The Good Pub Guide 199

GW00731421

The Good Pub Guide 1992

Edited by Alisdair Aird

Deputy Editor Fiona May

Additional research: Martin Hamilton, Esther Eidinow, Milly Taylor

BCA

LONDON · NEW YORK · SYDNEY · TORONTO

CONTENTS

Introduction

A cheaper steak and kidney pie?

This year, we have intensified our search for value in pubs by introducing a new symbol in the *Guide*: the £ symbol, which we have used to pick out pubs where we found good bargain food – worthwhile snacks costing £1 or less, or a choice of decent hot dishes costing £3 or less. Few pubs now meet these targets. But enough did win our bargain meals award to show that it can be done; all praise to them. We have also taken the steak and kidney pie as a standard measure of how much pubs are charging for food. We checked pie prices in 350 pubs, to see how they varied from pub to pub and place to place – and how much pub food prices have gone up in the last year. All these are good pubs, main entries in the *Guide*, where steak and kidney pie shows up as one of the dishes people really like. This is important, because it means that although there will of course be quality and quantity variations, we are broadly comparing like with like – pies that we and our readers have enjoyed eating. We have also found that the price of a steak and kidney pie tends to be quite a good indicator of how a pub's prices for other food work out. Our country-wide analysis of what pubs do charge for steak and kidney pie has shown up some interesting points.

In the average British pub, steak and kidney pie now costs £4.45. We found massive variations from county to county. In the most expensive counties, the average price worked out at least £1.50 more than in the cheapest counties. Using this steak and kidney yardstick, we'd rate as the bargain areas Derbyshire and Staffordshire (£3.70); the East Midlands – that is, Leicestershire, Lincolnshire and Nottinghamshire (£3.80); Lancashire/Merseyside and London (£3.90); Hertfordshire, the Midlands, and Scotland (£4); and Yorkshire and Northumbria (£4.15). Counties where pubs charge over the odds for this staple favourite are Oxfordshire (£5), Sussex and Gloucestershire (£4.95), and Buckinghamshire, Suffolk and Wiltshire (£4.80). But Berkshire takes the biscuit – a steak and pie lover there has to pay on average £5.35 to satisfy his appetite, a hefty 45 per cent more than it would cost him up in Derbyshire or Staffordshire.

There are of course plenty of pubs which buck the trend. In any one county, we found a wide range of prices for much the same quality. Individual pubs to praise for keeping their food prices generally down, and in particular their prices for a good steak and kidney pie below the £3 mark, are the Rising Sun at Tarporley in Cheshire, the Swan at Fradley in Staffordshire, the Blue Bell at Barnards Green in Hereford & Worcestershire (part of the Marstons Tavern Table

7

chain), the Black Dog at Belmont in Lancashire, the Sir John Borlase
Warren in Nottingham, the Lion of Morfe at Upper Farmcote
in Shropshire, the Crown at Bolton Percy in Yorkshire
and the Will's o' Nat's at Meltham there. All these have shown their
colours as true price-busters on the steak and kidney pie front. But
two pubs deserve special applause, for low food prices in areas
where other pub prices are going through the roof. These are the Ele
phant & Castle at Bloxham in Oxfordshire and the Six Bells at
Chiddingly in Sussex. The Six Bells in particular stands out as our
champion pub price buster of the year.

Over the year, our survey shows that pub pie prices have gone up
by an average of 9 per cent – very much in line with the general
index of retail prices, over the period in which we were checking
prices. Spot checks on the prices of other pub food indicate that
these have been rising in line with the same rate.

Beer prices – when will they hit the roof

With beer prices, it's a much sadder story. This year for the first
time we have carried out a rather ingenious price comparison, comparing how much a particular pub is now charging for a pint of beer
with how much that same pub charged last year. This gives a much
more accurate indication of how prices are rising than the more com
mon (and much easier) overall sample survey. In all, we were able to
check the price increase in 907 pubs, spread across England, Scotland and Wales.

In the country as a whole, the increase over the year worked out
at just over 16 per cent – around double the general rate of
inflation over the same period. We found this increase pretty
consistent, regardless of where the pub was. But we found some
interesting differences in other respects.

In general, the price rise has been steepest in pubs tied to one of
the country's six big national brewing combines. It has been least
steep in pubs tied to other, smaller brewers. To put the difference in
perspective, it's probably best to think of the price increases in terms
of actual money. On average, the price of a pint in a pub tied to a national brewer has increased over the year by 21p; in a pub tied to another smaller brewer, it has increased by 16p. Part of that increase
has nothing to do with the brewers, being higher duty and VAT. Dis-
counting that part means that in reality the price increase in pubs
tied to the national brewers has been nearly half as big again as the
increase in pubs tied to lesser breweries.

Prices in free houses have gone up by somewhere between the
two. However, if the free house gets its beer from one of the nationals, the increase has been much the same as in pubs directly tied to
the nationals.

One strand of the Government's action against the big brewers' monopoly hold on pub pricing has been to weaken the brewery tie by restricting the number of pubs each brewer can keep in its stable. Brewers have been converting many of their tenancies to leaseholds which don't count in totting up their tied pubs. So the hope would be that in these leasehold pubs prices will not move so sharply upwards as they would in the brewers' managed houses.

It does seem from our survey that this may in fact be happening, at least to some extent. While the increase in the Big Six's managed and tied-tenanted pubs worked out at 18 per cent or more, it was around 16 per cent in the case of their leasehold pubs. This is a hopeful sign for the future.

Another strand in the Government's action against the big brewers' monopoly has been the regulation under which a tied pub can buy a beer from some quite different brewery. Our survey showed that this is not working out well in practice. It's true that quite a lot of tied pubs do stock a so-called guest beer. But in practice these guest beers are almost always supplied through the tied brewer (a point which other surveys have sometimes failed to grasp). So we checked with the pubs which stocked guest beers to find out where they were getting them from. In most cases they were getting them through their parent brewery, which thus kept its hands firmly on the price reins. In our survey we found that only 17 per cent of the pubs tied to national brewers were exercising their right to buy a guest beer directly from a competing brewer. Only 4 per cent were both doing this and charging less for it than for the tied beers. This is too small a proportion to have any real practical effect on the market.

Part of the problem may be that many leaseholders, whatever the terms of their lease say, still see themselves as being in practice tied to the brewer from whom they bought the lease. Only a handful of leaseholders considered themselves as having free action on choice of beers. Almost all described themselves as being tied – so these leases in practice are not freeing pubs from the tie.

There may be more hope of effective competition from the smaller brewers. As we've said, their prices have gone up less fiercely. The list below shows the saving in pence per pint, compared with the nationals' prices, which we found with their smaller but most value-conscious competitors. We've included only those where there's a saving of at least 20p a pint.

Holts	49
Banks's	34
Bathams	32
Hoskins	30
Hardys & Hansons	30

Timothy Taylors	28
J W Lees	27
Clarks	26
Robinsons	26
Hook Norton	25
Donnington	24
Everards	24
Maclays	24
Thwaites	23
Smiles	22
Mansfield	21
Sam Smiths	21
Burtonwood	20

Pubs brewing their own beers typically save you around 22p a pint, by comparison with the big nationals.

As we've found year after year, beer prices vary widely from place to place. The most expensive areas are generally those in which the big brewers control a high proportion of pubs. In the cheapest, regional and local brewers tend to have a higher share of the market. Our survey showed that, in rough order of exorbitance starting with the costliest, the most expensive areas are London, Surrey, Sussex, Hampshire, Buckinghamshire, Kent, Oxfordshire, Berkshire and the Isle of Wight. Bargain areas, starting with the cheapest, are Lancashire/Merseyside, Cumbria, Derbyshire, Staffordshire, Cheshire, Yorkshire, Humberside, Hereford & Worcestershire and Shropshire. To put this in perspective, a pint now costs 40p more in Central London than in Manchester or Liverpool.

Some confusion

A smoke screen has been cast over the pricing and competition aspects by fundamental changes in the relationships between the various brewers themselves. In effect, Courage are handing over their pubs to Grand Metropolitan (Watneys), while Grand Met are handing over their breweries to Courage. So Courage are producing all the beers, Grand Met controlling the vast joint estate. This means that Courage, John Smiths, Ruddles, Websters and Wilsons are all products of a single firm. Ushers, however, which has been part of Grand Met, is as we go to press being floated off as a separate independent company.

Greenalls, the large Cheshire-based regional brewers, have also opted out of brewing. They have sold their beer brands to Allied. So Greenalls and their subsidiary beers Davenports, Shipstones, Simpkiss and Wem are now Allied beers, along with ABC, Ansells, Arrols, Benskins, Dartmoor, Friary Meux, Ind Coope, Tetleys, Taylor Walker, Tetleys Walkers and Peter Walkers.

Down in the west country Devenish have also stopped brewing. Their Cornish and Devenish beers are now produced by Whitbreads (along with Chesters, Flowers, Fremlins and Wethereds).

Some thoughts for 1992

With 1992 now on us, it's worth considering some of the things continental pub-equivalents do that British pubs don't do. For a start, there's the question of service. In Britain that too often means fighting your way to a bar, trying to catch the attention of a barman who'd clearly much prefer not to serve anyone, let alone you, and then lurching back through the crowds with glasses which have no extra rim space at the top to stop your drink slopping out over your fingers and maybe trousers. And this, mark you, is in a pub where a group of four people having lunch and a couple of drinks will be spending some £25. It's come to the point where one feels one's being done a favour if one's grudgingly allowed to borrow a battered and probably sticky tray to carry one's own drinks on.

Contrast that with the typical continental bar where, however humble your spending, a waiter comes and takes your order, then brings your drink. How unBritish that sounds – until one remembers that that was the general rule here too, until a few decades ago. Indeed there are still a very few pubs (such as the Ship in Longbenton up on Tyneside) which have kept their traditional service bells, and which still bring your drinks to your table as a matter of course. It would be great to see more pubs follow suit, as part of their contribution to 1992.

Year after year, we have pleaded for more sense about children in pubs. This is the only country in Europe which finds the question of children in public places so awkward. The main problem here is the inconsistency with which the law is applied. In law children under 14 are not allowed in those parts of a pub in which alcohol is being served, though they can be in a separate room. Practice however varies wildly from pub to pub (partly depending on how firmly the law is enforced locally). We will continue to press for a more uniform system – and one which meets more closely the needs of the times, and the ways in which people are now using pubs. Pubs are now very much more family places than they were between say 1910 and 1980, and the law should surely recognise the fact by changing the law which at present makes it illegal for families to use them. This time, we should say something about the other side of the coin. Children on the continent simply fit in. They are there as part of everyday social life, and they tend not to behave in the obtrusively spoilt way that all too often puts both publicans and other pub users off the whole idea of having children in pubs. On an inspection visit this year we were in one of the best pubs in this book (in fact the Crown in Southwold). It goes out of its way to make it easy for families to use the pub, and as a rule this works very well. But while we were there a couple eating lunch with young children let them scream and fuss for perhaps quarter of an hour, in spite of the obvious though politely concealed discomfort of several other tables full of people close to them. It must have wrecked a good many lunches that day.

Good pubs, good people

We've already mentioned the Six Bells at Chiddingly as a champion pub price-buster. Here are our awards for this year's other exceptional pubs.

Our award for the best all-round dining pub goes to the Angel at Hetton in Yorkshire, coping so well and in such a friendly way with the crowds who seek out its imaginative food.

For the best cheeseboard we pick the Royal Oak at Didsbury in Manchester; a close run thing, with the Mark Addy also in Manchester, the Shepherds at Melmerby in Cumbria and the Queens Head at Fowlmere in Cambridge running it close.

The year's finest fish pub is the Start Bay at Torcross in Devon; it has a head start over the competition as the landlord dives for some of it himself.

For the most stylish pub meal we select the Royal Oak at Yattendon in Berkshire.

For the best country cooking we choose the Hunters Lodge at Cornworthy in Devon – such an unassuming place that the quality of the cooking comes as a real surprise.

For the most spectacular coastal surroundings we pick the Ty Coch at Porth Dinllaen in Wales.

For wines by the glass, from a shortlist that includes the Nobody at Doddiscombsleigh, La Galoche in Tunbridge Wells, New Inn in Cerne Abbas, Squirrel at Hurtmore and Plough at Wistanstow, we choose as best of all the Crown in Southwold, Suffolk.

For superb beers we choose the Brunswick in Derby – as well as its fine range of bought-in beers, perfectly kept, it now has its own microbrewery.

Our whisky pub of the year is the Cadeby Inn at Cadeby in Yorkshire; not such a wide choice as the Cragg Lodge at Wormald Green up that way, but a really enlightened one.

For interesting country wines we choose the Ringlestone Inn at Ringlestone in Kent – again, not such a wide choice as some other places, but a perfect pub to taste them in.

For our outstanding character pub of the year, we choose the Falkland Arms at Great Tew in Oxfordshire.

For sheer extraordinariness we pick out the Highwayman at Sourton in Devon; out-Disneys Disney.

Our favourite country pub is the White Horse near Petersfield in Hampshire; nothing fancy, just honest character and warmth – with a splendid choice of beers and country wines, and good genuine food.

As our classic town pub of the year we choose Whitelocks in Leeds, a marvellously unchanging place.

Southwold in Suffolk wins our award as the best small town for the pub-lover; Edinburgh is the best city for pubs.

For unspoilt charm we select the Tuckers Grave at Faulkland in Somerset.

Our find of the year is the Crab & Lobster at Asenby in Yorkshire: good food in exceptionally enjoyable surroundings.

Our drinks man of the year is Alec Heard of the Ship at Conyer Quay in Kent – how he knows his way around those hundreds of wines, whiskies, liqueurs and malts is a mystery.

Our most welcoming licensee is Gianni Scoz of the Tally Ho in Hatherleigh, Devon; an Italian who shows just what a perfect English publican should be.

Our trail-blazers of the year are Chris and Jenny Phillips of the White Hart at Ford in Wiltshire; they have, one after the other, transformed no less than four other pubs before this into marvellously enjoyable places, and seem to have a magic touch in giving pub-lovers just what they want.

Landlord of the year is Alistair Cade of the Notley Arms in Monksilver; he has made that pub a remarkable haven of pleasure, and his skilful management makes sure that in spite of the many people who make it so busy it somehow never seems too busy or crowded – everything always goes smoothly.

Alan East of the Yew Tree at Cauldon in Staffordshire gets our special award as the man who, with his extraordinary collections of antique musical and other curiosities, and his general love of life, has brought most pleasure to readers of this *Guide* in its first ten years.

How the *Guide* Works

The Good Pub Guide is unique among annual guides. It is completely independent. It carries no advertising or sponsorship, and prohibits payment for inclusion – which depends purely on merit. Moreover it has no axe to grind: it is not linked to any pressure group, and as it is not just a part of some large organisation there is no risk of its editorial policy and standards being affected by anything other than the best interests of pub-goers. What really sets it apart from all other guides is its unique working method. It is the only Guide (not just in Britain but anywhere in the world) in which all the main entries have been inspected personally by the editorial team, almost always the Editor himself; and which at the same time has a country-wide information network gathering up-to-date news about pubs from thousands of individual reader/reporters.

This puts pubs through a two-stage sifting process. First of all, some 2,000 regular correspondents keep in touch with us about the pubs they visit, and another 6,000 readers have sent us at least some reports. Naturally, we depend most on the most recent reports – those we get in the months leading up to the *Guide* going to press. We also keep an eye on reports we've had in the previous year, for comparison – to see how consistent and reliable individual pubs are, and to spot any changes in standards. For this edition, we have analysed over 30,000 individual reports.

This keeps us up to date about pubs included in previous editions – our reporters warn us when a pub's standards have dropped (after a change of management, say), and it's their continuing approval that reassures us about keeping a pub as a main entry for another year. Very important, though, are the reports they send us on pubs we don't know at all. It's from these new discoveries that we make up a shortlist, to be considered for possible inclusion as new main entries. The more people that report favourably on a new pub, the more likely it is to win a place on this shortlist – especially if some of the reporters belong to our hard core of about five hundred trusted correspondents whose judgement we have learned to rely on. These are people who have each given us detailed comments on dozens of pubs, and shown that (when we ourselves know some of those pubs too) their judgement is closely in line with our own.

This brings us to the acid test. Each pub, before inclusion as a main entry, is inspected anonymously by the Editor, the Deputy Editor, or both. They have to find some special quality that would make strangers enjoy visiting it. What often marks the pub out for special attention is good value food (and that might mean anything from a well made sandwich, with good fresh ingredients at a low price, to imaginative cooking outclassing most restaurants in the area).

Maybe the drinks are out of the ordinary (pubs with several hundred whiskies, with remarkable wine lists, with home-made country wines or good beer or cider made on the premises, with a wide range of well kept real ales or bottled beers from all over the world). Perhaps there's a special appeal about it as a place to stay, with good bedrooms and obliging service. Maybe it's the building itself (from centuries-old parts of monasteries to extravagant Victorian gin-palaces), or its surroundings (lovely countryside, attractive water-side, extensive well kept garden), or what's in it (charming furnishings, extraordinary collections of bric-à-brac).

Above all, though, what makes the good pub is its atmosphere – you should be able to feel at home there, and feel not just that *you're* glad you've come but that *they're* glad you've come.

It follows from this that a great many ordinary locals, perfectly good in their own right, don't earn a place in the book. What makes them attractive to their regular customers (an almost clubby chumminess) may even make strangers feel rather out of place.

Another important point is that there's not necessarily any link between charm and luxury – though we like our creature comforts as much as anyone. A basic unspoilt village tavern, with hard seats and a flagstone floor, may be worth travelling miles to find, while a deluxe pub-restaurant may not be worth crossing the street for. Landlords can't buy the Good Pub accolade by spending thousands on thickly padded banquettes, soft music and luxuriously shrimpy sauces for their steaks – they can only win it by having a genuinely personal concern for both their customers and their pub.

Using the *Guide*

THE COUNTIES

England has been split alphabetically into counties, mainly to make it easier for people scanning through the book to find pubs near them. Each chapter starts by picking out pubs that are specially attractive for one reason or another.

Occasionally, counties have been grouped together into a single chapter, and metropolitan areas have been included in the counties around them – for example, Merseyside in Lancashire. When there's any risk of confusion, we have put a note about where to find a county at the place in the book where you'd probably look for it. But if in doubt, check the Contents.

Scotland and Wales have each been covered in single chapters, and London appears immediately before them at the end of England. Except in London (which is split into Central, North, South, West and East), pubs are listed alphabetically under the name of the town or village where they are. If the village is so small that you probably wouldn't find it on a road map, we've listed it under the name of the nearest sizeable village or town instead. The maps use the same town and village names, and additionally include a few big cities that don't have any listed pubs – for orientation.

We always list pubs in their true locations – so if a village is actually in Buckinghamshire that's where we list it, even if its postal address is via some town in Oxfordshire. Just once or twice, while the village itself is in one county the pub is just over the border in the next-door county. We then use the village county, not the pub one.

STARS

Specially good pubs are picked out with a star after their name. In a few cases, pubs have two stars: these are the aristocrats among pubs, really worth going out of your way to find. And just two pubs have three stars – the tops. The stars do NOT signify extra luxury or specially good food. The detailed description of each pub shows what its special appeal is and it's that that the stars refer to.

FOOD AND STAY AWARDS

The knife-and-fork rosette shows those pubs where food is outstanding. The bed symbol shows pubs which we know to be good as places to stay in – bearing in mind the price of the rooms (obviously you can't expect the same level of luxury at £12 a head as you'd get for £30 a head).

£ — NEW THIS YEAR

As part of our quest for food bargains in pubs, we have this year used this symbol to pick out pubs where we found decent snacks at £1 or less, or worthwhile main dishes at £3 or less.

RECOMMENDERS

At the end of each main entry we include the names of readers who have recently recommended that pub (unless they've asked us not to). Important note: the description of the pub and the comments on it are our own and not the recommenders'; they are based on our own personal inspections and on later verification of facts with each pub. As some recommenders' names appear quite

16

often, you can get an extra idea of what a pub is like by seeing which other pubs those recommenders have approved.

LUCKY DIPS – NEW STANDARD THIS YEAR

This year we have been able to raise the standard for entry to the Lucky Dip section at the end of each county chapter, which includes brief descriptions of pubs that have been recommended by readers, with the readers' names in brackets. As the flood of reports from readers has given so much solid information about so many pubs, we have been able to include only those which seem really worth trying. With most, the descriptions reflect the balanced judgement of a number of different readers. Many have been inspected by us. In these cases, LYM means the pub was in a previous edition of the *Guide*. The usual reason that it's no longer a main entry is that, although we've heard nothing really condemnatory about it, we've not had enough favourable reports to be sure that it's still ahead of the local competition. BB means that, although the pub has never been a main entry, we have inspected it, and found nothing against it. In both these cases, the description is our own; in others, it's based on the readers' reports. Where only one single reader has recommended a pub, we have now not included that pub in the list unless the reader's description makes the nature of the pub quite clear, and gives us good grounds for trusting that other readers would be glad to know of the pub.

Lucky Dip pubs marked with a ☆ are ones where the information we have (either from our own inspections or from trusted reader/reporters) suggests a firm recommendation. Roughly speaking, we'd say that these pubs are as much worth considering, at least for the virtue described for them, as many of the main entries themselves. Note that in the Dips we always commend food if we have information supporting a positive recommendation. So a bare mention that food is served shouldn't be taken to imply a recommendation of the food. The same is true of accommodation and so forth.

The Lucky Dips (particularly, of course, the starred ones) are under consideration for inspection for a future edition – so please let us have any comments you can make on them. You can use the report forms at the end of the book, the report card which should be included in it, or just write direct (no stamp needed if posted in the UK). Our address is The Good Pub Guide, FREEPOST, London SW10 OBR.

MAP REFERENCES

All pubs are given four-figure map references. On the main entries, it looks like this: SX5678 Map 1. Map 1 means that it's on the first map at the end of the book. SX means its in the square labelled SX on that map. The first figure, 5, tells you to look along the grid at the top and bottom of the SX square for the figure 5. The third figure, 7, tells you to look down he grid at the side of the square to find the figure 7. Imaginary lines drawn down and across the square from these figures should intersect near the pub itself.

The second and fourth figures, the 6 and the 8, are for more precise pin-pointing, and are really for use with larger-scale maps such as road atlases or the Ordnance Survey 1:50,000 maps, which use exactly the same map reference system. On the relevant Ordnance Survey map, instead of finding the 5 marker on the top grid you'd find the 56 one; instead of the 7 on the side grid you'd look for the 78 marker. This makes it very easy to locate even the smallest village.

Where a pub is exceptionally difficult to find, we include a six-figure reference in the directions, such as OS Sheet 102 reference 654783. This refers to Sheet 102 of the Ordnance Survey 1:50,000 maps, which explain how to use the six-figure references to pin-point a pub to the nearest 100 metres.

MOTORWAY PUBS

If a pub is within four or five miles of a motorway junction, and reaching it doesn't involve much slow traffic, we give special directions for finding it from the motorway. And the Special Interest Lists at the end of the book include a list of these pubs, motorway by motorway.

PRICES AND OTHER FACTUAL DETAILS

The *Guide* went to press during the summer of 1991. As late as possible before that, each pub was sent a checking sheet to get up-to-date food, drink and bedroom prices and other factual information. In the last year, we've found that prices have tended to increase by up to around 15% over the year – so you should expect that sort of increase by summer 1992. But if you find a significantly different price (with a few pubs this last year, some prices have jumped by over 30%) *please let us know*. Not every pub returned the sheet to us (if it didn't, we don't show a licensee's name after the brewery name at the end of the entry), and in some cases those that did omitted some prices. In such cases we ourselves were usually able to gather the information - especially prices – anyway. But where details are missing, that is the explanation. Again, this is something we'd particularly welcome readers' reports on.

Breweries to which pubs are 'tied' are named at the beginning of the italic-print rubric after each main entry. That means the pub has to get most if not all of its drinks from that brewery. If the brewery is not an independent one but just part of a combine, we name the combine in brackets. Where a brewery no longer brews its own beers but gets them under contract from a different brewer, we name that brewer too. When the pub is tied, we have spelled out whether the landlord is a tenant, has the pub on a lease, or is a manager; tenants and leaseholders generally have considerably greater freedom to do things their own way, and in particular are allowed to buy drinks including a beer from sources other than their tied brewery.

Free houses are pubs not tied to a brewery, so in theory they can shop around to get the drinks their customers want, at the best prices they can find. But in practice many free houses have loans from the big brewers, on terms that bind them to sell those breweries' beers – indeed, about half of all the beer sold in free houses is supplied by the big national brewery combines to free houses that have these loan ties. So don't be too surprised to find that so-called free houses may be stocking just as restricted a range of beers as openly tied pubs.

Real ale is used by us to mean beer that has been maturing naturally in its cask. We do not count as real ale beer which has been pasteurised or filtered to remove its natural yeasts. If it is kept under a blanket of carbon dioxide ('blanket pressure') to preserve it, we still generally mention it – as long as the pressure is too light for you to notice any extra fizz, it's hard to tell the difference. But we say that the carbon dioxide blanket is there.

Other drinks: we paid particular attention to picking out those pubs where the quality or range of wines is above the general pub average (gradually improving, though still well below what it should be). We're always particularly grateful to readers for reports on wine quality in pubs. We've also looked out particularly for pubs doing enterprising non-alcoholic drinks (including good tea or coffee), interesting spirits (especially malt whiskies), country wines (elderflower and the like) and good farm ciders. So many pubs now stock one of the main brands of draught cider that we normally mention cider only if the pub keeps quite a range, or one of the less common farm-made ciders.

Meals refers to what is sold in the bar, not in any separate restaurant. It means that pub sells food in its bar substantial enough to do as a proper meal – something you'd sit down to with knife and fork. It doesn't necessarily mean you can get three separate courses.

Snacks means sandwiches, ploughman's, pies and so forth, rather than pork scratchings or packets of crisps. We always mention sandwiches in the text if we know that a pub does them – if you don't see them mentioned, assume you can't get them.

The food listed in the description of each pub is an example of the sort of thing you'd find served in the bar on a normal day. We try to indicate any difference we know of between lunchtime and evening, and between summer and winter (on the whole stressing summer food more). In winter, many pubs tend to have a more restricted range, particularly of salads, and tend then to do more in the way of filled baked potatoes, casseroles and hot pies. We always mention barbecues if we know a pub does them. Food quality and variety may be affected by holidays – particularly in a small pub, where the licensees do the cooking themselves (May and early June seems to be a popular time for licensees to take their holidays).

Any separate *restaurant* is mentioned, and we give a telephone number if tables can be booked. We also note any pubs which told us they'd be keeping their restaurant open into Sunday afternoons (when, in England and Wales, they have to close their bars). But in general all comments on the type of food served, and in particular all the other details about meals and snacks at the end of each entry, relate to the pub food and not to the restaurant food.

Children under 14 are now allowed into at least some part of most of the pubs included in this *Guide* (there is no legal restriction on 14-year-olds going into the bar, though only 18-year-olds can get alcohol there). As we went to press, we asked pubs a series of detailed questions about their rules. *Children welcome* means the pub has told us that it simply lets them come in, with no special restrictions. In other cases we report exactly what arrangements pubs say they make for children. However, we have to note that in readers' experience some pubs set a time limit (say, no children after 8pm) that they haven't told us about, while others may impose some other rule (children only if eating, for example). If you come across this, please let us know, so that we can clarify the information for the pub concerned in the next edition. Even if we don't mention children at all, it is worth asking: one or two pubs told us frankly that they do welcome children but don't want to advertise the fact, for fear of being penalised. All but one or two pubs (we mention these in the text) allow children in their garden or on their terrace, if they have one. Note that in Scotland the law allows children more freely into pubs so long as they are eating (and with an adult); there are moves afoot to follow suit in England and Wales.

Dogs, cats and other animals are mentioned in the text if we know either that they are likely to be present or that they are specifically excluded – we depend chiefly on readers and partly on our own inspections for this information.

If an entry says something like 'on *Good Walks Guide* Walk 22' (or, in the Lucky Dips, 'on GWG Walk 22'), the pub is on one of the walks described in the book of that name by Tim Locke, published by Consumers' Association and Hodder & Stoughton.

Parking is not mentioned if you should normally be able to park outside the pub, or in a private car park, without difficulty. But if we know that parking space is limited or metered, we say so.

Telephone numbers are given for all pubs that are not ex-directory – new this year.

Opening hours are for summer weekdays. If hours are significantly different in winter, we note the differences. In the country, many pubs may open rather later and close earlier than their details show unless there are plenty of customers around (if you come across this, please let us know – with details). Pubs in England and Wales are allowed to stay open all day Mondays to Saturdays, from 11am (earlier, if the area's licensing magistrates have permitted) till 11pm; Scottish pubs have been allowed to do this for longer, and all-day opening is far more generally common there – outside cities, it's still quite rare in England and Wales, where pubs are still experimenting with the new hours which came into effect in 1988. Again, we'd be very grateful to hear of any differences from the hours we quote. You are allowed 20 minutes' drinking-up time after the quoted hours – half an hour if you've been having a meal in the pub.

Sunday hours are standard in law for all English and Welsh pubs that open on that day: 12-3, 7-10.30. But a few still stick to 2pm closing (we mention this when we know of it). In Scotland, a few pubs close on Sundays (we specify those that we know of), most are open 12.30-2.30 and 6.30-11, and some stay open all day. If we know of a pub closing for any day of the week or part of the year, we say so. The few pubs which we say stay closed on Monday do open on Bank Holiday Mondays.

Bedroom prices normally include full English breakfasts (if these are available, which they usually are), VAT and any automatic service charge that we know about. If we give just one price, it is the total price for two people sharing a double or twin-bedded room for one night. Otherwise, prices before the / are for single occupancy, prices after it for double. A capital B against the price means that it includes a private bathroom, a capital S a private shower. As all this coding packs in quite a lot of information, some examples may help to explain it:

£30 on its own means that's the total bill for two people sharing a twin or double room without private bath; the pub has no rooms with private bath, and a single person might have to pay that full price

£30B means exactly the same – but all the rooms have private bath

£30(£35B) means rooms with private baths cost £5 extra

£18/£30(f35B) means the same as the last example, but also shows that there are single rooms for £18, none of which have private bathrooms

If there's a choice of rooms at different prices, we normally give the cheapest. If there are seasonal price variations, we give the summer price (the highest). This winter – 1991-92 – many inns, particularly in the country, will have special cheaper rates. And at other times, especially in holiday areas, you will often find prices cheaper if you stay for several nights. On weekends, inns that aren't in obvious weekending areas often have bargain rates for two- or three-night stays.

We regret to say that an increasing number of incidents in which bookings have been 'lost' or otherwise mucked up make us now recommend that you confirm any booking in writing; and then to be doubly sure check by telephone that the inn has received your booking.

MEAL TIMES

As bar food service has become such a normal part of a pub's operations, pubs have become more consistent in the times at which they serve it. Commonly, it's served from 12-2 and 7-9, at least from Monday to Saturday (food service often stops a bit earlier on Sundays). If we don't give a time against the Meals and Snacks note at the bottom of a main entry, that means that you should be able to get bar food at those times. However, we do spell out the times if we know that bar food service starts after 12.15 or after 7.15; if it stops before 2 or before 8.45; or if food is served for significantly longer than usual (say, till 2.30 or 9.45).

Though we note days when pubs have told us they don't do food, experience suggests that you should play safe on Sundays and check first with any pub before planning an expedition that depends on getting a meal there. Also, out-of-the-way pubs often cut down on cooking during the week if they're quiet – as they tend to be, except at holiday times. Please let us know if you find anything different from what we say.

NO SMOKING

We say in the text of each entry what if any provision a pub makes for non-smokers. Pubs setting aside at least some sort of no smoking area are also listed county by county in the Special Interest Lists at the back of the book.

CHANGES DURING THE YEAR – PLEASE TELL US

Changes are inevitable, during the course of the year. Landlords change, and so do their policies. And, as we've said, not all returned our fact-checking sheets. We very much hope that you will find everything just as we say. But if you find anything different, please let us know, using the tear-out card in the middle of the book (which doesn't need an envelope), the report forms at the back, or just a letter. You don't need a stamp: the address is *The Good Pub Guide*, FREEPOST, London SW10 OBR.

Author's acknowledgements

This book would not be possible without the help of several thousand readers who so kindly send us reports on pubs – good and bad. I am full of gratitude to them, and always deeply aware of the great debt this book owes to their enthusiasm, in discovering new gems, keeping us right up to date on the many thousands of pubs their reports cover, and warning us when standards slip. Quite a number of readers send us literally hundreds of reports, and often describe in great detail the pubs they "test" for us. We've come to regard these as a sort of inner bodyguard of trusted pub-hunters, and I'd like to give special thanks to Gwen and Peter Andrews, Ian Philips, Thomas Nott, Derek and Sylvia Stephenson, Richard Houghton, Nick and Alison Dowson, TBB, WHBM, Brian Jones, Tony and Lynne Stark, Iain and Penny Muir, Jenny and Brian Seller, Lyn and Bill Capper, Joan Olivier, H K Dyson, Graham Bush, Roger Huggins, Tom McLean, Ewan McCall, Dave Irving, Wayne Brindle, Andy and Jill Kassube, John C Baker, Nigel Gibbs, E G Parish, Frank Cummins, Chris Raisin, John Evans, Brian and Anna Marsden, Dave Braisted, Simon Collett-Jones, Mr and Mrs P B Dowsett, Michael and Alison Sandy, Dr and Mrs A K Clarke, Reg Nelson, Phil and Sally Gibson, Derek Patey, Len Beattie, Charles Bardswell, P A and J B Jones, Peter Corris, John and Chris Simpson, Mr and Mrs Simon Turner, Robert Lester, Comus Elliot, Pauline Crossland, Dave Cawley, Neil and Anita Christopher, BKA, Michael and Jenny Back, A T Langton, Marjorie and David Lamb, Graham Gibson, Joan and Michel Hooper-Immins, Andrew and Ruth Triggs, Mike and Wendy Proctor, G T Jones, PLC, Mayur Shah, Alan Skull, Viv Middlebrook, John Innes, S V Bishop, Barry and Anne, Robert and Vicky Tod, Steve Mitcheson, Anne Collins, Caroline Wright, John Whitehead, Lee Goulding, Peter Griffiths, John abd Joan Wyatt, Richard Gibbs, Mrs Joan Harris, Laurence Manning, Frank W Gadbois, Anthony Barnes, Andy Morrissey, Gordon and Daphne, Steve and Carolyn Harvey, Peter and Rose Flower, David Wallington, KC, Mrs Margaret Dyke, Derek and Irene Cranston and SS.

Thanks too to Milly Taylor, Alison Thomas and Olivia Aarons – for the energy they put into working on the book.

Particular thanks, finally, to so many publicans for working so hard to give so much enjoyment to so many people.

Alisdair Aird

England

Avon   *see* Somerset

Bedfordshire   *see* Cambridgeshire

Berkshire

Though this is one of the very costliest areas for pubs, you can still find real food bargains here, especially at the Bell at Aldworth (one of the county's nicest country pubs). Snacks at the Pot Kiln at Frilsham (another beautifully rustic place) and the cheerful and very friendly Queen Victoria at Hare Hatch also stand out as attractively priced by any standards. At the opposite end of the scale, there's been a management buyout at the stylish Royal Oak in Yattendon: its food, though far from cheap, stands out for quality. Other pubs here that shine for good food include particularly the Swan at Inkpen (interesting Singapore-style dishes) and White Hart at Hamstead Marshall (where the Italian landlord does the cooking). And most enjoyable meals are also to be had at the friendly Crown in Cookham, the Ibex in Chaddleworth (an engaging new entry that could almost be renamed the Desert Orchid), the civilised and upmarket Bel & the Dragon in Cookham, the pretty little restaurant of the Jolly Farmer in Cookham Dean (another new entry, bought from its brewery by several dozen regulars), the Fox at Hermitage (new licensees doing well in this new entry, a dining pub quite handy for the M4), the Green Man at Hurst, the Dundas Arms at Kintbury (a lovely spot – and nice wines), the rather smart Bird in Hand at Knowl Hill, the Cricketers on Littlewick Green, the Fox & Hounds at Peasemore (another racehorse-country pub), and the Harrow at West Ilsley (just refurbished so charmingly that this year it gains a star award). Among the Lucky Dips at the end of the chapter, the Bunk at Curridge is an interestingly stylish little place with very promising food under its new regime – though at twice the price of the more unassuming food at the very friendly Red Lion at nearby Compton, another particularly promising pub; other Dips to single out include the Belgian Arms at Holyport, Seven Stars at Knowl Hill, Little Angel at Remenham, White Hart in Wargrave and Five Bells at Wickham.

ALDWORTH   SU5579   Map 2

Bell ★ £

A329 Reading–Wallingford; left on to B4009 at Streatley

For 200 years this unspoilt and old-fashioned country local has been in the same family and the welcome from the licensees and regulars is warm and friendly. The beamed bar has benches built around the panelled walls and into the gaps left by a big disused fireplace and bread oven – though there's still a woodburning stove; very well kept Arkells BBB and Kingsdown, Badger Best, Donnington SBA, Hook Norton, and Morrells Mild on handpump and good house wines are handed through a small hatch in the central servery. Lovely fresh hot crusty rolls are filled with cheddar (70p), ham, pâté or stilton (80p), roast turkey or tongue (90p), smoked salmon (£1.30), and Devon crab (£1.50); darts, shove-ha'penny, dominoes, chess and Aunt Sally. The quiet garden is at its best in summer, when it's filled with roses, mallows and lavender; Morris dancers, then. Close to the Ridgeway, the pub is popular with walkers on Sundays, and quieter on weekday lunchtimes. At Christmas, local mummers perform in the road by the ancient well-head (the shaft is sunk 400 feet through the chalk); steaming jugs of hot punch and mince pies are handed round afterwards. (Recommended by WHBM,

Gordon and Daphne, A T Langton, Nick and Alison Dowson, Richard Houghton, Bev and Doug Warwick)

Free house   Licensee H E Macaulay   Real ale   Snacks (11–2.45, 6–10.45)   Newbury (0635) 578272   Well behaved children in tap room   Open 11–3, 6–11; closed Mon (not Bank Holidays) and 25 Dec

BRAY   SU9079 Map 2
Crown

1 3/4 miles from M4 junction 9; A308 towards Windsor, then left at Bray signpost on to B3028

Friendly and pleasant, this 14th-century pub has a partly panelled, low-beamed main bar with leather-backed seats around copper-topped or wooden tables, old timbers conveniently left at elbow height where walls have been knocked through, and a cosy winter fire; some caricatures by Spy and his competitors on the walls, guns, pistols, and stuffed animals. Decent bar food includes, at lunchtime, sandwiches on request, a choice of well filled rolls (90p), consistently good fish mousse (£2.20), quiche (£3.20), Chinese barbecued pork (£4.50), and home-made puddings like Gaelic coffee trifle, mousses or apple pie (£1.85); in the evening the choice is more elaborate – lobster soup (£3.50), avocado and seafood (£4.50), frogs legs in garlic (£5.50), duck (£10.75), and steaks (from £11); vegetables are grown in their kitchen garden; summer Sunday barbecues. Well kept Courage Best tapped from the cask, and a fair choice of wines; piped music. The large back garden has tables under cocktail parasols, and there are more tables and benches in the flagstoned courtyard and vine arbour. *(Recommended by D J and P M Taylor, Graham Bush, TBB, J P Cinnamond; more reports please)*

Courage   Licensee Hugh Whitton   Real ale   Meals (not Sat lunchtime) and lunchtime snacks (12.30–2, 7.30–10)   Well behaved children welcome   Restaurant; closed Sun Maidenhead (0628) 21936   Open 10.30–3, 5.30–11

CHADDLEWORTH   SU4177 Map 2
Ibex

From A338 pass church and follow signs to Brightwalton

The landlord feels very much at home in the horse-racing country around this brick and flint village pub – he was a National Hunt jockey until three years ago and rode Desert Orchid to seventeen victories. The carpeted lounge has old-fashioned bench seating and refectory-style tables, prints on the walls, and a big winter log fire. Good bar food includes changing daily specials like mushrooms in a mango and madras sauce or chicken livers in a marjoram, cream and wine sauce (£3.25), chicken breast in a stilton and spring onion sauce (£5.50), liver in ale (£5.95), guineafowl with fresh mango (£8.95), and fresh fish; there's also a standard menu with soup, pâté, pies and steaks. More tables are set for evening meals in the sun lounge (and the snug little old-fashioned dining room); maybe piped music. The public bar has darts, dominoes and fruit machine. There are tables out on a sheltered lawn, and more on the terrace by the building which is lit up in the evening. As we went to press, this pub was tied to Courage, but there were plans for Morlands to take it over. *(Recommended by Chris Ball, Barbara M McHugh, J M Potter, HNJ, PEJ)*

See above   Tenant Colin Brown   Real ale   Meals and snacks   Restaurant   Children welcome   Chaddleworth (048 82) 311   Open 11–3, 6.30–11

CHIEVELEY   SU4774 Map 2
Blue Boar

4 miles from M4 junction 13: A34 N towards Abingdon, first left into Chieveley, bear left (signed Winterbourne, Boxford) and keep on until T-junction with B4494 – turn right towards Wantage, pub on right

The three rambling rooms of the beamed bar here are attractively old-fashioned, and furnished with high-backed settles, Windsor chairs and polished tables, and plush or brocaded cushioned stools; also, a variety of heavy harness (including a massive collar), hunting prints and photographs. The middle room has an unusual inglenook seat, and the left-hand room has a seat built into the sunny bow window with a fine view over unspoilt fields, and a roaring log fire. Wadworths IPA and 6X on handpump, quite a few malt whiskies and liqueurs; piped music. Bar food includes soup (£1.80), sandwiches (from £2.15; fillet steak £4.95), ploughman's (£3.95), salads (from £4.95), pasta of the day (£5.45), home-made burger (£5.95), beef curry or steak and kidney pie (£6.95), and puddings (from £2); friendly, professional service. There are tables among tubs and flowerbeds on the rough front cobbles. Standing on the picturesquely stunted ancient oak outside this thatched inn is the Blue Sandstone Boar, presented by Cromwell who stayed here in 1644 on the eve of the Battle of Newbury. *(Recommended by E J Knight, Ian Phillips, J M Potter, Andrew Winter, Gordon and Daphne, A Y Drummond, Simon Collett-Jones)*

Free house   Licensee Peter Ebsworth   Real ale   Meals and snacks   Restaurant Chieveley (0635) 248236   Well behaved children welcome   Open 11–3, 6–11 Bedrooms; £37S,£50B/£65B

COOKHAM   SU8884   Map 2

Bel & the Dragon ★

High Street; B4447 N of Maidenhead

This quietly civilised and restful old place has three well kept communicating lounge rooms with pewter tankards hanging from heavy Tudor beams, old oak settles, deep, comfortable leather chairs, and oak panelling; one room is no smoking. A smartly dressed (either in collar and tie or blue coat) and grave but friendly barman behind the very low zinc-topped bar counter serves well kept Brakspears PA and Old tapped from the cask, wines including decent ports and champagne, all the ingredients necessary for proper cocktails, and freshly squeezed orange juice. There are often free home-made crisps, olives or gherkins as well as good, if pricey, bar food: soup (£2.25), sandwiches (from £2.25, prawn and avocado £4, Scotch smoked salmon £6; toasties £3), ploughman's (£4; the walnut bread baked specially for them is very popular), lasagne (£4.50), cheese and ham omelette or Swiss veal sausage with onions (£5), home-made steak and kidney pie (£5.75), and puddings such as home-made cheesecake (£2); in summer and good weather snacks are also served in the garden or on the back terrace. There is no car park and street parking can be very difficult. The Stanley Spencer Gallery is almost opposite. *(Recommended by P A Devitt, TBB, Wyn and Syd Donald, JMC, Nigel Gibbs, Mike Tucker, Alison and Nick Dowson)*

Free house   Licensee F E Stuber   Real ale   Meals and snacks   Restaurant; closed Sun evenings   Bourne End (06285) 21263   Children in eating area of bar only   Open 11–2.30, 6–10.30 (11 Sat)

COOKHAM DEAN   SU8785   Map 2

Jolly Farmer

Off A308 N of Maidenhead, or from A4094 in Cookham take B4447 and fork right past Cookham Rise stn; can be reached from Marlow – fork left after bridge

In 1987 this part flint-faced, part brick village pub was bought from Courage by a consortium of its regulars. There are three little rooms, the middle of which is the main bar: a built-in brocade-cushioned settle by the window (and a tiny one by the bar counter), a few wheelback chairs and some tall bar stools on the quarry tiles, an old brick fireplace with a log-effect gas fire, and brass spigots, horse-harness and horsebrasses over the bar counter; at one end of the building an old-fashioned room has half-panelled walls, a small brick fireplace and a few tables and wheelback chairs, and at the other is an attractive dining room with starched pink and white tablecloths, a pretty built-in wall bench, and more wheelbacks. Good bar food includes doorstep sandwiches (from £1.70), home-made pâté (£2.85), deep-fried potatoe skins with delicious dips (£2.45), mushrooms in garlic butter (£3.05), pork chop in apple and cider (£5), home-made steak and kidney pie (£6.15), popular rack of lamb, and trout with sherry and almonds (£8.50); as we went to press they were doubling the size of the kitchen. Well kept Courage Best and Wadworths 6X on handpump; darts (early evening only; not Sat), dominoes and cribbage. Though it's very quiet on weekday lunchtimes, it does get busy at weekends. In front of the pub are some picnic-table sets and flowering tubs, and a very long side lawn has picnic-table sets and green metal tables and chairs, and a swing. The tiny village green and flint-faced church are opposite. *(Recommended by Ian Phillips, TBB, Patrick Stapley, R S Eades)*

Free house   Licensee Michael French   Real ale   Meals and snacks; no food Sun evenings   Restaurant; midnight supper licence   Marlow (0628) 482905   Well behaved children in restaurant lunchtimes   Open 11.30–3(4 Sat), 5.30–11

COOKHAM RISE   SU8984 Map 2
Old Swan Uppers

B4447 Cookham–Maidenhead

The broad worn flagstones spread throughout this genuinely welcoming, cosy pub – it's one of the things readers particularly like. The U-shaped bar has heavy black beams, cream walls over shiny black panelled dado, cushioned wall benches and stools, railway-lantern lamps, blow-ups of sepia cartes-de-visite and other Victorian photographs, and log fires – one of them pretty vast – in stripped brick fireplaces; two or three quieter dark blue plush booths are around on the left. The restaurant area rambles off on the right. Well kept Boddingtons, Eldridge Pope Royal Oak, Marstons Pedigree and Palmers Best on handpump, with a dozen or so decent malts; maybe unusual piped music in some areas. Under the new licensee, the bar food includes sandwiches, avocado and grapefruit in a raspberry sauce (£2.95), vegetarian dishes (from £3.25), deep-fried fresh fish (£5.50), and rack of lamb with a honey and lemon sauce (£8.95). Tables are set out on a fairy-lit back terrace, with some wooden ones at the front by the village road. *(Recommended by Richard Houghton, TBB, Peter Argent, Nick and Alison Dowson)*

Free house   Licensee Derek Walsh   Real ale   Meals and snacks (12–2, 7–10)   Restaurant (not Sun evening)   Bourne End (062 85) 21324   Children welcome   Open 11–3, 6 (7 Sat)–11; closed evening 25 Dec   Bedrooms; £26/£36

EAST ILSLEY   SU4981 Map 2
Crown & Horns

A34, about 5 miles N of M4 junction 13

This friendly, homely pub keeps an attractive range of rotating real ales, which typically includes Bass, Fullers London Pride, Morlands Original and Old Master, Theakstons Old Peculier and Wadworths 6X, with guests like Brakspears or King & Barnes Festive on handpump; a collection of 170 whiskies spans most of the world – Morocco, Korea, Japan, China, Spain and New Zealand. The partly panelled and beamed main bar has racing prints and photographs, and the TV is on for the racing in a side bar. Bar food includes sandwiches (from £1.25), home-made soup (£1.45), ploughman's (from £2.25), lasagne or moussaka (£3.95), liver and bacon casserole (£4.25), chicken breast with stilton and mushroom sauce or duck in a honey and orange sauce (£5.95), steak (from £8.75), game and venison pie in season, and puddings such as home-made treacle tart (£1.50); cheerful, efficient service. Skittle alley, darts, pool, bar billiards, shove-ha'penny, dominoes, cribbage, fruit machine, juke box and piped music. The pretty paved stable yard has tables under two chestnut trees. *(Recommended by Barry and Anne, Simon Collett-Jones, Mayur Shah, Mrs G L Carlisle)*

Free house   Licensees Chris and Jane Bexx   Real ale   Meals and snacks (12–2, 6–10)   East Ilsley (063 528) 205/545   Children in eating area, restaurant and TV room   Open 11–3, 6–11; closed evening 25 Dec   Bedrooms; £28B/£36B

Swan 🛏

Particularly well refurbished in open-plan style a few years ago, the bar in this old coaching inn is a stylish assortment of irregularly shaped nooks and corners, divided by low walls topped with broad polished woodwork; the main area has bentwood tables and armed chairs on an elegant pastel flowery carpet, a clock made from copper and oak salvaged from HMS *Britannia* (the last wooden three-deck battleship, 1862–1916), lots of local photographs, and a mix of diners and quietly chatting other customers; one area down by an elegantly arched 1930s fireplace is mainly for drinkers and has some pub cartoons on the walls. Good value home-made bar food includes sandwiches (from £1.35; prawn £2.75), several ploughman's (from £2.30), spaghetti with a bolognaise or vegetarian sauce (£3.30), cottage pie (£3.60), scampi (£4.90), with at least twenty further choices from a daily blackboard, such as local rabbit, pheasant, pigeon or venison, and puddings (£2); well kept Morlands Original and Old Masters on handpump; good friendly service. Darts, cribbage, unobtrusive fruit machine, faint piped music. There are picnic-table sets on a prettily trellised back terrace, and on a sheltered lawn with a play area. *(Recommended by H E Hental, HNJ, PEJ, R Tomlinson, Richard Houghton, Stan Edwards, A T Langton)*

Morlands   Tenant Michael Connolly   Real ale   Meals and snacks   No smoking restaurant (closed Sun evening) Children in eating area and restaurant   East Ilsley (063 528) 238   Open 10.30–2.30, 6–11   Bedrooms; £20(£31B)/£40(£49B)

FRILSHAM   SU5473   Map 2

Pot Kiln £

From Yattendon follow Frilsham signpost, but just after crossing motorway go straight on towards Bucklebury when Frilsham is signposted right

This striking brick pub is surrounded by wooded hills and peaceable pastures and has a warmly friendly, old-fashioned atmosphere. It's popular locally and has bare benches and pews, wooden floorboards, and a good log fire. Well kept Arkells BBB, Morlands Original and Old Speckled Hen, and Ringwood Fortyniner on handpump (kept under light blanket pressure), are served from a hatch in the panelled entrance lobby – which just has room for one bar stool. Good bar food includes filled hot rolls (from 95p), home-made soup (£1.50), a decent ploughman's (£2.70), lots of vegetarian dishes such as curry (£4.10) or lasagne (£4.75), steak and kidney pie (£4.95), fish pie (£5.25), and steak (£8.30); no chips, and vegetables are fresh. On Sundays they only do rolls and on Tuesday only soup and rolls; friendly service. The public bar has darts, dominoes, shove-ha'penny and cribbage; informal folk music on Sunday evenings – people get up to play more or less as the mood takes them. The back room/dining room is no smoking. There are picnic-table sets in the suntrap garden – warm enough even to sit out on a sunny March day. It's good dog-walking country, though they don't actually allow them in the main bar. *(Recommended by Nick and Alison Dowson, TBB, Gordon and Daphne, Ian Phillips, Keith and Sian Mitchell, Lyn and Bill Capper)*

Free house   Licensee Philip Gent   Real ale   Meals (not Sun) and snacks (12–1.45, 7–9.45)   Hermitage (0635) 201366   Well behaved children in dining room (not after 7.30)   Folk singing Sun evening   Open 12–2.30, 6.30–11

GREAT SHEFFORD   SU3875   Map 2

Pheasant

Under half a mile from M4 junction 14; A338 towards Wantage, then first left (pub visible from main road, and actually at Shefford Woodland, S of the village itself)

This white-painted tile-hung pub is conveniently placed for stop-offs from the M4. The four neat communicating room areas have racehorse prints on the walls, cut-away cask seats, wall pews and other chairs on their Turkey carpet, and well kept Wadworths IPA and 6X on handpump; good wines, several malt whiskies, and decent coffee. Bar food includes sandwiches (from £1.50), soup (£1.75; the carrot and coriander is quite spicy), ploughman's (£2.75; in winter they include a bowl of soup – £3.50), chilli con carne (£4), salads (from £5.50), trout (£6.75), steaks (from £8.25), and specials like kidneys in brandy and cream or chicken provençale; puddings (£2.50), and Sunday roast (£4.95). Darts, cribbage, dominoes, ring the bull – very popular – and video game in the public bar; piped music. Rustic tables in a smallish garden look over the fields. Mr Jones is also licensee at the Royal Oak at Wootton Rivers (see Wilts). *(Recommended by Alan Skull, R C Morgan, E W Denham, Simon Reynolds, Barbara and Norman Wells, K H Frostick, Tom Evans, Jerry and Alison Oakes, Stan Edwards, Greg Parston, BKA, Mr and Mrs H W Clayton)*

Free house   Licensees John and Rosa Jones   Real ale   Meals and snacks   Small restaurant   Great Shefford (0488) 39284   Children welcome   Open 11–3, 5.30–11

Swan

2 miles from M4 junction 14; on A338 towards Wantage

Tables on an attractive quiet lawn and terrace overlook the tree-hung stream with ducks and there may be weekend summer barbecues out here; the garden room shares the same view. Inside, there are dark green or dusky pink plush banquettes, and the public bar has darts, pool, a fruit machine, trivia, juke box and piped music; the budgerigar is called Jackie. Home-made bar food includes sandwiches (from £1.50), home-made soup (£1.75; the fish soup is good), ploughman's (from £2.95), lasagne (£3.95), salads (from £4.95), winter steak and kidney pie (£5.25), popular garlic prawns (£5.95), and puddings like banoffi pie (£2.50); well kept Courage Best and Directors on handpump; several malt whiskies. *(Recommended by Mr and Mrs H W Clayton, Dr and Mrs A K Clarke, Stan Edwards)*

Courage   Lease: Gwyn Chivers   Real ale   Meals and snacks (till 10pm)   Children welcome   Restaurant   Great Shefford (048 839) 271   Open 11–3, 6–11; closed evening 25 Dec

HAMSTEAD MARSHALL   SU4165   Map 2

White Hart 🏵 🛏

Village signposted from A4 W of Newbury

This extended cream-rendered tiled-roof Georgian house is pleasant and civilised, and the low-ceilinged, L-shaped bar has a central log fire, red plush seats built into the bow windows, red-cushioned chairs around oak and other tables, a copper-topped bar counter, and steeplechasing and other horse prints on its ochre walls. The popular bar food concentrates on meals rather than snacks: soup (£2.50), authentic pasta (from £3.50 starter, £5.50 main course) such as lasagne, fettucini and conchiglie, excellent spinach and ricotta pancakes, omelettes (£4.50), lamb kidneys sautéed with mushrooms and wine (£7.90), crispy roast half duckling with rich orange sauce (£9.90), delicious monkfish, grilled Dover sole (£12.50), and daily specials such as spare ribs (£7.90) or fish casserole (£10.50); home-made puddings like tiramisu or strawberry pavlova (£3); they make their own cassata (Mr Aromando, from Italy, does most of the cooking). Well kept Badger Best and Wadworths 6X on handpump; politely friendly service. No dogs (their own Welsh setter's called Sam, and the pony's called Solo). The flower-bordered and walled lawn is shaded by a lime tree, ancient pear tree and much younger eucalyptus. The bedrooms are in a converted barn across the courtyard. *(Recommended by Jane Buekett, R C Watkins, T Darling, Lyn and Bill Capper, Mr J C Bell, John Tyzack, Gordon and Daphne)*

Free house   Licensee Mr Nicola Aromando   Real ale   Meals and snacks (not Sun)   Restaurant (not Sun)   Kintbury (0488) 58201   Children in restaurant   Bedrooms; £40B/£55B   Open 12–2.30, 6.30–11; closed Sun, 25–26 Dec and 2 weeks in Aug

HARE HATCH

Queen Victoria £

Blakes Lane, The Holt; just N of A4 Reading–Maidenhead, 3 miles W of exit roundabout from A423(M) – keep your eyes skinned for the turning

A cheerful buzz of conversation fills this friendly two-roomed local. There's quite a concentration on food and it's the specials people tend to go for – often adventurous and always good value (most around £4.15): steak and kidney casserole, pasta dishes, filled tacos, baked leeks au gratin with hunky bread or pheasant in season. Also, sandwiches (from £1), winter soups (£1.10), ploughman's (£2.95), spicy sausage (£3.25), filled potato shells (from £3.50; the prawn is very popular), steak sandwich with chips (£3.95), several vegetarian dishes like broccoli and macaroni cheese, vegetable bake or cheese and nut croquette (£3.25), lamb masala (£4.15), steak (£7.45), and puddings like treacle and nut tart or cheesecakes. The bar has low beams, sturdy furnishings on the new carpet, a stuffed sparrowhawk, a delft shelf lined with Beaujolais bottles and lots of games from a fruit machine and video game to darts, cribbage, dominoes, solitaire and three-dimensional noughts and crosses; well kept Brakspears PA, SB, Mild and Old on handpump. There's a robust table or two in front by the car park. *(Recommended by TBB, David Warrellow, Simon Collett-Jones, Ian Phillips, D C and R J Deeming; more reports please)*

Brakspears   Tenant Ronald Rossington   Real ale   Meals and snacks (11.30–2.30, 6.30–10.30)   Reading (0734) 402477   Children welcome   Open 11–3, 5.30–11

HERMITAGE   SU5073   Map 2

Fox

2 1/2 miles from M4 junction 13: A34 towards Oxford, first right, then left on B4009

Even when one reader came here to eat with his 20-strong bowling team, the service stayed prompt and efficient. Extensive refurbishments have left an open-plan expanse of flowery red carpet with sage-green plush seats, some stripped brickwork, small wildfowl and sporting prints on roughcast white walls with shiny timbering; it's divided into two good-sized areas, and there's a log fire. Changing daily, the wide choice of good, popular bar food includes home-made soup (£1.90), very good value lunchtime French sticks filled with excellent bacon and cheese (the bacon is more like gammon), a huge helping of lovely beef, and nice cheese and prawn, salad of sautéed chicken livers with spring onions (£2.75), ploughman's with some unusual cheeses (£4.75), very good cauliflower cheese with bacon, crab and salmon tagliatelle, tasty steak and kidney pie, char-grilled pork chop with apple and cider sauce (£6.25), vegetarian dishes, and excellent Dover sole with herb butter (£9.75); every Wednesday evening they add a curry (£5.25) to the normal menu, and there's a monthly dining club (free membership; seven courses including wine and coffee £30). Well kept Courage Best with guests like Eldridge Pope and Theakstons Best on handpump; fruit machine, trivia, piped pop music. Outside, there are picnic-table sets under cocktail parasols on an attractively planted rose terrace, with another table down on a patch of grass (with a dog in a kennel); no dogs inside. *(Recommended by Tom Evans, Simon Collett-Jones, D J and P M Taylor, Richard Houghton, J V Dadswell, K J How)*

Free house   Managed: Simon Rudd, Andrew Latham   Real ale   Meals and lunchtime snacks   Restaurant   Hermitage (0635) 201545   Children in eating area of bar   Open 11–2.30, 6–11

nr HURLEY   SU8283   Map 2

Dew Drop

Just W of Hurley on A423 turn left up Honey Lane – look out for the IGAP sign; at small red post-box after large farm, fork right – the pub is down a right-hand turn-off at the first cluster of little houses

Outside this genuinely secluded brick and flint cottage are seats in the attractively wild sloping garden looking down to where white doves strut on the pub's red tiles; tubs of bright flowers and a children's play area. The main bar has a log fire at each end and simple furnishings; space is rather tight by the bar. Bar food includes ploughman's (£2), smoked salmon mousse (£2.30), mushrooms on toast (£3), pasta bake or seafood lasagne (£4), scampi (£4.50), and puddings like treacle tart (£1.50). Well kept Brakspears PA and Old on handpump and some good malt whiskies; cribbage. From his conversation and from the pictures on the wall, it's not difficult to discover the landlord's passion – golf. Popular with dog owners. *(Recommended by P A Devitt, R K Sutton, Ian Phillips, R J Walden, Nick Dowson; more reports please)*

Brakspears   Tenant Michael Morris   Real ale   Meals and snacks (not Sun evening) Children welcome   Littlewick Green (062 882) 824327   Open 11–2.30, 6.15–11

HURST   SU7972   Map 2

Green Man

Hinton Road; A321 Twyford–Wokingham, turn right into B3030, then NE just S of filling station in village centre, signposted Ruscombe

At lunchtime, the low-beamed, atmospheric bar here is full of the sound of contented cheerful conversation: black standing timbers, lots of alcoves and country pictures, horsebrasses and brass stirrups, tapestried wall seats and wheelback chairs around brass-topped tables on the green carpet, and an open fire at both ends (neatly closed in summer by black-and-brass folding doors). Some black japanned milkchurns serve as seats around the counter, which dispenses well kept Brakspears PA and SB and Old tapped from the cask. Popular bar food includes rolls (from £1), burgers (from £1.50), stilton ploughman's (£2.60), excellent chilli con carne, home-made pies like steak and kidney, pigeon or game (all £4.65), evening vegetarian dishes like nut roast Portuguese (£6.85), and steaks (from £8). Dominoes, cribbage and piped music (maybe Radio 1). Cribbage, dominoes, boules, Aunt Sally and a golf society; garden at rear. *(Recommended by TBB, Gordon and Daphne; more reports please)*

Brakspears   Tenant Allen Hayward   Real ale   Meals and snacks (12–2, 7–10; not Sun, not Mon evening)   Reading (0734) 342599   Open 11–2.30, 6–11

INKPEN   SU3564   Map 2

Swan ✿

Lower Inkpen; coming from A338 in Hungerford, take Park Street (first left after railway bridge, coming from A4); Inkpen is then signposted from Hungerford Common

It's the Singaporean food and warm welcome that draws people to this popular pub – spruced up inside and out this year. Fresh and fragrantly flavoured, the food might include fine oriental fish soup, excellent Szechuan prawns, chicken and lamb satay (£3.95), very good chicken curry, nasi goreng, popular Singapore noodles, excellent chicken with cashew nuts (£5.65), and beef rendang (£6.50); in the evening the only western-style dishes available are lamb cutlets or steaks, but there's a wider choice at lunchtime: broccoli and cheese quiche (£3.25), ploughman's (£3.75), home-made steak and kidney pie (£4.25), and lamb stew (£4.50); children's helpings. The Singapore connection shows in one or two other ways, too: a wicked gin sling, for instance, and deeply chilled lagers from Singapore, Thailand and China (as well as well kept Brakspears Bitter, Greene King Abbot, Hook Norton Best, and Mitchells ESB on handpump); Addlestones cider. A long, rambling row of rooms has a woodburning stove and log fire (including a big old fireplace with an oak mantlebeam between the bar counter and the restaurant area), well waxed flowery-cushioned pews and tables on the muted beige and brown carpet, and some traditional black-painted wall settles; at the bottom, heavily-beamed end are blond dining chairs and tables with a woodburning stove. A dice game called balut, fruit machine, quiet piped music, and magazines in one snug alcove up a couple of steps. The house claret is chateau-bottled for them by a friend with a house in Bordeaux – the licensees have a hotel and restaurant with them on the River Garonne. There are flowers out in front by the picnic-table sets, which are raised above the quiet village road. *(Recommended by Tony Triggle, Mrs Pat Crabb, Mayur Shah, TBB, Tony and Lynne Stark, W K Struthers, A W Dickinson, Gordon and Daphne)*

Free house   Licensee John Scothorne   Real ale   Meals and snacks (12–1.45, 7–9.30, not Sun evening, Tues lunchtime or Mon)   Restaurant   Inkpen (048 84) 326 Children in restaurant and bottom end of bar lunchtime and early evening   Open 11.30–2.30, 6.30–11; closed all day Mon, Tues lunchtime, and one week in January and September

KINTBURY   SU3866   Map 2

Dundas Arms 🛏

A4 Newbury–Hungerford; don't take the first signposted turning to Kintbury, but continue through Halfway, then take first left after about a mile; pub is after the River Kennet, but just before the Kennet and Avon Canal and the village itself

The waterside location here is lovely – between the River Kennet and the Kennet & Avon Canal – with banks of spring daffodils and lots of ducks; there's a lock just beyond the hump-backed bridge. Good bar food includes sandwiches (from £1.65; smoked salmon £2.95), soup (£2.50), crab au gratin (£3.80), smoked salmon pâté (£3.95), ploughman's (from £4.20), fresh pasta with pesto sauce (£4.25), gammon and egg (£5), smoked haddock with poached eggs or avocado, smoked chicken and prawn salad (£5.25), leek and gruyere pie (£5.30), steak and kidney pie (£5.75), home-cured gravadlax (£6.30), and puddings like bread and butter pudding (£2.50); good breakfasts. The partly panelled and carpeted bar has cream walls, one of which is covered with an outstanding array of blue and white plates. Well kept Adnams Bitter, Eldridge Pope Hardy, Fullers London Pride, and Morlands Bitter on handpump; there's a remarkable range of clarets in the good evening restaurant; tea or coffee; pleasant service. Fruit machine, juke box. The bedrooms are in converted ex-barge-horse stables, and their French windows open on to a secluded terrace. *(Recommended by Mrs Pat Crabb, Mrs M Lawrence, JMC, Lyn and Bill Capper, John C Baker, Tony and Louise Clarke, Alan Skull)*

Free house   Licensee David Dalzell-Piper   Real ale   Meals and snacks (not Sun, not Mon evening)   Restaurant (partly no smoking)   Kintbury (0488) 58263   Children welcome   Open 11–2.30, 6–11; closed Christmas to New Year   Bedrooms; £55B/£65B

KNOWL HILL   SU8279   Map 2

Bird in Hand

About 8 miles along A4 Reading–Maidenhead

This rather smart roadside inn has a spacious main bar with beams, cosy alcoves, dark brown panelling with a high shelf of willow pattern plates, some attractive Victorian stained glass in one big bow window, a red Turkey carpet on polished oak parquet, and a log fire. There's a centuries-older side bar, and a snug well padded back cocktail bar; pleasant, friendly atmosphere. Good home-made food includes a lunchtime cold buffet (£5.50 for as much as you want), as well as home-made soup (£1.75), sandwiches (open sandwiches from £2.10, club £3.85, sirloin steak £4.95), filled baked potatoes (from £2.45), chilli con carne (£3.95), changing daily hot dishes such as beef casserole with dumplings (£5.50), rabbit and hare in red wine, leek and port sauce (£5.95), and good home-made puddings (£2); the buffet area is no smoking. Well kept Brakspears PA and Old, and Youngs Special on handpump, an extensive wine list, and a few good malt whiskies, including the Macallan. The garden at the side is roomy and neatly kept. *(Recommended by David Warrellow, Mr and Mrs C H Garnett, D J and P M Taylor, John Baker, Dr J C Harrison)*

Free house   Licensee Jack Shone   Real ale   Meals and snacks (12–2.30, 6–10.30) Children in eating area and restaurant   Restaurant (not Sun evening)   Littlewick Green (062 882) 2781/6622   Open 11–3, 6–11   Bedrooms; £67B/£90B

LITTLEWICK GREEN   SU8379   Map 2

Cricketers

3 ³/₄ miles from M4 junction 9: A423(M) then left on to A4, from which village is signposted on left

This building is in three parts, the oldest of which, two identical cottages, date back some 400 years. There are cricketing prints and assorted memorabilia – including an extensive range of books on the subject – in the cheerful and well kept lounge, as well as maroon plush window seats and stools, lots of Windsor chairs, cartoons, and a substantial old factory clocking-in clock. Bar food includes sandwiches (from £1.50; toasties from £1.75), ploughman's (£3.50), good chilli con carne with potato skins, sour cream and chives or lunchtime ham and egg (£4), chicken curry (£4.25), steak and kidney pie (£4.50), tasty smoked haddock pasta with prawns and mushrooms (£4.75), beef and venison in ale (£5), and puddings like hot treacle tart (£1.75); evening dishes such as barnsley chop (£5) or steak (£6.50), and occasional summer barbecues; dishes are archly given cricketing pun names. Fullers London Pride, Morlands Original and Speckled Hen, and Wadworths 6X on handpump; cribbage, dominoes, fruit machine, and video game. The village green opposite is attractive. The National Trust's Maidenhead Thicket is just east on the A4, and there are woods along the A404 towards Marlow. *(Recommended by Amanda Dauncey, Joan and Tony Walker, TBB, A W Dickinson, Peter Maden, Hilary Robinson, Dr J C Harrison)*

Free house   Licensees John and Adrienne Hammond   Real ale   Meals and snacks (not Mon evening)   Maidenhead (0628) 822888   Children welcome   Open 11–3, 5.30–11; 11–11 Sat; closed 26 Dec

PEASEMORE   SU4577   Map 2

Fox & Hounds

Village signposted from B4494 Newbury–Wantage

The popularity of horse-racing locally is reflected here in a full set of Somerville's entertaining *Slipper's ABC of Fox-Hunting* prints, and one stripped-brick wall has a row of flat-capped fox masks. The two bars have brocaded stripped wall settles, chairs and stools around shiny wooden tables, and a log-effect gas fire (open to both rooms). Good bar food includes home-made soup (£2.25), a proper ploughman's (from £2.25), filled baked potatoes (from £2.75), pizzas to eat here or take away, home-made pies such as beef in beer or haddock and prawns (£4.75), vegetarian dishes like lentil bake or pasta shells in spicy tomato and mushroom sauce (£4.75), chicken breast filled with leek and stilton (£7.50), fresh whole lemon sole or fresh salmon, steaks (from £8.95), and their speciality beef Wellington (£11.50). Well kept Courage Best, John Smiths Bitter and Eldridge Pope Hardy on handpump, with a reasonable choice of wines; good service; darts, cribbage, backgammon, fruit machine and discreet juke box. A few picnic-table sets in front, by the quiet lane, look over to the rolling fields. *(Recommended by H E and M Wells, HNJ, PEJ; more reports please)*

Free house   Licensees David and Loretta Smith   Real ale   Meals and snacks (till 10pm)   Restaurant   Chieveley (0635) 248252   Children welcome away from bar and fruit machines   Open 11.30–3, 6.30–11

SONNING   SU7575   Map 2

Bull

Village signposted on A4 E of Reading; off B478, in village

The two atmospheric communicating rooms in this pretty and unpretentious old pub have cosy alcoves (one with a set of books), cushioned antique settles and low wooden chairs, newspapers on racks, inglenook fireplaces, beams in the low ceilings, and a penny-farthing. Well kept Brakspears SB, Flowers Original, Marstons Pedigree, and Wethereds SPA on handpump; chatty staff; soft piped music. Lunchtime bar food includes a good cold buffet with salads such as quiche or pies (£4.20) and mixed meats (£4.80); excellent breakfasts. The courtyard outside is particularly attractive with tubs of flowers and a rose pergola – though at busy times it may be packed with cars. If you bear left through the ivy-clad churchyard opposite, then turn left along the bank of the river Thames, you come to a very pretty lock. *(Recommended by Len and Sylvia Henderson, Cdr W S D Hendry, J R Williams, Gethin Lewis; more reports please)*

Whitbreads   Tenant Dennis Catton   Real ale   Lunchtime meals and snacks Restaurant   Reading (0734) 693901   Children in restaurant   Open 10–2.30, 5.30–11   Bedrooms; £35.25/£63.45

STANFORD DINGLEY   SU5771 Map 2
Bull

From M4 junction 12, W on A4, then right at roundabout on to A340 towards Pangbourne; first left to Bradfield, where left, then Stanford Dingley signposted on right

Partly divided into two by a couple of standing timbers hung with horse-brasses, the little bar in this friendly 15th-century pub has some red-cushioned seats carved out of barrels, a cushioned window settle and wheelback chairs on the red quarry tiles, heavy black beams, and an old brick fireplace; the other side is similarly furnished but carpeted, and decorations include an old station clock, some corn dollies and a few old prints. Good bar food includes popular soup (from £1.70, stilton £2.25), sandwiches on request, filled baked potatoes (from £1.65), ploughman's (from £2.50), savoury pancakes with a vegetarian or salmon and shrimp filling (£4.20), chilli con carne (£4.60), chicken provençale (£5.90), steaks (from £6.80), daily specials, and puddings like fruit crumble (£1.70). Well kept Bass, Brakspears, and Charrington IPA on handpump; ring-the-bull, occasional classical or easy listening music. There's also a simpler saloon bar with plush grey semi-circular banquettes and wheelback chairs, a tiny barrel-like bar counter, and another brick fireplace. In front of the building are some big rustic tables and benches, and to the side is a small garden with a few more seats. *(Recommended by Steve Huggins, Jerry and Alison Oakes, Simon Collett-Jones, Angus and Rosemary Campbell, R E Osborne, Keith and Sian Mitchell)*

Free house   Licensees Patrick and Trudi Langdon   Real ale   Meals and snacks (till 10pm; not Mon lunchtime)   Children in eating area of bar; not after 8.30pm; not Sat evening   Open 12–3, 7–11; closed Mon lunchtime

Old Boot
In summer the sloping south-facing back garden and terrace here – with their pleasant rural views – are a popular place to sit and there's a small livestock area where children are welcome; some tables outside in front, too. Inside, the neat bar has fine old pews, settles, country chairs and tables, attractive fabrics for the old-fashioned wooden-ring curtains, thoughtfully chosen pictures, an inglenook fireplace, and bunches of fresh flowers. Popular, tasty bar food includes home-made soup (£1.65), club sandwiches (from £1.90), smoked salmon and scrambled eggs on croûtons (£3.30), garlic mushrooms with bacon (£4.25), their own pie or hot baked avocado with prawns, cheese and bacon (£4.60), roasts (£5.10), chicken and stilton roulade (£6.25), steak (£9.25) and daily specials. Well kept Courage Best, Gales HSB, John Smith Bitter, and Wadworths 6X on handpump; malt whiskies; good service. *(Recommended by Lyn and Bill Capper, Stan Edwards, Mike Tucker, Syd and Wyn Donald, Keith and Sian Mitchell, Gordon and Daphne, Dr and Mrs R E S Tanner, M S Hancock, TBB, J Charles; more reports please)*

Free house   Licensees Mikala Evans, Leonard Overton   Real ale   Meals and snacks (till 10pm; till 9.30 Sun)   Restaurant (not Sun evening)   Reading (0734) 744292 Children welcome   Open 11–3, 6–11

WEST ILSLEY   SU4782 Map 2
Harrow ★

Signposted at East Ilsley slip road off A34 Newbury–Abingdon

There have been some substantial changes to this little downland inn this year. The two small bars have been carefully knocked together to keep the feel of separate areas but give more space. The walls have been repainted a dark terracotta making an excellent backdrop to the many mainly Victorian prints, there are big Turkey rugs on the floor, and the new mix of antique oak tables, unpretentious old chairs, a couple of more stately long settles and an unusual stripped twin-seated high-backed settle between the log fire and the bow window works very well; the cats are obviously finding life more comfortable now, though the friendly retriever seems still to prefer the outdoor life. The dining area (no smoking at lunchtime) is now next to the kitchen, which helps service, and new lavatories have been built on behind. Good, generously served bar food includes granary French rolls (from £1.85; curried chicken, mango chutney and mayonnaise £2), home-made soup (£1.95), mushrooms, garlic croûtons and bacon (£2.50), ploughman's (from £3), local sausages with home-made barbecue sauce (£3.75), rabbit pie with lemon, herbs and bacon (£3.95), walnut roulade with stilton and cauliflower filling (£4.75), marinated lemon chicken (£6.95), roast breast of duck with apples (£7.95), and puddings served with thick local cream like summer pudding or treacle tart (£2.20). Morlands, who started brewing in this village before they moved to Abingdon, supply the Original, Old Masters and Speckled Hen, kept well on handpump; coffee and teas (decaffeinated as well). Darts, cribbage, fruit machine and piped music. Picnic-table sets and other tables look out over the duck pond and cricket green, and a spacious children's garden has a notable play area with a big climber, swings, rocker and so forth – not to mention ducks, fowls, canaries, rabbits, goats and a donkey, and on our most recent visit even a horse lying basking in the sun (there are stables). The pub can be surprisingly lively – on show days, say, or if there's a cricket match going on. There are lots of walks nearby – the Ridgeway is just a mile away. Note they no longer do bedrooms. *(Recommended by A T Langton, Margaret Dyke, Simon Collett-Jones, Richard Houghton)*

Morlands   Lease: Mrs Heather Humphreys   Real ale   Meals and snacks (not Sun evening in winter)   East Ilsley (063 528) 260   Children welcome   Open 11–2.30 (3 Sat), 6–11

WINTERBOURNE   SU4572   Map 2

Winterbourne Arms

Not far from M4 junction 13; village signposted from B4494 Newbury–Wantage

This bustling and pretty village local has a comfortable atmosphere and a pleasant clutter of decorations – old bottles on strings, plates, smoothing-irons and lots of small pictures on the cream walls, and a slow-ticking wall-clock; off on the right you can find bar billiards. There's a log fire and brocaded small settles, chairs and stools on the flowery red carpet. Generous helpings of tasty home-made bar food include filled rolls (from £1.75), a range of ploughman's (from £3.25, tuna or spicy sausages £4.35), savoury quiche (£4.50), gammon steak (£6.75), several daily specials such as king prawns in garlic butter, good beef in Beaujolais or chicken breast in white wine and tarragon, and puddings (£2). Well kept Boddingtons, Flowers Original, Marstons Pedigree and Wethereds Bitter and SPA on handpump; friendly, homely service. Darts (not always in use), cribbage, dominoes, a tucked-away fruit machine, piped music. As the road is slightly sunken between the pub's two lawns, you can't actually see it from inside the bar – so the view from the big windows is rather peaceful. Picnic-table sets, and a big weeping willow outside; pleasant nearby walks to Snelsmore and Donnington. *(Recommended by Mayur Shah, Simon Collett-Jones, Carol and Mike Muston)*

Free house   Licensees Tony and Janet Tratt   Real ale   Meals and snacks (not Sun evening)   Restaurant (not Sun evening)   Chieveley (0635) 248200   Children in restaurant   Open 11.30–2.30, 6 (7 winter)–11; closed Mon lunchtime (except Bank Hols)

WOOLHAMPTON   SU5767   Map 2

Rising Sun

A4, nearly a mile E of village

Redecorated this year, this friendly pub keeps a fine selection of regularly changing real ales on handpump: Arkells BBB, Fullers London Pride, Hook Norton Best, Morlands Original, Ringwood Old Thumper, Theakstons Best, and Youngers IPA; several malts. The comfortable rambling lounge is decorated with small reproduction coaching prints; the public bar has darts, bar billiards, dominoes, cribbage, fruit machine and piped music. Popular, reasonably priced home-made bar food includes sandwiches (from £1.40), ploughman's (from £2.50), steak and mushroom pie or curry (£3.75), lasagne (£3.95), and steaks; friendly service. Seats outside at the back, where there's a swing. *(Recommended by Chris Fluck, E H and R F Warner, R Houghton; more reports please)*

Free house   Licensee Peter Head   Real ale   Meals and snacks (till 10pm) Restaurant   Woolhampton (0734) 712717   Children in restaurant   Open 11.15–2.30 (3 Sat), 6–11; closed 26 Dec

YATTENDON   SU5574   Map 2

Royal Oak ★ ⊘ ⇔

The Square; B4009 NE from Newbury; turn right at Hampstead Norreys, village signposted on left

This is the first inn we know of to have gone through the fashionable process of a management buy-out; everything continues as before, under the previous management team. The emphasis remains very much on the sophisticated restauranty food: fish soup with rouille and gruyere (£4.90), ploughman's (£5), salad of warm goat's cheese with lardons and croûtons (£6.90), crispy duck with salad frisée (£7.50), knuckle of pork with spring vegetables (£8.75), grilled escalope of salmon with spinach and beurre blanc (£9.95), grilled calves liver and bacon (£11.20), poached hake with a creamy sorrel sauce (£11.25), and puddings like home-made apple and rhubarb crumble with clotted cream (£4) or profiteroles with a hot chocolate sauce (£4.25); they will do sandwiches on request; for bar lunches you have to book a table. The lounge and prettily decorated panelled bar have an extremely pleasant atmosphere, log fires in winter, and a good range of well kept beers – Adnams Bitter, Badger Tanglefoot, and Wadworths 6X on handpump; good service. The pretty garden, replanted under the new regime, is now available for all visitors. The village – where Robert Bridges lived for many years – is very attractive. *(Recommended by W C M Jones, JMC, Gordon and Daphne, Gillian Savitz, Jim and Maggie Cowell, Dick Brown, Jamie and Ruth Lyons, TBB, Dr Sheila Smith, R J Walden, Simon Barber, Mike and Jill Dixon and friends, John and Pat Smyth, Bev and Doug Warrick)*

Free house   Licensee Julie Huff   Real ale   Meals and snacks (till 10pm)   Restaurant (closed Sun evenings)   Hermitage (0635) 201325   Children welcome   Occasional jazz evenings in garden   Open 11–2.30, 6–11; closed 25 Dec   Bedrooms; £60(£70B)/£70(£80B)

Lucky Dip

Besides the fully inspected pubs, you might like to try these Lucky Dips recommended to us and described by readers (if you do, please send us reports):

Aldworth [Haw Lane; B4009 towards Hampstead Norreys; SU5579], *Four Points*: Attractive thatched pub, main entry in last edition for its stupendous helpings of good value food; under a new regime there seems to have been a change of style though the place still has appeal — more news please *(Gordon and Daphne, LYM)*

☆ **Ashampstead** [SU5676], *Fleece & Feathers*: In beautiful rural spot with tables outside, comfortable free house with Windsor chairs and settles, guns, sporting prints, real ales inc Wadworths 6X, generous helpings of good food inc steaks and less usual items, friendly licensees and dog; small billiard room *(Geoffrey Medcalf, Richard Purser, Stan*

Edwards)

Aston [Ferry Lane; back rd through Remenham; SU7884], *Flower Pot*: A short stroll from Thames, with welcoming lounge bar, well kept Brakspears, bar food, friendly young service (not always quick); good garden with views over meadows to cottages and far side of river; on GWG68 *(Ian Phillips)*

Bagnor [SU4569], *Blackbird*: Very popular lunchtime for good value food; nr Watermill Theatre *(David and Christine Foulkes)*

☆ **Binfield** [Terrace Rd North; SU8471], *Victoria Arms*: Cleverly laid out with pleasing mix of old and new, good choice of seating areas, well kept Fullers Chiswick, London Pride and ESB, big display of bottled beers, reasonably priced bar food inc Sun; darts, fruit machine, piped music; children's room, summer barbecues in quiet garden *(Simon Collett-Jones, LYM)*

Binfield [B3034 from Windsor], *Stag & Hounds*: Low-beamed rambling pub which has been praised for imaginative bistro menu, atmosphere, service and well kept Courage, but no recent reports *(News please)*

Bisham [SU8485], *Bull*: Quietly chatty refined lounge bar with well kept Brakspears and Wethereds, friendly staff and bar food, though prominent concentration on restaurant *(Richard Houghton)*

Bracknell [Station Rd; SU8769], *Market*: Decent open-plan town pub with good service, well kept Ind Coope *(Richard Houghton)*; [London Rd], *Royal Oak*: Lively, like an old City pub, with well kept Courage and friendly, fast service *(Richard Houghton)*

Bray [SU9079], *Hinds Head*: Handsome old place with early Tudor beams, oak panelling, leather seats, smart restaurant; considerable potential *(LYM)*

☆ **Brimpton** [Brimpton Common; B3051, W of Heath End; SU5564], *Pineapple*: Popular thatched country pub, heavy low beams, stripped brick and timbering, rustic furniture on the tiled floor, rocking-chair by the fire; food inc sandwiches, pies, lots of filled baked potatoes, steaks, well kept Flowers Original, Wethereds and Whitbreads Pompey Royal and a good range of other drinks, side games area, maybe piped pop music; lots of tables on sheltered lawn, play area; open all day; children in eating area *(LYM — more reports please)*

Chieveley [East Lane; SU4774], *Hare & Hounds*: Has had well kept beer, very friendly atmosphere, good cheap food inc real chips in spick-and-span low-beamed bar full of bric-a-brac; skittle evenings; but no recent news *(Reports please)*

Cockpole Green [signed off A4 W of Maidenhead; SU7981], *Old Hatch Gate*: This rustic glory-hole with its cheap well kept Brakspears beers and happily Dickensian attitude seems at last to have closed: what a shame *(LYM)*

Cold Ash [SU5169], *Spotted Dog*: Currently on an upswing, with food worth watching *(L G and D L Smith)*

☆ **Compton** [E end, just off Streatley rd; SU5279], *Red Lion*: Doing particularly well under friendly young landlord, with well kept Morlands, good range of most attractively priced home-cooked food, and a real welcome for visitors despite being a proper country local; sizeable quiet garden with children's play area; children in eating area on right *(Stan Edwards, Gordon and Daphne, A T Langton, BB)*

Cookham [High St; SU8884], *Royal Exchange*: Pleasantly cosy, ivy-covered Benskins pub with low ceiling, dark panelling, bar food, real ale; useful back garden *(Nick Dowson, Alison Hayward)*

Cookham Dean Common [Harding Green; SU8785], *Uncle Toms Cabin*: Quaintly basic old-fashioned pub, quiet on weekdays; small bars with numerous oil lamps, friendly licensee and locals, pleasant atmosphere, well kept Benskins Best, home-made bar food and clean outside lavatories *(TBB)*

Cookham Rise [by Cookham Stn; SU8984], *Railway*: Clean and comfortable, with good range of very reasonably priced food lunchtime and evening, real ales such as Brakspears, Greene King Abbot and Wethereds; lots of railway memorabilia *(Peter Argent)*

☆ **Crazies Hill** [from A4, take Warren Row Rd at Cockpole Green signpost just E of Knowle Hill, then past Warren Row follow Crazies Hill signposts; also signed off A321 Wargrave—Henley — OS Sheet 175 map reference 799809; SU7980], *Horns*: Idiosyncratic combination of unassuming surroundings with ambitious food (limited Sun and Mon evenings, but can rise well above the ordinary, sometimes with good South-East Asian cooking) and well kept Brakspears PA and SB on handpump, decent wines, good collection of spirits; pleasant seats outside; quiet children may be tolerated in small bistro area until 7.30 *(TBB, LYM)*

☆ **Curridge** [3 miles from M4 junction 13: A34 towards Newbury, then first left to Curridge, Hermitage, and left into Curridge at Village Only sign — OS Sheet 174 map ref 492723; SU4871], *Bunk*: Stylish dining pub under promising new regime, with smart little stripped-wood tiled-floor bar on left, elegant stable-theme bistro on right with wooded-meadow views and conservatory; four well kept real ales, pricey but good bar food from steak or club sandwiches and warm herring-roe salad to wild salmon and char-grills; quick polite service and tables in neat little garden *(Gordon and Daphne, A T Langton, BB)*

Datchet [The Green; not far from M4 junction 5; SU9876], *Royal Stag*: Tasteful and cosily lit Tudor-style L-shaped bar with Allied real ales, friendly atmosphere, striking pillars dividing off dining area with decent food, piped music; in pretty village *(GB, CH, Graham Bush)*

East Ilsley [leaving village southwards; SU4981], *Star*: Good village local, lively and unpretentious, with attractive inglenook, beams, black woodwork; well kept Watneys-related and other real ales, attractively priced food from sandwiches up, faint piped music, garden behind with picnic-table sets and big play boot-house *(Barry and Anne, BB)*

Eton [High St; SU9678], *Crown & Cushion*: Proper pub with old-fashioned service, good choice of food, well kept Courage *(Richard Houghton)*; [Bridge St], *Watermans Arms*: Friendly local with good range of inexpensive, attractively served food inc lots of salads and good omelettes; well kept Courage, striking rowing and other decorations, pleasantly light and airy conservatory leading to enclosed yard; parking very difficult in tourist season *(Ian Phillips, LYM)*

Eton Wick [32 Eton Wick Rd; SU9478], *Pickwick*: Friendly local with Malaysian dishes besides more usual bar food inc soup, sandwiches and very good chilli con carne; Youngs beers *(Richard Nagle)*

Hampstead Norreys [Yattendon Rd; SU5376], *New Inn*: A main attraction's the spacious back garden with play area, goldfish pond and country views; straightforward inside, with well kept Morlands Old Masters and Speckled Hen, prompt friendly service, good value food with more elaborate evening dishes (not Mon or Tues), games in lively public bar; children welcome; bedrooms *(HNJ, PEJ, LYM)*

☆ **Holyport** [1 1/2 miles from M4 junction 8/9 via A308(M), A330; SU8977], *Belgian Arms*: Homely low-ceilinged village pub with interesting Belgian military uniform prints, well kept Brakspears, simple but tasty bar food (not Sun), pleasant conservatory used as evening restaurant, pleasant outlook over pond and charming green from garden with hens and goats beyond *(Lyn and Bill Capper, Keith and Sian Mitchell, Nick Dowson, William D Cissna, LYM)*

☆ **Holyport** [1 1/2 miles from M4 junction 8/9 via A308(M)/A330], *George*: Open-plan, but low ceiling, bay window with built-in seats and nice old fireplace give middle part some character; one end mainly drinking, the other mainly dining — decent plain cooking (inc popular club sandwiches with chips) and friendly and efficient service; neatly kept, Courage real ales, picnic-table sets outside; very busy lunchtime *(Richard Houghton, TBB, BB)*

Hungerford [Charnham St; 3 miles from M4 junction 14; town signposted at junction; SU3368], *Bear*: Civilised hotel bar with open fires, well kept real ales such as Wadworths 6X; bar food good but not copious nor cheap, restaurant; bedrooms comfortable and attractive, though expensive *(Andrea and Guy Bradley, Mr and Mrs P B Dowsett, Dick Brown, R Elliott, LYM)*

☆ **Hurst** [opp church; SU7972], *Castle*: Handsome traditional brick-built village inn with picnic-table sets overlooking its own bowling green; three cottagey rooms with

roaring fires, welcoming landlady and friendly staff, well kept Courage ales and good coffee, generous, decent home-cooked food; family dining area nearly as big as main bar; bedrooms *(Ian Phillips, D J and P M Taylor)*

☆ **Knowl Hill** [Bath Rd (A4 Reading—Maidenhead); SU8279], *Seven Stars*: Fairly smart, with extensive panelling, log fire, civilised and relaxed atmosphere; well kept Brakspears Mild, PA and Old, wide choice of wines, good range of simple bar food from sandwiches through vegetarian and other dishes to steaks, helpful service, fruit machine; big well laid out garden with summer barbecue and playhouse; a couple of attractive dogs; children's room *(TBB, Ian Phillips, LYM)*

Lambourn [Lambourn Woodlands; B4000, 2 1/2 miles towards Newbury; SU3278], *Hare & Hounds*: Old and unpretentious with modern extension; spacious bars, good choice of beers, wide range of good value food inc children's dishes, attentive quick service, unobtrusive piped music *(HNJ, PEJ)*

Littlewick Green [3 miles from M4 junction 9; A423(M) then left on to A4; SU8379], *Shire Horse*: Worth visiting for Courage's adjoining Shire Horse Centre (which is open Mar-Oct); comfortable, spacious and popular open-plan lounge bar, well kept Courage ales, piped music, tea house, play area by big side lawn, bar food *(LYM)*

Maidenhead [Queen St; SU8783], *Hand & Flowers*: Simple traditional Victorian town pub with prompt friendly service, Brakspears PA, nice relaxed atmosphere, separate food servery, fruit machine *(Simon Collett-Jones)*

nr **Maidenhead** [Marion Rd (A308 N)], *Robin Hood*: Friendly old low-ceilinged pub with fairly quiet piped music, bar food inc good omelettes, well kept Courage, garden with play area *(Anon)*

☆ *nr* **Maidenhead** [Pinkneys Green (A308 N); SU8582], *Golden Ball*: Well organised Brewers Fayre pub with pleasant decor, cosy atmosphere, well kept Whitbreads-related real ales, good food (steak and kidney pie recommended), fast friendly service; much refurbished, though the low-ceilinged bit by the open fire still has a rustic air; seats on peaceful lawn, open all day *(TBB, Amanda Dauncey, LYM)*

Maidens Green [Winkfield Rd; signs to Winkfield Plain W of Winkfield off A330, then 1st right; SU8972], *Cottage*: Cosy old pub doing well under current regime, with small flagstoned bar, really pleasant staff, well kept Badger Best tapped from the cask; great emphasis on the restaurant *(R Houghton, TBB)*

Marsh Benham [off A4 W of Newbury; SU4267], *Red House*: This very popular main entry closed in 1991 *(LYM — news please)*

Newbury [Market Pl; SU4666], *Old Waggon & Horses*: Pleasant views of Kennet from beamed and partly flagstoned riverside lounge bar, old fishing rods and stuffed fish behind counter, courteous, friendly service, unhurried civilised atmosphere; Courage beers, food from beef sandwiches to gammon, juke box, fruit machine *(Simon Collett-Jones, LYM)*; [Greenlands Rd; Stroud Green], *Plough*: Unspoilt little villagey pub on outskirts nr race course, well kept Courage Directors, friendly licensees, bar food inc filled baps *(David and Ruth Hollands)*; [Greenham Rd (A34)], *Railway*: This friendly little hotel was demolished in 1991

☆ **Old Windsor** [17 Crimp Hill, off B3021 — itself off A308/A328; SU9874], *Union*: Neat L-shaped bar with a couple of leather chesterfields, plush stools, lots of banknotes on beams, nostalgic show-business photographs, woodburner, fruit machine and piped pop music; Courage, Flowers and Theakstons, attractive copper-decorated restaurant, good value food here and in bar; white plastic tables under cocktail parasols on front terrace *(D W Boydell, Mayur Shah, Ian Phillips, Shirley Pielou, BB)*

Old Windsor [Crimp Hill], *Oxford Blue*: Nice jolly atmosphere, very well patronised, good lunchtime food, served pleasantly in garden-room extension; well kept real ale, lots of air force memorabilia, restaurant and garden; children's play area *(Shirley Pielou, Mayur Shah)*

Pangbourne [SU6376], *Copper Kettle*: Very pleasant bar in good hotel with well kept beers and good lunchtime bar snacks *(Cdr W S D Hendry)*; [opp church], *Cross Keys*: Simple but comfortable lounge with aviation photographs; Courage ales and decent bar food from sandwiches to steaks; popular Sun lunchtime barbecues on good largely covered back terrace, with decorative Japanese bridge over little stream; two interconnecting family rooms *(Keith and Sian Mitchell)*

☆ **Reading** [Kennet Side; SU7272], *Fishermans Cottage*: Good spot by lock on the Kennet, with lovely back garden; character decor, pleasant stone snug behind woodburning range, light and airy conservatory, almost a wine-bar atmosphere; well kept Fullers Chiswick, ESB and London Pride, small choice of wines, food ready to serve and cooked to order, pleasant service, small darts room *(Simon Collett-Jones, Len and Sylvia Henderson)*

Reading [35 Blagrave St], *Blagrave Arms*: Courage ales, good popular bar lunches inc immense hot beef sandwich with salad; lots of seats *(Ian Phillips)*; [Cholmely Rd, Newtown], *Eastgate*: Friendly Irish pub in not-so-smart area, very diverse regulars, well kept Courage, nice garden nr Kennet Canal; has been open all day Mon-Sat *(Liam Baldwin)*; [Mount Pleasant], *Greyhound*: Notable home-made pizzas *(Kev and Caron Holmes)*; [316 Kennetside], *Jolly Anglers*: Good unspoiled canalside local with couple of picnic-set tables on towpath; warm welcome, very reasonable food, Courage beers *(Ian Phillips)*; [Castle St, next to PO], *Sweeney Todds*: Looks like a pie shop with

various higgledy-piggledy rooms downstairs, waitresses bring superb traditional meat and game pies etc — inexpensive and very good, also take-aways; garden *(Mrs C F Peters)*; [part of Caversham Hotel, Caversham Bridge/Richfield Ave], *Three Men in a Boat*: Worth knowing for fine riverside position, with popular home-made food, well kept beer and terrace *(E G Parish)*; [Abbey St], *White Lion*: Civilised and comfortable modern Morlands pub with eclectic but spotless decor, limited but well presented bar food, piped music, pleasant terrace; can get crowded lunchtime *(Ian Phillips, A T Langton)*

☆ **Remenham** [A423, just over bridge E of Henley; SU7683], *Little Angel*: The food in this rather upmarket pub can be excellent, and they pull out all the stops in regatta week (prices approach restaurant levels, they add a service charge); the fish restaurant has been a particular attraction, as has their readiness to serve a wide choice of wines by the glass; well kept Brakspears, piped music, floodlit terrace *(D A Greer, LYM)*

Sindlesham [Bearwood Rd, off B3349; SU7769], *Walter Arms*: Has been comfortable dining pub with wide choice of good quickly served bar food, well kept Courage and decent bedrooms; but no recent reports *(News please)*

Slough [Park St; off A4 into Windsor Rd then Hershel St; SU9779], *Queen of England*: Straightforward pub winning friends with its exceptionally friendly welcome and extremely good value food; well kept Wethereds, music some nights *(TBB, A W Dickinson)*; [Windsor Rd], *Rising Sun*: Pleasant open-plan town local, busy but not boisterous; friendly service, well kept Bass, Charrington IPA and a guest beer; reasonable bar food Mon-Fri *(Richard Houghton)*; [Albert St], *Wheatsheaf*: Well kept Fullers in spacious oak-beamed bar, good value food, smallish suntrap garden *(A W Dickinson)*

Sonning [SU7575], *White Hart*: Praised in former editions, this hotel has been renamed the Great House and has moved out of our orbit

☆ **Streatley** [SU5980], *Bull*: Busy traditional pub with well kept Watneys-related real ales on handpump, friendly staff and regulars, good sensibly priced food in bar and restaurant; can get very busy; nr GWG97 *(A T Langton, Joan Olivier)*

Streatley, *Swan*: This smart complex has — at a hefty price — well kept real ales, well made bar food (just soup and sandwiches Sun), light evening meals (not Sun) in college rowing-club state barge, good service, traditional games, and a welcome for children, all in colourful grounds by the Thames; bedrooms luxurious, many with river views and own terraces *(Robert Kimberley, LYM)*

Tilehurst [Oxford Rd; SU6673], *Restoration*: Comfortable plum-coloured Victorian-style interior, friendly barmaids, good home-made hot pies and sandwiches, Allied and other real ales, games bar *(Geoffrey Medcalf, Richard Purser)*

Twyford [A4; SU7876], *Horse & Groom*: Reliable steak pub, substantial old place, with good snacks and real ale *(Ian Phillips)*

☆ **Waltham St Lawrence** [SU8276], *Bell*: Handsome and interesting 16th-century pub owned by local charity, in centre of pretty village; straightforward bar food (not Sun), good value restaurant, well kept and decently priced Brakspears, Tetleys and Wadworths, wide choice of whiskies, maybe piped music; pleasant back lawn; parking not always easy *(Ian Phillips, D J and P M Taylor, Comus Elliott, LYM)*

Warfield [Church Lane/A3095; SU8872], *Yorkshire Rose*: A former tea house, now a pub/restaurant with two separate areas; pub part is cosy with low beams and nice atmosphere, with many different age groups, and good service from uniformed staff; Brakspears and a guest beer, remarkably fine gents', good-sized car park *(Richard Houghton, TBB)*

☆ **Wargrave** [High St, off A321 Henley—Twyford; SU7878], *White Hart*: Spacious and friendly low-beamed lounge bar decorated to suit its 18th-century character, good value bar food, well kept Whitbreads-related real ales maybe inc Pompey Royal; restaurant, good-sized car park *(TBB, LYM)*

Wargrave [High St], *Bull*: Good atmosphere and open fire in low-beamed pub with well kept Brakspears and good value bar food; tables on covered terrace; bedrooms *(LYM)*

☆ **Wickham** [3 miles from M4 junction 14, via A338, B4000; SU3971], *Five Bells*: Small village inn firmly in racehorse country, with big log fire, lots of bric-a-brac behind the bar, bar food from sandwiches and a good ploughman's through popular steak and kidney pie to steaks (maybe an extra charge for credit cards), Ushers and Watneys-related real ales, garden with very well equipped play area; children in eating area; bedrooms *(Paul Evans, LYM)*

☆ **Windsor** [Datchet Rd — opp Riverside Stn, nr Castle; SU9676], *Royal Oak*: Clean, well run and spacious; beams, joists, some fine stained-glass screens, half panelling, red plush seating and armed Windsor chairs, old and well lit prints, and brick fireplace dividing off another similar room; airy eating room with big food serving counter — good choice of reasonably priced bar snacks and full meals; very efficient friendly service, maybe some traffic noise; white furniture in L-shaped concreted garden; under same ownership as Greyhound in Chalfont St Peter *(Dr and Mrs A K Clarke, John and Heather Dwane, Mrs A Crowhurst, BB)*

☆ **Windsor** [Castle Hill, opp Henry VIII Gate], *Horse & Groom*: Friendly little partly Tudor pub, nicest near the door; relaxed staff, well done straightforward cheap food, well kept Courage Best and Directors; surprisingly uncrowded, maybe loud radio music *(Wayne Brindle)*

Windsor [Thames St], *Adam & Eve*: Bustling young people's pub by theatre, well kept Bass and Charrington IPA, occasional barbecues in little back yard; don't try to park nearby *(Sidney and Erna Wells, LYM)*; [Thames St], *Donkey House*: In for its nice Thames location, with tables outside, but does have well kept Friary Meux Best, cheap food, friendly staff *(LYM)*

☆ **Winkfield** [A330, opp church; SU9072], *White Hart*: Neatly modernised well kept Tudor pub with ex-bakery bar and ex-courthouse restaurant (weekend concentration on this), bar food, Courage real ale, friendly staff, sizeable garden *(TBB, Mr and Mrs Damien Burke, LYM)*

Winkfield [B3022 towards Windsor; SU9272], *Hernes Oak*: Clean, warm and well run local with enterprising choice of spirits; bar food, children allowed in back room *(LYM)*

☆ **Wokingham** [from Wokingham inner ring rd left into Easthampstead Rd just after A329 Bracknell turn-off; turn right at White Horse, then left into Honey Hill — OS Sheet 175 map ref 826668; SU8068], *Crooked Billet*: Jolly and homely atmosphere in sprucely furnished weatherboarded country pub — pews, tiles, brick serving counter, crooked black joists; particularly well kept Brakspears PA, SB, Mild and Old on handpump, simple cheap food, nice mix of customers, communicating restaurant area (not Sun — bar food very limited Sun evening); seats and swings outside; children in restaurant; has been open all day *(Ian Phillips, W Bailey, Mrs A Crowhurst, Philip Harrison, LYM)*

☆ **Woodside** [off A322 Windsor—Ascot — look for blue/gold board; SU9270], *Duke of Edinburgh*: Pleasant, cosy atmosphere, well kept Arkells or Courage, friendly service, good bar food — especially fish, but cauliflower cheese and bacon and cheesecake also recommended; small garden, shame about the juke box *(TBB, Robert Kimberley)*

Woolhampton [off A4; SU5767], *Rowbarge*: Friendly country pub nr Kennet & Avon Canal, with lots of tables outside, beamed bar, panelled family room, big French-windowed dining room, tables in garden; good small choice of bar food inc freshly made sandwiches and Sun roasts; well behaved dogs allowed *(Dr and Mrs R E S Tanner, LYM)*

Buckinghamshire

Several new entries here, or pubs back in these pages after an absence, include the refreshingly unpretentious Red Lion at Chenies, the Swan at Denham (attractive village, good food, pretty garden), the hidden-away Seven Stars at Dinton, the friendly and relaxed Cross Keys in Great Missenden and (our best new find here this year) the extremely welcoming and very pretty Old Swan at Cheddington. The Bull at Bellingdon gains a food award this year – this dining pub is doing extremely well now, with very courteous service and interesting cooking. Other changes to note here include the cheerful and attractive Clifden Arms at Worminghall's escape from its brewery tie (it's now a free house); the Pheasant in a lovely spot at Brill has also "gone free". The civilised old Greyhound at Marsh Gibbon has started an unusual specialisation, in Thai food. The Red Lion at Stoke Green and Bull & Butcher in Turville, both long-standing favourites, have friendly new licensees. Other pubs that are currently doing particularly well in the county include the friendly Chequers at Fingest, the George in Great Missenden (remarkably wide choice of food), the very friendly Pink & Lily at Lacey Green (a fine all-rounder), the Red Lion near Princes Risborough (as nice a country pub as you'd hope to find in the Home Counties – and a friendly and simple place to stay), and the Old Crown at Skirmett (one of the best places for food in the Chilterns). The Swan at Ley Hill is another to note for good food; and it's well worth knowing that the Dog & Badger at Medmenham (quite handy for the Thames) now serves food all day; food's also a plus at the Old Thatched Inn at Adstock, the Bull & Butcher in Akeley (good lunchtime buffet), the Old Hare in Beaconsfield (imaginative), the Peacock at Bolter End, the Black Horse near Chesham, the Walnut Tree at Fawley, the unspoilt White Hart at Northend, the Crown at Penn (shows what can be done within the confines of a brewery food format) and the White Swan at Whitchurch. Among the Lucky Dip entries at the end of the chapter, pubs of particular note at the moment (virtually all of them inspected by us, so we can be sure they're worth a visit) include the Five Bells at Botley, Blue Flag at Cadmore End, Dinton Hermit at Ford, Old Sun at Lane End, Rising Sun at Little Hampden, Red Lion and perhaps White Lion at Marsworth, Stag at Mentmore, Kings Arms at Skirmett, Old Plow at Speen, Oak & Saw at Taplow, Old Swan at The Lee and Plough at Winchmore Hill; there's a good choice in Marlow, with something there to suit almost every taste.

ADSTOCK   SP7330 Map 4

Old Thatched Inn

Just N of A413, 4 miles SE of Buckingham

Spotlessly kept, this comfortable thatched village pub is popular for its very good, home-made food: soup (£1.75), grilled sardines (£4), lasagne (£4.50), sandwiches (from £2.25; toasties £2.50), chicken liver and bacon pâté (£2.50), tasty ratatouille au gratin, ploughman's (from £2.50; the stilton is excellent), grilled sardines (£4), pork curry (£5), chicken tikka or superb steak and kidney pie (£5.50), good scampi (£5.75), fresh trout (£6), sautéed lamb with rosemary and garlic or 10oz rump steak (£8.50), and puddings (£1.75). Well kept Adnams, Hook Norton, Morrells Bitter, Ruddles Best and County and Websters Yorkshire are tapped from the cask or on handpump; light blanket pressure on some; freshly squeezed orange juice, and as much tea or coffee as you can drink for 75p. The bar is decorated with antique hunting prints, copper and brassware, there are stripped beams and timbers, flagstones by the bar counter, and wheelback chairs and bays of green plush button-back banquettes in carpeted areas leading off; potted plants, fresh flowers and an open winter fire (with a log-effect gas fire in summer). Dominoes and cribbage. There is a dining conservatory which is attached to the restaurant. *(Recommended by K and E Leist, C G T Prince, Les and Jean Bradman, John Whitehead, Miss M James, A Clack, Karen and Graham Oddey, Marjorie and David Lamb, Mr and Mrs T F Marshall)*

Free house   Licensee Ian Tring   Real ale   Meals and snacks (12–2, 6–10) Restaurant (not Sun evening)   Aylesbury (0296) 712584   Children in restaurant Open 12–2.30, 6–11; closed 25 Dec

AKELEY   SP7037   Map 4
Bull & Butcher
The Square; just off A413

The lunchtime buffet in the small dining room of this friendly village pub has a wide range of decently made help-yourself salads with home-cooked beef or honey-roast ham, and home-made quiches and pies (around £4 to £6). There's also an evening steak bar (8oz rump £11 – which includes pudding and coffee; other dishes too, such as large gammon steaks, 8oz lamb noisettes and scampi). Well kept Fullers London Pride, Marstons Pedigree, Morlands Original, and a guest beer on handpump, good value wines by the bottle, several malt whiskies and farm cider. The rough-cast walls of the long open-plan bar are decorated with drawings of well known customers, there are red plush button-back banquettes, and on each side of a massive central stone chimney there are fires, with a third down at the end; the curved beams in this wood-floored lower bar area are unusual. Darts, shove-ha'penny, cribbage, dominoes, Sunday evening bridge club, piped music. Pleasant beer garden. *(Recommended by Paul and Margaret Baker, A M Neal; more reports please)*

Free house   Licensee Harry Dyson   Real ale   Lunchtime meals and snacks (not Sun) Steak bar   Lillingstone Dayrell (028 06) 257 (not Sun or Mon)   Children in eating areas   Occasional live entertainment   Open 12–3, 6 (6.30 Sat)–11

AMERSHAM   SU9597   Map 4
Kings Arms
High Street; A413

The black-and-white Tudor frontage here is extremely attractive and the rambling bar has lots of snug alcoves, heavy beams, high-backed antique settles, quaint old-fashioned chairs and other seats, and a big inglenook. Simple bar food includes toasted ham and cheese sandwich (£1.40), home-made soup (£1.35; the onion is good), filled French stick (£1.95), ploughman's (£2.55), open prawn sandwich (£3.25), salads (£3.70), steak and kidney pie (£3.95), and daily specials like fish pie, Hungarian goulash or pasta (£3.50-£3.95), and puddings such as fruit tart (£1.95); they also do cream teas between 3 and 5pm. Benskins Best and Greene King IPA on handpump, with Ind Coope Burton tapped from the cask behind the bar counter; friendly efficient service. Dominoes, cribbage and two popular monthly quiz competitions. In an attractive little flower-filled courtyard and coachyard there are seats, with more tables and a climbing frame beyond, on a tree-sheltered lawn; the goat is called Jocelyn. *(Recommended by TBB, R Tomlinson,*

Peter Hood, Barbara Hatfield, Michael and Alison Sandy, M Saunders, R M Savage, Jim and Becky Bryson)

Benskins (Allied) Licensee John Jennison Real ale Meals and snacks (all day until 9pm) Restaurant (not Sun evening or Mon – no pipes or cigars, and they ask other smokers to be considerate) Amersham (0494) 726333 Children in eating area of bar until 8pm Open 11–11

nr AMERSHAM SU9495 Map 4
Queens Head

Whielden Gate; pub in sight just off A404, 1 1/2 miles towards High Wycombe at Winchmore Hill turn-off; OS Sheet 165 map reference 941957

Delightfully unspoilt, this pretty little country local has a good pubby atmosphere, low beams, simple traditional furnishings, a good cigarette card collection, horsebrasses, and lots of brass spigots. There are flagstones by the big inglenook fireplace (which still has the old-fashioned wooden built-in wall seat curving around right in beside the woodburning stove – with plenty of space under the seat for log storage), a stuffed albino pheasant, and old guns. The friendly dalmatian is called Monty and there's also a tabby cat. Home-made bar food includes soup (£1.75), omelettes (£3), bean and vegetable bake (£3.50), pheasant pie or chicken and spinach mornay in filo basket (£4.75), and lots of pizzas (from £4). Well kept Benskins Best and Ind Coope Burton on handpump; darts, shove-ha'penny, dominoes, cribbage, fruit machine, and piped music. There are often summer barbecues in the garden behind (and Aunt Sally) – plump conifers, a small pond, attractive tubs of flowers on the terrace, swings and a climber. (Recommended by MBW, JHW, TBB, Jill Hampton, Brian Metherell, J H Walker)

Benskins (Allied) Tenants Les and Mary Anne Robbins Real ale Meals and snacks (till 10pm); not Sun evening Amersham (0494) 725249 Children in family room Open 11–2.30 (3 Sat), 5.30 (6 Sat)–11 (Sat evening opening 6)

ASTWOOD SP9547 Map 4
Swan

Main Road; village signposted from A422 Milton Keynes–Bedford

Some 300 years old, this partly thatched pub is warmly friendly and old-fashioned. The open-plan bar has low oak beams, antique seats and tables, and a log fire in the handsome inglenook. Bar food includes good home-made soup (£1), a choice of ploughman's (from £1.75), good quiche (£2.50), harvest pie (£2.80), steak sandwich in a freshly baked roll (£2.95), salads (from £2.95), roast chicken or scampi (£2.95), and 8oz steak (£6; in the restaurant their steaks run up to 2lb T-bone). Well kept Adnams Best, Everards Tiger, Flowers Original, Marstons Pedigree and Wethereds on handpump; friendly service; darts, shove-ha'penny, cribbage, dominoes, unobtrusive piped pop music. The quiet lawn at the back has tables under old fruit trees, and there are more seats out in front; handy for Stagsden Bird Gardens. (Recommended by Monica Darlington, Lyn and Bill Capper, Mr and Mrs J M Elden, Philip King; more reports please)

Free house Licensees Jim and Diane Nicklen and Paul Cribb Real ale Meals and snacks (not Sun evening) Restaurant Children in one part of bar and restaurant Open 11–2.30, 6–11 – maybe all day on bank hols and special occasions Two bedrooms North Crawley (023 065) 272; £25.50S/£35.75S

BEACONSFIELD SU9490 Map 2
Old Hare

A mile from M40 junction 2; 41 Aylesbury End, Old Beaconsfield

Several bars in this busy pub ramble about: to the right of the door a dimly lit end room has a big, very high-backed antique settle as well as more straightforward furniture (and a serving hatch); a lighter room has a big inglenook with a copper hood, and the rooms by the odd-angled bar counter are decorated with prints of hares, photographs and prints of the pub. Cheerfully efficient staff serve the varied and often imaginative food. At lunchtime there are daily specials like mushroom and hazelnut or brie and watercress soups (£1.95), prawn and courgette quiche (£3.50), liver and bacon casserole or sweet and sour pork or grilled brill (£4.75); there's also filled French bread or wholemeal baps (from £1.95), ploughman's (from £3.25), steak in ale pie (£3.95), salads (from £3.95), chilli spiced prawns and cod in rich tomato sauce (£4.25), and evening steak (£8.25); home-made puddings. Well kept Benskins Best, Ind Coope Burton and Tetleys Yorkshire on handpump, and guests like Adnams, Greene King Abbot, Marstons Pedigree or Wadworths 6X; lots of malt whiskies; no machines or music. The big, sunny back garden has lots of white plastic garden furniture and a couple of picnic-table sets and was packed on our warm lunchtime visit with local business people and ladies lunching. *(Recommended by Simon Collett-Jones, Andy and Jill Kassube, Richard Houghton, Ian Phillips; more reports please)*

Benskins (Allied) Manager A M Reed Real ale Meals and snacks (12–2, 7.30–10); no food Sun evenings Beaconsfield (0494) 673380 Open 11–2.30, 5.30–11; closed evening May 10 for annual street fair

BELLINGDON SP9405 Map 4

Bull 🛇

Signposted off A416 in Chesham; on Bellingdon Rd on N side of village

Very much a dining pub now, this spotlessly kept and very popular old brick cottage has added more tables and chairs to cope with the demand for their interesting food. There are built-in planked dark wood and red plush cushioned wall seats, vases of fresh flowers, and a bow window with a highly polished round table and built-in seats; beams in the slightly sloping ceiling, several attractive display cases, a big clock and barrel tops on the walls, an inglenook fireplace with horsebrasses on the mantlebeam, and a tiny room up some steps with quite a few old cattle prints. They don't do sandwiches or ploughman's now: soup (£1.50; the onion is recommended), mushrooms in tomato, garlic and red wine (£2.25), notable tuna and mushroom or seafood with fresh scallops pancakes (£4.25), beef, mushroom and Guinness pie or stuffed marrow (£4.50), salmon and mushroom pancake (£6), fresh crab and avocado mornay (£7), steaks (from £8), and puddings (from £2). Well kept Adnams, Benskins Best, Greene King IPA and Ind Coope Burton on handpump, and house wines and others served from the dark wood-planked bar counter; courteous, very efficient service; the friendly retriever is called Oscar. The pretty front garden has picnic-table sets, attractive barrels of flowers and a swing; food is served out here or on the large terrace with its attractive pergola. There are a few enamel signs on the wall by the car park, and a bus stop just outside. *(Recommended by Geoffrey Donald, Robert Gower, Simon Collett-Jones, Richard Nagle, David Wallington, Maurice Southon, P Saville, Les and Jean Bradman, Pat and Derek Wescott, Stephen King)*

Benskins (Allied) Tenants Jeff and Sue Steers Real ale Meals and snacks Cholesbury (024 029) 8163 Children in eating area of bar Open 11–2.30, 6–11; closed 24 and 25 Dec

BLEDLOW SP7702 Map 4

Lions of Bledlow

From B4009 from Chinnor towards Princes Risborough, the first right turn about 1 mile outside Chinnor goes straight to the pub; from the second, wider right turn, turn right through village

A fair number of walkers gather in this 16th-century pub. It's perched on a steep slope and beyond a sheltered crazy-paved terrace and a series of small sloping lawns, you can walk straight up into the hills and the steep beechwoods beyond. The inglenook bar has lots of heavy low beams, attractive oak stalls built into one partly panelled wall, other seats and an antique settle on its deeply polished ancient tiles, and marvellous views from the bay windows over a small quiet green to the plain stretched out below; log fires. Freshly cooked food includes soup, filled French bread and ploughman's, and changing daily specials. Well kept Courage Directors, Wadworths 6X, Wethereds and Youngs on handpump, with a guest beer. One of the two cottagey side rooms has a space game. *(Recommended by Lee Goulding, David Warrellow, J E Stanton, Mrs J Crawford, Margaret and Trevor Errington, Tony and Lynne Stark, Dr J C Harrison)*

Free house   Licensee F J McKeown   Real ale   Meals and snacks (not Sun evening) Restaurant (not Sun evening)   Princes Risborough (084 44) 3345   Children in side rooms and restaurant   Open 11–3, 6–11; closed evening 25 Dec

BOLTER END   SU7992   Map 4

Peacock

Just over 4 miles from M40 junction 5; A40 to Stokenchurch, then B482

You're made to feel welcome in this bustling, cheerful pub whether you've just come for a drink or to enjoy the wide range of popular food. The rambling bar is brightly modernised, has a good log fire in one alcove, and ABC and Bass on handpump; decent wines and coffee, and freshly squeezed orange juice. Efficiently served, the bar food includes ploughman's (£2.90), pizzas with various toppings (from £3.45), vegetarian kidney bean and mushroom provençal (£3.90), home-made lasagne (£4.50), a home-made beef and vegetable curry pie (£4.65), Chinese-style turkey breast (£5.75), 12oz rump steak (£9.25), puddings like home-made blackberry and apple pie (£1.95), and daily specials such as Italian beef topped with garlic bread, satays (made by a Thai lady), and cheesecake or syllabub; fish fresh from Billingsgate on Thursdays. Darts, cribbage and dominoes. In summer there are seats around a low stone table and picnic-table sets in the neatly kept roadside garden. The 'no children' is strictly enforced here. *(Recommended by A W Dickinson, Barbara Hatfield, David Warrellow, Margaret Dyke, C A Holloway, A C Morrison)*

ABC (Allied)   Tenant Peter Hodges   Real ale   Meals and snacks (till 10pm; not Sun evening)   High Wycombe (0494) 881417   Open 11–2.30, 6–11

BRILL   SP6513   Map 4

Pheasant

Windmill Rd; village signposted from B4011 Bicester–Long Crendon

By the time this edition comes out, Mr Carr will have bought this 17th-century pub from Allied Breweries. It's in a lovely spot beside one of the oldest post windmills still in working order, and picnic-table sets in the small, sheltered back garden look down towards Oxfordshire fading into a great distance. The quietly modernised and neatly kept bar has comfortable russet leatherette button-back banquettes in bays around its tables, a woodburning stove, and a step up to a dining area which is decorated with attractively framed Alken hunting prints – and which has the view. Bar food includes sandwiches (from £1.20), tagliatelle (£2.40), popular burgers (from £3.20), a notable ploughman's (£3.60), home-cooked honey roast ham with two eggs (£4.25), a wide choice of fresh fish (£4.95), steaks (from £9.40), and daily specials like home-made soup (£1.40), vegetarian dishes (from £3.20), home-made lasagne (£4.95) or lamb steak (£7.80); puddings such as home-made cheesecake (£1.60). Well kept Tetleys and Wadworths 6X on handpump; no dogs (they have three golden retrievers themselves). *(Recommended by Mr and Mrs T F Marshall, Duncan Stuart-Mills, Ted George, Geoffrey Medcalf, Richard Purser, David Lamb, R K Sutton)*

Free house   Licensee Mike Carr   Real ale   Meals and snacks   Restaurant Kingston Blount (0844) 237104   Children in restaurant   Open 11–3, 5.30 (6.30 Sat)–11; closed 25 Dec

CHALFONT ST PETER   SU9990 Map 3

Greyhound

High Street; A413

This pleasant and comfortable 14th-century inn has a long open-plan bar with brasses on the lantern-lit dark panelling, low beams, plenty of deep red plush seats, and a huge winter log fire in a handsome fireplace. Bar food includes sandwiches (from £1.35; toasties from £1.95), home-made soup (£1.75), ploughman's (from £2.65), hot beef sandwich (£2.75), filled baked potatoes (from £2.75), salads (from £3.95), and a choice of three roasts from their carvery (£5.25); friendly staff. Well kept Courage Best and Directors, Gales HSB, John Smiths, and Wadworths 6X on handpump from a good long counter; fruit machine. There are tables among flower tubs in the pretty front courtyard, with more on a sheltered lawn by the little River Misbourne; large car park. *(Recommended by Nigel Gibbs, Lyn and Bill Capper, Duncan Stuart-Mills, A M S Jeeves, JM, PM)*

Courage   Tenant John Harriman   Real ale   Meals and snacks (12–2.30, 7–9.30 – till 10 weekends)   Restaurant (midnight supper licence)   Gerrards Cross (0753) 883404 Children in eating area and restaurant   Open 11–11   Bedrooms; £42/£52.50

CHEDDINGTON   SP9217 Map 4

Old Swan

High St

This mainly thatched, cream-painted old building is very pretty in summer with its lovely hanging baskets and tubs, and side lawn with little wishing well and white garden furniture and picnic-table sets; slide and swings for children. Inside, there's a quietly civilised, friendly atmosphere in the right-hand bar rooms; a few tables with nice country-style chairs, a built-in wall bench and old-fashioned plush dining chairs on the bare boards, an inglenook with glass cabinets filled with brass on either side of it and quite a few horsebrasses, and little hunting prints on the walls; the other part is carpeted with simple furnishings, and darts. Well kept ABC Best, Tetleys and Wadworths 6X on handpump, ten malt whiskies, wines of the month (£4.25 a bottle), and popular mulled wine in winter. On the other side of the main door is a room with housekeepers' chairs on the rugs and quarry tiles and country plates on the walls, and a step up to a carpeted part with stripy wallpaper and pine furniture. The little dining room leads off here. Good home-made food can be eaten in the bar or restaurant and might include sandwiches (from £1.35), ploughman's (£2.30), vegetarian mixed platter (£3.95), steak and kidney pie or lasagne (£4.25), sardines (£4.85), chicken tarragon (£6.95), steaks (from £7.65), 18–20 oz Dover sole (£12.95), with specials like pork in honey and cider (£4.25), seafood platter (£4.75), fresh salmon salad (£5.25), and good banoffi pie, summer pudding or passion cake (£2.05); summer barbecues (sometimes with live music); very pleasant, efficient staff. Piped nostalgic pop, resident quiz evenings, fruit machine. *(Recommended by Lyn and Bill Capper, Richard Houghton, Gethin Lewis)*

ABC (Allied)   Tenant Paul Jarvis   Real ale   Meals and snacks (till 10pm) Restaurant   Cheddington (0296) 668226   Children in eating areas   Occasional live jazz   Open 11.30–2.30(3 Sat and Sun), 6–11; closed evening 25 Dec

CHENIES   TQ0198 Map 2

Red Lion

2 miles from M25 junction 18; A404 towards Amersham, then village signposted on right; Chesham Rd

Quiet midweek lunchtimes but lively and busy at weekends, this white-painted brick pub has a nicely relaxed atmosphere. The L-shaped bar has built-in wall benches by the front windows with beige or plum-coloured plush cushions, and wheelback chairs and plush stools around a mix of small tables; the walls are decorated with traction-engine photographs and prints, as well as advertising and other prints. Well presented bar food includes soup such as cream of mushroom (£1.95), wholemeal baps or French sticks (from £1.95), filled baked potatoes (from £2.50), ploughman's (from £3.25), vegetarian pancakes (£3.95), lamb pie (£4.95), butterfly prawns in chilli and ginger (£5.95), chicken dijonaise (£7.50), rump steak (£8.50), and daily specials such as chilli tacos (£3.95) and puddings like fresh strawberries (£1.95). Well kept Ansells Mild, Benskins Best, Ind Coope Burton and Tetleys on handpump; friendly service. Pretty hanging baskets and window boxes. The pub is convenient for Chenies Manor. *(Recommended by R M Savage, Mrs P R Walters, Mr and Mrs R P Begg, P Saville, Tony and Lynne Stark, Ian Phillips, Colin Price)*

Benskins (Allied)   Tenants Heather and Mike Norris   Real ale   Meals and snacks (till 10pm)   Rickmansworth (0923) 282722   Open 11–2.30, 5.30–11; closed 25 Dec

CHESHAM   SP9502   Map 4
Black Horse

The Vale; leaving Chesham on A416 towards Berkhamsted fork left at Hawridge 3, Colesbury 3 1/2

As well as the Grade II listed heavy-raftered separate barn with shelves of interesting old books, this pretty white-painted brick pub has black beams and joists, rough-plastered white walls, and an inglenook fireplace big enough to hold two tables in its small black-beamed original core; it opens into an extension with lots of heavy dark-lacquered tables, wheelback chairs and high-backed winged rustic settles. They specialise in home-made pies, with eight from beef, Guinness and orange to wild rabbit and tarragon with soft green peppercorns or pork, apricot and herb (£4.50); other generously served, good value bar food includes sandwiches, soup (£1.25), ploughman's (£2.75), venison sausages (£3.25), filled baked potatoes (from £2.50), salads (from £3.95), smoked trout fillets (£3.95), cold poached salmon with lemon mayonnaise or gammon and egg (£4.95); good Sunday roast. Well kept Adnams, Benskins Best, Glenny Wychwood Best, and Ind Coope Burton on handpump; polite, friendly service; unobtrusive piped music. There are lots of well spaced picnic-table sets and a climbing frame on the big back lawn, with more tables under cocktail parasols in front. They also own the White Lion at Marsworth. *(Recommended by Simon Collett-Jones, Les and Jean Bradman, Lyn and Bill Capper, Richard Houghton, Jan and Ian Alcock, JM, PM)*

Benskins (Allied)   Tenant Roger Wordley   Real ale   Meals and snacks (12–2, 6–9) Chesham (0494) 78465   Children early evening by appointment   Open 11–2.30, 6–11

DENHAM   TQ0486   Map 3
Swan

3/4 mile from M40 junction 1; follow Denham Village signs

In a quiet and charming street of old tiled buildings stands this recently redecorated pub. There are open fires, neat dark oak woodwork, stripped brickwork, and fresh flowers. Good interesting bar food served by courteous and efficient staff includes sandwiches, ploughman's, various salads, and a range of hot dishes (all around £3.75) such as steak and kidney pie, pan-fried chicken livers, seafood tagliatelle, oriental prawns, salt beef and deep-fried camembert with gooseberry or cranberry sauce; fresh puddings, and popular Sunday roasts (£4.95); no bookings, so get there early). Well kept Courage Best and Directors and John Smiths on handpump; fruit machine, piped music. The extensive back garden is floodlit at night, and leads from a sheltered terrace through a rose garden to a more spacious lawn with picnic-table sets and a children's play house; there may be donkeys in the adjoining railed paddock. *(Recommended by Marjorie and David Lamb, Stan Edwards, Lyn and Bill Capper, Ian Phillips)*

Courage   Tenant David Meredith   Real ale   Lunchtime meals and snacks   Denham (0895) 832085   Open 11–3, 5.30(6 Sat)–11

DINTON   SP7611 Map 4

Seven Stars

Stars Lane; follow Dinton signpost into New Road off A418 Aylesbury–Thame, near Gibraltar turn-off

So tucked-away that it's only those in the know who track it down, this pretty and charmingly run pub's nicest corner is in the public bar – where two highly varnished old built-in settles face each other across a table in front of a vast stone inglenook fireplace. The lounge bar is comfortably and simply modernised – spick and span under the beams and joists. These rooms are not large, but there's a spacious and comfortable restaurant area – and there are tables under cocktail parasols on the terrace and lawn of the sheltered garden. Good value bar food includes sandwiches (from £1.40), filled baked potatoes (from £2.10), a choice of ploughman's (£3.15), popular ham and egg (£3.15), quiche lorraine (£3.25), vegetable lasagne (£3.30), cod (£3.75), beef carbonnade (£4.10), gammon and egg (£4.90), steaks (from £8.75) and good dishes of the day such as pork schnitzel. Well kept ABC on handpump, friendly and efficient service, maybe piped music. *(Recommended by Lyn and Bill Capper, David Lamb)*

Ind Coope (Allied)   Tenants Rainer and Sue Eccard   Real ale   Meals and snacks (not Sun or Tues evenings)   Restaurant   Aylesbury (0296) 748241   Open 12–2.30, 6–11; closed Tues evening

FAWLEY   SU7586 Map 2

Walnut Tree

Village signposted off A4155 (then right at T-junction) and off B480, N of Henley

The imaginative bar food here concentrates on meals rather than bar snacks, with starters like baked mushrooms stuffed with pâté and cranberries (£3.25), good cold smoked lamb, baked avocado and prawns mornay (£3.85), giant kiwi mussels grilled with basil, garlic and parmesan cheese (£3.90), and main dishes such as vegetarian rosti (£4.55), duck breast with a honey, thyme sauce (£7.95), and pan fried liver with mushrooms and asparagus spears (£8.25); good puddings. Well kept Brakspears PA and SB on handpump, a good range of wines (including local English ones), and decent malt whiskies; efficient, polite service. Attractively simple furniture, a winter log fire and darts, dominoes, cribbage, fruit machine, juke box. The terrace is now glassed-in to provide more bar or restaurant seating; it is no smoking. The big lawn around the front car park has some well spaced rustic tables, with some seats in a covered terrace extension – and a hitching rail for riders. *(Recommended by TBB, Simon Collett-Jones, J M Potter, Margaret Dyke, R M Savage, Jill Hampton, Brian Metherell)*

Brakspears   Tenant Geoffrey W Knight   Real ale   Meals and snacks (till 10pm)   Restaurant   Turville Heath (049 163) 360   Children in eating area of public bar and in restaurant   Open 11–3 (2.30 in winter), 6–11; closed 25 and 26 Dec   Bedrooms; /£50S

FINGEST   SU7791 Map 2

Chequers ✍

Village signposted off B482 Marlow–Stokenchurch

On Sunday lunchtimes there's a particularly friendly and villagey atmosphere here as walkers and local churchgoers crowd in. The central room of the bar has some seats built into its black-painted wooden dado, an 18th-century oak settle and other chairs of varying ages from ancient to modern, and a big log fire; it's decorated with pistols, antique guns and swords, toby jugs, pewter mugs and decorative plates; a small eating room is no smoking. There's also a sunny lounge with comfortable easy chairs and French windows to the spacious garden. The whole pub is spotlessly kept. Promptly served by convivial, efficient staff, the bar food includes sandwiches (from £1.40), ploughman's (from £2.25), local spicy sausages (£2.50), popular spicy country vegetable soup (£2.95), cottage pie, lasagne or chicken and game pie (£4.25), steak and kidney pie (£5.25 – a special favourite here), roast lamb or liver and bacon, freshly caught trout (£6.50), hot avocado and prawns in cheese sauce (£6.75), vegetarian dishes (starters from £3.95, main courses £5.75), and puddings (£2.50); there's also a romantic restaurant. Well kept Brakspears PA, SB and in season Old Ale on handpump, and Symonds Scrumpy Jack cider; dominoes, cribbage, backgammon. Outside there are lots of tables under cocktail parasols among flowerbeds, and beyond this, quiet pastures slope up to beech woods, with views right down the Hambleden valley. Over the road is a unique Norman twin-roofed church tower – probably the nave of the original church. *(Recommended by Margaret Dyke, Maureen Hobbs, TBB, E and P Parkinson, Neil Barker, J E Stanton, David Lamb, Phil Bryant, M Saunders, Tony and Lynne Stark, Mr and Mrs T F Marshall, Richard Houghton, Mr and Mrs H W Clayton, A M S Jeeves, John and Karen Day)*

Brakspears   Tenant Bryan Heasman   Real ale   Meals and snacks (11–2.30, 6–9.45; not Sun evening)   Restaurant   Turville Heath (049 163) 335   Children in eating area of bar and small room   Open 11–3, 6–11

FORTY GREEN   SU9292   Map 2
Royal Standard of England

3 1/2 miles from M40 junction 2, via A40 to Beaconsfield, then follow sign to Forty Green, off B474 3/4 mile N of New Beaconsfield

An interesting collection of antiques fills this ancient pub: old rifles, powder-flasks and bugles, lots of brass and copper, needlework samplers, ancient pewter and pottery tankards, oak settles, finely carved antique panelling, and stained glass. The open fires have handsomely decorated iron firebacks – including one from Edmund Burke's old home nearby. Bar food prices have not changed since last year: good soup of the day (£1.25), ploughman's (£2.75), sausages and chips (£3.50), chicken (£4.25), lots of good summer salads, a range of home-made pies including venison or pigeon (from £4.25), fritto misto or vegetarian flan (£4.50), crab (£5) and salmon (£5.50). Well kept Brakspears SB, Eldridge Pope Royal Oak and Hardy, and Marstons Pedigree and Owd Rodger (the beer was originally brewed here, until the pub passed the recipe on to Marstons) on handpump; 28 malt whiskies, several Irish ones, and fruit wines; friendly service. There are seats outside in a neatly hedged front rose garden, or in the shade of a tree. Perhaps best visited during the week when it's less crowded. *(Recommended by Mr and Mrs W S Kennedy, Phil Bryant, Robert Gower, J E Stanton, Richard Houghton, Chris Raisin, A W Dickinson, Marjorie and David Lamb, A M S Jeeves, Philip Orbell, Jim and Becky Bryson, Tony and Lynne Stark, Andy and Jill Kassube, Peter Watkins, Pam Stanley, JM, PM, Dr J C Harrison)*

Free house   Licensees Philip Eldridge and Alan Wainwright   Real ale   Meals and snacks (12–2.30, 6–10.15)   Beaconsfield (0494) 673382   Children welcome   Open 11–3, 5.30–11

FRIETH   SU7990   Map 2
Yew Tree

Village, signposted off B482 N of Marlow, is in Bucks though it has an Oxon postal address

The bar in this rather smart old pub is comfortable and there are stripped beams and joists, animal and sporting pictures (look out for the entertaining fishing engravings by F Naumann), china and glass sparkling in corner cupboards, and horsebrasses and guns over the log fires at each end. Bar food includes steamed haddock with chive sauce (£4.50), bockwurst and sauerkraut (£4.95), lamb kebabs (£6.95), tasty stuffed poussin, and puddings such as pear and apple crumble with clotted cream. Well kept Ringwood Old Thumper, Ruddles County, Websters Yorkshire, and a beer brewed by Chilton Valley Wines called Old Barn Ale on handpump, and gluhwein and jaegertee in winter, fresh fruit punch in summer and lots of malt whiskies; decent wine and coffee; good, efficient if formal service. The neat front garden has tables on its lawn and small terrace – they serve out here too; there's also tethering space for horseriding clubs. *(Recommended by TBB, A W Dickinson, Simon Collett-Jones, Phil Bryant, J E Stanton, Richard Carpenter, K E P Wohl, R M Savage, TBB, Margaret Dyke)*

Free house Licensees Franz Aitzetmuller and Annie Beckett Real ale Meals (12–2, 5.30–10.30) Restaurant; closed Sun evening High Wycombe (0494) 882330 Children welcome Open 10–2.30, 5.30–11; all day in July and August

GREAT MISSENDEN SP8900 Map 4

Cross Keys

High St

There's a genuine old-fashioned atmosphere in this warm and friendly pub. The two rooms of the bar are separated by wooden standing timbers. One half is quarry-tiled with high wooden bar stools, an old leather chair and some stools, old sewing machines on the window sill, collectors' postcards, bar and small brewery mirrors on the walls, horse bits, spigots and pewter mugs on the beams by the bar, and well kept Fullers London Pride and ESB on handpump. The other half has bare boards, a bay window with a built-in seat overlooking the street, a high-backed settle, and a couple of housekeepers' chairs in front of the big open fire. The big waitress-served eating room is attractively furnished with a mix of old high-backed, slightly curved pine settles, captains' chairs and iron tractor seats, with traps and boxing gloves on some beams, lots of mugs and a few jugs hanging from other central ones, and a woodburning stove in the brick fireplace. Decent bar food includes home-made vegetable soup (£1.30), lovely fresh sandwiches (from £1.60), omelettes (from £2.90), sausage and egg (£2.95), ploughman's (£3.25), home-cooked gammon and egg (£4.50), and puddings (£1.95), with specials such as farmhouse vegetable escallope (£4.95) or salmon en croûte with asparagus spears (£5.40), and Monday evening fish and chips; welcoming staff. Popular Sunday evening quiz, table of magazines to read; piped Carpenters on our visit, darts, cribbage, dominoes, trivia. There are a couple of seats by the car park. *(Recommended by Lyn and Bill Capper, V H Balchin, Michael and Alison Sandy, Richard Houghton, JM, PM)*

Fullers Managers Mr and Mrs Stephens Real ale Meals and snacks (not Tues or Sun evening) Restaurant Well behaved children in restaurant Great Missenden (024 06) 5373 Live music planned Open 11–2.30, 5.30–11

George ★ ⊘

94 High St

The new chef in this very friendly 15th-century pub has introduced gargantuan roasts on Sunday lunch – whole hocks of pork and half shoulders of lamb (£5.25), as well as lots of offal dishes such as braised liver, stuffed hearts and sautéed kidneys. The food is served in a spaciously comfortable, straightforward room: fresh vegetable soup (£1.40), onion bhajis with cucumber and yoghurt raita (£2.75), pasta (£4.35), a daily fish dish, steak and kidney pie (£6.25), hot beef curry (£6.60), seafood pie (£6.65), chicken with tarragon (£7.70), and half honey roast duck (£10.70); several vegetarian dishes like wheat and walnut casserole or fruit nutlets (£5.65), and puddings such as spotted duck or treacle and nut tart (£1.95). On weekday lunchtimes there are also chips with a dip (85p), sandwiches (from £1.25), filled baked potatoes (from £2), ploughman's (£2.30), and chilli con carne (£2.95). On Friday and Saturday evenings they do two sittings. Well kept ABC Bitter, Fullers London Pride, Greene King IPA, and Wadworths 6X on handpump (under light blanket pressure), mulled wine in winter, tea, coffee and so forth; friendly, obliging service (they take great pains to train their staff carefully). The cosy two-roomed bar has timbered walls decorated with prints, attractively moulded heavy beams and little alcoves (including one with an attractively carved box settle – just room for two – under a fine carved early 17th-century oak panel), and a high mantlepiece holding Staffordshire and other figurines over the big log fire. A snug inner room has a sofa, little settles and a smaller coal fire;

shove-ha'penny, table skittles, dominoes, trivia and piped light music. There are plans to create bedrooms out of the function room, the licensees' personal flat and the Old Courthouse. *(Recommended by Simon Collett-Jones, J E Stanton, N P Hopkins, Les and Jean Bradman, Lyn and Bill Capper, Duncan Stuart-Mills, Mayur Shah, Mr and Mrs T F Marshall, Lyn and Bill Capper, Jamie and Ruth Lyons, E and P Parkinson, TBB, Peter Watkins, Pam Stanley, JM, PM, Jill Hampton, Brian Metherell)*

ABC (Allied)   Tenants Guy and Sally Smith   Real ale   Meals and snacks (12–2.15, 7–9.45); not evenings 25 and 26 Dec   Restaurant Fri–Sat evenings, Sun lunch   Great Missenden (024 06) 2084   Children in eating area and restaurant   Open 11–2.30 (3 Sat), 6–11; closed evening 25 Dec–evening 26 Dec

HAMBLEDEN   SU7886   Map 2

Stag & Huntsman

Village signposted from A4155

The pretty and neatly kept country garden here – floodlit at night – backs directly on to the Chilterns beechwoods. Inside, the compact, L-shaped little lounge bar has low-ceilings and upholstered seating and wooden chairs on its carpet; the attractively simple public bar has darts. Home-made bar food includes excellent smoked fish pâté (£2.70), spinach enchilada (£3.60), chicken curry or steak and kidney pie (£4.75), and smoked fish platter (£6.95). Well kept Brakspears PA and SPA, Luxters Barn Bitter, Wadworths 6X and Farmers Glory on handpump. The 'no children' policy is strictly enforced. The village is particularly pretty. *(Recommended by Richard Houghton, Simon Collett-Jones, E and P Parkinson, Gwen and Peter Andrews, David Warrellow, Harry Blood, T Galligan)*

Free house   Manager Mike Matthews   Real ale   Meals and snacks (not Sun evening) Restaurant   Henley (0491) 571227   Open 11–2.30(3 Sat), 6–11; closed evening 25 Dec   Bedrooms; £42.50S/£48.50S

IBSTONE   SU7593   Map 4

Fox 🛏

1 3/4 miles from M40 junction 5: unclassified lane leading S from motorway exit roundabout; pub is on Ibstone Common

This is a lovely spot for walkers with rolling fields and the Chilterns oak and beech woods beyond the nearby common. The inn has been considerably extended but the comfortable lounge bar has low 17th-century beams, high-backed settles and country seats, old village photographs on the walls, and log fires. In the public bar – which has darts, shove-ha'penny, dominoes, cribbage, fruit machine, and trivia – the pine settles and tables match the woodblock floor. The small dining area in the bar is no smoking. Home-made bar food includes sandwiches (from £1.40), several ploughman's (from £2.95), starters like soup or herrings (from £1.80), fresh fish such as smoked haddock, fish bake or sole (from £4.50), game or steak and kidney pies (from £5.35), and home-made puddings. Well kept Brakspears PA and SB, Luxters Barn Bitter, Tetleys, Wethereds Winter Royal, and a guest such as Greene King Abbot on handpump or tapped from the cask; Westons farm cider, and decent wines by the glass; friendly service. The neat rose garden is prettily lit by old lamps, and the pub overlooks the village common and its cricket ground. *(Recommended by J R Smylie, Mrs V Middlebank, Phil Bryant, Marjorie and David Lamb, P Craddock, A M S Jeeves, Dave Braisted, Dr J C Harrison)*

Free house   Licensees Ann and David Banks   Real ale   Meals and snacks (12–2, 7–10)   Turville Heath (049 163) 289/722   Children in eating area of bar   Bedrooms; £41S/£58.50S   Open 11–3(4 Sat), 6–11

LACEY GREEN   SP8100   Map 4

Pink & Lily

Parslow's Hillock; from A4010 High Wycombe–Princes Risborough follow Loosley

Row signpost, and in that village follow Great Hampden, Great Missenden signpost; OS Sheet 165 map reference 826019

Very friendly, efficient staff serve the nine real ales here, well kept on handpump: Boddingtons, Brakspears, Flowers Original, Glenny Dr Thirsty and Hobgoblin, Ind Coope Burton, Wadworths 6X and Wethereds. And though it's an airy, modernised dining pub, the little taproom has been preserved very much as it used to be in the days when this was a favourite pub of Rupert Brooke's: built-in wall benches on the red flooring tiles, an old wooden ham-rack hanging from the ceiling and a broad inglenook with its low mantlepiece – as well as shove-ha'penny, dominoes, cribbage and piped music. The airy main bar has low pink plush seats, with more intimate side areas and an open fire, and there's a Spanish-style extension with big arches and white garden furniture. Popular, genuinely home-made food includes sandwiches (from £1.30; toasties 25p extra; open sandwiches from £2.95), filled baked potatoes (from £2.75), ploughman's (from £2.95), salads (from £3.25), chicken, bacon and stuffing or steak and kidney pies or vegetarian curry (£3.75), a roast of the day (£4.95), 8oz sirloin steak (£7.50), and home-made puddings (£1.75); vegetables are fresh. The garden has a lot of rustic tables and seats. *(Recommended by Derek and Sylvia Stephenson, TBB, R Tomlinson, Simon Collett-Jones, Peter Churchill, Tony and Lynne Stark, Mike Tucker, Richard Houghton)*

Free house   Licensees Clive and Marion Mason   Real ale   Meals and snacks (not Sun evenings)   Beaconsfield (0494) 488308   Children over 5 if eating, in bottom bar only Open 11.45 (11 Sat)–3, 6–11

LEY HILL   SP9802 Map 4

Swan 🏅

Village signposted from A416 in Chesham

The cricket field and common are opposite the pub, and on the front and back terraces and side lawn are picnic-table sets, as well as pretty hanging baskets, tubs of flowers and a climbing frame. The partly no smoking rambling main bar has low heavy black beams, black oak props, snugs and alcoves with cushioned window and wall seats around country tables, an old kitchen range with a club fireguard, and another big fireplace. Bar food includes freshly made soup of the day (£1.50), sandwiches (from £1.60 – you can choose your own relish), ploughman's (£2.60 – you can choose your own fruit, pickle or type of bread), filled baked potatoes (£2.95), filled pitta pockets, fish or chicken and asparagus pies or lasagne (£3.95), winter steak and kidney pudding or game pie in port, fresh trout (£5.50), salmon steak (£6.50), and lots of steaks in sauces (from £6.60); puddings like old English trifle, summer pudding or crumbles (from £1.45), and children's menu with sandwiches, starters, main courses and puddings (from £1). Well kept Benskins Best, Ind Coope, Tetleys and Youngs Special on handpump. *(Recommended by Robert Gower, Simon Collett-Jones, Martin and Gill Searle, R M Savage, R C Vincent, TBB, Lyn and Bill Capper)*

Benskins (Allied)   Licensees Matthew and Teresa Lock   Real ale   Meals and snacks (not Sun evening or 25 Dec)   Chesham (0494) 783075   Children welcome away from bar   Open 11–2.30, 5.30–11

LITTLE HORWOOD   SP7930 Map 4

Shoulder of Mutton

Church St; back road 1 mile S of A421 Buckingham–Bletchley

The locals and staff (and Benjamin the alsatian) in this half-timbered partly thatched old pub are friendly, and there's a lot of character in the T-shaped bar. This has sturdy seats around chunky rustic tables, quarry tiles, a showcase of china swans, and a huge fireplace at one end with a woodburning stove. Good value bar food includes sandwiches (from £1.20), hot snacks (from £1.90), ploughman's (from £2.90), home-made steak and kidney pie (£4.90), shoulder of mutton in ale

(£7.50), rump steak (£8.50), and home-made daily specials such as vegetarian nut cutlet (from £3.50). Well kept Adnams and ABC Best on handpump; shove-ha'penny, cribbage, dominoes, and fruit machine in the games area, and piped music. French windows look out on the back garden with plenty of tables, and there's a quiet churchyard beside it. From the north, the car park entrance is tricky. (*Recommended by Karen and Graham Oddey, David Lamb, George Atkinson, Mrs R Horridge, Ian Phillips, Lyn and Bill Capper*)

ABC (Allied)   Tenant June Fessey   Real ale   Meals and snacks (not Sun evening, not Mon)   Restaurant   Winslow (0296) 712514; not Sun evening   Children in eating area of bar until 9pm   Open 11–2.30, 6–11; closed Mon lunchtime

MARSH GIBBON   SP6423   Map 4
Greyhound

Back road about 4 miles E of Bicester; pub SW of village, towards A41 and Blackthorn

Although the bar food in this quietly old-fashioned pub does include things like sandwiches, spaghetti bolognese (£3.80), and Hungarian goulash (£5.60), most of the dishes are now Thai: chicken and cashews, beef in oyster sauce or spare ribs in a special sauce (all £4.50), beef in an alcoholic, spicy, garlicy sauce (£4.70), and fresh tuna in black bean sauce or fresh salmon in pepper and celery (£5.60); half price for children. There are comfortable heavy-armed seats and tables with old Singer sewing machine bases, walls are stripped back to golden-grey stone, unusual hexagonal flooring tiles, stripped beams, and a finely ornamented iron stove. Well kept Fullers London Pride, Greene King Abbot and Dark Mild, Hook Norton Bitter and Theakstons Best on handpump; dominoes, cribbage, piped music. There's a small but pretty front garden with picnic-table sets, and a more spacious garden at the back, too, with swings and a climbing frame tucked among the trees. (*Recommended by Brian and Anna Marsden, Marjorie and David Lamb, Lyn and Bill Capper, Nick and Alison Dowson*)

Free house   Licensee Richard Kiam   Real ale   Meals and snacks (not Tues evening)   Thai restaurant   Stratton Audley (0869) 277365   Children allowed   Open 11–3, 6–11

MEDMENHAM   SU8084   Map 2
Dog & Badger

A4155 Henley–Marlow

This stone and brick timbered pub dates back to 1390 and a Roundhead cannon ball from the Civil War was found here during restoration – it's on a shelf above a table in the restaurant area. The big, busy bar is comfortably modernised and neatly kept, with banquettes and stools around the tables, low oak beams, soft lighting, brasses, a crossbow on the ceiling, patterned carpet and an open fire (as well as an illuminated oven). Attractively presented bar food includes good sandwiches or rolls (from £1.30, open prawn £3.55), enterprising filled baked potatoes or several versions along the ploughman's theme (from £3.60), pizza (half £2.50, whole £3.95), salads (from £4.65), vegetarian tagliatelle or savoury nutburger (£4.35), steak and kidney pie or spare ribs (£4.95), beef stir-fry (£5.25), rump steak (£5.95), and puddings such as deep-pan apple pie or treacle sponge (£2.25); in the evening there's also a table d'hôte menu which you can eat in the bar or restaurant (£10.75). Well kept Brakspears, Flowers Original, Wethereds, and a guest beer on handpump, and quite a few whiskies; unobtrusive piped pop music, fruit machine; efficient service. A pleasant short walk takes you down to the Thames. (*Recommended by Lyn and Bill Capper, Simon Collett-Jones, T Galligan; more reports please*)

Whitbreads   Lease: W F Farrell   Real ale   Meals and snacks (noon till 10pm)   Restaurant   Henley-on-Thames (0491) 571362   Children in eating area of bar   Open 11–3, 5.30–11; 11–11 summer

NORTHEND   SU7392   Map 4
White Hart

Old-fashioned, quiet and friendly, this pub has a cosy, unspoilt bar with some panelling, very low handsomely carved oak beams, good log fires (one in a vast fireplace), and comfortable window seats. Generous helpings of bar food include good home-made soup or sandwiches (£1.75), several very good ploughman's with pickles (from £2.95), cheese, tomato and basil quiche (£3.55), filled pancakes (£3.95), liver and bacon (£4.80), beef and cider or steak and kidney pies (£4.99), gammon steak and stilton (£6.80), and puddings (£1.95); they do a few things for those with small appetites (£2.20), and weekend specials. Well kept Brakspears PA, SB and Old on handpump; tea, coffee and hot chocolate; cribbage and dominoes. Hatch service in summer to the attractive, sheltered garden which also has a children's play area. The pub is popular with walkers and cyclists. The ladies' lavatory has been refurbished this year. *(Recommended by Pamela Harris, Simon Collett-Jones, TBB, Mrs Caroline Gibbins, R K Sutton, Dr and Mrs Peter Crosby, TBB)*

Brakspears   Tenants Frank and Barbara Nolan   Real ale   Meals and snacks (12–2, 7–10; all day Sat and bank hols)   Henley-on-Thames (0491) 63353   Children in top room (lunchtime only)   Trad jazz Fri evenings   Open 11–11; 11–2.30, 6.30–11 in winter   Bedrooms; £20/£30

PENN   SU9193   Map 4
Crown

B474

One of Watney's Country Carvery dining pubs, this popular creeper-covered place is neat and comfortable with an olde-worlde decor and well preserved medieval flooring tiles in one room. Efficiently served bar food includes home-made soup (£1.75), ploughman's (from £2.50), salads (around £4.25), and hot dishes such as chicken in tarragon, tasty goulash, steak and mushroom pie or lasagne (from £4.25), and puddings (from £1.75); quite a few tables tend to have been reserved. Well kept Ruddles Best and County and Websters Yorkshire on handpump; fruit machine, trivia, juke box or piped music. Fine views from the back terraces – on a ridge over 500 feet high – look out over rolling pastures and woodland. Tables among pretty roses face the 14th-century church in front and there are slides, swings, climbing frames and a wooden horse and cart for children. *(Recommended by Simon Collett-Jones, Les and Jean Bradman, Norman Hill, Chris Raisin, A M S Jeeves, Mr and Mrs F W Sturch)*

Trumans (Watneys/Courage) Manager Charles Hardman   Real ale   Meals and snacks   Restaurant; noon–9 Sun   Penn (049 481) 2640   Children in eating area and restaurant   Open 11.30–2.30, 6–11

nr PRINCES RISBOROUGH   SP8003   Map 4
Red Lion

Upper Icknield Way, Whiteleaf; village signposted off A4010 towards Aylesbury; OS Sheet 165 map reference 817040

This old inn is very much a friendly, peaceful and well kept local – much loved by Chilterns walkers. The low-ceilinged, cosy bar is simply furnished, and there are small prints on the walls, vases of flowers, an alcove of antique winged settles, and a log fire that Doggo, the big golden labrador, likes to lie in front of. Good bar food includes sandwiches (from £1.15), very tasty filled baked potatoes (from £1.85; the ham and cheese is recommended), excellent omelettes (from £3.75), home-made lasagne (£4.75), home-made curry (£5.50), and a popular four-course Sunday lunch (£8.95); weekday lunchtime daily specials like beef stew and dumpling or bubble and squeak, and super chips. Well kept Brakspears PA, Morlands PA and Hook Norton Best, and an occasional guest beer on handpump; cribbage, dominoes, and piped music. The pub is tucked up a quiet village lane close to Whiteleaf Fields (National Trust), and has a small front lawn and most attractive large back garden. (*Recommended by TBB, Peter Churchill, Jeremy Hayne, K and J O'Malley, David Wallington, Ian Phillips*)

Free house   Licensee R T Howard   Real ale   Meals and snacks (12–2, 6–9.30) Restaurant   Princes Risborough (084 44) 4476   Only children over 5 in restaurant Open 11.30–3, 5.30 (6 Sat)–11   Bedrooms; £22/£33

SKIRMETT   SU7790 Map 2

Old Crown ★ ⊘

High St; from A4155 NE of Henley take Hambleden turn and keep on; or from B482 Stokenchurch–Marlow take Turville turn and keep on

This unspoilt village pub is packed with 700 bric-a-brac items, paintings, antiques, bottles and tools. The small central room and larger one leading off have Windsor chairs, tankards hanging from the beams, and logs burning in the big fireplace; the little no smoking white-painted taproom has trestle tables and an old-fashioned settle by its inglenook fireplace. In the evenings and at weekends it's well worth booking a table if you want to enjoy the constantly changing, seasonal home-made bar food: very good soups such as carrot and coriander or tomato and basil (£2.20), deep-fried camembert with gooseberry conserve or ploughman's (£3.50), smoked fish terrine (£4.50), steak, kidney and mushroom pie (£6.50), fillet of pork with apricots or breast of chicken stuffed with cream cheese and asparagus (£8.25), escalope of poached Scotch salmon in a prawn and dill sauce (£8.85), bouillabaise (£9.45), and puddings like apple and blackcurrant pie (£2.65) or home-made chocolate truffle torte (£2.95). Well kept Brakspears PA, SB and Old Ale are tapped from casks in a stillroom, and served though a hatch; good value wine; dominoes, cribbage, and trivia. A sheltered front terrace has flower tubs and there are picnic-table sets under cocktail parasols, and a fish pond in the garden. Note that children under 10 are not allowed even in the pretty garden. The alsatian's called Bruno. (*Recommended by TBB, Richard Houghton, Miss J Powell, Norman Foot, John Day, J Maloney, Dennis and Pat Jones*)

Brakspears   Tenant Peter Mumby   Real ale   Meals and snacks (not Mon, except bank hols)   Restaurant (not Mon, except bank hols)   Turville Heath (049 163) 435   Well behaved children over 10 in restaurant   Open 11–2.30, 6–11

STOKE GREEN   SU9882 Map 2

Red Lion

1 mile S of Stoke Poges; on B416 come to roundabout and turn right for Wexham; pub is on left; OS Sheet 175 map reference 986824

Friendly new licensees have taken over this 17th-century former farmhouse and have redecorated and added new upholstery throughout. The main bar has robust high-backed settles forming alcoves, inglenook seats, lots of bric-a-brac, and well kept Bass and Charrington IPA on handpump from a chest-high bar counter; winter mulled wine and summer punch. Good value bar lunches are served in the pantry bar (though the food may be eaten anywhere in the pub): sandwiches, ploughman's with five different cheeses (from £2.95), salads (from £3.95), and daily-changing hot dishes like broccoli, potato and nut bake (£3.75) or home-made lasagne, tasty cottage pie and steak and kidney or turkey and ham pies (£3.95); in the evening most food is served in the back Stables restaurant which is connected to the main pub by a covered walkway. A large no smoking area is always open in the bar, next to the pantry; dominoes, cribbage, fruit machine, and piped music. There are picnic-table sets under cocktail parasols on the roundel of lawn in front of this attractive wisteria-covered tiled house, and they have summer barbecues on the sheltered back terrace. (*Recommended by Majur Shah, The Shinkmans, J E Stanton, TBB*)

Bass   Managers Michael and Lyn Smith   Real ale   Meals and snacks   Restaurant; closed Sat lunchtime and Sun evening   Slough (0753) 21739   Children in pantry bar (not evening)   Open 11–3 (2.30 in winter), 5.30–11; 11–11 Thurs and Fri; closed evening 25 Dec

TURVILLE   SU7690   Map 2

Bull & Butcher

In a pretty half-timbered village in a fold of wooded hills, this black-and-white timbered pub is a popular place to finish a walk. The comfortable low-ceilinged bar is partly divided into two areas and has cushioned wall settles and an old-fashioned high-backed settle by one log fire; a stable half-door lets in a breeze on warm summer days. Under the new licensee the bar food has changed little: winter baked potatoes with a range of fillings (£3.50), summer salads (£4.25), a vegetarian dish of the day (£3.50), beef in ale pie (£4.95), and very popular, locally made treacle tart. On winter Sundays they do a roast lunch (£4.95). Well kept Brakspears PA, SB and Old Ale on handpump; dominoes and cribbage. There are tables on a lawn by fruit trees and a neatly umbrella-shaped hawthorn; summer barbecues. The 'no children' is strictly enforced here. (*Recommended by TBB, P A Devitt, Norman Hill, Tony and Lynne Stark, Jonathan Neil-Smith, Bill and Jane Rees, Don Mather*)

Brakspears   Tenant Peter Hanson   Real ale   Meals and snacks (12–2, 6.30–9.45); not 25 and 26 Dec   Open 11–2.30, 6–11

WEST WYCOMBE   SU8394   Map 4

George & Dragon ✿

London Rd; A40 W of High Wycombe

In a fine village owned by the National Trust, this handsome inn is one of its most striking buildings. The rambling main bar is comfortably modernised but still has massive oak beams, sloping walls, a big log fire and a magnificent oak staircase (haunted by a wronged girl – there's also a poltergeist that hides things which turn up unexpectedly in odd places). Good, popular bar food includes sandwiches, home-made soup (£1.75; they do vegetarian ones, too), ploughman's with a choice of cheeses, oxtail stew (£4.10), a plate of smoked salmon or spinach and blue cheese pancakes (£4.25), very good home-made pies like ham, leek and cider or cumberland sweet lamb (£5.25), beef Wellington (£7.25), daily specials like fresh skate (£6) or pork kebab (£6.10), and home-made puddings. It gets crowded at weekends – you have to get there early for a seat. Courage Best and Directors and a guest beer on handpump. The arched and cobbled coach entry leads to a spacious, peaceful garden with picnic-table sets, a climbing frame and slides; the pub is on *Good Walks Guide* Walk 70. Nearby you can visit West Wycombe Park with its fine furnishings and classical landscaped grounds, the Hellfire Club's caves halfway up the hill, and at the top of the hill the church with its landmark tower-top golden ball in which the Club sometimes dined. We don't currently have the evidence to recommend this as a place to stay. (*Recommended by Pamela Harris, Gwen and Peter Andrews, C C Cook, Comus Elliott, David Wallinton, P A Devitt, K Leist*)

Courage   Tenant Phillip Todd, Manager Sonia Heath   Real ale   Meals and snacks (12–2, 6–9.30); not Sun evenings   High Wycombe (0494) 464414   Children in eating area of bar   Open 11.30–2.30 (3 Sat), 5.30–11   Bedrooms; £40S(£46B)/£46S(£55B)

WHITCHURCH   SP8020   Map 4

White Swan ★ ✿

10 High Street; A413 Aylesbury–Buckingham

Though Fullers have now taken over this popular, partly thatched old building, the friendly licensees are still here and so are most of their animals – Charlie the yellow labrador and the two cats, TC and Pi. The odd-shaped saloon bar has a few venerable leather dining chairs, a carved Gothick settle, seats built into squared honey-coloured oak panelling below a delft shelf, chunky elm tables, a longcase clock, fresh flowers, and a small open fire. A wide range of good value, wholesome bar food includes soup (£1.25), a huge choice of sandwiches or French bread rolls (from 90p; toasties from £1, triple deckers from £1.90), lots of ploughman's (from

£2.75), good hors d'oeuvres (£3.50), salads (from £3.25, ham and peach £4.50, mixed seafood £5.50), a variety of good omelettes (from £3.40), breakfast grill (£3.80), vegetable lasagne (£4.50), steak and Guinness pie (£4.95), tasty gammon and eggs (£5.25), evening rump steak (£7.50), and puddings; courteous and helpful service. Well kept Fullers Chiswick, ESB, and London Pride on handpump, quite a few whiskies, and cheap help-yourself coffee; sensibly placed darts, shove-ha'penny, dominoes, cribbage and piped music. Behind the pub, a rambling informal garden has picnic-table sets under trees. *(Recommended by J Whitehead, Gethin Lewis, Norman Hill, G S B G Dudley, Marjorie and David Lamb, R C Gandy, Mr and Mrs Allan Chapman, Lyn and Bill Capper)*

Fullers   Tenants Rex and Janet Tucker   Real ale   Meals and snacks (12–2, 6–9.45; Sun 12–1.45, not Sun evening)   Children in dining room   Open 11–2.30, 6–11

WORMINGHALL   SP6308   Map 4
Clifden Arms

4 1/2 miles from M40 junction 8: take Wheatley exit, and in Old London Road take first right on outskirts, passing Holton and Waterperry

After being a tenant for a good many years, the warmly friendly landlord has now bought the freehold of this exceptionally pretty 16th-century cottage from Allied. The cosy little lounge has old-fashioned seats, squint-timbered ochre walls, a roaring log fire in its big fireplace, and quite a forest of interesting bottles, brass powder-flasks, milk-yokes, black iron vices and tools (it's worth asking the landlord what the unfamiliar ones are for) hanging from its heavy beams. A cheerful lino-floored bar, also beamed, has a second fire. The kitchen has been revamped this year and the good value bar food includes sandwiches (from £1.40; steak £2.25, a monumental club sandwich named for a neighbouring American £4), marvellous home-made soup (£1.75), filled baked potatoes (from £2.75), sausage, bacon, beans and egg (£3.20), a hefty ploughman's (£3.50), various omelettes (£4), salads (from £5.50), chicken kiev (£6), sirloin steak (£10.25), and daily specials such as home-made pork curry or steak in ale pie (£4.25) or poached salmon steak (£5.50); puddings like apple flan (£1.50). Well kept Hook Norton Bitter, Morrells Varsity, and Tetleys Bitter on handpump, decent coffee. The restaurant is no smoking has been extended into the pool room. Cribbage, dominoes and piped music. This year Porty the Jack Russell has been joined by Tippy the cat. The garden loops around behind the house, with picnic-table sets in the orchard, a sheltered flower garden with roses, an ancient pump and well, a run of fancy poultry, a large pond with resident turtle (which they thought they'd lost when the pond dried up – he reappeared when it re-filled), and donkeys; the big play area has slides, a boathouse, log fort and giant red indian. The picturesque village has almshouses built in 1675 and the Norman church has a 15th-century tower and 14th-century chancel. Nearby Waterperry Gardens are worth a visit. *(Recommended by Dr Paul Kitchener, KC, TBB, Mrs S Fergy, Lyn and Bill Capper)*

Free house   Licensees Bob and Gwen Spencer   Real ale   Meals and snacks (11–3, 6–10)   Restaurant   Ickford (0844) 339273   Children in eating area of bar and restaurant   Open 11.30–3, 6–11

Lucky Dip

Besides the fully inspected pubs, you might like to try these Lucky Dips recommended to us and described by readers (if you do, please send us reports):

Adstock [Verney Junction; SP7330], *Verney Arms*: Notable for particularly good food, generally French-oriented but with some spicy specialities; well kept ABC, friendly landlord with pleasant dry sense of humour *(Dr Gordon Copp)*

☆ **Amersham** [High St, Old Town (A413); SU9597], *Eagle*: Really old, open-plan but with bags of character in three carpeted low-beamed eating areas, log fire supplemented by flame-effect gas fires, pictures of local towns and villages; good for lunch or Sat evening meals, particularly fresh fish specials (other evenings no food, and more of a young people's haunt); friendly, efficient, polite service, Adnams, Benskins and Tetleys ales; soft piped music, fruit machine; no food Sun *(Lyn and Bill*

Capper)

Amersham [High St], *Elephant & Castle*: Low beams, china, velvet and brasses in popular Whitbreads food pub with fine U-shaped bar counter, piped music; Wethereds on handpump *(LYM)*; [A404], *Saracens Head*: Comfortable, with Courage beers, good service and decent food inc good filled Yorkshire puddings; big games rooms, and back room with weekend discos *(Richard Nagle, LYM)*

Ashendon [Lower End; between A41 and A418 W of Aylesbury; SP7014], *Red Lion*: Adnams, Badger, Wadworths IPA and 6X and a guest beer, good straightforward bar food; closed Sun evenings except bank hols; two bedrooms *(T J Broughton)*

Aylesbury [1 Wendover Rd (A413 one-way); SP8213], *Aristocrat*: Cosy, lively but not boisterous, first-class friendly service, Fullers beers in top condition, food all day lunchtime onwards Tues–Sat, with afternoon break Mon; warm welcome, spotless lavatories *(Richard Houghton)*; [Market Sq], *Kings Head*: Famous 15th-century inn with wonderful period window lighting lofty bar, well kept Marstons Pedigree, good choice of bar food, extra seats in side room *(M C Barres-Baker)*

☆ *nr* **Aylesbury** [Gibraltar; A418 some miles towards Thame, beyond Stone — OS Sheet 165 map reference 758108], *Bottle & Glass*: Smart rather upmarket dining pub, inventively cooked main meals rather than traditional bar snacks, served in character surroundings; a main entry in last edition as it also had real ales and welcoming, cosy little bar area, but now seems to have abandoned these in favour of food service *(Gethin Lewis, LYM)*

Beaconsfield [London rd; SU9490], *Royal Saracens Head*: Worth a look for its striking timbered facade, attractive sheltered courtyard and, in one corner of the spreading open-plan bar, massive beams and timbers — but thoroughly breweryised, with lots of artificial plants and so forth; Wethereds real ale, Beefeater steak bar *(Andy and Jill Kassube, Phil Bryant, LYM)*

☆ **Botley** [Tylers Hill Rd; SP9702], *Five Bells*: Remote family-run country pub with good relaxing pubby atmosphere, pleasant and quiet; about eight well kept real ales, good value lunchtime bar food, good service, inglenook fireplaces; children in eating area; new regime settling in well *(Mr and Mrs F W Sturch, Richard Houghton, LYM)*

☆ **Bourne End** [Hedsor Rd — former Old Red Lion; SU8985], *Masons*: Friendly and cosy popular local refurbished a couple of years ago with attractive plain furniture; well kept reasonably priced drinks, very busy weekdays for cheap bar lunches inc excellent sandwiches, must book evening restaurant, which has special-offer weekday meals for two (not Mon) *(Miss M James, A Clack, TBB)*

Brill [Windmill St; SP6513], *Sun*: Good food in bar and restaurant, well kept ABC beers; could also be a good place to stay *(John Wheeler)*

☆ **Burnham** [Hawthorn Lane, Burnham Beeches; SU9381], *Stag*: Spacious pub with panelling, pink wallpaper, U-shaped brick counter, raised corners, leather-look sofas, cottagey tables and chairs, conservatory and upstairs restaurant; friendly polite service, Whitbreads and other real ales, jazz Weds; has been open all day, right by the woods *(Richard Houghton, Simon Collett-Jones)*

Burnham [Lent Rise Rd], *Pheasant*: Quiet old low-ceilinged pub with well kept Courage, horsebrasses, backgammon, nice atmosphere, good value meals and snacks, smiling service *(Richard Houghton, Dr and Mrs A K Clarke)*

☆ **Cadmore End** [B482 towards Stokenchurch; SU7892], *Blue Flag*: Several comfortable beamed areas divided by partitions and standing timbers; horsebrasses, advertising mirrors, particularly wide choice of well prepared food, several changing well kept real ales on handpump, piped Radio 1, rather bossy dog; attractive little restaurant, efficient uniformed staff, adjacent small modern hotel *(Dr J C Harrison, Richard Houghton, D C Ball, BB)*

Chalfont St Giles [High St, off A413; SU9893], *Feathers*: Cosy and cheerful low-beamed local, handy for Milton's cottage, with well kept Whitbreads-related real ales, comfortable settees, good open fires and seats outside *(LYM)*; [A413], *Pheasant*: Thoroughly refurbished, but keeping its 17th-century oak beams and stone fireplaces; popular for generous quickly served unambitious food; no smoking dining room *(Mr and Mrs T F Marshall, R M Savage)*

Cheddington [outside village, by canal bridge; SP9217], *Duke of Wellington*: Good value food, inc very generous good ploughman's *(Margaret and Trevor Errington, Lyn and Bill Capper)*; [Station Rd; by stn, about a mile from village], *Rosebery Arms*: Comfortable and friendly, with sofas as well as tables and chairs, good food (liver and bacon, steak and kidney pie, jugged kipper recommended), friendly service, Adnams Broadside, Charles Wells Eagle and Ind Coope Burton; separate restaurant area *(Lyn and Bill Capper)* @L-diP PUB TXT =

Chicheley [A422 — quite handy for M1 junction 14; SP9045], *Chester Arms*: Pleasant Greene King pub with public and lounge bars, comfortably furnished and friendly; wide choice of good value bar food from sandwiches up, inc superb nut roast *(Paul and Margaret Baker)*

☆ **Colnbrook** [1 1/4 miles from M4 junction 5 via A4/B3378, then "village only" rd; TQ0277], *Ostrich*: Handsome old-fashioned bar in striking Elizabethan pub with long and entertaining history; good open fire, bar food and real ale (not cheap), restaurant *(Ian Phillips, P Craddock, TBB, A M S Jeeves, LYM; more reports on new regime please)*

Colnbrook [also handy for M4 junction 5], *Red Lion*: Comfortable Courage pub with good basic food, pleasant atmosphere, a few picnic-table sets on back lawn *(Ian Phillips)*

☆ **Cuddington** [Upper Church St; village signposted from A418 Thame—Aylesbury; SP7311], *Red Lion*: Discreetly chintzy small lounge with big inglenook fireplace, well kept ABC Best and maybe Bass on handpump, bar food from sandwiches up, good restaurant, piped music, garden with play area *(BB)*

Denham [TQ0486], *Falcon*: Cosy and friendly open-plan pub, good range of beers inc Wethereds, good bar snacks *(B R Shiner)*

Dorney [Village Rd; SU9278], *Palmers Arms*: Now a "Groaning Board" dining pub nr Dorney Court, modern inside, and on most reports still well worth knowing for wide choice of bistro food inc garlic bread, filled baked potatoes, black pudding and bacon in garlic butter, Tues fish from Billingsgate, fondue evenings; Bass, good wine list; big car park, pleasant garden *(Richard Nagle, Ian Phillips, A W Dickinson; more reports on current regime please)*

Dunsmore [a mile off A413 Wendover—Gt Missenden — OS Sheet 165 map reference 862054; SP8605], *Fox*: Tucked-away Chilterns village pub, promising new lease of life as free house, with bright freshly decorated bar, substantial solid conservatory, well kept Hook Norton Old Hookey and Wadworths 6X, good food, big garden with tables, swings and climbers; on GWG71 *(P R Graham, LYM; more reports please)*

Farnham Common [Beaconsfield Rd (A355); SU9684], *Royal Oak*: Well run and relaxing, with Courage beers, fair choice of food (not cheap but generous), nice back garden *(Richard Houghton)*

☆ **Ford** [village signposted between A418 and B4009, SW of Aylesbury; SP7709], *Dinton Hermit*: Neat little stone cottage, locally popular (so get there early) for good value food (not Sun or Mon) from sandwiches and baked potatoes up, lots of puddings; well kept ABC Best, Bass and Tetleys on handpump, friendly efficient service, good atmosphere; comfortably modernised lounge with winter log fire, interesting scrubbed-table public bar with huge inglenook (and darts) on left, attractive sheltered country garden with play area *(Lyn and Bill Capper, BB; more reports on this nice pub please)*

Gayhurst [B526; SP8446], *Sir Francis Drake*: Odd Gothick traceried and pinnacled building, cosy inside, strong on spirits and cocktails (not cheap); sandwiches and so forth if they're not too busy, maybe interesting curries; tables in neat garden *(LYM)*

☆ **Great Brickhill** [Ivy Lane; SP9030], *Old Red Lion*: Picnic-table sets in pretty sheltered garden with fabulous view over much of Buckinghamshire and beyond; well furnished and clean inside, with well kept Whitbreads-related beers, quickly served filling food (not Sun evening), log fire, unobtrusive piped music; children in eating area *(Geoff Roynon, Ted George, LYM)*

☆ **Great Hampden** [corner of Hampden Common — OS Sheet 165 map reference 845015; SP8401], *Hampden Arms*: Pleasant and comfortable little two-room country pub by cricket-green common; good choice of well presented reasonably priced bar food inc very good fisherman's platter, real ales inc Greene King Abbot and Ind Coope Burton, friendly efficient young licensees; well placed for walkers *(Margaret Dyke, Marjorie and David Lamb)*

Great Horwood [SP7731], *Swan*: Particularly well kept Ruddles Best on handpump, very friendly licensees *(Karen and Graham Oddey)*

Great Kimble [Risborough Rd (A4010); SP8206], *Bernard Arms*: Cheerful atmosphere and reasonably priced food in spotless refurbished Benskins pub, quick lunchtime food, evening restaurant (not Sun) *(Gordon Leighton)*

☆ **Great Linford** [4 1/2 miles from M1, junction 14; from Newport Pagnell take Wolverton Rd towards Stony Stratford; SP8542], *Black Horse*: Just below Grand Union Canal — drinks can be taken out on the towpath (good walks along here), and garden has biggish play area; spacious and rambling, with genuinely pubby atmosphere, well kept Allied and guest beers on handpump, good range of popular bar food; children allowed in restaurant *(Jonathan and Jane Hagger, Geoff Roynon, LYM)*

Great Missenden [B488, a mile E; SP8901], *Barley Mow*: Free house with Fullers London Pride, Marstons Pedigree and another real ale on handpump, sizeable standard bar menu, welcoming landlord and labrador *(Gwen and Peter Andrews)*; [Mobwell], *Black Horse*: Comfortable two-bar pub with ABC Best, Adnams, Greene King Abbot and Tetleys, wide choice of bar food from sandwiches up; darts, fruit machines, unobtrusive piped music, lots of hot-air balloon pictures; picnic-table sets behind; base of hot-air ballooning club, around 60 flying Easter weekend, with bookable charity rides and other attractions such as biplane aerobatics *(Lyn and Bill Capper)*; [old London rd, E — beyond Abbey], *Nags Head*: Virginia creeper-covered small pub, well kept Ind Coope Burton and other ales, carefully prepared, quickly served straightforward food *(Mr and Mrs T F Marshall)*

Hanslope [SP8046], *Globe*: Old cottage-type pub worth knowing for garden with excellent children's area inc aviary; real ale, straightforward food inc Sun lunch, pleasant staff *(Gwyneth and Salvo Spadaro-Dutturi)*

Hawridge [The Vale; signed from A416 N of Chesham — OS Sheet 165 map reference 960050; SP9505], *Rose & Crown*: Big log fire in spacious open-plan bar, broad terrace with lawn dropping down beyond giving peaceful country views, play area, Allied and Watneys-related real ales, bar food; children allowed *(Stephen King, Tony and Lynne Stark, LYM)*

Hawridge Common [off A416 N of

Chesham; then towards Cholesbury;
SP9505], *Full Moon*: Has been popular
main entry, as delicious little country pub
with snugly comfortable low-beamed
rambling bar and spacious common-edge
lawn, kept marvellously traditional by
former tenants; since their early 1991
retirement there's been uncertainty over its
future but we're keeping our fingers crossed
— it could do really well as a free house
(LYM; news please)

Hedgerley [One Pin Lane; SE of M40
junction 2; junction Parish Lane/Collum
Green Rd — OS Sheet 175 map reference
968863; SU9686], *One Pin*: Cheerfully
welcoming if dimly lit family-run pub with
simple bar food, good service, well kept
Courage ales, neat garden *(Nick and Alison
Dowson)*

High Wycombe [Frogmore (A4128);
SU8593], *Bell*: Polite well organised staff,
adequate quickly served food, well kept
Fullers Chiswick, London Pride and ESB on
handpump, low lights and nice buzz of
conversation; popular with young people
evening and shoppers by day; handy for stn
*(Richard Houghton, Derek and Sylvia
Stephenson)*

Hyde Heath [village signposted off B485
Great Missenden—Chesham; SU9399],
Plough: Prettily placed local, with chatty
long bar, well kept Allied beers, quickly
served reasonably priced food, open fires *(G
R Peasson, LYM)*

Iver [TQ0381], *Gurkha*: Nice atmosphere in
pleasant bar; splendid food, spotless
lavatories *(N S Holmes)*; [146 Swallow St],
Oddfellows Arms: Spacious but cosy old
local with open fire, Courage and Youngs
beers, wide choice of bar lunches (not Sun),
dominoes and cribbage *(James M Goode)*;
[High St], *Swan*: Pleasant Courage pub with
interesting restaurant *(J E Stanton)*

Kingswood [A41; SP6919], *Crooked Billet*:
Decent straightforward food under
welcoming newish licensee *(Mr and Mrs T F
Marshall)*

☆ **Lane End** [B482 Marlow—Stokenchurch;
SU7991], *Old Sun*: Wide choice of good
value bar food (not Sun or Mon evenings) in
breweryised but still pleasantly laid out old
pub with winter log fires, well kept
Whitbreads-related real ales, unobtrusive
piped music, pub and garden games (it's
pretty outside); children welcome unless too
busy *(A M S Jeeves, Nick Dowson, Alison
Hayward, LYM)*

Lavendon [A428 Bedford—Northampton;
SP9153], *Green Man*: Well appointed
refurbished pub with good, varied food and
pleasant restaurant; useful 20% Mon
discount for OAPs *(T G Saul)*

☆ **Little Hampden** [up dead-end off back rd Gt
Missenden—Stoke Mandeville, W of A413;
SP8503], *Rising Sun*: In a lovely Chilterns
spot for walkers (on GWG71), with several
well kept real ales (particularly Adnams),
and food of restaurant quality — genuinely
creative and interesting, well worth the trip
if that's what you're after; but now hardly

the flexible and pubby place that the
location really calls for, and (though they do
weekday snacks, at a price) Sunday food's
confined to booked restaurant lunches;
closed Sun evening, all day Mon *(J E Stanton,
Geoffrey and Sylvia Donald, John Hawley, Mr
and Mrs T F Marshall, Andrea and Guy
Bradley, Peter Watkins, Pam Stanley, R M
Savage, Stephen King, LYM)*

Little Kingshill [Hare La; SU8999], *Full
Moon*: Very homely and almost cottagey,
with a real welcome; comfortably
modernised, with well kept Adnams,
Benskins Best and Tetleys on handpump,
pleasant garden *(Richard Houghton)*

Little Marlow [Sheepridge Lane; off A4155
at Well End; SU8786], *Crooked Billet*:
Lovely old cider house on country lane, with
ancient low beams in one cosy and
comfortable bar; pleasant staff and locals,
well kept Wethereds, excellent garden
(Richard Houghton)

☆ **Little Missenden** [signed off A413 W of
Amersham; SU9298], *Crown*: Friendly,
unspoilt local of character with Hook
Norton, Marstons Pedigree and Morrells
ales, all well kept; cheerful, friendly
landlord, nice garden; very popular
weekends *(J E Stanton, Joel Dobris)*

☆ **Littleworth Common** [Common Lane; 3
miles S of M40 junction 2 — OS Sheet 165
map reference 937864; SP9487], *Blackwood
Arms*: Unpretentiously rustic, with friendly
welcome, several changing real ales inc
rarities for the area such as Arkells or
Mitchells ESB, small choice of reasonably
priced food, roaring log fire, polite service
(though serving bar could be bigger at busy
times), basic garden *(Richard Houghton,
Barbara Hatfield, P R Graham)*

☆ **Littleworth Common** [2 miles from M40
junction 2, off A355], *Jolly Woodman*:
Fairly big, but beamed and pleasantly
cottagey, with welcoming atmosphere,
central fireplace, attractive range of
reasonably priced freshly cooked food from
seperate servery, Whitbreads-related real
ales, open all day; alone by the woods
(Christian Leigh, Barbara Hatfield, LYM)

☆ **Long Crendon** [Bicester Rd (B4011);
SP6808], *Angel*: Pleasantly refurbished
dining pub, partly 17th-century, warm and
spotless, with new conservatory-style dining
room; young welcoming staff, well kept real
ales, imaginative range of good generous
food, particularly fish and Sun roasts; not
cheap but good value *(D B Delany, Dr and
Mrs R E S Tanner)*

Long Crendon [Bicester Rd (B4011);
SP6808], *Chandos Arms*: Handsome
thatched building with well presented
reasonably priced food in two low-beamed
communicating carpeted bars, wooden
settles and other seats, lots of brass and
copper, Whitbreads-related real ales, no
piped music, friendly and efficient service;
log fire, darts and shove-ha'penny in one bar
(Phil Bryant, Norman Hill)

Lower Hartwell [Oxford Rd (A408);
SP7913], *Bugle Horn*: Very attractive

garden with mature trees, flowerbeds, tables under cocktail parasols; comfortable bar, well appointed restaurant and separate food bar, Allied real ales with a guest such as Adnams, unobtrusive piped music *(Lyn and Bill Capper)*

Ludgershall [off A41 Aylesbury—Bicester; SP6617], *Bull & Butcher*: Old low-beamed building doing well under newish licensees (he was a butcher); tastefully refurbished, all very clean and neat, with public bar, saloon and eating area with numerous jugs and bottles hanging from beams; Exmoor and Tetleys; food at notably low prices from ploughman's to lots of steaks, efficient friendly service, unobtrusive piped music; children in eating area, front lawn facing green *(Lyn and Bill Capper, Joan Olivier)*

Maids Moreton [SP7035], *Wheatsheaf*: Simple but cosy compact thatched pub with good reasonably priced straightforward food, small garden and friendly pub dog *(Chris Cook)*

☆ **Marlow** [St Peter St; first right off Station Rd from double roundabout; SU8586], *Two Brewers*: Attractive somewhat upmarket low-beamed bar with shiny black woodwork, nautical pictures and gleaming brasswork; sheltered back courtyard, glimpse of Thames from front benches; Whitbreads-related real ales and decent bar food (at a price), but concentration on restaurant, with bar users now left rather cramped except at quiet times — when it's well worth a visit; piped music, children in restaurant if not too busy; can park nearby — a special bonus for Marlow *(Philip Harrison, TBB, LYM)*

☆ **Marlow** [High St], *Chequers*: If large attractive gilt-and-plaster-ceilinged public bar dominated by young people and loud music, take refuge in charming little peaceful bar nr dining room (or tables out on pavement under cherry trees); wide choice of good food from sandwiches to lobster salad with plenty of mid-priced dishes, Brakspears ales, friendly and attentive service; open all day; bedrooms *(Cdr W S D Hendry, WHBM)*

☆ **Marlow** [West St (A4155 towards Henley)], *Ship*: Low-beamed town local with interesting warship photographs and nautical equipment in small twin side-by-side bars, straightforward bar lunches from sandwiches upwards, well kept Whitbreads-related real ales on handpump, pleasant staff, piped music, tables on back terrace, evening restaurant; open all day Fri–Sat, popular with young people weekend evenings; children in restaurant *(TBB, LYM)*

☆ **Marlow** [A4155, further out], *Hare & Hounds*: Ivy-clad cottage on outskirts with calm and intimate atmosphere in split-level dove-grey bar, two log-effect gas fires; charming licensee, Whitbreads-related real ales, wide choice of good bar food, popular restaurant *(Ian Phillips, Simon Collett-Jones)*

Marlow [Quoiting Sq], *Clayton Arms*: Unchanged gem, with particularly well priced Brakspears PA; try spotting two chairs the same in the pre-war side lounge;

really long-serving landlord and friendly locals *(Nick and Alison Dowson)*; *Coach & Horses*: Outstandingly clean and tidy, fresh flowers, well kept Courage, good range of food *(A Kilpatrick)*

☆ **Marsworth** [Vicarage Rd; SP9214], *Red Lion*: Partly thatched simple and unfussy pub, recently sold by Allied Breweries as free house, with well kept Banks & Taylors Shefford, Bass, Hook Norton Best and Wadworths 6X, good range from back food bar inc big thick sandwiches, good ploughman's, steak and kidney pie with shortcrust pastry; basic traditional furnishings and lively games area in tiled-floor main bar with two open fires, steps up to cosy parlour; obliging service, decent wines; tables in front, and in small sheltered butterfly-friendly back garden; short walk from impressive flight of canal locks; children in games area until 8.30 *(Michael Sandy, Stan Edwards, LYM)*

☆ **Marsworth** [Startops End — village signed off B489 Dunstable—Aylesbury], *White Lion*: Busy but cosy modernised pub nr canal, popular under current regime (same as Black Horse, Chesham — see main entries), with good choice of beers inc Exmoor, Greene King Abbot, good service, big helpings of reasonably priced food; good-sized children's room; good walks, on GWG110 *(Roxanne Chamberlain, Paul Coleman, Kathy Holt, BB)*

☆ **Mentmore** [SP9119], *Stag*: Small carpeted lounge bar with sturdy green leatherette seats around low oak tables, attractive fresh flower arrangements, open fire, and restaurant and public bar leading off; good value well presented bar food from sandwiches to main dishes, with wider evening choice; well kept Charles Wells Eagle, polite well dressed staff, charming sloping garden with floodlit pear tree; prices match the unusually civilised ambience *(Michael and Alison Sandy, Maysie Thompson, BB)*

Naphill [SU8497], *Black Lion*: Comfortable open-plan bar with aircraft pictures (Strike Command HQ nearby), conservatory dining extension, Courage and Youngs Special, fruit machine, maybe piped music, picnic-table sets in garden; super ladies'; Indian takeaways available lunchtime and evening *(Lyn and Bill Capper, Geoff Lee, BB)*

☆ **New Bradwell** [2 Bradwell Rd; SP8341], *New Inn*: Comfortable local by Grand Union Canal with some waterside tables, serving perfectly kept Charles Wells Eagle and Bombardier; food well prepared, with usual choice and a few more exciting dishes; dogs allowed *(Geoff Roynon, John Baker)*

Owlswick [SP7806], *Hare & Hounds*: Beautifully placed by old village green; two bars with nice atmosphere; changing real ales eg Fullers ESB and Ruddles, good service *(Richard Houghton)*

Penn [SU9193], *Horse & Jockey*: Useful for decent food served till 10pm; changing real ales such as Tetleys *(Mike Tucker)*; [Elm Rd], *Red Lion*: Comfortable and welcoming, with lovely winter fire, good value food, several Whitbreads-related real ales *(Mike Tucker)*

☆ **Penn Street** [SU9295], *Hit or Miss*: Imaginative food from sandwiches up in bar and spacious restaurant of comfortably modernised low-beamed pub with own cricket ground, and good cricket memorabilia; open fire, no piped music or fruit machines; Hook Norton and Marstons Pedigree, decent wines *(BKA, LYM)*

Preston Bisset [SP6529], *Old Hat*: Quiet and unspoilt, with old pew, built-in wall settle, open fires, sleeping dogs, and cottage-parlour atmosphere; very welcoming landlady with interesting stories, well kept Hook Norton; pretty village; well behaved children if early *(Gwyneth and Salvo Spadaro-Dutturi)*

Prestwood [Wycombe Rd; SP8700], *Polecat*: Newly refurbished, with considerably enlarged eating areas and new emphasis on good home cooking — enjoyably above average; keen, friendly service, convenient and spacious gentrified decor, Watneys-related real ales *(Mr and Mrs T F Marshall)*

☆ **Skirmett** [Fingest rd off B482 at Bolter End, then follow Skirmett signs; SU7790], *Kings Arms*: Country pub in quiet and attractive valley, with inglenook fireplace and log fire in traditionally furnished high-beamed bar with more modern extension, wide range of bar food (not Sun evening) inc unusual as well as traditional dishes, using fresh vegetables and maybe herbs from the garden, small restaurant; well kept Brakspears and Whitbreads-related real ales, decent wine list, good service; seats on side lawn, attractive if not spacious (and quite pricey) bedrooms; children in eating area and restaurant *(Sandra Kempson, R K Sutton, Mrs A M S Jeeves, LYM)*

Slapton [SP9320], *Carpenters Arms*: Good pub atmosphere, well kept real ales, quality home-cooked food at fair prices *(Geoff Payne)*

☆ **Speen** [Flowers Bottom Lane; rd towards Lacey Green and Saunderton Stn — OS Sheet 165 map reference 835995; SU8399], *Old Plow*: Wide choice of exceptional if upmarket bar food, inc lovely smoked salmon pot, good salads, fine ploughman's with home-baked bread, restaurant starters served as bar snacks, good home-made puddings; chocolate-box pub prettily tucked into deep fold of the Chilterns and surrounded by orchards, with oak beams, brick fireplaces, horsebrasses and harness in crisply cottagey interior; well kept Brakspears, decent wines, winter log fire; nice walks; good restaurant; bedrooms *(Roger and Lynda Pilgrim, Mrs V Middlebrook, R M Savage, LYM)*

Speen [Hampden Rd; SU8399], *King William IV*: Spotless and well run country dining pub inc no smoking dining room, good if not cheap straightforward food; real ales such as Flowers and Ruddles *(R M Savage, Roger and Lynda Pilgrim)*

☆ **St Leonards** [edge of Buckland Common — village signed off A4011 Wendover—Tring; SP9107], *White Lion*: Simple but neat open-plan Chilterns pub with old black beams, cushioned seats, log-effect gas fire; good value straightforward home cooking (no hot main dishes Sat, no food Sun); well kept Allied ales on handpump, friendly service, unobtrusive piped music, small but attractive sheltered garden; provision for children *(BB)*

☆ **Stewkley** [High St N; SP8526], *Swan*: Lovely old pub with fine choice of beers, good modestly priced food (sandwiches and plaice particularly commended), nice dining area, huge log fire, big fully enclosed garden with all sorts of children's activities and summer barbecue; children's room *(John Drummond, Mrs P R Walters)*

Stewkley [High St South], *Carpenters Arms*: Nice old building with good local atmosphere, doing well under newish management; warm and friendly service, extended dining area with worthwhile food, woodburning stove *(John Drummond, LYM)*

Stoke Poges [Wexham St; SU9983], *Plough*: Oak-beamed pub with friendly service, good helpings of simple food; Allied real ales *(P Saville)*

☆ **Stony Stratford** [High St; SP7840], *Bull*: Lively separate Vaults Bar with stone floor, wooden shutters, wooden benches and pine tables and chairs, lots of agricultural and other hardware hanging from ceiling and on bar, posters on walls; half a dozen or more real ales, food, friendly service; open all day, busy weekends, live folk Sun; bedrooms *(Dominic Woodfield, Liam Baldwin, Gwyneth and Salvo Spadaro-Dutturi, LYM)*

☆ **Taplow** [Station Rd; SU9082], *Oak & Saw*: Popular and friendly little local opp quiet attractive village green, with old photographs of area, quite cosy main bar, good mix of customers; decent weekday food (separate eating area), pleasant staff, well kept Courage and a guest such as Wadworths 6X, sensible prices; opens noon *(TBB, Richard Houghton, A W Dickinson, Richard Gibbs)*

☆ **The Lee** [Swan Bottom, back rd 3/4 mile N — OS Sheet 165 map reference 902055; SP8904], *Old Swan*: Attractive furnishings in four charming low-beamed interconnecting rooms, logs burning in cooking-range inglenook, spacious and prettily planted back lawns with play area; decent bar lunches and good range of well kept real ales, but evening food prices on the steep side *(E and P Parkinson, J E Stanton, JM, PM, Mark Evans, LYM — more reports please)*

The Lee [back roads 2 1/2 miles N of Great Missenden, E of A413], *Cock & Rabbit*: Stylish Italian-owned pub, more a country restaurant now, but with real ales such as Flowers, Morlands and Wethereds, decent wines, and big garden with tables on verandah, terraces and lawn; children in eating area and restaurant *(Andrea and Guy Bradley, Peter Watkins, Pam Stanley, LYM)*

Wavendon [not far from M1 junctions 13 and 14; SP9137], *Plough*: Lovely village pub, good variety of reasonably priced lunchtime food, good choice of wine by the glass, big garden *(Monica Shelley)*

☆ **Wheelerend Common** [just off A40; SU8093], *Brickmakers Arms*: Spacious panelled pub in attractive spot, with interesting shortish walks nearby; comfortable seats and tables, friendly, helpful staff, good value food, particularly steak and kidney pudding, decent range of beers; big garden, popular in summer, with children's play area; good-sized car park *(A J Vere, Dr Paul Kitchener)*

☆ **Winchmore Hill** [The Hill; SU9394], *Plough*: Clean and comfortably modernised spacious bar overlooking green, several interconnecting areas, some interesting nicknacks, wide choice of reasonably priced and generously served bar food, well kept real ales such as Theakstons and Youngers Scotch and IPA, neat helpful staff, piped music, tables on lawn with wishing well; restaurant named after landlady Barbara Windsor *(Richard Houghton, BB)*

Winchmore Hill [SU9394], *Potters Arms*: Good varied food from enterprising menu inc bargain big rump steak; lots of bottled foreign beers *(Geoffrey Donald)*

Winslow [Market Sq; SP7627], *Bell*: Elegant black and white timbered inn with plush hotel bar, decent bar food, all-day coffee lounge, pleasant inner courtyard, well kept Adnams, Marstons Pedigree and Wadworths 6X on handpump, decent wines, piped music; restaurant *(George Atkinson, Michael and Alison Sandy, Sidney and Erna Wells, Mr and Mrs Allan Chapman, LYM)*

Wooburn Common [Kiln Lane; SU9387], *Chequers*: Attractive bar with sofas and fire, welcoming licensees *(Geoffrey and Sylvia Donald)*; [Wooburn Common Rd; about 3½ miles from M40 junction 2], *Royal Standard*: Cleanly decorated and civilised, with well kept Whitbreads real ales, pleasant atmosphere, good imaginative range of bar food, seats and boules pitch out behind; busy weekend evenings; children welcome *(Ian Phillips, LYM)*

☆ **Wooburn Moor** [Watery Lane — OS Sheet 175 map reference 913898; SU9189], *Falcon*: Friendly little low-beamed pub with relaxing atmosphere, good mix of customers, well kept Whitbreads-related real ales with a guest such as Brakspears, attractive garden *(J E Stanton)*

Woughton on the Green [SP8737], *Olde Swan*: Good value bar food, particularly well kept Charles Wells, big garden with play area *(Derek and Sylvia Stephenson)*

Cambridgeshire and Bedfordshire

One of the nicest pubs here, the unspoilt little Cock at Broom, has friendly new licensees this year: so far, reports are good, with concentration still on its famous cheeses. The people who run the Kings Arms in Broomfield (see Essex main entries) have also taken on the prettily set Anchor up at Sutton Gault: more restauranty now, but good food. The new landlord at the Pheasant at Keyston is a chef with quite a track record; the old one (very popular in his time there) has now turned up at the White Hart at Bythorn – an extremely nice new main entry. Other newcomers to this edition are the Live & Let Live in Cambridge (very relaxed, with cheap food), the friendly Red Lion at Hinxton and the warm-hearted Bell at Odell (popular home cooking). In a sense, the Olde Plough at Bolnhurst is also a newcomer: it's finally reopened, handsomely rebuilt, after its fire. Other pubs to note particularly here include the Royal Oak on one of the largest village greens in England, at Barrington (good food, new conservatory), the Free Press in Cambridge (a favourite there), the Crafty Fox near Chatteris (relaxed and atmospheric as ever despite several interesting changes), the Three Tuns at Fen Drayton (good all round, including food), the Chequers at Fowlmere (currently on peak form, with stylish food and a really good choice of wines by the glass) and Queens Head there (a nice contrast, yet the wines here too are good), the Chequers at Keysoe (reliable food), the unchanging Queens Head at Newton (good simple food in basic but charming surroundings), the nice old Bell at Stilton, the Olde White Hart at Ufford (decent food) and that handsome old allrounder the Haycock at Wansford (lots of character still in spite of extensive recent changes). The Lucky Dip section at the end of the chapter includes a wealth of pubs in Cambridge, no less than three solid bankers in the small village of Eaton Socon, and two good but strongly contrasting places in Turvey. Others in this section that stand out as particularly worth a visit (most of them inspected by us) include the Hardwicke Arms at Arrington, Millstone at Barnack, Plough at Downham, Black Horse at Dry Drayton, Kings Head at Dullingham, George & Dragon at Elsworth, King William IV at Fenstanton, Woodmans Cottage at Gorefield, Live & Let Live near Hexton, King William IV at Heydon, Knife & Cleaver at Houghton Conquest, Black Horse at Ireland, Three Horseshoes at Madingley, Pike & Eel at Needingworth, White Horse at Shefford, Red Lion at Swaffham Prior, Tickell Arms at Whittlesford and Three Blackbirds at Woodditton.

BARRINGTON (Cambs)   TL3949 Map 5

Royal Oak

From M11 junction 11, take A10 for Royston; village signposted on right after 3 1/2 miles

Opposite one of the largest village greens in England, this thatched and heavily timbered pub has several rambling tile-floored rooms decorated with brass, copper, antlers and harness. The building itself dates back to the 14th century – look out for the fine Tudor brickwork above a mantlebeam in the large central chimney, now opened up as a sort of connecting lobby. Good bar food, served by friendly staff, includes a vast range of vegetarian food for which they were featured on Anglia television. Although they do have a restaurant, one menu serves throughout and customers can choose to sit where they like. They serve sandwiches (from £1.75), soup (£2.35), ploughman's (£3.25), omelettes (£3.90), salads (from around £3.75), home-made steak and kidney pie and curries (£4.70), prawn, ham and pepper pancake (£4.85) and pork stuffed with ham and cheese with mushroom sauce (£5.55); the good selection of vegetarian dishes includes a popular moussaka (£4.80), cashew caprice (a tagliatelle dish) or Challis cottage crumble (£4.85), nut cutlet (£5), and hazelnut, pineapple and pepper pancake (£5.65); puddings such as home-made apple pie or strudel and raspberry pavlova (£2.75). Well kept Adnams and Greene King IPA and Abbot on handpump; fruit machine and piped music. One of the restaurant areas is no smoking. They now have a conservatory adjacent to the restaurant. Seats and tables under cocktail parasols outside. *(Recommended by JF, John C Baker, Wayne Brindle, Paul Harrop, Drs M and K Parier, Derek Patey, Nigel Gibbs, Sandra Cook, NAC)*

Free house   Licensees Robert and Elizabeth Nicholls   Real ale   Meals and snacks (12–2, 6.30–10)   Restaurant   Cambridge (0223) 870 791   Children in eating areas Open 11.30–2.30, 6–11

BIDDENHAM (Beds)   TL0249   Map 5

Three Tuns   £

57 Main Road; village signposted from A428 just W of Bedford

In a lovely village, this friendly, bustling thatched pub has a good mix of customers, many of whom have come to enjoy the wide range of good bar food: from sandwiches (£1), excellent home-made soup (£1.10); they also do soup and a choice of sandwich for £1.70 – an idea it would be nice if other pubs copied) and pâté (£1.60), through several good, fresh ploughman's (£2), burgers (from £2.50) and salads (£3; prawn £3.80), to various hot dishes such as quiche, lasagne or chilli con carne (£3.80), home-made chicken casserole or steak and kidney pie (£4); children's menu (£1.40). Very well kept Greene King IPA and Abbot and Rayments on handpump; cheerful, prompt service. The comfortable lounge has low beams and country paintings on the walls, and the livelier public bar has table skittles as well as darts, dominoes, fruit machine, space game and piped music. Popular with families, the big, very well kept garden has doves and a dovecote. *(Recommended by Jerry and Alison Oakes, Klaus and Elizabeth Leist, Richard Dolphin, Colleen Holiday, J Morley, Pete Storey)*

Greene King   Tenants Alan and Tina Wilkins   Real ale   Meals and snacks (not Sun eves)   Bedford (0234) 354847   Children in small dining room   Open 11.30–2.30, 6–11

BOLNHURST (Beds)   TL0859   Map 5

Olde Plough   £

B660 Bedford–Kimbolton

After long and painstakingly careful refurbishment following a bad fire, this cottage has at last opened again – with extra space inside. The carpeted lounge bar has black beams, little armchairs around low tables, a leather sofa and a leather armchair, and a log fire in the big stone fireplace. What was the old kitchen is now a smallish dining bar with brocaded seats around tables ingeniously salvaged from oak barn fittings; its wooden ceiling uses boards from a Bedford church (another fire casualty). The public bar has a couple of refectory tables, settles and other seats on the flagstones, a big woodburning stove. The cats are called Chubbs, Blacky and Titch. Bar food should be along traditional lines – rolls and more substantial meals such as ploughman's, a half-pint of prawns or fish and chips (£2.50) and so forth; three-course Sunday lunch (£8.50). They serve Ruddles Best and County and Samuel Websters Choice on handpump and a range of country wines which are changed seasonally; darts, pool, hood skittles, cribbage, dominoes, a fruit machine and video game and also trivial pursuit and cards. As we went to press they were working on an upstairs restaurant and a function room. The pretty garden has an established rock bank (where there's the remains of a moat under trees), as well as rustic seats and tables, and a long crazy-paved terracewhich seats 30 and looks onto the pond. *(More reports please)*

Free house   Licensee M J Horridge   Real ale   Meals and snacks (12–2, 7–10; not 25 Dec)   Restaurant   Colmworth (023 062) 274   Well behaved children till 9pm   Open 12–2.30 (3 Sat), 7–11; closed 25 Dec

BROOM (Beds)   TL1743 Map 5

Cock ★ Ⓟ £

23 High Street; from A1 opposite northernmost Biggleswade turnoff follow Old Warden 3, Aerodrome 2 signpost, and take first left signposted Broom

Friendly new licensees have taken over this fine pub overlooking the village green. Little has changed in the pub itself, though of course the menu is different. The layout is attractively old-fashioned and the four rooms have simple latch doors, low ochre ceilings, stripped panelling and new farmhouse-style tables and chairs on the antique tile floors. A central corridor runs down the middle of the building, with the sink for washing glasses on one side (pewter mugs hang over it) and on the other steps down to the cellar. There's no bar counter: the very well kept Greene King IPA and Abbot is tapped straight from the cask in the cellar. The new licensees hope to have an additional eating area by the time this edition comes out, which they say will be in keeping with the character of this 270-year-old pub; until then food is being served at lunchtimes only as the pub is too busy in the evenings. Bar food includes soup (£1.50), toasted sandwiches (from £1.10), the ploughman's comes with a wide choice of cheeses – mostly English – and they also do a traditional ploughman's with two cheeses served with a mug of soup (£4.25). Other dishes include filled baked potatoes (from £1.35), hot beef or gammon rolls (from £2.75), and home-made chilli (£2.95); there are also daily specials such as large Yorkshire pudding filled with mince stew (£3.50), game pie or chicken and mushroom pie (£3.99). Winter log fires, hood skittles, darts, shove-ha'penny, cribbage, and dominoes in one front room, unobtrusive piped music; the pétanque pitch has gone but more picnic tables and parasols have been added to those on the terrace by the back lawn and there is now a fenced children's play area. *(Recommended by Michael Marlow, Roger Danes, M J Brooks, Mr and Mrs T F Marshall, George Atkinson, Dr Paul Kitchener, Margaret and Roy Randle, Colleen Holiday, Tony and Lynne Stark; more reports on the new regime, please)*

Greene King   Tenants Peter and Jackie Little   Real ale   Meals and snacks (not eves, until September)   (0767) 314411   Children away from drinks serving area   Live music monthly   Open 12–3, 6–11

BYTHORN (Cambs)   TL0575 Map 5

White Hart Ⓟ

Village signposted just off A604 Huntingdon–Cambridge

The Bennetts, who built up quite a following at the Pheasant at Keyston, have in the last few months turned this into a quietly distinguished pub/restaurant; we'd say it has a very bright future. The airily modern no smoking restaurant, rather smart, is at the back, and as we go to press food service is confined to that, with an interesting and good value set menu giving half a dozen choices of each course. Main courses might include roast guineafowl, saddle of venison with wild mushrooms, stirfry chicken with oyster sauce or magret of duck with a prune and brandy sauce; four courses £15.50, two (lunchtime) £12.95. The pub part, at the front, has several linked smallish rooms, individually furnished with soft leather chairs and stools, housekeepers' chairs, wing armchairs, a big leather chesterfield, attractive tables, rugs on stripped boards; there's a log fire in a huge brick fireplace, and books (new cooking ones) and magazines are truly for reading, not just decoration. Well kept Greene King IPA and Abbot and Rayments on handpump, a good choice of decent wines, free nuts, pleasant staff. Stables behind are in use. *(Recommended by John C Baker, BOB; more reports please)*

Free house   Licensees Bill and Pam Bennett   Real ale   Restaurant (not Sun evening, Mon)   Bythorn (080 14) 226   Children welcome   Open 11–3, 6–11; closed Mon, evening 25 and 26 Dec

CAMBRIDGE   TL4658   Map 5

Anchor

Silver St

In a marvellous position right by the river (where there are punts for hire – with a boatman if needed) this lively pub is very popular with university and foreign students. It's set out on several levels. By the entrance is an area with leatherette armchairs and a brick fire at one end, and a chesterfield, a couple of stools and another brick fireplace at the other; there's a mix of college and local photographs on the walls, and a few plants. The upstairs bar (closed in the afternoon) has a wooden bar counter with a modern glass and brass gantry, bar stools by stained-glass shelves that look over a plusher area, ceiling fans, and a huge domed glass light; the windows here have good riverside views. Downstairs, the cafe-bar (open all day) has settles, farmhouse chairs, hefty stools and round wooden tables on the bare boards, and a workmanlike brass footrail along the bar counter (where there's also a glass food cabinet). Steps take you down to a similar though simpler flagstoned room with picnic-table sets and display cabinets to do with brewing; French windows lead out to a suntrap terrace with more picnic-table sets and some tubs of flowers. Bar food includes sandwiches and ploughman's (£2.95); popular hot dishes here are steak pie or lasagne (£3.60) and Sunday roast (£3.95). Well kept Boddingtons, Castle Eden and Flowers Original on handpump; cheerful young service, piped music, various trivia and fruit machines and a juke box. *(Recommended by Andrew Morrissey, Nigel Gibbs, Wayne Brindle, Peter Churchill, Alan and Ruth Woodhouse)*

Whitbreads   Manager Alistair Langton   Real ale   Meals and snacks (12–2.30) not evenings   Cambridge (0223) 353554   Children in eating area only   Live jazz Tues   Open 11–11

Boathouse

14 Chesterton Road; one-way section of ring road, by A10 Ely turn-off

Big windows in an airy part of the bar here look over the riverside garden and its picnic tables and across to Jesus Green, and there are barges moored between the pub and a nearby lock. The bar itself consists of little partitioned snugs by net-curtained etched-glass windows on the roadside, a U-shaped serving counter, paisley-pattern wallpaper and dark Anaglypta, and bookshelves and small prints; up some steps (where the big windows are) hang oars and inverted sections of boats. Adnams, Boddingtons, Flowers IPA and Original, Fullers Chiswick, Greene King Abbot, Marstons Pedigree and Whitbreads Best and Castle Eden on handpump; piped music, two fruit machines. Bar food is quickly served from a side counter and includes filled rolls (from £1.35), soup (in winter, £1.75), burgers (£2.95, vegetarian £2.75), cottage pie (£4.25), half a roast chicken (£4.35), steak and mushroom and ale pie (£4.45); daily specials might include pork, tomatoes, herbs and white wine, seafood lasagne, seafood pie and vegetarian dishes such as aubergine lasagne (from £3.95–£4.40); puddings such as fruit pie, chocolate fudge cake (£1.75); traditional Sunday lunch – a choice of two roasts (£5.65). They are planning a children's menu for the weekends. They now have a function room upstairs which also operates as a no-smoking area. The pub dog, a border collie, is called Badger. *(Recommended by Jerry and Alison Oakes, Phil Bryant, Nigel Gibbs, Wayne Brindle, Ben Wimpenny)*

Whitbreads   Manager Robert Shearer   Real ale   Meals and snacks (12–2, 5.30–8.30, not Fri–Sun eves)   Cambridge (0223) 460 905   Children welcome   Open 12–11; winter 12–3, 5–11; closed 25, 26 Dec

Free Press

Prospect Row

Several readers' favourite Cambridge pub, this nicely unmodernised, characterful pub is simply furnished and one room is served from a hatch. The snug – which doubles as the eating area – is no-smoking, and half the pub is no-smoking at lunchtime. Good, wholesome bar food includes soup which is always vegetarian, such as curried parsley or carrot and orange or, in summer, chilled spinach and soured cream (£1.50), sandwiches (£1.75) and filled French sticks (£2.75); they do one main dish a day, in winter this might be beef stew or chicken cacciatore (£3.50–£4), while in summer they might include beef in horseradish sauce or a salad with meat, prawns or a pie (from £3); puddings also vary with the seasons, in summer they might be home-made treacle tart or raspberry shortcakes, in winter steamed puddings (all £1.65); you're advised to get there early if you want a seat. Well kept Greene King IPA and Abbot on handpump; friendly service. The sheltered and paved garden at the rear is quite a suntrap and is home for seven rabbits which have built their own burrows there – one of them is tame enough to be picked up. This is the only pub we know of that doubles as a boat club. *(Recommended by I M Kelly, Peter Argent, Andrew Morrissey, John and Joan Wyatt, Michael Spriggs, Alan and Ruth Woodhouse, Wayne Brindle, Drs M and K Parier, Pete Storey)*

Greene King   Tenants Chris and Debbie Lloyd   Real ale   Meals and snacks (12–2, 6(7 Sun)–8.30)   Cambridge (0223) 683 37   Children welcome   Open 12–2.30, 6–11; closed 25 Dec eve, all day 26 Dec

Live & Let Live £

40 Mawson Road; off Mill Road SE of centre

Cheerfully basic and relaxed, with bare boards, pale wood chairs around sturdy varnished pine tables, bare boards and brickwork, heavy timber baulks and interesting bric-a-brac, coming-events posters at one end. Equally basic generous bar food, all home-made (you can see the comings and goings in the kitchen), includes doorstep sandwiches (£1), huge ploughman's or cauliflower cheese (£2), steak and kidney pie and lots of other things with chips, beans and peas (£2.50–2.75 – the lasagnes and chilli are popular): the low prices attract many graduate students, and the atmosphere's chatty (no machines, piped music unobtrusive or absent). Quick and friendly bar service, good table clearance, well kept Marstons Burton, Merrie Monk, Pedigree and Exhibition Mild, and Nethergate and Old Growler on handpump. *(Recommended by Nigel Gibbs, Sandra Cook, Tony and Lynne Stark, Andrew Morrissey, Wayne Brindle, Peter Fenton)*

Free house   Licensee Margaret Rose Holliday   Real ale   Meals and snacks (not Sun evening)   Cambridge (0223) 460261   Children in eating area till 8.30   Open 12–2.30, 6–11

Tap & Spile £

Mill Lane

The favourite real ales in this popular riverside pub seem to be Batemans XXXB, Castle, Fullers London Pride, Mitchells Best, Nethergate and Wadworths IPA and 6X, but they change constantly and so far 180 different ales have been served from their eight handpumps; they also get beers direct from local microbreweries, and have farm ciders and English country wines. Kitchen chairs, chunky stools, settles and a mix of wooden tables sit on the bare boards (or ancient quarry tiles) of the busy U-shaped bar, there's an open brick fireplace, and miscellaneous decorations: lots of display cases with clay pipes or brewery taps and slings, photographs of college games teams, and oars with past names of Pembroke College rowers. Bar food includes sandwiches (but not mid-week lunchtime), beefburgers (from £1.75), filled baked potatoes (from £2.25), spring rolls (£2.65), sausages (£2.75), ploughman's (£4.25) and scampi (£4.45); daily specials include ratatouille (£2.30), macaroni cheese or cauliflower cheese (£2.50) or shepherd's pie (£2.95) and Sunday roast (£3.95). Pleasant and efficient male staff; dominoes, shove-ha'penny and piped pop music. The hanging baskets and window boxes are pretty in summer, and the main punt station is next door. There are approaching two dozen other pubs, mainly in the North of England, in this chain of Tap & Spile back-to-basics real ale pubs. (*Recommended by John and Joan Wyatt, Peter Churchill, Nigel Gibbs, Wayne Brindle, W H Bland, Frank Cummins*)

Brent Walker   Manager J H Gibbs   Real ale   Meals and snacks (12–2 only) Cambridge (0223) 357026   Children in eating area only   Open 11–11

Old Spring

Ferry Path (pub's car park is on Chesterton Road)

The gas lighting here creates an attractively subdued atmosphere (and quite a lot of heat if the pub is busy); electricity is more or less confined to lighting some of the countryside and romantic pictures. There are cushioned small settles, pews, stools and traditional tables on the bare boards, and earth-coloured plaster walls; also a conservatory. Well kept Greene King IPA and Abbot and Rayments on handpump, two fruit machines and a couple of open fires; piped music. The bar food menu changes every day and might include ploughman's (£2.75), chilli (£3.95) and steak and kidney pie (£4.50), vegetarian dishes might include quiches (£3.75), cauliflower cheese or lasagne (£3.95); there's a separate evening menu, a regular favourite is chicken tikka (£4.50) and daily specials; Sunday roast, and summer barbecues. (*Recommended by Phil Bryant, Wayne Brindle; more reports please*)

Greene King/Grand Met   Manager Adrian Brown   Real ale   Meals and snacks (12–2.30, 6.30–9.30)   Cambridge (0223) 357 228   Children welcome till 8 pm Open 11–3(4 Sat), 5.30–11; open all day Sat; closed pm 25 Dec

nr CHATTERIS (Cambs)   TL3883 Map 5

Crafty Fox 🏅

Pickle Fen; B1050 towards St Ives

Some changes afoot here although the character – very relaxed and chatty – is, if anything, more evident now; the emphasis is on a really hospitable and warm welcome. Redecoration is planned but the basic structure of the pub will remain the same. At the moment a more or less open screen divides the small drinking area around the bar from the charming eating part, with its mix of country kitchen chairs around a half-dozen tables, attractive wall seat built into a corner by the stone fireplace, fresh flowers, and soft lighting (some candles at night); fieldmouse paintings, avocet and hunting prints and a plan of the Spithead royal fleet review of 1977 decorate the walls. Thoughtfully prepared and almost entirely home-made, the bar food might include winter soup, sandwiches on request at lunchtime (£1.20), jacket potatoes (from 95p), main meals might include beefburgers (£2.15), steak and kidney pie (£3.50), swordfish (£6.15), chicken satay (£6.95) and steaks (from £8.95), they also do vegetarian dishes such as lasagne (£3.50-£4.50) and they say they are prepared to cook to order if people can't find what they want on the menu; puddings such as chocolate brandy cake, chocolate fondue, St Honoré de Cassis or apple crumble (£1.95). In summer the pub's great pride is an extensive conservatory terrace shaded by properly cared-for grape vines, with a small fountain, coloured lights, and they're planning renovations so that it can be used in winter as well; a barbecue for Sunday lunchtimes (though if you book in advance, they will arrange a do-it-yourself barbecue in the week); the shade netting is a useful idea. They plan to extend the terrace, taking up some of the sizeable car park. Well kept Home and Theakstons XB on handpump, and decent wines; piped music. They may start having a regular jazz band on Sunday lunchtimes. (*Recommended by Frank Gadbois, Phil Bryant, M J Brooks, Alan and Ruth Woodhouse*)

Free house   Licensees David Skeggs and Patrick Quinn   Real ale   Meals and snacks (12–5, 7–10, prepared to serve at any time)   Chatteris (035 43) 2266   Children welcome   May have live music Sun lunchtime   Open 11–11; 25 Dec may open for an hour

DUXFORD (Cambs)   TL4745 Map 5

John Barleycorn ⊘

Moorfield Rd; village signposted off A1301; pub at far end of village

Under its new thatch, this low, early 17th-century pub has exceptionally pretty hanging baskets, tubs and flowerbeds. The dimly lit bar is quietly chatty and attractively furnished with high-backed booth-type oak settles, some wheelback chairs and chunky country tables, and autumnal-coloured curtains to match the cushions; it's broken up by a brick pillar and a couple of standing timbers, and there's a raised brick fireplace with horsebrasses hung along the mantlebeam and a shotgun on the wall above, as well as a mix of old prints, decorative plates (including game ones), photographs of the pub, brass lamps, a ship's clock and some scales, horse bits and reins, and a stuffed hooded crow. The emphasis is very much on the popular food: toasties (from £2.30), filled baked potatoes (£2.85), generous ploughman's (from £2.90), spare ribs (£4.60), very good Turkish lamb with nuts and fruit, spiced beef with dumplings, venison, mushroom and vegetable pie or a choice of salads (£5.75). Well kept Greene King IPA and Abbot. Service is reserved but courteous. Dominoes, cribbage, shove-ha'penny, and piped music. There are a couple of picnic-table sets in front of the building, with more in the back garden along a little grass area surrounded by roses and flowering shrubs, and filled with birdsong; a converted barn with ancient timbers has some back-to-back seats, and there's a brick barbecue. *(Recommended by JF, Nigel Gibbs, Simon Reynolds, Mr and Mrs T F Marshall, Sandra Cook)*

Greene King   Tenant Henry Sewell   Real ale   Meals and snacks (12–2, 7–10)
Cambridge (0223) 832699   Open 12.30–2.30, 6.30–11; closed 25 Dec

ELTISLEY (Cambs)   TL2659 Map 5

Leeds Arms ⊨

The Green; village signposted off A45

Overlooking the large and peaceful village green, this clean and friendly pub has a beamed lounge bar made up of two rooms knocked together: red plush stools, pew-like cushioned wall benches, and a huge winter log fire with brass hunting horns and decorative plates on the mantelpiece; a third room, down some steps, is dominated by tables with cushioned wheelback chairs. Good value bar food includes sandwiches (from £1.50) and ploughman's (£2.50), though neither is served on Saturday evenings, home-made soup (£1.35), home-made cannelloni (£2.35), very good spiced mushrooms (£2.50) or frogs' legs in garlic butter (£3.35); their main dishes include lasagne (from £3.75), home-made curry or chilli con carne (£3.90), salads (from £4.50) and smoked haddock pasta with prawns and mushrooms (£5.75); a range of fish dishes such as pan fried trout with prawns (£4.75), and grills including steak (from £7.25); puddings include pina colada gateau, mississippi mud pie and strawberry romanoff gateau (from £1.85). Well kept Adnams and Greene King IPA on handpump; efficient service; darts, shove-ha'penny, cribbage, dominoes, a fruit machine sensibly set aside in an alcove, and piped music. They also sell confectionary. The garden has swings, slides and picnic-table sets among the silver birches on the lawn. The bedrooms, plainly furnished but comfortable and well equipped, are in a separate block beyond the garden. *(Recommended by TBB, J Barnwell, Rita Horridge, L W Baal, Wayne Brindle, Simon Collet-Jones, Barry and Anne, P J and S E Robbins, M McCrum, G and M Hollis)*

Free house   Licensee George Cottrell   Meals and snacks (12–2, 7–9.45)   Restaurant (12–2, 7–8.30 Sun)   (048 087) 283   Children 10 and over in restaurant except Sat eves   Open 11.30–2.30, 6.30–11; closed 25 Dec   Bedrooms; £35B/£42B

ETTON (Cambs) TF1406 Map 5

Golden Pheasant

Village just off B1443, just E of Helpston level crossing; and will no doubt be signposted from near N end of new A15 Peterborough bypass

A wide choice of well kept real ales on handpump in this former manor house includes Bass, Batemans XXXB, Courage Directors, Greene King IPA, Rayments and a guest beer such as Broadside each week on handpump, and some decent malt whiskies. The comfortable bar has high-backed button-back maroon plush settles built against the walls and around the corners, some spindleback chairs, prints of racing cars and birds on the walls, quite a high burnt ochre Anaglypta ceiling, little gilt fringe-shaded wall lamps, and an open fire. In the airy, glass-walled side room are some Lloyd Loom chairs around glass-topped cane tables. Good value bar food includes French onion soup, ploughman's (from £2.95), scampi or steak and kidney pie (£3.95), grilled trout (£4.25) and daily specials such as good cod and prawn pie; puddings such as cherry cheesecake, mississippi mud pie (all £1.90); barbecue summer Sunday lunchtimes; good, cheerful service. Fruit machine and well reproduced and chosen piped pop music. The stone-walled garden, surrounded by tall trees, looks out across flat countryside; pétanque is played here in summer. The big paddock is safe for children. *(Recommended by M J Morgan, John C Baker)*

Free house   Licensees Clive and Sue Philips   Real ale   Meals and snacks (12.30–2, 6.30–9.30; not Sun evening)   Restaurant   Peterborough (0733) 252387   Children in conservatory   Occasional live music   Open 11.30–3.30, 5.30–11 (all day Thurs–Sat); closed pm 25 Dec

FEN DRAYTON (Cambs)   TL3368 Map 5

Three Tuns ✪

High Street; village signposted off A604 NW of Cambridge

Beneath the moulded and very heavy early Tudor beams in this attractive thatched pub there are two inglenook fireplaces (one of which is usually alight), cushioned settles and an interesting variety of chairs, big portraits and old photographs of local scenes, brass plates on the timbered walls, and old crockery in a corner dresser. Pleasantly served by friendly staff, the bar food includes sandwiches with a choice of brown, white or French bread (from £1), home-made soup (£1.80), home-made chicken liver and bacon pâté (£2), Greek dips (£2.25), chicken satay with peanut sauce or ploughman's (£2.50), home-made dishes such as meaty or vegetarian lasagne (£3.80) or chicken curry (£3.90), salads (from £3), gammon with pineapple (£5), chicken kiev (£6), 8oz rump steak (£7.50); daily specials include a pie such as chicken and mushroom or steak and kidney (£4.05), leek and pasta mornay (£3.75), Barnsley chops (£6.50); and there are daily puddings like home-made apple pie (from £1.20). Greene King IPA and Abbot and Rayments on handpump, a range of malt whiskies, and sensibly placed darts, shove-ha'penny, dominoes, cribbage and fruit machine. A well tended lawn at the back has tables under cocktail parasols, apple and flowering cherry trees, and some children's play equipment. The unusual inn sign consists of three tiny barrels sitting on a pole, and the building may have been the medieval guild hall for the pretty village. It can get very crowded. *(Recommended by M D Hare, Gordon Theaker, Peter Churchill, M E A Horler)*

Greene King   Tenant Michael Nugent   Real ales   Meals and snacks (not Sun evening)   (0954) 30242   Children in eating area till 8pm   Open noon–2.30, 6.30–11

FOWLMERE (Cambs)   TL4245 Map 5

Chequers ✪

B1368

This civilised and rather upmarket 16th-century coaching inn has two warm and cosy comfortably furnished communicating rooms; upstairs there are beams, wall timbering and some interesting moulded plasterwork above the fireplace, and downstairs has prints and photographs of Spitfires and Mustangs flown from Fowlmere aerodrome and an open log fire. Look out for the priest's hole above the bar. Served by black-and-white dressed waiters, the interesting and often excellent bar food might include stilton and walnut pâté perfumed with port or soft herring roes with black butter and capers (£2.90), New Zealand mussels in garlic butter (£3.20) tasty mushrooms on garlic bread (£3.40), and a lovely hors d'oeuvres trolley (small £3.20, large £5.15); main meals include aubergine stuffed with mushrooms or tagliatelle, cream, mushrooms and prawns (£4.50), crab au gratin with sweetcorn (£5.35), pork escalope with mushroom and cream sauce (£5.80) and steaks (from £8.60) with puddings like crème brûlée or a fine summer pudding (£2.40). Nibbles on the bar on Sunday morning. Tolly and Original on handpump, freshly squeezed orange juice, a good choice of vintage and late-bottled ports by the glass; there's a cruover machine to keep the good choice of fine wines by the glass in perfect condition. The garden is particularly well looked after, with white tables under cocktail parasols among the flowers and shrub roses and the pub can now also boast a private conservatory/function room overlooking the garden with direct access to ample parking. *(Recommended by Charles Bardswell, Mr and Mrs T F Marshall, P S Vince, Maggie Jo St John, GB, CH, P A Devitt, Gwen and Peter Andrews, Miss S Lee, BHP, Nigel Gibbs, Sandra Cook, John Evans, Drs M and K Parier, J P Cinnamond, Miss S Lee)*

Camerons Lease: Norman Rushton Real ale Meals and snacks (12–2, 7–10, Sun –9.30) Restaurant Fowlmere (0763) 208369 Children welcome Open 12–2.30, 6–11; closed 25 Dec

Queens Head £

Long Lane; turn left by war memorial, pub on corner

Cheese is the special thing in this pretty thatched 17th-century cottage (from £2.60): they have up to 18 at a time, including several rarities, and serve half a dozen different breads – a current favourite is black bread (rye and fennel). The soup of the day is another good bet (£1.55, home-made with fresh ingredients); other food is limited to doorstep sandwiches (from £1.45, children's specials like chocolate spread £1.10), filled baked potatoes (from £1.60) and pâté (£2.20). Greene King IPA and Abbot on handpump, attractively priced decent wines, coffee; friendly, hard-working licensees. The main bar has simple furnishings such as farmhouse chairs and brocaded stools around wooden tables, some panelling, attractive old portrait photographs, and a few horsebrasses. Darts, shove-ha'penny, dominoes, cribbage, shut-the-box, fruit machine, and maybe a pop or general knowledge quiz; maybe piped music in this main bar. The quiet and cosy little beamed lounge bar has wheelbacks and other similar furniture, half-panelled walls and bar counter, a brick fireplace, and walls decorated with some prints, plates and horsebrasses. The sizeable garden has picnic-table sets and a new double boules pitch; they plan to add a non-working 1953 Fordson tractor for children to play on. *(Recommended by Rodney and Ruth Hewson, Charles Bardswell)*

Greene King Tenants Howard and Sue Gascoyne Real ale Lunchtime meals and snacks (12–2, 2.30 weekends) Fowlmere (0763)208288 Children welcome Open 12–2.30, 6–11; 12–4, 7–11 Sat – may stay open later afternoon, esp Sat, if busy

HINXTON (Cambs) TL4945 Map 5

Red Lion

2 miles from M11 junction 9, 3 1/2 miles from junction 10; just off A1301 S of Great Shelford

It's easy to sink down into the button-back red brocade wall banquette without noticing George the quiet amazon parrot perched above your head – till he softly says Hello, or asks for a Polo mint. Other livestock here includes a pair of cockatiels, and Jill the silver tabby. But the main thing here is the thriving atmosphere, owing so much to the warm personalities of the licensees. The bar's mainly open-plan, with a few big prints and quite a lot of smaller rustic pictures on the walls, and shelves of china in one corner. A good choice of bar food from sandwiches to an excellent value rump steak includes well prepared dishes of the day such as home-baked ham or lasagne (£3.50), spicy pork (£3.95) and a fine prawn curry (£4.25); the bar angles round to a back dining room. Well kept Adnams, Greene King IPA, Hook Norton Best, Marstons Pedigree and Nethergate on handpump, a good wine list, unobtrusive piped Radio 2. The garden outside this pretty white slightly jettied twin-gabled old building has picnic-table sets, a swing and a chicken ark. *(Recommended by Nigel Gibbs, Sandra Cook, John C Baker, Janet and Gary Amos, Norman and Barbara Wells)*

Free house   Licensee James Read Crawford   Real ale   Meals and snacks till 10 Restaurant   Saffron Walden (0799) 30601   Children 6 and over in restaurant   Open 11–2.30, 6–11

HOLYWELL (Cambs)   TL3370   Map 5

Olde Ferry Boat

Village and pub both signposted (keep your eyes skinned!) off A1123 in Needingworth

On the site of a monastic ferry house, this remote fenland pub has a gravestone in the bar apparently marking the resting-place of the resident ghost Juliet. The four rambling bar areas have window seats with views of the Great Ouse, red leather settees, a pretty little carved settle, low-beamed ceilings, timbered or panelled walls, and an old-fashioned atmosphere; one of the four open fires has a fish and an eel among rushes moulded on its chimney beam, and two rooms are no smoking. Well kept Adnams Broadside, Bass, Greene King Abbot and IPA, and a guest on handpump. Bar food includes home-made soup (£1.95), stilton and lamb pâté (£2.95), lunchtime ploughman's (£3.95), omelettes (£4.99), sausage, kidney and mushroom pie (£6.25), lasagne (from £5.90) and steak (£7.90); children's dishes (from £2.90); occasional food theme evenings; friendly, attentive service; fruit machine and piped music. The front terrace has tables under cocktail parasols, with more on a side rose lawn along the river – lovely to watch people messing about in boats. *(Recommended by Gwen and Peter Andrews, Mrs Richard Stewart, Brian and Jill Bond, P S Vince, Bob and Lesley Fawthrop, Nigel Gibbs, Chris Raisin, Miss R Murdoch, Michael and Betty Hall, M S Hancock, Ted George, Alison and Tony Godfrey, Andy Hick, J P Cinnamond)*

Free house   Licensee Richard Jeffrey   Real ale   Meals and snacks (12–2, 7–10) Restaurant (not Sun evening)   St Ives (0480) 63227   Children welcome   Open 11–3, 6–11   Bedrooms; £39.99/£49.50

HORNINGSEA (Cambs)   TL4962   Map 5

Plough & Fleece   ★

Just NE of Cambridge: first slip-road off A45 heading E after A10, then left at T; or take B1047 Fen Ditton road off A1303

There's a genuinely homely atmosphere in this small but rambling country pub, particularly in the black-beamed public bar with its high-backed settles and plain seats on the red tiled floor, plain wooden tables – including an enormously long slab of elm (with an equally long pew to match it) – butter-yellow walls, a stuffed parrot, and stuffed fox by the log fire. There is a new no smoking dining room – lots of wood and old bricks and tiles; by the time this edition comes out a new terrace should link it to the garden. The extensive range of often imaginative bar food includes home-made soup (£1.50), hot garlic cockles or home-made pâté (£2.45), devilled crab or vegetarian stilton and broccoli flan or tuna and prawn flan (£2.75), omelettes (£4.25), salads such as home-cooked ham or stuffed pepper (£4.30), popular Suffolk hot-pot (£4.25), honey-roast guinea fowl (£7.25) or barbary duck breast (£8.50), sirloin steak (£9) and beef Wellington (£10). Prices are slightly higher in the evenings. At lunchtimes there are also sandwiches (from £1.30, toasties from £1.50), ploughman's, and hot snacks; good puddings such as toffee apple pie or Northamptonshire chocolate pudding with rum-flavoured sauce (from £2); efficient service even under pressure. Well kept Greene King IPA and Abbot on handpump, half a dozen good malt whiskies and a couple of vintage ports; dominoes and cribbage. The mix of wild and cultivated flowers in the garden is a nice touch; picnic-table sets beyond the car park, and a herbaceous border is a children's play area with a rope ladder climbing into an old pear tree. *(Recommended by M J Brooks, Jamie and Ruth Lyons, Roy Y Bromell, E B Warrington, Alan and Ruth Woodhouse, Barry and Anne, Drs M and K Parier, Wayne Brindle, Robert and Elizabeth Scott, John Tyzack, Nick and Alison Dowson, KC, J P Cinnamond)*

Greene King Tenant Kenneth Grimes Real ale Meals and snacks (not Sun or Mon evening) No smoking restaurant Cambridge (0223) 860795 Open 11.30–2.30, 7–11; closed 25 and 26 Dec

KENNETT (Cambs) TL6968 Map 5
Bell

Bury Road; crossroads B1506/B1085, through Kentford on the Newmarket slip-road just off A45 Bury St Edmunds–Cambridge

The main attractions here are the half-dozen well kept real ales, and decent choice of tasty bar food. From an attractive and efficient servery this might include good home-made soup (£1.75), brunch (£3.95) or steak and stout pie (£4.95), and the ales might include Adnams, Nethergate and Theakstons Best; there is also a wide choice of malt whiskies and wines; obliging service. The rambling, Turkey-carpeted bar has lots of stripped country tables with Windsor armchairs and cushioned dining chairs, heavy oak beams, a brick inglenook and a freestanding fireplace; a tiled-floor room, used as an evening seafood bar, leads off. *(Recommended by Frank W Gadbois, Mr and Mrs C H Garnett, P Craddock, John Behle, G L Tong)*

Free house Licensees Mr and Mrs Colin Hayling Real ale Meals and snacks (12–2, 7–9.45; not Sun eves) Restaurant Newmarket (0638) 750286 Children in restaurant at lunchtime Trad jazz Tues evenings Open 11.30–2.30, 6 (Sat 6.30)–11; closed evenings 25 and 26 Dec Bedrooms; £27.50B/£35.50B

KEYSOE (Beds) TL0762 Map 5
Chequers

B660 N of Bedford

Consistently good bar food in this attractive pub includes home-made soups like tasty cheese and ale or carrot and mint (£1.75), sandwiches, (all £1.50), good ploughman's (£3.50), vegetarian courgette and cheese flan or tagliatelle (£4.50), lovely salads, chicken stuffed with stilton and chives or fried trout (£7.50), and steaks (from £8.45); puddings, such as coffee nut pudding in butterscotch sauce or fresh fruit pavlova, are all home-made (£2); Sunday roast lunch; children's helpings. The pub is often full, particularly in the evenings, when food may finish early because of the heavy demand. Well kept Hook Norton and guest beers such as Batemans, Moorhouses Pendle Witches Brew and Theakstons Old Peculier all from handpumps on the stone bar counter, and some malts. The two beamed bars are comfortably modernised and welcoming, and a central feature is the unusual stone-pillared fireplace. Darts, fruit machine, video game, piped music. The terrace at the back looks over the garden which has a wendy house, play tree, swings and a sand-pit. *(Recommended by M and J Back, Roger Danes, Dr R J A Jones; more reports please)*

Free house Licensee Jeffrey Kearns Real ale Meals and snacks (12–2, 7–10; not Mon) Children everywhere but main bar Bedford (0234) 708 678 Open 11–2.30, 6.30–11; closed Mondays, except Bank Holidays, and 25 and 26 Dec

KEYSTON (Cambs) TL0475 Map 5
Pheasant ⊘

Village loop road; from A604 SE of Thrapston, right on to B663

The new licensee here has worked in several top restaurants and early reports from readers suggest the food is really excellent – though by no means cheap. His menu includes game soup (£1.75), toasted brie or guinea fowl terrine (£2.95); main dishes might include plaice fillet, steak and kidney pie, cod, salmon and saffron pie or fusilli carbonara (£5.95), chicken breast with chasseur sauce or trout fillets with chive butter (£6.95), half a roast duck or poached salmon salad (£7.95) and steak (£8.25). Delicious puddings might include coconut parfait, chocolate truffle cake or toffee and date pudding (£2.95); Sunday roast (£14.95). Well kept Adnams, Batemans XXXB and a guest beer on handpump, and a superb selection of wines, by the glass as well as by the bottle. The extended and low-beamed main bar has a comfortable atmosphere, and leading off here is a room that used to be the village smithy: leather slung stools and a heavily carved wooden armchair among the Windsor chairs, heavy-horse harness on the high rafters, and an old horse-drawn harrow; the walls are decorated with old photographs of the pub. Some tables under cocktail parasols at the front are laid with tablecloths. No dogs. This is one of Ivo Vannocci's Poste Hotels. (Fans of Bill Bennett who was here before can track him down at the White Hart in Bythorn – see main entry above.) *(Recommended by John C Baker, Rita Horridge, P A Devitt, J Barnwell, A J Whiteman, John and Tessa Rainsford)*

Free house   Licensee Nick Steiger   Real ale   Meals and snacks (12–2, 6–10; not Christmas day or New Year's eve)   Restaurant   Bythorn (080 14) 241   Children welcome   Open 11–3, 6–11; closed eve Dec 25, all day 26 Dec

NEWTON (Cambs)   TL4349 Map 5

Queens Head ✪

2 1/2 miles from M11 junction 11; A10 towards Royston, then left on to B1368

A favourite among several readers, this pretty brick pub attracts people from some miles away to enjoy its unchanging straightforward character and freshly prepared, simple bar food. Furnishings in the main bar are traditional, with bare wooden benches and seats built into the walls and bow windows, a curved high backed settle on the yellow tiled floor, unusual seats in the fireplace, a loudly ticking clock, and paintings on the cream walls. The little carpeted saloon is broadly similar but cosier. Darts in a side room, with shove-ha'penny, table skittles, dominoes, cribbage, nine men's morris and a fruit machine. The range of bar food includes a good choice of sandwiches (from £1.30, smoked salmon £1.90), superb home-made soup (£1.60); in the evening and on Sunday lunchtime they serve plates of excellent quality cold meat, smoked salmon, cheeses and pâté (from £2.75). Well kept Adnams Bitter and Broadside tapped from the cask, with Old Ale in winter and Tally Ho at Christmas; English wines, including elderflower and raspberry. Seats at the front outside. Belinda the goose who used to patrol the car park unfortunately died but the licensee has plans for her to return to the bar – he is getting her stuffed! – and she also features on the pub sign, painted by the licensee's father and son. *(Recommended by Tim and Sue Halstead, Tony and Lynne Stark, Wayne Brindle, Alan and Ruth Woodhouse, Pete Storey, Drs M and K Parier)*

Free house   Licensee David Short   Real ale   Snacks (12–2, 6(Sun 7)–10)   Cambridge (0223) 870436   Children in games room   Open 11.30 (11 Sat)–2.30, 6–11; closed 25 Dec

ODELL (Beds)   SP9658 Map 5

Bell £

Horsefair Lane; off A6 S of Rushden, via Sharnbrook

There's a warm and friendly atmosphere in the five linked rooms that loop around the central servery of this pretty thatched stone village pub. It has quite a few handsome old oak settles as well as more neatly modern furniture, a log fire in one big stone fireplace, two coal fires elsewhere, and low ceilings with black shiny beams over on the right. The landlady's cooking, relying on fresh local ingredients, fills the pub with a contented lunchtime buzz. Generously priced food includes sandwiches (from £1.35), ploughman's (from £2.30), omelettes and speciality flans (from £2.60), ham and egg (£2.85), smoked haddock pancakes (£3.30), the usual fried dishes (£3.40), fish pie (£3.45), liver and bacon (£3.95), pies such as venison and bacon or steak and kidney (£4.50) and changing casseroles such as half a chicken in a curry and mango chutney sauce, or beef and bacon (£4.95; sometimes served smaller at lunchtime, £3.45). Good home-made puddings (£1.50ish) include pecan pie and a popular chocolate mousse spiked with brandy and Grand Marnier. Well kept Greene King IPA and Abbot and Rayments on handpump, faint piped music, efficient service. The garden running back to the Great Ouse has picnic-table sets, golden pheasants, cockatiels, and a goose called Lucy who likes being fed lettuce leaves. (*Recommended by S Holder, Margaret and Roy Randle, Maysie Thompson*)

Free house   Licensee Doreen Scott   Real ale   Meals and snacks (limited Sun lunchtime, not Sun evening)   Bedford (0234) 720254   Children in two rooms   Open 11–2.30, 6–11

SOUTHILL (Beds)   TL1542 Map 5
White Horse

From A603 E of Bedford, right on to B658; village signposted on right after 4 miles

The spacious garden here is popular with families, with its 7 1/4-inch gauge railway with diesel engines, bridges and a tunnel (children's rides 20p), garden shop, and children's games and play area. Inside, the comfortable main lounge is decorated with cricketing prints, 1930s cigarette picture cards, and framed old English currency notes, and a smaller, plainer public bar has comic railway pictures and prints among the harness; big woodburning stove. There's an interesting spotlit well in the dining room; Flowers IPA and Wethereds on handpump, darts, shove-ha'penny, dominoes, cribbage, table skittles, fruit machine and piped music. Bar food may include sandwiches – doorsteps or French rolls (from £1.40), and open (from £3.30) – ploughman's (from £3) and salads (from £5.25); hot meals include cod, spring rolls, sausages or quiche lorraine (£3.50), meaty or vegetable burgers (£4) and scampi (£5) and children's meals (£2); set Sunday roasts. Handy for the Shuttleworth Collection of old cars and early aeroplanes. (*Recommended by Maysie Thompson, Mrs R Horridge, Roger Danes; more reports please*)

Whitbreads   Lease: Anthony Roy Tofari   Real ale   Meals and snacks (12–2.30, 7–9.30; not Sun evening)   Restaurant (not Sun eves)   Hitchin (0462) 813364   Children in eating areas   Open 11–3, 6–11

STILTON (Cambs)   TL1689 Map 5
Bell

High Street; village signposted from A1 S of Peterborough

Carefully restored and modernised over the past few years, this handsomely rambling old coaching inn has a well in the sheltered cobbled and flagstoned back courtyard that is believed to date back to Roman times; picnic-table sets here, too. The two opened-up rooms of the attractive bar have sturdy upright wooden seats, plush-cushioned button-back banquettes built around the walls and bow windows, big prints of sailing and winter coaching scenes on the partly stripped walls, flagstones, floor tiles, and a large log fire in the fine stone fireplace. Well kept Marstons Pedigree, Ruddles County and Tetleys on handpump and a guest beer such as Adnams or Boddingtons; dominoes, backgammon, cards, Mastermind, a trivia machine and piped music. Stilton the cheese got its name originally from being sold to the inn's coaching customers (it's still possible to buy stilton cheese here) and thus widely travelled around the country, until then it had been known as the Quenby cheese and was actually made in Little Dalby and Wymondham up near Melton Mowbray; it's therefore no surprise that it still features prominently on the bar menu: snacks and starters include soup (£1.65), filled French sticks (from £1.95) terrine of stilton and hazelnut pâté (£2.95) and ploughman's (from £2.95); main dishes include curried lamb kidneys, liver and bacon in onion sauce

(£4.95), chilli (£5.35), sweet and sour chicken (£6.25) and steaks (from £6.75); puddings are from £1.95, or you can sample their blue stilton with traditional plum bread (£2.95); Sunday lunch from £8.95; very good, friendly service. The inn sign is a large and stately affair – a curlicued gantry and a coach-arch, with distances to cities carved on the courtyard side. *(Recommended by Mr and Mrs J M Elden, Wayne Brindle, J R Smylie, Mr and Mrs R J Foreman, Adam and Elizabeth Gorb, Chris Raisin, Roger Bellingham, Helen Roe, Phil Russell, Mr and Mrs R J Foreman, Mr and Mrs P A Jones, W H Bland, Kathleen Morley, A Jarman, Barry and Anne, F J Robinson, Eleanor Wallis, Alison and Tony Godfrey, D A Wilcock, Miss C M Davidson, L M Miall)*

Free house   Licensees John and Liam McGivern   Real ale   Meals and snacks Children in eating area until 7pm   Restaurant   Peterborough (0733) 241066   Open 11–2.30, 6–11   Bedrooms; £57B/£72B

SUTTON GAULT (Cambs)   TL4279   Map 5

Anchor 🏅

Village signed off B1381 in Sutton

Under its new licensees this riverside house has become even more of a dining pub, with most tables being reserved in advance. The food is very good indeed: home-made soup (£2), egg and prawns with tarragon mayonnaise (£2.95), chicken liver, port and hazelnut pâté (£3.25), button mushrooms in cream and garlic au gratin or chilled galia melon with passion fruit sorbet (£3.60), giant green lipped mussels or grilled dates wrapped in bacon on mild mustard cream sauce (£3.75); main dishes include chilli, or tagliatelle with bacon, mushrooms, garlic and cream (£5.75), chicken, leek and bacon crumble or steak, kidney and Guinness pie (£6.75), or breast of barbary duckling with orange and sherry sauce (£8.50); vegetarian dishes such as curried nut loaf in tomato and basil sauce or wholemeal vegetarian crumble (£5.75). There is a selection of outstanding puddings such as uncloying strawberry pavlova and chocolate/coffee roulade. Well kept Tolly Original tapped from the cask, good wine list, winter hot punch; they also do freshly squeezed orange juice (£1.30 a glass). The four heavily timbered rooms are lit with gas lights (from swan's-neck gas lamps) or candles, and furnished with antique settles, dining or kitchen chairs and well spaced, stripped and scrubbed deal tables; sloping floors, good lithographs and big prints on the walls, and three log fires. Shove-ha'penny, dominoes, cribbage, well reproduced piped classical music. Tables outside by the water, with fine views across the unspoilt countryside. No dogs. *(Recommended by Irene and Derek Cranston, Gwen and Peter Andrews, Brian and Jill Bond, Phil Bryant, Mrs V Constable, Mrs C Fairweather, R C Wiles, Gary Melnyk, J P Cinnamond)*

Free house   Licensees Robin and Heather Moore   Real ale   Meals and snacks (12–2, 6.30–9.30; Fri and Sat –10; Sun 7–9)   Ely (0353) 778537   Well behaved children in eating area at lunchtime and until 8.30 at night   Open 12–2.30, 6.30–11; closed 25 and 26 Dec

SWAVESEY (Cambs)   TL3668   Map 5

Trinity Foot   £

A604, N side; to reach it from the westbound carriageway, take Swavesey, Fen Drayton turn-off

Well liked locally, this comfortable pub is busy even midweek in winter. It's pleasantly decorated with well spaced tables and fresh flowers, and there's a light and airy conservatory. The bar food is good value and comes in big helpings; this pub specialises in daily fresh fish such as fresh plaice and haddock (£6), oysters, lobsters; other food includes sandwiches (from 95p), ploughman's (£3) and specials, with steak and kidney pie a firm favourite, and good Sunday roasts. Flowers Original and Ruddles on handpump; nicely made Pimms with Bergamot flower; efficient, friendly service. The enclosed garden of shrubs, trees and lawns is pleasant. The eating area of the bar is no-smoking. *(Recommended by Gordon L Smith, Adrian Acton; more reports please)*

Whitbreads   Tenants H J and B J Mole   Real ale   Meals and snacks (12–2, 6–9.30; not Sun evening)   Children in eating area   Open 11–2.30, 6–11; closed 25 and 26 Dec

UFFORD (Cambs)   TF0904   Map 5

Olde White Hart

From A15 N of Peterborough, left on to B1443; village signposted at unmarked road on left after about 4 miles

This nice old-fashioned pub is comfortable and friendly and popular for its bar food (best to book) which now includes more vegetarian and fish dishes; rolls and sandwiches (£1) and light snacks are served at lunchtime. Popular main dishes include home-made pies such as steak and mushroom and tuna and asparagus (£4.50) and weekly specials such as smoked salmon and lobster, spiced salami and pasta crème or spare ribs (£6); imaginative puddings. On Sunday lunchtime they do hot roast beef rolls (£1.30), and Sunday roast lunch; barbecues Thursday, Friday and Saturday evenings. An attractive stone chimney divides the lounge bar into two; there are pewter tankards hanging from the beam over the bar counter, wheelback chairs around dark tripod tables, and Boris the stuffed tarantula. The carpeted public bar has old-fashioned settles and dark tables. Well kept Home Bitter, Theakstons Best, XB and Old Peculier on handpump, and a large selection of world-wide bottled beers; several wines by the glass. The refurbished snug is furnished with wooden settles made by the landlord's father who also crafted the outdoor benches; darts, cribbage, dominoes, ring the bull and Connect Four. The sunny terrace has white metal seats and a canopy (for theme nights in summer and on wet days); the big, pretty garden with its children's play area now takes in the formerly overgrown Acre Meadow which is grazed by the pub's own sheep and goats. *(Recommended by M Morgan, Tom Evans, Wayne Brindle, Sarah Bullard)*

Home (S & N)   Tenants Chris and Sally Hooton   Real ale   Meals and snacks (12–2, 6–9.30; not Sun evening or Mon)   Restaurant   Stamford (0780) 740250   Children in eating area   Folk music on Sun eves, Summer Jazz Sun lunch and occasional live bands Thurs/Fri   Open 11–2.30 (till 3 Sat), 6–11; closed 25 Dec

WANSFORD (Cambs)   TL0799   Map 5

Haycock ★ 🚫 🛏

Village clearly signposted from A1 W of Peterborough

So many pubs and inns seem to lose all heart and soul when they extend that it's a real delight to find this one which seems to gain in appeal and character with each successive stage of what has become quite a formidable development. The old-fashioned style of the place has been firmly underlined by the extensions, and the particularly well-drilled staff seem to put a genuine enjoyment into their work that is all too rare elsewhere. The latest phase has been the opening up of an airy stripped brick eating bar by the garden which has dark blue and light blue basketweave chairs around glass-topped basket tables, pretty flowery curtains and nice modern prints of sunny conservatory or garden scenes; there's a food counter on one side, and doors open on to a big terrace with lots of tables. Another room has dark terracotta walls and three nice old oak settles with cushions, and two handsome stone arches that lead into the main bar; this has been refurbished and has dark terracotta walls, a sturdy dado rail above mulberry dado, more old settles with pretty blue cushions and some leather saddle stools. The front sitting room on the other side of the servery is furnished with warm light brown fabric walls and easy chairs and settees in brown zig-zag cloth, there is some squared oak panelling by the bar counter, a nice wall clock, and big log fire. There are two no smoking areas. The snag is that, although the quality is good, the bar food prices are high – a dish of fresh melon with fruit (£3.95), peeled prawns (£6.95) or two rollmop herrings (£5.45) with salads chosen from the cold buffet table; main courses include grilled sardines, mushroom stroganoff or baked pork chop (£7.95), sliced breast of chicken curried with rice and mango or seafood pancake (£8.25); home-made puddings (from £3.95). Those in a hurry can get sandwiches, or more quickly prepared pasta dishes such as rigatoni and tuna fish with cheese sauce or farfalle with cream and bacon (£7.95). Weather permitting, barbecues are held on the garden terrace (from £6.95). Well kept Adnams, Bass, Ruddles Best and County and Shefford all on handpump, a good range of decent wines by the glass – the cruover machine allows them to keep about 20 or so in very good condition – and properly mature vintage ports by the glass; freshly squeezed juices. The walled formal garden is spacious and attractive; boules and cricket and fishing. One of Ivo Vannocci's Poste Hotels. *(Recommended by Capt F A Bland, J R Smylie, W T Aird, Gordon Theaker, Tony Gayfer, Tony Bland)*

Free house   Licensee Richard Neale   Real ale   Meals and snacks (noon–11pm) Restaurant   Stamford (0780) 782223   Children welcome   Open 10.30–11 (Sat 10.30–3, 5.45–11)   Bedrooms; £68B/£90B

Lucky Dip

Besides the fully inspected pubs, you might like to try these Lucky Dips recommended to us and described by readers (if you do, please send us reports); pubs in Bedfordshire are picked out with the abbreviation Beds after the town name:

Alconbury [Main St, Alconbury Weston; TL1875], *White Hart*: Popular local with Watneys-related beers, food at useful prices — considering its closeness to the A1 *(Mr and Mrs Back)*

☆ **Arrington** [TL3250], *Hardwicke Arms*: Quaint creeper-covered coaching inn with elegant beamed and panelled lounge, high-ceilinged further room, friendly helpful service, good often imaginative lunchtime bar food, well kept Adnams, Bass and Greene King real ales; games room, tables in spacious outside area; next to Wimpole Hall; bedrooms *(Tom Evans, LYM)*

Babraham [just off A1307; TL5150], *George*: Staff friendly and efficient even on Newmarket race day, reasonably priced bar food, well kept beer *(Edward Stagg)*

☆ **Barnack** [Millstone Lane; off B1443 SE of Stamford; turn off School Lane nr the Fox; TF0704], *Millstone*: The local stone of this building is what they used also for Ely Cathedral and most of the Cambridge colleges — a fine old strongly traditional pub with wall timbers and high beams weighed down with harness, and a really good woodburning stove; several well kept real ales inc rarities like Moorhouses Pendle Witches Brew, busy and cheerful atmosphere, good choice of decent bar food from soup and sandwiches through omelettes and pies to gammon and trout, served apart in side area with pews; fruit machine, piped music, friendly service; children allowed in restaurant and snug *(A G Purkis, M J Morgan, John C Baker, Nic James, BB)*

Bartlow [TL5845], *Three Hills*: Pleasing 16th-century pub, warmly welcoming licensees, long bar with plenty of dark wood tables and matching bar stools, well kept Greene King IPA, very subdued pipe music, real family atmosphere, bar food, evening restaurant, Sun lunches; interesting hill forts nearby; shame the log fire's gone; licensees Steve and Sue Dixon helped by daughter; poor pork in stroganoff, poor chips with plaice, oniony salad *(Gwen and Peter*

Andrews, Barbara and Norman Wells)

Bedford, Beds [St Mary's St; TL0449], *Kings Arms*: Well kept open-plan town-centre pub, recently refurbished with plenty of space, small back bar up steps and big conservatory area; popular for wide range of food, served all the time *(Michael and Alison Sandy, LYM)*

Bourn [TL3256], *Duke of Wellington*: More than generous helpings of well cooked interesting food *(Maysie Thompson)*

Boxworth [TL3464], *Golden Bowl*: Worth knowing for good choice of vegetarian dishes; four real ales, pleasant ambiance and staff, good garden with children's play area *(Dr and Mrs D A Blackadder, D B Haunch)*

Bromham, Beds [Bromham Rd; A428, 2 miles W of Bedford; TL0050], *Swan*: Traditional comfortable village pub with open fires in both lounge (with dining extension) and public, good reasonably priced English-style food, Greene King IPA and Abbot, pleasant garden *(G Pell)*

☆ **Cambridge** [Dover St (off East Rd)], *Tram Depot*: Superbly designed and furnished conversion of former tramway stables, with long central skylight over upstairs area and glazed mezzanine, old furniture to match the bare brick and flagstones, faultless bar service, well kept beers from the Victoria at Earl Soham (under same ownership — see Suffolk main entries), good atmosphere — popular with young people; bar food (not Sat evening) *(Richard Houghton, Frank W Gadbois)*

☆ **Cambridge** [Tenison Rd], *Salisbury Arms*: Charles Wells pub with a dozen or so real ales inc lots of guest beers, good no smoking area, buoyant young atmosphere and decent basic lunchtime bar food; surprisingly high-ceilinged and spacious back bar, smaller front public bar, good staff, pub games, loud CD juke box, farm cider; weekday happy hour 6-7, maybe jazz Sun lunchtime *(Frank W Gadbois, Wayne Brindle, Nigel Gibbs, Andrew Morrissey, Tony and Lynne Stark, Drs M and K Parier, LYM)*

☆ **Cambridge** [85 Gwydir St], *Cambridge*

Blue: Well kept Banks & Taylors and other real ales in small and simply furnished two-roomed pub with university sports photographs, local paintings, food inc good choice of home-made pies (not Sun evening), friendly pubby atmosphere, sheltered terrace with children's climbing frame *(Michael Spriggs, Tony and Lynne Stark, Drs M and K Parier, Wayne Brindle, LYM)*

☆ **Cambridge** [Newmarket Rd], *Wrestlers*: Charles Wells pub, quiet lunchtime but lively evenings (free rock and other live music Thurs-Sat), wide choice of bar food from Thai chefs (tom yam particularly good), student atmosphere, pool table, six real ales such as Adnams Broadside and Mansfield Riding as well as Charles Wells Bombardier and Mild *(Phil Bryant, Frank W Gadbois)*

☆ **Cambridge** [Panton St], *Panton Arms*: Former brewery off the tourist beat, with two interesting bars, pleasant well furnished side courtyard; friendly bar service and very efficient, pleasant service of good home-made bar food (not Sat or Sun evenings) inc enterprising dishes — eg Armenian or Malaysian *(Frank Cummins, Dr and Mrs A K Clarke)*

Cambridge [Napier St], *Ancient Druids*: Shinily modern, with interesting own-brewed beers (viewing windows to microbrewery), wide choice of good value food (not Sun evening), air-conditioning; parking in adjacent multi-storey *(Wayne Brindle, Richard Houghton, Stephen R Holman)*; [Chesterton Lane], *Arundel House*: River-view hotel worth knowing for basement bar with good value freshly cooked food inc some unusual items such as pasta with smoked fish; Greene King Abbot *(Mr and Mrs K J Morris)*; [19 Bridge St], *Baron of Beef*: Traditional-style busy pub with lots of old photographs, panelling, Greene King ales under pressure from uncommonly long counter, pub food from buffet, friendly landlord *(Nigel Gibbs, Wayne Brindle, Ben Wimpenny)*; [Bene't St], *Bath*: Large bar with huge fireplace, earthenware jars, milk churns, etc, machines and four TVs (none of which intrude); plenty of seating and standing room, cheap cheerful food from Pizza Hut stand unobtrusively at back, well kept Whitbreads-related beers; good CD juke box, very popular with students — especially weekends *(Alan and Ruth Woodhouse, Julian Holland, Nigel Gibbs)*; [4 King St], *Cambridge Arms*: Unusual multi-level modern conversion of former brewery, comfortable and spacious, young lively atmosphere, Greene King IPA and Abbot, rather good food, sheltered courtyard, maybe jazz nights *(Wayne Brindle, Tony and Lynne Stark, LYM)*; [King St], *Champion of the Thames*: Good atmosphere, with good town-and-gown mix, good unobtrusive refurbishment *(William Pryce)*; [Midsummer Common], *Fort St George*: Comfortable riverside pub with river terrace in charming waterside position, interesting ancient core, Greene King real

ales, bar food, games in public bar; can get crowded *(Wayne Brindle, William Pryce, JF, LYM)*; [Barton Rd/Kings Rd], *Hat & Feathers*: Warm friendly atmosphere in bright local with good beer, darts *(JMC)*; [110 Water St, Chesterton; TL4660], *Pike & Eel*: Large plushly refurbished pub with conservatory and lovely river views, moorings, Greene King and Rayments ales, lunchtime food *(Wayne Brindle)*; [Thompsons Lane — next to Jesus Common], *Spade & Becket*: Fine spot by River Cam with numerous picnic-set tables on waterside terrace, river views from upper balcony and extensive conservatory, very friendly staff and decent pub food; parking may be difficult; children welcome *(Malcolm Ramsay, Wayne Brindle)*; [Regent St], *University Arms*: A chain hotel, but with several well kept real ales and useful bar food *(F Teare, Stephen R Holman, JF)*

☆ **Castor** [A47 W of Peterborough; TL1298], *Fitzwilliam Arms*: Long thatched pub popular for good range of food from sandwiches and good ploughman's to full meals, well kept Ind Coope Burton, pleasant chatty landlord *(Keith Stevens, Frank Davidson, T Mansell)*

☆ **Castor** [24 Peterborough Rd], *Royal Oak*: Old thatched pub with good value home cooking, well kept Allied real ales, several open fires, small traditional bar areas and sociable landlord; very busy weekends *(A G Purkis, T Mansell, LYM)*

☆ **Catworth** [High St; B660 between A45 (Kimbolton) and A604; TL0873], *Racehorse*: Plush lounge, parquet-floored dining extension with Persian rug, simply furnished public bar with racing silks (and games), and lots of racehorse pictures and club badges (some really old) throughout pub; well kept Adnams, Batemans and other real ales, good range of whiskies, log fire, modestly priced bar food from soup and sandwiches to steaks and mixed grill, friendly service, piped music; tables outside, stables behind; children welcome *(Janet Brown, George Atkinson, LYM)*

Clayhithe [TL5064], *Bridge*: Interestingly furnished beamed and timbered bar, and pretty garden by River Cam; good log fire, well kept Everards, bar food, usually friendly service; bedrooms in motel extension *(LYM)*

Clophill, Beds [back st; TL0837], *Stone Jug*: Good largely home-made food inc nice pies, well kept Banks & Taylors Shefford, Courage Directors and a couple of changing guest beers, unpretentiously friendly pleasant front bar, side lounge and darts areas and family area, couple of tables among flowers on small back terrace, picnic-table sets on road side; no food Sun, but bar nibbles *(Michael and Alison Sandy)*

☆ **Conington** [Boxworth Rd; TL3266], *White Swan*: Friendly country pub, good atmosphere, big garden, good range of consistent bar food, well kept Greene King IPA and Abbot, games room; restaurant *(Gordon Theaker, J D Maplethorpe, Wayne*

Brindle)

Coton [nr M11, junction 13: 2 miles W of Cambridge off A1303 — OS Sheet 154 map reference 412588; TL4058], *Plough*: This has now been taken under brewery management; the two couples who made it a popular main-entry dining pub have moved to the Crown at Hartest in Suffolk *(LYM)*

Cottenham [High St; TL4567], *White Horse*: Decent pub with reasonable bar food Tues-Fri, Brakspears and Flowers beers, back restaurant *(Phil Bryant)*

Croydon [TL3149], *Queen Adelaide*: Friendly landlord and staff, good choice of well kept real ales, big eating area with good range of reasonably priced pub; restaurant, children's room, large paddock with climbing frames *(Nigel Gibbs)*

☆ **Downham** [Main St; sometimes known as Little Downham — the one near Ely; TL5283], *Plough*: Fenland village pub doing particularly well under new management, good food cooked by husband eg particularly good chicken and white wine soup, chilli con carne and beef bourguignonne; Greene King beers *(John and Diana Jarrad, John C Baker)*

☆ **Dry Drayton** [off Park St, opp church; TL3862], *Black Horse*: Notably welcoming unspoilt local with particularly well kept Bass, warm decor with walk-round fireplace, good freshly cooked food inc plenty for vegetarians (attractive dining room), good beers; games area, garden, lovely quiet village spot *(Peter Churchill, J Kingsbury)*

☆ **Dullingham** [50 Station Rd; TL6357], *Kings Head*: Cosy dining pub, popular for wide and interesting choice of freshly made food, with lots of puddings; open fires, well kept Tolly and Original, good friendly service, fairy-lit seats out above the broad village green; children in family area *(J P Cinnamond, Maggie Jo St John, M Morgan, LYM)*

Eaton Bray, Beds [SP9620], *White Horse*: Old low-beamed dining pub rambling through timbered dividers, central servery, massive choice of food inc exotics, Allied real ales inc a guest such as Greene King IPA; not cheap; ranks of tables on back lawn *(ILP, MS)*

☆ **Eaton Socon** [Old Great North Rd; village signposted from A1 nr St Neots; TL1658], *White Horse*: Good value fresh food served quickly and pleasantly in rambling series of well kept low-beamed rooms inc one with high-backed traditional settles around fine log fire, several well kept Whitbreads-related real ales on handpump, relaxed chatty atmosphere, play area in back garden; children in eating areas; bedrooms *(Nigel Gibbs, Sandra Cook, M J Brooks, David Young, LYM)*

☆ **Eaton Socon**, *Waggon & Horses*: Beautifully presented food from home-made soup to mixed grills with specials such as chargrilled tandoori pork or beef stew with very light dumplings and fresh vegetables, good puddings, in pleasantly spacious

non-smoky open-plan beamed pub; good mix of customers *(Dr G M Regan, Nigel Gibbs, Sandra Cook)*

☆ **Eaton Socon**, *Crown*: Cosy little pub with two low-beamed bars, good range of beers such as Brains SA and Bitter, Hook Norton Best and Tetleys, maybe a cockatoo; moderately priced bar food (not Sun), open fire, nostalgic piped music, restaurant; no T-shirts *(Nigel Gibbs, Sandra Cook, Tina Hammond)*

Elm [Low Rd; TF4706], *Artful Dodger*: Real ales, snacks and meals seven days a week, good Sun lunchtime nibbles, pleasant semi-rural surroundings, jovial atmosphere, flexible afternoon hours; children in separate dining room *(Mike Morgan, E W and J Morgan)*

☆ **Elsworth** [TL3163], *George & Dragon*: Good atmosphere in pleasantly idiosyncratic pub with attractively furnished and decorated panelled main bar and quieter back dining area, wide choice of decent food inc good Sun carvery, Watneys-related and other real ales, open fire, unhurried pleasant service; nice terraces, play area in garden, restaurant *(Mr and Mrs K J Morris, LYM)*

Ely [Annesdale; TL5380], *Cutter*: Worth knowing for its idyllic riverside setting; good value food, well kept Watneys-related real ales *(Tony and Lynne Stark)*; [Silver St], *Prince Albert*: Good recently updated traditional pub with friendly landlord and particularly well kept Greene King IPA, Mild and Abbot; very nice garden *(Dr A K Wilkinson)*; [West End Rd, off Cambridge Rd], *West End House*: Friendly local comfortably updated by new landlord, well kept Watneys-related real ales and Mansfield Old Baily, log fire, nice garden *(Dr A K Wilkinson, Ian Turner)*

Everton, Beds [TL2051], *Thornton Arms*: Pleasant country local with well kept Charles Wells Eagle *(John C Baker)*

Fen Ditton [High St; TL4860], *Ancient Shepherds*: Cosy village pub with armchairs and sofas in pleasant lounge; decent food, pleasant friendly staff, well kept Tolly *(Wayne Brindle)*

☆ **Fenstanton** [High St; off A604 near St Ives; TL3168], *King William IV*: Well kept Greene King, civilised decor, very good atmosphere, friendly staff; wide choice of above-average food inc good ploughman's and help-yourself salad bar, also good restaurant; beautifully kept outside with flowers and so forth *(Richard Donaghy, J D Maplethorpe, Gordon Theaker)*

Fowlmere [High St; TL4245], *Swan House*: Pleasant atmosphere, friendly staff, good choice of reasonably priced good bar food, choice of well kept real ales; also restaurant/wine bar *(Eddy Stephens, Nigel Gibbs, Sandra Cook)*

☆ **Godmanchester** [London Rd; TL2470], *Exhibition*: Interesting decor, good choice of good bar food, well kept Watneys-related real ales

☆ **Gorefield** [Main St; TF4111], *Woodmans Cottage*: Friendly and spaciously modernised open-plan bar rambling around central servery, leatherette stools and banquettes, beams and open fires, welcoming staff and lively atmosphere, huge helpings of particularly good value home-made bar food inc two dozen specials and notable choice of puddings in side eating area, Adnams or Bass, separate games room, restaurant booked well ahead for weekend evenings and Sun lunch; seats out on verandah *(M and J Back, BB)*

☆ **Grantchester** [TL4455], *Red Lion*: Pleasant atmosphere in bright and cheerful bar of comfortable and spacious food pub; restaurant, sheltered terrace and good-sized lawn; the village is pretty, a short stroll from lovely riverside meadows *(R C Wiles, LYM)*

Grantchester, *Green Man*: Pleasant village setting, very friendly landlord, assorted student and antipodean customers, well kept Tolly, attractive layout *(Tony and Lynne Stark, LYM)*

Great Abington [off A604 Cambridge—Haverhill, and A11; TL5348], *Three Tuns*: Welcoming little peaceful local among interesting old houses opp village cricket field, well kept Greene King Abbot, big cheap sandwiches *(Jack Taylor)*

☆ **Great Chishill** [TL4239], *Pheasant*: Good atmosphere in friendly, cosy and comfortable local with sound choice of good food (not Sun lunchtime or Mon — nice fish), well kept Adnams and Greene King beers; charming garden; closed Mon lunchtime *(Nigel Gibbs, Sandra Cook, LYM)*

Great Eversden [High St (off A603); TL3653], *Hoops*: Busy but notably friendly village local, big garden, theme food evenings, Charles Wells ales; bedrooms *(Nigel Gibbs, Geoff Lee, Ron Gentry)*

Great Gransden [off B1046 Cambridge—St Neots; TL2755], *Crown & Cushion*: Nice spot in pretty village, friendly licensees, plentiful good value bar food (esp cold buffet), well kept Charles Wells; small garden with menagerie; children welcome *(P S Vince)*

Guyhirn [High Rd; TF3903], *Oliver Twist*: Attractive choice of food, reasonably priced considering the quality and quantity; good choice of ales *(Geoff Lee, E Robinson, Mike Morgan)*

☆ **Hail Weston** [just off A45, not far from A1 St Neots bypass; TL1662], *Royal Oak*: Picturesque thatched and beamed pub in quiet village nr Grafham Water; good value food from sandwiches and ploughman's up, cosy fire in winter, well kept Charles Wells, welcoming locals, nice big garden *(Andy and Jill Kassube, J D Maplethorpe)*

Harlington, Beds [a mile from M1 junction 12; A5120, 1st R to Harlington, R in village; TL0330], *Carpenters Arms*: Good atmosphere in big comfortable lounge, well kept Watneys-related ales, nice choice of very good food inc half a dozen specials and speciality ham pancakes in cheesy sauce; adventurous restaurant *(Michael and Alison Sandy)*

☆ **Harston** [48 Royston Rd (A10); nr M11 junction 11; TL4251], *Queens Head*: Solid,

reliable local with generous decent food (esp pies) served quickly, Greene King ales, no smoking area; garden *(Nigel Gibbs, Sandra Cook, Gary and Janet Amos, Mr and Mrs K J Morris, Peter Churchill)*

Hemingford Abbots [High St; TL2870], *Axe & Compass*: Thatched black-beamed pub with three bars (one acts as dining room), straightforward bar food (Tues-Sun lunchtime), Watneys-related real ales, TV room; delightful pub *(BKA)*

Henlow, Beds [TL1738], *Five Bells*: Good food in bar and relaxed dining room, inc home-made puddings *(Mr and Mrs G Wyse)*

☆ nr **Hexton**, Beds [Pegsdon; B655 a mile E of Hexton; TL1230], *Live & Let Live*: Typical snug little village pub with well kept Greene King beers, well prepared, cooked and presented food at reasonable prices (scrumptious steak and kidney pie), good service, entertaining parrot and lovely garden below Chilterns *(John Seward, Colleen Holiday, LYM)*

☆ **Heydon** [off A505 W of M11 junction 10; TL4340], *King William IV*: Packed with remarkable bric-a-brac of many types and ages, furnishings interesting too, in attractively lit rambling partly 16th-century beamed and timbered bar; garden with overflow from this, and paddock with animals — all good fun; several real ales, bar food; bedrooms (attractive but due for some updating) *(Gwen and Peter Andrews, Beti Wyn Thomas, J P Cinnamond, Wayne Brindle, Colleen Holiday, Andrew Morrissey, Drs M and K Parier, J W Deane, Sidney and Erna Wells, Nigel Gibbs, Sandra Cook, LYM)*

☆ **Histon** [High St; TL4363], *Red Lion*: Nice warm atmosphere, good range of well kept real ales and consistently good weekday lunchtime food, attractively presented and reasonably priced; obliging staff, real ales such as Tetleys *(Judith Trye, Phil Bryant, Barbara and Mike Williams)*

Houghton [TL2872], *Three Horseshoes*: French windows into garden from comfortable lounge, locals' bar with black beams and inglenook, well kept Watneys-related real ales, bar food (not Sun evening) inc lunchtime cold buffet; keen darts *(BKA, LYM)*

☆ **Houghton Conquest**, Beds [3 miles from M1, junction 11; TL0441], *Knife & Cleaver*: Well kept Banks & Taylors Shefford and Batemans on handpump, remarkable choice of old malts, blazing fire, maps, drawings and old documents, very good restaurant in pleasantly planted conservatory; delightful atmosphere *(Jenny and Brian Seller)*

☆ **Huntingdon** [TL2371], *Old Bridge*: Food not cheap, but always worth stopping for — very popular; fantastic salads — salmon or meats, and good wine by the glass; good service, great surroundings; bedrooms excellent, if expensive *(Syd and Wyn Donald, I H Rorison)*

Huntingdon, *George*: Quietly elegant and comfortable lounge bar off hotel lobby, decent straightforward bar food; bedrooms

(Buck Shinkman, LYM)

☆ **Ireland**, Beds [off A600 Shefford—Bedford — OS Sheet 153 map reference 135414; TL1341], *Black Horse*: Busy country free house, thoroughly refurbished but attractive and comfortable with its beamery and good log-effect gas fire; interesting and generous if not cheap bar food (not Sun evening) inc good fish dishes — very popular for this at weekends; Ruddles and Youngers IPA and No 3 on handpump; closed Mon; attractive restaurant *(Sidney and Erna Wells, A and J Jackson, Jim Froggatt, Denise Plummer)*

Isleham [TL6474], *Griffin*: Very old beamed inn with well kept Adnams and above-average bar food *(John C Baker)*

Kempston, Beds [16 Bedford Rd; TL0347], *Wellington*: Spotless dining pub, very cheerful; Charles Wells very well kept — though served through a North Country sparkler to give a creamy head *(John C Baker)*

Kensworth Common, Beds [B4540; TL0318], *Old Red Lion*: Handy for Whipsnade, recently comfortably extended with new restaurant conservatory; friendly licensees, decent food, Whitbreads-related real ales; good play area *(Mr and Mrs Reeves)*

Keysoe, Beds [Keysoe Row E (B660); TL0762], *White Horse*: Friendly landlord, wide choice of good value bar food, spacious garden, conservatory, Charles Wells ales *(S Holder)*

Kings Ripton [TL2676], *Unicorn*: Extended under current regime, with good choice of bar food at fair prices *(M Ollis)*

Little Staughton, Beds [TL1062], *Crown*: Warm welcome, good food at reasonable prices in bar and restaurant, with fresh vegetables and quality ingredients *(Mr and Mrs S Norman)*

☆ **Madingley** [TL3960], *Three Horseshoes*: Comfortably upmarket thatched restaurant/pub with elegant garden, food (not cheap) inc excellent seafood and good salad bar; nicely decorated small bar dining area, very clean, with Tolly and Original on handpump; children welcome; pretty village *(Maysie Thompson, Frank W Gadbois, R E Horner, JF, Gethin Lewis, LYM)*

☆ **Marholm** [TF1402], *Fitzwilliam Arms*: Attractive old thatched stone-built inn with comfortable and relaxing rambling three-room bar; very popular lunchtime for good value food, service cheerful and efficient; good big garden, Ind Coope beers; also known as Green Man from front topiary *(John C Baker, Tom Evans, T Mansell, Nic James, M Morgan)*

Maulden, Beds [TL0538], *White Hart*: Friendly thatched village local with nice low-ceilinged bar, restaurant and games room with pool table; well kept Whitbreads Castle Eden, covered wagon in front garden *(Colleen L Holiday)*

☆ **Needingworth** [Overcote Lane; pub signposted from A1123; TL3472], *Pike & Eel*: Marvellous peaceful riverside location, with spacious lawns and marina; roomy plush bar, easy chairs and big open fire in smaller room on left, and ambitious extensive glass-walled restaurant (food confined to this, but does include some bar-food things); well kept Adnams, Bass, and Greene King Abbot, friendly and obliging landlord, provision for children; pleasant if basic bedrooms, good breakfasts *(Alison and Tony Godfrey, Brian and Jill Bond, J D Cranston, Ted George, LYM)*

Odell, Beds [Little Odell; SP9657], *Mad Dog*: Cosy and friendly old thatched Greene King pub handy for Harrold-Odell Country Park, well kept Rayments Special, good choice of well presented moderately priced bar food from sandwiches up, good service, pleasant garden with genuine miniature fairground roundabout; popular Sun lunchtime *(Jenny and Brian Seller, T G Saul)*

☆ **Old Warden**, Beds [TL1343], *Hare & Hounds*: Cosy and unpretentious old local with wide choice of generously served bar food, pleasant efficient staff, comfortable lounge, Charles Wells beers, restaurant, garden with children's play area; beautiful village, handy for Shuttleworth collection *(Colleen Holiday, the Shinkmans)*

Peterborough [Thorpe Meadows; TL1999], *Boathouse*: Newish Greene King pub by River Nene and famous boating lake; open all day, food all day too; reasonable prices, summer barbecues; family room with satellite TV *(Nic James)*; [465 Oundle Rd, off A605 in Woodston], *Botolph Arms*: Interesting flagstoned former farmhouse, good food from extensive (if pricey) menu, Sam Smiths ales *(Nic James)*; [Parnwell Way], *Fox & Goose*: New Shipstones pub with emphasis on traditional, cosy furnishings; reasonable prices *(Nic James)*; [Thorpewood], *Greenkeeper*: Modern Greene King pub, food all day, sunken verandah overlooking golf course *(Nic James)*; [29 Church St, Stanground — S outskirts], *Woolpack*: On old course of River Nene, with own moorings, four Whitbreads-related real ales, weekend summer beer festivals; wartime memorabilia in back "museum" *(Nic James)*

Potton, Beds [TL2449], *Royal Oak*: Good choice of lunchtime food, esp roasts with plenty of fresh local vegetables *(Maysie Thompson)*

Pulloxhill, Beds [off A6 N of Barton le Clay — OS Sheet 153 map reference 063341; TL0633], *Cross Keys*: Good simply furnished beamed village pub, flooring tiles, fine old fireplace (sad about the electric fire), good plentiful reasonably priced food, carpeted lounge, very chatty and friendly long-serving licensees; restaurant with Sun evening trad jazz — sometimes George Chisholm, who lives near; pleasant garden, play area *(Sidney and Erna Wells)*

Ramsey [68 High St; TL2885], *George*: Now under same ownership as Bell in Clare (see Suffolk); long lounge bar off courtyard restored to show old beams, Greene King IPA and Abbot, Ind Coope Burton and Tetleys; overlooks golf course; bedrooms *(Anon)*

☆ **Ridgmont**, Beds [SP9736], *Rose & Crown*: Good value food, warm welcome, well kept Adnams, Charles Wells and Mansfield Riding; open fire in traditional low-ceilinged public bar, smarter lounge with masses of *Rupert Annual* covers, well laid out to take a good few people, charming staff; games inc darts and pool, maybe rabbits in long and attractive sheltered back garden, stables restaurant (not Mon or Tues evenings); children allowed in bar eating area; easy parking, good wheelchair access *(Michael and Alison Sandy, Nick Holmes, L M Miall, LYM)*

Rings End [TF4002], *Fishermans Haunt*: Friendly talkative landlord, Elgoods real ale, basic but tasty bar food, relaxed atmosphere — beautiful spot in summer, with good roach and rudd fishing *(Mike Morgan, E W Morgan)*

☆ **Riseley**, Beds [High St; off A6; TL0362], *Fox & Hounds*: 16th-century pub with good bar food inc generous and popular charcoal-grilled steaks using properly hung beef, good puddings; pretty beamed restaurant, welcoming landlord, well kept Charles Wells *(P J Simmons, Dr R J A Jones)*

☆ **nr Sandy**, Beds [Deepdale; B1042 towards Potton and Cambridge; TL2049], *Locomotive*: Reasonably priced food inc Sun roast and good trout, omelettes and specials, well kept Charles Wells, lots of railway memorabilia, big garden with views, restaurant area; handy for RSPB headquarters, can get very busy (and smoky); children allowed in eating area *(S Holder, Paul Gore, P Lloyd, Miss K Bamford, John C Baker, LYM)*

Sandy, Beds [TL1649], *Kings Arms*: Welcoming staff, pleasant locals, Timothy Taylors Special, good bar and restaurant food *(M Baatz); Lord Nelson*: Friendly, with well kept Whitbreads-related real ales, good range of bar food, darts and billiards in public area *(Jim Froggatt, Denise Plummer)*

☆ **Sawston** [High St (Cambridge Rd); TL4849], *Greyhound*: Cosy, friendly and comfortable, with open fire, Whitbreads-related real ales and Marstons Pedigree, fashionable imported lagers, big helpings of good value pub food inc vegetarian dishes, welcoming staff; restaurant area, big garden, good facilities for children *(S R Gilbert, Nigel Gibbs)*

Sharpenhoe, Beds [Harlington Rd; TL0630], *Lynmore*: Recent open-plan refurbishment with tables of all sizes in spacious lounge, beers such as Boddingtons, Tetleys and Wadworths 6X, big helpings of reasonably priced straightforward food, big wine glasses, nice atmosphere; back restaurant overlooking Sharpenhoe Clappers (NT); food not impressive, good but not great inc plough, chicken & ham or fishman pie *(Michael and Alison Sandy, A and J Jackson)*

☆ **Shefford**, Beds [Deadmans Cross; A600 towards Bedford; TL1141], *White Horse*: Friendly pub with well kept Banks & Taylors and Charles Wells, decent wines, good basic range of bar meals, restaurant area, family room and garden with slide, swings and summer evening barbecue; comfortable inside with armchairs, settee, books, inglenook fire, variety of prints; cheerful licensees *(Roger Danes, Frank Gadbois, Pete Storey)*

Shillington, Beds [TL1234], *Noahs Ark*: Four-table public bar, tiny lounge with three; well kept Greene King Abbot, friendly licensees, food bargains at odd hours eg mid-afternoon, late evening; decent play area inc beached boat; open all day but closed Tues afternoon *(Colleen Holiday)*

St Neots [towards Eaton Socon; TL1860], *River Mill*: Attractive pub in nice spot by river; family room *(Wayne Brindle)*

Stanford, Beds [TL1641], *Green Man*: Now a free house, with Boddingtons, Marstons Pedigree and Theakstons on handpump; interesting small pub, coal fires in all three connecting rooms, friendly staff, good value food, big garden with playground *(Jim Froggatt, Denise Plummer)*

Stow Cum Quy [B1102, off A1303 E of Cambridge; TL5260], *Wheatsheaf*: Good food in comfortable eating area; Greene King IPA, efficient service *(A Langan)*

Stretham [Cambridge Rd, Elford Closes (off A10 S of Stretham roundabout); TL5072], *Lazy Otter*: Riverside family pub with big bar and conservatory, helpful staff, well kept Adnams and Greene King, popular bar food, restaurant; waterside garden with family theme days and evening barbecues, boat moorings *(More reports please)*

Studham, Beds [Dunstable Rd; TL0215], *Bell*: Good bar food, Allied real ales, clean and attractive inside; side restaurant *(Les and Jean Bradman); Red Lion*: Handy for Whipsnade Zoo, in attractive spot with tables outside looking up to grassy common; cheerful modernish decor, good value bar food (not Sun), decent real ales *(Gary Scott, LYM)*

☆ **Sutton**, Beds [village signposted off B1040 Biggleswade—Potton; TL2247], *John o' Gaunt*: Cosy low-beamed bar, enterprising bar food, well kept Greene King IPA; lovely pink-washed low building nr fine 14th-century packhorse bridge with shallow ford taking cars past it; friendly service *(LYM)*

☆ **Swaffham Prior** [B1102 NE of Cambridge; TL5764], *Red Lion*: Welcoming and attractive village local with well kept Tolly Original, maybe Old Strong, wide range of food from ploughman's to steaks, separate dining lounge; unusually plush gents' *(Wayne Brindle, Geoff Lee, John and Tessa Rainsford)*

☆ **Tempsford**, Beds [TL1652], *Anchor*: Extensive roadhouse with lots for children, included as a useful break from A1, and notable for its big riverside gardens with outdoor chess and draughts, boules, fishing on the River Ouse; quickly served straightforward food, restaurant *(LYM)*

The Turves [W of March; TL3396], *Three Horseshoes*: Rather sprawling, by blacksmith's; comfortable inside, with family conservatory, well kept Elgoods and Greene King IPA, good food inc superb shark steak; French-run *(John C Baker)*

Toddington, Beds [64 High St; handy for M1 junction 12; TL0028], *Bedford Arms*: Well preserved Tudor pub with well kept Charles Wells Eagle; good provision for families *(P S Vince); Oddfellows Arms*: Small piney bars, warm and pleasant, with roaring coal fires, now Allied real ales, short choice of reasonably priced weekday food (not Sat) *(Michael and Alison Sandy, Ken Krober)*

Totternhoe, Beds [Church St; towards Eaton Bray — OS Sheet 165 map reference 989210; SP9821], *Old Bell*: Friendly and pleasant, with seven ever-changing well kept real ales inc a mild and a couple of strong ones, lunchtime bar food; plushly comfortable and opened out *(Michael Sandy)*

Trumpington [High St (A1309); TL4454], *Coach & Horses*: Has been comfortable and picturesque, with well kept beer, wide choice of generously served good food from hot and cold buffet, garden; but no reports since recent refurbishments *(I S Thomson, Charles Bardswell); Unicorn*: Large, well appointed welcoming pub with vast garden; wide choice of pub games, big helpings of good food, quite cheap for area *(Wayne Brindle)*

☆ **Turvey**, Beds [off A428, by church; SP9452], *Three Cranes*: Modern-feeling clean two-level bar with some stripped stone and woodburner, quiet and relaxed; simple, generous and reliable bar food from good sandwiches and ploughman's to mixed grills, well kept Adnams, Fullers ESB, Hook Norton Best and Wadworths 6X, decent wines and whiskies, pleasant staff, unobtrusive piped music; distinctive portico with jettied upper storey; restaurant, garden with climbing frame and occasional jazz evenings or barbecues *(Jonathan and Jane Hagger, JF, Michael and Alison Sandy, W H King, BB)*

☆ **Turvey** [Bridge St; A428 NW of Bedford — at W end of village], *Three Fyshes*: Great appeal for those who like rough-and-ready no-frills pubbiness and good beer — they brew their own, and have several good ales from other breweries, as well as farm ciders; lots of character, flagstones, inglenook fires, dogs and cats; good sandwiches and big crusty rolls, hot dishes from vegetarian specialities to steaks and venison; traditional games, summer barbecues; open all day Sat; children welcome *(Ted George, Nigel Gibbs, R C Gandy, David and Rebecca Killick, LYM)*

Upper Dean, Beds [TL0467], *Three Compasses*: Pretty, thatched pub with welcoming landlord, Charles Wells on handpump and good basic food from burgers to steaks *(Margaret and Roy Randle)*

West Wickham [High St; TL6149], *White Horse*: Cosy and friendly, good landlord, wide choice of good food priced for very hungry, hungry or peckish helpings; furnishings just right for a village pub, interesting decor, things to read *(Rodney and Ruth Hewson)*

Weston Colville [Weston Green; TL6153],

Fox & Hounds: Comfortable, with good range of good bar food inc English and some delicious Portuguese dishes *(D T Richards)*

☆ **Whipsnade**, Beds [B4540 E; TL0117], *Old Hunters Lodge*: Snug bar with roaring fire, good friendly service, good range of good value bar food, well kept Greene King or Websters, pleasant old-world restaurant; children welcome *(David Shillitoe, Geoff Payne)*

☆ **Whittlesey** [B1040 N; TL2799], *Old Dog in a Doublet*: Comfortable, clean and quiet riverside pub with clean tradional decor, bric-a-brac, old prints and well spaced, comfortable and solid seating; open fire, quick friendly service, reasonably priced standard bar food, well kept beer inc Adnams and Greene King Abbot, decent wines; fairly loud but varied piped music; popular with walkers on Hereward Way *(Mr and Mrs K J Morris, Louisa and Brian Routledge, Brian and Jill Bond, David Oakes)*

Whittlesey [Ramsey Rd], *Boat*: Riverside pub with simple public bar, small dining lounge, decent home-made bar food (steak and kidney recommended) at very reasonable prices, well kept Elgoods beer, some interesting whiskies and inexpensive wines; service always friendly and welcoming *(Nic James)*

☆ **Whittlesford** [off B1379 S of Cambridge; handy for M10 junction 10, via A505; TL4748], *Tickell Arms*: Still idiosyncratic and flamboyant, with quite an operatic feel, individual heavy furnishings in dim-lit bar, flower-filled conservatory, formal garden, distinctive food, classical music and high prices; closed Mon (except bank hols); quite unique in its way and well worth a try, though recurrent niggles seem to prevent universal appeal; the wines often a better bet than the beers *(Julian Proudman, Nigel Gibbs, Sandra Cook, JF, C R and M A Starling, John C Baker, Peter Hall, Frank W Gadbois, Noel Sephton, Wayne Brindle, J L Haywood Smith, LYM)*

☆ **Wisbech** [North Brink; TF4609], *Red Lion*: Pleasant, friendly pub on River Nene, nr centre and NT Peckover House; popular with local businessmen for good value well presented home-cooked lunches, good range of beers inc local Elgoods *(Keith and Aubrey Day, Mr and Mrs I J W Ferguson, Mike Morgan)*

Wisbech [Norfolk St], *Ferry House*: Quiet pub with good imaginative food, attractive open fire, pool table in back bar, changing real ales such as Courage Directors, Flowers Original and Whitbreads Castle Eden; dogs allowed, open all day Mon, Thurs-Sat *(Mike Morgan);* [Elm Rd], *Flower Pot*: Friendly, with good value food, well kept Greene King IPA and Abbot on handpump, darts and pool in public bar, children's play area in pleasant garden; dogs allowed *(Mike Morgan);* [Hill St, nr bus stn], *Horsefair*: Greene King pub with friendly but unhurried service, bar meals; brewers'-Regency-style decor, open all day, good choice of brandies *(Mike Morgan);*

[North Brink], *Rose*: Well kept real ales such as Adnams, Fullers London Pride and Marstons Pedigree; by the river, among Georgian buildings *(L Priest)*

Wisbech St Mary [TF4208], *Wheel*: Old-fashioned village inn with welcoming licensees, Elgoods ales, good value dining-room Sun lunch; play area; bedrooms *(E Robinson)*

Wistow [TL2780], *Three Horseshoes*: Delightful fenland free house, real ales, pleasant licensees, good food; comfortable bedrooms *(E Robinson)*

☆ **Woburn**, Beds [1 Bedford St; SP9433], *Black Horse*: Open-plan food pub with plenty of space and wide choice from sandwiches and baked potatoes to moderately priced steaks, also children's and vegetarian dishes and lots of summer barbecues in pleasant sheltered garden; well kept Everards, Marstons and Wadworths 6X on handpump, quick service, restaurant; open all day summer Sat and bank hols; handy for the Abbey; children in eating area and restaurant *(Michael and Alison Sandy, Monica Shelley, Colleen L Holiday, Lyn and Bill Capper, LYM)*

Woburn [18 Bedford St], *Magpie*: Small pleasant old-fashioned bar with old furniture and floor, well kept Watneys-related real ales and a guest such as Fullers ESB, good bar food inc lots of specials – not cheap but good value, popular restaurant; bedrooms *(Michael and Alison Sandy, Maysie Thompson)*

☆ **Woodditton** [Ditton Green; village signed off B1063 at Cheveley; TL6659], *Three Blackbirds*: Two snug bars in pretty thatched village pub, friendly and efficient service, well kept Tolly Bitter and Original, popular good value bar food from sandwiches and lunchtime ploughman's through home-cooked ham to good steaks and Sun roasts; piped music, pretty garden, restaurant Tues-Sat — where children allowed *(Mr and Mrs J Back, LYM)*

Cheshire

Major changes here include Greenalls, the regional brewer, opting out of brewing altogether: its pubs are now supplied by the national Allied Breweries, who have taken over brewing all Greenalls' former beer brands. There's a very friendly new licensee at the charming unspoilt White Lion at Barthomley, and new licensees are also proving popular at the Boot, our favourite Chester pub, the Copper Mine at Fullers Moor (its tie has switched from Boddingtons to Bass/Burtonwood), the Dun Cow at Ollerton (much to everyone's relief, its welcoming traditional character is undamaged) and the Dog at Peover Heath (food perhaps better than before, though service may need time to settle in). Pubs here that currently seem on peak form include the snug and attractive White Lion at Alvanley, the Cholmondeley Arms near Bickley Moss (really good food, nice conversion), the spotless and friendly Spinner & Bergamot at Comberbach, the Bells of Peover in its lovely position at Lower Peover, the Rising Sun at Tarporley (really cheap food in a nice little village pub) and the Smoker at Plumley (warm praise all round – and a food award newly granted). Pubs in the Guide for the first time (or back after an absence) are the well run and very popular canalside Barbridge Inn, the handsome old Alvanley Arms at Cotebrook, the cosy little Hanging Gate up in the hills near Langley, the warmly friendly and very individual Ring o' Bells at Overton (decent food), the Bulls Head at Smallwood (one of the nicest pub gardens we've ever seen) and the very companionable Ryles Arms up at Sutton. To southerners, a striking point is the large number of pubs here that have their own bowling greens, but perhaps the real Cheshire trademark is a certain comfortable almost well fed charm – very distinctive, and quite unlike other areas. This marks many of the pubs in the Lucky Dip section at the end of the chapter: there is of course a splendid choice in Chester itself, but other places that currently seem to be getting more than their fair share of particularly good pubs are Bollington (where the Vale is still our first choice), Mobberley, and the Parkgate waterfront. Individual rising stars in the Dip are the Cock & Pheasant at Bollington Cross, Ring o' Bells in Christleton, Parr Arms at Grappenhall, Carriers at Hatchmere, Davenport Arms at Marton, reopened Cheshire Hunt at Pott Shrigley and Old Ship at Styal. Other Dip pubs well worth a visit (almost all inspected by us) are the Maypole at Acton Bridge, Poacher at Bickerton, Combermere Arms at Burleydam, Fiddle i' th' Bag near Burtonwood, Ash Tree at Butley Town, Olde Red Lion at Goostrey, Pheasant at Higher Burwardsley, Swan With Two Nicks at Little Bollington, both entries in Lymm and Setter Dog at Walker Barn.

ALVANLEY SJ4974 Map 7

White Lion

2 1/2 miles from M56, junction 14; A5117 towards Helsby, bear left into A56 then quickly turn right, following village signpost; in village, turn right into Manley Road

Unless you get to this pretty and very popular black-shuttered white pub early, you may have to wait for a table – and you can't order food until you're seated. Generously served and well presented, readers feel it is well worth the wait: soup (£1), sandwiches (from £1.25, toasties from £1.35, steak barm-cake £1.75) and quite a wide variety of ploughman's (from £1.80), through home-made hot-pot or cottage pie (£1.90) and salads (from £3), to specials like home-made steak pie (£3.80), chicken chasseur (£4.50) or salmon and prawn pasta in a mornay sauce; puddings (£1.65). Greenalls Mild and Bitter on handpump; polite and friendly service. The low-ceilinged lounge has softly cushioned red plush seats and wall banquettes, decorative plates on the walls, and beer-steins, pistols, copper jugs and so forth hanging from its moulded black beams; piped music. The smaller public bar has darts and dominoes. Outside, there are rustic picnic-table sets on the grass by the play area (which has an assault course and sand-floored fortress), white tables and chairs under cocktail parasols, and attractive hanging baskets; an adjacent field has various ducks, geese and sheep, and the village church is opposite. *(Recommended by G T Jones, Mr and Mrs J H Adam, Brian and Anna Marsden, J W Sutton, Mr and Mrs J H Adam)*

Greenalls (Allied) Tenant Keith Morris Real ale Meals and snacks (12–2, 6–9.30) Frodsham (0928) 722949 Children welcome till 8pm Open 11.30–3, 5.30–11

BARBRIDGE SJ6156 Map 7

Barbridge Inn

Village signposted just off A51 N of Nantwich; OS Sheet 118 map reference 616566

Particularly well run, this comfortably modernised and very popular open-plan pub is prettily placed at the junction of the Shropshire Union and Middlewich canals, with an elegantly curvy little brick bridge down beyond its big waterside garden. This has a good many picnic-table sets (some under cover), a play house, climber, swings and slide, and summer barbecues; the narrow-boats alongside are an attraction (as are the free moorings, for their crews). A wide choice of well prepared and generously served home-made bar food includes sandwiches (from £1.40), filled baked potatoes (from £2.25), steak and kidney or chicken and ham pies (£5.25), beef in beer (£5.50), specials such as Scotch black pudding (£2.50), lasagne (£3.95), fresh fish which the licensee gets from the market, and grills like peppered fillet steak (£11.75), puddings (£2), and Sunday lunch (£6.95); the balustraded restaurant area, up steps, overlooks the canal. Well kept Boddingtons, Chesters Mild, Higsons Bitter and Theakstons Best on handpump, unusual malt whiskies, decent wines (the choice by the bottle is good); rack of daily papers, darts, bar billiards, fruit machines, cards, and piped music. There's a side conservatory, and children's area (the children's menu has a colouring page, with crayons from the bar). *(Recommended by Derek and Sylvia Stephenson, Chris Raisin, C H Stride, Martin Aust, Dr and Mrs C D E Morris, K Widdowson)*

Boddingtons (Whitbreads) Tenants Richard and Carol Sutton Real ale Meals and snacks Restaurant Wettenhall (027 073) 266 Children in family area 1960s music Fri evening and trad jazz every other Thurs Open 11–3, 5.30–11; 11–11 Sat; closed 25 Dec

BARTHOMLEY SJ7752 Map 7

White Lion ★ £

Village link signposted from M6 junction 16 exit towards Crewe

A warmly friendly new licensee has taken over this thatched 17th-century pub and early reports from readers happily suggest that little has changed. The simply furnished main room has attractively moulded black panelling, heavy oak beams in the low ceiling (one big enough to house quite a collection of plates), Cheshire watercolours and prints, an open fire, and latticed windows; up some steps, a second room has another open fire, more oak panelling, a high-backed winged settle, a paraffin lamp hinged to the wall, and sensibly placed darts, shove-ha'penny, cribbage and dominoes. Very cheap bar food includes filled rolls, soup (80p), cornish pasties, steak and kidney pie, home-made quiche or pâté (all £1), hot sirloin beef with onion in a bap (£1.40), and home-made apple pie (£1); in the evenings and on Saturdays and Sundays they only do rolls and pies. Well kept Burtonwood Bitter and Dark Mild on handpump. There's a peaceable view of the attractive village from the tables under the old yew tree or on the front cobbles. It can get very busy at weekends. The early 15th-century red sandstone church of St Bertiline across the road is worth a visit. (*Recommended by Martin Aust, Andy and Jill Kassube, John Davidson, Laurence Manning, R T and J C Moggridge, Mike and Wendy Proctor, Sue Holland, Dave Webster, L M Miall*)

Burtonwood　Tenant Terence Cartwright　Real ale　Snacks　Crewe (0270) 882242 Children in tap room lunchtime only　Open 11.30–3(4 Sat), 6–11

BELL O TH HILL　SJ5245　Map 7
Blue Bell

Signed just off A41 N of Whitchurch

The entrance to this black and white timbered building – with a massive central chimney – is through a great oak door by a mounting-block; you then find yourself in a small quarry-tiled hallway, with stairs up, and another formidable oak door on your right. This leads into three very heavily beamed communicating rooms, two served by hatch, and each with an open fire – the main bar's in an inglenook with an attractively moulded black oak mantlebeam. There's a cheerful mix of furnishings from comfortable plush wall seats and stripped country-kitchen tables (with bunches of flowers) to a nice little antique settle, as well as a few decorative plates, one or two dog or hunting prints and some strange curios on the walls. Quickly served good value bar food might include sandwiches, Somerset lamb chops (£4.40), Cumberland sausage mixed grill (£4.50), stuffed plaice, smoked cod and prawn cheesebake or chicken supreme in a sunnyside sauce (£4.85), and gammon steak (£5.20). Greenalls Bitter and Original on handpump, large glasses of French house wine (£1.20), dominoes, quiet piped music, and friendly service; fresh flowers in the ladies' lavatory. There are picnic-table sets among flowers on the front grass and opposite is a farm; the adjoining field may have cows and maybe a donkey or two. As we went to press this pub came up for sale: news please. (*Recommended by David and Anne Walker, Dr P D Putwain, Chris Raisin*)

Greenalls (Allied)　Tenant Mark Sumner　Real ale　Meals and snacks (12–2, 6.30–10)　(0948) 2172　Children in eating area of bar　Open 12–3, 6.30–11; closed Mon lunchtime and 25 Dec

BICKLEY MOSS　SJ5549　Map 7
Cholmondeley Arms ★ ⚲

Cholmondeley; A49 5 ½ miles N of Whitchurch

Most people come to this light and airy converted Victorian schoolhouse to enjoy the very good food. Dishes readers have particularly liked this year include delicious carrot or very creamy stilton soup (£1.85), ham, herb and cheese pancake in lovely sauce (£4.40), excellent omelettes (£3.95), filling and tasty steak and kidney pie, very good plaice or large salmon steak in wine sauce, excellent salmon and spinach lasagne (£4.75), popular salmon fishcakes with hollandaise, and wonderful syrup sponge pudding or home-made rum, raisin and walnut ice cream (from £2.10). Other food includes sandwiches (from £2.30), several children's dishes (£3), ploughman's (£3.30), a complicated terrine (£3.30), garlic mushrooms with bacon (£3.65), devilled kidneys on toast (£4.10), salads (from £4.95), hot beef curry (£5.75), gammon (£6.20), chicken piri piri (£6.95), steaks (from £8.75), and a very wide choice of home-made puddings (from £2). An old blackboard lists ten or so interesting and often uncommon wines by the glass, including a decent champagne; well kept Boddingtons, Marstons Pedigree and Ruddles on handpump; big (4 cup) pot of cafetière coffee, teas, and hot chocolate. The cross-shaped and high-ceilinged bar has masses of Victorian pictures (especially portraits and military subjects), patterned paper on the shutters to match the curtains, an open fire, a range of furnishings from cane and bentwood to pews and carved oak (with some of the old school desks above the bar on a gantry), and a great stag's head over one of the side arches. There are seats out on a sizeable lawn, and Cholmondeley Castle and gardens are close by. (*Recommended by Howard and Lynda Dix, B and D Sowter, W C M Jones, Olive Carroll, Tony and Lynne Stark, G T Jones, Martin Aust, John and Chris Simpson, P D Putwain, M Watson, Nick and Alison Dowson, Laurence Manning, Mike Beiley, J Scarisbrick, I T Parry, Susan Palmer, G A Price, Mr and Mrs J E Rycroft, Celia and David Watt, Wayne Brindle, J M Shaw, George Jonas*)

Free house   Licensees Julian and Virginia Harrison   Real ale   Meals and snacks (12–2, 6.30–9.30; 6–10 summer Sats); not 25 Dec   Cholmondeley (0829) 720300 Children welcome   Open 11–3, 6.30(6 Sat)–11; winter evening opening 7 (6.30 Sat); closed 25 Dec   Bedrooms; £30S/£40S

BOTTOM OF THE OVEN   SJ9872 Map 7

Stanley Arms ⚲

From A537 Buxton–Macclesfield heading towards Macclesfield, take first left turn (not signposted) after Cat & Fiddle; OS Sheet 118 map reference 980723

Consistently good bar food in this isolated moorland pub includes memorable daily specials, excellent steak sandwiches and popular big Sunday roasts, as well as generous helpings of sandwiches (from £1.40 not Sunday or bank holidays), home-made soup (£1.50), good ploughman's (£3.60), omelettes or home-cooked ham and egg (£3.95), lamb's liver and onions or tasty lasagne (£4.95), outstanding salads (from £5.70; dressed crab £6.50), steaks (from £6.40), half freshly roasted duckling with home-made orange, brandy and Grand Marnier sauce (£8.75), and puddings such as home-made lemon soufflé (from £1.50); evening prices are slightly more, and readers have praised the very good strips of beef in red wine sauce or fillet of pork in rosemary butter. Well kept Marstons Burton and Pedigree on handpump, and a good range of spirits; friendly service. The three cosy rooms have fresh summer flowers, open winter fires, little landscape watercolours on the ochre walls, and piped classical music. Two of them have lots of shiny black lacquered woodwork, subdued red and black flowery plush wall settles and stools, some dark blue seats, and low dimpled copper tables on the grey carpets; the third is laid out as a dining room, with pretty pastel tablecloths. It can get busy at the weekend. There are fine views out to the steep pastures that rise towards Shuttlingsloe; picnic-table sets on the grass behind. (*Recommended by Mr and Mrs B Hobden, Jill and Peter Bickley, Greenwood and Turner, G T Jones, J M Watson, Paul and Margaret Baker, Janet and Gary Amos, P J and S E Robbins, Laurence Manning, T Galligan*)

Marstons   Tenant Alan Harvey   Real ale   Meals and snacks (11.30–2.30, 7–10) Restaurant   Sutton (02605) 2414   Children in eating area and restaurant   Open 11.30–3, 7–11; closed 25 Dec

BRERETON GREEN   SJ7864 Map 7

Bears Head 🛏

1 3/4 miles from M6, junction 17; fork left from Congleton road almost immediately, then left on to A50; also from junction 18, via Holmes Chapel

Though this rather smart place does concentrate on its restaurant trade and well dressed pre-dinner parties can tend to dominate the bar around 8pm, it is much more of a relaxed local at other times. The rambling rooms have masses of heavy black beams and timbers, some traditional oak panel-back settles and ladder-back rush seats, a corner cupboard full of Venetian glass, and in a room at the back a modern, reconstructed fireplace with a brick back and a high front mantlebeam forming an inglenook; there are two serving bars, though only one is normally in use. A section of wall in one room (under glass for protection) has had the plaster removed to show the construction of timber underneath. Bar food consists of home-made soup (£1.40), sandwiches (from £1.60, excellent steak and onion £4.75), home-made pâtés, salads, home-made pasta dishes (£4.75), and daily hot dishes such as gammon with egg or pineapple, roast chicken or fried fillet of plaice (all £4.95), and sirloin steak; home-made puddings like chocolate roulade; courteous service from smart uniformed staff. Bass and Burtonwood Bitter on handpump, kept in fine deep cellars, and decent Italian wines; fruit machine, soothing piped music. A pretty side terrace by the black-and-white timbered inn has white cast-iron tables and chairs under cocktail parasols, big black cast-iron lamp clusters and a central fountain. *(Recommended by Laurence Manning, Stephen R Holman, Steve and Carolyn Harvey, Margaret and Roy Randle)*

Free house   Licensees Mr and Mrs Roberto Tarquini   Real ale   Meals and snacks (12–2, 7–10; not Sun evening)   Restaurant (not Sun evening)   Holmes Chapel (0477) 35251   Children in eating area of bar and in restaurant   Open 11–3, 6–11 Bedrooms; £42.50S/£55S

CHESTER   SJ4166   Map 7
Boot

Eastgate Row North

Many people's favourite Chester pub, this spic-and-span place does get very crowded at peak times – but even then the efficient staff manage to be friendly. The split-level downstairs bar has heavy beams and woodwork, oak flooring and flagstones, exposed wattle and daub behind glass panels, solidly built-in wooden furniture, the brewery's Yorkshire-rose emblem worked into stained-glass panels in the latticed windows, and a couple of framed Victorian newspapers; cribbage, dominoes, fruit machine, piped music. A handsome staircase takes you to an oak-panelled function room; beyond the food serving room is another lounge, with a black-leaded kitchen range and a collection of glass and pot boots. Well kept Sam Smiths OB and Museum tapped from casks downstairs. Under the new licensees, the bar food has remained the same: filled rolls, soup, pâté or hot beef sandwich, and ploughman's, filled baked potatoes, and quiche. The attractively landscaped zoo to the north of the city is good. *(Recommended by Graham Bush, Mr and Mrs J H Adam, Nick Dowson, Terry Buckland, Christopher Heathman, P A Crossland, D A Cawley, Graham Gibson, Jon Wainwright, Mr and Mrs P A Jones, H K Dyson)*

Sam Smiths   Managers John and Tania Green   Real ale   Lunchtime snacks   Chester (0244) 314540   No nearby parking   Open 11–3.30, 5.30–11; 11–11 Fri and Sat; closed 25 and 26 Dec

Falcon

Lower Bridge Street

Though the massive stone blocks of the base and the cellars go back some 700 years or more, much of this handsome timbered building dates from around 1600. The quiet, airy room upstairs (available for functions in the early part of the week) has a fine range of latticed windows looking over the street, and there's some interesting quatrefoil. Well kept Sam Smiths OB and Museum on handpump; soft drinks may be on the pricey side; fruit machine, piped music. Bar food includes open sandwiches, various salads and daily hot dishes (£3.35); the bar staff wear uniforms (it's that sort of place). It can get very crowded on Friday and Saturday evenings. *(Recommended by Graham Richardson, N P Hopkins, Simon Collett-Jones, J R Jewitt, Mr and Mrs J H Adam, Jenny and Brian Seller, P Corris, H K Dyson, Celia and David Watt)*

Sam Smiths   Manager Andrew Waller   Real ale   Meals and snacks (lunchtime, not Sun)   Children in upstairs bar lunchtime only – not Sat   Parking may be difficult Live music Sat lunchtime   Open 11–3, 5–11; all day Sat

CHURCH MINSHULL   SJ6661   Map 7
Badger

B5074 Nantwich–Winsford

This is one of the very few pubs we know with the village post office under the same roof. The friendly bar has straightforward, largely modern furnishings, though lots of stuffed animals lurking in nooks and crannies (particularly in the bar counter itself – and there's a badger peering out of a hole in a big wooden cask) give an unusual touch. Good food includes soup (£1.95), filled baps (from £2.75), Lancashire hot-pot (£2.95), plaice or fine cheese and onion quiche (£3.50), salads (from £3.95), home-made pies such as turkey and ham or steak and kidney (£4.25), steaks (from £5.95), and children's dishes (£1.50). Puddings are good (£1.75). The beers, well kept on handpump, are Marstons Mild, Best and Pedigree, and Oak Best, Double Dagger, Old Oak and Wobbly Bob; they also have several malt whiskies on optic including Macallan and Smiths; helpful service. The bare-boards public bar has pool, sensibly placed darts, and a fruit machine that takes 2p pieces; coal fires, piped music. There are picnic-table sets under cocktail parasols in the neat garden below the handsome village church, sheltered by shrubs and a flowering cherry, with some seats on a back verandah; besides a sundial and swings there may be rabbits. *(Recommended by P Corris, Mr and Mrs J H Adam, Derek and Sylvia Stephenson, John Scarisbrick, Chris Raisin, E G Parish, Charles Hall, G T Jones)*

Free house   Licensee Bernard Conwell   Real ale   Meals and snacks (12–2, 6–10; restricted Sun evening)   Restaurant   Church Minshull (027 071) 607   Children welcome   Open 11.30–3, 5–11; 11.30–11 Sat

COMBERBACH   SJ6477   Map 7

Spinner & Bergamot ⊗

Village signposted from A553 and A559 NW of Northwich; pub towards Great Budworth

Spotlessly kept and consistently bright and welcoming, this slated and pebbledashed pub has a warm winter log fire in each room. The front bar has some toby jugs hanging from the beams, one or two hunting prints on the cream textured walls, and red plush button-back built-in wall banquettes. The softly lit back dining room has country-kitchen furniture (some of oak), pretty curtains, and a big brick inglenook with a stripped high mantlebeam; brocaded wall seats in the neat red-tiled public bar. Generously served home-made bar food at lunchtime includes decent sandwiches (from £1.50; toasties or open sandwiches from £2), soup (£1.40), filled baked potatoes (from £2), fish mornay (£3), salads (from £3), steak and kidney pie (£4), gammon with egg or pineapple (£4.40), and fresh grilled plaice (£5.50); in the evening dishes are slightly more expensive and also include mushrooms filled with pâté and deep fried (£2.80), kofta curry (£4.80), excellent jumbo scampi in home-made batter (£6.20), and steaks (from £8.25). Daily specials, and Sunday roast (£4.20); vegetables are fresh. Well kept Greenalls on handpump; darts, dominoes, piped music, and a bowling green outside at the back – bowls can be hired; cheerful, efficient service. A hatch in the front lobby serves the white tables out on a sloping lawn, which has swings, a climber and assorted rabbits and birds (children not allowed in pub); there are lots of flower tubs and hanging baskets outside, bunches of fresh flowers inside. *(Recommended by John Watson, Syd and Wyn Donald, John Broughton, Dr S D Page, Brian and Anna Marsden, C F Walling, Simon Turner, Tony and Pat Young, A F C Young, G T Jones)*

Greenalls (Allied)   Tenants Doug and Mavis Hughes   Real ale   Meals and snacks (not Sun evening)   Restaurant; not Sun evening   Comberbach (0606) 891307   Open 11.30–3, 5.30–11

COTEBROOK   SJ5765   Map 7

Alvanley Arms ⇔

Junction A49/B5152, N of Tarporley

This 16th-century farmhouse has a main bar with neat high beams, a big open fire, fairly close-set tables (dining-height by the red plush wall banquettes around the sides and lower ones with plush stools in the middle), a few hunting and sporting prints, and brasses. On the other side of a pleasantly chintzy small hall is a quieter but broadly similar room with more interesting prints and a delft shelf of china. Very generous helpings of waitress-served food include sandwiches and salads, vegetarian dishes or chilli con carne (£3.95), lasagne or home-made steak pie (£4.05), honey-glazed lamb chops (£5.25), chicken tikka (£5.65), daily specials, puddings, and children's meals (£2.50); four gourmet evenings a year. Well kept Robinsons Mild and Best on electric pump and several malt whiskies; prompt and friendly service, fruit machine tucked away in a lobby. A side lawn by a pond with geese looks out over rolling fields and has fairy-lit picnic-table sets under a small cedar, and swings; food is not normally served out here. *(Recommended by P Corris, Theo Schofield, D I Baddeley, G T Jones)*

Robinsons   Tenants Mr and Mrs J White   Real ale   Meals and snacks (12–2, 6–9.30 Mon-Sat; 12–2, 7–9 Sun)   Candlelit restaurant   Little Budworth (0829) 760200 Children in eating area of bar and in restaurant   Open 11.30–3, 5.30(6 Sat)–11 Bedrooms; £25B/£50B

FADDILEY SJ5953 Map 7
Tollemache Arms

A534 Nantwich–Wrexham

The two rooms on the right in this little black and white, thatched and timbered 15th-century pub have dark glossy beams, upholstered, built-in wall settles and leatherette-cushioned cask seats around gleaming copper tables, particularly cottagey decorations – copper utensils, houseplants and so forth – and an open fire; the inner room, up a couple of steps, is the snugger of the two. The room on the left is laid out more conventionally, but like the others has lots of brass and copper, and shiny beams. The decent range of bar food includes tomato, orange and basil soup (£1.35), mushrooms stuffed with pâté in a French mustard and brandy sauce (£2.50), pork and leek sausages with stilton sauce (£3.95), steak and Guinness pie or lamb in rosemary and red wine (£4.25), 8oz fillet steak (£7.95), home-made puddings, and two Sunday roasts (£3.95). Well kept Greenalls Bitter on handpump; friendly service. Darts and dominoes in the back public bar; piped music. The neat small lawn, with a couple of substantial yew trees guarding the gate in its picket fence, has picnic-table sets and a black-and-white children's play house (that several doves enjoy as well). The pub is floodlit at night. *(Recommended by David and Rebecca Killick; more reports please)*

Greenalls (Allied)   Tenants Janice Brindley and Andy Bebbington   Real ale   Meals and snacks (not Mon)   Faddiley (0270) 74223   Children in eating area   Open 12–3, 7–11; closed Mon lunchtime

FULLERS MOOR SJ4954 Map 7
Copper Mine

A534 Wrexham–Nantwich, about a mile E of A41 junction

Refurbished under new licensees, the softly-lit, low-ceilinged rooms here have stripped beams and timbering, blacked stove doors set into the dividing wall, and separate seating areas; lovely views from all windows. The walls are covered with masses of copper-mining mementoes – blasting explosives and fuses, old lamps, and photographic tableaux of more-or-less tense moments in local mining history. Popular bar food ranges from traditional dishes to mushroom and stilton crêpes, tempura prawns, and steak medici (from £2.95-£7.95). Well kept Bass and Burtonwood Best on handpump; rack of magazines. There are picnic-table sets under cocktail parasols in the spacious grounds, and summer barbecues (weather permitting); this is a pleasant base for exploring the local countryside – there are good walks to Bickerton and Larkton Hills. *(Recommended by Mr and Mrs Crombleholme, Keith Croston, Eric Locker, Laurence Manning, Graham Gibson)*

Burtonwood/Bass   Lease: Geoffrey and Linda Aldridge   Real ale   Meals and snacks Restaurant   Tarporley (0829) 782293   Chidren welcome   Open 11–3, 6–11; 12–3, 7–11 winter

GOOSTREY   SJ7870 Map 7

Crown

111 Main Road; village signposted from A50 and A535

We're leaving this friendly village pub as a main entry even though, the day before this chapter of the book went to press, Peter McGrath (the tenant who had built up its reputation) heard his brewery was giving him a year's notice to quit, to take the pub into management. So he may still be there for some months – or by now he may have found a new place in which to excercise his talents. The two comfortable communicating rooms of the lounge bar have had a chaise longue and cushioned settles as well as more conventional seats, prints of some of Lowry's less well known paintings, and open fires. Popular bar food has included sandwiches, excellent stilton ploughman's, chilli con carne, southern fried chicken, and a lunchtime special, with evening extras such as rack of lamb or rump steak in the back bistro dining room; bookings are essential at weekends. An upstairs room can be booked for dinner parties, preferably not on Saturdays. Well kept Marstons Pedigree on handpump; piped music. Seats on the front terrace face the village road. *(Recommended by Richard Gibbs, G T Jones, Robbie Pennington, Simon Turner, H B Vanstone, Steve Mitcheson, Anne Collins, J Scarisbrick)*

Marstons   Licensee Peter McGrath   Real ale   Meals and snacks (not Mon, not Sun evening)   Restaurant (not Sun evening)   Holmes Chapel (0477) 32128   Children in eating area of bar   Jazz or folk Sun evening   Open 11.30–3, 5.30–11   Bedrooms

GREAT BUDWORTH   SJ6778 Map 7

George & Dragon

4 1/2 miles from M6, junction 19; from A556 towards Northwich, turn right into B5391 almost at once; then fork right at signpost to Aston-by-Budworth, Arley Hall & Gardens

A good cross-section of people (walkers leave their boots tidily in the porch) gather in this picturesque old pub to enjoy the relaxed and friendly atmosphere and well presented bar food. The rambling and panelled lounge has plenty of nooks and alcoves, copper jugs hanging from the beams, red plush button-back banquettes and older settles on its Turkey carpet, and a fine big mirror with horsebrasses on the wooden pillars of its frame. The public bar has a lively atmosphere and is simply furnished; darts, dominoes, and fruit machine; the piped music may sometimes be loud. At busy times families can use the upstairs restaurant which is no smoking then. Bar food includes soup (£1.15), sandwiches (from £1.50; the beef are good), good ploughman's (£3.45), vegetarian lasagne or roast meats (£3.95), superb ham and eggs, salads (from £4.25), swordfish steak (£5.25), and steaks (from £6.95); children's menu (£1.75), and Sunday roast. Well kept Ind Coope Burton, Tetleys Bitter on handpump, and some malt whiskies. The 11th-century church and village stocks are opposite the fine wrought-iron gantry that serves for an inn sign. *(Recommended by Tony and Lynne Stark, Col G D Stafford, R T and J C Moggridge, Lee Goulding, Simon J Barber, Derek and Sylvia Stephenson, Alan and Marlene Radford, TBB)*

Tetleys (Allied)   Lease: Malcolm and Lynne Curtin   Real ale   Meals and snacks Upstairs restaurant   Comberbach (0606) 891317   Children in eating area at lunchtime, restaurant in evening   Open 11.30–3, 6–11

nr LANGLEY   SJ9471 Map 7

Hanging Gate

Higher Sutton; follow Langley signpost from A54 beside Fourways Motel, and that road passes the pub; from Macclesfield, heading S from centre on A523 turn left into Byrons Lane at Langley, Wincle signpost; in Sutton (half-mile after going under canal bridge, ie before Langley) fork right at Church House Inn, following Wildboarclough signpost, then two miles later turning sharp right at steep hairpin bend; OS Sheet 118 ref 952696

This old drovers' pub was first licensed nearly 300 years ago – though it was built much earlier. The cosy little low-beamed rooms are simply furnished with small seats and modern settles by the big coal fires, a stuffed otter, and some attractive old photographs of Cheshire towns; they look out beyond a patchwork of valley pastures to distant moors (and the tall Sutton Common transmitter above them). Down stone steps an airier garden room has much the same view from its picture window; dominoes, juke box, and sitting space game. Reasonably priced bar food includes soup, sandwiches, and basket meals, with daily specials such as steak and kidney pie, chicken in tarragon wine, beef rogon josh or drunken bull (all £3.85). Well kept Border Bitter and Marstons Pedigree on handpump. There is a crazy-paved terrace outside. *(Recommended by Greenwood and Turner, Dave Irving, Adam and Elizabeth Gorb)*

Free house   Licensees John and Lyn Vernon   Real ale   Meals and snacks   Children in two rooms   Open 12–3, 7–11; closed 25 Dec

LANGLEY   SJ9471   Map 7
Leathers Smithy

From Macclesfield, heading S from centre on A523 turn left into Byrons Lane at Langley, Wincle signpost; in Langley follow main road forking left at church into Clarke Lane – keep on towards the moors; OS Sheet 118 map reference 952715

In a glorious setting – surrounded by rich upland sheep pastures, hills and pine woods and backed by the steep mass of Teggs Nose (a country park) – this friendly pub is popular with walkers; a couple of benches in front look across to the Ridgegate Reservoir. The lively, partly flagstoned right-hand bar has bow window seats or wheelback chairs, and gin traps, farrier's pincers, a hay basket and other ironwork on the roughcast cream walls. On the left, there are more wheelback chairs around cast-iron-framed tables on Turkey carpet, little country pictures and drawings of Cheshire buildings, Wills steam engine cigarette cards and a locomotive nameplate curving over one of the two open fires, and faint piped music. Hearty bar food includes sandwiches (from £1.40), beef pie (£2.70), ploughman's (from £3), lasagne (£3.60), vegetarian dishes (£3.80), cod or chilli con carne (£3.90), tasty steak and kidney pie (£4), good salads, and gammon and egg (£5.50); delicious puddings such as butterscotch and walnut fudge cake (£1.50). Ind Coope Burton, Jennings Bitter, and Tetleys Bitter and Mild on handpump, and farm cider. Gluwein in winter from a copper salamander, and a decent collection of spirits, including 40 malt whiskies and 10 Irish; dominoes, fruit machine. *(Recommended by G T Jones, Martin and Gill Searle, Steve and Carolyn Harvey, Brian and Anna Marsden, Christian Leigh)*

Tetleys (Allied)   Tenant Paul Hadfield   Real ale   Meals and snacks (not Mon evening)   Sutton (026 05) 2313   Children in own room Sat & Sun lunchtime only Occasional pianola music   Open 12–3, 7–11

LITTLE LEIGH   SJ6276   Map 7
Holly Bush   £

4 1/2 miles from M56 junction 10: A49 towards Northwich, pub just S of A533 junction

As last year's *Guide* went to press, there was a vigorous campaign to keep this pub open as a rare survival of the unspoilt farm/tavern; we still didn't know whether the representations made to the brewery and the planning authorities by many people including the *Guide* would secure its future. We did win a year's grace for the pub, under the widow of Albert Cowap who had done so much to keep it as it was. But that year runs out just before this edition will be published. There is again great pressure for the pub to be preserved, but we still don't know whether, when you read this, it will be as described – or fundamentally changed, or, even worse, turned into a private house. So, again fingers crossed. It's a fine timber-framed and thatched, old-fashioned farmhouse, with friendly service and locals, warm fires, varnished wall benches with sloping panelled backs around waxed and polished country tables, and two naval pictures on the wall; there's no bar – the Greenalls and Mild (on handpump) are served from the open doorway of a little back taproom; pork pies (50p), steak pies (60p), and sandwiches (from 90p). Darts and dominoes. *(Recommended by Graham Gibson, Tony and Lynne Stark; more reports please)*

Greenalls (Allied)   Tenant Mrs Suzanne Cowap   Real ale   Snacks   Weaverham (0606) 853196   Children in small snug, not after 9pm   Occasional folk music   Open 11–3, 5.30–11

LOWER PEOVER   SJ7474   Map 7

Bells of Peover ★

From B5081 take short cobbled lane signposted to church

The sheltered crazy-paved terrace in front of this graceful wisteria-covered pub faces a beautiful black and white timbered church (mainly fourteenth-century, with lovely woodwork inside; the stone tower is sixteenth-century); a spacious lawn beyond the old coachyard at the side spreads down through trees and rose pergolas to a little stream. Inside, it's spotlessly kept with warmly welcoming staff – even when very busy. The little tiled bar has side hatches for its serving counter, toby jugs, and comic Victorian prints, and the original lounge has antique settles, antique china in the dresser, high-backed Windsor armchairs, spacious window seat, and pictures above the panelling; two small coal fires. There's a second similar lounge. Bar food includes home-made soup (£1.30), good, fresh sandwiches (from £1.45; open sandwiches from £2.95), filled ba:ed potatoes (from £3.25), lasagne or home-made quiche (£4.20), home-made steak and kidney pie (£4.40), pretty salads with interesting fruit (from £4), good daily specials, and several puddings (from £1.85). Jacket and tie are advised in the restaurant. Very well kept Greenalls Best on handpump and several wines. *(Recommended by Barrie Hopwood, Harry McCann, Roy Cove, John Atherton, Dr S D Page, John Watson, Brian and Anna Marsden, Wyn and Syd Donald, Malcolm H Littler, John and Tony Walker, J L and J A Annandale, Dorothee and Dennis Glover, Adam and Elizabeth Gorb, Laurence Manning, N P Siesage, Mr and Mrs Simon Turner, John and Tessa Rainsford, Tony and Pat Young, H B Vanstone, Keith Mills, Tony and Lynne Stark, Graham Gibson, RT, J F Kent, Audrey and Brian Green, A F C Young, Steve Dark, Ralph A Raimi, John Broughton, Robert and Vicky Tod)*

Greenalls (Allied)   Tenant Dave Barker   Real ale   Meals and snacks (not Sat or Sun evening)   Restaurant; closed Sat lunchtime, Sun evening and all day Mon   Lower Peover (0565) 722269   Children in restaurant   Open 11.30–3, 5.30(6 Sat)–11

LOWER WHITLEY   SJ6179   Map 7

Chetwode Arms

2 1/4 miles from M56, junction 10; village signposted from A49 Whitchurch road

Three carpeted rooms lead off the small central servery here – one with a handsome heavy seat built right around its walls, and there's a snug little room with a settle and some chairs. The locals' bar is on the right, served by a hatch, with old green-cushioned settles, heavy mahogany tables, and darts, and dominoes. There's some farm equipment such as a miniature harrow and plough, horsebrasses, little country pictures on the walls, and a collection of china teapots and so forth; warm coal fires. Wholesome food includes home-made soup (£1.30), sandwiches (from £1.40), ploughman's (£3), salads (from £3.95), vegetarian quiche or kofta curry (£4.10), liver and onions (£4.30), fresh fillet of plaice or chicken tandoori (£5.35), and puddings (£1.80); Sunday roast (£4.60), and children's meals. Greenalls on electric pump; good service. Darts, pool, dominoes, piped music. The bowling green is beautifully kept and there's a big back lawn with swings. *(Recommended by Mr and Mrs B Hobden, M J Ridgway, Dr S D Page, Graham Bush, C F Walling, G T Jones, Andy and Jill Kassube)*

Greenalls (Allied)   Lease: Robert and Anita Southerton   Real ale   Meals and snacks Warrington (0925) 730203   Children welcome   Open 11.30–3, 5.30–11; all day Sat

MACCLESFIELD   SJ9271   Map 7

Sutton Hall Hotel ★ 🚫 🛏️

Leaving Macclesfield southwards on A523, turn left into Byrons Lane signposted Langley, Wincle, then just before canal viaduct fork right into Bullocks Lane; OS Sheet 118 map reference 925715

This fine and historic old baronial hall is reliably good for its friendly but smartly civilised atmosphere and well prepared, properly cooked food. The bar is divided up into separate areas by tall black timbers, and there are broad flagstones around the bar counter (carpet elsewhere), some antique squared oak panelling, lightly patterned art nouveau stained glass windows, and a raised open fire; furnishings are mainly straightforward ladderback chairs around sturdy thick-topped cast-iron-framed tables, and some unusual touches include an enormous bronze bell for calling time, a brass cigar-lighting gas taper on the bar counter itself, a suit of armour by another substantial stone fireplace, and a longcase clock. Popular bar food includes home-made soup (£1.45), open sandwiches (from £1.85, special toasties £3.25), lasagne (£4.95), steak and kidney pie (£5.25), specials like cold venison pie or vegetarian spinach pancakes (£5.25), and puddings (around £2). Well kept Bass and Mild, Marstons Burton and Stones Best on handpump, a guest such as Boddingtons, 30 malt whiskies, and decent wines. There are tables on a tree-sheltered lawn. They can arrange clay shooting, golf or local fishing. *(Recommended by Paul and Margaret Baker, Steve and Carolyn Harvey, Harry McCann, George Atkinson, Mr and Mrs B Hobden, Mike and Wendy Proctor, Mr and Mrs Simon Turner, Laurence Manning, D W Huebner)*

Free house   Licensee Robert Bradshaw   Real ale   Meals and snacks   Restaurant Sutton (026 05) 3211   Children allowed weekends only   Open all day   Four-poster bedrooms; £65B/£80B

MOBBERLEY   SJ7879   Map 7

Bird in Hand

B5085 towards Alderley

Rambling off the central servery in this partly 16th-century pub are several low-ceilinged little rooms with comfortably cushioned heavy wooden seats, small pictures on the attractive Victorian wallpaper, toby jugs and other china on a high shelf, wood panelling in the cosy snug, and a blazing winter fire; the top dining area is no smoking. Good bar food ranges from sandwiches (from £1.30; open sandwiches such as home-roasted ham with peach £3), home-made soup (£1.45), and ploughman's (£3.30), through salads (from £4.10), home-made steak and onion pie, fresh battered haddock or gammon with two eggs (£4.35), to puddings like home-made fruit pie (£1.95); daily specials such as giant yorkshire pudding filled with spicy sausage and onion gravy (£4.75), and roast Sunday lunch. Sam Smiths OB and Museum on handpump or tapped from the cask, and lots of malt whiskies; darts, dominoes and fruit machine. It can get crowded; seats outside. *(Recommended by Dave Irving, Brian and Anna Marsden; more reports please)*

Sam Smiths   Manager Andrew Towers   Real ale   Meals and snacks (not Sun evening)   Mobberley (0565) 873149   Children in eating area of bar   Open 11–3, 5.30–11; all day Sat

OLLERTON   SJ7877   Map 7

Dun Cow

A537 SE of Knutsford

A new licensee has taken over this comfortable country pub. The low-ceilinged lounge, sheltered by a wooden draught screen, has two blazing fires with a low wicker-seat chair (like a nursing chair with arms) by one of them, an oak settle squeezed into a little alcove, and small pictures and nice little oak chairs and tables in a corner snug. There are also traditional dark wood built-in seats, a couple of longcase clocks, a polished chest by the entry, and some large embroidered panels (particularly the one on the way through to the restaurant). The small taproom has dominoes; well kept Greenalls Bitter and Original on handpump. Good value bar food includes soup, sandwiches (from £1.75), seafood bake (£3.25), ploughman's (£3.95), and home-made steak and kidney pie (£4.50); Sunday lunch (£4.95). A few picnic-tables under the oak trees in front of the building. *(Recommended by J H M Broughton, J L and J A Annandale, Dave Irving; more reports on the new regime, please)*

Greenalls (Allied) Tenant Derek Shirley Real ale Meals and snacks (all day Sunday) Restaurant Knutsford (0565) 633093 Children in snug and separate back room Open 11.30–11; open all day Sunday; closed evening 25 Dec

OVER PEOVER SJ7674 Map 7
Whipping Stocks

Stocks Lane; just off and easily seen from A50 S of Knutsford

The countryside around this solidly-built, comfortable pub is attractive and level, with a pretty walk through to the church and hall; there are picnic-table sets in quite a spacious tree-sheltered garden with a barbecue and safe play area. Inside, and opening off the fairly spacious central bar area, are several rooms – each with a distinct style of its own (and one no smoking). Seats range from small linenfold wooden chairs to sturdy wall settles upholstered in rather a 1930s plush fabric, most rooms have neat fireplaces, and there's a good deal of oak panelling (the bar counter itself is staunchly oaken – with fine elbow and foot rests). Popular waitress-served home-made bar food includes sandwiches (from £1.30), filled baked potatoes (from £2.25), ploughman's (£2.90), salads (from £3), home-made quiche (£3.50), daily specials such as chicken curry or moussaka, puddings like home-made treacle tart (£1.50), and evening gammon (£4.05), and sirloin steak (£6.40). Well kept Sam Smiths OB on handpump, with Museum kept under light blanket pressure; fruit machine, trivia, and well chosen and reproduced piped music, welcoming landlord. The grey and white cat is called Smudge. *(Recommended by Roy Cove, John Watson, Dr S D Page, Mr and Mrs J H Adam, Brian and Anna Marsden, Miss R Murdoch)*

Sam Smiths Managers John and Johanne Eadie Real ale Meals and snacks Lower Peover (0565) 722332 Children in eating area of bar lunchtimes and early evening Open 11.30–3, 5–11

OVERTON SJ5277 Map 7
Ring o' Bells

Just over 2 miles from M56, junction 12; 2 Bellemonte Road – from A56 in Frodsham take B5152 and turn right (uphill) at Parish Church signpost

Quiet and warmly friendly (to children as well), this 17th-century local has lots of little rambling rooms. A couple have plush seats with windows giving a view past the stone church to the Mersey far below; one at the back has some antique settles, brass-and-leather fender seats by the log fire, and old hunting prints on its butter-coloured walls. Yet another – with beams, antique dark oak panelling and stained glass – leads through to a darts room (there's also shove-ha'penny, dominoes and cribbage but no noisy games machines or piped music) decorated with pinups. Consistently good, waitress-served lunchtime bar food (popular with businessmen) includes sandwiches, deep-fried camembert (£1.90), home-made steak and mushroom pie, vegetarian quiche, lasagne or spicy chilli (all £2.95), and plaice filled with prawn and mushroom (£3.40). Well kept Greenalls Bitter and Original on handpump from the old-fashioned hatch-like central servery; 84 different malt whiskies; piped music. The cats are called Basil and Blackberry India. *(Recommended by Graham Gibson, Andy and Jill Kassube, M A Cameron, R L Harris, Keith Mort)*

Greenalls (Allied) Tenant Shirley Wroughton-Craig Real ale Lunchtime meals and snacks Children welcome (not in bar itself) Frodsham (0928) 32068 Open 11.30–3.30, 5.30 (6 Sat)–11

PEOVER HEATH   SJ7973 Map 7

Dog 🏮

Off A50 N of Holmes Chapel at the Whippings Stocks, keep on past Parkgate into Wellbank Lane; OS Sheet 118 map reference 794735; note that this village is called Peover Heath on the OS map and shown under that name on many road maps, but the pub is often listed under Over Peover instead

Surrounded by sweeping country lanes stands this attractive, very busy inn with its pretty hanging baskets. Smartened up by the new licensees, there's an engaging series of small areas around the main bar with seats ranging from a little rocking chair, through wall seats (one built into a snug alcove around an oak table), to the handsome ribbed banquettes in the quiet and spacious dining room on the left; logs burn in one old-fashioned black grate and a coal fire opposite it is flanked by two wood-backed built-in fireside seats. Large helpings of popular bar food might typically include interesting home-made soups, a good choice of sandwiches (from £1.60), ploughman's with good cheeses (from £3.15), starters such as black pudding with mustard or chicken livers on toast (£3.45), main dishes such as duck and chicken pie, rabbit with herbs and mustard, ham shank with parsley sauce, cheese and mushroom pancake or roast beef or turkey (all £4.75 lunchtime, £5.45 evening), daily specials (£1 extra), and puddings like home-made crumbles and pies; bookings are essential; service is pushed at busy times. Well kept Boddingtons Bitter, Flowers IPA, Marstons Pedigree, Websters Choice, and Whitbreads Castle Eden on handpump, and quite a few malt whiskies; darts, pool, dominoes, and satellite TV in the taproom, and a tucked-away fruit machine. There are picnic-table sets out on the quiet lane. The licensees also own the Old Packet House in Altrincham. (*Recommended by Caroline Wright, Laurence Manning, Dr S D Page, Keith Mills, Mr and Mrs A B Taylor, D M Moss, Mr and Mrs Simon Turner*)

Free house   Licensees Frances and Jim Cunningham   Real ale   Meals and snacks (not Sun evenings or all day Mon)   Chilford (0625) 861421   Children in eating area of bar   Blues Mon evening, Country & Western Weds evening   Open 11.30–3, 5.30–11   Bedrooms; £30B/£55B

PLUMLEY   SJ7175 Map 7

Golden Pheasant

Plumley Moor Lane; signposted Plumley off A556 by the Smoker – see next entry

The sizeable garden outside this spacious pub has a neatly kept bowling green, picnic-table sets under cocktail parasols, and a climbing frame. The comfortably modernised open-plan rooms have one or two antiques – an odd sofa, a fine longcase clock – among the more conventional furnishings such as attractively upholstered built-in wall seats, a couple of elaborate antique flower prints and wooden partitions with stained-glass inserts, and an open fire. Bar food includes soup (£1.50), sandwiches (from £1.30), chilli con carne (£3.95), lasagne or fish pie (£4.25), and steak and kidney pie (£4.95); specials like steak in pepper sauce (£6.95) or duck breast in orange and ginger sauce (£9.30), and Sunday roast (£4.50); staff are smart and efficient. Very well priced Lees Bitter and Mild, and several malt whiskies; darts, juke box, fruit machine, with pool in a separate games room. (*Recommended by Bill Ryan, C F Walling, Richard Houghton, John Broughton; more reports please*)

Lees   Managers Chris and Anita Murphy   Real ale   Meals and snacks (12–2, 6–10) Restaurant   Lower Peover (0565) 722261   Children welcome   Open 11–3(4 Sat), 5.30–11   Bedrooms; £39B/49B

Smoker 🏮

2 ½ miles from M6 junction 19: A556 towards Northwich and Chester

Praise from readers about the home-made food here has been so enthusiastic this year that we've given it a Food Award: home-made soup (£1.30), sandwiches (from £1.35), a choice of 13 starters like good pâté or asparagus rolled in ham coated with cheese sauce (£2.70), and around 28 home-made main courses such as excellent kofta curry, hummus with pitta bread or vegetarian avocado pâté (£4.35), lovely fresh plaice, popular liver and onions, beef stroganoff or pork fillet in green peppercorn sauce (£5.10), lots of steaks (from £7.15), roast sirloin of beef or turkey, and puddings such as delicious lemon brûlée; chips and vegetables are freshly prepared. Well kept Robinsons Best and Mild on electric pump; 25 single malt whiskies and a decent choice of wines by the bottle. The three communicating rooms have comfortable deep sofas, cushioned settles, Windsor chairs, some rush-seat dining chairs, and open fires in impressive period fireplaces; they are decorated with a large collection of copper kettles, military prints on dark panelling in one room, a glass case containing a remnant from the Houses of Parliament salvaged after it was hit by a bomb in World War II, and an Edwardian print by Goodwin Kilburne of a hunt meeting outside the pub. Good, helpful service, friendly locals, and a relaxed atmosphere. Around this sixteenth-century thatched building are a cobbled front area and a sizeable side lawn with roses and flowerbeds. It's actually named after a favourite racehorse of the Prince Regent. *(Recommended by G T Jones, Dr S D Page, Robert and Vicky Tod, T Henwood, J R Smylie, W C M Jones, Bill Ryan, Mr and Mrs J H Adam, Sue Braisted, Michael Cochrane, Graham Gibson, A Wright, Audrey and Brian Green, Michael and Joan Melling)*

Robinsons Tenants John and Diana Bailey Real ale Meals and snacks (12–2.30, 7–10) Restaurant (not Sun evening) Lower Peover (0565) 722338 Children in eating area and restaurant Open 11–3, 5.30–11

RAINOW SJ9576 Map 7
Highwayman

A mile above village, NE along A5002 Macclesfield–Whaley Bridge

Overlooking the Cheshire Plain, this early 17th-century pub has a front terrace which is popular on fine summer evenings or weekends; nearby parking may be difficult then. The cosy little rooms have low beams, some antique settles and simpler cushioned seats around rustic wooden tables, and a winter coal fire each; the high bar counter is attractively covered with copper. Bar food includes home-made soup (£1.35), sandwiches (lunchtimes, from £1.40), black pudding (£2.35), a choice of half a dozen freshly made pizzas (from £2.65), savoury pancake rolls (£3.30), plaice goujons (£4.15), and specials like home-made steak and kidney pie (£4.15). Well kept Thwaites on handpump; darts and piped music. *(Recommended by Hilary Bill, Dave Irving, Andy and Jill Kassube, Michael Cochrane, Derek and Sylvia Stephenson, Janet and Gary Amos, Ian Briggs, G T Jones, H B Vanstone, Wayne Brindle)*

Thwaites Tenants Frank and Audrey Jones Real ale Meals and snacks Chilford (0625) 573245 Children away from bar lunchtimes only Open 11–3, 6.30–11; winter evening opening 7pm; closed evening 25 Dec

SMALLWOOD SJ8160 Map 7
Bulls Head

Newcastle Road; A50 N of Alsager

The garden here is quite special: lots of space in separate areas divided by shrub borders, cascading roses, little secluded walkways, a lusciously planted part by a small pond – most of the plants are propagated in one of their two greenhouses. There's also a side terrace with rustic seats, and a big well equipped play area including a superannuated tractor; summer barbecues. Inside, the beamed and timbered open-plan bar rambles around a central servery, giving the impression of several separate areas – varying carpet patterns, and the switch to woodstrip flooring in one place, help with this, as does the mix of seating styles and of table sizes. Attractively presented bar food includes particularly good soup (£1.60), sandwiches (from £1.95), ploughman's (£4.25), good fish dishes (from £4.25), generous and unusual salads (£5.95), chilli con carne, steak and kidney pie, cottage pie served with lettuce, beetroot and red cabbage, and nut and mushroom fettucini and other vegetarian dishes (all £5.95), dishes of the day such as fish pie, lamb rogon josh and ham and cheese pancake (£5.95), sirloin steak (£7.95), puddings (£2.50), and Sunday lunch (£5.95); efficient and friendly service, by neatly uniformed waitresses; well kept Ind Coope Burton and Tetleys on handpump, decent house wines, and 18 malt whiskies; piped pop music (perhaps rather obtrusive – but it does mean that no traffic noise from the busy road penetrates even when the pub is quiet). (*Recommended by Sue Holland, Dave Webster, Mr and Mrs D C Leaman*)

Ansells (Allied)   Lease: William Anderson   Real ale   Meals and snacks (12–2.30, 6.30–10)   Smallwood (0477) 500247   Children in eating area of bar   Open 12–3, 6(5.30 Sat)–11; closed 25 Dec

SUTTON   SJ9469 Map 7
Ryles Arms

Off A54 Congleton–Buxton, 2 ¾ miles E of A523 – signposted Sutton 2 ¾; or coming into Sutton from Macclesfield, fork right after going under aqueduct; OS Sheet 118 map reference 942694

Though most people tend to be older regulars here for the very generous helpings of hearty food, making this decidedly a very "Cheshire" dining pub, locals dropping in for a drink by the bar in their jeans obviously feel quite at home too; its success owes a lot to the light yet sure touch of the welcoming Irish landlord, a man who really notices things without being obtrusive about it. The part by the bar is basically two rooms knocked together, with comfortable seats and French windows to a terrace with metal and plastic chairs. On the right is more obviously a dining area (no smoking at eating times), though with some attractively individual furnishings; the family room is no smoking, too. The bar food includes soup (£1), sandwiches (from £1.40), smoked fish pâté (£2 – their pâté s are recommended), ploughman's (£2.50), basket meals (from £2.50), tuna and courgette quiche (£4), chicken curry, steak and kidney pie or a good lasagne (£4.50), gammon and egg (£5), duck and orange (£5.60) and sirloin steak (£8), with a fine pheasant casserole in season; vegetables are fresh; children's lunches (£2). Well kept Marstons Pedigree and Ruddles Best and County on handpump, a good choice of whiskies; fruit machine. Hilly pastures lined with sycamores and ashes are all around. (*Recommended by Mike and Wendy Proctor, Laurence Manning, Jill and Peter Bickley, Graham Simpson*)

Free house   Licensees Frank and Joan Campbell   Real ale   Meals and snacks   Sutton (02605) 2244   Children in family room at lunchtimes   Open 11.30–3, 6–11; open all day Christmas week but closed 25 Dec

TARPORLEY   SJ5563 Map 7
Rising Sun   £

High St; village signposted off A51 Nantwich–Chester

Even in mid-week this village pub has a lovely bustling friendly atmosphere. The low-ceilinged, beamed rooms have three open fires, character seats including creaky nineteenth-century mahogany and oak settles around the well chosen tables, an attractively blacked iron kitchen range, sporting and other old-fashioned prints, and a big oriental rug in the back room. Reasonably priced lunchtime bar food includes sandwiches (from £1.35), filled baked potatoes (from £1.60), home-made steak and kidney pie (£2.60), home-made cottage pie (£2.75), salads (from £2.90), plaice (£3.30), and vegetarian dishes (£4.50), with daily specials such as tandoori chicken or rabbit casserole (£4.50), and seafood lasagne (£5), and puddings (from £1.85); in the evening there are popular steaks (from £6.50) and Dover sole (£8.50); friendly service. Well kept Robinsons Best and Mild on handpump; fruit machine, maybe unobtrusive background music. It's a popular haunt of local cricketers and the bowls team. (*Recommended by M Joyner, Tessa Stuart, Mike Tucker, Joan Goodwin; more reports please*)

Robinsons   Tenant Alec Robertson   Real ale   Meals and snacks (11.30–2, 5.30–9;

not Sun evening or 25 Dec)   No smoking restaurant   Tarporley (0829) 732423
Children welcome lunchtime and in restaurant in evening   Open 11.30–3, 5.30–11

WESTON   SJ7352 Map 7

White Lion 🛏

3 1/2 miles from M6 junction 16; A500 towards Crewe, then village signposted on right

On the right in this little black-and-white timbered inn is the main room – divided into small areas by very gnarled black oak standing timbers; there's a very varied mix of seats from orange-cushioned modern settles to ancient oak ones, with plenty of smaller chairs, and black beams. The best settles are in a smaller room on the left – three of them, well carved in 18th-century style. Bar food includes home-made soup (£1), good sandwiches (from £1, batch cakes or toasties £1.50, steak £4.50), vegetarian quiche or lasagne (£2.95), ploughman's, a daily special or roast (all £3.25), gammon steak (£3.95), poached local Dee salmon (£5.75), steak (£7.25), and home-made puddings (£1). Well kept Ind Coope Burton and Tetleys on handpump, piped music, friendly service by smartly dressed staff; two no-smoking areas. Picnic-table sets shelter on neat grass behind, by the pub's own bowling green. The comfortable hotel part is discreetly built out behind. *(Recommended by Jacquie and Jon Payne, PLC, Laurence Manning, Geoff Lee)*

Free house   Licensee Mrs A J Davies   Real ale   Meals and snacks (not 25 or 26 Dec or 1 Jan evenings   Restaurant (not Sun evening)   Crewe (0270) 500303   Children in eating area of bar and in restaurant   Open 11–3, 6.30–11; winter evening opening 7; closed evening 25 Dec   Bedrooms; £45B/£55B

Lucky Dip

Besides the fully inspected pubs, you might like to try these Lucky Dips recommended to us and described by readers (if you do, please send us reports):

☆ **Acton Bridge** [Hilltop Rd; B5153 off A49 in Weaverham, then right towards Acton Cliff; SJ5975], *Maypole*: Spacious and quietly comfortable beamed bar, separate seating areas with some antique settles as well as more modern furnishings, friendly service, good value bar food, Greenalls Bitter and Mild on handpump, two coal fires, gentle piped music and good lighting; seats in well kept garden with orchard behind *(Mr and Mrs D Young, Wayne Brindle, P Corris, G T Jones, Dr and Mrs C D E Morris, Mr and Mrs J H Adam, BB)*

Acton Bridge [A49; SJ5975], *Horns*: Now under same ownership as Bears Paw, and popular with familes for expanded food range, new children's play area, occasional barbecues *(C F Walling)*

Adlington [Wood Lane North; by Middlewood Way linear park, and Macclesfield Canal — OS Sheet 109 map reference 936818; SJ9180], *Miners Arms*: Well kept, clean and welcoming, with Boddingtons on handpump, good value lunchtime specials and other food from sandwiches to evening steaks *(Cynthia and Grahame Rayden)*

Alderley Edge [about 250 yds past Royal Oak, off Heyes Lane (which is off A34); SJ8478], *Moss Rose*: Tucked-away terraced local, friendly, good value bar food, nice terrace by its own bowling green; open all day Sat and whenever there is bowling match *(K W Mills)*; [The Sidings, London Rd; off A34 by stn], *Queensgate*: Unique, with cobbles, row of mock shops, cocktail bar and restaurant; fine panelling, ornate ceiling, some good prints, Ruddles Best and County on handpump *(Graham Gibson)*

☆ **Alsager** [Sandbach Rd N; SJ7956], *Wilbraham Arms*: Good food, particularly the salads, and useful for families to be able to use both restaurant and bar menus in the pretty restaurant; tidy and spacious building with fine seats and fittings, well kept Robinsons, pleasant efficient staff, big garden *(Laurence Manning, the Shinkmans)*

☆ **Audlem** [Audlem Wharf — OS Sheet 118 map reference 658436; SJ6644], *Shroppie Fly*: Looking out over one of the long flight of locks here; clean and tidy inside, with one bar shaped like a barge, good canal photographs, collection of brightly painted bargees' china and bric-a-brac, seats on waterside terrace; quite a wide choice of good value food, well kept real ale on handpump, children in restaurant and room off bar *(Derek and Sylvia Stephenson, J R Jewitt, LYM)*

☆ **Barton** [A534 E of Farndon; SJ4554], *Cock*: Handsome sandstone country pub with log fires, traditional furnishings, black beams, snug alcoves, attractive prints, well kept McEwans 80/- and Youngers Scotch, bar food from soup and sandwiches to steak, tables outside; closed Mon lunchtime *(LYM; more reports please)*

☆ **Beeston** [Bunbury Heath; A49 S of

Tarporley; SJ5459], *Beeston Castle*: Well restored pub with good range of food inc fine smoked goose breast, enormous open sandwiches, Greek dishes; country and western and quiz evenings. Very good *(D T Taylor, C H Stride)*

☆ **Bickerton** [Bulkeley — A534 E of junction with A41; SJ5052], *Bickerton Poacher*: Consistently good atmosphere in old-fashioned comfortable rambling pub with poacher theme; up to five Marstons and Border or Burtonwwood real ales kept well, adequate bar food inc lots of game dishes, bistro; attractive barbecue extension around sheltered courtyard (summer Fri and Sat evenings, Sun lunchtime), with lots of live music and special events; children welcome *(Brian and Anna Marsden, Martin Aust, Simon J Barber, Dr P D Putwain, Mr and Mrs L G Smith, LYM)*

☆ **Bollington** [29 Adlington Rd, heading N off B5091 by railway viaduct — OS Sheet 118 map reference 931781; SJ9377], *Vale*: Originally three terraced houses, modernised and open-plan but with very relaxing homely atmosphere; home-cooked bar food, well kept Thwaites Bitter and Mild and Timothy Taylors Landlord on handpump, very friendly staff, log fire, neat woodside lawn with good play area; closed Mon lunchtime except bank hols; nr start GWG73 *(Lee Goulding, Tony and Pat Young, LYM)*

☆ **Bollington** [Grimshaw La], *Barge*: Newly opened in old silk mill by Macclesfield Canal — nicely renovated with good family room overlooking canal; Boddingtons and Pedigree well kept on handpump, good value food inc lots for children; easy access from canal but many steps from main entrance below; open all day; children most welcome *(Brian and Anna Marsden)*

☆ **Bollington** [Church St], *Church House*: Friendly bar staff and good choice of simple bar meals in cosy local with well kept Theakstons and Wadworths 6X *(Sue Corrigan, Bill Ryan)*

Bollington [foot of White Nancy end of Kerridge Hill — OS Sheet 118 map reference 937772], *Redway*: Converted cottages with old-time flavour, in particularly attractive spot — tables outside give view over Cheshire; free house, bar food, restaurant *(G T Jones)*

☆ **Bollington Cross** [SJ9277], *Cock & Pheasant*: Recently modernised and spaciously extended old Boddingtons pub, now popular for good value food in attractive dining room; relaxed atmosphere, well kept bitter, nice dark wood decor, beams, log fire, antique prints; pleasant family lounge, plenty of tables in garden, back playground *(Brian and Anna Marsden, Keith Mills, Adam and Elizabeth Gorb)*

Bosley [Leek Rd (A523); SJ9266], *Harrington Arms*: Lively local open for early evening food with Hartleys and Robinsons beers; some refurbishing might not go amiss *(Keith W Mills)*; *Queens Head*: Good Boddingtons, good ham sandwiches and

main meals *(Greenwood and Turner)*

Bradfield Green [A530 NW of Crewe; SJ6859], *Coach & Horses*: Good-looking building with fine atmosphere, bar food, Greenalls Bitter, Mild and Original on handpump, games area, restaurant *(P Corris)*

Buglawton [A54; SJ8763], *Church House*: Good Robinsons, good food, growing farm tool collection *(Greenwood and Turner)*

☆ **Burleydam** [A525 Whitchurch—Audlem; SJ6143], *Combermere Arms*: Wide choice of good bar food inc sandwiches, game, steaks and vegetarian dishes in attractive 16th-century village pub by open fields, lots of fine woodwork, leaded windows, comfortable wall seating and other chairs, pretty carpet; Bass, Marstons Pedigree, Springfield and Youngers on handpump, welcoming staff, open fires, restaurant; said to be haunted *(Mike and Wendy Proctor, Martin Aust)*

☆ **Burtonwood** [Alder Lane; 3 miles from M62 junction 9, signed from A49 towards Newton-le-Willows — OS Sheet 108 map reference 585930; SJ5692], *Fiddle i'th' Bag*: Three comfortable and spacious areas with many alcoves, brassware, pottery and lots of stuffed animals; popular lunchtime for good food inc fine hot-pot and good cold table; friendly staff, tables outside — unusually peaceful setting by canal and riverside *(Lee Goulding, Roderic Plinston)*

☆ **Butley Town** [A523 Macclesfield—Stockport; SJ9177], *Ash Tree*: Refurbished as family pub/restaurant, but done well, keeping three-room layout; friendly staff, good range of well cooked bar food inc splendid lunchtime buffet with fine ploughman's, hot dishes, daily specials; popular restaurant; nice winter coal fires, well kept Boddingtons on handpump, comfortable atmosphere *(Andy and Jill Kassube, Tony and Pat Young, LYM)*

☆ **Chester** [Watergate St], *Custom House*: Popular old pub with interesting three-room layout, lunchtime snacks, Marstons Mild, Bitter, Exhibition and Pedigree, efficient service, good evening atmosphere, fruit machine in lounge *(Sue Holland and Dave Webster, Mr and Mrs P A Jones, Mr and Mrs J H Adam)*

☆ **Chester** [Park St (by Roman Walls, off Albion St)], *Albion*: Another interesting three-room pub by city wall, carefully refurbished to keep Victorian character; good value generous lunchtime food, well kept Greenalls, masses of wartime memorabilia *(Jon Wainwright, Derek and Sylvia Stephenson, Mr and Mrs P A Jones)*

☆ **Chester** [1 Russell St, down steps off City Rd], *Old Harkers Arms*: Converted Victorian canalside building with several changing real ales (not cheap) such as Batemans, Boddingtons, Oak, Pendle Witches Brew and Thwaites, interesting malt whiskies, good choice of enterprising food; lots of bric-a-brac inc clock, piano, accordian, sepia nudes and a pile of books; very lively in the evening with super-efficient friendly staff, quiet lunchtime *(Graham*

Gibson, Andrew and Kathy Porter)

☆ **Chester** [Tower Wharf, Raymond St — behind Northgate St, nr rly], *Telfords Warehouse*: Another converted warehouse, popular and spacious, with big windows overlooking Shrops Union Canal basin; blond furniture, well kept Theakstons XB, Youngers IPA and Scotch (not cheap), bar food inc up to three dozen different cheeses at lunchtime; steps down to cellar wine bar (with decent wines), steps up to restaurant area; trad jazz Sun lunchtime, Tues evening *(Graham Gibson, Derek and Sylvia Stephenson, Terry Buckland)*

Chester [Garden Lane (off A540)], *Bouverie*: Well kept and well priced Greenalls, friendly locals and delightful staff *(T Buckland)*; [Lower Bridge St], *Clavertons*: Heavy beams, lots of nooks and crannies, concentration on wide range of well priced wines by the glass but well kept Lees Bitter and Moonraker too; interesting choice of quickly served bar food inc vegetarian dishes; impressive Georgian columned entrance leads also to antique market; juke box or piped music — popular with young people particularly at weekends; open all day *(Mr and Mrs J H Adam)*; [Westgate Row N, Watergate St], *Deva*: Pleasantly restored Greenalls pub in fine medieval building nr shops, good cheap quick bar food *(George Mitchell)*; [1 Liverpool Rd], *George & Dragon*: Promising under new father-and-son team, bar lunches seven days, good value steakhouse *(E G Parish)*; [Parkgate Rd — just off A540], *Good Intent*: In big garden of Mollington Banastre hotel but quite separate, with good food and service, several ales tapped from the cask *(E G Parish)*; [Lower Bridge St], *Kings Head*: Black and white timbered 17th-century inn with original woodwork, bar a pleasant meeting-place (may be busy evenings), with well kept Davenports on handpump and fruit machine; open all day, can get crowded evenings; eight bedrooms, some with four-posters *(Patrick Godfrey, T Buckland)*; [Northgate St], *Pied Bull*: Clean and comfortable with well kept Greenalls Original, lunchtime food, charming staff and contented customers *(Terry Buckland, G T Jones)*

☆ **Christleton** [Laneside (off A41); SJ4466], *Ring o' Bells*: Very civilised spacious lounge, popular with more mature couples; upmarket decor with settees, elegant tables, old prints, longcase clock; good food inc sandwiches and vegetarian lasagne, Bass and Stones on handpump; car park, some spaces reserved for disabled people *(E McCracken, M Joyner)*

Cotebrook [A49; SJ5865], *Fox & Barrel*: Friendly staff, welcoming fire, genuine hunting decorations, cosy corners and larger rooms, Greenalls Bitter tapped from the cask, good range of bar food inc flamboyant puddings, children's meals and baby foods, unobtrusive piped music *(F and J Hamer)*

☆ **Crewe** [Nantwich Rd (A534) opp rly stn; SJ7056], *Crewe Arms*: Quietly comfortable

spacious lounge tastefully decorated with Victorian pictures, marble-topped tables, alabaster female figures, curtained recesses, ornate ceiling; well kept Tetleys, good reasonably priced bar meals, welcoming atmosphere, helpful friendly staff, good parking; open all day; bedrooms *(Peter Argent, E G Parish)*

Daresbury [Old Chester Rd; SJ5983], *Ring o' Bells*: Comfortable inn with good choice of reasonably priced good food, well kept Greenalls Original and Mild on handpump, garden; Alice-in-Wonderland window — Lewis Carroll's father was vicar here; bedrooms *(W K Wilkinson, E G Parish)*

Dean Row [SJ8781], *Unicorn*: Consistently good food, seats outside; no dogs or children *(Mr and Mrs B Hobden)*

☆ **Delamere** [A54/B5152; SJ5669], *Fishpool*: Friendly new landlord and Welsh wife in bright, comfortable and attractive country pub with four small rooms, bottle collection, plates and brasses; good range of bar food, Greenalls Mild and Bitter on handpump; pleasantly placed nr Delamere Forest *(Graham Gibson, Mr and Mrs J H Adam, Chris Walling)*

Disley [Buxton Rd; E end of village, opp school; SJ9784], *Crescent*: Comfortable, friendly local with good value food inc a few more exotic specials under newish landlord *(Keith Mills)*; [Mudhurst Lane; Higher Disley, off old Buxton rd; SJ9784], *Moorside*: Big hotel with own small golf course, but does have well kept beer (at a price) and dining area as distinct from restaurant *(Bernard Phillips)*; [7 Buxton Old Rd], *Mousetrap*: Good straightforward bar lunches inc attractive sandwiches and excellent fry-up *(Glenda Jones)*

Duddon [A51 NW of Tarporley; SJ5265], *Headless Woman*: Useful country pub, not over-modernised, with impression of several little rooms, old timbers worked into walls, adequate food, Greenalls Bitter *(Graham Gibson, G T Jones)*

Foxtwist Green [nr Whitegate; SJ6268], *Plough*: Pleasant old building with several rooms, good service, Robinsons; popular with businessmen and OAPs lunchtime for above-average food; nr Whitegate Way (disused railway track) and other pleasant walks *(G T Jones)*

☆ **Gawsworth** [SJ8969], *Harrington Arms*: Basic farm pub with wood-screened narrow roomlets with fine carved bar counter; well kept Robinsons Best and Best Mild on handpump, simple food; tree-trunk tables outside *(LYM)*

Glazebury [SJ6796], *Foresters Arms*: Welcoming, comfortable and snug *(John Broughton)*

☆ **Goostrey** [Station Rd (towards A535); SJ7870], *Olde Red Lion*: Comfortable and attractive modernised open-plan bar, generally good bar food inc good ploughman's, friendly efficient service, Robinsons and Tetleys on handpump, unobtrusive piped music, restaurant, nice garden with play area; children welcome

(Steve Mitcheson, Anne Collins, H B Vanstone, G D and J A Amos, G T Jones, Roger Braithwaite, LYM)

Gorstage [Millington Lane; off A49 W of Northwich; SJ6173], *Oaklands*: Attractive rural inn with fair amount of land, country-house feel, meals, Theakstons Old Peculier; bedrooms *(Graham Gibson)*

☆ **Grappenhall** [nr M6 junction 20; A50 towards Warrington, left after 1 1/2 miles — OS Sheet 109 map reference 638863; SJ6486], *Parr Arms*: Friendly pub with good bar lunches (not Sun) inc notable ploughman's — its three very clean small rooms quickly fill; copper, pottery, coats-of-arms of defunct counties; pleasant spot by village church *(John Watson, C F Walling)*

Great Budworth [A559, about 4 miles from M56 junction 10 — OS Sheet 118 map reference 656778; SJ6578], *Cock*: Pleasant, busy country pub, two snugly traditional front rooms, with Greenalls Original on handpump; big back dining room with country views; lots of young people at weekends *(Lee Goulding)*

Hartford [SJ6472], *Red Lion*: Very nicely run, with good food — their scalloped potatoes are a great change from chips *(Wyn and Syd Donald)*

Haslington [A534 Crewe—Sandbach; SJ7456], *Hawk*: 15th-century, with low beams and brasses, Robinsons ales, bar food inc several daily specials and good puddings *(C F Walling)*

☆ **Hatchmere** [B5152; off A556 at Abbey Arms; SJ5672], *Carriers*: Refurbished pub with reasonably priced food lunchtime and evening, well kept Burtonwood Bitter and Mild on handpump; pleasant new landlord settling in well, but shame about the video game in split-level lounge with its heavy-horse prints and old brewery photographs; attractive garden leading down to lake, handy for Delamere Forest walks *(Graham Gibson, C A Wilkes, P Corris, C F Walling, G T Jones, Mr and Mrs J H Adam)*

Hatton [Hatton Lane; SJ6082], *Hatton Arms*: Quaint village pub with plush seats and winter fire in welcoming, homely lounge, dominoes, darts and cribbage in tap room, Greenalls beers, pleasant service, chatty locals *(Ian and Sue Brocklebank, Robert Timmis)*

Haughton Moss [Long Lane; off A49 S of Tarporley; SJ5856], *Nags Head*: Tiny old country pub with plain home cooking in side area, decent wine (wrongly located by us at Houghton Green in 1991 edition) *(W C M Jones)*

Heatley [Mill Lane; SJ7088], *Railway*: Old original railway pub with good bar food, superbly kept Boddingtons on handpump, friendly licensees *(A Gough)*

☆ **Higher Burwardsley** [off A41 S of Chester via Tattenhall or A534 via Harthill — OS Sheet 117 map reference 523566; SJ5256], *Pheasant*: A lovely place to stay, with comfortable bedrooms, beautiful views,

pleasant longish walks straight from the door and good fire in cosy restaurant; the bar with its open fire and attractive furnishings and decorations has been much enjoyed, too, but this last year there have been one or two signs of complacency on the food and service side — we hope only a temporary lapse, as on form (despite a newish food service area which is not to everyone's taste) this can be one of the nicest pubs in the county; at start of GWG72 *(D W Huebner, G W H Kerby, Julian Proudman, LYM; more reports please)*

☆ **Higher Whitley** [1 1/4 miles from M56 junction 10; A559 towards Northwich; SJ6280], *Birch & Bottle*: Clean and well decorated, with interesting prints and other memorabilia, open fires, well kept Greenalls Mild, Bitter and Original, polite, helpful and friendly staff, and wide range of decent reasonably priced bar food from first-class sandwiches up, attractively furnished conservatory; children allowed if eating, till 8.30 *(M J Ridgway, C F Walling, Roy Cove, Hugh Saddington, Andy and Jill Kassube, LYM)*

Hooton [A41; SJ3678], *Chimneys*: Handsome Gothic-style hotel with new conservatory, Bass on handpump from fine new bar made of handsome American wood with lovely brass footrest; grill room, dining room for residents. *(Graham Gibson, Mr and Mrs J H Adam)*

Kelsall [Chester Rd (A54); SJ5268], *Morris Dancer*: Clean and comfortable, with good food in bar and tapas extension, well kept Greenalls *(Mr and Mrs J H Adam)*

Knutsford [Tatton St; off A50 at White Bear roundabout; SJ7578], *Lord Eldon*: Compact former coaching inn, full of character, with Watneys-related and guest real ales, food inc vegetarian menu *(E G Parish)*; [Canute Pl], *White Bear*: Eye-catching black-and-white pub, immaculate inside with good select atmosphere, comfortable chairs on thick carpet, speciality pies, Greenalls beers *(E G Parish)*

☆ **Little Bollington** [A56, about 3 miles E of Lymm; SJ7286], *Olde No 3*: Cosy old pub with good atmosphere, coal fire; varied choice of good food, generous helpings, John Smiths beer; by Bridgewater Canal *(C F Walling, G T Jones, Bill Ryan)*

☆ **Little Bollington** [2 miles from M56 junction 7: A56 towards Lymm, then first right at Stamford Arms into Park Lane — use A556 to get back on to M56 westbound; SJ7286], *Swan With Two Nicks*: Beamed village pub with lots of brass, copper and other bric-a-brac, snug alcoves, antique settles in back room, log fire, good home-cooked bar lunches (Sun very popular), well kept Whitbreads-related real ales, tables outside, attractive surroundings inc Dunham Hall deer park; no dogs or children *(Dr S D Page, RT, Simon Turner, LYM)*

☆ **Little Leigh** [A49 by swing bridge; SJ6276], *Leigh Arms*: Popular baronial-style mock-Tudor pub set back by River Weaver, limited choice of tasty and inexpensive bar food inc vegetarian dishes and steaks; friendly service, well kept Burtonwood and Forshaws, country wines, restaurant, tables outside; children allowed in eating area *(C F Walling, P Corris; news of new regime please)*

☆ **Lower Peover** [Crown Lane; B5081, off A50; SJ7474], *Crown*: Attractive L-shaped bar with two rooms off, lots of Wedgwood and other plates, guns, cartoons and other decorations; popular bar food, relaxing atmosphere, Boddingtons on handpump, dominoes, good service *(Graham Gibson, C F Walling, Steve Mitcheson, Anne Collins)*

☆ **Lymm** [Eagle Brow — nr M6 junction 20; SJ6787], *Spread Eagle*: Considerable atmosphere and character in spacious well furnished village pub with three distinct areas, well kept Lees on handpump, good home-made bar food, cheery regulars (especially in small music-free snug), juke box, weekly jazz; parking may be difficult *(G T Jones, A Gough, Alan and Marlene Radford, Mr and Mrs Simon Turner)*

☆ **Lymm** [A6144 — OS Sheet 109 map reference 684874], *Bulls Head*: Clean and friendly low-beamed pub doing well under new landlord, relaxed atmosphere, decent straightforward bar food, well kept Hydes Mild and Bitter, reasonable prices, friendly service, occasional live music; has been open all day — popular with canal users in summer *(G T Jones, Pauline Crossland, Dave Cawley, Bill Ryan)*

☆ *nr* **Macclesfield** [A537 some miles out towards Buxton — OS Sheet 119 map reference 001719; SK0071], *Cat & Fiddle*: Britain's 2nd-highest pub, surrounded by spectacular moorland (though on a trunk road), with magnificent views; spacious spotlessly kept lounge, roomy flagstoned public bar, Robinsons real ales, bar food inc good value scampi; gets busy lunchtime in summer *(F Teare, P A Crossland, D A Cawley, LYM)*

Marbury [OS Sheet 117 map reference 562457; SJ5645], *Swan*: Rustic dining pub popular for good bar food, friendly and efficient service *(W C M Jones, Mr and Mrs K Virgin)*

☆ **Marton** [Manchester Rd; A34 N of Congleton — OS Sheet 118 map reference 850682; SJ8568], *Davenport Arms*: Good choice of very good value food served piping hot, well kept Wilsons and a decent pot of tea in very clean and spaciously modernised pub with pleasant friendly staff *(Mr and Mrs B Hobden, G T Jones)*

☆ **Mobberley** [Town Lane; down hill from sharp bend on B5185 at E edge of 30mph limit; SJ7879], *Roebuck*: Spacious and pleasant open-plan bar with long pews on richly polished floorboards, well kept Watneys-related real ales from the handsome bar counter, generously served good value bar food, attentive service, restaurant, seats in cobbled courtyard and garden behind, play area; the popular licensee is French, his Cheshire wife does the cooking; children welcome *(Simon J Barber, LYM)*

Mobberley [Wilsons Mill Lane], *Bulls Head*: Friendly and comfortable low-beamed village pub with soft lighting, good value food, well kept Tetleys, folk-singing landlord and own immaculate bowling green *(Mr and Mrs D C Leaman, BB)*; [Ashley Rd, towards Altrincham], *Chapel House*: Pleasant service and well kept Boddingtons in relaxing panelled lounge and small games room with darts, seats in courtyard; nr stn *(Lee Goulding)*; [Mobberley Rd, opp church], *Church*: Friendly pub with good range of better-than-average bar meals inc generous ploughman's and good filled baked potatoes, Greenalls beers; tables in courtyard, big garden with play area, own bowling green; children welcome *(Roger Taylor, E G Parish)*; [Paddock Hill — small sign off B5085 Knutsford—Wilmslow, OS Sheet 118 map reference 815796], *Plough & Flail*: Small three-roomed pub with good food in bar and restaurant, log fire *(John Watson)*

Mouldsworth [Station Rd; SJ5171], *Goshawk*: Well kept Greenalls Original, big helpings of well priced food inc vegetarian dishes, good service, plush comfort and family room; worth knowing for location nr Delamere Forest and big outdoor area inc good play area and bowling green *(C F Walling)*

☆ **Nantwich** [Hospital St — by side passage to central church; SJ6552], *Lamb*: Fine flower-decked old pub with comfortably sedate and beautifully kept spacious bar, well kept Greenalls Original, nicely presented quickly served bar food, traditional dining room, attentive staff *(W C M Jones, the Shinkmans)*

Nantwich [Oat Mkt], *Union Vaults*: Really cheap food with bargain two-course meals for OAPs, Marstons real ales, nice comfortable atmosphere with high-backed seats; in pedestrian precinct but parking adjacent *(E G Parish)*

Norley [Pytchleys Hollow — OS Sheet 117 map reference 572727; SJ5773], *Tigers Head*: Pleasantly refurbished and well run 17th-century inn nr Delamere Forest; good range of bar food, Burtonwood ale *(Mr and Mrs J H Adam)*

Over Peover [off A50 S of Knutsford; SJ7674], *Parkgate*: Attractive collection of small rooms in friendly pub with above-average bar food *(John Broughton)*

☆ **Parkgate** [The Parade; SJ2878], *Red Lion*: Victorian local on attractive waterfront with friendly landlady, well kept Tetleys, generous sandwiches, lovely cast-iron tables and 19th-century paintings *(Jenny and Brian Seller, Tony and Lynne Stark, Mr and Mrs J H Adam)*

Parkgate, *Old Quay*: Comfortable Whitbreads seafront pub, modern decor, reasonably priced Brewers Fayre food *(George Mitchell)*; [The Parade], *Ship*: Good views of estuary from picture windows, friendly and efficient service, good local Old Oak beer, reasonably priced well cooked food inc local fish and vegetarian dishes

(Robert and Vicky Tod)
Pickmere [B5391 NE of Northwich; SJ6977], *Red Lion*: Pleasant old-world village pub with good value food, friendly service, good atmosphere *(Mr and Mrs D C Leaman)*

☆ **Pott Shrigley** [Spurley Lane — OS Sheet 118 map reference 945782; SJ9479], *Cheshire Hunt*: Small-roomed country pub, recently reopened with small neatly refurbished rooms, two roaring winter fires, bar food inc good starters, vegetarian and children's dishes (may also be served 5.20-7; later evening food more costly), Boddingtons or Marstons Pedigree on handpump, friendly staff, piped music; tables on flagstoned terrace with pasture views, play area *(Graham Simpson, C A Wilkes, Richard Parr, LYM)*

Prestbury [SJ9077], *Bridge*: Friendly welcoming staff especially kind to infirm, aged customers; good bar meals from a regularly changing menu, comfortable seating, wood panelling; bedrooms *(Jill and Peter Bickley)*

Puddington [Woodbank; A540 nr A550; SJ3373], *Yacht*: Pleasant atmosphere, well kept Greenalls and decent bar food inc good sandwiches; lounge bar *(Mr and Mrs J H Adam, E G Parish)*

Runcorn [Wellington St, Old Town; SJ5183], *Wellington*: Basic friendly pub with well kept Marstons Burton, really cheap butties *(Greenwood and Turner)*

Sandbach [Newcastle Rd; 1 1/4 miles from M6 junction 17; SJ7661], *Old Hall*: Now too hotelish for a main entry, and the bar now takes second place, but this attractive Jacobean place does have Ruddles Best on handpump, reasonably priced food; smart service, comfortable bedrooms *(E G Parish, LYM)*; [Newcastle Rd], *Olde Black Horse*: Unusual old black and white pub in partly cobbled square (market day Thurs), with lots of character and good value food *(E G Parish)*

Stockton Heath [Victoria Sq; SJ6285], *Victors*: Wine bar, worth knowing for good choice of superbly presented very well cooked food *(W K Wilkinson)*

Stretton [just off M56 junction 10; A559 towards Northwich; SJ6283], *Ring o' Bells*: Immaculate three-roomed beamed country pub with popular new landlord, Greenalls beers, sandwiches *(Graham Gibson)*

☆ **Styal** [Altrincham Rd; B5166 nr Ringway Airport; SJ8383], *Old Ship*: Friendly welcome from cheerful staff and good Ruddles County, Websters, and Wilsons ales; open all day. Good bar lunches inc succulent casseroles and puddings, well kept Watneys-related real ales, cheerful service; has been open all day; NT village with nice walks in riverside woods; nr start GWG74 *(Len Beattie, Peter and Helen Noke)*

☆ **Swettenham** [off A54 Congleton—Holmes Chapel or A535 Chelford—Holmes Chapel; SJ8067], *Swettenham Arms*: Latest news is that a former landlord has returned to re-emphasise the classic local character of this prettily placed village pub, with well kept real ales and polished traditional furnishings in carefully restored beamed bar; bar food *(LYM; more reports please)*

Tarporley [A49/A51, a mile S; SJ5563], *Red Fox*: Spacious bar with pleasant conservatory, very rewarding bistro with helpful friendly service *(P J Taylor)*; [High St — village signposted off A49], *Swan*: Comfortably refurbished Georgian inn with well kept Greenalls on handpump, wide choice of bar food, restaurant, tables in pleasant garden, provision for children; comfortable and well equipped bedrooms *(Mr and Mrs P A Jones, W C M Jones, P J Taylor, LYM)*

Thelwall [B5157, nr M6 junction 20; SJ6587], *Pickering Arms*: Fine atmosphere in attractive low-beamed village pub with cobbled forecourt, good reasonably priced bar food lunchtime and evening, Greenalls Bitter and Mild and Stones on handpump; children allowed if eating *(P Corris)*

Tiverton [Wharton's Lock; Bates Mill Lane — OS Sheet 117 map reference 532603; SJ5660], *Shady Oak*: Worth knowing for its lovely position in open countryside by Shropshire Union Canal, with fine views to Beeston Castle, plenty of seats and good play area in waterside garden and terrace; basic bar, airy and comfortable lounge opening into carpeted conservatory, well kept Watneys-related real ales; juke box may be rather loud, service can slow when very busy, but food seems to be coming back into the reckoning; summer barbecues *(Mr and Mrs D C Leaman, the Shinkmans, J R Jewitt, Martin Aust)*

☆ **Walker Barn** [A537 Macclesfield—Buxton; SJ9573], *Setter Dog*: Remote and attractive extended moorland pub with fine bleak and windswept view; plain but pleasant inside, with well kept Marstons, reasonable choice of good food in small bar and restaurant, good service, roaring fire; handy for Teggs Nose Country Park *(G T Jones, P Grimshaw)*

Walleys Green [Wimboldsley; A530 Middlewich—Crewe, about 200 yds from main rly line — OS Sheet 118 map reference 684621; SJ6861], *Verdin Arms*: Pleasant inside, with meals lunchtime and evening, quiet atmosphere, Robinsons beers; small restaurant *(P Corris)*

Warrington [Winwick Rd (A49); SJ5686], *Lord Rodney*: Outstanding choice of real ales for area, such as Batemans, Friary Meux Best, Jennings, Robinsons, Tetleys Dark Mild and Bitter and Walkers; some eye-catching features *(Graham Gibson)*; [27 Buttermarket St], *Lower Angel*: Welcoming little two-bar pub, with two big pluses: besides his well kept tied Walkers beer, landlord gets through about ten barrels of interesting guest beers a week, with customer questionnaires moulding the choice; and he lets you bring in sandwiches from the excellent next-door bakery *(Ian and Sue Brocklebank, Greenwood and Turner)*; [Ballater Dr, Cinnamon Brow, New Town], *Millhouse*: Very low prices for both lunchtime food and Holts Mild and Bitter *(Greenwood and Turner)*

☆ nr **Warrington** [Fiddlers Ferry; leaving Warrington on A562 towards Widnes, keep eyes open as you pass Harris Carpets in Penketh then turn left by Red Lion Cavalier Restaurant (Tetleys); in Tannery Lane turn left again into Station Rd, park by rly and walk across — about 50 yds — OS Sheet 108 map reference 560863], *Ferry*: Picturesquely isolated between Manchester Ship Canal and Mersey, with comfortable easy chairs, old-fashioned settle and sofa as well as more modern seats in nautically decorated low-beamed bar, buffet bar food lunchtimes and Fri-Sat evenings, good river views, tables outside; provision for children, well kept Watneys-related real ales on handpump *(Alan and Marlene Radford, LYM)*

Wettenhall [SJ6261], *Boot & Slipper*: Small refurbished country pub with short choice of nicely presented bar food; dining room *(C F Walling, W C M Jones)*

☆ **Whiteley Green** [OS Sheet 118 map reference 924789; SJ9278], *Windmill*: Big prettily planted garden with summer bar and barbecues, spaciously modernised lounge, friendly helpful staff, good lunchtime bar food, well kept Boddingtons and Marstons Burton and Pedigree; provision for children; in attractive countryside nr Middlewood Way *(David Waterhouse, BB)*

☆ **Willaston** [Wistaton Rd — OS Sheet 117 map reference 329777; SJ3378], *Pollards*: Striking building based on 14th-century sandstone farmhouse, comfortable beamed and flagstoned bar, nice cushioned wall seats with some stone armrests; conservatory/lounge extension overlooking sizeable pleasant garden; Greenalls real ales, wide choice of good bar food, restaurant;

bedrooms *(Mr and Mrs J H Adam)*

Wilmslow [SJ8481], *King William*: Convenient for town centre, comfortably refurbished to keep small alcoves off bar; well kept Robinsons, choice of lunchtime snacks inc burger specialities, friendly atmosphere; children welcome *(Dave Irving)*

☆ **Wincle** [SU9666], *Ship*: Cosy and friendly 16th-century stonebuilt pub in nice spot with quaint little lounge and bar, well kept Boddingtons, Marstons Pedigree and maybe Courage Directors in summer, bar food, coal fire, comfortable family room with box of toys and fruit machine; tables in garden, nice Dane Valley walks, nr start GWG103; get there early weekends *(Tim Locke, Brian and Anna Marsden, D W Crossley, Greenwood and Turner, Mike and Wendy Proctor; more reports on new regime please)*

☆ **Wrenbury** [signed off A530 Nantwich—Whitchurch; SJ5948], *Dusty Miller*: Peaceful and attractive spot by Llangollen Canal, with big windows in; much modernised mill conversion, wide choice of bar food (not cheap), good no smoking area, well kept Hartleys XB and Robinsons, piped music, upstairs restaurant (not Sun evening); open noon-11, shorter winter hours; tables outside; children in restaurant *(J R Jewitt, P Craddock, Dave and Becky Killick, Robert and Kate Hodkinson, B and D Sowter, LYM)*

Wybunbury [Main Rd (B5071) — OS Sheet 118 map reference 699499; SJ6950], *Swan*: Charmingly placed by churchyard, with seats in garden, and in last edition a main entry for interesting food and good atmosphere; but tenant left summer 1991, taking his collection of unusual decorations — news of the new regime, please *(LYM)*

Cleveland   *see* Northumbria

Cornwall

Food in Cornish pubs has now improved strikingly. In the past, the county did not shine as a good place for pub food, but those days seem to be over. We'd now pick out in this department the beautifully placed Old Ferry at Bodinnick (good evening meals), the welcoming and unusual Cobweb in Boscastle (particularly low prices), the engaging Crows Nest up in the moorside village of that name, the enviable waterside Shipwrights Arms at Helford (particularly its summer cold table), the spotless and friendly Red Lion at Mawnan Smith (a new entry), the interesting Miners Arms at Mithian (lots of changes this year), the Victoria at Perranuthnoe (welcome back in the Guide after an absence), the Roseland at Philleigh (doing well all round), the popular and lively Blue Peter on Polperro harbour, the Lugger in a lovely spot at Portloe (another new entry), the friendly Crown at St Ewe (new restaurant this year), the fascinating Eliot Arms at Tregadillett (doing particularly well at the moment), the stylish Inn for all Seasons at Treleigh and the friendly and historic Wheel at Tresillian. Other pubs to mention particularly include two more new entries, the harbourside Lugger at Polruan and the unspoilt St Kew Inn, attractively set in the hamlet of that name; the Blue Anchor in Helston and Min Pin near Tintagel – sharply contrasting styles in pubs brewing their own beers; and the Heron at Malpas, Ship at Mousehole, Pandora near Mylor Bridge, Rashleigh Inn at Polkerris, Port Gaverne Hotel near Port Isaac (a lovely place to stay), Ship at Porthleven and Rising Sun in St Mawes – superb waterside positions. Other pubs here currently doing particularly well are the London Inn not far from Padstow harbour, the relaxed and friendly Turks Head in Penzance, the quietly friendly Old Inn at St Breward (the county's highest pub) and the warmly welcoming Logan Rock at Treen. In the Lucky Dip section at the end of the chapter current stars, almost all of them inspected by us, include the Napoleon in Boscastle, Cadgwith Cove at Cadgwith, Chain Locker and Kings Head among a fine choice of pubs in Falmouth, White Hart at Ludgvan, Royal Oak at Perranwell, Golden Lion in Port Isaac, Five Pilchards at Porthallow, Who'd Have Thought It at St Dominick, Falcon at St Mawgan, White Hart at St Teath, Long Cross at Trelights and Tinners Arms at Zennor; Truro has a decent choice of reliably good pubs. On the Isles of Scilly, the Turks Head on St Agnes stands out; the Atlantic on St Marys and New Inn on Tresco are also well recommended. A general point to watch in Cornwall is that Cornish Breweries/Devenish have now stopped brewing; their beers come from the national Whitbreads.

BODINNICK   SX1352   Map 1

Old Ferry Inn

The view from the bedrooms in this old inn is lovely – down the steep hillside and out over the River Fowey. There are three simply furnished little bar rooms – at one end there's a huge stuffed pike, a big clock and model ship, and the middle room has an old high-backed settle, mates chairs, built-in green leatherette wall seats, a gas fire, local photographs, a 44lb salmon in a glass case, and darts; a games room at the back – that actually burrows into rock at one end – has a window bench, a stag's head on one wall, and darts, shove-ha'penny, cribbage, dominoes, fruit machine and a television. Piped music. Bar food includes sandwiches (from £1; toasties 5p extra), soup or tasty pasties (£1.20), good ploughman's (from £2.75), and local ham (£4); decent breakfasts and very good evening meals in the dining room (3 courses £14.50); well kept Flowers Original and St Austell Tinners and a guest beer on handpump. Make sure your brakes work well if you park on the steep lane outside. The Hall Walk starts just above the village. *(Recommended by E A Simmons, E Fieldhouse, Freddy Costello, Jutta Whitley)*

Free house   Licensee Simon Farr   Real ale   Snacks   Evening restaurant   Polruan (0726) 870237   Children welcome   Open 11–3, 6–11; 12–2.30, 7–11 in winter   Bedrooms; £29(£35.50B)/£56(£71B)

BOSCASTLE   SX0990 Map 1

Cobweb £

B3263, just E of harbour

The atmosphere counts for a lot here – as does the warm welcome and good value food. The big bar has a lovely log fire, two or three curved high-backed winged settles against the dark stone walls, a few leatherette dining chairs, flagstones, and hundreds of old bottles hanging from the heavy beams. Quickly served, good value bar food includes sandwiches (from 90p, crab or prawn £2.40), soup (£1.30), ploughman's or basket meals (from £2), salads (from £3), lasagne (£3.75), gammon steak (£7), and steak (£7.50); daily specials and some vegetarian dishes. Well kept Bass, Exmoor Gold, St Austell Tinners, HSD, XXXX on handpump, with occasional guest beers; friendly service. Good juke box, darts, pool table (keen players here), video game, and fruit machine; the big communicating family room has an enormous armchair carved out of a tree trunk as well as its more conventional Windsor armchairs, and another cosy winter fire. Opening off this a good-sized children's room has a second pool table, and more machines. The tiny steeply-cut harbour nearby is very attractive, as is the main village climbing up above. *(Recommended by Genie and Brian Smart, John and Joan Calvert, David Heath, Barbara Wensworth, Sandra and Dave Price, Dr S E Martin, Dr L B Cook, H K Dyson, Helena and Arthur Harbottle, ACP, Richard Houghton, Mrs R Horridge, William D Cissna, C M Whitehouse, Nick Dowson, Alison Hayward)*

Free house   Licensee Ivor Bright   Real ale   Meals and snacks (11–2.30, 6–10) Restaurant (not Sun evening)   Boscastle (0840) 250278   Children in own room   Live entertainment Sat evening   Open 11–3, 6–11 (midnight Sat)

CHAPEL AMBLE   SW9975 Map 1

Maltsters Arms

Village signposted from A39 NE of Wadebridge; and from B3314

At its best, the food here can be really enjoyable: over the last year or two, dishes which have won particular approval from readers include the home-made soup (£1.95), ploughman's (£2.10 with decent West Country cheeses, nicely presented), chicken and ham pie (£3.95), sea bream, and lobster; also, moules marinière (£3.95) and evening dishes like popular veal (£8.55), 12 oz Aberdeen Angus steak (£9.45), and fresh local shellfish platter (£19.50), with puddings like treacle tart; they don't take table reservations. Ruddles County, Ushers Best and changing guest beers on handpump, kept under light blanket pressure. The rooms of the busy main bar have black oak joists in the white ceiling, partly panelled stripped stone walls, heavy wooden tables on the partly carpeted big flagstones, and a large stone fireplace; there's also a side room with Windsor chairs. Pool, dominoes, trivia, and piped music. Benches outside in a sheltered sunny corner. The local hunt meets here twice a year. *(Recommended by Martyn and Mary Mullins, T Nott, Alan and Sue*

Foulkes, Mr and Mrs R Gammon, Chris Newman, Deb Jay, H K Dyson, A K Ogilvie, C M
Whitehouse, Iain and Penny Muir)

*Free house   Licensees Jeffrey Pollard and Michael Munds   Real ale   Meals and
snacks   Wadebridge (0208) 812473   Children in eating area of bar   Occasional live
entertainment   Open 11–3, 6–11; winter lunchtime closing 2.30*

CONSTANTINE   SW7229   Map 1
Trengilly Wartha

Constantine signposted from Penryn–Gweek rd (former B3291); in village turn right just
before Minimarket (towards Gweek); in nearly a mile pub signposted left; at Nancenoy,
OS sheet 204, map reference 731282

Not far from the Helford River and tucked away on a quiet hillside, this pleasant
inn keeps a surprisingly wide choice of beers for the area: Courage Directors,
Exmoor, Fullers, St Austell and Theakstons tapped from the cask; also, local farm
cider, over 90 wines, 25 whiskies, overproof rums and many 'guest' drinks. The
low-beamed bar has an open woodburning stove with a built-in curved settle
beside it, modern high-backed settles facing each other across polished heavy
wooden tables, and – up a step – an eating area with some winged settles and
tables. Bar food includes home-made soup with home-made granary bread (£1.50),
pasties (from £1.60), filled baked potatoes (from £2), lunchtime ploughman's
(from £3.50), good calves' liver with mashed parsnips, vegetable pie (£4), salads
(from £4; dressed crab £7.50), a daily pasta dish (£4.40), 10oz sirloin steak (£9),
and daily specials like venison sausage (£3), seafood strudel (£4) or grilled Dover
sole (£8); home-made puddings such as gooseberry and apple crumble or rhubarb
and lemon tart (from £1.70). A cosy lounge has machine-tapestried wall benches, a
log fire and some harness, and a spacious front games room has darts, pool, bar
billiards, shove-ha'penny, cribbage, dominoes, shut-the-box, backgammon, fruit
machine, and video game. The attractive garden has some picnic-table sets.
*(Recommended by R and P F Shelton, Richard Houghton, Tim Barrow, Sue Demont, C A
Foden, G Atkinson, Tom Bowen, Charles and Mary Winpenny, Drs M and K Parier, Mr and
Mrs B E Witcher)*

*Free house   Licensees Nigel Logan, Michael Maguire   Real ale   Meals and snacks
(12–2.15, 6.30–9.30)   Restaurant (evening)   Falmouth (0326) 40332   Children in
family room and eating area of bar   Monthly summer Thurs live music   Open
11–3(2.30 winter), 6–11   Bedrooms; £32(£38B)/£38(£47B)*

CROWS NEST   SX2669   Map 1
Crows Nest

Signposted off B3264 N of Liskeard; or pleasant drive from A30 by Siblyback/St Cleer
rd from Bolventor, turning left at Common Moor, Siblyback signpost, then forking right
to Darite; OS Sheet 201 map reference 263692

The warm log fire here is very welcome on a cold, misty day when the old ruins of
the engine houses on the hills overlooking the hamlet can seem rather spooky.
There are bowed dark oak beams hung with lots of stirrups, bits and spurs, an
interesting table converted from a huge blacksmith's bellows (which still works)
and other polished tables, and an unusually long black wall settle by the big
fireplace as well as other more orthodox seats. On the right, and divided by a
balustered partition, is a similar area with old local photographs and maybe
flowers on the tablecloths. Bar food includes local fresh dressed crab salad (£4.50),
home-made cottage or steak and kidney pies, local whole plaice (£6), excellent
large gammon, and home-made puddings like treacle pudding, spotted dog
(£1.50) or lovely fresh pavlovas (£2.50). Well kept St Austell Tinners and HSD on
handpump; darts, dominoes, euchre, juke box, and fruit machine; helpful, friendly
service. On the terrace by the quiet lane there are picnic-table sets. *(Recommended by
R L Turnham, Martyn and Mary Mullins, Ian Phillips, John Kirk, David and Sarah Gilmore,
Charles and Mary Winpenny)*

St Austell   Tenant T W C Rosser   Real ale   Meals and snacks   Liskeard (0579) 45930   Children in eating area of bar   Open 11.30–11

HELFORD   SW7526 Map 1

Shipwrights Arms ★ Ⓟ

Off B3293 S of Helston

The waterside position here is lovely with terraces dropping down among flowers and palm trees to the creek's edge, and on summer evenings there are barbecues with prawns and steaks, and burgers for children. The top part of the terrace is roofed over with Perspex. Inside, yachtsmen congregate under the low shiny ochre ceiling by the bar counter and there are shark fishing photographs, lots of ship models and navigation lamps, sea pictures, drawings of lifeboat coxwains, and a collection of foreign banknotes behind the bar. At the other end, a dining area has oak settles, tables and waitress service; an open fire in winter. The very good summer cold table includes ploughman's and excellent crab and prawn and you can help yourself to as much (or as little) of the wide-ranging salads as you want (from £3.25); also, winter home-made hot dishes like lasagne or steak and kidney pie (£4), and evening beef in wine (£6.25). Well kept Flowers, Marstons Pedigree and a guest beer on handpump, and a decent choice of wines. Piped music. It does get very busy at peak times. *(Recommended by K Flack, Keith Stevens, Iain and Penny Muir, Gwen and Peter Andrews, Carol and Richard Glover, Mrs S M Judge, Bob Smith, H K Dyson, Ewan and Moira McCall, Wayne Stocuton, Brian Skelcher, Nick Dowson, Alison Hayward, Cliff and Karen Spooner, Steve Dark, Joan and Michael Melling, Drs M and K Parier)*

Cornish Brewery (Whitbreads)   Lease: Brandon Flynn and Charles Herbert   Real ale Meals and snacks (not Sun or Mon evenings in winter); tel Manaccan (032 623) 235 Children in eating area   Parking only right outside the village in summer   Open 11–2.30, 6–11

HELSTON   SW6527 Map 1

Blue Anchor

50 Coinagehall Street

The 15th-century brewhouse here is probably the oldest in the country and is still used to produce the Medium, Best, 'Spingo' Special and Extra Special ales at very reasonable prices – you are usually welcome to look around the brewhouse and cellar at lunchtime. A series of small, low-ceilinged rooms open off the central corridor with simple old-fashioned furniture on the flagstones, interesting old prints, some bared stone walls, and in one room a fine inglenook fireplace; a family room has video game, fruit machines, darts, dominoes and cards. Toasties (from 80p), pasties (£1), and ploughman's or pizzas (£1.50). Past this, and an old stone bench in the sheltered little terrace area is a skittle alley which has its own bar at busy times. The nearby Flambards Triple Theme Park has a lot of family attractions, and Godolphin House is well worth visiting. *(Recommended by Julian Proudman, Richard Houghton, H K Dyson, Carol Mason, Nick Dowson, Alison Hayward, Nigel Gibbs, Sandra Cook, David and Sarah Gilmore, Reg Nelson)*

Own brew   Licensees Sidney and Patricia Cannon   Real ale   Snacks   Helston (0326) 562821   Children in family room   Parking sometimes difficult   Open 11–3, 6–11, though they may open longer on Sat afternoons

LANNER   SW7240 Map 1

Fox & Hounds

Comford; junction A393/B3293; OS sheet 204 map reference 734399

This pretty white house has several warm and comfortable rambling areas with black beams and joists, some stripped stonework and dark panelling, greeny gold plush or deep pink cloth banquettes on the red carpet, and comical 1920s prints by

Lawson Wood; a woodburning stove in one granite fireplace, logs burning in another, and lots of summer flowers. A good range of bar food includes good soup, sandwiches (from £1.10), salads (local crab in season), first-rate whole lemon sole, gammon (£5.20), sirloin steak (£6.95), and puddings (from £1.65), with daily specials (£3.95). Well kept Bass and St Austell BB, Tinners and HSD tapped from the cask; fast, friendly service. Darts, fruit machine, juke box and piped music (in the restaurant). Outside is pretty, with hanging baskets and tubs of flowers, picnic-table sets on the front terrace, and more by swings and a climber on a sheltered and neatly kept back lawn. *(Recommended by R A Corbett, Dr Philip Putwain, Charles and Mary Winpenny, David and Sarah Gilmore, J C Proud, D J Devey)*

St Austell   Tenant Coral Snipp   Real ale   Meals and snacks (12–2, 7–10)   Children in eating area of bar and restaurant until 8.30   Restaurant   St Day (0209) 820251 Open 11–3, 6–11; 11–11 mid July–mid Sept; closed evening 25 Dec

LERRYN   SX1457 Map 1

Ship

Village signposted from A390 in Lostwithiel

The extended, partly no-smoking lounge bar in this attractively placed pub has old village photographs and trophies on the walls, brasses on beams, and a locally made grandfather clock; an old settle and table are virtually reserved for their longest serving customer. Home-made bar food includes sandwiches, pies like cheese and leek, Italian fennel, turkey and asparagus and steak and oyster, as well as chicken with honey and orange, and beef escoril. Well kept Bass, Courage Best, Eldridge Pope Hardy, Fergusons Dartmoor, and Wadworths 6X on handpump, and local farm cider; a separate room has sensibly placed darts, pool, dominoes, cribbage, fruit machines, and piped music. In front of the stone building by the flower borders, tubs and hanging baskets there are some picnic-table sets, with more on a sheltered back lawn which also has a children's play area. You can walk along the bank of the River Lerryn or through the National Trust woodland nearby. There is a self-catering flat for rent. *(Recommended by TBB, R L Turnham, Peter Watkins, Pam Stanley, R Elliott)*

Free house   Licensee Howard Packer   Real ale   Meals and snacks   Bodmin (0208) 872374   Children welcome   Open 11.30–3(2.30 winter), 6–11

LOSTWITHIEL   SX1059 Map 1

Royal Oak

Duke St; pub easily visible from A390 in centre

As well as an unusual range of real ales for Cornwall such as Bass, Flowers Original and IPA, Fullers London Pride, Marstons Pedigree and two or three guest beers on handpump, this 13th-century town pub also has a good choice of bottled beers, and draught ciders. The well kept lounge has captains' chairs and brown leatherette button-back banquettes on its patterned carpet, a couple of wooden armchairs by the gas-effect log fire, and walls stripped back to the old reddish granite. There's also a delft china shelf, with a small dresser in one inner alcove; piped music. Generous helpings of reliable bar food include sandwiches (lunchtimes from £1.10), soup (£1.25), ploughman's (lunchtimes from £2.35), basket meals (from £3.20), salads (from £3.50), broccoli and cream cheese pie (£3.75), steaks (from £6.75), very good scallops in cheese and white wine sauce (£6.95), and puddings (£1.35); children's (from £1.55). The flagstoned back public bar has darts, dominoes, cribbage, fruit machine and juke box, and younger customers. On a raised terrace by the car park, lined with cordylines, are some picnic-table sets. *(Recommended by H J Marchant, Kevin and Tracey Stephens, WHBM, Charles and Mary Winpenny, J M Fletcher, Peter Watkins, Pam Stanley, Roy McNeill)*

Free house   Licensees Malcolm and Eileen Hine   Real ale   Meals and snacks (12–2, 6.30–10)   Bodmin (0208) 872552   Children in restaurant   Open 11–3, 5.30–11 Bedrooms; £24(£26B)/£42(£46B)

MALPAS   SW8442 Map 1

Heron

Village signposted from A39 at main Truro roundabout

In warm weather, the slate-paved front terrace here is a popular place to eat, with its view over the wooded creek far below. The long, rectangular bar has an excellent collection of late 19th-century photographs of Truro and the surrounding countryside, brasses, bric-a-brac, and winter log fires. Good bar food includes generously filled sandwiches, pork satay or plaice goujons (£3.25), liver and bacon kebab with garlic bread (£3.95), home-made steak and kidney or turkey and ham pies (£4.25), mixed grill (£8.25), and home-made treacle tart (£1.75). Well kept St Austell Tinners and HSD on handpump; good service. Fruit machine, pool, video game, trivia and piped music. At weekends and in other busy periods, the pub can get exceedingly crowded – when nearby parking may not be easy (especially as there are double yellow lines outside the building). *(Recommended by P D Putwain, Charles Gurney, Patrick Young; more reports please)*

St Austell   Tenants Calvin and Anne Kneebone   Real ale   Meals and snacks   Truro (0872) 72773   Children welcome   Open 11–3, 6–11; 11.30–2.30, 7–10.30 in winter

MAWNAN SMITH   SW7728 Map 1

Red Lion

Off Penryn–Gweek rd (former B3291), via Budock Water, just W of Falmouth

Run by friendly young licensees, this spotless thatched village pub has several recently refurbished rooms that cluster around the central bar counter. The lounge has an unusual high ceiling, a warm woodburning stove in the big stone hearth at one end and another in the chimney stack at the other end, and some plates on the walls. A spacious, cream vertical planked public bar is decorated with local pictures, and fishing flies and rods, and the snug has harness and riding gear and more fishing tackle. Another small room, behind the restaurant, is no smoking. Generous helpings of good bar food at lunchtime include soup (£1.45), sandwiches (from £1.55), filled baked potatoes (from £1.75), ploughman's (from £2.85), ham and egg (£3.95), salads (from £3.95), and gammon steak (£6.50), with evening extras such as prawn and apple cocktail (£2.35) and lots of steaks (from £7.95); specials like moussaka (£3.95), steak and kidney pie (£4.25), and fresh local fish (from £6). Well kept Bass and Devenish JD and Cornish Original on handpump; newspapers to read. Darts, winter pool, dominoes, and fruit machine. Very clean lavatories. *(Recommended by Graham and Barbara Patrick, Hilary Roberts, Iain and Penny Muir)*

Devenish (Whitbreads)   Manager S P Galvin   Real ale   Meals and snacks Restaurant   Falmouth (0326) 250026   Children in eating area of bar   Occasional live music   Open 11–3, 6–11

METHERELL   SX4069 Map 1

Carpenters Arms

Village signposted from Honicombe, which is signposted from St Ann's Chapel, just W of Gunnislake on A390; pub signposted in village, OS Sheet 201, map reference 408694

Over the years little has changed in this 14th-century pub with its heavy black beams, massive stone walls, huge polished flagstones, and tiny windows. The friendly bar has a large slowly ticking clock, winged high-backed red leatherette settles in the various alcoves, brasses, and lots of succulent plants. A wide choice of bar food includes sandwiches (from £1.35), home-made soup (£1.60), excellent omelettes (from £2.90), vegetable curry (£3.95), good home-made steak and kidney pie (£4.75), puddings like home-made blackcurrant cake (£1.60), and children's dishes (£1.40). Well kept Bass, Flowers Original, Hoskins and Wadworths 6X on handpump or tapped from casks behind the bar, as well as good farm ciders and decent house white wine; piped music, sensibly placed darts, and fruit machine. Outside, by an old well, there are some sheltered tables. Cotehele, the lovely National Trust Tudor house by the head of the Tamar estuary, is a couple of miles further on through these narrow lanes. Please note, they no longer do bedrooms. (*Recommended by Brian and Anna Marsden, Philip and Trisha Ferris, John Kirk; more reports please*)

Free house   Licensees Douglas and Jill Brace   Real ale   Meals and snacks   Liskeard (0579) 50242   Children in eating area of bar   Open 11.30–2.30, 6.30–11

MITHIAN   SW7450 Map 1

Miners Arms ★ ⊘

By Easter 1992 the careful changes to this popular pub will have been completed. The atmospheric little back bar with its irregular beam and plank ceiling, bulging squint walls (one has a fine old wall painting of Elizabeth I), and a wood block floor won't change at all, nor will the cosy little room with its decorative low ceiling, lots of books and quite a few interesting ornaments. The kitchen is to be redeveloped and the lounge is to be extended to create more eating space – they are hoping to give the room the character back it lost during changes some years ago; one room is no smoking. The garden is to be landscaped, tables and a children's play area added, and the car park tarmacked. Though the choice of food here is not huge, it is of a very high quality and reasonably priced: sandwiches, soup (£1.75, wonderful home-made tomato soup with toasted garlic bread £1.80), tasty locally-made pasty (£2.05), exceptionally good ploughman's (from £3.25), crab bake with walnut bread (£3.50), popular garlic bread platter (camembert, plain garlic or tomato and basil breads, £3.95), vegetarian adzuki (£4.55), home-made steak and kidney, lamb and apple or smoked local fish pies (all £4.95), and sirloin steak (£8.25); home-made puddings like farmhouse crumble (£1.95) and children's dishes (£1.95). Well kept Cornish Original and Devenish JD on handpump, with guests like Flowers IPA and Marstons Pedigree, and farm cider; good, friendly service. Darts, pool, fruit machine and piped music; good winter fire. There are benches on the sheltered front cobbled terrace. (*Recommended by Mark Evans, Mr and Mrs D Devereux, Iain Heath, Ruth Davies, WHBM, Margo and Peter Thomas, Patrick Young, David and Sarah Gilmore*)

Devenish (Whitbreads)   Tenant Peter Andrew   Real ale   Meals and snacks (served throughout opening hours)   Restaurant   St Agnes (087 255) 2375   Children in cellar lounge and eating area of bar   Open 11–3, 6–11; 12–2, 6–11 in winter; closed evening 25 Dec

MORWENSTOW   SS2015 Map 1

Bush

Village signposted off A39 N of Kilkhampton

If this type of pub appeals to you, you'll like this particular one very much indeed: don't expect piped music, elaborate food or a welcome for children or dogs. It has a strong claim to be one of the very oldest (and most haunted) in Britain – part of it dates back just over 1,000 years (a Celtic piscina carved from serpentine stone is still set in one wall). There are ancient built-in settles and a big stone fireplace, and a cosy side area with antique seats, a lovely old elm trestle table, and a wooden propeller from a 1930 De Havilland Gipsy. An upper bar, opened at busy times, has built-in settles, and is decorated with antique knife-grinding wheels, miners' lamps, casks, funnels, and so forth. Well kept St Austell HSD and Winter Brew (December and January only), and guest beers such as Bass, Cotleigh Old Buzzard, Wadworths 6X and Farmers Glory on handpump or tapped from the cask behind the wood-topped stone bar counter (with pewter tankards lining the beams above it); quite a few malt whiskies and Inches cider. Simple bar food includes good, proper home-made soup (£1.10), sandwiches with ham off the bone or good locally-made pasties (£1.20), ploughman's with a bowl of home-made pickle (£1.75), home-made stew (£2), home-made fish or locally-made meat pies (£2.50), fresh crab roll (£2.50), and puddings like spotted dick or apple pie (£1.50). No chips. Darts, cribbage, dominoes and fruit machine. Seats outside shelter in the slightly sunken yard. Vicarage Cliff, one of the grandest parts of the Cornish coast – with 400-ft precipices – is a ten-minute walk away. (*Recommended by Tony and Lynne Stark, Roger and Carol Chisnall, TBB, Richard Cole, P and J McComb, Chris Newman, Deb Jay, Gary Phillips, William D Cissna, Nick and Alison Dowson, Steve Dark*)

Free house   Licensee J H Gregory   Real ale   Lunchtime meals and snacks (not Sun) Morwenstow (028 883) 242   Open 12–3, 7–11; closed Mon Oct-Mar

MOUSEHOLE   SW4726 Map 1

Ship

The character here hasn't changed much even though the main bar has been opened up, a new bar counter put in, the staircase moved and the wall moved out. There are built-in wooden wall benches and stools around low tables, black beams and panelling, sailors' fancy ropework, granite flagstones, and an open fire; windows overlook the harbour. Bar food includes sandwiches (from £1.40, excellent crab £2.90), enjoyable pasties (£1.50), fisherman's lunch (£3), lasagne (£3.70), crab salad (£5.50) and steaks (from £7). Well kept St Austell BB, HSD and Tinners on handpump, and several malt whiskies; friendly staff; winter pool and darts. The beautiful village does get packed in summer and over the Christmas period (when people come to visit the elaborate harbour lights). (*Recommended by Peter and Rose Flower, H K Dyson, Gwen and Peter Andrews, Margaret and Roy Randle, Patrick Stapley*)

St Austell   Tenants Michael and Tracey Madderns   Real ale   Meals and snacks (12–2.30, 6–9.30)   Restaurant   Penzance (0736) 731234   Children in eating area of bar   Summer parking can be difficult   Open 10.30–11; 10.30–2.30, 6–11 in winter Bedrooms; I£40B

nr MYLOR BRIDGE   SW8036 Map 1

Pandora ★ ★

Restronguet Passage: from A39 in Penryn, take turning signposted Mylor Church, Mylor Bridge, Flushing and go straight through Mylor Bridge following Restronguet Passage signs; or from A39 further N, at or near Perranarworthal, take turning signposted Mylor, Restronguet, then follow Restronguet Weir signs, but turn left down hill at Restronguet Passage sign

A farm in the 13th century, this lovely thatched pub was renamed the Pandora by Captain Edwards when his frigate of the same name (sent after the *Bounty* mutineers) was wrecked on the Great Barrier Reef in 1791. The setting – on a sheltered tidal waterfront – is at its best at high tide on a quiet day; to make the most of this there are lots of picnic-table sets in front and on a long floating jetty – where food and drink are served (weather permitting); quite a few people arrive by boat and there are showers for visiting yachtsmen. Inside, several rambling, interconnecting rooms have beautifully polished big flagstones, low wooden ceilings (mind your head on some of the beams), cosy alcoves with leatherette benches built into the walls, a kitchen range, and a log fire in a high hearth (to protect it against tidal floods); one area is no smoking. Bar food changes every few months and includes home-made soup (£1.50 or £1.80), sandwiches (from £2.25; local crab with cucumber and lettuce £3.95), burgers (from £3), fish pie (£4.50), salads (from £5.25), puddings like home-made treacle tart (from £1.80), and children's dishes (from £1.50). Bass, St Austell Tinners, HSD and BB on handpump from a temperature controlled cellar, and several malt whiskies; winter pool, shove-ha'penny, cribbage, and dominoes. It does get very crowded in summer, and parking is difficult at peak times. (*Recommended by Phil Bryant, Michael Bechley, Jim and Maggie Cowell, Andrew Morrisey, Keith Stevens, David Heath, Carol and Richard Glover, Iain and Penny Muir, H K Dyson, Malcolm H Littler, Gwen and Peter Andrews, WHBM, Gethin Lewis, R J Walden, Nick and Alison Dowson, W Bailey, S P Bobeldijk, Richard Houghton, Carol Mason, Patrick Young*)

St Austell   Tenants Roger and Helen Hough   Real ale   Meals and snacks (12–2.30,

*6.30–10 in summer)   Evening restaurant; sometimes closed in winter   Falmouth
(0326) 72678   Children in eating area of bar and restaurant   Open 11–11; 12–10.30
Sun; 11–2.30, 6.30–11 in winter*

PADSTOW   SW9175   Map 1
London

Lanadwell Street

A pub since 1802 – though originally three fishermen's cottages – this friendly local has two neatly nautical rooms with brass ships' instruments and sea photographs, comfortable furniture recently recovered in a quiet brocade, lots of red and cream woodwork, and an oak parquet floor. Bar food includes delicious sandwiches (good crab £2, and prawn £2.20), filled baked potatoes (from £2.75), ploughman's (£2.80), fish and chips (£3.30), salads (from £4, crab £5.25, prawn £5.50), megrin sole (£6.50), scallops rolled in bacon (£8), and steaks (from £9.50); on Sundays they do roast lunches only. Well kept St Austell BB, Tinners, and HSD on handpump, with XXXX under light blanket pressure; quite a few malt whiskies. Darts, dominoes, cribbage, euchre, and fruit machine. For vigorous walks you might try the old railway line as well as the coast path. It can get very busy in summer. There is a good bird garden nearby. *(Recommended by Tim and Lynne Crawford, Mr and Mrs B J Twigger, Cdr W S D Hendry, T Nott, H K Dyson, Iain and Penny Muir)*

*St Austell   Tenant Clive Lean   Real ale   Meals and snacks   Restaurant   Padstow
(0841) 532554   Children in restaurant   Open 11–4, 6–11   3 Bedrooms (not
Christmas week); £15/£30 – they hope to install showers for 1992*

PENDOGGETT   SX0279   Map 1
Cornish Arms

B3314

The two panelled rooms of the front bar in this slate-hung house (one of which is no-smoking at lunchtime) have high-backed built-in oak settles surrounding solid old wooden tables on the Delabole slate floor. Bar food includes sandwiches (from £1.50), ploughman's (£2.45), sausages (£2.50), beef stew (£4.75), liver and bacon (£5.95), local lemon sole (£8.95), and puddings like treacle tart (from £1.75). Well kept Bass, and Flowers IPA and Original tapped from the cask, and Pendoggett Special brewed for the pub on handpump. Good wines and several malt whiskies. The big, lively locals' bar has high-backed settles around stripped deal tables, a big woodburning stove, and darts, dominoes, cards, fruit machine, and occasional piped music. There are tables out on a corner terrace with a sea view down the valley. *(Recommended by Stephen R Holman, Mr and Mrs R Gammon, RJC, David Heath, Chris Newman, Deb Jay, H K Dyson)*

*Free house   Licensees Mervyn Gilmour and Paul Stewart   Real ale   Meals and
snacks   Restaurant   Bodmin (0208) 880263   Children in coffee room and
restaurant   Live music every two weeks   Open 11–11   Bedrooms; £42B/£69B*

PENZANCE   SW4730   Map 1
Turks Head

At top of main street, by big domed building (Lloyds Bank), turn left down Chapel Street

Even when this old pub is at its busiest, the atmosphere remains relaxed and friendly. The main bar has old flat irons, jugs and so forth hanging from the beams, pottery above the wood-effect panelling, wall seats and tables, and a couple of elbow rests around central pillars; a smaller side room is set out for eating, as is the downstairs cellar room (which has been a bar for several hundred years). A wide choice of seafood includes crab soup (£1.40), excellent grilled sardines, mussels in wine, tomato and garlic (£4.50), crevettes (from £4.15), crab salad (mixed meat £6.25, white meat £6.85), and cold seafood platter (£8.35); there's also plenty of non-seafood variety such as lunchtime sandwiches (from £1; filled French bread rolls from £1.30), filled baked potatoes (from £1.75) and ploughman's (from £2.95), as well as home-made soup (from £1.15), ratatouille topped with cheese (£3.50), good chicken curry (£4.50), meaty or vegetarian lasagne (£3.95), gammon steak (£5.80), and very good charcoal grilled steaks (from £7.60). No sandwiches or snacks on summer evenings. Devenish Steam, Boddingtons Bitter and Marstons Pedigree on handpump, and country wines; pleasant, helpful service; trivia and piped music; in the evening there can be quite a lively young crowd. The suntrap back garden has big urns of flowers. *(Recommended by R Tomlinson, Roger and Carol Chissnall, Mark Walker, R A Corbett, Peter Churchill, David Heath, Peter and Sue Darby, Pat and Malcolm Rudlin, Neil and Anita Christopher, Patrick Stapley, Richard Gibbs, RAB)*

Cornish Brewery (Whitbreads)   Tenant William Morris   Real ale   Meals and snacks (11–2.30, 6–10)   Restaurant   Penzance (0736) 63094   Children in cellar dining room   Open 11–3, 5.30(6 Sat)–11

PERRANUTHNOE   SW5329   Map 1

Victoria

Village signposted off A394 Penzance–Helston

The inn sign outside this friendly village pub shows a very young Queen Victoria indeed. Inside, the large L-shaped bar has exposed joists in its dark ochre ceiling, local coastal and wreck photographs, brocaded settles along its walls (some stripped to stone) and around polished wooden tables, and a neat coal fire; it angles round at the back on the left to a snug alcove; on the right, there's a more spacious family area with some higher-backed settles forming booths, a pool, darts, dominoes, cribbage, fruit machine, video game, juke box, and piped music. Good bar food includes sandwiches (from £1.40), filled baked potatoes (£3.25), home-made chicken curry (£3.50), home cooked beef or ham salad (£5.95), 12oz gammon steak (£7.95), and 12oz sirloin steak (£9.95); well kept Courage Directors and John Smiths Bitter on handpump. There are picnic-table sets under cocktail parasols in a sheltered stone-walled garden and by flowerbeds across the lane. The beaches of Mounts Bay are a couple of minutes' stroll away. *(Recommended by David Heath, E A George, Gwen Cranfield, Iain and Penny Muir)*

Courage   Tenant Chris Martin   Real ale   Meals and snacks (12–2, 6.30–9.30, not Sun evening)   Penzance (0736) 710309   Children in family room (except very young)   Open 12–3, 6.30–11   Bedrooms; £12.50S/£25S (no breakfasts)

PHILLEIGH   SW8639   Map 1

Roseland ★ ☺

The pretty paved front courtyard outside this charming old pub is a lovely place to sit in the lunchtime sunshine beneath the cherry blossom and in the company of many very tame small birds. Inside, there are bunches of fresh flowers, lots of old sporting prints and other pictures under the low beams, carefully chosen bar furnishings such as a nice oak settle and old-fashioned seats around the sturdy tables on the flagstones, and an old wall clock; good winter fire. Home-made bar food includes sandwiches (from £1.10 – the rare roast beef are good, toasties £2, fresh local crab £3.60), hot-pot or pea soup (£2), generous ploughman's (from £3), spinach and bacon pie, tasty seafood mornay or super salad niçoise (£4), steak and Guinness pie (£4), crab salad (£6), and puddings like chocolate biscuit cake or bread and butter pudding (£1.75). Well kept Devenish JD and Cornish Original on handpump from a temperature-controlled cellar, and winter hot toddies; dominoes, cribbage. The quiet lane leads on to the little half-hourly *King Harry* car ferry across a pretty wooded channel, with Trelissick Gardens on the far side. *(Recommended by Major and Mrs E M Warrick, Tony and Joan Walker, David Walker, David Wallington, Peter and Sue Darby, Carol and Richard Glover, Graham and Barbara Patrick, Charles and Mary Winpenny, Brian Skelcher, Iain and Penny Muir, Patrick Young, David and Sarah Gilmore, Robert Brown, T Galligan)*

Cornish Brewery (Whitbreads)   Tenant Desmond Sinnott   Real ale   Meals and snacks (not winter evenings)   Portscatho (087 258) 254   Children welcome   Open 11–2.30, 6–11; winter evening hours 7–10.30

POLKERRIS   SX0952 Map 1

Rashleigh

A rather remote descendant of the humble fisherman's tavern it used to be, this pub has tables by a figurehead on the stone terrace overlooking an isolated beach and attractively restored jetty and on to the far side of St Austell and Mevagissey Bays, many miles away; there are barbecues here in summer. Inside, the front part of the bar has comfortably cushioned seats, with local photographs on the brown panelling of a more simply furnished back area. Food includes an extensive lunchtime cold buffet (from £5), also soup (£1.20), sandwiches (from £1.30; open sandwiches from £4), ploughman's (£3.50), beef curry (£4), fish pie (£4.50), daily specials such as seafood cocottes (£6.50), vegetarian dishes (not Sun, Mon or Tues), chargrilled steaks (£9), and puddings (£1.50). Fergusons Bolsters Bitter, Ind Coope Burton, and St Austell HSD on handpump, and several malt whiskies; dominoes, cribbage, and piped classical music. This section of the Cornish coast path includes striking scenery, and there are safe moorings for small yachts in the cove. Though parking space next to the pub is limited, there's a large village car park. *(Recommended by Mr and Mrs P B Dowsett, Margo and Peter Thomas, J M Fletcher, David and Sarah Gilmore, ACP, Roy McNeill; more reports please)*

Free house   Licensee Bernard Smith   Real ale   Meals and snacks (11–2.30, 6–10) Restaurant   Par (072 681) 3991   Children in eating area of bar   Pianist Fri and Sat evenings   Open 11–3, 6–11; 11–11 Sat

POLPERRO   SX2051 Map 1

Blue Peter ★ ✪

The Quay; on the right-hand side as you go round the harbour – a brisk 10-minute walk from the public car park

In a village so popular with tourists, it's a pleasant surprise to find this atmospheric and friendly little pub. Reached by steps, the low-beamed and dimly-lit bar has bric-a-brac on the walls and beams, fishing nets, some boat pictures, a big naval shell by the coal fire, and a small winged settle, a polished pew, and a seat cut from a big cask (some of the other seats have, perhaps, seen better days). One window seat looks down on the harbour, another looks out past rocks to the sea. Hearty food includes sandwiches, home-made soup, filled baked potatoes, pizzas freshly cooked on the premises, and home-made hot dishes like beef and Guinness pie and Rangoon chicken curry with Basmati rice and poppadum. Daily specials such as fresh local trout grilled with garlic, a good, really hot chilli con carne and fresh seafood – which depends on what the local fishermen caught that morning; puddings, children's menu, vegetarian dishes and winter Sunday roasts. Well kept St Austell Tinners and HSD, a beer brewed for the pub and a guest beer such as Brains SA or Gibbs Mew Bishops Tipple on handpump, as well as strong farm cider. Darts, shove-ha'penny, cribbage, dominoes, fruit machine, space game, trivia and piped jazz and blues (rather obtrusive at times). The small V-shaped terrace at the top of the flight of steps up to the door has some slat seats. Near *Good Walks Guide* Walk 9. *(Recommended by Stephen R Holman, Dr John Innes, David Heath, K Flack, Mayur Shah, Carol and Richard Glover, David Warrellow, Charles Turner, Dr S E Martin, Dr L B Cook, Steve Dark, M Rowlinson)*

Free house   Licensees Tim Horn, Jennie Craig-Hallam, Terry Bicknell   Real ale Meals and snacks (12–2.30, 6–9.30)   Children in two upstairs family rooms   Jazz Sun lunchtime all year, light rock/blues Thurs Oct–May   Open 11–11; closed evening 25 Dec

POLRUAN SX1251 Map 1

Lugger

Reached from A390 in Lostwithiel; nearby parking expensive and limited, or steep walk down from village-edge car park; passenger/bicycle ferry from Fowey

A flight of steep stone steps take you up from the quay of this charming waterside village, to a pair of storm-cheating sliding doors. The left one opens into a traditional little lino-floored locals' bar. The main bar on the right is more geared to visitors, with its Turkey carpet, plush-cushioned wheelback chairs, big model boats, local boat photographs, fish tank and even a security TV camera keeping an eye on a further area up steps past the fireplace. But there are more traditional touches, such as the colourful window-boxes, the high-backed wall settles, and the beam-and-board ceiling. The upstairs food servery does a wide choice including pasties (£1), filled rolls (from £1), ploughman's (£2.50), salads (from £2.90), locally caught fish, dishes of the day such as chilli con carne (£3) and 8oz sirloin steak (£6.95); well kept St Austell Tinners and HSD on handpump, fruit machine, darts; good housekeeping. There are lovely views over the small harbour and across to Fowey. (*Recommended by Martyn and Mary Mullins, Ian Braid, Ian Blackwell, Iain and Penny Muir, D H Ashall*)

St Austell   Real ale   Meals and snacks   Children in family room   Open all day; 11–3, 6–11 in winter

nr PORT ISAAC   SX0080 Map 1

Port Gaverne Hotel ★ 🛏

Port Gaverne signposted from Port Isaac, and from B3314 E of Pendoggett

This is a particularly lovely place to stay with the sound of the sea from the comfortable rooms, early morning coffee at no extra charge, newspapers provided daily, very good restaurant food, and a warmly relaxed yet civilised atmosphere. The magnificent little bay is a stroll away (where there are occasional gig races in summer) and there are splendid clifftop walks all round. It's been run by the same friendly licensees for twenty-two years, and the well kept bars have big log fires, low beams, some exposed stone, flagstones as well as carpeting, a collection of antique cruets, and an enormous marine chronometer. In spring the lounge is filled with pictures from the local art society's annual exhibition in aid of the Royal National Lifeboat Institution (they also take part in the annual costumed four-legged race in aid of the same organization); at other times there are interesting antique local photographs. Many people praise the bar food, though the choice is not wide: sandwiches (from £1.25, excellent crab £2.50), home-made soup (from £1.75, crab £2.35), pâté (£1.95), ploughman's (from £2.25), cottage pie (£2.50), salads (from £3.50, half a lobster £9.25), home-made steak and kidney pie or a daily special (£4.95), with evening extras such as vegetarian lasagne (£3) and deep fried local plaice (£4.25). Sunday roast lunch (£5.25), half helpings for children, and there may be nibbles on the bar counter – cubes of cheese, biscuits and crispy bacon rinds. From Easter until 1st November it's served buffet-style in the dining room at lunchtime, and there is the same arrangement for Sunday lunchtime (when food stops at 1.30 sharp) throughout the year, but otherwise it's served in the bar or 'Captain's Cabin' – a little room where everything except its antique admiral's hat is shrunk to scale (old oak chest, model sailing ship, even the prints on the white stone walls). Well kept Flowers IPA and St Austell HSD on handpump, a good bin-end wine list with 60 wines, a very good choice of whiskies and other spirits such as ouzo and akvavit, and around 38 liqueurs; tea, coffee, and milk; quick, efficient service. Dominoes, cribbage and piped music, with darts, pool and a fruit machine in the renovated Green Door Club across the lane, which also has a big diarama of Port Isaac. A raised terrace outside has a good sea view (the bar does not). (*Recommended by H K Dyson, Paul Smith, Alan and Sue Foulkes, Tim Barrow, Sue Demont, TBB, T Nott, Freddy Costello, J H C Peters, Iain and Penny Muir, C M Whitehouse, Andrea and Guy Bradley, Steve Dark, Lyn and Bill Capper, Lesley Underhill, Steve Dark*)

Free house   Licensee Frederick Ross   Real ale   Meals and snacks (12–2, 7–10)   No smoking evening restaurant   Bodmin (0208) 880244   Children in restaurant and in Captain's Cabin in evening (served at 7pm)   Open 11–3, 5.30–11; closed 12 Jan to 22 Feb   Bedrooms; £39B/£78B; restored eighteenth-century self-contained cottages

PORTHLEVEN   SW6225   Map 1

Ship ★

There are marvellous views, both from the window seats in the bar and from the candle-lit dining room in this old fisherman's pub. It's set into steep rocks above a working harbour which is lit up at night and to reach it you have to climb a flight of rough stone steps. The knocked-through bar has log fires in big stone fireplaces and some genuine character, and there's also a summer cellar bar. Nicely presented bar food includes sandwiches (from £1.35; toasties from £1.85; 'leopard' sandwiches from £2.50 – you may like the bread so much that you feel frustrated you can't buy any to take away), filled oven-baked baked potatoes (from £1.95), ploughman's (from £3.50), salads (from £4.25), vegetable curry (£4.85), steak and kidney or tasty fish pies (£4.95), smoked haddock (£6.95), sirloin steak or crab thermidor (£7.95), seafood platter (£10.95), puddings (from £1.75), with evening dishes like an excellent big bowl of mushrooms in garlic (£2.95), and children's meals (from £1.95). Well kept Courage Best and Directors and John Smiths Bitter on handpump; dominoes, cribbage, fruit machine and piped music. Terraced garden. *(Recommended by Stephen R Holman, Tom McLean, R and Mrs P F Shelton, Iain and Penny Muir, E A George, Tom Evans, David and Sarah Gilmore, Mr and Mrs B E Witcher)*

Courage   Tenant Colin Oakden   Real ale   Meals and snacks (not winter Sun evenings)   St Mawes (0326) 572841   Children in family room   Parking can be difficult in summer   Open 11.30–11; 11.30–2.30, 7–11 in winter

PORTLOE   SW9339   Map 1

Lugger ⊘ 🍺

Off A3078, 2 miles S of Tregony

As this spotless little inn has a restaurant/hotel licence you have to eat (or stay) here. Well presented waitress-served bar lunches consist of soup (£1.75), pasties (£1.95), sandwiches (from £1.95, local crab or prawns are popular), filled baked potatoes (£2.50), seafood pâté (£2.75), ploughman's (£2.95), and salads (from £5, local crab £7). The low-beamed main room is an inner one, with lots of soft pink plush wing armchairs around low tables, and a fire at either end. A smaller outer room with a little corner bar (the beer is keg) has pale blue-green plush wall seats with a central love-seat, and looks down on the small rock cove – as do tables on a terrace just below, and the pretty evening dining room on the right; local wines and cider. There are scarcely enough houses here to call this a village, but it still has working fishing boats; a good friendly base for a fine stretch of the Coast Path. Not all the rooms have a sea view. *(Recommended by SJS, Keith Croxton, Dr and Mrs R E S Tanner, Joan and Michael Melling, J C Simpson)*

Free house   Licensees Colin and Stephen Powell   Morning coffee, bar lunches, teas, no smoking evening restaurant   Truro (0872) 501322   Open 12–2, last orders 9; closed 9 Dec–early Feb   Bedrooms; £41.10B/£92.20B inc dinner

SCORRIER   SW7244   Map 1

Fox & Hounds

Village signposted from A30; B3298 Falmouth road

This long, low white building – well set back from the road – is prettily decorated with hanging baskets and window-boxes, and has picnic-table sets under cocktail parasols in front. Inside, the long bar has creaky joists in the red ceiling, some vertical panelling, some stripped stonework, hunting prints, a stuffed fox, a fox mask, comfortable furnishings like red plush seats around dimpled copper tables, and big log fires; it's divided into sections by a partition wall and low screens. There is more seating in a no-smoking front extension, formerly a verandah. Popular, often inventive food is served by uniformed waitresses: home-made soup (£1.90), open sandwiches (from £2.70), filled baked potatoes (from £2.60), ploughman's (from £2.95), several vegetarian dishes (from £3.25), Lebanese kofta (£3.95), cold meat platter (£4.60), Thai chicken satay (£5.20), and sirloin steak (£7.80), with several evening extras. Well kept Devenish JD and Cornish Original on handpump, and some malt whiskies; fruit machine, piped nostalgic music. As we went to press the licensees told us that the pub might be taken back into brewery management in 1992; so there has to be an element of crossed fingers about this entry. *(Recommended by Chris Newman, Deb Jay, Gwen and Peter Andrews; more reports please)*

Devenish (Whitbreads)   Tenant D J Halfpenny   Real ale   Meals and snacks (till 10pm; not Mon evening except bank hols)   Redruth (0209) 820205   Open 11–2.30, 6(6.30 Sat)–11; winter Sun-Thurs evenings close 10.30; closed evening 25 Dec and all day 26 Dec

ST AGNES   SW7250 Map 1

Railway

Vicarage Rd; from centre follow B3277 signs for Porthtowan and Truro

There's a remarkable collection of shoes in this busy little pub – minute or giant, made of strange skins, fur, leather, wood, mother-of-pearl, or embroidered with gold and silver, from Turkey, Persia, China or Japan and worn by ordinary people or famous men. There's also some splendid brasswork (including one of the finest original horsebrass collections in the country), and a notable collection of naval memorabilia from model sailing ships and rope fancywork to the texts of Admiralty messages at important historical moments. Bar food includes home-made soup (£1.50), sandwiches (from £1.35), pasties (£1.50), home-made pie or vegetarian meals (£3.95), salads (from £3.95), and steak (£7.45). Well kept Devenish JD and Cornish Original on handpump under light blanket pressure; darts, fruit machine and piped music. When the locals are there in force it can get pretty crowded. *(Recommended by Iain and Penny Muir; more reports please)*

Cornish Brewery (Whitbreads)   Tenant Christopher O'Brien   Real ale   Meals and snacks   Children in eating area of bar and in restaurant   Open 11–11; may close winter afternoons

ST BREWARD   SX0977 Map 1

Old Inn

Old Town; village signposted off B3266 S of Camelford

The very worn carved stone in front of this quietly friendly old place is shrouded in mystery – it may be part of a Saxon cross. Inside, the two-roomed bar has banknotes and horsebrasses on the low oak joists that support the ochre upstairs floorboards, plates hanging on stripped stonework, and fine broad slate flagstones. Its inner room, with naif paintings on slate by a local artist (for sale cheaply), a good log fire, and cushioned wall benches and chairs around its tables, has a glass panel showing a separate games room with pool table, fruit machine and space game. The outer room has fewer tables (old ones, of character), a woodburning stove in the big granite fireplace, a piano and sensibly placed darts; also, dominoes, cribbage, juke box and piped music. Bar food includes sandwiches, cottage pie (£3.10), chicken creole or liver and bacon (£3.20), beef stroganoff (£3.40), ham and eggs (£3.80), and rump steak (£6.30). Well kept Bass and Ushers Best on handpump, cheap but decent coffee. Picnic-table sets outside are protected by low stone walls. The pub shares its hilltop with a church whose tower is a landmark for miles around; behind is open moorland, and cattle and sheep wander into the village. *(Recommended by D L Parkhurst; more reports please)*

Free house   Licensee Derek Judd   Real ale   Meals and snacks (12–2, 6–9)
Restaurant   Bodmin (0208) 850711   Children in eating areas and pool room   Open
12–3, 6–11

ST EWE   SW9746   Map 1
Crown

Village signposted from B3287; easy to find from Mevagissey

Run by the same friendly licensees for more than thirty years, this white cottage with its black paintwork has an unspoilt and traditional atmosphere. The bar has a roaring winter log fire with an ancient weight-driven working spit, 16th-century flagstones, a very high-backed curved old settle with flowery cushions, and long shiny wooden tables; shelves beside the fire have plates, a brass teapot and jug. The eating area has a burgundy coloured carpet, velvet curtains, and matching cushions to go on the old church pews. Good bar food includes fresh pasties (75p), egg mayonnaise (£1.10), sandwiches (from £1.10, local crab in season £2.75, open sandwiches £3), home-made soup (£1.40), ploughman's (from £2.60), filled baked potatoes (from £2.75), salads (from £4, fresh crab in season £6), gammon with egg or pineapple (£6.75), grilled lemon sole (£7.25), tasty steaks (from £7.50), and home-made puddings like fruit or very good mincemeat and brandy pies (from £1.30) and their special ice cream (£2.50). This year, they've opened a restaurant in what was the family room. Well kept St Austell BB on handpump, several malt whiskies and local wine; darts and fruit machine. There are several picnic-table sets on a raised back lawn. *(Recommended by Gwen and Peter Andrews, Mr and Mrs F Sherriff, Charles and Mary Winpenny, Peter Watkins, Pam Stanley, David and Sarah Gilmore, Iain and Penny Muir, Philip and Trisha Ferris, T Galligan)*

St Austell   Tenant Norman Jeffery   Real ale   Meals and snacks (12.30–2, 7.30–9.45)   Restaurant   Mevagissey (0726) 843322   Children in restaurant   Open 11–2.30, 6–11; closed evening 25 Dec   Bedrooms; I£30

ST KEW   SX0276   Map 1
St Kew Inn

Village signposted from A39 NE of Wadebridge

Tucked away in a small sheltered village, this charming local has an open kitchen range under a high mantlepiece decorated with earthenware flagons, black wrought-iron rings for hanging lamps or hams from the high ceiling, winged high-backed settles and varnished rustic tables on the lovely dark Delabole flagstones, a Windsor armchair, a handsome window seat, and pretty fresh flowers. Well kept St Austell Tinners and HSD tapped from wooden casks behind the counter (lots of tankards hang from the beams above it); good service. Waitress served food is the same in the bar and dining room: at lunchtime there is home-made soup (£1.10), ploughman's (£2.75), chicken kiev (£3.95) or lasagne (£4.50), and in the evening starters such as onion bhajee (£2.25) or chicken tikka (£2.95), main courses like fish pie and mushroom and nut fettucini (£4.50) and their speciality local sirloin steaks; children's (£2.10); summer barbecues. Picnic-table sets shelter between the wings of the pub, by a stone-trough pump on the front cobbles, and there's a big garden with lots of space for children, and Aneka the friendly goat; parking is in what must have been a really imposing stable yard. The church next door is lovely. *(Recommended by Mrs E Rayner, Barbara Wensworth, Iain and Penny Muir, H K Dyson, Nick and Alison Dowson, I S Wilson)*

St Austell   Tenant Steven Anderson   Real ale   Meals and snacks   St Mabyn (020 884) 259   Children in dining room, though no children under 6 in evenings   Open 11–2.30, 6–11; closed evening 25 Dec

ST MAWES   SW8537 Map 1

Rising Sun 🛏

The crazy-paved harbourside terrace outside this small hotel has sturdy slate-topped tables, with a low stone wall to sit on when those are full. There's an attractive conservatory bar with cane furniture, lots of brass, and white boarding, and a pubby front bar – popular with locals – which has simple furnishings and a big window seat overlooking the sea. Bar food includes broccoli and fennel soup (£1.30), sandwiches (from £1.75, crab £3.95), filled baked potatoes (from £2.25), ploughman's or salads (from £3.25), lamb curry (£3.75), scallop mornay (£6.25), and puddings like chocolate mousse (£1.35). Well kept St Austell BB and HSD on handpump, and several malt whiskies; fruit machine, winter darts. *(Recommended by Major and Mrs E M Warrick, David Heath, T and A Kucharski, C T and J M Laffin, Carol Mason, Robert Brown, T Galligan, Joan and Michael Melling)*

St Austell   Manager Stephen Busby   Real ale   Lunchtime meals and snacks   Evening restaurant (they do Sun lunch)   St Mawes (0326) 270233   Children in restaurant Open 11–11; 11–3, 6–11 in winter   Bedrooms; £35(£35B)/£70B)

ST MERRYN   SW8874 Map 1

Cornish Arms

Church Town; B3276 towards Padstow

For 21 years Mr Fitter has run this low stone building. It's simply furnished, with leatherette-cushioned oak wall settles and dining chairs around wooden tables, framed monthly rainfall figures for the past 20-odd years, photographs of local lighthouses facing a striking print of a lifeboat launch, and a coal-effect gas fire. The bar dates back to the twelfth or thirteenth century and has fine Delabole slate flagstones, neatly exposed ancient stonework, a sturdy mahogany serving counter, and a shining copper footrail. Simple bar food includes good pasties (£1.10), jumbo sausage (£1.55), ploughman's (£2.35), lasagne or plaice (£3.65), sirloin steak (£7.65), and Dover sole (to order); well kept St Austell Tinners and BB on handpump, and most attractively priced wines; quietly friendly service. On the left, there's a thickly carpeted ply-panelled games bar with winter pool, darts, cribbage, dominoes, fruit machines and a juke box; maybe quiet piped music. Picnic-table sets under cocktail parasols in front of this pretty cottage face the stone-built church; this can be a breezy spot. *(Recommended by Tim and Lynne Crawford, Iain and Penny Muir, Christopher and Heather Barton; more reports please)*

St Austell   Manager Peter Fitter   Real ale   Meals and snacks (in summer food is served until 10pm)   Children over 6 in eating area of bar until 9.30   Open 11–3, 6–11

TINTAGEL   SX0587 Map 1

Min Pin

Tregatta (B3263 S)

Min Pin stands for miniature pinscher (as shown on the inn sign) and the licensees have pictures of their prize-winning toy terriers and other dogs on the bobbly white walls. It's a cheerful, homely place – once a farmhouse – with well padded modern seats around the sturdy dark elm and other tables on the brightly patterned carpet of the main bar, and red leatherette furniture and a big open fireplace in the family room on the left; there's a restaurant beyond. Bar food includes soup (£1.50), garlic mushrooms, and ploughman's or giant filled yorkshire puddings (£3.50), with evening dishes such as pork and apple sage pie (£5.50), large local trout or prawn creole. The beers brewed here by Stephanie Hall (the young daughter of the family) use malt extract, but are very appetising, with a good clean finish: the pale, fragrant and well rounded Legend, and the hefty Brown Willy, named for Cornwall's highest hill; piped music. There's a two-level garden with trees behind and tables in the lower front part, which is prettily planted. *(Recommended by Sue Hallam, Richard Houghton; more reports please)*

Own brew   Licensees Keith, Marie and Stephanie Hall   Real ale   Meals and snacks   Restaurant   Tintagel (0840) 770241   Children in eating areas and in family room if eating   Open 11–3, 6.30–11; weekends only in winter (except Christmas and New Year weeks)   Bedrooms; £16S/£32S

TREBARWITH   SX0585   Map 1

Mill House Inn 🛏️

Signposted from B3263 and B3314 SE of Tintagel

There's unanimity about the lovely position here (a few minutes' walk through a secluded wooded valley with trout stream to the beach), and that's this 17th-century inn's strongest appeal. The big main bar has some stripped pine settles, pews, handle-back chairs and oak tables on its Delabole slate floor; an airy communicating extension has pine tables in side stalls. Home-made bar food can be eaten either in the bar, small restaurant or out on the terrace: sandwiches (from £1.05), home-made soup (£1.25), ploughman's (from £2.75), salads (from £4.10; crab £5.95), steak and kidney pie (£4.95), and steaks and grills (from £6.95), with daily specials like home-made pasties (£3.75), beef in beer (£4.35) or pork in mustard and pepper sauce (£5.95); home-made puddings like treacle tart (from £1.50) and children's menu (under £2). Well kept Flowers IPA and Original, Greene King Abbot, Marstons Pedigree, Wadworths 6X and a weekly changing guest beer on handpump or tapped from the cask; darts, pool, shove-ha'penny, dominoes, fruit machine, trivia, cards, and piped music; they also have football, cricket and spoof teams. The garden has terraces, waterfalls, a children's adventure play area, and a fenced area with friendly goats and sheep. *(Recommended by T Nott, John and Pat Smyth, H K Dyson, Richard Houghton, Peter Brabbs, ACP, Dr and Mrs B D Smith, Drs M and K Parier, C M Whitehouse)*

Free house   Licensee Kevin Howard   Real ale   Meals and snacks (11–10)   Evening restaurant   Camelford (0840) 770200   Children in eating area of bar and in restaurant   Live band Mon/Thurs/Fri/Sat evenings in main bar (not too loud)   Open 11–midnight; 11–3, 7–midnight in winter   Bedrooms; £22.50B/£45B

TREEN   SW3824   Map 1

Logan Rock

A long-established favourite with several readers, this well run and warmly friendly pub gets its name from an 80-ton teetering boulder which someone once tipped from its nearby clifftop fulcrum to show off his strength, and then had to pay a small fortune to have it hauled up the cliff again; it, like the pub, is owned by the National Trust. The low-beamed main bar (which has had a small half-wall removed to make room for more tables – thus losing the cosy little alcove), has high-backed modern oak settles, wall seats, old prints on the partly panelled walls telling the story of the Logan Rock, and a really warm coal fire. Bar food includes sandwiches (from £1.10, local crab when available £3), good pasties (£1.15), wholesome soup (£1.50), vegetarian quiche (£3.25), salads (from £3.50, crab £5.25), lasagne or a popular fish and egg dish they call the Seafarer (£3.50), scampi (£4.75), good charcoal-grilled steaks (from £6.50), and puddings like home-made fruit pie or crumble (£1.75); children's dishes (from £1.10). They will heat baby foods on request. Well kept St Austell Tinners and HSD on handpump, with XXXX kept under light blanket pressure, several malt whiskies; darts, table skittles, dominoes, cribbage, fruit machine and piped music, with space and video games, juke box, winter pool and another fruit machine in the family room across the way. Dogs are allowed in if on a lead. There are some tables in a small wall-sheltered garden, looking over fields, with more in the front court. *(Recommended by Gwen and Peter Andrews, Ian and Penny Muir, N W Acton, Julian Proudman, Graham and Barbara Patrick, Ewan and Moira McCall, David and Sarah Gilmore, Cliff and Karen Spooner, Patrick Stapley, Richard Gibbs, RAB)*

St Austell   Tenants Peter and Anita George   Real ale   Meals and snacks

Restaurant   St Buryan (0736) 810495 *(table service winter only)   Well behaved children in restaurant and family room   Open 10.30–3, 5.30–11*

TREGADILLETT   SX2940 Map 1

Eliot Arms ★ ⊘

Village signposted off A30 at junction with A395, W end of Launceston bypass

Readers have been delighted with this creeper-covered old house since it became a main entry last year. The atmosphere is quietly cosy, the staff efficient yet friendly and pleasant, and the food very good indeed. Every inch of wall of the charming warren of little softly lit rooms (there are at least five) is camouflaged with hundreds of horsebrasses, old prints, 66 antique clocks including 7 grandfathers, old postcards or cigarette cards grouped in frames, shelves of books and china. The furniture's a fine old mix, too, from high-backed built-in curved settles, through plush Victorian dining chairs, armed seats, chaise longues and mahogany housekeeper's chairs, to more modern seats; open fires, flowers on most tables, flower-printed cushions match the curtains, and the slate floors are partly carpeted; inoffensive piped music. A wide choice of food in generous helpings includes several ploughman's (from £2.85), daunting open sandwiches including a massive slab of rib of beef (£3.25 – £4.15 with chips), fresh herrings (£3.50), salads (from £3.50), tasty cheese and nut croquettes or home-made vegetable moussaka (£4.25), home-made curries (from £4.25), excellent scampi, lots of speciality charcoal grills (from £6.25), poached seafood platter in a creamy crab sauce (£7.25), Greek-style pork kebab (£7.95), and specials such as home-made pies (from £3.95), good fresh cod or scallops, and a big pork chop with stilton and apple (£5.50); lovely puddings. Well kept Devenish Royal Wessex, Flowers, and Whitbreads Best on handpump; darts, bar billiards, shove-ha'penny, table skittles, and fruit machine. A garden beyond the car park has picnic-table sets, a good climbing frame, swing and play house. *(Recommended by Martyn and Mary Mullins, Sandra and Dave Price, Peter and Sue Darby, TBB, Bob Smith, M and C Hardwick, Ian and Penny Muir, Alan and Audrey Chatting)*

Cornish Brewery (Whitbreads)   Lease: John Cook   Real ale   Meals and snacks (not 25 Dec)   Launceston (0566) 772051   Children in two front rooms   Open 11–2.30, 6–11   Bedrooms; £16/£30

TRELEIGH   SW7043 Map 1

Inn for all Seasons ⊘

From A30, take easternmost Scorrier turn-off, then immediate right on A3047 towards Camborne

The service in this restful place is particularly helpful: at one reader's request (and not on the menu) they produced two memorable beef salads. Other very good dishes might include excellent soup with home-made roll (£1.75), sandwiches (from £1.60), filled baked potatoes (from £2.45), spicy pasta and vegetable au gratin (£2.50), ploughman's (£2.95), salads (from £3.75; Newlyn crab £6.50), braised liver and onions or vegetable chilli (£3.95), aubergine and tomato bake (£4.75), pork in cider or beef curry madras (£4.95), stir-fried chicken with ginger or poached cod in mushroom sauce (£5.95), steaks (from £8.75), and home-made puddings like white chocolate torte, fresh fruit pavlova, sticky toffee pudding, and home-made ice cream (from £1.50); the fresh vegetables are perfectly cooked. Wadworths 6X served under light blanket pressure, and a wide range of drinks from the long and elegant bar counter; good coffee. The spacious and stylish lounge bar uses deep purples, soft pinks, and gentle greys and browns, the lighting (and the well reproduced piped music) is gentle, and the few old prints on the textured walls are carefully chosen. There are carefully staggered booths along the walls, quiet recesses, and separate islands with small easy chairs, plush banquettes, and black-lacquered chairs well spaced around solid dark tables. Broad windows, and white tables under cocktail parasols in front, look beyond the busy dual carriageway a couple of hundred yards away to distant rolling hills. *(Recommended by Alan and Eileen Bowker, Mrs M R Wilson, David Cardy)*

Free house   Licensees John Milan and Frank Atherley   Real ale   Meals and snacks
Restaurant (evenings Mon-Sat, Sun lunch)   Redruth (0209) 219511   Children in
restaurant and eating area of bar   Open 11–3, 5.30–11   Bedrooms; £35B/£50B

TRESILLIAN   SW8646   Map 1
Wheel

A39 Truro–St Austell

This spick-and-span pub was used by General Fairfax as his headquarters in the closing stages of the Civil War; Tresillian Bridge was where the Cornish Royalists finally surrendered to him. Watch for the low door as you go in. The two cosy and traditional original room areas have some timbering and stripped stonework, low ceiling joists, soft lighting, plush wall seats on the carpet, and steps from one part to another (though access for the disabled is quite reasonable); there's a further lighter and more spacious room. Generous helpings of good value bar food include soup (£1.10), large filled rolls (from £1.65; open sandwiches from £2.40), ploughman's (from £2.10), vegetarian dishes (from £2.80), salads (from £3; crab when available £6), good gammon (£4.80), steaks (from £8.25), home-made daily specials (£3.20), Sunday roast (£3.25), children's dishes (from £1.25; also small helpings off main menu) and puddings like home-made apple pie (£1.45). Well kept Devenish Royal Wessex on handpump, coffee and tea; particularly friendly service. Piped music; the pub can get very busy. The neat garden stretches down to a tidal stretch of the River Fal, and has a play area. *(Recommended by D P Pascoe, M McCartney, Mr and Mrs David Silcox, Mike and Lorna Weaver, Cdr W S D Hendry, Richard Houghton)*

Devenish (Whitbreads)   Tenant David Hulson   Real ale   Meals and snacks (till 10 Fri and Sat)   Truro (0872) 52293   Children in room with no bar   Open 11–2.30 (3 Sat or if busy), 6–11

Lucky Dip

Besides the fully inspected pubs, you might like to try these Lucky Dips recommended to us and described by readers (if you do, please send us reports):

☆ **Bodmin** [Dunmere, A389 NW; SX0467], *Borough Arms*: Neatly kept, with stripped stonework, lots of harness hanging from low joists, open fire, side room packed with old railway photographs and posters, decent piped music, fruit machine; big helpings of wholesome bar food (no sandwiches), well kept Devenish Cornish Original and Steam on handpump; picnic-table sets out among shady apple trees with good views over Dunmere woods, some traffic noise; can get very busy at lunchtime in season *(Mr and Mrs A J Land, Dr John Innes, Iain and Penny Muir, Andrea and Guy Bradley, BB)*

Bodmin [Crockwell St], *Hole in the Wall*: All sorts of bric-a-brac on walls and hanging from ceiling — brass bells, bugles and helmets, swords and muskets; smart new upstairs restaurant specialising in fish, bar lunches inc sandwiches, salads and hot dishes *(Cdr W S D Hendry)*

Bolventor [A30 on Bodmin Moor; SX1876], *Jamaica Inn*: Highly commercialised and very busy, but convenient for quite reasonable food, real ale and good service in clean and comfortable surroundings *(C T and J M Laffin, Tom McLean)*

☆ **Boscastle** [SX0990], *Napoleon*: Cosy partly 16th-century low-beamed slate-floored rooms and alcoves, normally quieter than our main entry here and preferred by some; enterprising mainly home-cooked bar food inc vegetarian dishes (though at quiet times it may seem nothing's "on"), lots of interesting Napoleon prints inc rare ones, well kept Bass and St Austell real ale, decent wines, darts, pool, sheltered terrace; piped music, children allowed in eating area; at top of very steep village *(Nick Dowson, Alison Hayward, H K Dyson, Iain and Penny Muir, LYM)*

☆ **Cadgwith** [SW7214], *Cadgwith Cove*: Lively atmospheric Devenish pub nr bottom of photogenic village, well kept beers, plenty of character and atmosphere, simple bar food inc good fresh local-crab sandwiches, spotless lavatories, maybe Fri singsongs; soon gets crowded, parking may be difficult *(Iain and Penny Muir, Vic and Reba Longhorn, M D Hare, Dr and Mrs R E S Tanner)*

☆ **Callington** [Newport Sq (A388 towards Launceston); SX3669], *Coachmakers Arms*: Reliable bar food, Bass on handpump, decent wines and efficient service in irregularly shaped timbered bar with appropriate old local advertisements; children in eating area and restaurant; bedrooms *(Miss P A Barfield, Brian Horner, LYM)*

☆ **Calstock** [off A390 via Albaston; SX4368],

Boot: Three-room pub with well kept real ales, decent wines by the glass and generous helpings of good bar food from sandwiches up (also separate upstairs restaurant), in lovely village on Tamar, with good walks nearby; friendly staff and locals; bedrooms *(John Kirk, John and Tessa Rainsford, M J Cochrane)*

☆ **Camborne** [Pendarves Rd; B3303 towards Helston; SW6440], *Old Shire*: Comfortable, homely family pub, friendly staff, good range of beers, interesting bar food, particularly good value evening help-yourself carvery/buffet, summer barbecues, children's area, garden; five bedrooms *(Gwen Cranfield, D P Pascoe)*

Charlestown [SX0351], *Rashleigh Arms*: Six real ales, good value bar and restaurant food, nice garden, good family room; comfortable bedrooms *(Mrs V Grant)*

Crackington Haven [SX1396], *Coombe Barton*: Hotelish-seeming big restaurant and bar area, but really worth knowing for good food; mainly holidaymakers but locals too *(Joan and John Calvert)*

☆ **Crafthole** [SX3654], *Finnygook*: Good friendly welcome in much modernised spacious lounge bar with wide choice of good value straightforward food, quick and friendly service; pleasant restaurant, good sea views from residents' lounge; bedrooms small but very comfortable, beautifully warm — very good value; bedrooms *(M and C McCrum, BB)*

Cubert [Trebellan; SW7858], *Smugglers Den*: Enormous inglenook, friendly staff, decent straightforward bar food, quiet restaurant, children's room with pub games etc; picnic-table sets outside, coarse fishing and campsite available *(Charles and Mary Winpenny, Margo and Peter Thomas)*

☆ **Devoran** [SW7939], *Old Quay*: Small, unpretentious pub overlooking Carnon River and its charming restored quay; notable pasties, good sandwiches and wide range of other food, well kept Devenish Cornish Original, and small suntrap terraced garden behind *(M W Turner, Dr Philip Putwain)*

☆ **Falmouth** [Custom House Quay; SW8032], *Chain Locker*: Strongly nautical harbourside pub, popular with locals and visitors alike; good choice of well kept real ales inc Devenish Cornish Original, pleasant buffet, quick service and lovely views from dining area; open all day at least in summer, waterside tables outside *(Rona Murdoch, T and A Kucharski, Colin Gooch, Keith Stevens, Michael Bechley, LYM)*

☆ **Falmouth** [Church St], *Kings Head*: Plenty of character in rambling bar with soft settees, easy chairs and firmer dining chairs, long thin serving counter done out like old-fashioned shop front; old plates and engravings, well kept Devenish real ales, bar food, winter log fire, piped music *(Mike Hallewell, T and A Kucharski, LYM)*

☆ **Falmouth** [Prinslow Lane, Swanvale], *Boslowick*: Reliably good reasonably priced bar food, consistently well kept Courage Best and Directors and courteous staff, in fine old black and white beamed and panelled manor house; plenty of seats inc plush sofas, log-effect gas fires; children's playpark *(J C Proud)*

☆ **Falmouth** [Maenporth Beach], *Seahorse*: Extensively modernised, almost a continental cafe/bar, with super view over beach and Fal estuary through smoked-glass facade or from terrace; Watneys-related real ales, chilled foreign beers, good value bar food, upstairs restaurant; part of new holiday complex *(Mike Hallewell, J C Proud)*

Falmouth [Church St], *Grapes*: Worth knowing for wonderful harbour view from two-level bar with Devenish real ales, pool table, juke box, usual bar food *(Michael Bechley)*; [Wodehouse Terr], *Seaview*: Free house with fantastic harbour view, good warm atmosphere, limited choice of food, well kept Bass, Courage Directors, Devenish Steam, Marstons Pedigree and Wessex *(Mike Hallewell)*; [The Moor], *Seven Stars*: Warmly welcoming old-fashioned town local with immaculate Bass, Flowers Original and St Austell HSD (maybe brought to your table in the snug) straight from the cask, simple snacks, tables on courtyard behind flower tubs; run as it has been for generations *(Gwen and Peter Andrews, T and A Kucharski, BB)*

☆ **Fowey** [SX1252], *Ship*: Some nautical touches in comfortable cloth-banquette main bar with well kept St Austell HSD and other real ales, juke box, coal fire; pool/darts room off on left, steps up to family dining room on right with big stained-glass window, good choice of usual bar food from sandwiches up through local fish to steak; very popular, good mix of locals and visitors; bedrooms old-fashioned, some oak-panelled *(Ian Blackwell, Jutta Whitley, David Warrellow, Iain and Penny Muir, BB)*

Fowey [from centre follow Car Ferry signs], *Galleon*: Great location with terrace over estuary; honest and down-to-earth, with good value, basic bar food; good rock music and pool table *(David Warrellow)*; [Town Quay], *King of Prussia*: Popular for harbour view from bow windows of upstairs bar, well kept St Austell Tinners and XXXX Mild, usual bar food down in family bar, efficient service; best at lunch, evenings the young people and thumping music may make you feel old at 27; bedrooms; the Polruan pedestrian ferry comes to the quayside steps opposite *(Iain and Penny Muir, Martyn and Mary Mullins, E H and R F Warner, LYM)*

☆ **Golant** [difficult approach from B3269; SX1155], *Fishermans Arms*: Superb spot with view of estuary from bar window and terrace looking down on garden; pleasant newish licensees, interesting copper, brass and old photographs; well kept St Austell Tinners, good sandwiches with thick-cut roast beef

Golant [SX1155], *Fishermans Arms*: Otherwise plain pub worth knowing for its attractive setting above River Fowey; (amount of parking depends on state of tide); full choice of bar food, efficient service, well kept real ales such as Courage Best and Directors, St Austell Tinners and Wadworths 6X; log fire, Dulux dog likes crisps *(David Warrellow, WHBM)*

☆ **Goldsithney** [SB3280; SW5430], *Crown*: Busy but friendly, with well kept St Austell beers inc very good Mild, limited choice of well prepared, generously and efficiently served restaurant; very pretty suntrap glass-roofed front loggia, a mass of colourful flower baskets and tubs *(Richard Houghton, Iain and Penny Muir)*

Gweek [SW7027], *Black Swan*: Friendly service, good food, well kept Devenish ales in revamped village inn *(Iain and Penny Muir)*

Halsetown [B3311 SW of St Ives; TL8130], *Halsetown*: Harness, copper and other bric-a-brac, big family room with fruit machines, pool and other games, Devenish ales, country wines, good range of bar food, friendly service; bedrooms *(Neil and Anita Christopher)*

☆ **Hayle** [Bird Paradise Park; SW5536], *Bird in Hand*: Busy barn-like place for families at the Bird Park (lunchtime Easter-end Oct, evenings not Sun July-early Sept), with own-brewed Paradise Bitter and strong Artists Ale, three or four well kept guest beers, decent food bar, evening pizzas and sometimes do-it-yourself barbecues; interesting upstairs four-table pool room, garden, play area *(Richard Houghton, Nigel Gibbs, Sandra Cook, David and Sarah Gilmore, Iain and Penny Muir, Brian Horner)*

☆ **Helford Passage** [SW7627], *Ferry Boat*: Big, friendly modern bar geared to high summer throughput, nice to sit out and watch the boats; wide choice of generous food, well kept St Austell ales, afternoon teas, efficient genuine service *(Iain and Penny Muir, Bob Smith, Hilary Roberts, M D Hare, BB)*

☆ **Helston** [Coinagehall St; SW6527], *Fitzsimmons Arms*: Large, bustling Devenish pub with lots of old woodwork, bric-a-brac and interesting corners, very friendly landlord, well kept real ales, reasonably priced bar food with generous veg; boxing memorabilia celebrating Helston-born Bob Fitzsimmons *(H K Dyson, Iain and Penny Muir, Reg Nelson)*

Helston [Church St], *Red Lion*: Friendly and lively young people's pub, mock old-world with lots of stripped softwood, loud music (live Weds), usual bar food inc pizzas, well kept Bass and Devenish real ales *(Iain Heath, Ruth Davies, Reg Nelson)*

nr Helston [Gunwalloe; signposted off A3083, S; SW6522], *Halzephron*: Clean and comfortable traditional pub looking over clifftop fields to sea; well kept Devenish beers, standard pub food, good log fire, tables outside; children welcome; bedrooms *(Iain and Penny Muir, LYM)*

Kestle Mill [A3058 SE of Newquay; SW8559], *Millers Apron*: Relaxing modernised bar with lots of red plush, comfortable settees, piped pop music; bar food, good restaurant, picnic-table sets on terrace by rock garden; four bedrooms *(Steve Hampson)*

Kilkhampton [SS2511], *New Inn*: Spacious well kept local with rambling interconnecting rooms, some traditional furnishings, fine woodburner, bar food, well kept Bass; children in good games room *(LYM)*

☆ **Lamorna** [off B3315 SW of Penzance; SW4424], *Lamorna Wink*: Has been popular main entry for location a few minutes' stroll from pretty cove (with good coast walks — nr GWG3), and fine collection of naval memorabilia and pictures; most find staff pleasant, but may be run too much for locals (particularly out of season) to please everyone; decent food inc huge baked potatoes, Devenish on electric pump *(C T and J M Laffin, Julian Proudman, Neil and Anita Christopher, K Flack, Carol and Richard Glover, LYM)*

Lands End [SW3425], *State House*: Very big comfortable conservatory extension overlooking sea, with Lands End Bar at N end, Longships Bar at S end, and dining room between, furnished in pretty bistro style with houseplants; seaview terrace, obliging staff, bar food; admission charge (lots of on-site entertainment); bedrooms good value *(T Nott, Gwyneth and Salvo Spadaro-Dutturi)*

Langdon [B3254 N of Launceston; SX3089], *Countryman*: Large, modernised, comfortable pub with Marstons Pedigree and Wadworths 6X on handpump and good range of pub food inc vegetarian dishes; children welcome *(Mel Landells)*

☆ **Lanlivery** [SX0759], *Crown*: Neatly kept pub with pleasantly pubby atmosphere, well kept Bass, good lunchtime bar food, evening restaurant, friendly efficient staff; bedrooms *(Graham and Barbara Patrick)*

Lanner [SW7240], *Coppice*: Cosy roadside inn, with Allied real ales and bar food; bedrooms *(Iain and Penny Muir)*

Lanreath [off B3359; SX1757], *Punch Bowl*: Flagstoned locals' bar and some antique settles etc in lounge, bar food, well kept real ales, local farm cider, good collection of malt whiskies, attractive village; warm bedrooms *(Julian Proudman, LYM)*

Lelant [Griggs Quay, Lelant Saltings; A3047 St Ives rd off A30; SW5437], *Old Quay House*: Well run open-plan bar, big garden overlooking Lelant bird marshes, Watneys-related real ales on handpump, good choice of wines, reasonably priced fresh food inc good help-yourself salad table, friendly service *(Theo Schofield)*; *Tyringham Arms*: Large family room with amusements inc big-screen satellite TV, real ales, good food inc cheap Sun lunch, tables outside *(D H Bennett)*

Longrock [old coast rd Penzance—Marazion; SW5031], *Mexico*: Cheerful local with big helpings of good food; warm-hearted and relaxed *(WMS, DHT)*

Looe [SX2553], *Old Salutation*: Appeals to

middle-aged, with plenty of good food, Watneys-related real ales *(Ted George)*; [Hannafore, W Looe], *Tom Sawyers*: Homely appeal, well kept Bass and Whitbreads-related real ales, pleasant staff, good home-made bar food (steak sandwich, ploughman's and Sun carvery recommended); evening restaurant; children welcome; nr GWG9 *(Mr and Mrs M Cockram)*

☆ **Ludgvan** [Churchtown; off A30 Penzance—Hayle at Crowlas — OS Sheet 203 map reference 505330; SW5033], *White Hart*: Very well reconstructed beamed and small-roomed 19th-century pub with great atmosphere, friendly landlady, paraffin lamps and loads of nick-nacks; well kept beer tapped from the cask, simple food, no piped music — a successful attempt to hold on to the past (WCs in period, too, which may not be so popular) *(WMS, Richard Gibbs, Iain and Penny Muir)*
Ludgvan, *Old Inn*: Pleasant village inn with warm welcome and well kept St Austell ales *(Iain and Penny Muir)*

☆ **Manaccan** [down hill signed to Gillan and St Keverne; SW7625], *New Inn*: Old thatched local in sleepy coastal village, decidedly individual if somewhat superannuated feel and furnishings in its two rooms, rather upmarket if sweatered clientele, well kept Devenish beers; some but not all readers still enjoying the food and welcome which gained it a main entry in previous editions *(Cliff and Karen Spooner, Julian Proudman, Gwen and Peter Andrews, R A Corbett, ACP, Carol and Richard Glover, Robert Brown, W Bailey, Iain and Penny Muir, Ewan and Moira McCall, Nick Dowson, Alison Hayward, LYM)*
Marazion [The Square; SW5231], *Cutty Sark*: Unpretentious but nice, with friendly atmosphere, well kept Cornish beers, decent wine, good food (particularly substantial fresh plaice) in bar and restaurant; bedrooms *(Helen Emmitt, Charles Park, Reg Nelson)*; *Fire Engine*: Welcoming St Austell local worth noting for fine views of St Michaels Mount from picnic-table sets on suntrap sloping lawn *(Iain and Penny Muir)*
Marhamchurch [off A39 just S of Bude; SS2203], *Bullers Arms*: L-shaped bar with half a dozen well kept real ales, quickly served conventional bar food, darts in flagstoned back part, pool room, piped pop music (maybe loud), restaurant; children welcome; a mile's walk to the sea; bedrooms *(Mrs R Horridge, Mandy and Michael Challis, LYM)*
Mawgan [SW7125], *Old Court House*: Quite a barn of a place, with some traces of its past as a courthouse, well kept Devenish, pleasant service, friendly locals, dogs and cat, wide choice of food *(Carol and Richard Glover, R Houghton)*
Mevagissey [Fore St; SX0145], *Fountain*: Delightful bar with open fire, old village photographs, good value food inc local fish, well kept St Austell beers *(Nic James)*; [quayside], *Sharks Fin*: Right on the pretty harbour, with bar reminiscent of smugglers'

cave (but very clean), reasonable choice of bar food at moderate prices; restaurant, and open all day in summer for food inc cream teas; bedrooms very good value *(Colin Laffan, Mrs S Stewart)*; [Fore St, nr harbour], *Ship*: Good food esp local fish, well kept St Austell, pleasant cheerful service; rather dark in places, with comfortable seats, interesting ships' memorabilia, friendly black and white cat; juke box in public *(Keith and Janet Morris, Nic James)*

☆ **Mitchell** [A30 Bodmin—Redruth; SW8654], *Plume of Feathers*: Lots of bric-a-brac and even a well in friendly and comfortable rambling bar with huge back open fire; sandwiches, choice of ploughman's, pies, curries and casseroles, Cornish Original and Devenish JD on handpump, good coffee, piped music, darts and winter pool; tables outside, with adventure playground and farm animals; children welcome *(Iain and Penny Muir, LYM)*
Mullion [SW6719], *Old Inn*: Shipwreck mementoes and crabbing pictures in long lantern-lit bar of thatched village inn, big inglenook fireplace, well kept Cornish Original and Devenish JD on handpump, home-cooked bar food inc choice of pizzas and often local fish, summer barbecues Tues-Sat, good games area (pool in winter), TV and small aviary in children's room, seats outside; bedrooms, and self-catering cottages *(M D Hare, Iain and Penny Muir, Wayne Stockton, LYM)*
Mylor Bridge [SW8137], *Lemon Arms*: St Austell pub with well kept real ales; handy for start or finish of very pretty walk *(H K Dyson)*
Newbridge [A3071 Penzance—St Just — OS Sheet 203 map reference 424316; SW4232], *Fountain*: Warm and dark, marvellously friendly local with winter log fire, armchairs and comfortable alcoves *(WMS, K Flack)*
Newlyn [Fore St (coast rd); SW4628], *Fishermans Arms*: Ancient fisherman's inn with fine nautical memorabilia, St Austell real ale, wonderful views of Mounts Bay and Marazion Sands *(Reg Nelson, Iain and Penny Muir)*
Newquay [Station Approach; SW8161], *Cavalier*: Friendly and enterprising, with cheap tapas as well as bar food from sandwiches to steaks and more elaborate evening dishes; real ales, open all day *(Cdr W S D Hendry)*
Newtown [Newtown in St Martin; the one off B3293, SE of Helston; SW7423], *Prince of Wales*: Comfortable and cosy village pub doing well under current regime, with wide choice of good fresh food, small restaurant, genuine welcome, well kept Devenish ale *(Iain and Penny Muir, D G King)*

☆ **Padstow** [Lanadwell St; SW9175], *Golden Lion*: Friendly local with pleasant black-beamed front bar, high-raftered back lounge with russet plush banquettes against the ancient white stone walls; good value lunches from soup and sandwiches inc fresh crab to ham and egg, scampi and so forth; evening steaks and fresh seafood; well kept

Devenish on handpump, piped music, juke box, fruit machines. Popular with locals and visiting boat crews *(Cdr W S D Hendry, Tim and Lynne Crawford, H K Dyson, BB)*

Padstow [Mill Sq; just off North Quay/Broad St], Old Ship: Tables on front courtyard of simple hotel tucked away behind harbour, bustling open-plan bar with well kept Whitbreads-related real ales on handpump, usual bar food, fruit machines, juke box or piped music, more tables in Perspex-roofed inner courtyard, live music Weds/Sat, children's room, open all day summer; 15 bedrooms *(Tim and Lynne Crawford, Keith and Janet Morris, BB)*; [North Quay], Shipwrights: Good harbour spot for open-plan low-beamed pub with flagstones, thorough nautical theme, reasonably priced food, St Austells beers *(Carol and Richard Glover, Iain and Penny Muir, BB)*

Paul [SW4627], Kings Arms: Pleasant and clean St Austell pub with well kept HSD, garden; tranquil spot opp church; bedrooms *(Iain and Penny Muir)*

Pelynt [B3359 NW of Looe; SX2055], Jubilee: Good open fire and Queen Victoria memorabilia in bright hotelish lounge bar, pool and other games in lively flagstoned public bar, bar food, real ale, barbecues in inner courtyard, good play area; comfortable bedrooms *(D P Ryan, Mr and Mrs Simon Turner, Dr John Innes, J A Scott, D C Bail, E A Simmons, Mrs D M Hacker, LYM; more reports please)*

Penryn [SW7834], Seven Stars: Cosy and popular Devenish pub notable for its exceptional collection of sparkling-clean brass platters and ornaments — perhaps the biggest in the country *(Keith Stevens, BB)*

Penzance [Chapel St; SW4730], Admiral Benbow: Impressive nautical artefacts and decent food and drink, though drinking areas can come under pressure when busy, and the specials advertised outside may be available only in the evenings; open all day summer *(Carol Mason, N W Acton, David Heath, Gwen and Peter Andrews, LYM)*; [Barbican; Newlyn rd, opp harbour after swing-bridge], Dolphin: Good maritime refurbishment, welcoming atmosphere, big windows over harbour, seats outside, reasonably priced quickly served bar food, St Austell ales, willing staff, big pool room with juke box etc; children in room off main bar *(Reg Nelson, Iain and Penny Muir, Derek Patey, LYM)*

☆ **Perranarworthal** [A39 Truro—Penryn; SW7839], Norway: Elaborate pastiche of small-roomed rustic pub, lots of pictures, country bygones, china, taxidermy and bric-a-brac; popular lunchtime bar food, restaurant, Devenish real ales, tables outside *(Gwyneth and Salvo Spadaro-Dutturi, Charles Gurney, BB)*

☆ **Perranwell** [off A393 Redruth—Falmouth and A39 Falmouth—Truro; SW7839], Royal Oak: Pretty cosily decorated beamed village pub with genuinely friendly atmosphere, bar food inc attractive

lunchtime buffet, well kept Devenish, good winter fire, provision for children, garden with picnic-table sets; only reason this very nice pub is not a main entry is absence of recent reports *(Margo and Peter Thomas, J C Proud, LYM)*

Pillaton [SX3664], Weary Friar: Old village pub with two comfortably spacious rooms linked at reception, well kept Courage Best and Directors, good coffee, pleasant staff and plentiful well presented bar food; attractive restaurant; bedrooms comfortable *(Ted George, LYM)*

Pityme [Pityme Farm Rd; SW9576], Pityme: Welcoming family pub with good food at very reasonable prices, efficient service, St Austell real ales, modern decor *(RJC)*

Polgooth [SW9950], Polgooth Inn: Lively rustic pub, formerly unashamedly basic but now entirely smoothed over, with well kept St Austell real ales, good range of popular food; particularly good with children — big family room and (up steep steps) outside play area *(Iain and Penny Muir, K J Lawry, LYM)*

Polperro [at edge of village nr main car park; SX2051], Crumplehorn Mill: Whitewashed inn with four separate areas inc attractive stripped stone and flagstone upper bar, its simple tables separated by curtains; log fire, beams and brasses, dim lighting, Bass and St Austell HSD and XXXX, muted music, generous reasonably priced food; bedrooms *(Dr John Innes, Carol and Richard Glover)*; [bear R approaching harbour], Noughts & Crosses: Cosy little low-beamed and panelled bar, upper family room and lower softly lit riverside bar with comfortable banquettes, pool table and fruit machines; good atmosphere especially for young people, Courage beers, piped music, usual bar food *(Mayur Shah)*; [by harbour], Three Pilchards: Small, cosy and friendly low-beamed local with well kept Courage Best and Directors on handpump; quickly served weekday food (limited out of season), open fire; open all day *(Mayur Shah, Martyn and Mary Mullins)*

Polzeath [SW9378], Pentire Rocks: Good service, well presented food; bedrooms *(M R Elley)*

Ponsanooth [A393 Penryn—Redruth; SW7537], Stag Hunt: Colin and Vicki Gilham who made this — and previously the Miners Arms at Mithian — popular main entries have moved up to the New Inn at Yealand Conyers (see Lancs main entries) *(LYM)*

☆ **Port Isaac** [SX0080], Golden Lion: Old pub in lovely steep village, nice view from the seat by the window; simple but good atmosphere, old pictures and photographs, good value lunchtime snacks (esp local pasties, fresh crab sandwiches and crab ploughman's), well kept St Austell Tinners and HSD, little roof terrace high over harbour; village at its best outside peak season, with wonderful cliff walks nearby *(Iain and Penny Muir, H K Dyson, David and Sarah Gilmore, LYM)*

☆ **Porthallow** [off B3293 in St Keverne, then signed; SW7923], *Five Pilchards*: Now a welcoming free house, with well kept changing real ales such as Devenish Cornish Original, Greene King Abbot and Wadworths 6X on handpump, country wines, reasonable range of lunchtime food, friendly staff, interesting local pictures; so close to the sea you can park on the foreshore with sailors anchoring outside; best out of season *(Alan and Eileen Bowker, Keith Stevens, David and Daphne Carter, Iain and Penny Muir)*

☆ **Porthleven** [Peverell Terr; SW6225], *Atlantic*: Stunning setting overlooking sea; large, open-plan lounge with alcoves, pleasant open log fire in granite fireplace, well kept Devenish real ales, wide choice of bar food with emphasis on local seafood *(Patrick Young)*

☆ **Portscatho** [SW8735], *Plume of Feathers*: Clean and lively pub in pretty fishing village; good value food (particularly soup, crab sandwiches), inc takeaways, from hatch in corner of main bar; small eating area, side locals' bar, well kept St Austell Tinners, well reproduced loudish pop music, efficient friendly staff; very popular with summer visitors; on South Cornwall Coastal path; dogs allowed *(WHBM, J and K Craddock, Iain and Penny Muir, David Wallington, David and Sarah Gilmore, BB)*

☆ **Poughill** [SS2207], *Preston Gate*: Attractive conversion of two cottages, flagstones, pews, mahogany tables, log fires, good value bar food, well kept Watneys-related real ales, some seats outside; village pronounced 'Poffle' *(Audrey and Keith Patchett, LYM)*

Redruth [Tolgus Mount; SW6842], *Tricky Dickies*: Relatively new Cornish Breweries pub, built of granite and slate to capture area's character; good choice of food and of beers, remote and full of character — very popular for eating out, Sun lunch notably cheap *(M P Hallewell)*

☆ **Roche** [SW9860], *Victoria*: Useful A30 stop — snug low-ceilinged bar, antique oak settles, oak panelling and a carved doorway, old ship furniture and farm tools, brass pots, mugs, measures and guns, even a man trap; popular food inc good home-made pasties, well kept St Austell ales, panelled children's room, cheery service, restaurant *(Patrick Young, LYM)*

Rosudgeon [SW5529], *Coach & Horses*: Nice friendly pub with good food, children's area *(D H Bennett)*

Sennen [OS Sheet 203 map reference 357255; SW3525], *First & Last*: Spaciously refurbished and (except in summer when it can get noisily busy) handy for Lands End; well kept real ales such as Wadworths 6X (cellar cooled by a spring which you can see through a viewing hole); pool table, friendly and helpful landlady, bar food inc good pasties *(Gwyneth and Salvo Spadaro-Dutturi, T Nott)*

☆ **Sennen Cove** [SW3526], *Old Success*: 17th-century fisherman's local in glorious spot beside big beach — view along Whitesand Bay is magnificent, esp outside the main holiday season; refurbished in suitably cottagey style with fishing/lifeboat/shipwreck decorations; friendly staff, good quickly served food, good range of real ales inc Bass, piped music; nr GWG2; pleasantly furnished bedrooms — good value winter weekends *(T Nott, Tom McLean, Gwyneth and Salvo Spadaro-Dutturi, Gwen and Peter Andrews, P and J McComb)*

St Buryan [SW4025], *St Buryan*: Simple pub with two bars and friendly landlord; part lino tiled, part carpeted, solid-fuel stove, tractor seats by bar, kitchen chairs and a few plain tables; horse collars and brass on modern stone wall, TV and plastic flowers; well kept Courage Best; juke box, darts, fruit machine *(RAB)*

☆ **St Dominick** [Saltash; a mile E of A388, S of Callington — OS Sheet 201 map reference 406674; SX3967], *Who'd Have Thought It*: Consistently good and often out-of-the-ordinary food (lunch orders may stop 1.30), charming waitresses and stunning Tamar views from dining area of tightly run entertainingly unCornish country pub — flock wallpaper, tasselled plush seats, Gothick tables, gleaming pottery and copper; well kept Bass and Devenish, decent wine by the glass; nr NT Cotele House *(T Nott, E A Simmons, David and Sarah Gilmore, Ted George, John Kirk, LYM)*

☆ **St Issey** [SW9271], *Ring o' Bells*: Cheerful well modernised village inn with well cooked food inc good beef, chips and fresh veg, with half helpings of some dishes (not puddings) for children; well kept Courage; bedrooms *(Christopher and Heather Barton, Tim and Lynne Crawford, LYM)*

☆ **St Ives** [Fore St; SW5441], *Castle*: Comfortable and friendly largish pub, well furnished and popular with locals; original pine panelling, old town photographs, maritime memorabilia, good value bar food, Devenish beers, good service and atmosphere, unobtrusive piped music; best out of season *(Donn and Jess Barrett, D J Penny, Reg Nelson)*

St Ives [Chapel St], *Three Ferrets*: Small, fairly basic free house with loudish music, Wadworths 6X, and good value food with bargain dishes *(D J Penny, Reg Nelson)*

☆ **St Just in Penwith** [SW3631], *Star*: Honest-to-goodness low-beamed local in windswept town not far from Lands End; interesting mining artefacts and ornaments, happy atmosphere, well kept St Austell ales tapped from the cask, satisfactory food inc good steak rolls, nostalgic juke box; little TV parlour, seats in small courtyard — which leads straight through to a farmyard; bedrooms comfortable, with huge breakfast served in delightful snug *(WMS, K Flack, WHBM, LYM)*

St Just in Penwith, *Miners Arms*: Another real local with traditional bar leading to games/pool room and modern bistro/food bar; reasonably priced food inc good seafood, Courage beers *(K Flack)*

St Mawes [SW8533], *Victory*: Lots of sailing and other sea photographs in unpretentious fishermen's and yachtsmen's bar, character landlord, well kept Devenish JD on handpump, simple bar food; seats out in the alley, a few steep yards up from the harbour; bedrooms simple but good value (don't expect an early night) *(W Bailey, David Heath, LYM)*

☆ **St Mawgan** [signed off A30; SW8765], *Falcon*: Recently renovated wisteria-covered stone inn doing well under current regime, with suntrap seats in sheltered cottage garden with views of peaceful, pretty village; well kept St Austell ales, inexpensive straightforward bar food (not sandwiches), friendly staff, children allowed in dining room; bedrooms *(Tim Barrow, Sue Demont, Charles and Mary Winpenny, D H Ashall, LYM)*

St Merryn [SW8874], *Farmers Arms*: Extensively renovated, with big central bar and food counter serving bright and spacious dining area; well disclosed by the works now a floodlit feature — 8ft of water in it makes changing the floodlights a challenge; children's games room with videos and so forth, and family room; bedrooms *(Cdr W S D Hendry)*

☆ **St Neot** [N of A38 Liskeard—Bodmin; SX1867], *London*: Beamed pub with two open fires, good imaginative home-made food and well kept beers served cheerfully; in very attractive village tucked away down tricky roads in wooded valley *(BMS, Pat & Malcolm Rudlin)*

☆ **St Teath** [B3267; signed off A39 SW of Camelford; SX0680], *White Hart*: Good food (sandwiches, Yorks puddings and steaks all praised) in welcoming village pub with snug slate-floored main bar, comfortable eating bar and lively games bar with darts, pool and juke box; well kept Ruddles County and Ushers Best, naval and marines memorabilia, open fire; bedrooms *(C M Whitehouse, Mr and Mrs David Silcox, Iain and Penny Muir, L A Mills, LYM)*

Stratton [SS2406], *Tree*: Interesting rambling pub with cosily attractive old-fashioned layout; news of new regime, please *(BB)*

Threemilestone [W of by-pass outside village; SW7844], *Oak Tree*: Spacious re-conversion from restaurant, well kept Wadworths 6X and Cornish Original on handpump, food inc hefty salads, friendly staff *(Michael and Alison Sandy)*

☆ **Trebarwith** [Trebarwith Strand; SX0585], *Port William*: Attractive spot, interesting bar area with pictures by local artists; now concentrating a lot on nicely served food inc fresh crab and other seafood, delicious home-made soups; four well kept real ales; outside terrace has lovely views; 11-11 Easter—Nov *(Major S C Thompson, Tim and Lynne Crawford)*

Trelights [signposted off B3314 Wadebridge—Delabole; SW9979], *Long Cross*: Spotless plush-and-varnish furnishings in modern bar with Victorian

stained-glass panels, unusual heptagonal bench around small central fountain, restrained maybe classical piped music, good house wines, well kept St Austell Tinners, good value bar food such as ploughman's, baked potatoes, burgers, salads and chicken; family room, further dining bar, cream teas; picnic-table sets around pool outside, good play area; remarkable garden under restoration (small charge), with lots of attractive ideas and some sweeping coast views; bedrooms comfortable and well furnished, many with good views *(E H and R F Warner, H K Dyson, BB)*

☆ **Trevaunance Cove** [The Beach; SW7251], *Driftwood Spars*: Converted tin-mine store nr beach with huge beams, thick stone walls, and log fires, bar done out like smugglers' inn, big family room, attractive dining room, well kept ales, good food using fresh ingredients, quick service; bedrooms comfortable *(Mr and Mrs A C Goundry, Freddy Costello)*

☆ **Truro** [Kenwyn St; SW8244], *William IV*: Elegantly tiled two-level conservatory dining room opening into flowery garden with plenty of tables; busy dark-panelled bar with slightly secluded raised areas, chamber-pots, bottles, scales, ewers and basins; good value buffet food inc daily hot specials, well kept St Austell beers *(Margo and Peter Thomas, Patrick Young, Sue Hallam)*

☆ **Truro** [Frances St], *Globe*: Several rooms around central serving area, nicely done out with old panelling and beamery, bottle-glass screens, mixed furnishings inc leather armchairs and sofas, taxidermy, old prints; good value help-yourself home-made bar food lunchtime and evening, well kept Devenish real ales *(D P Pascoe)*

Truro [Lemon Quay; by central car park], *Market*: Cosily redone with lots of oak, bentwood chairs, well kept Devenish Cornish Original and GBH on handpump, good bar food *(Patrick Young, LYM)*; *Old Ale House*: No spirits, but good choice of regularly changing real ales such as Fullers London Pride, Wadworths 6X and Youngs Special, and interesting country wines such as damson and birch; free peanuts *(Charles Gurney)*

☆ **Veryan** [SW9139], *New Inn*: Quietly welcoming one-bar village pub with good landlord, well kept St Austell tapped from the cask, good choice of food; very clean; bedrooms *(Richard Houghton, Iain and Penny Muir, David and Sarah Gilmore)*

Wadebridge [SW9872], *Molesworth Arms*: Comfortably plush main bar with three areas and interesting fireplace, classic Cornish locals' bar across coach entry, attractive restaurant in former back stables; good bar lunches, good choice of ales; doing well under current regime; bedrooms *(Cdr W S D Hendry)*; [Molesworth St], *Swan*: Pleasant open-plan bar, well kept St Austell Tinners and HSD, friendly staff, reasonably priced bar food, restaurant; bedrooms *(Anon)*

☆ **West Pentire** [SW7760], *Bowgie*: Friendly

atmosphere in hotelish lounge bar looking out over the rolling lawns of this magnificent headland to Crantock beach and the sea; good if not cheap beer (Flowers IPA and Original, a guest such as Marstons Pedigree) and food, newspapers and magazines available, soundproofed family room, good play area; children allowed in main part lunchtime; bedrooms well appointed —

Isles of Scilly

☆ **St Marys — Hugh Town** [The Strand; SV9010], *Atlantic*: Big cheerful low-beamed L-shaped harbourside pub done out interestingly with wrecked ship mementoes, lots of spars and heaps of marine bric-a-brac; substantial helpings of bar food inc good sandwiches, huge pasties, good chilli con carne, fresh fish, St Austell Tinners and HSD; happily absorbs locals, boat skippers and visitors of all sorts — pile your bags in a corner while you wait for a boat; family room, restaurant, small back balcony/terrace overlooking water; bedrooms in adjacent hotel *(Neil and Anita Christopher, Prof Peter Knight, Peter and Rose Flower, Dave Mead, TBB, BMS)*
Hugh Town [Silver St (A3110)], *Bishop & Wolf*: Basic food inc good crab sandwiches in friendly and comfortable bar (may get rather smoky when crowded), with nets, oars, lamps and so forth, St Austell ales, pool, fruit machine, unobtrusive piped music; big upstairs restaurant; open all day *(Margaret and Roy Randle, Dave Mead, GCS, Derek Patey, Peter and Rose Flower, Neil and Anita Christopher)*; [The Quay], *Mermaid*: Fine view of harbour from picture-window bar done up with maritime relics, rough wood, stone floor, large winter stove and dim lighting; music for young people in cellar bar; well kept Devenish real ales, bar food inc some fish, new licensees trying hard *(Peter and Rose Flower, Margaret and Roy Randle)*
☆ **St Agnes** [The Quay; SV8807], *Turks Head*: The islands' star licensees, John and Pauline Dart, have returned after a brief spell on the mainland to take over this small but cosy

good value *(Charles and Mary Winpenny, S P Bobeldijk, LYM)*
☆ **Zennor** [SW4538], *Tinners Arms*: Very promising — plain but reliable food and St Austell real ales in comfortable stripped-pine bar, in beautiful setting nr coast path *(Brian Skelcher, Paul and Elizabeth Wright, K Flack, Neil and Anita Christopher, Julian Proudman, LYM; more details of new regime please)*

and very friendly pine-panelled bar in idyllic surroundings, with magnificent sea and island views from the garden terrace; warmly welcoming service, good range of drinks — though not real ale — and snacks, particularly huge home-made pasties, at fair prices; open all day summer, boats from St Marys most nights during season; singsongs Sun and Thurs; ideal stop-off after trip to Bishop Rock *(Brian Barefoot, Peter and Rose Flower, Derek Patey, Pat and Malcolm Rudlin, TBB, Keith and Sian Mitchell, Dave Mead, Angie and David Parkes, Margaret and Roy Randle, GCS)*
St Martins [SV9215], *Seven Stones*: Quickly served bar snacks inc crab in friendly but bare bar, pool table; super views to Tresco and beyond; closed 5-7 *(Neil and Anita Christopher, Peter and Rose Flower)*; *St Martins*: Good choice of simple reasonably priced home-made bar food inc delicious quiches, sea views and friendly service in genteel lounge or on lawn of newish plush hotel (marble columns and so forth), in idyllic spot looking across to Tresco; Devenish Steam real ale; bedrooms *(Neil and Anita Christopher, Gwen and Peter Andrews)*
☆ **Tresco** [New Grimsby; SV8915], *New Inn*: Basic but friendly old cottage-style inn with decent bars, good choice of bar lunches such as sandwiches, soup and huge pizzas, more interesting evening food, decent wine, pool table; welcoming staff, nice garden, small swimming pool; comfortable bedrooms, a nice place to stay *(Neil and Anita Christopher, John and Ruth Roberts, George Atkinson, Peter and Rose Flower)*

Cumbria

New entries here, or pubs back in the Guide after an absence, include the traditional Angel on Alston's steep and picturesque main street (cheap food), the Coledale Inn in a fine fell-foot setting at Braithwaite, the civilised Travellers Rest just outside Grasmere, the idiosyncratic Old Crown up at Hesket Newmarket (brewing its own good beers), the unusual Snooty Fox in Kirkby Lonsdale (really interesting food), the beautifully placed Middleton Fells at Middleton, the well run Dalesman in Sedbergh (a comfortable place to stay) and the cheerful and well kept Queens Arms at Warwick-on-Eden (real home cooking). These are all in or particularly well placed for fine countryside. Indeed, this is probably the best region of England for finding pubs and inns in lovely surroundings – many in stunning locations, ideal for walkers. Pub food has become very good here now – often imaginative, not just the warming hearty food which has traditionally been the strong point of Lakeland and Pennine pubs. Other pubs here to note for good food include the Royal Oak in Appleby (a star award this year, for all-round excellence), the Hare & Hounds at Bowland Bridge (a popular dining pub), the Masons Arms on Cartmel Fell (now brewing very interesting beers; a particularly nice pub, with around half its food now vegetarian), the friendly Pheasant at Casterton, the Sun in Coniston, the lively old Sun in Kirkby Lonsdale, the Shepherds at Melmerby (lots of local produce, first-class cheeses), the friendly White Horse at Scales (currently doing specially well – in the running for a star award) and the Bay Horse just outside Ulverston (really innovative cooking). Other pubs on particularly good form at the moment include the very friendly Barbon Inn in the village of that name, the Sun at Bassenthwaite (a nice Italian/Lakeland mixture), the engagingly traditional New Inn at Brampton just by Appleby, the splendid Britannia in its lovely spot by Elterwater, the Blue Bell at Heversham (a new licensee), the Hare & Hounds at Levens, the Kirkstile Inn so strategically placed at Loweswater, the friendly Tower Bank Arms at Near Sawrey (handy for the Beatrix Potter farm), and the unpretentious Kings Arms at Stainton. The area's high proportion of free houses will appeal to people with a particular interest in beer, as will the good local ales produced by Jennings and Yates (and, on a smaller scale, by our main entry the traditional Sun in Dent); sadly, Robinsons who bought Hartleys some years ago closed its brewery in 1991 – the formerly prized XB now comes from Stockport. In the Lucky Dip section at the end of the chapter, pubs and inns showing particular appeal (most inspected by us) include the Queens Head at Askham, Hole in t' Wall in Bowness, Marys Chambers in Carlisle, Wainwrights at Chapel Stile, Old Posting House at Deanscales, Swan just outside Grasmere, Dog & Gun in Keswick, Shepherds at Langwathby, George in Penrith, Ship at Sandside, Newfield at Seathwaite, Fat Lamb between Sedbergh and Kirkby Stephen, Church House at Torver, Mortal Man at Troutbeck and Bay Horse at Winton.

AMBLESIDE   NY3804 Map 9

Golden Rule

Smithy Brow; follow Kirkstone Pass signpost from A591 on N side of town

This traditional Lakeland pub has a very local atmosphere – lots of chat and no piped music. The bar has lots of local country pictures and a few fox masks on the butter-coloured walls, horsebrasses on the black beams, built-in leatherette wall seats, and cast-iron-framed tables. The room on the left has darts, a fruit machine and dominoes; the one down a few steps on the right is a quieter sitting room. Well kept Hartleys Bitter and XB on handpump, good baps, filled French sticks and some meals. There's a back yard with tables, a small pretty summer garden, and wonderfully colourful window-boxes. Near the start of *Good Walks Guide* Walk 130. *(Recommended by H K Dyson, Peter Barnsley, D Swift, Graham Bush, Simon Tormey, Andrew and Ruth Triggs, A Parsons, Andy and Jill Kassube)*

Hartleys (Robinsons)   Tenant John Lockley   Real ale   Meals and snacks   Coniston (053 94) 33363   Children welcome   Nearby parking virtually out of the question Open all day

ALSTON   NY7246 Map 10

Angel £

Front Street (A689)

On the steep cobbled main street of this quaintly old-fashioned Pennine village, this is popular for quickly served family food including sandwiches (from £1; the open prawn one is quite a meal), home-made soup (£1.10), very popular Japanese prawns (starter £1.70, main £4.30), ploughman's (£2.50), salads (from £3), good Cumberland sausage (£3.20), mushroom and nut fettucini (£3.50), a well made steak and mushroom pie (£3.70), 12oz gammon and egg (£4.80), 8oz sirloin steak (£6.50), and puddings like sticky toffee or pavlova (£1.25); children's helpings, too. The black-beamed and timbered L-shaped bar has wheelback chairs and traditional black wall seats around dimpled copper tables, and logs burning in a big stone fireplace; well kept McEwans 70/- and Tetleys on handpump, darts, and juke box. A sheltered back garden has some seats. *(Recommended by R J Yates, Dave Braisted, Margaret and Roy Randle)*

Free house   Licensee J N E Ashcroft   Real ale   Meals and snacks (not Tues evening) Alston (0434) 381363   Children welcome   Open 11–4, 7–11   Bedrooms; £13/£26

APPLEBY   NY6921 Map 10

Royal Oak ★ ⊘ ⇌

Bongate; B6542 on S edge of town

We've had so much warm praise from readers for the friendly welcome and good service, excellent food at fair prices, decent choice of drinks, and clean, comfortable bedrooms, that this year we've decided to award this popular inn a star. The bar food is fresh and home-made and typically includes superb soup with home-made bread, lunchtime sandwiches such as home-cooked ham and beef (£1.25), traditional lunchtime ploughman's (£1.95), Cumberland sausage (made by hand by the local butcher's wife £2.75), hot pancakes stuffed with apple and stilton (£2.95), real brown Lancashire shrimps (£3.45), vegetarian dishes such as hazelnut and mushroom roast with carrot sauce or savoury crumble (£3.95), pie of the day, English gammon and egg (£4.95), cod and prawn pie (£5.25), and steaks (from £7.45); adventurous daily specials, children's meals (from £1.50), and puddings (from £2); the breakfasts are gigantic. Well kept Bass, Theakstons Best, local Yates Bitter, Youngers Scotch, and guest beers on handpump; several malt whiskies, and a carefully chosen wine list. The beamed lounge has old pictures on the timbered walls, some armchairs and a carved settle, and a panelling-and-glass snug enclosing the bar counter; there's a good open fire in the smaller, oak-panelled public bar; dominoes. Seats on the front terrace, among masses of flowers in tubs, troughs and hanging baskets, overlook the red stone church; the building itself is based on a partly 14th-century posting house. *(Recommended by Jill and Peter Bickley, S E Dark, Anthony Barnes, Adam and Elizabeth Gorb, Carol and Philip Seddon, S V Bishop, FG, JG, Gill and Maurice McMahon, Mel Landells, F J Robinson, Kathryn Ogden, George Hunt, Caroline Wright, Roger Etherington, David Young, Andy and Jill Kassube, Michael and Joan Melling, Mike Beiley)*

Free house   Licensees Colin and Hilary Cheyne   Real ale   Meals and snacks   Restaurant   Kirkby Thore (07683) 51463   Children welcome   Open 11–3, 6–11; closed 25 Dec   Bedrooms; £21.50B/£50B   See also entry under nearby Brampton

ASKHAM   NY5123   Map 9

Punch Bowl

Village signposted on right from A6 4 miles S of Penrith

One of the main attractions here is the pub's position – at the bottom of the lovely lower village green, and facing the wall of the Lowther estate. The good bar food is another: lunchtime sandwiches, good smokies (£2.65), deep-fried stilton (£3.20), fine ploughman's (£4.30), turkey bake (£4.85), fritters (£5.05), and steak (from £7.70). The rambling beamed bar has a mix of interesting furnishings that include an antique settle by an open log fire, Chippendale dining chairs and rushwork ladder-back seats around the sturdy wooden tables, well cushioned window seats in the white-painted thick stone walls, and local photographs and prints of Askham; the old-fashioned woodburning stove, with its gleaming stainless chimney in the big main fireplace, is now largely decorative. Well kept Boddingtons and Whitbreads Castle Eden on handpump, with guest beers kept under light blanket pressure; dominoes, cribbage and piped pop music, and in the separate public bar darts, pool, and fruit machine. There are tables out on a gravelled side terrace. *(Recommended by Peter Barnsley, Nigel Hopkins, W H Bland, Mr and Mrs G W Hodgson, Mrs P Cardy, D J Milner)*

Whitbreads   Lease: David Riley   Real ale   Snacks (lunchtime) and meals   Restaurant   Hackthorpe (093 12) 443   Children welcome   Live entertainment Friday evening once a month   Open 11.30–3, 6.30–11; 11–11 school holidays; 12–2.30, 7–11 winter   Bedrooms; £17.50/£35

BARBON   SD6383   Map 10

Barbon Inn ★ ☞

Village signposted off A683 Kirkby Lonsdale–Sedbergh; OS Sheet 97, map reference 628826

This civilised inn is a welcoming place with good, reasonably priced food and kindly service. Several small rooms lead off the main bar, each individually and comfortably furnished with carved 18th-century oak settles, deep chintzy sofas and armchairs, and lots of fresh flowers. Home-made bar food includes sandwiches (from £1.20), excellent soup (£1.35), tasty Morecambe Bay potted shrimps (£3.25), duck and chicken liver pâté (£2.85), Cumberland sausage (£3.75), platters and salads (from £3.50), home-roasted ham (£4.25), home-made steak and kidney pie (£4.95), sirloin steak (£8.50), and puddings like home-made fruit pie (£1.45). Well kept Theakstons Best and Old Peculier on handpump, and quite a few wines; dominoes and piped music. The neatly kept, sheltered garden is very prettily planted and floodlit at night; some paths and tracks lead up to the fells. New 18-hole golf course half a mile away and pony trekking 2 miles away. *(Recommended by Ray and Gwen Jessop, J E Rycroft, S V Bishop, John Atherton, MAC, I H Rorison, Michael and Joan Melling, A P Jeffreys, Barbara Wensworth, Ben Wimpenny, Hayward Wane, H K Dyson, M A and W R Proctor)*

Free house   Licensee Lindsey MacDiarmid   Real ale   Meals and snacks   Restaurant   Barbon (046 836) 233   Children welcome   Open 12–3ish, 6.30–11   Bedrooms; £24/£46

BASSENTHWAITE LAKE　NY2228 Map 9

Pheasant ★ 🏠

Follow Wythop Mill signpost at N end of dual carriageway stretch of A66 by Bassenthwaite Lake

Though this is very much a smart and civilised hotel, the two rooms of the bar are distinctly pubby. Linked by a fine wood-framed arch, they have rush-seat chairs, library seats, cushioned settles, hunting prints and photographs on the fine ochre walls, and a relaxed, old-fashioned atmosphere; the hatch at the low serving counter leads to the entry corridor through a traditional wood-and-glass partition. Good, freshly made lunchtime bar food includes soup (£1.35), ploughman's or Cumberland pork and ham pie (£3.25), salmon mousse (£3.40), smoked local Herdwick lamb with melon (£3.85), sweet smoked chicken (£4.10), and smoked venison, duck and Cumberland sauce (£4.65); they do main dishes in the dining room (which is no smoking). Well kept Bass and Theakstons Best on handpump, fresh orange juice, lots of malt whiskies, and English country wines. A large and airy beamed lounge at the back has easy chairs on its polished parquet floor and a big log fire on cool days; there are also some chintzy sitting rooms with antique furniture (one is no smoking). You can walk into the attractive beechwoods from the garden. A reader whose room booking was given up to someone else was told it was his fault for not confirming in writing (though he hadn't been told to do this); so do write to be on the safe side. *(Recommended by Jill and Peter Bickley, I H Rorison, Dennis Jones, M Box, Mr and Mrs Simon Turner, W H Bland, Hayward Wane, Richard Holloway, Mr and Mrs J E Rycroft, M A and W R Proctor, Simon Bates, D T Taylor, John and Anne McIver)*

Free house　Licensee W E Barrington Wilson　Real ale　Lunchtime snacks Restaurant　Bassenthwaite Lake (07687) 76234　Children in lounge and restaurant (not Sun)　Open 11(11.30 winter)–3, 5.30–10.30; till 11 Friday and Saturday; closed 24 and 25 Dec　Bedrooms; £48B/£86B

BASSENTHWAITE　NY2332 Map 9

Sun

Village itself, signposted off A591 a few miles NW of Keswick

The atmosphere here is notably friendly and the licensees (he's Italian, she's from the Lakes) are the sort of people who remember you if you go a second time – even months later. It's much used by locals and though it looks tiny from outside, its bar rambles around into areas that stretch usefully back on both sides of the servery. There are built-in wall seats and plush stools around heavy wooden tables, low 17th-century black oak beams, lots of brasses, and a good stone fireplace with big logs burning in winter. The favourite dishes here are meaty or vegetarian lasagne or cannelloni with garlic bread (£4.50), as well as minestrone soup (£1.30), salads (from £3.50), ploughman's (£3), steak and kidney pie or squid in batter (£4.50), gammon or excellent pork in mushroom sauce (£5), sirloin steak (£7.50), puddings such as apple pie (£1.75), and children's helpings (£2.50); the range is surprisingly wide for such a tucked-away place. Well kept Jennings with a guest like Tetleys on handpump; juke box (rarely used), fruit machine and in winter darts, dominoes and pool; no dogs. There are a few tables in the front yard by a neighbour's blackcurrant patch, in the heart of this charmingly close huddle of white houses looking up to Skiddaw and other high fells. *(Recommended by C A Holloway, Dr D Radley, Mr and Mrs L D Rainger, Mrs O Tarlow, Nigel Pritchard, Michael Wadsworth, D P Ryan, M A and W R Proctor, P J and S E Robbins)*

Jennings　Tenants Giuseppe and Josephine Scopelliti　Real ale　Meals and snacks (12–1.30, 6.30–8.30ish; not Sun evening)　Keswick (07687) 76439　Children in family room next to bar (no prams or pushchairs)　Open 12–3, 6–11; winter 12–2.30, 6.30–11

BEETHAM SD5079 Map 7

Wheatsheaf £ 🛏

Village (and inn) signposted just off A6 S of Milnthorpe

Busy at lunchtime and in the evening, this pleasant old pub is very handy for the old road to the Lakes. The lounge bar has attractive built-in wall settles, tapestry-cushioned chairs, a massive antique carved oak armchair, a cabinet filled with foreign costume dolls, fox mask and brush, lots of exposed beams and joists, and a calm old golden labrador. There's also a little central snug, and beyond that a tiled-floor bar with darts, dominoes and fruit machine; piped music. Reasonably priced bar food includes home-made soup (£1.05), sandwiches (from £1.30), good home-made pies like cottage with cheesy topping (£2.55) or steak and mushroom (£3.50), salads (from £2.55), sausage, liver and bacon (£2.70), fresh fish of the day (£3.60), salads (from £2.90), and steaks (from £6.15); Sunday lunch (£6.65) and a set evening menu in the dining room (£8.50); agreeable service. Thwaites Bitter on handpump, quite a few malt whiskies and wines, tea, coffee or milk. There's a fine black-and-white timbered cornerpiece – a glorified two-storey set of gabled oriel windows jettied out from the corner and into the quiet village street; the windows have sadly been recently damaged by lorries. (*Recommended by G Dobson, Robert and Vicky Tod, Dr T E Hothersall, Margaret and Roy Randle, A T Langton, K H Frostick, P W Brindle, P Lloyd, Miss K Bamford, Kathleen Morley, Maurice and Gill McMahon, Barbara M McHugh, Dr R Fuller*)

Free house   Licensee Mrs Florence Miller   Real ale   Meals and snacks (11.45–1.45, 6–8.45)   Restaurant   Milnthorpe (05395) 62123   Children in eating area till 8.30 Open 11–3, 6–11; closed 25 Dec evening   Bedrooms; £30B/£40B

BIGGAR SD1965 Map 7

Queens Arms

On Isle of Walney; follow A590 or A5087 into Barrow-in-Furness centre, then Walney signposted through Vickerstown – bear left on the island

Children enjoy coming to this pub because it's right next to a large beach – which may well be virtually empty, with only the curlews and wading birds for company; there's a nature reserve to the south. The snug little bar has an open fire in its stone fireplace, wheelback chairs and tapestried built-in banquettes, a delft shelf, and a good deal of brown varnish. Rustic seats and tables shelter in the yard, and opening off this there's a smallish eating room with high-backed settles forming booths around the tables and a more spacious restaurant. Bar food includes home-made soup, sandwiches (from £1.50), ploughman's (£3.75), home-made steak and kidney pie or lasagne, puddings such as lemon brûlée (£1.95), and specials like ham and mushroom pancake (£4.95) or roast rack of lamb (£5.95). Hartleys XB and occasional guest beers on handpump. To reach the pub, the road threads past a series of gigantic shipyard gates, weaves across a couple of great drawbridges, then tracks down the island. (*Recommended by TBB, Brian Jones; more reports please*)

Whitbreads   Tenant Cyril Whiteside   Real ale   Meals and snacks (not Mon) Restaurant   Barrow-in-Furness (0229) 471113   Children in eating area of bar   Open 11.45–3, 6.30–11; closed Mon except bank hols

BOOT NY1801 Map 9

Burnmoor

Village signposted just off the Wrynose/Hardknott Pass road, OS Sheet 89 map reference 175010

The landlord of this partly sixteenth-century, family-run pub shepherded for years on the hills around here and can suggest good walks – of which there is no lack, such as up along Whillan Beck to Burnmoor Tarn; and *Good Walks Guide* Walk

125 is nearby. There are seats outside on the sheltered front lawn, and it's close to Dalegarth Station (the top terminus of the Ravenglass and Eskdale light steam railway). Inside, the beamed and carpeted white-painted bar has an open fire, red leatherette seats and small metal tables. Generous helpings of quickly served bar food include delicious soup (£1), lunchtime ploughman's (£2.90), wholemeal cheese and onion flan (£2.90), breaded haddock (£3.50), cold beef or ham (£3.70), Cumberland game pie (£4.90), Wienerschnitzel (£5.40), sirloin steak (£7), and puddings (£1.20); children's menu (£2.30); they grow a lot of the vegetables themselves, and keep hens and pigs. Well kept Jennings Bitter and Cumberland on handpump; dominoes, juke box, pool room. *(Recommended by Miss A G Drake, Andy and Jill Kassube, Margaret and Roy Randle, Comus Elliott, A M Neal, Steve and Maureen Collins)*

Free house　Licensees Tony and Heidi Foster　Real ale　Meals and snacks (12–2, 6–9)　Restaurant　Eskdale (094 03) 224　Children welcome till 9　Open 11–3 (2.30 winter), 5–11　Bedrooms; £18.40/£37 (£40.90B)

BOWLAND BRIDGE　SD4289　Map 9

Hare & Hounds 🖙

Village signposted from A5074; OS Sheet 97 map reference 417895

This popular dining pub – down by the bridge itself – has a friendly atmosphere in its comfortably modernised bar. Stub walls divide it into smaller areas, and there are ladder-back chairs around dark wood tables on the Turkey carpet, blue and white china, reproduction hunting prints, a stuffed pheasant, and open fires; dominoes. The landlord used to play for Liverpool and England – as the team photographs and caps on the wall testify. Good bar food includes sandwiches (from £1.30; the turkey are good and thick), soup (£1.20), ploughman's (£3.85), pizzas (from £3.75), Cumberland sausage (£3.85), salads (from £3.85), coq au vin (£4.95), and steaks (from £7.95); good, prompt service. Well kept Tetleys on handpump, from a long bar counter with a cushioned red leatherette elbow rest for people using the sensible backrest-type bar stools. There are geraniums in hanging baskets and climbing roses on the walls, with picnic-table sets in the spacious garden at one side. *(Recommended by George Mitchell, A L Wark, G R Braithwaite, Andy and Jill Kassube, R C Watkins, Brian Jones, Dave and Kate Buckley, Peter Barnsley, N F Calver, TBB, Carol and Richard Glover)*

Free house　Licensee Peter Thompson　Real ale　Meals and snacks　Restaurant (residents only)　Crosthwaite (044 88) 333　Children welcome　Open 11–3, 5.30–11　Bedrooms; £29 (£29S)/£38 (£38S)

BRAITHWAITE　NY2324　Map 9

Coledale Inn

Village signposted off A66 W of Keswick; pub then signed left off B5292

Excellent walks straight from the door of this solid three-storey Lakeland house strategically placed at the foot of the Whinlatter Pass, with dramatic views of Skiddaw and of the much closer bracken-covered hills around the village. On a sunny day it's hard to beat the quiet garden, with its tables and chairs on the slate terrace beyond the sheltered lawn. Inside, the comfortable main bar has cushioned wall and window seats in two rooms connected by an arch, attractive informal flower arrangements (foxgloves, willow gentian and the like), a winter coal fire and little 19th-century Lakeland engravings; the green-toned bar on the right, with a bigger bay window, is more of a dining bar. Several readers have found the bar food just right for hungry walkers; vegetable soup (£1.10), sandwiches (from £1.30), filled baked potatoes (£2.35), salads (from £3.35), ploughman's (£3.55), Cumberland sausage (£4), vegetarian tortellini (£5.05), steak (£6.60), and puddings with custard or cream (£1.40) have all been recommended, with dishes of the day such as beef curry (£5.05) and several children's dishes (£1.45 – reversing the usual practice, they offer these in double helpings at double prices for adults).

The dining room is no smoking. Well kept Yates, Youngers Scotch, and a beer brewed locally for the pub on handpump; winter darts, fruit machine, piped music, friendly service. The fluffy pub dogs enjoy chasing passing dogs, so visitors should keep theirs on a lead. We've not yet heard from readers who've stayed here, but would imagine that it would be enjoyable. *(Recommended by KC, Andy and Jill Kassube, WFL, R K Sutton)*

Free house   Licensee Peter Mawdsley   Real ale   Meals and snacks   Braithwaite (059 682) 272   Children welcome   Open 11–11; may close winter afternoons if quiet Bedrooms £22.90S/£52.87S

BRAMPTON   NY6723 Map 10

New Inn

Off A66 N of Appleby – follow Long Marton 1 signpost then turn right at church; village also signposted off B6542 at N end of Appleby

In the second week of June the Committee of the Appleby Horse Fair pretty much uses this well kept and friendly 18th-century inn as its base, so it tends to get packed then – especially in the dining room, which becomes the special preserve of the gipsy women. It's a well proportioned, flagstoned and carpeted room with horsebrasses on its low black beams, well spaced tables, and a splendid original black cooking range at one end, separated from the door by an immensely sturdy old oak built-in settle. Good value home-made food is served here and includes soup (£1.15), chicken and duck liver pâté with Cumberland sauce (£1.95), potted shrimps (£2.35), the house speciality (caught by the landlord and locally smoked) smoked salmon (£3.60), pizzas (from £2.35), Cumberland sausage and egg (£3), chicken curry (£3.70), popular spinach roulade (£3.90), pork escalopes (£5.40), seafood mornay (£5.50), sirloin steak (£7.70), and puddings like fruit crumble or chocolate fudge cake (£1.50). They also do lunchtime sandwiches (from £1.15; steak £2.50) and ploughman's (£2.50); on Sundays, besides three-course lunches (£5.50, children £2.50), there's a more limited choice. The two cosy little rooms of the bar have a medley of seats including panelled oak settles and a nice little oak chair. There's a mass of local pictures, mainly sheep and wildlife; a stuffed fox is curled on top of the corner TV, and a red squirrel pokes out of a little hole in the dividing wall. Well kept Theakstons Bitter and XB, Whitbreads Castle Eden and Youngers Scotch on handpump; a good choice of whiskies with some eminent malts, and half a dozen English wines; friendly service, and no games other than dominoes. No dogs in bedrooms. *(Recommended by S V Bishop, Jill and Peter Bickley, Andy and Jill Kassube, Mrs S Fielding, Gill and Maurice McMahon, Paul and Janet Waring, Peter Adcock, Dave Braisted)*

Free house   Licensees Roger and Anne Cranswick   Real ale   Meals and snacks (not winter Tues)   Restaurant   Kirkby Thore (07683) 51231   Children till 9pm   Open 11–3, 6–11; closed Tues lunchtime Dec (open Christmas week), Jan and Feb Bedrooms; £18/£36

CARTMEL FELL   SD4288 Map 9

Masons Arms ★ ★

Strawberry Bank, a few miles S of Windermere between A592 and A5074; perhaps the simplest way of finding the pub is to go uphill W from Bowland Bridge (which is signposted off A5074) towards Newby Bridge and keep right then left at the staggered crossroads – it's then on your right, below Gummer's How; OS Sheet 97 ref 413895

This lovely old-fashioned pub keeps a staggering range of drinks, with some 250 bottled beers from all over the world, including thirty or so from around Britain; a helpful and comprehensive leaflet pre-empts at least some of the inevitable confusion. It's also one of the few pubs we know that has real German beer on draught – Furstenburg Export and Antonio, and Weizenthaler; new this year on draught is Belgian Liefmanskriek – a cherry beer based on a brown ale. Besides these, they keep Thwaites Bitter, Theakstons XB, and a guest beer. From their own micro-brewery they produce Amazon (light and hoppy but quite strong, and named for Arthur Ransome, the author of *Swallows and Amazons*, who used to live in the area), Big Six and Great Northern, as well as damson beer (based loosely on Belgian fruit beer but probably the first commercially brewed fruit beer in Britain – strong and dry) which will be a Christmas beer (though as they are just going into bottling their own beers it will be also be available all year round). Also interesting farm ciders and perrys and country wines, and espresso and cappuccino coffee. The main bar has low black beams in a bowed ceiling, country chairs and plain wooden tables on polished flagstones, needlework samplers and country pictures, a big log fire, and by it a grandly Gothick seat with snarling dogs as its arms. A small lounge has oak tables and settles to match its fine Jacobean panelling, and a plain little room beyond the serving counter has more pictures and a fire in an open range; the family room has an old-parlourish atmosphere; occasional piped music. The plentiful and wholesome food is now 50% vegetarian and includes soup (from £1.95), sandwiches, hazelnut and lentil pâté or ploughman's (£4.25), fisherman's pie or cajun chicken, Cumberland sausage and cider casserole (£6.25), and specials such as okra and cashew nut curry or creamy apple, onion and cheese bake (£4.50), tortellini stuffed with ricotta and served with tomato and basil sauce (£4.75), pan-fried breast of chicken with lemon and tarragon (£5.75), and lamb and apricot casserole (£6.25); puddings such as crunchy lemon freeze or chocolate berry bliss; service is coolly efficient. The setting is unrivalled – overlooking the Winster Valley to the woods below Whitbarrow Scar; a good terrace, with rustic benches and tables, makes the most of the view. They sell leaflets outlining local walks of varying lengths and difficulty. There are good self-catering flats in an adjoining stone barn. The stream of customers is inevitably at its heaviest at weekends and high season; it's often much quieter mid-week. (*Recommended by Bob Smith, Robert and Vicky Tod, Dave Braisted, J R Smylie, C Crockett, S Chauveau, T Lindmarker, Dr R H M Stewart, N E Stanton, H K Dyson, Mr and Mrs Simon Turner, Roger and Carol Chisnall, Dennis Jones, Martin and Gill Searle, David and Kate Jones, Rita Horridge, Richard Carpenter, Paul and Janet Waring, Mike Tucker, GB, A M Neal, Terry Glendenning, Paul Wreglesworth, Carol and Richard Glover, Andy and Jill Kassube, A Parsons, M A and W R Proctor, G Dobson, J Scarisbrick, Simon Bates, M H Box, Janet and John Towers, Steve and Maureen Collins, Barbara Wensworth, Graham Bush, Mrs V A Middlebrook, TBB, R J Yates*)

Own brew Licensees Helen and Nigel Stevenson Real ale Meals and snacks (12–2, 6–8.45) Crosthwaite (044 88) 486 Children welcome till 9pm Open 11.30–3, 6–11 Self-catering flats available

CASTERTON SD6379 Map 7

Pheasant 🐾 ⇐

A683 about a mile N of junction with A65, by Kirkby Lonsdale

Good personal service from the owners and staff make this neat and civilised white-painted inn a lovely place to stay. And the food is good, too. At lunchtime this includes home-made soups (£1.85), sandwiches (from £2.25), cheese omelette (£4.25), very good Cumberland sausage (£4.50), home-made steak and kidney pie (£4.75), gammon (£5.75), and puddings (£2.75); in the evening there is a far wider choice in the restaurant only. The two comfortably modernised rooms of the main bar have ladder-back chairs and antique tables, newspapers and magazines to read, and an open log fire in a nicely arched bare stone fireplace. Well kept Theakstons Old Peculier and Youngers Scotch on handpump, several wines, coffee and tea. The dining room and garden lounge are no smoking. There are some tables with cocktail parasols outside by the road. The nearby church (built for the girls' school of Brontë fame here) has some attractive pre-Raphaelite stained glass and paintings. (*Recommended by Mrs Norma Mundy, Jill and Peter Bickley, John Whitfield, Mr and Mrs J French, Diana Dickinson, Mr and Mrs C F Jolliffe, Wynne Hughesman, Mr and Mrs M V Melling, Thelma and George Clarke, TBB, P Lloyd, Miss K Bamford*)

Free house Licensee David Seed Hesmondhalgh Real ale Lunchtime bar meals and snacks (12–1.45, 6.30–9) Evening restaurant Kirkby Lonsdale (05242) 71230

Children welcome, though none under 7 in restaurant   Open 12–2.30(3 Sat),
6–10.30(11 Sat); closed Mon except bank hols, 25 and 26 Dec and Jan 5-Feb 5
Bedrooms; £37.50B/£52.50B

CONISTON   SD3098   Map 9

Sun 🕰 🛏

Inn signposted from centre

Spectacular bare fells surround this substantial stone inn and tracks from the lane lead straight up to the Old Man of Coniston. There are white tables out on the terrace, and a big, tree-sheltered garden runs down to a steep little beck. Fishing, riding and shooting can all be arranged for residents, and the start of *Good Walks Guide* Walk 126 is nearby. Inside, the back bar has lots of Lakeland colour photographs and some recalling Donald Campbell (this was his HQ during his final attempt on the world water speed record), cask seats (one pair remarkably heavy) as well as spindleback chairs and brown plush built-in wall benches around the traditional cast-iron-framed tables, and a small but very warm log fire; the floors are part carpeted, part handsome polished flagstones. Home-made bar food includes a good soup of the day such as tomato and tarragon (£1.10), sandwiches (from £1.15), pâté (£2.75), ploughman's (from £2.95), Cumberland sausage or tuna mornay (£3.75), cottage pie (£4.50), fisherman's pie (£4.75), and gammon steak (£5.25); puddings such as sticky toffee or real bread and butter pudding. Jennings, Marstons Pedigree and Tetleys on handpump and electric pump, from the deep sixteenth-century granite cellar, and lots of malt whiskies; friendly staff; darts, dominoes, piped music. The restaurant is no smoking. *(Recommended by Ian Coburn, Bob Smith, Peter Burton, Tony and Lynne Stark, Caroline Gibbins, Becky Carron, C Crockett, S Chauveau, T Lindmarker, Ed Birch, Mr and Mrs Simon Turner, Robert and Vicky Tod)*

Free house   Licensees Richard, Philip and Stephen Elson   Real ale   Meals and snacks (12–2, 6–9); not 25 Dec   Restaurant   Coniston (053 94) 41248   Children in eating area mealtimes only   Open 11–11   Bedrooms; £30(£35B)/£60(£70B)

CROSTHWAITE   SD4491   Map 9

Punch Bowl

Village signposted off A5074 SE of Windermere

The bar in this heavy-slated white 16th-century inn has been imaginatively reworked to give a lot of space in several separate areas. It's all spick and span, with close-fitted carpets, and there's a high-raftered central area by the serving counter with an upper gallery on either side; steps lead down into a couple of small dimly lit rooms on the right, and there's a doorway through into two more airy rooms on the left. Through here the furnishings are particularly comfortable, with well spaced tables, good hunting prints and open fires giving a relaxed feel. Generously served bar food includes home-made soup (£1.60), sandwiches (from £1.90; Mon-Thurs lunchtimes), salads (from £3.95), Cumberland sausage or home-made vegetarian lasagne (£4.50), curry of the day (£4.75), seafood mornay (£5.75), steaks (from £7.95), children's dishes (£2.75) and good puddings such as spiced apple crumble (£1.95). Well kept Theakstons Best and summer guest beers such as Theakstons Old Peculier or Youngers Scotch on handpump, and several malt whiskies; friendly, smartly dressed staff. Darts, pool, dominoes, unobtrusive piped music, fruit machine and juke box (tucked away down at the lower end). There are some tables on a terrace stepped into the hillside; dogs allowed. The bedrooms have four-posters. The pub is a meeting place for vintage-car enthusiasts about four times a year (money is raised for guide dogs for the blind). *(Recommended by Stephen R Holman, A A Worthington, J R Smylie, Anne and Tim Neale, Robert and Vicky Tod, Barbara McHugh)*

Free house   Licensee Anita L Crompton   Real ale   Meals and snacks   Restaurant   Crosthwaite (044 88) 237   Children welcome away from bar   Open 11.30–2.30(3

Sat), 6–11; winter evening opening 6.30; closed 25 Dec and 3 days in Jan   Bedrooms; £29B/£35B

DENT   SD7187 Map 10

Sun

Village signposted from Sedbergh; and from Barbon, off A683

This pretty and traditional little pub's own Dent Brewery, set up in a converted barn some three miles up in the Dale, now produces about 1,000 gallons a week, and supplies its Bitter and Ramsbottom to some other pubs and breweries in the area; they're also available here, of course, together with well kept Theakstons XB and Youngers Scotch on handpump. The bar has fine old oak timbers and beams (studded with coins), dark armed chairs, brown leatherette wall benches, lots of local snapshots and old Schweppes advertisements on the walls, and a coal fire; one of the areas is no smoking. Through the arch to the left are banquettes upholstered to match the carpet (as are the curtains). Generous helpings of good value bar food include home-made soup, sandwiches, home-made chicken curry (£2.95), home-made steak and kidney pie (£3.15), 12 oz Cumberland sausage (£3.25), rump steak (£4.35), and T-bone when available (£5.95); children's helpings, enormous breakfasts; friendly service. Darts, pool, dominoes, cribbage, fruit machine, and juke box (in the pool room). There are rustic seats and tables outside; it can get very busy in summer. *(Recommended by Ray and Gwen Jessop, Paul S McPherson, John Atherton, Mr and Mrs J H Adam, H K Dyson, Ruth Humphrey, Wayne Brindle)*

Free house   Licensee Martin Stafford   Real ale   Meals and snacks (not 25 Dec)   Dent (058 75) 208   Children welcome until 9pm   Open 11–2.30, 7–11, all day Sat and during school holidays   Bedrooms; £13.50/£27

ELTERWATER   NY3305 Map 9

Britannia Inn ★ 🛏

Off B5343

A happy mix of customers crowds into this popular little Lakeland pub to enjoy the friendly atmosphere and staff, well kept beer, and decent bar food. At the back is a small and traditionally furnished bar where ramblers are welcome (even with their muddy boots), and the front bar has settles, oak benches, Windsor chairs, winter coal fires, and a couple of window seats looking across to Elterwater itself through the trees on the far side; there's also a comfortable lounge. Well kept Jennings Bitter and Mild, Marstons Pedigree and Mitchells Bitter on handpump, Bulmers cider, over 20 malt whiskies, a well chosen, good value wine list, and country wines; darts, dominoes and cribbage. Good home-cooked bar food includes home-made soup (£1.15), lunchtime filled wholemeal baps (£1.15) and ploughman's (£3.25), filled baked potatoes (from £1.65), cheese and onion quiche (£4.35), salads, pork chop baked with cider, onions and apples or local rainbow trout (£4.65), daily specials, puddings like home-made bread and butter pudding (£1.75), and children's dishes (from £1.75); the restaurant is no smoking. The front terrace has chairs and slate-topped tables. Langdale and the central lakes are close by and there are tracks over the fells to Grasmere and Easedale. In summer, people flock to watch Morris and Step and Garland Dancers on the pretty village green. Near the start of the *Good Walks Guide* Walk 128. *(Recommended by Brian Jones, BKA, S D Samuels, Robert and Vicky Tod, Derek and Sylvia Stephenson, K and J O'Malley, Colin Pearson, Tony and Lynne Stark, J R Smylie, Dennis Jones, John Atherton, M Box, W H Bland, Ian Clayton, Hilary Thorpe, John Fazakerley, Andy and Jill Kassube, H K Dyson, Tim Locke, Mary and Lionel Tonks, M A and W R Proctor, Simon Bates, J Scarisbrick, BKA, Raymond Palmer, D J Cooke, Steve Dark, Barbara Wensworth)*

Free house   David Fry   Real ale   Meals and snacks   Restaurant   Langdale (096 67) 210 – changing in 1992 to (05394) 37210   Children welcome   Occasional morris dancing   Summer parking may be difficult   Open 11–11; closed 25 Dec and evening 26 Dec   Bedrooms; £43(£49S)/£48(£54S)

ESKDALE GREEN   NY1400 Map 9

Bower House ⛫

1/2 mile W of village towards Santon Bridge

An unusual bonus for a Lake District pub is the well tended and sheltered lawn and garden here. The lounge bar has cushioned settles and Windsor chairs that blend in well with the original beamed and alcoved nucleus around the serving counter, and there's a good winter fire; also, a separate lounge with easy chairs and sofas. Good value bar food includes sandwiches (from £1.20), home-made soup (£1.40), Cumberland sausage (£3.50), salads (from £4), lasagne (£4.50), gammon and egg or steak and kidney pie (£4.75), sirloin steak (£8.50), and daily specials (which can run out quite quickly) such as spicy prawns (£2.50), guinea fowl with fresh herb sauce or loin of lamb with mint and cucumber (£5.50), and home-made puddings like sticky toffee pudding or raspberry cheesecake (£1.75); the restaurant is no smoking. Well kept Hartleys XB, Ruddles, and Youngers Scotch on handpump, a reasonably priced wine list, and quite a few malt whiskies; dominoes. Close to *Good Walks Guide* Walk 125. Some bedrooms are in the annexe across the garden. (*Recommended by Simon Turner, Roger and Carol Chisnall, Graham Bush, Tim and Sue Halstead, Michael Brookes, Ian Briggs, Simon Baker, Peter Watkins, Pam Stanley, Andy and Jill Kassube*)

Free house   Licensee Derek Connor   Real ale   Meals and snacks (12–2, 6.30–9.30) Restaurant   Eskdale (0946) 723244)   Children welcome   Open 11–3, 6–11 Bedrooms; £39.25B/£53.50B

FAUGH   NY5155 Map 9

String of Horses ⛫

From A69 in Warwick Bridge, turn off at Heads Nook, Castle Carrock signpost, then follow Faugh signs – if you have to ask the way, it's pronounced Faff

This pretty 17th-century inn has Dutch blinds and lanterns, and more lanterns and neat wrought iron among the greenery of the sheltered terrace. Residents have the use of a Jacuzzi, sauna, solarium and small outdoor heated pool. Inside, the open-plan bar is made up of several cosy communicating rooms with heavy beams, fine old settles and elaborately carved Gothick seats and tables, as well as simpler Windsor and other chairs, panelling and Laura Ashley wallpaper. There are log fires in cool weather, brass pots and warming pans, and some interesting antique prints. Bar food includes sandwiches, home-made soup (£1.25), filled Yorkshire puddings or lunchtime ploughman's (£2.95), Cumberland sausage (£3.75), salads (from £4.25), good steak and oyster pie (£4.95), chicken tikka (£5.50), gammon with peach and cottage cheese (£5.75); also, daily specials and puddings (£1.95). Several malt whiskies and an extensive wine list; dominoes, fruit machine, and piped music. (*Recommended by Richard Holloway, Dr T E Hothersall, John and Anne McIver*)

Free house   Licensees Anne and Eric Tasker   Meals and snacks   Restaurant   Hayton (0228) 70297 or 70509   Children welcome   Occasional live music in restaurant Sat Open 11.30–3, 5.30–11   Bedrooms; £58B/£65B

GRASMERE   NY3406 Map 9

Travellers Rest

A591 outside village

Very friendly new licensees took over this late 16th-century inn in August 1990. The comfortable, beamed lounge bar is furnished with bluey-grey banquettes and cushioned wooden chairs around varnished wooden tables, there are local watercolours, suggested walks and coast-to-coast information on the walls, some horsebrasses by the bar counter, and piped classical music; just inside the door is a large, welcoming log fire. The no smoking dining room is similarly furnished as is the games room which is popular with families; pool, darts, shove-ha'penny, dominoes, fruit machine, video game, trivia, and juke box. A wide choice of entirely home-made bar food includes lunchtime ploughman's (from £3.75) and open sandwiches (from £3.85), as well as soup (£1.50), local trout pâté (£2.95), 8oz prime beefburger (£3.65), local Cumberland sausage and apple sauce (£4.45), vegetable chilli (£4.50), steak and kidney pie or chicken curry (£4.75), scampi (£5.75), steaks (from £7.75), daily specials, and puddings like hot sticky toffee pudding or fruit pies (£1.95). Well kept Jennings Bitter and Cumberland on handpump, and several malt whiskies. Outside is a side garden with picnic-table sets and a stream. There are lovely walks and wonderful scenery all around. *(Recommended by Janet and Paul Waring, S Fazackerly, H K Dyson, Peter Adcock, Bill Sykes)*

Free house   Licensees Lynne and Graham Sweeney   Real ale   Meals and snacks (12–3, 6–9.45)   Grasmere (096 65) 604   Children welcome   Live entertainment in winter   Open 11–11; closed 3–6.30 Sun   Bedrooms; £19.50/£39

nr HAWKSHEAD   SD3598   Map 9

Drunken Duck

Barngates; the hamlet is signposted from B5286 Hawkshead–Ambleside, opposite the Outgate Inn; OS Sheet 90 map reference 350013

Even though this old white pub is off the beaten track in peaceful hill country, it's always busy. Several pubby rooms have beams, good fires, cushioned old settles, blond pews, ladderback country chairs, and tapestried stools on fitted Turkey carpet, lots of landscapes, Cecil Aldin prints, and a big longcase clock. Daily-changing, home-made bar food includes filled rolls (£1.50), soup such as curried parsnip (£1.50), hummus or duck liver pâté (£2.75), Cumberland sausage casserole, vegetarian stroganoff or cauliflower and broccoli bake (all £4.75), chilli con carne (£4.95), deep-fried duck (£5.25), and lots of puddings such as jam or syrup roly poly or sticky toffee pudding (£2.25). Well kept Jennings, Marstons Pedigree, Tetleys Bitter, Theakstons XB and Old Peculier, and Yates Bitter on handpump; over 70 whiskies and Australian and New Zealand wines; darts. Seats on the front verandah look across to Lake Windermere in the distance; to the side there are quite a few rustic wooden chairs and tables, sheltered by a stone wall with alpine plants along its top, and the pub has fishing in a private tarn behind. Dogs welcome. *(Recommended by Bob Smith, B C Armstrong, I H Rorison, Dr John Innes, D Swift, Sally Palmer, MAC, R K Sutton, J R Smylie, Robert and Vicky Tod, H K Dyson, W A and S Rinaldi-Butcher, A T Langton, Tim and Sue Halstead, Viv Middlebrook, C F Walling, Andy and Jill Kassube, Andrew and Ruth Triggs, Simon Bates, Cathy Long, Bev and Doug Warrick, Greg Parston)*

Free house   Licensee Peter Barton   Real ale   Meals and snacks   Hawkshead (096 66) 347   Children in rooms away from main bar   Open 11.30–3, 6–11   Bedrooms; £40B/£59.50B

HAWKSHEAD   SD3598   Map 9

Kings Arms 🏠

The terrace here is a fine place to sit with its old-fashioned teak seats and oak cask tables around the roses and overlooking the central square of the delightful Elizabethan village. The low-ceilinged bar has red-cushioned wall and window seats and red plush stools on the Turkey carpet, and an open fire. Bar food includes home-made soup, lunchtime sandwiches (from £1.35), ploughman's (from £3.20), salads (from £3.50), lasagne (£4.45), home-made steak and mushroom pie (£4.65), and 8oz sirloin steak (£6.75), with specials like game pie, puddings (£1.85), and children's menu (£2.20); the restaurant is no smoking. Jennings and Tetleys on handpump, with Theakstons Best and Old Peculier under light blanket pressure, and quite a few malt whiskies; dominoes, fruit machine and piped pop music. The coins embedded in the oak beams of some of the bedrooms are very much in keeping with the picturesque old-fashionedness of the inn. They supply free permits to guests for the nearby public car park.

(Recommended by Dr John Innes, S Fazackerly, R W Challinor, W H Bland, N E Bushby, H K Dyson)

Free house   Licensee Rosalie Johnson   Real ale   Meals and snacks (12–3, 6–9.30) Restaurant   Hawkshead (096 66) 372   Well behaved children welcome   Open 11–11   Bedrooms; £23(£25.50B)/£37(£46B)

Queens Head

Attractive and friendly street-corner pub with a low-ceilinged, open-plan bar that's popular with diners: heavy bowed black beams, red leatherette wall seats and plush stools around heavy traditional tables on the discreetly patterned red carpet, and a few plates decorating one panelled wall; a snug little room leads off. Popular bar food includes home-made soup (£1.45), lunchtime sandwiches (from £1.75), ploughman's (£3.50), salads (from £4.75), tagliatelle carbonara or filled giant Yorkshire pudding (£4.95), beef goulash (£4.75), grilled gammon and steaks; the restaurant is no smoking. Well kept Hartleys XB and Robinsons Bitter on handpump; piped music. The village is a charming and virtually car-free network of stone-paved alleys winding through huddles of whitewashed cottages. *(Recommended by Dr John Innes, Jonathan Moorhouse, Mr and Mrs Simon Turner, W H Bland, James and Libby Cane, Viv Middlebrook, Dennis and Pat)*

Hartleys   Tenant Tony Merrick   Real ale   Meals and snacks   Restaurant Hawkshead (096 66) 271   Children in restaurant and eating area of bar   Occasional live jazz   Open 11–5, 6–11   Bedrooms; £28.50(£36)/£44(£51B)

HESKET NEWMARKET   NY3438   Map 9

Old Crown

Village signposted from B5299 in Caldbeck

Part of a stone terrace facing a long narrow green, with Caldbeck Fells rising behind, this is prettily placed in the lovely northern fringes of the Lake District that relatively few tourists reach. The little bar's very homely, with just four tables, comfortably serviceable chairs, a coal fire, shelves of well thumbed books (they have a lending library with a small donation to charity), a sleepy ginger cat and a friendly orangeman labrador called Blot ("as in on the landscape"). They brew their own interesting beers: Skiddaw Special (light and refreshing), Blencathra (darker and hoppier, though no stronger), Old Carrock (strong) and Doris's 90th (named for the landlady's mother's birthday in 1989); also Thwaites on handpump, a good few malt whiskies. Bar lunches consist of good stock-pot soup (£1.20), robust sandwiches (from £1.20, home-baked ham £1.40) and filled baked potatoes (from £1.40); in the evening there's quite an emphasis on Indian dishes such as chicken korma or vindaloo (£3.80) and rogon josh or kheema matar (£4.20), though they also do lasagne (£3.50) or trout (£4.20). Sunday lunch (£5.50). Service is friendly and pleasantly direct; everyone's treated as a real person. There's a fuller evening menu; the side dining room is small and simple, with a nice little upright stove. A public bar on the right has pool; darts, shove-ha'penny, dominoes, draughts and Trivial Pursuit. Though the bedrooms are simple, they are good value – especially considering the excellent breakfasts. *(Recommended by David Heath, Peter Krugman, Andy and Jill Kassube)*

Own brew   Licensees Liz Blackwood and Jim Fearnley   Real ale   Meals (evening, Sun lunchtime) and snacks   Caldbeck (069 98) 288   Children in dining room   Open 12–3, 5.30–11; may be closed winter lunchtimes   Bedrooms in next door cottage; £14/£28

HEVERSHAM   SD4983   Map 9

Blue Bell

A6 (now a relatively very quiet road here)

Once a vicarage, this white and partly black-timbered inn has pewter platters hanging from the beams in the bay-windowed lounge bar, an antique carved settle, comfortable cushioned Windsor armchairs and upholstered stools on the flowery carpet, small antique sporting prints on the partly panelled walls, and an open fire. One big bay-windowed area has been divided off as a children's room, and the long, tiled-floor, quieter public bar has darts and dominoes. Under the new licensee the bar food includes home-made soup (£1.25), open sandwiches (from £1.35), lovely Morecambe Bay potted shrimps or home-made quiche (£2.50), tasty home-made cottage pie (£2.95), locally baked steak and kidney pie (£3), and salads (from £4.85, fresh salmon £5.35). Well kept Sam Smiths OB on handpump, with Museum kept under light blanket pressure; helpful staff; pool, fruit machine, and piped music. Crossing over the A6 into the village itself, you come to a picturesque church with a rambling little graveyard; if you walk through this and on to the hills beyond, there's a fine view across to the estuary of the River Kent; the estuary itself is a short walk from the pub down the country road that runs by its side. *(Recommended by Mrs Joan Harris, Anthony Sargent, Caroline Gant, Andy and Jill Kassube, Maurice and Gill McMahon, Pamela E Roper, D J Cooke, Raymond Palmer, D T Taylor, Dr T W Hoskins, Bev and Doug Warrick)*

Sam Smiths   Manager T P Atherton   Real ale   Meals and snacks (11–2.30, 6–9.30) Restaurant   Milnthorpe (05395) 62018   Children welcome   Open 11–3, 6–11 Bedrooms; £46B/£68B

KIRKBY LONSDALE   SD6278 Map 7

Snooty Fox ⚲

Main Street (B6254)

Popular bar food here includes home-made soup with freshly baked soda bread (£1.65), interestingly filled baked potatoes (from £2.65), filled pancakes such as ricotta cheese and spinach (from £3.15), ploughman's (£3.90), fresh fettucini stir fry with chicken and vegetables (£4.25), prawns in a fiery Indian sauce or bacon, apple and sage crusty pie (£4.90), good farmers grill, tasty braised ham shank, home-made steak and kidney pudding (£5.10), cold pink roast sirloin of beef with salad (£5.40), haunch of venison marinated in red wine and cooked in a creamy elderberry wine sauce (£6.40), and home-made puddings such as delicious crumble (£2); huge breakfasts. Well kept Hartleys XB and Youngers Scotch on handpump, sensibly chosen wine list, country wines, and coffee or tea. Get there early, especially on Thursday – market day. There are several rambling rooms with mugs hanging from beams, eye-catching coloured engravings, stage gladiator costumes, stuffed wildfowl and falcons, mounted badger and fox masks, guns and a powder-flask, horse-collars and stirrups and so forth. Also, bar counters made from English oak, some oak panelling, country kitchen chairs, pews, one or two high-backed settles and marble-topped sewing-trestle tables on the flagstones, two coal fires, and shutters. Fruit machine and good juke box. There are tables out on a small terrace beside the biggish back cobbled stableyard. *(Recommended by Peter Barnsley, Rob Weir, Derek and Sylvia Stephenson, Rita Horridge, Joan and Dennis Bird, Andy and Jill Kassube, Barbara and Mike Williams, Anthony Barnes)*

Free house   Licensees Andrew Walker, Jack Shone   Real ale   Meals and snacks (12–2.30, 7–10)   Restaurant   Kirkby Lonsdale (0468) 71308   Children welcome 11–11; 11–3, 6–11 in winter   Bedrooms; £20(£25B)/£35B

Sun ⊨

Market St (B6254)

This lively and atmospheric little inn has several comfortably modernised, low beamed, rambling rooms with a large collection of some 300 banknotes (with another 200 yet to go up), maps, old engravings, and battleaxes on the walls, some of which are stripped to bare stone or have panelled dados; furnishings include green plush cushioned seats, captains' and spindleback chairs on the red carpet, stools by the long bar counter in the front room with good backrests, and winter fires. Good, homely bar food such as sandwiches, black pudding with mustard sauce (£2.30), home-made beefburger (£3.50), pizzas (choose your own topping from £3.75; takeaway service till 11pm), chicken and broccoli bake or feta cheese and spinach in filo pastry (£3.95), lamb and rosemary pie (£4.25), cajun fish with pilaf rice (£5.75), puddings (from £1.75), and daily specials. Well kept Boddingtons, Dent Bitter (from the Sun in Dent), and Youngers Scotch and No 3 on handpump, and 45 malt whiskies; quick, cheerful service; dominoes and piped music. There's an unusual pillared porch; the steep cobbled alley is also attractive. *(Recommended by Derek and Sylvia Stephenson, Anthony Barnes, Colin and Shirley Brown, K Croxton, JM, PM, Joan and Dennis Bird, Mr and Mrs R P Begg, Michael Marlow, Sarah Bullard)*

Free house   Licensees Andrew and Belinda Wilkinson   Real ale   Meals and snacks (11–2, 6–10)   Restaurant   Kirkby Lonsdale (05242) 71965   Children in eating area of bar   Open 11–11   Bedrooms; £20.50(£20.50B)/£36(£42B)

LANGDALE   NY2906 Map 9

Old Dungeon Ghyll 🏠

B5343

This is a real fell-walkers' and climbers' haven – you can almost watch them steam as they sit by the huge fire in the cosy, basic but characterful bar; furnishings are very simple, there are window seats cut into the enormously thick stone walls, and a grand view of the Pike of Blisco rising behind Kettle Crag. Marstons Pedigree and Owd Rodger, Theakstons XB and Old Peculier, Yates Bitter and guest beers on handpump, farm cider, and a fair range of malt whiskies; shove-ha'penny, dominoes and cards (absolutely no noisy games machines or piped music). Good value, home-made bar food includes home-made soup with home-made bread (£1), sandwiches (£1.20), beef casserole, lasagne, chilli con carne or fresh fish (from £3.50), and puddings (from £1); book if you are not a resident and want a full evening meal. It can get really lively on a Saturday night (there's a popular National Trust campsite opposite). The inn is dramatically surrounded by fells – including the Langdale Pikes flanking the Dungeon Ghyll Force waterfall which inspired Wordsworth's poem 'The Idle Shepherd Boys'. *(Recommended by BKA, H K Dyson, Tony and Lynne Stark, R Etherington, Steve Dark, Andy and Jill Kassube, Andrew and Ruth Triggs, Mike Beiley, R E Horner, Lesley Sones, Geralyn Meyler)*

Free house   Licensee Neil Walmsley   Real ale   Meals (12–2.30, 6–8.30; all day Sun) No smoking evening restaurant   Langdale (096 67) 272   Children welcome Occasional live music Weds evenings   Open 11–11; closed 23–26 Dec   Bedrooms; £22.50(£26.50B)/£45(£53B)

LEVENS   SD4886 Map 7

Hare & Hounds

Village signposted from A590; since completion of dual carriageway link, best approach is following route signposted for High Vehicles

Handy for Sizergh Castle, this pleasant village pub has an interesting display of old fire-engine artefacts. The low-beamed, carpeted lounge bar is furnished with a wicker-backed Jacobean-style armchair and antique settle on its sloping floor, as well as old-fashioned brown leatherette dining seats and red-cushioned seats built into the partly panelled walls. The tap room at the front is a snug place, and has darts, cribbage and dominoes; there's a golden-oldie juke box and a fruit machine in the separate pool room, down some steps. Well kept Vaux Samson and Wards on handpump. Bar food includes soup (£1.20), lunchtime sandwiches (from £1.30) or ploughman's (£3.85), plaice or tasty lasagne (£3.95), salads (from £3.95), steak and kidney pie (£4.05), puddings like home-made sticky toffee pudding (£1.80), with extra dishes in the evening such as gammon (£6.10) and steak (£7); children's dishes (from £2.25). *(Recommended by G Dobson, A T Langton, P W Brindle, I H Rorison, Andy and Jill Kassube, WAH, Maurice and Gill McMahon, Edward and Jean Rycroft, Ruth Humphrey, Simon Bates, Dr R Fuller, D T Taylor, J Scarisbrick)*

Vaux   Tenants Pat and Maggie Dolan   Real ale   Meals and snacks; no food Sun-Tues

evenings Oct–Mar   Milnthorpe (05395) 60408   Children in lounge bar and pool room only, until 8pm   Open 11–3, 6–11

LITTLE LANGDALE   NY3204 Map 9

Three Shires ⇔

From A593 3 miles W of Ambleside take small road signposted The Langdales, Wrynose Pass; then bear left at first fork

The extended back bar in this comfortable stone-built inn has stripped timbers and a beam-and-joist stripped ceiling, Lakeland photographs on the walls, a modern stone fireplace and chimney piece with a couple of recesses for ornaments, and antique oak carved settles, country kitchen chairs and stools on its big dark slate flagstones; an arch leads through to a small, additional area. Ruddles County and Websters Yorkshire on handpump, lots of malt whiskies, a comprehensive wine list, coffee, tea (with meals only), and hot chocolate; darts, cribbage. Bar food includes soup (£1.35), lunchtime sandwiches (from £1.40), good ploughman's (from £3.50), salads (from £3.95), Cumberland sausage (£4.25), home-made steak and kidney pie (£4.60), local trout (£5.60), sirloin steak (£8.95), daily specials, puddings (£1.75), and children meals (£2.50); in the evening, dishes are slightly more expensive; good breakfasts. There are lovely views from the terrace out over the valley to the partly wooded hills below Tilberthwaite Fells, and there are more seats on a well kept lawn behind the car park, backed by a small oak wood. The pub is on *Good Walks Guide* Walk 128. *(Recommended by R C Watkins, K Croxton, Ursula Thompson, M A Watts, M H Box; more reports please)*

Free house   Licensee Ian Stephenson   Real ale   Meals and snacks (no evening food Dec and Jan)   No smoking restaurant (closed Sun lunchtime)   Langdale (096 67) 215   Children in eating area of bar if eating – till 9pm   Open 11–11; 11.30–2.30, 8–10.30 in winter; closed 25 Dec   Bedrooms; £25/£50(£56B)

LOWESWATER   NY1222 Map 9

Kirkstile

From B5289 follow signs to Loweswater Lake; OS Sheet 89, map reference 140210

At the foot of soaring fells and not far from the water, this welcoming little inn is much used by walkers. The low-beamed and carpeted bar has a big log fire, comfortably cushioned small settles and pews, and partly stripped stone walls; there are fine views from the big bow windows in one of the rooms off here. Decent bar food includes home-made wholemeal filled rolls (from £1.30), good home-made soup (£1.50), filled baked potatoes (from £2.25), home-made pasty (£2.50), ploughman's (£3), bean and tomato casserole (£3.50), omelettes (from £3.85), grilled bacon chop, egg, mushrooms and tomato (£4.95), sirloin steak (£8.25), and puddings (£1.50); good breakfasts, lovely high teas, morning coffee. Well kept Jennings on handpump, a good choice of malt whiskies, and tea; darts, dominoes, cribbage, and a slate shove-ha'penny board; a side games room called the Little Barn has pool, fruit machine, video game and juke box. There are picnic-table sets on the lawn. *(Recommended by Dr and Mrs A K Clarke, Beryl and Tim Dawson, Theo Schofield, H K Dyson, Andy and Jill Kassube, D M and D E Livesley, Michael Brookes, Simon J Barber, Caroline Wright, P J and S E Robbins, Simon Bates)*

Free house   Licensees Ken and Shirley Gorley   Real ale   Meals and snacks (12–2.30, 6–9)   Restaurant (closed Sun)   Children welcome   Open 11–11   Bedrooms tel Lorton (090 085) 219; £28.50(£37B)/£37(£45B)

LOWICK GREEN   SD2985 Map 9

Farmers Arms

A590 N from Ulverston, then left on to A5092 after about 4 miles

Behind a massive wooden door several centuries old, the public bar of this busy, rambling old hotel has heavy beams, huge flagstones and a handsome fireplace with a big open fire; some seats are in cosy side alcoves. The hotel itself is across the yard, with its own plusher lounge bar, and a preserved spinning gallery. Bar food includes home-made soup, sandwiches, and daily specials such as stilton and walnut pâté (£2.95), spicy bean goulash (£4.45), venison sausage and Cumberland sauce or leek and ham crumble (£4.60), and giant Yorkshire pudding filled with game casserole or roast of the day (£4.85). Theakstons XB and Old Peculier or Youngers 80/- on handpump, a decent wine list and a good choice of spirits; dominoes, fruit and trivia machines, and piped music; also pool room and darts alley. *(Recommended by A J Lemm, Raymond Palmer, Andy and Jill Kassube, Mary and Lionel Tonks, Simon Bates; more reports please)*

Scottish & Newcastle   Manager Alan Lockwell   Real ale   Meals (12–2, 6–9; noon–9pm Sun) and snacks (all afternoon)   Restaurant   Greenodd (0229) 861376 or 861277   Children welcome   Open 11–11; closed 26 Dec and 1 and 2 Jan   Bedrooms; £28.50(£41B)/£51B

MELMERBY   NY6237 Map 10

Shepherds ⚲

About halfway along A686 Penrith–Alston

As well as a really wide choice of good cheeses (over 26 to choose from to have with your ploughman's, from £3 – the mature cheddar is *really* mature) and tasty home-made puddings, there might be soup (£1.40), pork and port pâté (£3.60), home-cooked ham (£4.50), plaice (£3.95), flavoursome Cumberland sausage and egg (£4.20), chicken curry, lasagne or steak and kidney pie (£5.30), beef bourguignonne (£6.20), a mountain of spare ribs, very tender spiced lamb with yoghurt or chicken breast Leoni (£5.90), and steaks (from £9.60); lots of daily specials like Italian baked chicken or roast duckling with blackberry sauce, vegetarian dishes such as chestnut and mushroom pie or spinach and feta cheese parcels (£5.20), surprise starters like pasta with strong gorgonzola, and Sunday roast lunch (£4.50). Only local produce and meat is used where possible, and there are nice touches such as their own dijon-style mustard (you can buy it over the counter) and home-made rolls; quick, friendly female table service. Best to get there early. It's a spacious place, with cushioned wall seats, sunny window seats, sensible tables and chairs, light-panelling, lots of pot plants, and an open fire; one room is no smoking. A games bar has darts, pool, dominoes, fruit machine, and juke box. Well kept Marstons Burton, Pedigree, Merrie Monk and Owd Rodger on handpump, as well as 46 malt whiskies, and English fruit wines. Hartside Nursery Garden, a noted alpine and primula plant specialist, is just over the Hartside Pass, and there are fine views across the green to the Pennines. *(Recommended by PLC, Jacquie and Jon Payne, Brenda Crossley, Paul S McPherson, Richard Holloway, Mr and Mrs J H Adam, Dr T E Hothersall, Mike and Wendy Proctor, Richard Holloway, Janet and John Towers, Andy and Jill Kassube, W H Bland, David Morrell)*

Marstons   Tenant Martin Baucutt   Real ale   Meals and snacks (11–2.30, 6–9.45) Children in eating area lunchtime and till 8.30   Open 10.30–3, 6–11; closed 25 Dec

MIDDLETON   SD6397 Map 10

Middleton Fells

A683 Kirkby Lonsdale–Sedbergh

The neatly kept and attractive garden here has pretty shrub and flower borders with sturdy old-fashioned teak benches, and a back terrace with more modern tables and seats; the individual children's playground is popular. The pub is surrounded by the quiet countryside of the Lune valley below the great fells that lead up to Calf Top. Inside, the open-plan bar has oak beams and leaning posts from the old cow stalls (it incorporates the old barn where there's a pool table, darts board and bar stools), green plush wall banquettes and stools, local photographs on the walls, lots of horsebrasses and brass ornaments (some made by the landlord), and a fireplace in local stone; the eating area has upholstered fiddleback chairs, more green plush banquettes and settles. Home-made bar food includes filled rolls (from £1.65), summer ploughman's (£3), main dishes like spare ribs, steak in ale pie, very good lamb and vegetable curry and lasagne (all £4.25), puddings (£1.75), and Sunday lunch (£6.50; children £2.95). Service is friendly; well kept Tetleys Bitter and Youngers Scotch on handpump; darts, pool, dominoes, fruit machine, and juke box (in pool room). *(Recommended by Mrs Joan Harris, Ray and Gwen Jessop, Richard and Sarah Elwell)*

Free house   Licensee John O'Neill   Real ale   Meals and snacks (not Mon Jan-March)   Sedbergh (05396) 20258   Children welcome   Open 11.30–3, 6.30–11; 12–2.30, 7–11 winter; closed Mon Jan-March

NEAR SAWREY   SD3796 Map 9

Tower Bank Arms

B5285 towards the Windermere ferry

Though this black and white pub can get crowded, backing as it does on to Beatrix Potter's farm, it remains a friendly place. The traditionally furnished, low-beamed main bar has a big cooking range with a lovely log fire, high-backed settles on the rough slate floor, local hunting photographs, a grandfather clock, and maybe Emma, Maxwell or Nelson the pub's labradors. Matthew Browns Mild, Theakstons Best, XB and Old Peculier, and Youngers Scotch on handpump, as well as 25 malt whiskies and wine bottled for the pub; darts, shove-ha'penny, dominoes and cribbage. Lunchtime bar food includes soup (£1.30), filled brown rolls (from £1.60), ploughman's (£3.30), home-made quiche (£3.75), and a home-made pie of the day (£4); more substantial evening main meals such as grilled gammon and eggs or Esthwaite trout (£5.50), venison or duckling (£6.50) and good, sticky puddings; helpful service. This is a good area for golf, sailing, birdwatching, fishing (they have a licence for two rods a day on selected waters in the area), and walking. *(Recommended by Mr and Mrs Simon Turner, Terry Glendenning, H K Dyson, Dr John Innes, Andy and Jill Kassube, D T Taylor, Ben Wimpenny, A T Langton, James and Libby Cane, Michael Brookes, Ruth Humphrey)*

Free house   Licensee Philip Broadley   Real ale   Meals and lunchtime snacks (not 25 Dec)   Restaurant   Hawkshead (096 66) 334   Children in eating area of bar lunchtime, in restaurant evening   11–3, 5.30(6 winter)–11   Bedrooms; £27.50B/£37.50B

OUTGATE   SD3699 Map 9

Outgate Inn

B5286 Ambleside–Hawkshead

Well kept and very friendly, this early 18th-century roadside pub has three comfortably modernised and neatly carpeted communicating room areas. The decor and furnishings vary from each to each – button-back wall banquettes as opposed to country-kitchen and housekeepers' chairs, exposed joists rather than plaster ceiling. One part has an alcovey feel with shelves of books and oddments in a cosy corner, in another big windows look out through the beech trees to steep pastures; but all have local photographs and country prints, often carefully lit; open fires. Popular bar food includes sandwiches (from £1.20), several starters, haddock (£3.80), home-made steak and kidney pie (£4.75), mixed grill (£5), steak (£7.65), children's dishes (from £1.80), and puddings. Well kept Hartleys XB and Robinsons on handpump, dominoes, fruit machine, and maybe restrained piped music. There are a couple of tables in front. *(Recommended by Sally Palmer, Roger Hodgson, A T Langton, H K Dyson, G J S May, D T Taylor, Terry Glendenning, Ben Winpenny, Kathleen Morley)*

Hartleys (Robinsons)   Tenants Ian and Katrina Kirsopp   Real ale   Meals and snacks   Hawkshead (096 66) 413   Children welcome till 9   Jazz Fri   Open 11–3, 6–11   Bedrooms; /£33

SCALES NY3427 Map 9

White Horse ⊘

A66 1 1/2 miles E of Threlkeld: keep your eyes skinned – it looks like a farmhouse up on a slope

Though the menu in this comfortable and friendly pub doesn't change much, the high standard of cooking and quality of the ingredients is as good as ever. It's generously served, made mainly from local produce and uses no convenience foods. At lunchtime (when it's advisable to get there early) there are open sandwiches, home-made soup (£1.50), savoury flan or delicious peach halves filled with garlic and herb cream cheese (£3.50), a good ploughman's (£3.75), potted shrimps with hot garlic bread or prawn open sandwich (£3.95), lovely Waberthwaite Cumberland sausage with mushrooms or superb Waberthwaite Cumberland ham with two free range eggs (£4.95); booking is often pretty much essential in the evening: pork fillet with sherry and mushroom sauce (£8.75), steaks (from £8.95), and seasonal specials like fresh Scotch salmon with dill mayonnaise (£8.25) or chicken breast with a mild curry cream sauce and pots of mango chutney, coconut and sliced banana (£8.75); tasty puddings such as excellent sticky toffee ginger pudding, home-made brown bread and honey ice cream or fresh strawberry meringue (£2.40). Well kept Marstons Burton and Pedigree on handpump, and some malts; cheery, efficient service, even when pushed. The beamed bar, which extends into the old kitchen (no smoking), has warm winter fires, dark oak high-backed settle-style seating upholstered in deep red, an unusual textured wall hanging showing a white horse on the fells, and candles and flowers on the tables; there's quite a hunting theme – hunting pictures and local hunting cartoons on the walls, and a growing range of locally mounted animals and birds native to the area; a cosy little snug is installed in what used to be the dairy; dominoes. There are wooden settles, flower boxes and tubs outside. From this isolated cluster of pub and farm buildings, tracks lead up into the splendidly daunting and rocky fells around Blencathra – which have names like Foule Crag and Sharp Edge. (*Recommended by Mrs E Morgan, Mr and Mrs T A Towers, Eddie Sach, Marc and Margaret Wall, Jill and Peter Bickley, PLC, Richard Carpenter, Maurice and Gill McMahon, A J Brown, Tony and Lynne Stark, Graham Bush, Anthony Sargent, Caroline Gant, S V Bishop, Richard Holloway, Richard Osborne, Mr and Mrs Simon Turner, Stephanie Sowerby, Pat and Dennis Jones, A M Neal, Lesley Sones, Geralyn Meyler, Caroline Wright, Mary and Lionel Tonks*)

Free house Licensees Laurence and Judith Slattery Real ale Meals and lunchtime snacks Threlkeld (07687) 79241 Only children over 5, only in eating area Open 11–3, 6–11; 12–2, 7–11 in winter; closed 25 Dec

SEDBERGH SD6692 Map 10

Dalesman 🛏

Main St

Stripped stone and beams, stuffed grouse and other creatures, Vernon Stokes gundog pictures, houseplants, tropical fish, a log-effect gas fire and cushioned seats around dimpled copper tables make for a lively mix of styles that somehow seems to underline the cheerful atmosphere in this comfortably modernised old pub. A buttery area through stone arches on the right has a wide choice of popular food including soup (£1.50), filled rolls and toasties (from £2), several starters or snacks such as garlic mushrooms (£2.85), filled baked potatoes (from £3.80), ploughman's (£4), salads (from £4), haddock (£4.30), moussaka, lasagne, omelette or steak and kidney pie (£4.95), local venison with walnuts and redcurrants (£6.50), salmon (£6.80), 10oz sirloin steak (£8.95), and lots of dishes of the day such as fresh crab (£3.50), vegetable biriani or mushroom feuilletines (£3.95) and honey-roast duck (£8.50); children's dishes (from £2.80), Sunday roast beef (£4.50), friendly service. Well kept Ind Coope Burton, Tetleys Bitter and Dark Mild, Youngers Scotch and an interesting beer brewed for the pub by Tetleys (nut-brown, slightly fuller-flavoured and less bitter than the regular brew) on handpump; several wines by the glass and malt whiskies; dominoes, fruit machine, and piped music. There are some picnic-table sets out in front; small car park. *(Recommended by Yvonne and Don Johnson, A Killick, William Mechan, G T Jones)*

Free house   Licensees Barry and Irene Garnett   Real ale   Meals and snacks, also breakfast 8.30–9.30   Sedbergh (053 96) 21183   Children in eating areas   Open 11–3, 6–11; all day school summer hols; closed evening 25 Dec   Bedrooms £18(£20B)/£36(£40B)

STAINTON   NY4928 Map 10
Kings Arms

1 3/4 miles from M6 junction 40: village signposted from A66 towards Keswick, though quickest to fork left at A592 roundabout then turn first right

The pleasant open-plan bar in this modernised old pub has leatherette wall banquettes, stools and armchairs, wood-effect tables, brasses on the black beams, and prints and paintings of the Lake District on the swirly cream walls; piped music. Good value bar food includes soup (95p), sandwiches (from £1.10, open sandwiches from £2.20), filled baked potatoes (£1.40), home-made minced beef pie (£2.50), salads (from £3.20), spinach and walnut lasagne (£3.30), local trout (£3.50), delicious farmhouse gammon with egg or pineapple (£4), and sirloin steak (£6); children's dishes (from £1.50), puddings (from £1), and Sunday lunch. Well kept Boddingtons and Whitbreads Castle Eden on handpump, coffee and tea; friendly staff. Sensibly placed darts, dominoes, fruit machine, fairly quiet juke box, piped music. Probably at its best in the evenings, when there's a good mix of locals and visitors. There are tables outside on the side terrace and a small lawn. *(Recommended by F J Robinson, Mrs Pat Crabb, Richard Holloway, Richard Dolphin, Mr and Mrs J H Adam)*

Whitbreads   Tenant Raymond Tweddle   Real ale   Meals and snacks   Penrith (0768) 62778   Children welcome if eating   Country and Western Sun evening once a month Open 11–3, 6–11

ULVERSTON   SD2978 Map 7
Bay Horse 🕹

Canal Foot signposted off A590 and then again by the large factory

Beautifully presented and very innovative, the range of food here might include home-made baps (£1.35), very tasty tomato, basil and orange soup (£1.35), home-made herb and cheese pâté with cranberry and ginger purée (£3.95), Cumberland sausage with onion and red pepper marmalade and apple sauce or home-made meat and potato pie (£4.75), minced lamb with tomato and almonds topped with egg custard or buttered macaroni with ham and mushrooms in a rich cheese and mustard sauce (£5.50), cod baked on sliced courgettes, apple and water chestnuts with a fresh herb cream sauce (£6.25), and home-made puddings (£2.50). There's also the grill with well hung Scotch steaks (from £11.50); three-course set lunch in the no-smoking conservatory restaurant (£12.50) – the view from here across to Morecambe Bay is outstanding; they hope to extend this room. Besides well kept Mitchells Best and ESB and guests such as Fullers, Marstons, Moorhouses and Timothy Taylors on handpump, there's a decent choice of spirits, and a wine list with a strong emphasis on New-World wines (the sweet Morris Old Liqueur Muscat from Australia, sold by the glass, is recommended); tea, coffee, hot chocolate and home-made shortbread. The civilised but pubby smallish bar has a huge but elegant stone horse's head, attractive wooden armchairs, some pale green plush built-in wall banquettes, glossy hardwood traditional tables, blue plates on a delft shelf, and black beams and props with lots of horsebrasses. Magazines are dotted about, there's a handsomely marbled green granite fireplace, and decently reproduced piped music; darts, shove-ha'penny, cribbage, dominoes, bagatelle, and Connect–4. Out on the terrace are some picnic-table sets. The owners also run an outstanding restaurant at their Miller Howe hotel on Windermere. (*Recommended by Neville Kenyon, C Crockett, S Chauveau, T Lindmarker, Maurice and Gill McMahon, Steve and Maureen Collins; more reports please*)

Free house Licensee Robert Lyons Real ale Lunchtime bar meals and snacks (not Mon) Restaurant (not Sun; closed Jan and Feb) Ulverston (0229) 53972 Children in eating area Open 11–3, 6–11 Bedrooms planned

WARWICK ON EDEN NY4657 Map 9

Queens Arms

2 miles from M6 junction 43: A69 towards Hexham, then village signposted

New licensees took over this cheery and well kept old pub as we went to press and were planning to redecorate the two-roomed bar with its roaring winter log fires. They've also placed a strong emphasis on seasonally changing home-made bar food, often using fresh vegetables from the garden: soup (£1.30), speciality burgers (from £2), large filled granary rolls (from £3), and main dishes like stir-fry chicken, fresh haddock fillets, steak and mushroom pie, stews with dumplings, liver and onions (all £3.50-£3.95), steaks (from £5.65), and puddings such as fruit crumbles or hot chocolate gateau (from £1). Well kept Ind Coope Burton and Tetleys on handpump; piped music. The neat side garden, with roses, marigolds and other flowers, has rustic tables and seats, and a well equipped play area. (*Recommended by S D Samuels, F A Noble, John Gillet, Lesley Jones, Geralyn Meyler*)

Free house Licensee David Hutton Real ale Meals and snacks Wetheral (0228) 60699 Children welcome Open 11.30–3, 5–11 Bedrooms; £28B/£38B

WASDALE HEAD NY1808 Map 9

Wasdale Head Inn 🛏

To NE of lake; signposted from Gosforth

Surrounded by steep fells, this gabled old hotel is popular with walkers and climbers, and Wastwater – the most severely grand of all the lakes – is nearby, surrounded by towering screes. The high-ceilinged, spacious main bar has fine George Abraham photographs on the walls, shiny panelling, cushioned settles on the polished slate floor, and a log-effect gas fire; there's an adjoining pool room, as well as a panelled and comfortably old-fashioned residents' bar and lounge. Well kept Jennings, Theakstons Best and Old Peculier and Yates on handpump, and a good selection of malt whiskies; pool, dominoes, cribbage. Home-made bar food includes soup (£1.40), locally potted shrimps (£3.25), cheese and onion flan (£4.75), steak and kidney pie (£4.10), cold platters (from £4.25), chicken casserole (£5.70), daily specials, and huge breakfasts. There's a self-catering cottage and two flats in converted inn buildings nearby. (*Recommended by R Tomlinson, Andy and Jill Kassube, Roger and Carol Chisnall, H K Dyson, Martin and Gill Searle, Comus Elliott, Kathleen Morley, Simon Bates, T Galligan*)

Free house Licensee Jaspar Carr Real ale Meals and snacks (11–3, 6.30–10) Restaurant Wasdale (094 67) 26229 Children in own room Open 11–11; mid Nov-mid March only open Fri evening, Sat, and Sun lunchtime Bedrooms (they only do dinner, bed and breakfast); no accommodation mid Nov-mid March (except 28 Dec-mid Jan); £51B/£99B

Lucky Dip

Besides the fully inspected pubs, you might like to try these Lucky Dips recommended to us and described by readers (if you do, please send us reports):

Alston [Main St; NY7246], *Turks Head*: Bar divides big front room into two areas, back lounge with cosy fire and small tables; friendly and obliging landlord, good value

food; Theakstons on handpump (*Margaret and Roy Randle*)
☆ **Ambleside** [North Rd; NY3804], *Unicorn*: Small backstreet village local with friendly

landlord and staff, well kept real Hartleys XB and Robinsons, occasional jazz band, good value food; bedrooms nice and quiet, with good breakfasts — good value *(H K Dyson, Andrew and Ruth Triggs, Simon Tormey)*

Ambleside [Lake Rd], *Churchill*: Comfortable hotel bar with real ales, coffee, fiiled French bread and all-day pastries; bedrooms *(Anon)*; [Lake Rd], *Royal Oak*: Busy local, S&N beers *(H K Dyson)*; *Wateredge*: A hotel not a pub, but worth knowing for good food; four big lounges with lake views, very good service; bedrooms comfortable *(D I Baddeley)* nr Ambleside [A592 N of Troutbeck; NY4007], *Kirkstone Pass*: Remote but cheery roadside mountain inn — the highest in Lakeland — with wide choice of whiskies, well kept beer, open fire, lively amusements, cheap simple food (all-day summer cafe); fine surrounding scenery; a useful shelter in bad weather, perhaps at its best in winter; bedrooms *(Simon Bates, H K Dyson, LYM)*

Appleby [Station Approach; NY6921], *Midland*: Worth knowing especially for railway buffs, as this severe-looking but comfortable building is right by the station on the famous Settle—Carlisle line, with railway memorabilia in its two smallish bars; well kept Marstons Pedigree on handpump, open all day *(John and Joan Wyatt, Peter Argent)*; [Market Sq/Boroughgate], *Tufton Arms*: Late Victorian hotel recently renovated, bar on right in period style with antique portrait photographs, contemporary ornaments, oak panelling, furniture fittingly a bit austere but inc a comfortable wall bench, Jennings and Youngers real ales, reasonably varied bar food inc good liver pâté, attentive quick service; seats in cobbled yard; bedrooms *(Anon)*

☆ Armathwaite [NY5146], *Dukes Head*: Good food, well kept Whitbreads Castle Eden, comfortable atmosphere and most concerned landlady; bedrooms *(Peter Griffiths, Mr and Mrs L D Rainger)*

Arnside [SD4678], *Albion*: Attractively plain corner pub with fine estuary views from bar and tables outside overlooking prom, pleasant atmosphere, well kept beer, simple food, no pop music; superb situation; nr start GWG124 *(MGBD, Graham Bush)*; [Promenade], *Olde Fighting Cocks*: Typical seaside pub, big comfortable lounge, cheery landlady, magnificent views over estuary and railway viaduct, well kept Thwaites, good bar food *(Andy and Jill Kassube)*

☆ Askham [village crossroads by lower green; NY5123], *Queens Head*: Popular village pub in attractive surroundings handy for Lowther Pk, bar food inc good steaks on sizzling platters, well kept Vaux and Wards, pleasant decor with gleaming copper and brass, friendly staff; children in back bar until 9; bedrooms comfortable and good value *(Ray and Gwen Jessop, John Atherton, J R Smylie, Roger Broadie, George Hunt,*

Kathryn Ogden, Jill and Peter Bickley, P Corris, Roger Etherington, Richard Holloway, LYM)

☆ Bampton [NY5118], *St Patricks Well*: Imaginative food inc own venison recipe and fresh veg, polite quick service, well kept beer, fine malt whiskies; bedrooms simple but excellent value, with good breakfasts *(S V Bishop, John Burgan, Hilary Irving, C A Holloway)*

Bardsea [SD3074], *Bradylls Arms*: Popular, pleasant dining pub overlooking Morecambe Bay *(Raymond Palmer)*

Barrow in Furness [off A590 Barrow—Ulverston, by abbey ruins; SD2069], *Abbey*: Next to Furness Abbey ruins, recently decently modernised — nice place for a drink and a snack in these beautiful surroundings *(Dave Buckley)*

Beckermet [NY0207], *White Mare*: Worth noting for remarkable value steak; Theakstons XB and Best *(Simon Turner)*

Blencow [NY4633], *Clickham*: Very comfortable, with real fires, quaint alcoves, good efficient service, good meals esp fish, steaks and home-made puddings; well kept Marstons inc Pedigree *(Andy and Jill Kassube)*

Boot [NY1801], *Woolpack*: Good choice of reasonably priced home-cooked food, Theakstons and Youngers IPA on handpump, nice garden; handy for Hardknott Pass; children welcome till 9 *(Andy and Jill Kassube)*

Borrowdale [Ravenscraig; NY2515], *Sca Fell*: Remote hotel with good Riverside Bar, just right for walkers *(R K Sutton)*

☆ Bowness on Windermere [SD4097], *Hole in t' Wall*: Ancient but lively pub with lots of rustic bygones in beamed and slate-floored lower bar, handsome if simply furnished panelled upper room with fine plaster ceiling; basic traditional wall seats etc, simple lunchtime food, well kept Hartleys XB on handpump, open fire, quick service; pool room, juke box; rustic tables in nice flagstoned courtyard; can get crowded *(Maurice Southon, Andy and Jill Kassube, Roy Butler, J R Smylie, Peter Barnsley)*

Bowness on Windermere [SD4097], *Royal Oak*: Good local just off main tourist beat, well kept Castle Eden *(Peter Barnsley)*

Brigsteer [OS Sheet 97 map reference 481896; SD4889], *Wheatsheaf*: Popular for well kept Castle Eden and bar food — esp soups, gammon sandwiches, Cumberland sausages with proper sauce *(A T Langton)*

☆ Buttermere [NY1817], *Bridge*: Sound lunchtime bar food served briskly in simple but comfortable lounge bar of extended stone hotel, well kept Theakstons Best, XB and Old Peculier on handpump, tables on flagstoned terrace; in a lovely spot, handy for Crummock Water and Buttermere — the pretty little village, at the start of GWG135, fills with walkers in summer (though they don't allow boots or walking gear here); evening restaurant; bedrooms *(Richard Holloway, H K Dyson, D Swift, Ben*

Wimpenny, Mr and Mrs Simon Turner)
Calder Bridge [NY0506], *Stanley Arms*:
Largish S & N pub with well kept
Theakstons Best and XB and Youngers IPA,
decent food *(Simon Turner)*

☆ **Cark in Cartmel** [SD3776], *Engine*:
Comfortably modernised pub which has
been well kept and popular, with lots of
brasses and flowers, good open fire, friendly
service, well kept Bass, good range of
whiskies and tables out by little stream; no
news since brewery said to be selling it *(A T
Langton, LYM; reports please)*

☆ **Carlisle** [Mary St, part of County Hotel;
NY4056], *Marys Chambers*: New
open-plan bar, clean and well kept, with
plenty of stripped pine; reasonably priced
food all day from local shrimps through
afternoon sandwiches to steak and kidney
pie or cook-it-yourself sizzler steaks;
Theakstons XB and guest beers, nostalgic
piped music, darts; open all day, handy for
stn; bedrooms *(Mr and Mrs P A Jones, Patrick
Godfrey)*

☆ **Cartmel** [The Square; SD3879], *Kings
Arms*: Relaxed rambling bar with heavy
beams but clean and bright decor, short
choice of popular bar food inc children's
helpings (pleasant service, but can
sometimes slow), well kept Whitbreads
Castle Eden; nice spot on attractive town
square; children welcome till 8.30 *(TBB,
Stephen and Sarah Lake, Barbara and Rory
Nical, J Scarisbrick, Ruth Humphrey, R A
Corbett, Malcolm Ramsay)*
Cartmel [off main sq], *Cavendish Arms*: Old
pub nr lovely 12th-century priory, well kept
Bass, promptly served bar food from
sandwiches to good steaks, clean WCs, good
service; nothing outstanding *(Mr and Mrs J H
Bloom, Andy and Jill Kassube, KC)*; *Royal Oak*:
Well kept Whitbreads-related real ales, good
value food inc tasty lamb chops and mixed
grill, pleasant landlord, clean pub; nice big
garden *(Rita Horridge, Andy and Jill Kassube,
J Scarisbrick, A T Langton)*
Castle Carrock [B6413 S of Brampton;
NY5455], *Weary Sportsman*: Warm and
friendly village local, bar snacks and meals,
no piped music, lovely old fire, Whitbreads
(Comus Elliott)

☆ **Chapel Stile** [B5343; NY3205],
Wainwrights: Pleasant and comfortable
rather than smart, in fine setting alongside
timeshare holiday cottages, with generous
helpings of quickly served good value food
inc children's dishes, well kept Theakstons
XB and Old Peculier on handpump, friendly
atmosphere *(Edward and Jean Rycroft, Arthur
and Mary Beck, H K Dyson, R C Watkins,
Dave Braisted, Andy and Jill Kassube, KC)*
Cockermouth [Main St; NY1231], *Brown
Cow*: Lovely clean pub with quick friendly
staff, generous helpings of good
home-cooked food, Theakstons ales; best to
get there early *(L H Lever)*
Coniston [SD3098], *Crown*: Quickly served
bar food, well kept Hartleys; bedrooms
(Andy and Jill Kassube); Red Lion: Popular

stone-built village pub, several rambling
rooms attracting lunchers and walkers,
pleasant front courtyard looking down High
St and over to Old Man; well kept
Theakstons Old Peculier and Youngers
Scotch *(Lee Goulding);* [Yewdale Rd],
Yewdale: Warmly welcoming landlord,
good bar food, well kept Boddingtons and
Castle Eden on handpump, smart
surroundings; bedrooms comfortable *(Andy
and Jill Kassube)*
Crooklands [A65/B6385, nr M6 junction
36; SD5384], *Crooklands*: Hotel dating to
16th century, good well priced usual bar
food, pleasant staff, good four-course set
meals in upstairs restaurant; bedrooms
(Andy and Jill Kassube)

☆ **Crosby Ravensworth** [NY6215], *Butchers
Arms*: Good value simple food inc splendid
puddings, well kept Marstons Pedigree,
Yates and Youngers Scotch on handpump,
very friendly young licensees (as is Sam the
spaniel), simple but comfortable furnishings,
interesting mountain photographs; pretty
Pennine village; children welcome *(Jill and
Peter Bickley, BB)*

☆ **Dean** [just off A5086 S of Cockermouth;
NY0825], *Royal Yew*: Comfortably
modernised village pub, Stones on
handpump, particularly good value food inc
fine steak, decent unobtrusive service *(C A
Holloway)*

☆ **Deanscales** [A5086 S of Cockermouth;
NY0927], *Old Posting House*: Interesting
old fittings surviving from posting and
coaching days in comfortably modernised
pub with very neat blue furnishings in
split-level bar extending round from servery,
some stripped stone, Lakeland and
heavy-horse prints, good value bar food from
soup, sandwiches, ploughman's and big
Yorkshire puddings through home-made
stews and pies to steaks and mixed grill; well
kept Jennings and Tetleys *(Frederick and
Eileen Ward, M E A Horler, BB)*
Eamont Bridge [handy for M6 junction 40;
NY5328], *Beehive*: One-room village pub
with Hartleys and Whitbreads beers, good
helpings of bar food; children allowed for
meals, play area *(P Corris, Andy and Jill
Kassube)*
Eskdale Green [NY1400], *George IV*:
Many-roomed, oak-beamed pub on
GWG125 which has been popular for wide
range of good value food, well kept
Marstons Pedigree and Theakstons on
handpump, good malt whiskies and wines;
three bedrooms *(Roy Goodwin; more news
please)*

☆ **Far Sawrey** [SD3893], *Sawrey*: Basic
take-us-as-you-find-us Claife Crier stable
bar with wooden stalls dividing tables,
harness on rough white walls, big helpings
of good simple food, well kept Jennings and
Theakstons, welcoming efficient staff; seats
on nice lawn look up to Claife Heights,
which have good views of Lake
Windermere; dogs allowed; nr GWG127;
bedrooms with good family rates *(Heather*

Martin, Robert and Vicky Tod, Mr and Mrs Simon Turner, Alan Wark)

☆ **Garrigill** [NY7441], *George & Dragon*: Friendly and informal 17th-century flagstone bar, good value well presented bar food, well kept beer, freshly cooked food running up to duck and game in stone-and-panelling dining room, good service; on dead-end road in beautiful scenery; bedrooms small but comfortable and clean — good value *(Richard Hooker)*

Glenridding [back of main car park, top of road; NY3917], *Travellers Rest*: Comfortable newish pub with keg beers, worth knowing for its position nr start of GWG132 and food suiting hungry walkers; well organised *(Nigel Hopkins, KC)*

Gosforth [The Square; NY0703], *Globe*: Appealing local in quiet village, hanging baskets and flowers outside, warm welcome in, good wholesome food and outstandingly well kept Theakstons and XB on handpump *(Andy and Jill Kassube)*; [off A595 and unclassified rd to Wasdale], *Wheatsheaf*: Small recently refurbished two-room pub with good food and growing range of well kept real ales inc Bass, Jennings and Marstons Owd Rodger; comfortable games room, helpful newish landlord — very promising *(Mr and Mrs Simon Turner)*

Grange over Sands [Grange Fell Rd; off B5277; SD4077], *Hardcrag Hall*: Elegant and quietly respectable 16th-century manor-house hotel with big log fires and smart locally popular food inc river trout in panelled rooms; bedrooms *(Andy and Jill Kassube)*

☆ **Grasmere** [main bypass rd; NY3406], *Swan*: Good pub lunches in relaxing old-fashioned hotel lounge popular with older people, oak beams, armchairs, velvet curtains, prints and swords, inglenook log fires, efficient obliging service; darts in small sometimes smoky decidedly male public bar, Tetleys (cold), tables in garden, picturesque surroundings; easy parking; THF, comfortable bedrooms *(John Gould, E Morgan, Michael and Joan Melling, R C Watkins, H K Dyson, J H Tate, G Dobson)*

Grasmere, *Tweedies*: Useful bar with well kept Ruddles County, good atmosphere, tartan-topped walls, normally friendly service *(Len Beattie)*; [in village itself], *Wordsworth*: Calm and well kept hotel with impeccably served light lunches in charming conservatory leading out from main bar; separate unpretentious beamed public bar (the Olive Branch) on left, which recent reports suggest is a second choice; comfortable bedrooms; nr start GWG129 *(Mrs Joan Harris, Lesley Sones, Geralyn Meyler, LYM)*

High Newton [just off A590 Lindale—Newby Bridge, towards Cartmel Fell; SD4082], *Crown*: Good value food inc quickly served Sun lunch, some live music; children welcome; bedrooms *(A T Langton)*

Hoff [NY6718], *New Inn*: Atmospheric little pub, full of friendly wellie-clad locals;

basic bar food — ploughman's etc; abundance of stuffed animals might not appeal to all *(Peter Adcock)*

☆ **Ireby** [NY2439], *Sun*: Typical working Lakeland local, white walls, beams, brasses and harness, red plush seats and polished tables; very clean and friendly, with good food, well kept Jennings, woodburning stove *(Marc and Margaret Wall, M A and W R Proctor)*

☆ **Kendal** [Highgate; SD5293], *Olde Fleece*: Smartly refurbished long bars with pleasant atmosphere and service, good helpings of useful bar food *(BKA, Len Beattie)*

Kendal, *Riverside*: Good choice of good food served by willing waitresses in lounge bar, also full meals in buttery; bedrooms *(A L Wark)*

☆ **Keswick** [Lake Rd, off top end Mkt Sq; NY2624], *Dog & Gun*: Cheerfully popular town local with old beams, high settles, partly slate floor (rest carpeted or boards), fine Abrahams mountain photographs, woodburning stove; well kept Theakstons Best, XB and Old Peculier, good bar food, nostalgic taped music; provision for children if eating, no dogs, open all day *(Simon Bates, H K Dyson, Andy and Jill Kassube, W H Bland, Ben Wimpenny, Andrew and Ruth Triggs, Pat & Dennis Jones, D J Cooke, Dick Brown, LYM)*

☆ **Keswick** [St John's St], *George*: Well worn flagstones, old beams, old-fashioned furnishings as well as modern banquettes in bustling main bar; snug black-panelled side bar with log fire (interesting Wordsworth associations), well kept Theakstons and Yates, good lively atmosphere; good value bar food, more upmarket restaurant; trout fishing; bedrooms comfortable *(Simon Bates, Dick Brown, LYM)*

Keswick [Lake Rd], *Four in Hand*: Cosy old panelled back lounge with hunting and local pictures, lots of bric-a-brac, open fire, good food (not Sun in winter); bedrooms *(Carol and Richard Glover)*; [off Market Sq; behind Queens Hotel], *Old Queens Head*: Plush seats down long low-beamed dim-lit modernised bar with low beams, bric-a-brac, bar food, upstairs room with juke box *(Carol and Richard Glover)*; [Crosthwaite Rd; by A66, a mile out], *Pheasant*: Warm welcome in small traditional Lakeland inn, bar lunches and evening meals using fresh local produce, well kept Jennings; bustling and friendly — where the locals eat; bar walls covered with caricatures of them; bedrooms cheap, with huge cheerful breakfast *(Jim Roberts)*

☆ nr **Keswick** [Newlands Valley — OS Sheet 90 map reference 242217], *Swinside*: Clean and friendly country inn in peaceful valley surrounded by marvellous crags and fells — tables outside, and picture-window upstairs dining room, have the view; wide choice of good straightforward bar food, Jennings Mild and Bitter, decent house wine; dogs not welcome; bedrooms; may not open winter lunchtimes *(KC, Richard Holloway, J M*

Watson)

Kirkby Lonsdale [SD6278], *Red Dragon*: Pleasant decor, good atmosphere, wide choice of good value standard food, well kept Jennings, friendly licensees *(Yvonne and Don Johnson, Derek and Sylvia Stephenson)*

☆ **Kirkby Stephen** [NY7808], *Kings Arms*: Cosy and formally comfortable oak-panelled lounge bar, darts and dominoes in easy-going main bar, friendly welcome for strangers, pleasant service, bar food inc good sandwiches and popular lunchtime cold table, well kept Whitbreads Trophy, tables in walled garden; children allowed in restaurant; bedrooms *(Brian Barefoot, LYM)*

Kirkby Stephen [4 Market St; NY7808], *White Lion*: Friendly local with well kept Marstons Burton and good food at sensible prices *(Len Beattie, George Hunt, Kathryn Ogden)*

Kirkcambeck [B6318 N of Brampton; NY5369], *Wheatsheaf*: Small, welcoming country pub with Greenalls beer, good if rather limited bar food and lovely log fire all year *(A J and E M Watts)*

Langwathby [A686 Penrith—Alston; NY5734], *Shepherds*: Good quickly served reasonably priced bar food, good decor in split-level bar, welcoming staff, tables outside, well kept beer *(Mr and Mrs P Yarwood, Dave Whiteley)*

☆ **Levens** [Sedgwick Rd, nr entrance to Sizergh Castle — OS Sheet 97 map reference 500872; SD5087], *Strickland Arms*: Pleasant, clean and comfortable stone-built local, friendly staff, well kept Theakstons Best, popular bar food, piped music *(M A and W R Proctor, I H Rorison, A T Langton)*

Lindale [B5277 N of Grange-over-Sands — OS Sheet 97 map reference 419805; SD4280], *Lindale*: Old coaching inn with wide choice of food in spacious bar and nice oak-beamed dining area (children welcome here); well kept Whitbreads-related real ales; bedrooms *(Bob and Ann Westbrook, Andy and Jill Kassube)*

☆ **Little Bampton** [NY2755], *Tam o' Shanter*: Out-of-the-way village pub made very comfortable by present licensees, with red plush banquettes and log-effect gas fire in big modernised lounge, extending into orderly dining area on right and neatly carpeted games area on left; well worth knowing for its good choice of well prepared and attractively presented food at sensible prices, inc cheap children's dishes; some picnic-table sets outside *(Mr and Mrs L D Rainger, BB)*

☆ **Middleton** [A683 Kirkby Lonsdale—Sedbergh; SD6386], *Swan*: Attractive country inn reopened after closure, with comfortable individual furnishings, good food and pleasant management; nice surroundings *(Mrs R S Young, LYM)*

☆ **Mungrisdale** [village signed off A66 Penrith—Keswick, a bit over a mile W of A5091 Ullswater rd — OS Sheet 90 map reference 363302; NY3731], *Mill Inn*: Lovely valley hamlet hidden away below Blencathra, tables on gravel forecourt and neat lawn sloping to little river, pleasant new landlord, simple bar, bar food and afternoon teas, Theakstons Best, lots of malt whiskies, separate restaurant; can arrange salmon and sea trout fishing on River Eden; seven clean and pleasant bedrooms (note that there's a quite separate Mill Hotel here) *(Anthony Barnes, Christopher Wickens, Andy and Jill Kassube, Mr and Mrs C R Douglas, LYM)*

Nether Wasdale [OS Sheet 89 map reference 125041; NY1204], *Screes*: Perfect setting in spectacular valley, lovely homely atmosphere, good value plain simple bar food, well kept Theakstons and Yates, good choice of malt whiskies; five bedrooms *(Andy and Jill Kassube)*; *Strands*: Good value food just right for fell-walkers, well kept Hartleys and Robinsons, friendly atmosphere, efficient service, piped music (can be on the loud side); bedrooms *(T Galligan, Mr and Mrs Simon Turner, Mr and Mrs D Johnson, KC)*

☆ **Oxen Park** [OS Sheet 97 map reference 316873; SD3287], *Manor House*: Good landlord in quiet and comfortably refurbished beamed pub with good coal fire, well kept Hartleys XB and Robinsons, good home cooking (not Mon or Tues evenings), nostalgic music; good facilities for the disabled; children welcome; bedrooms *(Terry Glendenning)*

Oxenholme [SD5389], *Station*: Well run and quiet unspoilt country pub, with log fire, simple food inc good soup and nourishing sandwiches, long-serving landlord, Whitbreads-related beers; no music except Sat night piano *(MGBD, A T Langton)*

Patterdale [NY3916], *White Lion*: Small friendly pub popular with walkers (nr GWG132), helpful staff, Boddingtons, sandwiches, pizzas etc at lunchtime, evening steaks; banquettes in alcoves; parking 100 yards away across road; bedrooms basic, but good views *(J M Watson, BKA)*

☆ **Penrith** [NY5130], *George*: Well run substantial hotel with old-fashioned lounge hall — oak panelling and beams, handsome plasterwork, oak settles and easy chairs around good open fire, big bow windows; reasonably priced lunchtime bar food, well kept Marstons Pedigree, lively back bar, restaurant; bedrooms *(Frank Davidson, LYM)*

☆ **Penrith** [Cromwell Rd/Castlegate; first roundabout coming from M6], *Agricultural*: The Cumberland sausage here really is something special; other good straightforward food, served promptly, and well kept Marstons in friendly old-fashioned bar *(Barbara Wensworth, J M Potter)*

Penrith, *Lowther Arms*: Smart and spotless, Matthew Brown Mild and Theakstons Best and XB, good value food, friendly efficient staff *(Bob Smith)*; [Gt Dockray], *Two Lions*: Old pub at one end of big central square, good value food in new restaurant, Castle Eden on handpump *(P Corris)*

Piel Island [accessible by ferry from Roa Island, nr Rampside SE of Barrow, or on foot from Walney at low tide; SD2364], *Ship*: Atmospheric pub on one of the small islands in the Walney Channel with two basic rooms, small bar in one, benches and tables in the other and 'throne' in one corner (landlord is, by tradition, the King of Piel); island consists of pub, ruined castle (English Heritage — free entry) and some cottages *(Brian Jones)*

Ravenglass [SD0996], *Ratty Arms*: Ex-railway bar (terminus for England's oldest narrow-gauge steam railway) with well kept beer, low prices, good value restaurant, pool table; can get crowded *(Comus Elliott, Andy and Jill Kassube, LYM)*

☆ **Ravenstonedale** [village and pub signed off A685 Kirkby Stephen—M6; NY7204], *Kings Head*: Neatly refurbisfied beamed bar with log fires, friendly staff, well kept Tetleys, decent bar food and good generous evening meals (booking suggested); children welcome; bedrooms (being refurbished too) *(Michael Marlow, Mike and Wendy Proctor, Frank Davidson, C and L H Lever)*

☆ **Ravenstonedale**, *Black Swan*: Discreetly comfortable, with some stripped stonework, tables in tree-sheltered streamside garden over road; good bar food, Hartleys and Youngers on handpump, friendly licensees; bedrooms *(SS, J E Rycroft, BB)*

Red Dial [NY2546], *Sun*: Old pub tastefully modernised and extended, very big helpings of quickly served bar food such as home-made soup, quiche or lasagne, gammon and sirloin steak; piped music, restaurant *(P R Rainger)*

☆ **Rockcliffe** [NY3661], *Crown & Thistle*: God food in generous helpings served quickly even at busy times, attentive service *(Mr and Mrs L D Rainger)*

☆ **Sandside** [B5282, OS Sheet 97 map reference 478808; SD4781], *Ship*: Extensive modernised pub with glorious view over the broad Kent estuary to the Lakeland hills; bar food, well kept Youngers real ales, decent wines, summer barbecues, tables out on grass by good children's play area; children allowed in eating area; bedrooms *(Dave & Kate Buckley, Brian Jones, MAC, LYM)*

Satterthwaite [SD3492], *Eagles Head*: Simple pub in small unspoilt Lakes village handy for Grizedale Forest with friendly new licensees, Thwaites on handpump, good value home-cooked chipless food eg sandwiches, baked potatoes, pies, lasagne, Cumberland sausage *(Caroline Gibbins, Becky Carron)*

☆ **Seathwaite** [Duddon Valley, nr Ulpha (ie not Seathwaite in Borrowdale); SD2396], *Newfield*: Friendly and traditional walkers' pub with standard choice of freshly prepared food, well cooked and nicely presented, inc good steaks; well kept Theakstons, good service, clean lavatories; bedrooms *(Maurice and Gill McMahon, D J Cooke)*

Sedbergh [Finkle St; A683; SD6692], *Red Lion*: Cheerful beamed local with stuffed

gamebirds and sporting dog prints, Marstons Mild, Burton and Pedigree on handpump, bar food from sandwiches through cottage pie and omelettes to steak, back games area; bedrooms *(Gwen and Peter Andrews, Paul S McPherson, BB)*

☆ nr **Sedbergh** [A683 Sedbergh—Kirkby Stephen], *Fat Lamb*: So splendidly remote that it's difficult to decide whether this moorland inn should be included under Sedbergh, Kirkby Stephen or Ravenstonedale; pews and piped music in brightly modernised two-room bar with log fire in traditional black kitchen range and good photographs of steam trains and local beagles; welcoming owners, usual bar food, Tetleys under light pressure, maybe piped classical music, restaurant, seats outside by sheep pastures; comfortable bedrooms with own bathrooms *(A P Jeffreys, Gwen and Peter Andrews, Paul S McPherson, Frank Davidson)*

Shap [NY5615], *Bulls Head*: Typical village local with friendly welcome and ample helpings of bar food *(Len Beattie)*

☆ **St Bees** [Main St; NX9712], *Queens*: Three simply furnished clean rooms inc dining area with big tables, well kept Boddingtons and McEwans 80/- or Theakstons, nice relaxed atmosphere, friendly service and big helpings of good home-made bar food; good start or finish for Wainwright's coast-to-coast walk *(Simon Turner, Len Beattie, Dr Keith Bloomfield)*

St Bees [Main St], *Oddfellows Arms*: Tiny terraced pub with well kept Jennings, attractive food, quiet friendly service; piped music, darts *(Simon Turner, Len Beattie)*

☆ **Staveley** [SD4798], *Eagle & Child*: Very good value simple but generous food in bright but comfortable little modern front lounge and more spacious carpeted bar; well kept, with small neat garden; bedrooms quite cheap *(Barbara M McHugh, BB)*

☆ **Talkin** [village signed off B6413 S of Brampton; NY5557], *Blacksmiths Arms*: Clean, bright and cheerful; well kept Theakstons Best and Old Peculier on handpump, good generous reasonably priced food, open fire; friendly licensees; five bedrooms *(Mr and Mrs L D Rainger, A J and E M Watts, Russell Taylor, G R Prest)*

☆ **Threlkeld** [old main rd, bypassed by A66; NY3325], *Salutation*: Friendly small village local used by fell-walkers, with lots of connecting rooms; open fire, cards and dominoes; big helpings of good food inc the formidable Sally (a no-holds-barred beefburger), well kept Matthew Browns and Theakstons Old Peculier on handpump, welcoming staff; can get crowded; big upstairs children's room with pool table and juke box (oldies) *(P J and S E Robbins)*

☆ **Tirril** [3 1/2 miles from M6 junction 40; A66 towards Brough, A6 towards Shap, then B5320 towards Ullswater; NY5126], *Queens Head*: Low beams, black panelling, traditional settles and inglenook fireplace in small original front part, friendly old-fashioned atmosphere, usual bar food,

Matthew Browns on handpump, decent wine, back area with pool, darts, juke box etc, partly no smoking restaurant; children welcome; bedrooms *(Alan Hall, John Atherton, LYM)*

☆ **Torver** [A593 S of Coniston; SD2894], *Church House*: Cosy low-beamed bar — open all day at least in summer — with splendid views over surrounding hills, big garden; reasonably priced good bar meals, small restaurant, changing well kept real ales, big garden; children welcome; spacious, airy bedrooms *(Dr and Mrs A K Clarke, Tony Hodge, Lisa Wilson, Nigel B Pritchard)*

☆ **Troutbeck** [Upper Rd, nr High Green — OS Sheet 90 map reference 411035; NY4103], *Mortal Man*: Currently doing well, with wide choice of good value generous bar food in generous helpings, in attractively pubby main bar with good log fire, friendly quick service, well kept Youngers Scotch, restaurant; on GWG130; warm, clean and comfortable bedrooms *(K W Schofield, Raymond Palmer, H K Dyson, Mrs W Knowles, I H Rorison, M Box, A T Langton, KC)*

Troutbeck, *Queens Head*: Low-beamed and dim-lit but lively rambling bar with interesting fireplace and lots of other things to look at, fine mountain views from seats

outside, reasonable choice of bar food, Watneys-related real ales, restaurant; darts, fruit machine and pool table; on GWG130; bedrooms; found closed 1991, news please *(Mrs E Morgan, Simon Bates, Ben Wimpenny, LYM)*

Ulverston [King St; SD2978], *Rose & Crown*: Old-fashioned with good food inc interesting seafood, well kept Hartleys inc Mild, quick service even when busy on Sat market day, good friendly atmosphere *(Ian D Coburn)*

Wigton [West St; NY2648], *Hare & Hounds*: Well decorated and comfortable old-world bar, very popular with locals; polite helpful staff, good helpings of attractively priced bar food inc home-made soup, filled baked potatoes, omelettes, trout with almonds, scampi; pool room *(P R Rainger)*

☆ **Winton** [just off A683; NY7810], *Bay Horse*: Lovely moorland setting for two low-ceilinged rooms decorated with Pennine photographs and local fly-tying, good atmosphere, friendly staff, big helpings of well cooked reasonably priced food inc fresh veg, well kept McEwans 80/-, Youngers and guest real ales; pool in games room; clean good value bedrooms *(Jill and Peter Bickley, LYM)*

Derbyshire and Staffordshire

Pub food prices have not increased here as steeply as they have in many other places this last year. It's beginning to stand out as a good area both for finding very cheap food and for eating well – but still getting good value – further up the scale. Our £ symbol is a guide to the food bargains here; for particularly good food we'd pick out the innovative Druid at Birchover (a staggering choice), the Izaak Walton at Cresswell (a newcomer to the Guide, taken over by licensees with a fine track record), the Lazy Landlord at Foolow (interesting specials), the Robin Hood at Holmesfield, the Royal Oak at Millthorpe, the Lathkil at Over Haddon (a nice place to stay, too), and the more homely Black Lion at Butterton and Packhorse at Little Longstone. Pubs doing well after a change of management include the Barrel near Foolow (now a free house), the comfortable Maynard Arms at Grindleford (very wide choice of food now), the Jervis Arms at Onecote (popular with families; an even wider range of real ales), the Greyhound at Warslow (exceptionally friendly, decent food) and the handsome Mainwaring Arms at Whitmore. Besides the Izaak Walton already mentioned, new main entries here (or pubs back in the Guide after an absence) are the good value Crown in Abbots Bromley, the friendly Watts Russell Arms in fine countryside at Alstonefield, the Swan at Fradley (one of the prettiest canalside spots in the country), the Colvile Arms by its bowling green at Lullington, and the Horseshoe at Tatenhill (good value food, a fine family garden). The area's most exceptional pub is without doubt the Yew Tree at Cauldon: very unsmart, but remarkable collections of antiques (especially musical ones), a heady informal atmosphere, and extremely low prices. This is a particularly good area for the beer lover. Burton on Trent's unique water produces many national and regional beers, from Allied's main brewery, Bass and Marstons. The Albion there is a place to find Marstons at its best; the Coopers Tavern (in the Lucky Dip section at the end of the chapter) will show Bass on top form, and the Devonshire Arms (another Dip) is a good place to sample Allied's top beer, Ind Coope Burton. Another main entry there, the Burton Bridge Inn, produces its own interesting beers in a small brewery just behind. Other pubs in the area brewing their own beers are the John Thompson near Melbourne (also using Trent water) and the Rising Sun at Shraleybrook, and the Brunswick in Derby has just inaugurated its own microbrewery. These last two have a fine range of other drinks, too; as has the Jug & Glass near Hartington. In the Lucky Dip, pubs currently showing particular merit (most of them inspected by us) include several in the small village of Ashley, the Devonshire Arms at Beeley, Sycamore at Birch Vale, Green Man at Clifton Campville, Alexandra in Derby, Queen Anne at Great Hucklow, Raddle at Hollington, Cheshire Cheese at Hope, Red Lion at Litton, Three Horseshoes at Longlane, Star at Penkridge, Olde Dog & Partridge in Tutbury and White Horse at

Woolley. The Old Crown in Shardlow, being taken over after this edition went to press by a couple who made a great success of another pub there, should be well worth visiting. The Greyhound at Penkhull, an interesting old pub which has had outstandingly cheap food, is an almost certain bet too, though changes there as we went to press were not yet quite finalised enough for us to be certain that a main entry would still be in order.

ABBOTS BROMLEY (Staffs) SK0724 Map 7

Crown 🛏 £

An unusual feature in this pleasant and comfortable village inn is the big painting in its public bar showing the village's unusual medieval-dress September horn dance. The antlers now used (which hang in the church) have been carbon-dated to about 1100, and the dance itself may be very much older – after all, these antlers may have replaced a long series of earlier sets. The modernised lounge bar has plush button-back banquettes, modern panelling, soft lighting, and fresh flowers. In the public bar there are darts, dominoes, cribbage, a video game, a juke box and a fruit machine; piped music. Bar food includes soup (£1.15), sandwiches (85p), ploughman's (£2.95), steak and mushroom pie or beef in Guinness (£5), barbecued ribs (£6.75) and steaks (from £7.50); vegetarian dishes and puddings such as bread and butter pudding or rice pudding (£1.75); well kept Bass on electric pump; efficient service. The bedrooms are good value. *(Recommended by R A Corbett, D S and Mrs T M Beeson, T Nott)*

Bass Tenant Steve Hayes Real ale Meals and snacks (11–2.30, 6.30–10) Restaurant Burton on Trent (0283) 840227 Children welcome Open 11–3, 6–11 Bedrooms; £19/34

ALREWAS (Staffs) SK1714 Map 7

George & Dragon £

High St; bypassed village signposted from A38 and A513

This cheerful village has three cosy low-beamed and flagstoned rooms opening off its central servery, with homely decorations such as lots of brass candlesticks and, in a big room at one side, a splendid collection of commemorative Royal china. Good value bar food includes filled rolls (from £1), sandwiches (from £1.30), toasties (from £1.50), soup (£1.25), burgers (from £1.25), mushrooms in garlic butter or home-made pâté (£1.80), filled baked potatoes (from £1.60), ploughman's (from £2.30), fillet of plaice or jumbo sausages (£3), omelettes (from £3), salads (from £3.25), steak and kidney pie cooked with Pedigree Bitter (£3.25) and deep-fried scampi (£3.50); puddings such as Mississippi mud pie or chocolate fudge cake (from £1.40) and a children's menu from £1; efficient service. Very well kept Marstons Pedigree on handpump; dominoes, cribbage, fruit machine, piped music. The attractive, partly covered garden has a terrace (where there are occasional barbecues), an aviary with cockatiels and other birds, white doves strutting along the tops of the walls and roofs, and a well serviced children's play area, with a swing, playboat and a play elephant. Please note that they no longer do accommodation. *(Recommended by T Nott, Dave Braisted, Graham Richardson, Alison and Tony Godfrey, Helen and Wal Burns, N P Hopkins; more reports please)*

Marstons Manager Mr John Greenway Real ale Meals and snacks (not Sun) Burton on Trent (0283) 790 202 Children in eating area of bar Open 11–2.30(3 Sat), 6–11

ALSTONEFIELD (Staffs)   SK1355 Map 7

George

Village signposted from A515 Ashbourne–Buxton

Ideally placed for walkers, this charming 16th-century inn has a pretty rockery in the sheltered and spacious back stableyard with picnic seats, and there are some stone seats beneath the pretty inn sign at the front; you can arrange with the landlord to camp on the croft. Inside, there's a fine collection of old Peak District photographs and drawings on the darkening cream walls, foreign banknotes on the beams in the low butter-coloured ceiling, a warm winter coal fire, and pewter tankards hanging by the copper-topped bar counter (where there may be a box of greeting cards, some depicting the pub, reproduced from paintings by a local artist). A more spacious family room is full of wheelback chairs around tables. Popular, good value food is ordered at the kitchen door: soup or sandwiches (£1.35), ploughman's (from £2.85), meat and potato pie, lasagne or home-made Spanish quiche (£4.10), smoked trout (£4.25), meat and potato pie or lasagne (£3.85), and fillet steak (£5.75); puddings (from £1); considerate service. Well kept Ansells and Ind Coope Burton on handpump; darts, dominoes, fruit machine. *(Recommended by Tom and Jeanne Barnes, A M Neal, Simon Velate, G T and J Barnes, Mike and Wendy Proctor, DC, Andy and Jill Kassube, Graham Bush, Steve Mitcheson, Anne Collins)*

Allied   Richard and Sue Grandjean   Real ale   Meals and snacks (till 10 evening) Alstonefield (033 527) 205   Open 11–2.30, 6–11; winter evening opening 7, closed 25 Dec

Watts Russell Arms

Hopedale

Down its quiet lane, this shuttered stonebuilt pub has picnic-table sets on its sheltered terrace, with more tables out behind. Inside, the impeccably clean carpeted bar has brocaded wall banquettes, high seats around the bar (which is made from copper-bound oak barrels) and wheelback chairs and carvers; blue china and brass platters on the white roughcast walls, lots of other bric-a-brac, brown joists in the ceiling, velvet curtains on brass rails, and an open fire below a copper hood. Well kept Mansfield Old Baily and Riding Mild and Marstons Pedigree on handpump; pleasant young staff; generous helpings of good, freshly cooked and well presented food – besides sandwiches, current favourites are all-day breakfast (£3.75), chilli con carne with fruit and salad (£3.85), prawns with pink peppered sauce (£4.50), 8 oz gammon (£5), 8 oz steak (£6.85), and puddings include home-made trifle (£1.30). Situated in the Peak District National Park, close to Dovedale and the Manifold Valley, it's popular with walkers and busy at weekends; darts, dominoes and piped Radio 2. *(Recommended by Tom and Jeanne Barnes, A S Clements, A C Lang, Steve Mitcheson, Anne Collins)*

Free house   Licensee G A Harrison   Real ale   Meals and snacks   Alstonefield (033 527) 271   Open 11.30–2.30, 6.30–11; opens ½-hour later winter

BAMFORD (Derbys)   SK2083 Map 7

Derwent

Main St (A6013)

Fairly handy for the Ladybower reservoir and the moors around it, this bustling and friendly, old-fashioned inn has several rooms leading off the carpeted hall with its old cushioned settle, books on bookshelves, and bar servery. Several rooms lead off, one of which has yokes, heavy-horse harness and trace shafts on the partly panelled walls, two bay windows, and an old-fashioned green plush wall seat curving all around it. Another has large sunny windows, lots of wooden tables and big pictures on its wood-effect panelling. There are usually lots of fresh flowers and potted plants. The games bar (with its local team photographs) has darts, dominoes, fruit machine, quiz machine and quiz league on Sundays; piped music. Well kept Stones Best, Wards Sheffield Best and two other real ales (unknown at the time of going to press) on handpump. Good value bar food ranges from soup

(£1.25), sandwiches (from £1.30), ploughman's or a delicious cheese platter (£2.50), to steak and kidney pie (£3.50) or lasagne (£3.75); home-made puddings such as sticky toffee pudding, fruit pies or treacle pie (£1.30). The charming little dining room has stripped-pine panelling. There are seats in the garden. *(Recommended by Lynn Sharpless, Bob Eardley, Roy Y Bromell, Dr K Bloomfield, RJH, Helen Roe, T Henwood, Neville Kenyon, Len Beattie, A M Neal, Jenny Cantle, Sue Holland, Dave Webster, Andy and Jill Kassube)*

Free house   Licensees David and Angela Ryan   Real ale   Meals and snacks (12–2, 7–10)   Restaurant   Hope Valley (0433) 51395   Children welcome   Quiz league on Sun, occasional live entertainment   Open 11–11   Bedrooms; £25.50(£28.50B)/£35(£40B)

BIRCHOVER (Derbys)   SK2462 Map 7

Druid 🏮

Village signposted from B5056

The emphasis here is very much on the extensive choice of excellent, innovative food. They do about 100 dishes every day, chalked up on three large blackboards, the following are served as starters or light lunches: szechuan spare ribs cooked in ginger, chilli, garlic and honey (£3.40), port and stilton pâté (£3.50), pots of prawns in hot garlic butter with apple and celery (£3.80), steamed savoury bake, rice, mushrooms, onion and tomato sauce (£4.70), almond risotto, rice, sultanas, onion, peppers, mushroom with peanut, garlic and honey sauce (£5.20), Rowtor medieval chicken with raisins, apricots, cinnamon, red wine and cloves (£7.20), Turkish lamb, cardamom, cummin, apricots, whole peppercorns, tomato and a side dish of minted yoghurt and garlic with chopped cucumber (£7.30), steamed trout served with a Russian walnut sauce (£8.20); puddings are home-made and change daily, they might include Bakewell pudding, or To Hell With Chocolate (all £2.30); half price helpings for children. In the evenings and at weekends, when it's often very crowded, it may be advisable to book for meals; friendly landlord and helpful staff. The bar itself is small and plain, with green plush-upholstered wooden wall benches, small dining chairs and stools around strightforward tables, and a little coal fire. The spacious and airy two-storey dining extension, candlelit at night, has pink plush seats on olive-green carpet and pepper-grinders and sea salt on all the tables. Well kept Marstons Pedigree on handpump and a good collection of malt whiskies, as well as cafetière coffee and a selection of teas; a small public bar has darts, dominoes, cribbage; well reproduced classical music. The pub's name was reputedly inspired, during the eighteenth-century craze for druids, by a strange cave behind it among the beech trees sprouting from the Row Tor. There are picnic-table sets in front. *(Recommended by L W Baal, Barry and Anne, Hilary Bill, I H Rorison, J Nothey, June and Tony Baldwin, John and Christine Simpson, Andrew Morrissey, MAC, Kathy Holt, M Joyner, N P Cox, Jane Buekett, P A Crosland, D A Cawley, Simon Velate, Curt and Lois Stevens, Hilary Sargeant, Norman Clarke, Mike and Wendy Proctor, A F C Young, Laurence Manning)*

Free house   Licensees Brian Bunce and Nigel Telford   Real ale   Meals and snacks Winster (0629) 650 302   Children in bar until 8, and must be eating   Open 12–3, 7–11; closed 25 Dec, 26 Dec pm

BRASSINGTON (Derbys)   SK2354 Map 7

Olde Gate

Village signposted off B5056 and B5035 NE of Ashbourne

There are no electronic games or piped music in this relaxed creeper-covered pub – just the sound of people chatting. The public bar on the right has pewter mugs hanging from one beam, embossed Doulton stoneware flagons on a side shelf, an ancient wall clock, and traditional furnishings such as rush-seated old chairs and antique settles (one ancient, partly reframed, black oak solid one); there's also a lovely old kitchen range with lots of gleaming copper pots and stone-mullioned windows that look across the garden to small silvery-walled pastures. On the left of a small hatch-served lobby, another beamed room has stripped panelled settles, tables with scrubbed tops, and a fire under a huge mantlebeam. Good value bar food changing day by day includes open sandwiches such as prawns or crab (from £2.75), home-cooked meat salads (from £3.95), tandoori chicken or Barnsley chops (£5.75), barbecued steaks, and very good puddings like lemon mousse or traditional English puddings with custard; they don't do chips; well kept Marstons Pedigree on handpump and in winter Merrie Monk and Owd Roger, and 20 malt whiskies; darts, cribbage, dominoes. The small front yard has a couple of benches – a nice spot in summer to listen to the village bell-ringers practising on Friday evenings (best from 8 to 9, as it's learners earlier). The Carsington reservoir is being developed to provide water sports and so forth. *(Recommended by Brian and Anna Marsden, Mike and Wendy Proctor, John and Christine Simpson, Andy and Jill Kassube, Lynne Sheridan, Bob West, Derek and Sylvia Stephenson)*

Marstons   Tenant Paul Scott Burlinson   Real ale   Meals and snacks (not Mon evening)   (062 985) 448   Open 12–2.30 (3 Sat, Sun), 6–11

BURTON ON TRENT (Staffs)   SK2423   Map 7

Albion

Shobnall Rd; from centre take B5234 to Abbots Bromley, continue past Marstons Brewery, pub on left directly after going under A38 flyover

The conservatory here – with cane chairs around marble-topped tables – is popular with families and leads out into a spacious fairy-lit garden with swings, a children's bar, a yew walk and a fenced-off stream. The huge attractively modernised carpeted lounge has stained-glass entrance doors, with the motto *Through this wide-opening gate none too early come, none return too late,* and the good solid furnishings include deep maroon swagged velvet curtains, nice Victorian reproductions on the flowery-papered walls, a long and efficiently staffed bar counter, and a side area, slightly raised behind a balustrade, with a button-back leather settee, great winged armchair and other more parlourish furnishings. The big public bar is comfortable and well decorated too, with pool, darts, fruit machine and a juke box in the bar, with piped music in the lounge and the conservatory. Bar food includes rolls (from 80p, hot meat ones £1.80), ploughman's (from £1.50), curry or steak and kidney pie (£3.45) and a roast of the day (£3.95), puddings (from £1); summer barbecues. Excellently kept Marstons Pedigree on handpump. *(Recommended by T Nott, Tim and Lynne Crawford; more reports please)*

Marstons   Manager Malcolm Wink   Real ale   Lunchtime meals and snacks   Burton on Trent (0283) 681 97   Children in conservatory   Open 10.30–2.30, 5.30–11; closed eve Dec 25

Burton Bridge Inn

24 Bridge St (A50)

This firmly unpretentious local is the tap for the small brewery behind. Beautifully kept on handpump, the ales are served in the little front bar: Burton Bridge, Burton Bridge XL, Porter and Festival; in winter they also serve Top Dog Stout and Old Expensive and in summer, Summer ale; traditional country fruit wines. The plain walls are hung with notices, awards and brewery memorabilia, simple furnishings include pews and plain tables; even when it's quiet people tend to spill out into the corridor. Bar snacks such as good filled cobs (from 80p), chip butties (95p), hot roast beef cob (£1.60), filled Yorkshire puddings with onion gravy (£1.75) and ploughman's (£2.10); dominoes and upstairs there's a skittle alley, with gas lighting and open fires, which can be hired for the evening, with a pie and pea supper or buffet if required. The brewery is down a long, very old-fashioned yard; the Tuesday tours are fun – ring to make a booking. *Recommended by Chris Raisin, Graham Doyle, Derek and Sylvia Stephenson; more reports please)*

Own brew   Licensee Kevin McDonald   Real ale   Lunchtime meals and snacks (filled cobs Sun)   Burton on Trent (0283) 36596   Open 11.30–3, 5.30–11

BUTTERTON (Staffs)   SK0756 Map 7

Black Lion ★ ⌨

Village signposted from B5053

This particularly friendly 18th-century stone inn is in lovely countryside not far from the Manifold valley, enjoying views over the Peak National Park, and close to various places of interest such as Sudbury Hall, Trentham Gardens and the Wedgwood China Factory. The area provides opportunities to enjoy many sporting activities, such as watersports, shooting, and the chance to fish the same rivers as Charles Cotton and Izaac Walton; there are many walks in the area and the pub is mentioned in many of the walking guides. Several homely rooms make up the rambling bar: one has a low black beam-and-board ceiling, a fine old red leatherette settle curling around its walls, comfortable bar stools with backrests, well polished mahogany and other tables, lots of brassware and china, and a good log fire. Off to the left, there are red plush button-back banquettes around sewing-machine tables and Victorian prints. An inner room has a parakeet called Sergeant Bilko who squawks loudly at regular intervals, a Liberty-print sofa and a fine old kitchen range. Good value bar food includes home-made soup (£1.30), various salads and sandwiches (from £1.40), huge lunchtime ploughman's (£3.50), steak and kidney pie or chicken breast (£3.95), vegetarian lasagne or tasty chicken curry (£4.25), and 10oz rump steak (£5.50), as well as daily specials such as cheese and vegetable pie, steak and mushroom casserole and turkey, ham and mushroom pie and puddings such as blackforest gateau or apple pie (£1.40); they now also have a carvery with a separate menu, which offers a selection of starters such as breaded mushrooms or pâté de champagne (£2.10), a roast joint of the day and a variety of steaks, and puddings such as spotted dick and custard, (main course, pudding and coffee £9.75, children's portion £3.75). McEwans 70/-, Theakstons Best and Youngers No 3 and a guest beer on handpump and several malt whiskies; a cocktail bar is open in the evenings; darts, shove-ha'penny, dominoes, cribbage, bar football, table skittles, fruit machine, and separate well lit pool room; piped music. Picnic-table sets and rustic seats on the prettily planted terrace look up to the tall and elegant spire of the local church, and across to the surrounding hills. Butterton is now a conservation village. *(Recommended by John and Christine Simpson, Alan and Ruth Woodhouse, Gwen and Peter Andrews, E Chilvers, Chris Raisin, Graham Doyle, Kevin Fields, Graham Bush, Simon Velate, J Scarisbrick, Mike and Wendy Proctor, A Wright, Mrs J Edwards, T Galligan; more reports please)*

Free house   Licensee Ron Smith   Real ale   Meals and snacks   Restaurant (not Sun evening)   Onecote (0538) 304 232   Children welcome   Monthly live entertainment; impromptu Sat evenings   Open 12–3, 7–11; closed Weds lunchtime   Bedrooms; £25B/£38B

nr BUXTON (Derbys)   SK0673 Map 7

Bull i'th' Thorn ★ £

Ashbourne Road (A515) six miles S of Buxton, nr Hurdlow; OS Sheet 119 map reference 128665

It's a pleasant surprise to find that at the core of this otherwise unassuming roadhouse is a striking medieval hall with handsome panelling, a massive central beam among a forest of smaller ones, and old flagstones stepping gently down to a big open fire; it's furnished with fine long settles and panelled window seats in the embrasures of the thick stone walls, an ornately carved hunting chair, a longcase clock, a powder-horn, and armour that includes 17th-century German helmets, swords, and blunderbusses and so forth. Straightforward bar food such as sandwiches (from 90p), ploughman's or cottage pie (£2.50), salads (from £2.75), steak and kidney pie, roast beef or scampi (£3.25); puddings such as fruit pie and cream (£1.25); morning coffee and Sunday roast lunch (£3.30). An adjoining room has darts, pool, dominoes, fruit machine, juke box and piped music; well kept Robinsons Best on handpump. The family room opens on to a terrace and big lawn, with swings, and there are more tables in a sheltered angle in front – where a lively carving over the main entrance depicts a bull caught in a thornbush; there are others of an eagle with a freshly caught hare, and some spaniels chasing a rabbit. They also have a function room which can be hired, and as well as the bed and breakfast accommodation they offer a holiday flat and adjacent field for caravans and camping. *(Recommended by Maysie Thompson, Mr and Mrs R Sherriff, Dennis Jones, Helen and Wal Burns, Margaret and Trevor Errington, Simon Velate, Gwen and Peter Andrews)*

Robinsons　Licensee G R Haywood　Real ale　Meals and snacks　Restaurant for special occasions and Sunday lunch　(0298) 833 48　Children in eating area and family room　Open 11–3(3.30 Sat), 6–11　Two bedrooms; £15\£25

CAULDON (Staffs)　SK0749　Map 7

Yew Tree　★　★　★　£

Village signposted from A523 and A52 about 8 miles W of Ashbourne; OS Sheet 119 map reference 075493·

This remarkable pub is quite unique. It's very much an unassuming, basic local with all that you'd expect from that – regulars dropping in and very cheap snacks and drinks. Yet it's absolutely entwined with the character of Alan East himself and all the amazing paraphernalia he has collected and packed into the old-fashioned and dimly lit rooms. He owns a pair of Queen Victoria's stockings which were used in an episode of *Lovejoy*, shown last January. There are ancient guns and pistols, several penny-farthings, an old sit-and-stride boneshaker, a rocking horse, swordfish blades, and even a fine marquetry cabinet crammed with notable early Staffordshire pottery; also, 18th-century settles, soggily sprung sofas, a four-person oak church choir seat with carved heads which came from St Mary's church in Stafford, and above the bar, an odd iron dog-carrier (don't ask how it works). The most unusual things are the working Polyphons and Symphonions – 19th-century developments of the musical box, often taller than a person, each with quite a repertoire of tunes and of the most elaborate sound-effects; go with plenty of 2p pieces to work them. And an expanding set of fine (and vociferous) longcase clocks in the gallery just above the entrance, a pianola with an excellent collection of piano rolls, a working vintage valve radio set, a crank-handle telephone and a sinuous medieval wind instrument made of leather. The atmosphere is basic but very friendly, and prices for the hot pork pies (50p), meat and potato pies or steak pies (55p), big filled baps (from 70p), quiche or smoked mackerel (£1.85) are remarkably low, as they are for the drinks – including Bass, Burton Bridge and M & B Mild on handpump or tapped from the cask, and some interesting malt whiskies such as overproof Glenfarclas. Darts, shove-ha'penny, table skittles (taken very seriously here), dominoes and cribbage. Hiding behind a big yew tree, the pub is difficult to spot – unless a veteran bus is parked outside. Dovedale and the Manifold Valley are not far away. All in all, an eccentric classic. *(Recommended by Andrew Morrissey, Brian and Anna Marsden, Andy and Jill Kassube, Graham Gibson, Lynn Sharpless, Bob Eardley, John and Christine Simpson, WAH, Greenwood and Turner, Robin and Christine Harman, Sarah Bullard, Graham Bush, A M Neal, Simon Velate, Laurence Manning, J Scarisbrick, Mike and Wendy Proctor, T Galligan, Tom McLean, Ewan McCall, Roger Huggins, Heather Sharland, Tim Locke, Sue Holland, Dave Webster, Chris Raisin, Graham Doyle)*

Free house　Licensee Alan East　Real ale　Snacks (generally something to eat any time they're open)　One cote (0538) 308 348　Children in Polyphon room　Pianola most nights – played by the landlord　Open 10–3 (4 if needed on Sat), 6–11

CRESSWELL (Staffs) Map 7

Izaak Walton

Village signposted from Draycott in the Moors, on former A50 Stoke–Uttoxeter

The Yateses, with a distinguished track record at the Red Lion at Ipstones and then the Poachers at Rudyard, have now transformed this into an upmarket dining pub with impressive food such as good home-made soups (£1), lunchtime open sandwiches (from £1.95, prawn £2.50), filled baked potatoes (£1.30-£2.30), starters, such as pâté or Japanese prawns (from £1.50), main course dishes such as chicken breast (£3.25), salads (from £3.50, prawn £4.25), steak and kidney pie (£3.95), chicken and broccoli bake (£4.25), steaks (from £8.45), and vegetarian dishes such as cheese or leek or mushroom or tomato flan or stuffed aubergines (£5.95), with specials such as double Barnsley lamb chops (£5.95), roast duck in orange sauce or rolled fillet of plaice filled with crab (£7.95); puddings such as chocolate fudge gateau (£1.95), strawberries and cream (£2.25) and pineapple surprise (£2.50). Three course Sunday lunch is £7.50 (£3.95 for children). The two rooms have gentle lighting, little country pictures, dried flowers on walls and beams, pastel flowery curtains; though there's a little settee in one window furnishings are mainly uniform solid country-kitchen chairs and tables in polished pale wood, going nicely with the fawn carpet – it's all very neatly kept. Well kept Marstons Pedigree on handpump; piped music. *(Recommended by J Scarisbrick)*

Free house   Licensees Anne and Graham Yates   Real ale   Meals and snacks (Mon-Thurs 12–2, 7–9.45, Fri & Sat 7–10)   Stoke on Trent (0782) 392265   Children welcome if kept away from bar   Open 11–2.30, 6–11; closed Dec 25 and 26

DERBY   SK3438   Map7
Abbey Inn

Darley Street; coming in from A38/A6 roundabout, take first left signposted Darley Abbey, then left into Old Road signposted to toll bridge, turning right just before the bridge itself

Parts of this carefully restored, smallish pub are all that's left of what used to be a powerful eleventh-century monastery, covering much of this area. The downstairs bar has studded oak doors, a refectory table and some shiny elm ones, William Morrisish brocaded stools and benches, a long pew, a big brick inglenook with stone chimneypiece, some massive stonework (leaning, in the case of the outer wall), and a brick floor. A spiral stone staircase leads up to a bigger and quieter bar where the restored stonework is more notable, especially in the modelling of the windows; the bow of a Viking longship is built into the wall, there are handsome reconstructed high oak rafters and trusses, and neat cushioned pews built into stalls around the tables. Lunchtime bar food includes sandwiches, and home-made main dishes such as lasagne, curry and various vegetarian dishes (from £3.25), and giant pies (£3.30). Well kept Sam Smiths Museum and Old Brewery on handpump; darts, shove-ha'penny, cribbage, dominoes, piped music, and quiz team every other Wednesday; quietly relaxed atmosphere. Besides a couple of sturdy teak seats outside, there are stone side-steps to sit on, and a stone well-head; customers tend to stray into the park opposite, by a weir on the Derwent. The pub has a cricket and football team and a sort of Viking Association (anyone can join) which holds occasional mock-battles; every April they hold the Darley Dash – a running race for charity. *(Recommended by Carl Southwell, Chris Raisin)*

Sam Smiths   Licensees Christine and Simon Meyers   Real ale   Lunchtime meals and snacks (Mon curry night 7.30–10pm, no food Sun)   Derby (0332) 558297   Children in eating area of bar until 7pm   Open 11–2.30, 6–11.30

Brunswick   £

1 Railway Terrace; close to Derby Midland railway station

In June of 1991, the micro-brewery here produced its first brew – a 1036OG pale bitter; they are using well water from the well they discovered during building work, which they are sure was used when they brewed beer here many years ago. They serve it alongside their remarkable range of other well kept ales – fifteen, ever-changing brews are always on offer. Regularly available are Batemans Mild (they always have a Mild on offer), Burton Bridge, Draught Bass, Hook Norton Bitter and Old Hookey, Marstons Pedigree, Theakstons XB and Best, Timothy Taylors Landlord, Wards Kirby and Sheffield and Youngers No 3 on handpump, with Theakstons Old Peculier tapped from the cask; ever-changing forthcoming beers are listed on a blackboard. Over four days around 3 October (anniversary of their opening) they have a beer festival, with many more ales on offer. A couple of farm ciders are always available, tapped from the cask. There are original flagstones throughout downstairs, and the high-ceilinged serving bar has heavy, well padded leatherette seats, whisky-water jugs above the dado, and a dark blue ceiling and upper wall, with squared dark panelling below. The no-smoking room is decorated with little old-fashioned prints and swan's neck lamps, and has a high-backed wall settle and a coal fire; behind a curved glazed partition wall is a quietly chatty family parlour narrowing to the apex of the triangular building. Darts, cribbage, dominoes, fruit machine, occasional piped music; good friendly service. Bar food includes pork pies (75p), filled rolls (from 90p – the hot beef, £1.30, are good), salads (from £2.50), vegetarian bean feast (£2.50), beef in Hook Norton Old Hookey (£2.90), meat and potato pie (£3), steak and kidney pie with suet crust (£3.50) and a roast beef dinner served in a giant Yorkshire pudding (£3.60); the beef and turkey are both home-cooked. There are seats in the terrace area behind. *(Recommended by Carl Southwell, Graham Bush, Andrew Stephenson, Derek and Sylvia Stephenson, Chris Raisin)*

Free house　Licensee Trevor Harris　Real ale　Lunchtime meals and snacks (rolls only Sun)　Restaurant　Derby (0332) 290677　Children in family parlour　Upstairs 2 folk clubs alternate Mon eves and occasionally Sun eves (usually last Sun in month), jazz Mon and Thurs evenings　Open 11–11

FENNY BENTLEY (Derbys)　SK1750 Map 7
Coach & Horses

A515 N of Ashbourne

Popular and quietly friendly, this former 17th-century coaching inn has old prints and engravings on the dark green leafy Victorian wallpaper and comfortable, ribbed green built-in wall banquettes in its nice little back room. There are more old prints in the front bar, which has flowery-cushioned wall settles and library chairs around the dark tables on its Turkey carpet, waggonwheels hanging from the black beams, horsebrasses and pewter mugs, and a huge mirror; two winter log fires. Quickly served good value bar snacks include filled baps and sandwiches (from 95p, toasties from £1.50), soup (£1.10), burgers (£1.30) and filled baked potatoes (from £1.80); the fuller menu offers a choice of starters such as smoked mackerel (£1.55), main meals such as savoury or Chinese pancake rolls (£3.25), salads (from £3.50), haddock or plaice (£3.50), spaghetti bolognese or chilli con carne (£3.75), steak and kidney pie, cottage pie or lasagne (and vegetarian lasagne) (£3.95), chicken or veal (£6.50), lemon sole with prawns or salmon in asparagus sauce (£6.75) and steaks from £7.95, including a very generous 16oz rump steak (they give you a free pint if you eat your plate clean). Well kept Bass on handpump, good coffee, unobtrusive piped music. There are picnic-table sets on the back grass by an elder tree, with rustic benches and white tables and chairs under cocktail parasols on the terrace in front of this pretty rendered stone house. *(Recommended by G V Price, WAH, Avril Harrison-Smith, Colin and Mary Meaden, Mrs J A Uthwatt, Mike and Wendy Proctor)*

Free house　Licensee Edward Anderson　Real ale　Meals and snacks　Restaurant Thorpe Cloud (033 529) 246　Open 11–2.30, 6.30(6 Sat)–11

FOOLOW (Derbys)　SK1976 Map 7
Lazy Landlord ✿

Village signposted off A623 Chesterfield–Chapel en le Frith

This maroon-shuttered pub is in the heart of a pretty village, close to the green and pond and surrounded by rolling moorland pasture. The central bar is simply furnished and steps from here lead down into a quietly relaxed room with unusually high ceiling joists, harness on stripped stone walls, a comfortable variety of seats including lots of maroon plush small dining chairs, pleasant tables with inlaid brass number-plates, and an open fire. On the other side, a dining room with more stripped stone has tables in snug individual stalls. The most interesting food

tends to be the half dozen or so specials of the day – a typical selection might
include starters such as grilled sardines (£2.25), goat's milk cheesecake with chives
(£2.65), main dishes such as rabbit with bacon and sage or sea bream with country
sauce (£5.95), pork medallions with wild mushrooms or lamb with basil and
mustard sauce (£6.75). The basic choice runs from sandwiches (from £1.50), soup
(£1.65) and starters such as potted shrimps (£2.65) through vegetable crumble or
steak and kidney pie (£4.85) to steaks (from £8.50); vegetables are fresh, cooked al
dente. Well kept Wards Sheffield Best and Darleys Thorne on handpump,
welcoming service, very quiet piped music. There are three picnic-table sets in front
of the pub which has fine Victorian etched and cut glass windows. *(Recommended by
Simon Velate, Dorothy and David Young, Neville Kenyon, Brian and Anna Marsden, Bill
Sykes; more reports please)*

*Free house   Licensees D W, M D and K G Holden   Real ale   Meals and snacks (12–2,
6–10)   Hope Valley   (0433) 30873 (from Feb 92 630 873)   Children welcome
Open 11.30–3, 6–11; closed 25 Dec*

nr FOOLOW (Derbys)   SK1976 Map 7

Barrel   £

Bretton; signposted from Foolow which itself is signposted from A623 just E of junction
with B6465 to Bakewell

New licensees have taken over this friendly traditional pub, which is the highest in
Derbyshire and enjoys spectacular views. The beamed bar is divided up into several
areas by stubs of massive knocked-through stone walls – the cosiest is at the far
end with a leather-cushioned settle, a built-in corner wall-bench by an antique oak
table, and an open fire. Decorations on the cream walls include local maps, an
aerial photograph, a rack of clay pipes, poems about the pub and a clock which
moves in an anti-clockwise direction; a delft shelf has lots of old glass and china
bottles, and there's a mix of seats. Bar food includes sandwiches (from 95p – the
crab ones are very good; double-decker 60p extra, toasties from £1.45), open
wholemeal baps (from £1.75, prawn or smoked salmon £2.80), quiche and salad
(£2.30), ploughman's or chicken, ham and mushroom pie (£2.80), smoked turkey
and cottage cheese salad (£3); puddings (£1.20). Bass and Stones on handpump; a
good choice of whiskies; darts, dominoes. From the breezy front terrace there are
fine views to the pastures below the high ridge. *(Recommended by D and B Carren, I H
Rorison, Helen and Wal Burns, Simon Velate, Wayne Brindle)*

*Free House   Licensee Derek Smith   Meals and snacks   Hope Valley (0433) 30856
Children welcome   Open 12–3, 6.30–11*

FRADLEY (Staffs)   SK1513 Map 7

Swan

Off A38 Burton–Lichfield, signposted Fradley Park; after a mile turn right at Fradley
Junction sign, then left at T-junction, then left along far bank of canal; OS Sheet 128,
map reference 140140

The location is what makes this cheerily unpretentious pub: the junction of the
Trent–Mersey Canal and the Birmingham Navigation system, with lines of brightly
coloured narrow-boats along the tree-lined banks. Inside, the room on the right is a
traditional lino-floored public bar. The lounge on the left is rather smarter, with
canal photographs and painted ware, red plush banquettes and dimpled copper
tables; it leads down into a Cellar Bar with its low vaulted brick ceiling painted a
dark red, more plush banquettes in its alcoves, and old waterway maps and
photographs. A back food servery (with fruit machine) dispenses big helpings of
food including wrapped filled rolls (75p), sandwiches (from £1.60), cheap specials
such as a good steak and kidney pie or lasagne (£2.95), ploughman's (£2.35),
salads (£3.65), various fish dishes such as lemon sole (from £3.85) and steaks
(from £5.96), puddings, such as cheesecake (from £1.30); children's menu (£2.10)
and a good-value Sunday lunch (get there early for a table); well kept Ansells Bitter
and Mild and Ind Coope Burton on handpump and a wide range of malt whiskies.

There are a few picnic-table sets out by the water. (*Recommended by Hilary Sargeant, Norman Clarke, Cliff Blakemore, Dr and Mrs C D E Morris, P A and J B Jones*)

Ind Coope (Allied) Tenant W A Smith Real ale Meals and snacks Burton on Trent (0283) 790330 Children if eating in Cellar Bar till 8.30 Open 11–3, 6–11

FROGGATT EDGE (Derbys) SK2477 Map 7

Chequers

B6054, off A623 N of Bakewell; Ordnance Survey Sheet 119, map reference 247761

A relaxing place to stop if out walking for the day and you can enjoy views over the attractive valley from white benches at the front; there are also tables on the back terrace. The Edge itself is up through the woods behind the inn. Inside, it's comfortable and old-fashioned with library chairs or small high-backed winged settles on the well waxed floorboards, an attractive, richly varnished beam-and-board ceiling, antique prints on the white walls (partly stripped back to big dark stone blocks), and a big solid-fuel stove. One corner has a big grandfather clock, another a nicely carved oak cupboard. Well kept Wards Sheffield Best on handpump, a good range of wines and 86 malt whiskies. Bar food includes a generous soup (£1.50), good home-cooked meat sandwiches (£1.40; prawn £3.25), ploughman's (£3), salads (from £2.95), chilli con carne (£3.50), steak and mushroom pie (£3.95), sirloin steak (£6.95) and puddings (£1.50). Quiz machine, juke box and piped music. (*Recommended by T J Broughton, Andrew Morrissey, I H Rorison, Simon Velate, Drs M and K Parier, Mr and Mrs A Gray, Frazer and Louise Smith*)

Wards (Vaux) Tenant Ian McLeod Real ale Meals and snacks (12–2, 6–9) Hope Valley (0433) 30231 Children in family room Open 11–3, 6–11 Bedrooms; £25/£35

GRINDLEFORD (Derbys) SK2478 Map 7

Maynard Arms 🛏

B6521 N of village

There have been a few changes since the new licensee took over this inn but the welcome is warm and the food seems as popular as ever. The spacious main bar has comfortable blue-coloured plush seats on the blue patterned carpet, some dark panelling, tapestry wall hangings, silver tankards above the bar, and a high ceiling. Off the hall there's a smaller green plush bar for restaurant diners only which is no-smoking. Bar food includes starters such as soup in a bonnet, that is served with a pastry bonnet (£1.05), a giant Yorkshire pudding with onion and herb pan gravy, devilled Essex whitebait or avocado and prawns (all £1.95), a range of sandwiches, from French bread (£1.75) to a toasted steak sandwich (£4.25), ploughman's (£2.95), full Derbyshire breakfast with chipped potatoes (£3.35), fish dishes include salmon fish cakes (£2.95) while there are meat dishes such as spicy minced beef (£3.45), giant Yorkshire puddings with sausage and onion gravy or slices of roast beef in gravy, steak and kidney pie or chicken and leek pie (£3.95) and steaks (from, minute steak, £3.50), vegetarian dishes such as cauliflower cheese (£1.95) and courgette and mushroom lasagne (£3.35); puddings such as treacle tart with custard, traditional apple pie and summer pudding (all £1.60). Well kept Boddingtons and Stones on handpump; piped music and darts. The restaurant looks out over the neatly kept garden to the valley. The sherry and fruit in the bedroom is a nice touch. (*Recommended by Jeremy and Vicki Elden, Harry Stirling, I H Rorison, June and Tony Baldwin, Maysie Thompson, N P Cox, Mike and Wendy Proctor, Simon Velate, D J and P M Taylor, Wayne Brindle, Win and Gordon Lambert, T Galligan*)

Bass Lease: David Brass Real ale Meals and snacks (12–2.30, 7–9.30) Restaurant Hope Valley (0433) 30321 Children welcome Open 11–11 Bedrooms; £59B/£72B

HARDWICK HALL (Derbys) SK4663 Map 7

Hardwick Inn

4 1/2 miles from M1 junction 29: A617 towards Mansfield, then in Glapwell turn right at Hardwick Hall signpost and keep on to the far side of the park; can also be reached from A6010 via Stainsby

Though it's now owned, along with its lovely park, by the National Trust, this 17th-century house was originally the lodge for the nearby Elizabethan Hall. There's a relaxed, old-fashioned atmosphere in the several separate rooms, and the carpeted lounge has varnished wooden tables, comfortably upholstered wall settles, tub chairs and stools, and stone-mullioned latticed windows. Bar food includes sandwiches, soup (95p), ploughman's (from £2.60), Lincolnshire sausage with egg (£2.75), home-made steak and kidney pie (£3.25), plaice or haddock (£3.40), a daily vegetarian dish (£3.60), salads (from £3.85), gammon and egg or pineapple (£3.95) and steaks (from £6.45); a daily special, puddings (£1.40), and children's menu (from £1.75). Well kept Theakstons XB and Youngers Scotch on handpump; friendly staff. *(Recommended by Tony Bland, Brian and Anna Marsden, T Henwood, Andrew and Ruth Triggs, Mr and Mrs P B Dowsett, I H Rorison, J Harvey Hallam, GB, Richard Dolphin)*

Free house Licensees Peter and Pauline Batty Real ale Meals and snacks (not Sun evening) Carvery restaurant (Tues-Sat, Sun lunchtime) Chesterfield (0246) 850245 Children in restaurant, 2 children's rooms and family room Open 11.30–3, 6.30–11

nr HARTINGTON (Derbys) SK1360 Map 7

Jug & Glass

Newhaven; on A515 about 1 mile N of junction with A5012; OS Sheet 119 map reference 156614

The sort of place you might easily speed past if you didn't know what was inside. There's a fine range of well kept real ales on handpump such as Kimberley Classic, Mansfield Old Baily, Marstons Pedigree, Owd Rodger and Stout from the keg, Ruddles Best and County, and a weekly guest beer; they now hold their mini beer festival on the first weekend of September with all beers (about 50 different traditional ales on tap from all areas of the country) at half price; freshly squeezed orange juice and country wines. Bar food includes home-made soup (£1), ploughman's (£3), breaded haddock or vegetable lasagne or stroganoff (£3.75), gammon with egg, pineapple and sausage (£6), steaks (from 7oz sirloin £7.25), and specials such as 24oz rib eye steak with full trimmings (£9.50) and 10–12oz swordfish steaks marinated, grilled and served with cream and wine sauce; they use local meat, and at 24 hours' notice will do a full leg of lamb, loin of pork or rib of beef to carve yourself (£9 each including starters, puddings and coffee, minimum four people – you can take home what's left; if you wish the landlord to carve there's a nominal change of half-a-pint!); puddings from £1. The cosy bar has a friendly atmosphere, simple furnishings, a cuckoo clock and a piano, lots of flowery china hanging from low beams, and winter coal fires (as well as central heating). Another room with flock wallpaper takes the overflow when the small main bar gets too crowded. In the attractive no-smoking dining room there's a stone-pillared fireplace with an old oak mantlebeam. Darts, dominoes, cribbage, fruit machine, juke box; piped music. The outside dining area has been extended and there are now 14 bench table and seats and parasols on the terrace.
(Recommended by John Scarisbrick, Jeanne and Tom Barnes, Jerry and Alison Oakes, Simon Velate, Mike and Wendy Proctor, John and Joan Wyatt)

Free house Licensee John Bryan Real ale Meals and snacks (11.30–2.30, 7–10) No-smoking restaurant Hartington (0298) 84224 Children welcome Open 11–4, 6–11 (winter evening opening 7)

HOLMESFIELD (Derbys)   SK3277 Map 7

Robin Hood

Lydgate; B6054 towards Hathersage

Consistently good food in this well kept, rambling ex-farmhouse includes home-made soup (£1.25), filled baked potatoes (£2.15), sandwiches (from £2.45, with chips and salad), ploughman's (from £3.75), spiced beef salad (£4.75), savoury moussaka or baked spiced ham (£4.95), grilled plaice or grilled gammon and pineapple (£5.25), seafood salad (£6.95), steaks (from £8.95), and vegetarian dishes such as moussaka, lasagne or stilton and walnut quiche (£4.95) with puddings such as bread and butter pudding, summer pudding or brandy snaps (£1.75); daily specials such as hot beef or lamb baps (£2.95)chicken, leek and ham pie (£4.95), tandoori chicken or seafood pancake (£5.50), lamb steak in cream and tarragon sauce (£6.25) and Dover sole (£9.50), daily puddings such as apple and blackberry crumble, raspberry surprise (from £1.80); children's portions from £2.50 and good, friendly service. Though booking is advisable at weekends, only half the tables are booked out at any time. The extended lounge area has exposed beams, chintz and paisley curtains, plush button-back wall banquettes around wood-effect tables, partly carpeted flagstone floors, and open fires; piped music. Outside on the cobbled front courtyard there are stone tables. The elevated position of the building means that it enjoys good views over Chesterfield and Sheffield; a number of footpaths into the famous Cordwell Valley start opposite the pub itself. (*Recommended by B and M A Langrish, Mr and Mrs R Gammon, Mr and Mrs N Baker, Mike Tucker, Dave Braisted*)

Free house   Licensees Chris and Jackie Hughes   Meals and snacks (11.30–2.30, 6.30–9.30)   Sheffield (0742) 890360   Children allowed indoors if eating but only till 8.30   Open 11.30–3, 6–11; winter evening opening 6.30   Bedrooms planned

LITTLE HUCKLOW (Derbys)   SK1678 Map 7

Old Bulls Head ★

Pub signposted from B6049

This popular pub in a quiet village surrounded by upland sheep pastures is immaculately kept. The two small rooms have old oak beams, thickly cushioned built-in settles, interesting collections of locally mined semi-precious stones, antique brass and iron household tools, and a coal fire in a neatly restored stone hearth. One room is served from a hatch, the other over a polished bar counter. Well kept Wards Sheffield Best from carved handpumps; bar snacks are simple and consist of sandwiches (£1.70) and ploughman's (£3); well reproduced classical music, dominoes. In the well tended, dry-stone-walled garden there's a fine collection of well restored and attractively painted old farm machinery. Note the restricted winter opening hours. As we went to press this came up for sale: news please. (*Recommended by Andy and Jill Kassube, Wayne Brindle, D and B Carron, Alan and Eileen Bowker, A and L Holden, Mike and Wendy Proctor*)

Free house   Licensee Geoff Hawketts   Real ale   Snacks (weekend lunchtimes only)   Hartington (0298) 871 097   Children welcome   Open weekdays 7–11, Sats 12–3, 7–11

LITTLE LONGSTONE (Derbys)   SK1971 Map 7

Packhorse

Monsal Dale and Ashford Village signposted off A6 NW of Bakewell; follow Monsal Dale signposts, then turn right into Little Longstone at Monsal Head Hotel

Though this cottagey place is popular with locals, the licensees are friendly to all their customers. Simple furnishings in the two small rooms range from country-kitchen chairs and cloth-cushioned settles to an odd almost batwinged corner chair, and there's a beam-and-plank ceiling, and open fires. Individual but discreet decorations include prettily hung decorative mugs, a collection of brass spigots, attractive landscape photographs by Steve Riley, blow-ups of older local photographs and the odd cornet or trumpet. They are planning to convert this arrangement, in the same style, so that there is a further room which will be used for dining and at the same time they plan to extend the menu. At the moment, good value bar food such as sandwiches (from £1.30), soup (£1.30), baps spread with dripping and generously filled with hot well hung beef or with hot pork, apple sauce and stuffing (£1.30), starters like spare ribs (which are a meal in themselves), prawn provençale or Stilton garlic mushrooms (from £1.30), ploughman's with a selection of cheeses (£3.55), main courses such as good cauliflower and leek bake (£3.75), chilli con carne or very tasty, filling steak and kidney pie (£4.30), lamb steak in stilton sauce (£5.50), duck with Cumberland sauce or sirloin steak (£7.50), and puddings (£1.50), such as apple pie with cream or brandy roulade. Well kept Marstons Burton and Pedigree on handpump; darts, dominoes, cribbage. In the steep little garden there are goats and rabbits. Please note, they no longer do bedrooms. *(Recommended by Derek and Sylvia Stephenson, David and Ruth Hollands, Andy and Jill Kassube, Mrs S M Judge, Roxanne Chamerlain, Mike and Wendy Proctor, Neville Kenyon, Simon Velate, A S Clements, A and L Holden, D W Crossley)*

Marstons   Tenants Sandra and Mark Lythgoe   Real ale   Meals and snacks   Great Longstone (062 987) 471   Well behaved children in eating area until 9pm   Open 11–3, 5–11; closed 25 Dec evening

LULLINGTON (Staffs)   SK2513   Map 7

Colvile Arms

Village signposted off A444 S of Burton

Nice to find such an unspoiled public bar these days: high-backed old winged settles (one with seats both sides, forming a corridor to a further plush snug with a Turkey rug on its flooring tiles), attractive Victorian fireplace, hatch service. The right-hand lounge is cosy too, with plush seats, lots of brass around a coal-effect gas fire, low beams – overall, a well cared-for feel, making for a most welcoming village pub. Well kept Bass, M & B Mild and Marstons Pedigree on handpump, good friendly landlord. Rustic seats around tables on a small sheltered back lawn overlook a neat bowling green. *(Recommended by David Gaunt, Chris Raisin)*

Free house   Real ale   Meals and snacks   Open 11–3, 6–11

nr MELBOURNE (Derbys)   SK3825   Map 7

John Thompson

Ingleby; village signposted from A514 at Swarkestone

Well kept lawns and flowerbeds outside this large, busy pub run down to the rich watermeadows along the River Trent, there are lots of tables on the upper lawn, and a partly covered outside terrace with its own serving bar. The spacious, modernised lounge has sturdy oak tables, some old oak settles, button-back leather seats, ceiling joists, antique prints and paintings, and a log-effect gas fire; a couple of smaller cosier rooms open off; pool, a fruit machine, a juke box in the children's room and a no-smoking area in the lounge. The beer brewed here is highly praised (you can buy their home-brew kits) and they also keep Marstons Pedigree on handpump. Good but straightforward bar food consists of sandwiches (£1 – nothing else on Sundays; the beef is excellent), then a set meal of soup (£1), a cold buffet (£3) or hot roast beef (£4.50, not Mondays) and pudding; summer barbecues. *(Recommended by Colin and Mary Meaden, Andy and Jill Kassube, Pete Storey, Dr Keith Bloomfield, Matt Pringle)*

Own brew   Licensee John Thompson   Real ale   Lunchtime meals and snacks (snacks only Sun; cold buffet only, Mon)   Derby (0332) 862469   Children in separate room Open 10.30–2.30, 7–11

MILLTHORPE (Derbys)   SK3276   Map 7
Royal Oak

B6051

In a quiet rural spot, this 17th-century pub is well known for its very good value home-made food: toasties and sandwiches such as bacon and black pudding (£1–£1.50), a wide choice of ploughman's, cottage pie (£2.85), ratatouille or Cumberland sausage (£3), seafood mornay, sweet and sour pork or chicken à la king (£3.60), lamb casserole (£3.65) or game pie (£4.95); puddings like bread and butter pudding, cherry cheesecake or fruit crumble (all £1.35). The characterful main room has bare stone walls, solid furnishings under the old oak beams and a winter log fire, and opens into a small, more comfortable and quieter lounge. Well kept and well priced Darleys Thorne and Wards Sheffield Best on handpump; selection of malt whiskies and quite a few spirits and liqueurs; cribbage and dominoes. The crazy-paved terrace under hawthorn, ash and other trees, has picnic-table sets – as does a side lawn further up; several good walks in the area. *(Recommended by J D Baines, M M Baines, Andrew Turnbull; more reports please)*

Free house   Licensees Harry and Elaine Wills   Real ale   Meals and snacks (not Sat-Sun evenings)   Sheffield (0742) 890 870   Open 11.30–2.30, 5.30–11 (11.30–3, 6–11 Sat); closed Mon lunchtime, except bank holidays

MONSAL HEAD (Derbys)   SK1871   Map 7
Monsal Head Hotel

B6465

Readers particularly like the lively, flagstoned bar in the old stables here. It's open all day, and has a big woodburning stove in an inglenook, cushioned oak pews around flowery-clothed tables in the stripped timber horse-stalls, and harness, horsey brassware, farm tools, and railway signs and lamps from a local disused station; steps lead up into a crafts gallery. The spacious high-ceilinged main front bar is set out more as a wine bar, with dining chairs around big tables; it's partitioned off from the restaurant area. Bar food includes sandwiches (from £1.20), and good home-made vegetable soup (£1.50), onion bhajis or garlic mushrooms (£1.60), vegetarian dishes such as aubergine and mushroom lasagne or bulgur wheat and walnut casserole (£3.50), fish dishes such as fillet of plaice (£3.75), home-made pies (from £4.95, rabbit pie or venison pie £7.25); there's a carvery in the lounge (steaks from £6.50); some of the main dishes can also be served as children's helpings but in the evenings there is also a children's menu (£1.75). Well kept John Smiths, Mansfield, Theakstons Old Peculier, a beer brewed for the pub and a regularly changing guest beer such as Adnams on handpump, as well as Westons Old Rosie cider; darts, shove-ha'penny, table skittles; quiet (and free) juke box. The pub's position above the steep valley of the River Wye is marvellous and gives good views from its balconies and the big windows of its lounge, though perhaps the best place for them is the terrace by the front car park. Both the restaurant and the bedrooms are decorated in authentically Victorian style. The back garden has a play area; on *Good Walks Guide* Walk 82. *(Recommended by Robin and Christine Harman, Roy Smylie, Mr and Mrs R Gammon, R Tomlinson, I H Rorison, Simon Velate, Matt Pringle, Michael Thomson, Derek Patey, Dr Paul Kitchener, Gill and Neil Patrick, Mike and Wendy Proctor, Giles Quick)*

Free house   Licensee Nicholas Smith   Real ale   Meals and snacks   Restaurant Great Longstone (062 987) 250   Children welcome, but not after 7 in Stable bar Open 11–11; closed 25 Dec   Bedrooms; £41.25B/50S

ONECOTE (Staffs)   SK0555   Map 7
Jervis Arms

B5053, off A523 Leek–Ashbourne

There are new owners here at the Jervis Arms, while the former landlord has now gone to The Raddle in Hollington (see Lucky Dip entries). This 17th-century pub has something for both adults and children and can, therefore, get busy at weekends. The irregularly shaped main bar has little hunting prints on the walls, window seats, wheelback chairs, two or three unusually low plush chairs, white planks over shiny black beams, and toby jugs and decorative plates on the high mantlepiece of its big stone fireplace. A similar if slightly simpler inner room has a fruit machine, and there are two family rooms (as well as high chairs and a mother and baby room). Quickly served good bar food includes soup (£1), ham, beef or cheese rolls (£1.30), tasty filled baked potatoes (from £2.75), ploughman's or generous home-cooked ham (from £3.25), roast topside of beef or steak pie (£3.75), roast chicken (quarter £3.75, half £5), vegetarian dishes such as curried nut, fruit and vegetable pie or savoury cheesecake (£3.95), and 12oz sirloin steak (£7), daily specials, all around £4, such as chicken tikka masala, tuna pasta bake or peppered pork; puddings such as meringue glacé (from £1.50), children's helpings (from £1). Well kept Bass, Ruddles County, Samuel Websters, Theakstons XB and Old Peculier and Youngers Scotch on handpump; friendly service. Dominoes, cribbage, fruit machine and piped pop music. The neat riverside lawn has picnic-table sets under cocktail parasols, and a couple of play trees with slides and swings (more facilities for children are planned), a little shrubby rockery behind, and lots of sheltering ash trees; a footbridge leads to the car park. A spacious barn behind the pub has been converted to self-catering accommodation. There are lovely moorland pastures above the village. *(Recommended by John Scarisbrick, Andy and Jill Kassube, Virginia Jones, Hilary Bill, Chris Raisin, Mike and Wendy Proctor, Geoffrey and Nora Cleaver, John Beeken)*

Free house   Licensees Robert and Jean Sawdon   Real ale   Meals and snacks (till 10 evening)   Onecote (0538) 304 206   Children welcome   Open 12–3, 7–11; closed 25 and 26 Dec   Self-catering barn (with two bedrooms); £150 a week for the whole unit

OVER HADDON (Derbys)   SK2066   Map 7

Lathkil ⊘ ⊨

Village and inn signposted from B5055 just SW of Bakewell

It's the easy-going atmosphere, very good food and warm, well equipped bedrooms that readers like so much in this marvellously positioned, popular inn. The airy room on the right has old-fashioned settles with upholstered cushions or plain wooden chairs, black beams, a delft shelf of blue and white plates on one white wall, original prints and photographs, a cheery fire in the attractively carved fireplace, and big windows. On the left is the spacious and sunny family dining area, which doubles as a restaurant in the evenings; at lunchtime the highly praised bar food is served here and includes home-made soup (£1.35), filled cobs (from £1.50), smoked mackerel salad (£3.35), lamb curry (£3.70), lasagne or quiche (£3.80), steak and kidney pie or beef and mushroom pie (£4.10), smoked trout (£4.30) and cold meats and salads (£4.35); home-made puddings (from £1.50). Well kept Wards Darleys Best Mild, Thorne and Sheffield Best on handpump and good breakfasts; piped classical music or jazz, shove-ha'penny, dominoes, cribbage. The pub is popular with walkers and there's even a place in the lobby to leave muddy boots. Best to get here early in good weather. The views sweep over the wooded slopes of Lathkill Dale, Youlgreave church tower and the village of Stanton in Peak, and if you follow the footpath to the east of the pub you can see the River Lathkill far below flowing over a series of weirs. In the centre of the village a couple of former dairy farmers have turned their farm buildings into the Lathkill Dale Craft Centre. *(Recommended by Caroline Wright, Dennis Jones, Derek and Sylvia Stephenson, Roy Smylie, Roy Cove, Greenwood and Turner, Mr and Mrs Sherriff, J and K Craddock, G V Price, Andy and Jill Kassube, Simon Maxwell, I H Rorison, Kathy Holt, Curt and Lois Stevens, Mike and Wendy Proctor, Gordon Theaker, Paul and Margaret Baker, Simon Velate, John and Joan Wyatt, Michael Thomson, Andrew Stephenson)*

Free house   Licensee Robert Grigor-Taylor   Real ale   Lunchtime meals and snacks   Evening restaurant (residents only, not Sun)   Bakewell (0629) 812501   Children in eating area of bar at lunchtime and in restaurant in evening   Open 11.30–3, 6–11; closed 25 Dec evening   Bedrooms; £32.50S/£60B

ROWARTH (Derbys)　SK0189 Map 7

Little Mill

Turn off A626 at Mellor signpost (in steep dip at Marple Bridge); fork left at Rowarth signpost, then follow Little Mill signpost; OS Sheet 110 map reference 011889

Tucked away down tricky roads in good walking country, this stone-slated white house has an an open-plan bar with comfortable little settees and armchairs on the Turkey carpet, stub walls, and bare brick pillars. Bar food includes soup (£1), sandwiches (from £1.30), black pudding (£1.50), tasty deep-fried mushrooms, doner kebab (from £2.20), ploughman's (£3.25), and home-made dishes such as lasagne (£2.75), chicken and mushroom pie (£2.65), steak and kidney pie (£3.75), lamb or chicken curry (£3.85), and puddings (£1.55). Banks's, Hansons, Robinsons Best Mild and Bitter on handpump and one extra strong which is changed on a regular basis such as Ruddles or Theakstons; quite a few malt whiskies; darts, pool, dominoes, fruit, space and trivia machine and juke box. The 1932 Pullman railway dining car (called the Derbyshire Belle) is converted into three well appointed bedrooms. Roses, honeysuckle and tubs of flowers decorate the front terrace and there are little lawns with ash trees, seats, swings and a climbing frame. (*Recommended by Bill Ryan, Lee Goulding, H B Vanstone, A M Neal, Ben Whitney, Pippa Redmond; more reports please*)

Free house　Licensee Christopher Barnes　Real ale　Meals and snacks (all day) Upstairs restaurant　New Mills (0663) 743178　Children welcome　Bands on Wed nights　Bedrooms; 25B/£35B; they also have two self-contained cottages　Open 11–11

SHARDLOW (Derbys)　SK4330 Map 7

Hoskins Wharf

3 1/2 miles from M1 junction 24; A6 towards Derby, pub on left

You reach the bar in this imposing late 18th-century converted canal warehouse by a counter-weighted drawbridge as one branch of the canal plunges through a sweeping arch in the building's centre. It's not a big room, and has stripped brickwork, heavy beams, brick flooring, simple furniture, some colourful narrow-boat nameplates, a picture window overlooking the canal basin – and plenty of chat. Bar food includes filled French sticks (£1.30), beefburger or breaded plaice (£3.25), chicken and chips (£3.35), ploughman's or cold meat platter (£3.50), chilli con carne (£3.65) and beef in ale pie (£3.75), with puddings such as blackforest gateau, death by chocolate (£1.70). An upstairs restaurant serves mainly grills, but includes cheap children's dishes and a bargain £4.99 steak lunch – may be served downstairs too, at lunchtime. Well kept Hoskins Beaumanor, Churchills and Penns on handpump, with a changing guest beer such as Vaux Samson; fruit machine, maybe darts and piped music. Outside there are picnic-table sets among weeping willows (and an unusually big dragon's-claw willow) on a grassy promontory between the canal branches, with more by a children's play area on a bigger stretch of grass behind; a very pretty spot. (*Recommended by Dr Keith Bloomfield, P A and J B Jones, Mrs P J Pearce, Andy and Jill Kassube, Carl Southwell, Andrew Stephenson, Dr P H Mitchell*)

Hoskins　Tenant David Holmes　Real ale　Meals and snacks (not Sat eve) Restaurant　Derby (0332) 792 844　Open 11.30–3, 6–11, 11.30–11 Sat (winter Sat 11.30–3, 6–11)

SHRALEYBROOK (Staffs)　SJ7850 Map 7

Rising Sun

3 miles from M6 junction 16; from A500 towards Stoke take first right turn signposted Alsager, Audley; in Audley turn right on the road still shown on many maps as A52, but now in fact a B, signposted Balterley, Nantwich; pub then signposted on left (at the T-junction look out for the Watneys Red Barrel)

The real attraction here is the own-brew beers produced in the brewery behind the pub – Rising, Setting, Sunlight and Sunstroke Bitters and a more powerful brew appropriately called Total Eclipse; they also keep half a dozen on handpump, rotating weekly from a cellar of around thirty, and typically including Adnams, Ashvine, Badger, Batemans XXXB, Courage Directors, Eagle, Hadrian Gladiator and Centurion, Mansfield, Oakhill, Pitfield Dark Star, Robinwood Old Fart, Sarah Hughes and Titanic; around 110 malts and 100 liqueurs, and Thatcher's and Westons Special Vintage ciders. The bar has a warm open fire, shiny black panelling and beams and timbers in the ochre walls, red leatherette seats tucked into the timberwork and cosy alcoves, brasses and some netting, and dim lighting. Bar food includes sandwiches, soup, a wide range of burgers (from £1.50), filled baked potatoes (£2), beef in ale casserole or gammon (£5) and a wide range of vegetarian foods. Dominoes, cribbage, fruit machine and piped music. There may be a minibus service to get you home. A notice in the window says 'No Students'. *(Recommended by John Scarisbrick, John Fazakerley, John Radford, Martin Aust, Alan Holden, Richard Houghton, Mike and Wendy Proctor, Dr M Owton, Sue Holland, Dave Webster, Pamela E Roper, Len Beattie)*

Own brew   Licensee Mrs Gillian Holland   Real ale   Meals and snacks (12–2.30, 6.30–10.30)   Restaurant   Stoke on Trent (0782) 720 600   Children till 8.30pm in bar, no restrictions elsewhere   Occasional live entertainment Fri and Sat evenings in upstairs function room   Open 12–3.30, 6.30–11; all day Sat

TATENHILL (Staffs)   SK2021 Map 7

Horseshoe £

Off A38 at A5121 Burton exit – then signposted; OS Sheet 128 map reference 203217

A decent remodelling of a village pub, this has several cosy communicating areas around its central servery, with a choice of moods – from the regulars on the tiles by the counter itself through the relaxed comfort of russet-cushioned wall seats in a square-panelled part with an open fire to the more sit-up chairs and tables in a self-contained side area with a woodburning stove. Very quickly served good value bar food includes home-made soup (£1), rolls and sandwiches (from 95p, a generous steak one £4.50), burgers (from £1.95), sausage, egg and chips (£2.40), omelettes (from £2.55), pizza (£2.60), ploughman's (from £2.80), filled baked potatoes (from £2.70), vegetarian dishes (£3.10), salads (from £3.10), a richly flavoured steak and kidney pie (£3.60), 8oz gammon and egg (£4.40), 10oz rump steak (£7.10) and children's dishes (from £1.90; also helpings of some main dishes); you must book for the Sunday lunch in the cosy pitched-roof two-level restaurant. Well kept Marstons Pedigree on handpump and Owd Rodger in winter; eight different kinds of beaujolais; dominoes, cribbage, fruit machine, piped music. The back garden's great attraction in good weather: plenty of tables either on the terrace or among small trees, and an ambitious play area including a fort and a huge timber climber. *(Recommended by T Nott, A S Maxted, George and Evelyne Smaylen)*

Marstons   Tenants Michael and Maureen Bould   Real ale   Meals and snacks (12–2, Tues-Sat 6–9.15)   Burton on Trent (0283) 64913   Children in family room or dining room   Open 11.30–3, 5.30–11; closed evening 25 Dec

WARDLOW (Derbys)   SK1874 Map 7

Bulls Head

B6465; village signposted off A623 W of Chesterfield

A welcome sight as you climb out of Cressbrook Dale, this heavy-slated white house is very much a dining pub with bar food such as home-made soup (£1), sandwiches (from £1.50, smoked salmon £1.95), ploughman's (£2.50), steak and kidney pie (£3.95), summer steak or chicken breast (£7.50), with puddings (£1.75) such as treacle sponge or apple and blackberry pie; there's a minimum charge of £3. Well kept Mansfield and Wards Sheffield Best on handpump; efficient service. The front part has deep green walls and plush button-back built-in wall banquettes, Turkey carpet, a lot of exposed stonework, some harness, and a coal-effect gas fire; behind is a red-carpeted room, with its tables more intimately set between winged settles forming individual stalls. There are tables on a small flagstoned terrace in front, and a couple on grass by sycamores behind; stone-walled small pastures stretch away on all sides. *(Recommended by John Beeken, Derek and Sylvia Stephenson; more reports please)*

Free house   Licensee Mrs Selina Wetherall   Real ale   Meals (booking strongly advised Fri-Sun) and snacks   Hartington (0298) 871 431   Children in eating area only   Open 11–2.30, 6.30–11   Bedrooms; l£35

Three Stags Heads

Wardlow Mires; A623 by junction with B6465

Delightfully unspoilt, the little parlour bar in this white-painted stone cottage has old leathercloth seats, a couple of antique settles with flowery cushions, two high-backed Windsor armchairs and simple oak tables on the flagstones, and a cast-iron kitchen range which is kept alight in winter; also, a double rack of pots (made in the barn which is a pottery workshop – they also make the majority of the plates used in the pub), a petrified cat in a glass case, and three live dogs. There's also a small, no smoking dining parlour with bookable tables and an open fire. Food is served all day from a regularly changing menu and home-made dishes might include cauliflower and tomato curry (£4.50), courgette and tomato casserole with cheese dumplings (£5), lamb and apricot tagine (£6.50), chicken and mushroom in red wine (£7.25) and rack of lamb (£8.50); there are always vegetarian, often vegan, dishes on the menu; no smoking dining room and friendly service. Theakstons Old Peculier and Youngers Scotch and No 3 on handpump; continental beers and lagers and fruit beers in bottles. Cribbage, dominoes, spoof, chess, and nine men's morris. The front terrace outside looks across the main road to the distant hills. Walkers – and their boots – are welcome. The car park is across the road by the petrol station. *(Recommended by Keith W Mills, D and B Carron, Andy and Jill Kassube, Simon Velate, Matt Pringle, Wayne Brindle)*

Free house   Licensees Geoff and Pat Fuller   Real ale   Meals and snacks (12–10 pm) Tideswell (0298) 872268   Children in eating area of bar before 8.30pm   Live folk/traditional blues Sat evening   Open 11–11, winter eve opening 7pm; closed lunchtime Mons (not bank hols) when evening opening is 7, and winter weekday lunchtimes

WARSLOW (Staffs)   SK0858 Map 7

Greyhound 🛏

B5053 S of Buxton

This plain slated stone building takes its name from the Buxton to Uttoxeter coach which used to stop here. It's run by particularly friendly people who serve good home-made bar food: soup (£1.20), sandwiches or home-baked rolls (from £1.20 – they home-cook their meat), ploughman's (from £3), home-made steak and kidney pie (£3.50), pork fillet in apple and cider sauce (£3.90), sirloin steak (£5.90), and daily specials that are chalked up on a board; puddings (from £1.50), children's menu (£1.70), traditional Sunday lunch (£3.50) – best to get there early then (and on Saturday evening); good breakfasts. Well kept Bass and a guest beer on handpump. The long beamed bar has elm-topped stools and cushioned oak antique settles, some quite elegant, on its carpet, a log fire, houseplants in the windows, and quietly restrained landscapes on the cream walls. Pool room, with darts, dominoes, fruit machine and table skittles; piped music from Bros to Beethoven. There are rustic seats out in front, with picnic-table sets under ash trees in the side garden. The village is just a short stroll from the Manifold Valley, and quite well placed for other Peak District features. The simple bedrooms are comfortable and clean and there are local information leaflets in the foyer. *(Recommended by Paul and Margaret Baker, Barry and Anne, Mr and Mrs Sherriff, P Corris, Mike and Wendy Proctor, Martin and Amy Evans, M G Clark)*

Free house   Licensee David Mullarkey   Real ale   Meals and snacks (not Mon lunchtime)   Buxton (0298) 84249   Children until 9pm in pool room and tap room Live music Sat (usually singer and guitarist)   Open 12–3, 7–11 (till 11.45 Sat); 12–2.30, 7–11 in winter (till 11.45 Sat); closed Mon lunchtime   Bedrooms; £14/£28

WETTON (Staffs)   SK1055   Map 7

Olde Royal Oak   £

A room in the garden has been opened up for families which has taken some of the pressure off the bar in this white-painted and shuttered stone village pub. The locals are friendly and welcoming and the variety in the rooms adds to the charm. The old part has small dining chairs around rustic tables, black beams supporting white ceiling boards, an oak corner cupboard, and a log fire in the stone fireplace. This extends into a more modern-feeling area, with another fire and a door into a carpeted sun lounge, which looks on to the small garden. Popular bar food includes sandwiches (from £1-£1.50), ploughman's (from £2.75 – the cheese for the Stilton version is made in nearby Hartington), and main dishes like sausages (£2.40), omelettes (from £2.85), ham and egg (£2.95), chicken or cod (£3.70), scampi or trout (£3.95), gammon (£4.20) and plaice (£4.40); puddings from £1.40. Eldridge Pope Royal Oak, Ruddles County and Best and Theakstons XB on handpump, several malt whiskies, and coffee; darts, dominoes and shove-ha'penny. It's set in National Trust and walking country, with places like Wetton Hill and the Manifold Valley nearby. Behind the pub is a croft suitable for caravans and tents. *(Recommended by WAH, J H G Owen, Greenwood and Turner, G T and J Barnes, Tony and Pat Young, Dr Keith Bloomfield, Andy amd Jill Kassube, Keith Bloomfield, John Scarisbrick, Simon Velate, T Galligan)*

Free house   Licensee George Burgess   Real ale   Meals and snacks (not winter Sun evenings)   Alstonefield   (033 527) 287   Children in family room and garden bar   Open 11.30–3, 6.30–11 (11–3, 6.30–11 Sat, winter 12–2.30, 7–11)

WHITMORE (Staffs)   SJ8141   Map 7

Mainwaring Arms   ★

3 miles from M6 junction 15; follow signs for Market Drayton, Shrewsbury, on to A53

The interconnecting oak-beamed rooms in this lovely stone building ramble up and down, in and out, with four open fires (one in a capacious stone fireplace in the lower room), some old-fashioned settles among comfortable more modern seats, and reproduction memorial brasses on the walls. Home-made bar food includes soup (95p), sandwiches (from £1.20, prawn sandwiches £2.20, French sticks £1.70), lamb hot-pot or beef stew served inside a large Yorkshire pudding (£2.95), a good summer cold buffet with salads and a choice of home-cooked meats (£3.50), chicken and mushroom, chicken in lemon and garlic or steak and kidney pie (£3.50), horseshoe gammon and egg (£5.50). Well kept Bass, Boddingtons, and Marstons Pedigree on handpump; wide range of foreign bottled beers and ciders; trivia machine. There are seats outside opposite the idyllic village church, and a cobbled barbecue area at the back. The local shoot may use it for gatherings. *(Recommended by John and Christine Simpson, T Nott, J Scarisbrick, Mike and Wendy Proctor, TBB, Niall and Jane, Laurence Manning; more reports please)*

Free house   Licensee Simon Hastings   Real ale   Lunchtime meals and snacks   Stoke on Trent   (0782) 680 851   Children in eating area, until 8pm only   Open 11–2.30 (3 Sat), 5.30–11

WRINEHILL (Staffs)   SJ7547   Map 7

Crown

Den Lane; pub signed just off A531 Newcastle-under-Lyme–Nantwich

The Davenhills have been running this spic-and-span and rather civilised country pub since 1978. It's been carefully refurbished with red plush wall settles, banquettes and stools around the dark cast-iron-framed tables on its carpet, patterned curtains on rings on rails, and attractive pictures ranging from little etchings of pottery kilns to big landscapes and old prints. At one end, there's a flagstoned inglenook with plush side seats and at the other, a second open fire in a stripped brick fireplace with black-iron side oven. Generously served good value bar food includes plaice (£3.45), lasagne (£3.50), scampi (£3.95), gammon (£4.50), and steaks (from the village butcher) and a good range of vegetarian dishes for under £4 (the landlady does most of the cooking and is vegetarian herself); well kept Bass and Marstons Pedigree on handpump; dominoes, well reproduced pop music, friendly service. *(Recommended by Mrs J Timmis; more reports please)*

Free house   Licensees Charles and Sue Davenhill   Real ale   Evening meals till 10pm (not weekday lunchtimes, not Sun evening)   Nantwich   (0270) 820472   Children only at lunchtime and early eve   Open 6–11 weekdays (closed lunch, except bank hols), 12–3, 7–11 Sat; usual Sun hours

Lucky Dip

Besides the fully inspected pubs, you might like to try these Lucky Dips recommended to us and described by readers (if you do, please send us reports):

☆ **Abbots Bromley**, Staffs [Bagot St; SK0724], *Royal Oak*: Clean and attractive refurbished dining lounge with pleasant service and good, varied reasonably priced food with Dutch influence; well kept Marstons Pedigree, interesting Oak Room restaurant *(Graham Richardson, Mr and Mrs K W Banks, Nigel Hopkins)*

Abbots Bromley [Main St], *Bagot Arms*: 18th-century coaching inn with genial landlord, open fire in lounge, Marstons Pedigree on handpump, bar food such as ploughman's and steak and kidney pie *(John Beeken)*

Acton Trussell, Staffs [nr M6 junction 13; off A449 Stafford rd; SJ9318], *Moat House*: In delightful grounds with big duck pond, looks like old manor house; friendly licensees, good service, log fires, dark beams, and nice variety of wooden and upholstered comfortable chairs; spacious bar divided into smaller areas by wooden beams, conservatory restaurant and nice country house-type atmosphere; food very good *(Keith Croxton)*

Alton, Staffs [SK0742], *Talbot*: Small cosy stone-built pub, good friendly staff, limited choice of good interesting food *(Mike and Wendy Proctor)*

☆ **Amington**, Staffs [Tamworth Rd; SK2304], *Gate*: Pleasantly refurbished and locally popular canalside pub with some concentration on food in lounge bar, also separate bar, Marstons ales, good-sized family room, good service, restaurant *(Graham Richardson, J Jewitt, E V Walder)*

☆ **Ashbourne**, Derbys [St Johns St; SK1846], *Smiths*: Narrow pub going a long way back, with small front area, comfortable snug and further family dining lounge with some interesting old furniture inc two carved antique settles and magnificent carved high-backed chair with high built-in cupboard; well kept Marstons, hearty helpings of good straightforward bar food, attractive service; piano singalong Fri, Sun *(WAH, Simon Velate, Dorothy and David Young, Greenwood and Turner)*

☆ **Ashford in the Water**, Derbys [SK1969], *Ashford Inn*: Clean, comfortably refurbished and well kept, with lots of gleaming brass, pleasant staff, good helpings of well prepared bar food with fresh veg, upmarket restaurant with emphasis on healthy eating; get there early to be sure of the good specials; Bass and Stones on handpump; bedrooms inc at least one four-poster; picturesque village, pleasant staff *(P A Crossland, D A Cawley, Neville Kenyon, BB)*

Ashford in the Water, Derbys [SK1969], *Bulls Head*: Friendly welcome, good service, food and beer *(Dr and Mrs James Stewart, DC)*

☆ **Ashley**, Staffs [signposted from A53 NE of Market Drayton; SJ7636], *Peel Arms*: Polished and plush, yet old-world appeal, with big open range, lovely garden, good friendly landlord, well kept Allied ales, popular food; very clean *(Laurence Manning, G T and J Barnes)*

☆ **Ashley** [Lower Rd (towards B5026)], *Robin Hood*: Old-world decor, oak beams, open fire, brown leather seats, unobtrusive piped music, well kept McEwans 70/- and 80/-, good well presented bar food, Sun lunches, keen young staff; separate dining room, well behaved children allowed *(G T and J Barnes)*

Ashley, *Meynell Arms*: New licensees doing well; good plain cooking, deep sofa, cast-iron stove and other old-fashioned touches in timbered, panelled and stripped stone lounge, games inc darts and table skittles in comfortable public bar, children in eating area *(G T and J Barnes, John C)*

Ashover, Derbys [SK3564], *Red Lion*: Attractive Victorian-style pub with impeccable service, short imaginative choice of good value bar food, small dining area with cheerful fire *(J B A Lynch)*

Bakewell, Derbys [Market Pl; SK2168], *Red Lion*: Town bar popular with young people, but worth knowing for good range of reasonably priced bar food, upstairs restaurant; Wards on electric pump *(A S Clements, Sidney and Erna Wells, Steve Mitcheson and Anne Collins)*; *Rutland Tavern*: Local of some character, with well kept Marstons Pedigree, simple food *(A S Clements)*

☆ **Balterley**, Staffs [Newcastle Rd; SJ7650], *Broughton Arms*: Clean and airy, with quick service, well kept Greenalls, sensible choice of well served bar food inc good value steaks *(Catherine and Andrew Brian)*

☆ **Bamford**, Derbys [Taggs Knoll — main rd; SK2083], *Anglers Rest*: Friendly staff in spotless pub with revolving door, warm atmosphere, wide choice of generous good value bar food (they make quite a thing of extra sauces), quick service *(Joan and John Calvert, Janet Brown)*

☆ **Baslow**, Derbys [SK2572], *Devonshire Arms*: Comfortably refurbished with good furniture and attractive decorations, good choice of reasonably priced food using some fresh ingredients from nearby Chatsworth (special sausages particularly good); evening restaurant meals, Marstons and Shipstones on handpump *(Pat and Tony Young, Dr Keith Bloomfield, ILP)*

Baslow, *Rutland Arms*: Village pub with pleasant helpful staff and decent food from sandwiches up *(Roy Y Bromell)*

☆ **Beeley**, Derbys [SK2667], *Devonshire Arms*: Also handy for Chatsworth, clean and very popular (sometimes overly so), with oak beams, stripped stone and flagstones, big log fires, well kept Theakstons (full range) and maybe Wards, straightforward food in bar and nice separate dining room; attractive rolling scenery; children welcome, with upstairs family room and own menu; service could perhaps do with a more personal touch *(Mike and Wendy Proctor, Dr Keith Bloomfield, S Corrigan, Simon Velate, Roxanne Chamberlain)*

Belper, Derbys [29 Chesterfield Rd; SK3447], *Queens Head*: Warm and cosy, with constant open fire, Rugby Union theme, well kept Allied beers, very cheap food *(Alan McCormick)*

Betley, Staffs [OS Sheet 118, map reference 753486; SJ7548], *Black Horse*: Pleasant and spacious, with Sat four-course dinner-dance and good value Sun lunch *(Martin Aust)*

☆ **Birch Vale**, Derbys [Sycamore Rd; from A6015 take Station Rd towards Thornsett; SK0287], *Sycamore*: Busy food pub with fountain in downstairs drinking bar and four connecting eating rooms, variously furnished, with wide choice of food from sandwiches to a good range of steaks inc do-it-yourself hot-rock sizzlers, also children's dishes and lots of rich puddings; piped music may be rather loud; spacious streamside gardens with good play area, pets' corner and summer drinks-and-ice-cream bar; restaurant open all day Sun, children welcome; bedrooms *(KC, Steve Mitcheson, Anne Collins, M A and W R Proctor)*

Brackenfield, Derbys [Matlock rd; SK3759], *Plough*: Cosy former 18th-century farmhouse on three levels, with oak beams, character, good bar meals inc some vegetarian; Bass, Mansfield Old Baily and Stones; big beautifully kept gardens with play area *(Mrs Parkes, Mrs Langford, Mrs Dobson)*

☆ **Bradley**, Staffs [SJ8718], *Red Lion*: Friendly 16th-century pub with particularly well kept Bass Special, sensibly priced good food inc good Sun lunch, friendly service *(Maurice and Gill McMahon, N P Hopkins)*

Branston, Staffs [Tatenhill Lane; off A5121 just SW of Burton; SK2221], *Bridge*: Pleasant waterside pub (good moorings outside Bridge 34) with good Pedigree from the barrel, basic supplies for boaters and caravanners; no food evenings; tables outside *(P A and J B Jones)*

☆ **Brewood**, Staffs [SK8808], *Admiral Rodney*: Well kept real ales, very good value food (particularly steaks), friendly service, separate games room; the Victorian-style refurbishment is perhaps a little overemphasised *(K Widdowson, C H Stride)*

Brindley Ford, Staffs [Fisher St; SJ8854], *Gardeners Rest*: Welcoming village pub popular for good choice of good value bar lunches inc fresh-cooked veg; nr Chatterley Whitfield Mining Museum, Tunstall *(Les and Jean Bradman)*

☆ **Burton on Trent**, Staffs [Cross St — a no entry — heading N down Station St, pass Bass Brewery then turn left into Milton St (from which pub has a back entrance); SK2423], *Coopers Tavern*: Fine example of highly traditional back tap room with chatty landlord and notably well kept Bass straight from imposing row of casks, cheap and nourishing hot filled cobs, pie and chips and so forth virtually throughout opening hours; the nearby Bass brewing museum is well worth a visit; children welcome *(Chris Raisin, Graham Doyle, LYM)*

Burton on Trent [opp Ind Coope brewery], *Devonshire Arms*: Decent pub with lots of little corners; particularly well kept Ind Coope Burton on handpump, good cheap food *(John Cattell)*

Buxton, Derbys [Bridge St; SK0673], *Railway*: Clean and popular food pub with good service, varied well cooked food inc imaginative salads and home-made puddings; good range of cocktails *(Dr V Randle)*

☆ nr **Buxton**, Derbys [Hurdlow Town; A515 Ashbourne Rd, about half a mile from the Bull i'th' Thorn; SK1166], *Duke of York*: Friendly, helpful landlord and good bar food inc children's dishes, served all day Sun; also children's menu; Robinsons real ale; can get busy *(R D Llewellyn, A J Francis)*

☆ **Castleton** Derbys [Cross St; SK1583], *Olde Nags Head*: Village hotel renovated to preserve character, though bar not large (and walkers with boots or packs excluded), open fires, antique furniture, well presented traditional bar food (perhaps the best pub food in the village); Bass, restaurant; bedrooms warm and comfortable but pricy *(Richard Fawcett)*

☆ **Castleton**, *Olde Cheshire Cheese*: Two comfortable communicating bar areas in slated white timbered pub; wide choice of rather pricy but generally good bar food, sensibly placed darts, leatherette seats around wooden tables, affable licensee, piped jazz; popular with young people; bedrooms *(Sidney and Erna Wells, Dr B A W Perkins, Roy Cove, David and Rebecca Killick, A S Clements, BB)*

Castleton [Cross St], *Bulls Head*:

Plain-speaking village pub with well kept Robinsons, warm fires, food (may be slow when busy) inc good Yorkshire puddings *(Matt Pringle, Robin and Christine Harman);* [High St/Castle St], *Castle:* Handsome flagstones, beams and stripped stonework in plush hotel bars, food in bar and restaurant, keg beers, open fires; open all day in summer, with tables outside; good location, on GWG81; bedrooms well equipped if rather pricy *(Dorothy and David Young, A S Clements, LYM)*

Charlesworth, Derbys [Glossop Rd; SK0193], *Travellers Call:* Good value bar food inc very hot chilli; busy Sun lunchtime *(Pauline Crossland, Dave Cawley)*

☆ **Cheddleton**, Staffs [Basford Bridge Lane, off A520; SJ9651], *Boat:* Narrow neatly furnished pub just above canal, low plank ceilings, well kept Marstons, welcoming atmosphere; handy for North Staffs Steam Railway Museum *(Mike and Wendy Proctor, Wayne Brindle, LYM)*

☆ **Chinley**, Derbys [A624 towards Hayfield; SK0482], *Lamb:* Old stone-built moorland pub, long and low, with three small rooms, fine stone fireplace, good friendly atmosphere, well prepared reasonably priced bar food served quickly once you order (though you may have to wait a while for a table), famous crown green bowler as licensee, Bass and other real ales on handpump; children allowed till 7 *(P A Crossland, D A Cawley)*

Chisworth, Derbys [A626 Glossop—Marple; SJ9992], *Hunters:* Warmly welcoming, with well kept Robinsons Mild and Bitter on handpump, bar food and imaginative meals — weekend booking recommended for the restaurant *(Dennis Jones)*

Chunal, Derbys [A624 a mile S of Glossop; SK0391], *Grouse:* Spacious and comfortable long bar with good bar food inc fine game soup, unobtrusive piped music, Thwaites Mild and Bitter under light pressure, interesting landlord; children allowed in upstairs restaurant *(Gwen and Peter Andrews)*

☆ **Church Broughton**, Derbys [OS Sheet 128, map reference 205337; SK2033], *Holly Bush:* Particularly good value simple home cooking and good dining-room Sun lunch in neat and attractively refurbished village pub, well kept Marstons Pedigree, friendly labradors *(Chris Raisin, Eric J Locker)*

☆ **Clifton Campville**, Staffs [SK2510], *Green Man:* Cosy and notably welcoming 15th-century village pub kept spick-and-span, with low beams, inglenook and chubby armchair in public bar, airy lounge, well kept Ind Coope and Tetleys, good value bar food inc fine sandwiches, efficient service; children in snug and family room, garden with swings and lots of pets *(M A and W R Proctor, F D Wood, Pete Storey, Graham Richardson, Chris Raisin, LYM)*

☆ **Colton**, Staffs [Bellamour Way; SK0520], *Greyhound:* Friendly oak-beamed pub with good value home-made bar food, log fire, well kept Banks's, small garden; children welcome *(Mrs B Spratt, Tim and Lynne Crawford)*

☆ **Consall**, Staffs [Consallforge; best approach from Nature Pk, off A522 — OS Sheet 118 map reference 000491; SJ9748], *Black Lion:* Basic and unspoilt, in remote and unusual canalside spot, with good coal fire, very cheap bar food, Marstons Pedigree and Ruddles County on handpump, character landlady, traditional games, piped music; children welcome; busy weekends, good walking area on edge of country park *(J Scarisbrick, R J Whiston, LYM)*

☆ **Derby** [Siddals Rd; SK3435], *Alexandra:* Imposing Victorian pub recently taken over and well revivified by Batemans, collection of beer bottles around walls, dark floorboards, railway pictures, well kept Batemans and several guests on handpump, cheery staff, decent varied food; no juke box but landlord will put on CD of your choice if he's got it *(Carl Southwell, Chris Raisin, P A and J B Jones)*

Derby [Harington St], *Baseball:* Restored Victorian pub in shadow of Francis Ley's famous white-elephant Baseball Ground, massive curving mahogany bar, food, eight real ales; bedrooms *(Anon);* [13 Exeter Pl], *Exeter Arms:* Extended but still traditional low-beamed pub with huge fireplace in lovely little snug, Marstons Burton, Pedigree and Merrie Monk on handpump *(Angie and Dave Parkes, Carl Southwell);* [Arleston La, Sinfin; SK3432], *Ferrers Arms:* Plush modern split-level bar, open fire in lounge, Everards and maybe other real ales *(Carl Southwell);* [Queen St, nr cathedral], *Olde Dolphin:* City's oldest pub, several rooms inc beamed and timbered bar, cosy snug, room with mementoes of Offilers brewery; Bass, Springfield Bitter and Mild on handpump, good value snacks upstairs all day *(Angie and Dave Parkes, Carl Southwell);* [204 Abbey St], *Olde Spa:* Friendly old tiled-floor local with Ind Coope Burton on handpump, separate games room, garden with fountain *(Carl Southwell)*

Dovedale, Staffs [Thorpe—Ilam rd; Ilam signposted off A52, Thorpe off A515, NW of Ashbourne; SK1452], *Izaak Walton:* Low beams, antique oak settles and chairs, log fire in massive central stone hearth, Ind Coope Burton on handpump, bar food, restaurant, morning coffee, afternoon tea; seats outside; alone in fine position on the peaceful sloping pastures of Bunster Hill; nr start GWG84; bedrooms comfortable *(Mike and Wendy Proctor, LYM)*

☆ **Eccleshall**, Staffs [Castle St; SJ8329], *George:* Oak-beamed bar attractively modernised to keep character and charm, well kept real ales such as Tetleys, tempting bar food, good atmosphere, friendly landlord, carvery; bedrooms comfortable *(Laurence Manning)*

Edale, Derbys [SK1285], *Old Nags Head:* Popular and roomy walkers' pub at start of Pennine Way; efficiently served substantial basic cheap food, open fire, well kept real ales; video games in airy back family room; can get busy during walking season — lovely countryside outside village; nr start GWG83 *(Helen and John Thompson, LYM)*

Elmton, Derbys [SK5073], *Elm Tree*: Softly lit and popular low-ceilinged rural pub with well kept Bass on handpump, food, pianist Weds/Sat *(R A Caldwell)*

Eyam, Derbys [Water Lane; SK2276], *Miners Arms*: Well entrenched and comfortably modernised food pub, locally popular for good lunches (no bar meals Mon, other days open 12.30) *(DC, LYM); Rose & Crown*: Most friendly and obliging service in clean well organised pub with plain but well produced and generously served food, Stones and Tetleys real ales *(DC, Dave Braisted)*

☆ **Farnah Green**, Derbys [follow Hazelwood signpost off A517 in Blackbrook, W edge of Belper; SK3346], *Bluebell*: Good food in smart, plush dining pub with discreetly decorated small rooms, sturdy tables out on terrace and in quiet gently sloping spacious side garden; restaurant with inventive cooking; well kept Bass *(BB)*

Flash, Staffs [A53 Buxton—Leek; SK0267], *Travellers Rest*: Isolated main-road hill pub included for its ranking as Britain's third-highest; vast number of keg beers, loud juke box, ditto decor, no shortage of amusement machines; nice views from back terrace, simple snacks *(LYM)*

Forton, Staffs [A519 Newport—Eccleshall; SJ7621], *Swan*: Large country pub with comfortable armchairs in carpeted lounge, spacious bar area, flame-effect gas fires, Boddingtons and Marstons ales, good straightforward bar food; restaurant (Fri-Sun) *(Keith Croxton)*

Glossop, Derbys [Manor Park Rd; SK0394], *Commercial*: Generous helpings of good reasonably priced food in newish restaurant area, very attentive service, well kept real ale, darts and juke box in pub part; children in restaurant *(Mr and Mrs W B Barnes, Steve Mitcheson, Anne Collins)*; [Milltown, off High St East (A57)], *Prince of Wales*: Old-fashioned character end-of-terrace pub, relaxing at lunchtime (food then), lively evenings; well kept Marstons *(Lee Goulding)* *(Steve Mitcheson, Anne Collins); Royal Oak*: Particularly good food *(Pauline Crossland, Dave Cawley)*

Grangemill, Derbys [A5012/B5056; SK2457], *Hollybush*: Well kept, clean and pleasant old inn with rural, old world atmosphere, prompt friendly service and good choice of nicely presented bar food *(W J Wonham)*

☆ **Great Hucklow**, Derbys [SK1878], *Queen Anne*: Charming family-run pub, interesting bar food, Tetleys and freshly squeezed orange juice, comfortable beamed bar with gleaming copper and open fire, two other rooms, one with French windows on to small terrace and pleasant garden with idyllic views; may be closed lunchtime — perhaps even Sat — in winter; children

welcome *(Francesca Lopez, Neville Kenyon)*

Great Longstone, Derbys [SK2071], *White Lion*: Well appointed and respectable, with friendly service, good reasonably priced food; charming village, beautiful countryside *(J W Martin)*

☆ **Grindon**, Staffs [signed off B5033 N of A523; SK0854], *Cavalier*: 16th-century country pub with engaging rustic garden, two traditionally furnished rooms with nice old-fashioned features; has had short choice of interesting bar food, Marstons Pedigree, Ruddles County and guest beers on handpump, unusual bottled foreign beers and malt whiskies; children in side family room and restaurant; has been closed Mon lunchtime and maybe other lunchtimes *(Steve Mitcheson, Anne Collins, Simon Velate, John Scarisbrick, Chris Raisin, LYM; news please — no reports since recent refurbishment)*

Halfpenny Green, Staffs [off B4176; on Shrops border SW of Wolverhampton; SO8291], *Royal Oak*: Pleasant Banks's pub with reasonable food inc good goulash *(Dave Braisted)*

☆ **Hathersage**, Derbys [SK2381], *George*: Substantial comfortably modernised old inn, picturesque outside; a nice place to stay (the back bedrooms are the quiet ones); popular lunchtime bar food, neat flagstoned back terrace by rose garden; nr start GWG80 *(LYM)*

☆ **Hayfield**, Derbys [Church St; SK0387], *George*: Comfortable, quiet and cosy, particularly around roaring coal fire; lots of local photographs, lunchtime food, well kept Burtonwood beers, seats out by picturesque main street of pretty village, stream nearby *(Steve Mitcheson, Anne Collins, Lee Goulding)*

☆ **Hayfield** [Little Hayfield; A625 N], *Lantern Pike*: Friendly little village inn, cosy and homely, doing well under new landlord; open fire in front room, back dining room (children allowed), tasty food; fine hill views from back terrace, served by window at side of bar; good value bedrooms *(Pauline Crossland, Dave Cawley)*

Hayfield, Derbys [Market St; off A624 Glossop—Chapel-en-le-Frith], *Pack Horse*: Dining pub, popular (and busy) for consistently good generous food; not really for drinkers, though tables and benches outside *(A and L Holden, Steve Mitcheson, Anne Collins); Royal*: Streamside hotel with friendly and relaxed part-panelled bar, good side room full of curios and toby jugs, real fires, lunchtime and evening food, well kept Websters Choice; bedrooms *(Mike and Wendy Proctor, Lee Goulding)*

Hednesford, Staffs [Mount St; SJ9913], *West Cannock*: Very pleasant and attentive licensees, well kept Bass, good value food lunchtime and evening at competitive prices; cosy Victorian-style parlour, pool table, tables outside *(John and Chris Simpson)*

☆ **High Offley**, Staffs [Bridge 42, Shrops Union Canal; SJ7826], *Anchor*: Unusual canal pub, very basic — two homely rooms in a house which has been in the family for over a century; basic sandwiches, 11 ciders as well as Marstons Pedigree and Owd Rodger and Wadworths 6X brought up from cellar, snacks; winter closed Mon-Weds *(C H Stride, P Lloyd, Miss K Bamford)*

☆ **Hollington**, Staffs [the one between Alton and Uttoxeter; SK0538], *Raddle*: Comfortable modern furnishings in neatly painted rambling up-and-down bar of extended stone pub, five well kept real ales on handpump, quite big upstairs family room with own servery, tables outside and big new play area beyond, sweeping country views; recently redeveloped by new licensees who made the Jervis Arms at Onecote a popular main entry, and should be well worth a visit as it settles in and gains character; their food's always been worth knowing, too *(G T and J Barnes, BB)*

Holloway, Derbys [SK3357], *Yew Tree*: Stone-built pub with two small lounges, larger dining extension, Wadworths 6X on handpump, bar food such as filled Yorkshire puddings and baked potatoes, welcoming staff, tables outside with splendid views; handy for National Tramway Museum, Crich; children welcome *(Roy Y Bromell, John Beeken)*

☆ **Hope**, Derbys [Edale Rd; SK1783], *Cheshire Cheese*: Good range of good bar food (not Sun evening) in cheerful little up-and-down oak-beamed rooms of 16th-century stone-built village pub; lots of old local photographs and prints, abundant coal fires, well kept Wards Sheffield Best and Darleys Best; children allowed in eating area; walkers welcome, nr start GWG81; bedrooms inc cottage over the road *(Shirley Pielou, Dr B A W Perkins, Patrick Godfrey, LYM)*

☆ **Hope**, Derbys [out towards Castleton], *Poachers Arms*: Village pub with several welcoming bars, good decor, efficient service, generous helpings of interesting and varied well cooked food inc adventurous vegetarian dishes; Fri evening electric organ; children welcome; bedrooms *(Dr B A W Perkins, D W Crossley, Mrs R M Morris, D J and P M Taylor)*

Hopwas, Staffs [SK1704], *Chequers*: Well kept Courage Best and Directors and good value quick bar food in open-plan pub nr Coventry Canal, seats up by water; piped music may be a little loud *(Joan and Michel Hooper-Immins, Graham Richardson, LYM)*

Hulme End, Staffs [SK1059], *Manifold Valley*: Good setting nr river in open countryside; large lounge bar with good atmosphere, open fire and skittles; well kept Darleys Dark, Thorne Best and Wards Sheffield Best, generous helpings of bar food and Sun lunches in separate dining room; provision for children *(J Scarisbrick, BB)*

Ilkeston, Derbys [out on A6096 towards Derby; SK4338], *Bartlewood Lodge*: Very comfortable Brewers Fayre pub with good family food; well equipped children's garden with animals *(Anon)*; [Dale Abbey, off A6096 Derby rd], *Carpenters Arms*: Nr Abbey ruins, Hermit's Cave and remarkable All Saints Church (part of which was

formerly the village inn); Ind Coope Burton on handpump, good range of bar snacks lunchtime and evenings; can get crowded weekends *(Alan and Eileen Bowker)*; [Durham St], *Durham Ox*: Friendly, popular little backstreet pub with well kept Wards, Darleys and Vaux, lunchtime snacks *(P A and J B Jones)*; [Market Sq], *Sir John Warren*: Large hotel with comfortable refurbished bar and lounge, well kept Hardys & Hansons *(P A and J B Jones)*

Ipstones, Staffs [B5053 (village signposted from A52 and from A523); SK0249], *Red Lion*: Gentle colour scheme and comfortable seats in friendly and well run pub overlooking valley, well kept Burtonwood Best on handpump, reliably good value bar food, games area, piped music *(SJC, LYM)*

☆ **Kings Bromley**, Staffs [SK1216], *Royal Oak*: Friendly, efficient service, wide choice of good value well presented food and well kept beer in basic but cosy bar with enjoyable atmosphere; pleasant dining room, garden (may be donkeys behind) *(Graham Richardson, Roger Braithwaite)*

Kings Newton, Derbys [nr M1 junction 24; SK3826], *Hardinge Arms*: Lots of cricketing memorabilia in pub with some original timbering in very old rambling front part, modern back extension, well kept Marstons, food inc good set Sun lunch; children welcome *(E E Hemmings, LYM)*

☆ **Kinver**, Staffs [A449; SO8483], *Whittington*: Striking black and white timbered Tudor house built by Dick Whittington's family, fine garden with pétanque, old-fashioned bar, good choice of lunchtime bar food (soup almost a meal in itself), attentive staff, roaring fire, Marstons Pedigree *(LYM)*

☆ **Kirk Ireton**, Derbys [SK2650], *Barley Mow*: Range of well kept real ales tapped from the cask in unspoilt and basic series of interconnecting rooms — no frills, lots of woodwork *(Andrew Turnbull)*

☆ **Ladybower Reservoir**, Derbys [A57 Sheffield—Glossop, at junction with A6013; SK1986], *Ladybower*: Charming stone pub in sharp-sided valley by beautiful reservoir, clean and comfortable open-plan layout, well kept Tetleys, Theakstons and Wilsons, popular and quick if not cheap food in eating area (try the onion gravy), discreet piped music, fox masks; stone settles outside, good views (many walks nearby) favourite *(P A Crossland, D A Cawley, KC, Steve Mitcheson, Anne Collins)*

Langley Mill, Derbys [Boat Lane, Stoneyford; SK4449], *Stonyford Lodge*: Formerly the Boat, now has carvery (Tues-Sat, and Sun lunch), bar food inc sandwiches, steak and kidney pie, scampi, roast beef; Bass and Boddington on handpump; bedrooms in motel wing *(Alan and Eileen Bowker)*

Leek, Staffs [outskirts; SJ9856], *Abbey*: Good choice of food under new landlords of old country pub with Bass and changing guest beer; spacious terrace, nice surroundings *(J Scarisbrick)*; [17 Osbourne

Rd], *Blue Mugge*: Typical friendly market-town pub with low-priced well kept Bass and Worthington, good cheap basic food; good games room, three other rooms (each dedicated to a personage such as Winston Churchill) *(J Scarisbrick, Sue Holland and Dave Webster)*

Lees, Derbys [just off Langley Common—Longford rd, off B5020 W of Derby; SK2637], *Black Cow*: Pleasant timbered lounge bar with two open fires, smaller quiet panelled lounge; run by friendly family, with good range of bar food lunchtime and evening inc toasted sandwiches; well kept Bass on handpump *(Graham Richardson)*

☆ **Lichfield**, Staffs [Tamworth St; SK1109], *Pig & Truffle*: Well worth knowing for fine range of well priced, nicely presented food — much very simple but really good, inc lots of fresh fish; faultless waitress service, well kept real ales, good coffee, friendly atmosphere; lavatories exceptionally clean; seats in sunny back yard *(J and B Grove, Ian Phillips)*

☆ **Lichfield** [Market St; one of the central pedestrian-only streets], *Scales*: Old-fashioned two-room pub with big etched window, delft shelf over dark oak panelling, Bass and M&B Springfield on electric pump, attractively planted suntrap back courtyard; bar food (lunchtime, not Sun) inc attractive cold table, friendly service, good coffee; small restaurant; children welcome *(Graham Richardson, LYM)*

Lichfield [B'ham Rd/Tamworth Rd], *Bald Buck*: Smartly comfortable and spacious town-edge pub with well kept Banks's, food, friendly service; easy parking nearby *(Patrick Godfrey, BB)*; [London Rd, just before A38 bypass], *Shoulder of Mutton*: Spacious and comfortably refurbished, with books, sofas, conservatory; good food bar with generous carvery and self-service vegetables; good choice of non-beer and low-alcohol drinks, pleasant service *(Dave Braisted, Brian and Genie Smart, Dave Braisted)*

Little Bridgeford, Staffs [nr M6 junction 14; turn right off A5013 at Little Bridgeford; SJ8727], *Worston Mill*: Fine building — former watermill, with wheel and gear still preserved, ducks on millpond and millstream in garden with play area, attractive conservatory; no reports since recent takeover by Marstons *(LYM; news please)*

☆ **Litton**, Derbys [SK1675], *Red Lion*: Cosy and pretty partly panelled village pub almost wholly given over to close-set bookable tables for its good food — British country cooking with French accent; snug low-ceilinged front rooms with warm open fires, bigger back room with stripped stone and antique prints; good service, Boddingtons; not open weekday lunchtimes *(LYM)*

Long Eaton, Derbys [High St; SK4933], *Old Cross*: Large L-shaped bar comfortably furnished with leather settees, bookshelves,

antique fireplace; good atmosphere, well kept Shipstones *(P A and J B Jones)*; *Turks Head*: Recently liberated free house increasingly popular for food, all home-cooked by new landlady — pies, curries, roasts and so forth (even the cabbage is done imaginatively, with bacon in it); Bass *(Anon)*

☆ **Longlane**, Derbys [SK2538], *Three Horseshoes*: Traditional village pub with well kept Marstons Pedigree and a guest such as Woodfordes or Burton Bridge, friendly welcome, open fire, no juke box; owned by group of locals wanting to keep it simple *(Derek Stephenson, Chris Raisin)*

Matlock Bath, Derbys [258 Dale Rd; SK2958], *County & Station*: Good food, well kept Marstons; bedrooms *(Greenwood and Turner, Carl Southwell)*

☆ **Melbourne**, Derbys [SK3825], *White Swan*: Strikingly restored to show ancient structure though interestingly there's a slightly modern feel to it — ambitious food inc good Sun lunch and popular puddings, attractive decorations, comfortable seats, chatty landlord, well kept Marstons Pedigree and Theakstons; pleasant narrow garden; children welcome *(Alan and Eileen Bowker, Paul and Margaret Baker, LYM)*

☆ **Melbourne** [Derby Rd (B587); between Stanton by Bridge and Kings Newton, N of village], *Sir Francis Burdett*: Good cheap food with help-yourself vegetables, inc vegetarian dishes and Sun roasts, well kept Bass, Marstons Pedigree and Theakstons with several guests such as Greene King Abbot, good stock of whiskies; 17th-century family-run pub with bar, lounge, family room, tables outside; friendly if detached doberman *(Jane James, Andy and Jill Kassube)*

Melbourne [B4587 S], *Melbourne Arms*: Substantial good value traditional bar meals such as cheap cottage pie with four veg; friendly staff, Bass *(Dave Braisted)*

Muckley Corner, Staffs [A5/A461; SK0806], *Muckley Corner*: Well run, friendly atmosphere and service, pleasant decor, separate dining area, sensibly priced food inc unusual dishes such as marlin, well kept beer; children allowed in dining room *(Graham Richardson)*

Nether Heage, Derbys [Spanker Lane; between A6 and A38 W of Ripley; SK3650], *Spanker*: Friendly and cosy, weekday food inc very good carvery popular with businessmen *(Jon and Jacqui Payne)*

Newcastle under Lyme, Staffs [Gallowstree Lane; off Keele Rd, a mile W of centre; SJ8445], *Dick Turpin*: Good food inc real sherry trifle, friendly staff, attractive situation and decor *(Joan Goodwin)*

Norbury Junction, Staffs [SJ7922], *Junction*: Busy pub with sensibly priced food inc good value carvery and well kept beer *(John and Christine Simpson, C H Stride)*

☆ **Penkhull**, Staffs [Manor Ct St; SJ8644], *Greyhound*: Pretty 16th-century pub, one of the oldest in the Potteries, with interesting features in its traditionally furnished rooms; we've had no reports since a major refurbishment and a change of management in summer 1991, but it has previously been a main entry for its quite outstandingly cheap food and well kept Allied real ales — should still be well worth a visit *(TBB, LYM; more reports please)*

☆ **Penkridge**, Staffs [SJ9214], *Star*: Good atmosphere and service in single bar with lots of old beams and nooks; well kept cheap Banks's ales, good value lunchtime bar food (busy then), open all day — handy for M6 junctions 12/13 *(John and Christine Simpson, C H Stride)*

Penkridge, Staffs [Penkridge Lock; SJ9214], *Boat*: Nice pub decorated with old prints and china, efficient table service, good value pub food with pizza and pie specialities *(C H Stride)*

Pilsley, Derbys [SK2471], *Devonshire Arms*: Friendly welcome in cosy village pub within walking distance of Chatsworth Farm and Craft Shops, smallish eating area with limited but good value food using fresh Chatsworth ingredients, Mansfield Riding and Old Baily and Stones *(Dr K Bloomfield, A F C Young)*

Renishaw, Derbys [A616, 2 miles from M1 junction 30; SK4578], *Sitwell Arms*: Comfortable high-ceilinged bar with well kept guest beers under current landlord, restaurant; bedrooms in well equipped extension *(Robert Caldwell, LYM)*

Rosliston, Derbys [68 Main St; off A38 SW of Burton; SK2416], *Plough*: Small, cosy country pub with log fires, Marstons on handpump, good choice of well presented lunchtime bar food (not Mon); very friendly service *(Mr and Mrs K Finch)*

Rudyard, Staffs [off A523 N of Leek; SJ9558], *Poachers*: The Yates who made this a very popular dining pub have now moved to the Izaak Walton at Cresswell — see main entries *(LYM)*

Rugeley, Staffs [Lichfield Rd; SK0418], *Eaton Lodge*: A Banks's Milestone restaurant/pub, with mock-Victorian decor, efficient, friendly service; food imaginative and well prepared; bedrooms *(Paul and Margaret Baker)*

Rushton Spencer, Staffs [Congleton Rd; off A523 Leek—Macclesfield at Ryecroft Gate; SJ9462], *Crown*: Quiet country pub in picturesque setting, busy front snug, bigger back lounge, games room with cribbage; food not extensive but varied, new Greek landlord adding dishes such as stifatho to prawn sandwiches, mushroom pancakes, meatballs and so forth; well kept Theakstons XB and Old Peculier and Youngers IPA *(John Scarisbrick, LYM)*

Sandiacre, Derbys [opp Padmoor Moorings; nr M1 junction 25; SK4736], *Red Lion*: Large, basic canalside pub with huge helpings of good cheap bar food, Hardys & Hansons real ales; restaurant *(P A and J B Jones)*

☆ **Sandonbank**, Staffs [B5066, off A51 in Sandon; SJ9428], *Seven Stars*: Useful food pub, warm and comfortable, with several cosy corners and two large open fires; wide

choice from sandwiches to steaks, Burtonwood on handpump; two pool tables (winter only), piped music; restaurant, children welcome, seats out behind *(David and Rebecca Killick, G R Braithwaite, LYM)*

Saverley Green, Staffs [Sandon Rd; off A50 Stoke—Uttoxeter; SJ9638], *Hunter*: So full of antiques that it's reminiscent of Yew Tree at Cauldon; good Sun lunch, well kept Friary Meux Best and Ind Coope Burton on handpump *(Greenwood and Turner)*

☆ **Seighford**, Staffs [3 miles from M6 junction 14 via A5013/B5405; SJ8725], *Holly Bush*: Neatly kept extended eating house with numbered tables, standard menu of grills and so forth inc some imaginative starters, full meals only Sun (children charged by height then) and maybe Christmas; piped music can be loud; neat back rose garden; related to Seven Stars at Brocton, Red Lion at Ipstones *(Hilary Sargent, D L Williams, A G Roby, Laurence Manning, David Williams, Chris Raisin, LYM)*

Shardlow, Derbys [Aston Rd (A6); SK4330], *Dog & Duck*: No reports since this formerly cosy old Marstons pub's sweeping 1991 transformation into a Taverners Table pub/restaurant; it used to have a spacious back garden with lots for children *(News please)*; [The Wharf — turn off at Navigation Inn, cross canal then immediately left], *Malt Shovel*: Given notice by Marstons, the tenants who made this canalside pub such a popular main entry, with tasty food, excellent service and lots of entertaining bric-a-brac, are leaving in 1991 — taking the decorations with them, and reopening in the Old Crown here, which should be well worth a visit *(Reports on both pubs, please)*; [143 London Rd], *Navigation*: Attractively refurbished, with big split-level lounge, snooker room, Laura Ashley decor, numerous artefacts and local photographs; Greenalls, Shipstones and Tetleys on handpump, bar food *(Alan and Eileen Bowker)*

Sparrowpit, Derbys [nr Chapel en le Frith; SK0980], *Wanted Inn*: Rugged stone building which has been praised for two real fires, lots of photographs of spectacular surrounding countryside, welcoming licensees and good home-cooked food, but no recent reports *(News please)*

Stone, Staffs [21 Stafford St; A520; SJ9034], *Star*: Canal photographs and exposed joists in intimate public bar, snug lounge and family room of simple eighteenth-century pub in attractive canalside setting; well kept Bass and M&B Springfield, friendly welcome, basic food, open fire in one room *(LYM)*

Sutton, Staffs [off B1040 Biggleswade—Potton; SJ7822], *Red Lion*: Rifles and brasses on the walls, traditional three-course lunch and their special pie, and beer tapped from the cask; big car park with fine view over rolling countryside and chickens wandering around; open 11-11 Sat *(Gwen and Peter Andrews)*

Swanwick, Derbys [SK4053], *Gate*: Proudly

kept Courage Directors in spacious, bright and comfortable roadhouse with horseshoe bar; filled rolls in bar, hot food in restaurant *(Michel Hooper-Immins)*

Taddington, Derbys [SK1472], *Queens Arms*: Comfortable, warm and welcoming little pub with friendly young landlord and good food; village by-passed by A6 *(Mr and Mrs R Gammon)*

Tansley, Derbys [A615 Matlock—Mansfield; SK3259], *Tavern*: Tastefully refurbished, with small restaurant section, well kept Ind Coope Burton and Tetleys, friendly atmosphere, good bar food inc more adventurous speciality main courses *(Dr K Bloomfield)*

Thorncliffe, Derbys [2 miles NE at N edge of the Morridge; pub named on OS Sheet 119; SK0360], *Mermaid*: Glorious isolation on lonely and exposed minor road in staggeringly beautiful scenery; two recently reurbished bars, with efficient young staff, Theakstons Best on handpump, reasonably priced bar food; restaurant with moor views; gliding club in field opp *(John Beeken)*; [OS Sheet 119, map reference 014584], *Red Lion*: On road to moors with nice views, busy for evening bar food — showing real imagination under current cheerful and efficient regime; mainly open-plan and much modernised, but with plenty of alcoves; Bass on handpump *(P Corris, DC)*

☆ **Ticknall**, Derbys [B5006 towards Ashby de la Zouch; SK3423], *Chequers*: Good fire in enormous inglenook fireplace of clean and cosy 16th-century pub with well kept Bass tapped from the cask, unusual spirits, good lunchtime filled baps and ploughman's (not Sun), seats in sizeable garden; nr Calke Abbey (NT) *(Carl Southwell, Graham Richardson, LYM)*

☆ **Ticknall** [7 High St], *Staff of Life*: Good atmosphere, good range of real ales inc three or four guest beers, and enormous gammons, sampled on several occasions, well cooked and good value for those with appetites *(Eric Locker, Carl Southwell, Brian McDermott)*

Ticknall [50 Main St (A514)], *Wheel*: Pleasant, welcoming landlord, well kept Bass, friendly service of simple but well prepared hot food; nr entrance to Calke Abbey *(E A Turner, Carl Southwell)*

☆ **Tideswell**, Derbys [SK1575], *George*: Simple bar with cushioned wall seats, small chairs, delft shelf with little toby jugs, coal fire; games room with pool and vigorous juke box on right; small tile-floored snug between; well kept Hardys & Hansons on handpump, good value simple bar food inc

brightly lit puddings cabinet; tables in front overlooking pretty village, and in sheltered back garden; good value bedrooms — pretty village with end-June well-dressing *(Simon Velate, Matt Pringle, D Ainsworth, BB)*

☆ **Tutbury**, Staffs [High St; off A50 N of Burton; SK2028], *Olde Dog & Partridge*: Extended Tudor coaching inn with spacious carvery (evening pianist), neatly kept and civilised but busy two-room bar, well kept Marstons Pedigree, lunchtime snacks (not Sun) inc sandwiches, efficient service; trim and attractive garden; children welcome; bedrooms very comfortable, with substantial breakfasts *(B M Eldridge, Robin Hillman, LYM)*

Whittington Moor, Derbys [Sheffield Rd (off A61 1 1/2 miles N of Chesterfield centre)], *Derby Tup*: Friendly no-frills basic pub with small snug, big lounge; has been praised for particularly wide and interesting range of superbly kept real ales, but no recent reports *(News please)*

Winster, Derbys [B5056 above village; SK2460], *Miners Standard*: Attractive and welcoming pub in White Peak District, with well kept Eldridge Pope and Marstons Pedigree on handpump, good reasonably priced bar meals till 10 from restaurant's chef, interesting photographs of lead mining, morris dancing and so forth; big open fires (unusual illuminated fireplace), geological samples *(Alan and Eileen Bowker, B O Jones, C J and L M Elston)*

☆ **Woolley**, Derbys [Badger Lane; off B6014, Woolley Moor; SK3760], *White Horse*: Friendly country pub, beautifully located with views of Amber valley and hills towards Matlock — lovely walking country; well kept Bass and guest beer eg Banks's & Taylors SOS; particularly good value food (not Sun evening) from splendid sandwiches to remarkably low-priced restaurant meals, reasonable wine, obliging service; children's play area *(R Caldwell, Derek and Sylvia Stephenson, Alan and Eileen Bowker)*

Youlgreave, Derbys [SK2164], *Bulls Head*: Small hotel in lovely walking country with two bars, real ales and quick bar food *(Lynne Sheridan, Bob West)*; [Church St], *George*: Bright, clean village local with helpful staff, well kept Home Bitter and Mild on handpump, basic but filling good value food, pleasant atmosphere, bar games; handy for Lathkill Dale and Haddon Hall, walkers welcome *(A E Alcock, John Beeken)*

Yoxall, Staffs [Main St; SK1319], *Crown*: Cheerfully popular village pub with good reasonably priced food using local produce, jovial landlord, well kept Marstons *(Dr and Mrs G J Sutton, Dr Keith Bloomfield)*

Devon

One of the very best parts of Britain for good pubs, this has a fine
range from delightfully basic anachronisms like the Drewe Arms at
Drewsteignton to stylish old inns like the White Hart in Exeter. The
county's best pub of all is the Nobody Inn at Doddiscombsleigh –
exemplary atmosphere, food and, particularly, wines and other
drinks. Indeed, perhaps Devon's real speciality is the ancient and
interesting country pub, often in fine surroundings, which surprises
and delights by the quality of its food – as at the Sloop at Bantham
(really fresh fish), the Drewe Arms at Broadhembury (again, superb
fish), the Butterleigh Inn, the Hunters Lodge at Cornworthy (huge
helpings, too), the Tuckers Arms at Dalwood, the Church House at
Harberton, the Rock at Haytor Vale, the Duke of York at Iddesleigh,
the Peter Tavy Inn (vegetarian dishes, keen prices), and Keith Floyd's
Maltsters Arms at Tuckenhay. Moreover, these places don't have a
monopoly on good food; Devon now scores so high all round on food
quality that there are too many award-standard pubs for us to list
individually here. Interesting new entries here, or pubs back in these
pages after a break, include the carefully refurbished Chichester Arms
at Bishops Tawton, the warmly welcoming old Coach & Horses at
Buckland Brewer, the interesting George at Chardstock (both of these
good places to stay at), the Hoops at Horns Cross, the spacious and
well run Nutwell Lodge at Lympstone, the friendly Old Smithy at
Welcombe and the China House in Plymouth. This last is a
remarkable new waterside pub in a fine old building, and a splendid
example of what the big brewers can do when they really set their
minds to it – in this case, it's Ansells (part of Allied Breweries).
Another less exemplary coup by Allied is the marketing of the beers
from this national combine's Plympton brewery; don't imagine from
the name they are now using (Fergusons Dartmoor) that you are
patronising some bravely independent local brewer. Indeed, for
drinkers Devon is not in general good news, as beer prices in the
county have been rising slightly more steeply than in most areas, and
are now rather above the national average. It's also difficult to find
really cheap food here, though it can be done – as at the Ebrington
Arms at Knowle. Among other main entries, pubs that are decidedly
on the up-and-up at the moment, and well in the running for a star
award, include the friendly Durant Arms at Ashprington (nice locals,
good food), the Cott at Dartington (perhaps better than ever now it's
recovered fully from its fire), the quaint Cherub in Dartmouth (good
fish cooking), the Italian-run Tally Ho at Hatherleigh (brewing its
own beers), the Church House at Rattery (friendly and villagey, with
good food) and the relaxing Cridford Inn at Trusham. Among the
Lucky Dip entries at the end of the chapter, the New Inn at
Broadclyst, Crabshell at Kingsbridge, Kestor at Manaton, Church
House at Stokenham and Otter at Weston also currently seem on a
clear upward trend.

ASHBURTON   SX7569   Map 1

London Hotel

11 West St

The spacious Turkey-carpeted lounge in this fine old coaching inn spreads back into a softly lit dining area with one wall curtained in red velvet, and furnishings include little brocaded or red leatherette armchairs and other seats around the copper-topped casks they use as tables; the clean white walls are largely stripped back to stone, and there's a central fireplace. The beers they brew – Bitter and IPA and Porter on handpump can also be sampled in Plymouth at the Mutton Cove, which Mr Thompson also runs. Bar food includes home-made oxtail or stilton and cider soup (£1.35), sandwiches (from £1.75), ploughman's (from £2.50), omelettes or salads (from £4), fresh local trout (£7), steaks (from £8.25), and puddings (£1.50); cribbage, dominoes, fruit machine and piped music. *(Recommended by Richard Houghton, R J Walden, M G Richards)*

Own brew   Licensee D F Thompson   Real ale   Meals and snacks (11–9.30) Restaurant Ashburton (0364) 52478   Children welcome   Open 11–11   Bedrooms planned

ASHPRINGTON   SX8156   Map 1

Durant Arms

Village signposted off A381 S of Totnes; OS Sheet 202, map reference 819571

This pretty and happy gable-ended cottage has a lower carpeted lounge (popular with families) furnished with settles, tables, chairs, red velvet curtains and a winter fire (there are two others as well). The old-fashioned upper bar has unusual cutaway barrel seats and a bay window overlooking the village street. In the simply furnished games bar there are darts, dominoes, cribbage and piped music. On the food side, readers continue to pick out the memorable home-made Brown Pot – filled with bacon, kidney and vegetables, cooked in stout and topped with pastry (£3.75); there's also sandwiches (from £1.50), liver and onions or venison casserole (£3.50), chicken curry or ham, chicken and mushroom pie (£3.75), whole plaice (£5.50), monkfish provençale (£6.95), whole lemon sole (around £8.50), and fillet steak with prawns in garlic butter (£9.95); friendly service. Bass, Palmers IPA, Tetleys and Wadworths 6X on handpump, 12 malt whiskies and Luscombe cider (summer only). The new puppy George II is as friendly as his predecessor. Tables in the sheltered back garden. *(Recommended by Neil Tungate, Margarate Drazin, Mrs J Cookson, S V Bishop, N H Harries, E H and R F Warner, John A Barker, M V and J Melling, R H Martyn, David and Flo Wallington, H K Dyson, Mr and Mrs L W Norcott, S V Bishop, G and M Stewart, Jacqui and Jon Payne)*

Free house   Licensees John and Gill Diprose   Real ale   Meals and snacks (11.30–2, 6.30–9.30)   Harbertonford (0803) 732240   Children in eating area of bar – not Sat evening after 7pm   Folk music Mon evening   Open 11.30–2.30, 6–11

Watermans Arms

Bow Bridge, on Tuckenhay road; OS Sheet 202, map reference 819571

Across the road from this popular place you can watch the ducks pottering about on the little Harbourne River, with maybe a heron in the tidal creek to the right. Inside there are high-backed settles and built-in black wall benches in the flagstoned front area of the bar, with more tables in a comfortable carpeted oak-beamed inner area. Generously served bar food includes home-made soup (different ones each day, £1.75), well filled rolls or sandwiches (from £2), home-made chicken liver pâté (£2.25), ploughman's with a choice of cheeses (from £3), home-made chicken and mushroom pie or mixed meat platter (£4.95), salads (from £4.15; fresh local crab £5.45), mixed seafood platter (£6.55), daily specials and vegetarian dishes. The new licensee has introduced several more Allied real ales on handpump: Ansells Best, Fergusons Dartmoor, Ind Coope Burton, Tetleys and a guest, with Addlestones and Luscombe ciders; dominoes and video game. *(Recommended by John A Barker, Roger and Ann Short, J K Conneen, S G Game, David and*

Ann Stranack, S V Bishop, Peter York, John Knighton, Alan Merricks, M Box, W C M Jones, Verity Kemp, Richard Mills)

Free house   Licensee Trevor Illingworth   Real ale   Meals and snacks (6.30–10 evening)   Partly no smoking restaurant   Harbertonford (0803) 732214   Children in eating area of bar and in restaurant   Open 11–3, 6–11

AXMOUTH   SY2591   Map 1

Harbour

B3172 Seaton–Axminster

This thatched stone pub, much bigger inside than it looks from outside, evokes the days when smugglers must have posted lookouts on the tower of the handsome church opposite, with its fine stone gargoyles: in the Harbour Bar, black oak beams and joists, a high-backed oak settle, brass-bound cask seats, an antique wall clock, and a huge inglenook fireplace with fat pots hanging from pot-irons. A central lounge has more cask seats and settles, and over on the left another room is divided from the dining room by a two-way log fireplace. At the back, a big flagstoned lobby with sturdy seats leads on to a very spacious and simply furnished family bar. Well kept Devenish Royal Wessex and Flowers IPA and Original on handpump, farm cider; efficient service; darts, pool, winter skittle alley, cribbage, maybe unobtrusive piped music. Bar food includes home-made soup (£1.35), sandwiches (from £1.25), a good few other snacks or starters such as garlic bread and cheese (£1.80), ploughman's (from £2.55), home-cooked ham (£3.85), cauliflower, courgette and pasta bake, steak and kidney pie (£4.35), salads (from £4.25) and evening gammon (£5.65) or rump steak (£6.90); daily specials, half helpings for children, and Sunday roast (£4.50). They have a lavatory for disabled people, and general access is good. There are tables in the neat flower garden behind. *(Recommended by Pauline Crossland, Dave Cawley, Chris Newman, Deb Jay, Mr and Mrs D V Morris, Barry and Anne, Jamie and Sarah Allan, Brian and Anna Marsden)*

Free house   Licensees Dave and Pat Squire   Real ale   Meals and snacks (not Mon, not winter Sun evenings, not 25 Dec)   Colyton (0297) 20371   Children in family room   Open 11–2.30, 6–11

BANTHAM   SX6643   Map 1

Sloop ⊘ ★

Off A379/B3197 NW of Kingsbridge

This village inn is in good surfing country – the sandy beach a few hundred yards over the dunes is one of the best for the sport on the south coast. The atmospheric, 16th-century building has a black-beamed bar with stripped stone walls, flagstones, country chairs around wooden tables, and easy chairs in a quieter side area with a nautical theme. Well kept Bass, Ruddles County and Ushers Best on handpump, Churchward's cider from Paignton and 25 malt whiskies. Bar food includes very popular fresh fish such as crab claws (£3.60), trout (£5.60), superb giant cod, excellent skate or giant whole plaice (all £6.65), lemon sole (£7.40), and whole Dover sole (£10.40); there's also pastie (95p), tasty home-made turkey broth (£1.40), granary-bread sandwiches (from £1.35, good fresh crab £2.50), basket meals such as home-made sausage (from £1.95), ploughman's (£2.90), a good range of salads (from £4.20, superb seafood £6.65) and good steaks using local meat (from £7.20). Home-made puddings such as lemon crunch or raspberry pavlova (£1.95), daily specials like home-made salmon pâté (£2.90) or vegetable pasta (£4.80), and hearty breakfasts for residents; there may be delays at busy times. Darts, dominoes, cribbage, table skittles, fruit machine, video game, trivia and piped music. Around a wishing well in the yard behind, there are some seats. *(Recommended by Geoffrey Medcalf, Richard Purser, M D Hare, Chris Newman, Deb Jay, Harry Stirling, P and J Shapley, Neil and Anita Christopher, W C M Jones, Ruth Roberts, Caroline and Adrian Skeates, Harry Stirling, David Wallington, R W Stanbury, Hilary Roberts, M V and J Melling, N P Cox, David and Ann Stranack, G Malcolm Pearce, Mr and Mrs L W Norcott, Mrs A Turner, Roy Isaac, Paul and Janet Waring)*

Free house   Licensee Neil Girling   Real ale   Meals and snacks (till 10 evening)
Restaurant   Kingsbridge (0548) 560489/560215   Children in eating area of bar
Open 11–2.30, 6(6.30 winter)–11   Bedrooms; £19.50(£23B)/£40(£45B); they also
have self-catering cottages

BERRYNARBOR   SS5646   Map 1

Olde Globe   ★

Village signposted from A399 E of Ilfracombe

Converted from three rambling, 13th-century cottages a few centuries ago, this highly atmospheric place has a series of dimly lit, homely rooms and alcoves with curved deep-ochre walls, bulging unevenly in places, as well as low ceilings, and floors of flagstones or of ancient lime-ash (with silver coins embedded in them); there are old high-backed oak settles (some carved) and red leatherette cushioned cask seats around antique tables. There's also a profusion of decorations – genuinely old pictures, priests (fish-coshes), thatcher's knives, sheep shears, gin traps, pitchforks, antlers, copper warming pans and lots of cutlasses, swords, shields and fine powder flasks. Well kept Ushers Best on handpump and several country wines; sensibly placed darts, skittle alley, pool room, dominoes, cribbage, fruit machine and piped music. Bar food includes sandwiches (from 95p), steak and kidney pie or pasties (£2.10), ploughman's (£2.15), salads (from £2.90), home-made spaghetti bolognese (£3.20), meaty or vegetarian lasagne (£3.40), scampi (£3.80), gammon (£4.95), steaks (£6.20; 16oz T-bone £8.50), with children's meals (£1.75), puddings (from £1.10), and good, traditional Sunday lunch (you have to book). The crazy-paved front terrace has old-fashioned garden seats, with an attractive garden beside it. *(Recommended by Vanessa and Peter Hurst, Philip and Trisha Ferris, Mr and Mrs L King, P M Bisby, John Drummond, Mr and Mrs S Harvey; more reports please)*

Ushers   Lease: Phil Bridle   Real ale   Meals and snacks (till 10 summer evenings)
Gaslit restaurant   Combe Martin (027 188) 2465   Children in own room with toys, in
eating area of bar and in restaurant   Live music summer Thurs evenings   Open
11.30–2.30, 6(7 winter)–11

BISHOPS TAWTON   SS5630   Map 1

Chichester Arms

Pub signposted off A377 outside Barnstaple

Much of Barnstaple has a busy, bustling feel these days, and both this village and the thatched pub itself are restoratively peaceful. The pub has been refurbished, with plush wall banquettes and cushioned wheelback chairs on its patterned carpet; but there are still low heavy beams, a solid old bar counter, uneven sloping floors and stout supporting timbers, with an open fire in one end wall stripped back to bare stone; the family room has its own bar, darts, pool, alley skittles, dominoes, fruit machine, video game and piped music, and doors out to a barbecue area. Good value bar food includes home-made soup (£1.20), sandwiches (from £1.25; toasties 20p extra), filled baked potatoes (from £2.25), home-made herb and spice jumbo sausage (£2.50), ploughman's (from £2.50), vegetarian quiche (£3.50), salads (from £3.75), beef curry or home-made steak and kidney pie (£3.95), gammon (£5.35), steaks (from £7.95), daily specials, puddings like home-made sherry trifle (from £1.65), children's dishes (from £1.85), and Sunday roast lunch; well kept Ushers Best on handpump. There are picnic-table sets on a flagstoned front terrace, with more in a sheltered back area. *(Recommended by Steve and Carolyn Harvey, David Wallington)*

Ushers   Lease: Hugh and Gay Johnston   Real ale   Meals and snacks (till 10)
Barnstaple (0271) 43943   Children in family room   Live music Sun   Open
11.30–2.30, 6.30–11; all day Sat

BRAYFORD SS6834 Map 1

Poltimore Arms

Yarde Down – three miles from village, towards Simonsbath; OS Sheet 180, map
reference 724356

This authentic Exmoor pub has a main bar with old leather-seated chairs with
carved or slatted backs, cushioned wall settles, a little window seat, some
interesting tables, and a beam in the slightly sagging cream ceiling with another
over the small serving counter; an inglenook fireplace has a woodburning stove,
and there are photos of hunt meetings, and hunting cartoons. The lounge bar has a
mix of chairs and a settle, Guinness and Fry's Chocolate prints, plants and a small
brick open fire; a plainly decorated games room has pool, darts, shove-ha'penny,
cribbage, dominoes, fruit machine and juke box; friendly cat. The decent range of
bar food includes sandwiches (from 90p, toasties 10p extra), home-made soup or
curried eggs (£1.10), omelettes (£1.25), ploughman's (from £2.60), salads (from
£3), home-made steak and kidney pie, lasagne or vegetarian nut croquette (£3.50)
and steaks (from £5.80), with extra evening dishes such as their speciality noisettes
of lamb (£4), fresh fish (from £4) and mixed grills (£7). Ushers on handpump,
Cotleigh Tawny tapped from the cask. In the side garden there are picnic-table sets
and a grill for barbecues. (*Recommended by R and P F Shelton, Steve and Carolyn Harvey,
B M Eldridge; more reports please*)

*Free house   Licensees Mike and Mella Wright   Real ale   Meals and snacks (12–2,
6–9.30; not 25 Dec)   Restaurant   Brayford (0598) 710381   Children in games room
and restaurant   Open 11.30–2.30, 6(6.30 winter)–11*

BROADHEMBURY ST1004 Map 1

Drewe Arms ★ ⊗

Village signposed off A373

In an attractive village of cream-coloured thatched cottages, this 15th-century inn
has a bar with neatly carved beams in its high ceiling, and handsome
stone-mullioned windows (one with a small carved roundabout horse). On the left,
a high-backed stripped settle separates off a little room with three tables, a mix of
chairs, flowers on sturdy country tables, plank-panelled walls painted brown
below and yellow above with attractive engravings and prints, and a big
black-painted fireplace with bric-a-brac on a high mantlepiece. The flagstoned
entry has a narrow corridor of a room by the servery with a couple of tables; darts,
shove-ha'penny, dominoes and skittle alley. The beautifully cooked, fresh local fish
is as popular as ever with readers: fresh scallops, half a fresh lobster, turbot, John
Dory, Dover sole, fillet of sea trout, whole plaice, brill, smoked eel, spider crabs
and so forth; also, really wonderful tomato soup, open sandwiches, delicious baby
lobster ploughman's, and daily specials that include two meat dishes such as local
venison or fillet of beef (£2.95–£8.95), and lovely puddings (£2.25). Bass, Cotleigh
Tawny and Otter Head and Ale (from a tiny brewery a few miles from the pub in
Luppitt) tapped from the cask, a comprehensive wine list (with good value house
wine), local cider, tea and coffee. A flower-filled lawn with picnic-table sets and
cocktail parasols stretches back under the shadow of chestnuts towards a church
which has a singularly melodious hour-bell. *Recommended by David Wallington,
Gordon and Daphne, Ruth Roberts, Patrick Young, Mr and Mrs G W Hodgson, Dr and Mrs
R J Williams)*

*Free house   Licensees Kerstin and Nigel Burge   Real ale   Meals and snacks (till 10)
Restaurant   Broadhembury (0404) 84267   Children in eating area of bar and in
restaurant; no small children after 8pm   Open 11–3, 6–11*

BUCKLAND BREWER SS4220 [Map 1]

Coach & Horses ⇐

Village signposted off A388 S of Bideford; OS Sheet 190, map reference 423206

Everyone reporting on this well preserved 13th-century thatched village pub has singled out the genuine warmth of the welcome from the landlord and his family. A good log fire burns in the big stone inglenook of the cosy lounge, another inglenook in the bar has a woodburning stove, there are heavy oak beams, comfortable seats including an attractive antique settle; a small back room serves as a children's room. Enjoyable food, with the more elaborate dishes served in a cosy little restaurant, includes home-made soup (£1.25 or £1.60), sandwiches (£1.25), burgers (from £1.25), filled baked potatoes (from £1.75), good ploughman's (from £2.60), ham and egg (£3.50), chilli con carne (£3.65), scampi (£3.85), salads (from £4), good value vegetarian lasagne (£4.20), trout (£4.40), very generous gammon (£5.85), 10oz steak (£7.85), and daily specials (from around £3.50), with vegetables running to braised celery, cabbage perked up with grated orange rind, or carrots done with basil; Sunday lunch (£4.25) – bookings preferred but not essential. Well kept Flowers IPA and Original and a guest beer such as Fullers ESB or Wadworths 6X, and Stonehouse's cider; darts, dominoes, shove-ha'penny, cribbage, fruit machine, video game. The two cats are called Amos and Benson. There are tables on a terrace in front, and in an attractive side garden with swings and slides. *(Recommended by Michael and Joan Johnstone, Mrs R Horridge, Alan Trenaman, Steve and Carolyn Harvey, Mr and Mrs W B Barnes)*

Free house Licensee K A Wolfe Real ales Meals and snacks Restaurant Horns Cross (0237) 451395 Well behaved children welcome Open 11–2.30, 5–11; closed evening 25 Dec Bedrooms; £22/£36

BURGH ISLAND SX6443 Map 1

Pilchard

Park in Bigbury-on-Sea and walk about 300 yards across the sands, which are covered for between six and eight hours of the twelve-hour tide; in summer use the Tractor, a unique bus-on-stilts which beats the tide by its eight-foot-high 'deck'.

Included primarily for its isolated island location, this thoroughly ancient pub (12th-century) has a small L-shaped bar with thick-walled embrasures and storm-shuttered windows which give a snug view of the tide inching across the sands, low chairs, settles edged with rope and others with high backs, cosy snug booths and lots of bare wood and stripped stone; lighting is by big ships' lamps hanging from the beam-and-plank ceiling and there's a good – though not always lit – log fire. The white-plastered back bar has pool, shove-ha'penny and dominoes; Ruddles County and Ushers on handpump; piped music. The licensees actually own the island; the art deco hotel nearby has been patronised by various alumni in its time – principally Agatha Christie (who used to write here) and the Duke of Windsor and Mrs Simpson. It can be very popular in season and there's an outside terrace overlooking the beach. *(Recommended by Pauline Crossland, Dave Cawley, Neil and Anita Christopher, Philip Orbell, Nick and Alison Dowson, Roger Huggins, John Burgan, David and Sarah Gilmore, John Knighton, Alan and Audrey Chatting)*

Free house Licensee Tony Porter Real ale Evening bistro Kingsbridge (0548) 810344 Children in bistro £1.50 car parking in Bigbury; cheaper by the Bay Cafe Open 11–11; 11–3, 7–11 in winter

BUTTERLEIGH SS9708 Map 1

Butterleigh Inn ✿

Village signposted off A398 in Bickleigh; or in Cullompton take turning by Manor House Hotel – it's the old Tiverton road, with the village eventually signposted off on the left

Relaxed and friendly, this 16th-century village inn has an unassuming series of little rooms with comfortable, well worn furnishings: an attractive elm trestle table and sensibly placed darts in one, old dining chairs around country kitchen tables in another and prettily arranged settles around the four tables that just fit into the cosy back snug. There are topographical prints and watercolours, pictures of birds and dogs, a fine embroidery of the Devonshire Regiment's coat-of-arms and plates hanging by one big fireplace. Well kept Cotleigh Tawny, Harrier and Old Buzzard on handpump and local farm cider; darts, table skittles, shove-ha'penny, cribbage, dominoes and piped music; jars of snuff on the bar. Very good bar food includes sandwiches (from £1.25), two or three vegetarian dishes such as peanut and lentil bake (£3.50), chilli sausages, grilled quail with port sauce (£5.25), 8oz fillet steak glazed with stilton (£7.95) or 16oz T-bone steak (£8.95) and puddings like chocolate and brandy pots, bread pudding and treacle tart. There are tables on a sheltered terrace and neat small lawn with a log cabin for children. *(Recommended by Mr and Mrs C H Garnett, Jim and Maggie Cowell, Gordon and Daphne, Alan and Eileen Bowker, Michael and Alison Sandy, Patrick Young, Graham and Glenis Watkins, Gill Graham)*

Free house   Licensees Mike and Penny Wolter   Real ale   Meals and snacks Bickleigh (088 45) 407   Open 12–2.30(3 Sat), 6–11   Bedrooms; £20/£30; also cottage sleeping four

CHARDSTOCK   ST3004   Map 1

George 🛏

Village signposted off A358 S of Chard

The best part of this neatly thatched village inn is the two-roomed original bar, mainly a dining area now, with massive beams, stone-mullioned windows, ancient oak partition walls, well converted old gas lamps, character furnishings and two good log fires, one with a couple of comfortable armchairs in front. There's a quietly enjoyable chatty atmosphere here, as the piped music is confined to an interestingly laid out two-level back bar (which also has a couple of fruit machines). Good bar food includes French onion soup (£1.75), sandwiches (from £1.75), ploughman's (from £2.50), deep-pan pizzas big enough to share (from £3), venison sausages (£3.65), vegetarian dishes such as a cashew "paella" (£3.95), chicken Kiev or steak and kidney pie (£4.25) and steaks (from £6.95); well kept Boddingtons or Flowers Original and Marstons Pedigree on handpump and a decent choice of wines and whiskies, neat and efficient staff; darts, alley skittles, table skittles and dominoes. There are some tables out in a back loggia by a flint-cobbled courtyard sheltered by the rather attractive modern extensions to the ancient inn, with more in a safely fenced grass area with a climber and swings; summer barbecues. The four bedrooms are in a well converted back stable block. The inn has an interesting booklet about its history. Excellent walks nearby. *(Recommended by P R MacCrimmon, E G Parish, Gordon and Daphne, Fiona Easeman, C Collins)*

Free house   Licensee Robert Potter   Real ale   Meals and snacks   Restaurant   South Chard (0460) 20241   Children in eating area of bar, restaurant and snug area   Jazz last Sat of month   Open 11.30–2.45(3 Sat), 6–11; closed Mon lunchtime in winter and lunchtime 25 Dec   Bedrooms; £35B/£42.50B

CHERITON BISHOP   SX7793   Map 1

Old Thatch ⊘

Village signposted from A30

This friendly 16th-century inn has a rambling, beamed bar, separated from the lounge by a large open stone fireplace (lit in the cooler months). Fergusons Dartmoor Best, Ind Coope Burton and Wadworths 6X on handpump; dominoes, cribbage, piped music. The range of good value, home-made bar food is extensive, and popular with readers: good soup (£1.10), filled French bread or toasties (from £1.65), imaginative starters such as sautéed kidneys with herbs, bacon and mushrooms (£1.95) or kedgeree (£2.20), ploughman's (£2.20), salads (£3.95), and hot dishes such as Boston dry hash (£2.75), deep-fried fish of the day (£2.95), tasty steak and kidney pudding (£3.75), a curry of the day served with cucumber raita, mango chutney and a poppadom or braised stuffed hearts (£3.95), excellent, large mixed grill (£4.25), Armenian lamb or seafood pie (£5.50), steak (£6.95), and enterprising puddings such as spiced bread pudding made with Guinness (£1.75);

pleasant, friendly service. Tables are bookable. In Dartmoor's National Park, it's popular with drivers from the A30. *(Recommended by E H and R F Warner, Iain and Penny Muir, G L Carlisle, Graham and Glenis Watkins, C A Foden, G Atkinson, R and Mrs P F Shelton, E H and R F Warner, John O'Gorman)*

Free house   Licensee Brian Bryon-Edmond   Real ale   Meals and snacks (12–2, 6.30–9.30)   Cheriton Bishop (0647) 24204   Open 12(11.30 Sat)–3, 6.30(6 Sat)–11; Mon–Thurs winter evening opening 7; closed first two weeks Nov   Bedrooms; £29B/£41B

CHURCHSTOW   SX7145   Map 1

Church House

A379 NW of Kingsbridge

The 13th-century arch of the main door dates back to the time when this pub was a Benedictine hospice; there's an atmospheric and historic feel in the bar, with cushioned seats cut into the deep window embrasures of the stripped stone walls, low and heavy black oak beams and a great stone fireplace with side bread oven. The long, cosy room is neatly kept and comfortable, with an antique curved high-backed settle as well as the many smaller red-cushioned ones by the black tables on its Turkey carpet, and a line of stools – each with its own brass coathook – along the long glossy black serving counter. Bar food, served at the curtained-off end of the bar, includes sandwiches (from £1.25), home-made soup (£1.50), ploughman's (from £1.95), fresh haddock (from £3.25), cottage pie (£3.25), devilled chicken (£3.75), salads (from £3.95), mixed grill (£6.45), rump steak (£6.95) and puddings like home-made fruit pies (£1.75); the carvery – fine roasts, help-yourself vegetables – is good value (£6.95 including home-made puddings), and you're advised to book. Bass, Ruddles County and Ushers Best on handpump; darts, cribbage, dominoes, euchre, fruit machine. Just inside the back entrance there's a conservatory area with a floodlit well in the centre, and there are seats outside. *(Recommended by Roger Huggins, P and J Shapley, Chris Newman, Deb Jay, Geoffrey Medcalf, Richard Purser, Carol Mason, Margaret and Trevor Errington, Mrs A Turner; more reports please)*

Free house   Licensee Nick Nicholson   Real ale   Meals and snacks (12–1.30, 6.30–9; not 25 or 26 Dec)   Carvery Weds–Sat evenings, Sun lunch   Kingsbridge (0548) 852237   Children in carvery   Open 11–2.30, 6–11; closed evening 25 Dec

COCKWOOD   SX9780   Map 1

Anchor

Off, but visible from, A379 Exeter–Torbay

The small, low-ceilinged and rambling rooms in this local have black panelling, good-sized tables in various alcoves, and a cheerful winter coal fire in the snug. Bass, Flowers Original and Eldridge Pope Royal Oak on handpump or electric pump, with rather a good wine list, and malt whiskies; darts, dominoes, cribbage, fruit machine, and piped music. Bar food still includes quite a few fish dishes under the new licensees: Torbay crab sandwiches (£2.65), crab and brandy soup (£3.50), grilled whole plaice or local cod steak (£4.95), and local crab platter (£6.50); there are also sandwiches (from £1.50), home-made soup (£2.30), various platters (from £3.25), and home-made cottage pie (£3.95); children's dishes (from £1.20); restaurant food can be eaten in the bar. Tables on the sheltered verandah overlook a quiet lane to yachts and crabbing boats in the landlocked harbour. Nearby parking may be difficult if it's busy. *(Recommended by Keith Steven, Nigel Hopkins, Chirs Newman, Deb Jay, Mike Hallewell, M Box)*

Heavitree (who no longer brew)   Lease: H C Barnes and C E Keyte   Real ale   Meals and snacks   Restaurant   Starcross (0626) 890203   Children in eating area of bar and restaurant   Open 11–11; 11–2.30 6–11 in winter

COLEFORD   SS7701 Map 1

New Inn 🛏️

Just off A377 Crediton–Barnstaple

The good range of home-made bar food (using fresh local produce where possible) in this old thatched inn typically includes tomato and rice soup (£1.90), pork and pheasant pâté (£2.95), bobotie (£4.25), mussels in cider or nut roast with garlic and tomato sauce (£4.95), hot beef creole (£6.50), chicken tikka (£6.95), salmon with pink peppercorns (£8.15), brill in wine and cream (£8.50), and puddings such as honey and walnut tart or boozy kiwi syllabub (£2.10). The bar is made up of four interestingly furnished areas spiralling around the central servery; there are some character tables – a pheasant worked into the grain of one – carved dressers and chests, ancient and modern settles, spindleback chairs, low dark green velour armchairs and plush-cushioned stone wall seats. The white walls are hung with paraffin lamps, antique prints and old guns, with landscape plates on one of the beams and pewter tankards on another; the resident parrot is entertaining. The servery itself has modern settles forming stalls around tables on the russet carpet, and there's a winter log fire. Flowers IPA and Original, Wadworths 6X and a guest beer such as Butcombe, Fullers or Hook Norton on handpump, and three or four dozen bin-end wines (including New World ones), with several malt whiskies; fruit machine (out of the way up by the door), darts, shove-ha'penny and piped music. By the stream outside there's an attractive courtyard and small garden. *(Recommended by Steve and Carolyn Harvey, George Atkinson, Mr and Mrs C H Garnett, C M Andrews, Lawrence Manning, Mrs K J Betts)*

Free house   Licensee Paul Butt   Real ale   Meals and snacks (till 10pm)   Restaurant Copplestone (0363) 84242   Children in eating area of bar and in restaurant   Open 11.30–2.30, 6–11   Bedrooms; £20(£27B)/£34(£42B)

COLYTON   SY2493 Map 1

Kingfisher

Dolphin St; village signposted off A35 and A3052 E of Sidmouth, in village follow Axminster, Shute, Taunton signpost

This straightforward pub (very much a local, but also warmly welcoming to strangers), has blue plush cushioned window seats, stools, sturdy elm wing settles and rustic tables, a big open fireplace and walls stripped back to stone. Glasses slotted into the two waggon-wheels hanging above the bar swing in unison when someone in the upstairs family room (where there's a useful box of toys) walks above the beamed ceiling; sensibly placed darts, dominoes, cribbage, fruit machine, video game and skittle alley. Well kept Badger Best and Flowers IPA, and one or two guest beers on handpump; they also have Farmer John's cider, from along the Exeter road a bit (the cider farm's open for visits). Bar food includes sandwiches (from £1.20, speciality prawn £2.50), filled baked potatoes (£2.60), sausages (£2.80), scampi (£4.50), home-made cheesecakes and fruit pies (from £1.60), and children's menu (£1.70). The terrace (where there are tables under cocktail parasols) has been extended this year to include a pergola, flowerbeds and water features; there's also a lawn and climbing frame for children. *(Recommended by Barry and Anne, Brian and Anna Marsden, Dr D M Forsyth, Quentin Williamson, Richard and Ann Jenkins)*

Free house   Licensee Graeme Sutherland   Real ale   Meals and snacks (till 10pm) Colyton (0297) 52476   Children in family room   Open 11–2.30, 6–11

COMBEINTEIGNHEAD   SX9071 Map 1

Coombe Cellars

Pub signposted off B3195 Newton Abbot–Shaldon

The long bar in this estuary pub has lots of nautical bric-a-brac and captains' chairs, with compasses set into the couch, and very large windows along its left-hand side giving a superb view up the River Teign. There's a family area off one end, three log-effect gas fires, and a Porthole bar (which was the original bar and is used by water-skiers and windsurfers – open all day at weekends) with barrel seats and tables, and more nautical bric-a-brac. Well kept Bass, Tetleys and Wadworths 6X on handpump, an extensive wine list, 10 malt whiskies, and farm cider on handpump; piped music. Bar food includes home-made soup (£1.45), sandwiches (from £1.75), a generous ploughman's on a big wooden platter (£2.95), basket meals (from £3.10), a pot of prawns with garlic mayonnaise (£3.35), five vegetarian dishes (£4.05), salads (from £5.65), pan-fried lemon sole fillets (£6.40), steaks (from £8), and daily specials like monkfish provençal (£5.25). Outside, pontoons and jetties with tables overlook the water, and there are big terraces and a fenced-in children's playground with a huge play galleon in the garden area. There are lots of water-sports facilities – the pub is the base for the South Devon Water Sports Association. (*Recommended by DPB, M and C McRum, Mr and Mrs W H Crowther, Joan Harris, M J Brooks, W Bailey, David and Sarah Gilmore*)

Free house   Licensee Simon Tyler   Real ale   Meals and snacks (11.30–2.15, 6.45–10.15)   Restaurant   Newton Abbot (0626) 872423   Children in eating area of bar   Open 11–3, 5.30–11 (Porthole bar open all day at weekends)

CORNWORTHY   SX8255 Map 1

Hunters Lodge 🅿

Off A381 Totnes–Kingsbridge 1/2 mile S of Harbertonford, turning left at Washbourne; can also be reached direct from Totnes, on the Ashprington–Dittisham road

Decidedly an unpretentious local, this conceals cooking that rises well above the average. The normal menu covers a remarkable range, with popular examples running from local pasties (£1.15) and fresh basil and tomato soup (£1.30), through stuffed mushrooms (£3.15), a memorable steak and kidney pie, sweet and sour crispy cod or garlicky prawns (£3.95) and gammon and egg, to various steaks (from £7.25), half a guinea fowl (£7.95), a special mixed grill (£10.75), crab, Dover sole or lobster, puddings (from £1.60), and Sunday roast lunch (£6.25); chips are good and helpings huge. As the two rooms of the little low-ceilinged bar have only around half a dozen red plush wall seats and captains' chairs around heavy elm tables, it can get crowded at holiday times. There's also a small and pretty cottagey dining room with a good log fire in its big 17th-century stone fireplace. Well kept and attractively priced Blackawton Special and Ushers Best on handpump; darts, dominoes, trivia, cards, chess, board games, and piped music; they have four dogs (only let loose after closing time). There are picnic-table sets on a big lawn stretching up behind the car park, with swings, a climbing frame and summer barbecues. (*Recommended by S V Bishop, P and J Shapley, David Hunn, Brian and Anna Marsden, Geoffrey Medcalf, Richard Purser, David Wallington, Nick and Alison Dowson, M G Richards, C J Parsons, S V Bishop*)

Free house   Licensee Robin Thorns   Real ale   Meals and snacks (12–2, 7–10) Cottagey restaurant   Harbertonford (080423) 204   Children in eating area of bar Open 11.30–3, 6.30–11; closed evening 25 Dec

DALWOOD   ST2400 Map 1

Tuckers Arms 🅿

Village signposted off A35 Axminster–Honiton

The informally furnished, flagstoned bar in this thatched medieval longhouse has a random mixture of dining chairs, a funky armchair, window seats, a pew, a high-backed winged black settle, oak stripped beams, a big inglenook log fireplace and a woodburning stove. A side lounge with shiny black woodwork has a couple of cushioned oak armchairs and other comfortable but unpretentious seats. Well kept Boddingtons, Flowers Original, Marstons Pedigree and Wadworths 6X on handpump, quite a few malt whiskies, and coffee; darts, shove-ha'penny, fruit machine, piped music, and skittle alley. Enterprising and well prepared bar food includes home-made soup (£1.65), potato skins with interesting dips (from £2.15), home-made vegetarian moussaka (£5.25), gammon with peaches (£5.55), fresh local trout with lemon and caper butter (£6.25), the notably popular 'tiddy': a big puff pastry with a changing home-made filling, such as pork loin in cider with cream and a hint of grain mustard (£6.75) or layers of salmon and asparagus in a white wine sauce (£6.95), rack of lamb with lemon, herbs and garlic (£7.55), steaks (from £8.55), breast of duck with fresh herbs, field mushrooms and bacon and served with a rich juniper berry and port wine sauce (£9.75), and puddings like sticky treacle sponge pudding or home-made apple tart (from £1.95); also a lunchtime and early evening light snack menu and daily specials. The inn is prettily decked with hanging baskets and big pots of flowers and there are some picnic-table sets. (*Recommended by JBM, Patrick Freeman, Mr Jennings, Mr and Mrs D V Morris, Mr and Mrs J L Jones, Dr D M Forsyth, Chris Raisin, Gordon and Daphne*)

Free house   Licensees David and Kate Beck   Real ale   Meals and snacks (till 10pm) Stockland (040 488) 342   Children in restaurant and skittle alley/garden room until 7.30   Open 11.15–3, 6–11; 12–2.30, 7–10.30 in winter   Bedrooms; £25S/£40S

DARTINGTON   SX7762 Map 1

Cott ⊘ ⇌

In hamlet with the same name, signposted off A385 W of Totnes opposite A384 turn-off

This picturesque Devonshire inn, one of the oldest in the country (it first got its licence in 1320), takes its name from the Dutchman Johanus Cott, who converted the original cottages into a staging post for his shepherds as they journeyed to Totnes with their flocks. Its outstanding feature is the thatched roof – at 183 feet one of the longest in the south of England – best admired from the benches in the crazy-paved courtyard where there are also attractive buckets of flowers. The heavy-beamed bar, as traditional as the outside, consists of communicating rooms with lots of polished brass and horse-harnesses on the whitewashed walls, big open fires, some flagstone flooring, and traditional carved cast-iron, copper-topped round tables in front of sturdy high-backed settles, some elaborately carved; a small area is set aside for non-smokers. Well kept Bass, Blackawton and Fergusons Dartmoor on handpump; Churchward's cider, a decent range of wines by the glass (including Soviet ones) and several armagnacs. Good home-made bar food, using fresh vegetables, includes a hot and cold lunchtime buffet: sandwiches, pies, and salads (from £3.95) and pork with crackling, apple sauce and stuffing, braised duck with cranberry gravy or fresh Brixham fish (all £4.95); in the evening there is fresh monkfish with smoked bacon, garlic, mushrooms and cream (£10.95), local guinea fowl flamed in apple brandy (£11.50), and medallions of beef fillet (£12.75); puddings (£2.30); considerate, cheerful service. There are good walks through the grounds of nearby Dartington Hall, and it's good touring country – particularly for the popular Dartington craft centre, the Totnes–Buckfastleigh steam railway and one of the prettiest towns in the West Country, Totnes. (*Recommended by Judith Pickett, N H Harries, David Wallington, S V Bishop, Paul and Janet Waring, Patrick Freeman, Bob and Margaret Grover, U W Bankes, M L Rantzen, Jim and Maggie Cowell, H K Dyson, Mr and Mrs Simon Turner, Caroline Wright, Susan Turner, Wayne Brindle, Roy McIsaac*)

Free house   Licensees Stephen and Gillian Culverhouse   Real ale   Meals and snacks (12–2, 6.30–9.30)   No smoking restaurant   Totnes (0803) 863777   Children in restaurant   Open 11–2.30, 6–11   Bedrooms; £48(£58B)/£53(£63B)

DARTMOUTH   SX8751 Map 1

Cherub ⊘

Higher St

This lovely 14th-century building is one of the very few British pubs listed officially as Grade I. It's shown a resilient attitude to the progress of time: it survived an 1864 fire which destroyed the southern end of the street, and the World War Two bombing which destroyed the north side; hence it's the oldest building around here. Consistently good bar food includes sandwiches, carrot and courgette soup

(£1.50, French onion £1.60), filled baked potatoes (from £2.60), smoked haddock in a white wine and cheese sauce (£2.95), ploughman's (from £2.95), pasta with peppers, sweetcorn, mushrooms and shallots or chilli con carne (£4.25), smoked chicken with broccoli and ham, fresh scallops or seafood pasta (£5.25), and specials like monkfish with chervil sauce (£9.50) or salmon, sole and trout with orange and lemon butter sauce (£11.50); quick, pleasant service. The comfortable bar has tapestried seats under creaky heavy beams, red-curtained leaded-light windows and an open stove in the big stone fireplace; a good atmosphere. Each of the two heavily timbered upper floors juts further out than the one below. Blackawton, Flowers Original, Ind Coope Burton and Wadworths 6X on handpump, several dozen malt whiskies, and English wines. The pub takes its name from a type of locally built wool-carrying boat. *(Recommended by Mrs J Cookson, Tony and Rosemary Kelly, P and J Shapley, Richard Dolphin, Andrew Sowray, Les King, Jutta Whitley, David and Ann Stranack, Mr and Mrs L W Norcott, John Knighton, Carol Mason, John R Jones, Roy McIsaac, Margaret and Trevor Errington, D I Baddeley, Mrs A Turner, Paul and Janet Waring; more reports please)*

Free house   Licensees John and Janet Hill   Real ale   Meals and snacks (till 10pm) Restaurant   Dartmouth (080 43) 2571   Children in restaurant   Open 11–3, 5–11

Royal Castle 🛏

11 The Quay

Some of the oak beams in this 350-year-old waterside hotel reputedly came from the wreckage of the Spanish Armada. The lively, left-hand, local bar is decorated with navigation lanterns, glass net-floats and old local ship photographs; big windows overlook the inner harbour and beyond to the bigger boats in the main one. A mix of tables ranges from scrubbed deal to polished mahogany and there are stripped pine country kitchen chairs and stools, mates' chairs and a couple of interesting old settles; one wall is stripped to the original stonework and there's a big log fire. On the right in the more sedate, partly no smoking Turkey-carpeted bar (closed afternoons), they spit-roast joints at lunchtime from October to April over the open range; there's also a Tudor fireplace with copper jugs and kettles (beside which are the remains of a spiral staircase) and plush furnishings, including some Jacobean-style chairs, and in one alcove swords and heraldic shields on the wall. Well kept Bass, Boddingtons and Worthington BB on handpump, quite a few malt whiskies, and summer punches made with local fruit wines; welcoming staff; cribbage, dominoes, fruit machine, trivia, and piped music. The range of generously served bar food includes lunchtime sandwiches (from £1.25, prawn or crab £2.75) and a choice of ploughman's (from £2.45), as well as home-made soup (£1.25), baked potatoes with hot or cold fillings (from £2.25), ham and turkey tagliatelli (£3.25), home-made steak and kidney pie or savoury nut burger with curried fruit chutney (£4.25), curry of the day or whole plaice (£4.75), steaks (from £7.25), daily specials like lobster, poached salmon or Dover sole, puddings such as home-made apple pie (£1.65), and evening extras like salads (from £4.75); maybe evening bar nibbles. *(Recommended by John A Barker, P and J Shapley, M V and J Melling, H K Dyson, Gwen and Peter Andrews, Mr and Mrs L W Norcott, John Knighton)*

Free house   Licensees Nigel Way and Richard Moore   Real ale   Meals and snacks (12–2.30, 6.45–8.45)   Restaurant   Dartmouth (0803) 833033   Children in two separate areas   Jazz or country & western Thurs, blues/popular music Weds and Sun Open 11–11   Bedrooms; £37B/£62B

DODDISCOMBSLEIGH   SX8586   Map 1

Nobody Inn ★ ★ ⊘ 🛏

Village signposted off B3193, opposite northernmost Christow turn-off

During the 21 years Mr Borst-Smith has been running this friendly, 16th-century inn, he has built up what is perhaps the best pub wine cellar in the country with a remarkable choice of 700 well cellared wines by the bottle, 15 by the glass kept oxidation-free, properly mulled wine in winter, and twice-monthly tutored tastings in winter (they also sell wine retail, and the good tasting-notes in their detailed list are worth the £2.50 it costs – anyway refunded if you buy more than £20-worth); there's also a choice of 250 whiskies, Gray's and Inch's farm ciders and usually well kept Barrons Devon Glory, Bass, Flowers IPA, Eldridge Pope Royal Oak and Youngs on handpump or tapped straight from the cask; coffee. The two highly atmospheric rooms of the lounge bar are attractively furnished with handsomely carved antique settles, Windsor and wheelback chairs, red leatherette benches and carriage lanterns hanging from the beams (some of which are original). A snug area by one of the big inglenook fireplaces is decorated with guns and hunting prints. The wide range of efficiently served bar food includes home-made soup (£1.50), sandwiches (from £1.75, made to order; good crab), coarse home-made ducks' liver, port and herb pâté (£2.60), sausage and mash (£2.70), good butterbean casserole (£2.55), macaroni cheese with ham (£1.60), good, enormous ploughman's (£2.70), vegetable pie (£3.90); eight or nine daily specials, puddings like home-made spiced bread pudding or warm treacle tart (from £1.80), and a selection of around 33 local cow, sheep and goat cheeses (each marked with little identifications flags) to eat here or take away (a choice of 6 £2.70). They serve baskets of fresh vegetables with the main dishes (or to have on their own), and also sell local honey and clotted Jersey cream. There are picnic-table sets on the terrace, with views of the surrounding wooded hill pastures. The medieval stained glass in the local church is some of the best in the West Country. *(Recommended by Roger Cunningham, Lynn Sharpless, Bob Eardley, Andrew Morrissey, Tony Walker, Kevin and Tracey Stephens, Dr Keith Louden, Nigel Hopkins, Elisabeth Kemp, P and J Shapley, Gwynne Harper, M and P Rudlin, Dr John Innes, D L Parkhurst, Mr and Mrs C H Garnett, M J Cochrane, J L and J A Annandale, June and Tony Baldwin, Dr Robin Hull, Brian Jones, D M and D E Livesley, Chris Raisin, R J Walden, John and Christine Simpson, David and Ann Stranack, Hilary Roberts, David Wallington, Ian Whitlock, Gwen and Peter Andrews, WHBM, Tim and Ann Newell, Laurence Manning, W Bailey, Steve Dark, Mrs Lili Lomas, Andrea and Guy Bradley, Gethin Lewis, Charles Gurney, Ewan and Moira McCall, Wayne Brindle, M D Hare, John D Blaylock, Lyn and Bill Capper)*

Free house   Licensee Nicholas Borst-Smith   Real ale   Meals and snacks (till 10 evening)   Evening restaurant (not Sun)   Christow (0647) 52394   Open 12–2.30, 6–11; winter evening opening 7; closed evening 25 Dec   Bedrooms (some in distinguished eighteenth-century house 150yds away); £21(£32B)/£33(£53B)

DREWSTEIGNTON   SX7390 Map 1

Drewe Arms

The basic and thoroughly original simplicity of this thatched village local may not appeal to all tastes: simple built-in wooden benches facing each other across plain tables, ochre walls with local team photographs and advertisements tacked to them, and no serving counter – the well kept real ale (typically Flowers IPA) and draught cider, which you can draw yourself, are kept on racks in the tap room at the back. A third room, used occasionally, has a notable herringbone-pattern Elizabethan brick floor. However the place is distinguished by the landlady Mabel Mudge, who's been running it for 72 years and is the oldest licensee in the country. Sandwiches or ploughman's (£1.25); darts and cards. Though nearby Castle Drogo (open for visits) looks medieval, it was built earlier this century. Near the start of *Good Walks Guide* Walk 19. *(Recommended by Dr Keith Louden, Tony and Lynne Stark, Ann Marie Stephenson, John Burgan, Hilary Irving, Gordon and Daphne, Nick and Alison Dowson, Phil and Sally Gorton, Robert Humphreys, Chris Raisin)*

Free house   Licensee Mabel Mudge   Real ale   Snacks   Open 11–2.30, 6–11

EAST DOWN   SS5941 Map 1

Pyne Arms ✪

Off A39 Barnstaple–Lynton; OS sheet 180, map reference 600415

The universally popular and reasonably priced bar food in this busy place includes home-made soup (£1.35), filled rolls and sandwiches (from £1.15), ploughman's (£2.55), home-made pâté (£2.65), home-cooked ham and egg (£3.25), mussels in season prepared in four different ways (£5.35), scampi provençal (£6.75), several veal dishes (£7.55), steaks (from £8.15), beef stroganoff (£8.30), and a range of puddings made in their own bakery (from £2.05); quick, friendly service. The bar itself, low-beamed and L-shaped, has lots of nooks and crannies, a very high-backed curved settle by the door (as well as more ordinary pub seating), some copper jugs, big barrels and a woodburning stove with horse harness and farm tools on the wall above it; the red walls are hung with horse-racing prints and Guinness and Martell placards, and up some steps is a small, no smoking galleried loft with more tables and chairs. A flagstoned games area has pine-plank wall benches, a shelf with old soda syphons, handbells, and a clock, some swan-necked wall lamps, antlers, racing and hunting prints and a piano; pool table, darts, shove-ha'penny, table skittles, cribbage, dominoes and fruit machine, trivia; juke box. Well kept Flowers IPA on handpump and five wines by the glass. The boisterous doberman is popular with visitors, though he isn't allowed in the bar. The Black Venus at Challacombe and the Station House at Blackmoor Gate are under the same management. Arlington Court is close by. *(Recommended by Adrian Zambardino, Debbie Chaplin, Mr and Mrs L King, P R Morley, Steve and Carolyn Harvey, Nicholas Kingsley, G W Warren, David Wallington)*

Free house   Licensees Jurgen and Elisabeth Kempf   Real ale   Meals and snacks (till 10pm)   Barnstaple (0271) 850207   No children under 5 and those over that age in the small galleried loft only   Open 11–2.30, 6–11; closed 25 Dec

EXETER   SX9292   Map 1

Double Locks ★

Canal Banks, Alphington; from A30 take main Exeter turn-off (A377/396) then next right into Marsh Barton Industrial Estate and follow Refuse Incinerator signs; when road bends round in front of the factory-like incinerator, take narrow dead end track over humpy bridge, cross narrow canal swing bridge and follow track along canal; much quicker than it sounds, and a very worthwhile diversion from the final M5 junction

There's quite a nautical theme in the bar of this ancient and remote lockhouse – more like a retired seafarer's cottage, really – with ship's lamps and model ships. Well kept Adnams Broadside, Eldridge Pope Royal Oak, Everards Old Original, Greene King Abbot, Marstons Pedigree, Wadworths 6X and guest beers on handpump or tapped from the cask, and Gray's and Inch's farm ciders; coffee, tea, and hot chocolate; darts, dominoes in the main bar, bar billiards in another; piped music and trivia; notably friendly service. Generous helpings of simple, home-made food include soup (£1.25), sandwiches (from £1.40), a generous mushrooms on toast (£2.50), ploughman's (from £3.10), salads (from £4), hot dishes such as vegetable bake or ham and eggs (£3), breakfast special (£4), steak and kidney or turkey and mushroom pies (£4.20), home-made puddings like sticky toffee pudding or chocolate biscuit cake (£1.90), and Sunday roast (£3.95); summer weekend barbecues (from £2.60). There are picnic-table sets and a well provisioned play area, with an old steam train and swings, out on the grass, and maybe quite a few dogs at weekends. *(Recommended by Chris Newman, Deb Jay, Andrew Morrissey, N Doncaster, Mr and Mrs D L Haddow, Gail Marie Hindson, RJC, Neil H Barker, Mr and Mrs C H Garnett, Cliff and Karen Spooner, Mrs F Smith, Simon Weinberger, Ruth Humphrey, Sue Hallam, Andrea and Guy Bradley, Lt Cdr G R D Jackson)*

Free house   Licensee Jamie Stuart   Real ale   Meals and snacks (11–10.30)   Exeter (0392) 56947   Children welcome away from main bar   Live music Weds and occasionally Thurs, Fri and Sat   Open 11–11

White Hart ★ 🛏

66 South St; 4 rather slow miles from M5 junction 30; follow City Centre signs via A379, B3182; straight towards centre if you're coming from A377 Topsham Road

A popular meeting place for centuries, this splendid, well run 14th-century inn has a rambling main bar with big Windsor armchairs and built-in winged settles with latticed glass tops to their high backs, oak tables on the bare oak floorboards (carpet in the quieter lower area) and a log fire in one great fireplace with long-barrelled rifles above it; big copper jugs hang from heavy bowed beams in the dark ochre terracotta ceiling, the walls are decorated with pictorial plates, old copper and brass platters (on which the antique lantern lights glisten) and a wall cabinet holds some silver and copper. In one of the bay windows, there's a set of fine old brass beer engines. From the latticed windows, with their stained-glass coats-of-arms, one can look out on the cobbled courtyard – lovely when the wisteria is flowering in May. The Tap Bar, across the yard, with flagstones, candles in bottles and a more wine-barish feel, serves soup (£1.55), sandwiches (from £1.85), baked potato with cheese and anchovy topping (£2.25), cold meats (from £4.50), steak and kidney pudding (£5.60), chicken and chestnut pie (£5.70), and charcoal-grilled rib of beef steak (£9.15). There is yet another bar, called Bottlescreu Bill's, even more dimly candlelit, with bare stone walls and sawdust on the floor. It serves much the same food, as well as a respectable range of Davy's wines and pint jugs of vintage port from the wood or tankards of buck's fizz, and in summer does lunchtime barbecue grills in a second, sheltered courtyard. On Sundays both these bars are closed. Bass and Davy's Old Wallop (served in pewter tankards in Bottlescreu Bill's) on handpump; piped music. Bedrooms are in a separate modern block. *(Recommended by George Sayer, G Lynes, Jim and Maggie Cowell, David and Fiona Easeman, Steve Huggins, Brian Jones, Robert and Gladys Flux, Mr and Mrs C H Garnett, Ruth Humphrey, WMS)*

Free house   Licensee Graham Frederick Stone   Real ale   Meals and snacks (till 10pm; not Sun)   Restaurant   Exeter (0392) 79897   Children in restaurant and eating area of bar   Open 11–3.30, 5–11 (all day Fri and Sat); closed evening 25 Dec   Bedrooms; £54.50B/£78B

EXMINSTER   SX9487   Map 1

Swans Nest ★

Pub signposted from A379 S of village

The rambling, heavily beamed bar in this strongly foody pub has groups of sofas and armchairs, some carved old-fashioned settles, lots of wheelback chairs, high-backed winged settles (set out as booths around the tables), grandfather clocks, and high shelves of willow-pattern platters and so on; a sensible no-smoking area extends from the long food servery. There's a large carvery with beef, pork, turkey and lamb (£6.45), a salad bar which offers poached salmon, crab, cold meats, pies and quiches and a choice of twenty or more salads, and dishes such as vegetable bake (£3.75), mushroom stroganoff (£4.75), fresh fish (delivered daily, from £4.95), beef in Guinness (£5.50), and chicken supreme (£7.25). Friendly service. Bass, Fergusons Dartmoor, Whitbreads Best and Worthington on handpump, a good choice of wines and country wines. There is a children's play park, eating area, and Sunday lunchtime entertainment. In the charmingly landscaped car park (with room for 200 cars) they ask you to drive forwards into the bays, to prevent exhaust damage to their fine shrubs. *(Recommended by D S and Mrs T M Beeson, S J Rice, Andrea and Guy Bradley, T Galligan, P and M Rudlin)*

Free house   Licensee A Amatruda   Real ale   Meals and snacks (12–2, 6–10) Children in own area   Dancing Fri-Sat evenings   Open 11–2.30, 6–11; closed 26 Dec

Turf ★

Continue past the Swans Nest (see previous entry) to end of track, by gates; park, and walk right along canal towpath – nearly a mile

You can't reach this isolated place by car – the walk is well worth the effort and takes about 20 minutes, along the ship canal to the mudflats (full of gulls and waders at low tide); or you can take a 40-minute ride from Countess Wear in their own boat, the Water Mongoose (bar on board; £3 adult, £2 child return, charter for up to 56 people £100 – free a couple of winter evenings a week). They also operate a 12-seater boat which brings people down the Exe estuary from Topsham quay (15 minute trip, adults £2, child £1). For those arriving in their own boat there is a large pontoon as well as several moorings. A considerable amount of careful redecoration has taken place over the last year and the pleasantly airy, high-ceilinged, bay-windowed rooms of the bar have two open fires as well as a woodburning stove, fresh flowers on low varnished tables, and broad bare floorboards; on the walls are big bright shorebird prints by John Tennent and cartoons with a nautical theme by Larry and Colin Page, and they hope to exhibit paintings by local artists. Well kept Boddingtons, Flowers IPA and Marstons Pedigree on handpump from the cask, and Green Valley cider made from locally grown organic apples; darts, cribbage, dominoes, trivia, and piped music. Straightforward bar food includes sandwiches (from £1.50; home-cooked beef with horseradish £2.25; fresh local crab £2.50), home-made soup (£1.60), salads (from £2), filled baked potatoes (from £2.50), mushrooms in a creamy herb sauce (£2.50), tomato, lentil and pasta bake, local mussels or black bean and vegetable curry (£3.25), sausage hot-pot (£3.95), beef casserole, curry or korma (£4.50), and home-made treacle and chocolate puddings (£1.50); cook your own barbecues (from £1.75); friendly, efficient service. The dining room is no-smoking. Below, on the big lawn running down to the shore, you can play French boules; there are also log seats, picnic-table sets and a beached cabin boat for children to play in; well behaved dogs welcome. (*Recommended by Brian Jones, P and M Rudlin; more reports please*)

Free house   Licensees Clive and Ginny Redfern   Real ale   Meals and snacks   Exeter (0392) 833128   Children welcome   Impromptu jazz, blues and rock   Open 11–3, 6–11; 11–11 summer Sats; winter weekdays 11–2.30, 6–10.30   Bedrooms; £16.50/£33

HARBERTON   SX7758   Map 1

Church House ♀

Village signposted from A381 just S of Totnes

The latticed glass on the back wall of the open-plan bar by the entrance to this ancient pub was in a window which had been walled off (probably to evade window tax) until Victorian times; it's almost 700 years old, and one of the earliest examples of non-ecclesiastical glass in the country. Similarly, the magnificent medieval oak panelling was only discovered behind some plaster when renovations were carried out in 1950. Furnishings include attractive 17th- and 18th-century pews and settles, the bar counter originally came from a bank, and there's a large inglenook fireplace with a woodburning stove; one half of the room is set out for eating. The wide range of popular, generously served bar food uses fresh local produce whenever possible and the owners have purchased 10 acres of neighbouring farmland on which they hope to grow limited amounts of vegetables and perhaps provide some of their own lamb and beef: sandwiches (from £1.30), home-made soup (£1.50; the crab is good), locally made sausages (£2.50), ploughman's (from £2.75), omelettes (from £3.50), fry-up (£4.25), tagliatelle with a blue cheese and walnut sauce (£4.50), superb steak and kidney pie, prawn curry (£5.75), three lamb cutlets (£5.95), rump steak (from £6.95), and puddings like treacle tart or bread and butter pudding (£1.95). Lots of daily specials such as fresh local fish (when available), deep-fried brie wrapped in bacon with a spicy redcurrant jelly (£3.25), pork tenderloin dijonnaise (£6.95) or poached salmon steak with prawn and dill sauce (£7.50); vegetables are clean and crisp. Bass, Courage Best and Directors and a weekly changing guest beer such as Brakspears Best, Eldridge Pope Hardy or Royal Oak, Hook Norton Old Hookey, Marstons Pedigree, Smiles Best and Wadworths 6X on handpump, as well as Churchward's farm cider and George Duboeuf wines; efficient and friendly service; dominoes, cribbage. The pub is in a steep little twisting village, pretty and surrounded by hills. (*Recommended by Mr and Mrs W H Crowther, Dorothee and Dennis Glover, S V Bishop, Roger Huggins, J K Conneen, David and Flo Wallington, John Affleck, D Faulconberg, D P Pascoe, WMS, David and Ann Stranack, Philip and Trisha Ferris, Mrs D B Broadhurst*)

Free house   Licensee Mrs Jennifer Wright   Real ale   Meals and snacks   Restaurant Totnes (0803) 863707   Children in family room   Local and visiting Morris team throughout summer, and jazz last Tues in month   Open 11.30–2.30(3 Sat), 6–11; winter lunchtime opening 12; closed evenings 25 and 26 Dec

HATHERLEIGH   SS5404 Map 1

George

The little front bar – mainly for residents – in the original part of this pleasant, 15th-century inn has an enormous fireplace, tremendous oak beams, stone walls two or three feet thick, and easy chairs, sofas and antique cushioned settles. Across the corridor from this there's an even smaller, and very simple bar, which is only open on market day (Tuesday). The spacious L-shaped main bar was built from the wreck of the inn's old brewhouse and coachmen's loft, and has beams, a woodburning stove and antique settles around sewing-machine treadle tables; a quieter no-smoking extension, with more modern furnishings, leads off this; darts, pool, cribbage, dominoes and piped music. Barrons Devon Glory, Bass, Whitbreads Castle Eden and a guest ale on handpump, a good range of Spey and Islay malt whiskies, Inch's farm ciders, tea and coffee. Bar food includes sandwiches (from £1.30), clubs £2.60), home-made soup (£1.60), filled baked potatoes (from £2), ploughman's (from £2.20), tagliatelle provençale (£3), lasagne (£3.85), steak and kidney pie (£3.75), fry-up (£4.50), steaks (£7.25), and puddings (£1.85); daily specials are chalked up on a board. In the flood-lit courtyard there are hanging baskets and window-boxes on the black and white timbering, and rustic wooden seats and tables on its cobblestones; what was part of the stables has now been turned into a walled cobbled garden. *(Recommended by Geoffrey Medcalf, Richard Purser, Chris Newman, Deb Jay, Helena and Arthur Harbottle, Cliff and Karen Spooner, G W Warren)*

Free house   Licensees Veronica Devereux and John Dunbar-Ainley   Real ale   Meals and snacks (12–2, 6–9.30)   Restaurant (closed Sun)   Okehampton (0837) 810454 Children in lower part of bar   Open 11–3.30, 6–11   Bedrooms; £30.50(£42B)/£40.50(£54B)

Tally Ho 🕭

Market St (A386)

You can view the spotless copper brewing equipment used by the hospitable Italian landlord of this ancient village pub through a big window in one building of the former back coach yard; he brews deep-coloured quite strongly hopped Potboiler with its sturdily appetising finish, Tarka Tipple, Nutters and Dark Mild, keeps a fine range of Italian wines, has a decent choice of malt whiskies, and does freshly squeezed orange juice. Though there are Italian notes like the good-value Wednesday pizza night, the old brass and copper espresso machine on the counter, and *bel canto* touches (not just in the piped music but maybe in special summer events), the pub's deeply English character is perfectly preserved: heavy beams, sturdy old oak and elm tables on the partly carpeted brick floor, two woodburning stoves (an armchair by one, the other in a very high-mantled smoking-chamber of a hearth, with a fox mask above it), decorative plates between the wall timbers, candles in bottles, fresh flowers, shelves of old bottles and pottery. Firmly home-made bar food includes pasties (£1.25), sandwiches (from £1.75), ploughman's (from £2.20), omelette (from £2.15), good sausages (£2.20), lasagne (£3.75), devilled crab (£3.95), a vegetarian dish, fritto misto (£7.95), sirloin steak (£8.75), puddings (from £1.75); barbecues on Thursday, very good continental breakfasts; darts, shove-ha'penny, cribbage, dominoes, fruit machine, trivia, maybe unobtrusive piped pop radio. The friendly boxer is called Boris. There are tables in the sheltered garden. The atmospheric little back dining room specialises in Italian dishes. Mr Scoz is a keen fisherman, and can arrange fishing on about eight miles of the Torridge. *(Recommended by Ann Marie Stephenson, Tony and Lynne Stark, Chris Newman, Deb Jay, R J Walden, Cliff and Karen Spooner)*

Own brew   Licensees Gianni and Annamaria Scoz   Real ale   Meals and snacks (not Sun lunchtime)   No smoking restaurant; closed Sun, Weds and Thurs in summer Hatherleigh (0837) 810306   Children over 8 in eating area of bar and in restaurant Open 11–2.30, 6–11   Bedrooms; £25B/£38B

HAYTOR VALE SX7677 Map 1

Rock ★ ⊘ ⇐

Haytor signposted off B3344 just W of Bovey Tracey, on good moorland road to Widecombe

Locals and a good mix of visitors come to this civilised Dartmoor inn to enjoy the relaxed, friendly atmosphere and wide choice of good food. The two communicating rooms of the partly panelled bar have good winter log fires (the main fireplace has a fine Stuart fireback), polished antique tables (candlelit at night), easy chairs, oak Windsor armchairs and high-backed settles, and old-fashioned prints and decorative plates on the walls. The ground floor dining room is no smoking – as is the restaurant. Bar food includes delicious home-made soup (£1.35), sandwiches (from £1.20, ham, asparagus and pineapple £3.55), omelettes made with fresh local free range eggs, ploughman's (from £2.95), quiche of the day (£3.25), vegetarian dishes (from £3.95), rabbit surprise (£4.25), excellent curries such as lamb and mint (£4.75), mussels in garlic butter and white wine (£4.25), salads (from £4.75), beef in walnuts, celery and Guinness or beef and venison pie (£4.95), fresh fish from Brixham (when available, from £4.95; red mullet with mustard butter £7.95), grilled lamb cutlets (£6.55), steaks (from £7.25), a good range of puddings such as raspberry montiechristie, treacle tart, bread and butter pudding and steamed puddings (from £1.35), and Sunday roast; there may be delays during busy periods. Well kept Bass and Eldridge Pope Dorchester and Royal Oak on handpump, teas and coffee; courteous service. The winter Friday-night break – you pay for a meal for two in the restaurant and get free overnight accommodation – is good value. The village itself is just inside the National Park, and the inn is well positioned for golf, horse riding and fishing. The big garden is pretty and well kept. (*Recommended by John Burgan, Hilary Irving, Tony and Lynne Stark, Dr Keith Louden, Nigel Hopkins, Philip Orbell, Jan and Keith Grant, Miss Madeleine Selby, June and Tony Baldwin, Romey Heaton, M Saunders, Helena and Arthur Harbottle, Bob Smith, D M and D E Livesley, Mr and Mrs Simon Turner, Tony and Alison Sims, D I Baddeley*)

Free house   Licensee Christopher Graves   Real ale   Snacks (not Sun or bank hol) No-smoking restaurant   Haytor (0364) 661305/661465   Children in restaurant Open 11–2.30, 6(6.30 winter)–11   Bedrooms; £27.50(£37.50B)/£49(£55B)

HENNOCK SX8380 Map 1

Palk Arms

Village signposted from B3193; also good road first right turn after leaving Chudleigh Knighton on B3344 for Bovey Tracey

Changes here this year include a new restaurant with better views, and a larger, better equipped kitchen. The main bar has a large log fire in a stone fireplace and downstairs from the lounge bar is an attractive bread oven. Fergusons Dartmoor on handpump, and fresh coffee; darts, cribbage, fruit machine, juke box, and piped music. Bar food includes soup (£1.20), sandwiches (from £1.50), macaroni cheese (£2.50), ploughman's (from £2.55), salads (from £3.50), and puddings (£1.60); very good breakfasts. The picnic-table sets on the back lawn have magnificent views over the spread of the Teign Valley, which can also be enjoyed from the restaurant. Close to the Hennock reservoirs which is good for fly-fishing. (*Recommended by Graham and Brenda Blair, Hu' and Eve Deverson; more up-to-date reports please*)

Free house   Licensees Jim and Judith Young   Real ale   Meals and snacks Restaurant   Bovey Tracey (0626) 833027   Children in family room   Open 12–3, 7–11; closed Mon morning except bank hols   Bedrooms; £14/£28

HOLNE SX7069 Map 1

Church House ⊘ ⇐

Village signed off B3357 2 or 3 miles W of Ashburton

The lower bar in this Grade II-listed medieval inn has stripped pine panelling, and an atmospheric carpeted lounge bar has a 16th-century heavy oak partition and an 18th-century curved elm settle; there are fine moorland views from the pillared porch (popular with regulars). Blackawton Bitter and 44, Fergusons Dartmoor and Palmers IPA on handpump, and local farm cider, organic apple juice from a local farm, local mineral water, decent house wines, coffee and tea; darts, dominoes, cribbage, and table skittles in the public bar. Bar food includes filled baked potatoes (from £2.50), ploughman's (from £2.75), ham and eggs with sauté potatoes or leek, bacon and potato pie (£3.75), three-egg omelettes (from £3.75), vegetable casserole with yoghurt topping or large, tasty steak and kidney pie (£4.25), salads (from £4.50), whole plaice (£5.75), steaks (from £7.50), daily specials, and puddings (from £1.75); 3-course Sunday lunch (£7.50); they use local and organic produce, and try to accommodate special diets; pleasant and helpful staff. The quarter-hour walk from the Newbridge National Trust car park to the pub is rather fine, and there are many other attractive walks nearby, up on to Dartmoor as well as along the wooded Dart valley. Charles Kingsley (of *Water Babies* fame) was born in the village. *(Recommended by P M Bisby, David Wallinton, Andrew Fowles, Philip and Trisha Ferris, B and J Derry, Philip Orbell, David and Shirley Way, Mrs A Crowhurst, Wayne Brindle, Mr and Mrs D Hampton, M D Hare, David and Flo Wallington)*

Free house   Licensees N E and W J Bevan   Real ale   Snacks (not evening) and meals No-smoking restaurant   Poundsgate (036 43) 208   Children in eating area of bar and in restaurant until 9pm; not in restaurant in evening if under 10   Local musicians last Fri in month   Open 12–2.30, 6.30–11   Bedrooms; £17.50(£22.50B)/£30(£40B)

HORNDON   SX5280   Map 1

Elephants Nest ★

If coming from Okehampton on A386 turn left at Mary Tavy inn, then left after about 1/2 mile; pub signposted beside Mary Tavy inn, then Horndon signposted; on the Ordnance Survey Outdoor Leisure Map it's named as the New Inn

This isolated old pub on the lower slopes of Dartmoor has an amusing elephant mural in the bar, as well as cushioned stone seats built into the windows, captains' chairs around the tables, large rugs and flagstones, a beams-and-board ceiling, and a good log fire on cool days. Another room – created from the old beer cellar and with views over the garden and beyond to the moors – acts as a dining or function room or an overspill from the bar on busy nights. Bar food includes home-made soup (£1.20), good granary rolls (from £1.20), ploughman's (from £2.60), chilli con carne (£2.85), steak and kidney pie (£3.60), puddings (£1.70), vegetarian dishes and daily specials, and evening extras like curry (£3.60) or local trout (£5.10); fresh vegetables are 90p extra. Well kept Boddingtons, Palmers IPA, St Austells HSD and Websters Yorkshire on handpump, with up to 32 summer guests; Bulmers draught cider; sensibly placed darts, dominoes, cards, fruit machine and piped music; efficient service. The three dogs are allowed the run of the pub. Outside on the spacious, flower-bordered lawn are some wooden benches and tables. Though you can walk from here straight on to the moor or Black Down, a better start (army exercises permitting) might be to drive past Wapsworthy to the end of the lane, at OS Sheet 191, map reference 546805. *(Recommended by K and J O'Malley, David and Kate Jones, M and P Rudlin, Michael Simmonds, Dorothee and Dennis Glover, R A Corbett, Julian Proudman, N W Acton, Jacquie and Jon Payne, Mayur Shah, Harry Stirling, Mr and Mrs Simon Turner, Brian Jones, J C Proud, Wayne Brindle, Helena and Arthur Harbottle)*

Free house   Licensees Nick and Gill Hamer and Peta Hughes   Real ale   Meals and snacks (11.30–2, 7–10)   Mary Tavy (0822) 810273   Children in two areas away from bar   Folk music 2nd Tues of month   Open 11.30–2.30(3Sat), 6.30–11; closed evening 25 Dec   Bedrooms; £14B(£28B)

HORNS CROSS   SS3823 Map 1

Hoops

A39 Clovelly–Bideford (and just W of village)

Run by an enterprising ex-Royal Marines Captain, this neatly kept, 13th-century thatched inn has an ancient well set into the red carpeted floor of the oak-beamed bar, logs burning in big inglenook fireplaces, cushioned window seats, sturdy leather-seated oak settles, and paintings and old photographs of the pub on the walls; leading off here is a small, similarly furnished children's room with another fireplace. Decent bar food includes baked potatoes, burgers and steaks; Boddingtons, Flowers IPA and Original and Marstons Pedigree on handpump kept under light blanket pressure, and a good wine list; darts, cribbage, trivia, and piped music. Across the sheltered central courtyard – where there are picnic-table sets – is a cafe-style summer family room. They have planning permission to convert outbuildings into seven self-catering cottages. (*Recommended by Peter Bisby, E Fieldhouse, Tony Bland, Colin and Evelyn Turner*)

Free house   Licensees Derek and Marjorie Sargent   Real ale   Meals and snacks Restaurant; closed Sun evening   Horns Cross (0237) 451222   Children in own room and eating area of bar   Open 11–3, 6–11   Bedrooms; £20(£30B)/£40(£54B)

HORSEBRIDGE   SX3975 Map 1

Royal ★

Village signposted off A384 Tavistock–Launceston

This simple, old-fashioned place was originally called the Packhorse, and got its present name for services rendered to Charles I (whose seal is carved in the doorstep). Inside, it feels as if it can't have changed much since Turner slept on a settle in front of the fire, so that he could slip out early to paint the nearby bridge. In the right-hand room there are vertically panelled cushioned stall seats around neat old tables, some mates' chairs and wheelback chairs, and harness and brasses on the stripped stone walls; the one on the left has cushioned casks and benches around three tables on the slate floor, and bar billiards, sensibly placed darts and piped music. There's another small room, called the Drip Tray, for the overflow at busy times. The good variety of freshly cooked bar food includes a wide choice of lunchtime ploughman's (£2.35), moussaka, fisherman's pie or lasagne (£2.50), four vegetarian dishes (from £4), and venison in wine or duck in orange (£5.15), and puddings (£1.55); no chips or fried food; food service stops promptly at 2. Besides the beers brewed on the premises – Tamar, Horsebridge Best and the more powerful Heller – they also keep Bass, Eldridge Pope Royal Oak and Marstons Pedigree on handpump, and country wines. The covered area in the garden, presided over by Fred, the resident jackdaw, also has budgies, finches, cockatiels and so forth, and a big terrace with seats, a rose arbour and hanging baskets. They don't allow children. (*Recommended by Amanda Dauncey, Catherine and Andrew Brian, Mark Evans, D L Parkhurst, Richard Houghton, Graham and Glenis Watkins, Phil Gorton, David and Sarah Gilmore, Mr and Mrs Simon Turner, M L Hooper-Immins, PB, HB*)

Own brew   Licensees T G and J H Wood   Real ale   Meals and snacks (12–2, 7.15–9.30; not Sun evening)   Open 12–3, 7–11

IDDESLEIGH   SS5708 Map 1

Duke of York ⊘ ⇌

B3217 Exbourne–Dolton

Splendidly relaxed and very friendly, this largely 14th-century thatched pub is very much somewhere you can feel at home – whether you've dropped in for a casual chat and drink or to enjoy the generously served, truly home-made food. There are flowers and lit candles in bottles on the well spaced stripped country tables, and a housekeeper's chair by one big high-mantled stone fireplace – where logs may be burning even in summer. Home-made bar food using fresh local produce where possible is chalked up on a blackboard and includes home-made soup (£2), filled baked potatoes (from £3), pitta bread filled with hot, spicy merguez sausages (£2.75), a fair ploughman's (from £3.25), outstanding ham (cooked in local cider) and egg (£4), steaks (from £7.50), and changing specials such as smooth duck liver and orange pâté (£3), vegetable curry (£4), breast of chicken with port and wild mushroom sauce (£5), and puddings like sticky toffee pudding or brown sugar meringues with summer fruit purée (£2.20); children's helpings where possible, and summer self-service salad bar. Well kept Cotleigh Tawny and Old Buzzard, Eldridge Pope Hardy, Mitchells ESB, Palmers and Smiles tapped from the cask, Inch's farm ciders, several malt whiskies, and 32 bin-end wines; shove-ha'penny, cribbage, dominoes and sensibly placed darts. Through a small coach arch is a little back garden with some picnic-table sets under cocktail parasols, with a slide, and a rabbit hutch in the owners' part. Good fishing nearby; and if you stay you're well placed to take particular advantage of dinner in the charming little dining room – fine, interesting cooking. (*Recommended by Tony and Lynne Stark, Mrs R Horridge, David Wallington, Marianne Pryor, Mr and Mrs J D Cranston, G R Cleaver, R W Stanbury*)

Free house   Licensees Trish and John Colvill   Real ale   Meals and snacks Restaurant (Tues-Sat evenings; must book before noon)   Hatherleigh (0837) 810253 Children in eating area of bar and in restaurant for Sunday buffet   Morris dancers and occasional country storytellers   Open 11.30–3, 6.30–11; closed Mon winter evenings Bedrooms; £20/£22.50

KINGSKERSWELL   SX8767   Map 1

Barn Owl

Aller Rd; just off A380 Newton Abbot–Torquay – inn-sign on main road opposite RAC post

The new entrance, reception area and lavatories have been completed in this 17th-century farmhouse, and the residents' lounge will be finished shortly. One room has antique dark oak panelling, a decorative wooden chimney piece, an elaborate ornamental plaster ceiling, and grand furnishings such as a couple of carved oak settles and old-fashioned dining chairs around the handsome polished tables on its flowery carpet. Two other rooms have been stripped back to low black oak beams, with polished flagstones and a kitchen range in one. The wide choice of bar food ranges from home-made soup (£1.50), sandwiches (from £2.30, crab £3.50), filled baked potatoes (from £2.95), ploughman's (from £3.20), quite a few salads (from £4.50; fresh local salmon £7.95), fresh fillet of plaice (£4.95), fresh fillet of sole (£5.50), gammon (£6.25), steaks (from £9), mixed grill (£9.75), puddings (£1.95), and specials like liver and bacon casserole (£5.25) or prawn and mushroom pancakes (£5.75). Fergusons Dartmoor and Ind Coope Burton on handpump and several malt whiskies; log fires throughout. There are picnic-table sets in a small sheltered garden. (*Recommended by Steve Huggins, D I Baddeley, M Saunders, B A Cox; more reports please*)

Free house   Licensees Derek and Margaret Warner   Real ale   Meals and snacks (till 10)   Evening restaurant (not Sun)   Kingskerswell (0803) 872130   Open 11.30–2.30, 6.30–11; closed 25 Dec   Bedrooms; £47.50B/£60B

KINGSTEIGNTON   SX8773   Map 1

Old Rydon   ★   ⊘

Rydon Rd; from A381 Teignmouth turn off A380, take first real right turn (Longford Lane), go straight on to the bottom of the hill, then next right turn into Rydon Rd following Council Office signpost; pub is just past the school, OS Sheet 192, map reference 872739

The covered terrace here is now a heated conservatory with newly planted bougainvillea, jasmine, oleander, plumbago and grape vines. The small, cosy bar has cask seats and upholstered seats built against the white-painted stone walls, a heavy beam-and-plank ceiling with lots of beer mugs hanging from them, and a big winter log fire in a raised fireplace. There are a few more seats in an upper former cider loft, now a gallery facing the antlers and antelope horns on one high white wall. Popular, home-made bar food, changing daily depending on what fresh ingredients they've bought, might include vegetarian pancake filled with stir-fried vegetables in a peanut and soy sauce (£2.20), local smoked trout and egg mayonnaise (£2.50), baked potato filled with garlicky mushrooms, sweetcorn and tarragon stroganoff (£3.95), nasi goreng, Brixham fisherman's crumble or braised leg of lamb in caper, cream, white wine and lovage sauce (all £4.95), and outstanding seafood salad (£6.95). Well kept Bass, Wadworths 6X and a changing guest ale on handpump. A covered side terrace has some seats, with more in a nice biggish sheltered garden, which has a swing. *(Recommended by Mrs J Cookson, G L Carlisle, Jim and Maggie Cowell, Nigel Hopkins, Steve Huggins, M Saunders, J C Proud, B A Cox, E H and R F Warner)*

Free house   Licensees Hermann and Miranda Hruby   Real ale   Meals and snacks Restaurant   Newton Abbot (0626) 54626; closed Sun   Children upstairs till 8pm Very occasional live music   Open 11–2.30, 6–11

KINGSTON   SX6347   Map 1

Dolphin

Off B3392 S of Modbury (can also be reached from A379 W of Modbury)

Near the imposing village church, this yellow-shuttered 16th-century house is a peaceful and civilised place, with an informal bar made up of several knocked-through beamed rooms, and furnished with rustic tables and cushioned seats and settles around their bared stone walls. Well kept Courage Best and Directors, Marstons Pedigree and Wadworths 6X on handpump. Generously served bar food includes home-made soup (£1.65), lunchtime sandwiches (from £1.50) and ploughman's (from £3.25), chicken and apple in a curry mayonnaise (£3.25), chicken curry or steak and kidney pie (£4.50), vegetarian nut roast with cheese sauce (£4.95), shellfish bake (£6.95), puddings like home-made treacle tart (£1.95); and evening grills (from £5.95). Sunday roast, and children's meals (from £2). There are tables, swings, a children's summer snack bar and summer barbecues in the garden. Half a dozen tracks lead down to the sea, and unspoilt Wonwell Beach, about a mile and a half away. *(Recommended by WMS, Jane and Mark Hayward, D and B Carron; more reports please)*

Courage   Tenant Barry Fryer   Real ale   Meals and snacks (till 10)   Kingsbridge (0548) 810314   Children in family room and eating area of bar until 9pm   Open 12–2.30, 6–11

KNOWLE   SS4938   Map 1

Ebrington Arms £

Pub signposted just off A361, in village two miles N of Braunton

The two opened-up rooms of the carpeted lounge in this busy place have red plush stools around low tables, some pews, cushioned seats built into the stripped-stone outer walls (the inner ones are white), a copper-plated chimney breast, and a friendly atmosphere; the walls and black joists are decorated with lots of brass, prints, plates and pewter mugs. A snug bar has darts, shove-ha'penny, cribbage, space game and a fruit machine; separate pool room. Popular bar food includes home-made soup (£1.40), ploughman's (from £2.50), tasty cauliflower cheese with ham (£2.80), chilli con carne (£2.90), good turkey curry (£2.95), cottage pie (£3.20), tagliatelle (£3.25), steak, mushroom and Guinness pie (£4.25), popular cockles, mussels and prawns in white wine and cream (£4.75), and puddings such as tangy lemon pie or fruit crumble; children's menu and Sunday roast. Bass on handpump; juke box and piped music. There's a candlelit dining area up one or two steps at one end. Tess the dog is warmly welcoming. *(Recommended by John Drummond, Mrs R Horridge, P R Morley, Richard Fawcett, E V Walder, Philip and Trisha Ferris; more reports please)*

Free house   Licensee Alex Coombs   Real ale   Meals and snacks   Restaurant; closed Sun Jan-Easter   Braunton (0271) 812166   Children welcome   Open 10–3, 6–11

KNOWSTONE   SS8223   Map 1

Masons Arms   ★   ★   ⊘   ⇒

Village signposted off A361 Bampton–South Molton

In a lovely quiet position opposite the village church, this unspoilt 13th-century thatched inn has a good mix of chatty locals and visitors, and the landlord is most helpful about places to visit and so forth – and likely to remember your name on a second visit. To catch the mood of the house-style, we don't think we can improve on last year's phrase: engagingly homely and almost soporifically relaxed. The small main bar has substantial rustic furniture on the stone floor, ancient bottles of all shapes and sizes hanging from the heavy medieval black beams, farm tools on the walls, and a fine open fireplace with a big log fire and side bread oven. A small lower sitting room has pinkish plush chairs around a low table in front of the fire and bar billiards. Good, farmhousey bar food includes widely praised home-made soup (£1.40) and pâté (£1.95 – the walnut and cheese one is quite special), ploughman's with good fresh cheese and butter in a pot (£2.95), fried plaice or salads (£3.25), home-made pies, varying from day to day, like cheese and leek or rabbit and venison (£3.60), home-made curry (£4.60), fritto misto (£5.45), and puddings like excellent toffee pudding (from £1.25); specials such as hummus with garlic bread (£2.25), falafel with tatiki (£2.50), baked ham with cider sauce (£4.25), and fresh salmon mayonnaise (£5.95); very good value Sunday lunch, and a popular Thursday curry night with half-a-dozen to choose from, along with 5 or 6 sambals (this has proved so popular that there are now two other nights as well); they also have theme nights about once a month, usually with live music, a special menu and a special drink. They often sell home-made marmalades, fruit breads or hot gooseberry chutney over the counter. Well kept Hook Norton and Badger Best, Cotleigh Tawny and Wadworths 6X tapped from the cask, farm cider, a small but well chosen wine list, and coffee and teas; several snuffs on the counter; darts, shove-ha'penny, table skittles, dominoes, cribbage, and monthly general knowledge quiz (proceeds to charity). Charlie the engaging bearded collie likes to join you on a walk – at least part of the way; the cats are called Archie and Allie. We should make clear that the place to stay award reflects the distinctive character of the pub, much enjoyed by many readers who have stayed here – and by us. The level of comfort and somtimes of housekeeping is not however up to everyone's expectations. *(Recommended by Tony and Lynne Stark, Mr and Mrs B Dymott, Jim and Maggie Cowell, M P Furmston, Derek and Margaret Wood, Steve and Carolyn Harvey, Mr and Mrs C H Garnett, N W Acton, Roger and Carol Chisnall, Mr and Mrs David Williams, Michael and Joan Melling, Alan and Julie Wear, G W Warren, Virginia Jones, Prof M P Furmston, Cliff and Karen Spooner, Audrey and Roger Adcock, David Wallington)*

Free house   Licensees David and Elizabeth Todd   Real ale   Meals and snacks No-smoking restaurant (closed Sun and Tues evenings)   Anstey Mills (039 84) 231 Children welcome away from bar   Occasional live entertainment   Open 11–3, 7–11; closed evenings 25 and 26 Dec   Bedrooms; £26.95(£31S)/£43.90(£52S); dogs £1.50

LUSTLEIGH   SX7881   Map 1

Cleave

Village signposted off A382 Bovey Tracey–Moretonhampstead

The cosy, low-ceilinged lounge bar here has attractive antique high-backed settles, pale leatherette bucket chairs, red-cushioned wall seats and wheelback chairs around the tables on its patterned carpet; fresh flowers in summer and big log fires in winter. A traditionally furnished second bar has darts, dominoes, cribbage, and a fruit machine. Reasonably priced, tasty bar food includes home-made soup (£1.75), sandwiches (from £2.30) and ploughman's (from £3.20), with lunchtime dishes like cheese and onion flan or home-cooked ham (£3.65), home-made lasagne (£4.50), and home-made steak, kidney and Guinness pie (£4.95), and evening hot chilli con carne (£4.35), roast pork (£5.95), whole local trout (£8.95), fillet of salmon (£10.45), and puddings like delicious chocolate mousse; generous breakfasts for residents; friendly service. The real ale changes regularly, typically including Bass, Flowers IPA and a guest beer on handpump. The neat and pretty sheltered garden runs round the thatched 15th-century building. The out-of-the-way village is close to *Good Walks Guide* Walk 18. *(Recommended by Steve Huggins, Peter Churchill, Graham Patrick, Mayur Shah, Romey Heaton, L J B and J M Reynolds, S J Breame, Genie Krakowska Smart, Paul and Janet Waring)*

Heavitree (who no longer brew) Tenants A and A Perring Real ale Meals and snacks No-smoking restaurant Lustleigh (064 77) 223 Open 11–3, 6–11 Children in family room Parking may be difficult Three bedrooms; £25l£40

LYDFORD SX5184 Map 1

Castle ★ 🛏

Next to the village's daunting, ruined 12th-century castle, this charming pink-washed Tudor inn has a twin-roomed bar furnished with country kitchen chairs, high-backed winged settles and old captains' chairs around mahogany tripod tables on big slate flagstones; unusual stained-glass doors. One room, where the bar food is served, has masses of brightly decorated plates, some Hogarth prints, an attractive grandfather clock, low lamp-lit beams, a sizeable open fire and, near the serving counter, seven Lydford pennies hammered out in the old Saxon mint in the reign of Ethelred the Unready, in the 10th century; the second room has an interesting collection of antique stallion posters. The new licensees are hoping to introduce their own smokery for hams and fish, and other home-made dishes include seafood risotto (£3.75), Thai curry or kedgeree (£4), steak and kidney pie (£4.25), lots of salads with cold roast meats, and game. Fergusons Dartmoor Best, Strong and Cockleroaster, Ind Coope Burton, Tetleys and Wadworths 6X on handpump, and mulled wine; sensibly placed darts, shove-ha'penny, cribbage, dominoes, and piped music. The well kept garden has an adventure playground and barbecue area. The pub is close to a beautiful river gorge (owned by the National Trust), and the village itself was one of the four strongpoints developed by Alfred the Great as a defence against the Danes. *(Recommended by Tony and Lynne Stark, Chris Newman, Deb Jay, Julian Proudman, Mary and Peter Clark, Drs McCarthy and Mutch, John Evans, Mrs E Rayner, P M Rowntree, Mr and Mrs Simon Turner, J A Scott, R W Stanbury, Nick Dowson, Alison Hayward, Drs M and K Parier, Wayne Brindle, Mr and Mrs P C Clark)*

Free house Licensees Mary and Clive Walker Real ale Meals and snacks (12–2.30, 6–9.30) Partly no smoking restaurant Lydford (082 282) 242 Children in eating area of bar and in restaurant Open 11–3, 6–11 Bedrooms; £25(£35B)l£35(£45B)

LYMPSTONE SX9984 Map 1

Nutwell Lodge

Exmouth Road (A376, on the Exeter side)

The sort of place you might easily drive straight past, this big dining pub turns out to be attractively and spaciously furnished inside, thoughtfully laid out, and notably well managed. There's a sensible variety both of table sizes and of seating styles, so that you can feel you've found your own private spot in what is after all a very extensive and commodious place. Dark beams and joists, pillars, formal flower arrangements, tasteful pictures and pink-shaded candlebulb wall lamps set the mood, and one of the log-effect gas fires has a couple of button-back leather armchairs by it; the Moon-Riverish piped music is perhaps a shade obtrusive. Neat bow-tied staff man a good long bar counter, with particularly well kept Bass Triangle and respectable sherries and house wines but no nuts or crisps. A separate food counter serves decent straightforward food in big helpings, including home-made soup (£1.50), sandwiches (from £1.85, good crab £2.45), ploughman's (£3.50), vegetarian dishes (£5.50), salads (from £5.50), coq au vin (£5.50), and lots of steaks (from 6oz rump £6.95), whole fresh Brixham lemon sole (£8.95), and puddings (£1.95). There's a carvery with four joints, two pies and help-yourself vegetables (lunchtime £5.95, evening £6.95; three courses £8.95); part of the eating area is no smoking. An attractive lower room can be booked for parties. Some picnic-table sets out under cocktail parasols; exemplary car parking. *(Recommended by Pat Woodward, C A Foden, G Atkinson)*

Free house   Licensees Bruce and Pat Jefford   Real ale   Meals and snacks (till 10)
Topsham (0392) 873279   Children welcome   Open 11–3, 6–11

LYNMOUTH   SS7249 Map 1

Rising Sun ⇌

Mars Hill; down by harbour

The setting of this thatched 14th-century inn is lovely – looking over boats in the little harbour to the sea and in its own residential garden. The modernised panelled bar has uneven oak floors, black beams in the crooked ceiling, some stripped stone at the fireplace end, cushioned built-in stall-seats, and latticed windows facing the harbour. Ushers Best on handpump; friendly service; piped music. Good lunchtime bar food includes home-made soup (£1.85), filled rolls (from £1.95), filled baked potatoes (£2.65), ploughman's, steak, mushroom and Guinness pie or spicy sausages and eggs (all £3.85), crispy battered cod (£5.25), and seafood platter (£5.95); the best place to eat in is the small oak-panelled dining room. The comfortable bedrooms are mostly up the hill in the adjoining cottages, in one of which Shelley reputedly spent his honeymoon with his 16-year-old bride, Harriet. Near *Good Walks Guide* Walk 20; the steep walk up the Lyn valley to Watersmeet (National Trust) and Exmoor is particularly pleasant. *(Recommended by Chris Newman, Deb Jay, John Drummond, John Hickman, Dr T H Harrison, Andrew and Barbara Macdowall, Carol Mason, J A Scott, Jean and Hugo Thomas, D R Tyler, N C Dickerson, John Drummond)*

Free house   Licensee Hugo Jeune   Real ale   Lunchtime meals and snacks
No-smoking restaurant   Lynton (0598) 53223   Children in restaurant   Open 11–3, 5.30–11; 11–2.30, 6.30–11 in winter   Bedrooms; £35B/£70B

MILTONCOMBE   SX4865 Map 1

Who'd Have Thought It ★

Village signposted from A386 S of Tavistock

The atmospheric, black-panelled bar in this white-painted pub – dating back at least to the 16th century – has colourful plates on a big black dresser, cushioned high-backed winged settles around a woodburning stove in the big stone fireplace, rapiers and other weapons on its walls; two other rooms have seats made from barrels. Darts, dominoes, cribbage, fruit machine, and piped music; well kept Bass, Blackawton Headstrong, Eldridge Pope Royal Oak, Exmoor and Wadworths 6X on handpump; efficient, friendly staff. Generous helpings of popular bar food include granary bread sandwiches (from £1.50, good crab when available £2.15), generous ploughman's (lunchtime only, from £2.70), basket meals (from £3.50), good platters (from £4.95), grills (from £5.75), and puddings like cherry or blackcurrant pie with clotted cream (from £1.40); specials like home-made soup (£1.75), steak and kidney pie (£3.75), or braised steak in red wine. Sunday lunchtime food is restricted to sandwiches, ploughman's and basket meals. There are picnic-table sets on a terrace with hanging baskets, by the little stream. It's handy for the lovely gardens of the Garden House at Buckland Monachorum and for Buckland Abbey. *(Recommended by Geoffrey Medcalf, Richard Purser, Roger and Ann Short, J Whitley, Dr K A and S F Louden, Gwen and Peter Andrews, Hilary Roberts, Helena and Arthur Harbottle, R J Walden, Andy and Jill Kassube, Mr and Mrs Simon Turner, Wayne Brindle)*

Free house   Licensees Keith Yeo and Gary Rager   Real ale   Meals and snacks (restricted Sun lunchtime)   Yelverton (0822) 853313   Folk club Sun evening in lower bar   Open 11.30–2.30(3 Sat), 6.30–11

MORETONHAMPSTEAD   SX7585 Map 1

White Hart 🛏️

The large lounge bar in this civilised hotel is furnished with oak pews from the parish church, armchairs, plush seats and stools; the hall has a splendidly large-scale 1827 map of Devon by Greenwood, and in the lively public bar there are leatherette seats and settles under a white beam-and-plank ceiling; darts, cribbage, dominoes, fruit machine and piped music. Well kept Bass and Fergusons Dartmoor on handpump, and Luscombe farm cider. Decent bar food includes sandwiches, soup (£1.65), home-made pasty (£2), vegetable quiche, home-cooked ham, or lasagne (all £3.50), vegetable curry (£3.75), chicken and ham pie (£4.25), salads (from £4.25), a roast of the day (£6), grilled local trout (£7.50), grilled salmon steak (£8.25), steaks (£8.95), and puddings like treacle tart with clotted cream (from £1.85); daily specials, cream teas from 3pm, and Sunday roast; no children's helpings but an extra plate is available. You can sit on a pew among the flowers in the small back courtyard. Comfortable bedrooms. Well placed for Dartmoor. (*Recommended by Steve Dark, Chris Short and friends; more reports please*)

Free house   Licensee Peter Morgan   Real ale   Meals and snacks (12–2, 7–8.30); afternoon cream teas   No smoking restaurant and evening grill-room Moretonhampstead (0647) 40406   Children in eating area of bar   May have to park in the public car park, a short walk away   Open 11–11; closed 25 and 26 Dec Bedrooms; £37.50B/£57.50B

NEWTON ST CYRES   SX8798 Map 1

Beer Engine

Sweetham; from Newton St Cyres on A377 follow St Cyres Station, Thorverton signpost

An old station hotel popular with young people at weekends, and under the same management as the Sleeper at the Royal Clarence Hotel in Seaton, this pub brews its own beer – Rail Ale, Piston Bitter and the very strong Sleeper; you can observe the brewing process from the downstairs cellar bar. The spacious main bar has partitioning alcoves, Windsor chairs and some button-back banquettes around dark varnished tables on its red carpet; darts, shove-ha'penny, dominoes and cribbage; fruit machine and video game in the downstairs lobby. There's a simple range of food, including sandwiches, speciality sausages or vegetarian dishes (£3.25), steak and kidney pie (£3.75), gammon (£4.50), and 8oz rump steak (£6.95); obliging service. There's a real ale / real train link-up with Exeter at the weekends. (*Recommended by Roger Cunningham, Richard Houghton, Brian Jones*)

Own brew   Licensee Peter Hawksley   Real ale   Meals and snacks (12–2, 6.30–10) Exeter (0392) 851282   Children in eating area of bar   Rock and blues Fri and Sat evenings (cellar bar open till midnight) and folk and jazz Sun lunchtimes   Open 11.30–2.30, 6–11; 11.30–11 Sat

NORTH BOVEY   SX7483 Map 1

Ring of Bells

Off B3212 W of Moretonhampstead; can be reached direct from there, too

Set back from the village green (a lively place during the traditional mid-July Saturday fair), this 13th-century village inn has a simply furnished, opened up and carpeted main bar with bulgy white walls and horsebrasses on its beams. Well kept Fergusons Dartmoor, Ind Coope Burton, Marstons Pedigree, Wadworths 6X and guest beers on handpump or tapped from the cask, and Addlestones and Gray's farm ciders in summer; darts, pool in winter, cribbage, dominoes, fruit machine, video game, and piped music. Bar food includes good home-made curried parsnip soup (£1.95), Brixham plaice or chilli con carne (£4), a generous ploughman's or salads with game pie and cold meats (£4.50), and evening steaks (£7.50). Three courses in the restaurant (£12.50). Seats on the terrace are well sheltered by the mossily-thatched white buildings around it, and on the attractively bordered lawn there are summer lawn skittles and a good children's play area; summer swimming pool for residents. Fishing, golf, shooting and pony-trekking can be arranged for guests, and the inn is well placed for some of the most interesting parts of Dartmoor. *(Recommended by Nigel Hopkins, Gwen and Peter Andrews, Cliff and Karen Spooner, D J Devey, David and Christine Foulkes, Mr and Mrs Simon Turner, Ruth Humphrey, PB, HB, Janet and Paul Waring, GSS)*

Free house   Licensee Anthony Rix   Real ale   Meals and snacks   Restaurant Moretonhampstead (0647) 40375   Children in eating area of bar and in restaurant Open 11–3, 6–11   Bedrooms; £27.50B/£50B

PETER TAVY   SX5177   Map 1

Peter Tavy ★ ✪ £

Off A386 nr Mary Tavy, N of Tavistock

Interesting vegetarian dishes, a good range of real ales, and a relaxed, welcoming atmosphere cause this tiny pub to fill up very quickly, even on a mid-week lunchtime in winter. The particularly atmospheric low-beamed bar has high-backed settles on the black flagstones by the big stone fireplace (which usually has a good log fire on cold days), smaller settles in stone-mullioned windows, entertaining DIY graffiti on the low beams, and a snug side dining area; darts. Friendly staff serve the bar food that includes soup (£1.18; game £1.30), creamy cashew nut fingers and meaty or vegetarian pasties (all £1.28), wholemeal quiche (£1.40), butterbean, leek, sweetcorn and mushroom pie (£1.63), ploughman's (£2.85), cauliflower croustarde (£4.25), and chilli con carne (£4.35). Well kept Bass, Boddingtons, Butcombe, Eldridge Pope Royal Oak, Exmoor Gold, Tetleys, Wadworths 6X and Whitbreads Castle Eden on handpump or tapped from the cask; fruit wines. Picnic-table sets among fruit trees in a small raised garden have peaceful views of the moor rising above nearby pastures. This year there are new inside lavatories and a new car park. *(Recommended by Gerald Cleaver, R C Vincent, Mr and Mrs Crombleholme, Julian Proudman, John Wilson, R A Corbett, Wayne Brindle, Peter Maden, Hilary Robinson, Cliff and Karen Spooner, Amanda Dauncey, R J Walden, Steve Dark)*

Free house   Licensees Mr and Mrs P J Hawkins   Real ale   Meals and snacks (not 25 Dec)   Restaurant   Mary Tavy (0822) 810348   Children in restaurant and eating area of bar   Nearby parking often difficult   Open 11.30–2.30(3 Sat), 6.30–11

PLYMOUTH   SX4755   Map 1

China House ★

Marrowbone Slip, Sutton Harbour, via Sutton Road off Exeter Street (A374)

This striking new conversion by Allied Breweries has been catching the attention of our West Country readers in the last few months. It's right on the water, surrounded by a wooden terrace jettied out on baulks above the marina, with a spacious upper verandah with even better views over to the Barbican up below what used to be the hoist loft when this was a warehouse. Plymouth's oldest building, it's had an interesting history since its 17th-century origins as a naval storehouse, going through various transmogrifications until Cookworthy started his porcelain factory here (hence the name) in 1768. Inside is very spacious and lofty, with flagstone floors, bare slate and stone walls, great beams running across and strung with nets, kegs and fishing gear – even a clinker-built boat – so as to give an upper gallery. On the left is the main bar area, with plain wooden seats and plenty of locals around dark tables in front of a good log fire – all very chatty, comfortable and relaxed; a small restaurant is over on the right. Good home-made food includes fine garlic bread (95p), lunchtime open sandwiches (£1.95), home-made soup with garlic bread (£2.25), baked potatoes in mushroom sauce (£2.95), vegetarian moussaka or chicken and celery curry (£3.95), and steak and kidney pie (£4.35), with evening starters like potato skins with chilli dip (from £2.25) and main courses such as fettucini (£4.35), sweet and sour pork (£7.35), rack of lamb with barbecue sauce (£7.55), king prawns in garlic butter (£8.55), fresh fish (when available), and puddings like ginger and gooseberry flan (£2.25). Well kept Fergusons Dartmoor Best and Strong on handpump; two fruit machines, piped music. In front of the pub are some picnic-table sets, with benches on the verandah. *(Recommended by Lindy May, Kim Phipps, Jill Shore, Charles Gurney, Catherine and Andrew Brian, Paul Redgrave)*

Ansells (Allied)   Tenant Mo Law   Real ale   Meals and snacks   Restaurant   Plymouth (0752) 260930   Live jazz Sun, Tues and Thurs evenings   Open 12–3, 6–11

nr POSTBRIDGE   SX6579 Map 1
Warren House

B3212 1 3/4 miles NE of Postbridge

Remote on Dartmoor (and a valuable refuge after a walk), this rustic place is simply furnished with easy chairs and settles under a beamed ochre ceiling; there are also wild animal pictures on the partly panelled stone walls, and dim lighting (fuelled by the pub's own generator); even in high season it keeps quite a local atmosphere as it's something of a focus for this scattered moorland community. The fire at one end of the bar is said to have been kept continuously alight since 1845, though one reader claims to have heard of one occasion when it was briefly extinguished. Bar food consists of good pasties (£1.20), sandwiches (from £1.50), home-made soup (£1.75), ploughman's (£3), courgette and mushroom lasagne (£3.75), and home-made steak and kidney pie (£4.50). Flowers Original, Whitbreads Best and Wadsworth 6X on handpump, farm cider and a range of country wines. Darts, pool, dominoes, fruit machine, video game, and piped music. This road is worth knowing, as a good little-used route westward through fine scenery. *(Recommended by M and P Rudlin, John Evans, Elisabeth Kemp; more reports please)*

Free house   Licensee Peter Parsons   Real ale   Meals and snacks (noon–9.30 in summer)   Tavistock (0822) 88208   Children in family room   Open 11–11; 11–2.30, 5.30–11 in winter

RATTERY   SX7461 Map 1
Church House

Village signposted from A385 W of Totnes, and A38 S of Buckfastleigh

One of the oldest pubs in Britain – the spiral stone steps behind a little stone doorway on your left as you go in probably date from about 1030 – this has a homely open-plan bar with massive oak beams and standing timbers, large fireplaces (one with a little cosy nook partitioned off around it), Windsor armchairs, comfortable leather bucket seats and window seats, and prints on the plain white walls; the dining room is separated from this room by heavy curtains. Fergusons Dartmoor, Ind Coope Burton and Tetleys Bitter or a guest beer on handpump, 35 wines, 30 malt whiskies and farm cider. Bar food includes home-made soup (£1.65), ploughman's with good cheeses (from £2.80), vegetarian fry-up (£3.25), salads (from £3.35), excellent home-made quiche (£3.85), good value smoked salmon (£3.85), chicken and cranberry curry (£4.35), tasty steak and kidney pie (£4.80), rump steak (from 6oz £6.10), home-made puddings like treacle tart (£1.80), and daily specials like rabbit and ham pie (£4.95), fresh salmon and asparagus mornay (£5.30), fresh fish dishes, and roast guinea fowl (£6.25); the local cheeses are good; amiable staff and locals. Outside, there are peaceful views of the partly wooded surrounding hills from picnic-table sets on a hedged courtyard by the churchyard. The original building here probably housed the craftsmen who built the Norman church, and may then have served as a hostel for passing monks. *(Recommended by J S Evans, Keith Stevens, F and J Sherwood, S V Bishop, Margaret Drazin, Jutta B Whitley, Brian Jones, Philip Orbell, PADEMLUC, John Evans, Mr and Mrs L W Norcott, H K Dyson, S V Bishop, E A Simmons, Amanda Dauncey)*

Free house   Licensees Mr B and Mrs J J Evans   Real ale   Meals and snacks   Buckfastleigh (0364) 42220   Children in dining room and eating area of bar   Open

11–2.30, 6–11 (midnight supper licence); 11–2.30, 6.30–10.30 in winter; closed evenings 25 and 26 Dec

SANDY PARK SX7189 Map 1

Sandy Park Inn

Just off A382 N of Moretonhampstead

Mike Wootton the new licensee has actually worked here for seven years and intends to keep things very much as they are. The small black-beamed bar is an inviting place: built-in pale brown varnished wall seats with red fabric cushions, wings and rather high backs, stripped kitchen or mahogany tables, big black-iron fireplace, black beams in the ochre ceiling; the original doorway is blocked by the greyhound's huge wicker basket. Well kept Boddingtons, Brakspears, Flowers Original and Marstons Pedigree on handpump or tapped from the cask; cribbage, dominoes, and cards. Bar food includes soup (£1.65), pasties or pâté (£2.25), salads (£3.50), and lasagne or pies (under £4.25). Sturdy benches beside the honeysuckle outside the thatched white house look out to the pretty surrounding wooded hills. *(Recommended by Pearl and Steve Munns, Nick and Alison Dowson, PB, HB; more reports please)*

Free house   Licensee Mike Wootton   Real ale   Meals and snacks   Small restaurant Chagford (064 73) 3538   Children in own room   Open 11–11; 11–3, 5–11 in winter; closed evening 25 Dec   Bedrooms; £12.50/£25

SHEEPWASH SS4806 Map 1

Half Moon 🛏

Off A3072 Holsworthy–Crediton at Highampton

This buff-painted and civilised building takes up one whole side of the colourful village square – blue, pink, white, cream and olive thatched or slate-roofed cottages. The neatly-kept and friendly carpeted main bar has solid old furniture under the beams, lots of fishing pictures on the white walls, and a big log fire fronted by slate flagstones. Lunchtime bar food is attractively straightforward, including sandwiches (£1.50, toasted £1.75), soup or pastie (£1.75), ploughman's (£2.75) and salads (£3.50). Bass and Courage Best on handpump (well kept in a temperature-controlled cellar), a fine choice of spirits and a good wine list; darts, fruit machine and a separate pool room. Salmon or trout fishing can be arranged on nine miles of the Torridge for non-residents as well as residents. *(Recommended by Chris Newman, Deb Jay, Steve and Carolyn Harvey, W H Mecham, Peter Bisby, R J Walden; more up-to-date reports please)*

Free house   Licensees Benjamin Robert Inniss and Charles Inniss   Real ale   Snacks (lunchtime)˜ Evening restaurant (must book)   Black Torrington (040 923) 376 Children in eating area of bar   Open 11–2.30(3.30 Sat), 6–11   Bedrooms; £28B/£56B

SIDFORD SY1390 Map 1

Blue Ball ★ ⊘ 🛏

A3052 just N of Sidmouth

The low, partly-panelled lounge bar in this well kept and friendly 14th-century thatched village inn has upholstered wall benches and Windsor chairs under the heavy beams, a lovely winter log fire in the stone fireplace (there are two other open fires as well), and Boddingtons, Devenish Royal Wessex, Marstons Pedigree and Whitbreads PA on handpump, kept well in a temperature-controlled cellar. The food (particularly fresh local fish on crushed ice) is displayed enticingly at the back of the bar area; this might include good crusty white or wholemeal sandwiches (from £1.20, crab £2), a very generous ploughman's (from £2.60), omelettes (£3.50), salads (from £3.50), cheese and asparagus flan (£3.75), home-made steak and kidney pie (£4.25), and good steaks (from 8oz rump £7.50); puddings (£1.60), traditional roasts on Sunday and Thursday lunchtimes and evenings, and very good breakfasts (with free papers); efficient service. A plainer public bar has darts, dominoes, cribbage and a fruit machine; piped music. Tables on a terrace look out over a colourful walled front flower garden, with more on a bigger back lawn, where there are summer barbecues; also a safe swing, see saw and play house. *(Recommended by Denzil Taylor, Harry Stirling, Mr and Mrs G Turner, Paul and Janet Waring, Harry McCann, Robert and Gladys Flux, M G Creed, John Kirk, Mr and Mrs D V Morris, John Bowdler, Harry Stirling, Neil and Anita Christopher, Mr and Mrs D A P Grattan, E Mitchelmore, Gordon and Daphne, Brian and Anna Marsden, E A George)*

Devenish   Tenant Roger Newton   Real ale   Meals and snacks (11–3, 6.30–10)   Well behaved children in eating area and family room   Sidmouth (0395) 514062   Open 10.30–2.30, 5.30–11   Bedrooms; £20/£32

SLAPTON   SX8244   Map 1
Tower

Signposted off A379 Dartmouth–Kingsbridge

Up a narrow village lane, this ancient pub is overhung by the ivy-covered ruin of a 14th-century chantry. The low-ceilinged bar has small armchairs, low-backed settles and some furniture made from casks on the flagstones, two open log fires (lit whenever it gets chilly), evening candlelight, and a warm, happy atmosphere. The pool room has now been furnished with old pews and tables. On handpump, the ten real ales include Badger Tanglefoot, Gibbs Mew Bishops Tipple, Exmoor, Eldridge Pope Royal Oak, Palmers IPA, Wadworths 6X and two summer guests; good Italian wine by the glass. The Italian licensee's pasta dishes are popular – lasagne, broccoli pasta or spaghetti bolognese (£5.20) and seafood special (£8.25); there are also fresh granary baps, excellent pizzas (from £4.20), and fresh sole or steak (£10.50). Dominoes, fruit machine, video game and piped music. There are picnic-table sets on the quiet back lawn. *(Recommended by Chris Newman, Deb Jay, P and J Shapley, Les King, Roger Huggins, J E Stanton, Steve Huggins, G W Warren, R J Walden, R W Stanbury, Steve Dark, David and Ann Stranack)*

Free house   Licensees Keith and Kim Romp, Jan Khan, Carlo Cascianelli   Real ale Meals and snacks (12–2.30, 6.30–9.30)   Restaurant   Kingsbridge (0548) 580216 Children in own two areas   Open 11.30–2.30(3Sat), 6–11   Bedrooms; £15.50/£31

SOURTON   SX5390   Map 1
Highwayman   ★

A386 SW of Okehampton; a short detour from the A30

The meticulous workmanship, unrestrained imagination and sheer eccentricity of this pub's remarkable design will take your breath away. The porch (a pastiche of a nobleman's carriage) leads into a warren of dimly lit stonework and flagstone-floored burrows and alcoves, richly fitted out with red plush seats discreetly cut into the higgledy-piggledy walls, elaborately carved pews, a leather porter's chair, Jacobean-style wicker chairs, and seats in quaintly bulging small-paned bow windows; the ceiling in one part, where there's an array of stuffed animals, gives the impression of being underneath a tree, roots and all. The separate Rita Jones' Locker is a make-believe sailing galleon, full of intricate woodwork and splendid timber baulks, with red-check tables in the embrasures that might have held cannons. They don't do real ale, but specialise in farm cider, and food is confined to a range of pasties (£1); service is warmly welcoming and full of character; old-fashioned penny fruit machine. Outside, there's a play area in similar style for children with little black-and-white roundabouts like a Victorian fairground, a fairy-tale pumpkin house and an old-lady-who-lived-in-the-shoe house. You can take children in to look around the pub but they can't stay inside. *(Recommended by Gwynne Harper, A M J Chadwick, Mr and Mrs Crombleholme, Peter Woods, Mayur Shah)*

Free house   Licensees Buster and Rita Jones and Sally Thomson   Snacks (10–1.40,

*6–10)   Bridestowe (083 786) 243   Open 10–2, 6–10.30; closed 25 and 26 Dec
Bedrooms; £15/£30*

SOUTH POOL   SX7740   Map 1

Millbrook

Off A379 E of Kingsbridge

As this is one of the tiniest pubs in the book, be prepared for a bit of a squash at weekends, though there are more seats out in front on a sheltered flowery terrace. The little back bar has drawings and paintings (and a chart) on its cream walls, clay pipes on the beams, handsome Windsor chairs, a chintz easy chair, and fresh flowers. Bar food includes home-made soup such as celery and apple (£1.30), sandwiches (from £2, excellent crab £3.50), filled baked potatoes (from £2.50), ploughman's with mature cheddar or stilton (£2.50), cottage pie (£3.25), cauliflower with cheese and bacon, chicken curry or fish pie (all £3.50), crab salad (£5.25), and puddings such as apple cider cake or treacle tart (£1.65). Bass tapped from the cask, and farm ciders; darts and euchre in the newly renovated public bar. You can get here in the Kingsbridge/Salcombe ferry, and Southpool Creek is only a few moments' stroll away where the pub has mooring facilities for visiting yachts and small boats. *(Recommended by Dorothee and Dennis Glover, Philip and Trisha Ferries, Bruce and Zoe Fraser, D P Pascoe, Steve Huggins, R J Walden, Roy McIsaac, Margaret and Trevor Errington, John Knighton)*

Free house   Licensees Arthur and Cindy Spedding   Real ale   Meals and snacks (12–2, 6.15–9.30)   Kingsbridge (0548) 531581   Open 11–3, 5.30–11; 11–2.30, 6.30–11 in winter; may open longer in summer to cover high tide

SOUTH ZEAL   SX6593   Map 1

Oxenham Arms   ★   ⍁   ⊘

Village signposted from A30 at A382 roundabout and B3260 Okehampton turn-off

First licensed in 1477, this atmospheric inn has grown up around the remains of a Norman monastery, built here to combat the pagan power of the neolithic standing stone that still forms part of the wall in the family TV room behind the bar (there are actually twenty more feet of stone below the floor). It later became the Dower House of the Burgoynes, whose heiress carried it to the Oxenham family. The beamed and partly panelled front bar has a lovely relaxed atmosphere, Windsor armchairs around low oak tables and built-in wall seats, as well as elegant mullioned windows and Stuart fireplaces. Apart from the monolith, the small family room has beams, wheelback chairs around polished tables, decorative plates and another open fire. Consistently good bar food includes tasty soup (£1.25), sandwiches (from £1.45; the rare roast beef are particularly good), a generous ploughman's (£2.75), fish and chips (from £3.50), excellent home-made steak, kidney, mushroom and Guinness pie (£3.95), salads (from £3), grilled local trout (£4.75), and good daily specials such as lamb, onion and sultana pie or spicy chicken (£3.95) or salmon in puff pastry and cajun prawn creole (£4.25). Bass and St Austell Tinners tapped from the cask, 47 bin end wines, and coffee; darts, shove-ha'penny, dominoes and cribbage. There's further monastic evidence in the imposing curved stone steps leading up to the garden, and a sloping spread of lawn. The courtyard is now a car park for residents. *(Recommended by Kevin and Tracey Stephens, Tony and Lynne Stark, Jutta B Whitley, Chris Newman, Deb Jay, Peter Adcock, C A Foden, G Atkinson, June and Tony Baldwin, Janet and Paul Waring, Diane Duane-Smyth, Peter Sutton, Tom Espley, John and Christine Simpson, Joel Dobris, Patrick Stapley, Laurence Manning, S P Bobeldijk, Jonathan N C Jenson, Neil and Anita Christopher)*

Free house   Licensee James Henry   Real ale   Meals and snacks   Restaurant Okehampton (0837) 840244   Children welcome   Open 11–2.30, 6–11   Bedrooms; £32.50(£40B)/£40(£50B)

STAVERTON SX7964 Map 1

Sea Trout 🛏

Village signposted from A384 NW of Totnes

There are sea trout and salmon flies and stuffed fish on the walls of the neatly kept rambling beamed lounge bar here, with a stag's head above the fireplace, and cushioned settles and stools on its carpet; the main bar has low banquettes, soft lighting and an open fire. Well kept Bass, Fergusons Dartmoor, Ruddles Best and Wadworths 6X on handpump, as well as farm ciders, some malt whiskies, tea and coffee; friendly, attentive staff. There's also a public bar, popular with locals, with a pool table, darts, trivia and fruit machines and juke box. Good, popular bar food includes home-made soup (£1.35), sandwiches (from £1.65), burgers (meaty or nut, from £2.50), ploughman's (from £2.70), superb home-made pork sausages with herb or apple (£3.25), home-cooked ham (£3.95), home-made steak and kidney pie (£4.50), salads (from £4.75), local trout or gammon (£4.95), and steaks (from £6.95); daily specilas (from £3.95), children's dishes (from £2.50), puddings, and good Sunday lunch. In the pretty garden, they plan to install pagoda-style seating on crazy paving among stone-walled flower borders and build a new waterfall under a weeping willow. They can arrange fishing for you on the River Dart, and a station for the Torbay Steam Railway is not far away. *(Recommended by Steve and Carolyn Harvey, N H Harries, Patrick Freeman, Steve Huggins, J K Conneen, S P Bobeldijk, John Russell, Brenda Hall, S V Bishop, W C M Jones, Mrs Joan Harris, Mr and Mrs M A Stockman)*

Free house Licensees Andrew and Pym Mogford Real ale Meals and snacks (12–2, 7–10) Restaurant (closed Sun evening) Staverton (080 426) 274 Children over 6 in eating area of bar Jazz Tues evening Open 11–3, 6–11; closed evening 25 Dec, and 26 Dec Bedrooms; £36B/£47B

STOCKLAND ST2404 Map 1

Kings Arms ✿

Village signposted from A30 Honiton–Chard

Though there is a pubby back bar, it's the dark beamed, elegant dining lounge with its solid refectory tables, attractive landscapes, medieval oak screen (which divides the room into two), and great stone fireplace across almost the whole width of one end, that most people head for. A very wide choice of excellent bar food might include cauliflower soup (£1.50), tricolori salad or Portuguese sardines (£2.50), lovely Pacific prawns in garlic and white wine sauce (£4.50), chicken tikka masala or rack of lamb (£6.50), beef stroganoff (but using cream and pickled dill cucumber instead of soured cream) or seafood in filo pastry (£7.50), excellent darne of wild salmon in lobster and dill sauce, half a roast duck or fillets of sole with crabmeat (£9.50), and puddings such as apple and strawberry strudel or sherry trifle (from £2); booking is essential. At lunchtime there are simpler snacks too, including sandwiches (from £1), ploughman's (from £2), meaty or vegetarian pancakes or omelettes (£3.50), burgers (from £3.50), steak and kidney pie (£3.50), salads (from £4.50), and steaks (from £7.50); Sunday roast. Well kept Badger Best, Exmoor and Ushers on handpump, decent wines and brandies, a good choice of whiskies – particularly strong on island single malts, coffee and teas. At the back, a flagstoned bar has leatherette chairs and seats built into the stripped high dado of its bare stone walls; it leads on to a carpeted darts room with two boards, another room with dark beige plush armchairs and settees (and a fruit machine), and a neat ten-pin skittle alley (the pub fields six teams, Monday, Wednesday and Friday in winter; on Thursdays there's a keep-fit class); table skittles, cribbage, dominoes, video game, and pervasive piped classical music. There are tables under cocktail parasols on the terrace in front of the cream-faced thatched pub, with more by a weeping willow in the sheltered back garden. Well behaved dogs allowed.

(Recommended by JBM, S J Rice, M McCartney, Dr W M Owton, Gordon and Daphne, P Freeman, Mr and Mrs D V Morris, D Baddeley, G W Warren, Mayur Shah)

Free house   Licensees Heinz Kiefer and Paul Diviani   Real ale   Snacks (lunchtime) and meals   Restaurant   Stockland (040 488) 361   Varied live music Sun   Well behaved children welcome   Open 12–3, 6.30–11; closed 25 Dec   Bedrooms; £20B/£30B

STOKE GABRIEL   SX8457 Map 1

Church House   ★

Village signposted from A385 just W of junction with A3022, in Collaton St Mary; can also be reached from nearer Totnes; nearby parking not easy

There's an exceptionally attractive medieval beam and plank ceiling in the lounge bar of this early 14th-century, flower-covered pub, as well as a black oak partition wall, a huge fireplace still used in winter to cook the stew, window seats cut into the thick butter-coloured walls, decorative plates and vases of flowers on a dresser. The mummified cat in a case, probably about 200 years old, was found during restoration of the roof space in the verger's cottage three doors up the lane – one of a handful found in the West Country and believed to have been a talisman against evil spirits. Home-made bar food includes soup, sandwiches, filled baked potatoes (from £2.30, prawns £3), ploughman's (from £2.80), cottage pie, chicken curry and chilli con carne (£4.25), and maybe Dart salmon (£6.50). Darts, cribbage, and fruit machine in the little public locals' bar; piped music. The Bass on handpump is particularly well kept, unusually fed from a temperature-controlled cellar at a higher level or tapped from the cask. There are picnic-table sets on the little terrace in front of the building. Relations with the Church of England (which still owns it) go back a long way – witness the priest hole, dating from the Reformation, visible from outside. They also run another pub, the Whitchurch Inn, Whitchurch near Tavistock. (*Recommended by Les King, Neil Tungate, Mrs A Turner, R H Martyn, John Knighton, B A Cox*)

Bass   Tenants Geoff and Paul Bradford   Real ale   Meals and snacks; cream teas in summer   Stoke Gabriel (080 428) 384   Open 11–11; winter 11–3, 6–11 but open all day Sat

TIPTON ST JOHN   SY0991 Map 1

Golden Lion   🍺

Pub signposted off B3176 Sidmouth–Ottery St Mary

Originally a straightforward railway inn, this bustling village local has a softly-lit bar with a comfortable old settee, red leatherette built-in wall banquettes, an attractive Gothick carved box settle, a carved dresser, and a longcase clock; also, lots of guns, little kegs, a brass cauldron and other brassware, bottles and jars along a delft shelf, and plenty of fresh flowers. A wide choice of reasonably priced home-cooked bar food here includes home-made soup (£1.20; good crab bisque £1.40), sandwiches (from £2.10), ploughman's (from £2.75), quiche, lasagne or chilli con carne (£3.75) and salads (from £4.95; seafood £7.25), with grills such as gammon (£6.60) and steaks (from £7.50); home-made puddings (from £2), daily specials like sweetbreads with bacon (£2.80), a roast, vegetarian dishes (£3.75), rabbit in mustard pie or pigeon breasts in stout (£4.95), and chicken tikka; Sunday roast; friendly service. Well kept Bass, Flowers IPA and Whitbreads Best on handpump, Inch's cider, a good choice of wines, and coffee; darts, dominoes, open fire. There are pretty summer hanging baskets, a few picnic-table sets on the side lawn, a pretty walled area, and a terrace with summer barbecues and food-theme evenings. The restaurant is no smoking. (*Recommended by Gary Marchant, Richard Dolphin, Dr D M Forsyth, Mrs M R Sale, Robert and Gladys Flux, Gordon and Daphne*)

Heavitree (who no longer brew)   Tenants Colin and Carolyn Radford   Real ale   Meals and snacks   Small no smoking restaurant, best to book   Ottery St Mary (0404) 812881   Children in room attached to bar   Open 11–3, 6–11   Two bedrooms; £19.91S/£37.48S

TOPSHAM SX9688 Map 1

Bridge ★

2 1/4 miles from M5 junction 30: Topsham signposted from exit roundabout; in Topsham follow signpost (A376) Exmouth on the Elmgrove Road

The utterly old-fashioned layout and character of this 16th-century ex-maltings remains happily unchanged over the years. And Mrs Cheffers continues to keep a wonderful choice of real ales – tapped from the cask in the cosy inner sanctum where only the most regular of regulars sit – that might include Adnams Broadside, Badger Tanglefoot, Bass, Eldridge Pope Royal Oak, Exmoor Bitter and Gold, Fullers ESB, Gibbs Mew Bishops Tipple, Marstons Pedigree and Owd Rodger, Theakstons Old Peculier, Wadworths 6X and Wiltshire Old Devil. The cosy little parlour, partitioned off from an inner corridor with leaded lights let into the curved high back of one settle, is decorated with a booming grandfather clock, crossed guns, swords, country pictures and rowing cartoons, and mugs hanging from the beams; a bigger room is opened at busy times. Food is confined to pasties (85p), sandwiches (£1.10) and ploughman's (£2.50). *(Recommended by Vanessa and Peter Hurst, Chris Newman, Deb Jay, David Evans, RJC, Mr and Mrs C H Garnett, Gordon and Daphne, Dr M I Crichton)*

Free house   Licensee Mrs Phyllis Cheffers   Real ale   Snacks   Children welcome Open 12–2, 6–10.30 (11 Fri and Sat)

Globe 🛏

2 miles from M5 junction 30: Topsham signposted from exit roundabout; in Topsham, keep straight on into Fore St where the inn has a small car park

In the narrow main street of this pretty little waterside town stands this relaxed and civilised 16th-century coaching inn. The heavy-beamed bar is comfortably furnished with red leatherette seats around the big bow window, a big panel-back settle, heavy wooden armchairs, and good sporting prints on the dark oak panelling, with an open fire under the attractive wooden mantelpiece. Good value bar food includes home-made soup (£1.25), smokies (£1.50), ploughman's (£2.25), bacon, egg and kidneys (£2.75), and home-made pies such as rabbit or steak and kidney (£3); beside the main restaurant there's a snug little eating room with its own fire; friendly service. Well kept Bass, Ushers Best and Worthington Best on handpump. There are seats out in a small sheltered and partly covered courtyard. *(Recommended by Vanessa and Peter Hurst, Joan Harris, P Argent, Gordon and Daphne, L and J, Graham and Glenis Watkins; more reports please)*

Free house   Licensee Denys Price   Real ale   Meals and snacks   Restaurant; closed Sun   Topsham (0392) 873471   Children in eating area of bar   Open 11–11 Bedrooms; £30B/£40B

TORCROSS SX8241 Map 1

Start Bay ⊘

A379 S of Dartmouth

People sometimes queue outside this popular, thatched, 14th-century pub before it opens to make sure they get an early choice of the large selection of very fresh and generously served seafood (the landlord and manager go fishing and diving as often as possible): cod and haddock come in three sizes – medium (£3.30 or £3.40), large (£4.40 or £4.50) and jumbo (£5.30 or £5.40 – truly enormous); plaice is served in medium (£3.40) and large (£4.50) varieties; there's also skate (£4.50) and a much praised seafood platter, with crab, prawns, cockles, mussels and smoked mackerel (£7.25). Other food includes sandwiches (from £1.40), soup (£1.50), ploughman's (£2.75), gammon (£4.95) and steaks (from £7.20), with puddings (from £1.30), specials like spinach and mushroom lasagne (£3.40), local scallops (when available and often straight out of the sea), and whole lemon sole or monkfish tails (£6.95); they warn of delays at peak times, though service is organised and efficient. Well kept Flowers IPA and Marstons Pedigree on handpump, Addlestones cider, Merrydown country wines, coffee and tea. The unassuming – and often busy – main bar has wheelback chairs around plenty of dark tables or (round a corner) back-to-back settles forming booths, photographs of storms buffeting the pub and country pictures on its cream walls, and a winter coal fire; a small chatty drinking area by the counter has a brass ship's clock and barometer; one area is no smoking as is part of the family room. The good winter games room has pool, darts, shove-ha'penny, dominoes, video game, and juke box; there's more booth seating in a family room with sailing boat pictures. Fruit machine in the lobby. On the terrace are some picnic-table sets looking out over the three-mile pebble beach. The freshwater wildlife lagoon of Slapton Ley is just behind the pub. *(Recommended by Patrick Freeman, P and J Shapley, D I Baddeley, Paul and Janet Waring, W C M Jones, Richard and Ann Jenkins, David and Ann Stranack, Joan and Michael Melling, Chris Short and friends, D I Baddeley)*

Heavitree (who no longer brew; Whitbreads tie)   Tenant Paul Stubbs   Real ale Meals and snacks (11.30–2, 6–10)   Children over 14 in eating room   Open 11.30–2.30, 6–11; closed evening 25 Dec

TORRINGTON   SS4919 Map 1

Black Horse 🛏

High St

Though this ancient and pretty twin-gabled inn is reputed to have collected at least one ghost, the licensees – a notably friendly couple – haven't seen anything, though they're convinced their dogs have. The bar on the left has a couple of fat black beams hung with stirrups, an oak counter, a comfortable seat running right along its full-width window, and chunky elm tables; on the right, a lounge has a striking ancient black oak partition wall, a couple of attractive oak seats, muted plush easy chairs and a settee. The restaurant is oak-panelled. Generously served bar food (the licensees' son is the chef) includes sandwiches (from 85p), soup (£1.10), filled baked potatoes (from £1.30), ploughman's (the stilton is excellent) or salads (from £2.10), good chicken, ham and mushroom pie (£2.75), vegetable lasagne (£3), chilli con carne or home-made steak and kidney pie (£3.10), steaks (from £5.95), good value daily specials, children's dishes (from £1.45), promptly served Sunday roast lunch, and good breakfasts; the vegetables are fresh and cooked just right; well kept Ruddles County and Ushers Best on handpump; darts, shove-ha'penny, cribbage, dominoes, fruit machine, trivia; well reproduced piped music, friendly cat. A black horse in a cut-out silhouette prances along the inn-sign's gantry. Handy for the RHS Rosemoor garden and Dartington Crystal. *(Recommended by John and Joan Nash, David Watson, TBB, Steve and Carolyn Harvey, B A Ferris, K R Harris, R W A Suddaby)*

Ushers   Lease: David and Val Sawyer   Real ale   Meals and snacks (not Sun evening) Restaurant   Torrington (0805) 22121   Children in lounge and restaurant (no young children in restaurant, evening)   Open 11–3, 6(6.30 Sat)–11   Bedrooms; £14B/£24B

TOTNES   SX8060 Map 1

Kingsbridge Inn

Leechwell St; going up the old town's main one-way street, bear left into Leechwell St approaching the top

Parts of this busy place – the oldest in Totnes – date back to the ninth century. The rambling bar has low heavy beams, broad stripped plank panelling, bare stone or black and white timbering, and comfortable peach plush seats and wheelbacks around rustic tables on the clover and peach carpet. There's an elaborately carved bench in one intimate little alcove, an antique water pump and a log-effect gas fire; part of the pub is no smoking. Lunchtime bar food includes soup such as spinach and orange (£1.30), sandwiches or filled French bread (from £1.50), platters (from £2.75), herring fillets with mustard sauce (£2.80), tuna, mozzarella and black olive pizza (£2.95), spicy pasta and vegetable bake or lamb curry with poppadum and cucumber raita (£4.25), Italian fennel casserole (£4.50), casserole of local wild pigeon breasts (£4.95), and steak and kidney pie (£5.25), with moussaka (£4.60), poached salmon steak with cucumber sauce (£6.50), and steaks (from £7.70) in the evening; home-made puddings such as strawberry and rhubarb tart or summer pudding (£2.30). Bass, Courage Best and Directors and Fergusons Dartmoor Best on handpump, local farm cider, several wines, teas and cappuccino or espresso coffee; pleasant service. Nearby ancient Leechwells is worth the walk down and back up a steep hill (reputed to have healing properties). Dogs allowed (on a lead). *(Recommended by P and J Shapley, Steve and Carolyn Harvey, David Wallington, June and Tony Baldwin, P Argent, Mrs Joan Harris, H K Dyson, Carol Mason, Joseph J Lewy, Ian Blackwell)*

Free house   Licensees Paul and Rosemary Triggs, Martyn and Jane Canevali   Real ale   Meals and snacks (11–2, 6–10; not 25 Dec)   Children in eating area of bar Local groups Weds evening   Open 11–2.30, 5.30–11; closed evening 25 Dec

TRUSHAM   SX8582 Map 1

Cridford Inn

Village and pub signposted from B3193 NW of Chudleigh, just N of big ARC works; 1 1/2 very narrow miles

You'll find a warm welcome and a lovely relaxed atmosphere in this 14th-century oak-beamed longhouse (which, oddly, has a corrugated iron roof). There are cushioned window-seats, pews and chapel chairs around kitchen and pub tables, stout standing timbers, old hunting prints, a couple of guns and display cases of cartridges on white-painted uncoursed stone walls, rugs on flagstones, some stained glass in the windows, and a big woodburning stove in the stone fireplace. Good, reasonably priced bar food includes sandwiches (from £1.10), home-made soup (£1.50), filled baked potatoes (from £2), smoked mackerel pâté or smoked venison (from £1.50), macaroni cheese, liver and bacon casserole or speciality sausages (£3.50), and dishes from the restaurant menu such as trout or casseroles (from £4), and steaks (from £8); well kept Exmoor on handpump, with Bass, Cotleigh Old Buzzard and an interesting weekly guest beer tapped from the cask, local award winning cider, country wines. Darts, dominoes, cribbage, fruit machine, trivia and juke box in the end family room. The suntrap terrace in front of the pub has sturdy rustic benches and tables under cocktail parasols, and a small play area. The little hamlet is largely modern. *(Recommended by Dr John Innes, Brian Jones, John Russell, Brenda Hall, Phil and Sally Gorton, Gordon and Daphne, Mayur Shah)*

Free house   Licensees Tony and Mike Shepherd   Real ale   Meals and snacks Restaurant   Chudleigh (0626) 853694   Children welcome (till 8 evening)   Open 11–3, 6(7 winter)–11   Bedrooms; £20B/£35B

TUCKENHAY   SX8156 Map 1

Maltsters Arms ⊗

From A381 S of Totnes take Ashprington road in Harbertonford, then after 3 miles turn right over river to pass Watermans Arms; or take Ashprington road out of Totnes, keeping on past Watermans Arms

To make the most of the superb cooking you would really have to eat in the light and airy (if rather pricey) restaurant with its picture windows looking over the wooded creek below. But bar snacks have been excellent too, and everything including the bread, mayonnaise and pastries is home-made: watercress soup (£2.50), lovely fresh salmon or rare roast beef sandwiches (£3.50), very good cheese platter (£3.75), exceptionally good sausages (£4), grilled kipper or three Mediterranean prawns with mayonnaise (£5.50), huge prawn cocktail (£5.95), cold poached salmon (£7.75), sirloin steak (£9.75), and puddings like treacle tart or pears poached in red wine and served with a raspberry coulis (from £3.50). Bass, Blackawton, Exmoor and Ind Coope Burton on handpump, decent wines, a wide selection of malts, an interesting brandy list, freshly squeezed orange juice, and coffee; friendly service. At one end is a snug little room with a couple of fat leather armchairs (which the young ginger cat favours), a sofa, other chairs and small tables, Victorian fish prints, some stuffed fish in glass cabinets, a cabinet of vintage fishing books, and a fire. This is linked by the long, narrow bar with its stools, fishing rods on the ceiling, and jars of cockles, pickled eggs, mint imperials and jelly babies on the counter, to the room at the other end (on the left of the door as you go in). This has red-painted vertical panelled seats and stripped kitchen tables on the wooden floor, lots of small fish prints three-to-a-frame, and a model sailing ship over the log fire; dominoes, cribbage, bagatelle, lots of board games, including Trivial Pursuit, and a juke box with an interesting repertoire. There are creekside tables and popular summer barbecues (the fresh sardines are popular). No bedrooms, but there's a smart B & B next door in a converted wine warehouse. You can reach the pub by boat. (Recommended by Mrs J Cookson, A Lord, S V Bishop, John Watson, Mr and Mrs W H Crowther, Alan Merricks, Paul and Janet Waring, J and K Craddock, John A Barker, Barbara Wensworth, Catherine and Andrew Brian, Mr and Mrs T A Towers, W C M Jones, David and Ann Stranack, Dennis Heatley, David Wallington)

Free house   Licensees Keith Floyd/John Pitchford   Real ale   Meals and snacks (12–2.30, 7–10)   Restaurant   Harbertonford (0803) 732350   Children in eating area of bar   Open 11–3, 6–11

UGBOROUGH   SX6755   Map 1

Anchor

On B3210; village signposted from Ivybridge (just off A38 E of Plymouth)

Under the present regime bar food here definitely takes second place to the restaurant, which there's considerable emphasis on. But the oak-beamed public bar is still a pleasant place, with wall settles and seats around the wooden tables on the polished woodblock floor, and a log fire in its stone fireplace; there are Windsor armchairs in the comfortable carpeted lounge. Bar food includes home-made soup (£1.55), sandwiches or basket meals (from £2.05), home-made pizzas (from £3), lasagne (£4), hot-rock grills (from £8.45), daily specials like wild rabbit or game casserole (from £2), and home-made puddings such as treacle tart (from £1.60). Well kept Bass, Ruddles, Tetleys and Wadworths 6X tapped from the cask, with guests beers, quite a few malt whiskies, and half a dozen or more ports. Darts, cribbage, dominoes, fruit machine and piped music. This is an attractive village, unusual for its spacious central square. (Recommended by Reginald Richer, T Nott, Mr and Mrs Finch, David and Flo Wallington, John Evans, C T and J M Laffan, M J Clifford, Mayur Shah, R J Walden, Peter Woods; more reports please)

Free house   Licensees Sheelagh and Ken Jeffreys-Simmons   Real ale   Meals and snacks (not 25 Dec)   Restaurant   Plymouth (0752) 892283   Children in eating area and in restaurant   Jazz alternate Mons, guitarist Sat monthly   Open 11.30–3, 5–11   Bedrooms; £30B/£40B

WELCOMBE   SS2218   Map 1

Old Smithy

Village signposted from A39 S of Harland; pub signposted left at fork

There are plenty of seats in the pretty, terraced, sheltered garden of this friendly, thatched pub, and the lane going past leads eventually to parking down by Welcombe Mouth – an attractive rocky cove. Inside, the carpeted open-plan bar has log fires at both ends of the room, button-back banquettes and wheelback chairs and little snug windows; the old forge is now the restaurant; piped music. Quickly served and reasonably priced bar food might include sandwiches (from £1), soup (£1.30), ploughman's (from £2), lasagne (£3.75), steaks (from £6.25), and puddings (£1.75). Well kept Butcombe and Marstons Pedigree on handpump, and three draught ciders; charming, helpful service. Darts, dominoes, fruit machine, pool and video game. (Recommended by Mr and Mrs J H Adam, Joanna Stevens, Stephen Goodchild, Roy Bromell)

Free house   Licensee Mr Marshall   Real ale   Meals and snacks (12–3, 6.30–10)

Restaurant   Morwenstow (028 883) 305   Children welcome   Fornightly live music
Open 11–11; 11–2.30, 7–11 in winter; closed 25 Dec   Bedrooms;
£15(£16B)/£30(£32B)

WINKLEIGH   SS6308 Map 1

Kings Arms

Off B3220, in village centre

There are a couple of large fish tanks (with some real rarities) and a parrot in the
attractive beamed main bar here, as well as some old-fashioned built-in wall settles,
scrubbed pine tables and benches on the flagstones, dim lighting, and a log fire in a
cavernous fireplace; a two-way fireplace with a wood-burning stove separates the
bar from the no smoking restaurant (where they've found the original well). Good,
home-made bar food includes vegetable soup, game pâté (£2.75), cheese and nut
roast or lasagne (£3.50), cod and leek cobbler (£3.95), venison pie (£4.95),
poached salmon in vermouth (£5.50), and puddings like sticky toffee pudding and
old English lemon possett (£2.25). Ruddles Best and Ushers Best on handpump
from a temperature-controlled cold room; friendly service; dominoes, well
reproduced piped pop music. There are a couple of white tables by a small pool in
the little side courtyard, sheltered by large shrubs. The pub is on the edge of the
village square. (Recommended by Gerald Cleaver, Alan and Heather Jacques, Jonathan N C
Jensen, Karen Spooner, Michael and Joan Melling, John D Blaylock)

Free house   Licensee Nigel Rickard   Real ale   Meals and snacks; light snacks only Sun
evening; not Mon   No smoking restaurant; not Sun evening   Winkleigh (0837)
83384   Children over 6 welcome   Open 11–3, 6–11; closed Mon   Self-contained
cottage for weekly let

WOODBURY SALTERTON   SY0189 Map 1

Diggers Rest   ★

3 1/2 miles from M5 junction 30: A3052 towards Sidmouth, village signposted on right
about 1/2 mile after Clyst St Mary; also signposted from B3179 SE of Exeter

Perhaps at its best out of season when things tend to be less crowded, this friendly,
newly thatched Tudor pub has comfortable old-fashioned country chairs and
settles around polished antique tables, a dark oak Jacobean screen, a grandfather
clock, heavy black oak beams, and plates decorating the walls of one alcove;
there's a log fire at one end and an ornate solid fuel stove at the other. The big
skittles alley is popular with families and is open for them in July and August, and
there's a games room with pool, alley skittles, and video game. Well kept Bass,
Fergusons Dartmoor and Flowers IPA on ancient handpumps, and local farm
cider; sensibly placed darts in the small brick-walled public bar. Decent bar food
includes home-made soup, sandwiches (from £1.85, local crab £2.15),
ploughman's (from £2.95), prawns in garlic (£3.25), home-made curry, turkey pie
or cold gammon (all £3.95), daily specials such as cashew nut paella or steak and
kidney pie (from £2.95) and puddings (£1.75). The terrace garden has views of the
countryside. (Recommended by Graham and Glenis Watkins, Peter F Newman, John D
Blaylock, Michael and Alison Sandy, Brian and Anna Marsden)

Free house   Licensee Sally Pratt   Real ale   Meals and snacks (12–1.45, 7–10; not 25
Dec)   Woodbury (0395) 32375   Children in family room   Open 11–2.30, 6.30–11;
closed evening 25 Dec

Lucky Dip

Besides the fully inspected pubs, you might like to try these Lucky Dips recommended to
us and described by readers (if you do, please send us reports):

Abbotskerswell [SX8569], *Court Farm*:
Beams and flagstones, front garden, well
kept Flowers IPA, Eldridge Pope Thomas
Hardy, food very good if not cheap *(Steve
Huggins)*
Alswear [A373 South Molton—Tiverton;

SS7222], *Butchers Arms*: Well kept friendly local, bright lounge, generous food, children allowed in basic pool room, guest ales such as Butcombe; bedrooms *(Steve and Carolyn Harvey)*

Ashburton [West St; SX7569], *Exeter*: Simple pub with 12th-century origins, friendly staff, good cheap food, Euddles ale *(Bernard Phillips, David Walker)*; [centre], *Royal Oak*: Pleasantly unpretentious real pub, with Bass, Palmers, Tetleys and Websters Yorkshire, food inc well filled French bread (eg lovely local ham), good value ploughman's and fish and chips *(Joan Harris)*

Avonwick [B3210 1/2 mile from A38; SX7157], *Mill*: Friendly service, big helpings of bar food, increasing emphasis on restaurant side (busy carvery, famous Sun roasts), Bass on handpump, attractive surroundings, children's area, big car park *(John Evans)*

Axmouth [SY2591], *Ship*: Devenish real ales, rather good food with seafood emphasis, polite service, lots of embroidered folk dolls, attractive garden with convalescent owls, cuddly samoyeds *(Brian and Anna Marsden, LYM)*

Aylesbeare [A3052 Exeter—Sidmouth, junction with B3180; SY0392], *Halfway*: Old free house with high views over Dartmoor; exceptionally wide food choice inc some unusual puddings, reasonable choice of beers and wines *(E V M Whiteway)*

Barnstaple [Boatport St; SS5533], *Corner House*: Lots of panelling, Toby jugs, plates on delft shelf, character customers; well kept Bass and guest beers such as Exmoor, bar food, remarkable swing doors in gents'; handy for Queens Hall theatre *(Gerald Cleaver)*

Beer [Fore St; ST2389], *Anchor*: Friendly, clean pub with lots of atmosphere, good choice of well kept ales and of locally caught fish, well presented; bedrooms *(S J Rice)*

Beesands [SX8140], *Cricket*: Notably friendly landlord in plain beachside local with Marstons Pedigree and Whitbreads Best on handpump and children's room; people tend to take their drinks over to the rocks and look at the tide and the Start Point lighthouse *(Roger Huggins)*

Belstone [SX6293], *Tors*: Dartmoor-edge country local with good reasonably priced food, well kept beer *(Mr and Mrs W H Crowther)*

Bickington [A383 Ashburton—Newton Abbot; SX7972], *Dartmoor Half Way*: Much extended but warm and friendly, with huge helpings of good value food with many vegetables, well kept Bass; open all day *(Mary Springer, Steve Huggins)*

Bickleigh [A396, N of junction with A3072; SS9407], *Trout*: Comfortable and spacious dining pub which has had good atmosphere, efficient service, well kept Bass and Courage Directors, restaurant, tables on pretty lawn, provision for children; no reports since up for sale last year; good-sized well equipped bedrooms *(LYM; news please)*

☆ **Bigbury** [St Anns Chapel; B3392 N; SX6647], *Pickwick*: Rustic-style main bar with well kept Bass, Flowers and maybe Palmers, local Stancombe cider tapped from the cask, good choice of bar food inc good fresh prawn sandwiches, very friendly bar staff, piped music; pool and other games in spacious newer and plainer family extension — children treated very well; restaurant; bedrooms *(John Drummond, LYM)*

☆ **Blackawton** [OS Sheet 202, map reference 807509; SX8050], *Normandy Arms*: Quaint 15th-century pub in remote, pretty village, welcoming licensees; interesting bars hark strongly back to World War II (when this village was used as secret rehearsal ground for Normandy landings); log fire, well kept Blackawton Bitter and Forty-Four, wide choice of decent bar food inc good steaks, restaurant; children away from main bar, well behaved dogs welcome; lots of tractors; good value bedrooms, clean and comfortable *(Henry and Caroline Gibson, W Bailey, Roger Sims)*

☆ **Blackmoor Gate** [SS6443], *Old Station House*: Big purpose-built dining pub based on former station house, in same local chain as Pyne Arms, East Down (see main entries), with similar food, Marstons Pedigree; expanse of Turkey carpet with churchy pews and plush dining chairs, soft red lighting, lovely view, more character in nice no smoking area with grandfather clock, big games area with two well lit pool tables, darts and juke box, pleasant service, picnic-table sets on terrace; skittle alley; children under five only in small family room *(Steve and Carolyn Harvey, Mike Hallewell, J A Scott, BB)*

☆ **Blagdon** [Higher Blagdon; pub (and Aircraft Museum) signed off A385 leaving Paignton; SX8561], *Barton Pines*: Spaciously converted mock-Elizabethan 19th-century mansion, with extensive provision for families (caravans in grounds), wide range of decent food from sandwiches to mixed grills, well kept Fergusons Dartmoor, grand gardens giving views out to sea and over to Dartmoor *(LYM)*

Bolham [A396, a mile N of A361 nr Tiverton; SS9515], *Hartnoll Country House*: Roadside Georgian hotel with lounge, south-facing conservatory, decent real ale, straightforward bar food; tables on big lawn with swift river at bottom; nr Knightshayes Ct (NT) *(GB)*

Bovey Tracey [towards Haytor Vale; SX8278], *Edgemoor*: Attractive white-painted hotel on hill up to moors, with hard-working new management and staff; good value food (booking advisable); nice local prints; bedrooms *(Romey Heaton)*

Bow [A3072 W of Crediton — OS Sheet 191, map reference 724018; SS7201], *White Hart*: Beamed bar with settles and huge inglenook; small dining room, tap room with pool and games, skittle alley, neat garden; well kept Bass and Flowers on handpump, reasonably priced food *(Alan and Heather Jacques)*

☆ **Bradworthy** [SS3214], *Pigs Ear*: Good fun, with pig decorations all over walls and ceiling — even two house-trained Vietnamese pot-bellied pigs running around bar; real fire in inglenook, interesting bellows and knife sharpener, cuddly cat, well kept Flowers Original, St Austell HSD, Whitbreads Best, Stonehouse's cider, delicious parsnip wine, very good value food from sandwiches and baked potatoes up; nr Tamar Lakes; bedrooms attractive, welcoming staff *(Mrs R Horridge)*

☆ **Brampford Speke** [off A377 N of Exeter; SX9299], *Agricultural*: Refurbished village local in same stable as Salterton Arms, Budleigh Salterton, with gallery where children allowed, picnic-table sets on sheltered terrace, good value food inc some interesting dishes, upstairs restaurant, well kept Courage, friendly prompt service *(Brian Jones, Gary Marchant)*

☆ **Branscombe** [upper village; signed off A3052 Sidmouth—Seaton; SY1988], *Fountain Head*: Interesting 14th-century pub beautifully placed in lovely sheltered combe village, lots of stone, flagstones, beams, panelling, log fires, good value bar food (not Weds evening, nor winter evenings unless booked; Sun lunchtime stops 1.30), well kept Badger Best and Tanglefoot and Devenish, friendly dog and quick staff, small children's room, outside lavatories; good value self-catering flat and cottage *(Dewi Jones, Barry & Anne, Patrick Freeman, Jamie and Sarah Allan, Gordon and Daphne, LYM)*
Branscombe [lower village], *Masons Arms*: Rambling low-beamed bar in very busy 14th-century inn just up from the sea, not far from interesting donkey sanctuary, and attractive in summer for its pretty tables outside and in winter for its roaring log fire, sometimes used for spit-roasts; well kept Bass, Badger Best and Tanglefoot, bar food, restaurant (evenings/Sun lunch); bedrooms comfortable and attractive, though not cheap; children not welcome inside *(Laurence Manning, S J Rice, D M Forsyth, Mr and Mrs W E Potter, Jamie and Sarah Allan, Jacquie and Jon Payne, N H Harries, LYM)*
Braunton [SS4836], *Williams Arms*: Very popular recently extended pub, bar food and good carvery *(P R Morley)*
Bridestowe [SX5189], *White Hart*: Delightful inn, consistently good food and service *(Dr and Mrs T H Harrison)*
Bridford [SX8186], *Bridford*: Pleasant welcome and friendly service in long, spacious bar with tropical fish, chess, a couple of armchairs, well kept real ales, inexpensive food; good tables outside *(Dr and Mrs Ralph Wright)*

☆ **Broadclyst** [Whimple Rd; SX9897], *New Inn*: Unusual and varied good bar food with fresh ingredients and home-made bread in isolated converted farmhouse with stripped brickwork, boarded ceiling, low doorways, unpretentious furnishings inc comfortable chairs around roaring log fire, country and horsey bygones; friendly service, well kept real ales, decent wines, palatial skittle alley *(J R Carey, Mrs Joan Harris, Mr and Mrs D V Morris)*
Broadclyst [B3121, by church], *Red Lion*: Well appointed pub on village green, stripped bricks and beams, open fire, helpful staff, well kept Bass and Tetleys, generous decent food; seats outside *(K R Harris)*
Buckland Monachorum [SX4868], *Drakes Manor*: Friendly beamed and oak-panelled village pub full of copper and china, with orange banquettes, well kept Courage, cheap generous home-cooked food, fruit machines; in Dartmoor-edge village with notable garden — the Garden House *(Dr Keith Louden)*

☆ **Budleigh Salterton** [Chapel St; SY0682], *Salterton Arms*: Friendly service and wide range of reasonably priced good food bring crowds in summer — salads particularly crab, vegetarian dishes, lasagne, fish, fresh vegetables and puddings and ice creams all praised, lunchtime snacks too, evening concentration on meals in comfortable upper gallery; main L-shaped bar with plush wall seats, lots of train and other prints, nautical mementoes, small open fires, neat uniformed staff, well kept Bass, Charrington IPA and John Smiths; children allowed upstairs *(Simon Collett-Jones, Mrs Joan Harris, Brian Jones, Denzil Taylor, Peter F Newman, Michael and Alison Sandy, BB)*
California Cross [SX7052], *California*: Newish combination of riding stables with big rambling three-bar pub, amazing display of bottles and butterflies; separate games room with skittles and farm tools; Blackawton and Fergusons Dartmoor, straightforward upstairs restaurant; opp caravan and camping site *(David Wallington)*

☆ **Calverleigh** [B3221 Tiverton—Rackenford; SS9214], *Rose & Crown*: Clean, quiet and welcoming, with well kept beers, decent choice of good value generous food, lots of fresh flowers, cheerful licensees; skittle alley *(Audrey and Roger Adcock, Jack and Dorothy Rayner)*
Chagford [Mill St; SX7087], *Bullers Arms*: Low-key unpretentious local, comfortable and very clean, with good value home cooking inc plenty of vegetarian dishes, well kept changing real ales, coal-effect gas fire, helpful landlord, summer barbecues *(Robert Humphreys, John Wilson)*; *Ring o' Bells*: Busy but spacious and comfortable old black-and-white local, log-effect gas fire with adjacent pin-table, friendly licensee and nice tabby, well kept Wadworths 6X and farm cider, good home-made bar food, restaurant *(John Wilson)*

☆ **Challacombe** [B3358 Blackmoor Gate—Simonsbath — OS Sheet 180, map reference 695411; SS6941], *Black Venus*: Part of the same local chain as the Pyne Arms, East Down, but not the feel of a "chain" pub, and though the basic menu is the same local readers say the food, especially fish, can be particularly good (the owner may cook here); low-key atmosphere in snug rooms with low beams, pews, decent chairs, stuffed birds, woodburning stove and big open fire, separate games room; children allowed in eating area (not under 5), dogs maybe by arrangement; bedrooms *(Irene and Peter Cranston, Steve and Carolyn Harvey, Simon Reed, David Eversley, Suzanne Gilpin, E Evans, D S and T M Beeson, BB)*

☆ **Chillington** [SX7942], *Chillington Inn*: 17th-century village inn with very good food in old-world atmosphere; small restaurant, evening booking essential — Dart salmon, lobsters; comfortable bedrooms, weekend breaks *(David and Ann Stranack, Mr and Mrs T A Towers)*

☆ **Chittlehamholt** [off A377 Barnstaple—Crediton, and B3226 SW of South Molton; SS6521], *Exeter Inn*: Freshly decorated beamed bar in 16th-century thatched inn, a couple of cask armchairs by the fire as well as mates' chairs and so forth, matchbox and foreign banknote collections, well kept Ushers Best and Websters Yorkshire on handpump, Hancock's farm cider, bar food from sandwiches and ploughman's through local trout, piped music; children allowed in eating area, some tables outside; restaurant, comfortable bedrooms *(Steve Dark, Ann Marie Stephenson, Steve and Carolyn Harvey, LYM)*

☆ **Christow** [Village Rd; SX8385], *Artichoke*: Pleasant little thatched local built lengthways down hillside, so open-plan bar has different levels; popular straightforward bar food, cheerful service; attractive village, nr Canonteign Waterfalls and Country Park; three comfortable good value bedrooms *(Gordon and Daphne, Jim and Maggie Cowell)*

Chudleigh [SX8679], *Coaching House*: Recently refurbished 17th-century coaching inn with spacious lounge bar, food counter serving good food from soup and sandwiches to coq au vin and steaks, inc children's dishes, well kept Allied real ales on handpump, friendly efficient staff, piped music, live music some evenings; bedrooms *(Neil and Anita Christopher)*

Chudleigh Knighton [SX8477], *Clay Cutters Arms*: Genial thatched village local with generous simple good value food inc local rabbit pie, big winter log fires, Flowers IPA and Eldridge Pope Royal Oak, popular games area, seats on side terrace and in orchard; bedrooms *(John Kirk, LYM)*

☆ **Clearbrook** [off A386 Tavistock—Plymouth; SX5265], *Skylark*: Good Dartmoor views from popular and spacious pub with generous good value bar food, well kept beer, children's room off car park; can get crowded in season *(Charles Gurney, DHT, Ted George)*

Cockington [SX8963], *Drum*: Friendly new regime in spacious beamed pub with settles and other seats, Fergusons real ale, usual bar food, piped music, juke box; skittle alley, front terrace and superb gardens *(Steve Huggins)*

Cockwood [SX9780], *Ship*: Very well run, with reasonably priced good beer and good food with fish as the speciality *(John McGee)*

Colaton Raleigh [A376; SY0787], *Otter*: Clean and attractive little pub, lots of flower tubs and baskets around big garden, fast efficient family meals, Watneys-related real ales, children's playground and separate children's bar, capacious car parks *(Mrs M R Sale)*

Combe Martin [SS5847], *Dolphin*: Pleasant location with wide range of beers inc Exmoor, also local Scrumpy; usual bar food served generously till quite late *(Richard and Ann Jenkins)*

Countisbury [A39, E of Lynton — OS Sheet 180, map reference 747497; SS7449], *Exmoor Sandpiper*: A lot of character in the string of low-beamed ancient rooms that forms the bar, bar food inc good sandwiches, well kept Bass, Exmoor and Flowers IPA on handpump, unusual whiskies, several log fires, friendly efficient staff; good position opp moorland church, on GWG22; children welcome; bedrooms comfortable though not cheap, dogs allowed *(J P Berryman, W H Mecham, Lynne Sheridan and Bob West, Mr and Mrs P A Jones, LYM)*

Crediton [High St; SS8300], *Ship*: Unpretentious town pub with very helpful staff, Bass and good, plain, decent food *(K R Harris)*

☆ **Croyde** [off B3231 NW of Braunton; SS4439], *Whiteleaf*: A guest house not a pub, but a firm recommendation for truly imaginative all-fresh food and good wines in comfortable surroundings, at modest cost; dogs accepted; listed by us as it's where the Wallingtons can now be found — among the country's top publicans in their time some years ago at the Rhydspence, Whitney on Wye *(BOB)*

☆ **Croyde**, *Thatched Barn*: Highly commercial extended thatched inn nr fine surfing beach, interesting original features still to be found in rambling but largely modernised bar, well kept Courage ales, largely home-made bar food inc local fish and good puddings, loud piped music, provision for children, morning coffee served from 10am, restaurant *(H F H Barclay, LYM)*

Dartmouth [Sandquay; SX8751], *Floating Bridge*: Clean and friendly, with well kept Watneys-related real ales on handpump, good choice of food, cheery landlord, nice atmosphere *(Les King, H K Dyson);* [Smith St], *Seven Stars*: Busy long black-beamed oak-panelled bar, Courage Best and Directors, piped pop music and fruit machine; upstairs restaurant, children's room, efficiently served and well priced popular food *(H K Dyson, BB)*

nr **Dartmouth** [Henborough Post; B3207 3 miles out], *Sportsmans Arms*: Friendly, good atmosphere, well kept beer *(John A Barker)*

Dawlish [Beach St; SX9676], *Exeter*: Friendly landlord, well kept Bass, bar food inc good ploughman's *(Alan and Heather Jacques);* [Marine Parade], *Marine*: Well renovated family pub with views of Lyme Bay and Exmouth, good value meals, well kept Ansells Best Mild and Dartmoor Best; bedrooms good *(C P Houghton)*

☆ **Devonport** [6 Cornwall St; SX4555], *Swan*: Lively riverside local with eight or more real ales, enormous good value doorstep sandwiches, live music most nights with extended opening till midnight *(Amanda Dauncey, Charles Gurney)*

☆ **Dittisham** [The Level; SX8654], *Red Lion*: Good friendly local with well kept beer and reasonably priced food from toasties up, inc lobster with notice; family room *(John A Barker, Keith Stevens, Jon and Jane Fawbert)*
Dittisham, *Ferry Boat*: Most notable for its peaceful waterside position, with big windows overlooking the boats, and the little foot-ferry you call by bell; Courage beers, simple but rather pricey food *(H K Dyson, Helen Emmitt, Keith Stevens, David and Ann Stranack, LYM)*
Down Thomas [SX5050], *Langdon Court*: Hotel lounge, but genuinely relaxed and friendly, with ornate bar, nice fire, country views — also from picnic-table sets outside; Flowers IPA and Whitbreads guest ale, good value fresh straightforward food with daily fish speciality; dogs allowed; children's room; comfortable bedrooms *(C G Thompson, Brian and Anna Marsden, A D Atienza); Mussel*: Courage pub notable for huge playground with play house, tree slide, swings and so on as well as child-sized picnic-table sets; several picnic-table sets under cover; good value food, children in eating areas *(Brian and Anna Marsden)*

☆ **Drewsteignton** [Fingle Bridge — OS Sheet 191, map reference 743899; SX7390], *Anglers Rest*: Sprucely airy and spacious bar, in idyllic wooded valley by 16th-century packhorse bridge; reasonably priced food inc children's meals (not Sun), efficient service, well kept Cotleigh and Courage or John Smiths real ales, brisk summer business in tourist souvenirs; winter opening times more restricted; easy parking; good walks nearby, inc GWG19 *(Helen Crookston, John Burgan, Hilary Irving, Pauline Crossland, Dave Cawley, RJC, LYM)*

☆ **Dunsford** [signed from Moretonhampstead — OS Sheet 191, map reference 813891; SX8189], *Royal Oak*: Good value bar food, esp sandwiches and vegetarian dishes, in light and airy lounge bar of village inn, well kept real ales, friendly family service, pool room, small restaurant, provision for children, Fri barbecues, good value bedrooms *(Tania Lamberton, LYM)*
East Budleigh [SY0684], *Sir Walter Raleigh*: The tenant who made this village pub a popular main entry for his good home cooking, and the cheerful atmosphere he (and his dog) generated, has now left; it now has the usual bar food with some fish specials, Devenish and Flowers real ales, and a neat bar with dining area; the village itself, and its church, is well worth a visit *(LYM; reports on new regime please)*
East Prawle [SX7836], *Pigs Nose*: Cheery and bustling pub on green, open fire, hatch for ordering well cooked plain food (inc children's helpings), Flowers and Wadworths 6X, easy chairs and sofa, pig cards on low beams, pig posters on walls; pool, darts; dogs allowed on a lead;

children's room; nr start GWG12 *(Roy McIsaac, S P Bobeldijk, M Box, Philip and Trisha Ferris)*
Ermington [SX6353], *Crooked Spire*: Emphasis on restaurant with friendly service and massive helpings of decent food inc good steaks *(John Evans)*
Exbourne [SX6002], *Red Lion*: Well kept Flowers Original and greatly improved layout and decor under new landlord *(R J Walden)*

☆ **Exeter** [The Close; SX9292], *Well House*: Lovely position, with big windows looking over the close to the cathedral (though trees partly block the view in summer); open-plan bar divided by inner walls and partitions, lots of Victorian prints, limited choice of popular bar lunches inc good salads; Bass, Flowers, Exe Valley and interesting guest beers *(R Hodgins, Mrs Joan Harris, BB)*
Exeter [Bonhay Rd], *Mill on the Exe*: Free house in fine position on River Exe, reconstructed from materials of disused mill — old bricks and timbers, comfortable chairs, good choice of hot and cold food, quick friendly service; tables out on terraces *(E V M Whiteway); [The Quay], Prospect*: Former pair of 17th-century cottages, in lovely relatively quiet spot on terrace over River Exe next to newly renovated quay, handy for ferry to Maritime Museum; congenial main bar area with settles around panelled walls, wide range of food in large dining area up a few steps, helpful staff *(Helen Crookston, Michael and Alison Sandy); [Martins Lane], Ship*: Photogenic 14th-century pub just off the Cathedral Close, with well kept Bass, Flowers IPA and Original on handpump, fish inc good Torbay sole *(Stephen R Holman, Neil H Barker, LYM); [High St North], Turks Head*: Quiet, with long two-level book-lined lounge bar, wide choice of bar food, Flowers Original on handpump, good staff; upstairs Beefeater restaurant *(Gwynne Harper, LYM); [Haven Banks], Welcome*: Characterful old Devenish pub on Exeter Ship Canal, most notable for free folk music Sun lunchtime — anything up to 20 musicians, thrilling atmosphere; real ale *(Gerald Cleaver)*
Exwick [Exwick Rd; SX9093], *Thatched House*: Friendly local with well kept Ruddles and good value food from sandwiches to steaks *(Keith Mason, Linda Criddle)*

☆ **Filleigh** [off A361 N Devon link rd; SS6627], *Stags Head*: 16th-century thatched inn run by cheerful and efficient family, with clean coordinated furnishings, good range of generous food, well kept Bass and wide range of other beers, friendly atmosphere; bedrooms comfortable and good value *(Graham and Jane Smithard, Sue North)*
Fremington [SS5132], *New Inn*: Good value food; shady car park *(D S and T M Beeson)*

☆ **Georgeham** [Rock Hill; above village — OS Sheet 180, map reference 466399; SS4639], *Rock*: Oak beams, old red quarry tiles, open fire, pleasant mix of country furniture inc traditional wall seats, good chatty atmosphere, with well kept Watneys-related real ales, local farm cider and good range of bar food inc good soup, filled French bread, home-cooked dishes; darts, fruit machine, unobtrusive piped music; further room with pool and food cabinet, tables under cocktail parasols on front terrace, pretty hanging baskets; doing well under new regime

Great Torrington [Well St; SS4919], *Hunters*: Friendly, welcoming landlord, well kept Whitbreads, good bar food, especially lunchtime; open all day *(Gerald Cleaver)*

Hartland Quay [SS2522], *Hartland Quay*: Worth knowing for good isolated position with interesting cliff formations above the stony beach and quay *(Mrs R Horridge)*

Hawkchurch [ST3400], *Old Inn*: Thoughtfully updated old pub keeping its atmosphere; good straightforward food, dogs welcome; nice village *(P R MacCrimmon)*

Hemerdon [SX5657], *Miners Arms*: Friendly and attractive low-beamed pub in picturesque Dartmoor countryside, wide range of well kept beers such as Bass, Marstons Pedigree, Ruddles, Sam Smiths; cheap food, big garden with play area *(Jenny and Neil Spink)*

Hemyock [ST1313], *Catherine Wheel*: Good range of interesting and well cooked dishes at reasonable prices, staff pleasant and friendly; restaurant *(Tim Gilroy)*

Holbeton [SX6150], *Mildmay Colours*: Good cheerful atmosphere, wide choice of good value bar food (inc vegetarian dishes), upstairs evening carvery and Sun lunch (best to book); front terrace has lovely views *(C G Thompson)*

☆ **Honiton** [Fenny Bridges; A30 4 miles W; ST1500], *Greyhound*: Big well run thatched Country Carvery dining pub, heavy beams, lots of red plush, deliberately old-fashioned style; quickly served good value bar food, carvery, Ushers on handpump, provision for children, comfortable well equipped games room; bedrooms *(Mr and Mrs F W Sturch, Dr D M Forsyth, LYM)*

nr Honiton [Fenny Bridges], *Fenny Bridges*: Well kept bar, good quick service, good choice of real ales, wide choice of decent food inc half-price children's dishes, restaurant; garden *(Dr and Mrs R E S Tanner)*; [Putts Corner; A375 S, junction with B3174; SY1496], *Hare & Hounds*: Large, plush and smart, with big lounge bar, smaller wood-and-tiles tap room; comfy sofas as well as more normal furnishings, stuffed birds; four well kept changing beers, good choice of roasts etc, smart restaurant *(Michael and Alison Sandy, Denzil Taylor)*

Horns Cross [A39; SS3823], *Coach & Horses*: Small country free house with good atmosphere, welcoming landlord and quickly served decent bar food; can get crowded *(Tony Bland)*

☆ **Ideford** [SX8977], *Royal Oak*: Lively old-world thatched local, friendly, dark and cosy, with lots of Victorian and Edwardian regalia and flags; well kept Bass and Whitbreads, character landlord, raised log

fire *(Phil Gorton)*

Ilsington [SX7876], *Carpenters Arms*: Friendly and pleasantly unspoilt local, Whitbreads beers *(Phil and Sally Gorton)*

Ivybridge [SX6356], *Hunting Lodge*: Long room with two bars, restaurant at end, pleasant service (reduced prices for elderly); emphasis on good value food *(John Evans)*

☆ **Kenn** [signed off A380 just S of Exeter; SX9285], *Ley Arms*: Simply furnished and welcoming old flagstoned village pub well restored after fire some years ago, cosy tap room and larger bar, big inglenook, choice of well kept beers on handpump inc Bass and Flowers, roomy dining area with bar food inc vegetarian and good value children's dishes (or they can have half-price helpings of other dishes), carvery *(Brian Jones, Jim Cowell, Gordon and Daphne, Dr John Innes)*

Kennford [just off A38; SX9186], *Gissons*: Popular roadhouse recently rebuilt after fire, wide range of good food (best to book), comfortable furniture, well stocked bar *(E V M Whiteway)*

☆ **Kentisbeare** [3 1/2 miles from M5 junction 28, via A373; ST0608], *Wyndham Arms*: Bustling well run village local, comfortable armchairs, big squashy sofas each side of big log fire, tables tucked into walls of long beamed main bar and out in sheltered courtyard; shortish but varied and well balanced choice of good value generous bar food, well kept Flowers IPA and Original, daily papers; games room, candlelit restaurant *(Margaret and Roy Randle, Bill and Jane Rees, David Gaunt, BB)*

☆ **Kilmington** [A35; SY2797], *Old Inn*: Friendly and welcoming thatched village local with character bar, comfortable inglenook lounge, good value bar food (children's dishes attractively priced), Bass and Charrington, good open fires, traditional games and skittle alley, restaurant, children's play area in nice garden *(Pauline Williams, Dr W M Owton, David Gaunt, Brian and Anna Marsden, LYM)*

☆ **Kingsbridge** [edge of town; SX7344], *Crabshell*: Friendly atmosphere, very obliging service, well kept Bass and Charrington IPA, warm winter fire, good bar food — particularly ploughman's, filled rolls and crab sandwiches at lunchtime, more elaborate evening seafood; attractive waterside spot, fine view over moorings *(WMS, Dorothee and Dennis Glover, M Box, Mr and Mrs W H Crowther)*

Kingsbridge [Church St], *Dodbrooke*: Two small cottage rooms, friendly, comfortable and cosy, good well presented basic bar food, popular with locals — good evening atmosphere *(WMS)*

Kingswear [SX8851], *Ship*: Good atmosphere, old beams, Whitbreads-related real ales, bar food *(H K Dyson)*

Lamerton [A384 Launceston—Tavistock; SX4476], *Blacksmiths Arms*: Good value generous fresh food, children very welcome *(J F and R Haynes)*

☆ **Landscove** [Woolston Green — OS Sheet

202, map reference 778662; SX7766], *Live & Let Live*: Homely but immaculate sunny open-plan bar, friendly licensees — he was bursar at Dartington—woodburner, well kept Ind Coope Burton, bar food inc good curry, tables in small orchard; next to Methodist chapel, facing over moors towards Dart valley *(Patrick Freeman, LYM)*

☆ Lee [SS4846], *Grampus*: Attractive 14th-century pub with nice quiet garden, just a stroll up through the village from the sea, in lovely fuchsia valley; well kept Flowers on handpump, good sheep's-cheese ploughman's and other food *(Alan and Heather Jacques, B M Eldridge, LYM)*

Littlehempston [SX8162], *Tally Ho!*: Lovely, warm and inviting pub with well kept Bass and good food *(Steve Huggins)*

☆ Loddiswell [SX7148], *Loddiswell*: Courage pub, genuinely old, clean and bright; open fire, good choice of freshly cooked nicely served food inc fine steak and kidney pudding, traditional puddings, fresh fish daily in summer *(Gladys and Robert Flux, N P Cox)*

☆ Lower Ashton [off B3193; SX8484], *Manor*: Small friendly two-bar pub with four or five real ales tapped from the cask, good generous home-made food (not Mon) such as beef provençale, cauliflower bake and half-a-dozen bistro-type dishes; garden overlooking Teign Valley *(Colin May, R Hodgins, P Cowlard)*

Luppitt [OS Sheet 192, map reference 169067; ST1606], *Luppitt*: Tiny room in a farmhouse (three's a crowd), and a games room; well kept Whitbreads tapped from the cask, no food, closed Sun and maybe other times *(Phil Gorton)*

☆ Luton [Haldon Moor; SX9076], *Elizabethan*: Comfortable and welcoming, interesting range of local food such as rabbit, trout and sea fish, good local atmosphere in front bars, Devenish and other real ales, good staff, unobtrusive piped music *(Phil and Sally Gorton, Peter F Newman)*

☆ Lutton [pub signed off Cornwood—Sparkwell rd — OS Sheet 202, map reference 597596; SX5959], *Mountain*: Beams, log fires, some stripped stone, a high-backed settle, old-fashioned polished tables and Dartmoor views, also seats on verandah and vine-arbour terrace; generous helpings of well done bar food till 10 inc fine soups, well kept Exmoor, Ind Coope Burton and Wadworths 6X, local farm cider, unspoilt, friendly take-us-as-you-find-us atmosphere; children in eating area and small family room; no dogs (two in residence, with cats) *(T Nott, D J K Waltho, Brian and Anna Marsden, Philip and Trisha Ferris, Dr Keith Louden, LYM)*

Lynton [Castle Hill; SS7149], *Royal Castle*: Marvellous spot, 500 ft above sea with spectacular views from bars, terrace, restaurant and the good value bedrooms; Edwardian country-house atmosphere despite ongoing refurbishment under new owners; Exmoor and Pompey Royal on

handpump, good value bar food *(Mr and Mrs P A Jones)*

☆ nr Lynton [Rockford; Lynton—Simonsbath rd, off B2332 — OS Sheet 180, map reference 755477], *Rockford Inn*: Traditional village local, beamed split-level bar attractively decorated with farm tools and Lynmouth prints; well kept real ales such as Cotleigh Tawny, Courage Best and Directors, good bar food (meals rather than snacks in the evening), friendly licensees; beautiful Exmoor spot on East Lyn nr Doone valley, on GWG22 and nr NT walks at Watersmeet; Exe fishing; limited parking; six bedrooms *(Derek and Sue Hammond)*

☆ Malborough [SX7039], *Old Inn*: Quiet yet thriving village pub with quick polite service, good choice of reasonably priced bar food inc fine mussels and smart puddings, children's room *(Margaret and Trevor Errington)*

☆ Manaton [SX7581], *Kestor*: Smartly refurbished with interesting barn decor, clean and comfortable; well kept changing real ales such as Marstons Pedigree and Wadworths 6X, farm cider, wide range of good value, wholesome and original home cooking inc excellent open sandwiches, open fire, cheerful and helpful service; splendid Dartmoor-edge location; attractive bedrooms *(Nigel Hopkins, Genie and Brian Smart, Peter Maden, Hilary Robinson, Murray J Daffern, Eric Locker)*

Marsh [ST2510], *Flintlock*: Well kept and attractive, with welcoming staff, modest drinks prices, bar food inc good specials and salads *(D I Baddeley)*

☆ Meavy [SX5467], *Royal Oak*: Unpretentious village pub in attractive spot on green of Dartmoor village, L-shaped main bar with rustic tables, smaller attractively traditional public bar, good atmosphere, simple home-made food, well kept Courage on handpump; tables outside; owned by the parish council *(Peter Adcock, Philip and Trisha Ferris, LYM)*

☆ Merrivale [SX5475], *Dartmoor*: Refurbished pub with Courage and another real ale on handpump, good choice of country wines, open fire, good value lunchtime bar food, maybe early morning coffee, efficient service, roadside garden; good Dartmoor views, nr bronze-age hut circles, stone rows and crystal-clear river, at start of GWG15 *(Cliff and Karen Spooner, Peter Churchill)*

Modbury [SX6551], *Exeter*: Friendly refurbished old inn with bay-windowed bar, good straightforward food, well kept Ruddles, coffee and tea from 10am all day in summer; children in carvery lunchtime and early evening; bedrooms particularly well equipped *(Peter and Rose Flower, David and Flo Wallington)*

☆ Molland [SS8028], *London*: Basic and unspoilt time-warp pub on edge of Exmoor, but clean, with stag-hunting memorabilia, old photographs, big table in middle of main room; friendly welcome; fine beer, roaring log fire, dim lighting, cheap sandwiches, good ploughman's, one dog and countless cats; next to one of the most unspoilt churches in the country *(Phil Gorton, C J Parsons, Anthony Barnes)*

☆ Monkton [A30 NE of Honiton; ST1803], *Monkton Court*: Roomy and attractively laid out beamed main bar, snug side areas, efficient friendly service, well kept Courage, good choice of reliable bar food; provision for children, spacious relaxing garden; bedrooms *(Mr and Mrs J W Gibson, Mrs Joan Harris, LYM)*

☆ Moreleigh [B3207; off Kingsbridge—Totnes in Stanborough, left in village — OS Sheet 202, map reference 767527; SX7753], *New Inn*: Unrestored and very local, farming and riding customers, with locals playing cribbage and darts in middle, big inglenook at one end with old tables, chairs and benches, ochre ceiling, interesting pictures; comfortable and dark, with candles in bottles — seems little changed in a century; good standard food inc bargain smoked salmon, good whitebait, really cheap steak and kidney pie; well kept Palmers or Whitbreads tapped from the cask, decent wines by the bottle *(David and Flo Wallington, WMS)*

☆ Mortehoe [free parking by church; village signed with Woolacombe from A361 Ilfracombe—Braunton; SS4545], *Ship Aground*: Welcoming village pub by church, in good coastal walking country (Morte Point, Bull Point, Lee, Woolacombe Warren); open-plan, with leatherette wall seating, massive tree-trunk tables, lots of nautical brassware, log fire; well kept Flowers Original, Exmoor and a guest beer, good if not cheap or quick bar food, friendly staff; piped music may be loud; children in restaurant and games room; has been open all day in summer *(WHBM, Anthony Barnes, J A Scott, Christopher and Heather Barton, LYM)*

Morwellham [part of Morwellham Quay restored village; SX4469], *Ship*: Restaurant rather than pub now, but worth visiting as part of this interesting English Heritage restored copper-mine and shipping village; waitresses in period costume, drinks to suit — you can even dress the part yourself *(Freddy Costello)*

☆ Newton Abbot [East St; SX8671], *Olde Cider Bar*: Only Devon pub with just a cider licence — splendid range from 40-gallon casks behind bar, and good value country wines; very local, with basic wooden stools and wall benches, little changed in over a century (house rule — no pint glasses for women); simple cheap snacks, small games room with machines *(WMS, Phil Gorton, Andrew Morrissey)*

Newton Abbot [East St], *Jolly Abbot*: Old-world, with beams, welcoming licensees and cheerful customers; good value home-made food, well kept ales inc guests *(Tony Powell)*; *Jolly Farmer*: Barn decor, decent food, well kept Courage Best and Directors; skittle room, juke box *(Steve Huggins)*

☆ nr Newton Abbot [Abbotskerswell; A381 2 miles S], *Two Mile Oak*: Well kept Eldridge Pope Royal Oak, good log fires, beams, lounge with secluded candlelit alcoves, black-panelled traditional public bar with lots of brasses, wide choice of reasonably priced bar food, seats on back terrace and nicely planted garden *(Steve Huggins, LYM)*

Newton Ferrers [Riverside Rd East; SX5448], *Dolphin*: Small but comfortable waterside pub in very pretty village, nice views; friendly staff, particularly well kept Bass on handpump from barrels racked at back of bar, reasonably priced bar food *(Graham and Glenis Watkins, Paul Hussell)*

Newton St Cyres [SX8798], *Crown & Sceptre*: Bright, airy bars inc children's area, well kept Bass and good value food; terrace and bridge over small river to garden with play area *(Steve Huggins)*

Newton Tracey [5 miles S of Barnstaple on B3232 to Torrington; SS5226], *Hunters*: Friendly old pub with pleasant decor, Marstons Pedigree, good food, real fire, juke box and fruit machines; children in eating area or skittle alley; tables outside, play area *(Mel Landells)*

☆ No Mans Land [B3131 Tiverton—South Molton; SS8313], *Mountpleasant*: Cheerful roadside pub with friendly staff, well kept Butcombe and other beers, decent wines, good home cooking; children's room *(D W Backhouse, David Whalley)*

North Tawton [SS6601], *Copper Key*: Neatly repainted and rethatched, cosy and comfortable inside, with friendly service, well kept Marstons Pedigree, decent food *(S Watkins, R J Walden)*

Noss Mayo [SX5447], *Swan*: Right to water, in lovely village; Courage Best and Directors, generous straightforward food with some more original dishes maybe using fresh fish and herbs brought in by locals, friendly service, open fire; children welcome, some tables outside *(Jutta Whitley, Dr Keith Louden)*

Otterton [SY0885], *Kings Arms*: Well placed in centre of delightful old-world village, recently refurbished, with good bar meals and reasonable ale in comfortable surroundings *(E G Parish)*

☆ Paignton [27 Esplanade Rd; SX8960], *Inn on the Green*: Airy family bar, extensively refitted 1991 and a major feature of the front; open all day, with remarkably wide choice of popular sensibly priced food, good facilities for children, Watneys-related real ales, live music nightly; seats outside looking over green to sea; bedrooms in adjoining self-catering apartments *(Alan and Audrey Chatting, Carol Mason, LYM)*

Paignton [Torquay Rd], *Half Moon*: Spacious pub with reasonably priced food inc Sun lunch, back garden; children allowed *(Jane Moir)*

Parkham [SS3821], *Bell*: Thatched local with lots of nooks and crannies, open fire, real ales such as Bass, Flowers IPA and Original and Fullers London Pride, old-fashioned furniture, good value food

(Gerald Cleaver, LYM)

☆ Parracombe [off A39 Blackmoor Gate — Lynton — OS Sheet 180, map reference 668448; SS6644], *Fox & Goose:* Small local with remarkable range of good food from sandwiches to swordfish, friendly, unrushed service, Flowers IPA *(Dick Brown, Mr and Mrs J H Adam)*

Payhembury [ST0801], *Six Bells:* Welcoming village local on green, delightful atmosphere, limited range of wholesome bar food *(Stephen Goodchild)*

☆ **Plymouth** [Old George St; Derrys Cross, behind Theatre Royal; SX4755], *Bank:* Clean and comfortable conversion of former bank, dark wood railings dividing varying levels, conservatory area upstairs (children allowed here) leading to small garden, good service, good value food in wide variety all day (queue while it's done, take it on tray), well kept Fergusons Dartmoor and Strong; busy at lunchtime despite large size, popular younger people evenings; may have live jazz sometimes *(Brian and Anna Marsden, Catherine and Andrew Brian, Ted George, Ian Phillips, Mayur Shah, Sue Corrigan, Andy Kassube, Jenny Shephard)*

Plymouth [Barbican], *Pilgrims:* Worth visit for location opp fish mkt overlooking harbour; stylish furnishings, Whitbreads beers, video screens, jazz-based discreet music; cafe-type menu, extensive but not pricy *(Mayur Shah);* [Saltram Pl; back of Plymouth Hoe, behind Moat House], *Yard Arm:* Pleasant naval-theme pub on several levels with interesting woodwork; popular with businessmen at lunchtime, well kept Courage beers, generous standard food, cheerful service *(T Nott, C A Gurney, M J Cochrane, Mark Walker)*

☆ **Postbridge** [B3212; SX6579], *East Dart:* Central Dartmoor hotel by pretty river — it has some 30 miles of fishing; cheerful open-plan bar with long tables and good mix of locals, tourists and hikers, more intimate enclosed area, good fire virtually all year, efficiently served bar food inc really hot curries, well kept Exmoor and other real ales, farm cider, pool room; children welcome; bedrooms *(R Tomlinson, BB)*

☆ **Poundsgate** [SX7072], *Tavistock:* Ancient Dartmoor pub with gorgeous garden; original flagstones and fireplaces inside, wide choice of fairly priced standard food inc good home-prepared dishes, great puddings, good value Sun lunch, also open for breakfast, afternoon tea (May-Sept); Courage Best and John Smiths, welcoming efficient service; very popular in summer, a proper local out of season *(Philip and Trisha Ferris, Mr and Mrs Fleetwood, Amanda Dauncey)*

☆ **Princetown** [SX5873], *Plume of Feathers:* Warm welcome, efficient service, two log fires, interesting solid slate tables, well kept Bass and St Austell HSD and Tinners, cheap straightforward food inc good pasties; handy for walking Dartmoor; children welcome; new bedroom extension, bunkhouse and camping *(David and Kate*

Jones, Amanda Dauncey, Gwyneth and Salvo Spadaro-Dutturi, Dr W M Owton)

☆ **Rackenford** [SS8518], *Stag:* Largely early 13th-century, with massive walls, stone-flagged entrance passage, settles around large open fire, lots of atmosphere; well kept Cotleigh on handpump, bar food; dining room; bedrooms *(Audrey and Roger Adcock, D W Backhouse, BB)*

☆ **Ringmore** [SX6545], *Journeys End:* Interesting old-fashioned furnishings in panelled but unfussy lounge, entertaining china pig collection, comfortable new back conservatory overlooking attractively planted big garden; wide range of generously served bar food, usually six or more well kept real ales, farm cider; evening restaurant; not far from the sea; bedrooms comfortable and well equipped *(A D Atienza, John Knighton, LYM)*

☆ **Roborough** [off B3217 N of Winkleigh; SS5717], *Olde Inn:* Up to half a dozen constantly changing real ales all from independent breweries, inc interesting ones from far off, in cheery simple thatched local with welcoming young licensees; also farm cider, country wines, decent simple food, open fires, sensibly placed darts, some tables outside; folk Tues, jazz Thurs, 78s wind-up disco Sun; may be open all day Sat; children only in small garden, not in pub *(R Hodgins, Gerald Cleaver, C M Andrews, Marianne Pryor, BB)*

Rockford [SS7547], see under Lynton

Salcombe [off Fore St nr Portlemouth Ferry; SX7338], *Ferry:* Three storeys of stripped-stone bars (not all open out of season) look out over sheltered flagstoned waterside terrace to picturesque estuary; Palmers real ales, bar food, restaurant, games bar; can get crowded summer; the many steps make it unsuitable for disabled people, and some prices are on the high side *(LYM)*

☆ **Sampford Courtenay** [B3072 Crediton—Holsworthy; SS6301], *New Inn:* Cheerful open-plan low-beamed bar in 16th-century thatched pub, open fires, friendly staff, well kept Bass, Flowers IPA and Original, varied menu inc good toasties, ploughman's, children's helpings; pleasant garden with swings and play house, lovely flower-filled village *(Helena and Arthur Harbottle)*

☆ **Sampford Peverell** [16 Lower Town; a mile from M5 junction 27, village signed from Tiverton turn-off; ST0214], *Globe:* Spacious and comfortably modernised bar with good range of reasonably priced food inc popular Sun lunch, well kept Flowers IPA and Original, friendly service, piped music, games in public bar, pool room, skittle alley, tables in front; open all day; children allowed in eating area and family room *(K R Harris, LYM)*

Sandy Gate [nr M5 junction 30, on Topsham rd; SX9691], *Blue Ball:* Particularly good children's play area; good choice of food at reasonable prices *(RJC)*

Scorriton [SX7068], *Tradesmans Arms:*

Clean open-plan pub with good Dartmoor-edge views (the tables outside don't make the most of these), well kept Fergusons Dartmoor on handpump, decent low-priced food; large children's room; bedrooms *(Roger Huggins);*

Shaldon [SX9372], *Ness House*: Hotel in lovely spot on Ness headland, with seats out on lawns, bar food *(Pauline Crossland, Dave Cawley);* [Ringmore Rd; B3195 to Newton Abbot; SX9372], *Shipwrights Arms*: Good chatty atmosphere in village local with big helpings of good value food served till late, river views from back garden; parking can be difficult *(Dave Mead, LYM)*

Shiphay [SX8865], *Devon Dumpling*: Spaciously modernised, with upper barn loft and courtyard garden; Courage Best and Directors and expanding choice of reasonably priced food; aquarium, occasional live music *(Steve Huggins)*

☆ **Sidmouth** [Old Fore St; SY1287], *Old Ship*: Partly 14th-century, with shiny black woodwork, close-set tables and ship pictures in its three opened-together rooms, roomier raftered upstairs bar, fair-priced food inc good ploughman's and local fish, well kept real ales such as Boddingtons, Marstons Pedigree, Wadworths 6X; dogs allowed; just moments from the sea, so can get crowded in summer; bedrooms *(Prof H G Allen, Stephen R Holman, Robert and Vicky Tod, BB)*

Sidmouth [High St], *Tudor Rose*: Spacious, with pre-1960 bric-a-brac such as wooden slot machine, Bass on handpump, wide choice of bar food inc local plaice, rabbit casserole; good coffee, pleasant staff, restaurant *(A H Whitfield)*

☆ *nr* **Sidmouth** [Bowd Cross, junction B3176/A3052; SY1089], *Bowd*: Spacious thatched dining pub, clean, warm and comfortable, with soft lighting, expanse of Turkey carpet, gentle piped music and nice family room; well kept Devenish and a guest beer; has been open all day; particularly good garden *(Gordon and Daphne, Mr and Mrs G Turner, Brian and Anna Marsden, Dr D M Forsyth, LYM)*

Slapton [SX8244], *Queens Arms*: L-shaped bar with plush banquettes, usual bar food with quite a lot of fish, cream teas, Eldridge Pope Royal Oak and Palmers, open fire, fruit machine and sensibly placed darts; tables in garden; well behaved children allowed *(Heather Martin)*

Sourton [Prewly Moor, A30/A386 roundabout; SX5490], *Prewly Moor Arms*: Unpretentious, with reasonably priced good food inc meat from an organic farm *(A M J Chadwick)*

South Molton [SS7125], *Old Coaching Inn*: Very comfortable bar in big but cosy pub; good range of beers and well served good food *(K R Harris)*

South Tawton [off A30 at Whiddon Down or Okehampton, then signed from Sticklepath; SX6594], *Seven Stars*: Unpretentious village pub in quiet countryside, good helpings of simple decent

bar food, well kept Ind Coope Burton, Palmers and Wadworths 6X, farm cider; pool and other bar games, a couple of good-natured dogs, folk club last Sun in month; restaurant (closed Sun and Mon evenings winter); children welcome; bedrooms *(PB, HB, LYM)*

☆ **Spreyton** [SX6996], *Tom Cobbley*: Welcoming litle village local, good home-cooked food inc special curry evenings (booking needed), well kept Cotleigh Tawny and occasional guest beers, darts and cards, lovely garden with summer barbecues; busy at weekends; spotless bedrooms *(Anon)*

Sticklepath [off A30 at Whiddon Down or Okehampton; SX6494], *Devonshire*: This 16th-century thatched village inn, of great potential, closed 1991 *(News please)*

☆ **Stoke Fleming** [SX8648], *Green Dragon*: Friendly old beamed and panelled village pub with well kept Bass and Flowers, good value bar food, enterprising choice of takeaway picnics, good service *(Mark Jackson, Louise Mee)*

☆ **Stokeinteignhead** [SX9170], *Chasers Arms*: 16th-century thatched dining pub with particularly good food inc exceptional ploughman's and steak and kidney pie; well kept Eldridge Pope Dorset IPA, fine range of house wines, quick, friendly service *(J R Carey, Mr and Mrs P A Jackson)*

☆ **Stokenham** [opp church, just off A379 Dartmouth—Kingsbridge; SX8042], *Church House*: Busy, lively pub, so popular for its wide range of well presented bar food, especially local fish and seafood, hot curries and own-grown vegetables, that it's now open-plan throughout for this; well kept Bass and Flowers, friendly bustling landlord, family area through arch, tables in decent garden with swings *(David and Ann Stranack, Roger Huggins, Steve Huggins, A R Tingley, S P Bobeldijk, Dr B C Moyse, Miss D Brewster)*

☆ **Stokenham**, *Tradesmans Arms*: Pretty 15th-century thatched cottage with plenty of neatly kept antique tables in civilised bar, piped classical music, bar food strong on fresh fish — the honey-baked gammon and Madras curry are popular, too; fine range of malt whiskies, Bass and a couple of other real ales such as Adnams, picnic-table sets outside (nice surroundings), restaurant, no provision for children; tiny car park *(WMS, R J Walden, LYM)*

Tedburn St Mary [village signposted from A30 W of Exeter; SX8193], *Kings Arms*: Old inn with big log fire in long cosy open-plan bar, generally good if not cheap food (not Sun evening) in eating area at one end, games area around corner at other end, a couple of well kept real ales, local cider; children allowed in eating area; bedrooms *(Cdr W S D Hendry, LYM)*

Thelbridge Cross [OS Sheet 180, map reference 790120; SS7912], *Thelbridge Cross*: Beamed bar with log fire, friendly service, food in bar and restaurant; bedrooms, moor views *(C J Parsons)*

☆ **Thorverton** [SS9202], *Dolphin*: Engaging village inn run by cheerful brother and sister, simple bar with sensibly placed darts and pool, heavily velvet-curtained lounge spreading from conventionally furnished bar area through low easy chairs and comfortable settees into cosy dining room; bar food inc notable steak and kidney pie, Flowers IPA and Original and Wethereds Winter Royal on handpump; winning dogs and cat, entertaining special evenings, tables out under ancient wisteria and in small garden; bedrooms good value *(Paul and Margaret Baker, BB)*

☆ Topsham [Ferry Rd; SX9688], *Passage*: Attractive waterside pub with good genuine food (not Sun evening) inc fresh fish and good steaks, well kept Bass and Flowers IPA and Original, plank panelling, black oak beams, flagstones, seats on shoreside terrace, restaurant; open all day Sat, very busy summer weekends *(G S Jaques, JBM, LYM)*

Topsham, *Lighter*: Spacious and well kept plushly refurbished quayside pub with panelled alcoves; tall windows looking out over lock-keepers' cottage and tidal flats, efficient food bar, well kept Badger real ales; good choice of board games; children in eating area; bedrooms *(Steve Huggins, BB)*; [High St], *Lord Nelson*: Concentration on good range of food inc competitively priced specials and good vegetables; pleasant service, well kept real ales inc Marstons Pedigree *(Ray Hassell)*

☆ Torbryan [most easily reached from A381 Newton Abbot—Totnes via Ipplepen; SX8266], *Old Church House*: Wide choice of generous home-cooked food and several real ales in ancient pub, its flagstones carpeted now, with several comfortable and discreetly lit lounge areas, and snug plush-cushioned Tudor-panelled bar on right; friendly staff, piped music, evening restaurant; children allowed in family room; bedrooms in new extension excellent *(Peter Turl, Gwen and Peter Andrews, Margaret and Trevor Errington, Mr and Mrs R Clarke, LYM)*

Torquay [Park Lane; SX9264], *Hole in the Wall*: Small dark flagstoned bar with lots of character, Courage beers on handpump, much naval memorabilia, old local photographs, chamber-pots; friendly licensees and customers, open all day *(Jim and Maggie Cowell)*

Totnes [Fore St, The Plains; SX8060], *Royal Seven Stars*: Spacious, airy, plush hotel with well kept Ruddles County *(H K Dyson, P Argent)*; [Steamer Quay Rd], *Smugglers*: By River Dart with tables outside, good reasonably priced food, big family room *(Jane Moir)*

Tytherleigh [A358 Chard—Axminster; ST3103], *Tytherleigh Arms*: Comfortable and friendly spacious bar with good range of food from soups to local fish and steaks, three real ales, good pubby atmosphere; bookable tables in bar and restaurant; attractive village; children allowed if eating *(Tim Brierly, E G Parish)*

☆ Ugborough [SX6755], *Ship*: Very tidy and attractive, with pleasant efficient service, wide choice of good food in bar and restaurant (worth booking) inc interesting fish dishes *(David and Flo Wallington, Philip and Trisha Ferris, W H Mecham)*

Upottery [ST2007], *Sidmouth Arms*: Quaint and spacious old pub in charming village; well stocked bar, bar food; comfortable bedrooms *(PB, HB, E Streeton, Dr D Forsyth, Betty and Norman Gregory)*

West Down [the one up nr Ilfracombe; SS5142], *Crown*: Nice village pub with fine choice of beers, good choice of food inc children's and vegetarian, family room, discreet back pool/darts room, fine big garden behind *(John Drummond)*; [The Square], *Long House*: Not a pub, a cottage hotel, but worth knowing for really good pub lunches, reasonably priced — and open all day *(John Drummond)*

Westleigh [1/2 mile off A39 Bideford—Instow; SS4628], *Westleigh*: Friendly village pub with exceptional views over the Torridge estuary from its neatly kept garden, with good safe play area; usual food inc good home-made burger; children allowed *(Mrs S Y Sadler, LYM)*

☆ Weston [ST1200], *Otter*: Doing well under friendly new owners, former managers of White Hart, Exeter, with wide choice of good pub food from sandwiches to steaks, Sun lunches, Bass, Flowers IPA, Marstons Pedigree and Eldridge Pope Hardy, good inexpensive wines; pleasant, relaxed atmosphere with log fire in old fireplace, low and heavy old oak beams, thick pillars and walls, ex-chapel seating (one with lectern and bible), antique tables, candles, comfortable chairs near fire, interesting bric-a-brac; tables on lawn leading to River Otter — wildfowl encouraged by judicious winter feeding *(P M Bisby, Gordon and Daphne, Dave & Kate Buckley, J R Carey)*

Whiddon Down [A30; SX6992], *Post*: China and hundreds of horsebrasses, wide choice of good generous food, friendly atmosphere, Flowers Original and guest ale, family room, skittle alley, small garden *(Neil and Anita Christopher, K R Harris)*

Whimple [off A30 Exeter—Honiton; SY4097], *New Fountain*: Attractive village pub, civilised and snug, with decent food all sessions; the Jacksons who made their mark here are now at the Cove House, Chesil — see main entries *(Ruth Halling, A H Whitfield)*

☆ Widecombe [SX7176], *Old Inne*: Attractive old pub in beauty-spot village; comfortably rebuilt in the 1970s, with good friendly service, well kept Ushers, wide choice of reasonably priced food inc some unusual things and children's dishes, big log fire, newish restaurant area, good garden; very busy summer *(Les King, Mr and Mrs Fleetwood, LYM)*

☆ Widecombe [turning opp Olde Inn, down hill past long church house — OS Sheet 191, map reference 720765], *Rugglestone*: Unspoilt and welcoming little basic pub in beautiful setting, with landlady who sits in bar with the locals and goes out and gets their well kept reasonably priced Bass for them — if she isn't around, they bang the table with their empty glasses; little stream runs under the road and past front of the pub *(Paul Hussell, M and P Rudlin, Gordon and Daphne)*

Winkleigh [off B3220; SS6308], *Seven Stars*: Friendly village pub with Bass, real fire, CD juke box *(Gerald Cleaver)*

Woodland [signed off A38 just NE of Ashburton; SX7968], *Rising Sun*: Carefully restored after fire — even the key collection on the bar's beams has been replaced; pleasant grounds in isolated country setting, well kept Boddingtons, decent if not cheap food *(Mike Hallewell, LYM)*

Yelverton [by roundabout A386 Plymouth—Tavistock; SX5267], *Rock*: Real ales inc well kept Bass, quick bar service, good evening bar food inc children's dishes

and delicious treacle sponge, comfortable seats, fruit machine, welcoming staff, family room; bedrooms *(Mr & Mrs S Turner, G S Jaques)*

Zeal Monachorum [signed off A377 Crediton—Barnstaple at Lapford — OS Sheet 191, map reference 724038; SS7203], *Waie*: Part of working farm, welcoming and friendly; large, airy rather plain front lounge/dining area, functional back tap room, pool room, Bass, good home-made standard food, low prices; also squash courts, indoor pool, sauna, skittle alley *(Alan and Heather Jacques)*

Dorset

Some lovely countryside situations here, lots of friendly licensees, some very imaginative food. New main entries (or pubs back in the Guide after an absence) are the traditional George in Bridport (good choice of food), the charming old New Inn at Church Knowle, the busy Bakers Arms at Lytchett Minster (amazing collections) and the Hambro Arms at Milton Abbas, a delightfully placed dining pub. Pubs with something of a change of mood under new licensees include the White Hart at Bishops Caundle (this dining pub is as busy as ever), the Cove House at Chesil (the Jacksons, who made a name for their food at the New Fountain at Whimple, are making the most of fish landed virtually under their noses), the engaging Sailors Return at East Chaldon (popular cheap food), the prettily refurbished Drovers at Gussage All Saints, the Mitre tucked away at Sandford Orcas (they're doing bedrooms now), the Ilchester Arms at Symondsbury (in contrast, the new people here – from Zimbabwe – have stopped doing them; they're concentrating on fish cooking), and the Langton Arms at Tarrant Monkton. Other pubs to note as being on particularly good form at the moment include the Ilchester Arms in Abbotsbury (a nice old place, just redecorated), the very friendly Spyway at Askerswell, the New Inn at Cerne Abbas (excellent wines by the glass; a star award this year for all-round quality), the warmly friendly Saxon at Child Okeford (it's now a free house), the Fox at Corfe Castle (another pub freed from its tie, with some interesting internal changes), the Greyhound there (lots of seafood), the stylish Museum at Farnham (gains a place-to-stay award this year), the friendly Pilot Boat in Lyme Regis (excellent food; approaching a star award for all-round quality now), the Marquis of Lorne at Nettleton (doing very well for food and as a place to stay), the Three Horseshoes at Powerstock (outstanding fish, though you do pay for it) and the Shave Cross Inn (low prices, charming surroundings). We are sad to have to record the closure of the Tigers Head, a particularly nice little pub in Rampisham – a favourite of many readers. In the Lucky Dip section at the end of the chapter, three pubs which have changed hands or been otherwise changed too recently for inspection are currently winning particularly warm approval from readers: the Thimble at Piddlehinton, Kings Arms in Shaftesbury and Springhead at Sutton Poyntz. Other notable Dip entries (most of them inspected pubs, kept out of the main entries only by a relative lack of recent reports from readers) are the Inn in the Park in Branksome Park, Gaggle of Geese at Buckland Newton, Fox at Corscombe, Acorn at Evershot, Fiddleford Inn at Fiddleford, White Horse at Hinton St Mary, Avon Causeway at Hurn, Scott Arms at Kingston, Smugglers at Osmington Mills, New Inn at Stoke Abbott, Crown at Uploders, New Inn at West Knighton, Castle at West Lulworth and Wise Man at West Stafford.

ABBOTSBURY   SY5785   Map 2

Ilchester Arms 🛏

B3157

Redecoration is planned in October by the new managers, but they say that essentially the old look will remain the same. At the moment, the rambling beamed bar in this handsome old inn is made up of three main sitting areas where there are over 1,000 prints – including a profusion of swan pictures – on the walls; also, red plush button-back seats and spindleback chairs around cast-iron-framed and other tables on Turkey carpet, some brocaded armchairs in front of the open log fire, stirrups, horsebrasses, and hunting horns on the beams, a stag's head, and some stuffed fish. Generous helpings of popular bar food include soup (£1.50), home-made curry (£4.25), steak and kidney pie (£4.50), salads (£4.75), deep-fried chicken with bacon (£4.95), and home-made puddings (all £2); children's menu (from £1.95), breakfasts are served in the sizeable and attractive no smoking conservatory. Well kept Devenish Royal Wessex, Wadworths 6X and a guest beer on handpump, red wine bin ends, and malt whiskies; darts, dominoes, quiz machine, board games and piped music. As the delightful village of golden stone and thatch attracts a lot of visitors, it's useful to know that there is a fair sized car park through the coach arch. The nearby swannery has been famous for centuries for its hundreds of nesting pairs, and in season there are pochard, tufted duck, goldeneye, brent geese, widgeon and (since 1982) a flamingo; the inn is handy for the coast, the Abbey, and the sheltered 20-acre gardens (closed winter) with unusual tender plants and peacocks; lanes lead from behind the building into the countryside. (*Recommended by Dick Brown, Steve Huggins, Robert and Gladys Flux, Heather Sharland, Major E M Warrick, J E Stanton, John and Joan Calvert, A D Sherman, G W H Kerby, I R Pinnock, Pat Woodward, Mr and Mrs J H Adam, Carol Mason, Mrs A Turner*)

Devenish (Whitbreads)   Managers Mr and Mrs Doyle   Real ale   Meals and snacks Restaurant   Dorchester (0305) 871243   Children welcome anywhere except main bar   Live entertainment every second Friday   Open 11–11   Bedrooms; £35B/£55B

ASKERSWELL   SY5292   Map 2

Spyway ★ ⊘ £

Village signposted N of A35 Bridport–Dorchester; inn signposted locally; OS Sheet 194 map reference 529933

Run by a particularly friendly, helpful licensee, this isolated pub is very popular for its excellent and reasonably priced food: a fine choice of generous ploughman's such as hot sausages and tomato pickle (£2.50) or home-cooked ham with sweet pickle (£2.75), three-egg omelettes (£2.25), haddock or plaice (£2.95), a wide selection of salads (from £2.95), and specials like sausage and onion, country or game pies, and lasagne or curry; evening dishes like lamb cutlets (£4.50) and steaks (£7.50), and puddings such as chocolate alabama fudge cake (£1.40) or cheesecake (£1.50). Well kept Ruddles County, Ushers Best and Websters Yorkshire on handpump, as well as country wines, around 40 whiskies and 14 pure Dorset apple juices. The cosy and characterful little rooms have old-fashioned high-backed settles, cushioned wall and window seats, a longcase clock, fine decorative china, harness and a milkmaid's yoke; there's also a new dining area decorated with blue and white china, old oak beams and timber uprights. Darts, shove-ha'penny, table skittles, dominoes and cribbage. In the pretty little back garden are ducks and other pets. The views over these steep downs just in from the coast are lovely, and the lane past the pub opens on to many paths and bridleways. (*Recommended by Caroline Wright, Alan Skull, Nick and Alison Dowson, Mr and Mrs R G Dawes, Mr and Mrs D V Morris, Lynn Sharpless, Bob Eardley, David Wingrove, Olive Carroll, Robert and Gladys Flux, John Watson, P J Hanson, Mrs J A Gardner, Mr and Mrs B E Witcher, John Fazakerley, WMS, John and Christine Simpson, L H J King*)

Free house   Licensees Don and Jackie Roderick   Real ale   Meals and snacks   (030) 885 250   Children in eating area of bar   Open 10–3, 6–11

BISHOPS CAUNDLE   ST6913   Map 2
White Hart

A3030

There's been another change of management at this busy dining pub. The big irregular shaped lounge bar has handsomely moulded low beams, ancient panelling, a good variety of seats and tables in decent wood, dark red curtains, and nice lamps. Mostly home-made, the bar food includes French sticks (from £1.75), filled baked potatoes (from £2.50), a wide range of ploughman's including vegetarian pâté or blue vinney made in the village Caundle (from £3.20), salads from £3.75; main meals include lasagne or fried chicken (£3.95), home-made chilli con carne or turkey curry (£4.25) and a choice of home-made pies such as chicken and mushroom or ham, leek and cider (£4.35); there are separate selections – for those with less appetite, such as turkey curry and rice or lasagne (from £2), for vegetarians – including a nut roast with tomato and celery sauce (£3.95) or home-made pancake with spinach, stilton, celery, apple and cider (£4.25) – and for children (£2); puddings such as home-made profiteroles or Dorset apple cake (£1.75, £1.25 for smaller portions). Well kept Badger Best and IPA Eagle Bitter on handpump; alley skittles, a fruit machine and piped music. The biggish garden – floodlit at night – has a children's play area with trampolines, a play house with slides, and pet rabbits. *(Recommended by Brian Chambers, Major and Mrs E M Warrick, John and Joan Nash, L Walker, Laurie Nutton, John Fazakerley, Mr and Mrs J H Adam, W F C Phillips)*

Badger   Manager Mr A J Walken   Real ale   Meals and snacks (12–2, 7–10)   Bishops Caundle   (0963) 23301   Children in eating area   Open 11–2.30, 6 (winter 6.30)–11

BOURTON   ST7430   Map 2
White Lion ⊗

Pub signposted off A303; the narrow lane is actually opposite B3092 signposted to Gillingham

Though this ex-coaching inn is a very welcome stop for holidaymakers on their way to the West Country, it's full of jolly locals, too. The two main bar rooms have broad flagstones, 18th-century woodwork, beams, a warm woodburner and big open fires, window seats, and old-fashioned furniture. Across the entrance corridor is the tiny traditional village bar and there's a partly no-smoking room up a couple of steps that is set out for eating: built-in settles around a medley of tables. Generous helpings of bar food might include sandwiches (from £1.40), a marvellous ham and vegetable soup (£1.50), a wide range of ploughman's (from £2.30), home-cooked ham and egg (£3.40), salads (from £3.50), vegetarian dishes such as spinach and walnut lasagne or beans and peppers simmered in a spicy coconut sauce (£3.65), steak and kidney or pork and apple pie (£3.65), beef in red wine with sautéed vegetables (£3.95), fresh local trout (£4.75), fresh Scotch salmon in a prawn, grape and cream sauce (£6.65), evening Scotch steak with brandy sauce, and puddings such as torte or jam roly-poly (£1.50); best to book for the three-course Sunday lunch; breakfasts from 9.30–10.45am. Well kept Ruddles Best and County, Ushers Best and Ashvine Tanker and Challenger, both brewed in a pub nearby, on handpump, with guests like Bass, Smiles and Wadworths 6X; farm ciders and perry; shove-ha'penny, cribbage, dominoes, fruit machine, and quiet piped music. There are picnic-table sets in the several attractive garden areas which surround the rose- and clematis-covered old stone pub; regular weekend lunchtime barbecues. *(Recommended by Bernard Phillips, Nick and Alison Dowson, TBB, John and Joan Nash, Mr and Mrs B E Witcher, R J Walden, S V Bishop, Ewan and Moira McCall, Hazel Morgan, Dorothy Leith, M D Hare, Stephen Lambert, R W Stanbury, T Galligan)*

Ushers (Watneys: leashold)   Licensee Christopher Frowde   Real ale   Meals and snacks (Breakfasts 9.30–10.45, 11–1.45, 6–9)   Partly no smoking evening restaurant Gillingham (0747) 840866   Children in eating areas (till 8, unless over 14)   Monthly live entertainment and barbecue nights   Open 10.30–2.45, 6–11; 11–11 Sat

BRIDPORT   SY4692 Map 1

George ⊘ £

South St

Readers have not been put off even when they've found this old-fashioned and consistently friendly town local bursting at the seams. There are country seats and wheelback chairs set around the sturdy wooden tables on the flowery carpet, upholstered seats in knobby green cloth built against the gold and green papered walls, and a winter log fire. The good home-made food is cooked to order by the licensee, using only fresh local produce and might include soup, (£1.30), sandwiches, home-made pâté, over a dozen omelettes, Welsh rarebit and bacon; while daily specials might include home-made shepherd's pie (£2.75), smoked mackerel fillet (£3), local pork chop with white wine and mustard sauce (£3.25) or fettucine bolognese (£3.50); a selection of vegetarian dishes such as mushrooms à la grecque or stuffed pepper (from £2.75); puddings include home-made apple tart and Loseley ice creams. You order at the bar and there is table service. Well kept Palmers Bridport, IPA and Tally Ho on handpump, up to seven calvados, and freshly squeezed orange or grapefruit juice and apple juice from a local cider farm; an ancient pre-fruit machine ball game and Radio 3 or maybe classical or jazz tapes; there is a no smoking area. Most readers are very happy with this pub which is not especially smart, but others express the view that the housekeeping should be more of a priority. (*Recommended by N Hardyman, I T Parry, P R MacCrimmon, Dennis Jones, David and Fiona Easeman, Michael Manser*)

Palmers   Tenant John Mander   Real ale   Meals and snacks (not Sun lunch, or night out of season, bank holiday Mons, evening of last Thurs in August   Bridport (0308) 23187   Children in separate room by bar   Open 10am–11pm (9am for continental breakfast every day); closed 25 Dec   Bedrooms; £18.50/£37

CERNE ABBAS   ST6601 Map 2

New Inn ★ ⊘ 🛏

14 Long Street

For sheer all-round quality, we've decided to award this friendly 15th-century inn a star this year. The comfortable L-shaped lounge bar has oak beams in its high ceiling, seats in the stone-mullioned windows with a fine view down the main street of this attractive stone-built village, and a warm atmosphere. Real care is taken over the food which comes in big helpings and includes sandwiches (£1.85, smoked salmon £3.10), home-made soup (£1.85), help-yourself salad (£2.50), ploughman's (from £3.10), beefburger or quiche lorraine (£3.50), omelettes (from £3.50), whitebait, deep-fried camembert or garlic mushrooms (£3.95), pan-fried rainbow trout (£6.55), cream and garlic lamb (£6.85), steaks (from £9.15); there are also daily meat, fish and vegetarian specials. Eldridge Pope Dorchester, Hardy and Royal Oak on electric pump, a very good wine list (not long, but interesting and attractively priced) – there's also a dozen by the glass in good condition, often unusual, changing weekly – and ten malt whiskies; considerate service; piped music; several tables are set aside for non-smokers. Behind the old coachyard there are tables on a sheltered lawn, and being enclosed, it's safe for children. A couple of the bedrooms have four-posters. This was originally a guest house for the Benedictine abbey; it's on *Good Walks Guide* Walk 29, which focuses on the Cerne Giant above the village. (*Recommended by Tony Shepherd, Mark Barker, J R Williams, David Wingrove, JM, PM, Dr BCM, Joan and Michel Hooper-Immins, Jerry and Alison Oakes, John Evans, Pat Woodward, R J Walden, A P Hudson, Carol Mason, Cathy Long, R W Stanbury, Chris Newman, Deb Jay*)

Eldridge Pope   Tenant Paul Edmunds   Real ale   Meals and snacks   Cerne Abbas (0300) 341 274   Children in eating area of bar   Open 11–2.30, 6–11   Bedrooms; £25/£40

Royal Oak

Long Street

This friendly 500-year-old pub, a typical Dorset stone-built structure, is set in a large garden. It sells well kept Eldridge Pope Dorchester, Hardy and Royal Oak on handpump from the uncommonly long bar counter; ten wines by the glass, fifty-three by the bottle. The row of three communicating rooms has sturdy oak beams, flagstones, neat courses of stonework decked out with antique china, brasses and farm tools, lots of shiny black panelling, and big log fires. Carefully prepared home-made bar food includes winter soup (£1.85), sandwiches (all £1.85) and a dish of the day such as beef in beer or lamb in orange and red wine (£4.95); classical piped music. There are seats outside. The pub is on *Good Walks Guide* Walk 29. *(Recommended by JM, PM, David Lamb, Alan Skull, E G Parish, A P Hudson, Gordon and Daphne)*

Eldridge Pope   Tenant Paul Edmunds   Real ale   Meals and snacks   Cerne Abbas (0300) 341274   Open 11–2.30, 6–11 (Sat 11–11); closed evening 25 Dec

CHEDINGTON   ST4805 Map 1

Winyards Gap

A356 Dorchester–Crewkerne

From the cast-iron tables on the terrace in front of this modernised old inn and from window seats inside, there's a marvellous view over the Axe Valley and the Blackdown and Quantock Hills which is described at length in Thomas Hardy's *At Winyard's Gap*; the attractively planted and sheltered garden has more seats. The stroll from behind the pub to the monument is pleasant, and you can walk on through the woods to the village itself. Beamed and comfortably furnished with plenty of seating, the bar is decorated with lots of pottery, brasses and copper. Bar food includes home-made soup, filled rolls and a variety of home-made pies such as local venison, beef and game pie cooked with elderberry wine, or braising steak with oysters cooked with Guinness. There's a choice of light meals such as filled baked potatoes or crispy mushrooms with garlic dip (from £2.50), ploughman's with local ham or cheese (£3.10) and kedgeree (£4.25); fuller meals include curries (from £4), Dorset cream chicken (£5), a choice of fish dishes (from £3.50) and steaks (from £5.25). They serve over twelve home-made traditional puddings daily such as jam roly-poly or spotted dick; children's menu and vegetarian food; Sunday roasts for which it's best to book a table. They have also installed a hot-dog machine which serves Bockwurst sausages in real French baguette bread. They boast sixteen beers from around the world and well kept Exmoor Gold and Stag and Flowers Original with a guest ale on handpump; polite staff. Darts, pool, table skittles, fruit machine, juke box, a function room and a spacious and comfortably furnished skittle alley. The alcove area is designated a no smoking area. *(Recommended by T Greenfield, Bob Smith, Mr and Mrs D V Morris, G T Rhys)*

Free house   Licensees Clive and Pam Martin   Real ale   Meals and snacks   (0935) 891244   Children in dining area   Country and western/folk Sun evenings   Open 11–3, 6.30(7 in winter)–11   Self-catering flats in converted barn; £12.50

CHESIL   SY6873 Map 2

Cove House 🏆

Entering Portland on A354, bear right following Chiswell Only signs: keep eyes skinned for pub, up Big Ope entry on right

Overlooking Chesil Beach and the sea, this warmly friendly pub has tables under parasols out on the sea-wall promenade – only about thirty or forty metres from the sea edge and a marvellous place to catch the sunsets, which can be glorious. The bar on the right is simply furnished, with polished floorboards and local shipwreck photographs gently underlining the maritime feel; it opens into a dining room on the left. The new licensees have made the food here really something to reckon with, concentrating on fresh local ingredients – including fish straight from the boats just down the beach. Bar food includes snacks such as good daily soups (£1.50) and sandwiches (from £1.40), four or five types of ploughman's (from £2.65), sweet-cured herrings (£2.95) and home-cooked ham (£3.95). A fuller à la carte menu includes smoked mackerel pâté (£2.75) or tuna and pasta salad (£3) to start, with main meals such as whole scampi tails in batter (£4.75), sweetcorn and mushroom crumble (£5.75), chicken breast in provençale sauce (£6.50) and steak (£9.95). In the evening there's more, for example smoked salmon with buckwheat cakes (£3.95) and salmon plus smoked salmon pie (£8.95). They rotate through eighteen real ales, such as Greene King Abbot, Devenish Wessex, Marstons Pedigree and Wadworths 6X, with one being changed every month; helpful service and piped music. If you go out by the gents' at the back you can see the massive masonry which has let it stand up to the storms (though after a particularly bad one, pebbles from the beach have been known to rattle down the chimney). Dogs allowed. *(Recommended by Charles Bardswell, WHBM, Roger Huggins, Ian Phillips)*

Devenish   Tenant Pat Jackson   Real ale   Meals and snacks (12–2, 7–9.30, not Sun eve)   Restaurant   Portland (0305) 820895   Children in restaurant only   Open 11–2.30(Sat 3), 6.30–11 (closing times flexible)

nr CHIDEOCK   SY4292   Map 2

Anchor

Seatown; signposted off A35 from Chideock

What marks this old pub out is its position – alone by a seaside cove, on a Dorset Coast Path and in front of the Golden Cap pinnacle, the signal station used by 17th-century smugglers. There are tables out on the front terraces, above a shallow stream bisecting the beach. Besides all that there is quite a summer bustle, with a nearby caravan site – so some readers (particularly those with children) like that a lot, others might prefer the out of season peace when it's altogether quieter. The two bars have simple but comfortable seats around neat tables, low white-planked ceilings, some sea pictures and interesting photographs of local scenes, and winter fires; one table and the family room are no smoking. Bar food includes home-made soup (£1.45), sandwiches (from £1.35, crab £2.60), filled baked potatoes (£1.70), ploughman's (from £2.75), ham and egg (£3.10), curry (£3.20 with a larger version for £5.65), pizzas (from £3.65), home-made steak and mushroom pie (£4.20), and salads (from £4.65, lobster with 24 hours' notice £4.65, local crabmeat £7.65); daily specials such as seafood lasagne or venison casserole; puddings such as apple and blackcurrant pie or chocolate St Emilion, all served with clotted cream (£1.55); children's menu (from £1.50) and afternoon clotted cream teas in summer. Well kept Palmers BB, IPA and Tally Ho on handpump, under light top pressure during the winter; freshly squeezed orange juice, and a decent little wine list; darts, table skittles, cribbage, dominoes, fruit machine, a carom board and piped, classical music. There are plans for an extension to be made to the family room, which will mean improved facilities for the kitchen, cellar, ladies' lavatories and 2 ensuite rooms to let, overlooking the beach. *(Recommended by Gwen and Peter Andrews, P R MacCrimmon, Dennis Jones, Jamie and Sarah Allan, Neil and Anita Christopher, N A Shaw)*

Palmers   Tenant David Miles   Real ale   Snacks (served all afternoon in summer) and meals (no food winter Sun evenings)   Children in family room   Occasional folk/blues winter Sat evenings   Open 11–11; 11–2.30, 7–11 in winter; closed evening 25 Dec

CHILD OKEFORD   ST8313   Map 2

Saxon   £

Gold Hill; village signposted off A350 Blandford Forum–Shaftesbury and A357 Blandford–Sherborne; from centre follow Gillingham, Manston signpost

Both the licensees and locals in this little village pub go by the notice in its bar: *There are no strangers here, only friends yet to meet.* It's a quietly clubby room with a log fire, and leads through a lethally low-beamed doorway into a rather more spacious side room with a mix of tables including an attractive mahogany one in the centre, plank-panelled dado, and a big woodburning stove in its brick and stone fireplace. Bar food's simple but neatly presented and good value, including lots of sandwiches (from £1, prawn £3.25), toasties (£1.25), filled baked potatoes (£1.65), ploughman's (from £2.70), a wide choice of hot dishes such as a daily curry or home-cooked ham (£3.35), plaice, chilli con carne or shepherd's pie (£3.60), filled Yorkshire puddings (from £4.25), chicken kiev or home-made steak and kidney pie (£4.75) and steaks (from 8oz rump £7.95), with several dishes of the day including a vegetarian dish); puddings such as raspberry and redcurrant pie or meringue surprise (£2.30); children's menu (from £1.40). Well kept Bass and Exmoor on handpump; maybe quite well reproduced piped music, shove-ha'penny, cribbage, dominoes. Besides their dogs (Bass, a golden retriever and Sebastian, a bearded collie) and cats (William, Henry, and Thomas), they allow dry dogs on leads; the back garden has an attractively planted border, slide, contented rabbits in neat hutches, goldfish, a couple of small paddocks with an entertainingly wide variety of fowls from khaki campbells to vociferous geese, two goats called Polly and Thea and, finally, George, a Vietnamese Pot-bellied pig, who apparently labours under the misapprehension that he is a dog. *(Recommended by Barbara McHugh, Donald Smith, Nigel Paine, Brian Chambers, Crawford Reid)*

Free house   Licensees Roger and Hilary Pendleton   Real ale   Meals and snacks (11.45–1.45, 7–9.30); not Sun or Tues evenings   Child Okeford (0258) 860310 Children welcome in top bar   Open 11.30–2.30, 7–11   Two bedrooms; £15/£30

CHURCH KNOWLE (Isle of Purbeck)   SY9481 Map 2
New Inn

A few changes at this relaxed, popular pub – the restaurant has been completely refurbished, while in the rest of the pub, carpet replaces the parquet flooring, there are Windsor chairs, decorative wooden chairs and old-fashioned tables, and the decoration on the stripped stone walls now includes brass and lots of antiques, as well as the urns and china. Decent bar food includes home-made soup (£1.45), sandwiches (from £1.35), ploughman's (£2.35), lasagne (£4), steak and kidney pie (£4.60), game pie (£7.95), steak with prawns and mushrooms (£9.50), they specialise in fresh crab and lobsters; puddings such as hot treacle tart, spotted dick and hot cherries in brandy (from £1.90); they do picnics to take away. Boddingtons, Marsden Pedigree and Newquay Steam on handpump. Darts, alley skittles, fruit machine and piped music .*(Recommended by L Walker, Derek Patey; more reports please)*

Devenish (Whitbreads)   Tenant Mr Estop   Meals and snacks   Restaurant   Corfe Castle (0929) 480357   Children welcome in one of the bars   Open 11–3, 6(7 in winter)–11

CORFE CASTLE (Isle of Purbeck)   SY9681 Map 2
Fox

West Street, off A351; from town centre, follow dead-end Car Park sign behind church

Some changes at this cosy and unspoilt old pub: they have rebuilt the kitchens and enlarged the bar and lounge bar, and the gardens. During the building, they also uncovered a well which they have incorporated into the lounge, covering it with glass and lighting it from within; it stands in front of the fireplace which is made from stone from the castle and so dates from pre-1300. In the popular tiny front bar the single heavy oak table has been replaced with smaller tables and chairs, there's a good old engraving of the ruined castle among other pictures above the ochre panelling, lighting by one old-fashioned lamp, and hatch service. As we went to press, they were changing and extending their bar food and didn't yet have details about dishes or prices, but their cooking has been enjoyed as good value. Well kept Ansells, Gibbs Mew Bishops Tipple, Ind Coope Burton, Sussex, Tetleys and Wiltshire all on handpump; good dry white wine. The attractive suntrap garden is divided into secluded areas by flowerbeds and a twisted apple tree, is reached by a pretty flower-hung side entrance, and has good views of the castle. The surrounding countryside is very fine and the pub is on *Good Walks Guide*

Walk 25. There's a local museum opposite. They're quite strict about excluding children. *(Recommended by Simon Collett-Jones, E G Parish, Jonathan Warner, Jerry and Alison Oakes, Steve and Carolyn Harvey, Ian Phillips, Stephen King, M E Hughes)*

Free house   Licensee Miss A L Brown   Real ale   Meals and snacks   Corfe Castle (0929) 480449   Open 11–3, 6.30–11; closed 25 Dec

Greyhound

A351

The National Trust now own this old-fashioned pub set just below the ramparts of the castle. The three small low-ceilinged areas of the main bar have mellowed oak panelling, a collection of old bottles, diver's helmet, old photographs of the town on the walls, and flowers on each table; there's also a no smoking family area. Fresh local seafood is the speciality here: excellent Poole cockles (£2), Mediterranean prawns sautéed in garlic (£4.50), very good fresh crab salad, and fresh lobster or mixed seafood platter (£8); other bar food includes large filled rolls (from 80p), home-made soup, a good choice of filled baked potatoes (from £2.50), various ploughman's (£2.80), lasagne or steak and kidney pie (£3.50), and salads (from £5); daily specials and seafood are chalked up on a blackboard. Well kept Boddingtons, Flowers Original, Whitbreads Strong Country, Winter Royal (October–April) and a guest beer on handpump; friendly service; darts sensibly placed in the back room, pool (winter only), fruit machine, trivia, and juke box. There are benches outside. *(Recommended by WHBM, Dr C S Shaw, Simon Collett-Jones, Quentin Williamson, Derek Patey, J P Cinnamond, Mrs R F Warner, Barbara and Norman Wells, M E Hughes)*

Whitbreads   Tenant R A Wild   Real ale   Meals and snacks (11.30–2, 6.30–9; not 25 Dec)   Corfe Castle   (0929) 480205   Children in family area   Open 11–3, 6–11; winter evening opening 6.30; closed 25 Dec

CRANBORNE   SU0513   Map 2

Fleur-de-Lys ⌖

B3078 N of Wimborne Minster

This pleasant pub has an attractively modernised, oak-panelled lounge bar and a more simply furnished beamed public bar with well kept Badger Best and Tanglefoot on handpump, farm cider, and some malt whiskies. Bar food includes sandwiches (superb very fresh crab £2.25), home-made steak pie (£4.75), gammon and venison pie (£6.95), lemon sole (£7.75) and vegetarian dishes like creamy leek crumble, nutty mushroom layer and cream cheese and spinach cannelloni (£4.45) and daily specials (£4.45); home-made puddings such as raspberry pavlova (£1.90). Very good value Sunday lunch, but it gets very busy on Sundays, so it's best to get there early. Darts, shove-ha'penny, dominoes, cribbage, fruit machine, and juke box. There are swings and a slide on the lawn behind the car park. Thomas Hardy stayed here for part of the time that he was writing *Tess of the d'Urbervilles*, and if you fork left past the church you can follow the downland track that Hardy must have visualised Tess taking home to 'Trentridge' (actually Pentridge), after dancing here. *(Recommended by Jerry and Alison Oakes, Dr S Rae, Gethin Lewis, Maysie Thompson, W C M Jones, John and Anne McIver, Mrs J A Gardner, Mary Springer)*

Badger   Tenant Charles Hancock   Real ale   Meals and snacks (not 25 Dec or evening 26 Dec)   Cranborne (072 54) 282   Children in eating area of bar, room for very small children and babies   Open 10.30–2.30, 6–11   Bedrooms; £27S(£29B)/£40S(£42B)

EAST CHALDON   SY7983   Map 2

Sailors Return   £

Village signposted from A352 Wareham–Dorchester; from village green, follow Dorchester, Weymouth signpost; note that the village is also known as Chaldon Herring; Ordnance Survey sheet 194, map reference 790834

New licensees have taken over this extensively renovated old pub. It's carefully kept its original character – the low-ceilinged stone-floored core now serves as a coffee house. The newer part has open beams showing the roof above, uncompromisingly plain and simple furnishings, and old notices for decoration; the dining area has solid old tables in nooks and crannies. Bar food is good quality and served in huge helpings, it includes sandwiches (from £1, filled French sticks from £1.50) and home-made soup (£1.30); light meals and starters include burgers (from £1.65), local smoked mackerel (£1.95), deep fried scampi (£2.05), filled baked potatoes (from £2.10) and ploughman's (from £2.85); main meals include home-cooked ham (£2.55), salads (£3.10), a quarter roast chicken (£2.80), home-made steak and kidney pie (£3.25), and a variety of steaks (from £7.25); also, fresh local fish or daily specials like chicken and asparagus lasagne (£3.75) or whole local plaice (£3.95), and children's meals (from £1.35). Well kept Strong Country, Wadworths 6X and guest beers on handpump, country wines, and farm cider. Darts, shove-ha'penny, table skittles, dominoes, and piped music. Benches, picnic-table sets and log seats on the grass in front look down over cow pastures to the village, which is set in a wide hollow below Chaldon Down; from nearby West Chaldon a bridleway leads across to join the Dorset Coast Path by the National Trust cliffs above Ringstead Bay. *(Recommended by Marjorie and David Lamb, Brian Smart, Jerry and Alison Oakes, Dr and Mrs R E S Tanner, D Swift, Jonathan and Helen Palmer, Nic James)*

Free house   Licensees Bob and Pat Hodson   Real ale   Meals and snacks   Partly no smoking restaurant   Dorchester (0305) 853847   Children in restaurant   Open 11–2.30, 7–11

EAST LULWORTH   SY8581 Map 2

Weld Arms 🐟 £

B3070

Relaxed and rather homely, the main bar in this thatched white house has a couple of long oak-panelled settles and a pair of pews among more regular seats, some big oak tables, and assorted easy chairs by the fireplace where there are likely to be fresh flowers from the rambling garden in summer, and where you may be able to roast your own chestnuts in winter (donations to RNLI). Reflecting the enthusiasm of the licensee (who's a single-handed Transatlantic man and has entered the 1992 race from Plymouth, England to Newport, USA) are the ensigns which drape the yellowing ceiling, and newspaper sailing clippings, yacht pennants and nautical charts behind the bar. Lunchtime bar food includes home-made soup (£1.40), sandwiches (from £1.30 with prawn or crab sandwiches or a steak roll £2.20), burgers (from £1.40), a wide choice of ploughman's (from £2), good home-made cottage pie (£2.50), while lunchtime specials, all at £4.40, might include veal and vegetable pie, savoury spiced pork casserole, seafood crêpe topped with cheese or a 1/2 pint jug of prawns; children's menu from £1.70. They also have an à la carte menu which includes duck kebabs with an orange sauce (£2.50), baked avocado filled with bacon and prawns (£3.70), English veal pan-fried in spinach, cheese, wine and cream sauce, salmon and cod in fennel sauce, baked in filo pastry (£8.50); good home-made puddings (£2); a wide choice of pizzas on Sunday night. Well kept Royal Wessex on handpump; courteous service. There's a smaller, snugger bar on the left (not always open) and a back family room, with darts, shove-ha'penny, dominoes, cribbage, fruit machine and decent unobtrusive piped music. Behind the building are picnic-table sets, swings and a climbing frame. *(Recommended by Janet Brown, Barry and Anne, Karen Tangaere, Dick Brown, Rob Weeks, Keith and Sian Mitchell, David and Marjorie Lamb)*

Devenish   Tenant Peter Crowther   Real ale   Meals and snacks   West Lulworth (092 941) 211   Children welcome   Open 11.30 (11 Sat)–2.30, 6.30–11   Bedrooms; £16/£28

FARNHAM   ST9515   Map 2

Museum 🍺

Village signposted off A354 Blandford Forum–Salisbury

The Coopers Bar in this solid brick building is the one to head for: calm and civilised, with local pictures by Robin Davidson, green cloth-cushioned seats set into walls and windows, piped classical music, and an inglenook fireplace. As well as sandwiches (from £2.50 with very lavish salad), ploughman's (£3.25), steak and kidney pie (£4.95), steak and oyster pudding or grilled lamb cutlets (£5.25) there are weekly specials such as fresh salmon (from £5.25) and puddings such as Dorset apple cake, chocolate fudge cake and various crumbles (all £1.95); excellent breakfasts. Besides particularly well kept Badger Best and Wadworths 6X and two guest beers, such as Abbots or Marstons Pedigree, on handpump, they keep a large range of decent wines, local country wines and some malt whiskies; darts, dominoes, pool, fruit machine, juke box and, in the lounge bar, piped classical music with jazz in the evenings. There's a most attractive small brick-walled dining conservatory, leading out to a sheltered terrace with white tables under cocktail parasols, and beyond an arched wall is a garden with swings and a colourful tractor. The green-corrugated locals' side bar has darts and a fruit machine. Good value, simple bedrooms in converted former stables. The rustic village is largely thatch and flint. (Recommended by Brian Chambers, J A Gardner, WHBM, Nigel Paine and others)

Free house   Licensee John Barnes   Real ale   Meals and snacks (12–1.45, 7–9.30) Tollard Royal (0725) 516 261   Children in conservatory   Occasional live entertainment   Open 11–3, 6–11; closed 25 Dec, eve 26 Dec   Bedrooms; £35B/£45B

GODMANSTONE   SY6697   Map 2

Smiths Arms   £

A352 N of Dorchester

Charles II is supposed to have stopped here to have his horse shod – it was originally a smithy. The little bar has some antique waxed and polished small pews around the walls, one elegant little high-backed settle, high leather bar stools with comfortable backrests, and National Hunt racing pictures, and a warm atmosphere. Well kept Ringwood Best tapped from casks behind the bar; polite, helpful staff; piped music. Good home-made food includes sandwiches (from £1.10, prawn £1.65), ploughman's (from £2.45), jumbo sausage (£2.50), quiche (£2.75), chilli con carne (£2.90), chicken (£3.15), a range of salads (from £3.55), home-cooked ham (£3.65), scampi (£4.25), with daily specials such as broccoli au gratin or curried prawn lasagne (£3.25), topside of beef (£4.70); puddings (from £1.30) might include treacle tart, strawberry flan, bread pudding or raspberry gateau. You can sit outside on a crazy-paved terrace or on a grassy mound by the narrow River Cerne – and from here you can walk over Cowdon Hill to the River Piddle. No children allowed inside. (Recommended by JM, PM, Michael and Harriet Robinson, Carol Mason; more reports please)

Free house   Licensees John and Linda Foster   Real ale   Meals and snacks (12–2, 6–9.45)   Cerne Abbas   (0300) 341 236   Open 11–3, 6–11; winter evening opening 6.30

GUSSAGE ALL SAINTS   SU0010   Map 2

Drovers

Village signposted off B3078 Wimborne Minster–Cranborne at Horton Inn; pub then signposted

There's been another change of ownership at this partly thatched village pub. The two main areas are divided up by the big brick fireplace, and there are beams, sturdy country chairs around the tables on the quarry tiles or carpet, pink-shaded wall lamps, and a few pictures, plates and guns on the white walls. Good value home-made bar food, particularly popular on Sunday lunchtimes, includes soup (£1.50), sandwiches (from £1.35), ploughman's (from £2.75), omelettes (from £3.75), salads (from £4.50), steak and mushroom pie, chicken curry, roast of the day or lasagne (£4.95), trout (£5.95), and various chargrilled steaks (from 8oz sirloin £7.95). Dishes of the day might include rabbit casserole (£4.50), whole Poole plaice (£4.75), duck and apricot pie (£5.95) or poached salmon steak in prawn and champagne sauce (£7.75); a children's menu (from £1.75) and vegetarian dishes such as mushroom and nut fettucini (£4.95); puddings from £1.85. Well kept Flowers Original, Marstons Pedigree, Ringwood, Wadworths 6X and a guest beer on handpump and country wines; maybe piped radio. From the picnic-table sets on the front lawn you look across to low rolling farmland; there's a good children's play area. *(Recommended by WHBM, Jerry and Alison Oakes, Roy McIsaac, E W B and M G Wauton; more reports please)*

Free house   Licensees Mrs Krystina Radwanski and Gina Evans   Real ale   Meals and snacks   Children in eating area of bar only   Open 11–2.30, 6–11

LANGTON HERRING   SY6182 Map 2
Elm Tree ✪

Village signposted off B3157

The emphasis here is placed firmly on the interesting and popular home-made food. From a wide choice this might include sandwiches (from £1.20), home-made soup, always a choice of two of which one is vegetarian (£1.95), a wide selection of ploughman's (from cheese to tuna to lemon pâté, from £3.25), hot and spicy beef casserole (£4.95), a choice of three quiches such as prawn and stilton or ham and peach (£5.75), prawn stuffed garlic bread or chinese chicken and nut casserole (£6.25), fruity lamb curry or 8oz steak (£6.75), Scotch salmon and lemon butter (£7.50), lots of daily specials which might include a pasta bake such as seafood (scollops, tuna and prawns, £6.25) or a vegetarian version such as cauliflower, cheese and onion (usually slightly cheaper at about £4.95), king prawns in garlic butter or chicken wrapped in bacon with stilton sauce (£6.25); a daily choice of four home-made puddings such as chocolate fudge cake, cheesecake or a fruit crumble and home-made ice creams such as rhubarb and strawberry, chocolate, pear and ginger and the enduring favourite banana and butterscotch (all from £2); there is a children's menu but the chef will also prepare smaller versions of the main menu. Devenish Royal Wessex on handpump kept under light top pressure; freshly squeezed orange and grapefruit juice and English country wines; piped music. The two main carpeted rooms have beams and walls festooned with copper, brass and bellows, cushioned window seats, red leatherette stools, Windsor chairs, and lots of tables; there is a central circular modern fireplace in one room, an older inglenook (and some old-fashioned settles) in the other. The traditionally furnished extension gives more room for diners. Outside in the pretty flower-filled sunken garden are colourful hanging baskets, flower tubs, and tables; a track leads down to the Dorset Coast Path, which here skirts the eight-mile lagoon enclosed by Chesil Beach. *(Recommended by David Wingrove, W J Wonham, Cathy Long, D K and H M Brenchley, W F C Phillips, Peter Hall, Carol Mason; up-to-date reports please)*

Devenish (Whitbreads)   Tenants Anthony and Karen Guarraci   Real ale   Meals and snacks   Dorchester   (0305) 871257   Children welcome   Open 10–2.30, 6.30–11

LYME REGIS   SY3492 Map 1
Pilot Boat ✪

Bridge Street

Friendly and welcoming towards customers of all ages, this very busy old smugglers' pub offers an astonishingly wide choice of waitress served food. The food here is very good and they are now including more fresh fish dishes among the daily specials; the menu includes sandwiches (from £1.15, delicious crab £2.75), home-made soup (£1.95; the fish one is wonderful), very good huge ploughman's (£2.95), excellent crab pâté with crusty thick wholemeal toast and cold, fresh butter in a scallop shell or mushrooms in a cream and cheese sauce (£3.50), a wide selection of fish dishes (from £4.75, local trout £6.50, whole grilled lemon sole £7.95), beef lasagne (£4.75) and steak and kidney pie (£4.95), salads (from £5.25, home-cooked ham £5.75, local crab £7.25), steaks from £8.50, and a good choice of vegetarian dishes (from £3.95 for asparagus quiche, also nut and mushroom loaf £5.95 which is a vegan dish); puddings such as lemon meringue pie, delicious treacle and nut tart or bread pudding, and a children's menu (from £1.95; no half-helpings of adult food); specials and fresh fish are chalked up on a blackboard, and the side salads are outstanding. They now also do a Christmas Day lunch and a dinner and dance on New Year's eve. Well kept Palmers Bridport, IPA and Tally Ho on handpump, and a decent wine and liqueur list. The light, airy bar has comfortable blue plush seating and decorations such as local pictures, Navy and helicopter photographs, lobster-pot lamps, sharks' heads, an interesting collection of local fossils, a model of one of the last sailing ships to use the harbour, and a notable collection of sailors' hat ribands. At the back, there's a long and narrow lounge bar overlooking the little River Lym. Darts, dominoes, cribbage. Not far from the sea and beaches. They now have a terrace outside and a large new restaurant which also serves as a function room and provides a venue for the new Lyme Jazz Festival. *(Recommended by Mr and Mrs P B Dowsett, Bob Smith, David Lamb, Barry and Anne, Peter Argent, BCM, TOH, Alan Skull, Stan Edwards, Mr and Mrs D V Morris, F E Bartholomew, Michael and Alison Sandy, Stan Edwards, Jon and Jacquie Payne, Patrick Freeman, Cdr G F Barnett, M L Hooper-Immins, Brian and Anna Marsden, Richard Parr)*

Palmers   Licensee W C Wiscombe   Real ale   Meals and snacks (12–2.30, 6–10 in summer)   No smoking lounge bar and part of new restaurant   Lyme Regis (029 74) 43157   Children welcome   Occasional live entertainment   Open 11–3, 6–11, (winter 11–2.30, 7–11)

LYTCHETT MINSTER   SY9593 Map 2

Bakers Arms

Dorchester Road

Behind the misleadingly small thatched white facade here is a large, bustling, well run pub with some extraordinary collections. There's a complete set of £5, £1 and 10/- English notes and English silver and gold coins since 1837, army badges, some antique Dorset buttons, cigarette cards, models, watches, holograms, a good collection of English stamps, and a run of annual statistics on some 60 items from 1900 onwards; also birds' eggs (shown with pictures of the birds), a glass beehive with working bees, and a 1940s Wurlitzer juke box (previously owned by Elton John) with the original records. Video displays tell you when you can collect your order from the efficient food counter: home-made soup (£1.50), sandwiches (£1.85), ploughman's (£2.25), help-yourself salad bar (from £3.25 up to £7.60 with steak), their speciality, steak and kidney pie (£4.95) and daily specials which might include vegetable quiche or beef in Guinness; puddings (from £1.60) such as Dorset apple cake. Well kept Flowers Original, Wadworths 6X and Whitbreads; fast service and the eating area of the bar is no-smoking; piped music and a fruit machine. Behind the pub, with tables beside it, is an adventure playground. *(Recommended by Derek Patey, Rob Weeks, Nigel Gibbs, Stan Edwards)*

Free house (part tie to Whitbreads)   Licensee Roy Forrest   Real ale   Meals and snacks   Children in eating area   Open 11–2.30, 6–11; closed 25 and 26 Dec

MILTON ABBAS   ST8001 Map 2

Hambro Arms 🕐 🛏

Like the beautifully landscaped village, this pretty dining inn is a powerful draw in the tourist season for its pleasant atmosphere, friendly service and good food: sandwiches (£1.50), ploughman's (£2.25), broccoli mornay or vegetable quiche (£4.50), steak and mushroom pie or beef and oyster pie (home-cooked to order £5.95), game pie (£6.95), salmon en croûte (£7.95) and beef wellington (£8.95), with puddings such as summer pudding or treacle sponge with custard (£2.25). The beamed front lounge bar, reached through a maze of stone corridors, has a bow window seat looking down over the village, captains' chairs and round tables on the carpet, and in winter an excellent log fire. Well kept Devenish Wessex Best and Flowers IPA on handpump; darts, juke box and fruit machine in the cosy back public bar. The outside terrace has some tables and chairs and a handcart is decorated with attractive plants. *(Recommended by BKA, H J Marchant, George Pugh, J R Williams, Mr and Mrs J H Adam)*

Devenish (Whitbreads) *Tenants Ken and Brenda Baines* *Real ale* *Meals and snacks* *Milton Abbas (0258) 880 233* *Children in dining room or (over 10) in public bar* *Open 11–2.30, 6–11* *Bedrooms; £25B/£50B*

NETTLECOMBE SY5195 Map 2

Marquis of Lorne 🎯 🛏️

Close to Powerstock and can be found by following the routes described under the entry included for that village – see below

Though the journey to reach this charming, well kept 16th-century pub is tricky, the drive is through quiet, peaceful countryside and once there the views are lovely, the staff very friendly and the food excellent. It's popular locally and with visitors and the chatty main bar has a log fire, green plush button-back small settles, round green stools and highly varnished tables on a flowery blue carpet, and doberman and rottweiler photographs; a similar side room decorated in shades of brown opens off it. Generous helpings of bar food include sandwiches which vary daily, home-made soup (from £1.45), filled, deep fried mushrooms with mayonnaise dip (£2.25 starter, £3.75 main course), devilled whitebait (£2.85 starter, £4.05 main course), basket meals (from £3.05), ploughman's (£3.50), spaghetti bolognese (£3.65), salads (from £3.95), home-made game pie or grilled gammon with pineapple (£6.70), chicken cooked in hot chilli and tomato sauce with peppers, onions, olives and baby corn or roast guinea fowl cooked in a red wine sauce (£8.75), half honey roast duck with mushrooms (£9.80), and T-bone steak (£10.95); a separate menu provides a wide choice of vegetarian dishes such as mixed hazelnut salad (£1.95), tagliatelle pasta with mushrooms and cashew nuts topped with cheese (£2.95), Tibetan roast made with buckwheat, onions, mushrooms, spinach, walnuts and herbs with mushroom sauce or quorn Mexican – quorn marinaded in spicy sauce with peppers, corn, chillies, onions and olives (£6.95) and vegetarian moussaka (£7.50); superb Sunday lunch and good breakfasts. Well kept Palmers Bridport and IPA on handpump; darts, bar billiards, shove-ha'penny, dominoes, cribbage, table skittles, trivia and piped music. Outside, the summer hanging baskets are pretty, and the big garden has masses of swings, climbing frames and so forth among the picnic-table sets under its apple trees. The earth-fort of Eggardon Hill is close by. *(Recommended by David and Debbie, Jack and Barbara Smale, Margaret Dyke, Bill and Jane Rees, P J Hanson, Mr and Mrs D V Morris, Roger Pool, Roger and Deborah Dawes, I T Parry, Dr R B Crail, David Wingrove, Heather Sharland, Maureen Hobbs, C A Hall, D S Moxham)*

Palmers *Tenant Robert Bone* *Real ale* *Meals and snacks* *Partly no smoking restaurant* *Powerstock (030 885) 236* *Children welcome* *Open 11–2.30, 6.30(Sat 6)–11; closed 25 Dec* *Bedrooms; £21(£23B)/£42(£46B)*

PLUSH ST7102 Map 2

Brace of Pheasants

Village signposted from B3143 N of Dorchester at Piddletrenthide

Beautifully placed in a quiet sheltered valley, this 16th-century thatched pub has a good size play garden with swings and an aviary, and a lawn which slopes up towards a rookery; there's an attractive bridleway walk behind, to the left of the wood, over to Church Hill – and it may be best to walk to this pub as parking space is rather limited. Inside, the well run and very friendly beamed bar has good solid tables and some oak window seats as well as the Windsor chairs, fresh flowers, and a heavy-beamed inglenook at one end with cosy seating inside the old fireplace and a good log fire at the other. Popular bar food includes home-made soup (£1.75), crab savoury (£3), ploughman's (from £3.25), really excellent smoked pheasant pâté (£3.25), salads (from £5.50), steak, kidney and mushroom pie or gammon and pineapple (£5.75), fish pie (£5.85), pheasant in red wine (£7.95), char-grilled steaks (from £8.95), and duck with apple and calvados (£9.50); specials like scallops and mussels in pastry, pernod and cream (£3.25), or chicken and coconut curry or game sausages with redcurrant and lemon sauce (£4.50), breast of pheasant with elderberry wine and orange (£8.50), trio of game breasts with redcurrant and port sauce (£9.25) and steamed halibut with dijon and cream sauce (£9.50) and children's menu (from £1.50). There are always four well kept real ales on handpump, such as Abbots Greene King, Bishops Tipple, Burtons and Wadworths 6X; darts, alley skittles, and dominoes. The golden retriever is called Scallywag and the labradors Becky and Bodger. Keith Andrew's orchid nursery is next door. (Recommended by Simon Reynolds, Michael Pritchard, John Knighton, Caroline Wright, P A Barfield, John Kirk, Mrs Vivien Warrington, Miss S Lee, Chris Newman, Deb Jay; more reports please)

Free house   Licensees Jane and Geoffrey Knights   Real ale   Meals and snacks (12–2, 7–10pm)   No smoking restaurant   Piddletrenthide (030 04) 357   Children in family room and restaurant   Open 11.30–2.30, 7–11

POWERSTOCK   SY5196 Map 2

Three Horseshoes ⊘

Can be reached by taking Askerswell turn off A35 then keeping uphill past the Spyway Inn, and bearing left all the way round Eggardon Hill – a lovely drive, but steep narrow roads; a better road is signposted West Milton off the A3066 Beaminster–Bridport, then take Powerstock road

A warm welcome can be expected at this popular and secluded dining pub; the cooking is imaginative – quite imaginative enough to justify the high prices. They concentrate on fresh fish, and each day, depending on the local catch, they have up to ten different fish dishes, such as grilled sardines, a properly made fresh fish soup (£3.50), mussels (£5.50), fish pie – their best seller (£6.50) – grilled whole plaice (£7.50) and bourride (£9.50), and they now do a seafood grill – half a lobster, scallops, oysters, clams and mussels grilled with garlic butter (£14.50); other food includes sandwiches, a self-help salad bar, spinach pancake with cheese sauce (£3.95), and a range of pies with hand-raised pastry – turkey and ham, pork, game – all at £4.95, and half-price for children. Good breakfasts with home-made marmalade. Well kept Palmers Bridport and IPA on handpump; freshly-squeezed fruit juice. The comfortable L-shaped bar has country-style chairs around the polished tables, pictures on the stripped panelled walls, and warm fires. On the neat lawn perched steeply above the pub there are charming views, as well as swings and a climbing frame. You can book six-hour fishing trips, there are nearby trout ponds, and plenty of beach casting. They have been asking for a whole night's room rate as an advance deposit. (Recommended by Patrick Freeman, Stan Edwards, Miss S J Ebbutt, Mr Jennings, Mr and Mrs Woodger, David Wingrove, David and Debbie, Alan Skull, I T Parry, Heather Sharland, Mrs M T Garden, Mr and Mrs G Turner)

Palmers   Tenant P W Ferguson   Real ale   Meals and snacks   No smoking restaurant   Powerstock (030 885) 328   Children welcome   Open 11–3, 6–11 Bedrooms; £24/£44(£55B)

SANDFORD ORCAS   ST6220 Map 2

Mitre £

Village signposted off B3148 and B3145 N of Sherborne

The general balance of opinion among visitors seems to be that the new licensee here is doing well (though Philip and Brenda Hayes, who left in late 1990, were a hard act to follow). The small bar has red leatherette wall benches and big flagstones, and leading off here is the bigger L-shaped dining room which has cream walls, plain tables on the flagstones, and a big woodburning stove set in the stripped-brick end wall; there's a no smoking area. Popular bar food includes sandwiches (from £1), baked potatoes (from £2), omelettes (from £2.50), ploughman's (£2.85), steak and kidney pie (£3.75), steaks (from £7.25), puddings like sticky toffee pudding (£1.75), and they hold special theme nights on Fridays when they serve the specialities of one particular country. Courage Directors and John Smiths on handpump, cider made in the village, and decent house wines; a fruit machine, bar billiards in winter, quiz nights and piped music. There are picnic-table sets up on the grass above the car park, a play area for children, and facilities for the disabled. (*Recommended by W E Parker, John and Joan Nash, Mr and Mrs R H Martyn, Jonathan and Helen Palmer, E G Parish, D A B and J V Llewelyn, Paul and Monica Mann, D Baddeley, Mrs Frances Smith, Mrs J A Gardner, R M Savage; more reports on the new regime, please*)

Free house   Licensee Ron Gower   Real ale   Meals and snacks (12–2.30, 7–10) Restaurant   Corton Denham (096 322) 271   Children welcome   Appropriate live entertainment on theme nights   Open 10–11   Bedrooms; £15S/£30S

SHAFTESBURY   ST8622   Map 2

Ship

Bleke Street; you pass pub on main entrance to town from N

Round the corner from Golden Hill, the steep terraced street of the nostalgic Hovis TV advert (which is behind the Town Hall), is this unpretentious seventeeth-century pub. There are seats built into the snug black-panelled alcove facing the main bar counter and on the left there's a panelled but similarly furnished room. Well kept Badger Best and Tanglefoot on handpump; darts, pool, cribbage, dominoes, dice games, mexican and straatje, a juke box and piped music. Bar food includes sandwiches, tuna and prawn puffs (£2.50), lasagne (£3.50), steak and kidney pie (£3.75), salmon en croûte or plaice filled with lobster thermidor (£4.50), and daily specials. (*Recommended by Marjorie and David Lamb, T Nott, Ian Phillips, Gordon and Daphne, Mr and Mrs J H Adam*)

Badger   Tenants Rene and Karen Broers   Real ale   Meals and snacks   Shaftesbury (0747) 53219   Children in eating area of bar   Open 11–3, 5–11; all day Thurs-Sat

SHAVE CROSS   SY4198   Map 1

Shave Cross Inn   ★   ⊘   £

On back lane Bridport–Marshwood, sigposted locally; OS Sheet 193, ref 415980

The original timbered bar in this thatched partly 14th-century pub is a lovely flagstoned room with one big table in the middle, a smaller one by the window seat, a row of chintz-cushioned Windsor chairs, and an enormous inglenook fireplace with plates hanging from the chimney breast. The larger carpeted side lounge has a dresser at one end set with plates, and modern rustic light-coloured seats making booths around the tables. Apart from a choice of excellent ploughman's (from £2.25), the bar food includes haddock fillet or very good sausages (£2.60), steak sandwich (£3.25), vegetarian chilli or mushroom and spinach lasagne (£3.75), a selection of salads that include home-cooked ham (from £3.45), kebabs of sweet and sour pork and spicy lamb (£5.50) and char-grilled steaks (£7.75); daily specials might include lamb and apricot pie or chicken, ham and leek pie or moussaka (£3.75) or a selection of fresh local seafood – oysters, prawns, lobster or crab; puddings such as Dorset apple cake or hot chocolate fudge cake (from £1.70) and children's meals (from £1.95). Well kept Badger Best, Bass and Eldridge Pope Royal Oak on handpump, cider in summer, and country wines. Friendly, polite staff. Darts, alley skittles, dominoes and cribbage. The pretty flower-filled sheltered garden has a thatched wishing well and a goldfish pool. There's a children's adventure playground, an interesting mural, and a small secluded campsite for touring caravans and campers. (*Recommended by Lynn*

Sharpless, Bob Eardley, D A R Glover, Miss J Woodman, Barry and Anne, JM, PM, Mr Jennings, D C Barker, David Lamb, Caroline Wright, Jamie and Sarah Allan, Patrick Freeman, Mr and Mrs B E Witcher, Mrs Sue Fergy, Barbara M McHugh, Gethan Lewis)

Free house   Licensees Bill and Ruth Slade   Real ale   Meals and snacks (not Mon, except bank hols)   Bridport (0308) 68358   Children in eating area of bar   Open 12–3, 7–11; closed Mon (except bank hols)

SYMONDSBURY   SY4493   Map 1

Ilchester Arms ⚥

Village signposted from A35 just W of Bridport

Warmly friendly new licensees from Zimbabwe have taken over this pretty old thatched inn and brought with them their family (so they now no longer do bedrooms) and Jess, the jack russell. One side of the open-plan bar has rustic benches and tables, seats in the mullioned windows, and a high-backed settle built into the bar counter next to the big inglenook fireplace; the other side, also with an open fire, has candle-lit tables and is used mainly for dining in the evening and at weekends. They specialise in fresh fish, emphasising that they are not a fast-food operation; to start they serve calamari or scampi (£3.25), butterfly prawns (£3.35) or scallops au gratin (£3.95), whole fish such as four sardines (£4.75), silver whiting or plaice (£6.25), lemon sole or ten tiger prawns (£7.50), dover sole or brill (£9.75), they also serve fish steaks or fillets such as shark (£5.50), Scotch salmon (£7.25) or sea bass (£9.75), while specials might include whole brown crab (£5.75), half an English lobster (£9.25) or, for two, a whole turbot (£20.75). If you're in a hurry they also buy in some fish frozen and serve this more quickly (from £4.50). Other dishes include ploughman's (£2.95), chicken (£4.25), steak and kidney pie (£4.75) and pigeon breasts marinated in cider and herbs, then pan-fried in butter and cream (£6.25). For vegetarians there is a crumble of aubergines, tomato, garlic, mushrooms, peppers and onions (£4.50); children's menu from £1.95; puddings such as treacle tart or apple dumpling (£2.50); decent wines. Darts, dominoes, cribbage, and a separate skittle alley (with tables); piped music. There are tables outside in a quiet back garden by a stream. The high-hedged lanes which twist deeply through the sandstone behind this village of pretty stone houses lead to good walks through the wooded low hills above the Marshwood Vale. *(Recommended by Alan Skull, Jamie and Sarah Allan, David Wingrove, Mr and Mrs D V Morris, Steve Huggins, Martin and Anne Pearson, G T Rhys, Neil and Anita Christopher, Anne Wallbank, Mrs F Smith, Mrs Sue Fergy)*

Devenish   Tenants Steve and Babs Bulling   Real ale   Meals and snacks (not Sun eves)   Restaurant   Bridport (0308) 22600   Well behaved children welcome   Open 11.30–3, 6.30–11; winter 12–2.30, 7–11

TARRANT MONKTON   ST9408   Map 2

Langton Arms

Village signposted from A354, then head for church

Next to the village church, this 17th-century pub has a main bar with settles forming a couple of secluded booths around tables at the carpeted end, window seats, and another table or two at the serving end where the floor's tiled. Bar food includes lentil and onion soup (£1.25), ploughman's (£2.60), steak and kidney pudding or mushroom florentine (£3.25), gammon steak (£4.50), steaks (from £6.50), puddings such as pancakes with lemon, jam or maple syrup, or chocolate and nut fudge (£1.20), and specials such as garlic prawns or lamb with orange and tarragon, and oxtail in Guinness; they also hold nights when they specialise in pizza and curry. To be sure of a table, it's best to get there early. The public bar, with a big inglenook fireplace, has darts, pool, shove-ha'penny, cribbage and juke box, with a skittle alley with its own bar and more tables also has a fruit machine. Well kept Flowers Original, Gales HSB, Marston Pedigree, Ringwood, Wadworths 6X, with weekly guest beers on handpump or tapped from the cask; Pimms in summer, mulled wine in winter, quite a few wines, and malt whiskies. There's a barbecue in the pretty garden. There are tracks leading up to Crichel Down above the village, and Badbury Rings, a hill fort by the B3082 just south of here, is very striking. *(Recommended by Margaret Drazin, Mrs S Yoxall, Mr Jennings, Jerry and Alison Oakes, Mrs R F Warner, C T and J M Laffin, M J D Inskip)*

Free house   Licensees David and Lesley Schuster   Real ale   Meals and snacks   Restaurant   Tarrant Hinton (025 889) 225   Children welcome   Occasional live music   Open 11.30–2.30, 6–10.30   Bedrooms; £32B/£48B

WEST BEXINGTON   SY5387   Map 2

Manor Hotel 🏇 🍽

Village signposted off B3157 SE of Bridport, opposite the Bull in Swyre

This old stone building – the ancient Manor House of Bessington, now West Bexington, was first mentioned in the Domesday Book. On the same level as the spreading south-sloping garden, the busy pubby cellar bar in this well kept hotel has small country pictures and good leather-mounted horse brasses on the walls, black beams and joists, heavy harness over the log fire, red leatherette stools, low-backed chairs (with one fat seat carved from a beer cask), and soft lighting. A handsome no smoking Victorian-style conservatory has airy furnishings and lots of plants. Very good bar food includes home-made soup and sandwiches, specials such as lamb noisettes, vegetarian lasagne or vegetarian chilli bake (£6.35), escalope of pork fillet in sherry sauce (£6.75), prawn tagliatelle or baked hake in Indonesian sauce (£6.95) or grilled bream with anchovy butter (£7.95). Well kept Eldridge Pope Royal Oak, Palmers Bridport (which here carries the pub's name) and Wadworths 6X on handpump; malt whiskies; alley skittles and a function room. The conservatory extension to the bar provides a no smoking area. The garden has picnic-table sets on a small lawn with flowerbeds lining the low sheltering walls, and there's a much bigger side lawn with a children's play area. The sea is just a stroll away (past the bungalows which make up most of this village), and the walks along the cliff are bracing. *(Recommended by Major and Mrs E M Warrick, Mr and Mrs Frostick, Roy Wilson, Marjorie and David Lamb, Richard Parr, Lynne Sheridan, Bob West, W F C Phillips, I R Pinnock)*

Free house   Licensee Richard Childs   Real ale   Meals and snacks (12–2, 7–10pm)   Restaurant   Burton Bradstock (0308) 897785   Children in eating area only   Open all day   Bedrooms; £40.80B/£68.50B

WORTH MATRAVERS   SY9777   (Isle of Purbeck) Map 2

Square & Compass   £

At fork of both roads signposted to village from B3069

A favourite of many readers for its never-changing, unspoilt atmosphere, this old pub has been in the Newman family for eighty-five years. The old-fashioned main bar has wall benches around the elbow-polished old tables on the flagstones, and interesting local pictures under its low ceilings. Marstons Pedigree, Tanglefoot, Whitbreads Pompey Royal and Strong Country are tapped from a row of casks behind a couple of hatches in the flagstoned corridor (local fossils back here, and various curios inside the servery), which leads to a more conventional summer bar; farm ciders. Reasonably priced bar snacks include filled rolls (from 60p, crab sandwiches £1.40), home-made pasties and pies (from 75p–90p for a sausage pie); cards and dominoes. There are seats outside on a side lawn that looks down over the village rooftops to the sea showing between the East Man and the West Man (hills that guard the sea approach); on summer evenings you can watch the sun set beyond Portland Bill. The pub is at the start of an OS Walkers Britain walk and on *Good Walks Guide* Walk 25. *(Recommended by David Warrellow, Derek Patey, Rob Weeks, Barbara and Norman Wells, Steve and Carolyn Harvey)*

Whitbreads   Licensee Ray Newman   Real ale   Snacks (11–3, 6–11)   Worth Matravers   (0929) 439 229   Children in family room   Occasional live music   Open 11–3, 6–11

Lucky Dip

Besides the fully inspected pubs, you might like to try these Lucky Dips recommended to us and described by readers (if you do, please send us reports):

Almer [just off A31 Wimborne Minster—Bere Regis; SY9097], *Worlds End*: This charming 15th-century L-shaped thatched pub (with Badger real, wide choice of good value food and good big play area) was sadly gutted by fire in 1991; the local hope is that rebuilding will re-create it as before

Ansty [Higher Ansty; ST7603], *Fox*: Still has interesting collection of some 800 toby jugs and lots of colourful plates, but cold table and carvery-style food service give a less personal impression than in the old days; food good though, with wide choice of puddings; well equipped children's bar with games and pool table, skittle alley with own bar, piped pop music (can be intrusive); strong local beer brewed for the pub, under pressure but interesting; small swimming pool, caravan site nearby; bedrooms (*Keith and Sian Mitchell, LYM*)

Beaminster [ST4701], *Greyhound*: Small and homely, with friendly staff, good beer and reasonably priced if limited food (*Dennis Jones*)

☆ **Bere Regis** [West St; SY8494], *Royal Oak*: Down-to-earth friendly pub with well kept open-plan modernised bar, good range of low-priced and well made bar food, Flowers Original and Whitbreads Strong Country on handpump, woodburning stove, sensibly placed darts, cribbage, fruit machine; dining room; open all day Fri and Sat; bedrooms (*BB*)

Blandford Forum [Market Pl; ST8806], *Greyhound*: Nicely decorated, spacious and comfortable, with relaxed atmosphere, Badger beers and good, reasonably priced bar food; attractive flowers in tubs and baskets, outside seats (*Richard Burton*)

Bournemouth [423 Charminster Rd; SZ0991], *Fiveways*: Busy, friendly town pub with usual pub food, Eldridge Pope real ales, no smoking area, good games room (*Brian Chambers*)

☆ **Branksome Park** [Pinewood Rd; off A338 on edge of Poole, towards Branksome Chine — via The Avenue; SZ0590], *Inn in the Park*: Small hotel bar well worth knowing for well kept Adnams, Ringwood and Wadworths real ales, good value bar food (not Sun evening) and attractive dining room (children allowed), tables on small sunny terrace; very popular weekends when car park full of hot hatches; quiet pine-filled residential area, nice steep walks down to sea; comfortable bedrooms (*WHBM, Michael and Rachel Brookes, Mary Springer, LYM*)

Bridport [Barrack St, off South St; SY4692], *Tiger*: Friendly free house with straightforward good value bar food, Bass and Wadworths 6X on handpump; pool room, skittle alley, juke box; bedrooms (*D Stokes*)

Broadmayne [SY7286], *Black Dog*:

Comfortably modernised spotless village pub with good value food from sandwiches through kidney pie and so forth to steaks; friendly and caring staff (*T R G Alcock, LYM*)

Broadstone [Waterloo Rd; junction A349/B3074; SZ0095], *Darbys Corner*: Large comfortably refurbished pub with three areas (one no smoking) radiating from central bar; big helpings of decent food, welcoming new licensees, Badger Best and Tanglefoot (*Win and Reg Harrington, WHBM*)

☆ **Buckhorn Weston** [ST7524], *Stapleton Arms*: Spacious comfortable lounge, snug, games bar (two pool tables) and nicely furnished restaurant; piped classical music, wide choice of reasonably priced food inc children's helpings and good Sun lunches, friendly locals and landlord, good choice of real ales such as Exmoor, Palmers, Wadworths 6X and Wethereds on handpump, plenty of tables in back garden (*D A B and J V Llewelyn, Mr and Mrs B E Witcher*)

☆ **Buckland Newton** [ST6904], *Gaggle of Geese*: Quiet free house in secluded village, genial licensees, well kept real ale, bar food, elegant bar with distinguished furnishings, spacious pool/snooker and skittle rooms; attractive garden with pond and big play area; goose auction twice a year, other country events; five bedrooms (*N J Hogg, Robert and Elizabeth Scott*)

☆ **Burton Bradstock** [SY4889], *Anchor*: Friendly, cheap and cheerful, comfortable and clean, with plenty of room and courteous staff; well kept Courage Best, good choice of bar food till 10, inc good puddings (*Dr R B Crail, Jacquie and Jon Payne*)

☆ **Burton Bradstock** [SY4889], *Three Horseshoes*: Attractive thatched inn with comfortable carpeted lounge, Palmers real ales inc Tally Ho, pleasant willing staff, good choice of bar food from sandwiches up inc children's dishes, restaurant; clean lavatories, no piped music, pleasant shingle beach a few minutes' drive away (with NT car park); nice atmosphere, but can get packed out in summer; bedrooms (*F Costello, Roy Wilson*)

☆ **Cerne Abbas** [Main St; ST6601], *Red Lion*: Cosy and picturesque oak-beamed pub, pleasantly refurbished, with well kept real ales such as Wadworths 6X, good atmosphere, generous helpings of well cooked straightforward food, quick friendly service; small but pleasant and tidy garden; good value bedrooms (*D K and H M Brenchley, David and Debbie, J L and S J Power, Marjorie and David Lamb*)

☆ **Charlton Marshall** [A350 Poole—Blandford; ST9004], *Charlton Inn*: Attractively refurbished oak-beamed bars with wide choice of generously served food from sandwiches through hot dishes such as tipsy crab pie, well kept Badger Best and Tanglefoot, quick friendly service, unobtrusive piped music, small garden *(Neil and Anita Christopher, S Watkins)*

☆ **Charminster** [A352 N of Dorchester; SY6793], *Three Compasses*: Friendly village pub with well kept Devenish Royal Wessex, good value food, skittle alley, family room with colour TV; bedrooms *(Stan Edwards)*

☆ **Chetnole** [ST6007], *Chetnole Arms*: Small comfortable local in very quiet village, generous helpings of straightforward bar food, well kept real ale, no piped music, genial landlord *(A P Hudson)*

☆ **Chideock** [A35 Bridport—Lyme Regis; SY4292], *George*: Thatched 17th-century pub with plush seats in simple dark-beamed lounge, wide choice of straightfoward bar food, well kept Palmers real ales, big log fire, family room with pool, darts and other games, various household pets, juke box, tables in back garden; nr GWG23; bedrooms *(John Kirk, Jamie and Sarah Allan, Neil and Anita Christopher, Win and Gordon Lambert, Brian and Anna Marsden, LYM)*
Chideock, *Clock*: Attractive thatched village inn with pleasant mix of styles and furnishings in open-plan bar, well kept Devenish, table skittles, brightly lit pool table; restaurant, simple bedrooms; nr GWG23 *(Neil and Anita Christopher, BB)*

☆ **Child Okeford** [on lane entering village from A357 Sturminster Newton—Blandford], *Union Arms*: Claret-coloured furnishings in bar and restaurant extension from original traditional core, where high-backed settles huddle around woodburning stove in big stone fireplace; well kept Hook Norton Best and a couple of interesting guest beers on handpump, discreet piped music, lunchtime bar food, some concentration on restaurant; pleasant licensees *(D A B and J V Llewelyn, LYM)*
Christchurch — see Winkton

☆ **Colehill** [off A31 E of Wimborne — OS Sheet 195, map reference 032024; SU0201], *Barley Mow*: Comfortable thatched, beamed and panelled genuine country pub with splendid winter fires and pretty garden; children allowed in eating area; in 1991 the Parkers who made it a popular main entry for very good value food, well kept Badger and guest ales and friendly efficient service moved to the Lost Keys at Wimborne, and we have no news yet of the new regime *(LYM; reports please)*
Corfe Castle [Furzebrook; A351 2 miles towards Wareham; SY9383], *Halfway*: Unpretentious Whitbreads pub, not spoilt — outside lavatories; pleasant atmosphere, well patronised, good choice of bar food showing Greek influence *(Derek Patey)*
Corfe Mullen [A31 W of Wimborne Minster; former Coventry Arms; SY9798], *Famous Old Trout*: Substantial Devenish development around former Coventry Arms, five inter-communicating bars, two restaurant areas; wooden or flagstone floors,

period furnishings and low ceilings repainted in smoky ochre *(Anon)*

☆ **Corscombe** [off A356 Dorchester—Crewkerne; outskirts, towards Halstock; ST5105], *Fox*: Idiosyncratic pub with obvious horse and hunting connections, friendly greyhound called Katie, old-fashioned furnishings and interesting decorations, well kept real ales such as Devenish JD and Exmoor tapped from the cask, short choice of bar food inc good sandwiches and interesting ploughman's; seats across quiet lane on streamside lawn *(Chris Raisin, Olive Carroll, L Walker, LYM)*

☆ **Dorchester** [High East St], *Kings Arms*: Hotel bar with comfortable armchairs, well kept real ales, wide choice of freshly prepared bar food (not cheap), open fire; close associations with Nelson and Hardy's *Mayor of Casterbridge*; bedrooms (the Lawrence of Arabia suite and the Tutenkhamen have to be seen to be believed) *(A P Hudson, Heather Sharland, M A Vann, LYM)*

☆ **Dorchester** [Monmouth Rd], *Bakers Arms*: Former bakery (as the big surviving steel oven doors show), now a friendly town pub with well presented simple home-made food from sandwiches to steaks, at fair prices, well kept Eldridge Pope ales, small sunny garden *(Nic James, Steve Huggins)*
Dorchester [Weymouth Ave; by Dorchester Sth Stn], *Stationmasters House*: Newish Eldridge Pope brewery tap, imaginative food from sandwiches up with railway-theme names, lots of old loco pictures etc, Hardy and Dorchester on handpump; tables on terrace; good children's room *(Joan and Michel Hooper-Immins)*

☆ **East Stour** [A30, E towards Shaftesbury; ST7922], *Kings Arms*: Attractively refurbished family-run free house with local paintings in comfortable lounge, restaurant (not Mon) beyond tanks of catfish, traditional public bar; generous bar food from toasted open sandwiches through steak and kidney pie to a big mixed grill with interesting specials such as ham and pineapple omelette, Bass and Charrington IPA or Worthington BB, no piped music; tables outside; children welcome *(Brian Chambers, Lyn and Bill Capper)*

☆ **Evershot** [off A37 8 miles S of Yeovil; ST5704], *Acorn*: After some dissent recent reports have spoken favourably of bar food from sandwiches to steaks, several changing real ales, decent wines and good service, in comfortable L-shaped bar with stripped stone, fine old fireplaces, pretty furnishings; games in public bar, good service, piped music; attractive Hardy walking country; children in skittle alley and restaurant; bedrooms comfortable *(M S Hancock, Mr and Mrs J H Adam, Roy Wilson, Jonathan and Helen Palmer, Heather Sharland, LYM)*
Evershot, *Strangway Arms*: Clean, comfortable and homely country pub with good food, plenty of space and friendly staff *(K R Harris)*

☆ **Fiddleford** [A357 Sturminster

Newton—Blandford Forum; ST8013], *Fiddleford Inn*: Vast flagstones in nicely furnished bar, wide choice of bar food (not cheap), interesting well kept real ales inc guest beers, good garden with play area; bedrooms clean and comfortable, with substantial breakfasts *(Brian Chambers, LYM)*

Halstock [ST5407], *Quiet Woman*: Spacious, clean and warm, with open fire, separate dining area, good helpings of typical bar food, skittle alley, pleasant back garden with well equipped play area; children allowed away from bar *(Brian Chambers)*

☆ **Hinton St Mary** [just off B3092 a mile N of Sturminster; ST7816], *White Horse*: Friendly atmosphere in light and cheerful extended lounge bar with cushioned settles and chairs, popular for wide choice of generous fresh food inc good fish; quick service, no piped music, Wadworths 6X; darts in larger public bar, booking recommended for good restaurant Sun lunch; quiet village with superb manor house and medieval tithe barn *(Brian Chambers, Barbara M McHugh, S Watkins, Donald Smith)*

☆ **Hurn** [village signed off A338, then follow Avon, Sopley, Mutchams sign — OS Sheet 195, map reference 136976; SZ1397], *Avon Causeway*: Expansively comfortable hotelish lounge with interesting railway decorations, six or more real ales under light blanket pressure, bar food from sandwiches to steaks inc children's dishes (there's an airy Moroccan-theme family room); outside they've kept the pre-war bypassed station platform complete with Pullman-car restaurant, also lots of tables — quiet woodland around; open all day, jazz Sun evening; piped music may be rather too obtrusive (bedrooms over bar may suffer, but otherwise comfortable and well equipped) *(Richard Houghton, Michael and Rachel Brookes, Rob Weeks, Bernard Phillips, Ian and Catherine Harvey, LYM)*

☆ **Kingston** [B3069; SY9579], *Scott Arms*: Efficient family food service (not cheap, but inc good applecake) in barn bar extension, well kept Devenish, Wadworths 6X and perhaps Flowers Original in rambling and interesting original core, children's area, superb view of Corfe Castle from garden; on GWG25, in beautiful village; bedrooms comfortable; new management late 1990 *(J E Stanton, A and J Jackson, John Fazakerley, Barbara and Norman Wells, R J Walden, Adrian M Kelly, M E Hughes, W J Wonham, P A Barfield)*

Knap Corner [B3092 S of Gillingham; 1/2 mile N of East Stour A30 Shaftesbury—Sherborne; ST8023], *Crown*: Small pub which has been praised for gorgeous log fire, friendly atmosphere, well kept Wiltshire Stonehenge, Old Grumble and Old Devil on handpump and good choice of decent food, but no recent reports *(News please)*

Leigh [the one nr Sherborne; ST6208],

Carpenters Arms: Friendly renovated village local with well kept Butcombe, good choice of reasonably priced food lunchtimes and most evenings, central fireplace, skittle alley, snooker and pool tables *(Peter Argent, Brian Chambers)*

Longham [A348 Ferndown—Poole; SZ0698], *Angel*: Popular food pub with substantial helpings from sandwiches up, inc good home-made steak and kidney pie; friendly service; piped music, and can get crowded, especially weekends *(Chris Cook)*; [Ringwood Rd], *Bridge House*: Greek-owned, with polite service, well kept beer, sunny tables overlooking river; bar food (not cheap); bedrooms *(Bernard Phillips)*

Lyme Regis [Broad St; SY3492], *Royal Lion*: Old-fashioned dark-panelled many-roomed bar with food, games room, restaurant; bedrooms *(LYM)*

☆ **Marnhull** [B3092; ST7718], *Crown*: Lots of atmosphere in attractive thatched inn, with oak beams, old settles and elm tables, broad flagstones and big log fire much as they were when Hardy modelled the Pure Drop at Marlott on it, in *Tess of the d'Urbervilles*; small more modern lounge (a bit of a trek from here to the lavatories), generous bar food from sandwiches through omelettes to steak, well kept Badger Best; children in eating area; also restaurant; bedrooms good value *(Dr and Mrs A K Clarke, Lyn and Bill Capper, LYM)*

Marnhull [Burton St], *Blackmore Vale*: Sadly the Hirons who made this Badger pub such a popular main entry for good value food have now left — we'd be grateful for news of them *(LYM)*

☆ **Melbury Osmond** [Roman Rd, Drive End; ST5707], *Rest & Welcome*: Clean, cosy, warm and welcoming little pub; limited bar good choice of straightforward food, well kept beer, good service *(T Billington, H J Stephens)*

☆ **Morden** [off B3075, between A35 and A31 E of Bere Regis; SY9195], *Cock & Bottle*: Enjoyably unspoilt country local with genuine welcome for strangers; scrupulously clean, with Badger Best and Tanglefoot and simple but good food — good ingredients tastefully presented *(WHBM)*

Mosterton [High St; ST4505], *Admiral Hood*: Wide range of food, especially fish, in quietly popular thatched 18th-century dining pub with neatly furnished spacious L-shaped bar, well kept Watneys-related real ales on handpump, coal fire in handsome stone fireplace, quick service, simple skittle alley *(Jacquie and Jon Payne, BB)*

Motcombe [just NW of Shaftesbury; ST8425], *Coppleridge*: Promising recent conversion from farm, well presented reasonably priced food, good choice of beers (inc genuine Czech Budweiser) and spirits *(Anon)*

☆ **Mudeford** [beyond huge seaside car park at Mudeford Pier — OS Sheet 195, map reference 182916; SZ1891], *Haven House*: Quaint old part-flagstoned heart to much-extended pub with Devenish and Wadworths 6X, bar food from sandwiches to crab salad; family cafeteria, tables on sheltered terrace; under new regime not as cheap as it was, but worth knowing for its unique seaside position — you can walk by the sea for miles from here *(Ian Phillips, LYM)*

☆ **Osmington Mills** [off A353 NE of Wareham; SY7381], *Smugglers*: Thatched stone pub, much extended but popular for the way it's been done — soft lighting, cosy corners, log fires, appropriate woodwork and nautical decorations; good value efficiently served bar food, partly no smoking restaurant, Courage Best and Directors and Ringwood Old Thumper on handpump, piped music (may be loud), streamside garden with good play area and thatched summer bar — just moments above the sea; children in eating area; open all day summer, bustling then (holiday settlement nearby); bedrooms *(W F C Phillips, P A Barfield, Barbara and Norman Wells, Sidney Wells, Eric J Locker, Barbara M McHugh, Brian Chambers, David Fowles, LYM)*

Parkstone [Parr St, Lower Pkstone; SZ0391], *Bermuda Triangle*: Interestingly decorated free house with three regularly changing real ales, several good continental lagers on draught and many other beers from around the world; good lunchtime food, friendly German landlady, good local atmosphere *(Malcolm Penney, Eody Beilby)*

☆ **Piddlehinton** [SY7197], *Thimble*: After two changes of regime latest news is that this lovely old thatched country pub is if anything better than ever: the little beamed bar (planning permission for an extension) attractively refurnished, with good choice of food, well above average, from sandwiches up, well kept Badger and other real ales, open fires, welcoming helpful service; tables in garden with summer house, barbecues, stream and little bridge; homely good value bedrooms, with decent breakfasts *(Bernard Phillips, Peter and Rosemary Woods, Brian Chambers, Dr S Rae, Hazel Astley)*

Piddletrenthide, *Poachers Arms*: Relaxed and unpretentious but very friendly, with good, plain pub food; bedrooms large, comfortable and purpose-built round garden and pool *(Michael and Harriet Robinson)*

☆ **Poole** [28 Market St (opp Guildhall, which is signed off A348) — OS Sheet 195, map reference 009903; SZ0190], *Angel*: Well run spacious and relaxed lounge with cool and careful decor, decent bar food from efficient separate servery, Watneys-related real ales and decent wines, tables and barbecues in back courtyard, restaurant and modern bedrooms; can get crowded with young locals in the evenings *(J S Rutter, LYM)*

☆ **Poole** [The Quay], *Lord Nelson*: Lively and friendly big maritime-theme waterside pub with interesting corners, friendly staff, well kept Badger and Gales beers on handpump, lunchtime food, locals inc genuine harbour folk; live music some nights, outside seats *(Nigel Gibbs)*

Poole [Sandbanks Rd, Lilliput], *Beehive*: Popular for spacious family eating area, good food — not cheap but worth it — well kept beer, big play area *(Mr and Mrs A P Reeves)*; [Market St], *Guildhall*: Small well run pub with well kept Devenish and good house wine; a find for its superb seafood *(John Kirk)*

☆ **Portland Bill** [SY6870], *Pulpit*: Comfortably refurbished, with well kept Gibbs Mew real ales, friendly obliging staff, piped music, food in bar and restaurant; in interesting spot nr Pulpit Rock, with great sea views *(Sidney Wells)*

Rampisham [OS Sheet 194, map reference 561023; ST5602], *Tigers Head*: Sadly we lost this fine main-entry pub in 1991, when the tenant lost his legal battle to stay in the face of the village-landlord's plans to close the pub and convert it to domestic dwellings *(LYM)*

☆ **Shaftesbury** [Bleke St; ST8622], *Kings Arms*: Major new dining-pub refurbishment by Badger, with country-cottagey furnishings, well chosen lamps, pictures, lots of china and other bric-a-brac, big inglenook fireplace, some stripped masonry, lots of partly timbered divisions to give feel of series of separate rooms; lavatory for disabled people, baby-changing room, open all day; managed by the Symondses, who were very popular at the White Hart, Bishops Caundle *(Brian Chambers)*

☆ **Shaftesbury** [The Commons], *Grosvenor*: Old wisteria-covered coaching house; now a THF hotel, but public bar used by locals, with cheap bar food inc soup, big ploughman's, one or two hot dishes and help-yourself salads; ask Reception if you can see the magnificently carved oak 19th-century Chevy Chase sideboard in the first-floor lounge (not always possible as used for private meetings); bedrooms *(Brian Chambers, Barbara M McHugh, T Nott)*

Shaftesbury [High St], *Mitre*: Good choice of meals, promptly served and well prepared, in straightforward lounge bar with lovely view; bedrooms *(Marjorie and David Lamb, LYM)*; [150 yds from bottom of Gold Hill], *Two Brewers*: Good range of well kept real ales, very cheap lunchtime food, pleasant landlady, clean and nicely furnished inter-connecting bars *(Ted George)*

Sherborne [Westbury; off Half Moon St; ST6316], *Britannia*: Attractive and welcoming 18th-century inn nr abbey, comfortable main lounge bar with end dining area, public bar with pool table and dartboard; bedrooms meticulously kept *(J M and S A Smither)*; [Horsecastles], *Skippers*: Imaginative bar food inc good fish, local and other cheeses, and interesting guest beers — but happily more locals than tourists *(Robert W Buckle, Dr and Mrs A K Clarke)*

Southbourne [Overcliff Dr; about 2 miles W of Hengistbury Head; SZ1591], *Commodore*: Whitbreads pub with new furnishings, giant brass ceiling fans, reasonably priced bar food inc ploughman's and good brunch; worth knowing for fine sea views from picture windows *(WHBM)*

Stoke Abbott [off B3162 and B3163 W of Beaminster; ST4500], *New Inn*: Good home-made food (not Mon evenings except bank hols) inc imaginative vegetarian dishes, well kept Palmers real ales, helpful service, comfortable beamed bar with big log fire and good horsebrass collection, charming garden; children in no smoking dining room; good bedrooms *(Leo Black, Felicity Vincent, G Parker, LYM)*

☆ **Studland** [SZ0382], *Bankes Arms*: The special feature is the wonderful peaceful spot above one of England's best beaches, giving good views of Poole Harbour and Bournemouth Bay; filling bar food (there may be a delay at trippery times), strong Whitbreads-related real ales, log fire; nr start GWG26 and south-western Coast Path; bedrooms clean and comfortable *(Barbara Hatfield, Derek Patey, Barbara and Norman Wells, E G Parish, Dave Irving)*

Studland [Beach Rd], *Manor House*: Ancient hotel with pubby atmosphere in small bar, very good beer and food — but you have to eat unless you're staying; closed early part of year *(E G Parish)*

☆ **Sturminster Marshall** [A350; SY9499], *Black Horse*: Above-average bar food inc good mushrooms wrapped in bacon, and well kept Badger beers, in smart but genuine pub with personal service from welcoming family (also restaurant); handy for NT Kingston Lacey *(WHBM, Dr and Mrs A K Clarke)*

☆ **Sturminster Newton** [A357; ST7814], *Red Lion*: Small, homely and cosy, with warmly welcoming staff, pleasant unhurried service, relaxing atmosphere, well kept beers, good reasonably priced food, log fire *(John Knighton)*

☆ **Sutton Poyntz** [SY7083], *Springhead*: Welcoming new tenants providing good food (inc fine seafood fresh daily from Weymouth) and attentive service in comfortably furnished big bar and adjoining restaurant area; nice spot facing willow-edged stream, with play area in big garden; the Jacksons (formerly of the New Fountain at Whimple) are now to be found at the Cove House in Chesil (see main entries) *(Stan Edwards, Brian Chambers, Roy Wilson, D A Clarke)*

Swanage [Sandbanks Rd; opp Burlington Rd; SZ0278], *Crows Nest*: Locally popular for food in bar and restaurant, attractive secluded garden; children in family room *(E G Parish)*; [Durlston Rd], *Durlston Castle*: Now a Bass pub, sympathetically refurbished, with wooden floors throughout; pleasant lighting, book-lined bar with hanging boat; good bar food, stunning views over bay, particularly from upstairs restaurant *(Jonathan and Polly, Derek Patey)*; [Burlington Rd], *Grand*: Good bar food, friendly helpful staff, fine view from conservatory; bedrooms *(Derek Patey)*; [1 Burlington Rd], *Pines*: Large well furnished bar with splendid long counter, very popular lunchtime for good bar food, served with

style; bedrooms good *(Roy Wilson)*

☆ **Tarrant Gunville** [Tarrant Hinton; ST9212], *Bugle Horn*: Attractive country pub, tastefully and comfortably furnished, with welcoming licensees, well kept Ringwood and Wadworths 6X, good choice of usual bar food inc genuine old-fashioned ploughman's; seats in garden *(WHBM, Brian Chambers, Barbara M McHugh, JM, PM)*

Tarrant Keynston [ST9304], *True Lovers Knot*: Enthusiastic young couple transforming atmosphere of this village pub without altering basic character; straightforward food, children in eating area, big garden *(WHBM)*

Three Legged Cross [SU0805], *Old Barn Farm*: Well organised dining pub which has kept character; good friendly service, decent beer, food well served and interesting *(SJC)*

☆ **Trent** [ST5918], *Rose & Crown*: Relaxed atmosphere in converted farmhouse with log fire, flagstone floors, good oak settles, nice pictures and new dining conservatory — very organised food, with chef in whites; Fullers London Pride, Oakhill and Wadworths 6X, good service, fresh flowers, books, no piped music; picnic-table sets behind; children welcome *(Lyn and Bill Capper)*

☆ **Uploders** [SY5093], *Crown*: Good food from soup through steak and kidney pie and vegetarian dishes to steaks or sole, and delicious home-made puddings — oven cooking, no microwave; two dining areas, inc beamed former stable with good wooden tables and chairs; well kept Badger, good service, tables on small back lawn *(Jon and Jacquie Payne, Mr and Mrs R G Dawes, J L Simpson, Barbara M McHugh)*

☆ **Upwey** [B3159, nr junction A354 — OS Sheet 194, map reference 666845; SY6684], *Masons Arms*: Friendly and largely unspoilt local decorated with photos of submarines and Ark Royal, fine collection of caps, shillelaghs and all sorts of plates, prints, fox brushes and oddments; Devenish ales, particularly good value bar food inc filled Yorkshire puddings and fine salads, skittle alley; attractive garden, big children's play area *(Stan Edwards)*

Verwood [SU0808], *Monmouth Ash*: Lounge bar with dining area, public bar and back skittle alley/children's room; well kept Badger, reasonable choice of fairly priced food *(Dave Irving)*

☆ **Wareham** [South St; SY9287], *Quay*: Two spacious stripped-stone bars, open fire, friendly young bar staff, modest but generous bar food inc vegetarian dishes, trendy music, good beer; charming quayside spot, parking nearby can be difficult *(Derek Patey)*

Wareham [41 North St; A351, N end of town; SY9287], *Kings Arms*: Popular thatched town local with two traditional bars separated by flagstoned corridor to back counter serving well kept Whitbreads Strong Country and Pompey Royal; reasonably priced bar snacks (not Fri—Sun evenings), may be smoky; back garden

(Derek Patey, LYM); [top of Church Ope Cove], *Mermaid*: Good reasonably priced food, friendly landlord, well kept Gibbs Mew, good position; children's room, skittle alley; bedrooms *(N A Shaw)*; [Town Cross], *Red Lion*: Good value food from sandwiches to generously garnished pies such as turkey and mushroom, with home-made puddings; bedrooms *(G M K Donkin)*

Wareham Forest [Coldharbour; Wareham—Bere Regis — OS Sheet 195, map reference 902897; SY8683], *Silent Woman*: Friendly, with well kept Badger ales, good choice of tasty bar food, peanuts on counter, military insignia on walls, interesting case of books; lounge bar extended into new stripped-masonry dining area with country bygones, access for wheelchairs; on GWG28 *(Chris Aslett)*

West Bay [SY4590], *Bridport Arms*: Well kept Palmers, good choice of bar food inc good crab sandwiches (served late at lunchtime), friendly service, nice atmosphere — especially in public bar; bedrooms *(Dennis Jones)*

☆ **West Knighton** [off A352 E of Dorchester; SY7387], *New Inn*: Spotless refurbished stone building, plenty of seats (and character), warm welcome; attractive home cooking in bar and reasonably priced restaurant, Devenish on handpump, country wines, skittle alley, children's room; garden, lots of flower tubs, pleasant setting in quiet village with wonderful views *(C A Hall, Dr R B Crail)*

☆ **West Lulworth** [B3070; SY8280], *Castle*: Attractive thatched inn with good food and wine in dining room, popular bar food in lively flagstoned booth-table public bar (piped music may be loud), cosy more modern-seeming smaller lounge bar, well kept Devenish real ales, traditional games and helpful staff; barbecues and outdoor chess on lawn above steep rose beds, lots of fine walks inc GWG27; comfortable bedrooms *(Richard Dolphin, J P Cinnamond, J E Stanton, M E Hughes, Dr S E Martin, Dr L B Cook, Nic James, LYM)*

☆ **West Stafford** [SY7289], *Wise Man*: Clean and comfortable thatched 16th-century pub with lots of toby jugs hanging from beams in lounge; particularly welcoming service, well kept Devenish, decent wines and country wines, wide choice of good value generous food; nr Hardy's cottage *(John Voos, C W Campbell, Nic James)*

Weymouth [by stn, Brownlow St; off Ranelagh St; SY6778], *Brownlow*: Basic but comfortable with plates and dishes above bar, food all day, Gibbs Mew Salisbury and Stonehenge, gentle piped music, pool table, children's room *(Peter Argent)*; [Trinity Rd], *Old Rooms*: Character fisherman's pub with

fine harbour views, basic food inc succulent crab or prawn sandwiches, Devenish beers, very friendly landlord formerly of the Royal Oak, Cerne Abbas *(Joan and Michel Hooper-Immins)*; *Park*: Reliable if rather straightforward good value food, pleasant atmosphere, well kept Eldridge Pope beers *(Michel Hooper-Immins)*

☆ **Wimborne Minster** [Victoria Rd, W of town; SZ0199], *Lost Keys*: Formerly the Green Man, now a free house, taken over 1991 by the Parkers (who previously made a success of the Barley Mow at Colehill); three connecting rooms off central bar, pleasantly furnished with red plush banquettes; notably hospitable welcome, Bass and Wadworths 6X on handpump, good bar food inc well filled sandwiches, restaurant *(WHBM)*

Wimborne St Giles [SU0212], *Bull*: Good bar food inc super ploughman's, local ham, fresh Cornish fish; Badger real ale *(Wm Mechan)*

Winfrith Newburgh [A352 Wareham—Dorchester; SY8084], *Red Lion*: Part of hotel, but has been enjoyed for pubby feel, good helpings of decent food presented well, quick service; bedrooms *(Brian Smart, David Lamb; news of new regime please)*

☆ **Winkton** [B3347 nearly 3 miles N of Christchurch; SZ1696], *Fishermans Haunt*: Modernised and much extended series of interconnected bars with some interesting furnishings, bar food from sandwiches to hot dishes inc children's meals, well kept Bass, Courage Directors, Devenish and Ringwood Fortyniner, garden tables, cheerful staff; children allowed in eating area and restaurant; bedrooms *(M Joyner, LYM)*

☆ **Winkton** [Bockhampton Rd, via Burley Rd, off B3347 — OS Sheet 195, map reference 166962; SZ1696], *Lamb*: Comfortable and relaxing country pub with friendly staff, good choice of bar food (chilli recommended), well kept real ales such as Marstons Pedigree, Ringwood Best, Old Thumper and Porte, darts, restaurant; garden, nice setting *(Richard Houghton, N P Attwell)*

Winterbourne Abbas [A35 W of Dorchester; SY6190], *Coach & Horses*: Spacious refurbished food pub (bedrooms too), which has been popular for reasonable prices, wide choice, generous servings, welcoming atmosphere and attentive staff, but no recent reports *(News please)*

Yetminster [High St; ST5910], *White Hart*: Welcoming and comfortable low-beamed village pub with stone-mullioned windows and lots of nooks and crannies; good choice of food, well kept Bass and Oakhill Bitter; garden and play area; well behaved children allowed *(Peter Argent)*

Durham   *see* Northumbria

Essex

Food in pubs here has been improving so much recently that the county can now be counted as above average for eating out; and on the whole prices are more reasonable than in most areas within striking distance of London. Drinks prices too are lower than the national average in those Essex pubs which are tied to local or regional brewers (but otherwise rather higher). Pubs here which we'd pick out particularly for food include the Kings Arms at Broomfield (very good meals, decent wines too), the consistent Swan at Chappel (with its attractive rather continental sheltered terrace), the handsome old Marlborough Head at Dedham (quite imaginative), the Cock & Bell at High Easter (can be very good indeed), the Cricketers at Rickling Green (a nice place to stay), the Eight Bells at Saffron Walden (doing very well under the current regime) and the Green Man at Toot Hill (recently bought out from its brewery, with lots of wines by the glass). These last three are all new main entries, or back in the Guide after a break. The Bell at Castle Hedingham and White Hart at Great Saling deserves special mentions as interesting buildings; the Black Bull at Fyfield for buying itself out of its brewery tie; Seabrights Barn at Great Baddow for the great efforts it makes to keep children – and their parents – happy; the Rainbow & Dove at Hastingwood for its vibrant cheerfulness, very relaxing for a place so close to the motorway; the Bell at Horndon on the Hill for proudly preserving the standards of a proper country pub; the Crooked Billet at Leigh on Sea for its attractive waterfront position; the Green Man at Little Braxted and Viper at Mill Green for their peaceful and pretty country locations; the friendly White Horse at Pleshey for all its bric-a-brac; and the Hoop at Stock for its fine range of splendidly kept real ales. In the Lucky Dip section, pubs that are currently moving up the charts include the Barge at Battlesbridge, Horse & Groom in Chelmsford and Fox & Goose nearby, Plough at Great Chesterford, Fox at Mashbury, Ferryboat at North Fambridge, Golden Lion in Rochford and Fleur de Lys at Widdington.

ARKESDEN   TL4834 Map 5

Axe & Compasses ★

Village signposted from B1038 – but B1039 from Wendens Ambo, then forking left, is prettier; OS Sheet 154, map reference 482344

The rambling and comfortable carpeted saloon bar in this attractive pub is distinctively furnished with cushioned oak and elm seats, quite a few easy chairs, old wooden tables, lots of brasses on the walls, and a bright coal fire. The smaller public bar, with cosy built-in settles, has sensibly placed darts, dominoes, and a fruit machine. Greene King IPA and Abbott and Rayments Special on handpump, good house wines, and several malts. In the evening there are food themes which change with the day; on Tuesday, fresh fish and scampi from Lowestoft (from £5.50); Wednesday, an £8.75 meal with steak, plaice or chicken kiev; Thursdays traditional English cooking (from £5); Fridays and Saturdays a grander range of full meals as well as bar snacks; Sundays, roast lunches (£10) and evening pasta (£5.95). At lunchtime the food includes home-made soup such as tomato or minestrone (£1.60), generous wholemeal sandwiches (from £1.65), various ploughman's (from £2.95; the stilton one is good), sausages, fish and grills with good, big chips, home-made daily specials (around £5.50), and puddings such as lemon soufflé (from £2.25); friendly, helpful staff. There are seats outside, on a side terrace with colourful hanging baskets; maybe popular barbecues. The village is pretty. *(Recommended by Gwen and Peter Andrews, K and J O'Malley, Wayne Brindle, Maggie Jo St John, Michael C Ennis, Maysie Thompson, Adrian Kelly, JM, PM)*

Greene King   Tenant Jerry Roberts   Real ale   Meals and snacks   Restaurant; closed Mon evening   Saffron Walden (0799) 550272   Children in restaurant   Occasional 60s evenings   Open 11–2.30, 6–11

BELCHAMP ST PAUL   TL7942   Map 5
Half Moon

Cole Green; Belchamp St Paul is on good back road Great Yeldham–Cavendish; the Belchamps are quite well signposted within the Sudbury-Clare-Sible Hedingham triangle

Close to the attractive village green, this white thatched building has good walks in the surrounding countryside. The beamed lounge area has a glass-fronted solid fuel stove, cushioned built-in wall benches and Windsor chairs on the dark red carpet, and a snug cubby by the serving counter. The lively locals' bar has darts, dominoes, fruit machine, and piped music; in summer, a bar in the back beer garden serves soft drinks and so forth. Bar snacks range from sandwiches (from £1.45), home-made soup (£1.75), ham or mixed cheese ploughman's (£3.20), and really good locally made sausages (£2.95), to more substantial meals (particularly in the evening) such as nut cutlet with cream and mushrooms or tomato and cheese sauce (£5.95), chicken in a cream and champagne sauce (£7.50), and peppered sirloin steak (£8.50); puddings (from £2.35); with 36 hours' notice they'll prepare more elaborate dishes. Adnams Southwold, Greene King IPA and Abbot and Nethergate Bitter on handpump from the temperature-controlled cellar, with Old Growler in winter; they also have Hackerpschorr, a full-flavoured real lager from Munich. *(Recommended by Gwen and Peter Andrews, Barbara and Norman Wells; more reports please)*

Free house   Licensees Bob and Denny Horsfield   Real ale   Meals and snacks (till 10pm; not Sun or Mon evenings)   Restaurant; closed Sun evening   Clare (0787) 277402   Well behaved children welcome   Open 11.30–2.30, 7–11.20; closed evening 25 Dec

BROOMFIELD   TL7010   Map 5
Kings Arms ✿

Village signposed off new A130 bypass N of Chelmsford

From a good bar menu that changes daily, the dishes served in this half-timbered village pub include home-made soup such as chicken and mushroom (£1.95), home-made duck liver, Cointreau and orange pâté (£3.50), dressed Cromer crab with mayonnaise, tuna oak smoked in dark rum or walnut and vegetable pie with spicy tomato sauce (all £3.95), Elizabethan chicken roasted with honey and almonds (£4.95), mixed kebabs (£5.25), fillet of fresh cod with a crispy cheese and light garlic topping or pork chop with mushroom, onion, tarragon and mozzarella cheese topping (£5.95), freshly roasted Thaxted duckling with brandied blackberries (£6.75), steaks (from £9.75), puddings like fresh fruit salad or hot chocolate fudge cake (£2.50), children's meals (from £1.75). Well kept Tetleys and a guest beer like Adnams, Batemans, Crouch Vale, Mauldons, Nethergate, Ridleys or Ruddles on handpump, good wines by the glass or bottle, as well as regular coffee, cappuccino with whipped cream, espresso, and hot chocolate with whipped cream, pot of tea; pleasant, helpful staff. The two heavy-beamed and dimly lit rooms of the bar have a quietly relaxed and chatty atmosphere, and are divided by a central brick chimney with arched brick fireplaces on either side (one with an unusual shuttered painting of the pub above it); there are brocade-cushioned reddish country chairs, some plush built-in window seats, and a mix of tables including a rather fine one built around a central standing timber; one side is more set out for eating – pleasantly so, with flowers on the tables. Fruit machine, quiet piped music. There are some picnic-table sets in front of the pub by particularly pretty tubs and hanging baskets, though the road that runs alongside is very busy. *(Recommended by Gwen and Peter Andrews, R C Morgan, George Atkinson)*

Ind Coope (Allied)   Licensee Robin Moore   Real ale   Meals and snacks (12–2, 6.30–9.30 or 10 Sat)   Chelmsford   (0245) 440258   Children in eating area of bar Open 11–2.30, 6.30–11; closed 25 and 26 Dec

CASTLE HEDINGHAM   TL7835   Map 5

Bell

B1058 E of Sible Hedingham, towards Sudbury

Besides seats on a small terrace in the car park, there's a fine big walled garden behind the pub – an acre or so, with grass, trees and shrubs. The popular, beamed and timbered saloon bar has Jacobean-style seats and Windsor chairs around oak tables, and some steps, beyond the standing timbers left from a knocked-through wall, lead up to a little gallery. A games room behind the traditionally furnished public bar has dominoes and cribbage; piped pop music. Bar food includes soup (£1.40), two sausages in a bap (£2.10), ploughman's (£2.40), half pint of smoked prawns with garlic dip (£3), lasagne (£3.50), steak and Guinness pie or lamb hot pot (£3.70), haddock and prawn gratinée (£4.20), sirloin steak (£6.30), and hot treacle tart (£1.90); well kept Greene King IPA and Abbot and Rayments tapped from the cask. Lucia the Great Dane may be ambling around – best not to bring your own dog. *(Recommended by Karen and Graham Oddey, WHBM, JM, PM, Barbara and Norman Wells, David Cardy, Gwen and Peter Andrews)*

Grays (who no longer brew)   Tenant Mrs Sandra Ferguson   Real ale   Meals and snacks (till 10pm, till 9.30 Sun; not Mon evening except bank holidays)   Clare (0787) 60350   Well behaved children welcome (not in public bar)   Jazz every last Sun lunchtime in month   Open 11.30–3, 6–11; closed evening 25 Dec

CHAPPEL   TL8927   Map 5

Swan

Wakes Colne; pub visible just off A604 Colchester–Halstead

The very sheltered suntrap cobbled courtyard is a lovely place to be on a fine day; it's got a slightly continental flavour with its parasols, big tubs overflowing with flowers, and French street signs, and is flanked on one side by the glass wall of the restaurant extension. The relaxed and friendly bar area is a spacious, rambling and low-beamed affair, with one or two swan pictures and plates on the white and partly panelled walls, banquettes around lots of dark tables, and red velvet curtains on brass rings hanging from wooden curtain rails; some standing oak timbers divide off side areas, and there are a few attractive tiles above the very big fireplace (log fires in winter, lots of plants in summer). Consistently good bar food includes filled French rolls (£1.30), sandwiches (from £1.35; the rare beef is excellent), ploughman's (from £2.95), chicken curry, gammon steak, very good fresh cod or rock eel or first class home-made steak and kidney pie (all £3.95), and 12 oz sirloin steak (£7.95). Greene King IPA and Mauldons Bitter on handpump, a good selection of wines by the glass, and decent coffee; faint piped music; pool, cribbage, fruit machine, space game and juke box in the biggish well furnished public bar. The garden (through which runs the River Colne) has picnic-table sets on grass stretching away from the big car park, and just below this is a splendid Victorian viaduct, which carries the Colne Valley Steam Railway; the Railway Centre itself, a must for steam enthusiasts, is only 1/4 mile away. *(Recommended by Prof S Barnett, Barbara and Norman Wells, Gwen and Peter Andrews, JM, PM, Gill and Doug Green, Mayur Shah, John Evans)*

Free house   Licensees Terence Martin and M A Hubbard   Real ale   Meals and snacks (till 10pm)   Restaurant   Clare (0787) 222353   Children over 5 in restaurant and eating area of bar   Open 11–3, 6–11

DANBURY   TL7805 Map 5

Anchor

Runsell Green; just off A414 Chelmsford–Maldon

Popular with locals, the open-plan, heavily beamed and sturdily timbered bar here has masses of brass and copper around its fireplaces (including an engaging clock with a tinkling chime), decorative plates on the cream walls, and comfortable plush settles and stools around simple modern oak tables; the no-smoking conservatory/family room becomes a restaurant in the evening. Well kept Adnams, Bass and Charrington IPA on handpump, and an extensive wine list; fruit machine and juke box in a side room. Bar food includes sandwiches (£1), soup (£1.95), ploughman's or home-made pâté (£2.75), seafood or vegetable lasagne (£3.15), salads (from £3.95), steak and kidney pie (£5.95), and puddings (£2.20). The raised lawn in front of this listed building (which was probably originally a yeoman farmer's in the 15th century) has picnic-table sets; swings behind. *(Recommended by Gwen and Peter Andrews, Nigel Gibbs, Shirley Pielou; more reports please)*

Charrington (Bass)   Licensee Mr Aris   Real ale   Meals and snacks (not Sun evening) Evening restaurant   Danbury (024 541) 2457   Children welcome away from main bar   Open 11–3(4 Sat), 6–11

DEDHAM   TM0533 Map 5

Marlborough Head ♀

Standing opposite Constable's old school, this early 18th-century pub serves good bar food such as soup (£1.35), sandwiches (from £1.35), strips of chicken and ham with apple mayonnaise or herring fillets with sour cream (£2.50), bacon, mushroom and tomato quiche (£3.90), fried spicy cajun shrimps (£4), lentil croquettes with a spicy tomato sauce (£4.25), fresh fillet of cod or beef and mushroom pie (£4.75), Aga-roasted back bacon steak with peaches (£5), English leg of lamb steak with caramelised shallot sauce or hare casserole (£5.50), sirloin steak (£9.50), and puddings like home-made treacle tart (£2) or sherry trifle (£2.75); get there early if you want a table. There's a wealth of finely carved woodwork in the cheerful central lounge; the refurbished beamed and timbered bar is popular for eating, with many tables (which have a numbered pebble for ordering food) in wooden alcoves around its plum-coloured carpet. Well kept Adnams Best and Benskins Best on handpump, freshly squeezed orange juice, and coffee; pleasant service. Seats in the garden at the back (part of which is now the car park). *(Recommended by Syd and Wyn Donald, Gill and Doug Green, Maysie Thompson, John and Karen Day, Prof S Barnett, Paul S McPherson, Gwen and Peter Andrews, R C Morgan, Barbara and Norman Wells, David Cardy, Tony Gayfer, Jenny Cantle)*

Ind Coope (Allied)   Licensees Brian and Jackie Wills   Real ale   Meals and snacks Colchester (0206) 323250 or 323124   Children in Royal Square Room   Open 11–3, 6–11; closed evenings 25 and 26 Dec   Bedrooms; £30S/£47.50S

FYFIELD   TL5606 Map 5

Black Bull

B184, N end of village

Mr Smith has now bought the freehold for this 15th-century pub from Charringtons and has changed the real ales on handpump to Courage Best and Directors, and Wadworths 6X. It's popular at lunchtime with businessmen and older people for its wide choice of food: stockpot soup (£1.20), sandwiches (from £1.35), ploughman's (from £2.10), filled baked potatoes (from £2.10), good chicken satay with peanut sauce (£2.65), ratatouille with garlic bread (£2.80), smokies (£2.95), chilli con carne or spinach and mushroom lasagne (£3.15), steak and kidney pie (£3.50), Mediterranean prawns (£5.95), wing of skate with lemon butter (£6.60), steaks (from £7), and duck breast with honey and lemon (£7.50). The pub has been recently extended to include new kitchens and a connected eating area; other communicating rooms have low ceilings, big black beams, standing timbers, and cushioned wheelback chairs and modern settles on the muted maroon carpet. Well kept Bass and Charrington IPA on handpump, darts, cribbage, piped music, fruit machine. By the car park, an aviary under a fairy-lit arbour has budgerigars and cockatiels, and there are picnic-table sets on a stretch of grass further back, and to the side of the building. *(Recommended by Joy Heatherley, JF, Derek Patey, Margaret and Roy Randle, Alan and Ruth Woodhouse, Caroline Wright)*

Free house   Licensee Alan Smith   Real ale   Meals and snacks   Fyfield   (0277) 899225   Children in eating area of bar   Open 11–2.30, 6.30–11

GREAT BADDOW   TL7204 Map 5
Seabrights Barn

From A12 Chelmsford bypass, take A1007 to Galleywood; turn right at lights and go right through village – pub on right

This fine conversion of a derelict 16th-century barn very much caters for families. There's a children's bar menu (£2.95) and certain free meals in the restaurant, a large enclosed garden with play equipment and a pets corner with six goats, chickens, rabbits and two aviaries, a decent no smoking conservatory-style family room off the main bar with cane plush-cushioned seating, ceiling fans, trivia and a television with cartoons, and a magician on Sunday lunchtimes. The rest of the pub is airy and spacious with the original high raftered and beamed ceiling, and is furnished with very high-backed farmhouse and other sturdy plush cushioned chairs, tractor-seat stools along the brick, wooden-topped bar bar counter, and rustic decorations. At one end there's an upper gallery, at the other a small cosy area separated from the main room by standing timbers; bright artificial hanging baskets. Also, an attractive little dining room, and a big restaurant. Bar food includes home-made soup (£1.10), sandwiches (£1.35), filled potato skins (from £2.15), ploughman's (£2.50), seafood crêpe (£2.95), filled baguettes (from £3.65), cajun chicken grill (£3.75), omelettes (£3.95), vegetable casserole (£4.45), home-made steak and Guinness pie, burgers or seafood lasagne (£4.95), rump steak (£7.85), daily specials like ribs (£2.50) or liver and bacon casserole (£3.25), and puddings (£2.15); Sunday lunch. Well kept Adnams Best and Broadside, Greene King IPA and Abbot, and Rayments on handpump, a good choice of wines, coffee and tea. Fruit machine, video game, CD juke box, piped music. The terrace has picnic-table sets, umbrellas, two football tables and a barbecue. It gets very busy at weekends; big car park. *(Recommended by SJC, Gwen and Peter Andrews; more reports please)*

Free house   Licensees Stephen Gormley and Ian Jones   Real ale   Meals and snacks (12–2.30, 6–10.30)   Partly no smoking restaurant; open noon–10pm Sun Chelmsford (0245) 478033; open all day Sat and Sun   Children welcome   Live entertainment inc Sun lunch magician for children   Open 12–3, 6–11

nr GREAT HENNY   TL8637 Map 5
Henny Swan

Henny Street; A131 from Sudbury, left at Middleton road at foot of Ballingdon hill; OS Sheet 155, map reference 879384

This very popular small pub has a cosy L-shaped and timbered lounge with well cushioned seats on the swirly carpet, lots of horsebrasses on the beams, and a big fireplace with a log-effect gas fire; a partly no smoking Victorian-style conservatory leads on to a terrace in the garden, where there's a pond and rustic benches among the willows on a riverside lawn. Decent bar food includes sandwiches (from £1.35), soup (£1.40), ploughman's (from £2.60), scampi (£4.35), pork steaks (£4.95), game pie (£5.50), whole grilled lemon sole (£6.50), roast young duckling (£7.65), steaks (from £7.95), roast pheasant (£8.95), daily specials, and puddings (from £1.49). Well kept Greene King IPA and Abbot on handpump, and coffee; maybe Radio Chiltern. Fishing permits are available and barbecues and a boar roast are held on summer Sundays (weather permitting).

(Recommended by Gwen and Peter Andrews, P Craddock, Prof S Barnett, Bernard Phillips, Barbara and Norman Wells, John Evans, Mrs E J Pateman, Alison Findlay)

Greene King   Lease: P A Underhill   Real ale   Meals and snacks (till 10pm Fri and Sat; not Sun evening)   Restaurant; not Sun evening   Twinstead (0787) 269238   Children in eating area of bar and in restaurant until 9pm   Occasional Morris dancing; Greek evening, and August Carribean barbecue with steel band   Open 11–3, 6–11; closed evening 25 Dec

GREAT SALING   TL7025 Map 5
White Hart
Village signposted from A120

This flower-decked Tudor pub has an attractive and characterful timbered lounge bar with Windsor chairs on its antique tiles, guns hanging behind the bar, and a stairway up to a little gallery with roughly timbered walls and easy chairs on its wide oak floorboards. Well kept Ridleys IPA and a guest like Adnams Extra on handpump; darts, dominoes, chess, draughts, and a fruit machine in the public bar. Bar food is marked out by the generous giant huffer sandwiches, a long-standing speciality and much loved by readers (from £1.35), and ploughman's (from £2.50). Cheerful service. As well as the usual picnic-set tables outside, there's a bench built right round the trunk of a fine lime tree. *(Recommended by Peter Andrews, SJC, Denny Lyster, James Turner; more reports please)*

Ridleys   Tenants Ken and Elaine Lavery   Real ale   Snacks; not 24–26 Dec Restaurant Tues-Sat evenings   (0371) 850341   Children in restaurant   Open 11–3, 6–11

GREAT YELDHAM   TL7638 Map 5
White Hart
Poole Street; A604 Halstead–Haverhill

Run by a welcoming, helpful licensee, nice to talk to, this striking Tudor house has a cosy bar with heavy beams and oak panelling, winged easy chairs, settees and wall settles, attractive antique Morland prints and a log fire; it opens into an extension, giving the feel of three separate room areas. Decent bar food includes sandwiches (from £1.30), delicious leek and potato soup (£2), ploughman's (£3.25), three local pork sausages in French bread (£3.50), omelettes (from £3.50), ravioli, mushrooms, prawns in a tomato, cream and tabasco sauce (£4.25), deep-fried split prawns or sirloin steak (£6.50), and dishes of the day such as splendid steak and Guinness pie, fresh fish from Lowestoft (from £4.50) or top rump of beef in plum, red wine and caraway sauce (£4.75), and puddings such as super raspberry meringue (£2.50). Well kept Nethergate on handpump, coffee and tea. The timbered and jettied building is surrounded by well kept lawns, where white cast-iron tables stand among lots of trees and shrubs; Samuel Pepys is said to have endorsed the original licence application. *(Recommended by Jill and Phillip Gilbert, Barbara and Norman Wells, Mrs Elizabeth Willis)*

Free house   Licensee David Smillie   Real ale   Meals and snacks (not Sun evening) Restaurant (not Sun evening)   Great Yeldham (0787) 237250   Children welcome Open 11–2.30, 6.30–11; closed Sun evening

HASTINGWOOD   TL4807 Map 5
Rainbow & Dove
1/4 mile from M11, junction 7; Hastingwood signposted from exit roundabout

Three small low-beamed rooms open off the main bar area in this rose-covered, tiled cottage. The one on the left is particularly snug and beamy, with the lower part of the wall stripped back to bare brick and decorated with old golf clubs, brass pistols and plates. Elsewhere, there are big brass platters, brass horseshoes and so forth, with horse-collars, the odd halberd and boomerang, and even a collection of garden ornaments in one fireplace. Popular straightforward lunchtime bar food includes sandwiches (from £1.10; toasties 10p extra), ploughman's (£3), pizza (£3.25), ham and egg (£3.50), two braughing sausages (£3.60), breaded plaice (£4.20), rump steak (from £8.25), and daily specials (from £3); evening soup (£1.60), trout (£5.50), and gammon (£6); Tetleys on handpump; piped music. Picnic-table sets under cocktail parasols, on a stretch of grass hedged off from the car park, are bordered by an 18-hole putting course and a paddock; there may be a children's summer bar out here at busy times (weekends, say), and there are summer Sunday evening barbecues. *(Recommended by JF, George Atkinson, Nigel Gibbs, Geoff Lee, Joy Heatherley, Derek Patey, Billy Dee, Nicky Morris, L M Miall)*

Benskins (Allied)   Lease: A R Bird   Meals (not Mon evening) and snacks   Children in eating area   Open 11.30–2.30, 7(6 Sat)–11

HIGH EASTER   TL6214   Map 5
Cock & Bell

The Easters are signposted from the Rodings, on B184/A1060

This timbered 14th-century pub is in the centre of the village and has a pleasantly local atmosphere. The heavily oak-beamed lounge bar is furnished with comfortably cushioned Windsor chairs and vases of fresh flowers. A cheerful second bar has the oldest dragon-beam ceiling in Essex, as well as a log fire. Well kept regularly changing beers such as Crouch Vale IPA, Eldridge Pope Hardy, Hook Norton, and Shepherd Neame Bitter and Spitfire on handpump, and a decent choice of wines. At its best the restaurary bar food – not cheap – can be very good: sandwiches (from £1.10), ploughman's (from £2.95), home-made quiche lorraine or tagliatelle bolognese (£3.95), steak and mushroom pie (£4.95), various vegetarian dishes, cold meats and hors d'oeuvres (£5.95), steaks (from £6.95), and children's menu (from £2); you can also choose dishes from their restaurant menu; Sunday roast lunch (£9.95, child £5.95), and maybe summer barbecues. There's a terrace and garden with a play area outside. *(Recommended by Adrian Kelly, SJC, JF, Caroline Wright, WTF)*

Free house   Licensee Barrie Day   Real ale   Meals and snacks   Children welcome Restaurant   Chelmsford (0245) 31296   Children welcome   Open 12–2.30, 7–midnight (supper license)

HORNDON ON THE HILL   TQ6683   Map 3
Bell

M25 junction 30 into A13, then left into B1007 after 7 miles

The 60-odd hanging baskets, troughs and old flower-filled mangles around the picnic-table sets and fountain in the sheltered back yard here have again won first prize in the local floral competition. Seats in a bow window at the back of the open-plan bar have views over the fields, and there are some antique high-backed settles, plush burgundy stools and benches, flagstones or highly-polished oak floorboards, and timbering and panelling; the fossilised objects hanging from the ceiling are hot-cross buns – collected, one a year, since 1900, though perhaps the wood carvings hanging from a block on the panelling and collected over much the same period are more edifying. Good bar food includes ploughman's, winter stew and dumplings (£3.95), fillet of cod baked in puff pastry (£4.50), chicken and chestnut pie (£4.85), and marinated leg of lamb steak or breast of chicken with mustard (£5.50). Well kept Bass and Charrington IPA on handpump, and 85 wines – listed on a blackboard with notes on what to drink with your food (you can also buy them off-sales). This is quite a centre for sporting activities: they have a ski club, a team in the London to Brighton cycle ride, and are coming up to their 16th year of the monthly Fun Runs, which take place every second Wednesday in summer (7pm start); the village cricket team are keen. On the last weekend in June the High Road outside is closed (by Royal Charter) for period-costume festivities and a crafts fair; the pub holds a feast then. *(Recommended by Joy Heatherley, Graham Bush, Mr and Mrs B Hobden, JF, Ian Phillips, Derek Patey, J P Day, David Cardy)*

Bass   Licensee John Vereker   Real ale   Meals and snacks   Restaurant
Stanford-le-Hope (0375) 673154   Well behaved children welcome   Open 11–2.30(3
Sat), 6–11; closed evenings 25 and 26 Dec   Bedrooms in house two doors away; I£48B

LAMARSH   TL8835 Map 5

Red Lion

From Bures on B1508 Sudbury–Colchester take Station Road, passing station; Lamarsh
then signposted

In winter, readers very much enjoy sitting by the huge log fire in the big brick
16th-century fireplace here, overlooking the River Stour and the Suffolk
countryside. The softly lit, timbered bar has tables and small pews by the front
windows, in stalls with red velvet curtain dividers, and in a timbered-off area
(which has pool, darts, fruit machine, video game, and trivia); unobtrusive piped
music. Good value bar food shows some eclectic touches such as excellent pea and
bacon or mushroom soup (£1.15) or the Greek-style tuna salad with feta cheese
(£4.95), as well as sandwiches (from £1.55), filled baked potato (£2.25),
ploughman's (from £3), spaghetti bolognese or ham and egg (£3.95), a substantial
double burger (£4), pork loin in mushroom sauce (£4.25), excellent mixed grill
(£6.25), steaks (rump £7.50), good rare roast beef on Sundays (£4.95), and
home-made puddings such as cherry pie (£1.65). Well kept Adnams and Greene
King IPA on handpump, and decent dry white wine by the glass; friendly staff.
There are swings in the biggish sheltered sloping garden. *(Recommended by Gwen and*
Peter Andrews, Derek Patey, Alison Findlay, Prof S Barnett,)

Free house   Licensees John and Angela O'Sullivan   Real ale   Meals and snacks
Restaurant   Bures (0787) 227918   Children in eating area and restaurant   Open
11–3, 6–11; 11–11 Sat

LEIGH ON SEA   TQ8385 Map 3

Crooked Billet

51 High St; from A13 follow signpost to station, then cross bridge over railway towards
waterside

The unspoilt lounge bar here has two big bay windows, cushioned seats facing into
the room built in around the walls, shiny yellowing walls decorated with
photographs of local cockle smacks, and a solid fuel stove; on the left, the
bare-floored public bar has a huge log fire, more photographs, and sensibly placed
darts, shove-ha'penny, and cribbage. Well kept Adnams, Ind Coope Burton,
Taylor-Walker, and Tetleys on handpump, with guest such as Marstons Pedigree,
Wadworths 6X, and Youngs on handpump. Straightforward snacks such as filled
rolls, ploughman's, chilli con carne and hot-pots. The big terrace has an outside
servery which is used on fine afternoons when the pub is closed; it's set by the
ancient wooden salt store and the sea wall, overlooking the shellfish boats in the
old-fashioned working harbour. They don't mind you eating cockles, shrimps or
jellied eels out here, from Ivy Osborne's marvellous stall, just down the lane (it
shuts at 10pm). *(Recommended by Jenny Cantle, Ian Phillips; more reports please)*

Ind Coope (Allied)   Manager Alan Downing   Real ale   Lunchtime meals and snacks
(not Sun)   Southend on Sea (0702) 714854   Open 11.30–3, 6–11

LITTLE BRAXTED   TL8314 Map 5

Green Man

Kelvedon Road; village signposted off B1389 by NE end of A12 Witham bypass – keep
on patiently

This quiet and pretty tiled brick house is tucked away on an isolated lane and has
picnic-set tables in the sheltered garden behind. Inside, the cosy, traditional little
lounge has a collection of 200 horsebrasses and some harness, as well as mugs
hanging from a beam, a lovely copper urn, and an open fire. Well kept Ridleys is

dispensed from handpumps in the form of 40mm brass cannon shells, and there are several malt whiskies; piped music. The tiled public bar leads to a games room with darts, shove-ha'penny, dominoes, cribbage, fruit machine, and video game. Good value bar food includes sandwiches (from £1.05, good steak), filled baked potatoes (from £1.55), hot locally-baked French bread filled with ham off the bone, sardines, chicken, turkey, beef or even meaty haggis brought from Scotland (from £1.40), ploughman's, salads (from £4.85) and lasagne, beef curry or chilli con carne. *(Recommended by Gwen and Peter Andrews, Anthony Barnes, John and Karen Day; more reports please)*

Ridleys Tenant Eion MacGregor Real ale Meals and snacks (12–2, 7.30–10.15) Malden (0621) 891659 Children in eating area of bar Open 11–3, 6(6.30 winter)–11

LOUGHTON TQ4296 Map 5
Gardeners Arms

2 1/4 miles from M11, junction 5; in Loughton, turn left on to A121, then right at war memorial and Kings Head on right; 103 York Hill

An unexpected find up its narrow lane, this pleasant old pub has a relaxed open-plan bar with low ceilings (except in one place, where it soars up to the full height of the pitched roof), old theatre billings, prints, engravings and pencil drawings of this and other picturesque old inns (including some by Cecil Aldin) on the walls, two or three delft shelves, some figured plates, an aged kitchen clock, guns above the beam where the bar opens into the restaurant area, and a couple of open fires. Bar food includes sandwiches (from £1.30, toasties from £1.45, steak £3.60), ploughman's (£2.70), omelettes (£3.10), salads (from £3.70), lasagne (£4.20), home-cooked ham and eggs (£4.30), steak, kidney and mushroom pie (£5.20), steak (£7.60), puddings (£1.65), and daily specials; as it's all freshly cooked, they warn of delays of 20–30 minutes with some dishes. Adnams, Ruddles County and Websters Yorkshire on handpump; fruit machine, piped music. There are spreading views to parts of Epping Forest from the picnic-table sets on the side terrace; there's also a little front verandah. *(Recommended by Joy Heatherley, Derek Patey, Robert Lester)*

Watneys Tenant Robert Worrell Real ale Lunchtime meals and snacks (not Sun) Restaurant 081 508 1655 Children in restaurant Open 11–2.30(3 Sat), 6–11; closed evening 25 Dec

MILL GREEN TL6400 Map 5
Viper

Mill Green Rd; from Fryerning (which is signposted off *north-east bound* A12 Ingatestone bypass) follow Writtle signposts; OS Sheet 167, map reference 640019

The two little rooms of the lounge in this homely pub have pale hessian walls (the log fireplace is in a stripped brick wall), spindleback seats, armed country kitchen chairs, and tapestried wall seats around neat little old tables, vases of flowers in summer, low ochre ceilings, and maybe the 17-year-old tortoiseshell cat (very partial to crisps). The parquet-floored tap room (where booted walkers are directed) is more simply furnished with shiny wooden traditional wall seats, and beyond there's another room with country kitchen chairs and sensibly placed darts. Bar snacks include soup (£1.15), good sandwiches (from £1.20, toasties from £1.30), Hawaiian toast (£2), ploughman's (from £2.50), and chilli con carne (£2.60). Well kept Ruddles Best and County on handpump from the oak-panelled bar counter; shove-ha'penny, dominoes, cribbage and a fruit machine. The garden has masses of nasturtiums, foxgloves, geraniums and lathyrus around the tables on a neat lawn, with honeysuckle and overflowing hanging baskets and window boxes on the pub itself; and all around is an oak wood, leading off to a bank of sweet chestnuts. Popular with walkers. *(Recommended by Karen and Graham Oddey, Derek Patey, WTF, J S Rutter)*

Trumans (Watneys) Tenant Fred Beard Real ale Snacks Ingatestow (0277) 352010 Open 11–2.30(3 Sat), 6–11

NEWNEY GREEN   TL6507 Map 5

Duck

Village signposted off A414 W of Chelmsford

Popular with businessmen at lunchtime, this friendly pub has a large, attractively furnished beamed bar with wheelback chairs, lots of tables tucked between high-backed booth seats, and some more unusual seating such as the great curved high-backed settle in one of the alcoves; there are also ancient-looking pictures and old farm and garden tools on the partly dark-panelled and partly timbered walls, a wind-up gramophone, and a coal-effect gas fire in a big two-faced brick fireplace draped with hop bines; part of the eating area is no smoking; fruit machine, piped music. Under the new licensee, bar food includes filled baps or sandwiches (from £1.50) and ploughman's (£2.75 – both these at lunchtime only), basket meals (from £2), ham and eggs (£3.25), gammon or vegetarian lasagne (£5), salads (from £5.25), sirloin steak (£9.50), a daily special, evening extras such as chicken kiev (£5.50) or duck à l'orange (£6.50), and puddings (£1.75); you're given a big wooden duck with your number on when you order. Well kept Bass, Boddingtons, Charringtons IPA, Flowers Original, Whitbreads Castle Eden, and a guest beer on handpump or tapped from the cask, several malt whiskies, and coffee. The garden by the huge car park has tables under cocktail parasols, lit by old streetlamps; there are two big lily-ponds (with anti-heron defences for the goldfish) in a rockery, and a hollow play tree with swings for children, a slide and a treehouse. (Recommended by Derek Patey, J and F Gowers, Gwen and Peter Andrews, Jenny Cantle)

Free house   Licensee Lee Hughes   Real ale   Snacks (lunchtime) and meals Chelmsford (0245) 421894   Children in eating area of bar and in restaurant   Open 11.30–3, 7.30–11; closed Mon (not bank hols)

PELDON   TL9916 Map 5

Rose

B1025 Colchester–Mersea, at junction with southernmost turn-off to Peldon

The atmosphere here is jolly and friendly – and that's its main appeal. The cosy, cream-walled bar is furnished mostly with antique mahogany and the occasional, rather creaky, close-set table; one or two standing timbers support the low ceiling with its dark bowed oak beams, brass and copper decorate the mantlepiece of the gothick-arched brick fireplace, and there are chintz curtains in the leaded-light windows; the large conservatory with its white tables and chairs and potted plants is no-smoking. The food servery, beside a stripped pine dresser on an old-fashioned brick floor, does sandwiches, lasagne (£4.65), and steak and kidney pie (£4.85), and so forth; other alcovey areas lead off here. Adnams on handpump and quite a few wines. The garden has good teak seats, a swing and a seesaw, as well as two ponds – the ducks have been known to wander expectantly among the tables. (Recommended by Gwen and Peter Andrews, Malcolm and Cynthia Pollard, Gill and Doug Green, JM, PM)

Free house   Licensee Alan Everett   Real ale   Meals and snacks   Restaurant; only Fri and Sat evening   Peldon (020 635) 248   Children welcome away from main bar Open 11–11   Bedrooms; £25S/£35S

PLESHEY   TL6614 Map 5

White Horse

Signposted with Howe Street off A130 Dunmow–Chelmsford

By the tiny bar counter in this relaxed and very friendly 15th-century pub, a snug room has brick and beamed walls, a comfortable sofa, some bar stools and a table with magazines on the brick floor, and a sonorous clock. Brick and half-timbered walls divide the main rooms which are decorated with jugs, tankards, antlers, miscellaneous brass items, a ship's bell, a shelf of books and old bottles, and several prints, and furnished with wheelback and other chairs and a mix of dark wooden tables; one fireplace has a woodburning stove, another big brick one has horsebrasses along the mantlebeam, and yet another has an unusual curtain-like fireguard. Popular bar food includes huffers (from £1.50), ploughman's or lots of filled baked potatoes (from £2.50), a tasty pie named after the pub or lasagne (£3.50), vegetarian dishes such as lentil crumble or spinach and mushroom lasagne or curry (£4), trout (£6.50), 6oz fillet steak (£7.50), venison in red wine (£9), rack of lamb (£10.50), and puddings like spotted dick and custard (£2.50). Well kept Boddingtons, Nethergate, and Morlands Speckled Hen on handpump, and good wines; fruit machine. A large dining room has sturdy furniture, lots of plants, glass cabinets with over 1,500 miniatures, and an old-fashioned stove in the brick fireplace. Doors from here open on to a terrace with white plastic garden furniture, a grass area with similar seating and a few picnic-table sets, and a children's play area with slide, swings and a see-saw. The hanging baskets and flowering tubs are lovely. The cat is called Tigger. *(Recommended by Gwen and Peter Andrews, Caroline Wright, Tony Beaulah; more reports please)*

Free house Licensees John and Helen Thorburn Real ale Meals and snacks (12–3, 7–10ish) Restaurant; not Sun evening Pleshey (024 537) 281 Well behaved children allowed Open 11–3, 7–11

PURLEIGH TL8401 Map 5

Bell

A414 E from Chelmsford, then right into B1010 after 5 miles; village signposted on right, pub by church at top of hill

Set on the only hill for miles (and with good views from its bow window over hedged flatlands to the Blackwater estuary), this popular and well kept pub serves good food, including sandwiches (£1), pizza (£1.85), ploughman's (£2), ham and egg (£2.60), salads (from £2.70), and plaice or scampi (£3.50); anyone not using the bar will have a 50p service charge added to the price of their food; friendly service. The rambling main bar has heavy black beams and timbers, cushioned wall banquettes and Windsor chairs on the carpet, and a huge log fire. Well kept Adnams and Benskins Best on handpump (the landlord encourages moderate drinking for drivers); dominoes, cribbage, trivia. Picnic-set tables on the side grass also have estuary views; New Hall Vineyard is closeby. *(Recommended by Graham Bush, Alison Findlay; more reports please)*

Ind Coope (Allied) Robert A Cooke Real ale Lunchtime meals (not Sun) and snacks Malden (0621) 828348 Open 11–3, 6–11

RICKLING GREEN TL5029 Map 5

Cricketers Arms ⊘ ⇌

Just off B1383 N of Stansted Mountfitchet

The softly lit and comfortable saloon bar, its two bays divided by standing timbers, has brown brocade button-back built-in wall banquettes, masses of cricketer cigarette cards, a big cricketing painting and a good log fire; maybe unobtrusive piped music. Good reasonably priced changing bar food, all home-made using fresh ingredients, includes sandwiches (from £1.10), soup (£1.25), filled baked potatoes (from £1.25), starters such as piquant taramasalata (£1.75) or soft roes (£2.25), a choice of ploughman's (£2.50), a good value fry-up (sausage, egg, bacon, tomatoes, mushrooms 30p each, chips 50p or 75p), mussels done in various ways such as marinière or a lightly curried version of mouclade (from £3.25), vegetable stroganoff (£3.50), liver and bacon (£4.25), steak and kidney pie (£4.50), 8oz sirloin steak (£6.75), and tempting puddings. Wednesday is fresh fish night – cod, plaice or haddock collected from Billingsgate (£3.25). Well kept Tolly Original and Dark Mild on handpump, with a monthly guest beer such as Felinfoel Double Dragon, good coffee (served with a jug of cream), friendly efficient staff – including "the Management", an engagingly manipulative standard poodle called Lulu. There's a very heavily beamed small stone-floored side family dining area, a modern back restaurant (usefully they do a second sitting at 3 for their genuinely no-rush Sunday lunch – booking only), and a separate front bar with pool, darts, cribbage, dominoes, fruit machine and juke box. A sheltered front courtyard has picnic-table sets overlooking a particularly good village cricket green. The bedrooms are in a modern block behind – handy for Stansted Airport, with a courtesy car for guests. (Recommended by Gwen and Peter Andrews, Caroline Wright, Kevin Perkins)

Free house   Licensees Tim and Jo Proctor   Real ale   Meals and snacks (12–2, 6.30–10)   Restaurant   Rickling (079 988) 322   Children in family room   Open 11–3, 6–11   Bedrooms; £50B/£55B

SAFFRON WALDEN   TL5438 Map 5

Eight Bells ⊗

Bridge Street; B184 towards Cambridge

There's been great relief among readers that the new regime here has not let down the high standards set by the tenant who had previously built up its reputation for good food. Quickly served by friendly, helpful staff the home-made food now includes fresh fish from Lowestoft or Billingsgate such as dressed Cromer crab (£4.35), and plaice, skate with capers and black butter and salmon in white wine (£6.10), as well as other dishes like soup (£1.70), ploughman's (from £3.25), good omelettes (from £4.35), lasagne or mushroom thermidor (£5.40), steak, kidney and mushroom pie or saffron-gilded chicken (£6.10), char-grilled steaks (from £10.20), puddings such as chocolate brandy pot or butterscotch fudge cake (£2.05), and children's menu (from £1.65). The neatly kept open-plan bar is divided up by the old timbers of a knocked-through wall, and has modern oak settles forming small booths around its tables; there's a family room in the tiled-floor tap room. Well kept Ind Coope Burton and Tetleys on handpump, and decent wines, and coffee; fruit machine. The restaurant, in a splendidly timbered hall with high rafters, has high-backed settles forming booths, and a very long refectory table. There are seats in the garden. Nearby Audley End makes a good family outing, and the pub is near the start of Good Walks Guide Walk 107. Please note, they no longer do bedrooms. (Recommended by Gordon Wrigley, Mrs Richard Stewart, Gwen Andrews, A W Lewis, C C Cook, D Cardy, JF, Mrs C M John)

Ind Coope (Allied)   Manager David Gregory   Real ale   Meals and snacks (noon–9.30; Mons 12–2.30, 6–9.30)   Weekend restaurant   Saffron Walden (0799) 22790   Children in family room   Open 11–3, 6–11

STOCK   TQ6998 Map 5

Hoop   £

B1007; from A12 Chelmsford bypass take Galleywood, Billericay turn-off

Even when this friendly pub is at its most crowded, the atmosphere stays friendly and relaxed and the staff cope splendidly – the extension has helped, too. There's an outstanding range of real ales and they normally have at least Archers, Adnams Bitter and Mild, Crouch Vale, Exmoor, Felinfoel, Hook Norton Old Hooky, Mauldons, Nethergate, and Wadworths 6X on handpump or more likely tapped from the cask, with Timothy Taylors Landlord every fortnight, and two or three guest beers such as Brains Red Dragon, Robinsons Mild and Palmers Tally Ho; however the best time to catch it is on the May Day weekend, when around a hundred real ales are available; also farm cider, decent wines by the glass, and mulled wine in winter. To the left there are brocaded wall seats around dimpled copper tables, with a cluster of brocaded stools on the right – where there's a coal-effect gas fire in the big brick fireplace. Sensibly placed darts (the heavy black beams are studded with hundreds of darts flights), cribbage and dominoes. Good value bar food, available all day, includes sandwiches (from 90p), soup (£1), filled baked potatoes (from £1.20), omelettes or sausage pie (from £2), ploughman's (from £2.50), home-cooked ham and egg (£2.80), and home-made dishes like steak and kidney pie, rabbit stew and dumplings or braised liver (all £3.50), and puddings such as home-made blackcurrant and apple pie (£1). There are lots of picnic-table sets in the big sheltered back garden, which is prettily bordered with flowers and where they have occasional summer barbecues and maybe croquet (or boules on the front gravel). The dog is called Misty and the cat Thomas. *(Recommended by Graham Bush, Richard Houghton, Gwen and Peter Andrews, George Atkinson, Karen and Graham Oddey, P and J McComb, Jenny Cantle)*

Free house   Licensee Albert Kitchin   Real ale   Meals and snacks (all day)   Stock (0277) 841 137   Children in eating area of bar   Open 10am–11pm

TILLINGHAM   TL9903   Map 5

Cap & Feathers   ★

B1027 N of Southminster

Under the new licensees, early reports from readers who know this warmly relaxed, tiled and white clapboarded village pub seem to suggest little has changed. The bar, divided into three snug areas, has uneven low beams, timbers, sturdy wall seats (including a venerable built-in floor-to-ceiling settle), little wheelback chairs with arms, a homely dresser and a formidable woodburning stove; one parquet-floored part has bar billiards, sensibly placed darts, and table skittles – there's another set in the attractive family room, and they have shove-ha'penny, cribbage and dominoes. Bar food features the succulent and distinctively flavoured products of their own smokery – thinly sliced beef as a starter (£2.50), cod and trout (£4.30), and maybe specials such as pheasant. Other home-cooked dishes include ploughman's, fish pie, vegetarian lasagne or vegetarian savoury sausages (all £3.95), sirloin steak (£6.50), mixed grill (£6.65), and home-made puddings like apple crumble or mandarin cheesecake. The fine range of drinks includes well kept Crouch Vale Woodham and Best, SAS, Essex Mild and in winter Willie Warmer, with Thatcher's farm cider, and fruit wines. There are a few picnic-table sets under birch trees on a small side terrace. *(Recommended by Gwen and Peter Andrews, Alison Findlay, Jenny Cantle, Maurice Southon, Derek Patey)*

Crouch Vale   Managers Neil and Carole Clack   Real ale   Meals and snacks Tillingham (0621) 779212   Children in family room   Open 11–3, 6–11   Three bedrooms; £15/£30

TOOT HILL   TL5103   Map 5

Green Man

Village signposted from A113 in Stanford Rivers, S of Ongar; and from A414 W of Ongar

Mr Roads has now bought the freehold of this pub from Watneys, and as we went to press they were deciding which real ales to serve – at the moment it's still Ruddles Best and Websters Yorkshire on handpump. Well chosen wines from five wine merchants include forty different well served champagnes by the bottle (many pinks, including their *doyenne*, Veuve Clicquot), with one sold by the glass, and over 100 wines (they have a wine of the week); there are also Beaujolais tastings. Good bar food includes soup (£2), ploughman's (from £2.25), mushrooms with garlic and diced bacon or grilled herring with oatmeal (£2.70), home-made pies like steak and kidney (from £4), wild rabbit with herb dumplings (£4.95), fillet of pork with cider and pimentoes (£5.90), and baked salmon in pesto sauce (£6.95); friendly service. There may be nibbles of cheddar and cheesy biscuits. The main emphasis is on the long dining lounge a step up from here, with candlelit tables, fresh flowers, and attractively figured plates on a delft shelf. In the evenings they take bookings for tables in here, but only for 7.30; after that, when you turn up they put you on a queue for tables that come free. A smallish and simply furnished area by the bar has mushroom plush chairs and pale mustard leatherette stools and settles, one or two hunting prints above the dark varnished wood dado, brass platters on a shelf just below the very dark grey-green ceiling, and an open fire; darts around the other side, shove-ha'penny, dominoes, cribbage and piped music. In summer, there's a lovely mass of colourful hanging baskets, window-boxes and flower tubs, prettily set off by the curlicued white iron tables and chairs. Many more picnic-table sets on the grass behind have a fine view over the quiet rolling fields and woods to North Weald. *(Recommended by David Lamb, P Craddock, Joy Heatherley, JF, Gwen and Peter Andrews)*

Free house   Licensee Peter Roads   Real ale   Meals and snacks (not 25 Dec)   Restaurant   North Weald (037 882) 2255   Children over 10 only   Open 11–3, 6–11

WOODHAM WALTER   TL8006   Map 5

Bell

A414 E from Chelmsford; village signposted on left after about 6 miles

This lovely tiled and timbered Elizabethan building has a neatly kept, but friendly and informal, lounge bar that is divided into irregularly-shaped alcoves on various levels, with old timbers and beams, comfortable seats and a log fire. The bar food is standard – sandwiches, soup, local sausage in French bread, home-made curry or steak and kidney pie (£3.95), and daily specials; there's a prettily decorated dining room in a partly panelled gallery up steps from the main bar. Benskins Best, Ind Coope Burton, and Tetleys Bitter on handpump. *(Recommended by Karen and Graham Oddey, Mayur Shah, Gwen and Peter Andrews; more reports please)*

Ind Coope (Allied)   Manager Mrs Lorraine Terris   Real ale   Meals (not Sun evening) and snacks   Danbury (0245) 413437   Well behaved children welcome   Open 12–3, 6–11

Cats

Back road to Curling Tye and Maldon, from N end of village

For some reason, he won't tell us why, the landlord has been trying to keep this charming country pub out of the Guide. But as we've explained to him, letting licensees decide for us which pubs *not* to include would damage our independence almost as much as allowing other landlords to pay for their inclusion. So here it is again, delightfully peaceful in summer with its well kept garden, looking out over quiet fields. The L-shaped bar is a rambling affair, full of interesting nooks and crannies and traditionally decorated, with low black beams and timbering set off well by neat white paintwork, and shelves of china cats, continually being added to by customers; open fire. The food is simple and straightforward, and the Adnams Southwold and Broadside, Greene King IPA and Abbot and Rayments Special on handpump particularly well kept; friendly service. *(Recommended by Karen and Graham Oddey, Gwen and Peter Andrews, Jenny Cantle, Quentin Williamson; more reports please)*

Free house   Real ale   Snacks   Open 11–2.30ish, 6.30ish–11; may close if not busy in winter

---

Lucky Dip

Besides the fully inspected pubs, you might like to try these Lucky Dips recommended to us and described by readers (if you do, please send us reports):

☆ **Abridge** [Market Pl (A113/B172); TQ4696], *White Hart:* Large open-plan riverside pub, recently refurbished, with Bass and Charrington IPA on handpump, good value food, RAF fighter-bomber pictures, piped pop music — popular with young people evenings; live jazz Weds, some weekends *(Robert Lester, George Atkinson, R P Hastings)*

Abridge [London Rd (A113)], *Maltsters Arms:* 16th-century pub with open fires in two small bars, lots of beams with water jugs, warm, welcoming atmosphere; Greene King beers; popular evenings with young people *(Robert Lester)*

☆ **Althorne** [TQ9199], *Huntsman & Hounds:*

Popular extended thatched country local with open fire, low beams, brasses, plates, mugs and foreign banknotes; well kept Greene King IPA and Abbot, good bar food, friendly staff, unobtrusive piped music, decent garden *(LYM)*

☆ **Ardleigh** [A137 towards Colchester; TM0529], *Wooden Fender:* Comfortably modernised open-plan beamed bar with good freshly prepared standard bar food and good Sun lunch; well kept Adnams, Greene King IPA and Abbot and Marstons Pedigree on handpump, prompt service, log fire, character landlord, piped music, restaurant allowing children, tables in garden with pool *(M Morgan, Gill and Doug Green, E G Parish,*

Norman and Barbara Wells, John Baker, E G Parish)

Ashdon [back rd Saffron Walden—Haverhill; TL5842], *Rose & Crown*: 17th-century pub with small rooms, one with original gothic lettering and geometric patterns; big helpings of good food in bar and restaurant, real fire, Greene King Abbot, resident dogs; pool room *(Adrian Pitts, J Johnson)*

☆ **Bannister Green** [off A131 or A120 SW of Braintree; TL6920], *Three Horseshoes*: Comfortable but unpretentious village pub with well kept Ridleys (good value weekday happy hour, not Fri); welcoming atmosphere, open fire, operatic piped music, wide choice of food from lunchtime huffers, ham and egg and so forth to more elaborate evening dishes (not Mon evening); traditional games, picnic-table sets on wide village green and among trees in garden; children welcome, open all day Sat summer *(Ian Phillips, Nigel Gibbs, Mrs K J Betts, LYM)*

Basildon [Felmore (off A132); TQ7389], *Watermill*: Large modern pleasantly barn-style bar, good Beefeater restaurant, facilities for the disabled; bedrooms well equipped *(A J Brown)*

☆ **Battlesbridge** [Hawk Hill; TQ7894], *Barge*: Pleasantly old-fashioned, low-ceilinged and cosy, with good value bar lunches, barge pictures, well kept Taylor-Walker, good service; children's room; by art and craft centre *(Derek Patey, Jenny Cantle, Gail Miller)*

Beaumont [byroad between B1035 and B1414; TM1724], *Swan*: Friendly landlord, tasty sandwiches, nice uncrowded atmosphere; pretty well tended garden *(Mrs P J Pearce)*

☆ **Beazley End** [off B1053 N of Braintree; TL7428], *Cock*: Welcoming and relaxing beamed lounge with open fire, village bar with pool and darts, restaurant decorated with corn dollies; well kept local real ales inc one brewed for them by Mauldons, decent wine, good choice of bar food inc fresh fish, Sun lunch, friendly service, maybe piped music; no dogs *(Gwen and Peter Andrews, Norman and Barbara Wells)*

Billericay [High St; TQ6794], *Chequers*: Beams and timbers, refurbished but with lively atmosphere; well kept Allied beers, juke box, slot machines *(Karen and Graham Oddey)*

☆ **Birchanger** [nr M11 junction 8 — right turn off A120 to Bishops Stortford; TL5022], *Three Willows*: Small pub with well kept Greene King IPA and Abbot and Rayments, cheap wines, wide range of bar food inc good fresh fish Tues *(P Thorogood, M J Morgan)*

Blackmore [The Green; TL6001], *Prince Albert*: Good bar food inc some vegetarian dishes, welcoming landlord, brass tankards hanging from ceiling, log fires, Bass and Charrington IPA on handpump; darts in snug *(Robert Lester, Derek Patey)*

Bocking [Bocking Churchstreet; TL7525], *Retreat*: Dating to 16th century, with exposed brickwork, 30ft well in one bar,

neat conservatory, quiet but genuine welcome, well kept Watneys-related beers with a guest such as Adnams, log-effect gas fire, bar food, attractive restaurant *(Gwen and Peter Andrews)*

Bradwell [A120 Braintree—Colchester; TL8022], *Swan*: Decent choice of reasonably priced varied food, good friendly service, Greene King beers, beams and standing timbers, nice atmosphere, pleasant layout and lighting *(Gill and Doug Green, Dave Braisted)*

Bradwell on Sea [Waterside; TM0006], *Green Man*: Interestingly furnished flagstoned 15th-century pub with games room and garden, decent bar food; interesting village with one-man lockup, old church nearby, path over field to sea *(E G Parish, LYM)*

Broadley Common [Common Rd; TL4207], *Black Swan*: Attractive low tiled white local, unpretentious and friendly, with low beams, snug, public and lounge bars; plenty of space outside *(Joy Heatherley)*

Bumbles Green [Nazeing Common Rd; TL4004], *King Harolds Head*: Friendly, welcoming and quite spacious, with pretty flower-baskets and window-boxes, Courage Directors, reasonably priced bar food, Sun roasts; piped music *(Joy Heatherley)*

☆ **Burnham on Crouch** [The Quay; TQ9596], *White Harte*: Old-fashioned yachting inn overlooking anchorage, with high ceilings, oak tables, polished parquet, sea pictures, panelling and stripped brickwork; bar food from sandwiches to boiled ham, lamb chops and so forth, well kept Adnams and Tolly, restaurant; children allowed in eating area; bedrooms *(LYM)*

Canfield End [Little Canfield; A120 Bishops Stortford—Dunmow; TL5821], *Lion & Lamb*: Comfortable open-plan multi-level dining pub, with good waitress-served home-cooked bar food inc fresh generously filled sandwiches, good vegetarian dishes, children's dishes; central red-brick fireplace, imposing grandfather clock, sizeable restaurant, well kept Adnams and Ridleys; tables on terrace and in family garden; handy for Langthornes nursery *(Mrs M C Lutyens)*

☆ **Chelmsford** [Roxwell Rd; TL7006], *Horse & Groom*: Popular well furnished mock-Tudor place with pleasant staff, thriving but relaxed atmosphere, well kept Watneys-related real ales, good reasonably priced food inc lots of salads (not Sun); tables outside *(Gwen and Peter Andrews, M Morgan)*

Chelmsford [Lower Anchor St], *Orange Tree*: Neat, cheerful and spacious yet cosy, with pleasant efficient service, good value lunchtime bar food (not Sun) inc good huffers, terrace with climbing plants and waterfall; easy wheelchair access; darts, gas fires, unobtrusive piped music, occasional live music *(Brian Quentin)*

☆ *nr* **Chelmsford** [Cooksmill Green; A414 5 miles W — OS Sheet 167, map reference 638052], *Fox & Goose*: Spaciously extended well kept dining pub, lots of beams and alcoves, lively but not boisterous evening atmosphere, decent food inc good home-made puddings, well kept Watneys-related real ales, neatly dressed but friendly young staff, unobtrusive piped music; pretty garden with pond and fountain, and climbing tree for children; well behaved children allowed weekends *(Mrs P J Pearce, Gwen and Peter Andrews, LYM)*

☆ **Chignall Smealy** [TL6711], *Pig & Whistle*: Pleasant country local with coal fire, brasses and farm tools, well kept Adnams on handpump, guest beers tapped from the cask, reasonably priced straightforward bar food; piped music *(Derek Patey)*

Chigwell [Lamborne Rd, Lamborne End; TQ4693], *Two Brewers*: Nice country pub with good range of beers and bottled lagers *(Martin Chandler)*

Chipping Ongar [High St; TL5502], *Royal Oak*: Homely wallpaper gives private-house feel to lounge at back of small old pub; friendly landlord, well kept Wethereds *(Quentin Williamson)*

☆ **Clavering** [B1038 Newport—Buntingford, Newport end of village; TL4731], *Cricketers*: Spacious yet cosy and attractive L-shaped dining pub with low beams and two open fires; well kept Flowers and Wethereds, wide choice of good imaginative well presented bar food, restaurant, outside tables *(A M Kelly, Maysie Thompson)*

☆ **Coggeshall** [West St (towards Braintree); TL8522], *Fleece*: Handsome yet unpretentious Elizabethan pub next to Paycocke's (lovely timber-framed house open pm summer Weds, Thurs and Sun); exposed bricks, finely carved beams, handsomely lit fireplace, well kept Greene King and Abbot on handpump (and a good winter concoction called Lumumba), good straightforward pub food (not Tues evening), friendly licensees and chatty locals; play area in spacious sheltered garden; provision for children; has been open all day Mon-Fri *(Gwen and Peter Andrews, Barbara and Norman Wells)*

☆ **Coggeshall** [main st], *White Hart*: 15th-century inn with lots of low dark beams, library chairs and one or two attractive antique settles around oak tables, seats in bow windows, flower prints and fishing trophies on cream walls, good bar lunches, well kept Adnams, freshly squeezed orange juice and decent wines and coffee; bedrooms comfortable *(JF, BB)*

Coggeshall [7 West St], *Cricketers*: Small local, generous plain home cooking, friendly staff, cosy log fire *(Alison Findlay, M Morgan)*; [91 Church St; turn off main st opp Post Office and Barclays Bank, then bear right], *Woolpack*: Particularly handsome timber-framed Tudor inn recently sold by Allied Breweries, softly lit period lounge, interesting bar food, well kept Adnams, log fire, piped music; children welcome; bedrooms comfortable *(LYM; reports on new regime please)*

☆ *nr* **Coggeshall** [Pattiswick (signed from A120 about 2 miles W of Coggeshall — OS Sheet 168, map reference 820247)], *Compasses*: Secluded beams-and-tiles country pub, spacious, comfortable and attractively decorated; wide range of well presented and generous good value bar food, Greene King IPA and Abbot and Mauldons (named for the pub) on handpump, log fire, traditional pub games, fruit machine, unobtrusive piped music; restaurant; spreading lawns, orchard, play area, surrounding farmland *(David Cardy, Gwen and Peter Andrews, Barbara and Norman Wells)*

☆ **Colchester** [East St; TM0025], *Rose & Crown*: Carefully modernised handsome Tudor inn, timbered and jettied, parts of a former gaol preserved in its rambling beamed bar, good value bar food, Tolly real ale; comfortable bedrooms *(Barbara and Norman Wells, LYM)*

Colchester [Castle St, off Roman Rd], *Forresters Arms*: Very backstreet local with well kept Whitbreads-related ales on handpump, particularly good varied lunchtime food *(R P Beavis)*; [Lexden Rd], *Tap & Spile*: Formerly the Hospital Arms; now has vast succession of real ales, and keeps much of the old charm, with cases of rugby club ties, cricketer photographs, some flagstone flooring; tables in small back courtyard, busy but efficient and pleasant staff, good lavatories *(Norman and Barbara Wells, M Morgan)*

Crays Hill [TQ7192], *Shepherd & Dog*: Cosy uncontrived local atmosphere, well kept Allied real ales, bar food, new conservatory, garden *(Graham Bush)*

☆ **Cressing** [TL7920], *Three Ashes*: Spick and span, with copper jugs, brasses and china cabinet, well kept Greene King IPA, decent bar food, obliging service, restaurant a couple of steps down from bar; no music *(Gwen and Peter Andrews)*

Cressing [TL7920], *Willows*: Very pretty, cosy pub with lots of ornaments and knick-knacks, good range of bar food, pleasant staff, extended restaurant section *(Alison Findlay, Gill and Doug Green)*

Danbury [TL7805], *Griffins Head*: One reader remembers lime juice after church every Sun in the 1930s while her parents had a beer in the old saloon; this 17th-century coaching inn has now been tastefully converted, with a Chef & Brewer restaurant in the former public bar, the modern dresser fitting in well with the ancient beams; Watneys-related real ales, attentive service even when busy *(Gwen and Peter Andrews)*

Debden Estate [The Broadway (A1168); TQ4398], *Sir Winston Churchill*: Smart two-bar pub, recently refurbished, with WWI, WWII and Churchill prints, Watneys-related real ales; two pool tables in public bar *(Robert Lester)*

Dedham [TM0533], *Anchor*: Friendly service and atmosphere, beer kept well, good home-made food — the Sun barbecue's a real joy *(R Dooley)*; *Sun*: Comfortably refurbished, nicely carved Tudor beams and panelling; friendly, attentive staff, wide choice of bar food from hefty sandwiches and burgers to steaks, restaurant; bedrooms *(Barbara and Norman Wells, LYM)*

East Tilbury [Princess Margaret Rd; TQ6877], *Ship*: Quiet, old-fashioned little country pub open till 4, with two bars, friendly staff, well kept Courage and good value food; nice garden; nr Victorian coalhouse fort *(A J Brown)*

Easthorpe [village signposted from A12; TL9121], *House Without A Name*: Heavy-beamed and timbered Tudor pub which has been praised for good choice of real ales, good log fire, usual pub food, friendly service; but found closed spring 1991 *(LYM; news please)*

☆ **Feering** [B1024; follow Kelvedon signpost off A12; TL8720], *Old Anchor*: Old and picturesque, with spreading well kept rambling beamed bar, popular bar food inc big help-yourself salads, efficient staff, Watneys-related real ales, log fire, pool area, well reproduced piped music; carvery restaurant, tables in sheltered garden; open all day Sat; bedrooms *(Mrs P J Pearce, Gill and Doug Green, LYM)*

Finchingfield [TL6832], *Fox*: Genuinely pubby welcome, straightforward food, in splendidly pargeted pub overlooking beauty-spot village green *(Gwen and Peter Andrews, Barbara and Norman Wells); Red Lion*: Nice local, well kept Ridleys *(JM, PM)*

Fordstreet [A604 2 miles W of A12; TL9126], *Queens Head*: Spacious and well kept, beams with lots of tankards, wall and window banquettes, aquarium, games room with darts and pool, good sensibly priced generous food *(Alison Findlay, Gill and Doug Green, Sylvia Findlay)*

☆ **Fuller Street** [The Green (off A131 Chelmsford—Braintree, towards Fairstead); TL7416], *Square & Compasses*: Old converted cottage with lots of brass, exposed beams, well kept Ridleys, good reasonably priced home-cooked bar food; piped folk music (live first Fri of month), maybe Morris dancing; on Essex Way *(Gwen and Peter Andrews)*

Furneux Pelham [TL4327], *Brewery Tap*: Notable for spacious garden with neat lawns and glorious flowers; friendly, with good reasonably priced traditional pub food and well kept Greene King and Rayments — no longer actually a brewery tap *(Sidney and Erna Wells)*

☆ **Gestingthorpe** [OS Sheet 155, map reference 813375; TL8138], *Pheasant*: Simple country pub with attractive old-fashioned furnishings, popular and often interesting lunchtime food, well kept ales inc Adnams, Greene King IPA and Nethergate, open fire; children welcome *(Gwen and Peter Andrews, Norman and Barbara Wells, LYM)*

☆ **Gosfield** [TL7829], *Green Man*: Warm welcome and genuinely individual feel, well kept Greene King IPA and Abbot on handpump, decent wines, L-shaped saloon with plenty of seats around bar, tables in alcove, lovely old fireplace, small dining room off; home cooking well above average, using good fresh ingredients and often running to really imaginative dishes, yet atmosphere kept simple and unpretentious, with homely mix of decorative styles *(Gwen and Peter Andrews)*

Gosfield [A1017 Braintree—Halstead], *Kings Head*: Recently extended and doing well under new licensees who concentrate on food *(Barbara and Norman Wells)*

Great Burstead [A129 Billericay—Wickford; TQ6892], *Duke of York*: More restaurant than pub, excellent food, well kept Greene King IPA and Abbot *(Graham Bush)*

☆ **Great Chesterford** [High St; 2 miles E of M11 junction 9; TL5143], *Plough*: Classic beamed village pub, recently extended, with open fire, friendly and relaxed atmosphere; doing well under current regime, with good bar food, well kept Greene King IPA and Abbot tapped from the cask, handy garden with farm animals; peaceful village *(John C Baker, P Thorogood, Barbara and Norman Wells)*

Great Easton [2 miles N of Dunmow, off B184 towards Lindsell; TL6025], *Green Man*: Quiet refurbished country pub with better-than-average food *(MBW, JHW)*

Great Hallingbury [Bedlars Green; handy for M11 junction 8; A120 towards Dunmow, 1st fork right — OS Sheet 167, map reference 524204; TL5119], *Hop Poles*: Small, clean and well kept, handy for walks in Hatfield Forest; good value Sun roast beef with crisp veg and fresh Yorkshire pudding, good range of attractive puddings; Benskins Best and Ind Coope Burton *(Mrs Imogen Perkin)*

Great Horkesley [TL9730], *Rose & Crown*: Under new regime; attractively restored, with good bar snacks, real ale, decent wines, no music; restaurant *(Richard Goss)*

Great Waltham [A130; TL6913], *Beehive*: Cheerfully extrovert Ridleys pub, pleasant attentive service, well kept IPA, decent wine, piped music not too obtrusive; village far nicer now it's bypassed *(Gwen and Peter Andrews)*

Great Warley Street [TQ5890], *Thatchers Arms*: Pretty pub by village green, Chef & Brewer restaurant, well kept Watneys-related real ales, good atmosphere, varied choice of decent food *(Derek Patey, A M Kelly)*

Hadleigh [London Rd (A13); TQ8087], *Waggon & Horses*: Large, tastefully modern restaurant-pub, open all day for meals, though must book for evening (when they often have special early offers); no real ale; children welcome *(A J Brown)*

Halstead [Bridge St; TL8130], *Bull*: Attractive old inn, enterprising new landlord, candlelit bistro section in spacious beamed main bar with wide choice of well presented substantial dishes; Adnams, Greene King, Ruddles and guest beers, fruit machine, trivia, and maybe rather obtrusive piped music; restaurant; bedrooms *(Barbara and Norman Wells)*

Hatfield Heath [overlooks biggest village

green in Essex, junction of several roads;
TL5215], *White Horse*: Friendly village pub
on big green; dining area off main lounge
opens on to pleasant lawn; solid wooden
benches and a mix of interesting tables;
Greene King ales, decent wines by the glass,
bar food *(R P Hastings)*

☆ **Herongate** [Dunton Rd — turn off A128
Brentwood—Grays at big sign for Boars
Head; TQ6391], *Old Dog*: Long and
narrow, with dark beams, open fire, friendly
and relaxed, comfortable back lounge, wide
choice of well kept local and other real ales,
good choice of lunchtime bar food (only
snacks weekends); dogs allowed;
picnic-table sets on front terrace and in neat
sheltered side garden *(Graham Bush, Karen
and Graham Oddey, George Atkinson, LYM)*
Herongate [Billericay Rd, Ingrave], *Boars
Head*: Busy and popular for food;
Watneys-related real ales *(Derek Patey)*
High Ongar [The Street; TL5603], *Foresters
Arms*: Friendly, with easy-going locals, well
kept Adnams and Greene King Abbot,
decent bar food *(Colleen Holiday)*
Kirby le Soken [TM2221], *Ship*: Old
pink-washed beamed building with very
friendly service, wide choice of good value
food, friendly service; open all day *(Margaret
and Trevor Errington)*
Langdon Hills [Staneway; TQ6786],
Crown: Big, lively pub in country park,
open all day; good atmosphere, popular
with locals in evening, good value meals inc
2lb steak *(A J Brown)*
Little Baddow [North Hill, towards Hatfield
Peverel; TL7807], *Rodney*: Low-beamed
country pub with bright brasses, open fire,
friendly atmosphere, well kept Adnams,
decent food (Nelson memorabilia in dining
area), welcoming staff; pool room, terrace
and garden *(Gwen and Peter Andrews)*

☆ **Littlebury** [TL5139], *Queens Head*:
Congenial connecting beamed areas, good
bar food inc some inventive dishes, well kept
Adnams, Marstons Pedigree and Websters
Yorkshire, restaurant *(Robert Mitchell)*
Loughton [Jessel Dr; TQ4296], *Cottage
Loaf*: Good recent refurbishment, yet still a
friendly and homely two-bar local, with
considerate landlord, Watneys-related real
ales and a guest such as Youngs Winter
Warmer on handpump, darts in saloon, pool
in public *(Robert Lester)*; [2 Church Hill
(A121)], *Kings Head*: Smartly refurbished
upmarket open-plan pub with Greene King
IPA and Websters Yorkshire on handpump,
good atmosphere, Sun DJ *(Robert Lester)*;
[165 Smarts Lane], *Victoria*: Recently
smartly refurbished as single open-plan bar
with raised dining area, plenty of wood, nice
fireplace; good atmosphere, chatty landlord
and friendly staff, good choice of well kept
beers, good home-cooked food, garden with
geese, rabbits and birds *(R W Grey)*

☆ **Manningtree** [Manningtree Stn; out towards
Lawford; TM1031], *Station Buffet*:
Privately run as a free house, with interesting
well kept real ales from the long
marble-topped bar, etched windows, just

three little tables and a handful of
unassuming seats — very pre-war feel; big
helpings of good low-priced rather
old-fashioned home-cooked food, quick
service, friendly staff and customers *(L W
Baal, John Baker)*

☆ **Margaretting Tye** [TL6800], *White Hart*:
Secluded pub in quiet surroundings by
village green, with lots of tables in well kept
garden, barbecue, ponies in adjoining
paddock; wide choice of good value
generous simple food, well kept Adnams and
Broadside, Mauldons, Greene King IPA and
a guest beer on handpump, friendly staff,
good mix of customers; some live music
(Mike Beiley, Gwen and Peter Andrews)

☆ **Mashbury** [TL6411], *Fox*: Alone in lovely
countryside, doing well under newish
licensees, stone-floor beamed lounge,
old-fashioned long tables, well kept Adnams
and Ridleys tapped from the cask, decent
wine, generous home cooking (may take
time), smiling service even under pressure;
convivial atmosphere, no music *(Gwen and
Peter Andrews)*

☆ **Matching Tye** [TL5111], *Fox*: Comfortable
and friendly low-beamed 17th-century
building, good choice of ploughman's and
interesting filled baked potatoes; lots of fox
pictures, peaceful garden in lovely rural
surroundings *(Alan and Ruth Woodhouse)*
Monk Street [formerly the Greyhound;
TL6128], *Countryman*: Still very much a
pub despite tasteful restaurant and motel
extensions; Adnams Southwold on
handpump, decent food, obliging staff and
Italian manager *(Gwen and Peter Andrews)*

☆ **Moreton** [TL5307], *Moreton Massey*:
Spacious open-plan beamed bar,
comfortable and attractive, with good
imaginative bar food, friendly service, well
kept changing real ales such as Adnams,
Boddingtons, Fullers London Pride and
Greene King Abbot, good choice of wines;
popular with locals as well as diners, darts in
second smaller bar; restaurant *(Alan and
Ruth Woodhouse)*
Mountnessing [Roman Rd; TQ6297],
Prince of Wales: Pleasant, popular rambling
beamed pub; conservative bar meals, well
kept Ridleys IPA *(John C Baker, P
Thorogood)*

☆ **Navestock** [Horsemans Side (off B175);
TQ5397], *Alma Arms*: Popular,
comfortable, low-beamed free house with
emphasis on tasty good value food —
scampi, curries, steak and kidney pie and
salmon all recommended, also bargain
three-course lunch; well kept ales such as
Adnams, Greene King IPA and Abbot,
Rayments BBA and Youngs Special; busy
but unspoilt atmosphere, good service *(Mrs
Sylvia Robinson, Peter Andrews, Derek Patey)*

☆ **North Fambridge** [The Quay; TQ8597],
Ferryboat: Quaint little 15th-century
weatherboarded pub in remote riverside
spot, with low beams, flagstones or tiles, old
benches, nautical memorabilia, log fire,
old-fashioned atmosphere and lighting; well
kept Adnams and an Allied beer, decent

wine, reasonably priced bar and restaurant food, quietly friendly atmosphere, dry-witted landlord; yachtsmen in summer; children in family room *(Gwen and Peter Andrews, Graham Bush)*

North Shoebury [Frobisher Way (behind ASDA); TQ9485], *Parsons Barn*: Attractively old-world former barn, with five or six real ales, good value bar food, friendly service *(Anon)*

North Weald [Ongar Rd (B181); TL4904], *Kings Head*: Mr Toby dining pub in ancient building, with good choice of food inc popular Sun lunches, Charrington IPA on handpump; building several centuries old *(Robert Lester)*

☆ **Norton Heath** [just off A414 Chelmsford—Ongar; TL6004], *White Horse*: Strong emphasis on good food (Tues-Sat lunchtimes) in comfortably modernised long 16th-century timbered bar, Courage Directors on handpump, unobtrusive piped music; bar billiards, farm tools; restaurant (Tues-Sat evening, Sun lunch); closed Mon *(Gwen and Peter Andrews)*

Orsett [off A13/A128 roundabout; TQ6481], *Cock*: Big, lively evening pub with well kept Courage beers and good value food; live music Tues and Thurs, open all day *(A J Brown)*

☆ **Paglesham** [TQ9293], *Plough & Sail*: Attractive old dining pub in pretty spot nr marshes, warm and friendly atmosphere, well kept Watneys-related beers, quick helpful service, good choice of decent bar food (all day at least in summer) inc good seafood, also carvery; very popular on warm summer evenings *(Jenny Cantle, Mike Beiley, C Sharpe)*

Paglesham [East End], *Punchbowl*: Pretty and beautifully kept; good food *(Jenny Cantle, C Sharpe)*

Peldon [TL9916], *Plough*: Pretty little tiled and white-boarded unpretentious village local, popular for genuinely fresh fish and seafood; cheerfully busy evenings and weekends *(Jan and Ian Alcock, BB)*

☆ **Purfleet** [Tank Hill Rd/High St; TQ5578], *Royal*: Small pub, happily not over-refurbished, in comfortable hotel, well kept real ale, good bar lunches and riverside Beefeater restaurant, efficient service; magnificent Thames views from tables on terrace *(A J Brown, Derek Patey)*

Radley Green [off A414; TL6205], *Thatchers Arms*: Small, cosy local with Adnams Extra and Ridleys IPA on handpump, games, reasonable prices; garden, big football pitch *(Robert Lester)*

Radwinter [B1053 E of Saffron Walden — OS Sheet 154, map reference 612376; TL6137], *Plough*: Pleasant inn with good food and well kept Greene King and Marstons; bedrooms good value and comfortable *(JM, PM)*

Ridgewell [A604 Haverhill—Halstead; TL7340], *Kings Head*: Unpretentious much modernised small Tudor pub with good value bar food, well kept Greene King IPA

and Abbot on handpump, local World War II memorabilia inc Dambusters print, signed James Stewart photograph, huge brass shellcases; pool and other games in airy public bar, piped music, a few tables in roadside garden *(BB)*; *White Horse*: Low-beamed and comfortable, bar covered in old pennies, particularly good value food with nicely served real butter and sauces; good service, tables outside *(John and Bridget Dean)*

☆ **Rochford** [35 North St (one-way); TQ8790], *Golden Lion*: Small and cosy though open-plan, with friendly landlord, good value lunchtime snacks, nice local atmosphere and seven well kept changing real ales such as Adnams, Crouch Vale, Fullers London Pride, Greene King IPA and Abbot and a Mild; unusual attractive stained-glass panels, back car park; can get very busy *(Nigel Gibbs, Graham Bush, Richard Houghton)*

Rochford [1 Stambridge Rd], *Cherry Tree*: Good food, pleasant comfortable atmosphere, new dining conservatory leaves the pub proper for snacks and drinks; very good service *(Ian Phillips)*

☆ **Rowhedge** [Quay; TM0021], *Anchor*: Splendid position overlooking River Colne with its swans, gulls and yachts; well kept Watneys-related real ales, fishing bric-a-brac, good atmosphere, ample helpings of good value food such as fresh plaice, restaurant *(Mrs P J Pearce)*

☆ **South Weald** [Weald Rd (off A12); TQ5793], *Tower Arms*: Well kept beers such as Adnams, Greene King IPA and Abbot and Youngs Special, friendly staff, attractive conservatory restaurant, nice secluded garden with boules; picturesque village; children allowed away from bar *(George Atkinson, Derek Patey, Gerry and Beverley Markham, P Thorogood)*

Southend [Tichfield Ave; by Prittlewell Stn; TQ8885], *Railway*: Open-plan pub with notably good value well presented lunchtime food at low prices, well kept Websters Yorkshire *(Lee Goulding)*

☆ **Stanway** [London Rd; TL9324], *Swan*: Big yet friendly local with well kept beer and several oak-beamed rooms inc pretty dining room (where children are allowed) for good bar lunches and evening meals; cheerful service, big open fire *(Barbara and Norman Wells)*

☆ **Stisted** [A120; TL7924], *Dolphin*: Heavily beamed and timbered if rather brightly lit, with comfortable banquettes, quiet atmosphere, Adnams Extra and Ridleys PA tapped from the cask, straightforward food in lounge, separate bar with darts etc, tables outside, children in eating area; open all day Sat *(Alison Findlay, C M Vipond, LYM)*

Stisted [The Street], *Onley Arms*: Friendly cheerful licensees, properly kept Ridleys — and their almost Belgianly extensive range of bottled beers; speciality bar snack is a sort of Germanic hot dog *(John C Baker)*

☆ **Stock** [B1007 towards Galleywood — OS Sheet 167, map reference 704004; TQ6998],

Ship: Particularly good food in old plastered building tucked behind trees, with oak furniture in beamed bar, modern extension; Paines EG and Tolly Original on handpump, restaurant *(Patrick Young)*

Stock [The Square (just off village st)], *Bear*: Pleasant character bars, warm and cosy (gas fires), with well kept Allied beers, good bar food; restaurant *(Karen and Graham Oddey)*

☆ **Thaxted** [Bullring; TL6130], *Swan*: Four-gabled late 15th-century inn, partly carpeted slate-floored circular bar, well refurbished and pleasantly pubby, with plain wooden chairs and settles, soft lighting, good piped music; Greene King IPA and Abbot and several well kept guest beers such as Courage Directors and Eldridge Pope Royal Oak; sandwiches in bar, other food in cellar restaurant; bedrooms comfortably modernised, all with own bathroom *(Gwen and Peter Andrews, JM, PM)*

Thaxted [Mill End], *Star*: Old beams, well kept Ind Coope Burton, pleasant staff, decent straightforward food *(JM, PM)*

Theydon Bois [Station Approach, nr B172; TQ4599], *Railway Arms*: Small friendly village local with good atmosphere, well kept Flowers and Greene King Abbot *(Robert Lester)*

Thorpe le Soken [High St; TM1922], *Bell*: Nice cosy two-level pub with generous helpings of good food, fairly priced; good service and atmosphere, easy parking *(Gill and Doug Green)*

Toppesfield [TL7337], *Crawley Arms*: 300-year-old pub with darkly furnished bar, Adnams Southwold, Greene King IPA and Charles Wells Bombardier on handpump and well cooked, attractively presented food; garden with cats, a spaniel-cross, guinea pigs, and goats; also a tearoom *(Gwen and Peter Andrews)*

Vange [A13 Basildon roundabout; TQ7185], *Five Bells*: Comfortably refurbished Toby dining pub with Bass and Charrington IPA, good value bar food, welcoming landlord *(E G Parish)*

☆ **Waltham Abbey** [very handy for M25 junction 26; A121 towards Waltham Abbey, then follow Epping, Loughton sign from exit roundabout; TL3800], *Volunteer*: Spacious open-plan roadhouse with several separate areas, attractive conservatory, interesting decorations; bar food inc lots of chow mein dishes and big pancake rolls prepared by Chinese landlady, alongside usual things, in enormous helpings; well staffed, with McMullens beer, some tables on side terrace, pretty hanging baskets; nice spot by Epping Forest, can get very busy weekends *(Joy and Peter Heatherley, Kevin Perkins, BB)*

Wendens Ambo [B1039 1 1/2 miles W; TL5136], *Bell*: Small pub with well kept Allied real ales, tasty usual bar food with good puddings, nice garden, friendly service *(A Langan)*

☆ **Widdington** [High St; TL5331], *Fleur de*

Lys: Clean and unpretentious village pub, spacious low-beamed L-shaped bar with copper kettles, lots of little country prints, good log fire, half a dozen changing well kept real ales such as Adnams, Charles Wells Bombardier, Courage Directors, Nethergate and Wadworths 6X, decent house wines, friendly staff, wide choice of generous reasonably priced good bar food inc local game, dining room on right (children allowed here), pool table and video games in plain back public bar, picnic-table sets on side lawn; handy for Widdington Wildlife Park *(Gwen and Peter Andrews, Alan and Ruth Woodhouse, BB)*

Witham [113 Hatfield Rd (B1389); TL8214], *Jack & Jenny*: Spacious L-shaped bar, comfortable chairs and sofas, pool table at one end, relaxing atmosphere (though piped pop music may be loud); well kept Courage and other ales, standard bar food at reasonable prices lunchtime and after 6; dining conservatory, family room, garden *(Gwen and Peter Andrews)*

Wivenhoe [TM0321], *Rose & Crown*: Friendly quayside pub with good river views, jovial licensee, warm fire; seafood stall outside in summer, good fish and chip shop nearby *(Jan and Ian Alcock, Gill and Doug Green)*

Woodham Ferrers [Main Rd; TQ7999], *Bell*: Timbered building with extension toning in; warm, friendly and clean, wide choice of food, several malt whiskies, good coffee; unobtrusive fruit machine, pool table; duck pond in sheltered garden with picnic-table sets *(Dr and Mrs John Davidson)*

Woodham Mortimer [TL8104], *Hurdlemakers Arms*: Quiet tucked-away local looking like a cosy house, open fire in simply furnished flagstoned lounge with cushioned settles, low ceiling and timbered walls; reliable food, well kept Greene King IPA and Abbot, good darts alley in public bar, picnic-table sets well spaced among trees and shrubs outside *(Jenny Cantle, BB)*; [A414 Danbury—Maldon], *Royal Oak*: Quite spacious, very welcoming; interesting bar food, good evening restaurant *(Shirley Pielou)*

Wormingford [B1508; TL9331], *Crown*: Peaceful old pub with big garden, good food, no music and friendly service; Greene King real ale *(Prof S Barnett)*

Writtle [TL6706], *Wheatsheaf*: Well kept Greene King Abbot and IPA in friendly, neat and cosy pub with hearty sandwiches and super-efficient landlord *(Frank Gadbois)*

Youngs End [A131 Braintree—Chelmsford, nr Essex Show Ground; TL7319], *Green Dragon*: Comfortable and popular dining pub, with lots of little alcoves and attractive barn restaurant (usefully open Sun afternoon); well kept Greene King, lots of bar food, pleasant staff, green dragon play area and barbecue outside *(Gwen and Peter Andrews)*

Gloucestershire

A fine choice of places to stay in here, usually in attractive surroundings, including the friendly Kings Head at Bledington (good innovative food), the atmospheric Noel Arms in Chipping Campden, the Lamb at Great Rissington (still good despite sharp price rises), the Black Horse at Naunton (sophisticated atmosphere, good food), the New Inn at North Nibley (very cheap wholesome food, good real ales), the Horse & Groom at Oddington (decent food); also (new discoveries, or inns back in these pages after a break) the lovely Wyndham Arms at Clearwell, the relaxed and friendly New Inn at Coln St Aldwyns (closed for quite a while, now reopened as an upmarket inn), the Fossebridge Inn at Fossebridge (first-class food and service), and the ancient Ostrich at Newland in the Forest of Dean. Other interesting new entries, or pubs to welcome back after a leave of absence, are the civilised old Kings Arms in Chipping Campden (what is it about this Cotswold village that nurtures so many good pubs?), the tiny but warmly friendly Plough at Cold Aston (good food), the handsomely reworked Kilkeney Inn at Kilkenny (the work of the Phillipses, who have given us so many other good Gloucestershire pubs – though they've already moved on), the very simple Halfway House at Kineton, and the friendly Bathurst Arms at North Cerney (imaginative food, lots of real ales). A good many other changes in the county include new licensees at the Black Horse in Amberley (reports very complimentary on the new regime), the simple Brockweir Inn up above the Wye at Brockweir (they plan to add a small restaurant), the quaint Plough at Ford (the asparagus feasts are to continue), the Boat at Redbrook on the Wye (the friendly new landlord is cleaning it up without damaging its character) and the busy and cheerful Ram at Woodchester (good food). Among all these changes it's good to note some utterly changeless pubs, like the timeless waterside Boat at Ashleworth Quay, the delightful Bakers Arms at Broad Campden (cheap good food), the Green Dragon at Cowley (doing particularly well, excellent food and service), the eccentric Tunnel House at Coates, the civilised and friendly Swan at Southrop (good food, again) and the Queens Head in Stow on the Wold where the winds blow cold (a proper old-fashioned Cotswold market-town pub). On the whole, food and drinks prices are a shade below the national average here, and food is often particularly worth noting; besides pubs already mentioned, we'd pick out for this the evening meals in the Gardeners Arms at Alderton, the busy Village Pub at Barnsley, the civilised yet friendly Crown at Blockley (particularly good fish), the small and welcoming Ebrington Arms at Ebrington (simple but good), the stylish Hunters Hall at Kingscote and the cheery Royal Oak in Painswick. In the Lucky Dip section at the end of the chapter, pubs which have very recently been going up in readers' estimation include the Catherine Wheel in Bibury, Hare & Hounds at Foss Cross, Canning Arms at Hartpury, Pickwick at Lower Wick, Churchill at Paxford and Corner Cupboard in

Winchcombe. Other Dip pubs already strongly in the reckoning, almost all of them inspected by us, are the Craven Arms at Brockhampton, Colesbourne Inn at Colesbourne, Wild Duck at Ewen, Glasshouse Inn at Glasshouse, Fox at Great Barrington, Royal Oak at Gretton, Golden Ball at Lower Swell, Kings Arms at Mickleton, Apple Tree at Minsterworth, Redesdale Arms in Moreton in Marsh, Egypt Mill at Nailsworth, Black Horse at North Nibley, Butchers Arms at Oakridge Lynch, Snowshill Arms at Snowshill and Mill at Withington.

ALDERTON   SP0033 Map 4

Gardeners Arms

Village signposted from A438 (now officially the B4077)
Tewkesbury–Stow-on-the-Wold

Contrary to our usual practice, the food award here refers to the evening restaurant which specialises in local game and good meats cooked by the landlord-chef; the lunchtime bar snacks are also good and might include sandwiches, ploughman's (£2.95), various salads (from £3.95), melon or avocado with prawns (£4.25), hot Indonesian smoked mackerel and salad (£5.95), and fresh poached salmon (£6.95). The smart, old-fashioned, L-shaped bar has a fine collection of interesting nineteenth-century prints on its cream walls – sporting, political, and scurrilous French literary ones by J-J Granville, old mugs and tankards hanging from its sturdy beams, high-backed antique settles and other good solid seats, and a good winter log fire; the atmosphere is relaxed and the two friendly labradors are called Sally (17 years old, yellow) and Captain (chocolate). The more straightforward public bar has been made more cosy with leather settees and sensibly placed darts; well kept Flowers Original, Wadworths 6X and Whitbreads PA on handpump. There are tables outside, where a partly covered crazy-paved back courtyard and a second terrace open on to a well kept garden, and barbecues are planned for summer. *(Recommended by E V Walder, Alan and Heather Jacques, Robert Brown, Bob Smith, PADEMLUC, Dick Brown, Chris Raisin, Iain and Penny Muir)*

Whitbreads   Tenant Jack Terry   Real ale   Snacks (lunchtime, not Sun) and Sun roast lunch   Evening restaurant (closed Sun pm and Mon pm in winter), though they do Sun roast lunch   Cheltenham (0242) 620 257   Children welcome   Singer-guitarist Thurs evening   Open 11–2 (2.30 Sat), 6.30–11; closed 25 Dec

AMBERLEY   SO8401 Map 4

Black Horse

Village signposted off A46 Stroud–Nailsworth; as you pass village name take first very sharp left turn (before Amberley Inn) then bear steeply right – pub on your left

This is set on the edge of Minchinhampton Common – a unique high cow-grazed plateau dotted with buildings (and prehistoric remains), enjoying remarkable views of the much more crumpled and folded surrounding hills. The simply furnished carpeted bar has wheelback chairs, green-cushioned window seats, a few prints on the plain cream walls, and a fire in a small stone fireplace; one window gives a striking panoramic view of the woods and stone villages tucked into the steep folds of the hillside opposite. Teak seats and picnic-table sets on a back terrace (with barbecue) have the same glorious view, as does a conservatory extension of the neat restaurant. On the other side a lawn with pretty flowers and honeysuckle has more picnic-table sets. The well kept real ales come from far afield (mainly north): Davenports, Fullers London Pride, Greene King Abbot, Hook Norton Best, Ind Coope Burton, Mitchells, Tetleys and Timothy Taylors Landlord. Good bar food includes soup (£1.75), ploughman's or spinach pancake (£3.15), roast pork with crackling (£4.95) and swordfish steak (£5.95). Darts. *(Recommended by P Freeman,*

Carol and Mike Muston, Tom McLean, Roger Huggins, Ewan McCall, Roger Entwistle)

*Free house   Manager E Abendanon   Real ale   Meals and snacks (12–2, 7–10.30)
Restaurant   Amberley (0453) 872556   Children welcome   Open 11.30–2.30 (Sat 3),
6–11*

AMPNEY CRUCIS   SP0602 Map 4

Crown of Crucis   £

A417 E of Cirencester

Very much a dining pub, this popular place is perhaps at its busiest at weekends, particularly Sunday lunchtime. Served by cheerful and efficient staff, the bar food includes home-made soup (£1.10), lunchtime sandwiches (from £1.25, toasties from £1.50), basket meals (from £2.50), ploughman's (£2.60), cauliflower, bacon and tomato mornay (£3.95), herb pancakes filled with mushroom, spinach and nuts or lasagne (£4.30), mushroom and herb terrine or honey baked ham salad (£4.35), salmon aand asparagus pancakes or brunch – lamb's liver, bacon, sausage, tomato, fried egg and chips (£4.75), and steaks (from £6.95) and puddings (from £1.75); children's menu (from £1.80). The spacious bar is sympathetically and comfortably modernised, and serves well kept Archers Village, Marstons Pedigree and Tetleys on handpump. There are lots of tables on the grass at the back, by a stream with ducks and maybe swans. *(Recommended by Mrs Pat Crabb, JMC, Laurence Manning, D Irving, R Huggins, T McLean, E McCall, M J B Pearson, E Davies, Mr and Mrs J H Adam, Patrick Freeman, Barbara M McHugh, Mr and Mrs P B Dowsett, Alastair Campbell, John and Pat Smyth, P and R Woods)*

*Free house   Licensee R K Mills   Real ale   Meals and snacks (12–2.30, 6–10)
Restaurant   Poulton (0285) 851806   Children in restaurant and eating area of bar
until 8pm   Open 11–11; 1–2.30, 6–11 in winter; closed 25 Dec   Bedrooms;
£47B/£58B*

ASHLEWORTH QUAY   SO8125 Map 4

Boat   £

Ashleworth signposted off A417 N of Gloucester; Quay signed from village

The timeless quality of this delightful and rather special 15th-century riverside cottage is beautifully preserved by the two ladies who've been running it in exactly the same charming way – with help now from a friendly younger woman – for so many years. The front parlour has a great built-in settle by a long scrubbed deal table facing an old-fashioned open kitchen range with a side bread oven and a couple of elderly fireside chairs; there are rush mats on the scrubbed flagstones, houseplants in the window, fresh garden flowers, and old magazines to read. A back parlour with rugs on its red tiles has plump overstuffed chairs and a sofa, a grandfather clock and dresser, a big dog basket in front of the fire, shove-ha'penny and cards (the front room has darts and a game called Dobbers). A pair of flower-cushioned antique settles face each other in the back room where Arkells, Smiles and a full range of Weston's farm ciders are tapped from the cask; they do lunchtime rolls or bread and cheese (75p). In the front, a suntrap crazy-paved courtyard, bright with plant tubs in summer, has a couple of picnic-table sets under cocktail parasols, with more seats and tables under cover at the sides. It's set back from the embankment of this peaceful curve of the River Severn, which has a good slipway here; the medieval tithe barn nearby is striking. *(Recommended by Ewan McCall, Tom McLean, Roger Huggins, Nick and Alison Dowson, Phil Gorton, Martin Morris, Derek and Sylvia Stephenson)*

*Free house   Licensees Irene and Sybil Jelf   Real ale   Lunchtime snacks   Painswick
(0452) 702 72   Occasional Morris Men in summer   Open 11–2.30, 6–11; closed
evening 25 Dec*

AWRE   SO7108   Map 4

Red Hart

Village signposted off A48 S of Newnham

Very un-mass-produced in its building, architecture and internal character, this surprisingly tall, three-storey pub is in an out-of-the-way village between the River Severn and Forest of Dean. The L-shaped bar has big prints on the walls, a deep glass-covered well, a stuffed pheasant on the mantlepiece over the good log fire, and a back area where a bale of straw swings from pitched rafters; fruit machine. Bar food includes home-made soup (£1.95), sandwiches (from £1.50), ploughman's (from £2.90), omelettes (from £3.25), cottage pie (£4.30), gammon and egg (£5.55), sirloin steak (£8.55), daily specials, and home-made puddings (£1.55). Well kept Banks's and Wadworths 6X on handpump, several malt whiskies and freshly squeezed orange juice; friendly service. They have a juke box trivia and football video game. There are picnic-table sets on the sheltered back lawn, with more out in front. *(Recommended by Gwynne Harper, R and M Wallace, D A Lloyd, Robert Brown, Roger Price, Andrew and Barbara Macdowall)*

Free house   Licensee John Bailes   Real ale   Meals and snacks 12–2, 7–10 Restaurant   Dean (0594) 510220; midnight supper licence; closed Sun and Mon evenings (except bank hol weekends)   Children welcome   Pianist/organist Sat evening   Open 11–2.30, 7–11

BARNSLEY   SP0705   Map 4

Village Pub

A433 Cirencester–Burford

Enjoyable, varied bar food in this very busy, friendly pub includes sandwiches (from £1.50, prawn £2.50), filled baked potatoes (£2.50), mushroom and hazelnut pâté (£2.50), ploughman's (£2.75), Gloucester sausages or nut and lentil cutlet (£4.25), salads (from £4.50), chilli or roast chicken (£4.50), mild curried bean and vegetable casserole (£4.95) and specials such as skate wings (£5.25), and beef in Guinness or chicken in white wine and tarragon (£5.45), with puddings such as apple crumble or raspberry syllabub (all £1.80). The comfortable, communicating rooms have low ceilings, walls (some stripped back to bare stone) decorated with gin-traps, scythes and other farm tools, several winter log fires, and plush chairs, stools and window settles around the polished tables. Well kept Flowers IPA and Wadworths 6X on handpump, and a range of country wines; cribbage, dominoes, piped pop music. The sheltered back courtyard has plenty of tables, and its own outside servery. *(Recommended by Dave Irving, Roger Huggins, Tom McLean, Ewan McCall, Maysie Thompson, Mrs Pat Crabb, Ken and Norma Guyll, John Watson, Mrs J A Gardner, Sidney Wells, L Walker, Jean and Edward Rycroft, D J Cooke, David and Christine Foulkes, Philip King, Caroline Wright, P and R Woods, John Broughton, Alan Skull, N P Cox)*

Free house   Licensee Miss S Stevens   Real ale   Meals and snacks (not 25 Dec) Restaurant   (0285) 740 421   Children in eating area and restaurant   Open 11–3, 6–11; closed 25 Dec   Bedrooms; £28.75B/£43.05B

BISLEY   SO9005   Map 4

Bear

Village signposted off A419 just E of Stroud

Full of character, this elegant rather Gothick little stone building – formerly a courthouse and lockup – has a meandering L-shaped bar with a long shiny black built-in settle and a smaller but even sturdier oak settle by the front entrance; this faces an enormously wide recently opened-up stone fireplace (not very high – the ochre ceiling's too low for that). At the back there's a tropical fish tank opposite the bar counter, which has well kept Boddingtons, Flowers Original, Wadworths 6X and Whitbreads PA on handpump; several malt whiskies. Bar food includes sandwiches (from £1.25), filled baked potatoes (from £1.40), basket meals such as

chicken or scampi (from £2.55), ploughman's (from £2.75), chilli con carne
(£2.95), cottage pie (£3.50), king-size Yorkshire pudding filled with steak and
kidney cooked in Guinness (£4.95) and evening steaks (from £8.80); there's a
separate stripped-stone no-smoking dining area. The landlord is welcoming and
interesting; table skittles, shove-ha'penny, dominoes, cribbage, trivia machine, and
faint piped music. A small front colonnade supports the upper floor, and the
sheltered little flagstoned courtyard made by this has a traditional bench (and a
dog water-bowl); as well as the garden, there's quite a collection of stone
mounting-blocks. The striking stone-built steep village is well off the beaten track,
so one of the Cotswolds' more hidden treasures. *(Recommended by Neil and Anita
Christopher, Roger Huggins, Ewan McCall, Tom McLean, Dave Irving, A H J Sale, Carol and
Mike Muston)*

*Flowers (Whitbreads)   Tenant D Stevenson   Real ale   Meals and snacks (not Sun or
Mon eve)   (0452) 770265   Children indoors lunchtime only   Open 11–2.30 (3 Sat),
6–11 – they may stay open longer in the afternoon if busy; closed 25 Dec*

BLEDINGTON   SP2422 Map 4

Kings Head 🚫 🛏

B4450

The menu in this 15th-century inn changes twice a day and at lunchtime the
popular bar food might include excellent soup (£1.50), salads (from £2.75),
sausages or a delicious hot roast beef sandwich (£2.95), aubergine and tomato au
gratin, savoury chicken pancake or basil and mozzarella (£3.95), chestnut and
courgette parcels with orange sauce (£4.25), smoked salmon and dill pasta or
braised kidneys (£4.50), tasty spare ribs (£4.95), and home-made steak, mushroom
and wine pie (£5.50), with specials such as hot blackpudding, apple and bacon
(£3.25), lamb's liver, red wine and thyme, baked cod cutlet parcels or fresh basil
tagliatelle (£4.25) and jugged hare (£4.95); in the evening they have an à la carte
menu which might include starters like squid salad in lime and mustard, crab and
cucumber mousse or deep-fried camembert (£2.95), walnut roulade stuffed with
asparagus and quail's eggs in a light wine cheese sauce (£3.25), main dishes such as
sliced lamb's kidneys braised with red wine, bacon and parsley (£5.95), local fresh
trout (£7.25), steaks from the chargrill start at £8.95, fillets of salmon and sole
layered with caviar wrapped in pastry, oven-baked and served with fresh spinach
sauce (£9.50). Well kept Hook Norton Best, Tetleys, Wadworths 6X and guest
beers on handpump from the antique bar counter, local ciders in the summer and a
good choice of malt whiskies; friendly service. The central main bar has a cheery
log fire in the stone inglenook (which has a big black kettle hanging in it),
high-backed wooden settles, gateleg or pedestal tables, and some beams –
including a heavy vertical one next to the serving counter. The lounge looks on to
the garden; piped music. The public bar has pool, bar billiards, shove-ha'penny,
dominoes, fruit machine, and juke box, with aunt sally in the garden. Tables on
terraces at the front look over the attractive village green with its ducks and
stream, and in summer months, Morris Dancers regularly perform in the
courtyard; the landscaped garden has a children's play area. *(Recommended by Mr
and Mrs P B Dowsett, Douglas Hain, E A George, Mr and Mrs H Dainton, Dr M V Jones, Dr
Sheila Smith, Alan Skull, Roger and Jenny Huggins, Laurence Manning, David Stanley, Sue
Garner, Iain and Penny Muir)*

*Free house   Licensees Michael and Annette Royce   Real ale   Meals and snacks (not
Sun eves)   Partly no-smoking restaurant – closed Sun evenings   Kingham (0608) 658
365   Children in restaurant and garden room extension   Open 11–2.30, 6–11
Bedrooms; £27B/£45B*

BLOCKLEY   SP1634 Map 4

Crown ★ ⊘

High Street

Now that a separate airy room on the left of the bar serves the very good fresh fish dishes, the bar itself has a more pubby atmosphere again: an antique settle and more recent furnishings, and off this is the snug carpeted lounge with an attractive window seat, Windsor chairs around traditional cast-iron-framed tables, a winter log fire; steps lead up into a little sitting room with easy chairs. This in turn leads through to another spacious dining room. The atmosphere is smart and civilised and the service friendly and good. As well as sea bream, mackerel, halibut, herring, sprats, whitebait, whiting, salmon, Dover sole, skate, plaice, monkfish, eel, red and grey mullet, sardines, trout, shark, lobster, crab, king prawns (from £3.50-£13.95), there's sandwiches, home-made soup (£1.95), melon with port or avocado with stilton (£3.95), spaghetti bolognese (£5.50), lamb cutlet, jugged hare or steak and kidney (£6.95), coq au vin (£7.25), beef stroganoff (£9.95) and steaks (minute steak £7.95, sirloin au poivre £11.95), and good home-made puddings (£2.45); Sunday lunch. Well kept Butcombe, Courage Directors and a guest beer on handpump, and a good selection of wines; you can sit out in front and have your drinks handed down from the window by the bar counter. Fruit machine and piped music (or piped Radio 2). Close to Batsford Park Arboretum. *(Recommended by H K Dyson, E V Walder, Dr and Mrs James Stewart, JMC, M A and C R Starling, Carol and Mike Muston, Ruth and Andrew Triggs, Mrs M E Lawrence, Ted George, Robert and Vicky Tod, Mrs J A Gardner, Cynth and Malc Pollard, William D Cissna, Laurence Manning, Mr and Mrs P B Dowsett, Adrian Pitts, Iain and Penny Muir)*

Free house   Licensees Jim and Betty Champion   Real ale   Meals and snacks   Restaurant   Blockley (0386) 700245   Children over 12 in eating area of bar   Open 11–3, 6–11   Bedrooms; £49.50B/£66.50S(£72.50S)

BOURTON ON THE HILL   SP1732 Map 4

Horse & Groom 🛏

A44 W of Moreton-in-Marsh

In summer, the flowers and hanging baskets outside this quiet, roadside pub are very pretty. Inside, an attractive, high-beamed little lounge bar has cricketing cartoons and steeplechasing photographs on the stripped-stone walls, flowery-cushioned easy chairs, and a large log fire. There's a local atmosphere in the bigger, orthodoxly furnished public bar; sensibly placed darts, cribbage, dominoes and fruit machine; Bass on handpump. Bar food includes soup (£1.15), sandwiches (from £1.25), omelettes (£3.25), chicken and chips or lasagne (£3.95), gammon and egg (£5.95), trout (£4.95), and steak (£6.35). Handy for the Batsford Park Arboretum and for Sezincote. *(Recommended by H K Dyson, Robert Brown, B and J Derry, David Allison, Barry and Anne, Joan Morgan, Wayne Brindle)*

Free house   Licensee J L Aizpuru   Real ale   Meals and snacks   Restaurant (not Sun or Mon evenings)   Evesham (0386) 700413   Children over 10 only   Open 11–2.30, 6.30–11   Double bedrooms; /£32S

BROAD CAMPDEN   SP1637 Map 4

Bakers Arms ⊘ £

Village signposted from B4081 in Chipping Campden

As we went to press the tenants were negotiating to buy the freehold of this delightful small pub from Whitbreads. Already they are using beer from micro-breweries or pubs brewing their own beer and are getting supplies from Butcombe, Donnington and Mitchells, and the Beer Engine in Newton St Cyres (see Devon main entries) and Jolly Roger in Worcester (see H & W Lucky Dip entries); they'll also keep Home Bitter, Theakstons Best and XB and two other real ales on handpump. The kitchen will be moved to give a room with more tables (and allow for new inside lavatories). Nicely presented food includes herby tomato soup (£1.15), excellent garlic bread (a whole stick, £1.60), ploughman's (from £1.65), salads (from £2), light meals such as macaroni cheese (£2.75) or mushroom and nut fettucini (£2.95), chicken, ham and leek pie (£2.95), vegetable chilli (£2.80), a variety of lasagnes (all £3.25), fisherman's pie or moussaka (£3.35) and daily specials, with puddings such as apricot crumble flan or hot chocolate fudge cake (£1.30); children's menu at lunchtime and until 7.30 in the evening. The beamed bar has a good pubby atmosphere, a pleasantly mixed bag of tables and seats around the walls (which are stripped back to bare stone), a log fire under a big black iron canopy at one end with a rocking chair beside it, and another at the other end. The oak bar counter is attractive, and there's a big framed rugwork picture of the pub; efficient, friendly service; darts, cribbage, dominoes. There are white tables under cocktail parasols by flower tubs on a side terrace and in the back garden, some seats under a fairy-lit arbour, and a well provisioned play area; Aunt Sally. (*Recommended by H K Dyson, E V Walder, M J Ridgway, Philip and Trisha Ferris, Marjorie and David Lamb, Richard Parr, Joan Morgan, Joy and Peter Heatherley, Caroline Wright, Gethin Lewis, Ted George, PADEMLUC, Miss D Baker, Pam Adsley*)

See above   Licensees Carolyn and Tony Perry   Real ale   Meals and snacks (noon–2.30, 5.30 (6.30 in winter)–9.45   (0386) 840 515   Children in eating area Open 11.30–3, 5.30(6.30 winter)–11; closed 25 Dec, evening 26 Dec and lunchtime first Sat after Spring Bank Hol, for local Scuttledown Wake

BROCKWEIR   SO5401 Map 4
Brockweir Inn
Village signposted just off A466 Chepstow–Monmouth

Popular with walkers, this friendly and simple 17th-century pub has a bare-stone-walled main bar with sturdy settles on quarry tiles in the front part, and brocaded seats and copper-topped tables in a series of carpeted alcoves at the back; there are lots of community notices and a local atmosphere. The bare-floored public bar is traditionally furnished, and has darts, pool and a fruit machine; piped music. Well kept Bass, Boddingtons, Hook Norton Best and a guest beer each week on handpump, three farm ciders also with a guest that changes regularly. Simple bar food includes sandwiches (£1.30), home-made soup (£1.25), pizzas (from £3.65), lasagne (£3.75, vegetarian £3.65), home-made steak and ale pie (£3.95) and puddings such as hot apple cake and strawberry (from £1.25); barbecues during the day and evening in the summer, and they plan to open a restaurant. A covered courtyard at the back opens into a sheltered terrace. You can walk from here up steep sheep-pastures to Offa's Dyke Path and the Devil's Pulpit, with views over the Wye and Tintern Abbey. Canoeing, horse riding and salmon fishing are available locally. (*Recommended by Jacqueline Davis, David Young, D and B Carron, Drs M and K Parier; more reports please*)

Free house   Licensees Howard and Claire Shields   Real ale   Meals and snacks (12–2, 7–10)   Tintern (0291) 689 548   Children welcome   Open 11.30–3, 6–11 Bedrooms; £20/£35

CHEDWORTH   SP0511 Map 4
Seven Tuns
Queen Street, Upper Chedworth; village signposted off A429 NE of Cirencester; then take second signposted right turn and bear left towards church

The two bars here have completely different characters. The basic bar on the left is OK for people in wellies or with children, and opens into a games room with darts, dominoes, juke box, pool, and fruit machine. While on the right, the smart but cosy lounge has a quiet, peaceful atmosphere, comfortable seats, decent tables, sizeable antique prints, tankards hanging from the beam over the serving bar, a partly boarded ceiling, and a good winter log fire in the big stone fireplace; there's also a skittle alley (which can be hired). Both the house pâtés such as stilton with herbs and the puddings (from £1.30) such as jam roly-poly, apple and blackberry pie and profiteroles come in for special praise; other food includes a vegetarian dish such as spinach and nut lasagne (£3.40), a good steak and kidney pie (£3.60), sandwiches and dishes of the day. Well kept Courage Best and Directors and Centurion or Fosseway on handpump; they serve Scrumpy Jack on handpump and mulled wine in winter; welcoming, hard-working staff. There are picnic-table sets under cocktail parasols on a side terrace, and older tables and seats over the lane in a little walled raised terrace with a stream running through it and forming a miniature waterfall outside; this steep collection of stone houses does seem to collect a lot of water and in wet weather the car park can be a bit mucky, though this may be because of their collection of rare-breed hens. *(Recommended by E V Walder, Comus Elliott, Roger Huggins, Ewan McCall, Tom McLean, Dave Irving, J M Potter, Mrs A M Stephenson, Mr and Mrs P B Dowsett, A H J Sale)*

Courage   Licensees Barbara and Brian Eacott   Real ale   Meals and snacks (not winter Mon lunchtime, not 25 Dec), Aug Bank Holiday Mon pig roast   (0285) 720 242 Children welcome, but not in lounge bar   Open 12–2.30, 6.30–11; closed winter Mon lunchtime, and may close 2.30 if licensees have a lot to do

CHIPPING CAMPDEN   SP1439 Map 4

Kings Arms

Run by friendly, hardworking licensees, this elegant small hotel has a comfortable and old-fashioned bar with some handsomely carved black beams, a fine stone inglenook fireplace (there are log fires throughout winter) and some big bay window seats. Bar food is good and well presented and might include soup (£1.60), country pâté (£3), pasta provençale (£4.25), lamb's kidney (£4.75) steak and kidney pie (£5.75), and hot game pie (£6.50), with puddings (all £1.75) such as sherry trifle, banoffi pie and mousse. They have a very extensive wine list – 120 by the bottle and 15 by the glass. They are kind to children and provide colouring cards and crayons to keep them amused during mealtimes. There are seats in the gardens behind. Handy for the attractive nearby gardens of Hidcote and Kiftsgate Court. *(Recommended by David Williams, Dr and Mrs Frank Rackow, Peter Lloyd, J B Craig; more reports please)*

Free house   Licensee Mr Earnshaw   Meals and snacks (12–3, 6–9.30   Restaurant Evesham (0386) 840 256   Children welcome   Open 11–11   Bedrooms; £20(£25B)/£40(£50B)

Lygon Arms

The young locals make for quite a lively atmosphere in the small bar here: stripped high-backed settles and green plush stools around the dimpled copper tables on the flowery carpet, a variety of horse photographs and hunting plates on the stripped stone walls, and a curious stone-slate roof over the stone-built bar counter. Generously served, good bar food includes filled rolls (from 95p) and sandwiches (from £1.25), filled baked potatoes (£2.60), starters such as home-made soup (£2), home-made chicken liver pâté (£2.95), main courses such as home-made chilli con carne (£4), clam fries with blue cheese dressing (£4.10), home-made lasagne (£4.65), home-made steak and kidney pie (£4.90) and steak (from £7.95), with daily home-made specials such as salmon and prawn quiche, pork and apricot casserole and chicken with lymeswold, vegetarian meals (from £3.25) and puddings (£1.85); good breakfasts and afternoon teas, daily June to October, and at weekends from November to May. Well kept Donnington SBA, Hook Norton Best, John Smiths, Ruddles Best and Wadworths 6X on handpump, and some interesting wines by the glass; friendly staff. Darts and skittle alley. A few white cast-iron tables are set out in the sheltered inner courtyard. *(Recommended by Barry and Anne, H K Dyson, Alan and Eileen Bowker, Andrew and Ruth Triggs, Ann-Alicia Court, Richard Parr, Lynne Sheridan, Bob West, Simon Collett-Jones)*

Free house   Licensee I G Potter   Real ale   Meals and snacks (11.30–2.30, 6–10, afternoon teas, daily June-Oct, weekends Nov-May)   Evening raftered steak-and-wine bar   Evesham (0386) 840318   Children in good family room and in eating area of bar   Folk music Sun evening   Open 11–11 (not Tues), winter 11–2.30, 6–11 Bedrooms; £22.50/£38

Noel Arms 🍺

The bar in this 14th-century inn has farm tools, horseshoes and gin traps on the bare stone walls, casks hanging from its beams, attractive old tables, seats and settles among the Windsor chairs, and a coal fire; there's also a conservatory. The small lounge areas are comfortable and traditionally furnished with coach horns, lantern lighting, and some stripped stonework, and the reception area has its quota of pikes, halberds, swords, muskets, breastplates and armour, and some 17th-century carved chairs and other oak antiques. Recommended bar food includes sandwiches (from £1.60, open prawn sandwich £3.75), soup (£1.45), hot filled baps (£2.45), spaghetti bolognese (£3.75), spanish omelette (£4.25) and puddings (£1.75). Bass, Hook Norton Best and Theakstons XB on handpump, and a good choice of malt whiskies; in the bar you can choose from the restaurant wine list. There are seats in the coachyard. *(Recommended by H K Dyson, J Roy Smylie, Andrew and Ruth Triggs, Simon Collett-Jones, Alastair Campbell)*

Free house   Licensee Neil D John   Real ale   Lunchtime meals and snacks Restaurant   Evesham (0386) 840317   Children in restaurant and eating area of bar Open 11–3, 5.30–11 in winter   Bedrooms; £55B/£75B

CLEARWELL   SO5708 Map 2

Wyndham Arms 🍺

B4231, signposted from A466 S of Monmouth towards Lydney

The licensees have been running this smart and well kept country inn for 18 years. It's a lovely place to stay, being close to both the Wye Valley and the Forest of Dean, but has a good local following too. The stylish beamed bar has red plush seats and red velvet curtains, a collection of flat-irons by the log-effect gas fire in its spacious stone fireplace, and two big unusual patchwork pictures on its bared stone walls. Good lunchtime bar food includes open sandwiches (from £3.95), ploughman's (£3.95), hot pasta dish of the day, deep-fried soft herring roes, snails with garlic and parsley butter, prawn curry, and fried squid rings with szechuan sauce (£4.95), deep-fried mushrooms stuffed with chicken liver or cheese and herb pâté (£5.55), vegetarian dish of the day (£5.75), 8oz steak (£6.25), smoked local wild salmon (£6.55), home-made puddings (£2) and there's a children's menu; excellent breakfasts. Well kept Bass on handpump; cribbage and dominoes. There are seats out on the well kept stone-terraced lawns. They have two flat-coated retrievers – Sam and his son Theo – and welcome other dogs. *(Recommended by David Heath, R A Corbett, Neil and Anita Christopher)*

Free house   Licensees John and Rosemary Stanford   Real ale   Meals and lunchtime snacks   Restaurant and grill room   Dean (0594) 833 666   Children welcome   Open 11–3, 5.30–11   Bedrooms; £35B/£70B

COATES   SO9700 Map 4

Tunnel House

Village signposted off A419 W of Cirencester; in village follow Tarlton signposts, turning right then left; pub up track on right just after railway bridge; OS Sheet 163, map reference 965005

Reached by a pot-holed track, this eccentric and very relaxed place is rather like a clubhouse or even an idealised version of a students' union bar (it's certainly popular with students from the Royal Agricultural College in Cirencester). There are friendly dogs and cats, a python – called Pythagoras – secured in a glass case by the bar, and an unusual mix of furnishings such as massive rustic benches and seats built into the sunny windows, a haphazard mixture of easy chairs, a sofa, and little spindleback seats; lots of enamel advertising signs, race tickets, air travel labels, dried flowers hanging from its beams, and a well carved wooden fireplace for one of the several open fires. Bar food includes bacon or sausage butties (£1.40), burgers (£1.70), chilli (£3.60) and chicken with barbeque sauce (£3.80). Well kept Archers Best and Wadworths 6X on handpump; darts, shove ha'penny, pinball, dominoes, space game, trivia game, fruit machine and huge juke box (there may be a TV on). They now run boat trips into the canal tunnel when there's enough water. *(Recommended by Pamela Sterling, Robert Brown, Dr M V Jones, Jim and Becky Bryson, Patrick Freeman, A J H Sale, Mrs Lili Lomas, Caroline Wright)*

Free house Licensee Chris Kite Real ale Meals and snacks (12–2, 7–10) (0285) 770 280 Children welcome Open 11–3, 6(7 winter)–11; 11–11 Sat

COLD ASTON SP1219 Map 4
Plough

Village signposted from A436 and A429 SW of Stow on the Wold; beware that on some maps the village is called Aston Blank, and the A436 called the B4068

Cool on a hot summer's day and warm and cosy in winter, this tiny and very friendly 17th-century pub is divided into snug areas by standing timbers and by one built-in white-painted traditional settle facing the stone fireplace. There are pictures on the walls, a very old photograph of the pub on the mantlepiece, low black beams, simple old-fashioned seats on the flagstone and lime-ash floor, and a happy mix of customers. Generous helpings of good bar food include home-baked filled rolls and ploughman's, nicely filled baked potatoes (from £2.55), home-made pies (from £3.60), chilli specials (£3.95), home-baked ham salad (£4.35). Well kept Wadworths 6X and IPA on handpump, with Norbury's farm cider; darts, cribbage, dominoes, quoits and piped easy-listening music. The small side terraces have picnic-table sets under cocktail parasols. *(Recommended by Sharon Hancock, E V Walder, Gordon and Daphne, Peter and Rosemary Woods, Dave Irving, Roger Huggins, Tom McLean, Ewan McCall, Mr and Mrs P B Dowsett)*

Free house Licensee J A King Real ale Meals and snacks Cotswold (0451) 21459 Open 11–2.30, 6.30(7 winter weekdays)–11 Bedrooms; l£35B

COLN ST ALDWYNS SP1405 Map 4
New Inn ☞

On good back road between Bibury and Fairford

This 16th-century stone free house had been a popular main entry for a good long time, so hearts sank when it was bought by a property developer who shut it down with a view to turn it into flats. A vigorous local campaign encouraged the council to overturn that proposal, and now after a gap of two years, it has opened as an upmarket inn that lots of readers have enjoyed. A central log fire in a neat stripped stone fireplace with wooden mantlebeam and willow-pattern plates on the chimney breast divides the two rooms of the bar. There are oriental rugs on the red tiles, low beams, some stripped stonework around the bar servery and hops above it, and a mix of seating from library chairs to stripped pews; down a slight slope, the further room has a log fire in an old kitchen range at one end. The atmosphere is relaxed and friendly. Home-made bar food includes sandwiches (from £2), ploughman's (from £2.75), fresh asparagus or shell-on mussels with white wine and garlic (£3.95), lasagne (£4.25), seafood pancake (£4.75), baked fillet of cod with a tomato coulis or pan-fried trout fillets with lemon butter (£5.25), steak and kidney pie (£5.25) and 6oz steak (£6), with home-made puddings (from £2) such as black forest gateau, crème caramel and lemon mousse. Well Kept Flowers IPA, Hook Norton Best, Marstons Pedigree and Wadworths 6X on handpump; pleasant, friendly service; cribbage, dominoes, cards, chess and draughts. There are seats on the small terrace in front and a garden across the driveway. The peaceful Cotswold village is very pretty. *(Recommended by Joan Olivier, Mr and Mrs P B Dowsett, Jonathan Warner, CDMC, Dave Irving, Roger Huggins, Tom McLean, Ewan McCall, Susan Sinclair, Joan Olivier)*

Free house Licensee C R Knight Real ale Meals and snacks Evening restaurant Coln St Aldwyns (0285) 750 651 Children in eating area only Jazz/folk Sun eves Open 11–11, winter 11–3, 6–11 Bedrooms; £30.40B/£50.70B

nr COWLEY   SO9614 Map 4

Green Dragon ★ ⊘

Cockleford; pub signposted from A435 about 1 1/2 miles S of junction with A436 – or follow Elkstone turn-off; OS Sheet 163, map reference 969142

This attractive stone-fronted pub is so popular that it's best to get there before 1pm if you want a seat – inside or out. Service is quick and friendly, the atmosphere lively, and bar food consistently good. It changes every week and might include cream of onion and mussel soup (£1.50), courgette and thyme pâté (£1.75), meatballs (minced beef with onions, garlic and cinnamon) in a sauce of red wine, tomatoes, peppers and marjoram, pork fillet with apple and stilton sauce or mushroom stroganoff (£4.50), steak and kidney pie, swordfish steak with a sauce of prawns, mussels and mushrooms, or West African ground-nut stew (£4.75), steaks (from £8.50), with puddings such as banoffi pie, chocolate roulade, maple and walnut pie, and cranberry cheesecake (£1.50). There's a lunchtime family carvery on Sundays. Archers Golden, Bass, Boddingtons, Flowers Original, Hook Norton Best, Smiles Exhibition, Theakstons Old Peculier and Wadworths 6X on handpump or tapped from the cask; wines that include a local one, and farm cider. The two bars have country kitchen chairs and tables, big flagstones as well as some red carpet, a collection of foreign banknotes pinned to some of the beams, logs burning all year in a spacious stone fireplace, and a woodburning stove in a big stone fireplace. They ask customers to dress decently. They have a self-contained function room which is available for hire, and will seat 40–90 people; it has terraces outside overlooking Cowley lake and the River Churn. There are lovely local walks, with maps provided. *(Recommended by E V Walder, John and Joan Wyatt, F H Thompson, WHBM, Alan Skull, Roger Huggins, Tom McLean, Ewan McCall, Dave Irving, Owen Barder, Eleanor Grey, A J H Sale, Martin Richards, Maureen and Pat Campbell, John Matthews, C E Power, Mrs Y M Healey, Mrs Lili Lomas, Christopher and Heather Barton, G D Collier, Mrs Joan Harris, R and S Bentley, N P Cox, Patrick Freeman, Lord Evans of Claughton, Caroline Wright)*

Free house   Licensees Barry and Susan Hinton   Real ale   Meals and snacks (11.15–2, 6.15–10 Mon-Sat; 12–2 (2.30 carvery), 7.15–10 Sun   Coberley (0242 87) 271 Children in restaurant and in carvery for Sun lunch   Jazz Mon evening, folk Weds evenings   Open 11–2.30, 6–11, Sat 12–3, 7–10.30

EBRINGTON   SP1840 Map 4

Ebrington Arms

Signposted from B4035 E of Chipping Campden; and from A429 N of Moreton-in-Marsh

In a quiet and pretty village, this well run small inn has a friendly mix of local countryfolk and visitors. The nice little flagstoned and low-beamed bar has recently made sturdy traditional furnishings – including seats built into the airy bow window, a big stone fireplace (with a roaring fire in winter), and a slightly raised woodfloored area. A lower room, also beamed and flagstoned, has stripped country-kitchen furnishings and another enormous log fireplace. Quickly (and generously) served decent simple bar food includes sandwiches (£1.30, sirloin steak baguette £3.35), hearty soups (£1.55), good ploughman's, egg and chips (£1.95), ratatouille (£2.85), omelettes (from £3.35), lasagne (£3.45), cottage pie (£4.45), fresh cod (£4.55), gammon and eggs or chicken, ham and tarragon pie (£4.95), a good steak and kidney pie (£4.95) and steaks (from 8oz sirloin £9.15). Particularly well kept Donnington SBA, Hook Norton Best and Theakstons XB on handpump, Bulmer's farm cider, decent coffee; absolutely no piped music or games machines – just an old-fashioned harmonium, dominoes, cribbage and darts. The two friendly welsh springers (not allowed in during food times) are called Cymro and Rhys. An arched stone wall shelters a terrace with picnic-table sets under cocktail parasols. You can count on good breakfasts if you stay – we'd be grateful too for reports on the bedrooms as we'd expect this to deserve our place-to-stay award. Handy for Hidcote and Kiftsgate. *(Recommended by Dr Keith Bloomfield, S V Bishop, Gethin Lewis, Pat Woodward, Margaret and Trevor Errington, D G Clarke)*

Free house　Licensees Gareth Richards and Andrew Geddes　Real ale　Meals and snacks (not Sun evening)　Paxford (038 678) 223　Children in dining room　Open 11–2.30, 6–11; closed 25 Dec　Bedrooms; /£35B

FORD　SP0829　Map 4

Plough

B4077

In the past, there have been ups and downs here, and the pub's appeal has been strongest for those prepared to take things as they find them, and to be treated not as anyone special – an appeal that's been very strong indeed. But between the time this edition goes to press and the time it gets into the bookshops, new licensees will have taken over. Things unlikely to change include the beamed and stripped-stone bar with its old settles and benches around the big tables on its uneven flagstones, oak tables in a snug alcove, and log fires; and of course the famous April-June asparagus feasts (£8) – the first asparagus spears to be sold at auction in the Vale of Evesham usually end up at this ancient, rambling inn. Other bar food has included sandwiches (from £1.25), soup (£1.75), garlic mushrooms (£2.45), ploughman's (£3.50), lasagne, chillies and curries (all around £3.75), home-made pies such as steak and kidney pie (£4.75), mixed grill (£6.25), and a trucker's breakfast from 9am. Well kept Donnington BB and SBA on handpump; darts and dominoes. There are benches in front, with rustic tables and chairs on grass by white lilacs and fairy lights. Look out for the llama farm between here and Kineton. *(Recommended by PLC, E V Walder, Michael and Alison Sandy, Laurence Manning, Gordon and Daphne, Victoria Logue, A Triggs, P B Dowsett, G D Collier, Mrs S McGreevy, Iain and Penny Muir)*

Donnington　Real ale　Meals and snacks　(038 673) 215　Children welcome Pianist　Open 11–3, 6–11　Bedrooms; £17.50/£35

FOSSEBRIDGE　SP0811　Map 4

Fossebridge 🗗 🛏

A429 Cirencester–Stow on the Wold

Particularly good – although expensive – food in this handsome Georgian inn might include starters such as spring onion and tomato soup (£1.75), warm croissant filled with mushroom and cream cheese sauce or shelled mussels in a rich prawn sauce (£3.75), and smoked scotch salmon (£5.95); main course dishes include tagliatelle topped with creamy chicken sauce or hot quiche lorraine (£5.50), strips of pork loin in sweet and sour sauce or chicken cajun (£6.75), grilled salmon or roast leg of lamb (£7.50), and puddings such as fruit crumble or sticky toffee pudding with butterscotch sauce (£2.50); at lunchtime only they also do filled baked potatoes (£2.95), ploughman's (£3.50), and assorted cold meats with salad (£5.25); vegetables are good. Well kept Marstons Burton and Pedigree on handpump, large glasses of wine, a useful choice of good malt whiskies, and as much coffee as you like. Service is helpful, smiling and unobtrusive. The two attractive bars, linked by arches, have beams in the sloping ceiling, prints, reproductions of old maps, decorative plates and copper pans on the walls, oriental rugs on flagstones, and traditional wooden chairs, wall benches and tables; there's also a fine log fire up at the waist-high level of the original floor. A more modern area houses an attractive restaurant. There are tables out on the streamside terrace and a spacious lakeside lawn. Handy for the Chedworth Roman villa (you can walk all the way from the inn, along the pretty river valley). *(Recommended by Laurence Manning, Mrs Jane Leeds, M A and C R Starling, Mrs P J Rattle, Dr T E Hothersall, M W Grubb, David Eversley, Suzanne Gilpin, E Evans)*

Free house　Licensees Mr and Mrs F J Winfield　Real ale　Meals and snacks Restaurant　Fossebridge　(0285) 720 721　Children welcome　Bedrooms; £35B/£45B　Open 11–3, 6–11

GREAT RISSINGTON   SP1917 Map 4

Lamb ⇐

You can sit out in the sheltered hillside garden here – which has a play area and aviary – and walk, via disused gravel pits that are now a habitat for water birds, to Bourton on the Water. Inside, the cosy two-room bar has wheelback and tub chairs with cushioned seats grouped around polished tables on the light brown carpet, a nook under the stairs with a settle and table, and a log-effect gas fire in the stone fireplace. The walls are hung with photographs of the thirteen guide dogs that the inn and customers have raised money for, a history of the village, plates, pictures, an interesting collection of old cigarette and tobacco tins, and a plaque donated by the only survivor of a bomber that crashed in the back garden in 1943. Bar food is truly home-made (apart from one pudding) and includes sandwiches, home-made soups using fresh vegetables (£2.25), home-made chicken liver pâté with brandy and garlic (£2.50), stuffed mushrooms (£3.25), sardines in garlic butter (£4.50), poachers pocket pie (£4.95); on Sunday the menu is limited to a roast lunch and ploughman's. Well kept Bass, Hook Norton Best and Wadworths 6X on handpump; a decent wine list, country wines, and farm cider. One of the chintzy bedrooms in the warren of small stairs and doors has a four-poster carved by the landlord; there's an indoor swimming pool. *(Recommended by H K Dyson, Jean and Christopher Cowan, Ruth and Andrew Triggs, A Y Drummond, Frank Cummins, Tom McLean, Roger Huggins, Ewan McCall)*

Free house   Licensees Richard and Kate Cleverly   Real ale   Meals and snacks   Restaurant   Cotswold (0451) 20388   Children in eating area of bar   Open 11–2.30, 6.30–11; closed 25 and 26 Dec   Bedrooms; £28(£30B)/£34(£42B)

GUITING POWER   SP0924 Map 4

Olde Inne

Village signposted off B4068 SW of Stow on the Wold (still called A436 on many maps)

The gently lit bar in this snug stone cottage has attractive built-in wall and window seats (including one, near the serving counter, that's the height of the bar stools), small brocaded armchairs, and a winter log fire in an unusual pillar-supported stone fireplace. The public bar is furnished like the main bar but has flagstones and stripped stone masonry, as well as sensibly placed darts. The licensee is welcoming and helpful, and the white cat is friendly, too. Bar food includes country pâté (£2.75), cod (£3.95), lasagne (£4.25), steak and kidney pie or barbecued pork chop (£4.95). Hook Norton Best and Theakstons Best and XB on handpump, a selection of malt whiskies. Tables on a strip of gravel in front look over the quiet lane to a gentle slope of field, and at the back the pleasant garden overlooks more fields. *(Recommended by Chris Ball, Derek and Sylvia Stephenson, R W Grey, HNJ, PEJ, M A and C R Starling, Iain and Penny Muir, Caroline Wright, J Bramley)*

Free house   Licensees Kenneth and Paula Thouless-Meyrick   Real ale   Meals and snacks   Restaurant   Guiting Power   (0451) 850 392   Children in eating area and restaurant   Open 11.30–2.30, 5.30–11

HYDE   SO8801 Map 4

Ragged Cot

Burnt Ash; Hyde signposted with Minchinhampton from A419 E of Stroud; or (better road) follow Minchinhampton, Aston Down signposted from A419 at Aston Down airfield; OS Sheet 162, map reference 886012

Red cushioned window-seats in this Grade II listed building overlook the garden and its line of chestnut trees, and there's stripped stone, black beams, a traditional dark wood wall settle by the end fire, and a relaxed, chatty atmosphere; off to the right is a no-smoking restaurant area. Home-made bar food includes onion soup (£1.50), pizzas (£2.95), pâté (£2.75), cauliflower cheese or omelettes (£3.25), steak and kidney pie (£4.95), gammon (£5.95) and steaks (from £8.50); well kept Courage Directors, John Smiths Yorkshire, Marstons Pedigree, Theakstons Best or

XB and Uley Old Spot on handpump; they offer eight malt whiskies and over fifty wines; service is kind. There are picnic-table sets outside, and at holiday times a pavilion-like garden bar may be used. There are bedrooms in an adjacent converted barn. (*Recommended by John Broughton, Ewan McCall, Roger Huggins, Tom McLean, Dave Irving, Margaret Dyke, Patrick Freeman, Carol and Mike Muston*)

Free house   Licensees Mr and Mrs M Case   Real ale   Meals and snacks Non-smoking restaurant   Brimscombe (0453) 884 463/731 333   Children over 10 in restaurant   Open 11–2.30, 6–11   Bedrooms; £45B/£55B (4-poster £65B)

KILKENNY   SP0018   Map 4

Kilkeney Inn 🏮

A436 nr Cheltenham – OS Sheet 163, map reference 007187; if this hamlet is not shown on your map look for Dowdeswell

Originally a row of cottages right by the road but now set well back from it, this small inn has been carefully brought up to date, giving an airily spacious, bright and open bar with neatly alternated stripped Cotswold stone and white plasterwork, and gleaming dark wheelback chairs around the tables. Up at the other end of the same long bar a proper drinking area, with well kept Courage Best, Hook Norton Best, John Smiths and Wadworths 6X on handpump (and decent wines), preserves a thrivingly pubby feel. At the back, it opens into a comfortable new dining conservatory. At lunchtime (and on Sunday evenings) the good bar food includes sandwiches (from £2.50), ploughman's (£2.90), pâté (£3.25), courgette and broccoli bake (£3.75), and chicken and mushroom pie (£3.95); there's also waitress-served à la carte food such as French onion soup (£1.75), cheese and herb pâté or melon pieces in rum with pineapple and kiwi fruit (£2.25), sautéed pigeon breast (£2.95), and main courses such as crisped vegetables with garlic and basil sauce in puff pastry or diced steak in red wine with mushrooms under a puff pastry top (£5.35), chicken with fresh tarragon and cream sauce (£6.95), lemon sole with herb and lime butter (£8.25), a wood lettuce and lamb fillet salad with cashew and tangerine dressing (£7.50), duck breast with black cherry and brandy sauce (£8.25), and grilled salmon with dill sauce (£7.75). Vegetables are lightly cooked and (like the puddings, from £1.80) served generously – service is friendly and good. Attractive Cotswold views, good parking. (*Recommended by John and Joan Wyatt, Roger Huggins, Tom McLean, Ewan McCall, Dave Irving, I R Smith, Mrs V Middlebrook*)

Free house   Licensees John and Judy Fennell   Real ale   Meals and snacks Restaurant   Andoversford (0242) 820341   Open 11.30–2.30, 6.30–11; closed 25 Dec

KINETON   SP0926   Map 4

Halfway House

Village signposted from B4068 and B4077 W of Stow on the Wold

You can sit outside this pretty little stone house in the narrow flagstoned front terrace, which is separated from the slow, quiet village lane by tubs of bright flowers on top of a low stone wall, or on the sheltered back lawn where there are also children's swings. The unpretentious bar has some old ancient farm tools and pictures at one end, and beams at the other; it's more the good mix of customers and well kept Donnington BB and SBA (fresh from the nearby brewery) on handpump that you notice. Simple bar food such as sandwiches or rolls (£1.40), soup (£1.40), ploughman's (£2.60), nut cutlets (£2.75), vegetarian lasagne (£3.75), steak and kidney pie (£4), fillet steaks (from £9); note that they like prior notice for vegetarian food; attentive, friendly licensees. Darts, dominoes, cribbage, cards, a fruit machine and juke box. The pub does warn that the landlord's otherwise friendly boxer cannot abide other dogs. (*Recommended by E V Walder, Barry and Anne, Mr and Mrs C B Scott-Morton, HNJ, PEJ*)

Donnington   Tenants Derek and Jean Marshall   Real ale   Meals and snacks (11.30–1.30, 6.30–9.15)   Restaurant   Guiting Power (0451) 850 344   Children welcome lunchtime   Open 11–2.30, 6–11 all year   Bedrooms; £15/£30

KINGSCOTE   ST8196 Map 4

Hunters Hall ★ ⦵

A4135 Dursley–Tetbury

There's something to suit all tastes in the elegant series of high-beamed connecting rooms in this smart creeper-covered building: a comfortable miscellany of easy chairs, sofas and a fine old box settle as well as some more elementary seats, velvet curtains, exposed stone walls and good winter log fires. The lower-ceilinged public bar has sturdy settles and oak tables on the flagstones in front of another big log fire, and a back room – relatively untouched – is popular with local lads playing pool; darts, shove-ha'penny, and fruit machine. Bar food, generally served from a buffet in an airy end room, includes lunchtime sandwiches (not Sunday), goat's cheese wrapped in filo pastry (£2.95)mussels in white wine, smoked trout, very good steak and kidney pie (£4.75), turkey and ham pie or seafood pancakes (£5.25), salads such as rare beef or mixed meats (£5.75), charcoal-grilled steaks (from £7.25), and salmon (£7.75); excellent breakfasts; there's more space to eat in the Gallery upstairs. Bass, Hook Norton Best, Smiles Best, Uley Old Spot and Wadworths 6X on handpump, and quite a few wines by the glass. The big garden has weekend summer barbecues and is good for families with a big play area at the far end which has a fortress of thatched whisky-kegs linked by timber catwalks, as well as a climber and swings. *(Recommended by Roger Huggins, Tom McLean, Ewan McCall, Dave Irving, Mr Jennings, J R Williams, Barry and Anne, Alastair Campbell, G D Collier, Cherry Knott, D A B and J V Llewelyn, N P Cox, Patrick Freeman, Carol and Mike Muston)*

Free house   Licensee David Barnett-Roberts   Real ale   Meals and snacks   Restaurant (sandwiches not on Sun)   (0453) 860 393   Children in eating area of bar, restaurant and gallery   Open 11–3, 6(6.30 in winter)–11; closed 25 Dec   Bedrooms; £44B/£54B

nr LECHLADE   SU2199 Map 4

Trout

St John's Bridge; a mile E of Lechlade on A417

Originally an almshouse, this became an inn in 1472 and was known as 'Ye Sygne of St John Baptist Head' until 1704 when the name was changed to Trout. Ancient fishery rights are still held by the pub. The low-beamed main bar is partly panelled and decorated with trout and stuffed pike, and there's a flagstone part by the serving counter which has Courage Best and Directors and John Smiths on handpump; darts, shove-ha'penny, dominoes and Aunt Sally. Opening off here is a snug area, once the ground-floor cellar, which has wooden tables and settles, and fishing prints on the walls. A third bar leads on to the spacious Thameside garden, which has plenty of tables by the old walnut tree, boules, a summer bar and marquee; there are fine views from here over the meadows towards Lechlade. Varied bar food includes home-made soup (£3.25), ploughman's (£3.75), home-made pâté (£4.50), vegetarian spaghetti with different sauce every day (£4.95), four types of home-made pizza (from £5.95), mediterranean fish stew (£6.50), 8oz rump steak (£9.95), and two specials, one with grilled trout and one smoked trout; the helpings are very large, so they are prepared to cook the same dishes in smaller helpings for reduced prices; children's menu (from about £3.50). Occasional piped music; quick, courteous service, and the friendly pointer is called Blucher. *(Recommended by Mr and Mrs P B Dowsett, Robert Brown, Ted George, Lyn and Bill Capper, Joan Olivier, S V Bishop, Alastair Campbell, Wayne Brindle, Patrick Freeman, Neil and Anita Christopher, John Bramley)*

Courage   Tenant R G Warren   Real ale   Meals and snacks   Restaurant; closed Sun Faringdon (0367) 52313   Children in restaurant   Jazz Tues evenings and in marquee in summer   Open 11–2.30, 6–11; 11–11 summer Sats

LITTLE WASHBOURNE   SO9933   Map 4

Hobnails

B4077 (though often mapped still as the A438) Tewkesbury–Stow on the Wold; 7 1/2 miles E of M5 junction 9

Parts of this traditional pub are five hundred years old and it's been run by the same family for 248 years. The snug little front bar has old wall benches by a couple of tables on its quarry-tiled floor and low sway-backed beams hung with pewter tankards, and there's a more modern, carpeted back bar with comfortable button-back leatherette banquettes. They specialise in a wide range of large and generously filled baps, which range from sausage and fried egg (£1.80), through liver and onions (£2.90) and chicken and mushroom in creamy sauce (£4.35), to steak with egg and mushrooms (£6.05); there's also a choice of soups (£1.95) and other starters, macaroni cheese (£4.50), a good selection of interesting vegetarian dishes (£4.70), lasagne (£5.05), curries (£5.35) and lamb hot-pot (£5.60), and a wide range of home-made puddings such as treacle and lemon tart, tyrolean chocolate gateau or french fruit flan (£2.40). Well kept Flowers IPA and Original, Wadworths 6X and Whitbreads PA on handpump; cheerful, helpful service. Darts, shove-ha'penny, fruit machine, piped music. A separate skittle alley (with tables) is for hire Monday to Friday evenings. Between the two buildings, and beside a small lawn and flowerbed, there's a terrace with tables. *(Recommended by Bob Smith, VL, Pat Woodward, Michael and Alison Sandy, Andrew and Barbara Sykes, Frank Cummins)*

Whitbreads   Licensee Stephen Farbrother   Real ale   Meals and snacks (12–2, 7–10) Restaurant   Alderton (024 262) 0237   Children in eating area and restaurant, family room at weekends   Open 11–2.30, 6–11; closed 25, 26 Dec

NAILSWORTH   ST8499   Map 4

Weighbridge

B4014 towards Tetbury

What one reader liked about this busy stone-built pub was that although the food is very good, he felt able to enjoy a drink without someone pushing a menu under his nose. The three little downstairs rooms, with walls either crisply white or stripped to bare stone, have attractive antique settles and small country chairs; the one on the left has its black beam-and-plank ceiling thickly festooned with black ironware – sheepshears, gintraps, lamps, cauldrons, bellows; there are log fires in each. Up some steps is a raftered loft with candles in bottles on an engaging mix of more or less rustic tables, and some unexpected decorations such as a wooden butcher's block. You can walk from here into the sheltered garden rising behind the pub, with swings and picnic-table sets under cocktail parasols. An unusual feature of the bar menu is the popular two-in-one pies with steak on one side and cauliflower cheese on the other, say (£4.80 large, £3.60 small), also shepherd's (£3.30), steak and mushroom or turkey, sweetcorn and pepper (£3.60); other bar food includes cottage rolls or toasties, filled baked potatoes, ploughman's, tasty hot pizzas, and salads, and at least ten vegetarian dishes every day. Well kept Courage Best and Directors and Wadworths 6X on handpump, and 18 wines by bottle or the glass. *(Recommended by Robert Brown, Roger Huggins, Tom McLean, Ewan McCall, Bob Timmis, Pamela Sterling, John Broughton, Martin and Gill Searle, G D Collier, BKA, E A George, Janet Tomalin, Capt and Mrs D S Kirkland, H K Dyson)*

Free house   Licensee J M Kulesza   Real ale   Meals and snacks   Children in two rooms away from bar   Open 11–2.30, 7 (6.30 Sat)–11

NAUNTON   SP1123   Map 4

Black Horse ⊘ ⇌

Village signposted from B4068 (shown as A436 on older maps) W of Stow on the Wold

On a quiet village lane, this L-shaped little inn has a sophisticated atmosphere in its unpretentiously furnished bar: black beams and some stripped stonework, polished elm cast-iron-framed tables, simple country-kitchen chairs and built-in oak pews, flagstones and flooring tiles, and a big woodburning stove. A good range of food includes home-made soup (£1.50), pâté (£2.50), lunchtime ploughman's (from £2.50), chicken breast or seafood platter (£4.50), tasty gammon with egg or pineapple (£6.50), delicious roast duckling, and succulent Scotch steak (£9), with specials such as lovely smoked prawns (£3.50), lasagne (£4), and pork chop with apple and calvados sauce (£6.50), and puddings like lemon brûlée or pecan and maple syrup tart (£2); chips are crisp; last orders for Sunday lunch 1.30 prompt. Well kept Donnington BB and SBA, several wines, shove-ha'penny, cribbage, dominoes, sensibly placed darts, fruit machine and juke box (which could be quieter at times); some tables outside. Note that they don't allow children. *(Recommended by PADEMLUC, Laurence Manning, Ruth and Andrew Triggs, Andy and Jill Kassube, Maureen and Pat Campbell, Mrs Carol A Riddick, Adrian Pitts, George Atkinson, Iain and Penny Muir)*

Donnington Tenants Adrian and Jennie Bowen-Jones Real ale Meals and snacks (not 25 Dec) Restaurant Guiting Power (0451) 850378 Open 11–2.30, 6–11; closed eve 25 Dec Two bedrooms; £17.50/£30

NEWLAND   SO5509 Map 4

Ostrich 🛏

B4231 Lydney–Monmouth, OS Sheet 162, map reference 555096

Prettily placed in a charmingly picturesque village above the River Wye, this consistently welcoming small inn dates back to the 13th century. Its spacious but cosily traditional low-ceilinged bar has huge logs burning in a fine big fireplace decorated with a very capacious copper kettle and brass-bound bellows. It's comfortably furnished with cushioned window seats and wall settles and rod-backed country-kitchen chairs. A good choice of bar food freshly prepared to order includes lunchtime filled rolls (£2) and ploughman's (£3.50); and soup (£2), several starters or tapas dishes such as devilled mushrooms or garlic king prawns £2), vegetarian food such as cashew balls or portuguese nut roast (£5), pies such as steak and oyster or venison (£5–5.50), fish such as salmon (£5.50) or turbot, steaks, venison steak and roast barbary duck (£7.50), with puddings such as bread and butter or summer pudding (around £2). They bake all their own bread. Well kept Boddingtons and Marstons Pedigree on handpump, and a pair of frequently changing guests such as Greene King Abbot and Theakstons Old Peculier; a good range of decent wines, a dozen or two malt whiskies. Service is just right – attentive and pleasant without being too effusive; Sunday newspapers out, maybe unobtrusive piped classical music, tables out in small garden. If you stay, count on big breakfasts. *(Recommended by Frank Cummins, Dr John Innes, C C Cook, Dick Brown)*

Free house Licensees Richard and Veronica Dewe Real ale Meals and snacks Children in dining room Open 11.30–3, 6–11 Bedrooms; £20/£30

NORTH CERNEY   SP0208 Map 2

Bathurst Arms

A435 Cirencester–Cheltenham

Warmly welcoming, this pink Cotswolds inn has a good range of real ales on handpump: Brains, Courage Best, Flowers Original, Gibbs Mew Bishops Tipple, Hook Norton Best, Ind Coope Burton, Tetleys, Wadworths 6X and Wethereds Winter Royal. The large choice of imaginative food includes generous lunchtime sandwiches (from £1.70), soup (£1.80), ploughman's with two types of chutney, then starters such as mushroom provençale with tagliatelle (£2.60), local goat's cheesecake (£2.90), swiss mushroom soufflé (£3.10), main dishes such as spinach and mushroom lasagne (£5.10), pan-fried duck with fresh white peaches (£6.95) and timbale of lemon sole stuffed with langoustine and apple with cider sauce (£10.50) with puddings such as strawberries deep-fried in Guinness and brandy butter and served with caramel (£2.40). The beamed and black-panelled bar has high-backed antique settles and nice window seats, Windsor chairs on the Turkey carpet, pewter tankards above the serving counter and a splendid stone fireplace; the quite separate Stables Bar has cribbage and dominoes. They hold summer barbecues most weekends, lunchtime and evening on the pretty front lawn. *(Recommended by A J H Sale, Michael Richards, John Evans, Mrs M Hatchwell)*

Free house   Licensees Mr and Mrs F A C Seward   Real ale   Meals and snacks   Restaurant   Children in eating area   North Cerney (028 583) 281   Open 11–3, 6–11 all year   Bedrooms; £30(£40B)/£35(£45B)

NORTH NIBLEY   ST7496   Map 4

New Inn ★ 🏠

Waterley Bottom, which is quite well signposted from surrounding lanes; inn signposted from the Bottom itself; one route is from A4135 S of Dursley, via lane with red sign saying Steep Hill, 1 in 5 (just SE of Stinchcombe Golf Course turn-off), turning right when you get to the bottom; another is to follow Waterley Bottom signpost from previous main entry, keeping eyes skinned for small low signpost to inn; OS Sheet 162, map reference 758963

There's a fine collection of breweriana here – particularly antique handpump beer engines, including the ones actually used to dispense the well kept real ales: Cotleigh Tawny, Greene King Abbot, Smiles Best and Exhibition, Theakstons Old Peculier, and WB (a bitter brewed for the pub by Cotleigh), as well as guests. Mrs Sainty also keeps Inch's cider and a good range of malt whiskies. Wholesome, home-made and value-for-money, the bar food includes filled brown baps, toasted sandwiches, ploughman's, chilli con carne (£3.10), lasagne (£3.50), tasty steak and onion pie (£3.70), with puddings like peach and banana crumble (£1.20); well cooked, plentiful breakfasts. The carpeted lounge bar has cushioned Windsor chairs and varnished high-backed settles against the partly stripped stone walls, and sensibly placed darts, dominoes, shove-ha'penny, cribbage, and quiz games in the simple public bar; piped music. Outside, there's a beautifully kept rose terrace, the garden beyond, and then a bowl of quiet pastures, rising to a fringe of woods; at the far end of the garden, is a small orchard with swings, slides and a timber tree-house. To stay here (it's pleasant walking country) you have to book a long way ahead – and best not to arrive outside opening hours. *(Recommended by Barry and Anne, A M Kelly, M J Cochrane, Alan Skull, Drs M and K Parier, Nigel Cant, Patrick Freeman, Roger Huggins, H K Dyson, Carol and Mike Muston, Andrew Sowray)*

Free house   Licensee Ruby Sainty   Real ale   Meals and snacks   (0453) 543 659 Open 12–2.30, 7–11   Two bedrooms; £17.50/£35

ODDINGTON   SP2225   Map 4

Horse & Groom 🏠

Upper Oddington; signposted from A436 E of Stow on the Wold

Run by two brothers, this attractive inn has a handsome antique oak box settle among other more modern seats, decent tables, just a few horsebrasses on the dark 16th-century oak beams in the ochre ceiling, stripped stone walls with some harness and a few brass platters, pale polished flagstones, a big log fire, and hunting-print curtains for smallish windows. Good value bar food includes good sandwiches (from £1.35), soup (£1.50) and ploughman's (£3), lasagne or vegetarian dishes (£4.20), steak and kidney pie (£4.70), trout (£5.25) and puddings such as pavlova or treacle tart (£2); Sunday roast (£5.25) and children's meals (£2). Hook Norton Best, Wadworths 6X and a guest beer on handpump; Taunton cider. A quarry-tiled side area with a fine old polished woodburner has pool; also, darts and piped music. There are picnic-table sets on the neat lawn below the car park, with apple trees, a fine play area including an enormous log climber, a budgerigar aviary, a hut housing fat rabbits, and Aunt Sally; beyond a rose hedge is a pretty water-garden where there are large trout. The bedrooms are not large, but quaint and comfortable, and the candlelit dining room is pretty. They plan to have built a family room by the spring which will have a video game in it. *(Recommended by Prof and Mrs J L Evans, BHP, Laurence Manning, Sir Nigel Foulkes, Mr and Mrs T A Towers, Derek and Sue Hammond, Tim Brierly, Jamie and Ruth Lyons, Simon Collett-Jones, G and M Hollis)*

Free house   Licensees Russell and Stephen Gainford   Real ale   Meals and snacks
Restaurant   (0451) 30584   Children in eating area of bar   Open 11.30–2.30, 6–11;
winter evening opening 6.30; closed 25 and 26 Dec   Bedrooms; £28.50S/£47S

PAINSWICK   SO8609   Map 4
Royal Oak

St Mary's St

This cheerful and friendly local has a lounge bar with a lovely panelled oak door, an elegant oak settle, seats and copper-topped tables made from barrels, some walls stripped back to silvery stone, and an open fire in the massive chimney which divides the room into two parts. There's a second bar on the left, and a small sun lounge facing a sheltered suntrap courtyard with wisteria and colourful pots of geraniums and calceolarias. Good bar food ranges from sandwiches (from £1.20), home-made soup (£1.70), ploughman's (from £2.30), home-made pâté (£2.50) and salads (around £4.95, salmon £5.95), to an enterprising range of hot dishes, changing every day, but typically including chicken breast stuffed with cheese and mustard or chicken kiev, with a fish dish on Thursdays; well kept Boddingtons, Flowers Original and Whitbreads PA on handpump; juke box. It's well positioned in the centre of a charming small hillside town of old stone buildings, narrow alleys and antique shops, and handy for St Mary's churchyard with its 99 yew trees.
(Recommended by E W Denham, Barry and Anne, Andrew and Ruth Triggs, Robert Brown, Shirley Allen, Cherry Knott, Barbara M McHugh, BKA, Mr and Mrs G Turner, R and S Bentley, H K Dyson, E W Denham, Carol and Mike Muston)

Flowers (Whitbreads)   Tenant Mr Morris   Real ale   Meals and snacks (not Sun)
Painswick   (0452) 813 129   Children in eating area only   Nearby parking may be difficult   Open 11–3, 6–11; closed 25 Dec

REDBROOK   SO5410   Map 4
Boat

Pub's inconspicuously signed car park in village on A466 Chepstow–Monmouth; from here 100-yard footbridge crosses Wye (pub actually in Penallt in Wales – but much easier to find this way); OS Sheet 162, map reference 534097

A friendly new licensee has taken over this wonderfully positioned pub and has – without changing too much of the unspoilt and relaxed atmosphere – cleaned up the bars, added some new furniture, re-done the lavatories, and tidied up the garden. The snug has been lightened up, too, with new curtains, fresh paint, and the suspended ceiling stripped out to show the original arched ceiling it had hidden. The main bar has local photographs, landscapes, a wall settle, a grey-painted piano and a woodburning stove; it's still got its tiled floor – and the easy-going atmosphere which has always been its trademark. There are twelve ales on offer, tapped straight from casks behind the long curved bar counter, the line-up changes weekly, and might include Batemans XXXB, Greene King Abbot, Hook Norton Old Hookey, Morlands Speckled Hen, Oakhill, Theakstons Best, XB and Old Peculier, Thwaites, Worthington BB and Wadworths 6X; also farm cider, country wines; cribbage, dominoes and a space game. Bar food includes soup (£1.25), filled baked potatoes (from £1.20), crab mousse (£1.50), ploughman's (£2.60), ratatouille or cauliflower and broccoli cheese (£2.80), turkey and mushroom crumble or creamed chicken livers (£3.40), rabbit in white wine and mushroom sauce (£3.45), locally smoked salmon (£4.20) with puddings such as bread and butter pudding or triple chocolate pudding (£1.40). There are splendid views of the valley from the steep terraced garden (prettily lit at night), which has tables among little waterfalls and a pond cut into the rocks.
(Recommended by Robert Brown, Michael and Alison Sandy, R A Corbett, Neil and Anita Christopher, Gwynne Harper, Julian Proudman, Rob Harrison, Jerry and Alison Oakes, B Jeepies, John Burgan, Hilary Irving; more reports on the new regime, please)

Free house   Licensee Steffan Rowlands   Real ale   Meals and snacks   (0600)712 615   Children in separate snug   Folk music Tues, jazz Thurs   Open 11–3, 6–11

SAPPERTON   SO9403   Map 4

Daneway £

Village signposted from A419 Stroud–Cirencester; from village centre follow
Edgeworth, Bisley signpost; OS Sheet 163, map reference 939034

The Thames and Severn Canal (about 500 yards away) is being partially restored
by a canal trust, and it was for the tunnel workers that this cheerful, friendly place
was built in the late 18th century. On a sloping lawn bright with flowerbeds and a
rose trellis, lots of old picnic-table sets look down over the remains of the canal
and the valley of the little River Frome. The pub's car park is built over what used
to be one of its locks – you can still see the corner-stone of the lock gates. It's on
Good Walks Guide Walk 89. Inside, there's a remarkably grand and dominating
fireplace, elaborately carved oak from floor to ceiling, and racing and hunting
prints on the attractively papered walls. Lunchtime bar food includes filled rolls
(75p, not Sundays; bacon and mushroom £1.80), ploughman's (from £2.20), filled
baked potatoes (£2.20), lasagne (£3.50), and beef and Guinness pie (£4.20), with
evening extras like gammon steak (£5.50) and rump steak (£7.25); puddings such
as hot apple pie (£1.30). Well kept Archers Best and a beer brewed for the pub
(from a local brewery) on handpump and electric pump, Wadworths IPA on
handpump, and 6X tapped from the cask, also regular guest beers and local farm
cider. Darts, dominoes, shove-ha'penny, and ring-the-bull in the public bar, which
has a big inglenook fireplace; quoits. There may be a vintage motor cycle club
meeting in the car park on summer Wednesdays. *(Recommended by E V Walder, Roger
Huggins, Tom McLean, Ewan McCall, Dave Irving, HNJ, PEJ, A Y Drummond, Mrs Lili
Lomas, Barry and Anne, Chris Raisin, Carol and Mike Muston)*

*Free house   Managers Liz and Richard Goodfellow   Real ale   Meals and snacks
Cirencester (0285) 760 297   Children in small family room off lounge   Open 11–2.30
(3 Sat), 6.30–11*

SIDDINGTON   SU0399   Map 4

Greyhound

Ashton Rd; village signposted from industrial estate roundabout in Cirencester
through-traffic system; and from A419 (northbound only)

There's a chatty, friendly atmosphere here, with locals and visitors welcomed alike.
On the right, the biggish lounge bar has lots of copper and brass on the beams and
ochre walls, with a few hunting prints, Edwardian hat feathers, some
black-lacquered farm tools, and china and other bric-a-brac, and an old
herringbone brick floor (carpeted at the far end). By one of its two big log fires is a
red plush wing armchair, but otherwise there's a happy mix of high-backed winged
settles, high dining chairs, chapel seats and so forth, and good tables – mainly
stripped pine, but one fine circular mahogany one. A wide choice of good value bar
food includes sandwiches (from £1.55), filled rolls (from £1.80), soup (£1.85),
omelettes (from £2.15), filled baked potatoes (from £2.30), ploughman's (from
£2.95), soup or garlic mushrooms (£1.85), omelettes (from £2.05), prawns in
garlic (£3.20), salads (from £3.30), and hot dishes such as vegetable gratin (£4.10),
chicken curry (£4.65), rainbow trout (£5.15) and steaks (from £9.75), with crisp
sauté potatoes, good salad garnishes and fresh puddings such as chocolate fudge
pavlova (£1.85); well kept Wadworths IPA and 6X and Badger Tanglefoot on
handpump; the public bar has darts, table skittles and fruit machine; piped music.
There are picnic-table sets and older seats among lilacs, apple trees, flower borders
and short stone walls behind the car park. *(Recommended by Mr and Mrs P B Dowsett,
Dr and Mrs A K Clarke, Mrs Lili Lomas, John and Joan Wyatt, Tom McLean, Ewan McCall,
Roger Huggins)*

*Wadworths   Tenant Bob Flaxman   Real ale   Meals and snacks (12–2, Mon-Thurs
7–10, Fri-Sat–10.30, Sun 7–10)   (0285) 653 573   Open 11.30–2.30, 6.30–11;
evening opening Sat-Mon 7; closed 25 Dec and evenings 26 Dec, 1 Jan*

SOUTHROP   SP1903 Map 4

Swan 🏮

Village signposted from A417 and A361, near Lechlade

This rather civilised country pub is mainly popular for its choice of enterprising and home-made bar food. At lunchtime, this might include stilton and onion soup or mushroom and hazelnut pâté (£2.65), smoked haddock and prawns in a creamy sauce (£3.15), cottage pie with chips and peas (£3.65), goat's cheese wrapped in puff pastry with cranberry sauce or avocado with smoked chicken in a coronation sauce (£4.20), grilled sardines with garlic buttered new potatoes or buckwheat pancake filled with chicken, bacon and mushrooms (£5), and fresh salmon (£5.50); in the evening the prices are slightly higher, but the range of dishes increases and might include charcoal grilled whole smoked prawns or deep-fried camembert with cranberry and orange sauce (£3.30) among the starters, and there are main dishes like charcoal grilled leg of lamb pieces in a mushroom and fresh sage sauce or roast breast of Somerset duck with blackcurrant and cassis sauce (£8.95), and Southrop beef Wellington (£9.30), there are also lunchtime and evening specials. Morlands Original and guest beers such as Hook Norton Best and Fullers London Pride on handpump, and a short but good selection of wines by the bottle; friendly staff (and cats). The extended low-ceilinged front lounge has cottagey wall seats and chairs, and winter log fires, and beyond it is a spacious stripped-stone-wall skittle alley, well modernised, with plenty of tables on the carpeted part, and its own bar service at busy times; fruit machine and trivia in the public bar. There are tables in the sheltered garden behind. *(Recommended by E V Walder, Alan Skull, Simon Reynolds, Peter Burton, David Lamb, Margaret Dyke, Paul Harrop, Tom McLean, Ewan McCall, Roger Huggins, A J H Sale, Jenny and Brian Seller, P B Dowsett, Frank W Gadbois, Patrick Freeman, Mrs J Crawford)*

Free house   Licensee Patrick Keen   Real ale   Meals   Restaurant   Southrop (036 785) 205   Children welcome   Open 12–2.30, 7–11

ST BRIAVELS   SO5605 Map 4

George 🛏 £

The three rambling rooms in this pleasant place have old-fashioned built-in wall seats, some booth seating, green-cushioned small settles, toby jugs and antique bottles on black beams over the servery, and a large stone open fireplace. A Celtic coffin lid dating from 1070, discovered when a fireplace was removed, is mounted next to the bar counter. Bar food includes soup (£1.50), vegetarian burger (£1.70), ploughman's or chicken and chips (£2.50), salads (from £3.50), cheese and broccoli flan (£4), lasagnes (meat, vegetable and seafood from £4.50), home-made chilli (£4.50), home-made steak and kidney pie (£5), salmon steak (£5.50), and fresh local trout (£6.50), with daily specials such as rabbit stew and a variety of gateaux and hot puddings (£2); they do not do children's meals but will provide smaller or half portions of some main meals. Well kept Badger Tanglefoot, Marstons Pedigree and Wadworths 6X on handpump; cribbage, dominoes and piped music. Outside the pub there are tables on a flagstoned terrace at the back that overlook a grassy former moat to a silvery stone 12th-century castle built as a fortification against the Welsh, and later used by King John as a hunting lodge; there are more tables among roses and shrubs and an outdoor chess board. *(Recommended by Michael and Alison Sandy, Julian Yorke, Robert Brown, Mr and Mrs D Devereux, Alan Skull, Donald Godden)*

Free house   Licensees Maurice and Cherry Day   Real ale   Meals and snacks (not Mon-Thurs evenings)   Dean (0594) 530228   Children in eating area of bar up till 8.30pm   Open 12–2.30, 7–11   Bedrooms; /£40

STANTON   SO0634 Map 4

Mount

Village signposted off B4632 (the old A46) SW of Broadway; Old Snowshill Road – take no through road up hill and bear left

The position here is lovely – up a steep, quiet lane looking back down over the pretty golden stone village; on a good day you can see across to the Welsh mountains. The atmospheric original bar has cask seats on big flagstones, heavy-horse harness and racing photographs, black beams, and a big fireplace. A spacious extension, with some big picture windows, has comfortable oak wall seats, cigarette cards of Derby and Grand National winners, and an aquarium of goldfish and angel fish. Well kept, reasonably priced Donnington BB and SBA on handpump, and farm cider; friendly staff. Darts, dominoes, cribbage, fruit and space machines and piped music; they also race woodlice in winter. Generally decent bar food includes sandwiches (from £1.50, tasty toasties £2.50), ploughman's (from £3.40), chicken and broccoli lasagne (£3.95), daily specials, and puddings (£1.25); at busy times there may be PA announcements when food is ready; barbecues in summer. You can play boules on the lawn, and there are seats on the terrace; on *Good Walks Guide* Walk 88. It does get very busy at peak times. *(Recommended by Laurence Manning, Alan and Heather Jacques, Robert Brown, Neil and Anita Christopher, I H Rorison, BHP, Miss P de Earthe Bond, A C Morrison, David Young, Bob Smith)*

Donnington   Tenant Colin Johns   Real ale   Meals and snacks (not Sun evening) Stanton   (038 673) 316   Children welcome if well behaved   Open 11–3, 6–11; 11–11 Sat; closed 25 Dec

STOW ON THE WOLD   SP1925 Map 4

Queens Head

The Square

Local people come to this charming, old-fashioned pub to enjoy themselves, though it's popular with visitors, too. The spacious flagstoned back bar has lots of beams, a couple of attractive high-backed settles as well as wheelback chairs, public school football team colours on a back wall, and a big log fire in the stone fireplace; piped opera in here (not in front), darts, shove-ha'penny and fruit machine. The busy stripped-stone front lounge is packed with small tables, little Windsor armchairs and brocaded wall banquettes. Bar food includes sandwiches (from £1.50), very good soup or filled baked potatoes, flans for vegetarians such as broccoli flan or faggots (£3.50), and steak and kidney pie and puddings such as delicious apricot crumble or toffee pudding; Donnington BB and SBA on handpump are particularly well kept; mulled wine in winter; quick, helpful service. A green bench in front of this charming building, under the climbing rose and the hanging baskets, looks across the pretty square, and in a back courtyard there are some white tables. Two dogs. *(Recommended by Joan and Michel Hooper-Immins, Keith Croxton, R E Horner, Jim and Becky Bryson, Andy and Jill Kassube, Sheila Keene, A Triggs, N P Cox, Simon Collett-Jones, Adrian Pitts, Iain and Penny Muir, Keith Croxton)*

Donnington   Tenant Timothy Eager   Real ale   Meals and snacks (not Sun)   (0451) 30563   Children in back bar   Occasional jazz Sun   Open 11–2.30, 6(6.30 Sat)–11

nr STOW ON THE WOLD   SP1925 Map 4

Coach & Horses

Ganborough; A424 2 1/2 miles N of Stow; OS Sheet 163, map reference 172292

Good value and genuinely home-made, the bar food in this welcoming and popular Cotswold stone pub might include game soup (£1.55), sandwiches (from £1.55; toasties from £1.70), cottage pie (£1.95), basket meals (from £2.45), filled baked potatoes (from £2.65), ploughman's (from £2.85), lasagne or a vegetarian dish of nuts and onion topped with potato, cheddar cheese and toasted almonds (£2.95), curried chicken (£3.60), home-made steak and kidney pie or chicken kiev (£4.70) and steaks (from £6.95), with specials such as winter stew made with Donnington beer (£2.95), and smoked salmon and asparagus quiche with various salads (£4.95); puddings such as fruit crumble or rich chocolate mousse (from £1.55); occasional barbecues summer Sunday evenings and on bank holidays. Being so close to the brewery, the Donnington XXX, BB and SBA are well kept on handpump; cheerful, polite staff. The bar area has leatherette wall benches, stools and Windsor chairs on the flagstone floor, and steps up to a carpeted part with high-backed settles around the tables; it's decorated with good wildlife photographs and coach horns on its ceiling joists, and there's a winter log fire in the central chimney-piece. Darts, dominoes, fruit machine and juke box. There are seats outside, on a terrace and a narrow lawn. The attached field is where their german shepherd, Candy, and their very likeable but not-very-bright irish wolfhound, Kelly, play; they also have a goat and occasional horse, and are a site for Caravan Club members; slide and swings for children. *(Recommended by Derek and Sylvia Stephenson, E V Walder, Mr and Mrs A G Gillanders, G T and J Barnes, John and Joan Wyatt, Iain and Penny Muir)*

Donnington   Tenants Andy and Sarah Morris   Real ale   Meals and snacks, summer food service times more flexible (open till 9.30, 10 at weekends)   (0451) 30208   Children in eating area   Occasional duo pop/country during summer, and always on New Years Eve   Open 11–3 (later if busy), 6–11; winter lunchtime closing 2.30; closed 25 Dec

WOODCHESTER   SO8302 Map 4

Ram 🏮

South Woodchester, which is signposted off A46 Stroud–Nailsworth

Always busy and cheerful, the attractive L-shaped beamed bar has three open fires, some stripped stonework, country-kitchen chairs, several cushioned antique panelled settles around a variety of country tables, and built-in wall and window seats. The range of well kept real ales on handpump is enterprising, with Archers Village, Boddingtons, Hardington, Hook Norton Old Hookey, Marstons Burton, Uley and two guest beers each week. Inviting and interesting, the very popular bar food includes various ploughman's, curries, spinach roulade or beef and oyster pie (£4.45), chicken tikka or lamb and asparagus pie (£4.95), and puddings such as lemon lush pie or chocolate roulade (£2.15). Service, even when pushed, remains polite and prompt. Sensibly placed darts, and a fruit machine. There are spectacular views down the steep and pretty valley from picnic-table sets on the terrace by tubs of flowers and an unusually big hibiscus. *(Recommended by Roger Huggins, Tom McLean, Ewan McCall, Dave Irving, Carol and Mike Muston, Mrs D Summers, Margaret Dyke, Maureen Hobbs, M Rowlinson, Colleen Holiday, Pete and Rose Flower, BKA, Mrs Lili Lomas, John and Joan Wyatt, M A and C R Starling, Robert and Vicky Tod, Patrick Freeman)*

Free house   Licensees Michael and Eileen McAsey   Real ale   Meals and snacks (12–2, 6.30–9.30)   (0453) 873 329   Children in eating area of bar   Impromptu piano   Open 11–3 (Sat 4, 3 in winter), 6–11

Lucky Dip

Besides the fully inspected pubs, you might like to try these Lucky Dips recommended to us and described by readers (if you do, please send us reports):

Ampney St Peter [OS Sheet 163, map reference 089013; SP0801], *Red Lion*: Friendly and unpretentious village local; closed weekday lunchtimes *(Dave Irving, Roger Huggins, Tom McLean, Ewan McCall)*
Andoversford [SP0219], *Royal Oak*: Attractive rooms separated by big open fire, raised eating area almost in rafters on left, typical Cotswolds bar on right leading to games room with darts and pool *(Roger Huggins, Ewan McCall, Tom McLean, Dave Irving)*
Apperley [SO8628], *Farmers Arms*: Old-world, cosy and comfortable, with good bar food lunchtime and evening every day, Bass, Hook Norton and Wadworths 6X *(Mr and Mrs K Guyll)*
Avening [ST8897], *Weighbridge*: Pleasantly unchanging, with decent food, civilised atmosphere, Courage or Wadworths 6X *(Tom McLean)*
Berry Hill [SO5713], *Pike House*: Warm welcome, particularly good reasonably priced wide-ranging food inc imaginative vegan meals *(J Bryan)*
☆ **Bibury** [SP1106], *Catherine Wheel*: Three-room pub in famously beautiful village (so does get very popular), with nice pubby atmosphere, friendly young landlord, good open fire in front bar, back bar cosier and more relaxed, well kept Courage Best, good choice of well cooked generous food in

dining room inc good Sun lunch, picnic-table sets in attractive quiet garden; fruit machine and piped music can be intrusive *(Dr M I Crichton, Mr and Mrs P B Dowsett, H K Dyson, Jim and Becky Bryson, Peter and Rose Flower, Margaret Dyke, Roger Huggins, Tom McLean, Dave Irving, I R Smith, Ewan McCall, M Joyner)*

Bibury, *Swan*: Hotel in lovely spot on River Coln, very comfortable bar with sturdy deep-cushioned wooden chairs, relaxing atmosphere, Websters beer, lunchtime bar snacks/buffet (not cheap), good service *(Andrew and Ruth Triggs)*

Brierley [SO6315], *Swan*: Warm welcome, big sandwiches and home-made hot dishes, Bass, Flowers Original and IPA and Marstons Pedigree on handpump *(Robert K Mundy)*

☆ **Brimpsfield** [Nettleton Bottom; A417 Birdlip—Cirencester, by start of new village bypass — OS Sheet 163, map reference 943137; SO9413], *Golden Heart*: Partly 16th-century stone-built country local, under new regime and recently refurbished but keeping its huge open fireplace, appropriate old furniture and three cosily distinct areas; friendly atmosphere, bar food such as ploughman's or steak and kidney pie with nursery puddings (maybe not winter weekday lunchtimes), Bass and three other real ales tapped from the cask, reworked garden; good walks nearby *(Neil and Anita Christopher, Alan Skull, Roger Huggins, Tom McLean, Ewan McCall, Dave Irving, Phil Gorton, Martin Morris, LYM)*

Broadoak [SO7013], *White Hart*: Spacious and comfortable beamed bar, big evening restaurant, terrace overlooking River Severn; has been praised for well kept Whitbreads-related real ales, wide range of cold dishes with good helpings of some hot food, quick friendly service and welcome for children, but no recent reports *(News please)*

Broadwell [off A429 2 miles N of Stow on the Wold; SP2027], *Fox*: Cleanly civilised village pub in lovely spot opp spreading village green, with flagstones, three local Donnington beers on handpump, above-average home-cooked food, obliging service; bedrooms *(P and R Woods, John and Joan Wyatt, Laurence Manning)*

☆ **Brockhampton** [the one between Andoversford and Winchcombe — OS Sheet 163, map reference 035223; SP0322], *Craven Arms*: Pleasant, comfortably modernised low-beamed pub with popular food, well kept local real ales on handpump, short but good wine list, generally good service; several rooms with log fire, stripped stonework, mainly pine furniture, nice garden; lovely walk up to Bellas Knapp for the views *(John and Joan Wyatt, Derek and Sylvia Stephenson, PADEMLUC, Mrs Joan Harris, P Woodward, Iain and Penny Muir, Alan Skull)*

Cambridge [3 miles from M5 junction 13 — A38 towards Bristol; SO7403], *George*: Busy and popular dining pub with attractive decor, good value bar food, well kept

Marstons Pedigree, pleasant service; restaurant, garden with barbecues and play area, summer caravan site; best to book at weekends *(W C M Jones, Tom Evans, Neil and Anita Christopher); White Lion*: Popular with caravanners in summer; good choice of real ales, good value bar food inc authentic pizzas *(J R Jewitt)*

Chaceley Stock [SO8530], *Yew Tree*: Spacious river-view dining room in rambling country pub down long lane, good choice of reasonably priced food inc vegetarian, decent wine list, friendly staff, various different bar areas inc 15th-century core and big games area; attractive waterside lawns, Severn moorings; prone to flooding which can close it for long periods *(Neil and Anita Christopher, LYM)*

Charlton Kings [Cirencester Rd; SO9620], *Clock Tower*: Large recently modernised Banks's pub in converted ex-stable block of former Lilleybrook Hotel, cheap real ales inc very popular Mild, roaring trade in Sun lunches; very clean *(Iain and Penny Muir, John and Joan Wyatt)*

Cheltenham [Portland St; SO9422], *Cotswold*: Well kept Wadworths, simple pub food from brightly lit cabinet, warm and welcoming if sometimes smoky atmosphere *(Alan Skull, Paul Harrop, E V Walder)*

☆ **Cirencester** [W Market Pl; SP0201], *Slug & Lettuce*: Lively town pub with a good deal of character, flagstones, bare boards, interesting furnishings inc good big tables, hearty log fires; Courage real ales, bar meals, piped music, children welcome; tables in inner courtyard *(Roger Huggins, Ewan McCall, Tom McLean, Patrick Freeman, Mr and Mrs A G Gillanders, LYM)*

Cirencester [Blackjack St, between church and Corinium Museum], *Golden Cross*: Small and busy brightly lit local, worth knowing for very cheap food; Arkells, friendly landlord, children welcome *(Margaret and Trevor Errington, Roger Huggins)*

☆ **Cliffords Mesne** [OS Sheet 162, map reference 699228; SO6922], *Yew Tree*: Comfortable and well laid out, doing well under current owners, with good bar food (not Mon), well kept beer, friendly service; good restaurant; children welcome; good starting point for walk up May Hill (NT) *(Kay and Eric George)*

☆ **Coberley** [A436 Brockworth—Andoversford, just SW of junction with A435 Cheltenham—Cirencester; SO9516], *Seven Springs*: Unusual and comfortable reworking of airily lofty and spacious stone barn, with good food area, snugger side areas and sloping pond-side garden; Courage beers, maybe a pianist or organist; children allowed daytime — has been open all day *(John Miles, John and Joan Wyatt, LYM)*

Coleford [Joyford, signed off B4432 at Globe and Home Centre in Five Acres — OS Sheet 162, map reference 580134; SO5813],

Dog & Muffler: Well placed for walkers, with cosy bar, long back conservatory overlooking verandah and secluded lawn surrounded by high hedges; tables with linen and fresh flowers, nicely cooked and presented straightforward food, well kept Sam Smiths on handpump, friendly and welcoming service, log-effect gas fire *(Frank Cummins)*

☆ **Colesbourne** [A435; SO9913], *Colesbourne Inn*: Popular comfortably refurbished pub/hotel with friendly landlord, huge log fire, good atmosphere, settles and oak tables; well kept Wadworths 6X, Famrers Glory and Old Timer, wide range of bar food inc game and ploughman's with unusual cheeses, smart waitresses *(Mr and Mrs P B Dowsett, Patrick Freeman)*

Cranham [nr church — OS Sheet 163, map reference 897129; SO8912], *Black Horse*: Small friendly local, with generous helpings of freshly cooked proper food *(Tom Evans)*

Duntisbourne Abbots [A417 N of Cirencester — OS Sheet 163, map reference 978091; SO9709], *Five Mile House*: Rare unspoilt survivor, very basic; high-backed settle dividing snug from entrance hall, flagstoned second room with its seats around table in bay window formerly used by toll keeper and Courage tapped from casks behind primitive bar counter *(Phil Gorton, Martin Morris, Dave Irving, Tom McLean, Ewan McCall, Roger Huggins)*

Edge [A4173 N of Stroud; SO8509], *Edgemoor*: Modernised food pub notable for the striking valley views through its big picture windows; Whitbreads-related ales under light carbon dioxide blanket, unobtrusive piped music, children in eating area *(Neil and Anita Christopher, Mr and Mrs W H Crowther, LYM)*

Elkstone [Beechpike; A417 6 miles N of Cirencester — OS Sheet 163, map reference 966108; SO9610], *Highwayman*: Rambling low-beamed rooms with stripped stone, alcoves, antique settles among more modern furnishings, log fires; popular food running up to steaks, wide choice of lunchtime open sandwiches and ploughman's, children's dishes, Arkells on handpump, piped music; outside play area; children in eating area, two family rooms and restaurant *(LYM)*

☆ **Ewen** [signed from A429 S of Cirencester; SU0097], *Wild Duck*: Small 16th-century hotel with stylishly old-fashioned furnishings in high-beamed main bar, civilised atmosphere, old paintings, entertaining parrot at liberty, decent bar food — which like the drinks is not cheap; Bass and Wadworths 6X on handpump, shove-ha'penny, piped music, tables in attractive sheltered garden; can get very busy, dogs allowed; bedrooms comfortable and pleasantly furnished, though bathrooms not heated *(Mrs Lili Lomas, PADEMLUC, Neville Kenyon, Dr and Mrs A K Clarke, Patrick Freeman, Mr and Mrs P B Dowsett, Alastair Campbell, D A Lloyd, Robert and Vicky Tod, Neil and Anita Christopher, LYM)*

☆ **Foss Cross** [A429; SP0609], *Hare &*

Hounds: Cosy old roadside pub with two big log fires, reasonably priced food inc good fresh pasta and spicy Indian dishes, family eating area (pub especially welcoming to them), good range of well kept real ales such as Hook Norton, Marstons Pedigree, Theakstons Old Peculier and Wadworths 6X, good coffee, very efficient service, no music, good big back restaurant popular for weekend carvery and Sun lunch; nice area outside, good car park *(John Drummond, Roy Bromell, Mr and Mrs P B Dowsett, P A and J B Tucker)*

☆ **Frampton Mansell** [off A491 Cirencester—Stroud — OS Sheet 163, map reference 923027; SO9102], *Crown*: Attractive spot above village and steep wooded valley, quiet stripped stone lounge bar with dark beam-and-plank ceiling, wall banquettes and ladder-back dining chairs, darts in public bar, Archers Village and Wadworths 6X on handpump, good generous cold buffet, restaurant; children in eating area, teak seats outside; comfortable bedrooms *(John Bowdler, Tom McLean, Roger Huggins, Ewan McCall, Mrs Lili Lomas, LYM)*

☆ **Glasshouse** [by Newent Woods; first right turn off A40 going W from junction with A4136 — OS Sheet 162, map reference 710213; SO7122], *Glasshouse*: Carefully unspoiled basic country tavern, with decorative plates, fine British Match poster and open fires in cavernous hearth of kitchen bar, changing well kept real ales such as Butcombe and Flowers or Theakstons tapped from the cask, ploughman's and plain basket meals, seats on grass outside facing remarkable topiary "cottage"; fine nearby woodland walks *(Janet Tomalin, LYM)*

☆ **Gloucester** [Bristol Rd], *Linden Tree*: Attractive decor in long thin bar with further room beyond, lively welcoming atmosphere, good range of changing well kept real ales such as Batemans, Hook Norton Best, Marstons Owd Rodger, Wadworths 6X and Farmers Glory, well prepared reasonably priced food, friendly service *(Brian Jones)*

Gloucester [Southgate St; part of New County Hotel, between Greyfriars and Blackfriars], *County*: Good value bar lunches, Marstons Pedigree and Burton on handpump, very friendly service, pleasant bar; bedrooms *(Joan and Michael Hooper-Immins, Tom Evans)*; [Tewkesbury Rd], *Queens Head*: Conscientious young chef in refurbished tenanted pub with obliging staff; well presented food, ample helpings and real ingredients; full range of Whitbreads real ales and guests *(Tom Haggett)*; *Tailors House*: Friendly pub nr cathedral, well kept Whitbreads PA *(Iain and Penny Muir)*; [docks entrance], *Tall Ships*: Wadworths pub, very handy for docks museums, recently refurbished in U shape with bottom part a raised dining area and pool table down one side out of sight; fairly simple inexpensive food inc good sandwiches and ploughman's, good tuna bake and uncommonly good chips; Adnams and a guest beer such as Batemans XB as well as 6X, juke box *(Derek and Sylvia Stephenson)*

☆ **Great Barrington** [signed off A40 Burford—Northleach; SP2013], *Fox*: Proper low-key old Cotswold inn, nothing fancy, with stripped stonework, rustic furniture, plain good value bar food, well kept Donnington inc Mild, skittle alley, sheltered terrace by River Windrush (tempting pipe crosses it to opposite field with horses); bedrooms inexpensive, hearty breakfasts *(Comus Elliott, HNJ, PEJ, Alan Skull, Michael and Alison Sandy, Robert Timmis, A P Hudson, Mr and Mrs J H Adam, LYM)*

☆ **Gretton** [signed off B4077 E of Tewkesbury; SP0131], *Royal Oak*: Entertaining medley of furnishings in long series of flagstoned or bare-boarded rooms, old prints, beams, dim lighting inc candles in bottles, stripped country chairs and tables in dining conservatory with good views, tables on terrace and in big garden with play area (on weekends Great Western Steam Railway stops here); enterprising and original bar food, well kept Courage-related and other real ales, friendly young service; folk music Weds *(Derek and Sylvia Stephenson, LYM; more reports please)*

☆ **Hartpury** [Ledbury Rd; SO7924], *Canning Arms*: Attractive, cheerful and welcoming, in lovely surroundings, with friendly licensees and good genuinely home-cooked food inc fine vegetable pie and proper chips; varying well kept beers tapped from the cask, decent wine, real fire *(Chris Richardson, Simon Richards)*

Hartpury [Hamms Lane], *Rising Sun*: Good, reasonably priced bar food inc superb specials and good value Sun lunches, friendly service; children welcome, play area outside; comfortable bedrooms *(Mae and Brian Postlethwaite)*

Kelmscot [SU2599], *Plough*: Friendly and cosy little country pub in Wm Morris's village; bedrooms *(Dave Irving)*

☆ **Kemble** [outside village; A433 Cirencester—Tetbury — OS Sheet 163, map reference 981986; ST9897], *Thames Head*: Cottagey stripped-stone back bar with pews, log-effect gas fire in big fireplace; country-look dining room with another big gas fire; more traditional locals' front bar with real fire, games, pool room; well kept Arkells Bitter and 3B on handpump, good friendly service, seats outside, children welcome; food interesting and inventive — we'd like more reports since the latest change of management *(Frank W Gadbois, DGC, Mr and Mrs P B Dowsett, Neil and Anita Christopher, LYM)*

☆ **Lechlade**, *Red Lion*: Good range of reasonably priced well prepared food (waiters Fri/Sat evenings), friendly helpful service, well kept Arkells *(Derek and Sylvia Stephenson, Marjorie and David Lamb, G M K Donkin)*

Lechlade, *Crown*: Decent bar food from sandwiches up, helpful and friendly service,

good arrangements for wheelchairs; nr church *(G M K Donkin, Joan Olivier)*; [The Square], *New Inn*: Comfortable lounge bar in largish hotel, popular for good value bar lunches; choice of beers, big open fire, restaurant, superb Thames-side garden (mooring allowed); bedrooms *(P B Dowsett, Wayne Brindle)*; [A417 towards Cirencester], *Three Horseshoes*: Worth knowing for decent food served quickly *(G M K Donkin)*

Leighterton [off A46 S of Nailsworth; ST8291], *Royal Oak*: Rather spartan decor, with well kept Butcombe, Green King Abbot, Hook Norton and Uley Old Spot on handpump, straightforward bar food, friendly landlord; quite handy for Westonbirt Arboretum *(Margaret Dyke, P and R Woods)*

Little Barrington [A40 W of Burford; SP2012], *Inn For All Seasons*: Good bar food and service; warm, comfortable and attractive; good bar choice, especiallly of spirits; bedrooms *(F M Bunbury)*

Lower Lydbrook [Vention Lane; pub signposted up single-track rd from B4228 NE of village — OS Sheet 162, map reference 597168; SO5916], *Royal Spring*: Particularly attractive spot, with pretty garden built around stream dropping down steep coombe on edge of Forest of Dean; pews and high-backed settles in long beamed lounge looking down valley, usual bar food, log fire, keg beers; play area, pets' corner; children welcome, folk Thurs *(Gwen and Peter Andrews, Neil and Anita Christopher, Robert Brown, LYM)*

☆ **Lower Swell** [B4068 W of Stow on the Wold (sometimes still called A436 on maps); SP1725], *Golden Ball*: Neat and simple local inn — no pretensions to much atmosphere — with well kept Donnington BB and SBA from the pretty brewery just 20 minutes' walk away, good range of ciders and perry, friendly landlord, generously served bar food inc imaginative salads and good game pie; games area behind log fireplace, occasional barbecues, Aunt Sally and quoits in pleasant streamside garden; evening restaurant, no food Sun evening; very clean simple bedrooms, good value *(M H Box, John and Joan Wyatt, Miss A G Drake, Mr and Mrs P B Dowsett, C A Holloway, LYM)*

☆ **Lower Wick** [ST7196], *Pickwick*: Very good welcome in clean and well refurbished free house with plentiful well presented home-cooked food from ploughman's through spinach florentine and choice of fresh fish to steaks, with children's dishes and deliciously fattening puddings and ice creams; Bass, John Smiths and Theakstons; children welcome *(Mrs Heather Fuller, Nigel Cant)*

Meysey Hampton [SU1199], *Masons Arms*: 1990 renovation wearing in nicely, looking more lived-in; well kept beer, friendly staff, big open fire at one end; has bedrooms now *(Dave Irving, Roger Huggins, Tom McLean, Ewan McCall, Mr and Mrs P B Dowsett)*

☆ **Mickleton** [B4632 (ex A46); SP1543], *Kings Arms*: Comfortable and relaxed L-shaped lounge bar with rugs on parquet, plush-cushioned window seats and small settles, brocaded chairs and stools, well spaced tables; good choice of low-cost snacks and particularly good value filled home-baked rolls — remarkably popular lunchtime with older people; pleasant staff, Flowers IPA and Original on handpump, some tables outside; handy for Hidcote and Kiftsgate, even Stratford, so busy weekends; opens 10, closes earlyish *(Hope Chenhalls, E V Walder, A C Morrison, Margaret Dyke, Peter Lloyd, BB)*

Mickleton, *Butchers Arms*: Clean and tidy pub with friendly atmosphere and staff, good choice of food (half helpings for children as well as own menu), cosy atmosphere, and well kept Flowers ales; outside garden with fishpond *(R W Grey)*

☆ **Minchinhampton** [Minchinhampton Common; Nailsworth—Brimscombe — on common fork left at pub's sign], *Old Lodge*: Partly 16th-century, superbly placed on high NT common, with good range of interesting real ales inc local Uleys, friendly service, food which can be imaginative and good value; interconnecting rooms with unusual mix of ageing furniture, nice pub dog *(Roger Huggins, Tom McLean, LYM)*

☆ **Minchinhampton**, *Crown*: Happy, welcoming Cotswold-stone pub on market sq of historic village, well kept Flowers Original on handpump, decent wines, good hot and cold bar food, open fires, darts and dominoes *(H K Dyson)*

☆ **Minsterworth** [A48 S of Gloucester; SO7716], *Apple Tree*: Originally 17th-century farmhouse, comfortably and well refurbished as Whitbreads Wayside Inn, keeping oak beams and open fires; friendly service, unobtrusive piped music, well kept Whitbreads-related real ales, wide choice of usual food presented well (home-made steak and kidney pie consistently good value), big garden ideal for children with safe enclosed play area; open all day — lane beside leads down to the Severn, a good way of avoiding east bank crowds on a Bore weekend *(Jacquie and Jon Payne, C A Merrett, Christopher and Heather Barton, G D Collier, David Gethyn-Jones)*

Miserden [OS Sheet 163, map reference 936089; SO9308], *Carpenters Arms*: Cotswold stone pub with lots of wood inside, food good inc formidable help-yourself lunchtime summer buffet; evening tables set for meals (main courses and puddings); Whitbreads-related real ales, closed Mon except bank hols; strictly no children and may close early — could be very good indeed if atmosphere more warmly pubby *(Mrs Lili Lomas, T R Smith, Gordon and Kathy Lewis)*

☆ **Moreton in Marsh** [SP2032], *Redesdale Arms*: Well renovated and comfortably pubby bar and buttery in old-fashioned but lively country-town hotel with good log fires, well kept Courage Directors; food, though not cheap, above normal pub standards inc first-class veg and home-made

ice cream, served by helpful staff; bedrooms *(P Knight, Barry and Anne)*

Moreton in Marsh, *Black Bear*: Busy two-bar local, full range of Donnington beers, clean and welcoming, food lunchtime and evening *(Iain and Penny Muir, R E Horner)*; [High St], *White Hart Royal*: Comfortable partly 15th-century THF inn with blazing inglenook fire in room off main bar, Bass from the cask, bar food; bedrooms simple but comfortable — good value *(Ms P Woodward)*

☆ **Nailsworth** [ST8499], *Egypt Mill*: Former mill tastefully converted to pub, with working mill wheel in one room, static machinery in second area, Ind Coope Burton and Wadworths 6X on handpump, good bar food, quick service, good upstairs restaurant; can get crowded at weekends, occasional jazz evenings; children welcome, no dogs; high time they fixed the car park *(Tom McLean, Ewan McCall, Roger Huggins, J R Jewitt)*

Newent [SO7225], *Black Dog*: Well placed on main square, with plenty of parking and tables in front; old-fashioned bars with big fireplaces; friendly locals; food cheap and good, well kept beer *(George Sayer)*; [Church St], *George*: Comfortable 17th-century inn with open fire, friendly staff, good well priced bar food inc children's dishes, Bass; opp Shambles museum; bedrooms *(E A George)*

☆ **North Nibley** [B4060; ST7496], *Black Horse*: Straightforward village pub with particularly good feel about it, with efficient friendly staff, Flowers Original, Whitbreads PA and a guest beer on handpump, wide range of generous fresh home-cooked bar food served till 10; popular restaurant Tues-Sat evenings, Sun lunchtime, tables outside; bedrooms not large, but clean and comfortable, most with shower and private lavatory, good breakfasts *(B and J Derry, WHBM, Carol and Mike Muston)*

Northleach [Market Pl; SP1114], *Red Lion*: Comfortable and friendly, with good value well presented simple bar food, popular Sun roast, open fire, well kept Courage Directors; nr World of Mechanical Music — polyphons, musical boxes, autopianos, clocks *(E V Walder, Michael Stiffin, Hilary Wood)*; [Square; SP1114], *Union*: Comfortably refurbished yet keeping Cotswold feel, attractive food; bedrooms *(Sidney and Erna Wells)*

Norton [Wainlode Hill; SO8523], *Red Lion*: On Severn, looking over to Malvern Hills, plenty of outside seating; Flowers Original and IPA and two ciders on handpump, bar food *(Robert K Mundy)*

Nympsfield [SO8000], *Rose & Crown*: Pretty Cotswold stone village inn covered with roses and climbers; comfortable inside, with Whitbreads-related and other real ales, good choice of food inc good value ploughman's, seats outside; bedrooms *(Alastair Campbell)*

☆ **Oakridge Lynch** [signed off Eastcombe—Bisley rd; SO9102], *Butchers*

Arms: Above a particularly steep and twisty village — luckily the good-sized car park is on the level top road; big neatly modernised rambling carpeted bar with low beams, big fireplace, some stripped stonework, good range of well kept real ales such as Archers, Butcombe, Ind Coope Burton, Ruddles Best and County, decent wines; good imaginative bar lunches, restaurant (Weds-Sat evenings, Sun lunch), reasonable prices, friendly atmosphere, skittle alley *(Ewan McCall, Tom McLean, Roger Huggins, Mrs J M King, Mrs Lili Lomas, Dave Irving, Mrs A Crowhurst, BB)*

☆ **Parkend** [SO6208], *Woodman*: Welcoming fairly big Forest of Dean pub on village green, comfortably worn in and lively without being noisy, with long heavy-beamed bar, wide choice of good value food from sandwiches to steaks inc monthly foreign "theme" dishes, children's menu and Sun lunch; well kept Flowers Original and Marstons Pedigree on handpump, two fireplaces (flowers in one), saws and blades on the wall, good service; darts, fruit machine, juke box; children and small dogs at one end; bedrooms *(Frank Cummins, Dr John Innes, Jean Smith, B J Smith, E H and R F Warner, Annette Keith, Mr and Mrs D Coates)*

☆ **Paxford** [B4479], *Churchill*: Quaint and out-of-the-way, with two little knocked-together flagstoned rooms, simple furniture, former commode full of old books, toy car collection; currently doing well, with welcoming licensees, well kept Hook Norton Best and Old Hookey, good cheap coffee, honest simple bar food, small garden with picnic-set tables *(E V Walder, Iain and Penny Muir, M Joyner)*

Perrotts Brook [A435; SP0105], *Bear*: Worth knowing for nice location, and capacity for both wheelchairs and children *(Robert Brown)*

☆ **Prestbury** [Mill St; SO9624], *Plough*: Unspoilt thatched village pub with flagstones and panelling in basic but roomy back taproom, looking unchanged since 1950s with its grandfather clock, big log fire, well kept Flowers and Whitbreads tapped from casks behind bar, and plenty of Cotswolds characters; good bar food, small but cosy lounge, pleasant back garden *(P J Simmons, Bob Timmis, B M Eldridge)*

☆ **Purton** [just upstream from Sharpness village on left bank of Severn estuary — ie not pub of this name in nearby Berkeley; SO6904], *Berkeley Arms*: Wonderful quiet Severn estuary view, you can see (and walk) for miles, from waterside pub with character — L-shaped room with high-backed settles, no food, no noise; caravanning allowed in field behind in summer when no risk of flooding *(Tom McLean, Ewan McCall, Roger Huggins, N W Acton, Dave Irving)*

Purton, *Berkeley Hunt*: Very basic old-world traditional pub with well kept Wadworths 6X from quaint serving bar between two rooms; pleasant canal setting, basic food *(Tom McLean, Ewan McCall,*

Roger Huggins, Dave Irving, D Price)

Quenington [SP1404], *Keepers Arms*: Cosy, clean and tidy stripped-stone pub with mugs hanging from low beams, well kept Flowers, decent-sized meals at reasonable prices; waitress service; no car park or piped music; pretty village *(Mr and Mrs P B Dowsett, P Freeman)*

☆ **Sapperton** [OS Sheet 163, map reference 948033; SO9403], *Bell*: Well kept Flowers Original, Wadworths 6X and Whitbreads PA, good value straightforward food and welcoming landlord in spacious but warm and cosy L-shaped lounge with big tables; darts, quoits, fruit machine, log fire, tables on small front lawn; fine walks from here — it's on GWG89; well behaved children welcome — a popular family pub at weekends *(Mr and Mrs P B Dowsett, Cliff and Karen Spooner, Roger Huggins, John Miles, Tom McLean, Ewan McCall, Mrs Lili Lomas, Michael Richards, Dave Irving)*

☆ **Selsley** [just SW of Stroud; SO8304], *Bell*: Pleasant village pub worth knowing for its panoramic views and position on common, popular with walkers of the Cotswold Way; friendly staff and locals, wide range of reasonably priced home-cooked bar food, Whitbreads-related real ales and Uley Old Spot on handpump, piped music, live some nights, fruit machine in public bar *(Alastair Campbell, Margaret Dyke, Cherry Knott)*

☆ **Sheepscombe** [village signposted from B4070 NE of Stroud, and A46 N of Painswick; SO8910], *Butchers Arms*: Has been very popular with many readers as simple village inn with cheerful atmosphere, low prices, well kept Flowers Original and Whitbreads PA under light carbon dioxide blanket, plain lunchtime bar food (only light ploughman's on Sun), fine views from bay windows and seats outside; very simple bedrooms, good value; no news since landlord warned us he was leaving, with threat of closure of pub by Whitbreads *(News please)*

Shipton Moyne [off B4040 Malmesbury—Bristol; ST8989], *Cat & Custard Pot*: Village local, with friendly landlord and atmosphere; concentrating a bit more on food, with good simple bar food such as ham and eggs; restaurant extension; Whitbreads-related real ales; pretty village *(Roger Huggins, D K Andrew, BB)*

☆ **Slad** [SO8707], *Woolpack*: Friendly village local, very small, with well kept Flowers Original and Wadworths 6X, welcoming landlord, good range of bar food; one of the settles is Laurie Lee's usual seat *(H K Dyson, BKA, Roger Huggins, Ewan McCall, Tom McLean)*

Slimbridge [Shepherds Patch — OS Sheet 162, map reference 728042; SO7303], *Tudor Arms*: By swing bridge across Gloucester and Sharpness ship canal, handy for Wildfowl Trust; good varied reasonably priced home-cooked bar food and evening restaurant; straightforwardly comfortable, lively and welcoming; children's room; bedrooms in small building next door *(John*

Broughton)

Sling [Clements End; SO5807], *Montague:* Plain, friendly pub with cheap food inc good value children's dishes *(Michael and Rachel Brookes); Orepool:* Under new ownership and extended in character, with friendly welcome, good beer and food; children catered for *(PB, HB)*

☆ **Snowshill** [SP0934], *Snowshill Arms:* Well kept Donnington BB and SBA, log fire, efficiently served popular food (inc Tannoy system for back garden, which has a good play area — and a skittle alley); more airy inside than many Cotswold pubs, with charming village views from bow windows; cheery atmosphere, helpful Italian licensee and English wife, prices notably low for the Cotswolds; children welcome if eating; handy for Snowshill Manor *(Richard Parr, Maysie Thompson, P Knight, Iain and Penny Muir, Mrs Lili Lomas, Margaret and Trevor Errington, Curt and Lois Stevens, P L Knight, William D Cissna, Klaus and Elizabeth Leist, Caroline Wright, LYM)*

Staunton [A4136, Forest of Dean — OS Sheet 162, map reference 548126; SO5513], *White Horse:* Popular Forest of Dean pub with swings and climbing frame in big garden, well kept Whitbreads-related real ales, wide choice of good value bar food inc Sun lunch; on GWG199 *(Neil and Anita Christopher, Dick Brown)*

Stow on the Wold [The Square; SP1925], *Old Stocks:* Good value bedrooms in well run simple hotel with well kept Ruddles in cosy, clean and welcoming small bar, reasonable bar food, subdued piped music, friendly barman; seats on pavement and in sheltered garden *(Mr and Mrs P B Dowsett, BB)*

Stroud [1 Bath Rd; SO8504], *Clothiers Arms:* Nr derelict railway, with obliging landlords (one is Italian — they do superb, authentic spaghetti napolitana) and good real ale from small breweries; lots of bric-a-brac, difficult to find a table (let alone avoid smoke) Sat lunchtime *(John and Joan Wyatt)*

Tetbury [Market Pl; ST8893], *Crown:* Popular old inn doing well under current regime, with open fires in lounge, back dining conservatory, friendly efficient service, Whitbreads-related real ales, wide choice of bar food from sandwiches to steaks; bedrooms *(Lyn and Bill Capper, Roger Huggins)*

nr **Tetbury** [A433 towards Cirencester, nr Cherington], *Trouble House:* 17th-century pub with well kept Wadworths on handpump, simple low-priced bar food from sandwiches up; basic bar, comfortably redecorated cosy lounge with open fire and fruit machine, further room leading off for bar billiards, darts and juke box *(Tom McLean, Roger Huggins)*

Tewkesbury [52 Church St; SO8932], *Bell:* Handsome old inn currently doing well, welcoming and comfortable plush bar with some neat William and Mary oak panelling, black oak beams and timbers, medieval

leaf-and-fruit frescoes, tapestries and big log fire; bar food inc ploughman's, pies and salads, restaurant, well kept Banks's, Bass and Wadworths 6X on handpump; garden above Severnside walk; comfortable bedrooms *(Andrew and Ruth Triggs, Barry Gibbs, Maysie Thompson, BB)*

Toddington [A46 Broadway—Winchcombe, junction with A438 and B4077; SP0432], *Pheasant:* Attractively served good food at reasonable prices, friendly staff, tables in garden with children's play area; close to Gloucs & Warwicks Railway *(Mr and Mrs D Coates)*

☆ **Twyning** [SO8936], *Village Inn:* Welcoming village pub with good atmosphere, helpful staff, good if not cheap bar food (may be limited Mon and Tues), well kept beer, decent wines; beer and wines good, dogs allowed; pretty garden *(W C M Jones, Robert and Vicky Tod)*

Uley [The Street; ST7898], *Old Crown:* Nice atmosphere and friendly landlord in unpretentious bar with good value generous bar food inc children's dishes, Uley Best and Old Spot and Whitbreads PA on handpump, darts and fruit machine, unobtrusive piped music *(Alastair Campbell, Patrick Freeman)*

Wanswell Green [SO6901], *Salmon:* Comfortable, cosy and clean village pub, good food well served in bar or dining room, Flowers real ale; very attentive to young children; big front play area *(K R Harris)*

Westonbirt [A433 SW of Tetbury — OS Sheet 162, map reference 863904; ST8690], *Hare & Hounds:* Pleasant old-fashioned hotel bar with decent lunches, positive helpful staff, Wadworths IPA and 6X, pleasant gardens; handy for Arboretum; children allowed — but limited space for families; bedrooms *(Ewan McCall, Roger Huggins, Tom McLean, GSB)*

☆ **Whitminster** [A38 1 1/2 miles N of M5 junction 13; SO7708], *Old Forge:* Pleasant and friendly old beamed pub with small restaurant; good choice of beers and wines, very good home-made bar food with fresh veg *(Richard and Ann Jenkins, Joan Olivier)*

☆ **Winchcombe** [High St; SP0228], *Corner Cupboard:* Comfortable village local with armchairs in lounge, good taproom with well kept Uley and other real ales on handpump, decent wines by the glass, good choice of whiskies, no piped music or games; well prepared bar food, more imaginative evening meals based on fresh local produce in small restaurant; attractive small back garden *(Bob Timmis, P L Knight, Mrs Joan Harris, David Gethyn-Jones, Mr and Mrs J H Adam)*

Winchcombe [High St, nr church], *Plaisterers Arms:* Well kept Ind Coope Burton, generous sensibly priced bar food *(Bob Timmis)*

☆ **Withington** [signed off A436, A40; from church go S, bearing left — OS Sheet 163, map reference 032153; SP0315], *Mill:* Fine mossy-roofed old stone building with cosy little side rooms off rambling beamed bar, interesting antique seats, good log fire, lovely streamside gardens (summer barbecues) and fine location in peaceful valley — gets very busy weekends; children allowed, Sam Smiths real ales, usual bar food from ploughman's to steaks; games bar, piped music (can be intrusive); still a very popular place, though recent reports not entirely unmixed *(Mrs Lili Lomas, G D Collier, P B Dowsett, Gordon and Daphne, Margaret and Roy Randle, Dr and Mrs James Stewart, Ewan McCall, Tom McLean, Roger Huggins, Ann Marie Stephenson, Paul Harrop, L Cossins, LYM)*

Woodchester [Church Rd, North Woodchester; SO8302], *Royal Oak*: Unspoilt village local with lots of beams and exposed stonework, two bars, Adnams, Bass and Wadworths IPA and 6X; two restaurants, one no-smoking, worth booking for the good soups, fish, home-made pies, steaks and so forth *(Tony Ephgrave, Tom McLean, Roger Huggins, Ewan McCall)*

Hampshire

This is by no means a cheap county. Drinks average 10p or 15p more than the national average, though you can cut your bill by using a pub tied to one of the area's local or regional brewers – with the bonus that one of them, Gales, does a fine line in traditional country wines. Moreover, food prices are on the high side, with only one really good pub (the Coach & Horses at Rotherwick) able to scrape into our bargain food category. One reason for this is that the quality of the food in Hampshire pubs is decidedly a cut above the average – you may be paying a bit extra, but what you get is often better, too. For value on these terms, we'd pick out particularly the friendly and unspoilt Sun at Bentworth, the consistently popular and warmly welcoming Red Lion at Boldre, the Fox at Bramdean (this year it earns a food award for the sheer quality that goes into things which elsewhere might seem quite ordinary), the relaxed and unfussy Five Bells at Buriton (a new entry), the New Forest Inn at Emery Down (its specials are the things to go for), the engaging Olde Whyte Harte near the water at Hamble, the Old Beams at Ibsley (good value, quick service), the Leather Bottle at Mattingley, the Filly at Setley, the White Lion at Soberton (these three all good well run country pubs), the old-fashioned Harrow at Steep, the Tichborne Arms at Tichborne (particularly enterprising snacks, as well as good main dishes), the George at Vernham Dean (fresh veg from the pub's garden) and cottagey Boot nearby, the stylish Chequers at Well, the Test-side Mayfly near Wherwell (particularly for its unusually wide range of cheeses), and the Wykeham Arms in Winchester – currently doing specially well all round, and worth a word of special praise for its good wines by the glass. Other pubs to note particularly are the Hobler at Battramsley (for its lively appeal), the Milbury's at Beauworth (a remarkably deep well in this interesting building), the Jolly Sailor for its fine waterside position at Bursledon, the High Corner at Linwood for its good summer garden, and the Jekyll & Hyde at Turgis Green (food all day at this well run roadside stop-off). In the Lucky Dip section at the end of the chapter, pubs which as we go to press show in readers' reports as currently on the up-and-up include the Flower Pots at Cheriton, Foresters at Frogham, Red Lion at Mortimer West End, Wellington Arms at Stratfield Turgis and Barley Mow at Winchfield; and judging by its new licensees' time at the Vine in Stockbridge, the Boot in Houghton ought quickly to come into the reckoning. Other notable Dips, almost all inspected by us, include the Globe in Alresford, Fox & Hounds at Bursledon, Fox & Hounds at Crawley, Queen at Dummer, Hen & Chicken at Froyle, Chequers at Pennington, Alice Lisle at Rockford, Red Lion and perhaps Grapes in Southampton, Three Lions at Stuckton, Bugle at Twyford, Brushmakers Arms at Upham, Hoddington Arms at Upton Grey and Cartwheel at Whitsbury.

ALRESFORD   SU5832 Map 2

Horse & Groom

Broad St; town signposted from new A31 bypass

Several rambling nooks and crannies give the open-plan bars here a pleasantly secluded feel: black beams, timbered walls partly stripped to brickwork, old local photographs, shelves of earthenware jugs and bottles, and neat settles and Windsor chairs – though perhaps the most enjoyable place to sit is at the tables in the three bow windows on the right, looking out over the broad street. Well kept Flowers Original, Fremlins, Marstons Pedigree and Whitbreads Strong Country on handpump; coal-effect gas fire. Bar food includes sandwiches (from £1.75), soup (£1.95), good ploughman's (from £2.95), sausages (£3.60), salads (from £4.25), tasty home-made steak and kidney pie (£4.25), gammon (£5.95) and steaks (from £7.50), with puddings (£1.50); they warn of some delays at busy periods. *(Recommended by BKA, Bernard Phillips; more reports please)*

Whitbreads   Licensees Robin and Kate Howard   Real ale   Meals and snacks Alresford   (0962) 734 809   Children welcome   Open 11–2.30(3 Sat), 6–11

BATTRAMSLEY   SZ3099 Map 2

Hobler

A337 a couple of miles S of Brockenhurst; OS Sheet 196, map reference 307990

You need to have a sense of humour to eat here – the menu may be punctuated with broad-minded jokes, and there are management-made graffiti in the gents. Divided by the massive stub of an ancient wall, the distinctively lively black-beamed bar is furnished with lots of tables, red leatherette bucket seats, pews, little dining chairs and a comfortable bow-window seat; also, guns, china, New-Forest saws, the odd big engraving, and several customer photographs on the walls. The cosy area on the left is black-panelled and full of books. Generous helpings of bar food include filled baked potatoes (from £2.95), ploughman's (from around £2.95), salads (from £4.50), steak and kidney pie or chicken pies (£4.50), seafood such as red snapper (£6.95) or fresh lobster, half a shoulder of lamb (£6.95), steaks (from £8.95) and lots of daily specials. It is very popular, so get there early for a table in the main building (many are booked in the evening). Well kept Flowers Original, Wadworths 6X and a high-gravity guest such as Bunces Old Smokey on handpump, and a good range of malt whiskies and wines (including some expensive bargains by the bottle); friendly golden labrador. There's more seating out in a comfortable alpine-style log cabin with a hefty woodburning stove, and in summer a spacious forest-edge lawn has a summer bar and marquee, a huge timber climbing fort for the good play area, and a good few picnic-table sets, beside a paddock with ponies, donkeys and hens. The landlord now also runs the slightly bigger Turf Cutters Arms, East Boldre, near Burley; this has a similar atmosphere and menu. *(Recommended by Ken and Barbara Turner, P Corris, Phil and Sally Gorton, H E Hental, Andrew Gale, Paul Brown, John and Chris Simpson, Dick Brown, Michael and Rachael Brookes, Mrs G Evans)*

Whitbreads   Licensee Pip Steven   Real ale   Meals and snacks (12–2, 6–10, not eves Dec 25 and 26)   (0590) 232 91   No children inside, no dogs   Jazz Tues   Open 10–2.30, 6–11; closed 25 Dec eve

BEAULIEU   SU3802 Map 2

Montagu Arms 🖛

The semi-circular bar counter here is shaped like part of a wine press and the wine list is unusually interesting. The stylishly comfortable bar is divided into quiet separate areas by low curtain-topped partitions and sweeping arches, is decorated in an understated colour-scheme of cool greens, and has a big Cecil Aldin hunting print as well as attractive little local landscapes on the walls. Bar food includes filled baked potatoes (from £1.70), soup (£1.85), ploughman's (from £3.50), chilli con carne (£3.95), salads (from £4.50), cheese and onion pie (£4.50), beef goulash or steak and kidney pie (£4.95) and roast pork (£5.50), with puddings such as apple and blackurrant pie or strawberry syllabub (£1.75); quick, friendly service; the dining area is no smoking. Well kept if not cheap Boddingtons, Marstons Pedigree, Wadworths 6X and Whitbreads Best on handpump, a wide range of malt whiskies and decent coffee; unobtrusive piped pop music. The inn, very solidly built in the early 1920s and decorously comfortable and well run, is off to one side, with a pretty lake just beyond it. Picnic-table sets in the front courtyard look down to the Palace gates. *(Recommended by WHBM, E G Parish, S Watkins, M E Hughes, Mrs A Turner)*

Free house Licensee Mr Osmond Real ale Meals and snacks Restaurant Beaulieu (0590) 612 324 Children welcome Open 11–11 Bedrooms; £67.90B/£95.90B

BEAUWORTH SU5726 Map 2

Milbury's

Turn off A272 Winchester/Petersfield at Beauworth 3/4, Bishops Waltham 6 signpost, then continue straight on past village

Surrounded by a Bronze Age cemetery – the Mill Barrow, hence the pub's name – this carefully restored, cheerful place has sturdy beams, broad flagstones, stripped masonry and massive open fireplaces (with good winter log fires). Furnishings inside and out in the garden are in character with the pub's considerable antiquity. In a side area overlooked by a little timber gallery (and safely grille-covered) is a well cut nearly 300 feet into the chalk and carefully spot-lit so that in its narrow depths you see the twinkle of water reflections; the massive treadwheel beside it used to be worked by a donkey. Well kept Courage Best and Directors, Gales HSB and John Smiths on handpump; some malt whiskies and a range of over 100 wines. Bar food, largely home-made using local ingredients, includes home-made soup (£1.40), a choice of ploughman's (from £2.65), salads (from £3.90), prawn and spinach pancake (£4.10), beef in Guinness pie (£4.35), gammon (£5.20), and steak (from £8.95), with children's dishes (£2.50), a good choice of home-made puddings such as Bavarian cheesecake or hazelnut meringue (from £1.75) and Sunday roasts (£4.25). Sunday brunch (£4.65, served 9.30–11.15) comes with Sunday papers; weekend summer barbecues; efficient, cheerful service. *(Recommended by Michael Bechley, Pamela Harris, Barry and Anne, Lynn Sharpless, Bob Eardley, E U Broadbent, W J Wonham, Jerry and Alison Oakes, Lynn Sharpless, Roger Mallard, Donald Godden, John and Chris Simpson, Patrick and Mary McDermott, Prof A N Black, Bev and Doug Warrick, Jacquie and Jon Payne, Dr S E Martin, Dr L B Crook)*

Free house Licensees Jan and Len Larden Real ale Meals and snacks (12–2, 7–10; 12–2.30, 7–10.30 Fri and Sat) Restaurant (0962) 771 248 Children welcome, except main bar Open 11–3, 6–11 Bedrooms; £28.50/£38.50(£46.50)

BENTLEY SU7844 Map 2

Bull

A31 Farnham–Alton, W of village and accessible from both directions at W end of dual carriageway Farnham bypass

This pleasant little tiled white pub has two traditionally furnished low-beamed rooms; besides country and old master prints, there are several comical prewar Bonzo prints – particularly in the left-hand room, which has a dimly lit back alcove with a tapestried pew built around a nice mahogany table, and a log-effect gas fire in a big old fireplace. Good bar food ranges from sandwiches (from £1.10), home-made soup (£1.40) and basket meals (from £2.25), through ploughman's (from £2.95), lasagne (£3.95), salads (from £4.25) and home-made steak and kidney pie (£4.25), to steaks (from £6.95) and puddings (all £1.95). Courage Best and Directors and Wadsworth 6X on handpump and a fine range of wines; darts, fruit machine, piped music. There are tables on the side terrace, by a fairy-lit Wendy house on stilts. It's under the same management as one of our Lucky Dip entries, the Hen & Chicken down the road at Froyle. *(Recommended by Mr and Mrs*

C H Garnett, John and Heather Dwane, S J Rice, WHBM, Tim and Ann Newell, Dr John Innes; more reports please)

Courage   Licensees Peter and Mary Holmes   Real ale   Meals and snacks (till 10, Sun–Thurs evening, 10.30 Fri and Sat)   Restaurant   Bentley (0420) 22156   Children in eating area and restaurant   Occasional pianist Tues   Open 11–11

BENTWORTH   SU6640   Map 2

Sun

Sun Hill; from the A339 coming from Alton the first turning takes you there direct; or in village follow Shalden 2 1/4, Alton 4 1/4 signpost

In 1635 this tucked-away country pub started life as two cottages, and there are still just two little communicating rooms – both with low beams and fat woodburning stoves in big fireplaces. The one on the right has a brick-tiled floor and lacy tablecloths (but not at all twee), and on the left are bare boards and scrubbed deal tables. A mix of seats includes high-backed antique settles, pews and schoolroom chairs, and there are old-world prints, corn dollies and blacksmith's tools. A lively local atmosphere, and quick, friendly service. Generous helpings of good, fresh bar food such as sandwiches (from £1.50), ploughman's (from £2.50), filled baked potatoes (£3.50), plaice, juicy ham and egg, cottage pie, lasagne and vegetarian dishes (£4.50), trout (£6.25) and 8oz sirloin steak (£7.75). Zulu the black collie cross likes playing chase the matchstick with you. There's a jack russell called Datchet. There are a couple of picnic-table sets under cocktail parasols by the quiet lane. *(Recommended by W K Struthers, Richard Houghton, Dr John Innes; more reports please)*

Free house   Licensee Jeremy McKay   Real ale   Meals and snacks (12–2, 6–9.30) (0420) 62338   Open 11–3, 6–11; closed 25 Dec

BOLDRE   SZ3298   Map 2

Red Lion ★ ☺

Village signposted from A337 N of Lymington

We've not heard of anyone, once enticed in, who has been disappointed in this warmly friendly, atmospheric pub. Its row of four, black-beamed rooms are decorated with a profusion of chamber-pots, as well as hunting pictures and landscapes, heavy-horse harness, needlework, heavy urns and platters and daintier old bottles and glasses, farm tools, gin traps and even man traps. The end room has pews, wheelback chairs and tapestried stools, and a pretty collection of old bottles and glasses in the window by the counter. Consistently popular bar food includes home-made soup, good sandwiches (from £1.90), ploughman's or avocado and prawns (£3.10), smoked salmon (£4.10), and salads (from £5.10). For once even the basket meals (from £3.10) are something special, running to duck with fresh orange soaked in wine (£4.90). This year's favourites have been their new daily specials, which might include pasta and vegetables in cheese sauce (£3.10), lambs' kidneys in sherry (£3.90), vegetable casserole (£4.10), quiche (£5.10), and beef in Guinness with dumplings (£5.50). Also new this year is a range of puddings which runs from the usuals (apple pie, gateaux) to an interesting range of ice creams such as chocolate dream (with maple syrup and walnut) or coupe sunrise (lemon, cassis and raspberry sorbets). Quick, helpful service; it's advisable to get there early if you want a table – it really does fill up, especially at weekends. Well kept Eldridge Pope Dorchester and Royal Oak on handpump. The pub is conveniently placed on the fringes of the New Forest and near the Lymington River; in summer the area in front of it is a riot of colourful flowerbeds. *(Recommended by Bernard Phillips, H E Hental, Rob Weeks, John and Christine Simpson, Jane Buekett, Mr and Mrs A Dean, John Mason, Paul Brown, Mrs J A Gardener, M C Howells, B A Cox, Dick Brown, M E Hughes, Mr and Mrs J A Oxley, Ken and Barbara Turner, W C M Jones)*

Eldridge Pope   Licensees John and Penny Bicknell   Real ale   Meals and snacks (11–2.15, 6–10.15)   Restaurant   Lymington (0590) 673177   Open 10.30–3, 6–11, 11–11 in summer school hols, with food all day

BRAMDEAN   SU6128   Map 2

Fox ✪

A272 Winchester–Petersfield

This much modernised dining pub proves that food doesn't have to have fancy names or elaborate ingredients to be first-class. Here, familiar pub standbys win really warm approval from readers for outstanding quality: sandwiches (from £2) including really excellent beef or pork, and vegetables exciting more praise than the humble cabbage usually dreams of aspiring to, as well as good soup (£2.25), ploughman's (£3.50), a fine locally smoked trout (£3.95), king prawns with mayonnaise or mussels and prawns in sherry and garlic butter (£5.25), cauliflower cheese or battered cod (£5.95), and beef stroganoff (£7.50). Service is attentive and friendly. The well kept open-plan bar has black beams, tall stools with proper backrests around its L-shaped counter, and comfortably cushioned wall pews and wheelback chairs; the fox motif shows in a big painting over the fireplace, and on much of the decorative china. Well kept Marstons Burton and Pedigree on handpump, and decent coffee; sensibly placed darts in the games room, fruit machine, unobtrusive piped music. At the back there's a walled-in patio area, and a spacious lawn spreading among the fruit trees, with a really good play area – trampoline as well as swings and a seesaw. Unfortunately, a real fox massacred the hens in the run which have starred in previous editions (missing one cockerel roosting up a tree) and they haven't been replaced. *(Recommended by R and Mrs P F Shelton, Dr John Innes, Jon Barnes, H E Hental, M W Grubb, Colin Laffan, Mr and Mrs Foreman, Nigel Gibbs, John H Walker, Alan Skull, R Elliott, Prof A N Black)*

Marstons   Licensee Mrs Jane Inder   Real ale   Meals and snacks   Bramdean   (0962) 771 363   Open 10.30–2.30(3 Sat), 6–11; closed 25 Dec

BURITON   SU7420   Map 2

Five Bells ✪

Village signposted off A3 S of Petersfield

The relaxed, unfussy atmosphere of an unpretentious country pub combines here with decidedly good food: the specials in particular, served with carefully cooked fresh vegetables, are always worth attention – maybe fresh mussels (£2.95), deftly herbed and crisply fried chicken breast, and a generous and very gamey game pie. Other dishes, more meals than snacks, include soup (£1.50), crispy cod roes with a garlic dip or fresh sardines (£2.50), several vegetarian dishes such as courgette and tomato flan (£3.50), chicken tandoori (£3.95), rabbit casseroled with cider and mustard (£5.50) and a good deal of fresh fish and seafood such as crab mornay (£5.50). The lounge on the left is dominated by the big log fire; a mix of simple furnishings, fresh flowers on tables, old photographs on partly stripped brick walls, a rather worn turkey carpet on oak parquet. The public side, with some ancient stripped masonry, has a woodburning stove, old-fashioned tables, sensibly placed darts, shove-ha'penny, cribbage, dominoes, trivia machine, fruit machine, piped nostalgic pop music, and an end alcove with cushioned pews, old fishing prints, and board games such as Scrabble (with a referee dictionary). Well kept Badger Tanglefoot, Ballards Best, Friary Meux Best, Fullers London Pride, Ind Coope Burton and Tetleys on handpump, quick service. There are a few tables on sheltered terraces just outside, with many more on an informal lawn stretching back above the pub. *(Recommended by Peter Ames, Ian and Wendy McCaw)*

Free house   Licensee John Ligertwood   Real ale   Meals and snacks (till 10) Restaurant   (0730) 63584   Children in restaurant   Jazz last Mon in month, folk music each Weds   Open 11–2.30(3 Sat), 5.30–11

BURSLEDON   SU4809   Map 2

Jolly Sailor

2 miles from M27 junction 8; A27 towards Fareham, then just before going under railway bridge turn right towards Bursledon Station, keeping left into Lands End Road and bearing left past the station itself

This wonderfully positioned, old-fashioned pub has tables out in the waterside garden under a big yew tree, and even on the wooden jetty, looking out over the picturesque bustle of this popular Hamble yachting harbour. There's a children's bar out here at busy times. Bow windows give the same view in the airy front bar, which has a nautical decor of ship pictures, nets and shells, and Windsor chairs and settles on its floorboards; the beamed and flagstoned back bar, with pews and settles by its huge fireplace, is more authentically in the *Howards Way* mood. Well kept Badger Best and Tanglefoot, Everards Old Original, Gales HSB and Wadworths 6X on handpump; fruit machine and piped music. Besides sandwiches, current bar food favourites are mushrooms cooked with cream, white wine and garlic (£3.35) and beef and mushroom pie (£4.95). They specialise in fresh fish at weekends; pleasant service. The path down to the pub from the lane is steep. *(Recommended by Michael Bechley, D A Greer, Tony and Lynne Stark, J H Walker, Mr Cowell)*

Badger   Managers Ron and Anne May   Real ale   Meals and snacks   Restaurant Bursledon (0703) 405 557   Children in eating area and restaurant   If parking in lane is full use station car park and walk   Open 11–2.30, 6–11(Sat 11–11)

CHALTON   SU7315   Map 2
Red Lion

Village signposted E of A3 Petersfield–Horndean

This, the county's oldest pub, may date partly from 1150 – when a workshop here was site office for the rebuilding of the Norman church opposite. The heavy-beamed and panelled bar has an ancient inglenook fireplace with a frieze of burnished threepenny bits set into its mantlebeam, and is furnished with high-backed traditional settles and elm tables. A modern restaurant extension leads off. Gales BBB and HSB on handpump, and a variety of country wines; reasonably priced bar food such as toasted sandwiches or filled rolls (from £1.40), home-made soup (£1.65), stilton ploughman's (£2.95), steak and mushroom pie (£3.65), lamb's liver (£4.15), grilled gammon steak (£4.45) and a choice of home-made puddings (£2.10); though there's now a restaurant, food can be served throughout the pub. Tables outside; the pub's popular with walkers and riders, and fairly close to the extensive Queen Elizabeth Country Park. *(Recommended by A Blackler, N J Clark, Jacqueline Davis, John and Chris Simpson; more reports please)*

Gales   Tenant Mr Worth   Real ale   Meals and snacks (not Sun eves)   (0705) 592 246   Children in lounge bar   Open 10.30–2.30, 6–11; closed 25 Dec eve

DROXFORD   SU6018   Map 2
White Horse

4 miles along A32 from Wickham

Handy for Portsmouth or even Southampton, this 16th-century coaching inn has a rambling lounge bar made up of a series of small intimate rooms: attractive and comfortable refurnishings, low beams, bow windows, alcoves and log fires. The public bar is larger and more straightforward, with cribbage, dominoes, pool, fruit machine, video game and CD player. Bar food includes sandwiches (from £1.40), soup (£2), hot crusty french sticks (£2.55), ploughman's (from £3), salads (from £4.05), some good vegetarian dishes (£4.85) and pies, gammon (£4.95), brace of smoked quail (£5.65), steak (£9.15) and puddings (£2.25); children's helpings (£1.80); welcoming, professional service. Well kept Courage Best, Gales HSB, Marstons Pedigree, Morlands Old Speckled Hen and Wadworths 6X on handpump; they're about 5p cheaper in the public bar. There are tables on a courtyard comfortably sheltered by the building's back wings. *(Recommended by Mel and Phil Lloyd, A D Bulmer, Mrs Y M Healey, HEG, Simon Collett-Jones; more reports please)*

Free house   Licensee Sidney Higgins   Real ale   Meals and snacks (12–2, 7–9.45) No-smoking restaurant   Droxford   (0489) 877 490   Children in family room and restaurant   Open 11–3, 6–11   Bedrooms; l£40B(£50B)

EMERY DOWN   SU2808 Map 2

New Forest Inn ★ ⊘

Village signposted off A35 just W of Lyndhurst

The staff here come in for particular praise from readers – impressively efficient even when really busy yet always warm and friendly. And the food, too, is good, with daily specials being so popular that they're often gone by 1 o'clock: giant prawns wrapped in bacon with cheese and garlic, the daily pasta dish, salmon in champagne sauce, pigeons in cream and raisin sauce or beef with stilton and celery. They also do soup (£2.25), various ploughman's with warm cottage loaves (from £2.75), crab pâté, particularly good mushrooms in garlic (£3.50), Cumberland sausage (£3.50), and particular specialities such as curry with poppadoms, avocado and bacon or fresh fruit and cottage cheese salad (£5.25), gammon (£6.25), pork fillet in a green peppercorn sauce or king prawns in garlic sauce (£7.25) and steaks (from £8.75). Puddings include a light and fluffy toasted lemon brûlée, hot apple and cider pudding or treacle and walnut tart (£2.25); vegetables are properly cooked, and the sauces are interesting. Flowers Original, Wadworths 6X and Whitbreads PA on handpump, good coffee. The softly lit bustling open-plan bar has russet plush settles, wall seats, and smaller chairs around good solid tables, antlers, fox masks, a big china owl and smaller china forest animals, country prints and old photographs of the area, a couple of log fires, and soft lighting. The well kept three-level back lawn is a hive of animal activity, with white rabbits, a pony looking over the post-and-rails fence, maybe lambs or kids in the side stables, and up to four Old English sheepdogs; lovely walks nearby. The car park fills up quickly at busy times. *(Recommended by H K Dyson, Kathy Holt, H E Hental, A N Black, Gwen and Peter Andrews, John and Chris Simpson, Simon Collett-Jones, Tim and Ann Newell, Helen Roe, Gethin Lewis, P Craddock, Peter Churchill, Jerry and Alison Oakes, W K Struthers, Mrs J A Gardner, Jacquie and Jon Payne, Mr Cowell, Mike and Jill Dixon, David Goldstone, Tom Espley, Roy McIsaac, Dr John Innes, Peter Hall, GB, CH, M and C Hardwick, Kenneth Sharp, Dick Brown, M E Hughes, Karen Tangaere, Cliff Blakemore)*

Whitbreads   Lease Sue and Nick Emberley   Real ale   Meals and snacks (11.30–2, 6–9.30; 7–9 Sun)   (0703) 282 329   Children welcome   Open 11–2.30, 6–11 (10.30 winter weekdays)   Bedrooms; £25B/£50B

nr FAWLEY   SU4503 Map 2

Jolly Sailor

Ashlett Creek; from A326 turn left into School Road, signposted Fawley 1/2; at Falcon pub crossroads take Calshot road, then fork left almost at once

Not far from the magnificent Rothschild rhododendron gardens at Exbury (at their best in May or early June, and they now sell plants), this well kept small pub has a comfortably modernised bar here with soft banquettes, red velvet curtains, and a central flame-effect fire; there are lots of photographs of Southampton liners on the walls. Bar food under the new licensees includes soup, sandwiches, and – customers' current favourites here – vegetarian lasagne, chilli or curry (£3.95), seafood platter (£4.25), and haddock and broccoli mornay (£5.25). Boddingtons, Flowers Original and Wadworths 6X on handpump; darts, shove-ha'penny, fruit machine, trivia, juke box, piped music. The restaurant overlooks the busy shipping channel, where curlews and sandpipers strut at low water, and beyond to the distant bustle of Southampton Water; picnic-table sets on the side lawn have a similar view. *(Recommended by Richard Marjoram, W C M Jones, Mike and Jill Dixon, John and Joan Calvert; more reports please)*

Whitbreads   Managers Mr and Mrs S James   Real ale   Meals and snacks (not Mon evening)   Restaurant   Fawley (0703) 819 305   Children in eating area   Once a month, Sun pm, 50s and 60s music   Open 11–11

HAMBLE   SU4806 Map 2

Olde Whyte Harte

3 miles from M27 junction 8; on B3397 (High Street)

This friendly place has low beams in the flagstoned bars that were originally Tudor ships' timbers and still have some of their old fastenings; there's a fine inglenook fireplace with the Charles I coat-of-arms on its iron fireback (and a hat display above the mantlepiece), a three-foot-thick wall at the back that may even go back to the 12th century, and old maps and charts, rope fancywork, mugs and copper pans. Very good value home-made bar food includes sandwiches and toasties, cottage pie (£2), steak and kidney pie (£3.95), and sirloin steak (£5.95). Good service; Gales Best, BBB and HSB on handpump, and lots of country wines; cribbage, fruit machine, regular quiz nights and piped music. Besides barrel seats on the small front terrace, there is a back terrace by the sheltered lawn and garden. Popular with yachtsmen at the weekends. (*Recommended by Simon Collett-Jones, Alan Skull, John and Christine Simpson, Dr J D Bassett, Mr Cowell*)

Gales   Manager D Kerans   Real ale   Meals and snacks   (0703) 452108   Children in separate room   Open 11–2.30, 5–11

IBSLEY   SU1509 Map 2

Old Beams

A338 Ringwood–Salisbury

Surprisingly large behind its thatched front, this busy pub has a strong emphasis on food; there's a huge choice, including an appetising cold buffet, soup (90p), sandwiches (from £1.55), ploughman's (from £2), steak and kidney pie or steamed beef pudding (£5.30), lamb chops, veal casserole, chicken chasseur or beef in ale (£5.45), a roast (£5.85), and venison (£5.95). Eldridge Pope Royal Oak, Gibbs Mew Bishops Tipple, Ind Coope Burton, Ringwood Best and Old Thumper and Tetleys from handpump, a decent choice of wines by the glass and some foreign bottled beers. The oak-beamed main room is divided by wooden panelling and a canopied log-effect gas fire, and there are lots of varnished wooden tables and country-kitchen chairs under the good oak beams; the front half of the pub is no smoking. The garden behind has picnic-table sets among its trees. (*Recommended by Mike Rising, Alan Skull, Rob Weeks, Ian Phillips, Mr and Mrs G Turner*)

Free house   Licensees R Major and C Newell   Real ale   Meals and snacks (12–2, 7–10)   Restaurant   Ringwood (0425) 473387   Children welcome   Open 11–2.30, 6–11

KINGS WORTHY   SU4933 Map 2

Cart & Horses

A3090 E of Winchester, just off A33

In front of this picturesque pub are some heavy wooden tables, with more in the sheltered garden behind which also has a play area with several trampolines, a see-saw and a Wendy house; summer barbecues. Inside, the public bar has various rambling alcoves with cushioned settles and some milk-churn seats, and darts and bar billiards – there's also a separate skittle alley. The spacious, comfortable lounge is half no-smoking, and largely given over to eating. The range includes filled rolls (£1.50), soup (£1.65), filled baked potatoes (from £2.85), a variety of vegetarian and pasta dishes (£3.95), pies such as beef and Guinness, cod and prawn, beef and walnut or game (£4.95), and puddings such as chocolate gateau (£1.95); children's dishes (£1.60). Well kept Marstons Burton, Pedigree and Owd Rodger on handpump, Bulmer's cider, and country wines. (*Recommended by Martin and Gill Searle, Keith Houlgate, David Shillitoe, Mr and Mrs Foreman; more reports please*)

Marstons   Tenant David Lee Smith   Real ale   Meals and snacks   Restaurant   Winchester (0962) 882360   Children in family and dining rooms   Open 11–3, 6–11 (all day on bank holiday weekend)

LANGSTONE   SU7105   Map 2
Royal Oak

High Street; last turn left off A3023 (confusingly called A324 on some signs) before
Hayling Island bridge

The 18th-century Langstone Gang used to land their smuggled brandy here,
floating it in on submerged rafts to avoid *The Griper*, the Excise brig which
patrolled the harbour. Seats in the bow windows and benches in front of the
appropriately picturesque pub look out over the water – at high tide swans come
right up, with the ebb the saltings between here and Hayling Island fill with wading
birds. The flagstoned bar is simply furnished with Windsor chairs around old
wooden tables on the wooden parquet and ancient flagstones, and two open fires
in winter. Bar food is much what you'd find in other Whitbreads Wayfarers Inns,
including home-made soup (hearty here), French bread well filled with ham or
cheese, ploughman's (£2.95), vegetarian dishes, home-made hot dishes such as
lasagne or various curries (£3.85), seafood mornay (£4.10), rib of beef (£4.95),
and rump steak (£7.50). Well kept Boddingtons, Flowers Original, Gales HSB,
Marstons Pedigree and Whitbreads Strong Country on handpump, as well as
Bulmer's cider; smartly dressed staff. At the back of the pub is a pets' corner with
goats and rabbits. (*Recommended by Phil and Sally Gorton, Col G D Stafford, Phil Bryant,
Nigel Gibbs, D J Cooke, Jacqueline Davis*)

*Whitbreads   Manager Hilary Wallace   Real ale   Meals and snacks   Restaurant
Portsmouth (0705) 483125   Children in eating area and restaurant   Parking at all
close may be very difficult   Open 11–11*

LINWOOD   SU1910   Map 2
High Corner

Linwood signposted via Moyles Court from A338 (and also from A31); follow road
straight up on to heath and eventually pub signposted left down a gravelled track; OS
Sheet 195, map feference 196107

In summer this thatched pub is very popular – partly for its New Forest position
and partly for the big neatly kept woodside lawn with well spaced picnic-table sets
and a sizeable children's play area; they have cook-yourself barbecues (or you can
pay a little extra and they'll do the cooking). Inside, a series of rooms rambles
beyond the main serving bar, and there's a family room, no-smoking glazed
verandah lounge and a separate stable bar. Bar food includes home-made soup
(£1.45), sandwiches (from £1.85), ploughman's (from £3 – the venison sausage is
good), crisp mushroom fritters (£3.35), vegetable curry (£4.25), scampi or smoked
fish crumble (£4.45), home-made steak, kidney and mushroom pie or trout
(£5.35), a choice of steaks (from £7.95), and puddings such as home-made fruit
mousse or sherry trifle (from £1.60). Well kept Boddingtons, Flowers Original and
Wadworths 6X on handpump; darts, shove-ha'penny, dominoes, cribbage, fruit
and trivia machine, space game, unobtrusive piped music, squash court. Close to
Good Walks Guide Walk 40. (*Recommended by John and Christine Simpson, Mr and Mrs
A P Reeves, Jacquie and Jon Payne, M Rising, Celia and David Watt, WHBM, W K Struthers,
Mrs G Evans; more reports please*)

*Free house   Licensees Lin and Roger Kernan   Real ale   Meals and snacks (12–2,
7–10)   Restaurant (all day Sun)   (0425) 473 973   Children in four family rooms
Open 11–3, 6–11 (11–11 Sat; winter 11–2.30, 7–10.30)   Bedrooms; £45.50B/£66B*

MATTINGLEY   SU7358   Map 2
Leather Bottle

3 miles from M3, junction 5; in Hook, turn right-and-left on to B3349 Reading Road
(former A32)

Well run by friendly, efficient staff, this brick-and-tiled pub has a beamed main bar
at the front with good inglenook fireplaces (one with a ticking metal clock over it),
brocaded built-in wall seats, little curved low backed wooden chairs, red plush bar
stools, some sabres on the cream wall, and red velvet curtains. At the back is the
characterful cottagey second bar with lots of black beams, an antique clock,

country pictures on the walls (some stripped to brick), lantern lighting, sturdy inlaid tables with seats, and a red carpet on bare floorboards. Well kept Courage Best tapped from the cask, Directors on handpump and a guest bitter, decent coffee; fruit machine, maybe unobtrusive piped music. Good value bar food includes sandwiches (from £1.25, toasted ham and egg – named a Tom Special for one of the regulars – £2.60, steak £3.90), soup (£1.70), lots of ploughman's (from £2.80), sweetcorn and mushroom pizza (£4.10), salads (from £4.60), ham and egg (£4.90), 8oz burgers (£4.60), lemon sole (£5.20), char-grilled half-chicken (£6.20), and steaks (from 8oz sirloin £10.30), with puddings such as lemon brûlée and steamed syrup sponge (from £1.90). In summer the tubs and baskets of bright flowers, wisteria, honeysuckle and roses are a riot of colour; there's also a neat, tree-sheltered garden. The licensees run another pub in Hampshire, the Swan at North Warnborough, on which we have no recent reports. *(Recommended by David Evans, Nick and Alison Dowson, Mr and Mrs C H Garnett, Simon Collett-Jones, Mayur Shah)*

Courage   Lease Richard and Pauline Moore   Real ale   Meals and snacks (12–2, 7–10)   (0734) 326371   Children in eating area   Open 11–2.30, 6–11

MINLEY   SU8357   Map 2
Crown & Cushion

From A30 take B3013 towards Fleet, then first left turn signposted Minley, Cove, Farnborough

The 'Meade Hall' behind this tiled and timbered pub is perhaps the most interesting feature here: a lively pastiche of an ancient feasting place, with two very long communal refectory tables, smaller candlelit tables in intimate side stalls, broad flagstones, a huge log fire, and a veritable armoury of scythes, pitchforks and other rustic ironmongery festooning its rafters and timbers (it also has anachronistic piped music and slot machines). The efficient food counter serves a good range of home-cooked meats and fresh salads (from £3–£4), ploughman's (£3), and at lunchtime a varied choice of hot dishes such as lasagne, chillies and pies (about £3.80), or generous cuts from a huge joint, with three vegetables (£4.75, not Sunday). In the evening they add toasted sandwiches (from £1.50, served with chips), burgers (£2–£3), basket meals (from £3.50), and puddings (all £1.50). Ruddles Best and County and Websters Yorkshire on handpump, with country wines, mead (of course) and a couple of draught ciders. The separate original pub part is comfortable, and has darts, dominoes, cribbage and a fruit machine. Its name commemorates the closest that anyone has come to stealing the Crown Jewels – Colonel Blood from nearby Minley Warren was caught here in 1671 with them in his saddlebags, after a subtle raid on the Tower of London. If you look hard enough, you'll see that the yew tree outside is cut in the shape of a cushioned crown; there are picnic-table sets across from it overlooking the woodside cricket ground. *(Recommended by Klaus and Elizabeth Leist, Tim and Ann Newell, Mr and Mrs C H Garnett, Dr R Fuller)*

Watneys/Grand Met   Manager Mr Bickup   Real ale   Meals and snacks   (0252) 545253   Children welcome lunchtime only   Bar open 11.30–2.30, 5.30–11, Sat 11–11; Meade Hall 11.30–2.30, 7–11

NEWTOWN   SU6113   Map 2
Travellers Rest

Church Road – E of village, which is signposted off A32 N of Wickham

One reader who had last visited this pretty little tile-hung roadside cottage in 1947 was very pleased to find, on a revisit, that it hasn't been spoilt. The two small rooms of the uncomplicated bar have been only gently brought upmarket, keeping well cushioned housekeepers' chairs, a winged settle, leatherette armed chairs, built-in cushioned wall seats, and above all the chatty atmosphere warmly fuelled by locals and friendly new licensees. Bar food includes sandwiches, ploughman's and hot dishes such as home-made steak and kidney pie (£3.20) and chicken in red wine (£3.90), with a dish of the day that in summer tends to fresh seafood, in winter more towards game such as pheasant or venison. They do their best to keep up a supply of their own vegetables. Well kept Gibbs Mew Wiltshire, Salisbury and Bishops Tipple on handpump, and locally made fruit wines; darts, dominoes, fruit machine, piano. The pretty back garden is floodlit at night; they are planning to build a conservatory there, where children could be catered for. *(Recommended by C H Stride, HNJ, PEJ, Margaret Drazin, Richard Houghton, Mr Cowell)*

Gibbs Mew   Tenants Brenda and Roy Etherington   Real ale   Meals and snacks (12–2, 7.30–10.15; not Sun eve)   Monthly gatherings for piano singalongs, Irish or folk music, and occasional Morris dancers   Open 11–3, 6–11; closed 25 Dec eve

OVINGTON   SU5531 Map 2

Bush ★

Village signposted from A31 on Winchester side of Alresford

This unpretentiously atmospheric pub, tucked away down a leafy lane, has a slightly upmarket feel – at least at quiet times, when its appeal is definitely strongest; it's scarely large enough to accommodate crowds without strain, though service stays good when it's busy. The dimly lit, low-ceilinged bar has a roaring fire on one side with an antique solid fuel stove opposite, cushioned high-backed settles, elm tables with pews and kitchen chairs, and masses of old pictures in heavy gilt frames on the green walls; it can get really busy, but service is good. Badger Best, Eldridge Pope Royal Oak, Gales HSB and Wadworths 6X, on handpump and tapped from the cask; a good choice of wines. Bar food – not cheap – includes home-made soup (£2), sandwiches (from £2), ploughman's (from £3), mussels in garlic butter (£5.25), steak and kidney pie (£5.95), trout (£6.75) and a seafood platter (£8.95), with specials such as smoked chicken and strawberry salad (£5.25), macaroni cheese (£5.95), baked loin of shark or gigot of lamb with peppercorn sauce (£6.95); puddings such as fruit pie (£2.30), children's dishes (£2.30), and a roast Sunday lunch (£6.75), when the choice of other dishes may be more limited; it's worth booking on summer weekends. The tree-sheltered pergola dining terrace outside has white wrought-iron tables by a good-sized fountain pool, and there are lots of seats (and quiet walks) by the river; handy for the A31 – though the pub itself is peacefully placed in the Itchen valley. *(Recommended by Margaret Dralin, R Heaton, Mike Rising, Julian Proudman, David Hunn, Mrs V Middlebrook, John and Christine Simpson, Prof A N Black, Ian Phillips, Richard Houghton, Robert and Elizabeth Scott, HEG, S J Rice)*

Free house   Licensee Robert Middleton   Real ale   Meals and snacks   Restaurant (not Sun)   Alresford (0962) 732764   Nearby parking may be difficult   Children in restaurant and eating area of bar until 9pm   Open 11–2.30, 6–11

nr PETERSFIELD   SU7423 Map 2

White Horse ★ ★ ★

Priors Dean – but don't follow Priors Dean signposts: simplest route is from Petersfield, leaving centre on A272 towards Winchester, take right turn at roundabout after level crossing, towards Steep, and keep on for four miles or so, up on to the downs, passing another pub on your right (and not turning off into Steep there); at last, at crossroads signposted East Tisted/Privett, turn right towards East Tisted, then almost at once turn right on to second gravel track (the first just goes into a field); there's no inn sign; alternatively, from A32 5 miles S of Alton, take road by bus lay-by signposted Steep, then, after 1 3/4 miles, turn off as above – though obviously left this time – at East Tisted/Privett crossroads: OS Sheet 197 coming from Petersfield (Sheet 186 is better the other way), map reference 715290

As we've said before – don't come to this remote 17th-century pub with the wrong expectations. This gets its three stars (and some readers say give it a fourth) because it is the epitome of the English Country Pub, with the strong dose of relaxed take-us-as-you-find-us homeliness which that should imply. Always at its best when Jack himself is there (as he almost always is – he's been licensee nigh on 20 years now), it owes a great deal to his down-to-earth Lancashire good-heartedness. From the outside it doesn't look special, and some of the furnishings in the two charming and highly idiosyncratic parlour rooms have seen better days, but their individuality is undeniable: old pictures, farm tools, drop-leaf tables, oak settles, rugs, stuffed antelope heads, longcase clock, a fireside rocking-chair. Then there's the range of beers – a dozen or so good real ales, including their own very strong White Horse No Name, as well as Ballards Best, Bass, Courage Best and Directors, Eldridge Pope Royal Oak, King & Barnes Sussex and Broadwood, Ringwood Fortyniner and a guest bitter; two dozen country wines, some sparkling, are tapped from small china kegs; shove-ha'penny, dominoes, cribbage. Bar food includes sandwiches (from 90p, toasties £1.20), good thick soup (£2 – winter only, as it's done overnight on the Aga), good baked potatoes, very good ploughman's (from £2.75), salads (from £3.95), a vegetarian dish, and a few home-made hot dishes most days, such as a genuine hot-pot, cottage pie or beef and venison pie. They've usually got local eggs for sale, including organic free range ones, and in season pheasants too. There are of course times (not always predictable, with Sundays – even in winter – often busier than Saturdays) when the place does get packed. Rustic seats (which include chunks of tree-trunk) and a terrace outside; as this is one of the highest spots in the county it can be quite breezy. There are caravan facilities in the nearby field, which is regularly used for pony club meetings – or maybe for the odd Tiger Moth plane to land in. *(Recommended by Brian Jones, Mike Rising, David Evans, Phil and Sally Gorton, David Hunn, John and Christine Simpson, Barbara Hatfield, Lynn Sharpless, Bob Eardley, TBB, Jutta Whitley, Gordon and Daphne, Mrs Lili Lomas, Gordon Mott, Ian Phillips, Tim and Ann Newell, John Burgan, Hilary Irving, WHBM, Alan Skull, Robert and Elizabeth Scott, M Rising, Jacqueline Davis, Robert Sear, Canon K C A Wills, M K C Wills, Celia and David Watt)*

Free house   Licensee Jack Eddleston   Real ale   Meals (sandwiches only Sun and bank holidays) and snacks   (042) 058 387   Children not allowed in   Open 11–2.30(3 Sat), 6–11

ROMSEY   SU3521   Map 2

Luzborough House

3 miles from M27 junction 3; A3057 towards Romsey, but turn right at A27

Originally a keeper's cottage, this big, carefully lit pub, redecorated for its friendly new managers, has a bright and attractive high-raftered main bar with high-backed stools by ledges around stripped-brick pillars, a sofa and easy chairs, and plenty of standing space around the bar counter. The variety of smaller rooms has a more intimate feel. There's the popular, elegant cream-panelled 18th-century dining room decorated with attractive landscapes, a neat conservatory with white cast-iron tables opening off it, and a snug 16th-century country kitchen with low beams and a huge woodburning stove in its inglenook fireplace. Well kept Boddingtons, Flowers Original and Whitbreads Strong Country on handpump. Bar food includes soup (£1.15), sandwiches (from £2.45), ploughman's (from £2.80), steak and kidney pie (£3.70), scampi (£4.25), gammon (£4.45), chicken kiev (£5.95) and puddings such as apple pie or various gateaux (from £1.30). On the spacious walled lawn are picnic-table sets under cocktail parasols, as well as a slide and sprung rockers. They plan occasional live entertainment. *(Recommended by Mrs Richard Stewart, Jon and Jacqui Payne, T Galligan, E U Broadbent)*

Whitbreads   Real ale   Meals and snacks (12–10)   Restaurant   Romsey   (0794) 523 816   Children welcome everywhere except bar area   Open 11–11

ROTHERWICK   SU7156   Map 2

Coach & Horses ⊘ £

4 miles from M3, junction 5; follow Newnham signpost from exit roundabout, then Rotherwick signpost, then turn right at Mattingley, Heckfield signpost; village also signposted from A32 N of Hook

A fine choice of well kept real ales is kept on handpump in this busy village pub – popular with local business people – dispensed at the servery in the parquet-floored inner area: maybe Badger Best and Tanglefoot, Charles Wells Bombardier and Eagle, Marstons Pedigree, Ringwood Old Thumper, Theakstons Old Peculier and Wadworths Farmers Glory and 6X. Well cooked, straightforward bar food includes sandwiches (from 90p, open prawn £2.35), ploughman's (from £1.95), smoked trout pâté (£1.95), home-made burger (£2.25), a variety of home-made pizzas (from £2.15), chilli con carne (£2.75), gammon and egg (£4.45), mixed grill (£6.45) and steaks (from £6.25); on Sundays there's a good carvery; pleasant service. The two small beamed front rooms each have a stripped brick open fireplace, interesting furniture such as oak chairs, and a fine assortment of attractive pictures; one is carpeted and the other has neat red and midnight blue flooring tiles. The partly creeper-covered, 16th-century building is surrounded by tubs and baskets of flowers in summer, and there are rustic seats and picnic-table sets under cocktail parasols; the terrace has been extended. *(Recommended by Geoff Lee, Mike Rising, Richard Houghton, Mr and Mrs C H Garnett, Simon Collett-Jones, SJC, Alan Skull, P W Knatchbull-Hugessen, Mayur Shah, Susan Grossman, Patrick Freeman, WHBM, TBB, Patrick and Mary McDermott, KC, Gordon and Daphne, Ian Phillips, John and Christine Simpson)*

Free house (leased from Badger)   Licensee Mrs Terry Williams   Real ale   Meals and snacks (12–2, 7–10; carvery only, Sun lunchtime)   Restaurant   Rotherwick (0256) 762542   Children welcome   Open 11–2.30, 5.30–11

SETLEY   SU3000 Map 2
Filly

A337 Brockenhurst–Lymington

Two spacious rooms in this neat and busy New Forest pub have lots of horsebrasses on the beams, dark ochre ceilings and dark red walls, little wooden kegs, cork and glass net-floats, tackle blocks, and antlers; one area has long cushioned antique settles and built-in pews, the other has spindle-back chairs around oak tables with a couple of cosy alcoves; lighting is dim, fireplaces capacious and piped music discreet. Popular bar food includes sandwiches and filled rolls (from £1.50, toasted from £1.75), filled baked potatoes (from £1.95), ploughman's (from £3.50), home-made lasagne or chilli con carne (£3.95), salads (from £4.50), steak and mushroom pie, seafood platter or scampi (£4.75), a decent choice of vegetarian dishes, and steaks (from £7.95); food orders are announced over loudspeakers. The interesting range of beers – Bass, Palmers IPA, Ringwood Best and Old Thumper – are well kept on handpump; the alsatian's called Tess. There are a few picnic-table sets on neat grass at the back. *(Recommended by H E Hental, P Corris, John and Christine Simpson, Mr and Mrs J A Oxley, Dick Brown, Paul and Margaret Baker, A J Dourleyn, Jacquie and Jon Payne)*

Free house   Licensees Tony and Lynn Bargrove   Real ale   Meals and snacks (till 9.30, 10 Fri and Sat evening)   (0590) 23449   Children welcome   Open 11–2.30, 6.30 (Sat 6)–11

SOBERTON   SU6116 Map 2
White Lion

Village signposted off A32 S of Droxford

The rambling, carpeted bar on the right in this pleasant tiled and white-painted country pub is simply furnished with red-cushioned pews and scrubbed tables, a picture of Highland cattle, a woodburning stove, and in a lower area a big photograph of HMS *Soberton*. The irregularly shaped public bar has more pews with built-in wooden wall seats, and darts. Carefully cooked and attractively presented, the bar food ranges from home-made soup (£1.50), filled French bread (from £1.75), and ploughman's (from £2.95), through filled baked potatoes and omelettes (both from £3.50), lots of pasta dishes (from £3.75), avocado and tomato bake, fish pie or crispy cod (£4.25), sauté of kidney with sherry or supreme of chicken with garlic and herbs (£5.95), lamb cutlets with honey and rosemary (£6.25), monkfish provençale and rice (£7.50) and steak (from £8.75); specials include sweet and sour dishes (£5.25), stir fry beef (£5.75) and moules marinières (£5.95); they also do smaller helpings for children on request. There's a Sunday buffet, and theme evenings celebrate such dates as Bastille Day appropriately; friendly service; Flowers Original, Fremlins, Marstons Pedigree, Wadworths 6X and Whitbreads Strong Country and Pompey Royal. There are attractive views over the quiet green to the tall trees of the churchyard, and picnic-table sets in a sheltered garden with swings, a slide and climbing bars, and on a suntrap fairy-lit terrace; they roast pigs on bank holidays out here (if it rains, there's an awning for the terrace), and may have children's entertainment in the afternoon then. It tends to get busy at weekends. (*Recommended by Barry and Anne, Michael Beckley, Mr Cowell, M K C Wills, Mel and Phil Lloyd*)

Whitbreads   Tenants Rod and Joanie Johnson   Real ale   Meals and snacks (at any time)   Restaurant (open noon–10.30 Sun)   Droxford (0489) 877346   Children welcome in lower lounge and restaurant   Open 11–2.30, 6–11 (11–3, 7–10.30 Sat)

STEEP   SU7425   Map 2

Harrow ⊘

Village signposted from A325 and A3 NE of Petersfield; from Petersfield on Alton rd turn right at Steep Garage, go past church to bottom of hill

The charming atmosphere in the little public bar of this unchanging and unspoilt country tavern is marvellously old-fashioned, in a way that somehow conjures up upper-class Land Girls dipping their toes into the local life of the wartime Village Pub – with its tiled floor, built-in wall benches around scrubbed deal tables, good log fire in the big inglenook, stripped pine wallboards, nostalgic fading or drying wildflowers, and dominoes or cribbage. But a major draw that you'd never have found in those hard times is the massively generous scale on which they serve their simple home-cooked food. Excellent soups overflow from old-fashioned bowls (£2), sandwiches using their home-baked bread (from £1.50) can seem uncommonly filling, and other choices include outstanding home-made Scotch eggs (£1.15), huge ploughman's (from £4.50), lasagne, cauliflower cheese or shepherd's pie (£4.50), and salads (from £5.75) served on an enormous carving plate. Boddingtons, Flowers Original and Strong Country tapped from casks behind the counter, country wines, and good soft drinks including locally made apple juice; friendly staff, even when under pressure. The big, free-flowering garden has lots of tables; children are allowed only out here. We're all hoping that the new Petersfield bypass won't intrude on this idyll. (*Recommended by Gwen and Peter Andrews, Simon Collett-Jones, Ian Phillips, John and Christine Simpson, Pat and Derek Westcott, Steve and Carolyn Harvey, Jean T Crosley*)

Free house   Licensee Edward C McCutcheon   Real ale   Snacks   Petersfield (0730) 62685   Open 11–2.30(3 Sat), 6–11

STOCKBRIDGE   SU3535   Map 2

Vine

High St (A30)

Though many of the tables here may be laid for eating and it's often advisable to book at the weekend, the open-plan bar has kept its distinctly pubby feel. There's an interesting combination of woodwork, brickwork and papered walls, a delft shelf of china and pewter, and old-gold velvet curtains. Generously served good value bar food includes sandwiches, home-made soup (£1.50), home-made pâté (£1.95), stuffed mushrooms with stilton sauce (£2.75), deep-fried brie with cranberry sauce (£2.85), avocado, bacon and blue cheese salad (£3.25), Cumberland sausages (£5.85), spinach, mozzarella and ratatouille in filo pastry (£5.95), ragout of salmon and mushrooms with fresh basil (£6.95) and entrecote steak (£8.95), and puddings such as crème brûlée or apple strudel (£1.85). Favourite specials include smoked turkey breast with mange tout salad (£4.95) and loin of pork with honey and ginger (£6.95); they warn of delays with some dishes. Flowers Original, Brakspears and Wadworth 6X on handpump, and they hope to introduce guest beers soon; a small but decent wine list; darts, dominoes, maybe piped music. The garden behind runs down to a carrier of the River Test. *(Recommended by John and Christine Simpson, T Galligan, Ron Gentry, W C M Jones, John Baxter, Celia and David Watt, Joan and John Calvert; reports on new regime please)*

Whitbreads   Tenants John Green and Christopher Henshaw   Real ale   Meals and snacks (12–2.30, 7–10)   Restaurant (teas 3.30–5.30)   Andover (0264) 810652   Children welcome, no children under 15 after 9pm   Open 11–11   Bedrooms; £20/£40

TICHBORNE   SU5630   Map 2

Tichborne Arms ⊗

Village signed off A31 just W of Alresford

In rolling countryside, this attractive and friendly thatched pub serves imaginatively straightforward, fresh bar food that includes home-made soup (£1.50), sandwiches (from £1.20, prawn £2.50, lots of interesting toasties from £1.60), liver and bacon nibbles with a home-made dip (£2), ploughman's (from £2.75 – the ham version is specially good), baked potatoes with a fine range of fillings (from £3.10), salads (from £4.25), home-made daily specials such as macaroni cheese with chopped ham and tomato (£4.10), fresh asparagus, cheese and prawn quiche (£4.25), beef cobbler or steak and mushroom pie (£4.65) and locally caught trout (£5.95), with puddings, all home-made, such as a hotly tipped fudge and walnut flan or lemon cheesecake (from £1.50); they warn of delays at busy times. The comfortable, square-panelled room on the right has pictures and documents on the walls recalling the bizarre Tichborne Case – when a mystery man from Australia claimed fraudulently to be the heir to this estate, a log fire in an attractive stone fireplace, wheelback chairs and settles (one very long), and latticed windows with flowery curtains. On the left, a larger and livelier room, partly panelled and also carpeted, has sensibly placed darts, shove-ha'penny and a fruit machine; well kept Courage Best and Directors and Wadworths 6X tapped from the cask, and country wines; quick friendly service. There are picnic-table sets outside in the big well kept garden. *(Recommended by R and Mrs P F Shelton, Mrs V Middlebrook, Philip and Trisha Ferris, H E Hental, David Lamb, J M Potter, Lynn Sharpless, Bob Eardley, Dr and Mrs M I Crichton, Richard Sachs, Steve and Carolyn Harvey, SJC, PLC, John and Heather Dwane, Mr and Mrs G Turner, H G Allen)*

Free house   Licensees Chris and Peter Byron   Real ale   Meals and snacks (12–1.45, 6.30–9.45)   (0962) 733 760   Open 11.30–2.30, 6–11

TURGIS GREEN   SU6959   Map 2

Jekyll & Hyde

A33 Reading–Basingstoke

The sheltered and attractively planted garden behind this rambling main-road pub has lots of picnic-table sets under cocktail parasols, with swings, a slide and a climber, as well as lots of games – cricket, swingball, rounders and so forth. Inside, various areas open off each other, with black beams and joists, cream-painted walls, wheelback chairs around rather rustic oak tables, and some more individual furnishings. The dining area up a few steps looks down into the main bar area through timbered openings, and a back room has a fine winged and high-backed settle among more modern furnishings, and big Morland and Landseer prints. They always keep five real ales on handpump. though these change occasionally; as we went to press they were Badger Best and Tanglefoot, Charles Wells Eagle, Everards Old Original and Wadworths 6X. Well presented bar food includes sandwiches (£2), soup (£2.50), spinach and bacon au gratin (£3.50), ploughman's (£3.75), salads (from £4.30), seafood platter (£4.55), club sandwich (£4.65), steak loaf (£4.85), scampi, vegetarian lasagne or another pasta dish (£4.95), pork and herb sausage (£5.95), steak and kidney pie (£6.50), and plenty of puddings (from £1.95); children's dishes, and Sunday roast (£6.25). There are lavatories for the disabled. *(Recommended by Simon Collett-Jones, Roger Mallard, Patrick and Mary McDermott, Nigel Gibbs, Peter Churchill; more reports on new regime please)*

Free house   Licensees David and Yvonne Anderson   Real ale   Meals and snacks
(8.30am–10pm Mon-Fri, 11am–10pm Sat, 12–2.15, 7–9 Sun)   Children in eating area
and back room   Open 8.30am (for breakfast)–11pm, 11–11 Sat

VERNHAM DEAN   SU3456   Map 2

George

On the old coach road going NW from Hurstbourne Tarrant; follow Upton signpost
from A343; or from A338 5 miles S of Hungerford follow Oxenwood signpost and keep
on

Delightfully run, this attractive country pub has a rambling open-plan beamed bar
with a lovely polished elm table, traditional black wall seats built into the panelled
dado, some easy chairs, a log fire in its big inglenook fireplace, and a relaxed and
friendly atmosphere. Good home cooking includes sizeable toasted sandwiches
(£1.70), soup with home-made stock, various ploughman's, and daily hot dishes
such as gently garlicky mushrooms with a bacon and cheese topping (£2.50),
corned beef hash or layer pie (cheese, bacon and onion layered into pastry, £3),
and winter rabbit stew; vegetables now come from the pub's own garden, and its
flowers adorn the tables. Well kept Marstons Burton and Pedigree on handpump;
cribbage, dominoes and fruit machine. There are tables in the pretty garden behind.
(Recommended by A J Stevens, L Walker, HNJ, PEJ, Gordon and Daphne, M J Whitehouse;
more reports please)

Marstons   Tenants Mary and Philip Perry   Real ale   Meals and snacks (not Sun eve)
(0264) 87 279   Well behaved children in family room, lunchtime   Open 11–2.30 (3
Sat), 6–11

nr VERNHAM DEAN   SU3558   Map 2

Boot

Littledown; on Upton side of Vernham Dean follow Vernham Street signposts

Charmingly small (despite a side extension) this downland flint pub has an original
low-beamed white-panelled bar – where there's barely space for a pair of tables by
the attractive inglenook fireplace; maybe piped music. The conservatory has
dominoes, cribbage, table skittles and shove-ha'penny, and there's a collection of
model boots and shoes in a corner cupboard; a family room acts as an overflow.
The decent range of bar food includes a weekly specials board, with such dishes as
home-made soup (£1.95), brie wedges and salad (£2), smoked salmon (£2.30),
ratatouille or macaroni pie (£4.20), lamb in a caper and sour cream sauce or
Indonesian pork (£4.80), and rump steak (£7), while puddings might include
spotted dick and custard (£1.70) or raspberry pavlova (£2); they also do
sandwiches (from £1.25; good ham with brown bread and mustard £1.75),
ploughman's or basket meals (from £3), and children's dishes (from £1.25). Badger
Best, Hook Norton Old Hookey, Marstons Burton and Pedigree and Wadworths
6X tapped from casks on trestles, and a couple of dozen malt whiskies; welcoming
service. There are tables on a terrace and in the well kept garden, with an old
paddock used as a children's play area; the more secluded side garden is the one
most favoured by readers without children. *(Recommended by Tony and Lynne Stark,*
Dr M I Crichton, Dr C S Shaw, W K Struthers, Gordon and Daphne, HNJ, PEJ)

Free house   Licensees Neale and Helen Baker   Real ale   Meals and snacks   Children
in dining room and conservatory   Open 12–3, 6–11; 12–2.30, 7–11 winter; closed
Mon except bank holidays

WELL   SU7646   Map 2

Chequers ⊘

5 miles W of Farnham; off A287 via Crondall, or A31 via Froyle and Lower Froyle
(easier if longer than via Bentley); from A32 S of Odiham, go via Long Sutton; OS Sheet
186, map reference 761467

Now run with deceptively informal efficiency by the same people as the Sporting Page and Front Page in London (in our view, doing a lot to raise pub standards in the capital), this snug little pub has found warm favour with readers. As with their London pubs, there's a firm emphasis on food, with enterprising dishes like grilled avocado with hot cheshire cheese (£3.50), good mussels, melt-in-the-mouth cheese en croûte, various salads such as warm bacon, apple and walnut (£3.90), pasta such as fusilli with smoked trout, avocado and cream (£4.20), mussels cooked in wine or cider (£4.50), sirloin steak sandwich (£4.75), plenty of fresh fish, delivered daily (around £5), veal escalope parmigiana (£5.25), and puddings such as treacle tart (£2.25) or banoffi pie (£2.50). The bar – full of alcoves – has low beams, wooden pews and old stools, books on a shelf for reading (not just show), GWR carriage lamps, a few horse brasses, panelled walls with lots of 18th-century country-life prints, and old sepia photographs of locals enjoying a drink; it all adds up to a nice cheerful atmosphere. Well kept Boddingtons, Flowers, Marstons Pedigree and Wadworths 6X on handpump, and decent wines. In the back replanted and tidied-up garden are some picnic-table sets; at the front, there's a rather idyllic vine-covered front arbour (last year they made wine for cooking from the grapes). (*Recommended by A W Dickinson, Mr Hellin, KC, Philip and Trisha Ferris, David and Gill Aspey, Mrs J A Blanks, Mr and Mrs J Foreman, J S Evans, K J Lawry*)

Free house   Licensees Christopher Phillips and Hugh Stanford   Real ale   Meals and snacks (12–2.30, 7–10)   Restaurant   Basingstoke (0256) 862605   Children in restaurant   Open 11–3, 5.30–11

nr WHERWELL   SU3941   Map 2
Mayfly

Testcombe; A3057 SE of Andover, between B3420 turn-off and Leckford where road crosses River Test

Even when this fine old place is very busy (which it invariably is at peak times) service remains efficient and good-tempered. If you want to eat, it's best to get there early to enjoy in comfort their exemplary range of cheeses – around three dozen to choose from, served from a separate counter with fresh crusty wholemeal bread (£2.75); there can be queues on busy days. Other popular dishes include home-made quiche (£2.75), smoked trout (£3.20) or smoked chicken (£3.30), and a selection of cold meats such as chicken tandoori or topside of beef (from £3.30) served with big helpings chosen from eight or so attractive salads (70p extra each), and puddings such as treacle tart or cheesecake (£2). In the winter they add hot dishes such as braised oxtail or steak and vegetable pie. The spacious, beamed and carpeted bar has fishing pictures and bric-a-brac on the cream walls above its dark wood dado, Windsor chairs around lots of tables, two woodburning stoves, and bow windows overlooking the water. Well kept Flowers Original, Strong Country and Wadsworth 6X on handpump, in winter sensibly kept under light blanket pressure; there's a conservatory restaurant over on the right. The memorable views from the peaceful tables by the fast-flowing River Test are much loved by readers. (*Recommended by R Tomlinson, Mr and Mrs C H Garnett, Norman Hill, M W Atkinson, Roy McIsaac, Barbara M McHugh, T Nott, Brian Barefoot, R Elliott, Mr and Mrs D W Fisher, John Coatsworth, Dr and Mrs A K Clarke, R J Walden, M J Dyke, Roger Mallard, Jan and Ian Alcock*)

Whitbreads   Managers Barry and Julie Lane   Real ale   Meals and snacks   (0264) 860 283   Children in conservatory and top bar area only   Open 11–11

WINCHESTER   SU4829   Map 2
Wykeham Arms ★ ⊘ ⇌

75 Kingsgate Street (Kingsgate Arch and College Street are now closed to traffic; there is access via Canon Street)

Deservedly popular, this interesting town pub is very well run by notably friendly, efficient licensees and their staff. And although there is quite an emphasis on the highly praised food even at lunchtime, it remains essentially a pub – somewhere you'd be just as welcome if a drink was all you wanted. The stylish series of rooms radiating from the central bar are furnished with 19th-century oak desks retired from nearby Winchester College, a redundant pew from the same source, kitchen chairs and candlelit deal tables, big windows with swagged paisley curtains, a piano carrying quite a load of houseplants, and lots of fresh flowers. The snug no-smoking room at the back, known as the Watchmakers, is decorated with a set of Ronald Searle 'Winespeak' prints, a second one is panelled, and all of them have a log fire; two-thirds of the total bar area is no smoking after 8pm on Friday and Saturday. Well presented bar food might include tomato and broccoli soup (£1.95), vignotte cheese and cucumber lunchtime sandwiches (£2.25) and toasties such as smoked ham with gruyere (from £2.30), smoked haddock and chive ramekins (£2.95), ploughman's (from £2.95), sausage and egg plait or cottage pie (£4.25), cauliflower cheese, fresh pasta carbonara or chilli con carne (£4.50), chicken and sweet pepper or pork and apricot casserole (£5.25), and puddings (£2.95) such as honey and walnut tart or wine and fruit jelly. In the evening, when prices are slightly higher, they add things like stilton and loganberry pie or venison, port and cherry terrine (£2.95), cheese and chive wholemeal tart (£5.95), Itchen trout baked with fresh mint and orange (£8.25), pork fried with mushrooms, wine and whole grain mustard (£8.50), rack of lamb with pineapple chutney and port wine glaze (£9.25), and yet more puddings – raspberry and cassis trifle, say, or fresh strawberries with rose-scented cream. The award-winning range of wines by the glass runs to over 20, and the Eldridge Pope Dorchester, Hardy and Royal Oak on handpump are well kept. There are tables on a covered back terrace, with more on a small but sheltered lawn. Residents have the use of a sauna; the inn is very handy for the Cathedral. (*Recommended by Brian Jones, Simon Collett-Jones, Robert Gomme, Margaret Dralin, Lynn Sharpless, Bob Eardley, Ann and John Cox, Peter Argent, Mr and Mrs W H Crowther, John and Christine Simpson, Robert and Elizabeth Scott, Barbara Hatfield, Barbara M McHugh, Quentin Williamson, Steve and Carolyn Harvey, Ann Stranack, John Moate, Cdr J W Hackett, Tony and Lynne Stark, David Young, Alison Hayward, Nick Dowson, R W Stanbury*)

Eldridge Pope   Lease Mr and Mrs Graeme Jameson   Real ale   Meals and snacks (not Mon evening or Sun)   Winchester   (0962) 53834   If the small car park is full local parking may be difficult – don't be tempted to block up Kingsgate Street itself   Open 11–11   Bedrooms; £59.50B/£69.50B

Lucky Dip

Besides the fully inspected pubs, you might like to try these Lucky Dips recommended to us and described by readers (if you do, please send us reports):

Aldershot [Waterloo Rd; from A325 into High St then at Texaco garage past FC turn left; SU8650], *Albion*: Good backstreet local, spotless, with well kept Gales HSB, Best, Light Mild and winter XXXXX, bar billiards in public bar, pleasant licensees (*R Houghton*)

☆ **Alresford** [The Soke, Broad St (extreme lower end); SU5832], *Globe*: Lovely view of 12th-century ponds from back windows and garden; good if not particularly cheap bar food till 10, well kept Gales HSB and Watneys-related real ales on handpump, friendly staff, quite a lot of local or historical display material; piped music; open all day, nearby parking can be difficult (*Tim and Ann Newell, John Kimber*)

Alresford [West St], *Swan*: Reasonably priced bar food inc children's dishes and good salad bar, friendly service, Courage real ale; a lot of energy's been going into refurbishment; bedrooms clean and comfortable (*BDS, Philip and Trisha Ferris*)

☆ **Alton** [Church St; SU7139], *Eight Bells*: Attractive, often busy low-beamed old-world bar full of bric-a-brac, five well kept Allied and guest beers on handpump, friendly barman (*Derek Patey, Tim and Ann Newell*)

☆ **Ampfield** [A31 Winchester—Romsey; SU4023], *White Horse*: Spacious and comfortable, with log fire, pleasant staff, good choice of food with some distinctive dishes as well as sandwiches, ploughman's, baked potatoes and so forth, at reasonable prices; decent wine, well kept Wadworths 6X (*Mrs J A Blanks, Dr and Mrs A K Clarke*)

Ampfield, *Potters Heron*: Good value bar food in comfortably done-up pub (*Peter Argent*)

☆ **Ball Hill** [Hatt Common; leaving Newbury on A343 turn right towards East Woodhay — OS Sheet 174, map reference 423631; SU4263], *Furze Bush*: Clean and airy decor, pews and pine tables, good bar food, well kept real ales inc Bass and Marstons Pedigree on handpump, decent wines by the bottle, tables on terrace and in good-sized sheltered lawn and orchard with play area; well behaved children allowed, no smoking area in dining room (*N S Holmes, LYM*)

☆ **Basing** [Bartons Lane (attached to Bartons

Mill Restaurant), Old Basing; SU6653],
Millstone: Remarkable choice of well kept
real ales tapped from the cask in unusual,
busy converted mill in lovely setting by
River Lodden; simple decor, decent good
value food, well kept ales, good service, big
garden; the star is for lunchtime (young
people tend to dominate atmosphere
evenings) *(Patrick and Mary McDermott,
Chris Fluck)*
Basing [A30, Old Basing], *Hatch*: Large
roadside pub with pleasant atmosphere,
good beer and food, and big open-plan bar;
tables outside, open all day *(Chris Fluck)*
☆ **Bighton** [off B3046 in Alresford just N of
pond; or off A31 in Bishops Sutton — OS
Sheet 185, map reference 615344; SU6134],
Three Horseshoes: Traditional two-bar
village local, friendly licensees, good simple
food, open fire in lounge, lots of bric-a-brac
in basic public bar, well kept Gales inc Dark
Mild and Winter, fresh flowers in spotless
lavatories, geese in garden *(R Houghton,
Lynn Sharpless, Bob Eardley, P R Ferris)*
☆ **Bishops Sutton** [former A31 on Alton side of
Alresford — now bypassed; SU6031], *Ship*:
Friendly, pleasant and cosy local with
relaxed atmosphere, good varied bar food
quickly served, discreet piped music *(Mr and
Mrs H M M Tickner, LYM)*
Bishops Waltham [The Square; SU5517],
Crown: Whitbreads Brewers Fayre pub
keeping some period character,
straightforward bar food, friendly staff,
small terrace; parking for disabled drivers
next to pub *(Michael Bechley)*; *White Horse*:
Unspoilt and friendly little country pub with
well kept Worthington BB and wide choice
of good food *(Tony and Lindsay Gray)*
Bishopstoke [SU4619], *River*: Spacious pub
popular with families, with interesting things
to look at and places for children to sit and
play *(Mel and Phil Lloyd, Peter Argent)*
Blacknest [OS Sheet 186, map reference
798416; SU7941], *Jolly Farmer*: Newly
built replacement for country pub destroyed
by 1989 explosion which only the skittle
alley survived; oak-raftered main bar with
good open fire and big bay window, family
room, restaurant, good bar food served till
10.30 inc children's dishes, quick service by
relaxed and friendly staff, spotless
housekeeping, a lot of obvious pride in the
place; family room, tables on sheltered
terrace and in garden *(G and M Stewart)*
☆ **Botley** [The Square; SU5112], *Bugle*: Well
decorated beamed bar with Flowers and
Whitbreads Strong County on handpump,
busy evenings with popular bar food inc
good fresh seafood, quick pleasant service;
restaurant *(John and Christine Simpson)*
☆ **Braishfield** [Newport Lane; SU3725],
Newport: Unreconstructed local with geese,
ducks and chickens roaming garden, two
decidedly unsmart old-fashioned bars,
down-to-earth landlords, superbly kept
Gales inc Mild, good range of country
wines, decent coffee, quickly served
sandwiches and so forth *(Lynn Sharpless, Bob
Eardley, Peter Argent, John and Chris
Simpson)*
Bramshaw [SU2615], *Bramble Hill*: Though
a hotel, worth knowing as a quiet New
Forest eating refuge *(H E Hental)*
☆ **Bransgore** [Highcliffe Rd; SZ1897], *Three

Tuns: Friendly, comfortable and attractive
pub in older part of village, with open fire,
well kept beer, good bar lunches, evening
restaurant *(WHBM)*
Bransgore [Burley Rd], *Carpenters Arms*:
Family pub popular for reasonably priced
bar food — fish and chips and so forth *(DJ)*
☆ **Brockenhurst** [Lyndhurst Rd; SU2902],
Snakecatcher: Unusual — long and narrow,
tables neatly set with pink mats and napkins,
and candlelit at night; friendly quick service,
display of jugs and so forth, well kept
Eldridge Pope Royal Oak and ten decent
wines by the glass, bar food from wide
choice of sandwiches to steaks, inc some
interesting dishes and children's food *(Tom
Evans, WHBM)*
Brockenhurst [by rly stn], *Morant Arms*:
Good licensees in clean pub with good value
food; tables outside, children's play area *(H
R Bevan)*
Brook [B3078 NW of Cadnam; SU2714],
Green Dragon: Small, friendly traditional
pub with lots of New Forest paraphernalia
on the walls; good choice of food; away
from main tourist area *(Dr John Innes)*
☆ **Bucklers Hard** [SU4000], *Master Builders
House*: Lovely spot by the water in carefully
preserved Montagu-estate village; beamed
and timbered bar with big log fire, good
self-service food bar in separate room,
friendly service, well kept Ind Coope
Burton; can get crowded, part of a
substantial hotel complex *(WHBM, Peter
Argent, R W Stanbury, Patrick Young)*
☆ **Burghclere** [off A34 — OS Sheet 174, map
reference 462608; SU4761], *Carpenters
Arms*: Well kept and friendly, small and
busy, with big helpings of reasonably priced
bar food, Watneys-related real ales,
unobtrusive piped music, fruit machine,
garden; small evening fixed-price restaurant;
opp Sandham Memorial Chapel (NT),
Stanley Spencer's masterwork *(Robert and
Elizabeth Scott)*
Burley [on back rd Ringwood—Lymington;
SU2003], *Queens Head*: Low-beamed
timbered and panelled Tudor pub
completely (and smartly) refurbished to
concentrate now on wide choice of food inc
ploughman's and so forth; good log fire,
well kept Flowers Original and Whitbreads
Strong Country on handpump, piped music;
gift/souvenir shop in courtyard — pub can
get packed in summer; provision for
children *(Dr John Innes, LYM)*
☆ **Bursledon** [Hungerford Bottom], *Fox &
Hounds*: Chef & Brewer popular especially
with young people for handsomely rebuilt
ancient Lone Barn behind — long oak-trunk
table, lantern-lit side stalls, jolly rustic
atmosphere and lots of interesting farm tools
and equipment, food bar, well kept
Watneys-related real ales with a guest beer
such as Gales; children allowed, seats out in
sheltered fairy-lit flagstone courtyard with
electric ride and small pets' corner; games
and juke box in main pub *(Keith Houlgate,
Peter Argent, John and Christine Simpson,
LYM)*
☆ **Cadnam** [by M27, junction 1; SU2913], *Sir
John Barleycorn*: Lovely old thatched pub
with two big log fires in spotless, cosily
divided long open-plan bar; pot plants,
hunting and game prints, good choice of

generous home-made food inc good salads, well kept Flowers Original and Whitbreads Strong Country on handpump, friendly staff; garden with barbecue *(Mike and Jill Dixon, Bill and Jane Rees)*

Charter Alley [White Hart Lane; off A340 N of Basingstoke; SU5957], *White Hart*: Good local with woodburner in small front bar, games in larger back bar, skittle alley; interesting and varied superbly kept real ales, warm welcome *(Richard Houghton)*

☆ **Cheriton** [just off B3046 towards Beauworth — OS Sheet 185, map reference 581282; SU5828], *Flower Pots*: Unspoilt village local now freed from its brewery tie, with well kept Archers, Bunces and a guest strong ale tapped from the cask in homely parlourish bar, low-priced food from new kitchen, friendly landlady taking genuine interest in customers, traditional games in public bar, old-fashioned seats on front grass; bedrooms good value though very simple; good breakfasts *(Dr C S Shaw, Lynn Sharpless, Bob Eardley, R Blatch, R and Mrs P F Shelton, R Elliott, Phil and Sally Gorton, D C Kennedy)*

☆ **Crawley** [signposted from A272 and B3420 NW of Winchester — OS Sheet 185, map reference 428347; SU4234], *Fox & Hounds*: Strikingly built almost Tyrolean pub matching interesting estate village, meticulous craftsmanship inside with elegant timbering and oak parquet; log fire in lounge, very wide choice of good bar food inc some interesting dishes, well kept Gales and Wadworths 6X on handpump, quick unobtrusive service, tables outside, children allowed in restaurant; well equipped bedrooms *(Dr and Mrs A K Clarke, W A Gardiner, Peter Hall, R A Bellingham, G Shannon, LYM)*

Crawley [on A272], *Rack & Manger*: Good choice of Marstons beers, friendly landlord, pleasant garden with good children's facilities *(Peter Argent)*

Crondall [SU7948], *Castle*: Pleasant unpretentious Fullers pub in village backstreet, ESB and London Pride on handpump, bar cat fond of crisps; shame about the juke box *(Dr M Owton)*; *Hampshire Arms*: Popular local with friendly service and quick food inc good ploughman's *(John Evans)*

Crookham [SU7852], *Black Horse*: Pleasant, unspoilt beamed pub, decent food, well kept Courage *(Dr and Mrs A K Clarke)*

☆ **Denmead** [Forest Rd, Worlds End; SU6211], *Chairmakers Arms*: Well kept Gales BBB, HSB, and XXXL and (from separate counter) wide choice of bar food from spectacular sandwiches to steaks in spacious communicating rooms of simply decorated but comfortable pub surrounded by paddocks and farmland; friendly service, no music *(Mel and Phil Lloyd, HNJ, PEJ, Richard Houghton, LYM)*

☆ **Dummer** [1/2 mile from M3 junction 7; SU5846], *Queen*: Very handy for motorway, with emphasis on quickly served good value food from notable sandwiches to steaks served till 10; bar agreeably pubby, with beams, lots of alcoves, log fire, well kept Courage Best and Directors, John Smiths and Wadworths 6X, well reproduced pop music; tables on terrace and in neat back garden; children allowed in restaurant

(Richard Gibbs, WHBM, Len and Sylvia Henderson, KC, Jutta Whitley, LYM)

Dunbridge [Barley Hill; SU3126], *Mill Arms*: Nice Test Valley spot, plenty of walks; pleasant decor, hunting pictures, wide choice of good home-made food, well kept Adnams and Worthington Best, good choice of wines, courteous and accommodating staff, attractive garden with terrace and fountain; largish straightforward restaurant with piped music and conservatory; children welcome *(Keith Hollins, Ali Mitchell)*

☆ **Dundridge** [Dundridge Lane; off B3035 towards Droxford, Swanmore, then right towards Bishops Waltham — OS Sheet 185, map reference 579185; SU5718], *Hampshire Bowman*: Simple isolated downland pub, cosy and unspoilt, with well kept Archers and Gales ales tapped from the cask maybe under light blanket pressure, short choice of good value straightforward food, friendly civilised service; tables on spacious lawn; children welcome *(A R and B E Sayer, Derek and Sylvia Stephenson, LYM)*

Durley [SU5116], *Alma*: Good beer, efficient service, and wide choice of good value food *(Adrian Brown)*

☆ **East Meon** [Church St; signed off A272 W of Petersfield, and off A32 in West Meon; SU6822], *George*: Massive slabs of timber make up some of the furnishings in the cosy areas which loop around the central servery — up to three log fires, candlelit dining room, scrubbed deal, beams and saddlery; wide choice of good value food from spick and span separate servery, Ind Coope, Gales and other real ales; comfortable good value bedrooms *(D Gilbert, J S Rutter, Jacqueline Davis, LYM)*

East Stratton [SU5439], *Plough*: Simple but good village pub with courteous, efficient staff *(R and E Harfield, Dr J L Innes)*

East Tytherley [SU2929], *Star*: Comfortable; well kept Gales *(Peter Argent)*

☆ **Everton** [SZ2994], *Crown*: Friendly landlord, very expert on rare whiskies; also well kept Whitbreads-related real ales in this traditional two-bar local with good service, decent bar lunches in eating area *(Comus Elliott)*

Faccombe [SU3858], *Jack Russell*: Hilltop village free house opp pond, lovely views nearby; good bar food inc some interesting home cooking and particularly good fish, polite attentive service, tasteful new conservatory restaurant extension, spotless housekeeping; no dogs despite name *(HNJ, PEJ)*

☆ **Farnborough** [Rectory Rd; nr Farnborough North stn; SU8753], *Prince of Wales*: Unpretentious local, Edwardian with some more recent antiquing, good range of changing real ales, decent malt whiskies, popular bar food, first-class service, good mix of customers, clean lavatories *(Richard Houghton, Peter Griffiths, Dr R Fuller)*

☆ **Farringdon** [Crows Lane, Upper Farringdon (follow Church sign off A32 S of Alton); SU7135], *Rose & Crown*: Clean, bright and friendly local, simple mainly modern bar furnishings but with old tools on joists, back dining room, Marstons and other well kept real ales, decent wines, good value food in bar and restaurant; tables, swings and bouncy ride in neat back garden (*HEG, Dr R B Crail*)

Farringdon [Gosport Rd (A32 S of Alton), Lower Farringdon; SU7035], *Royal Oak*: Good value generous food, esp game pie and curries, in relaxed and attractive beamed pub with friendly, efficient staff; good coffee (*TOH, Ian and Joan Jagor*)

☆ **Fordingbridge** [14 Bridge St; SU1414], *George*: Listed for its outstanding waterside position, with tables out on terrace and in sun lounge; warm welcome, comfortable bar, attentive service, bar food — esp salad bar (*Roy McIsaac, WHBM*)

Four Marks [A32 Alton—Alresford; SU6634], *Windmill*: Popular family pub with good value bar food, carvery Thurs-Sat evening and Sun-Weds lunchtime, good range of real ales; adventure playground, skittle alley (*A J Blackler*)

☆ **Fritham** [SU2314], *Royal Oak*: Thatched New Forest pub, Flowers and Whitbreads Strong Country tapped from the cask for two unspoilt and basic bars, one with high-backed settles and stairs, pots and kettles hanging in wide old chimney; tables outside, climbing frame, various animals wandering nearby; no food beyond pickled eggs, but your own sandwiches welcome; children in back room; start GWG40 (*R A Corbett, LYM*)

☆ **Frogham** [SU1713], *Foresters*: Busy forest-edge local, good value bar food from sandwiches up inc several unusual dishes (plans for extending back eating area), friendly atmosphere, interesting changing choice of well kept real ales inc ones from distant small breweries, farm cider, wooden settles, tables on front verandah; connections with Drovers at Gussage All Saints — see Dorset main entries (*WHBM*)

☆ **Froxfield Green** [Alton—Petersfield rd; SU7025], *Trooper*: Large 19th-century pub recently bought out of its brewery tie; high moulded ceilings and ornate bar counter but bare-boards style, nice atmosphere; Bass, Ringwood and guest beers such as Wadworths, cheap but interesting wines, candlelight, simple bar food inc good evening steaks (space for this has been limited, but plans for more of an eating area); good character landlord (*HEG, Phil Gorton*)

☆ **Froyle** [Upper Froyle; A31 Alton—Farnham; SU7542], *Hen & Chicken*: Busy and popular for wide choice of food, verging on the approach of a family restaurant rather than of a pub, generously served (till 10), and inc sandwiches and other pub snacks; good value Sun lunch (booking recommended); antique settles and oak tables among more modern furnishings, huge fireplace, good choice of well kept real ales such as Adnams Broadside, Brakspears SB, Courage Best and Wadworths 6X on handpump; unobtrusive piped music, tables outside, play area (*Tim and Ann Newell, S J Rice, Ian Phillips, Les and Jean Bradman, Hazel R Morgan, Adrian Zambardino, Debbie Chaplin, Caroline Wright, Peter Argent, L A Dormer, Patrick and Mary McDermott, LYM*)

Gosport [SZ6199], *Windsor Castle*: Town pub with unusually wide choice of bottled beers from around the world, lots of whiskies; Gales ales on handpump or tapped from the cask, good juke box; can get crowded (*Keith Stevens*)

☆ **Grateley** [SU2741], *Plough*: Typical old village local, helpful and friendly staff, good-sized lounge, big open fire, good choice (particularly evening) of generous nicely presented bar food served quickly in smart little candlelit dining area, well kept Gibbs Mew Wiltshire and Salisbury, subdued piped music (*R Elliott, HNJ, PEJ*)

☆ **Hamble** [High St; 3 miles from M27 junction 8; SU4806], *Bugle*: Large, extended yachtsmen's pub, neat, tidy and comfortable, with varied bar food, Watneys-related and other real ales, river views from restaurant and terrace (*John and Christine Simpson, A J Castle, Peter Argent, BB*)

Hamble [High St], *King & Queen*: Popular (particularly with young people) and traditional, lots of tables in courtyard, good value food, live music Thurs (*John and Christine Simpson*)

☆ **Hambledon** [Broadhalfpenny Down; about 2 miles E towards Clanfield; SU6414], *Bat & Ball*: Attractively placed much-extended dining pub with decent food, Allied real ales, relaxing atmosphere, pleasant log fire and long cricketing history — lots of memorabilia in restaurant (*Jacqueline Davis, P R Ferris, N J Clark, LYM*)

☆ **Hambledon** [West St], *Vine*: Welcoming well furnished old pub with two bars, nice prints, lots of farm tools, old banknotes and so forth; well prepared straightforward food, well kept ales such as Courage, Gales, Morlands, Marstons and Wadworths, shove-ha'penny, darts (*Richard Houghton*)

Hambledon [Hipley], *Horse & Jockey*: Busy at lunchtimes for reasonably priced nicely presented food; welcoming efficient service in clean, civilised surroundings; attractive spot (*R WJ, HNJ, PEJ*)

Hammer Vale [Hammer Lane; between A3, A287 and B2131 W of Haslemere; SU8832], *Prince of Wales*: Open-plan local with good choice of food, nice atmosphere, pleasant licensees, Gales ales (*Richard Houghton, LYM*)

Hawkley [Pococks Lane; SU7429], *Hawkley Inn*: Renovated (more open-plan) and reopened under new management; accommodating to walkers (on Hangers Way footpath), good food esp puddings, decent choice of wines and good guest beers such as Ballards and Hook Norton, no smoking area, friendly locals and staff, pleasant garden, good juke box; interesting new back restaurant (*Philip and Trisha Ferris, the Friday Night Club*)

Hayling Island [9 Havant Rd (A3023); SU7201], *Maypole*: Large, relaxed two-bar local, pleasant landlord, well kept Gales HSB, Butser and Dark Mild, good helpings of lunchtime food (*Richard Houghton, Robert Sear*) [Havant Rd] *Yew Tree*: Friendly recently renovated open-plan bar, wide range of well cooked and reasonably priced food, well kept real ales, decent garden; children well catered for (*Derek Walling, Chris Fluck*)

Hazeley [B3011 N of H Wintney — OS Sheet 186, map reference 742591; SU7459], *Shoulder of Mutton*: Popular pub, well kept Courage, pleasant atmosphere with quiet piped music; most tables set for good if not cheap food *(Mr and Mrs C H Garnett)*

☆ Heckfield [B3349 Hook—Reading (still called A32 on some maps); SU7260], *New Inn*: Wide range of food running up to steaks in very extensive rambling but well organised open-plan bar, some traditional furniture and a couple of good log fires as well as the many well spaced dining tables, friendly atmosphere, well kept Badger Best and Tanglefoot and Courage Best, helpful staff, unobtrusive piped music; restaurant (not Sun); bedrooms in comfortable and well equipped extension *(Ian Phillips, Mr and Mrs C H Garnett)*

Highclere [Andover Rd (A343 S of village); SU4360], *Yew Tree*: Spruce plushly refurbished bar with big log fire, family area off and bedrooms; has been popular for good straightforward bar food, Wadworths 6X and Whitbreads-related real ales on handpump, decent wines and discreet piped music, but no reports since found closed earlier in 1991 *(LYM; news please)*

☆ Hill Head [Cliff Rd; SU5402], *Osborne View*: Lovely Solent views, well kept Badger Best and Tanglefoot, usual bar food, friendly welcome and bustling waitresses, restaurant, trad jazz Sun evenings; straightforward modern style inside, but pleasant, and possibility of redevelopment this coming year; right by bird reserve *(Keith Stevens, Jacqueline Davis, SJC, D Swift, Michael Bechley)*

☆ Hook [London Rd — about a mile E; SU7254], *Crooked Billet*: Spaciously welcoming refurbished pub with homely open fires, good atmosphere, well kept beer and good range of soft drinks, wide choice of good bar food from sandwiches to steaks all day; attractive garden with stream and ducks (some traffic noise out here); children welcome, dogs may be allowed *(WHBM)*

☆ Horndean [London Rd; SU7013], *Ship & Bell*: Comfortable, quiet, clean and relaxed, with friendly service, good choice of reasonably priced bar lunches, well kept Gales beers from the brewery next door; bedrooms *(Nigel Gibbs, Jacqueline Davis)*

Horsebridge [about a mile SW of Kings Somborne — OS Sheet 185, map reference 346303; SU3430], *John o' Gaunt*: Well prepared fresh food — very popular on fine weekends *(P and J McComb)*

Houghton [S of Stockbridge; SU3432], *Boot*: Should be well worth knowing, as refurbished and taken over summer 1991 by the Hardings who previously made the Vine in Stockbridge a popular main-entry dining pub *(News please)*

☆ Hursley [SU4225], *Kings Head*: Polite, efficient service, Bass and other well kept real ales, wide range of good reasonably priced snacks *(Peter Argent, H E Hental)*

☆ Keyhaven [SZ3091], *Gun*: Wide choice of good value simple bar food and well kept Whitbreads-related real ales in busy old villagey pub overlooking boatyard; garden, good walk along spit to Hurst Castle with Isle of Wight views *(John Mason, Comus Elliott)*

☆ Kingsclere [SU5258], *Crown*: Pleasant atmosphere in long comfortable partly panelled lounge with popular home-cooked food, Courage real ales, central log fire;

games in simpler public bar, children in family room; bedrooms comfortable *(LYM)*

☆ Langstone [A3023; SU7105], *Ship*: Spacious pub in attractive spot by sea, lovely view from bar and upstairs restaurant, seats out by water; cheerful log fire, wide choice of generous usual food, well kept Gales, country wines *(N E Bushby, Mrs J A Blanks)*

☆ Lasham [SU6742], *Royal Oak*: Comfortable, friendly country pub in attractive spot nr gliding centre, with Courage Best, Eldridge Pope Royal Oak, Marstons Pedigree and Wadworths 6X; wide choice of popular food in bar and restaurant (ham and eggs and home-made apple pie particularly good); tables outside *(Nigel Gibbs, Patrick and Mary McDermott, Derek Patey)*

Lee on the Solent [Manor Way; SU5600], *Bun Penny*: Welcoming Whitbreads local, also Gales HSB and Wadworths 6X on handpump, usual bar food not too pricey, public bar a favourite haunt of HMS *Daedalus* trainees, secluded well kept garden; civilised lounge; genial manager goes out of his way to help disabled people *(Michael Bechley)*

Long Sutton [off B3349 S of Odiham; SU7347], *Four Horseshoes*: Pleasant country pub with nice landlord, chatty locals, good choice of lunchtime food inc several vegetarian dishes, Gales HSB, Butser and Mild or Winter, log fires, conservatory *(R Houghton)*

☆ Longparish [B3048 off A303 just E of Andover; SU4344], *Plough*: Pleasant open-plan pub/restaurant with popular bar food from sandwiches to steaks inc good fresh fish, Sun lunches, well kept Whitbreads-related real ales, good value wine, restaurant allowing children over 4, piped music *(D I Baddeley, Peter Burton, Mary Springer, R Elliott, LYM)*

☆ Lower Froyle [SU7544], *Anchor*: Popular, clean and brightly lit pub, well tucked away and said to date to 14th century, with well in bar; friendly helpful staff, good range of beers, piped music, friendly atmosphere, good varied straightforward bar food from well made sandwiches up; good restaurant *(R G E Mallin, Mrs H M T Carpenter)*

Lower Wield [SU6340], *Yew Tree*: More restaurant than pub, but welcoming and spotless, with small but imaginative choice of good food, well kept Marstons Pedigree *(Dr C S Shaw, Gordon Smith)*

Lymington [High St; SZ3295], *Angel*: Largely home-made bar food in spacious darkly decorated modernised hotel bar with Eldridge Pope real ales on handpump, and reputedly a Naval ghost; children in buffet bar; clean bedrooms *(M E Hughes, Edwin H Bradshaw, LYM);* [Southampton Rd (A337)], *Toll House*: Good value food from sandwiches and ploughman's to steaks; friendly *(W H Mecham, Mrs Poolman)*

Lyndhurst [High St; SU2908], *Mailmans Arms*: Attractive, with well kept Marstons, splendid service, huge helpings of unusual bar meals *(Bernard Phillips)*

Marchwood [off A326; SU3810], *Pilgrim*: Smart old-world extended thatched pub with well kept Bass, Charrington IPA and Courage Directors and good, straightforward food *(N E Bushby, BB)*

Medstead [Castle St; SU6537], *Castle of Comfort*: Homely old-fashioned village pub with Courage Best and Directors, outstandingly cheap soup, rolls, sandwiches, toasties and ploughman's; children's play area, long sunny front verandah (*P R Ferris*)
Milford on Sea [SZ2891], *Red Lion*: Good beer and fish inc genuine moules marinières and local flounder (*K C Hunt*)
☆ **Mortimer West End** [off Aldermaston rd at Silchester sign; SU6363], *Red Lion*: Country dining pub with emphasis on good imaginative bar food; beams, panelling, timbers, stripped masonry, Badger Best and Tanglefoot, quiet piped music, good log fire, welcoming staff; seats on small flower-filled terrace by quiet road; doing well since latest change of regime (*Richard Houghton, David Shenton, LYM*)
☆ **Nether Wallop** [village signed from A30 or B2084 W of Stockbridge; SU3036], *Five Bells*: Simple but welcoming country local with modestly priced wholesome food, well kept Marstons real ales on handpump inc Mild, long cushioned settles and good log fire in beamed bar, pictures of helicopter aerobatics, friendly licensee; bar billiards and other traditional games in locals' bar, small restaurant, provision for children; seats outside, well equipped play area (inc omnivorous goat) (*Philip and Trisha Ferris, WHBM, A N Black, LYM*)
New Milton [SZ2495], *Tower*: Good free house, welcoming landlord, good reasonably priced bistro upstairs (*B R Shiner*)
☆ **North Gorley** [Ringwood Rd; just off A338; SU1611], *Royal Oak*: 17th-century thatched and beamed pub with Whitbreads-related ales, happy busy licensees, smart young staff, generous helpings of reasonably priced good food, children in family room; big back garden with swings and climber (*Jeanne and Tom Barnes*)
North Warnborough [The Street; SU7351], *Anchor*: Proper friendly village pub, no music, simple food inc superb sandwiches (*Mrs M Tulip*)
☆ **Oakhanger** [off A325 Farnham—Petersfield; SU7635], *Red Lion*: Big log fire in cosy and comfortable lounge, good food (separate eating area), well kept Courage, friendly service (*Ian Phillips, G and M Stewart*)
Oakhanger, *Sun*: Standard pub food, well cooked; well kept beer; no children allowed in, but large, pleasant garden (*KC*)
☆ **Odiham** [High St; A287; SU7450], *George*: Small and comfortable old-fashioned back bar with nice garden outlook, well kept Courage Best and Directors and John Smiths, some wines by the glass, pleasant staff, bar food inc good sandwiches; bedrooms (*Mr and Mrs E H Warner, Mr and Mrs C H Garnett, LYM*)
Odiham [Church Sq], *Bell*: Unusual and welcoming local attractively placed in pretty square opp church and stocks; walls and ceiling festooned with bric-a-brac, good bar food (not weekends), well kept Courage Best and Directors; restaurant (*Ralf Zeyssig*)
☆ **Owslebury** [SU5123], *Ship*: Unspoilt downland village pub particularly worth knowing for magnificent views from two peaceful garden areas; small and old-fashioned inside, with usual bar food (good fresh rolls on Sun), friendly staff, well

kept Marstons real ales (*Lynn Sharpless, Bob Eardley, Michael and Harriet Robinson, H E Hental, Richard Houghton, LYM*)
☆ **Pennington** [Ridgeway Lane; marked dead end from A337 roundabout W of Lymington by White Hart; SZ3194], *Chequers*: Tucked-away yachtsmen's local, simple yet stylish — attractive pictures, plain chairs and pews, polished floorboards and quarry tiles; good interesting bar food changing in line with what's available fresh, can take quite a time to prepare but served till 10; five well kept real ales such as Flowers Original, Gales HSB and Wadworths 6X, loud but well reproduced pop music, pub games, tables out in courtyard and neat garden; children in eating area; restaurant; open all day Sat (*W K Struthers, Ken and Barbara Turner, John Mason, LYM*)
☆ **Pennington** [21 North St], *Musketeer*: Popular local with lots of musketeer memorabilia, half a dozen interesting well kept real ales such as Brakspears PA, Felinfoel Double Dragon and Premium and Ringwood Best on handpump, pleasant atmosphere (*H K Dyson, Mr and Mrs D Hutchings*)
☆ **Petersfield** [College St; SU7423], *Good Intent*: Welcoming and spotless 16th-century beamed and timbered local, thickly carpeted and comfortable, with good log fires; well cooked and presented bar food, efficient service, cosy restaurant (*Paul and Margaret Baker, Phil and Sally Gorton*)
☆ **Pikeshill** [SU2908], *Waterloo Arms*: Agreeably furnished 300-year-old thatched pub with log fire, four Whitbreads-related ales on handpump, unusually good wine list; dogs welcome, and properly pubby atmosphere, though food's the main attraction, from decent toasties or baked potatoes to amazing game platter for two (notice required); good puddings (*WHBM*)
Portsea [84 Queen St; SU6400], *George*: One-room nautical pub with pubby leather seats and panelling in front, more comfortably plush at back, friendly staff, regulars and cats, well kept Flowers Original, Marstons Pedigree, Merrie Monk and Owd Roger on handpump, excellent fish dishes; handy for Naval Heritage Centre, open all day Thurs and Fri; bedrooms (*Andy and Jill Kassube*)
☆ **Portsmouth** [High St; SU6501], *Dolphin*: Spacious and well run highly refurbished pub, Whitbreads-related real ales, wide range of food inc good ploughman's and fish, friendly service, video games; open all day Sat (*Dr J Barrie Jones, Michael Bechley, E A George, Andy and Jill Kassube*)
☆ **Portsmouth** [High St, Old Town], *Sally Port*: Recently completely refurbished, with good bar food, particularly in winter, well kept Marstons, very friendly and efficient staff; spotless, notable for its quiet position in an otherwise busy city; said to have been a favourite of Nelson; restaurant; bedrooms (*M J D Inskip*)
Portsmouth [Camber Dock], *Bridge*: Interesting spot on busy quay of the old harbour, opp ferry and fishing-boat quay; pine tables and paving-slab floors, good snacks, Marstons Pedigree (*M J D Inskip*); [Bath Sq], *Still & West*: Tourist pub listed

for its marvellous position by harbour mouth, with upstairs windows and terraces seeming almost within touching distance of the boats and ships; Gales ales *(M J D Inskip, Nigel Gibbs, Mayur Shah, LYM)*; [off Grand Parade, Old Town], *Wellington*: Friendly and busy little traditional pub with well kept beer, bar food, juke box *(Colin Gooch, Andy and Jill Kassube)*

☆ **Ringwood** [A31 W of town — OS Sheet 195, map reference 140050; SU1505], *Fish*: Clean, pleasant and restful comfortably modernised bar with woodburning stove and huge log fire, plain eating area where children allowed, lawn by River Avon; good value straightforward freshly prepared food from sandwiches up, Whitbreads-related real ales, discreet fruit machines *(Ian Phillips, LYM)*

Ringwood [Market Pl], *Star*: Stripped bricks, old beams, big log fire, nice feel, chatty welcoming staff; good range of inexpensive food from sandwiches to steaks, and of real ales *(Ian Phillips)*

☆ **Rockbourne** [signed off B3078 Fordingbridge—Cranborne; SU1118], *Rose & Thistle*: Popular main entry in previous editions, but closed after tenant's suicide last year; later sold by Whitbreads to local syndicate who were doing it up most promisingly but had not reopened it in time for proper assessment for this edition *(News please)*

☆ **Rockford** [OS Sheet 195, map reference 160081; SU1608], *Alice Lisle*: Friendly thoughtfully modernised open-plan bar with well kept Gales and guest beers, country wines, good straightforward bar food inc children's helpings, large popular conservatory-style eating area, efficient staff, baby-changing facilities; garden with good play area, ducks, peacock and lots of rabbits; attractive position on green, on outskirts of New Forest *(David Eversley, K R Tangacre, Rodney Middleton, BB)*

☆ **Romsey** [Middlebridge St; SU3521], *Three Tuns*: Cosy old-world pub, popular at lunchtime for good choice of bar food; friendly experienced staff, well kept Whitbreads-related real ales *(Joan and John Calvert, Peter Argent)*

Romsey [Church St], *Abbey*: Good choice of food, efficient service, well served Courage Best and Directors *(P Argent, R N Haygarth)*; [21 Bell St], *Angel*: Large L-shaped bar, eating area and courtyard attractively decorated with window baskets and tables and chairs; popular for good value lunches; Whitbreads-related ales, good coffee, small restaurant particularly popular with older people; bedrooms *(Gwen and Peter Andrews, Joan and John Calvert)*; [Greatbridge (A3057 towards Stockbridge)], *Dukes Head*: Long low-beamed cottage, row of three rooms with big log fire each end; country feel, good range of reasonably priced well cooked food *(Ian Phillips)*; *Old House At Home*: Partly thatched, with food which some say is the best value here, well kept Gales; spotless *(W K Struthers)*

☆ **Sarisbury** [Sarisbury Green; 2 1/2 miles from M27 junction 9 — left on A27; SU5008], *Bat & Ball*: Spacious and comfortably laid-out Whitbreads Brewers Fayre family food pub, efficient service, Legoland

playroom and outdoor play area, tables on sheltered back terrace; well kept Whitbreads-related real ales, fruit machine, unobtrusive piped music; afternoon teas *(BB)*

Selborne [SU7433], *Queens*: No reports since summer 1991 management change on this nicely placed country inn, which has had well kept Courage Best and Directors, limited choice of good generous bar food in main bar and log-fire lounge bar; children's area in garden, and good value bedrooms *(News please)*; *Selborne Arms*: Popular with walkers, with fine inglenook fireplace in friendly comfortable village bar, wide range of bar snacks imaginatively presented, smarter lounge, garden with good provision for children *(Ian Phillips)*

☆ **Sherfield on Loddon** [SU6857], *White Hart*: Homely and welcoming, with lovely soft-seated bow window where the ostlers used to wait for coaches (and coaching-days message rack over big inglenook fireplace); friendly efficient service, generous helpings of decent food, well kept Courage, tables outside *(David Lamb, Mayur Shah, LYM)*

☆ **Sopley** [B3347 N of Christchurch; SZ1597], *Woolpack*: Rambling low-beamed local with promising newish regime, wide choice of bar food inc imaginative home-made dishes, well kept Whitbreads-related real ales; conservatory looking down on little stream, bridge across to play area, picnic-table sets on terrace; pub games, unobtrusive piped music; children in eating area and family room *(Mr and Mrs D J Rutter, LYM)*

☆ **Southampton** [55 High St, off inner ring rd; SU4212], *Red Lion*: Behind ordinary town-pub facade is unusual and unexpected great galleried medieval hall with lofty rafters, timbered walls decorated with arms and armour, Tudor panelling; Watneys-related real ales, cheap Chef & Brewer bar food noon to 9.30 (open all day) at ranks of long tables in lower-ceilinged back dining area (children allowed here); piped music can be loud, and evenings young people can take over *(John and Chris Simpson, Ian Phillips, Brian Jones, D J and P M Taylor, LYM)*

☆ **Southampton** [Oxford St], *Grapes*: Masses of Victorian pictures on dark wallpaper above tiled dado, delft shelf, dim oil-type lamps, lots of chamber-pots hanging from ceiling, floor-length red fringed tablecloths; roaring log fire, pianola with flashing coloured lights, skeleton in rubber mask; well kept Whitbreads-related real ales, quick pleasant waitress service, good range of reasonably priced lunchtime food — small back eating area with black and white tiled floor and tented ceiling; live music some nights — not for sensitive ears; parking on nearby meters can be virtually impossible at lunchtime when pub is popular with local business people — busy evenings too *(Jim and Becky Bryson, Brian Jones)*

Southampton [163 University Rd, Highfield], *Hedgehog & Hogshead*: New own-brew pub with real ales brewed in the bar; wide variety of home-cooked food, piano most evenings; from the people who started the Firkin brew-pubs in London *(Anon)*; [St Marys St], *Joiners Arms*: Live bands most nights, from blues (typically Sun) to folk (Fri); back walls covered with black and white publicity shots, front bar often much quieter, with a Victorian feel, popular with locals; Eldridge Pope real ales with a guest such as Brains SA, friendly staff *(David Culpin)*; [Mt Pleasant Rd], *Old Farm House*: Good home-cooked lunchtime food (not Sat) and four real ales; said to have medieval origins *(M J Whittemore)*; [Adelaide Rd], *South Western Arms*: Good bare-boards-and-beams atmosphere, very popular with young people; well kept Archers Headbanger, Courage Directors and Stokers, with guest beers such as Hook Norton Old Hookey; locally popular as Nellies Nob *(Dr W M Owton)*; [Oxford St], *Willows*: Colourful decor, three levels with milk-churn bar stools, tables in nice snug corners; good range of well kept real ales such as Fullers London Pride and Ringwood Old Thumper and Fortyniner; lively Irish band Fri *(David Culpin)*

☆ Southsea [Albert Rd; opp Kings Theatre; SZ6498], *Wine Vaults*: The beers brewed on the premises, and ten or so well kept changing guest beers, make this spacious but unpretentiously honest pub popular with real ales fans and students; friendly staff, wooden floors and panelling, upstairs wine bar/restaurant serving very reasonably priced food from sandwiches up, with strong vegetarian/wholefood leanings *(Nigel Gibbs, Andy and Jill Kassube, Karen and Graham Oddey)*

Southsea [15 Eldon St], *Eldon Arms*: Spacious pub with interesting choice of reasonably priced food in restaurant; good choice of wines, well kept Eldridge Pope beers and guests such as Brains SA, darts and cricket teams; popular with Polytechnic students; ornate green-tiled facade *(Nigel Gibbs, Joan and Michael Hooper-Immins)*; [Esplanade], *Jolly Sailor*: Welcoming pub on front, beautiful log fire, well kept beers, nice if not cheap menu, great atmosphere *(Martin Chandler)*

Southwick [High St; SU6208], *Red Lion*: Nicely placed, with good-humoured welcome and competitively priced good food *(J E Romney)*

Sparsholt [SU4331], *Plough*: Consistently good lunchtime bar food, with weekend menu concentrating on quickly prepared dishes as they are so busy; well kept Flowers, good facilities for young children (popular with retired people too), plenty of outside tables *(Joan and John Calvert, Peter Argent)*

☆ St Mary Bourne [SU4250], *Bourne Valley*: Roomy and comfortable airy bar, friendly staff, good range of standard bar food at moderate prices, good small restaurant, big wild garden at back and smaller one at side; can get busy lunchtime; well equipped bedrooms *(HNJ, PEJ)*

☆ St Mary Bourne, *Coronation Arms*: Friendly neatly kept village local with welcoming landlord, well kept Marstons, usual pub food, Sun lunches; handy for Test Way walks; bedrooms *(BB)*

☆ Steep [Church Rd; Petersfield—Alton, signposted Steep off A325 and A272; SU7425], *Cricketers*: Solidly comfortable furnishings in spacious and airy lounge,

wide choice of generous fresh home-cooked food, well kept Gales ales, notable collection of malt whiskies, unobtrusive piped music; former back public bar is now a restaurant; friendly dogs, picnic-table sets on back lawn with swings and play-house; comfortable good value bedrooms *(John Sterry, LYM)*

☆ Stockbridge [bottom end of High St; A272/A3057; SU3535], *White Hart*: Interesting bar broken up into lots of small areas, oak pews and other seats, antique prints, shaving-mug collection, lots of china on beams of small side restaurant; usual bar food till 10, Sun lunches, cook-yourself summer barbecues, Bass and Charrington IPA on handpump, country wines; children allowed in restaurant; bedrooms *(John Baxter, Joan and John Calvert, LYM)*

Stockbridge [High St], *Grosvenor*: Comfortable old country-town hotel with pleasant efficient service, limited bar food inc good plaice and daily specials, piped music; not a lot of seating; big well kept garden behind *(John Baxter, Mrs Joan Harris, WHBM, BB)*

☆ nr Stockbridge [Leckford (A30 E) — OS Sheet 185, map reference 404367], *Leckford Hutt*: Comfortable settles, easy chairs and settees in main bar with welcoming fire and lots of mugs and tankards, second bar with table games, quoits, quiet fruit machine and impressive row of chamber-pots; good value food from sandwiches to steaks inc children's and even dogs' dishes; Marstons Best and Pedigree, friendly atmosphere, garden behind; children in lunchtime family area *(Lynn Sharpless, Bob Eardley, J Barnhill)*

☆ Stratfield Saye [SU6861], *New Inn*: Open-plan country pub with distinct areas, friendly and efficient new management, bright but relaxed atmosphere, well kept real ales such as Adnams Bitter and Mild, Badger Best and Tanglefoot and a guest; popular bar food *(Richard Houghton, R E C Griffith)*

Stratfield Saye [West End Green], *Four Horseshoes*: Real English pub with cheerful public bar, quieter lounge, enthusiastic landlord and properly kept Morlands *(John C Baker)* @L-DIP STAR = ☆

Stratfield Turgis [SU6960], *Wellington Arms*: Elegant small country inn with individual furnishings in restful and attractively decorated tall-windowed two-room lounge bar, part with polished flagstones, part carpeted; decent bar food inc good beef sandwiches, well kept Badger, open fire, garden; comfortable well equipped bedrooms *(Col G D Stafford)*

☆ Stuckton [village signposted S of Fordingbridge, by A338/B3078 junction; SU1613], *Three Lions*: Warmly welcoming pub-restaurant with wide choice of interesting and unusual wholesome food served generously inc good nursery puddings; good service, decent wines, well kept Allied and other ales on handpump; now chiefly a restaurant rather than a pub (so no longer a main entry), but the neat and airy bar, with lots of fresh flowers, has a good choice of enterprising lunchtime snacks (not Mon); closed Sun evening and Mon in winter, maybe two weeks' summer hol *(Gillian Savitz, Hope Chenhalls, LYM)*

☆ Swanwick [Swanwick Lane (A3051); handy

for M27 junction 9 — OS Sheet 196, map reference 515097; SU5109], *Elm Tree*: Pleasant old pub, much enlarged, with plenty of atmosphere in its several rooms — the far one is the most comfortable; well kept Courage and other ales, wide range of good food, quick friendly service; restaurant can be used for bar meals during week; children welcome *(John and Christine Simpson, J H Walker, Michael Bechley)*

Swanwick [handy for M27 junction 9 — A27, by Bursledon Bridge], *Spinnaker*: Recently refurbished, overlooking river and yacht moorings; Watneys-related real ales, good bar snacks, small restaurant *(N E Bushby)*

Sway [SZ2798], *Hare & Hounds*: Whitbreads pub doing well under energetic new licensee, well spaced tables in main bar, good choice of food from ploughman's through rabbit casserole to sole or salmon; children and dogs welcome; pretty in summer, with big garden and New Forest surroundings *(WHBM)*

Tadley [Broadhalfpenny Lane; Common, just E of A340; SU6061], *Treacle Mine*: Rather isolated free house with well kept Badger, Wadworths and guest; though open-plan keeps feel of three bars; pleasant staff *(Richard Houghton)*

☆ Tangley [Tangley Bottom; towards the Chutes — OS Sheet 185, map reference 326528; SU3252], *Fox*: Small, smart pub with well kept Courage ale, extensive wine list, chatty landlord, quick service, wide choice of good home-cooked food in bar and pleasant restaurant — booking needed here *(HNJ, PEJ)*

Tangley [SU3252], *Cricketers Arms*: Good cricketing prints and fine fireplace in stylishly simple small bar, L-shaped extension with more modern furnishings and more cricketing decorations; well kept Whitbreads-related real ales on handpump, friendly service, generous bar food inc a couple of hot dishes (not Thurs lunchtime), rustic seats on well kept terrace, small caravan site *(Dr M I Crichton, LYM)*

Thruxton [signposted off A303 flyover; SU2945], *White Horse*: Low-beamed thatched pub with very friendly service, old-fashioned atmosphere, well kept real ales such as Bunces Best, Wadworth 6X and guests eg Ringwood Porter; real cottage-style fire, bargain food *(Richard Houghton)*

☆ Timsbury [Michelmersh (A3057 towards Stockbridge); SU3423], *Bear & Ragged Staff*: Busy and spacious Whitbreads country pub, interesting choice of popular bar food from sandwiches to steaks, real ales, good service, log fire, gardens front and back with play area; open all day *(Peter Argent, I H Rorison, K H Frostick)*

Titchfield [East St; off A27 nr Fareham; SU5305], *Wheatsheaf*: Warm welcome, good choice of changing food, Gales and Ruddles real ales; lots of character, interesting history *(Cliff Blakemore); Fishermans's Rest*: Beautiful location opp Titchfield Abbey on River Meon; good changing choice of food, well kept beer *(D D O'Neill)*;

Totton [Eling Quay; SU3612], *Anchor*: Rough-and-ready honest working pub in peaceful setting by creek nr ancient Tide Mill (NT) itself; really cheap food, no frills or fancies; surrounded by redundant quayside buildings *(Ian Phillips)*

☆ Twyford [SU4724], *Bugle*: Spacious and convivial open-plan pub with fish nets and pressure gauges hanging from beams of former public bar area, walking sticks on its walls; emphasis on very wide choice of food inc unusual dishes of the day, which you collect when your number is called by microphone; well kept Eldridge Pope Dorchester on handpump, a good many wines by the glass, polite friendly staff, plenty of well spaced tables *(Roger Huggins, Barbara M McHugh, Mr and Mrs W H Crowther, J A C Maule)*

Twyford, *Dolphin*: Traditional village pub with two bars, friendly welcome, good choice of reasonably priced food and Marstons Pedigree and Best on handpump *(Derek Annis);* [High St], *Phoenix*: Friendly, cheerful landlords in long bar, lots of seating, big brick fireplace, WW2 aeroplane prints on walls, Marstons Best and Pedigree and good choice of Gales country wines, good value standard food, back skittle alley, seats outside *(Lynn Sharpless, Bob Eardley)*

☆ Upham [Shoe Lane — village signposted from B2177 (former A333) and from Winchester— Bishops Waltham downs rd; SU5320], *Brushmakers Arms*: Friendly and comfortably modernised L-shaped bar with dark red wall settles and other stools, low-priced home-cooked bar lunches inc good sandwiches, well kept Bass and a guest beer such as Morlands Old Masters on handpump, big woodburning stove, lots of ethnic brushes as decoration, tables in sheltered smallish back garden, fruit machine; nearby parking can be difficult *(John and Joan Calvert, GSS, J H Walker, BB)*

☆ Upton Grey [SU6948], *Hoddington Arms*: Smart little local with good imaginative restaurant-level cooking, well kept Courage Best and Directors, welcoming service *(Mr and Mrs C H Garnett, PLC, G and M Stewart)*

☆ Warnford [A32; SU6223], *George & Falcon*: Popular, spacious and comfortable country pub with wide range of beers and extensive choice of good generous food, prompt friendly service, piped light classical music *(Alan and Sharron Todd, Colin Gooch)*

☆ Warsash [Fleet End Rd, Locks Heath — OS Sheet 196, map reference 509062; SU4906], *Jolly Farmer*: Popular beamed local with knick-knacks and farming pictures, reasonably priced generous home-cooked bar food (fish and lobsters a speciality), well kept Marstons Pedigree and Whitbreads Strong Country, welcoming Irish landlord, efficient staff, comfortable restaurant; good-sized garden with adventure playground and barbecue *(Keith Houlgate, N E Bushby, W Atkins, D Bushby, Ian Jagor)*

Warsash [Shire Rd], *Rising Sun*: Much-refurbished Whitbreads pub listed for its riverside position, with best views for diners upstairs *(M J D Inskip)*

☆ West Meon [High St; SU6424], *Thomas Lord*: Attractive village local with strong cricketing influence and welcoming family atmosphere; well kept Flowers and Whitbreads, good simple range of generous good value food inc delicious fish, helpful service *(M K C Wills, Mr and Mrs D Barnes)*

West Wellow [nr M27 junction 2; A36 2 miles N of junction with A431; SU2919], *Red Rover*: Good choice of well cooked and presented bar food, friendly staff, real ales *(K R Harris)*

☆ **Weyhill** [A342, signed off A303 bypass; SU3146], *Weyhill Fair*: Lively local popular for Gales HSB, Marstons and Morrells on handpump, with weekly guest beers such as Batemans Mild tapped from the cask in the cellar, and for swiftly served big helpings of well prepared food; spacious lounge with easy chairs around wood-burner, elm-slab tables, other solid furnishings, prints of stamp designs, old advertisements and fair poster, pleasant atmosphere; smaller family room away from bar *(Richard Houghton, R Elliott, Michael and Alison Sandy, BB)*

Weyhill [A342], *Star*: Friendly pub with good value food, Gales ales *(Patrick Godfrey)*

Wherwell [SU3941], *White Lion*: Cosy pub with cheerful welcome, good straightforward home-cooked bar food and Sun roasts (worth booking), good housekeeping and service, friendly atmosphere, log fire, no piped music; no food Sun evening *(A J Stevens, Lynn Sharpless, Bob Eardley)*

☆ **Whitsbury** [follow Rockbourne sign off A354 SW of Salisbury, turning left just before village; or head W off A338 at S end of Breamore, or in Upper Burgate; SU1219], *Cartwheel*: Well placed country pub with pleasantly pubby atmosphere, horse-racing decorations, five well kept real ales, wide choice of generous bar food inc good sandwiches, pleasant mix of customers from green wellies through trainers to motor-cycle boots; dogs allowed; weekly barbecue in secluded garden with play area; steep walk through fields behind for good views (at start of GWG37); children allowed in restaurant when not in use *(WHBM, Richard Houghton, Roy McIsaac)*

☆ **Wickham** [Wickham Sq; SU5711], *Kings Head*: Interesting building, lively and well run, with Gales ales and nearly 150 whiskies, friendly atmosphere, good log fire, good range of bar food — not many tables, so get there early; further bar behind skittle alley *(Barry and Anne)*

Winchester [Guildhall; SU4829], *Abbey*: Reliable for tasty food served by chef in lounge with no smoking area *(Joan and John Calvert)*; [Wharf Hill], *Black Boy*: Wide range of real ales inc interesting guest beers, usual lunchtime bar food (may be limited weekends), good juke box (or occasional discos) making it lively in the evening; bays of button-back banquettes in main L-shaped bar, separate rustic barn bar open busy evenings, seats outside *(Alison Hayward, Nick Dowson, LYM)*; [The Square, between High St and cathedral], *Eclipse*: Picturesque partly 14th-century pub with heavy beams and timbers, though furnishings not special; friendly attentive staff, Whitbreads-related real ales, bar food; very handy for cathedral *(Lynn Sharpless, Bob Eardley, Peter Argent, R Elliott, LYM)*; [Kingsgate Rd], *Queen*: Transformed by current licensees, two comfortably cottagey bars with cricket prints in one, open fire in other, friendly staff, real ales inc Marstons Pedigree, good reasonably priced food (not Weds or Sun evenings) inc choice of Sun roasts; children's helpings; big garden very popular with young people *(Lynn Sharpless, Bob Eardley)*; [57 Stockbridge Rd], *Roebuck*: Friendly and comfortable, with good food, wine and Marstons Pedigree *(Philip and Trisha Ferris)*; Royal Oak Passage, off pedestrian High st], *Royal Oak*: Cheerful town pub included for its no-smoking cellar bar (not always open in the evenings), visually not special, but its massive 12th-century beams and even a Saxon wall give it some claim to be the country's oldest drinking spot; well kept Whitbreads-related real ales and maybe a guest such as Wadworths 6X, usual bar food (not winter evenings) *(T Nott)*

☆ **Winchfield** [Winchfield Hurst; SU7753], *Barley Mow*: Delightful pub close to Winchfield wharf of Basingstoke canal; large helpings of good home-cooked food, friendly staff, well kept beers *(Andrew Bennett, Mr and Mrs C H Garnett)*

Wolverton [Towns End; off A339; SU5558], *George & Dragon*: Pleasant open-plan, low-beamed country pub with well prepared simple bar food, helpful staff, well kept beers *(Chris Fluck, J V Dadswell)*

Hereford & Worcester

Always a good place for lovely old pubs with friendly staff, this is increasingly an area for good food in distinctive and attractive pubs. We'd note particularly the Blue Bell at Barnards Green (an excellent example of a brewery dining pub – a new entry), the Little Pack Horse in Bewdley (chatty and cheap), the restaurantish Roebuck at Brimfield, the prettily placed old Cottage of Content at Carey, the ancient Pandy at Dorstone, the eccentrically maritime Little Tumbling Sailor in Kidderminster, the stylish and imaginative Talbot at Knightwick, the popular Crown & Sandys Arms at Ombersley (also imaginative dishes) and the friendly and bustling Kings Arms there, the Ancient Camp in its breath-taking setting at Ruckhall Common, the pretty Loughpool at Sellack, the warmly welcoming Peacock just outside Tenbury Wells (another new main entry), the handsome old Rhydspence at Whitney on Wye, the Butchers Arms at Woolhope (currently doing very well indeed), the Crown there (very cheerful young licensees) and the nice Anchor over the river at Wyre Piddle. The Fleece at Bretforton deserves a special mention for its beautifully preserved interior, virtually unchanged for centuries; the Monkey House at Defford for its curiosity value (licensed to sell only cider and tobacco – unspoilt is quite inadequate as a word to describe it). Though few pubs here stand out as specially cheap, the area is on balance clearly cheaper than the national average – good value for both drinks and food. In the Lucky Dip section at the end of the chapter, pubs we'd pick out as particularly appealing (most of them inspected by us) include the Green Dragon at Bishops Frome, Little Kipper House at Bradley Green, Collin House at Broadway (currently on a decided upswing), Mug House at Claines, Firs at Dunhampstead, White Swan at Eardisland, Old Mill at Elmley Castle (another "comer"), Old Bull at Inkberrow, Royal George at Lyonshall, Cliffe at Mathon, Slip at Much Marcle, Hope & Anchor in Ross on Wye, Olde Anchor at Upton upon Severn, Coach & Horses at Weatheroak Hill, Boat at Whitney on Wye and Sun at Winforton.

BARNARDS GREEN   SO7945 Map 4

Blue Bell

B4208/B4211, SE edge of Great Malvern

This *Guide* includes only very few of the newish breed of family dining pubs which most of the national and big regional breweries have established under family names such as Henry's Table, Brewers Fayre and so forth. We've found that mostly these do give reliably good value, and tend also to have more individuality than their family names imply. But standardisation does mean that most don't stand out as sufficiently memorable to deserve a main entry. The Blue Bell is a happy exception, handsomely reconstructed and extended in summer 1990 as a Marstons Tavern Table; and its position, nestling under the Malvern Hills, is a bonus. So is the fact that, though much is set aside for diners, there's plenty of space (and a good welcome) if you just want a drink. It's kept a good deal of old-worldiness, and though open-plan has been well divided into areas on various levels each with its own character, with carved oak beams, walls stripped to brick, panelled or papered in an attractive floral pattern, big Victorian pictures and houseplants. The varnished tables, well arranged for dining, have assorted cushioned carvers, kitchen and dining chairs. A wide choice of good value food includes soup (95p), sandwiches (from £1.40), burgers (£2.40), steak and kidney pie (£2.95), several vegetarian dishes (from £2.95), chilli con carne (£3.10), ploughman's (£3.25), char-sui turkey breast or chicken tikka masala (£4.35) and rump steak (£5.65), with children's dishes, and specials such as lunchtime quiche or cod (£3.95), or in the evening chicken breast in a wine and mushroom sauce (£5.25). Well kept and very reasonably priced Marstons Burton and Pedigree on handpump, friendly quick service, fruit machine, unobtrusive piped music; lavatories for the disabled. The garden is attractive and well kept; they plan quite an ambitious children's play area. *(Recommended by Frank Cummins, Mr and Mrs P B Dowsett)*

Marstons   Manager Mr Millichip   Real ale   Meals and snacks (12–2, 6.30 or earlier in summer–9.30; till 10 Fri, Sat)   Malvern (0684) 575031   Children allowed if eating   Open 11.30–3, 6–11; closed evening 25 Dec

BEWDLEY   SO7875   Map 4

Little Pack Horse ★

High Street; no nearby parking – best to park in main car park, cross A4117 Cleobury road, and keep walking on down narrowing High Street; can park 150 yds at bottom of Lax Lane

For all its eccentricities and oddities, this charming little pub is far from twee. The small rooms have a chatty, relaxed atmosphere, and lots of old photographs and advertisements, clocks, wood-working tools, Indian clubs, a fireman's helmet, an old car horn, an incendiary bomb, and a wall-mounted wooden pig's mask that's used in the pub's idiosyncratic game of swinging a weighted string to knock a coin off its ear or snout. There are roughly plastered white walls, low beams, pews, red leatherette wall settles, and a mixed bag of tables on the red-tiled floor. Reasonably priced and very tasty, the bar food includes home-made soup (£1.60; the cream of broccoli is good), large filled baked potatoes (£2.85), prawns (half-pint £3.25), lasagne (£3.55), omelettes (£3.75), chilli con carne or chicken in a curry and apricot sauce (£3.95), gammon with pineapple or home-baked ham salad (£4.25), the hefty Desperate Dan pie (£4.65), and severn shark steak or sirloin steak (£5.45); with puddings such as deep apple pie or jam roly poly with custard (£1.60). Well kept Ind Coope Burton and the good value strong Lumphammer ale that's brewed for the chain (even non-beer-drinkers seem to like it) on handpump, house wine, and well made coffee; woodburning stove; darts, dominoes, fruit machine and sweet box for children. Dogs allowed (one unfailing visitor is a good-natured alsatian cross called Pepper). You can buy a mug in each of the 'Little' pubs and at the end of your tour you get a bonus one free. This quiet riverside town is full of attractive buildings. *(Recommended by Paul Denham, Nicola Brown-Denham, Joy Heatherley, Roger Huggins, R H Martyn, Wayne Brindle)*

Free house   Licensee Peter D'Amery   Real ale   Meals and snacks (sandwiches weekdays only)   Bewdley   (0299) 403 762   Children welcome anywhere but bar area   Open 11–3, 6–11, Sat 11–11; closed eve 25 Dec

BREDON   SO9236   Map 4

Fox & Hounds

4 1/2 miles from M5 junction 9; A438 to Northway, left at B4079, then in Bredon follow To church and river signpost on right

The big comfortable main bar in this neatly thatched, modernised pub is split into areas by dressed stone pillars and has carpet on the flagstones, a central woodburning stove, stripped timbers, maroon plush and wheelback chairs around attractive mahogany and cast-iron-framed tables, and elegant wall lamps; there's a large rooflight and a clever mirror-like window. A smaller side bar has an open fire at each end, settles, and assorted wooden kitchen chairs and wheelbacks. Enjoyable food includes home-made soup (£1.65), ploughman's (from £2.95), braised faggots (£3.95), chicken curry (£4.25), salmon and broccoli bake topped with creamed potato or chicken chasseur braised with a sauce of mushrooms, onions and tomatoes (£4.95), and steaks (from £7.50), daily specials and good puddings. Well kept Boddingtons, Marstons Pedigree and, rarely enough, a beer direct from a different brewer than the one the pub's tied to, Banks; prompt friendly service; darts, cribbage, shove-ha'penny, dominoes, fruit machine and piped music. Beside the pub with its colourful hanging baskets are picnic-table sets, some under Perspex, a barbecue and thatched Wendy house. Dogs allowed – the pub has two terriers of its own. *(Recommended by Frank Cummins, Derek and Sylvia Stephenson, PADEMLUC, A Triggs, Richard Parr, Brian and Anna Marsden, Robert and Vicky Tod)*

Flowers (Whitbreads) Lease Michael Hardwick Real ale Meals and snacks (12–2, 6.30–10; not Sun evening) Restaurant Bredon (0684) 72377 Children welcome Open 11–3, 6.30–11

BRETFORTON SP0943 Map 4

Fleece ★ ★

B4035 E of Evesham: turn S off this road into village; pub is in centre square by church; there's a sizeable car park at one side of the church

This is one of the finest old country pubs in Britain. Originally, it was a farm owned by one family for nearly 500 years, but in 1848 they turned it into a pub and ran it until 1977 when Lola Taplin, the great-granddaughter of the original licensee, left it to the National Trust, to preserve as it is. She had run it single-handed since the war. All the furnishings are original, many of them heirlooms: a great oak dresser holds a priceless 48-piece set of Stuart pewter, there's a fine grandfather clock, ancient kitchen chairs, curved high-backed settles, a rocking chair, and a rack of heavy pointed iron shafts, probably for spit roasting, in one of the huge inglenook fireplaces. Three open coal fires warm the pub during winter and cold weather. Also, massive beams and exposed timbers, worn and crazed flagstones (scored with marks to keep out demons), and many more antiques such as a great cheese-press and set of cheese moulds, and a rare dough-proving table. The room with the pewter is no-smoking. Well kept Hook Norton Best, M & B Brew XI, Uley Pigs Ear and Shipwrecked – from the Jolly Roger in Worcester (see Lucky Dips); country wines and farm ciders. Bar food includes sandwiches (from £1.10), ploughman's (from £2.50), Gloucester sausages (£2.90), lasagne (£3.50), steak and kidney pie (£3.80), locally cured gammon (£4.50), and steak (£5.95); they do barbecues; friendly staff. They don't sell pre-packed snacks such as crisps or nuts, because the original owner who sold the pub to the National Trust refused to do so. Darts, cribbage, dominoes, or shove-ha'penny. In summer, when it gets very busy, they make the most of the extensive orchard, with seats on the goat-cropped grass that spreads around the beautifully restored thatched and timbered barn, among the fruit trees, and at the front by the stone pump-trough. There's also an adventure playground, a display of farm engines, barbecues, and maybe anything from Morris dancing, a vintage car rally or a sheep-shearing, spinning and weaving demonstration to the merriment of their Friday-to-Sunday festival on the first weekend in July, with up to 30 real ales, bands and pony-rides. They also hold annual asparagus auctions at the end of May. No dogs (they have their own). *(Recommended by Phil Clissitt, Ness Turner, Klaus and Elizabeth Leist, D G Clarke, Jerry and Alison Oakes, Lynne Sharpless, Bob Eardley, Jed and Virginia Brown, J Barnwell, Jim and Maggie Cowell, PLC, Andrew Morrissey, Roger Huggins, Tom MacLean, Ewan McCall, David Evans, Alan and Heather Jacques, MAC, Mike Rising, M Joyner, Brian Jones, D G Clarke, Michael and Alison Sandy, Joan Olivier, R A Corbett, Edward Burlton Davies, Mr and Mrs C Moncreiffe, Helen and Wal Burns, Andy and Jill Kassube, Lynne Sheridan, Cynth and Malc Pollard, Bob West, A Triggs, D Godden, Philip Orbell, Alison and Tony Godfrey, N P Cox, Barbara Wensworth)*

Free house Licensee Norman Griffiths Real ale Meals and snacks (not Mon evening) (0386) 831 173 Children in no-smoking Pewter Room Occasional live entertainment Open 11–2.30, 6–11

BRIMFIELD   SO5368   Map 4

Roebuck 🜋 🍺

Village signposted just off A49 Shrewsbury–Leominster

You get an idea of the style of this civilised dining pub from the fact that they serve olives and friandises (good ones) before your bar meal comes. This is excellent, though by no means cheap, and might include good soups (£2.70), starters or light snacks such as crab pot or ploughman's with home-made pickles (£4.50), rabbit terrine with red onion and apple chutney (£5.20), steak and kidney pie (£5.90), baked queen scallops stuffed with mushroom and garlic butter (£7), grilled salmon with chive cream sauce (£9.50), and puddings like home-made ice creams, bread and butter pudding with apricot sauce (£4.50) or fresh lemon tart (£4.70), and British cheeses with home-made oat cakes and walnut and sultana bread (£4.50); vegetables are good and they use organic produce whenever possible; caring, pleasant staff. The wine list is remarkably good, particularly strong on the better burgundy and rhône growers and éleveurs, and New World wines; good coffee. The quiet and traditional little back lounge bar has dimpled copper-topped cask tables, decorative plates mounted over dark ply panelling and a small open fire. A little panelled front snug leads through to a public bar with pool and darts; shove-ha'penny, table skittles, fruit machine, trivia, juke box, cribbage, and dominoes. The popular big-windowed side restaurant is elegant and modern. Incidentally, there's a family connection with the Walnut Tree at Llandewi Skirrid. *(Recommended by Mr and Mrs W H Thomas, P J Hanson, Cynthia McDowall)*

Free house   Licensees John and Carole Evans   Meals and snacks (till 10pm; not Sun or Mon or 25 and 26 Dec)   No-smoking restaurant   Brimfield (058 472) 230   Children welcome (there's a highchair)   Open 12–2, 7(6.30 Sat)–11   Bedrooms; £35B/£60B

CAREY   SO5631   Map 4

Cottage of Content 🍺

Village, and for most of the way pub itself, signposted from good road through Hoarwithy

To go through one of the entrances to this very pretty, isolated country inn means walking over headstones. Connected by an alcove with an antique settle, the two attractive and comfortable bars have dark oak beams, more antique settles, some timbering and panelling, rugs on the wooden floor, fresh flowers and plants, and an open coal-burning range. Good, popular bar food includes sandwiches (from £1), soup (£1.25), potted chicken and lemon tarragon (£2), ploughman's or sausage and egg (£2.50), faggots or stuffed aubergines (£3.50), lasagne or breaded plaice (£3.95), croissants filled with chicken and asparagus (£4.25), steaks (from £8.50), and duckling with orange and honey glaze (£10.50); good breakfasts. Well kept Bass, Hook Norton Best and Old Hookey and Marstons Pedigree on handpump, with 60 wines, 30 single malt whiskies and Rosie's cider; darts, dominoes and cribbage. Tables on a back terrace look up to a steep expanse of lawn, and there are a couple more on the front terrace facing a little stream and the very quiet village lane. *(Recommended by Andy and Jill Kassube, B T Estill, C C Cook, Barrie Hopwood, Patrick Freeman, Gwen and Peter Andrews, Julian Proudman, Peter and Rose Flower, Cliff and Karen Spooner, Col D G Stafford, John and Joan Wyatt, Mr and Mrs M Wall, Tony and Lynne Stark, M J Penford)*

Free house   Licensee Mike Wainford   Real ale   Meals and snacks (till 10pm Fri and Sat)   Carey (0432) 840242   Children welcome   Open 12–2.30(3 Sat), 7(6 Sat)–11; winter evening opening 7; closed 25 Dec   Bedrooms; £30B/£42B

DEFFORD   SO9143   Map 4

Monkey House

Woodmancote; A4104 towards Upton – immediately after passing Oak public house on right, there's a small group of cottages, of which this is the last

The only sign that this pretty black-and-white thatched cottage is a pub is a notice by the door saying 'Licensed to sell cider and tobacco'. There is no bar, just a hatch beside the door where very cheap Bulmer's Medium or Special Dry cider, tapped from wooden barrels, is poured by jug into pottery mugs. In good weather, you stand outside with the bull terrier and the hens and cockerels that wander in from an adjacent collection of caravans and sheds; they now have two horses called Murphy and Mandy. Or you can retreat to a small side outbuilding with a couple of plain tables, a settle and an open fire. They don't serve food (except crisps and nuts), but allow customers to bring their own. It's set back from the road behind a small garden with one or two fruit trees. The name came from a drunken customer some years ago who fell into bramble bushes and insisted he was attacked by monkeys. *(Recommended by Phil Gorton, Martin Morris, Roger Huggins, Tom MacLean, Ewan McCall, Dave Braisted, Peter and Rose Flower, T Nott)*

Free house   Licensee Graham Collins   Open 11–2.30, 6–10.30 (11 Sat); closed Mon evening, Tues

DORSTONE   SO3141   Map 6

Pandy 🔓

Pub signed off B4348 E of Hay-on-Wye

Dating back eight centuries, this fine half-timbered building is Herefordshire's oldest inn and is surrounded by most attractive, partly wooded gentle hills. The main room – on the right as you go in – has a relaxed, friendly atmosphere, heavy beams in the ochre ceiling, stout timbers, upright chairs on its broad worn flagstones and in its various alcoves, and a vast open fireplace with logs. In summer when they have a wider choice of daily-changing bar food there might be sandwiches, hummus and hot pitta bread (£2.50), fresh pasta or pan-fried sardines in garlic (£3.95), mushroom and nut stroganoff (£4.65), rabbit pie (£4.95), fresh cod in parsley sauce or a variety of pies (£5.25), halibut in prawn and mushroom sauce (£7.25), and guinea fowl in port wine sauce (£7.95), with puddings such as home-made tarts or home-made chocolate and crème de menthe mousse (£1.75), and ice cream made from local sheep's milk such as pistachio, brandy and almond or brown bread; the big helpings make the prices good value. Very well kept Bass, and Hereford Supreme (from a local brewery), and Boddingtons, which is alternated with a guest ale, all on handpump; most Scotch whiskies and all major Irish ones, and unlimited coffee. A games area with stripped stone walls and a big woodburning stove has pool, darts, cribbage, dominoes, quoits, old-fashioned juke box, trivia and fruit machine, and they hold quiz evenings; a side extension has been kept more or less in character. There are picnic-table sets in the neat side garden (which has a play area). *(Recommended by Gwyneth and Salvo Spadaro-Dutturi, SLH, Mrs Joan Harris, Miss S Le Huray, Cliff and Karen Spooner, D Morris, Adrian Pitts; more reports please)*

Free house   Licensees Chris and Margaret Burtonwood   Real ale   Meals and snacks (12–2, 7–9.45, not winter Mon and Tues lunchtime)   Children welcome   Visiting Morris Dancers and ceilidh band in summer, other occasional live entertainment   Open 12–3, 7–11; closed winter Mon and Tues lunchtime

FOWNHOPE   SO5834   Map 4

Green Man 🛏

B4224

In 1485 this bustling old place appeared in the deeds as The Naked Boy. It was then a coaching inn on what was the main road from Hereford to Gloucester, and in the 18th and 19th centuries the Petty Sessional Court was held here – you can still see the iron bars to which the prisoners were chained, the cell, and the Judge's bedroom with its special lock. The rather stately lounge has comfortable armchairs under its high oak beams, long cushioned settles agains the timbered ochre walls (which are hung with small pictures and brasses), seats set into tall latticed windows, and a big log fire. A second smaller but broadly similar bar has darts and dominoes; piped music. Good value bar food in generous helpings includes sandwiches (from £1.20, toasties £2.60), soup (£1.40), ploughman's (£2.70), roast local chicken (£3.10), salads (from £3.10), lasagne (£3.80), home-made steak pie or trout with almonds (£4.65), rump steak (£6.50), puddings (£1.50) and children's menu (£2.55). Well kept and attractively priced Hook Norton Best, Marstons Pedigree and Sam Smiths OB on handpump, and local ciders; helpful staff. The residents' lounges are no-smoking. The quiet garden behind this striking black-and-white inn has robust benches and seats around slatted tables among the trees and flowerbeds of the big back lawn, where they serve coffee and afternoon tea in good weather; there's also a play area. It's only half a mile to the River Wye. *(Recommended by Andy and Jill Kassube, E V Walder, Bernard Phillips, G W H Kerby, E A George, J P W Bowdler, Mr Jennings, Patrick Godfrey, Peter and Rose Flower, D I Baddeley, Cliff and Karen Spooner, Col D G Stafford, Helen and John Thompson, M J Penford)*

Free house Licensees Arthur and Margaret Williams Real ale Meals and snacks (till 10 evening) Two restaurants Fownhope (0432) 860243 Children in eating area of bar Open 11–2.30, 6–11 Bedrooms; £31.75B/£44.50B

HANLEY CASTLE SO8442 Map 4

Three Kings £

Pub signposted (not prominently) off B4211 opposite castle gates, N of Upton upon Severn

The little tiled-floor taproom on the right in this atmospheric and pretty country pub is separated off from the entrance corridor by the monumental built-in settle which faces its equally vast inglenook fireplace. The hatch here serves well kept and low-priced Butcombe Bitter, Jolly Roger Shipwrecked and Theakstons Best, with a guest beer on handpump, malt whiskies and farm cider. On the left, another room is decorated with lots of small locomotive pictures, has darts, dominoes, shove-ha'penny and cribbage. A separate entrance leads to the comfortable timbered lounge with little leatherette armchairs and spindleback chairs arounds its tables, another antique winged and high-backed settle, a neatly blacked kitchen range and an unchanging atmosphere. A short choice of reasonably priced home-cooking includes soup (75p), sandwiches (from 80p, toasties £1), omelettes (from £1.50), ploughman's (from £1.95), good chicken en croûte with soft cheese, breaded plaice stuffed with prawns and mushrooms or with broccoli and cheese (£4.25), salmon en croûte (£6), beef wellington (£6.75) and grilled fillet steak, when available, (£8.50); be warned that they say that the specials may take at least half an hour to prepare; puddings such as blackberry and apple pancake rolls and cream or chocolate trufito (from £1.25). Bow windows in the three main rooms, and old-fashioned wood-and-iron seats on the front terrace, look across to the great cedar which shades the tiny green. *(Recommended by PADEMLUC, B T Smith, Lynne Sheridan, Bob West, Derek and Sylvia Stephenson, Mr Jennings, Frank Cummins, Frank Gadbois, Mr and Mrs J H Adam, David Braisted)*

Free house Licensee Mrs Sheila Roberts Real ale Meals and snacks (not Sun evening) Upton Upon Severn (0684) 592686 Children in side room Live music Sun evening, folk club alternate Thurs Open 11–2.30 (may not open lunchtime if no customers – best to ring first), 7–11 Bedrooms; £20B/£35B

KEMPSEY SO8548 Map 4

Huntsman

Green Street Village – signposted down Post Office Lane off A38 S of Worcester, in Kempsey; OS Sheet 150, map reference 869491

A favourite with several readers, this unaffected village local has a cosy, chatty atmosphere in the two well kept small rooms on the right. There are horse and games pictures on the plain swirly plaster walls, well cushioned oak seats around attractive old waxed kitchen tables in window alcoves, hop bines over the little corner bar counter, and a small fire in the stone fireplace; beyond is a dining area appropriately named the Rookery Nook. On the left a lower room has lots of leatherette armchairs around its walls, and a trivia machine; cribbage, dominoes, a fruit machine, piped music and a full-size skittle alley. Bar food includes sandwiches (from £1.50), soup (£1.35), ploughman's (from £2.35), home-made steak and kidney pie (£4.55), vegetarian gratin (£4.65), gammon and egg (£5.60), chicken kiev (£6.25) and steaks (from £7.50), with puddings (£1.60); well kept Banks's or Jolly Roger on handpump. Under cocktail parasols on the side lawn, are some rustic slabby benches and picnic-table sets; the calmly friendly great dane is called Sam. *(Recommended by Mrs J Crawford, Dave Braisted, PADEMLUC; more reports please)*

Free house Licensee Neil Harris Real ale Meals and snacks (not Sun or Mon evenings) Restaurant Worcester (0902) 820336 Children welcome Open 12–3, 6–11; closed 25 Dec, evening 26 Dec

KIDDERMINSTER SO8376 Map 4

Little Tumbling Sailor ⊘

42 Mill Lane; from Mill St, which is signposted off ring road by A442 Bridgnorth exit, fork right at General Hospital up narrow lane

Several rooms radiate from the central servery in this entertaining maritime-theme pub. The navy-blue walls and the ceilings are packed with ships' wheels and badges, nautical brassware, net-floats, hammocks, anchors, oars, a naughty figurehead, a particularly rich collection of naval photographs with the relevant sailor's hat riband for each ship, masses of other ship pictures, model ships, and rope fancywork; also, red and blue leatherette seats around cast-iron-framed tables. Interesting bar food includes filled french sticks (£1.20), home-made soup (£1.45), mushroom stroganoff or red dragon pot (a tofu dish) (both £3.45), chilli (£3.95), chicken curry or fillet of plaice in cheese sauce (£4.25), chicken, ham and mushroom pie (£4.45), Desperate Dan pie (£4.65, vegetarian £3.95), and specials such as black country platter (£4.25), minty lamb pie (£4.50), salmon (£5.50) and grilled trout (£5.50), with home-made puddings such as chocolate mosaic, blackcurrant cheesecake, pastry pies and gateaux (£1.50). Well kept Ind Coope Burton and the chain's own Lumphammer on handpump, and house wine; fruit machine, trivia machine, and piped pop music. They sell their own pink seaside rock, key rings, printed T-shirts, and edited paper *The Lark*. The little sheltered garden has a trawler's deckhouse, wave-making machine, sand pit and even a substantial mock-up of a lighthouse for children. *(Recommended by A M J Chadwick, PLC, Rob and Gill Weeks, Paul Denham, Nicola Brown-Denham, Roger Taylor)*

Free house Licensee Mr Wilks Real ale Meals and snacks (12–2, 6.30–10, not 25 Dec) Kidderminster (0562) 747 527 Children welcome Music night Mon (from 50s and 60s to Folk and Irish) Open 11–3, 6–11; closed 25 Dec

KNIGHTWICK SO7355 Map 4

Talbot ⊘ ⇌

Knightsford Bridge; B4197 just off A44 Worcester–Bromyard

This quiet 14th-century inn is family run – the licensee's two sisters, Annie and Elisabeth, doing the cooking. It's the original, enticing food (though they do traditional dishes as well) that attracts most comment: filled french sticks (£1.30, open salad sandwich £1.60), excellent soup, such as iced or hot borage and cucumber or fresh minestrone (£1.50), ploughman's (from £3), crispy baskets with mushroom, baby corn and gorgonzola, red pepper and green bean terrine or chicken and sorrell quenelles (£3.95), main courses such as liver and bacon (£5.50), vegetarian dishes such as courgette and tomato casserole with cheese dumplings or spicy pheasant eggs with potato and yoghourt (£5.95), pork piquante or lamb noisettes with mushroom duxelles (£7.50), rack of lamb with creamy horseradish sauce or gruyere and pistachio (£8.95), roast duck with orange sauce (takes half an hour, £9.50), and sirloin steak (£10.95), with puddings such as fresh apricot streusel, Malvern apple pudding, fresh nectarine crumble, rum and raisin cheesecake and citrus curd and nutty roulade (from £2.30); the fresh vegetables are well cooked. The same food is served in the small restaurant, (note that there is a service charge for non-residents); especially civilised breakfasts with linen tablecloths and napkins, home-baked bread and home-made marmalade. Well kept Bass, Flowers IPA, Jolly Roger and Tetleys on handpump – and, more cheaply, Banks's, and good wines by the glass. The big rambling lounge has a variety of interesting seats from small carved or leatherette armchairs to the winged settles by the tall bow windows, heavy beams, entertaining and rather distinguished coaching and sporting prints and paintings on its butter-coloured walls, and a vast stove which squats in the big central stone hearth; there's another log fire, too. The well furnished back public bar has darts, pool on a raised side area, fruit machine, space game and juke box. Well behaved dogs welcome. Some of the bedrooms, clean and spacious, are above the bar. There are some old-fashioned seats outside, in front, with more on a good-sized lawn over the lane (they serve out here too). This settlement is mentioned in the Domesday book.

(Recommended by P and J Shapley, Brig J S Green, Chris Newman, Deb Jay, P and J Shapley, Lynn Sharpless, Bob Eardley, Mrs J A Blanks, M A and C R Starling, Paul Denham, Nicola Brown-Denham, Mr Jennings, PLC, John and Karen Day, Peter Burton, Robert and Vicky Tod, Nigel Gibbs, Dr M Owton, C M Whitehouse, T Nott, John Bowdler, Gwen and Peter Andrews, John Gillett, Mr and Mrs J M Elden)

Free house   Licensee J P P Clift   Real ale   Meals and snacks   Restaurant Knightwick   (0886) 21235   Children welcome   Open 11–11; closed 25 Dec evening   Bedrooms; £23(£29B)/£39(£52.50B)

LEDBURY   SO7138 Map 4

Feathers 🛏

High Street; A417

This striking, mainly 16th-century timbered hotel is very elegant to look at; the top floor was added a century later – from across the street you can see the differences. Inside, there's a relaxed atmosphere in the spreading beamed and timbered Fuggles Bar which is broken up into areas by attractive brick pillars: one or two old oak panelled settles, comfortable upholstered seats, pleasantly individual cloth banquettes built into bays, some blond squared panelling, and fresh flowers on a variety of solid tables. Decorations include 19th-century caricatures, fowl prints on the stripped brick chimney breast, hop bines draped liberally over the beams, some country antiques, and soft lighting from picture lamps, one or two tablelamps and old-fashioned wall lamps. Big curtained windows look over the rather narrow coachyard. There's also a more formal lounge by the reception area with high-sided armchairs and settees. Good bar food served on hand-made pottery such as home-made soup (£1.90), starters which can also be eaten as a main course such as grilled sardines (£2.45), chicken livers wrapped in bacon with sherry sauce (£2.80) or tagliatelli with prawns and mussels in a tomato and herb sauce (£3.10), and main courses such as pasta and vegetable bake (£4.95), home-made asparagus and parma ham quiche (£5.10), braised steak with a port wine sauce (£5.90), grilled supreme of salmon (£6.45) and daily specials. Bass, Felinfoel Double Dragon, Worthington BB and a guest beer, and a 70 bin-end wine list.

(Recommended by Joan and Tony Walker, F and J Hamer, John Bowdler; more reports please)

Free house   Licensees D M Elliston and Manson Malcolm   Real ale   Meals and snacks (till 10pm Fri and Sat; afternoon teas)   Restaurant   Ledbury (0531) 5266/7 Children welcome   Open 10–2.30, 5.30–11; closed evening 25 Dec   Bedrooms; £55.50B/£78B

OMBERSLEY   SO8463 Map 4

Crown & Sandys Arms 🌳

Coming into the village from the A433, turn left at the roundabout, into the 'Dead End' road

The very good – and often imaginative – home-made food in this friendly and pretty Dutch-gabled white pub is so popular that it's best to get there early to secure a seat. Daily specials might include mussels in season (£3), fresh fish (from £4), vegetarian lasagne (£4.30), nut roast (£4.35), and liver, bacon and onions or pork goulash (£4.95); other dishes include very good soups (£1.25), sandwiches (from £1.20, toasties from £1.40), ploughman's (from £2.25), cold sugar-baked ham or home-made curry (£4.25), steak and kidney pie (£4.75), gammon (£5.95) and 10oz local sirloin steak (£8.15), with home-made puddings (£1.85), and children's dishes (£1.30). Well kept Bass, Hook Norton Best and Old Hookey and a range of guest beers like Ruddles Best and County on handpump, decent wines and coffee, teas and hot chocolate with whipped cream and chocolate flakes. The lounge bar has black beams and some flagstones, comfortable Windsor armchairs, antique settles, a couple of easy chairs and plush built-in wall seats, old prints, maps and ornamental clocks (which are for sale) on its timbered walls, and log fires; no smoking at five tables; dominoes, cribbage. There are picnic-table sets in the garden behind the building. The antique shop and picture framer's in the back stables opens on Tuesday, Friday and Saturday. No dogs. *(Recommended by Robert and Vicky Tod, Brian Jones, J Barnwell, Paul Denham, Nicola Brown-Denham, Dave Braisted, A Kilpatrick, PLC, A T Langton, Phil Clissitt, Ness Turner, Peter Burton, Brian and Anna Marsden, Michel Hooper-Immins, J S Rutter, Barbara M McHugh, Alan and Marlene Radford, John Bowdler, Kenneth Krober, Roy McIsaac)*

Free house   Licensee R E Ransome   Real ale   Meals and snacks   Restaurant   Worcester (0905) 620252   Well behaved children allowed until 7pm (no prams, push-chairs or carrycots)   Open 10.30–3, 5.30–11; closed 25 and 26 Dec   Bedrooms; £20(£30B)/£47B

Kings Arms ✿

There's a good mix of customers in this bustling and very friendly Tudor pub. The atmosphere is pleasant and informal and the comfortable rooms ramble around various nooks and crannies full of stuffed animals and birds and a collection of rustic bric-a-brac. One room has Charles II's coat of arms moulded into its decorated plaster ceiling; he's reputed to have been here in 1651. A wide choice of regularly-changing home-made bar food includes sandwiches (from £1.50, weekday lunchtime), appetising home-made soup (£1.80), home-made pâtés that include a vegetarian cream cheese and cashew nut one (£3.50), and main dishes like home-made steak and kidney pie (£4.75), home-made gingered chicken and sweetcorn casserole (£5.75), fresh dressed crab (£7.25), tiger prawns (£7.50), sirloin steak (£7.75), and quite a few excellent puddings such as home-made rhubarb and apple crumble, treacle and nut tart or chocolate and brandy mousse (£1.85). Well kept Bass and Boddingtons on handpump, with a decent range of malt whiskies; two good log fires (one in an inglenook); quick cheerful service; no dogs. The licensees intend to extend the kitchen, creating better staff facilities and larger dining areas, enabling them to establish no- smoking areas. A pretty tree-sheltered courtyard has tables under cocktail parasols. *(Recommended by J K Conneen, PLC, Keith Croston, Phil Clissitt, Ness Turner, Joan and Tony Walker, Paul Denham, Nicola Brown-Denham, Brian Bannatyne-Scott, Rona Murdoch, W C M Jones, Frank Cummins, C M Whitehouse, Robert and Vicky Tod, Barbara M McHugh, Hilary Sargeant, Norman Clarke)*

Free house   Licensees Chris and Judy Blundell   Real ale   Meals and snacks (12.15–2.15, 6–10 Mon-Sat, noon–10 Sun)   Worcester   (0905) 620 142   Children over 6 welcome up to 8.30pm   Open 11–3, 5.30–11

PEMBRIDGE   SO3958   Map 6

New Inn

Market Square; A44

Beautifully set in the centre of this black-and-white town and overlooking the church – which has an unusual 14th-century detached bell tower beside it – this ancient place has tables on the cobblestones between it and the open-sided 16th-century former wool market behind it. Inside, there are heavy beams and timbering, aged oak peg-latch doors, elderly traditional furnishings including a fine antique curved-back settle on the worn flagstones, and a substantial log fire. Bar food served on old willow china plates includes good soup, sandwiches (£1.25), mushrooms in garlic or pâté on French bread (£3), smoked chicken and hot crispy bacon salad (£3.25), leek and mushroom croustade (£3.75), lamb cutlets in redcurrant and port wine sauce (£4.50) and puddings, such as banana fudge flan or cider syllabub (£1.50). Flowers Original, Whitbreads West Country PA and a guest such as Marstons Pedigree on handpump or tapped from the cask, and a few malt whiskies; cribbage, shove-ha'penny, dominoes and quoits. There are massive stones below the black-and-white timbered walls that date back some seven hundred years, and it used to house the Petty Sessions court and jail. (*Recommended by Paul Denham, Nicola Brown-Denham, Robert and Vicky Tod, P Freeman, PLC, Barbara McHugh, Brian and Anna Marsden, C M Whitehouse, Cliff and Karen Spooner, Brian Skelcher, R W Stanbury*)

Whitbreads   Tenant Jane Melvin   Real ale   Meals and snacks   Restaurant   Pembridge (054 47) 427   Children welcome everywhere but main bar   Open 11–3, 6–11; closed 25 Dec   Bedrooms; £16/£32

RUCKHALL COMMON   SO4539   Map 4

Ancient Camp   ⊘   ⇥

Ruckhall signposted off A465 W of Hereford at Belmont Abbey; then pub signed, down narrow country lanes and finally a rough track

Even on a grey day, the tucked-away setting here is lovely. You can sit (or eat) on the long front terrace at the white tables and chairs among roses and look down over the River Wye and beyond. Inside it's well kept and rather smart, and the central beamed and flagstoned bar is simply but thoughtfully furnished with comfortably solid green-upholstered settles and library chairs around nice old elm tables. On the left, a green-carpeted room has matching sofas around the walls, kitchen chairs around tripod tables, a big Victorian architectural drawing of the imposing Ram Mills in Oldham (the family firm), and a good few sailing pictures. On the right, there are simple dining chairs around stripped kitchen tables on a brown carpet, and stripped stonework; nice log fire. The food, all home-made, is quite something, including sandwiches (from £1.35), soup (£1.75), taramasalata (not the over-pink stuff) or good garlic mushrooms (£3.25), ploughman's (from £3.25), lovely cannelloni with ricotta cheese and spinach or with spicy meat filling (£4.95), Greek shepherd's pie (£5.25), and pan fried garlic chicken (£5.95). Well kept Whitbreads West Country PA and Woods Parish on handpump, decent wines and spirits, kind service; good log fires, maybe unobtrusive piped music. When you set off for a walk, Jack the hunt terrier may come part of the way. (*Recommended by Jerry and Alison Oakes, Jim and Maggie Cowell, M A and C R Starling, Mr Jennings, J P W Bowdler, Maureen Hobbs, Denny Lyster, Peter and Rose Flower, John and Ann Prince, Maryon and David Beer, Fiona Hellowell*)

Free house   Licensees David and Nova Hague   Real ale   Meals and snacks (not Sun evening, not Mon)   Restaurant – closed Sun and Mon   Golden Valley (0981) 250449   Children welcome lunchtime only; only residential if over 10   Very occasional live entertainment   Open 12–2.30, 6(7 Sat)–11; closed winter Mon   Bedrooms; £30S/£44S

SELLACK   SO5627   Map 4

Loughpool   ★   ⊘

Back road Hoarwithy–Ross on Wye; OS Sheet 162, map reference 558268

The central room in this pretty pub has kitchen chairs and cushioned window seats around plain wooden tables, sporting prints and bunches of dried flowers, beams, a mainly flagstoned floor, and a log fire at each end. Other rooms lead off, with attractive individual furnishings and nice touches like the dresser of patterned plates. Very good bar food includes soup (£1.50), pâté (£2.50), sausages (£3.50), moussaka (£4.50), pasta in a delicious ham and mushroom sauce, courgette and cheese bake (£4.75), chicken curry (£5), gammon in apple and cheese sauce (£5.75), chicken, bacon and broccoli lasagne (£6), salmon in lemon and prawn sauce (£8.25), and puddings (around £1.50). Well kept Bass, M & B Springfield and Wye Valley Hereford on handpump. The neat front lawn has plenty of picnic-table sets. *(Recommended by PLC, David Hunn, Mr and Mrs P B Dowsett, Julian Proudman, G Gossins, Mrs C S Priest, Mr and Mrs K Guyll, Jacqueline Davis, Helen and Wal Burns, Caroline Wright, Cliff and Karen Spooner, Pamela and Merlyn Horswell, Mrs Joan Harris, Audrey and Brian Green, J Penford, Gwyneth and Salvo Spadaro-Dutturi)*

Free house   Licensee Karen Whitford   Real ale   Meals and snacks   Restaurant   Harewood End (098 987) 236   Children in eating area of bar only   Open 12–2.30, 7–11; closed 25 Dec

TENBURY WELLS   SO6168   Map 4

Peacock ⊘

Worcester Rd; A456 about 1 1/2 miles E

Just outside the attractive little town, this is actually on the Shropshire side of the River Teme. Under the present welcoming landlady, it's developed a really warm and welcoming atmosphere. The front lounge bar is simply but attractively decorated, with a good log fire and hop bines. The most popular place to sit is the big-windowed bay with cushioned settles and dining chairs around its three tables. Up a step opposite are more tables, set for the good food. All home-made and generously served, this includes sandwiches (thick slices of home-baked bread, from £1.75), soup (£1.95; or served as a main course £2.60), ploughman's (£3), mushroom and broccoli bake (£3.75), three-bean vegetarian chilli, liver and bacon casserole or lasagne (£3.95), salads, steak and kidney pie (£4.50), fresh plaice (£5.25), most days a special such as chicken tikka with pilau rice (£4.95), and several good substantial puddings such as Caribbean ginger cake with hot rum fudge sauce (£1.95); the dining area has an evening restaurant menu, as well as this bar food. A side games room has two pool tables; also darts, fruit machine, video game and juke box; well kept Bass and Marstons Burton and Pedigree on handpump, Weston's cider. There are two rather engaging cats; no dogs. *(Recommended by Mrs B Wooldridge, Jamie and Sarah Allan, Frank Cummins)*

Free house   Licensee Andrea Holden   Real ale   Meals and snacks (not Sun evening in winter)   Tenbury Wells (0584) 810506   Children welcome   Monthly live music, usually Weds   Open 12–3, 6–11

WEOBLEY   SO4052   Map 6

Olde Salutation

Village signposted from A4112 SW of Leominster; and from A44 NW of Hereford (there's also a good back road direct from Hereford – straight out past S side of racecourse

Separated by a few steps and standing timbers, the two areas of the quiet lounge in this 500-year-old pub have brocaded modern winged settles and smaller seats, a couple of big cut-away cask seats, wildlife decorations, a hop bine over the bar counter, and logs burning in a big stone fireplace; it's divided by more standing timbers from a neat restaurant area (where there's piped music), and there's a separate smaller parquet-floored public bar with sensibly placed darts, fruit machine, space game and juke box; dominoes and cribbage. Bar food includes soups such as cream of broccoli (£1.60), liver and onions, mushroom, ham and garlic gratin or chilli con carne (£3.95), tuna melt, sweet and sour ribs or chicken curry (£4.25), grilled gammon with pineapple and egg or cod in cheese sauce (£4.95), and breast of pheasant with red wine sauce (£5.95). The three-course Sunday lunch (£5.95) is a bargain, and instead of sandwiches they serve hot roast in french bread (£2.85). Well kept Boddingtons, Hook Norton Best and Marstons Pedigree on handpump, Weston's ciders, over 50 wines and quite a good collection of whiskies. There are picnic-table sets under cocktail parasols on a sheltered back terrace. The pub looks straight down the broad street of this picture-book village. *(Recommended by Andrew and Ruth Triggs, J Harvey Hallam, Brian and Anna Marsden, G Richardson; more reports please)*

*Free house   Licensees Chris and Frances Anthony   Real ale   Meals and snacks
Restaurant (not Sun eve, or all day Mon)   Weobley   (0544) 318 433   Children in
eating area of bar and conservatory only   Open 11–3, 7–11, all day Sat; closed 25
Dec   Bedrooms; £18(£24B)/£28.50(£41B), 4-poster £46B*

WHITNEY ON WYE   SO2747   Map 6

Rhydspence ★ ⊗ ⊨

Pub signposted off A438 about 1 ½ miles W of Whitney

The Welsh border follows the line of the little stream running past this fine
timbered building, so it's fun to place one foot in Hereford & Worcester and the
other in Powys. The rambling beamed rooms are furnished with old library chairs
and cushioned wall benches built into the heavily timbered walls, magazines and
newspapers are set out to read, and there's a fine big stone fireplace in the central
bar. Particularly good bar food which changes every three months includes
home-made soup (£2.10), ploughman's (from £3.95), home-made burger (£3.85),
the Landlord's Favourites ('Hammy' or 'Fishy' from £3.95), pastie (£3.75),
home-made lasagne (beef, seafood or vegetarian) or spinach and mozzarella pie
(£4.95), tandoori chicken or beef curry (£5.25), and steak and kidney pie (£6.25);
the delicious puddings such as chocolate roulade, Norwegian cream or Maron
Mon Blanc are especially popular in the evenings and on Sunday lunchtimes. The
cottagey dining room is pretty; big breakfasts. Well kept Bass, Marstons Pedigree
and Robinsons Best on handpump, decent wines, ten malt whiskies, and farm cider
on handpump; darts, dominoes, shove-ha'penny and cribbage; no dogs. The
terrace and lawns look across to the lovely Wye Valley and hills beyond; quoits.
Full marks for the get-you-home service for locals. *(Recommended by D A R Glover,
Mrs C S Priest, Miss J Woodman, David Williams, Maysie Thompson, P Freeman, Brian
Skelcher, Paul McPherson, Jacqueline Davis, Colin Laffan, Cliff and Karen Spooner, John
Bowdler, Robert and Kate Hodkinson, Tony and Lynne Stark, Helen and John Thompson, M J
Penford, Gary Phillips)*

*Free house   Licensees Peter and Pam Glover   Real ale   Meals and snacks
Restaurant   Clifford (049 73) 262   Children welcome   Open 11–2.30, 7–11
Bedrooms; £25.60B/£51.20B*

WOOLHOPE   SO6136   Map 4

Butchers Arms ★ ⊨

Signposted from B4224 in Fownhope; carry straight on past Woolhope village

Together with a local man, Nick Squires – who has worked here for many years –
has become joint licensee. Readers tell us that nothing has changed and all the staff
remain their ever-efficient and caring selves. Both the welcoming twin bars have a
log fire, simple but traditional furnishings, some old pictures and engravings, and a
big sedately ticking clock. Using good fresh ingredients, the bar food includes
lunchtime sandwiches (from £1.10), and favourites such as mushroom, butterbean
and basil stew (£4.50), rabbit and bacon pie (£4.95), lamb and cranberry casserole
or cod pie (£5.25) and puddings (£1.75). Well kept Hook Norton Best and Old
Hookey, Marstons Pedigree and a guest beer on handpump, Westons farm cider,
decent coffee; generous breakfasts; friendly cat – dogs not welcome. Sliding French
windows behind the tiled and timbered house lead out to a charming terrace by a
tiny willow-lined brook. The bowl of fruit in the spotless bedrooms is a nice touch.
*(Recommended by Lynn Sharpless, Bob Eardley, Elisabeth Kemp, M A and C R Starling, Paul
S McPherson, Andy and Jill Kassube, Michael Stiffin, Hilary Wood, John and Helen
Thompson, D H Farr, Mr Jennings, George Sayer, Gordon Theaker, Ken and Norma Guyll,
Patrick Freeman, Jacqueline Davis, F A Owens, Tony and Lynne Stark, Simon Reynolds, J and
A Prince, Colin and Caroline)*

*Free house   Licensees Nick Squires and Charlie Power   Real ale   Meals and snacks
(11.30–2.15, 7–10, 10.30 Fri and Sat)   No-smoking restaurant   Fownhope   (0432)
860 281   Children in restaurant   Open 11.30–2.30, 6.30–11   Occasional folk
musicians and Morris Dancing   Bedrooms; £25/£39*

Crown 🍴

In village centre

Run by cheerful and efficient young licensees, this very popular pub serves generous helpings of reasonably priced bar food such as soup (£1.40), several starters or light snacks such as potted stilton and mushrooms or smoked haddock in wine, cream and cheese sauce (£2.20), and a very wide choice of main dishes including broccoli and cheddar quiche, cauliflower and potato bake or various omelettes (£3.95), lamb and cranberry casserole, steak and kidney pie, chicken and asparagus lasagne (£4.15), scampi or deep-fried chicken (£4.20), double lamb chops or grilled trout (£5.20) and steaks (from £6.50); excellent home-made puddings (£1.55 – they change every 8 weeks and are made by the landlady) like baba au rhum, coconut and jam tart, apricot clafoutti, and crème brûlée; note that one of the two bars is bookable, and, although in all other respects the menu is the same, sandwiches and ploughman's are not served in this bar. Well kept Hook Norton Best and Smiles Best on handpump, and occasional guest beers; Weston's and maybe Stowford Press farm cider, decent wines; good service. The lounge bar is light and airy with good wildlife photographs and little country pictures on the cream walls, dark burgundy plush button-back built-in wall banquettes and stools, a timbered divider strung with hop bines, stripped pine dado, and open fires; very quiet piped music. There are picnic-table sets under cocktail parasols on the neat front lawn; darts, summer quoits (though it's difficult to imagine the bar being empty enough to use them). *(Recommended by Derek and Sylvia Stephenson, Mr and Mrs J H Adam, W L Congreve, Andy and Jill Kassube, Peter Lloyd, B H Stamp, O M Bisby, Cliff and Karen Spooner, A S Maxted, Hilary Beggs, M J Penford)*

Free house   Licensees Neil and Sally Gordon   Real ale   Meals and snacks (till 10, one bar has bookable tables; not 25 Dec)   Fownhope (0432) 860 468   Well behaved children allowed, though customers with under 10s are asked to check with licensee, to avoid there being too many at one time   Open 12–2.30, 6.30–11; winter evening opening 7

WORCESTER   SO8555   Map 4

Farriers Arms

Fish Street; off pedestrian High Street, just N of the cathedral

The licensee sells (and signs) her book on pressed flowers in the snug little black-beamed lounge bar here, which also has some copper-topped tables, attractive old seats, and a grandfather clock carved with writhing lizards; piped music. The more rambling and simpler public bar has sensibly placed darts, shove-ha'penny, dominoes, cribbage, an old penny arcade machine (which works with 2p pieces), a fruit machine, and trivia. Decidedly well priced food includes soup (£1.25), hummus with hot pitta bread (£1.75), ploughman's (£2.25), a vegetarian dish of the day (£2.50), beef and mushroom pie or home-made quiche (£3.25), honey-roast ham (£3.75), puddings like tipsy trifle or treacle tart (£1.50), and a daily special. Well kept Courage Best and Directors on handpump. Dogs allowed. Tables on the sheltered terrace have their own summer servery. Very handy for the cathedral. *(Recommended by George Sayer, Peter Burton, G T Rhys, C H Stride; more reports please)*

Courage   Tenant Nona Pettersen   Real ale   Meals and snacks (11–9, with a half-hour gap between 2.30–3)   Worcester   (0905) 2769   Open 10.30–11

WYRE PIDDLE   SO9647   Map 4

Anchor 🍴

B4084 NW of Evesham

Tables by the windows in the big airy back bar have a first-class view down to the River Avon and its barge moorings, and on over the Vale of Evesham and Bredon Hill; the terrace shares the same view as does the big lawn that slopes down to the water. It's a comfortable, well kept pub and under the new licensee the popular bar food includes substantial soup (£1.40), open filled baps (from £1.85), an honest ploughman's (from £3), courgettes provençale, home-made steak and kidney pie or hot locally smoked chicken with home-made apricot chutney (£4.60), whole fresh trout (£4.90), steaks (from £7.90), and puddings like good home-made meringue concoctions (£1.55) and lovely hot stuffed peaches (£1.95). Well kept Boddingtons Best, Fowers Original and Hook Norton on handpump; fruit machine. The little lounge has a good log fire in its attractively restored inglenook fireplace, comfortably upholstered chairs and settles, and two beams in the shiny ceiling. *(Recommended by John and Karen Day, Bob Timmis, J Barnwell, P Craddock, John Bowdler, Frank Cummins, Dr and Mrs K J Lower; more reports on the new regime, please)*

Whitbreads   Lease: J M Senior   Real ale   Meals and snacks (not Sun evening) River-view lunchtime restaurant   Pershore (0386) 552799   Children welcome   Open 11–2.30, 6–11

Lucky Dip

Besides the fully inspected pubs, you might like to try these Lucky Dips recommended to us and described by readers (if you do, please send us reports):

Abberley [SO7667], *Manor Arms*: Good place to stay, bedrooms warm and comfortable, with good breakfasts; bar food, Banks's ales, restaurant *(NWN)*

☆ **Abbey Dore** [SO3830], *Neville Arms*: Upmarket lounge bar, welcoming and enjoyable country bar, beautiful Golden Valley views, friendly landlord, good cheap bar food, well kept beers and good coffee *(Caroline Wright, Canon K Wills)*

Ashton under Hill [Elmley Rd — OS Sheet 150, map reference 997378; SO9938], *Star*: Tastefully modernised Whitbreads local, Marstons Pedigree, small choice of straightforward food inc superb ham *(Derek and Sylvia Stephenson)*

Aston Crews [B4222 — village signposted off A40 at Lea; SO6723], *Penny Farthing*: Comfortably modernised stonebuilt pub with internal well feature, has been popular for good value food, well kept Bass and Hook Norton Old Hookey on handpump, pretty valley views from airy big-windowed restaurant, garden tables and bedrooms, but no recent reports *(BB)*; [off B4222], *White Hart*: Hilltop village pub with easy chairs among other seats in low-beamed bar with huge fireplace, other rooms leading off; Banks's and Wadworths 6X on handpump, bar food, pub games, tables in attractive surroundings outside *(LYM)*

Badsey [B4035 2 miles E of Evesham; SP0743], *Round of Gras*: Long flagstoned and comfortably refurbished bar and dining area, home-cooked fod inc bargain asparagus suppers (around May), friendly efficient service, Flowers real ale, fruit machines, maybe pop music; no dogs *(Dr and Mrs G J Sutton, Robert and Vicky Tod, BB)*

☆ **Beckford** [SO9735], *Beckford*: Doing well under current regime, wide choice of food inc exceptional puddings, well kept Courage Directors, Home, Theakstons Best and XB on handpump; old-fashioned feel, with good service *(Derek and Sylvia Stephenson)*

Belbroughton [High St (off A491); SO9277], *Queens*: Interesting building in lovely village, busy at lunchtime for reasonably priced food; well kept Marstons, paintings for sale in lounge *(Dave Braisted); Talbot*: Banks's Wayfarer Tavern dining pub, straightforward popular food, well kept beers, garden *(J Barnwell)*

☆ **Berrow** [A438 Tewkesbury—Ledbury just E of junction with B4208; SO7934], *Duke of York*: Friendly dining pub with two connected bar areas, Flowers real ales, popular good value food, with good fresh vegetables; attentive licensees, log fire, small back restaurant, spacious lawn *(H B Walton, BB)*

Bewdley [50 Wyre Hill (off A456); SO7875], *Black Boy*: Immaculately kept, comfortable, quiet and welcoming, with limited bar food and impressive militaria *(Brian Skelcher)*

☆ **Bishops Frome** [just off B4214 Bromyard—Ledbury; SO6648], *Green Dragon*: Character flagstoned pub with exceptional range of well kept real ales, esp from the north — eg Timothy Taylors and even Caledonian; good choice of straightforward bar food, excellent log fire, games room, seats outside; children welcome, no dogs; open all day Sat (and can get crowded); a most attractive place, though not consistently welcoming enough to ensure a main entry *(Cliff and Karen Spooner, Derek and Sylvia Stephenson, Geoff Wilson, Ken and Norma Guyll, LYM)*

Bishops Frome [B4214], *Chase*: Attractively decorated small inn with tables outside and comfortable bedrooms; has been praised for warm welcome (for children too), well kept Hook Norton and good home-made bar food, but no recent reports *(News please)*

Bournheath [Dodford Rd — OS Sheet 139, map reference 935735; SO9474], *Gate*: Attractive dining pub which has been popular for good value food, good range of beer and friendly service, but no recent reports *(News please)*

☆ **Bradley Green** [2 Feckenham Rd (B4090 E of Droitwich); SO9862], *Little Kipper House*: Formerly the Red Lion, bigger than other pubs in the Little chain but decor just as zany — all sorts of bric-a-brac from endless imitation kippers and other smoked foods on ceiling to venerable marine diesel called Jane, even a full-blown Boston herring smack and steam engine in car park; food inc monster pies and real kippers (also sold to take away), real ales inc Lumphammer beer; children welcome, big garden with play area (PLC, Dave Braisted, Helen and Andy Ward, Graham Bush, Paul Denham, Nicola Brown-Denham)

Bransford [off A4103 SW of Worcester; SO7852], Bear & Ragged Staff: Recently refurbished; good bar and restaurant food, pleasant staff (E A George)

Bredenbury [A44 Bromyard—Leominster; SO6156], Barneby Arms: Spacious clean pub with wide choice of usual food inc some unusual dishes (George Sayer)

☆ Broadway [Main St (A44); SP0937], Lygon Arms: Stately Cotswold hotel, owned by the Savoy group, well worth visiting for the strikingly handsome building itself, with interesting old rooms rambling away from attractive if pricey oak-panelled bar; sandwiches all day; imaginative bar food in adjoining more intimate wine bar, with wooden tables and pleasant service; tables in prettily planted courtyard, well kept gardens; children allowed away from bar; bedrooms smart and comfortable (A Triggs, JMC, M Joyner, LYM)

☆ Broadway [Collin Lane; marked Gt Collin Farm on OS Sheet; follow Willersey sign off A44 NW — OS Sheet 150, map reference 076391], Collin House: Though a hotel, concentrates heavily on good range of freshly cooked good interesting lunchtime bar food (not Sun) inc popular duck casserole; smallish but cosy bar with good log fire and bookable tables; tables outside, restaurant, pleasant staff, good coffee (Peter Lloyd, Roy Y Bromell, W Lawrence)

Broadway [Church St], Crown & Trumpet: Welcoming Whitbreads local off main tourist beat, reasonably priced attractive food inc eg duck and bacon pie, home-made puddings; well kept Boddingtons and Flowers, beams, timbers, settles (Iain and Penny Muir, David Stanley, Sue Garner); [Main St (A44)], Horse & Hound: Comfortable, clean and spacious old Cotswold pub with discreet piped music in lounge, pleasant helpful staff, Flowers IPA and Original, varied choice of good bar food from ploughman's to steaks, courteous service (Iain and Penny Muir)

Bromsgrove [Worcester Rd; SO9570], Olde Black Horse: Pleasant partly 17th-century building with Charles I connections; M & B beers, reasonably priced food (Dave Braisted)

☆ Broughton Hackett [A422 Worcester—Alcester — OS Sheet 150, map reference 923543; SO9254], March Hare: Interesting pub with well cushioned stripped pews, country-kitchen chairs and tables, wing armchair, rugs on tiled floor, glass-covered deep floodlit well; has been very popular for notable bar food inc some

unusual dishes, pleasant service, well kept real ales, good wines by the glass and large steak restaurant, but no reports since its take-over by Marstons (not Sun evening); tables in garden with corner water feature, more with assault climber, provision for children inside (H R Bevan, C E Power, EML, BB; news please)

Callow End [SO8349], Bluebell: Tenanted rather modern-decor Banks's pub with good value bar food inc good cheeses for ploughman's and some oriental flavours, pleasant staff; busy, with separate locals' bar and free entertainment some nights (Tom Haggett)

Callow Hill [Elcocks Brook — OS Sheet 150, map reference 010645; SP0164], Brook: Good value food, friendly service, welcoming fire (Mr and Mrs W H Thomas); [nr Wyre Forest visitors' centre], Royal Forester: Ancient inn restored and smartened up by new licensee; well kept real ales, pleasant service, bar food (Paul Denham, Nicola Brown-Denham)

Chaddesley Corbett [off A448 Bromsgrove—Kidderminster; SO8973], Fox: Good carvery, good choice of puddings; M & B ales, friendly atmosphere (W H and E Thomas)

Charlton [the one nr Evesham; SP0145], Gardeners Arms: Simple comfort, with food from ploughman's to good hot dishes, back dining area, well kept Whitbreads, staff friendly even when busy; caters well for children, big pleasant garden with swings (Dave Irving)

☆ Claines [3 miles from M5 junction 6; A449 towards Ombersley, then leave dual carriageway at second exit for Worcester; village signposted from here, and park in Cornmeadow Lane; SO8558], Mug House: Ancient pub actually inside a country churchyard, decidedly plain and simple decor, low doorways, heavy oak beams, well kept cheap Banks's Bitter and Mild, minimal choice of basic but generous snacks (not Sun), sizeable garden merging into farmland with view of the Malvern Hills; children allowed in snug away from servery (Dr and Mrs A K Clarke, LYM)

Clifton upon Teme [SO7162], Red Lion: Clean and civilised old pub in attractive village, pleasant service, lovely beamed bedrooms (Gordon and Daphne)

☆ Clows Top [A456 Bewdley—Tenbury — OS Sheet 138, map reference 717719; SO7171], Colliers Arms: Capacious wayside dining pub, cleanly decorated in modern style without pretensions, comfortable atmosphere, full choice of food, log fires, well kept Ansells Bitter and Mild and Ind Coope Burton, pleasant welcome, efficient service, immaculate lavatories; no dogs (Frank Cummins, Paul Denham, Nicola Brown-Denham)

☆ Conderton [southern slope of Bredon Hill — OS Sheet 150, map reference 960370; SO9637], Yew Tree: Good atmosphere in beamed and flagstoned local with well kept Banks's Bitter and Mild, Marstons Pedigree and Weston's farm cider on handpump, bar food; shame about the juke box and fruit machine *(Alan and Heather Jacques, Derek and Sylvia Stephenson)*

Cropthorne [SO9944], *New Inn*: Lots of gleaming brass and ornamental plates in very busy pub, popular for generous good value food; large garden with many tables *(G T and J Barnes)*

Crowle [SO9256], *Old Chequers*: Friendly efficient staff and consistently good food in comfortably refurbished pub *(Mrs V A Middlebrook, PADEMLUC, Norman Clarke and Hilary Sargeant)*

☆ **Cutnall Green** [SO8768], *Live & Let Live*: Simple, small and narrow, with wide range of good reasonably priced home-made food (even frozen take-aways); pretty garden *(R E and L J Rosier)*

Defford [SO9143], *Defford Arms*: Friendly, with well kept Davenports, interesting choice of food, spacious interesting garden *(Derek and Sylvia Stephenson)*

Drakes Broughton [A44 Pershore—Worcester; SO9248], *Plough & Harrow*: Friendly and attractive rambling lounge, well kept Flowers, particularly good value salads and other food inc Sun lunch; tables nicely set behind by old orchard; has been open all day *(Mr and Mrs D C Leaman, Richard Parr)*

Drayton [SO9076], *Robin Hood*: Homely, comfortable atmosphere, open fires, low beams, friendly efficient service, well kept Ansells and Ind Coope Burton on handpump, good varied bar food very reasonably priced inc short but interesting range of vegetarian dishes; good walks nearby *(Louisa and Brian Routledge)*

Droitwich [High St; SO9063], *Talbot*: Cheap bar food inc baked potatoes, huge hot pork sandwiches with stuffing, a few main dishes; very friendly *(Margaret and Trevor Errington)*

☆ **Dunhampstead** [just SE of Droitwich; pub towards Sale Green — OS Sheet 150, map reference 919600; SO9160], *Firs*: Many friendly regulars track down this relaxing and very tucked-away country local, with traditional yet gently upmarket furnishings, good value straightforward bar food inc interesting specials, well kept Bass, restaurant; a nice spot in summer, handy for canal users *(Barbara M McHugh, R E and L J Rosier, Mr and Mrs M Cockram, Doreen and Ray Whiteoak, Robert and Vicky Tod, LYM)*

☆ **Eardisland** [A44; SO4258], *White Swan*: Generous helpings of good well priced food in attractive old oak-beamed pub with gleaming copper, good log fires, well kept Marstons Pedigree, magazines and books to read; cosy dining room, good garden behind with retired tractor for children; lovely black-and-white village *(Mrs B Warburton, Mrs Joan Harris, Ian Phillips, J H C Peters, Cliff and Karen Spooner)*

Eckington [B4080; SO9241], *Anchor*: Doing well under current regime, comfortable and welcoming, with good food (booking needed weekends and evenings),

Allied and Hook Norton real ales; games machines and piped music in main bar *(PADEMLUC)*

☆ **Elmley Castle** [Mill Lane — village signposted off A44 and A435, not far from Evesham; SO9841], *Old Mill*: Friendly new licensees for former mill house in pleasant surroundings just outside picturesque old-fashioned village, tables in attractive sheltered garden looking over village cricket pitch to Bredon Hill; good choice of food (lunchtime, Weds-Sat evenings) inc good ploughman's and pies, some vegetarian dishes; neat L-shaped lounge, well kept real ales *(Pam Adsley, Alan and Heather Jacques, Joan and Tony Walker, Mr and Mrs K Guyll, LYM)*

☆ **Elmley Castle**, *Queen Elizabeth*: Ancient rambling locals' local, in pretty and old-fashioned village below Bredon Hill; attractive old-fashioned tap room, haphazard medley of periods in decoration and furnishings, friendly licensee and locals, well kept Marstons real ales, maybe piped classical music *(Derek and Sylvia Stephenson, A L Willey, LYM)*

☆ **Fladbury** [Chequers Lane — OS Sheet 150, map reference 996461; SO9946], *Chequers*: Peaceful, friendly and comfortable, dating back to 14th century; inexpensive well prepared food attractively presented, service most attentive, well kept creamy Banks's real ale; restaurant (using beams from former stables); comfortable bedroom extension *(Iain and Penny Muir, Andrew Cooke)*

Flyford Flavell [just S of A422 Worcester—Alcester; SO9754], *Boot*: Old-fashioned 18th-century pub with well kept Flowers and Marstons Pedigree, varied good food *(A J Woodhouse)*

Forhill [Lea End Lane/Icknield St (Birmingham AZ p 121 5F); SP0575], *Peacock*: Small, homely low-beamed pub alone in picturesque countryside, yet on the edges of Birmingham *(Lynne Sheridan, Bob West)*

Hanley Swan [B4209 Malvern—Upton — OS Sheet 150, map reference 813429; SO8142], *Swan*: Pleasant place with varnished wooden tables, tub chairs, light Anaglypta walls and a few horsebrasses in spacious carpeted lounge, public bar, tables and swings on lawn; pleasant service, well cooked and presented traditional food, well kept Banks's and Flowers Original and Weston's cider on handpump *(Frank Cummins)*

☆ **Hardwicke** [B4348 — OS Sheet 161, map reference 273437; SO2644], *Royal Oak*: Pleasant and relaxed, civilised yet friendly, with unpompous landlord; small bar with benches along two walls, good value bar food, Marstons Pedigree, simple restaurant, flowers on tables; fruit machine; comfortable bedrooms, good breakfasts — handy for Hay on Wye *(Janet Tomalin, B R Shiner)*

Harewood End [A49 Hereford—Ross; SO5327], *Harewood End*: Welcoming modernised country pub popular for wide range of good value food inc fine steak and kidney pie and curry *(Mrs Joan Harris)*

Hartlebury [B4193 E of Stourport; SO8470], *White Hart*: Busy straightforward pub handy for the castle and museum; well kept Bass and Highgate Mild, good helpings of cheap food *(John Brooks)*

Harvington [A450; SO8774], *Dog*: Good value food and Banks's beer in interesting sample of brewery architecture over the ages *(Dave Braisted)*

Hereford [69 St Owens St], *Barrels*: Lively local, far from plush, but well worth visiting for their four own-brewed Wye Valley real ales at prices to relish *(Iain and Penny Muir)*; [Bridge St/King St], *Orange Tree*: Well run comfortably refurbished partly panelled pub with good lunchtime food and Marstons Pedigree; nr cathedral *(JM, PM, Cdr John Hackett)*

☆ **Hoarwithy** [signposted off A49 Hereford—Ross on Wye; SO5429], *New Harp*: Well kept and friendly simple village local with nice bow-window seats, good simple food at attractive prices inc good value baps, well kept Flowers Original and Whitbreads Castle Eden on handpump, decent wines, games area around corner; picnic-table sets on yew-sheltered lawn beside pretty flower garden; children welcome; in attractive village close to River Wye, unusual Italianate church worth a visit; bedrooms good value, in cottage across road *(Caroline Wright, E A George, Maureen Hobbs, BB)*

Holt Heath [A443/A4133; SO8162], *Red Lion*: Free house with Ansells and a guest beer such as Wadworths, tasty snacks, reasonable prices *(Dave Braisted)*

Honeybourne [SP1144], *Thatched Tavern*: Old-world thatched pub with two rooms off bar, good choice of reasonably priced food, well kept Flowers and guest beers, dogs allowed (the owners' old english sheepdog is very friendly — as are staff) *(Pat and Clive Sherriff)*

Howle Hill [Kiln Green, Walford; closed weekday lunchtime, opens 7.30 (or after *Coronation Street*) — OS Sheet 162, map reference 601196; SO6020], *New Buildings*: Very old-fashioned, unchanged for years, with flagstones, real fire, Flowers and lots of ciders; many locals, also ideal for walkers and their dogs; big garden; children seemed not objected to, at least Sun lunchtime *(Salvo and Gwyneth Spadaro-Dutturi)*

☆ **Inkberrow** [A422 Worcester—Alcester; set well back — OS Sheet 150, map reference 015573; SP0157], *Old Bull*: Friendly new landlord for handsome black and white Tudor pub with big inglenook log fire, flagstones, oak beams and trusses, and some old-fashioned high-backed settles among the predominantly more modern furnishings; the model for the Archers' Bull in Ambridge; Whitbreads-related real ales and a guest such as Marstons Pedigree on handpump, decent bar lunches from sandwiches and ploughman's up; seats outside; children

allowed in eating area; open all day summer, with afternoon tea *(Joan and Tony Walker, Frank Cummins, J R Smylie, Barbara M McHugh, Phil Clissitt, Ness Turner, A Triggs, LYM)*

☆ **Kidderminster** [Comberton Hill, in stn; SO8376], *King & Castle*: Wide choice of good value food, half a dozen well kept changing real ales, railway memorabilia; by Severn Valley Steam Rly *(Paul Denham, Nicola Brown-Denham)*

Kidderminster [Chester Rd], *Land Oak*: Expensively and tastefully refurbished as part of the Milestone chain, cheerful attentive staff, wide range of good food in big helpings *(David and Ruth Hollands)*

Kingstone [OS Sheet 149, map reference 423357; SO4235], *Bull Ring*: Well kept Whitbreads Castle Eden and Marstons Pedigree, warm welcome, pleasant village location; bar food, juke box in public bar; children allowed in lounge *(Salvo and Gwyneth Spadaro-Dutturi)*

☆ **Kington** [Church Rd (A44); note this is the Herefs one, handy for Hergest Croft Garden, Hergest Ridge and Offa's Dyke Path, at SO3057], *Swan*: Attractively redesigned airy bar overlooking square, efficient welcoming service, good value food, well kept Allied ales, good evening restaurant; children welcome; at start of GWG93; bedrooms clean and simple, with good breakfasts *(Neil and Anita Christopher, Alison and Tony Godfrey)*

Kington [Victoria Rd], *Olde Tavern*: Plain 1900ish parlour with ochre walls and ceiling, dark brown woodwork, commemorative china, no counter — beer brought from bank of handpumps in back stillroom; kept by same family for a century *(Tim Locke)*; [Bridge St], *Talbot*: Friendly people, well kept Bass, good toasties and salads *(Ruth Locke)*

☆ **Leominster** [West St; SO4959], *Talbot*: Attractive hotel with carpeted and polished wood floors, heavy oak beams, gleaming copper, armchairs, antique settles and handsome log fires in delightful bay-windowed entrance bar; bedrooms *(More reports please)*

☆ **Lyonshall** [SO3355], *Royal George*: Good varied well presented food, all home-made, with lots of daily specials, in three bar rooms off central servery and new tastefully furnished dining room; cheerful, obliging and friendly staff, no smoking area, no music, well kept Flowers, good reasonably priced wines; bedrooms *(Mr and Mrs D G Wood)*

☆ **Malvern** [Graham Rd; SO7845], *Royal Malvern*: Appealingly old-fashioned, with good bar food inc superb rare beef sandwiches and vegetarian dishes; particularly well kept Woods Special on handpump *(Derek and Sylvia Stephenson)*

Malvern [British Camp, Wynds Pt; SO7641], *Malvern Hills*: Bass and good lunchtime buffet with soup and dish of day in comfortable hotel lounge; good bedrooms, fine scenery *(SVB)*

☆ **Mamble** [just off A456 Bewdley—Tenbury Wells — OS Sheet 138, map reference 690717; SO6971], *Dog & Duck*: Two rooms with stripped pine tables, pale wood chairs, deep red stippled walls and ceiling, modern beams, grey and black carpets and curtains; woodburner, fresh flowers and other attractive decorations, copper-topped bar; has been popular for decent food inc plenty of vegetarian dishes, using fresh natural ingredients, and well kept Hook Norton Best; but no reports since new ownership earlier in 1991 *(Frank Cummins, Dave Braisted; news please)*

☆ **Mathon** [SO7345], *Cliffe Arms*: Old black and white timbered pub in pleasant spot, tiny low-beamed rooms full of nooks and crannies and perhaps in line for some external redecoration; well kept Flowers, Hook Norton Best and Marstons Pedigree, good bar food (not Sun or Mon, not Tues evening) from delicious sandwiches up; also newish evening restaurant (Weds-Sat evening, Sun lunch; bookings only); streamside garden; children welcome *(Mr and Mrs W H Thomas, Lynne Sheridan, Bob West, Mr and Mrs W H Crowther)*

Monkland [W of Leominster; SO4657], *Travellers Rest*: Nice inside; wide choice of bar food inc children's menu, friendly licensees, flowers and candles in separate dining room *(Margaret and Trevor Errington)*

Mortimers Cross [A4110/B4362 NW of Leominster; SO4264], *Mortimers Cross*: Country pub doing well under new owners, with good food, improvements to main rooms inc good open fire *(A K Thorlby)*

Much Birch [Ross Rd; A49 S of Hereford; SO5131], *Axe & Cleaver*: Emphasis on restaurant, with good choice of food; also neat little bar with well kept beer, open fire and good bar food — though service may be slow *(JH)*

☆ **Much Marcle** [off A449 SW of Ledbury; take Woolhope turning at village stores, then right at pub sign; SO6633], *Slip*: Quite outstanding spacious flower garden around secluded country pub run by ex-nurseryman, among Weston's cider orchards, with play area some way off; pleasantly chatty atmosphere, small choice of carefully cooked bar food inc good value specials, well kept Flowers Original and local cider; straightforwardly furnished neat lounge on left angling around to family area, fruit machine in public bar, conservatory, unobtrusive piped music; very popular with older people at lunchtime, more villagey in the evening; service can slow down at peak times, and booking recommended *(John and Bridget Dean, Paul S McPherson, BB)*

☆ **Munsley** [Trumpet; A438 Hereford—Ledbury; SO6641], *Verzons*: 19th-century hotel with good choice of decent food in long bar-cum-bistro on left, well kept Hook Norton, friendly atmosphere; restaurant on right; bedrooms *(J H C Peters)*

Newbridge Green [B4211, off A4104 just W of Upton upon Severn; SO8439], *Drum &*

Monkey: Good value unpretentious food, well kept Banks's Mild and Bitter, Donnington BB and Wadworths 6X, pleasant, quick and efficient service, welcoming landlord; restaurant *(Derek and Sylvia Stephenson)*

Newtown [A4103 Hereford—Worcester, junction with A417; SO6145], *Newtown*: Good reasonably priced food, well kept Flowers, attentive licensee; very popular with older people, not a lot of space though *(J H C Peters)*

Oddingley [Smite Hill; near M5 junction 6 — A4538 towards Droitwich, then first right — OS Sheet 150, map reference 901589; SO9059], *Pear Tree*: Lots of nooks and crannies, good choice of bar food especially seafood *(J S Rutter)*

Offenham [by R Avon; SP0546], *Bridge*: Perhaps easier to find by boat than by road (the bridge went years ago, as did the ferry that replaced it); well kept Bass, appetising food, play area by water *(Dave Irving)*

☆ **Pensax** [B4202 Abberley—Clows Top; SO7269], *Bell*: Consistently good interesting food in unspoilt and warmly welcoming 19th-century pub with several changing well kept real ales, open fires, prompt friendly service; dining room extension with good view over hills towards Wyre Forest, opening on to wooden sun deck; children welcome *(PLC, Paul Denham, Nicola Brown-Denham)*

☆ **Pershore** [Bridge St; SO9445], *Millers Arms*: Takes some beating for value, no starters or puddings but particularly good home-made dishes such as really nicely done mushroom tagliatelle; a Wadworths pub, with guest beers eg Adnams Broadside and Badger Tanglefoot; more of a young people's pub in the evening *(Derek and Sylvia Stephenson)*

Pixley [SO6639], *Trumpet*: Pleasant old attractively timbered rambling pub, popular bar lunches *(Barbara M McHugh)*

Romsley [B4551 towards Halesowen; SO9679], *Sun*: Very good value food inc particularly reasonably priced mixed grill; well kept beer, good atmosphere *(Roger Huggins, Dave Braisted)*

☆ **Ross on Wye** [Riverside; coming in from A40 W side, 1st left after bridge; SO6024], *Hope & Anchor*: Notable for its position by the river, with big-windowed family extension looking out on flower-lined waterside lawns; boating theme in cheery main bar, snugger Victorian-style upstairs lounge and dining room, good reasonably priced bar food inc children's helpings, well kept M&B Springfield and Marstons Pedigree on handpump, silver band summer Sun evenings, maybe steam yacht trips from its own quay — busy weekends; dogs allowed *(H R Bevan, M J Penford, Mr and Mrs D Coates, Jim and Maggie Cowell, LYM)*

☆ **Severn Stoke** [A38 S of Worcester; SO8544], *Rose & Crown*: Old black-and-white pub with front bar (good fire) and back room, both with lots of character, low beams, assorted knick-knacks, several real ales; food not cheap but worth it, inc superb

salads, children's dishes; huge garden with
picnic-table sets and play area, several cats;
children allowed in back room *(Brian and
Anna Marsden)*

Shatterford [Bridgenorth Rd; SO7981], *Red
Lion*: Free house with several real ales such
as Everards, Marstons and Ruddles, bar and
restaurant meals *(Patrick Godfrey, Dave
Braisted)*

Shobdon [SO3962], *Bateman Arms*:
Comfortable two-bar local, friendly
licensees, well kept Flowers Original and
Woods, reasonably priced bar and
restaurant food *(Derek and Margaret Wood)*

Spetchley [Evesham Rd; SO8953], *Berkeley
Arms*: Pleasant pub with real ales, good
range of home-cooked bar food and
friendly, helpful staff *(R K Sutton)*

St Owens Cross [SO5425], *New Inn*:
15th-century coaching inn with friendly
young owners, medley of furnishings, bar
food from sandwiches to steaks, well kept
Smiles, restaurant; bedrooms good value —
on main rd, but double glazing helps *(J A
Dowsett, Jamie Lyons, Ruth Harrison)*

Staunton on Wye [SO3645], *New Inn*:
16th-century inn with good bar food from
sandwiches to steaks, Brains and
Theakstons, friendly landlord *(Andrew and
Ruth Triggs); Worlds End Lodge*: One of the
few licensed Youth Hostels; well kept
Marstons Pedigree, Weston's cider, good
vegetarian and vegan menu, low prices,
games room; relaxed atmosphere; part of an
outdoors centre; bedrooms basic but cheap
and comfortable, with good breakfasts
(Philip Thomas, SLH, D Morris)

☆ **Stoke Lacy** [A465 Bromyard—Hereford,
just N of village; SO6249], *Plough*:
Modernised pub by Symonds' cider plant,
comfortable and clean, with friendly service,
good range of generously served home-made
bar food inc fresh veg in bar and restaurant;
Greenalls real ales, choice of ciders,
restaurant *(M A Watts, Anthony
Nelson-Smith, Dave Braisted)*

☆ **Stoke Pound** [Sugarbrook Lane; Bridge 48,
Worcester & Birmingham Canal — OS
Sheet 150, map reference 962679; SO9667],
Queens Head: Large modern
air-conditioned locally popular canalside
dining pub, comfortably plush, with wide
choice of beers, friendly atmosphere, good
straightforward bar food inc seafood
specialities, evening carvery, restaurant;
service quick even when busy; Sun lunch
very popular (booking advised); friendly,
helpful staff; good canal walks, camping site
(Frank Cummins, F H Sommer, C H Stride)

☆ **Stoke Works** [Shaw Lane; a mile from M5
junction 5 — OS Sheet 150, map reference
938656; SO9365], *Bowling Green*:
Attractive building with well kept Banks's
Bitter and Mild, good atmosphere, friendly
service, short choice of good value food inc
good sandwiches and children's dishes; big
though not pretty garden, and its own
bowling green; handy for
Worcester—Birmingham Canal *(Barry and
Anne, Brian Jones)*

☆ **Symonds Yat** [Symonds Yat West; SO5616],
Old Ferre: Lively and attractive pub
overlooking river, with real ale, good value
restaurant meals inc huge mixed grill; nr
start GWG90; has small boat for 30-min
river trips, and own hand-pulled ferry
*(Lynne Sheridan, Bob West, Mr and Mrs J H
Adam)*

Symonds Yat [Symonds Yat E, by ferry —
OS Sheet 162, map reference 562159],
Saracens Head: Riverside spot next to ferry
with friendly staff, Bass ales and fair choice
of bar food, good puddings; simple decor,
satellite TV, pool; rather crowded in season
(Neil and Anita Christopher)

☆ **Tenbury Wells** [High St; SO6168], *Ship*:
Lots of dark wood, well kept Ansells, wide
range of good reasonably priced bar meals
concentrating on seafood, semi-separate
dining room (smarter yet more intimate),
notable Sun lunch, good coffee, attentive
service, warm atmosphere; good back bar
with pool and so forth; bedrooms
comfortable *(M B P Carpenter)*

Ullingswick [SO5949], *Three Crowns*:
Pleasant no-frills country local with limited
food inc good ploughman's, candles on
tables, well kept Allied beers; small
attractive lawn with good views *(Mrs Joan
Harris, J Penford)*

Upper Sapey [B4203 Bromyard—Great
Witley; SO6863], *Baiting House*: Two small
bars, old fireplace, well kept Banks's and
Flowers, good bar food; in good spot with
fine views *(Dave Braisted)*

☆ **Upper Wyche** [from Walwyn Rd (B4218)
heading W, first left turn after hilltop, on
right-hand bend, on to Chase Rd; SO7643],
Chase: Small rather quiet country pub on
Malvern Hills, well kept Donnington BB and
SBA and two Wye Valley real ales, limited
but good interesting bar food inc
adventurous soups, lovely fresh veg; fine
views from charming lounge; closed Tues
(Derek and Sylvia Stephenson)

☆ **Upton upon Severn** [far end High St;
SO8540], *Little Upton Muggery*: Another in
the Little chain, given its character by
hundreds of mugs hanging from ceiling; a
young person's pub, warm atmosphere, pine
tables on sawdust-powdered floor, enjoyable
food, well kept beers inc the usual
Lumphammer *(Ron and Audrey Davidson,
Mr and Mrs P B Dowsett, Dave Braisted)*

☆ **Upton upon Severn** [High St], *Olde Anchor*:
Picturesque 16th-century pub with
old-fashioned furnishings, old black timbers
propping its low ceiling, lots of copper, brass
and pewter, good fire in unusual central
fireplace; well kept Watneys-related real
ales, reasonably priced straightforward bar
food; has been open all day summer, can get
crowded evenings then; Paul Soden who
made this even more popular in the earliest
editions of this book for its own-brewed
beers and lively atmosphere is now brewing
at the Jolly Roger in Worcester *(WHBM,
PLC, A Triggs, Mr and Mrs P B Dowsett,
LYM)*

Upton upon Severn [Riverside], *Swan*:

Formerly a popular main entry, with beams, sofas, easy chairs, antique settles, log fires, imaginative food, well kept real ales, decent wines and waterside lawn; but closed for long period 1991 after Severn flooding *(News please)*

☆ **Weatheroak Hill** [Icknield St — coming S on A435 from Wythall roundabout, filter right off dual carriageway a mile S, then in village turn left towards Alvechurch; SP0674], *Coach & Horses*: Plush-seated two-level lounge bar, tiled-floor public bar and new restaurant extension, in country pub notable for well kept range of ten or so interesting real ales; decent choice of cheap simple food, good chatty atmosphere, piped music, good garden with plenty of seats on lawns and upper terrace; children allowed in eating area *(Mike and Wendy Proctor, Lynne Sheridan, Bob West, J Barnwell, Frank Cummins, LYM)*

☆ **Wellington Heath** [SO7141], *Farmers Arms*: Spacious, comfortable and friendly, with above-average food, very obliging service; tables on sunny terrace overlooking pretty wooded valley *(P J Brooks, Dr L Hughes)*

☆ **Whitney on Wye** [SO2747], *Boat*: Large and beautifully kept redbrick pub with lovely views of river and far beyond from big windows; very wide choice of consistently good generous home-cooked food with fine puddings; comfortably furnished, warm and friendly; bedrooms *(Dr Michael Smith, Paul McPherson, BB)*

Wigmore [SO4169], *Olde Oaken Bucket*: Old-world front bar, elegant candlelit back lounge with shelves housing collection of butter dishes; good choice of good value food inc steaks, back garden *(Paul McPherson)*

☆ **Willersey** [hotel signed off A44 about 2 miles E of Broadway; SP1238], *Dormy House*: In beautiful peaceful setting, smart hotel with cosy Cotswold bar and eating area in original 17th-century farmhouse core; good cold buffet and changing hot dishes (not cheap, but worth it), decent house wine, good coffee, young keen staff, good lavatories; inner courtyard with tables under cocktail parasols, more tables on front terrace, attractive and extensive garden overlooking golf course and distant hills; bedrooms *(JMC, S V Bishop, Roy Bromell)*

☆ **Winforton** [A438 14 miles W of Hereford; SO2947], *Sun*: Neatly kept, tidy and friendly stripped-stone pub with pleasant mix of country furnishings, two woodburners, generous helpings of quite individual bar food, good play area in garden; children allowed in eating area; closed Tues *(Mrs Joan Harris, Barry and Anne, N W Kingsley, Mike Tucker, N W Kingsley, Cliff and Karen Spooner, Dave Braisted, LYM)*

Wolverley [B4189 N of Kidderminster; SO8279], *Lock*: Pleasant pub by canal lock, comfortable lounge bar with welcoming fire and friendly staff, wide and interesting food choice, well kept Banks's, good coffee *(Roy Bromell)*

☆ **Worcester** [London Rd, about 1/2 mile from centre], *Little Worcester Sauce Factory*: One of the oddest of these odd and exuberantly decorated Little pubs, the bizarre decor a sauce-hater's nightmare; sashimi has turned up alongside the good value food along the lines of others in the chain; well kept beers inc Lumphammer *(PLC, Hilary Sargeant, N P Clarke, Dave Braisted, E V Walder)*

Worcester [50 Lowesmoor], *Jolly Roger*: Down-to-earth and decidedly unassuming place notable for the good very low-priced beers brewed on the premises; also no-nonsense food *(Derek and Sylvia Stephenson, PLC, Iain and Penny Muir)*

Wychbold [A38 towards Bromsgrove; part of Webbs Garden Centre — open 10-5 — OS Sheet 150, map reference 929670; SO9265], *Thatch*: Not a pub (part of Webbs Garden Centre, open 10-5, with wines licence) but worth noting for good value snacks and meals in pleasant surroundings *(Mr and Mrs W H Crowther)*

Yarpole [SO4765], *Bell*: Friendly efficient service in spacious rambling lounge with cretonne banquettes, nice flowers, lots of bric-a-brac, sunny south aspect, well kept Woods, varied food; children's play area, animals, stables; handy for Croft Castle and Berrington Hall *(Patrick Freeman, Brian and Anna Marsden)*

Hertfordshire

Of the counties around London, Hertfordshire now stands out as relatively good value, for pubs. Drinks prices – in contrast to other parts of the home counties – are scarcely higher than the national average. And quite a few pubs are now selling food which strikes us as good value too, particularly when quality is taken into account. These include the lively Fox & Hounds at Barley (brewing its own ales again, after a break of a few months), the busy and comfortable Bricklayers Arms at Flaunden, the very popular clean and friendly Green Man at Great Offley, the cheerful Coach & Horses at Newgate Street (its character landlord counts for a lot, too), all four main entries in St Albans (the closest town to London for a really good choice of character pubs serving decent food and beer at sensible prices), the thriving Sow & Pigs near Wadesmill (particularly attractive prices for its good straightforward food – which even includes a pauper's lunch for less than the price of some newspapers), and the enjoyable George & Dragon at Watton at Stone (decent wines here, too). Other pubs here that stand out as being well worth a visit include the Elephant & Castle at Amwell (a proper old country pub with a most attractive summer garden), the popular old Brocket Arms in its lovely spot at Ayot St Lawrence, and the cottagey little Moon & Stars at Rushden – very welcoming and relaxing. In the Lucky Dip section at the end of the chapter, pubs (almost all of them inspected by us) which currently stand out as particularly attractive include the Two Brewers at Chipperfield, Horns near Datchworth, Green Dragons at Flaunden and at London Colney, Alford Arms at Frithsden, Cabinet at Reed (a particularly fine pub we're always surprised we get so very few reports on), Plume of Feathers at Tewin, Coach & Horses at Thorley Street and both entries at Whitwell. Pubs very recently moving sharply up in readers' estimations which we have not yet been able to inspect ourselves are the Boat at Berkhamsted, Bull at Cottered, Three Horseshoes at Hinxworth and Plough near St Albans.

ALDBURY   SP9612 Map 4
Valiant Trooper

Village signposted from Tring and under a mile E of Tring railway station; Trooper Road (towards Aldbury Common)

Family run for the last eleven years, this partly white-painted, tiled brick house has a happy hour between 6 and 7pm when the real ales (Eldridge Pope Hardy, Fullers ESB and London Pride, Greene King Abbot and Marstons Pedigree on handpump) are £1.10 a pint; their spirits are always £1.50 or £2 for doubles and they do farm cider. The lively first room, beamed and tiled in red and black, has built-in wall benches, a pew and small dining chairs around the attractive country tables, and a woodburning stove in its inglenook fireplace. In the brown-carpeted middle room there's some exposed brick work and spindleback chairs, and the far room has nice country kitchen chairs around individually chosen tables, and a brick fireplace; decorations are mostly antique prints of cavalrymen. Fairly limited bar food includes open sandwiches or filled baked potatoes (£2.75) and chilli con carne (£3.70). Shove-ha'penny, dominoes, cribbage; dogs welcome. There are some tables in the small, prettily flowered garden at the back. The pub is in good walking country – it's on *Good Walks Guide* Walk 109. *(Recommended by Dave Gardiner, Sidney and Erna Wells, Ted George; more reports please)*

Free house   Licensee Dorothy Eileen O'Gorman   Real ale   Meals and snacks (not Sat or Mon evenings or all day Sun)   Restaurant; not Sun evening   Aldbury Common (044 285) 203   Children in eating area of bar lunchtime and up till 7pm   Open 12–3, 6–11; 12–11 Sat

AMWELL   TL1613   Map 5
Elephant & Castle

Village signposted SW from Wheathampstead

In summer this well run old pub is popular for its neat and secluded back garden (children and dogs not allowed here) and for its floodlit front lawn where there are picnic-table sets spaced well apart among fruit trees and weeping willow and where dogs and children are welcome; barbecues (weather permitting) and weekend Morris dancers, barber shop quartet and baroque quartet. Inside, there are no machines or piped music and the low-beamed main bar has a 200 foot well shaft as well as an inglenook fireplace, some panelling (other walls stripped to the timbered brick), and low leatherette-cushioned stalls and high-backed bucket seats on the red and black tiled floor. Decent bar food includes sandwiches, ploughman's, home-made chilli con carne and pies (£3.75) and chicken and fish dishes (£4); help-yourself salads (from a choice of 10) with all meals. Four changing real ales on handpump from a choice of Adnams, Ansells, Benskins, Boddingtons, Ind Coope Burton, Marstons, Tetleys, Wadworths 6X and Youngs; 18 malt whiskies from small distilleries. *(Recommended by Nick Dowson, David Shillitoe, Michael and Alison Sandy, Mr and Mrs F E M Hardy)*

Free house   Licensee Stewart Willett   Real ale   Meals and snacks (not Sun) Wheathampstead (058 283) 2175; closed Sun   Open 11–3, 5.30–11; all day summer Sats; closed 25 Dec

AYOT ST LAWRENCE   TL1916   Map 5
Brocket Arms ★

B651 N of St Albans for about 6 miles; village signposted on right after Wheathampstead and Marshall's Heath golf course; or B653 NE of Luton, then right on to B651

Well run and cared for, this popular 14th-century country pub has added two ensuite bedrooms and opened a garden bar and children's play area in the walled gardens behind the building. The two atmospheric and old-fashioned rooms have orange lanterns hanging from the sturdy oak beams, a big inglenook fireplace (often too hot to sit in), a long built-in wall settle in one parquet-floored room, and a wide choice of piped music from Bach to pop. Bar food includes soup (£1), ploughman's (£3), pâté (£3.50), and summer buffet lunches such as beef salad or chilli con carne (£4.50) and fresh salmon salad (£5.50). A wide range of beers on handpump such as Adnams, Greene King Abbot and IPA, Marstons Pedigree and Wadworths 6X with guests such as Banks & Taylors SOD, Fullers ESB, Gales HSB and Hook Norton Old Hookey, as well as Rosies farm cider; darts and dominoes. The pub is on *Good Walks Guide* Walk 108. Just over the road are the romantic ivy-hung ruins of a medieval church. *(Recommended by Nick and Alison Dowson, Bill Sykes, BKA, J E Stanton, Barbara Wensworth, Michael and Alison Sandy, Gary Scott, Tony and Lynne Stark)*

Free house   Licensee Toby Wingfield Digby   Real ale   Meals and snacks (not Sun or Mon evenings)   Partly no smoking restaurant (not Sun evening)   Stevenage (0438) 820250   Children in restaurant   Open 11–2.30(3 Sat), 6–11   Bedrooms; £40(£60B)/£55(£65B)

BARLEY   TL3938 Map 5

Fox & Hounds ★ ✪

Junction 10 of M11 then A505 towards Royston, then left on to B1368 after 4 miles

After a gap of seven months, they've starting brewing again here and as well as Old Dragon and Flame Thrower they are hoping to extend the range, as well as serving Theakstons Best, XB and Old Peculier (rare to get all three down South); also, two farm ciders, malt whiskies, and a good selection of wines by the glass or bottle. The low ceilinged and alcovey rambling rooms are well furnished – one of the stripped wood tables has a brightly-painted cast iron base which used to be a wringer; there are substantial log fires on both sides of a massive central chimney, and a friendly cat. The dining area with its odd-shaped nooks and crannies was originally the kitchen and cellar; the conservatory is no-smoking. Mostly home-made bar food includes sandwiches (from £1.20), generous whitebait (£2.75), garlic mushrooms (£2.10), spare ribs (£2.95), curries and vegetarian dishes (from £3.25), lasagne (£4.25), steak and kidney or ham and sweetcorn pies (£4.35), scallops, prawns and mushrooms in white wine (£5.65), poached salmon, steaks (from £6.25), and daily specials; friendly staff and lots of locals. There's a fine range of games, from darts (two league darts teams), bar billiards and dominoes (two schools), to shove-ha'penny, cribbage, fruit machine and juke box; also a league football team. The garden is well equipped for children, and there's a skittle alley and a barbecue area. They run a mini-bus service for customers. *(Recommended by JM, PM, Maggie Jo St John, Nigel Gibbs, Richard Houghton, Beti Wyn Thomas, Colin and Evelyn Turner, David Eversley, Charles Bardswell, SJC, Colleen Holiday, Nigel Gibbs, Sandra Cook, Tony and Lynne Stark, Gwen and Peter Andrews, Denise Plummer, Jim Froggatt, Jill Hampton)*

Own brew   Licensee Rita Nicholson   Real ale   Meals and snacks (till 10pm in summer)   Restaurant   Royston (0763) 848459   Children welcome (not too late Sats)   Open 11.45–2.30, 5.45–11; 11.30–3, 5.30–11 Sat; 12–2.30, 6–11 winter

FLAUNDEN   TL0100 Map 5

Bricklayers Arms

Village signposted from Bovingdon, on B4505 Hemel Hempstead–Chesham; Hogpits Bottom – from village centre follow Boxmoor, Bovingdon road and turn right at Belsize, Watford signpost

Though this comfortable, busy pub places quite a strong emphasis on the food the atmosphere in the bars remains nicely local, particularly at weekends. The low-beamed bar has buff leatherette armchairs and dark brown painted traditional wooden wall seats, open winter fires, and stubs of knocked-through oak-timbered walls that give a snug feeling to the three original rooms. There's a back dining room. On weekday lunchtimes the bar menu is used throughout the whole pub: sandwiches, soup (£1.80), prawn stroganoff (£3.45), prawn and halibut roll (£3.95), cottage pie (£4.20), vegetable bake (£4.75), curried chicken breast (£5.70), beef in ale pie (£6.50), grilled Dover sole (£8.40), steaks (from £8.50), and daily specials; the evening and Sunday lunch menu used in the back dining room is broadly similar. Adnams, Brakspears, Fullers London Pride and two guests on handpump; friendly staff. There are picnic-table sets and tables with cocktail umbrellas on a lawn surrounded by foxgloves along its sheltering hawthorn and ivy hedges. Just up the Belsize road there's a path on the left, through woods, to more Forestry Commission woods around Hollow Hedge. *(Recommended by D B Delany, Les and Jean Bradman, Gordon Leighton, T Kenny, R M Savage, BKA, Douglas Bail, Mr and Mrs F W Sturch)*

Free house   Licensee A P Power   Real ale   Meals and snacks (not Sun evening)   Restaurant   (0442) 833322   Open 11–2.30(3 Sat), 5.30(6 Sat)–11; winter evening opening 6

GREAT OFFLEY   TL1427   Map 5

Green Man ★

Village signposted off A505 Luton–Hitchin

This country pub is deservedly popular – it's clean and well kept, has a decent atmosphere, and good food and friendly staff. The rambling bars have low moulded beams, lots of antique farm-tool illustrations, wheelback and spindleback chairs around simple country tables, some stripped brick, and a woodburning stove and fruit machine on the left. The larger and more airy right-hand room has lots of little countryside prints and one or two larger pictures, a cabinet of trophies, cushioned built-in wall seats as well as the chairs around its tables, another big woodburner (with a row of brass spigots decorating the chimneypiece), and fruit machine. Bar food includes soup (£1.25), generous sandwiches and large filled rolls (from £2), filled baked potatoes (from £2.05), ploughman's (from £2.50), cottage or chicken, ham and leek pies (£4.10), a good lunchtime spread of help-yourself salads (from £5.50), gammon (£5.75), and puddings like apple pie (£2); the meat is supplied by the local butcher and the turkeys come from a local farm. Well kept Banks & Taylors Shefford, Boddingtons, Flowers Original, Greene King IPA and Abbot and Marstons Pedigree on handpump, with a decent choice of wines by the glass; friendly cat, piped music. Curlicued iron tables and chairs on the flagstoned terrace have a grand view beyond the lawn with its rockery, pond and little waterfall, to the flatter land below, stretching for miles to the east. There's a profusion of flowers in hanging baskets and tubs, and at the front are some swings and a slide. The licensee runs another pub (and fish restaurant) round the corner, the Prince Henry. *(Recommended by Michael and Alison Sandy, David Shillitoe, The Shinkmans, Lyn and Bill Capper, R A Reeves, K and J Morris, George Mitchell, Roger Broadie, Sidney and Erna Wells)*

Free house   Licensee Raymond H Scarbrow   Real ale   Meals and snacks (cold food is served 11.30–11pm)   Restaurant   Offley (046 276) 256   Children welcome   Open 10.30am–11pm; closed Sun afternoons

NEWGATE STREET   TL3005   Map 5

Coach & Horses

B153 W of Cuffley then first right just outside village

The open-plan bar in this engaging country pub has a friendly atmosphere, good winter fires at either end, a relaxing mix of carpet and large flagstones, cosy built-in wall settles, subdued lighting and perhaps piped music or Radio Essex; the remains of some wall ends create an illusion of separate little rooms. Popular bar food includes tasty home-made soup, a wide range of sandwiches or toasties (from £1.35; Reg's Special £3), excellent ploughman's (from £3.30), and home-made specials like steak and kidney or chicken pie, macaroni cheese or beef curry (£4.15); vegetarian dishes. Well kept Adnams, Benskins Best and Greene King Abbot on handpump; cribbage, dominoes, juke box and piped music. There are tables on a lawn with high trees around it, and more on the forecourt. There are walks in nearby rolling fields (lots of paths) or in vast woods such as the Great Wood country park (from the Northaw road, take the B157 towards Brookmans Park). *(Recommended by Anne Delnevo, Ian Macro, P S Vince, John and Karen Day, Nick and Alison Dowson)*

Benskins (Allied)   Tenant Reg Newcombe   Real ale   Meals and snacks (12–2, 6–9; not Sun)   (0707787) 2326   Children in family room   Open 11–3, 5.30–11

PUCKERIDGE   TL3823   Map 5

White Hart ✇

Village signposted from A10 and A120

As the licensees say themselves, this is a small family-run pub with a dining room, not a first-class restaurant, so the heavy-beamed, rambling bar has a character of its own with its pewter tankards, horsebrasses and coach horns; there are lots of wooden armchairs, wheelback chairs and button-back banquettes, and the fireplace has a massive carved mantlebeam. Well kept McMullens Bitter and AK Mild and Greene King Abbott on handpump kept under light blanket pressure; darts, shove-ha'penny, cribbage, dominoes, fruit machine, and piped music. The extensive menu can be eaten anywhere in the pub though tables in the dining room are bookable: sandwiches (from £1.25), ploughman's (from £2.75), lots of starters such as soup (£1.70), home-made venison pâté or fresh prawns with garlic butter (£2.95) or insalata di mare (octopus, squid, prawns and mussels in olive oil £3.25), main courses like home-made tomato pancakes with thermidor sauce (£3.25), home-made lasagne, fresh oven-roasted turkey or country lentil crumble (£5.50), fresh local trout stuffed with prawns and garlic butter (£5.95), seafood platter (£6.75; if you manage to finish it completely they will give you a voucher for £6.75 to deduct from your next meal), and rump steak (from £8.75); children's menu (from £1.10; they can also have a half helping of the main menu for half the price); good, friendly service. There are two sittings on Saturday evening. There are seats and swings in the floodlit garden by a paddock with chickens, roosters, ducks, goats, rabbits, sheep and ponies, and more under a thatched shelter built around a spreading tree. (Recommended by George Atkinson, Gwen and Peter Andrews, Phil Bryant, C A Holloway, John Whitehead, Stephen King, Colin and Evelyn Turner, Jill Hampton, Brian Metherell)

McMullens   Tenants Colin and Rita Boom   Real ale   Meals and snacks (12–2, 6.30–9.30)   Restaurant Ware (0920) 821309   Children in eating area of bar and in restaurant (under 5 with prior permission only)   Open 11–2.30, 5.30–11; 11–11 Sat; closed evenings 25 and 26 Dec

RUSHDEN   TL3031   Map 5
Moon & Stars

Village signposted from A507 Baldock–Buntingford, about 1 mile W of Cottered

This unspoilt and cottagey country pub has a villagey public bar with a heavy-beamed low ceiling, vast inglenook fireplace, Greene King IPA, Abbot and KK Mild on handpump, and maybe Fred the splendid friendly labrador; this room connects at the front with the lounge bar which has lots of tables. Bar food includes sandwiches (from £1.20), home-made liver and bacon pâté (£2), ploughman's (from £3), ham and egg (£3.75), huge Yorkshire puddings with big fillings (£3.95), gammon (£5.95), steak (from £6.50), and a hot daily special such as home-made steak and kidney pie (£4.50); fresh fish and chips Thursday evenings (£3.60), Sunday roast (£4.95) and home-made cakes and chutney for sale over the bar; small, decent wine list; darts, dominoes, shove-ha'penny, cribbage, a fruit machine, and pétanque. A garden at the back has tables, a climbing frame and swings; also benches in front. The pub was originally a row of three cottages. Due to complaints, the licensees have regrettably had to ban children under 14. (Recommended by Charles Bardswell, John Whitehead; more reports please)

Greene King   Tenants Robbie and Gill Davidson   Real ale   Meals and snacks (not Sun evening)   (076 388) 330; no bookings Thurs evening   Open 12–2.30, 6–11; winter evening opening 7; closed evening 25 Dec and all day 26 Dec

ST ALBANS   TL1507   Map 5
Fighting Cocks

Off George Street, through abbey gateway (you can drive down, though signs suggest you can't)

Though this was called the Round House when it first opened as an alehouse in 1600, it gets its modern name from a small area down steps in the modernised bar which used to be part of the Stuart cock-fighting pit. There are heavy low beams, a good log fire in the inglenook fireplace, a stuffed cock in a cabinet, some pleasant window alcoves, and other nooks and corners. Bar food includes open rolls (from £1.95), ploughman's (from £2.50), salads (from £3.50), lasagne (£3.95), and steak in ale or chicken and mushroom pies (£4.25). Well kept Benskins Best, Ind Coope Burton and Tetleys on handpump; fruit machine, video game and piped music. The surroundings are very attractive: seats in the garden, then beyond that lots of ducks on the River Ver, a lakeside park, and the Roman remains of Verulamium. *(Recommended by Ted George, Nick and Alison Dowson, Duncan Stuart-Mills)*

Benskins (Allied)   Manager Joe Capanella   Real ale   Lunchtime meals and snacks   St Albans (0727) 865830   Children in family room only   Open 11–11; 11–3, 6–11 in winter

Garibaldi

61 Albert Street; off Holywell Hill below White Hart Hotel – some parking at end of street

Behind an unassuming backstreet facade is this lively, brightly lit and refurbished Victorian pub. The well kept bar angles around the central island servery and there's a little tiled-floor snug up some steps; a separate food counter on a lower level opens out into a neat and cosy little no-smoking conservatory. There's a fairly regular crowd of mainly youngish people – but our older readers enjoy it too. Good value home-made bar food includes sandwiches, home-made soup (£1.50), mushroom stroganoff (£3.25), lamb casserole with cranberries (£3.75), and steak in ale pie (£4.25); friendly service. Well kept Fullers Chiswick, London Pride and ESB; cribbage, dominoes, trivia, fruit machine, decent piped pop music; they have their own cricket team. There are a few picnic-table sets in the side yard. *(Recommended by Wayne Brindle, Nick and Alison Dowson, TBB, P S Vince, Michael and Alison Sandy)*

Fullers   Manager Paul McFarlane   Real ale   Meals and snacks   St Albans (0727) 55046   Children in eating area of bar   Open 11–3, 5–11; all day Fri and Sat

Goat

Sopwell Lane; a No Entry beside Strutt and Parker estate agents on Holywell Hill, the main southwards exit from town – by car, take the next lane down and go round the block

With its boisterous atmosphere and friendly staff, this fine old pub is popular with a wide mix of customers. The network of linked rooms contains a profusion of eye-catching decorations – stuffed birds, chamber pots, books and prints. Tasty bar food ranges from good value, tasty sandwiches (from 80p) and winter soup (£1.55), through pizzas (from £2.80), burgers or chilli con carne (£3.75), a pasta dish (from £3.75), and steak and mushroom pie (£3.95), to steaks and home-made puddings (£1.80). The wide selection of fairly priced real ales includes Greene King IPA and Abbot, Hook Norton Best and Old Hookey, Marstons Pedigree, Rayments and Wadworths 6X and winter Old Timer on handpump. Fruit machine, video game, piped music and Sunday evening quiz. There are tables on the neat lawn-and-gravel back yard. *(Recommended by S Corrigan, Mrs G Walsh, P S Vince, Wayne Brindle, BKA, Nick and Alison Dowson, K W Mills)*

Devenish (Whitbreads)   Tenant Mr Ginn   Real ale   Meals and snacks (not Sun evening)   St Albans (0727) 833934   Children in eating area of bar if eating   Jazz Sun lunchtime and Tues evening, pop Mon evening   Nearby parking may be rather difficult   Open 11–2.30(3 Sat), 5.30(6Sat)–11; closed 25 Dec

Rose & Crown £

St Michaels Street; from town centre follow George Street down past the Abbey towards the Roman town

There's a marvellously relaxed and rather civilised atmosphere in this unchanging and elegantly facaded pub. Service is never less than friendly and efficient and the lunchtime bar food is good value and filling: really excellent home-made vegetable soup (£1.50), ploughman's (£2.65), cheese, potato and onion pie (£2.50), chicken, ham and mushroom pie (£2.95), wheat, walnut and tomato casserole (£3), winter casserole like beef and dumplings or sausage and peppers (from £3), lasagne or steak and kidney pie (£3.25), and puddings like spotted dick or apple and blackberry pie (£1.50). Well kept Adnams, Benskins, Greene King Abbott and Tetleys on handpump, and farm ciders, some whiskies, lots of country wines, winter hot punch and tea or coffee; unusual crisps and a selection of snuffs. The beamed public bars have unevenly timbered walls, old-fashioned wall benches, a pile of coffee-table magazines, and black cauldrons in a deep fireplace. Darts (placed sensibly to one side), shove-ha'penny, dominoes, cribbage, fruit machine, and juke box. There's always a selection of books and records for sale – proceeds go towards the RNLI and buying guide dogs. Lots of tables and benches along the side and at the back of the pub with shrubs and roses, flowerbeds and hanging baskets. (*Recommended by Michael and Alison Sandy, George Atkinson, Mrs G Walsh, Gill and Doug Green, Wayne Brindle, Richard Houghton, A W Dickinson, Christian Leigh*)

Benskins (Allied)   Tenant John Milligan   Real ale   Lunchtime meals and snacks (11.30–2.15)   St Albans (0727) 51903   Folk Thurs evening   Evening parking may be difficult   Open 11–2.30(3 Sat), 5.30(6 Sat)–11

WADESMILL   TL3517 Map 5

Sow & Pigs

Thundridge (the village where it's actually situated – but not marked on many road maps, which is why we list it under nearby Wadesmill); A10 just S of Wadesmill, towards Ware

Cheerfully run, this unassuming and comfortable pub has a small, traditional central bar with plank-panelling, lots of little piggies in a glass cabinet by the bar, an attractive wall clock, a small ship's wheel and binnacle under a collection of military badges, and a rustic table supported by two barrels in the bay of the cosy window seat. More spacious rooms lead off on both sides – on the right the dining room, with big copper urns hanging from dark beams, massive rustic tables and a big nautical chart; the area on the left has a timber part divider, and a couple of steps half way along, helping to break it up. Well kept Adnams, Benskins Best and Ind Coope Burton on handpump or tapped from the cask. They really know how to make sandwiches – the roast beef done with dripping (£1.35), smoked salmon (£2.10) and steak (£3.15) are all recommended. Other well priced bar food includes a pauper's lunch (30p), very good home-made soup (£1.20), ploughman's (£2.20), steak and kidney pie or delicious bacon and onion roly-poly (£3.25) and a bargain three-course steak lunch (£5.75). There are picnic-table sets under cocktail parasols, with their own service hatch, on a smallish fairylit grass area behind by the car park, sheltered by tall oaks and chestnut trees. (*Recommended by Nigel Gibbs, Mrs G Walsh, M B P Carpenter, John Whitehead, C A Holloway*)

Benskins (Allied)   Tenant Willie Morgan   Real ale   Snacks (any time during opening hours) and meals   Restaurant   Ware (0920) 463281   Children in restaurant   Open 11–2.30, 6–11

WATTON AT STONE   TL3019 Map 5

George & Dragon ★

Village signposted off A602 about 5 miles S of Stevenage, on B1001; High St

The carpeted main bar in this enjoyable place has country kitchen armchairs around attractive old tables, dark blue cloth-upholstered seats in its bay windows, an interesting mix of antique and modern prints on the partly timbered ochre walls, and a big inglenook fireplace. A quieter room off, with spindleback chairs and wall settles cushioned to match the green floral curtains, has a nice set of Cruikshank anti-drink engravings above its panelled dado. Popular bar food includes thick tasty soup (£1.30; Corsican fish soup £3.60), sandwiches (from £1.40), ploughman's (£2.85), button mushrooms in olive oil with tomato and coriander (£3.25), an evening hot snack (£3.50), a lunchtime dish of the day (£4.25), salads (from £4.25), fillet steak in a bread roll (from £6.60), pigeon breast and diced turkey (£5.50), and puddings (£1.80); they only take credit cards on bills over ten pounds. Proper napkins, good house wines by half-pint or pint carafes, and a selected house claret; the good restaurant doesn't impinge on the pub itself. There's also an official dress code – it's best if you at least wear shirts with sleeves; be warned that it's likely to be crowded by 12.30. Friendly, efficient service, and daily papers set out to read at lunchtime; fruit machine. There are picnic-table sets in a small shrub-screened garden, and the pub is handy for Benington Lordship Gardens. *(Recommended by Nicky Moore, Ken and Barbara Turner, Nigel Gibbs, Colleen Holiday, TBB, Charles Bardswell, A C Morrison, C A Holloway, Neville Kenyon, David Shillitoe, Barbara Wensworth)*

Greene King   Lease: Kevin Dinnin   Meals and snacks (12–2, 7.15–10; not Sun) Restaurant   Ware (0920) 830285   (not Sun)   Children in restaurant   Open 11–2.30, 6–11; closed evening 25 Dec)

WESTMILL   TL3626   Map 5

Sword in Hand

Village signposted W of A10, about 1 mile S of Buntingford

The comfortable bar in this pretty pub has lots of photographs of classic cars and local houses, and pictures of local scenes on the black and white timbered walls, cushioned seats on the Turkey carpet, and a log fire. Darts, cribbage, and piped music; the playful little dog is called Scruffy. It's best to get here early if you want to eat: soup (£1.75), ploughman's (from £2.50), lasagne or pies such as lamb and rosemary or steak and kidney (£4.50), steaks (from £6.95), and puddings (£1.95). Well kept Greene King IPA and Abbott, Rayments and a guest such as Tetleys or Ind Coope Burton. There are tables on a partly crazy-paved sheltered side garden under the pear tree. The licensee, a classic-car enthusiast, holds regular shows in the spacious two-acre back garden in summer and meetings in the pub in winter. The village (rows of tiled or thatched cottages) is particularly pretty. *(Recommended by C A Holloway, Charles Bardswell, John Whitehead, Colleen Holiday, Sidney and Erna Wells)*

Free house   Licensees David and Heather Hopperton   Real ale   Meals and snacks (not 25 Dec)   Restaurant   Royston (0763) 71356   Well behaved children allowed Open 11–2.30(3 Sat), 6–11   Bedrooms planned

---

Lucky Dip

Besides the fully inspected pubs, you might like to try these Lucky Dips recommended to us and described by readers (if you do, please send us reports):

☆ **Ardeley** [OS Sheet 166, map reference 310272; TL3027], *Jolly Waggoner*: Friendly and genuine country pub with two unspoilt bars, wide range of good home-cooked bar food; well kept Greene King ales *(Charles Bardswell, P S Vince)*

☆ **Ashwell** [69 High St; TL2639], *Rose & Crown*: Friendly, clean and comfortable village local, popular with all ages; public bar with darts and food bar with open fire, Greene King and Rayments ales, good well presented food, pleasant staff, pretty garden; attractive village *(Nick Holmes, Nigel Gibbs, Charles Bardswell, Sidney and Erna Wells)* **Ashwell** [by church], *Bushel & Strike*: Characterful building with well kept Charles Wells beer, good food served efficiently; attractive village *(Tony and Lynne Stark, Charles Bardswell)*; [nr stn], *Jester*: Popular nicely decorated bar in sizeable hotel, well kept real ales such as Fullers Chiswick and Wethereds Winter Royal, beautifully set up restaurant area; bedrooms *(Colleen Holiday)*

☆ **Ayot Green** [off B197 S of Welwyn — OS Sheet 166, map reference 222139; TL2213], *Waggoners*: Popular and well kept, with three small cosy areas, lots of mugs hanging from low ceiling, good bar food inc

outstanding moussaka served on Wedgwood china, separate eating area, four or five real ales, young friendly staff, garden; wooded walks, on GWG108 *(GB, CH, Nick Dowson)* **Baldock** [just off A1, rd into town; TL2434], *George IV*: Comfortable roadside pub with reasonably priced bar food and Greene King ales *(Nigel Gibbs)*

☆ **Berkhamsted** [Gravel Path; SP9807], *Boat*: Marvellous canalside spot, with waterside tables and weekend barbecues, good varied lunchtime food, well kept real ales inc Fullers Chiswick, ESB and London Pride, fine choice of wines inc New World ones, friendly and efficient service, good atmosphere *(G D Wheatley, E J Mooring, David Oakes, Mrs J Kitchen, O Travers)* **Bishops Stortford** [Rye St; TL4820], *Fox*: Well kept Greene King and other real ales, interesting, well prepared and very cheap food, friendly, intelligent and noisy atmosphere, consciously basic decor *(John C Baker)*; [London Rd], *Old Bulls Head*: Well kept Adnams and Allied real ales, friendly and efficient service, well prepared bar lunches inc good bacon sandwiches and home-made sausages, good if more expensive evening food (Weds-Sat) esp

Indian dishes, weekend barbecues; nice garden overlooks River Stort *(SJC, John C Baker)*; [Bridge St], *Star*: Recently refurbished, rambling and rustic; pleasantly busy, usual bar food, unobtrusive machines, friendly staff, seats in courtyard *(Ruth and Alan Woodhouse)*

☆ **Bourne End** [Winkwell; narrow lane off A41; TL0206], *Three Horseshoes*: Cosy and homely little canalside pub, said to date back to 16th century, by tiny swing-bridge; low ceilings, loads of gleaming horsebrasses and harness, two big inglenook fireplaces one with bread oven; small rooms inc cosy snug reserved for the over-30s, Greene King and Allied real ales, limited but good cheap lunchtime food (not Sun), tables on waterside terrace *(Ted George)*

Bramfield [OS Sheet 153, map reference 291157; TL2915], *Grandiston Arms*: Pleasant softly lit Benskins pub with low ceilings, log fire and attractive garden *(Nick and Alison Dowson)*

Burnham Green [TL2516], *White Horse*: Popular Benskins pub with varied seating, waitress-served dining area, log-effect gas fire, pleasant atmosphere, efficient staff *(Nick and Alison Dowson)*

Chandlers Cross [TQ0698], *Clarendon Arms*: Large, popular pub in attractive setting with pleasant verandah; has been praised for cheap plain bar lunches (not Sun) and choice of well kept ales, but no recent reports *(News please)*

Chapmore End [off B158 Hertford—Wadesmill; TL3216], *Woodman*: Tiny two-roomed village pub by pond with well kept Greene King tapped from the cask, big garden with fowl *(Tony and Lynne Stark, P S Vince)*

☆ **Chipperfield** [The Common; TL0401], *Two Brewers*: Relaxed and genuinely pubby spacious dark-beamed main bar, with cushioned antique settles and a good choice of well kept real ales; lunchtime bar food (not Sun) from comfortable bow-windowed lounge, good buffet; a THF, but long and low, overlooking a pretty tree-flanked cricket green; children allowed in lounge and restaurant; open all day Sat; bedrooms *(Kathy Holt, TBB, R C Morgan, David Oakes, LYM)*

Chipping [off A10; TL3532], *Countryman*: Beams and timbering, traditional settles, open fire, farm tools, wide choice of bar food, well kept real ales, restaurant, piped music; big pleasant garden; children in restaurant *(Sidney Wells, LYM)*

☆ **Chorleywood** [from M25 junction 17 exit roundabout follow Heronsgate signpost, pub on right; TQ0295], *Land of Liberty, Peace & Plenty*: Spotless, with good range of substantial bar food (not Thurs or Sun eves); friendly staff, well kept Courage and John Smiths, decent coffee, maybe unobtrusive piped music; children's play area, several pub dogs inc one of no mean bulk *(Mr and Mrs F W Sturch, Kathy Holt)*

Chorleywood, *Garden Gate*: Good moderately priced food with Caribbean specialities, good service, real ales; handy for walkers on nearby common; children welcome *(Geoffrey and Sylvia Donald, LYM)*; [Chorleywood Bottom], *Old Shepherd*: Unassuming local looking over green, well kept ales inc Wadworths 6X, good homely food even Sun lunchtime at low prices, friendly atmosphere *(Quentin Williamson, R Houghton)*; [Heronsgate Rd, The Swillet], *Stag*: Neat nicely carpeted dining lounge with Allied real ales, bar food from sandwiches up (not Sun or Mon eves); no piped music or fruit machines, tables on back lawn, children's play area *(Lyn and Bill Capper, Douglas Bail)*; [Rickmansworth Rd (A404 just off M25 junction 18)], *White Horse*: Tastefully refurbished old pub with well kept Greene King IPA and Abbot and Rayments, quickly served bar lunches *(Nigel Gibbs, Richard Houghton)*

Codicote [High St; TL2118], *Bell*: Comfortably modernised old pub, generous helpings of good bar food, handsome restaurant, well kept Flowers and Wethereds on handpump, good friendly service, piped music, fruit machine; tables on terrace; bedrooms *(John Whitehead, Lyn and Bill Capper)*

Coleman Green [OS Sheet 166, map reference 189126; TL1812], *John Bunyan*: Nice old pub with friendly atmosphere, good log fire, oak panelling, McMullens ales, good food at reasonable prices, children's play area in big garden, quiet weekday evenings, closes early then *(H Glew, J Ramalho, Mr and Mrs F E M Hardy)*

Colney Heath [TL2005], *Crooked Billet*: Good range of well kept real ales and lots of unusual bottled beers in traditional tiled bar and lounge — definitely no frills, but friendly service, straightforward bar food, summer barbecues, pets' corner in garden, maybe children's ponies to ride in summer; partly covered terrace *(John Whitehead, Nick and Alison Hayward, LYM)*; [Sleapshyde, just off A414 N — OS Sheet 166, map reference 203070], *Plough*: Pleasantly refurbished beamed Allied pub, cosy and clean, with good real fire, well kept beer and friendly atmosphere *(Nick and Alison Dowson)*

☆ **Cottered** [TL3129], *Bull*: Charming pub, spacious and comfortable, doing well under current friendly but busy young landlord; varied well served good bar food particularly popular lunchtime with older people, Adnams and Greene King ales, log fire, attractive small restaurant, big well kept garden with boules and play area *(Peter and Gail Hickman, Sidney and Erna Wells, Charles Bardswell)*

Cottered, *Bell*: Sadly this handsome thatched pub, popular with readers, was sold by Allied to Greene King, who have now closed it with the aim of selling it as a private house

Croxley Green [Rickmansworth Rd (A412); junction Watford Rd/Baldwins Lane — OS Sheet 176, map reference 087959; TQ0795], *Two Bridges*: Comfortably refurbished and relaxing place with attractive muted decor, sofas, easy chairs, books and so forth, well kept Allied real ales, efficiently served bar food; open 8am-11pm inc breakfast and afternoon tea *(Mayur Shah, Ian Phillips, LYM)*

Dane End [Great Munden; from Dane End go two miles past the Boot — OS Sheet 166, map reference 352234; TL3321], *Plough*: Included for the unique full-size Compton theatre organ in the comfortable and lofty lounge extension that's been built specially to house it; otherwise, usual bar food, well kept Greene King IPA and Abbot and Rayments, friendly local atmosphere *(J P Day, LYM)*

☆ **nr Datchworth** [Bramfield Rd, Bulls Grn; TL2717], *Horns*: Pretty 15th-century country pub with rugs on brick floor, big inglenook, low beams or high rafters, seats out among roses on the crazy paving; good pub food worth waiting for, well kept Flowers Original and Wethereds on handpump, good cider and coffee *(John Whitehead, L McGlenn, Charles Bardswell, LYM)*

Epping Green [back rd Cuffley—Little Berkhamsted — OS Sheet 166, map reference 297068; TL2906], *Beehive*: Cosy and popular local, Greene King Abbot and Ind Coope Burton *(Nick and Alison Dowson)*

☆ **Essendon** [West End Lane — off B158, which with Essendon and B1455 is signposted off A414 Hatfield—Hertford; TL2708], *Candlestick*: Friendly local with comfortable two-room mock-Tudor lounge, brightly lit public bar with games; generous helpings of cheap simple food (not Sat-Mon evenings), well kept McMullens and AK Mild, log fires, good service; plenty of seats outside, alone in country *(John Whitehead, BB)*

Flamstead [High St; TL0714], *Three Blackbirds*: Attractive low-beamed pub with quick friendly service, good value food, well kept Websters Yorkshire *(Mr and Mrs P A Stevens, David Shillitoe)*

☆ **Flaunden** [TL0100], *Green Dragon*: Neat and comfortable partly panelled pub with traditional untouched 17th-century tap bar, well kept Marstons Pedigree and other real ales such as Eldridge Pope, good reasonably priced bar food, darts and shove-ha'penny; charming well kept garden with summer-house and aviaries; where Guy Burgess last sighted in England *(Richard Houghton, Marjorie and David Lamb, David Wallington, LYM)*

☆ **Frithsden** [from Berkhamsted take unmarked rd towards Potten End, pass Potten End turning on right then take next left towards Ashridge College; TL0110], *Alford Arms*: In attractive countryside with tables out in front, and brewing its own real ales in tiny brewhouse; simple bar food, local atmosphere, good service even when busy, piped music (not obtrusive) in games area; live music Weds, open all day Sat *(Lyn and Bill Capper, R Houghton, LYM)*

Great Offley [TL1427], *Prince Henry*: Comfortable and relatively uncrowded, with 1920s-style furnishings and decor, wide choice of good value bar food, Greene King IPA and Abbot and Marstons Pedigree, good fish restaurant, popular Sun carvery *(Michael and Alison Sandy)*; [towards Kings Walden], *Red Lion*: Pleasantly old-fashioned smart country pub, sometimes more horses outside than cars; well kept Flowers, Marstons Pedigree and Wethereds, good food inc set Sun lunch, friendly service; bedrooms *(Michael Sandy, Billy Dee, Nicky Morris)*

Harpenden [469 Luton Rd (A1081 on way in from M1 junction 10); TL1314], *Fox*: Under new licensee lounge bar carefully extended with lots of dining tables for wide range of good value food; Allied real ales well kept, service good *(Michael and Alison Sandy)*; [East Common], *Three Horseshoes*: Attractively surrounded by quiet common, with tables on lawn and terrace; weekday food, well kept Brakspears and Whitbreads-related real ales, children welcome; has had jazz Tues *(David Shillitoe, Duncan Stuart-Mills, LYM)*

Hatfield [Park St, Old Hatfield; TL2308], *Eight Bells*: Recently re-opened after careful renovations by Allied, old low-beamed place with Oliver Twist connections; well kept Benskins Best and Ind Coope Burton on handpump, decent reasonably priced bar food *(Nick and Alison Dowson, Dr Gordon Copp)*; [Mill Green, off A1000 towards Welwyn Gdn City — OS Sheet 166, map reference 241099], *Green Man*: Small, cosy local with efficient friendly service, well kept Allied ales, good value sandwiches and ploughman's (lunchtime, not Sun), coal-effect gas fire; tables in garden, handy for Hatfield House *(Robin Perkins)*; [89 Great North Rd, off A414 N edge of town, S of Tesco — OS Sheet 166, map reference 232096], *Wrestlers*: Brass, beams and brazier-type fire; pleasant atmosphere, well kept Benskins Best and Ind Coope Burton, friendly staff, big garden *(Nick and Alison Dowson)*

☆ **Hertford** [Fore St], *Salisbury Arms*: Comfortably traditional English country-town hotel which has been praised for good Chinese food alongside more usual bar food inc outstanding sandwiches, well kept McMullens ales inc AK Mild and friendly waitress service, but no recent reports *(News please)*

☆ **Hertford** [Old Cross], *Woolpack*: Riverside McMullens pub next to brewery with attractive sawdust-and-bare-boards rambling bar, big beams, heavy stripped furniture, open fire, lots of dried flowers, foliage, stoneware jars, bottles, farm tools, tradesmen's boards; limited but impressive range of bar food, attractively presented and wholesome, inc beautiful ploughman's *(Ruth and Alan Woodhouse)*

Hertford [The Folly], *Old Barge*: Very popular well run canalside pub concentrating largely on vegetarian food; well kept Benskins Best, Ind Coope Burton, Tetleys and Youngs Special *(Nick and Alison Dowson, LYM)*

☆ **Hinxworth** [Main St, just off A1(M); TL2340], *Three Horseshoes*: Charming old thatched village pub with beamed and timbered bars and big brick inglenook; small dining extension leads to big garden with swings and climbing frames; Greene King IPA and Abbot and wide choice of good food (not Sun evening, Mon) inc children's dishes, freshly home-cooked so there may be a wait; friendly licensees, Weds singalong *(Sidney Wells, KC)*

Hitchin [Chapelfoot; B656, 2 miles towards Codicote; TL1925], *Royal Oak*: Greatly refurbished Brewers Fayre pub, with reconstructed barn, attractive decor, helpful staff — very friendly *(Margaret and Trevor Errington)*

Ickleford [TL1831], *Old George*: Rambling heavy-beamed Tudor pub by churchyard, good value simple but substantial food pleasantly served, Greene King beers; very quiet midweek lunchtime *(G L Tong, LYM)*

☆ **Kings Langley** [60 High St; TL0702], *Rose & Crown*: Lots of character in very welcoming pub with good warm fires, attractive pictures and lamps, Allied and several guest real ales; jazz/live bands four nights a week and Sun lunchtime *(TBB)*

☆ **Knebworth** [Park Lane, Old Knebworth; TL2320], *Lytton Arms*: Friendly, well managed pub with character, welcoming bar staff, decent bar food running up to steaks inc good choice of starters and puddings, long bar serving eight weekly changing beers (not cheap) and espresso coffee, friendly service, fruit machines; clean garden with barbecues and children's play equipment *(Joe and Stephanie Wylot, P Verdier, Colleen Holiday)*

☆ **Lemsford** [A6129 towards Wheathampstead; TL2111], *Crooked Chimney*: Well run spacious open-plan dining pub popular for family Sun lunch; central feature fireplace, well kept Allied real ales, restaurant and garden by fields *(John Whitehead, Nick and Alison Hayward, LYM)*

☆ **Lemsford**, *Sun*: Cheerful and popular low-beamed and timbered pub nr River Lea, well kept Courage, good generously served bar meals; can be busy and noisy in evenings but kept tidy *(John Whitehead, Nick Dowson, LYM)*

☆ **Letchmore Heath** [2 miles from M1 junction 5; A41 towards Harrow, first left towards Aldenham, then signed right; TQ1597], *Three Horseshoes*: Best point is lovely position opp duck pond on tree-shaded green; pretty and cottagey little flower-decked local with low ceilings, wide choice of standard weekday lunchtime bar food (snacks Sat), well kept Benskins Best and Ind Coope Burton on handpump, maybe faint piped music, white tables outside; can get crowded *(Olive Carroll, Ian Phillips, Philip Harrison, A C Morrison, LYM)*

☆ **Little Hadham** [The Ford; TL4422], *Nags Head*: Friendly 16th-century country local with well kept Greene King and Rayments, good food using fresh ingredients; restaurant; children welcome *(LYM)*

☆ **London Colney** [Waterside; just off main st by bridge at S end; TL1704], *Green Dragon*: Neatly kept and friendly, with soft lighting, lots of beams and brasses, well kept Adnams and Allied real ales, good atmosphere, good value straightforward lunchtime bar food (not Sun); pretty setting, tables out by quiet riverside green *(Nick Dowson, LYM)*

☆ **Much Hadham** [B1004; TL4319], *Bull*: Attractively straightfoward inglenook public bar, comfortable brocade-banquette lounge, cosy family dining room and spacious back garden; has been popular for good choice of food inc half-price children's helpings and rich puddings and well kept Allied ales, but no reports yet on new regime *(LYM; news please)*

Northaw [B157; TL2802], *Two Brewers*: Well furnished dining pub with cosy-sized rooms off low-ceilinged centre, good choice of food and well kept Benskins; pretty village *(A M Kelly)*

Pimlico [just outside Hemel, between Leverstock Green and Bedmond; TL0905], *Swan*: Unpretentious, with militaria and good choice of bar food; garden has genuine Percival Proctor trainer aircraft, Bofors anti-tank gun and 'ride-on' two-man torpedo from WW2 *(Stan Edwards)*

Pirton [TL1431], *Cat & Fiddle*: Homely pub facing village green, well kept Charles Wells real ales, bar food, swing on back lawn *(Colleen Holiday, LYM)*

☆ **Potters Crouch** [leaving St Albans on Watford rd via Chiswell Green, turn right after M10 — OS Sheet 166, map reference 116052; TL1105], *Holly Bush*: Small whitewashed pub with highly polished good biggish tables and other dark wood furniture, lots of pictures, plates, brasses and antlers, old-fashioned lighting; Benskins Best and Ind Coope Burton, reasonable simple food, efficient service, big garden with picnic-table sets; gets very popular *(BKA, Christian Leigh)*

Redbourn [Redbourn Rd (A5183); nr M1 junction 9; TL1012], *Chequers*: Roomy old oak-beamed Chef & Brewer pub in attractive open countryside; popular for good atmosphere, good value food (inc wide choice of specials), well kept Watneys-related real ales; back terrace and big garden by stream, nice restaurant; children welcome *(Mr and Mrs D Gritten, John Whitehead)*

☆ **Reed** [High St; TL3636], *Cabinet*: Ancient tiled and weatherboarded pub, friendly, relaxed and parlourish, with spacious lounge extension, charming garden with children's summer bar; reasonably priced bar food, wide choice of well kept real ales tapped from the cask, warm welcome *(LYM)*

☆ **Rickmansworth** [TQ0594], *Scotsbridge Mill*: Comfortably converted water mill — River Chess runs through building and through grounds crossed with narrow bridges; Whitbreads-related real ales, bar food, wider choice in extensive rambling two-floor Beefeater restaurant; tables out behind in plenty of space, nice countryside

(Lyn and Bill Capper)
Sandridge [High St; TL1610], *Rose & Crown*: Civilised and comfortable Groaning Board dining pub, friendly and relaxed, with four well kept real ales such as Flowers and Wadworths 6X, wide choice of generous food inc imaginative dishes as well as standards; welcoming service; dates to 15th century *(Michael and Alison Sandy, John Whitehead)*

☆ **St Albans** [Holywell Hill; TL1507], *White Hart*: Friendly but civilised hotel with considerable character and charm, and long and entertaining history; comfortable bar with antique panelling, handsome fireplaces and furnishings; bar food and accommodating restaurant, Allied real ales on handpump *(LYM)*

☆ **St Albans** [36 Fishpool St], *Lower Red Lion*: Lively and friendly beamed free house, well kept Adnams, Fullers London Pride, Greene King Abbot and Youngs Special on handpump, gas-effect log fires, plenty of seating; good value interesting bar food inc big steak sandwiches; in conservation area, pretty garden; bedrooms reasonably priced, though share bathrooms; huge breakfast *(Richard Houghton, P S Vince)*
St Albans [6 London Rd], *Peahen*: Comfortable Victorian-style McMullens pub, long, low lounge with gas-type lamps, display cases of Victoriana, decent bar food, real ale, piped Radio 1; basic separate public bar *(Michael and Alison Sandy)*; [Lower Dagnall St], *Verulam Arms*: Attractive one-room pub, clean and friendly, with well kept Allied and guest beers, good value bar food inc German specialities *(David Fowles)*

☆ nr **St Albans** [Tyttenhanger Green; off A414 E — OS Sheet 166, map reference 182059], *Plough*: Well run and spacious, with fine open fire, ten or so well kept real ales on handpump, bar billiards, walls festooned with old beer bottles and knick-knacks, loads of old aircraft magazines; friendly young staff, good value standard bar food (no Sun lunch), tea, coffee, garden *(Nick Dowson, M B Porter, P S Vince)*

☆ **Tewin** [Upper Green Rd; TL2714], *Plume of Feathers*: Pleasant old beamed building, keeping pub atmosphere despite emphasis on food, with low ceilings and some character furnishings; food in bar and restaurant interesting, well cooked and well presented, staff friendly and helpful, landlord unusually attentive; good choice of beers and wines, warm fires *(John Whitehead, Nick and Alison Dowson, Mrs S Mills, Julia Morrison, David Barrow)*
Tewin, *Rose & Crown*: Refurbished Greene King pub with well kept beers, promising food, good welcoming service, good outside terrace *(John Whitehead)*

☆ **Thorley Street** [A1184 Sawbridgeworth—Bishops Stortford; TL4718], *Coach & Horses*: Generous helpings of bar food and quick, pleasant service in tastefully furnished and extended popular dining area, good family facilities; well kept Allied beers, decent wine;

children's play area *(R C Vincent)*

☆ **Tring** [London Rd (A41); Wigginton; SP9310], *Cow Roast*: Interesting two-level 17th-century inn with huge inglenook, decent choice of good value bar food up to steaks, upmarket restaurant; well kept Allied real ales with a guest such as Youngs Special, good coffee, efficient welcoming staff; restaurant; superb garden with children's play area, barbecue very popular with families *(Tony Swindells, Dave Gardiner, R M Savage)*
Walkern [TL2826], *White Lion*: Comfortable and welcoming old pub, popular for bar food and small restaurant, cosy alcoves and low beams, nice inglenook *(Charles Bardswell, LYM)*; *Yew Tree*: Clean and friendly, McMullens real ale, open fire, good choice of bar food at lower than average prices for the area *(Laurence McGlenn)*

☆ **Watford** [11 Stamford Rd; off Langley Rd, itself off St Albans Rd nr Watford Junction Stn; TQ1196], *Nascot Arms*: Backstreet corner local with two connected bars reminiscent in decor of bar in guest house — but wonderful welcoming landlord, staff and atmosphere, very cosy and comfortable; Greene King beers in top condition inc XX Dark, popular lunchtime food, terrace *(Richard Houghton, Stan Edwards)*

☆ **Wheathampstead** [Marford Rd; E edge of town — OS Sheet 166, map reference 184138; TL1716], *Nelson*: Newly refurbished small local with half a dozen well kept real ales, several good fires, reasonably priced food, pleasant landlord; comfortable and welcoming *(John Whitehead, H Glew, J Ramalho, Nick Dowson)*
Wheathampstead, *Swan*: Good friendly welcome, smart obliging service in clean and well kept pub under new management, relaxed atmosphere, three real ales; no food Sun *(John Whitehead)*
nr **Wheathampstead** [Gustard Wood; off B651 1 1/2 miles N, towards Shaws Corner], *Cross Keys*: New licensees at simple, friendly and clean local, prettily tucked away in woodland; Allied real ales with a guest such as Greene King IPA, simple bar food, picnic-table sets in orchard *(Margaret and Trevor Errington, Geoff Lee, LYM)*; [Nomansland Common; B651 1/2 mile S — OS Sheet 166, map reference 176127], *Wicked Lady*: Whitbreads Brewers Fayre dining pub with several areas inc a no-smoking one, separate food servery, family conservatory extension; fruit machines and piped music, well kept Whitbreads-related real ales; big lawn with good play area *(BKA, PW, PS, LYM)*

☆ **Whitwell** [B651; TL1820], *Eagle & Child*: Cosy, welcoming and popular, with friendly licensees, attractively moulded beams, attractive inglenook, good food, Whitbreads-related real ales; darts in snugly clubby public bar, good play area in back garden *(Sidney Wells, Colleen Holiday, Fay Reid, LYM)*

☆ **Whitwell** [67 High St (B651)], *Maidens Head*: Very clean local with good value food from sandwiches and good ploughman's to heft steaks, well kept McMullens tapped from the cask, amusing and friendly staff, interesting ley-ring collection, seats in safe children's garden away form the road *(S R Willett, A J Jennings, J Hobson)*

Wildhill [off B158 Brookmans Pk—Essendon; TL2606], *Woodman*: Basic local in fairly remote spot with open-plan bar, small homely lounge, low-priced Greene King IPA and Abbot *(Nick Dowson)*

Wormley [West End; TL3605], *Woodman*: Very comfortable and relaxed, with well kept McMullens AK and Country *(John C Baker)*

Humberside

Humberside is definitely a place for good value in pubs. Drinks prices here are well below the national average, and a far higher proportion of pubs than usual here – picked out by the £ symbol – meet our targets for bargain food. It's not just a question of cheapness, either, as the bargains are often really good, such as the buoyant filled Yorkshire puddings at the Half Moon at Skidby (they say the secret's using really fresh eggs – even a day or two older and the batter won't rise so well). Other pubs here, at very reasonable prices which have not increased as sharply as in most areas, serve bar food that's well above average in quality: the particularly welcoming Plough at Allerthorpe, the old-fashioned Seabirds at Flamborough (emphasis on fresh fish), the friendly Gold Cup tucked away at Low Catton (its Sunday lunch is particularly popular), the Pipe & Glass at South Dalton (thoroughly re-established now after its post-fire rebuilding, with real imagination showing in its kitchen) and the popular Three Cups at Stamford Bridge. Two other pubs deserving a special mention are the White Horse in Beverley – for its remarkably unspoilt charm; and the harbour-edge Minerva in Hull – for the beers it brews on the premises. Note that the Gate up at Millington has stopped doing bedrooms now; but in return very comfortable ones can be found at a new entry here, the friendly Feathers at Pocklington (a Tuesday meeting-place for half the East Riding, it seems). Pubs of above-average merit in the Lucky Dip section at the end of the chapter include the Boot & Shoe at Ellerton, Light Dragoon at Etton, George at Hull (these first three all inspected by us) and Downe Arms at Little Driffield. In general, the low-to-medium-priced family dining pubs which the Nottingham-based regional brewery Mansfield are setting up in Humberside are good value. And the Brewers Arms at Snaith is notable for its fine Old Mill real ales brewed nearby.

ALLERTHORPE   SE7847 Map 7

Plough

Off A1079 nr Pocklington

There's a genuinely friendly welcome and a relaxed atmosphere in this pretty white house. And the generous helpings of good bar food are quite a plus, too: Yorkshire pudding and onion gravy or home-made soup (£1.30), open sandwiches (from £1.50), ploughman's (£2.75), salads (from £3.50), spare ribs in a secret sauce or home-made curry (£4), gammon and egg (£4.50), sirloin steak (£7.50), daily specials like pork stroganoff, lovely fresh haddock or cod, and chilli con carne, vegetarian dishes on request, puddings (from £1.75), children's menu (from £1.30), and good Sunday roast. The two-room lounge bar has snug alcoves (including one big bay window), hunting prints, some wartime RAF and RCAF photographs (squadrons of both were stationed here), matchboxes glued to the ceiling at the end of the bar, and open fires. The games – pool, dominoes, shove-ha'penny, cribbage, fruit machine, video game, and juke box – are in an extension. Well kept Theakstons Best, XB and Old Peculier, and Youngers IPA on handpump, and coffee; piped music. There are tables on the grass outside; handy for the attractive lily-pond gardens and stuffed sporting trophies of Burnby Hall. *(Recommended by Heather Croft, Roger Bellingham, Colin and Mary Meaden, Ken and Norma Guyll, I R Rorison, Andy and Jill Kassube)*

Free house   Licensee David Banks   Real ale   Meals and snacks   Restaurant
Pocklington (0759) 302349   Children welcome   Open 12–3, 7–11

BEVERLEY   TA0340   Map 8

White Horse ('Nellies') £

Hengate, close to the imposing Church of St Mary's; runs off North Bar Within

Though John Wesley preached in the back yard in the mid 18th century, this fine
unspoilt building actually dates from around 1425. The small rooms have a
carefully preserved Victorian feel – quite without frills: bare floorboards, brown
leatherette seats (with high-backed settles in one little snug), a gas-lit
pulley-controlled chandelier, a deeply reverberating chiming clock, antique
cartoons and sentimental engravings, and open fires – one with an attractively tiled
fireplace. Well kept Sam Smiths OB and Museum on handpump, and remarkably
cheap food – sandwiches (from 70p), fish and chips or chicken and mushroom pie
(£2.75), and ploughman's; darts and pool. (*Recommended by Andy and Jill Kassube,
Paul Harrop, DC; more reports please*)

*Sam Smiths   Manager Mr Southern   Real ale   Lunchtime meals and snacks   Evening
restaurant; closed Mon   Hull (0482) 861973   Children welcome   Folk Mon, Jazz
Weds, occasional weekend bands   Open 11–11; closed 25 Dec*

FLAMBOROUGH   TA2270   Map 8

Seabirds ✪

Junction of B1255 and B1229

Just right after a blowy walk on the cliffs, this friendly slightly old-fashioned place
remains popular for its very good value food – with particular emphasis on the
fish: lunchtime sandwiches and ploughman's, good soup (£1.35), good garlic
scallops or mussels, omelettes (from £3), home-made steak and kidney pie (£3.50),
fresh local haddock and plaice (£3.60), grilled ham and eggs (£4.70), fresh crab or
local lobster salads, poached salmon (£5.85), sirloin steak (£8.50), daily specials
like excellent smoked haddock and broccoli quiche (£3.75), beef kremeskies
(£4.25), and pheasant in port (£5.45), and puddings (£1.40). Camerons Strongarm
on handpump; over 35 wines, and a large selection of whiskies and liqueurs;
friendly staff. The public bar is full of shipping paraphernalia, and old framed
photographs of Flamborough, and leading off this is the lounge, which has pictures
and paintings of the local landscape, a mirror glazed with grape vines, and a
woodburning stove; there's also a whole case of stuffed seabirds along one wall.
Darts, dominoes, fruit machine and piped music. There's now a family room in the
garden with a video game. (*Recommended by Roger Bellingham, P G Topp, N H White,
Colin and Mary Meaden, Barbara Wensworth, D J Milner, Tony and Penny Burton, Jan and
Ian Alcock, Syd and Wyn Donald, David and Rebecca Killick*)

*Free house   Licensees Keith Rostron and Mrs J Riding   Real ale   Meals and snacks
(not Sun or Mon winter evenings)   Summer restaurant   Bridlington (0262) 850242
Children in eating area of bar and restaurant   Open 11–3, 6.30–11*

HULL   TA0927   Map 8

Minerva £

From A63 Castle Street/Garrison Road, turn into Queen Street towards piers at central
traffic lights; some metered parking here; pub is in pedestrianised Nelson Street, at far
end

This interesting pub fronts on to a pedestrian area facing the old landing stage
from which the Humber Ferry used to sail. Several thoughtfully refurbished rooms
ramble all the way around a central servery: interesting photographs and pictures
of old Hull (with two attractive wash drawings by Roger Davis), a big chart of the
Humber, comfortable seats, a tiny snug with room for just three people, and a
back room (which looks out to the marina basin, and has darts) with a profusion

of varnished woodwork. Besides well kept Tetleys Bitter on handpump, the pub brews its own Pilots Pride (you can see into the microbrewery from the street). Lunchtime bar food includes sandwiches (from £1), chicken curry or chilli (£2.90), beef cobbler (£2.95), and steak pie (£3.05); in the evening there are burgers, plaice, chicken kiev (£3.50), steaks and puddings (£1.25). Darts, dominoes, and fruit machine. Piped music from the fine reproduction Wurlitzer juke box (the real 'works', with the records, are actually in a completely different place) is loud and clear. *(Recommended by T Nott; more reports please)*

Own brew (Tetleys–Allied)   Licensee John Harris McCue   Real ale   Meals and snacks (12–2, 6–8; not Sun evening)   Hull (0482) 26909   Children in eating area of bar only   Open 11–11 in summer; 11–4, 6–11 Mon-Thurs in winter; closed 25 Dec

Olde White Harte ★ £

Off 25 Silver Street, a continuation of Whitefriargate (see previous entry); pub is up narrow passage beside the jewellers' Barnby and Rust, and should not be confused with the much more modern White Hart nearby

A good mix of people gives this ancient tavern a proper town pub atmosphere. There are polished flooring tiles, carved heavy beams supporting black ceiling boards, attractive stained glass windows over the bow window-seat, and brocaded Jacobean-style chairs in the inglenook by a fireplace decorated with delft tiles. The curved copper-topped counter serves well kept Youngers IPA and No 3, Theakstons XB on handpump and 14 malt whiskies. Simple, traditional bar food includes sandwiches (from 80p, hot beef £1.90), salads or ploughman's (from £1.65), and lasagne (£2.25); Sunday lunch; courteous, speedy service. A handsome old oak staircase takes you up past a grandfather clock to a heavily panelled room where on St George's Day 1642 Sir John Hotham, the town's Governor, decided to lock the gate at the far end of Whitefriargate against King Charles, depriving him of the town's arsenal – a fateful start to the Civil War. There are seats in the courtyard outside. *(Recommended by T Nott; more reports please)*

Youngers (S & N)   Managers Gary and Anne Sowden   Real ale   Meals and snacks 11.30–2   Lunchtime restaurant   Hull (0482) 26363   Children in restaurant   No nearby parking   Open 11–11 Mon to Fri, 11–4, 6–11 Sat

LOW CATTON   SE7053   Map 7

Gold Cup ✪

Village signposted with High Catton off A166 in Stamford Bridge or A1079 at Kexby Bridge

The large garden and back paddock here have geese, Shetland ponies, goats and guinea fowl. Inside, the three communicating rooms of the comfortable lounge have open fires at each end, red plush wall seats and stools around good solid tables, flowery curtains, some decorative plates and brasswork on the walls, and a friendly atmosphere. The back games bar is comfortable too, with a well lit pool table, darts, dominoes, fruit machine, video game and well reproduced music. Popular bar food includes sandwiches (from £1.25), soup (£1.30), crusty rolls (from £1.95), giant Yorkshire pudding sandwich, scrumpy spiced ham, grilled gammon or steak, mushroom and Guinness pie, and a vegetarian dish (all £3.95), and chicken kiev (£4.75). Well kept John Smiths and Tetleys on handpump, good coffee, decent wines; friendly service. The restaurant is very popular, so it's best to book, particularly for Sunday lunch. *(Recommended by John and Christine Simpson, H Bramwell, Tim Gilroy, N P Hodgson)*

Free house   Licensees Ray and Pat Hales   Real ale   Snacks (not Fri or Sat evenings) and meals (11.30–2, 7–9.30)   Restaurant (not Sun evenings)   Stamford Bridge (0759) 71354   Children welcome   Open 11.30–3.30, 7–11; closed Monday lunch (except bank hols) and evening 25 Dec

MILLINGTON   SE8352 Map 7

Gate

Village signposted from Pocklington

This welcoming 16th-century pub has modern simple furnishings as well as an antique settle with wings and a high back, black beams supporting the ochre planks of the ceiling, and a big stone fireplace. Plates decorate the main beam over an opening through to another room furnished entirely in yew wood (the age of the trees used has been put at 1,500 years); this room has a set of antlers above its log fire. Cheap and well kept Ind Coope Burton, Tetleys and Theakstons Bitter on handpump, and several malt whiskies. Bar food includes sandwiches, home-made steak, mushroom and Guinness pie (£3.50), sirloin steak (£6), mixed grill (£6.50). Darts, pool, dominoes, and trivia in a back room. There is now a garden; good Wolds walks and remarkable East Riding views from just up the hill. Please note, they no longer do bedrooms. *(Recommended by Lee Goulding, John Burgan, Hilary Irving; more reports please)*

Free house   Licensees Paul and Suzanne Jackson   Real ale   Meals and snacks (not Mon evening)   Restaurant – must be booked   Pocklington (0759) 302045   Children in eating area of bar   Open 12–2, 7–11; closed Mon-Thurs lunchtimes and evening opening on those days 7.30

POCKLINGTON   SE8049 Map 7

Feathers 🛏️

56 Market Place; sigposted off A1079 York–Hull

Nineteen members of the Royal Philharmonic Orchestra tell us they've found this a very accommodating place to stay in. The well equipped bedrooms are now in a good modern block around what used to be the old cattle yard; you no longer run the risk of being put in the former Number 7, haunted by breathy chills and dragging noises thought to be linked to the 1810 murder of a maid here by a highwayman who was later hanged outside. The spreading open-plan lounge has comfortable banquettes and a cheerful market-town atmosphere (especially on market day itself, Tuesday). Good value bar food includes soup (£1.05), Yorkshire pudding with onion gravy (£1.45), sandwiches (£1.55, hot beef and onion £1.80), burgers (£1.70), ploughman's (£2.75), chicken (£3.55), scampi or steak and ale pie (£3.60), salads (from £3.65), gammon (£4) and rump steak (£5); just roast and pie on Sunday; good breakfasts. Well kept Theakstons Best and Youngers Scotch and No 3 on handpump; friendly staff, helpful long-serving licensees. *(Recommended by Steve Merson and others)*

S & N   Managers Ken and Wilma Suttle   Real ale   Meals and snacks   Restaurant   Pocklington (0759) 303155   Open 11–11   Bedrooms; £34B/£48B

SKIDBY   TA0133 Map 8

Half Moon ⚲ £

Main Street; off A164

If you want to enjoy the loaf-sized but feather-light Yorkshire puddings here it's best to arrive early; there are various fillings from £2.05 for onion and gravy, £2.50 with vegetarian gravy, £3.95 for roast beef – so popular that they get through around 60,000 eggs and 7,000lb of flour a year. Other food, efficiently served, includes soup (£1.15), chilli con carne (£2.45), ploughman's (£2.50), steak and kidney pie (£3.40), and puddings (from £1.20); they serve afternoon sandwiches (3–5.30, not Sun); friendly staff. There's an old-fashioned partly panelled front tap-room with a tiled floor, long cushioned wall benches, old elm tables, a little high shelf of foreign beer bottles and miniatures, and a coal fire. The more spacious communicating back rooms have a lighter and airier atmosphere, and an unusually big clock. Darts, dominoes, fruit machine, video game, trivia, and piped music; John Smiths on handpump. The landscaped garden area beside the car park has a children's play area with a suspended net maze, and there are plans for a family room, terrace and barbecue area. A black and white windmill is nearby. (*Recommended by M J Morgan, PLC, Dave Braisted, Dr R Fuller, Dr James Haworth*)

John Smiths (Courage) *Tenants Peter and Diane Madeley* Real ale *Meals and snacks (till 10pm; till 2.30 Sun lunchtimes; afternoon sandwiches 3–5.50)* Children welcome up to 8.30 *Country and Western Tues; 60s last Fri of month* Open 11–11; closed one day over Christmas

SOUTH DALTON SE9645 Map 8

Pipe & Glass ✪

Village signposted off B1248 NW of Beverley

Popular food in this tiled white pub changes daily, and a typical menu might include sandwiches (£1.55), leek and celery soup or Yorkshire pudding and onion gravy (£1.65), dim sum (£2.65), tagliatelle, bacon and peppers or cheese and broccoli quiche (£3.95), fresh crab salad (£4), chicken piri piri or steak and mushroom pie (£4.25), good prawn madras and poppadoms or gammon (£4.50), grilled fillet of plaice (£5.25), excellent duck in cherry sauce, and rump steak (£8.25); Sunday lunchtime food is restricted to the carvery in the old separate stable block. Ruddles Best and Whitbreads Castle Eden on handpump, and decent malts, brandies, and wines; darts, shove-ha'penny, cribbage, dominoes, and piped music. Both bars have beams, leather seats around the walls and in the bow windows, some high-backed settles, old prints, and log fires; there's also a conservatory. In summer, the hanging baskets are charming, and there are tables on a quiet lawn by the edge of Dalton Park, with a children's play area, flower borders, a very fine yew tree, ginger cats and maybe kittens. The village itself is best found by aiming for the unusually tall and elegant spire of the church, visible for miles around. (*Recommended by Roger Bellingham, Duncan Stuart-Mills; more reports please*)

Free house *Licensee Malcolm Crease* Real ale *Meals and snacks (till 10pm; not Mon)* Restaurant *Dalton Holme (0430) 810246* Children welcome *Open 11.30–2.30, 7–11; closed Mon and 25 Dec*

STAMFORD BRIDGE SE7155 Map 7

Three Cups

A166, W end of town; as it's actually over the Derwent Bridge it is just inside the N Yorks border

Once a farmhouse, this busy inn has a spacious bar area with oak beams, extensive panelling, lots of bare ochre brick walls (including an arched stripped partition dividing the two rooms), and green banquettes, library chairs, stools and low armchairs around dark rustic tables; there's a rare annotated *Vanity Fair* cartoon of the nobs at Newmarket in 1885, and in the pleasant alcove at one end are shelves of books, sepia photographs, and an open fire with a hand-turned bellows machine. Popular bar food includes a carvery (Tuesday-Sunday, £4.95), as well as soup (£1.30), filled rolls (£1.50), burgers (from £2.50), ploughman's (from £2.95), home-made lasagne (£3.75), gammon (£4.75), steaks (from £7.45), and puddings (£1.80); children's meals (from £1.70). Well kept Bass and Tetleys on handpump; fruit machine, piped music. Rustic tables run along the front terrace, with more tables on the back lawn, swings and a big shoe house. (*Recommended by G T Jones; more reports please*)

Bass *Tenants Ian and Gill McEnaney* Real ale *Meals and snacks (12–2, 7–10)* No-smoking restaurant *Stamford Bridge (0759) 71396* Children welcome *Open 12–2.30, 7(6.45 Sat)–11* Bedrooms; £20B/£30B

Lucky Dip

Besides the fully inspected pubs, you might like to try these Lucky Dips recommended to us and described by readers (if you do, please send us reports):

Barnetby le Wold [close to M180 junction 8, opp rly stn; SE0509], *Station*: Comfortable lounge with train pictures, has been praised for well kept Wards inc Dark Mild on handpump and interesting good value bar food, but no recent reports *(News please)*

Barton upon Humber [13 Whitecross St; TA0322], *Volunteer Arms*: Two small cosy rooms furnished plainly with sturdy ex-sewing-machine tables and dark wall seats; small beer mat collection, well kept Burtonwood, bar food — book for Sunday lunch; relaxed atmosphere *(Lee Goulding)*

☆ **Beverley** [TA0340], *Beverley Arms*: Comfortable and well kept THF hotel with spacious and traditional oak-panelled bar, well kept real ales, choice of several places to eat inc covered former coachyard, now very much an internal part of the building with an impressive bank of former kitchen ranges; good bedrooms *(LYM)*

Beverley [Dog & Duck Lane], *Dog & Duck*: Basic central pub with very cheap food and nice atmosphere *(Caroline Wright)*; [Saturday Mkt], *Kings Head*: Spacious L-shaped bar opening into two small dining rooms, good bar food even Sun lunchtime, Mansfield real ales; bedrooms *(DC)*

Bishop Burton [Main St; A1079 Beverley—York; SE9939], *Altisidora*: Low-beamed modernised lounge with comfortable alcoves, now a Mansfield Landlords Table family food pub; nr pretty pond in lovely village green *(LYM)*; *Dog & Duck*: Recently refurbished big old pub with an older, slightly smoky public bar, and a long bar more for eating; good Mansfield and Riding ales, good food, delightful service *(Dr R Fuller)*

☆ **Brandesburton** [village signposted from A165 N of Beverley and Hornsea turn-offs; TA1247], *Dacre Arms*: Good value generous bar food in rather vividly modernised but friendly and comfortable pub with choice of well kept real ales on handpump, good service, restaurant; children welcome *(M B P Carpenter, LYM)*

Brandesburton, *Black Swan*: Recently reopened as good value Mansfield Landlords Table family dining pub; good staff *(N H White)*

Brantingham [southern edge; SE9429], *Triton*: Spacious and comfortably refurbished, with good choice of usual bar food, restaurant with French windows to terrace, tables in sheltered garden with play area, conservatory bar; now under same management as Dacre Arms, Brandesburton *(BB)*

Bridlington [184 Kingsgate (A165, just outside); TA1867], *Broadacres*: Large, popular pub with Watneys-related real ales on handpump, good log fires, well planned layout inc snack bar, Watneys Country Carvery restaurant and children's room; has

been praised for good food inc superb local haddock, good service, but no recent reports *(News please)*; [Market Pl], *Packhorse*: Clean and welcoming, with good value home cooking, cosy polished decor; children welcome — separate room for unaccompanied ones, serving good soft drinks *(W B Gray)*

Broughton [just off M18, junction A15/A18; SE9608], *Briggate Lodge*: Good bar food and Websters Yorkshire in bars of new hotel, good restaurant — good break-point for journeys using Humber Bridge; bedrooms *(E J Cutting)*

Cleethorpes [Taylors Ave; TA3008], *Lynton*: Refurbished as Toby Grill; waitresses polite and don't hurry you, good steaks, good choice of puddings and well kept ale *(Kevin Barwood)*

☆ **Cottingham** [TA0633], *Tiger*: Comfortably refurbished pub, with friendly landlord and staff, well kept Bass on handpump, generous helpings of reasonably priced bar food *(David Gaunt, John Burgan, Hilary Irving)*

Ellerker [SE9229], *Black Horse*: This former main entry is really now functioning too much as a restaurant to be counted as a proper pub *(LYM)*

☆ **Ellerton** [signed off B1228 — OS Sheet 105, map reference 705398; SE7039], *Boot & Shoe*: Low-beamed 16th-century cottage with comfortable and friendly old bar, fair-priced standard evening bar food (not Mon, but Sun lunch too — when it can get crowded), well kept Old Mill and Tetleys on handpump and three winter log fires; pub games, good-sized garden behind, restaurant; children till 9; has been closed weekday lunchtime, winter Sat lunchtime *(Andy and Jill Kassube, LYM)*

☆ **Etton** [3 ½ miles N of Beverley, off B1248; SE9843], *Light Dragoon*: Roomy and comfortable village pub in rolling Wolds country, popular for wide range of good value bar food; two atmospheric dimly lit comfortable rooms, inglenook fireplace, well kept Youngers Scotch and IPA on handpump, garden with play area; occasional folk music *(Lee Goulding, Ann Griffiths, LYM)*

☆ **Flamborough** [junction B1255/B1229; TA2270], *Royal Dog & Duck*: Warm and friendly, with homely atmosphere in snug back bar and several other rambling rooms; generous helpings of popular food in efficient restaurant, keg beers; children allowed; bedrooms *(Barbara and Norman Wells, Tony and Penny Burton, Anthony Sargent, Caroline Gant, LYM)*

Great Driffield [TA0258], *Bell*: Good food inc wide choice of help-yourself salads, good friendly service, wide range of beers, decent wine, coffee and tea *(Roger Bellingham)*

Grimsby [Brighowgate; TA2609], *County*: Popular bar which has been praised for well kept Youngers, comfortable reasonably priced bedrooms with terrific breakfasts throughout the morning; but no recent reports *(News please)*

Halsham [B1362 Hedon—Withernsea; TA2727], *New Stag*: Quiet pub isolated in bleak countryside on winding back rd; very relaxed atmosphere, keg beers, no food, lots of bric-a-brac collected by enthusiastic landlord in simple bar divided by part-glazed panel from bar billiards room *(Lee Goulding)*

Hedon [TA1928], *Shakespeare*: Cosy village local, small L-shaped bar with thousands of beermats on beams, old framed brewery advertisements, real fire; friendly service, at least five real ales inc Darleys, Vaux Samson and Wards, juke box; gets very busy; bedrooms *(Anon)*

☆ **Hull** [Land of Green Ginger, Old Town; TA0927], *George*: Handsomely traditional long Victorian bar, lots of oak, mahogany and copper, cheap bar lunches, well kept Bass and Stones on handpump, thriving atmosphere, piped music; handy for the fine Docks Museum; children allowed in plush upstairs dining room; open all day *(LYM)*

☆ **Hull** [150 High St (in Old Town to S of centre, quite near Olde White Harte], *Olde Black Boy*: Little black-panelled low-ceilinged front smoke room, lofty 18th-century back vaults bar (with juke box strong on golden oldies, fruit machine, TV]; well kept Tetleys Mild and Bitter, bar food, friendly staff, interesting history *(BB)*

☆ **Hull** [alley off Lowgate; look out for huge blue bell over pavement], *Olde Blue Bell*: Well kept Sam Smiths OB on handpump and good value simple lunchtime food inc traditional Sunday lunch, in snug old three-room pub refurbished in traditional style; nr market *(BB)*

Hull [King St (Market Pl]], *Kings*: Interesting, newish bar in Old Town, mix of dark corners and bright open areas; exceptionally popular, with queues at weekends *(Lee Goulding)*; [Bricknell Ave], *West Bulls*: Large Toby pub/restaurant with good food and welcome *(John C Gould)*

Kirkburn [signed off A163 SW of Great Driffield; SE9855], *Queens Head*: Usual bar food with lunchtime summer carvery, well kept Watneys-related real ales, decent wines, tables among flowers and fruit-trees in pretty garden, galleried restaurant (Sun lunchtime, Tues-Sat evenings); children welcome; open all day summer *(LYM)*

☆ **Little Driffield** [Downe Arms; TA0158], *Downe Arms*: Friendly village pub with attractive decor and good choice of good reasonably priced food; restaurant *(Mrs Barbara Head, N H White)*

North Dalton [SE9352], *Star*: Upmarket village pub overlooking big pond, has been praised for enthusiastic young licensees, well kept Tetleys, good food and comfortable

bedrooms; but no recent reports *(News please)*

Rawcliffe [High St — OS Sheet 105, map reference 685229; SE6823], *Neptune*: Cheerful helpful staff, reliably good standard food — particularly fish; bar food Sun lunchtime too; very maritime theme *(DC)*

Redbourne [Main St; SK9799], *Red Lion*: Well kept and pleasant, with decent food — an oasis; bedrooms *(P A Devitt)*

☆ **Sledmere** [junction B1252/B1253 NW Gt Driffield; SE9365], *Triton*: Small and simple 18th-century inn with high-backed settles, good log fire, well kept Tetleys and Youngers Scotch, simple but generous bar food (not Mon lunchtime); games and juke box in public bar; in attractive spot; children welcome; bedrooms *(Gwen and Peter Andrews, I H Rorison, LYM)*

☆ **Snaith** [10 Pontefract Rd; SE6422], *Brewers Arms*: Good mill conversion, with exposed joists, brick and timber bar counter, light conservatory-style dining area with pine ceiling, green plush chairs, Turkey carpet and lots of plants; notable for the fine Old Mill and Bullion from their own brewery; bedrooms *(T Nott)*

South Cave [SE9231], *Fox & Coney*: Theakstons and Youngers ales, food inc good sandwiches and beef salad; promising young landlord *(Dr R Fuller)*

☆ **Sutton upon Derwent** [B1228 SE of York; SE7047], *St Vincent Arms*: Cosily panelled front parlour with high-backed settles, brass, copper and plates, further lounge, dining room and restaurant; wide choice of popular if rather pricey bar food till 10, well kept Courage or John Smiths and a guest such as Batemans XXX, unusually good choice of wines by the bottle; big garden; children welcome *(Gwen and Peter Andrews, PJP, LYM)*

☆ **Walkington** [B1230; SE9937], *Ferguson Fawsitt Arms*: Attractive mock-Tudor bars with wide choice of home-cooked hot dishes from airy flagstoned food bar, tables out on terrace, games bar with pool table *(John Burgan, Hilary Irving, LYM)*

☆ **Welton** [village signposted from A63 just E of Hull outskirts; SE9627], *Green Dragon*: Spaciously and spotlessly refurbished as Mansfield Landlords Table family dining pub; decent standard food in restaurant part (only sandwiches in bar), good service; notable as the real-life scene of the unglamorous arrest of Dick Turpin *(John Burgan, Hilary Irving, LYM)*

Wilberfoss [off A1079 E of York; SE7351], *Oddfellows Arms*: Open-plan, interesting pictures and plates on delft shelf, Bass and Stones, busy but pleasant service, decent bar food inc rabbit pie, vegetarian dishes and old-fashioned puddings; good coffee *(Arthur and Mary Beck)*

Isle of Wight

It seems all change in the island's pubs this year. For a start, Whitbreads have sold many of the pubs formerly tied to them to Gales, a Hampshire brewer based in Horndean (and famous for its traditional country wines, which are therefore becoming more of an island speciality). The shake-out in the brewing industry following the government's moves to weaken the national brewers' monopoly hold on prices is having less happy effects, too. In particular the big brewers have been giving many of their long-serving tenants notice to quit (either to take back a core of their most profitable pubs under direct brewery management, or to dispose of pubs that they see less prospect of a lucrative return from). This has happened to the tenant of the White Lion at Arreton, one of the island's nicer pubs. Other changes here are happier. In particular, we have four fine new main entries. The very unaffected local Red Lion at Freshwater does really good value food and has decent wines by the glass; the Seaview Hotel in Seaview, a nice place to stay at yet with a thoroughly pubby bar, has some particularly good food; the snug little Crown at Shorwell's a happy chatty place to spend an evening; and the Spyglass makes the most of its splendid position above the sea in Ventnor – a really good pub. There's real promise in the Lucky Dip at the end of the chapter, too, particularly at the Crab & Lobster at Bembridge, Pier View in Cowes, Hare & Hounds up at Downend and Pointer at Newchurch.

ARRETON   SZ5486 Map 2
White Lion

As we went to press, the licensees who have made this comfortable white house popular with readers heard that (as with many other tenants) their brewery was giving them notice. This does not necessarily mean they will go, but does put an obvious question-mark over the pub's future. We hope for a solution which will preserve its good qualities – a quiet, welcoming atmosphere, pleasant staff, and good value home-made food. This includes sandwiches (from £1.40), winter soup, ploughman's (from £2), and salads (£3); good English cheeses and no fried food. The communicating rooms of the roomy, beamed lounge bar have partly panelled walls decorated with guns, shining brass and horse-harness, and cushioned Windsor chairs on the brown carpet. The smaller, plainer public bar has dominoes and winter darts. Flowers and Whitbreads Strong Country tapped from casks behind the bar with an interesting cask-levelling device; piped music. There's a family Cabin Bar (full of old farm tools) in the pleasing garden and you can also sit out in front by the tubs of flowers. The village church is 12th century and houses the Isle of Wight Brass Rubbing Centre; a craft village nearby. *(Recommended by P Corris, Martyn and Mary Mullins, Henry Peter, Charles Owens, T Nott, Roger Danes, John and Pat Smyth)*

Whitebreads   Tenants David and Maureen James   Real ale   Meals and snacks (11.45–2.30, 7–10.30)   Children in family room and eating area   Open 11–4 (3 winter), 7–11

BONCHURCH   SZ5778   Map 2
Bonchurch Inn

Bonchurch Shute; from A3055 E of Ventnor turn down to Old Bonchurch opposite Leconfield Hotel

The charming Italian licensee and his English wife cook good Italian food and in summer serve it in a flower-filled courtyard enclosed by the buildings worked into the steep rock slope. This might include minestrone soup (£1.40), spaghetti bolognese (£3.50), cannelloni with spinach (£3.75), antipasto (£3.95), risotto seafood (£3.90), and puddings like a proper zabaglione (£2); also, half pint of prawns with vodka sauce (£4.25), vegetarian dishes, chicken cordon bleu (£5.50), rump steak (£5.90), and fresh crab, lobster, sole and halibut. Burts, Flowers and Marstons Pedigree tapped from the cask, fresh orange juice, Italian wines and coffee; darts, bar billiards, shove-ha'penny, dominoes and cribbage. The high-ceilinged and friendly public bar is partly cut into the steep rocks of the Shute, and conjures up an image of salvaged shipwrecks with its floor of narrow-planked ship's decking, folding chairs of the sort that old-fashioned steamers used to have and solid fuel stove in one corner; there's also a smaller saloon. Other bar food includes sandwiches (from £1.20, toasties 20p extra), home-made minestrone soup (£1.40), pizza napoletana (£2.60), quiche lorraine or ploughman's with a choice of cheddar or pâté (£2.85), deep fried squid (£3.10) cold salad platter (from £3.50), antipasto with meats, prawns and pâté (£3.85), 8oz steak or chicken kiev or grilled halibut steak (£5.50), cannelloni, lasagne or grilled fillet of plaice (£3.50), venison and port wine (£6), and puddings (from £1.75) including zabaglione (£1.95). Another converted stable, with a splendid arched entrance and across the cobbled courtyard, is now a café. *(Recommended by MCG, Roger Danes, Andrew Stephenson; more reports please)*

Free house   Licensee Ulisse Besozzi   Real ale   Meals and snacks (11.30–2.15, 6–10.30)   Restaurant   Ventnor (0983) 852611   Children in eating area of bar and in restaurant   Open 11–3, 6–11   Bedrooms; £18/£35

CHALE   SZ4877 Map 2

Clarendon / Wight Mouse ★

In village, on B3399, but now has access road directly off A3055

The buoyant holiday atmosphere of the perky Wight Mouse bar has a warm appeal for families. It's an extended, rambling place, its original core hung thickly with musical instruments, with guns, pistols and so forth over its open fire. At one end, it opens through sliding doors into a pool room with dark old pews and large antique tables, video game and juke box. At the other end is an extension with more musical instruments, oars and even part of a rowing eight hanging from its high pitched ceiling, lots of china mice around a corner fireplace, big decorative plates and other bric-a-brac; there are modern pine pews and blond kitchen chairs here. Turkey-carpeted family room extends beyond a two-way coal-effect gas fire, with quite close-set pews around its tables, hunting prints and more decorative plates. It leads out to the sheltered back lawn, with a boules pitch, lots of play things and a distant sea view. There are more picnic-table sets out in front, too. Big helpings of locally produced and home-made bar food include sandwiches (from £1.30, fresh crab £2.60, toasties 25p extra), home-made soup (£1.40), ploughman's (from £2.30), burgers (from £3.20), ham and eggs (£3.40), salads (from £3.40), Wiener schnitzel (£3.80), home-made pizzas (from £4.20) and scampi or Mexican hot chilli con carne in taco shells (£4.40), fisherman's platter or gravadlax (£5.90), giant mixed grill (£6.50) and steaks (from £7.90) and a range of vegetarian dishes (from £3.10); puddings such as home-made meringue nests filled with fruit, cream, ice cream and nuts (£1.50); there's also a children's menu and service is friendly and efficient. Well kept Boddingtons Bitter, Burts VPA, Marstons Pedigree, Wadworths 6X and Whitbreads Strong Country on handpump, and an outstanding choice of around 365 whiskies as well as some uncommon brandies, madeiras and country wines; darts at one end, dominoes, fruit machine, piped music. They run a pick-you-up and drop-you-home mini-bus service for four or more people (£3 per person). The hotel is named after a ship which was wrecked just off shore here in the Great Storm of 1836. *(Recommended by Les and Jean Bradman, Joan and John Calvert, Phil Clissitt, Ness Turner, Andrew and Helen Hole, John Thorndike, Henry Peters, J Barnwell, GB, CH, Pat and Derek Westcott, Alan and Sharron Tod, Paul Sweetman, John Farmer, A Sweatman, R G Tickner, Andrew Stephenson, Alan and Audrey Chatting, Charles Owens, Roger Danes)*

Free house   Licensees John and Jean Bradshaw   Real ale   Meals and snacks all day

(12–3, 7–10 Sun)   Restaurant   Isle of Wight (0983) 730431   Children in eating areas and three family rooms   Live music every night and summer Sun lunchtimes (not so loud that conversation is drowned)   Open 11am-midnight   Bedrooms; £23(£26B)/£46(£52B)

nr COWES (EAST)   SZ5095 Map 2

Folly

Folly Lane – which is signposted off A3021 just S of Whippingham

Big windows here look out over the boats as do picnic-table sets on the water's-edge terrace and they have their own pontoon mooring for visiting yachtsmen, as well as a VHF radio-telephone, a wind speed indicator, a barometer and a chronometer. Around the old timbered walls are venerable wooden chairs and refectory-type tables, shelves of old books and plates, railway bric-a-brac and farm tools, old pictures, and brass lights. They even have their own mail collection boxes, showers and a launderette. Good bar food includes seafood pie (£4.30), and steak pie or tenderloin of pork in apple and cider sauce (£4.50). Boddingtons, Wadworths 6X and Whitbreads Strong Country on handpump and a wide choice of rums such as West Indian amber; darts, pool, video game, and piped music. There's a good children's playroom, and a landscaped garden. Close to Osborne House. *(Recommended by J Barnwell, Peter Blood, Ian Phillips, W E Parker, John and Pat Smyth, Alan and Audrey Chatting)*

Whitbreads   Licensees Peter and Barbara Handtschoewercker   Real ale   Meals and snacks   Restaurant   Isle of Wight (0983) 297171   Children in eating area of bar and family room   Weds and Thurs country swing, Fri and Sat Hawaiian skiffle jazz, Sun Irish folk   Open 11–3, 6.30(6 Sat)–11; winter evening opening 7

FRESHWATER   SZ3484 Map 2

Red Lion £

Church Place; from A3055 at E end of village by Freshwater Garage mini-roundabout follow Yarmouth signpost and brown sign to Hill Farm Riding Stables, then take first real right turn signed to Parish Church

This is tucked well enough out of the way to have kept a genuinely welcoming local atmosphere, and on our autumn visit they'd just held the annual pumpkin competition, with a hundredweight winner. It's mainly flagstoned, with bare boards at one end, and quite a few rather worn but comfortable and attractive brocaded settees; other furnishings are sturdily country-kitchen in style, and there's a good mix of pictures and china platters on the walls. Bar food includes particularly good well filled sandwiches (from £1.20), filled baked potatoes or ploughman's (from £2.25), lasagne or macaroni cheese (£2.50), salads (from £3.75), and good value daily specials such as smoked haddock pasta with mushrooms and prawns (£2.95), turkey breast in a home-made onion and lemon sauce (£3.75), and trout and almonds (£4.25); well kept Flowers Original, Gales HSB and Marstons Pedigree on handpump, four wines by the glass, open fires, unobtrusive piped music, fruit machine, darts and cribbage. There are picnic-table sets on a sheltered back lawn edged by neat flowerbeds. The church next door has a Norman tower. *(Recommended by J P Berryman, Pat and Derek Westcott, T Nott)*

Whitbreads   Tenant Bryan Farrant   Real ale   Meals and snacks (11.30–2, 6.30–10); not 25 Dec   Isle of Wight (0983) 754925   Children welcome   Guitarist Thurs   Open 11.30–3(4 Sat), 5.30(6 Sat)–11

SEAVIEW   SZ6291 Map 2

Seaview Hotel ⊗ ⇔

High Street; off B3330 Ryde–Brading

From outside this looks like just another small residential seaside hotel; in fact, it has original bar food in its interestingly decorated front bar, a splendidly pubby old-fashioned back bar, a highly regarded evening restaurant, and very comfortable, attractively furnished bedrooms. The particular point of interest in the bay-windowed turkey-carpeted front bar is the splendid array of naval and merchant ship photographs; it has a line of close-set tables down each side, and a pleasantly chatty relaxed atmosphere. The good freshly made bar food includes sandwiches (from £1.60; fresh local crab when available £2.50), a choice of soups (£1.95), ploughman's or onion bhajees (£2.95), pike and leek terrine or a particularly popular little pot of baked crab flavoured strongly with tarragon (£3.70), seafood pasta (£3.95), scampi (£5.90), local lobster (from £7.95), and puddings like treacle sponge pudding (£1.95); good crusty rolls, so a shame about the melty wrapped butter pats. The back bar is dimly lit, with bare boards, ochre walls, good nautical pictures, quite a bit of marine bric-a-brac, traditional pub furnishings and a log fire; Burts and Ind Coope Burton on handpump; darts, shove-ha'penny, cribbage and dominoes. Tables on the front terrace and in the sun porch have a view of the sea and across to the south coast; there are more tables in a sheltered inner courtyard. (*Recommended by Henry Peters, J P Berryman, Mrs J A Blanks, J Barnwell, Harry McCann*)

Free house   Licensees Nicholas and Nicola Hayward   Real ale   Meals and snacks   Restaurant; closed Sun evening   Seaview (0983) 612711   Children in eating area of bar   Open 10.30–3, 6–11   Bedrooms; £43B/£65B

SHALFLEET   SZ4189   Map 2
New Inn

A3054 Newport–Yarmouth

There are plans to extend the snug bar here into the present kitchen area to create a no smoking restaurant/children's room; the kitchen will be moved to a more central area behind the main bar. The garden is to have new furniture and a barbecue. The partly panelled, flagstoned public bar has a boarded ceiling, scrubbed deal tables, a cushioned built-in settle and Windsor chairs, and a roaring log fire in the big stone hearth with guns and an ale yard hanging above it; in the beamed lounge bar there are Windsor chairs and wall banquettes around the stone walls. Bar food includes sandwiches (from £1.50, crab £2.50), ploughman's (from £2.75), home-made lobster bisque (£3.50), crab salad (around £5.50), steaks, and daily specials such as mackerel caught by the landlord (£2.25), kebabs (£3.75) and seafood pizzas (£3.95). The fresh fish is bought from the previous landlord who owns his own small trawler and lobster boat; the selection might include prawns, prawn curry, poachers pie, and Dover sole, and fresh crab and lobster when available; in winter there are live mussels and oysters; seafood platters (£14-£50). On handpump or tapped from the cask are Boddingtons, Flowers Original, Gales HSB, Wadworths 6X and Burts VPA (the landlord deserves praise for getting this direct from the local brewery and pricing it much more cheaply than his tied beers); local fruit wines and strong draught bottled ciders. (*Recommended by Freddy Costello, HNJ, PEJ, R A Corbett, Henry Peters, T Nott, Peter Adcock, Mrs J A Blanks, Anne and Tim Neale, Alan and Audrey Chatting*)

Whitbreads   Lease: Andy and Jane Thomas   Real ale   Meals and snacks   Restaurant   Isle of Wight (0983) 78314   Children in eating area of bar   Occasional folk music and Morris Dancers   Open 11–11; 11–3, 6–11 in winter

SHANKLIN   SZ5881   Map 2
Fishermans Cottage

Bottom of Shanklin Chine

It's the setting that makes this thatched cottage special. From the seats on the terrace you can look straight out onto the beach, and though you can drive to the pub, a path (for which there's a charge in season) zigzags down the picturesquely steep and sinuous Chine. The flagstoned rooms have low beams and photographs, paintings and drawings of the pub on their stripped stone walls. Bar food includes sandwiches, burger (£1.90), ploughman's (from £2.20), chicken nuggets (£2.65), and prawn or crab salad (£3.95). Coffee is served from 10.30 and there is a range of country wines; darts, a fruit machine and piped music. *(Recommended by P Corris, Mr and Mrs P C Clark, T Nott, Andrew Stephenson, Tony and Penny Burton, Roger Danes)*

Free house   Licensees Mrs A P P Springman and Miss M L Prince   Meals and snacks Isle of Wight (0983) 863882   Children in eating area of bar   Occasional jazz summer Weds evenings   Open 11–3, 7–11; open Fri night-Sun night only 1 Nov–1 March

SHORWELL   SZ4582 Map 2

Crown

B3323 SW of Newport; OS Sheet 196, map reference 456829

The big back garden is a delight in summer: picnic-table sets and white garden chairs and tables well spaced out by a little stream where trout wait for delicacies to drift down from the oak trees overhead or the lilies alongside, and white doves circle the dovecot; there are robust wooden slides, and children like the footbridge across from the car park. Inside, the small beamed two-room lounge bar has a good deal of shiny black woodwork, old country prints, blue and white china in a carved dresser, other character furnishings and a winter log fire. Black pews form bays around tables in a stripped-stone room off to the left, with another log fire. The atmosphere is snug and friendly; the one problem is finding a seat. Bar food includes sandwiches (from £1; hot sausage £1.60), soup, ploughman's (£2.50), vegetarian quiches or curry (£3.95), steak and kidney pie (£3.95), and 8oz sirloin steak, with evening specials such as chicken in brandy sauce, salmon, sole or plaice; puddings such as crumbles (from £1.50). Boddingtons, Flowers and Whitbreads Strong Country and winter Pompey Royal tapped from the cask; friendly young staff; Sunday quiz night, faint piped music. *(Recommended by HNJ, PNJ, T Nott, Alan and Audrey Chatting, Anne and Tim Neale, P Corris, Michael and Harriet Robinson)*

Whitbreads   Tenant M Grace   Real ale   Meals and snacks (till 10pm)   Isle of Wight (0983) 740293   Children in eating area of bar   Open 10.30–3, 6–11

VENTNOR   SZ5677 Map 2

Spyglass

Esplanade, SW end; road down very steep and twisty, and parking can be difficult

The position alone, with the good-sized terrace perched just above the sea, would make this well worth visiting, but the pub itself is an excellent example of how careful design rooted genuinely in local traditions can give even a recently refitted place considerable depth of character. It's cleverly broken up into snug separate areas including a carpeted no-smoking room at one end and a family area (with piped pop music) at the other. Most is quarry-tiled, with pews around traditional pub tables, and throughout there's a great deal of nautical memorabilia, much of it with local associations and most well worth a close look. Bar food includes sandwiches (from £1.10), filled baked potatoes (from £1.30), ploughman's (from £3), vegetarian lasagne or chilli con carne (£3.75), pint of prawns (£4.95), steaks, half lobster (£13.95), and puddings (£1.95). Well kept Ind Coope Burton and a beer brewed for the pub by Gibbs Mew on handpump, with changing guest beers tapped from the cask; on special occasions such as a lifeboat support week there may be half a dozen or more. Fruit machine, efficient staff, no objection to dogs or muddy boots; well used by locals and has a good thriving atmosphere. The terrace has a boat rocker for children. *(Recommended by Reg Tickner, Martyn and Mary Mullins, David Culpin, Henry Peters, T Nott, R C Bickerton)*

Free house   Licensees Neil and Stephanie Gibbs   Real ale   Meals and snacks; afternoon tea in summer   Isle of Wight (0983) 855338   Children welcome   Live music every night and Sun lunchtime (piano, jazz, folk)   Open 11–11; 11–3, 6–11 in winter

Lucky Dip

Besides the fully inspected pubs, you might like to try these Lucky Dips recommended to us and described by readers (if you do, please send us reports):

☆ **Bembridge** [Forelands, off Howgate Lane — look for sign into Foreland Fields Rd; OS Sheet 196, map reference 655873; SZ6587], *Crab & Lobster*: Prettily refurbished in parlour style, with clifftop coastguard-station and Solent views from front window, usual bar food, not cheap considering the size of the helpings, small restaurant area, welcoming service, well kept Whitbreads beers, 1950s piped music — rather loud in the lavatories; if you get there early or late you'll avoid coach tours; bedrooms *(T Nott, Roger Danes, Henry Peters, Peter Blood)*

Carisbrooke [Calbourne Rd; B3401 1½ miles W; SZ4687], *Blacksmiths Arms*: Pleasant pub with superb Solent view from small garden behind, very friendly helpful landlord, spotless neat bars, usual range of bar food at attractive prices inc excellently presented fresh salads; no piped music, largeish car park; nr donkey sanctuary *(HNJ, PEJ)*

☆ **Cowes** [25 High St; SZ4896], *Pier View*: Victorian pub with efficient pleasant service, good bar food inc original dishes, well kept Flowers and Marstons Pedigree, good choice of house wines; fresh flowers, unobtrusive piped music, prints of sailing ships, plates and keys on the walls *(Jutta B Whitley)*

Cowes [High St], *Vectis*: Basic stone-floored pub almost at sea level — flood marks inside; friendly atmosphere and landlord, cheap Burts, juke box and games machines *(David Culpin)*

☆ **Downend** [B3056, at crossroads; SZ5387], *Hare & Hounds*: Unspoilt local feel in little white thatched cottage with big log fire and some interesting touches in flagstoned L-shaped main bar, decent island photographs in more modern area on right, sentimental prints and noticeable juke box in games area with well lit pool room, usual bar food, well kept Burts on handpump, old-fashioned seats out in garden with wide views; by Robin Hill Country Park which has good play area *(A J Woodhouse, Henry Peters, BB)*

☆ **Fishbourne** [Fishbourne Rd; from Portsmouth car ferry turn left into no through road; SZ5592], *Fishbourne Inn*: Pleasant surroundings, atmosphere and friendly service; good food, esp puddings *(Henry Peters, J Barnwell)*

Freshwater Bay [SZ3484], *Albion*: Big bar overlooking bay, neat quick service, generous salads and hot dishes, well kept beer; terrace; bedrooms comfortable *(Mrs M R Sale, Henry Peters)*

Gurnard [Princes Esplanade; SZ4795], *Woodvale*: Nice spot with good garden facing Solent, well done interior, good range of usual pub food quickly served, Whitbreads-related real ales on handpump with Gales HSB, Marstons Pedigree and a guest; clean and tidy *(L A Mills)*

Hulverstone [B3399 — OS Sheet 196, map reference 398840; SZ3984], *Sun*: Thatched village pub worth knowing for pleasant well kept gardens looking over to the sea, and play area; simple family food, Gales ales *(T Nott, Henry Peters)*

☆ **Newchurch** [OS Sheet 196, map reference 562855; SZ5685], *Pointer*: Unassuming village local with green leatherette banquettes, flock wallpaper, old local photographs and a couple of fishtanks in lounge, L-shaped games bar on right, straightforward well prepared bar food at fair prices, well kept Flowers IPA and Original on handpump, good range of country wines *(Henry Peters, T Nott, Mrs C Spence, T K Baxter, BB)*

Ningwood [A3054 Newport—Yarmouth, a mile W of Shalfleet — OS Sheet 196, map reference 399892; SZ3989], *Horse & Groom*: Big Whitbreads pub with good home-cooked food in chargrills, fossils in partly stripped limestone wall, new old-world settles, Windsor chairs, brocaded banquettes, bare brickwork, black-stained rough woodwork *(T Nott, Peter Adcock, Charles Owens)*

☆ **Niton** [off A3055; SZ5076], *White Lion*: Refurbished by Whitbreads, with some character surviving, friendly landlord, good reasonably priced food (esp Sun lunches and exotic puddings), children's menu, Whitbreads-related real ales at a price; tables at a premium in the evening *(P Corris, J Barnwell, Bob and Viv Oldfield)*

Rookley [Niton Rd; pub signed off A3020; SZ5183], *Chequers*: Reopened 1990 after being sold by Whitbreads; spacious plush refurbishment in extensive lounge bar looking over road to rolling downland, small log fire, livelier partly flagstoned games area on left, well kept real ales on handpump; picnic-table sets out on grass, with realistic play house in safely fenced play area *(LYM)*

☆ **Seaview** [Esplanade; B3340, just off B3330 Ryde—Brading; SZ6291], *Old Fort*: Good value generous buffet, well served, fresh decor, natural wood furnishings, real ales, pleasant atmosphere of diners and drinkers mingling, fine sea views *(Pat and Derek Westcott, J Barnwell)*

Shanklin [Chine Hill; SZ5881], *Chine*: Quite basic pub with Formica-style furnishings, but well worth knowing for its lovely wooded setting on side of chine with good views out to sea; three bars, big family conservatory with flowers and magnificent vine; cheap food, cheap Burts ales; children allowed away from bar *(Andrew Stephenson)*; [High St Old Town; A3055 towards Ventnor — OS Sheet 196, map reference 584812; SZ5881], *Crab*: Picturesque thatch, but inside rather suburban-feeling, with standard food, well kept Flowers Original and Whitbreads Strong Country on handpump, games and children's room; open all day, very popular with tourists *(SJC, M C Howells, LYM)*

St Lawrence [SZ5376], *St Lawrence*: Superb Channel view from main bar, well above shore level on the tortuous Undercliff rd; friendly helpful staff, quickly fills lunchtime for well presented bar food inc good salad counter and separate salad bar-room *(HNJ, PEJ)*

☆ Whitwell [High St; SZ5277], *White Horse*: Refurbished pub with nice atmosphere, two separate seating areas next to main bar area, and log fire; Gales HSB, BBB, XXXD, and their new Best Bitter on handpump, wide range of food inc good garlic mushrooms *(Martyn and Mary Mullins, Reg Tickner)*

☆ Wootton Bridge [SZ5492], *Sloop*: Big busy brewery food pub, efficient, friendly and good value, in nice spot with lovely view over creek and boats *(Ian Phillips, Alan and Audrey Chatting, Henry Peters)*

Wroxall [SZ5579], *Star*: Cosy quarry-tiled public bar with big open fire, remarkably cheap Burts; nr start GWG42 *(Phil and Sally Gorton)*

☆ Yarmouth [Quay St; SZ3589], *George*: Pleasantly relaxing nautical-theme bar, good food swiftly and courteously served, friendly staff; bedrooms comfortable *(Tessa Stuart, Henry Peters, Tim Brierly)*

☆ Yarmouth [St James' Sq], *Bugle*: Lively recently redecorated bar with counter like galleon stern; food from well filled sandwiches to grills and seafood salads, well kept Flowers Original and Marstons Pedigree on handpump, restaurant, children's room, sizeable garden, maybe impressive summer barbecues; nr GWG40; big airy bedrooms — ask for one that's not over the bar *(Freddy Costello, Peter Adcock, P A Barfield, Henry Peters, Pat and Derek Westcott, LYM)*

Yarmouth [nr ferry terminal], *Kings Head*: Largeish pub/hotel with several well appointed plush and comfortable bars and lounges inc a no-smoking one; friendly attentive staff, wide range of excellently presented food in ample helpings inc good choice of fresh fish; good range of beers, piped music; bedrooms *(HNJ, PY7)*

Kent

Quite a few changes in this county include new licensees for the Dove at Dargate (lovely garden), the Spotted Dog at Penshurst (gorgeous views from its garden) and the fine old George & Dragon at Speldhurst; in all three, the changes seem to be going down well. The Ship at Conyer Quay has shrugged off its tie to Whitbreads, giving its extrovert landlord full rein to introduce a more remarkable choice than ever of wines, spirits and beers. Other pubs here that are doing specially well at the moment include the interesting old Three Chimneys at Biddenden, the relaxed Gate at Boyden Gate by Marshside (a proper country local), the Brown Trout just outside Lamberhurst (very pleasant staff, good fresh fish), the George at Newnham (lovely food in charming surroundings), the Ringlestone Inn (good food, lots of real ales and country wines – earning a star award for the first time this year), the Bell at Smarden (lovely atmosphere), La Galoche Bar in Tunbridge Wells (lots of wines by the glass, fine bar lunches – why don't more small hotels have bars like this?), Sankeys at the Gate there (good fish again, and an excellent choice of wines by the glass) and the Pepper Box up at Ulcombe (homely and chatty – yet another pub for good fresh fish). Interesting new main entries here are the Plough at Ivy Hatch (unusually tempting food in attractive surroundings), the Elephants Head near Lamberhurst (a fine old pub, carefully updated), and the Bottle House near Penshurst (quietly friendly, with good food – very relaxing). Among the Lucky Dip entries at the end of the chapter, pubs currently on an upswing include the White Horse at Bridge, Black Bull at Cliffe, Coopers Arms in Rochester, Chequers at Smarden and Compasses at Sole Street; others to note particularly here are the Woolpacks at Brookland and at Chilham, Carpenters Arms at Eastling, Fordwich Arms at Fordwich, Rose & Crown near Ivy Hatch, Duck at Pett Bottom, Black Horse at Pluckley, Star at St Mary in the Marsh, Grove Ferry at Upstreet and Bull at Wrotham (most of these have been inspected by us).

nr BIDDENDEN   TQ8538 Map 3

Three Chimneys ★

A262, a mile W of village

Readers' reports show that the last year has been a good one for this busy, friendly country pub. A series of small, very traditionally furnished rooms have low oak beams, old settles, some harness and sporting prints on the walls, and good winter log fires. Bar food varies with the seasons, but a choice of four starters, four main courses and four puddings might include curried apple soup (£1.90), asparagus and parmesan pancakes (£3.05), a quiche such as broccoli (£4.60), scallop and mushroom pie (£5.50), rabbit casserole (£5.65), cold salmon steak with green mayonnaise (£5.75), and glazed pear tart (£2.70) or buttered brazil cheesecake (£2.75). There is a useful overspill Garden Room, popular with families, where you can book tables and there are extras such as ploughman's (from £2.85) or sirloin steak (£8.75); as this part isn't licensed you have to carry your drinks in from the main bar. Besides a range of well kept real ales tapped from the cask, including Adnams Best, Fremlins, Goachers (from Maidstone), Harveys Best and Old in winter, Marstons Pedigree, and Wadworths 6X, they keep local cider, and their sensible wine list includes several half bottles. The simple public bar has darts, shove ha'penny, dominoes and cribbage. The garden is nicely planted with flowering shrubs and shrub roses, and shelters the neatly kept lawn in a series of gentle curves. Just down the road from Sissinghurst. (Recommended by Maysie Thompson, Peter Barnsley, Terry Buckland, Adrian Pitts, Mrs Richard Stewart, Mrs J A Blanks, John Burgan, Hilary Irving, Dr BCM, Tony and Lynne Stark, Peter Neate, John Highley, Norman Foot, John Evans, Mr Stoner, R and E Harfield, Mrs C Hartley, William D Cissna, John and Joan Nash)

Free house   Licensees C F W Sayers and G A Sheepwash   Real ale   Meals and snacks (till 10pm)   Restaurant   Biddenden (0580) 291472   Children in Garden Room Open 11–2.30, 6–11; closed 25 and 26 Dec

BOUGH BEECH   TQ4846 Map 3

Wheatsheaf

B2027, S of reservoir

Thought to have been a 15th-century royal hunting lodge, this quiet old pub has a smart bar with a massive stone fireplace and an unusually high ceiling with lofty timbers. A couple of lower rooms lead off and are divided from the central part by standing timbers. Decorations include a stag's head, cigarette cards, swordfish spears, and – over the massive stone fireplace which separates off the public bar – a mysterious 1607 inscription reading Foxy Galumpy. Bar food includes sandwiches (from £1, toasties 5p extra), soup (£1.30), home-made pâté (£1.45), omelettes (from £1.95), ploughman's (from £2.50), home-cooked ham with egg (£3.90), and steaks (£7.75); home-made puddings such as walnut, apple and raisin steamed pudding (£1.60), and children's dish (£1.70). Well kept Eldridge Pope Hardy, Fremlins and Flowers on handpump. The public bar has an attractive old settle carved with wheatsheaves, buffalo horns over its fire, and shove-ha'penny, dominoes, cribbage, quizzes, fruit machine; piped music. A pretty sheltered lawn with flowerbeds, fruit trees, roses, flowering shrubs, and a children's rustic cottage stretches behind the building. (Recommended by R Bennett, Mrs Richard Stewart, Heather Martin; more reports please)

Whitbreads   Tenant Ron Smith   Real ale   Meals and snacks (not Weds or Sun evenings)   Children in area set aside for them by public bar   Open 10 (10.30 Sat)–2.30, 6–11; closed lunchtime 25 Dec

BOUGHTON ALUPH   TR0247 Map 3

Flying Horse ⌦

Boughton Lees; just off A251 N of Ashford

Weekly matches are held in summer on the broad cricket green in front of this friendly 15th-century pub, and there are seats in the rose garden. The open-plan bar has fresh flowers on many tables, hop bines around the serving area, comfortable upholstered modern wall benches, horsebrasses, stone animals on either side of the blazing log fire, and lots of standing space. Further inside, age shows in the shiny old black panelling and the arched windows (though they are a later Gothic addition). Good bar food includes sandwiches, liver and bacon or Russian fish pie (£4), home-made steak and kidney pie (£4.20), first-class cold meat salad, and poached salmon (£5.50). Well kept Courage Best and Directors and guests like Fullers London Pride or Wadworths 6X on handpump, and a good wine list that includes their own labelled house wine. Darts, shove-ha'penny, cribbage, dominoes, fruit machine and piped music. (Recommended by Kevin and Tracey Stephens, Werner Arend, David Gaunt, Mrs A Crowhurst; more reports please)

Courage   Tenant Howard Smith   Real ale   Meals and snacks   Ashford (0233) 620914   Children in dining room only   Jazz Sun evening   Open 11–3, 6–11; 11–11 summer Sats   Bedrooms; £18(£20S)/£27(£29S)

BOYDEN GATE TR2265 Map 3

Gate Inn ★

Off A299 Herne Bay–Ramsgate – follow Chislet, Upstreet signpost opposite Roman Gallery; Chislet also signposted off A28 Canterbury–Margate at Upstreet – after turning right into Chislet main street keep right on to Boyden; the pub gives its address as Marshside, though Boyden Gate seems more usual on maps

The licensee is keen to emphasise that this charming country local is just that – a proper country pub with a relaxed, friendly atmosphere, and not a dining pub with waiter service. The bar has pews with flowery cushions around tables of considerable character, hop bines hanging from the beam, a good winter log fire (which serves both quarry-tiled rooms), and attractively etched windows; there are photographs on the walls – some ancient sepia ones, others new ('MCC' here stands for Marshside Cricket Club – the pub is a focus for many other games, too), and part of the area is no smoking. Bar food consists of enterprising sandwiches with lots of pickles (from 90p), home-made vegeburger or garlic mushrooms (£1.50), ploughman's with home-boiled bacon (£2.85), home-made ratatouille flan (£2.95), home-made spicy sausage hot-pot (£3.25), and puddings like prize-winning bread pudding (95p); they use organically grown local produce where possible, and encourage children to share their parents' food (with their own cutlery and plate provided). Well kept Shepherd Neame Bitter, Spitfire, Bishops Finger and Old tapped from the cask, and coffee; sensibly placed darts, as well as shove-ha'penny, dominoes, cribbage, trivia, children's board games, and Thursday evening quiz. In summer, it's lovely to sit outside at the picnic-table sets on the sheltered side lawn and listen to the contented quacking of a million ducks and geese (they sell duck food inside – 5p a bag). (*Recommended by Nick Haslewood, Rob and Gill Weeks, Mr and Mrs J H Adam, L M Miall*)

Shepherd Neame Tenant Christopher Smith Real ale Meals and snacks (available during all opening hours) Children welcome (family room) Piano Thurs lunchtime and Sun evening Open 11–2.30(3 Sat), 6–11

CHIDDINGSTONE TQ4944 Map 3

Castle

Village signposted from B2027 Tonbridge–Edenbridge

Records show a building called Waterslip House here in 1420, and the pub's stone foundations probably go back as far as that – so it could be where Anne Boleyn found shelter when she was stranded in a terrible blizzard on her way to nearby Hever. It's been an inn since 1730 and like the rest of the beautiful village is owned by the National Trust. The neatly modernised beamed bar has well made settles forming booths around the tables on its partly carpeted oak floor, cushioned sturdy wall benches, an attractive mullioned window seat in one small alcove, and latticed windows. Bar food includes home-made soup (£1.95), open sandwiches (from £2.75), home-made pâté (£3.25), filled baked potatoes (from £3.25), ploughman's (from £3.55), very hot chilli con carne or a daily pasta dish (£4.35), salads (from £6.55), steak and kidney pie or casseroled venison (£7.95), and puddings such as home-made cheesecake (£2.15). Well kept Larkins Sovereign, Shepherd Neame and Harveys Sussex on handpump; over 150 wines (including house wines) by the bottle, and coffee. The public bar – popular with locals – has darts, shove-ha'penny, dominoes and cribbage. The back garden is pretty, with a small pool and fountain set in a rockery and tables on a brick terrace and neat lawn; there's also a barbecue bar here. (*Recommended by Neil H Barker, David Hunn, Miss P M Hayes, W G Harvey, Mrs Terry Buckland, Ruth Humphrey, Richard Houghton, Cynth and Malc Pollard, Christian Leigh, Mrs C Hartley, Heather Martin*)

Free house Licensee Nigel Lucas Real ale Meals and snacks (11–2.45, 6–10.45) Restaurant Penshurst (0892) 870247 Children in eating area of bar Open 11–3, 6–11

CHILHAM   TR0753   Map 3

White Horse

Village signposted off A252/A28 W of Canterbury; pub in centre

A couple of white tables outside this well kept old pub give a perfect view of the timber-framed Tudor houses in the exceptionally pretty village square. Inside, the comfortably modernised open-plan lounge bar spreads around the neat central bar servery and has a massive fireplace with the Lancastrian rose carved at the end of its mantlebeam – a relic of the Wars of the Roses, uncovered only in 1966, during refurbishments. The handsomely carved ceiling beams are as old, and there's a theory that two skeletons found under the floor were victims of a skirmish in the 14th-century Peasants' Revolt. Bar food includes sandwiches (from £1.30), soup (£1.50), platters (from £2.95), salads (from £3.60), and daily home-made hot dishes such as curry (£3.75) or lamb casserole and steak and kidney pie (£3.95). Flowers, Fremlins and Wadworths 6X on handpump; dominoes, sensibly placed darts, piped music. The grand park of nearby Chilham Castle makes a good outing. *(Recommended by John and Bridget Dean, Dr J H Shears, Robert and Elizabeth Scott, S V Bishop, Simon Bates, Simon Collett-Jones; more reports please)*

Whitbreads   Manager L R Terry   Real ale   Meals and snacks (not Tues evening) Restaurant   Canterbury (0227) 730355   Open 11–11

CHIPSTEAD   TQ4956   Map 3

George & Dragon

39 High Street; 1 1/4 miles from M25 junction 5: A21 S, then A25 towards Sevenoaks, then first left

Though the furnishings in the open-plan bar of this busy dining pub are modern, they do tone in with the heavy black beams (some of them nicely carved), and oak tables and Windsor chairs on the geometric carpet; upright timbers divide the room into smaller, cosier areas, two of which have open fires. At lunchtime, bar food includes soup (£1.40), sandwiches (from £1.45), ploughman's (from £2.45), ham and egg (£3.85), home-made steak and kidney pie or farmhouse grill (£4.95), with evening dishes such as mussels in garlic (£3.30), seafood bake (£4.75), steaks (from £9.50), and puddings (from £1.10). Well kept Courage Best and Directors and a guest such as John Smiths or Youngs on handpump; piped music. There are tables on neatly kept grass beside roses and tall trees, behind the car park. *(Recommended by E G Parish, TBB; more reports please)*

Courage   Tenants Mr and Mrs F J Varley   Real ale   Meals and snacks (till 10pm) Open 11–3, 5.30–11

COBHAM   TQ6768   Map 3

Leather Bottle

2 1/2 miles from M2 junction 1; village signposted from A2 (towards London) on B2009

Dickens often used to end up at this ancient half-timbered house after strolling through the park of Cobham Hall, and mentions it fondly in *Pickwick Papers*. In amongst all the decorations you'd expect, there are some truly interesting prints of Dickens characters, including early postcards and teacards. The large, open-plan bar serves sandwiches (£1.95), ploughman's (£4.50), salads (£4.95) and a daily hot dish such as curry or vegetable bake (£4.50), beef and Guinness pie or lasagne (£4.95), and roasts (£5.95). Ruddles County and Websters Yorkshire; fruit machine. Tables are laid out on the extended back lawn and in the orchard at the bottom there's a large fish pond with a children's play area and an outdoors summer tuck shop. The village itself is pretty, with medieval almshouses, and outstanding brasses in the church. *(Recommended by Adrian Pitts, P W Brindle, Hank Hotchkiss, Brendan Moran)*

Trumans (Watneys)   Manager Michael Eakins   Real ale   Meals and snacks (12–3, 7–9)   Restaurant; closed Sun evening   Meopham (0474) 814327   Children in bar

annex and in restaurant   Open 10.30–3, 5.30–11; 10.30–11 Sat   Bedrooms;
£37/£54(£72B 4-poster)

CONYER QUAY   TQ9665 Map 3
Ship

From A2 Sittingbourne–Faversham turn off towards Deerton St (signposted) then at
T-junction turn left signposted Teynham, Sittingbourne; Conyer signposted from
Teynham

In an attractive creekside position, the rambling and cosy little rooms here have
fishing nets hanging from low planked ceilings, wooden floors, wall boards,
various nautical nick-nacks and a notice-board with boating advertisements. Mr
Heard has bought the freehold from Whitbreads so there's a much increased choice
of beers on the five handpumps; changing continually and well kept on handpump,
there might be any one of 30 real ales (they have a happy hour every night between
6 and 7 – 7–8 Sundays – when doubles are priced as singles and pints of beer or
cider are 10p cheaper). For southern England, his range of more than 175 malt
whiskies is incredible; he also runs a whisky trail with prizes, and runs to a further
75 blended scotches, Irish whiskeys and bourbons, more than 160 wines (14 by the
glass or carafe and 14 half-bottles), over 150 liqueurs, 25 rums, 20 ports, and 50
cognacs, armagnacs and other brandies. He keeps 60 bottled beers and local
Biddenden cider on handpump. Bar food includes toasties (from £1.20),
ploughman's (from £2.45), various fried fish dishes (£2, and an incredible range of
95), chilli con carne or curry (£3.45), vegetarian dishes (from £3.45), home-made
shepherd's or steak and kidney pies (£3.95), local oysters (£4.50), local rainbow
trout or dressed crab salad (£4.95). Dominoes, cribbage, various board and card
games, and a quiz each Tuesday evening at 8.30; also piped music. Used
paperbacks are sold and exchanged – proceeds to charity, and there are reference
books and magazines for use whilst in the pub; the lavatory walls are covered with
plaques of printed graffiti and there's a blackboard and chalk to write your own.
Tables on a narrow gravel terrace face the water packed with small boats. During
opening hours they can supply you with groceries. *(Recommended by M A and C R
Starling, L M Miall, H Paulinski)*

*Free house   Licensee Alec Heard   Real ale   Meals and snacks (till 10.30pm)
Restaurant   Teynham (0795) 521404   Children in restaurant   Open 11–3, 6–11
(midnight supper licence)*

DARGATE   TR0761 Map 3
Dove

Village signposted from A299

Surrounded by strawberry fields and orchards, this pretty honeysuckle-clad brick
house is well known for its lovely garden: roses, lilacs, paeonies and many other
flowers, picnic-table sets under pear trees, a dovecot with white doves, a rockery
and pool, and a swing; summer barbecues. A bridlepath leads up into Blean Wood.
Inside, it's carefully refurbished, there's a good winter log fire, and well kept
Shepherd Neame Bitter and Spitfire on handpump (can also be served by the jug),
quite a few wines, and some malt whiskies; unobtrusive piped music. Under the
new licensee bar food includes sandwiches, filled baked potatoes (from £2.50),
meaty or vegetarian lasagne (£3.20), home-made pies (£4.95), and 14–16oz fresh
Dover sole (£10.95). *(More reports please)*

*Shepherd Neame   Tenant Simon Blount   Real ale   Meals and snacks (not Sun
evening)   Restaurant   Canterbury (0227) 751360   Children in eating area of bar
Open 11–3, 6–11*

GROOMBRIDGE   TQ5337 Map 3
Crown

B2110

The room most popular with locals in this pretty tile-hung Elizabethan house has logs burning in the big brick inglenook, lots of old teapots, pewter tankards and so forth, a long copper-topped serving bar, and a relaxed, chatty atmosphere. The end room, normally for eaters, has fairly close-spaced tables with a variety of good solid chairs, a log-effect gas fire in a big fireplace, and an arch through to the food ordering area. The walls, mostly rough yellowing plaster with some squared panelling and some timbering, are decorated with small topographical, game and sporting prints (often in pretty maple frames), and a circular large-scale map with the pub at its centre; some of the beams have horsebrasses. There's a small, new private dining room – converted from the old kitchen – best to book. Quickly served on an entertaining assortment of plates old and new, the tasty food includes various ploughman's (£2.70), home-made steak and mushroom pie or chicken curry (£4.50), poached Scotch salmon (£5.50), vegetarian dishes, and daily specials such as rack of lamb (£4.70), or coronation chicken (£4.80); Sunday roast (£5) in restaurant. Well kept Harveys PA, with guests like Adnams and Wadworths 6X on handpump, good value house wines (by the glass as well), and local Biddenden cider; shove-ha'penny, cribbage. The nicest place to sit outside is at the picnic-table sets on the sunny front brick terrace or on the steep, neatly kept village green. Across the road is a public footpath beside the small chapel which leads, across a field, to moated Groombridge Place and fields beyond. *(Recommended by E G Parish, K Flack, Miss P M Hayes, H Martin, W G Harvey, Maggie and Derek Washington, Mrs C Hartley, Mr and Mrs J H Adam)*

Free house   Licensees Bill and Vivienne Rhodes   Real ale   Meals and snacks (not Sun evening)   Restaurant Tunbridge Wells (0892) 864742; not Sun evening   Children in snug and restaurant   Open 11–2.30, 6–11   Bedrooms; £19/£35

nr HADLOW   TQ6349 Map 3
Artichoke

Hamptons; from Hadlow–Plaxtol road take first right (signposted West Peckham – the pub too is discreetly signposted, on an oak tree); OS Sheet 188, map reference 627524

Decorations in the two rooms of this ancient and pretty country cottage include lots of gleaming brass, country pictures (mainly hunting scenes), some antique umbrellas and old storm lamps; one room has an inglenook fireplace and is decked out with jugs, kettles, pots, pans and plates, and the other has a woodburning range. There are cushioned high-backed wooden settles, wooden farmhouse-kitchen chairs, upholstered wrought-iron stools matching unusual wrought-iron, glass-topped tables on its Turkey carpet, beams in the low ceilings, and soft lighting. Home-made bar food such as ploughman's (£3.25), quiche lorraine (£4.25), lasagne (£4.75), steak and kidney pie or mixed grill (£5.25), prawn salad or chicken kiev (£6.25), and sirloin steak (£8.75), with specials such as Barnsley lamb chop (£6.25) and winter casseroles and curries. Fullers London Pride, Greene King Abbot and Youngs Special on handpump, with a good range of spirits. On a fairy-lit front terrace with a striped awning are some seats, with more built around a tall lime tree across the lane. *(Recommended by Beverley James, Maurice Southon, Tony and Lynne Stark, Norman Foot; more reports please)*

Free house   Licensees Terence and Barbara Simmonds   Real ale   Meals (not winter Sun evenings)   Restaurant (Fri and Sat evenings)   Plaxtol (0732) 810763   Children in eating area of bar   Open 11.30–2.30, 6.30–11; closed winter Sun evenings

IVY HATCH   TQ5854 Map 3

Plough ♟

Coach Rd; village signposted off A227 N of Tonbridge

Food in this relaxed and friendly village pub shows real imagination; changing day by day, it might in the evening include French onion soup (£2.50), vegetarian parcels in a tomato and chilli coulis (£3.50), mushrooms with chicken mousse and smoked salmon in puff pastry or salmon and broccoli terrine (£4), tagliatelle bolognese (£4.95), warmed avocado, bacon and blue cheese salad (£4.95/5.95 depending on size), liver and bacon (£6), seafood gratinée (£6.75), chicken done with mango (£7.50) and guineafowl done with sherry and orange (£9); at lunchtime they do ploughman's, ratatouille (£3.95), avocado salad (from £4.95), crispy duck salad (£6.50), seafood gratinée (£6.95), and puddings like French apple flan (£3). The bar has several cosy room areas, candlelit at night, with soft banquettes in a snug off on the left, small well cushioned settles and attractive country chairs around good solid tables in the main part, and round behind on the right another snug area – which leads on through to the elegant and comfortable back conservatory restaurant. Well kept Benskins Best, Brakspears, Fremlins and Marstons Pedigree on handpump, decent wines, very efficient friendly service – and a warm hum of contented conversation. There are picnic-table sets on gravel in front, and in a fairy-lit sloping back garden with its own summer bar and barbecue (and on our visit unobtrusive 1970s disco music wafting gently out of the sheltering shrubs). *(Recommended by Jenny and Brian Seller)*

Free house   Licensee Mr Edwards   Real ale   Meals and snacks (not Sun evening) Restaurant (evening Tues-Sat)   Plaxtol (0732) 810268   Open 11–3, 6–11; closed Sun evening

LAMBERHURST   TQ6635 Map 3

Brown Trout ♟

B2169, just off A21 S of village nearly opposite entrance to Scotney Castle

They really go out of their way to please everyone at this very popular dining pub, and even when exceptionally busy service remains prompt and friendly. A fly in the ointment is that to enjoy the food, you may have to book ahead – on Saturday evenings this may mean weeks in advance. The menu is strongest on fish with starters such as soft roes on toast (£3) or a heap of mussels (Sept–March £3), six oysters (£4), and Mediterranean prawns in garlic butter (£4.95), and main courses like an 8–10oz fresh fillet of plaice (£4.25), wing of skate (£6.25), dressed crab with prawns (£6.75), 16/18oz Dover sole (£9.95), and whole lobster (£12); there are non-fishy dishes like soup (£1.95), chicken (£4.50), escalope of veal à la crème (£5.95), and steaks (from £8.75). The remarkable value daily specials may include fresh huss, grilled trout in herb butter, and a pair of gammon steaks or white crabmeat with prawns. The serving counter is still decidedly the centre of the bar, which has beams thickly hung with copper and brass, small country prints (mainly of trout fishing) on the russet hessian walls, and a thoroughly unstuffy and relaxed atmosphere. With only eight or nine tables in the small bar itself, in summer they certainly need the overflow into the biggish extension dining room; on the way through, there's a big and remarkably well stocked aquarium. Well kept Flowers IPA and Fremlins on handpump, and a large choice of wines; side fruit machine, faint piped music. Even in winter the pub is bright with hanging baskets and tubs of pansies – and very pretty in summer, with picnic-table sets under cocktail parasols on the sloping front grass, opposite a big converted oast house with unusually tall black-rendered brick kiln roofs; large, safe garden behind the pub with swings, slides and trampolines. *(Recommended by Win and Reg Harrington, P Gillbe, Ian, Liz and Wendy Phillips, BCM, Don Mather, Miss P M Hayes, W G Harvey, M J Brooks, Mrs C Hartley, Win and Reg Harrington, Robert M Deeley, Mrs Carol A Riddick, A J Castle, Robert and Elizabeth Scott, Dave Braisted)*

Whitbreads   Lease: Joseph Stringer   Real ale   Meals and snacks (till 10pm) Restaurant   Tunbridge Wells (0892) 890312   Children welcome   Open 11–3, 6–11

nr LAMBERHURST   TQ6535 Map 3

Elephants Head

Hook Green; B2169 towards Tunbridge Wells

The newish landlord has done a sensitive job of opening up this ancient half-timbered stone-based country pub. It still keeps the feel of the formerly separate cosy brick-floored snug on the left, though its huge fireplace now shares the job of warming the whole rambling bar with a big woodburning stove in the middle. There are maroon plush cushioned pews and bentwood chairs around dark-topped cast-iron-framed tables on polished oak boards, stripped beams, cream walls with some timbering, and a hop bine over the substantial counter which serves well kept Harveys Sussex, Mild and Armada from handpump; the atmosphere is relaxed and chatty. A wide range of good bar food includes sandwiches, ploughman's with good cheeses, a fine steak and kidney pie under a huge balloon of puff pastry (around £4) and good steaks; they use local suppliers. Behind there are picnic-table sets under cocktail parasols on a brick terrace and on the neat grass beyond, which look out over fields towards a wood-sheltered hop garden; there's a play area. There are one or two tables out in front, too, by a sweep of green. A small side room has darts and a fruit machine. (Recommended by Hope Chenhalls, Richard Gibbs, BHP; more details on food prices please)

Harveys   Licensee T J Flanagan   Real ale   Meals and snacks (maybe not Mon evening)   Restaurant   Lamberhurst (0892) 890279   Open 11–3, 6–11

LUDDENHAM   TQ9862 Map 3

Mounted Rifleman

3 1/2 miles from M2 junction 6; follow Faversham signpost to A2, turn left on to A2, then follow Oare, Luddenham signpost; take first left turn (signposted Buckland, Luddenham), then turn right just before railway crossing; OS Sheet 178, map reference 981627 – hamlet marked as Elverton

It's easy to drive straight past this unchanging old brick house, remote in a quiet orchard, without even realising it's a pub. The two simply furnished, communicating rooms have bare benches, kitchen chairs and the like on their bare floorboards, some hunting prints on the ochre walls, and a truly old-fashioned standard of welcoming hospitality; behind the bar is the former scullery with stone sink, Aga and kitchen table. Well-kept Fremlins is tapped in the cellar and brought up on a tray, and summer sandwiches are served with home-pickled onions and eggs; darts. There are a couple of tables out behind by the roses on the way to the vegetable patch. (Recommended by Phil Gorton; more reports please)

Free house   Licensee Bob Jarrett   Real ale   Snacks   Teynham (0795) 522464 Open 11–3, 6–11

NEWNHAM   TQ9557 Map 3

George ★ ⊘

44 The Street; village signposted from A2 just W of Ospringe, outside Faversham

The flower arrangements in this distinctive 16th-century pub are beautiful, and like everything else here, chosen with care: early nineteenth-century prints (Dominica negroes, Oxford academics, politicians), a cabinet of fine rummers and other glassware, a collection of British butterflies and moths, prettily upholstered mahogany settles, dining chairs and leather carving chairs around candlelit tables, table lamps and gas-type ceiling chandeliers, and rugs on the waxed floorboards; hop bines hang from the beams and there are open fires. Varied and interesting food cooked by Philip and Lesley Powley might include sandwiches (from £1.10), delicious soup (£1.35), cheese-topped cottage pie (£3.40), a good variety of ploughman's and salads (from £3.95, avocado and prawns £5.50), pasta of the day (£4.50), vegetarian parcel (£5), steak and kidney pie or pudding (£5.75), trout meunière (£6.95), fillets of sole dieppoise (£7.75), rack of lamb (cooked pink

£8.25), steaks (from £9.25), puddings such as chocolate roulade or an old-fashioned suet pudding (£2.50), and specials such as piquant chicken livers on a bed of sliced courgettes (£3.60), salad of smoked quail breasts with nuts and walnut oil dressing (£3.80), okra à la creole (£4.95), rabbit and herb mustard cream hot-pot (£5.95) or salmon trout fillet en croûte with samphire and herb hollandaise (£8.20), and Kentish cherry pancakes (£2.50); game in season, local fruit and vegetables used as much as possible, and they try to cater for those with special diets. No credit cards. Well kept Shepherd Neame Old on handpump with Best and Spitfire kept under light blanket pressure, four wines by the glass, and unobtrusive, well reproduced and interesting piped music; shove-ha'penny, cribbage, dominoes, fruit machine, trivia. There are picnic-table sets in a spacious sheltered garden with a fine spreading cobnut tree, below the slopes of the sheep pastures. Dogs allowed (drinking bowl in lobby). *(Recommended by S E Dark, Derek Patey, Judith Regan, Mrs D M Hacker, S Blaxland, Simon Reynolds)*

Shepherd Neame Tenant Simon Barnes Real ale Meals and snacks (till 10pm; not Sun evening, not Mon) Well behaved children allowed Open 10.30–3, 6–11

OARE TR0062 Map 3

Shipwrights Arms ★

Ham Road, Hollow Shore; from A2 just W of Faversham, follow Oare–Luddenham signpost; fork right at Oare–Harty Ferry signpost, drive straight through Oare (don't turn off to Harty Ferry), then left into Ham Street on the outskirts of Faversham, following pub signpost

Situated in the middle of marshland, 3ft below sea level, this 17th-century pub has three original and cosy little bars separated by standing timbers and wood part-partitions or narrow door arches and filled with a medley of seats from tapestry cushioned stools and chairs through some big Windsor armchairs to black wood-panelled built-in settles forming little booths. Lighting is by generator (and water is pumped from a well), and there are hops and pewter tankards hanging over the bar counter, copper kettles, boating pictures, flags or boating pennants on the ceilings, several brick fireplaces, and a woodburning stove. Bar food might include filled rolls, soup, various ploughman's, corn beef hash or fish crumble, and beef in beer. Well kept Adnams Broadside, Batemans Mild and XXXB, Shepherd Neame Old, Youngers IPA and No 3 and Youngs Special tapped from casks behind the counter; farm ciders, including their own called Looney Juice; cribbage and piped music. A larger room with less atmosphere but considerably more light has a food hatch where a loudspeaker tells you your food is ready. The lane is long and extremely bumpy, and the small front and back gardens outside the white weatherboarded and tiled pub lead up a bank to the path above the creek where lots of boats are moored. As we went to press – not having had our fact checking sheet returned by the pub – we tried repeatedly to make contact by telephone but found their line was 'spare'. So we regret that there is a risk of some change which we cannot find out about. Please let us know. *(Recommended by K Flack, M Rising; more reports please)*

Free house Real ale Meals and snacks Children welcome Open 10.30–3, 6–11; 11–11 Sat; closed evening 25 Dec

PENSHURST TQ5243 Map 3

Bottle House

Coldharbour Lane, Smarts Hill; leaving Penshurst S on B2188 fork right up hill by telephone box at Smarts Hill signpost, then bear right towards Chiddingstone and Cowden

Tucked away from the village, this has long been a popular retreat for locals in the know, but has recently been winning approval for a wide choice of good food, including soup (£2) filled baked potatoes (£3.50), ploughman's (from £3.50), salads (around £4.50), seafood platter, garlic-spiced smoked mackerel or chilli con carne (£5.25), braised liver and bacon, kippers with parsley butter or steak and kidney pie (£5.50), home-potted beef or dressed crab (£6.25), salmon (£7.95) and steaks (from sirloin, £9.95), with good puddings (£2.50) and Sunday lunch. The bar is unpretentious and friendly, with black beams in an ochre ceiling, a fire with a small collection of old bottles on its brick mantlepiece, wheelback and other chairs, and big windows looking out over picnic-table sets under cocktail parasols on a neat raised suntrap lawn to quiet fields and oak trees. Well kept Ind Coope Burton, Tetleys and Youngs on handpump, unobtrusive piped music. *(Recommended by Ian Whitlock, Colin Laffan, Cynth and Malc Pollard, H Martin)*

Free house   Licensees Gordon and Val Meer   Real ale   Meals and snacks (not Sun evening)   Restaurant (evenings not Mon, Sun lunch)   Children welcome (no babies) Open 11–2.30, 6–11

Spotted Dog

Smarts Hill; going S from village centre on B2188, fork right up hill at telephone box: in just under 1/2 mile the pub is on your left

From the rustic tables and benches on the split-level terrace and garden outside this quaint tiled and white weatherboarded house there's an idyllic summer view: 20 miles of countryside, with the lush upper Medway valley curling round towards medieval Penshurst Place. The neatly kept and heavily beamed and timbered bar, licensed since 1520, has a fine brick inglenook fireplace, attractive moulded panelling in one alcove, and some antique settles as well as wheelback chairs on its rugs and tiles. On the food side, the home-made puddings come in for universal approval – spotted dick, apple and apricot pie, plum tart and so forth (£2.25), and a good choice of other dishes includes soup (£1.85), other starters such as garlic mushrooms (£2.95), open sandwiches (home-cooked ham £2.85), filled baked potatoes or ploughman's (from £3.65), good if not Cumbrian-sized local Speldhurst sausages (£4.25), vegetable curry and other vegetarian dishes (£4.45), pies like steak and kidney or chicken and ham (£5.25), and steak (£9.25). No longer tied to Whitbreads, it now has King & Barnes Sussex, Ruddles Best and Wadworths 6X on handpump, and Old Spotty – a Best Bitter brewed specially for the pub by Courage. The wine list is good (lots from the New World, even one from Penshurst); friendly and noticeably polite staff, unobtrusive piped music. *(Recommended by Catherine and Andrew Brian, BCM, M E A Horler, Klaus and Elizabeth Leist, Sharon Baruch, David Hunn, Peter Neate)*

Free house   Licensee Andy Tucker   Real ale   Meals and snacks   Restaurant Penshurst (0892) 870253   Children in restaurant and eating area   Open 11–2.30, 6–11; closed 25 Dec

PLUCKLEY   TQ9243 Map 3

Dering Arms ⊘ ⇌

Near station, which is signposted from B2077 in village

The Food Award to this striking old Dutch-gabled pub is chiefly for the beautifully presented specials which are chalked up on a board – potted crab (£2.75), vegetable chilli (£3.95), 6 oysters (£4.95), a home-made pie such as turkey, banana and red pepper, supreme of chicken in port and green peppercorn sauce or fillet of salmon in orange, chervil and cream sauce (£8.45), good fillet of halibut in coarse grain mustard sauce or whole crab salad (£8.95), and grilled lemon sole (£9.25); other good bar food includes sandwiches (from £1, toasties 10p extra), tasty home-made soup (£1.85), various ploughman's (£2.85), local pan-fried trout with lemon and hazelnuts or rump steak (£7.95), and puddings like lovely fruit salad or banana pancake (£2.25); good breakfasts. They also have gourmet evenings every six weeks. Well kept Goachers Maidstone Light, a beer they brew for the pub, and winter Old, Shepherd Neame Spitfire and Youngs Special on handpump or tapped from the cask, decent wines, and local cider. Simply but attractively decorated bars have a good variety of solid wooden furniture on the wood and stone floors, log fires, and a relaxed, friendly atmosphere; darts, bar billiards, dominoes, and juke box. *(Recommended by Richard Gibbs, Lynn Sharpless, Bob Eardley, Anthony Barnes; more reports please)*

Free house   Licensee James Buss   Real ale   Meals and snacks (not Sun evening)
Restaurant; closed Sun evening   Pluckley (023 384) 371   Children in eating area of
bar   Occasional live music   Open 11.30(11 Sat)–3, 6–11   Bedrooms; £28/£36

RINGLESTONE   TQ8755   Map 3

Ringlestone ★ ✇

M20 junction 8 to Lenham/Leeds Castle; join B2163 heading N towards Sittingbourne
via Hollingbourne; at water tower above Hollingbourne turn right towards Doddington
(signposted), and straight ahead at next crossroads; OS Sheet 178, map reference 879558

This year we've awarded a star to this popular country pub for its friendly,
welcoming staff and enthusiastic, hard-working landlord, lots of well kept real ales
and country wines, and imaginative – though not cheap – food. The central room
has farmhouse chairs and cushioned wall settles on the brick floor, tables with
candle lanterns set into ropework centrepieces, old-fashioned brass and glass lamps
on the bare brick walls, and a woodburning stove and small bread oven in an
inglenook fireplace. An arch from here through a wall – rather like the *outside* of a
house, windows and all – opens into a long, quieter room with cushioned wall
benches, tiny farmhouse chairs, three old carved settles (one rather fine and dated
1620), similar tables, and etchings of country folk on its walls (bare brick too).
Regulars tend to sit at the wood-panelled bar counter, or liven up a little
wood-floored side room. At lunchtime, the help-yourself hot and cold buffet is
very good and worth the queues: good soup, herrings in madeira or chicken and
pineapple (£2.55), sausage, apple and onion plait or lasagne (£2.95), garlic chicken
or lamb and coconut curry (£3.95), and a choice of 12 salads; puddings like
home-made summer pudding laced with strawberry wine or fruit crumble (£2.75),
and clotted cream ice creams; there's also crab pâté (£3.95), pies like lamb and
apricot, ham, leek and cider or beef in ale with walnuts (£6.85); vegetables or
potatoes of the day £2.35 extra; no chips or fried food. Changing well kept real
ales tapped from casks behind the bar or on handpump and chalked up on a board
might include Adnams, Archers Headbanger, Batemans, Felinfoel Double Dragon,
Fremlins, Gales BBB and HSB, Mitchells ESB, Palmers Tally Ho!, Shepherd Neame
Bishops Finger and Spitfire, Theakstons Old Peculier, and a beer from the local
brewers Goachers (although they sometimes use a guest beer) called Ringlestone;
they can be quite pricey; over 24 country wines (including sparkling ones); 10%
discount on all drinks (including off-sales) at lunchtime (not Sun). Shove-ha'penny,
cribbage, dominoes, and piped pop music (maybe light disco in the evening when
there are more young people). There are picnic-table sets on the large raised lawn
above a rockery with waterfalls and a fountain, and troughs of pretty flowers
along the pub walls. Well behaved dogs welcome. *(Recommended by Michel
Hooper-Immins, Kevin and Tracey Stephens, Mr and Mrs C H Garnett, JF, Mr and Mrs R
Gammon, Mrs K J Betts, S E Dark, Judith Regan, Tony and Lynne Stark, Dave Braisted,
David Cardy, E G Parish)*

Free house   Licensee Michael Millington-Buck   Real ale   Meals and snacks
Restaurant   Maidstone (0622) 859900   Children welcome (under gentle supervision)
Occasional Morris dancers in summer   Open 11–3, 6.30–11; closed evening 25 Dec
Bedrooms planned

ST MARGARET'S AT CLIFFE   TR3644   Map 3

Cliffe Tavern Hotel ⇔

High Street

Very handy for the Ramsgate or Dover ferry, this well kept, friendly place – set
back from the National Trust coastal cliffs – has tables on the quiet back lawn
sheltered by a high flint wall and bordered by a pretty rose garden. The bar has
settles, local prints, and a striking picture of a World War Two aerial dogfight
above the village; there's also a larger open-plan lounge. Very good, often
imaginative food includes sandwiches, home-made soups like spinach, pea and
mint or carrot, orange and coriander (£1.95), chicken satay, puff pastry parcels

filled with brie, home-made pies such as steak and kidney, cottage or chicken
(£3.95), several vegetarian dishes like aubergine and red bean goulash with sour
cream or vegetable korma with roasted sesame seeds (£4.95), whole lemon sole
(£7.80), and puddings; lovely big breakfasts; there's a dining area next to the back
bar. Well kept Adnams, Ruddles County and Shepherd Neame Best on handpump,
and their own label house wine; helpful, courteous staff; fruit machine. Most of
the bedrooms are in two little cottages across the yard from the main building.
Near *Good Walks Guide* Walk 43, and the Pine Gardens are worth visiting.
(*Recommended by Jim Froggatt, Denis Plummer, John Baker, Revd L J and Mrs Melliss, Alec
Lewery, Marie Enright, David and Joyce Knight, Hank Hotchkiss, John and Joan Nash, Mrs K
J Betts, Margaret Dyke, Jane Palmer*)

*Free house   Licensee Christopher Waring Westby   Real ale   Meals and snacks
Dover (0304)   852749   or 852400   Children welcome   Open 11–3(3.30 Sat), 6–11,
though they may stay open longer in afternoon if trade demands   Bedrooms;
£34.25B/£46.50B*

SELLING   TR0456   Map 3
White Lion

3 1/2 miles from M2 junction 7; village signposted from exit roundabout; village also
signposted off A251 S of Faversham

Formerly a coaching inn, this friendly and homely old place has an unusual
semi-circular bar counter, pews on stripped floorboards, and two huge brick
fireplaces (with a spit over the right-hand one). Generous helpings of bar food
include sandwiches (from £1), home-made soup (£1.95), delicious garlic and herb
pâté (£2.95), ploughman's (from £2.95, the stilton has been praised), salads (from
£4.75), home-made vegetarian stilton and sweetcorn quiche (£5.75), chicken
coconut curry (£5.95), steaks (from £6.75), lunchtime specials such as traditional
beef pudding or steak, kidney and mushroom pie (£4.50), puddings (£2.25), and
very popular Sunday roasts (£4.50). Well kept Shepherd Neame Best on
handpump, with decent wines by the glass; fruit machine, video game, maybe quiet
piped music – the landlord's a trumpet-player. The garden has a thriving
community of budgerigars, canaries, zebra finches, button quail, golden pheasants,
rabbits and guineapigs, with their young, and Timmy the cat. (*Recommended by Paul
Harrop, Colleen Holiday, Comus Elliott; more reports please*)

*Shepherd Neame   Tenant Anthony Richards   Real ale   Meals and snacks (till 10pm)
Restaurant   Canterbury (0227) 752211   Children welcome (own room)   Jazz last
Tues evening of the month   Open 11–3, 6.30–11; closed 25 Dec*

nr SMARDEN   TQ8842   Map 3
Bell ★

From Smarden follow lane between church and The Chequers, then turn left at
T-junction; or from A274 take unsignposted turn E a mile N of B2077 to Smarden

Summer or winter, this popular pub has a marvellous relaxed and friendly
atmosphere. The snug little back rooms have pews and the like around the simple
candlelit tables, bare brick or ochre plastered walls, brick or flagstone floors, low
beams, and an inglenook fireplace. Part of the lively front bar is set aside for
families with children, and also has darts, pool, shove-ha'penny, cribbage,
dominoes, fruit machine, video game, and juke box. One bar is no smoking. Good
bar food includes home-made soup (£1.40), sandwiches or toasties (from £1.50,
rump steak £2.95), home-made pâté (£2.10), ploughman's or pizza (from £2.65),
home-made shepherd's pie or basket meals (£3.15), salads (from £3.75), tender
home-made steak and kidney pie (£4.45), gammon steak with pineapple (£4.85),
steaks – including perfectly cooked fillet (from £7.45), and daily specials such as
fish mornay or cumberland pie; puddings like home-made chocolate crunch cake
(£1.50). They only do light snacks on Sunday lunchtimes. Well kept Flowers
Original, Fremlins, Fullers London Pride, Goachers Maidstone, Harveys, Shepherd
Neame and Ringwood Old Thumper on handpump; also, six wines by the glass,

and local Biddenden cider. You can sit out at the side, among fruit trees and shrubs, admiring the pub, which is hung with fancy tiles and covered with roses. Every second Sunday in the month at midday, there is a gathering of vintage and classic cars (the pub is packed then). Basic continental breakfasts only. *(Recommended by Mrs C Hartley, R G and S Bentley; more reports please)*

Free house   Licensee Ian Turner   Real ale   Meals and snacks (till 10pm or 10.30pm Fri and Sat; not Sun lunchtime)   Smarden (023 377) 283   Children in front family area of bar   Open 11.30(11 Sat)–2.30(2 Sat), 6–11; closed 25 Dec   Bedrooms; £16/£28

SOUTHFLEET   TQ6171   Map 3
Black Lion

Coming from A20, keep on B262 disregarding Southfleet sign off left, then turn left in Betsham; or if you do go into Southfleet, keep straight on through village past The Ship

Through the remains of a timbered wall, the two room areas of the main bar in this long thatched village pub open together and have a thriving local atmosphere. There's a mix of furnishings, including some shiny copper tables and a carpet on the quarry tiles of the quieter part away from the serving counter – and one particularly comfortable tubby little easy chair by the raised open fire over there on the right. There is a second smaller bar on the left, with steps up to a handsome restaurant. Bar food includes home-made soup (£1.70), ploughman's (£3.50), chilli con carne (£5.70), lamb and mango curry or gammon (£6.20), coq au vin (£6.50), and sirloin steak chasseur (£8.50), with puddings like home-made apple pie (£2.50). Well kept Ruddles Best and County and Websters Yorkshire on handpump, and notably helpful, welcoming staff. Fruit machine; Harry the friendly airedale may wander in towards closing time. The big shrub-sheltered back garden has a pleasant variety of well spaced seating, with a good barbecue; it's backed by open fields. *(More reports please)*

Watneys   Tenant A V Ray   Real ale   Meals and snacks (till 10pm)   No smoking restaurant (closed Sun)   Southfleet (0474) 832386   Children in eating area of bar and in restaurant   Open 11–2.30, 6–11

SPELDHURST   TQ5541   Map 3
George & Dragon

Village signposted from A264 W of Tunbridge Wells

This distinguished old pub is based on a manorial great hall dating back to 1212, and has antique cushioned settles and Windsor chairs, panelling, snug alcoves, heavy beams (installed during 'modernisation' in 1589 – until then the room went up to the roof), a massive stone fireplace, and some of the biggest flagstones you can find anywhere – it's said that Kentish archers returning from their victory at Agincourt rested on them in 1415. Bar food includes sandwiches (from £2.50), ploughman's (£3.50), main dishes like sautéed lamb's liver and bacon with onion gravy, gammon or grilled fillets of plaice (from £4.50), and puddings (£2.50). Well kept Harveys BB and PA and Fullers London Pride on handpump, and lots of malt whiskies; cribbage. It can get very crowded at weekends, especially in the evenings. The striking first-floor restaurant under the original massive roof timbers serves good but expensive food and is served by a quite splendid wine cellar – a place for special occasions. There are white tables and chairs on the neat little lawn, ringed with flowers, in front of the building. *(Recommended by Mike and Joyce Bryant, Klaus and Elizabeth Leist, D H K Reakes, Miss P M Hayes, W G Harvey, Heather Martin, Prof and Mrs C G Wall, S D Samuels, Mrs C Hartley, Richard Gibbs)*

Free house   Licensee Mr Wright   Real ale   Meals and snacks (till 10pm)   Restaurant; closed Sun evening   Langton (0892 86) 3125   Children in eating area of bar and in restaurant (over 5)   Open 11–3, 6–11

STAPLE   TR2756 Map 3

Black Pig

Barnsole Road, follow signs to village hall; pub signposted from Wingham–Sandwich back road through Staple, on the Sandwich side of the village

Most of the beams in this ancient half-timbered pub came originally off the Spanish Armada ships. The rambling main bar has comfortable chairs on the carpet, an unusual fireplace with a sort of semi-inglenook which may originally have been a smoking cabinet, a heavy beam-and-plank ceiling, and a friendly atmosphere. Bar food includes sandwiches (from £1.25), ploughman's (£2.75), lasagne (£3.95), steak and kidney pie (£4.20), and fresh seasonal fish such as plaice (£3) or trout (£4.20); puddings (£1.95). Well kept Adnams, Everards Tiger, Greene King IPA, Marstons Pedigree, Tetleys and Uley Old Spot on handpump; darts, pool and snooker, fruit machine, video game, and piped music; seats in the garden, where there are amusements for children. (*Recommended by Paul and Margaret Baker, Cynth and Malc Pollard, Mr and Mrs J H Adam, John Knighton, M Y Simon, L M Miall; more reports please*)

Free house   Licensees Graham and Clair Gould   Real ale   Meals and snacks Restaurant – with dance floor   Dover (0304) 812361   Children welcome away from bar servery   Blues Fri evening   Open 11–3, 6–11; 11–11 summer Sats and bank hol Mons

STOWTING   TR1242 Map 3

Tiger

The simplest route if coming from S is to turn left off B2068 signposted Stowting, straight across crossroads, then fork right after 1/4 mile and pub is on right; coming from N, follow Brabourne, Wye, Ashford signpost to right at fork, then turn left towards Posting and Lyminge at T-junction

Parts of this peaceful country pub date back to the 17th century, and there are shelves of little kegs, stone jugs and copper pots, an abundance of hop bines draped from the high ceiling, and an open fire at each end of the main bar; simple furnishings consist of plain chairs and dark pews built in against the walls, candles stuck into bottles, faded rugs on the dark floorboards, and some floor-to-ceiling plank panelling. Good home-made bar food includes sandwiches (from £1.50), lovely soup (£1.95), ploughman's with good ham, prawns (from £2.60), baked potato filled with stilton (£2.75), vegetarian dishes (from £3.75), tasty lasagne, home-made pies (£4.75), whole local plaice (£4.95), moist whole local trout (£5.50), weekly specials, and lovely puddings (from £1.80). Well kept Boddingtons, Everards Tiger, Greene King Abbot, King & Barnes and Tetleys on handpump, and farm cider; darts, piped music. Outside, picnic-table sets and other tables sit on the front terrace, some under a thinly planted arbour. (*Recommended by Marcus Adams, Anne Delnevo, Ian Macro, Mr and Mrs J H Adam, David and Diana Livesley*)

Free house   Licensees Alan and Linda Harris   Real ale   Meals and snacks (till 10pm)   Restaurant   Lyminge (0303) 862130   Children welcome   Jazz Mon evening   Open 11.30–3, 6.30–11; 11–11 summer Sats

TUNBRIDGE WELLS   TQ5839 Map 3

La Galoche ⊘ ⇌

Mount Edgcumbe House Hotel, The Common

At lunchtime, the good home-made bar food – from a menu that changes daily – seems particularly popular: fish soup with rouille (£3), crudités with guacamole or soft roes on toast (£3.25), shii-take mushrooms papillon (£3.95), curried vegetables with cashew nuts, lamb's liver and bacon or good pojarski smitane (meatballs with herbs and garlic and a sour cream, mushroom and white wine sauce, £6), various game birds roast or en salmis (from £7), grilled halibut with anchovy butter (£7.25), baked African sea bass or veal in wild mushroom and vermouth sauce (£7.75), and beef stroganoff (£8.75); puddings like summer pudding or profiteroles (from £2.75), and an excellent cheeseboard includes 30 different French cheeses (£3.35 for French bread and as many as you want to taste). Occasional 'special' weeks feature food and wine from particular areas, together with tutored tastings. Well kept Bass on handpump, up to 20 wines (including champagne) by the glass, and 25 bottles of wine under £10. It's also a friendly place to drop in for a drink. The characterful little bar (actually part of a small, well-run hotel on the Common) is built into the rock, and has a tiny cavern-like area to one side, a long built-in slatted pine wall seat, solid pine tables, bar stools against the slatted pine bar counter (where on Sundays there may be prawns and mussels to pick at and newspapers to read), and bright modern prints and cartoons. The small two-roomed restaurant is most attractive and overlooks the Common. *(Recommended by Mrs J A Blanks, H Martin, Stephen R Holman, Ralf Zeyssig, Miss P M Hayes, W G Harvey, Patrick Stapley, RAB, the May families, Mrs C Hartley)*

Free house   Licensees David and Susan Barnard   Real ale   Meals and snacks (till 10pm)   Restaurant; closed Sun   Tunbridge Wells (0892) 26823   Children Sat and Sun mornings only   Open 12–3, 6.30–11   Bedrooms; £40S/£65S

Sankeys at the Gate 🕸

39 Mount Ephraim (A26 just N of junction with A267)

Bar food here specialises in fish which is bought direct from source (wherever possible) or kept in their seawater tank: fish soup with rouille and gruyere (£3.50), stuffed Cornish clams (£4.50), baby scallops with breadcrumbs and garlic (£5.50), 6 oysters (from £5.50), Mediterranean prawns (hot with chillis and lime or cold with home-made mayonnaise £8.50), wing of skate with capers and black butter (£8.50), baked Scottish salmon (en croûte £10), medley of steamed fresh fish with tarragon cream (£13.50), dressed Cornish rock crab (£14), grilled Dover sole (£15.20), and plateau de fruits de mer (£16). Well kept Harveys from an antique beer engine, and a decent wine list. Plans are still afoot to make the downstairs area in this Victorian house more of a bistro/bar with a no-smoking area and decorations such as Spy and fish prints, old maps and bottles; this will lead to the garden where there are seats. *(Recommended by J A Snell, Kit Read, R G and S Bentley; more reports please)*

Free house   Licensee Guy Sankey   Real ale   Meals and snacks (not Sun or days listed below)   Restaurant   Tunbridge Wells (0892) 511422; closed Sun   Children welcome   Open 12–3, 6–11; closed Sun, bank holiday Mons, and 25 and 26 Dec

ULCOMBE   TQ8550   Map 3

Pepper Box

Fairbourne Heath (signposted from A20 in Harrietsham; or follow Ulcombe signpost from A20, then turn left at crossroads with sign to pub)

Quietly chatty and friendly, the cosy little low-beamed hop-strung bar in this cottagey country pub has flock wallpaper, some very low-seated Windsor chairs, wing armchairs and a sofa by the huge inglenook log fire, and copper kettles and pans on window sills and standing timbers. A side area (with enticing puddings in a cold cabinet at one end) is more functionally furnished for eating; there's a separate rustic little dining room, very snug and ideal for dinner-parties. The good value home-cooked food is strong on fish, with daily additions such as crab pâté (£3), grilled whole plaice or lemon sole (£5) joining the regular choice of fresh taramasalata (£3), fish pie (£5) and plaice fillets wrapped around prawns (£5.50). Other dishes include sandwiches (from £1.25), soup (£1.50), ploughman's (from £2.80), ham and eggs (£3.95), salads (from £3.95), stir-fried chicken (£4.65), and steaks (from £7.50); on summer Sundays it's cold food only. Well kept Shepherd Neame Best and Bishops Finger kept under light blanket pressure; piped music. The garden (with a caravan beside it) has tables among trees, shrubs, flowerbeds, a small pond and a swing; even if you don't catch a glimpse of the deer that come up, you may meet Jones the tabby tom, the other two cats, or Boots the plump collie. (*Recommended by Robert and Fiona Ambroziak, Jenny and Brian Seller, Derek and Sylvia Stephenson; more reports please*)

Shepherd Neame   Tenants Geoff and Sarah Pemble   Real ale   Meals and snacks (till 10pm; not Sun)   Maidstone (0622) 842558   Guitarist/vocals Sun evening   Open 11–3, 6.30–11; closed 25 Dec

WHITSTABLE   TR1166   Map 3

Pearsons ⌀

Sea Wall; follow main road into centre as far as you can, turning L into Horsebridge Rd; pub opposite Royal Free Fishers & Dredgers; parking limited

The reason for coming to this cheery place is to enjoy the consistently good, very fresh seafood: cockles (£1.20), rollmops or peeled prawns (£1.75), delicious crab sandwiches (£1.80), smoked salmon sandwiches (£1.95), smoked mackerel (£2.10), king prawns (£4.95), local oysters in season, and seafood platter (£8.30), with changing fresh fish or shellfish specials; also, other sandwiches (from £1.10) and ploughman's (£1.95). In the downstairs bar, small areas are divided by stripped brickwork and decorated with sea paintings, old local photographs, a ship's wheel, and lobster pots; a lower flagstoned part gets most of its submarine light from a huge lobster tank. Well kept Flowers Original, Fremlins and Wethereds Winter Royal on handpump; decent house wines, piped pop music, fruit machine. Upstairs, in two or three pleasantly close-packed dining rooms, there's a wider choice (as well as a sea view from some tables – downstairs the sea wall gets in the way); efficient, friendly service. There are some picnic-table sets outside between the pub and the sea. (*Recommended by Nigel Gibbs, Mayur Shah, L M Miall: more reports please*)

Whitbreads   Tenant Michael Wingrove   Real ale   Meals and snacks (11.30–2.30, 6–9.30)   Partly no smoking restaurant   Whitstable (0227) 272005   Children welcome   Open 11–3, 6–11

Lucky Dip

Besides the fully inspected pubs, you might like to try these Lucky Dips recommended to us and described by readers (if you do, please send us reports):

☆ **Aldington** [TR0736], *Walnut Tree*: Friendly old smugglers' pub dating back to early 14th century with interestingly old-fashioned kitchen bar and lively local public bar; reliable home-made bar food from sandwiches up, well kept Shepherd Neame on handpump, sheltered garden with pool and summer barbecues; children allowed in eating area and restaurant (*Win and Reg Harrington, LYM*)

☆ **Appledore** [Station Rd; TQ9529], *Railway*: Friendly family pub with wide choice of good bar food, well kept real ales, good log fires, big dining room, tables in garden; bedrooms in small motel wing (*Leo and Pam Cohen, Ken and Barbara Turner*)

☆ **Aylesford** [handy for M2 junction 3 or M20 junction 6, via A229; 19 High St; TQ7359], *Little Gem*: Quaint and ancient really small pub, friendly, cosy and dimly lit, with lots of atmosphere and unusually enterprising choice of real ales; bar lunches and evening snacks, children in eating area, piped radio (*Michael Bourdeaux, Kevin and Tracey Stephens, LYM*)

Aylesford [High St], *Chequers*: Good spot on river with superb views; spare decor, but warm and comfortable, with good range of beers, big helpings of food, friendly staff (*P B Godfrey, W Stockton*)

Barham [The Street; TR2050], *Duke of Cumberland*: Pleasant and spacious two-bar local with Whitbreads-related real ales, big helpings of good value straightforward lunchtime food; bedrooms, caravan site (*L M Miall*)

Bean [TQ5872], *Black Horse*: Comfortable, with restaurant and family area; main appeal for families is big courtyard with plenty of seats, summer barbecues, monkey and bird cages around edge, grass, pond and play things (*Mrs S Y Sadler*)

Bearsted [Plantation Lane; TQ7955], *Plantation*: 17th-century pub doing well under new regime, with Boddingtons beer, good bar food, nice old-fashioned atmosphere (*Comus Elliott*)

☆ **Benenden** [The Street (B2086); TQ8033], *King William IV*: Unspoilt but rather upmarket small low-ceilinged village local with cushioned pews, kitchen chairs, a good log fire, well kept Shepherd Neame and Mild; games in public bar, small garden; decent food (not Mon evening or Sun) (*Geoff* *and Julie Bond, Miss P T Metcalfe, Mrs C Hartley, LYM; more reports on new regime please)*

Borden [The Street; just off A249; TQ8862], *Tudor Rose*: Well refurbished village free house with well kept Fremlins and Shepherd Neame, wide choice of good bar food, warm welcome, big conservatory restaurant, good service, upstairs evening carvery (Tues-Sat), garden behind for children, ample parking; open all day *(Jeff Seaman)*

☆ **Boughton Street** [3/4 mile from M2 junction 7, off A2 — note that this is called Boughton Street on most maps, though most people just call it Boughton; TR0559], *White Horse*: Carefully restored by Shepherd Neame, cosy and interesting dark-beamed bars; decent food all day (opens 7 for breakfast) from sandwiches to steak with interesting dishes in communicating restaurant area, well kept Shepherd Neame on handpump, reasonable choice of wines, cheery helpful staff; tables in garden; children allowed; bedrooms comfortable and well equipped — back ones quiet *(Colleen L Holiday, LYM)*

Boughton Street [167-169 The Street], *Garden*: Small 17th-century hotel and restaurant (not a pub), worth knowing for comfortable accommodation, relaxed atmosphere, good service and decent food *(Harry McCann)*

Brabourne [Canterbury Rd, East Brabourne; TR1041], *Five Bells*: Good food and service, pleasant staff *(M J D Inskip)*

☆ **Brasted** [High St (A25), 3 miles from M25 (Sevenoaks junction) — OS Sheet 188, map reference 469550; TQ4654], *Bull*: Friendly local with well kept Shepherd Neame ales, good choice of good home-made food inc many vegetarian dishes in intimate dining lounge, separate public bar with darts and maybe skittles, polite service; tables in garden; children welcome *(R J and F J Ambroziak, M E A Horler, Keith Widdowson)*

☆ **Brasted** [A25], *White Hart*: Friendly and efficient staff in spacious relaxing lounge and sun lounge; well kept Bass and Charrington IPA in Battle of Britain bar with signatures and mementoes of Biggin Hill fighter pilots, big neatly kept garden; good value generous bar food, restaurant; can get very busy weekends; children welcome; bedrooms very clean if rather old-fashioned *(M E A Horler, LYM)*

Brenchley [TQ6741], *Rose & Crown*: Generally good if not cheap home-made food in sturdily timbered old inn with comfortable seats around rustic tables, several real ales, friendly service, piped music, children in eating area, restaurant and family room, seats on terrace, garden with play area; well equipped bedrooms *(Mrs C Hartley, LYM)*

☆ **Bridge** [off A2; TR1854], *White Horse*: Particularly good generous food inc excellent Sun lunch in smartly comfortable series of rooms inc civilised restaurant, Fremlins and Whitbreads on handpump, charming service, daily papers, guns on

walls; pleasant village *(Peter Robinson, Michael and Jennie Bukht, Nick Haslewood)*

Broadstairs [High St; TR3967], *Prince Albert*: Friendly, polite and good service, comfortable seating, pleasant relaxed atmosphere; quiet piped music, reasonable prices *(Neil H Barker)*

☆ **Brookland** [just off and signed from A259 about 1/2 mile out of village; TQ9825], *Woolpack*: Friendly local dating from 14th century (some of the ship's timbers may be older) in quite remote part of Romney Marsh, food from excellent toasties to vast mixed grill, very low entrance door and ceiling, nice big fire in capacious inglenook, well kept Shepherd Neame, streamside garden *(Richard Gibbs, Mike and Joyce Bryant)*

☆ **Burham** [Church St (nr M2 junction 3); TQ7361], *Golden Eagle*: Run much as restaurant — rather close-set bookable seats — but worth knowing for inventive, freshly cooked and nicely presented Malaysian and other food at reasonable prices; well kept Whitbreads-related real ales, striking Medway and North Downs view (pity about the pylons), lots of jugs and mugs hanging from impressive beams; one reader whose booking was mixed up did not feel well treated *(Peter Griffiths, Keith Widdowson)*

Burham [Church St], *Toastmasters*: Good range of real ales, big helpings of good food *(Trevor Fenning)*

Canterbury [The Friars; just off main St Peters St pedestrian area], *Canterbury Tales*: Pleasant, clean and airy lounge with good, fresh bar food, Brakspears, Hook Norton, and Shepherd Neame Bishops Finger *(Peter Robinson);* [3 Church Lane], *Simple Simons*: Step down through two-piece door with sliding spy-hole into basic beamed and flagstoned pub, very popular with students; young friendly staff, good piped music — often R & B; well kept real ales such as Fullers London Pride, Theakstons Old Peculier and Youngers No 3 *(David Culpin);* [Watling St], *Three Tuns*: 16th-century, with friendly and comfortable beamed bar areas, conservatory, decent reaonably priced food, real ale, piped music, children's room; bedrooms generously sized *(Sidney Wells, Neil Calver)*

☆ **Capel Le Ferne** [A20 towards Folkestone; TR2439], *Valiant Sailor*: Big neatly kept roadside pub, warm welcome, well kept Flowers Original, generous good value lunchtime food, comfortable lounge with settees and armchairs; they ask for respectable dress; useful for North Downs Way *(G A Broughton)*

☆ **Challock** [Church Lane; TR0050], *Chequers*: Low prices for usual bar food in tastefully modernised 17th-century village-green pub with friendly service, Courage ales *(Rob Harrison)*

Charing Heath [TQ9249], *Red Lion*: Friendly and unspoilt country pub, Shepherd Neame beers, no juke box *(Mr and Mrs J H Adam)*

Chartham Hatch [Hatch Lane; between A2

and A28 W of Canterbury; TR1056], *Royal Oak*: Old-fashioned and unspoilt real village local with well kept Shepherd Neame ales (*Comus Elliott*)

☆ **Chilham** [off A28/A252; TR0753], *Woolpack*: Interestingly renovated cheery bar, with pews, sofa, little armchairs, inglenook fires, well kept Shepherd Neame ales, low-priced bar food, restaurant, unobtrusive piped music; children in restaurant till early evening; bedrooms (*S V Bishop, Simon Collett-Jones, Jim Froggatt, Denise Plummer, John and Joan Nash, Simon Bates, John and Tessa Rainsford, LYM*)

☆ **Chillenden** [TR2653], *Griffins Head*: Unpretentious well run rural pub in attractive, quiet spot, stone floor, beams, big fireplace with roaring winter fire, two other rooms, restaurant; good range of beers, enjoyable meals such as veal escalopes and firm vegetables (few traditional snacks), good seating in and out (*Ian Whitlock, L M Miall*)

☆ **Cliffe** [TQ7376], *Black Bull*: Good authentic Far Eastern as well as more standard lunchtime bar food, Bass, Batemans, Stones, Youngs and guest beers, decent wines; L-shaped bar, darts/pool room, quiet juke box, no machines; comfortable and popular weekday evening basement restaurant with 80ft well (*D A Lloyd*)

Coopers Corner [B2042 Sevenoaks—Edenbridge; TQ4849], *Frog & Bucket*: Basic pub crowded for loud live music evenings and Sun lunchtime; well kept Theakstons Best and Youngers, lots of seating outside, barbecues, climbing frame; children welcome (*Judith Regan*)

Cowden [TQ4640], *Fountain*: Good two-bar local in nice old village, well kept beer, log fire, darts, good piped music, snacks (*Richard Gibbs*)

Crockham Hill [on Vanguard Way; TQ4450], *Royal Oak*: Useful for good walking country; wide choice of reasonable food (some home-grown veg), well kept Friary Meux Best, service unhurried (*W J Wonham*)

Crouch [TQ6155], *Olde Chequers*: Basic good food at reasonable prices, friendly staff, nice sunny terrace, popular restaurant (*Mr and Mrs R Gammon*)

Deal [Strand; TR3752], *Kings Head*: Attractively decorated seafront pub with tables overlooking water, attentive staff, good value food (*M W Atkinson*); [Strand], *Lifeboat*: Plush bar with helpful licensees, lunchtime food; loud evening piped pop music (*Dr J Barrie Jones*); [Strand], *Red Lion*: Attractive seafront pub, comfortable inside, Watneys-related real ales (*R Bennett*)

Dover [Dover Rd, Waldershare; TR2848], *High & Dry*: Recently refurbished, with warm welcome, good choice of reasonably priced food (*Colin Franks*)

Dunton Green [A224, Polhill; TQ5157], *Polhill Arms*: Attractive roadside pub overlooking Sevenoaks, well kept beer, pleasant restaurant, spectacular gardens (*E G Parish*)

East Peckham [Bullens Lane; TQ6648], *Addlestone*: Good plain working pub in hop and apple country; Flowers IPA and Fremlins on handpump, bar snacks (Sun too) inc good value cheese ploughman's, good collection of horse paraphernalia, helpful, friendly licensees (*Jenny and Brian Seller*)

☆ **Eastling** [off A251 S of M2 junction 6, via Painters Forstal; TQ9656], *Carpenters Arms*: Lace tablecloths, cottagey bric-a-brac, oak beams and big fireplaces front and back, with warm welcome, food (not Sun evening) in bar and restaurant, well kept Shepherd Neame, decent wines, some seats outside the pretty house; children allowed in restaurant; has been open all day (*Wayne Stockton, Anthony Barnes, LYM*)

☆ **Edenbridge** [High St; TQ4446], *Old Eden*: A Whitbreads Wayside inn, but full of old beams and individuality: high-roofed barn structure with upstairs food gallery; nice atmosphere, good food inc interesting specials, well kept Marstons Pedigree and Fremlins (*Dave Braisted, Comus Elliott*)

☆ **Edenbridge** [High St], *Crown*: Cheerful local with Tudor origins and not over-modernised, popular for straightforward bar food, with good service, real ales such as Friary Meux Best; one of the last pubs to have kept its 'gallows' inn-sign stretching right across the road (*Andy and Jill Kassube, LYM*)

Edenbridge [Swan Lane; TQ4446], *Swan*: Shady picnic-table sets outside flower-decked country pub, lunchtime and evening food, hard-working management (*E G Parish*)

Elham [St Marys Rd; TR1743], *Kings Arms*: Consistently well run, above-average bar food, very attractive bar and dining room, good open fire (*L M Miall*)

☆ **Eynsford** [TQ5365], *Malt Shovel*: Popular Victorian local with interesting decor (and reputed ghost), well kept Courage Best and Directors, good choice of cheap generous bar food (maybe not if restaurant busy eg Sun lunchtime); friendly staff (*P Gillbe*)

☆ **Finglesham** [The Street; just off A258 Sandwich—Deal; TR3353], *Crown*: Pleasant country pub, good friendly service, wide choice of reasonably priced bar food, popular old-world restaurant with inglenook fireplace and flagstones (*Mrs P Williams*)

Fordcombe [TQ5240], *Chafford Arms*: Beautiful garden with arbours and pretty lawns and shrubberies; Fremlins and Whitbreads real ales, local cider, interesting menu with a bias towards fish (also good if not over-generous crab sandwiches, good ploughman's); not cheap, service may slow (*Klaus and Elizabeth Leist, Jenny and Brian Seller*)

☆ **Fordwich** [off A28 in Sturry; TR1759], *Fordwich Arms*: Handsomely built and comfortable, with spacious garden by River Stour, welcoming winter fire, Fremlins and Marstons Pedigree, generous straightforward food, discreet piped music; parking may be difficult *(Mayur Shah, Jim Froggatt, Denise Plummer, LYM)*

Fordwich, *George & Dragon*: Friendly Beefeater by river and handy for Stodmarsh nature reserve, Whitbreads-related real ales, usual bar food; notable for character bedrooms *(Jim Froggatt, Denise Plummer)*

☆ **Four Elms** [B2027/B269 E of Edenbridge; TQ4648], *Four Elms*: Well kept Courage Directors, amazing range of bar food, generously served and reasonably priced, restaurant; friendly, with central open fire; children allowed in one not so welcoming room; handy for Chartwell *(Paul Evans, TOH, N P Davies, H Martin)*

☆ **Goudhurst** [A262 W of village; TQ7238], *Green Cross*: Good, interesting home-cooked bar food, good choice of real ales inc distant rarities (though atmosphere not really very pubby); beamed dining room for residents; bedrooms light and airy, good value *(Jas E Cross)*

☆ **Goudhurst**, *Star & Eagle*: Striking medieval inn with settles and Jacobean-style seats in heavily beamed hotelish open-plan bar, well kept Whitbreads-related real ales on handpump, decent bar food, tables behind with pretty views; polite service; children welcome; character bedrooms, well furnished and comfortable; parking can be difficult *(Mr and Mrs Foruria, Jas E Cross, LYM)*

Gravesend [7 Town Pier, nr ferry; TQ6473], *Three Daws*: Large timbered Tudor pub with interesting history, recently reopened; wide range of food in bar and restaurant; superb Thames views, interesting bric-a-brac, real ale, good service; two mins from car parks; children welcome *(Ann Stableford, A J Brown)*

Greenhithe [Old Town; TQ5874], *Pier*: Riverside position the main thing, fine views of the Dartford Bridge; local artist's old sailing barge pictures, children in room off bar, concrete terrace *(Mrs S Y Sadler)*

☆ **Hadlow** [Ashes Lane (off A26 Tonbridge Rd); TQ6349], *Rose Revived*: Friendly and attractive 16th-century pub with decent choice of well kept beers inc Harveys and King & Barnes, good bar food inc well filled fresh sandwiches *(Kit Read)*

☆ **Hawkhurst** [A268 towards Rye; TQ7730], *Oak & Ivy*: Comfortable and traditional old panelled pub with good atmosphere, friendly and efficient staff, generous good value home cooking, well kept Whitbreads-related real ales and roaring log fires; attractive restaurant *(Alan Merricks, C T and J M Laffan)*

Hawkinge [TR2339], *Cat & Custard Pot*: Well kept Shepherd Neame Spitfire on handpump, decent straightforward food, lots of RAF memorabilia *(Marcus Adams)*

Headcorn [High St; TQ8344], *George & Dragon*: Good atmosphere, open fires, very good food lunchtime and evening — crab pâté, soups, steak and kidney pie, steaks and puddings all recommended, chips exceptional *(Mrs C Hartley)*

Heaverham [Watery Lane — OS Sheet 188, map reference 572587; TQ5658], *Chequers*: Good country pub with two bars, lots of birds in big garden; good range of beers, reasonably priced bar food *(Geoff and Julie Bond)*

Herne [Herne Common; TR1865], *Fox & Hounds*: Very comfortable, exceptionally good value set meals *(E G Parish)*

Hever [TQ4744], *Henry VIII*: Country pub with good-sized pondside lawn and Boleyn connections *(C A Holloway, LYM)*

Higham [Gravesend Rd; TQ7171], *Sir John Falstaff*: Efficient and friendly, with varied reasonably priced food in bar and restaurant — substantial, well presented and fresh; children welcome *(Ann Stableford)*

☆ **Hodsoll Street** [TQ6263], *Green Man*: Attractive and well kept pub by village green; well prepared interesting food inc good value cold buffet, friendly staff, log fire, well kept Flowers and Fremlins *(Dr B A W Perkins, A S Maxted)*

Hollingbourne [Pilgrims Way; TQ8454], *Pilgrims Rest*: Well kept real ales such as Adnams, Fremlins, Shepherd Neame and Wadworths 6X, bar food, good Sun lunch in restaurant, friendly service, big real fire, darts and pool in separate area, unobtrusive juke box *(Keith Widdowson)*; [Eyhorne St (B2163), off A20 — OS Sheet 188, map reference 833547)], *Windmill*: Comfortable and welcoming bar with various different levels and alcoves around central servery; food, well kept Whitbreads-related real ales, sunny garden with children's play area *(Mr and Mrs R Gammon)*

Horsmonden [TQ7040], *Gun & Spitroast*: Attractive upmarket pub overlooking village green, with comfortable and spacious lounge; has been praised for good value bar food from generous sandwiches to spit roasts, with well kept Ind Coope Burton and restaurant, but no recent reports *(News please)*

☆ **Ide Hill** [off B2042 SW of Sevenoaks; TQ4851], *Cock*: Pretty pub, old but comfortably modernised, on charming village green, with decent straightforward bar food (not Sun evening, only snacks Sun lunchtime), well kept Allied and other ales, fine log fire, bar billiards, piped music, some seats out in front; handy for Chartwell and nearby walks — so gets busy, with nearby parking sometimes out of the question *(TOH, LYM)*

Ide Hill [TQ4851], *Crown*: Simple local with food inc good sandwiches, real ales, unobtrusive piped jazz, darts, small back garden with picnic-table sets; seats on attractive village green *(Judith Regan, Lyn and Bill Capper)*

☆ **Ightham Common** [Common Rd; TQ5755], *Harrow*: Modest but comfortable two-bar pub notable for well presented substantial fresh bar food; well kept Fremlins and King & Barnes Sussex on handpump, separate restaurant evenings and Sun; bedrooms *(Derek and Sylvia Stephenson)*

☆ **nr Ivy Hatch** [Stone Street; TQ5754], *Rose*

& Crown: Good value fresh bar food with Italian influence (particularly on puddings), in pleasant bar with some stripped masonry and fine collection of jugs hanging from ceiling; well kept Whitbreads-related real ales, decent wines, restaurant overlooking orchards; friendly staff, nice dog; can get booked up weekends; spacious garden with Fri evening summer barbecues, children's room in barn; handy for Igtham Mote (NT), on GWG49 *(C R and M A Starling, Derek and Sylvia Stephenson, Mr and Mrs E H Warner)*

☆ **Kingsgate** [Kingsgate Ave; TR3870], *Fayreness*: Outstandingly beautiful setting by shingle beach, warm welcome, consistently good bar food, well kept Youngs, efficient service; can get crowded *(JG, Mr and Mrs J H Adam)*

☆ **Lamberhurst** [B2100; TQ6735], *Horse & Groom*: Pleasant and welcoming two-bar local, well kept Shepherd Neame, good food in bar and restaurant area, darts, massive tie collection; bedrooms *(M Box, Richard Gibbs)*
Lamberhurst [High St], *George & Dragon*: Large rambling pub with well kept Harveys, Greene King Abbot and Ruddles on handpump, good choice of food inc substantial puddings, genial licensees; bedrooms, quieter behind *(Roderick Plinston, A J Castle)*; [Lamberhurst Down], *Swan*: Family pub next to Lamberhurst vineyards, food imaginative and good without being too expensive, friendly efficient service, good wine *(Derek Howse)*
Langton Green [just off A264; TQ5538], *Grange*: A Roast Inn, comfortably adapted from impressive former private house; above-average food, good service *(E G Parish)*
Larkfield [New Hythe Lane (nr M20 junction 3); TQ7058], *Monks Head*: Old-world low-beamed local dating back to 16th century; four small bar areas, one up steps, with two big fireplaces; has been praised for well kept Courage Best and Directors on handpump and interesting weekday bar food, but no recent reports *(News please)*

☆ **Leigh** [Powder Mills — OS Sheet 188, map reference 568469; TQ5446], *Plough*: Well kept and popular timbered country pub with cosy unspoilt atmosphere, huge log fire, variety of seating places, good range of real ales, consistently good generous reasonably priced bar food, Sun lunches in capacious old barn carvery; juke box, good service even when crowded (which it can be) *(Audrey and Brian Green, Mr and Mrs G Lacey, John Kimber)*
Loose [TQ7552], *Walnut Tree*: Shepherd Neame pub with limited but good food *(Trevor Fenning)*
Lower Hardres [TR1552], *Three Horseshoes*: Old-fashioned furnishings in country pub with choice of real ales, bar food inc wide choice of cheeses for ploughman's *(Comus Elliott, LYM)*
Luddesdown [TQ6766], *Golden Lion*: Simple traditional pub with big woodburning stove as well as open fire, well

kept real ales inc Ind Coope Burton, good value well presented simple bar lunches, attentive quick staff; handy for M2 junction 2, yet in peaceful valley for walkers *(Jenny and Brian Seller, D Thomas, LYM)*
Maidstone [Gabriels Hill; TQ7656], *Bull*: Big and old-looking, with friendly bar staff and quick straightforward food upstairs *(Alec Lewery)*; [Holland Rd/Wheeler St], *Greyhound*: 1940s-style public/lounge bar with well kept Shepherd Neame beers and good food; garden, car park; dogs allowed *(Michael Ranger)*
Marden [TQ7444], *West End*: Delightful village free house with well kept beers inc Fullers, low beams, attractive bar food *(Comus Elliott)*

☆ **Martin** [TR3346], *Old Lantern*: Popular old-world 17th-century pub with comfortable lounge, good log fire, well kept Watneys-related real ales and a guest beer, food usually good and reasonably priced, service usually cheerful and friendly; plenty of tables in attractive gardens; at its best at quiet times *(A Y Drummond)*
Martin Mill [Station Rd; TR3446], *Ugly Duckling*: Neat and tidy, with benches out in front, bar food inc good home-made scotch broth, shellfish stall outside with good choice of dressed crab, king prawns etc; good house wines; gets very busy, as big camp/caravan site nearby *(Alec Lewery, Marie Enright, Dr J Barrie Jones)*
Matfield [TQ6541], *Star*: Wide choice of good value bar food from home-made steak and kidney pie to steaks; very friendly, lots of locals; restaurant in 500-year-old back part, formerly butcher's *(Margaret and Trevor Errington)*
Nettlestead [B2015 Pembury—Maidstone; TQ6852], *Hop Pole*: Spacious carpeted bar with interesting prints, copper and brass ornaments, well kept Fremlins and Harveys, courteous friendly service, unobtrusive piped music, tables out in pleasant back area; good value varied and generous food; in hop and orchard country; children in quite small restaurant *(Mr and Mrs Peter Reeves)*
New Romney [Dymchurch Rd; TR0624], *Plough*: Big choice of low-priced meals in long bar with log fire, games and pool room; restaurant *(A H Denman)*
Oad Street [nr M2 junction 5; TQ8662], *Plough & Harrow*: Nice old village pub opp new craft centre with several real ales, pleasant landlord, well priced food *(Comus Elliott)*
Offham [TQ6557], *Kings Arms*: Attractive village pub with well kept reasonably priced Courage Best and bar food; delightful village *(Comus Elliott)*

☆ **Otford** [TQ5359], *Bull*: Well kept Courage Best and Directors, bar food, pleasant efficient staff, attractive garden, good family room; nr GWG47 *(Geoff and Julie Bond)*
Otford [High St], *Crown*: Well presented food inc fine Sun lunch *(R Johnstone)*; [66 High St], *Horns*: Well kept old pub with cheap snacks, well kept real ales inc Harveys and King & Barnes, log fire in big

inglenook; nr GWG47 *(Geoff and Julie Bond)*

Pembury [TQ6240], *Black Horse*: Well modernised to keep cosy and traditional feel, friendly staff, well kept Adnams, Harveys and Youngs, quick food; children's garden neat and well kept *(Terry Buckland, Martin Aust)*

☆ **Penshurst** [village centre; TQ5243], *Leicester Arms*: Pleasant atmosphere in well kept hotel bar with quiet corners; decent bar food inc good steak and kidney pudding here and in eating area extended and improved by new owners; good friendly service; on GWG50; decent bedrooms *(Jas E Cross, Mrs Richard Stewart, Win and Reg Harrington, Colin Laffan)*

☆ **nr Penshurst** [Hoath Corner; first R off B2188 S of village, then right again — OS Sheet 188, map reference 497431], *Rock*: Ancient beamed pub with inglenook, well kept Fremlins and Marstons Pedigree, bar food inc outstandingly generous ploughman's (all they do on Sun); ring the bull, tables outside; on GWG50 *(Jenny and Brian Seller)*

Petham [Stone St; TR1251], *Slippery Sams*: Friendly, well managed pub with good imaginative food in unspoilt beamed bar and restaurant *(Paul and Margaret Baker)*

☆ **Pett Bottom** [off B2068 S of Canterbury, via Lower Hardres — OS Sheet 179, map reference 161521; TR1552], *Duck*: Remote tile-hung cottage with two small rooms, big 17th-century fireplace, plain furnishings — can be packed out for expensive bar food inc interesting pies; Shepherd Neame and a couple of guest beers, decent wines by the glass, local cider, piped music; side restaurant; tables in sizeable garden; children allowed in smaller room *(Paul and Margaret Baker, Mr and Mrs J H Adam, Judith Regan, LYM)*

☆ **nr Plaxtol** [Sheet Hill; from Plaxtol, take Tree Lane from war memorial and church, straight through Yopps Green; from A227 nearly a mile S of Ightham, take unmarked turning beside lonely white cottage Bewley Bar, then right at oast house signposted Plaxtol; TQ6053], *Golding Hop*: Secluded and idiosyncratic country pub with suntrap lawn fenced off from small stream, interesting range of well kept real ales tapped from the cask, good farm ciders (it's even made its own), simple bar food (not Mon evening), straightforward country furniture; music can be loud, may have spit-roast pig on bank hols — when it gets very busy; children not allowed in (even to use lavatory) *(Maureen Preston, Derek and Sylvia Stephenson, LYM)*

☆ **Pluckley** [TQ9245], *Black Horse*: Cosy and busy old low-beamed local, reputedly haunted, with interesting rounded-top Dering windows, vast inglenook with unusual brazier-type fire, dark oak settles; friendly staff, huge amiable black cat, good if rather pricey home-made bar food inc good puddings, well kept Whitbreads-related and Marstons real ales, clean lavatories; big area given over to restaurant serving tasty business lunches; nicely laid out garden *(Jenny and Brian Seller)*

Ramsgate [Harbour Parade; opp end of rd to Sally Line; TR3865], *Harveys*: Good atmosphere, wood floor, plain wooden tables, beams; four real ales on handpump, attractive food — separate eating area *(John Atherton)*

☆ **Rochester** [10 St Margarets St; TQ7467], *Coopers Arms*: Interesting and comfortable old local, spotless, with quaint, friendly atmosphere; pleasant decor, brisk lunchtime trade for tasty bar meals; handy for castle and cathedral *(Barbara Hatfield, Comus Elliott, Gordon Mott)*

Rochester [High St], *Britannia*: Pleasant lunchtime food with well priced food — not fancy but nice; real ales inc Greene King IPA and Abbot and Theakstons Old Peculier on handpump *(Marcus Adams)*

Romney Street [TQ5461], *Fox & Hounds*: Very clean, in lovely walking countryside, with bar food up to steaks, lots of copper kettles, buckets and ships' fittings, big fireplace, two pool tables at one end, Courage real ale, seats out in front *(Keith Widdowson)*

Ryarsh [The Street; TQ6659], *Duke of Wellington*: Good bar food in well kept refurbished Tudor pub *(D Thomas)*

☆ **Sandgate** [Brewers Lane — main rd towards Hythe, then 100 yds or so after it emerges on to seafront park opp telephone box on R (beware high tides) and walk up steep cobbled track beside it; [TR2035], *Clarendon*: Sparely furnished tucked-away pub with friendly licensees, consistently well kept Shepherd Neame, bar food inc delicious clams, splendid dog *(Andy and Jill Kassube)*

Sandgate [High St], *Ship*: Small unpretentious front bar with friendly atmosphere, genuinely old furnishings; passage to another small back room; good value home-made food, good service, well kept Allied real ales, seats outside *(Andy and Jill Kassube)*

Sarre [TR2565], *Crown*: Delightful village inn comfortably refurbished by Shepherd Neame, well kept real ale *(Comus Elliott, Mr and Mrs J H Adam)*; *Kings Head*: Nice atmosphere, good beer, pleasant staff *(Comus Elliott)*

Selling [Perry Wood; from M2, keep right on through Selling; TR0456], *Rose & Crown*: Old pub, garden surrounded by woodland; enormous logfire, mix of furnishings inc wooden settle, good home-made food, Boddingtons, Fremlins and Shepherd Neame on handpump *(Paul Harrop)*

Sevenoaks [Godden Green; just E of Sevenoaks; TQ5355], *Bucks Head*: Lovely spot by duckpond on green, cosy inside, with standard bar food, prompt cheerful service, well kept Courage ales; nr GWG49, handy for Knole Park (NT); *(T W Hall, TOH)*; [London Rd nr stn], *Halfway House*: Pleasant atmosphere, friendly new licensees, attentive staff, good range of reasonably priced food *(Geoff and Julie Bond)*

Shatterling [Pedding Hill; A257 Ash—Wingham; TR2658], *Green Man*: Good lively bar, reasonably priced restaurant *(Mr and Mrs J H Adam)*

Shipbourne [TQ5952], *Chaser*: Extensively refurbished by former owners of Royal Oak Hotel in Sevenoaks — a good track record for their food; in attractive spot by church, concentrating on food in bar and restaurant; Harveys real ale; 15 bedrooms *(Anon)*

Shoreham [High St; TQ5161], *Crown*: Pleasant pub in lovely village, friendly landlord and staff, good choice of bar food, real fire, three separate bars, Greene King IPA and Abbot, piped music, picnic-table sets in garden *(Keith Widdowson)*

Shottenden [TR0454], *Plough*: Country free house, very popular summer and weekends, with at least five well kept beers on handpump and changing guests; good choice of reasonably priced bar food; children welcome, big garden safe for them, barbecues *(Steve Linter)*

Sissinghurst [TQ7937], *Bull*: Staff welcoming, Flowers, Fremlins and Whitbreads well kept, food good *(Stephen R Holman)*

☆ **Smarden** [TQ8842], *Chequers*: Comfortable old-world pub full of character, with beams, log fire, varied choice of really good reasonably priced food inc vegetarian dishes and seasonal veg, pleasant tables outside; bedrooms good value, with exceptionally good breakfasts *(Dr and Mrs Fisher, A W Woods, Geoff and Julie Bond, J E Hilditch)*

☆ **Sole Street** [the one above Wye; TR0949], *Compasses*: Largely unspoilt 16th-century country pub with sheep, goats, aviary and playthings in big attractive garden, friendly rustic atmosphere, efficient service, affable landlord, wide choice of good value bar food inc good pies, Shepherd Neame real ales, choice of local farm ciders, log-effect gas fires, bar billiards, piped music *(Miss M L Margetts, Mrs S Y Sadler, John McGee, LYM)*

☆ **Southfleet** [High Cross Rd, Westwood; coming from A2, keep on B262 into Betsham where you turn left — or coming through Southfleet keep straight ahead past The Ship], *Wheatsheaf*: Thatched and beamed Tudor pub kept simple inside — padded barrel chairs, traditional high-backed settles, sloping heavy beams, inglenook with big woodburner; well kept Courage Best and Directors, simple bar lunches (not weekends) inc cheap day's special, spontaneous folk music, occasional Morris dancers; big lawn above car park, and tables around sizeable softly floodlit pond *(Des Thomas, LYM)*

St Margarets at Cliffe [TR3644], *Smugglers*: Plush chesterfield sofas around front log-burner, big semi-circular central bar, darts area at back; quiet piped music, Marstons Pedigree and Scrumpy Jack on handpump *(Jim Froggatt, Denise Plummer)*

☆ **St Mary in the Marsh** [TR0628], *Star*: Remote partly flagstoned pub with haunting beeswax smell, log fire, good bar food at moderate prices, welcoming family service,

Shepherd Neame tapped from the cask and Harveys on handpump, friendly cats, small restaurant area; by small, attractive church; nice bedrooms, with views of Romney Marsh *(Jim Froggatt, Denise Plummer)*

☆ **Stalisfield Green** [off A252 in Charing; TQ9553], *Plough*: Beautifully placed well run pub, with varied well presented home-cooked food; interesting landlord *(John McGee)*

Tonbridge [Stafford Rd, The Slade; TQ5946], *Stafford Arms*: Good value newish carvery Tues-Sun, Flowers IPA; an oasis *(Peter Finzi)*

Tunbridge Wells [Mount Ephraim; behind Royal Wells Hotel; TQ5839], *Beau Nash*: Decent food, good atmosphere, terrace with leafy corners and picnic-table sets under cocktail parasols; children welcome *(E G Parish, William D Cissna, Mr and Mrs A P Reeves)*; [Mount Ephraim (A264)], *Brokers Arms*: Free house with Harveys Bitter, welcoming owners, cosy log fires, good mix of ages and genuine locals; giant helpings of good well priced bar food inc particularly good grills and fish; good value upstairs restaurant *(Miss P M Hayes, W G Harvey)*; [Denny Bottom, Rustall — Toad Rock signed off A264 W; TQ5639], *Toad Rock Retreat*: Pleasant pub nr the famous Rock, with central stone fireplace dividing comfortable saloon and dining area from simple public bar with piped music and machines; lots of beamery, cigarette cards, horse-racing mementoes; well kept Boddingtons and Wadworths 6X, popular with office people lunchtime for wide choice of food; small quiet terrace; children welcome *(Terry Buckland)*

☆ **Upstreet** [Grove Ferry; off A28 towards Preston; TR2263], *Grove Ferry*: Lovely position, with big riverside garden, full-length windows looking out on the water, nautical hardware, wide choice of generously served good bar food with stacks of fresh veg, restaurant, good Sun lunchtime carvery; well kept King & Barnes and Youngs on handpump, welcoming fire; very popular in good weather *(D Savage, Jim Froggatt, Denise Plummer)*

☆ **Warren Street** [just off A20 at top of North Downs — OS Sheet 189, map reference 926529; TQ9253], *Harrow*: Immaculate dining pub with extensive comfortably modernised low-beamed bar, very neatly furnished; quietly low-key atmosphere, flowers and candles, faint piped music, big woodburner; attentive service, generous helpings of well cooked food, Shepherd Neame and a guest beer such as Batemans on handpump; bedrooms *(Mr and Mrs Graham, John C Baker, BB)*

☆ **Weald** [village signposted off A21; in centre, turn left into Scabharbour Rd; TQ5450], *Chequer Tree*: Spacious and neatly modernised country pub with fairy-lit terraces, quite a big pond, lots of room up on the spreading lawns among trees and shrubs, and summer barbecues; bar food till 10 (not Sun or Mon evenings), well kept

Watneys-related real ales on handpump, flagstoned games area, restaurant (not Sun evening); children allowed in eating area and restaurant *(Simon Velate, LYM)*

Westerham [Market Sq; TQ4454], *George & Dragon*: Welcoming licensees in Chef & Brewer with good pubby atmosphere, good service, decent traditional Sun lunches, Watneys-related real ales *(E G Parish, Andy and Jill Kassube)*

☆ **Wickhambreaux** [TR2158], *Rose*: Attractive old building both inside and out, friendly atmosphere, well kept beer, good bar food inc fine sandwiches and ploughman's; pretty village *(G A Broughton)*

Wingham [TR2457], *Red Lion*: Neatly modernised and comfortable ancient inn, pleasant and friendly, with good varied bar food, well kept Whitbreads-related real ales on handpump; restaurant; bedrooms *(Judith Regan, LYM)*

☆ **Worth** [The Street; TR3356], *St Crispin*: Busy but relaxed and friendly partly 15th-century village pub, completely refurbished, with well kept beer inc guests, reasonably priced good bar food, restaurant, nice waitresses; pleasant garden, nice spot nr beach and golf courses; bedrooms *(Mrs R Horridge)*

☆ **Wrotham** [signposted 1 ¾ miles from M20, junction 2; TQ6159], *Bull*: Civilised food all day at linen-covered tables in character room of 14th-century inn with three log fires, inc traditional lunchtime and evening bar dishes and good value Sun lunch; well kept Whitbreads-related real ales, decent wines, friendly landlady, children welcome; though it's now more restaurant than bar it's still enjoyable and attractive — like the village around it; bedrooms, ample parking *(Dr James Haworth, M A and C R Starling, M J Brooks, LYM)*

Wye [village signed off A28 NE of Ashford; Upper Bridge St; TR0546], *New Flying Horse*: Comfortably modernised 17th-century beamed inn, pleasantly light, friendly atmosphere, locals at bar; wide choice of substantial bar food, well kept Shepherd Neame ales inc Old; attractive garden with Japanese influence; bedrooms pleasant — especially those in converted outbuildings — with good breakfasts *(E G Parish)*; *Tickled Trout*: Charming riverside spot, with tables out on waterside lawn and newish conservatory/restaurant; bar done out with heavy timbering, stripped brickwork and copper tables, straightforward bar food, Whitbreads-related and Marstons real ales on handpump; children allowed in eating area and restaurant; nr start GWG46 *(Geoff and Julie Bond, LYM)*

☆ **Yalding** [Yalding Hill; TQ7050], *Walnut Tree*: Ancient beams, inglenook, antiques and interesting pictures, with good bar food inc fine ploughman's, well kept Whitbreads-related real ales, restaurant, immaculate lavatories; bedrooms *(Jenny and Brian Seller)*

Lancashire
(including Greater Manchester and Merseyside)

This stands out as one of the cheapest areas in Britain for pub food and drink. Indeed, this last year prices here have if anything gone up by slightly less than in other areas, so the value margin is widening. And some really good food can be found in pubs here, as for instance at the Moorcock up by Blacko, the Assheton Arms in the pretty village of Downham (currently doing particularly well, it gains a food award this year), the Bushells Arms at Goosnargh (food is what gains it its place in the Guide), the Mark Addy and Royal Oak in Manchester (marvellous cheap cheese meals), the Devonshire Arms in the Mellor that's near Stockport (a new entry; beware that another Devonshire Arms in the other Mellor north of Manchester is an unlicensed hotel), the Hark to Bounty in its attractive Forest of Bowland village of Slaidburn, the friendly New Inn at Yeoland Conyers (another new entry), and the Inn at Whitewell, another Forest of Bowland pub and in many ways Lancashire's most attractive inn – currently doing particularly well all round. Look for our new £ symbol to spot the many food bargains in other pubs here. Changes to note here include friendly new licensees doing well at the Plough at Eaves near Broughton, continued expansion at the Owd Nells at Bilsborrow (a place for a cheerful family outing, with food all day), and a change of regime at the Station at Broadbottom. Besides the two already mentioned, new main entries, or pubs back in the Guide after a break, are the cheerful Black Dog up on the moors at Belmont (one of the very cheapest pubs we've found in the whole country), the civilised Cavendish Arms at Brindle (so charmingly rooted in the earlier years of this century), and the well run Rock at Tockholes (relaxing, with lovely views). All these, like a good few other main entries, are in attractive places. In the Lucky Dip at the end of the chapter, lovely surrounding countryside is at least part of the appeal of these pubs which we'd pick out as deserving special attention (almost all of them inspected by us): the Red Pump at Bashall Eaves, Coach & Horses at Bolton by Bowland, Lord Raglan up above Bury, Rams Head at Denshaw, Diggle Hotel at Diggle, Strawbury Duck at Entwistle, Golden Ball at Heaton with Oxcliffe, Egerton Arms near Heywood, Romper outside Marple, Tandle Hill Tavern in Middleton, Owd Betts on the moors near Rochdale, Victoria at Tockholes and Church at Uppermill. Other Dip pubs currently on an upswing are the Malt 'n' Hops in Chorley, Black Horse at Croston, Horns at Goosnargh, White Bull at Ribchester and Royal Oak at Riley Green, and we'd also pick out the Dunk Inn at Clayton le Moors, Harpers at Fence and Waggon at Mottram (again, we've inspected most of these). Manchester has a great many pubs well worth a try, and both Liverpool and Stockport have quite a few.

Holts pubs can be relied on for low prices: the Dip includes several interesting ones.

nr BALDERSTONE (Lancs)   SD6332 Map 7
Myerscough Hotel

Whalley Rd, Samlesbury; A59 Preston–Skipton, over 3 miles from M6 junction 31

Popular at lunchtime with businessmen and workers from British Aerospace opposite, this quiet pub has a cottagey atmosphere, nice ink and pen drawings of local scenes, a painting of the month by a local artist, lots of brass and copper, well made oak settles around dimpled copper or heavy cast-iron-framed tables, beams, and soft lighting; the serving counter has a nice padded elbow rest. Good value, well kept Robinsons Best and Mild on handpump, and several malt whiskies; shove-ha'penny, dominoes, and fruit machine. At lunchtime, bar food includes home-made soup (£1.20), sandwiches (from £1.50; the open ham is good), ploughman's or steak escalopes on granary barm cake (£3.20), steak and kidney pie (£3.55), roast beef or gammon and egg (£3.95), 6oz sirloin steak (£5.95), and puddings (£1.50), with daily specials like beef curry or grilled liver and bacon (£3.50). There are picnic-table sets, bantams and their chicks, and rabbits in the garden. (*Recommended by Mrs Pat Crabb, P Corris, Len Beattie, Mr and Mrs J H Adam, Lee Goulding, Len Beattie*)

Robinsons   Tenant John Pedder   Real ale   Meals and snacks (12–2, 6.30–8.30; not Sun evening)   Mellor (0254 81) 2222   Well behaved children in small room till 8.30 Open 11.30–3, 5.15–11

BELMONT (Lancs)   SD6716 Map 7
Black Dog £

A675

From two long benches on the sheltered sunny side of this 18th-century pub there are delightful views of the moors above the nearby trees; there's a track from the village up Winter Hill and (from the lane to Rivington) on to Anglezarke Moor, and paths from the dam of the nearby Belmont Reservoir. The original unpretentious small rooms have antiques and bric-a-brac from railwaymen's lamps, bedpans and chamber-pots to landscape paintings, as well as service bells for the sturdy built-in curved seats, rush-seated mahogany chairs, and cosy coal fires; there are various snug alcoves, one of which contains what was the village court. Bar food includes home-made soup (£1; they do a winter broth with dumplings), sandwiches (from £1; steak barm cake £1.20), ploughman's (from £2.30), steak and kidney pie, gammon, lamb cutlets or scampi (£2.90), vegetable or chicken curry (£3), salads, and steaks (from £5); as food is cooked to order there may be a bit of a wait. Well kept and remarkably cheap Holts Bitter and Mild on handpump, and morning coffee. An airy extension lounge with a picture window has more modern furnishings; pool, shove-ha'penny, dominoes, cribbage, fruit machine and piped classical music (which the landlord likes to whistle along to). (*Recommended by Graham Bush, Bill Ryan, Michael Rooke, Ben Wimpenny, J E Stanton, Jim and Maggie Cowell*)

Holts   Tenant James Pilkington   Real ale   Meals and snacks (not Mon or Tues evenings except for residents)   Belmont (020 481) 218   Children welcome away from bar   10-piece orchestra four times a year   Open 12–4, 7–11   Bedrooms; £29.50B/£42B

BILSBORROW (Lancs)   SD5139 Map 7
Owd Nells

St Michaels Road; at S end of village (which is on A6 N of Preston) take Myerscough College of Agriculture turn

Becoming more and more of a place for an outing, this very popular pub by the canal is sprouting quite a little thatched village of craft shops and so on (there's a tea shop, too) – as well as a substantially increased hotel side; an indoor pool and gym, more bedrooms, another children's play area and cricket field and small pavilion are planned. The spacious three or four communicating room areas have a mix of brocaded button-back banquettes, stable-stall seating, library chairs and other seats, high pitched rafters at either end, and lower beams (and flagstones) by the bar counter in the middle. A good choice of decent bar food includes home-made soup (£1.15), cheese and pickles (£2.35), local potted shrimps (£2.75), hot roast beef sandwich (£3), steak and kidney pudding (£3.95) and minute steak (£5.50), with afternoon sandwiches (from £1.95), and late-evening snacks such as deep-fried courgette strips (£1.85), mussel casserole (£2.50) and fresh prawns (£3.50); efficient waitress service. Well kept Boddingtons, Flowers, Fullers, Timothy Taylor, Wethereds, Whitbreads Castle Eden and weekly guests on handpump, wines including a bargain house champagne, draught cider, tea and coffee; video game, fruit machine, football machine, Connect Four, and unobtrusive piped pop music. There are colourful seats out on this large white house's terrace, part of which is covered by a thatched roof; a small walled-in play area has a timber castle. *(Recommended by John Atherton, Jim and Maggie Cowell, Jim and P Isaacs, Janet Brown, Adrian Steen, F Teare)*

Free house   Licensee Roy Wilkinson   Real ale   Meals (12–8) and snacks (all day) Next-door restaurant; open all day inc Sun   (0995) 40010/40020   Children welcome Morris dancing in square, craft demos   Open 11–11   Bedrooms; £30.15B per room

BLACKO (Lancs)   SD8541   Map 7

Moorcock ⊘

A682; N of village towards Gisburn

One reader found himself sitting next to people who had come all the way from Stockport just for the ham salad (£3.95). The other bar food – almost entirely home-made – is also outstandingly good. There's quite a continental theme, with garlicky Italian and Austrian dishes such as excellent bratwürst (£3.95), authentic goulash (£4.25) and schweinschnitzel (£4.75), as well as soup (£1.50), a substantial ploughman's (from £2.95, with proper little pots of butter), pâté (£1.95), chilliburger or savoury pancakes (£3.95), vegetable biryani or stuffed peppers (£3.95), steak and kidney pie (£4.25), whole ham shank in a light mustard sauce (£4.75), halibut mornay (£5.25), steaks (from £5.50 for minute steak), and lots of daily specials like salmon steak with hollandaise sauce; puddings such as cheesecake or good fruit pies (£1.75) and Sunday roasts (£4.75); efficient, friendly service. The bar is spaciously comfortable, with breath-taking views from the big picture windows, a lofty ceiling, and cream walls hung with brass ornaments. Well kept Thwaites Bitter and Best Mild on handpump; friendly sheepdog. The attractively landscaped back garden is very busy at weekends, though quieter during the week. They no longer do bedrooms. *(Recommended by Michael and Joan Melling, Len Beattie, Dave and Kate Buckley, John Watson, Kathryn Ogden, George Hunt, Gwen and Peter Andrews, Andy and Jill Kassube, Simon Bates, Andrew Stephenson)*

Thwaites   Tenant Elizabeth Holt   Real ale   Meals and snacks   Restaurant   Nelson (0282) 64186   Children welcome   Open 11.30–2.30, 6.30-midnight (supper licence); open all day Sun; closed 25 Dec

BLACKSTONE EDGE (Gtr Manchester)   SD9716   Map 7

White House

A58 Ripponden–Littleborough, just W of B6138

Walkers and hikers can leave their muddy boots in the long enclosed porch of this imposing 17th-century moorland pub. The cosy main bar has a large-scale map of the area and a Turkey carpet in front of a blazing coal fire; the snug Pennine Room opens off here, with brightly coloured antimacassars on its small soft settees. To the left, a spacious room has a big horseshoe window that looks out over the moors, comfortable seats around its tables, and coloured pins on a map of the world showing where foreign visitors have come from. Good helpings of homely bar food include home-made vegetable soup (£1), sandwiches (from £1.60, steak £1.90), Cumberland sausage with egg (£2.75), quiche lorraine (£2.85), lasagne or home-made steak and kidney pie (£3.25), salads (from £3.50), and 8oz sirloin steak (£6.75); also, daily specials and home-made apple pie (£1); children's meals (from £1.50). Well kept John Smiths and another beer such as Exmoor Gold, Marstons Pedigree, Moorhouses Pendle Witches Brew or Robinwood Old Fart on handpump, farm cider, and malt whiskies; trivia, fruit machine. *(Recommended by Carol and Richard Glover, Comus Elliott, Andrew Hazeldine; more reports please)*

Free house Licensee Neville Marney Real ale Meals and snacks (11.30–2, 7–10) Restaurant Littleborough (0706) 78456 Children welcome until 9pm Open 11.30–3, 7–11

BRIERFIELD (Lancs)   SD8435 Map 7
Waggon & Horses £
Just over 1/2 mile from M65 junction 12; A682 signposted Brierfield, pub on left

This warmly chatty and thoroughly welcoming place – not much to look at from the busy road – has been beautifully and lovingly restored. Though there's a high-ceilinged carpeted central area with plush stools, some cream tilework, heavy maroon woodwork and attractively cut and etched glass, especially around the servery itself, the real delight is in the small rooms leading off. Our own favourite is the one at the back on the left: soft gas lighting, ochre Anaglypta walls with good reproductions of Renoir nudes, heavy button-back wall seats in old gold plush, a couple of elegant Regency-striped chairs, thick flowered curtains, dark red ceiling, a figured walnut piano and a coal fire in a period fireplace with decorative tiles. Three other small rooms, also with fires, each have their own devotees (and one has darts). Well kept Thwaites Bitter and Mild on handpump (a two-hour happy hour on Saturday lunchtime), decent half bottles of wine and some malt whiskies; some tables out on a side terrace; shove-ha'penny, dominoes, fruit machine and piped music. Good value home-made bar food includes sandwiches, chilli con carne (£2.25), shepherd's or steak and mushroom pies (£2.50), lasagne (£2.80), gammon cooked with peaches (£3) and roast Sunday lunch (£3.50); service is warmly friendly and efficient. The pyrenean mountain dog is called Sebastian, and the pub is a short stroll from the Leeds to Liverpool canal. *(Recommended by Dr P A Stevenson, Dr John Martindale, Len Beattie, Brian Jones, Dr Thomas Mackenzie)*

Thwaites Tenant Kevin D Edwards Real ale Meals and snacks (lunchtime) (0282) 63962 Children welcome until 8pm Open 11.30–2.30, 5–11.30; 11–11 Fri and Sat

BRINDLE (Lancs)   SD6024 Map 7
Cavendish Arms
3 miles from M6 junction 29; A6 towards Whittle-le-Woods then left on B5256

Though this civilised pub dates back to the 18th century, its style is decidedly 1920s or earlier, with several small rooms around a central servery, comfortable seats, little partitions, discreet flowery curtains, lots of pictorial plates and Devonshire heraldic devices in plaster on the walls, and – what particularly sets the mood – stained-glass medieval-style scenes set into the latticed windows. Well kept Burtonwood Best and Mild on handpump, a good choice of malt whiskies, neat and friendly staff. Bar food includes soup (£1.25), filling open teacakes (from £1.70), ploughman's (from £3.50), home-made beef pie (£3.75), home-made lasagne or crispy battered cod (£4.25), roast beef and Yorkshire pudding (£4.50), daily specials, and puddings (£1). There are white metal and plastic tables and chairs on a terrace by a rockery with a small water cascade, with another table on a small lawn behind; a nice spot, by an attractive stone church. *(Recommended by Graham Bush, Jim and Maggie Cowell)*

Burtonwood Tenant Peter Bowling Real ale Meals and snacks (11–2, 5.30–9; not Sun, Mon or Tues evenings) (025 485) 2912 Children welcome until 9pm Open 11–3, 5.30–11; all day Sat

BROADBOTTOM (Gtr Manchester) SJ9993 Map 7

Station

Just E of present end of M67; village signposted off A57 in Mottram; the train from Manchester Piccadilly (every half-hour, more often in rush hours) takes 25 minutes

By the time the *Guide* is published, this attractive stone building – a virtually derelict station only a few years ago – will be in new hands. We're hoping the new licensees won't change too much. Most of the railway influence remains notably in one of the (no-smoking) restaurant areas done up as a dining-car on the Orient Express, down to details like the curved and lofted carriage roof, tulip lamps, masses of little vertical mirrors and a showy slave-lampholder. The bar itself, which opens straight on to the platform, has a similar Victorian style, with a sturdy brass footrest and elbow rest for the bar counter, blue-and-pink walls with Anaglypta dado and inset bookshelves, prints large and small, elaborate brass lamps, and blue curtains on fat wooden rails. Stairs (which divide the bar roughly into two) lead up to a second, galleried restaurant area, with banquette seating in booths, and a striking art deco stained-glass ceiling. Bar food has included soup, sandwiches, ploughman's, salads, steak and kidney pie, and vegetarian dishes, with children's dishes and puddings; black-and-white uniformed staff. Banks's Mild and Bitter on handpump; piped music. *(Recommended by Roy Cove, H B Vanstone, P A Crossland, D A Cawley, Keith Mills)*

Free house Licensees Larry and Irene Duggan Real ale Meals and snacks Restaurants Mottram (0457) 63327; open all day Sun Children welcome Live music Thurs evening Open 11.30–3, 5.30–11; all day Sun

nr BROUGHTON (Lancs) SD5235 Map 7

Plough at Eaves

4 1/2 miles from M6, junction 32: take M55 turn-off, then A6 N, then after about 1 mile N of Broughton traffic lights, first left into Station Lane; after canal bridge bear right at junction, then left at fork; pub on the right; OS Sheet 102, map reference 495374

Neat but pleasantly unfussy furnishings in the two low-beamed bars of this homely old country pub include lots of wooden casks, rush-seat chairs around dark wooden tripod tables, an antique oak linen chest and corner cupboard, a couple of guns over one good copper-hooded open fire with a row of Royal Doulton figurines above another, and little latticed windows. Well kept Thwaites Bitter on handpump; darts, shove-ha'penny, dominoes, cribbage, fruit machine, and piped music. Under the friendly new licensee bar food includes soup (90p), sandwiches (from £1.95), quiche of the day (£2.25), popular Cumberland sausage and egg (£2.95), gammon (£3.35), vegetable lasagne (£3.95), sirloin steak (£7.95), daily specials such as hot roast lamb sandwich (£2.25), fish pie (£3.50) and mixed grill (£9.95); puddings (£1.50), children's meals (£2.25) and Sunday roast. There's a well equipped children's play area at the back, and metal and wood-slat seats and cast-iron-framed tables running along the front by the quiet lane. *(Recommended by Robert and Lesley Fawthrop, Mel Landells, Graham Bush, R Tomlinson, Jim and Maggie Cowell, John Atherton)*

Thwaites Tenant June Daniel Real ale Meals and snacks (12–2.30, 6.30–9.30) Restaurant Catforth (0772) 690233 Children welcome Open 12–3, 6.30–11

BURNLEY (Lancs) SD8332 Map 7

Coal Clough House

Coal Clough Lane; between Burnham Gate (B6239) and A646; OS Sheet 103, map reference 830818

The notably well decorated lounge in this elegant Victorian dining pub has lots of oak panelling, an elaborately moulded high plaster ceiling, a lovely carved mantelpiece around the big open fireplace, and antique prints; the front sun lounge is popular, particularly with lunchtime businessmen. The conservatory and part of the family room are no smoking. Bar food, from the Millers Kitchen, includes sandwiches (from £2.25), ploughman's (from £3.25), steak and kidney pie or vegetable lasagne (£3.95), rump steak (£5.25), puddings (£1.95), Sunday roast (£3.95), children's meals (£2.50) and senior citizens' meals (£2.25); efficient service from well dressed bar staff; fruit machine, piped music. There are tables outside on the terrace by the wisteria, and beside the roses and mature trees on the lawn. *(Recommended by Len Beattie, Carol and Richard Glover, John Atherton, Andrew Stephenson; more reports please)*

Greenalls   Manager Stephen Hayes   Meals and snacks (12–2.30, 6–9.30; 6–10 Fri and Sat, all day Sun)   Burnley (0282) 28800   Children in family room   Karaoke Mon and Thurs evenings   Open 12–3.30, 6–11; 12–11 Sat (till 10.30 Sun); closed 25 Dec

nr DARWEN (Lancs)   SD6922 Map 7
Old Rosins

Pickup Bank, Hoddlesden; from B6232 Haslingden–Belthorn, turn off towards Edgeworth opposite the Grey Mare – pub then signposted off to the right; OS Sheet 103, map reference 722227

Big picture windows here make the most of the views over the moors and down the wooded valley. Lots of mugs, whisky-water jugs and so forth hang from the high joists of the extensive open-plan lounge, which is comfortably furnished with red plush built-in button-back banquettes, and stools and small wooden chairs around dark cast-iron-framed tables; the walls are hung with small prints, plates and old farm tools, and there's a good log fire. Boddingtons, Flowers and Timothy Taylors on handpump, lots of malt whiskies and coffee; fruit machine and piped music. Good value, interesting food ranges from home-made soup (£1), sandwiches (from £1.55; open sandwiches from £2.85) and ploughman's (£2.85), through pork satay (£2.25), salads (£3.35), and home-made pizzas (from £3.35), to freshly battered plaice (£3.55), beef in Old Peculier (£3.75), chicken tikka (£4), and sirloin steak (£6.95); puddings (£1.60) and children's meals. There are picnic-table sets on a spacious crazy-paved terrace, but what was the lawn is now a car park. *(Recommended by Greg Turner, A G Roby, Roger Taylor, Len Beattie, Carol and Richard Glover)*

Free house   Licensee Bryan Hankinson   Real ale   Meals and snacks (noon–10)   Restaurant   Darwen (0254) 771264   Children in eating area of bar and in restaurant   Open 12–11   Bedrooms; £35B/£55B

nr DELPH (Gtr Manchester)   SD9808 Map 7
Horse & Jockey

Junction of A62 and A670

As well as good local walks, including one down to the site of a Roman fort by Castleshaw reservoir, this isolated pub is not far from the Pennine Way. Inside, the two dimly-lit, cosy and atmospheric rooms are comfortably furnished with settees, easy chairs and Windsor chairs, and one room is panelled and served from a high hatch. A good range of well kept, changing real ales on handpump runs through Marstons Mild and Owd Rodger, Moorhouses Pendle Witches Brew and Timothy Taylors Bitter and Landlord and changing guest beers; prices are very low. The gents is pretty rustic. There are lovely views over the high moors. *(Recommended by R J August, Gary Scott, Andrew Triggs; more reports please)*

Free house   Licensee David Kershaw   Real ale   No food   (0457) 874283   Open 7–11; 1–2.30, 7.30–11 Sat

DOWNHAM (Lancs)   SD7844 Map 7
Assheton Arms ⊘

From A59 NE of Clitheroe turn off into Chatburn (signposted); in Chatburn follow Downham signpost; OS Sheet 103, map reference 785443

Before this busy pub even opens there's often a queue of people outside, waiting to get their teeth into the wide choice of good bar food. Reasonably priced and generously served, this includes tasty home-made ham and vegetable soup (£1.45), sandwiches (not Saturday evening or Sunday lunchtime; from £2), stilton pâté (£2.60), delicious potted Morecambe Bay shrimps (£3.50), home-made steak and kidney pie or cauliflower and mushroom provençale (£4.50), good grilled plaice (£5.25), succulent grilled ham with free-range eggs (£5.50), seasonal game pie (£6.10), steaks (from £8.75), puddings (from £1.75), and children's dishes (£2.50); the chips are excellent. The rambling, beamed and red-carpeted bar has olive plush-cushioned winged settles around attractive grainy oak tables, some cushioned window seats, and two grenadier busts on the mantlepiece over a massive stone fireplace (that helps to divide the separate areas). Well kept Marstons Pedigree, Whitbreads Bentleys Yorkshire and Castle Eden on handpump; piped music; young, helpful staff. The pub nestles on a pastoral slope opposite the church and there are picnic-table sets under cocktail parasols. The stonebuilt village, spreading out along a duck-inhabited stream, is charmingly preserved in traditional style by the Asshetons – the family of Lord Clitheroe – who've been here since 1558. *(Recommended by Greg Turner, M V Melling, Harry McCann, Robert and Vicky Tod, Olive Carroll, KC, Mr and Mrs Harry McCann)*

Whitbreads   Tenants David and Wendy Busby   Real ale   Meals and snacks (till 10pm)   Clitheroe (0200) 41227   Children welcome   Open 12–3, 7–11

EDGWORTH (Lancs)   SD7416 Map 7
White Horse

A676 N of Bolton, then left onto B6391; village signposted on right about 1/2 mile after Turton Tower; pub on Bury St

Of particular interest in this snug village pub is the profusion of highly lacquered, dark brown oak panelling, much of it carved. Lots of copper jugs and so forth hang from the beams, there are a couple of log fires (not always lit), a brass ship's clock and barometer, a grandfather and other old clocks, and plush button-back wall banquettes curved around wooden or dimpled copper tables. Well kept Matthew Browns Mild and Bitter, Theakstons XB and Youngers IPA and No 3 on handpump; darts, pool, cribbage, dominoes, fruit machine, video game, trivia and juke box. Bar food includes rump steak muffins and filled baked potatoes (from £1.65), good home-made steak or chicken pies (£3), home-made curries and chilli con carne (£3.45). Large balcony and small garden. *(Recommended by B Taylor, G T Jones, Ben Wimpenny, R C Gandy; more reports please)*

Matthew Browns (S & N)   Tenant Alan Parry   Real ale   Meals and snacks (not Sat evening)   (0204) 852377   Children welcome until 8.30   60s Disco Weds and Thurs evening; Irish folk every 2nd Sun lunchtime   Open 11–11; closed winter weekday afternoons

GARSTANG (Lancs)   SD4845 Map 7
Th'Owd Tithebarn   ★

Signposted off Church Street; turn left off one-way system at Farmers Arms

The dining area in this converted, creeper-covered canalside barn is particularly pleasant – more like a farmhouse kitchen parlour really, with an old kitchen range, prints of agricultural equipment on the walls, low beams – and waitresses in period costume with mob-caps. The rest of the bar has masses of antique farm tools, stuffed animals and birds, and pews and glossy tables spaced out on the flagstones under the high rafters. Simple bar food includes home-made vegetable soup (£1.65), ploughman's (£2.65), salads (from £2.85), steak and kidney pie (£3.95), a choice of roast meats (£4.25) and ham and eggs (£4.50); puddings (£1.75), and a good children's menu (from 85p). Lots of country wines, and a fine antique bar billiards machine. Outside, there's a big stone terrace where you can sit watching the boats and ducks; it can get very busy at weekends. Upstairs is the small Lancaster Canal Museum. *(Recommended by Mike Tucker, Anthony Barnes, Graham Bush, M A and W R Proctor, John Fazakerley, Carol and Richard Glover, John and Christine Simpson, J P Cinnamond)*

Free house Licensees Kerry and Eunice Matthews Meals and snacks (not Mon)
Restaurant (0995) 604486 Children in dining area Open 11–3, 7(6 Sat)–11; closed
Mon (though not lunchtime bank hol Mons)

GOOSNARGH (Lancs)   SD5537   Map 7

Bushells Arms 🏵

4 miles from M6 junction 32; A6 towards Garstang, turn right at Broughton traffic
lights (the first ones you come to), then left at Goosnargh Village signpost (it's pretty
insignificant – the turn's more or less opposite Whittingham Post Office)

Included for its enormously impressive range of home-made bar food, this very
busy dining pub has dishes that include soups from a choice of around 100, one of
the favourites being lovage (£1), falafel or crispy samosas (£1.80), home-made
brawn (£2.50), cheese and broccoli flan (£4), Lebanese kofta, Syrian potato
omelette or very popular steak and kidney pie (£4.50), a Greek beef stew, pork
chop with apple, cider, and calvados or poulet basque (all £5.50), chicken and
stilton roulade (£6), and puddings like apricot and sultana cheesecake, pineapple
and ginger spice cake and rhubarb and strawberry crumble (£1.75); crisp and fresh
vegetables include tasty potatoes, done with garlic, cream, peppers and parmesan,
children's dishes (£1.75), and traditional local shortbread flavoured with caraway
seeds and known as Goosnargh cakes (the place is pronounced Goozner,
incidentally). Delays at peak periods – mainly Saturday night. Two areas of the
spacious, modernised bar are no smoking – and there are lots of snug bays, each
holding not more than two or three tables and often faced with big chunks of
sandstone (plastic plants and spotlit bare boughs heighten the rockery effect); also
soft red plush button-back banquettes, with flagstones by the bar; fruit machine,
and maybe piped 1960ish music. Boddingtons Bitter on handpump, a good choice
of wines (including some New World ones), and several malt whiskies.
(Recommended by Kathryn Ogden, Greg Turner, Mike Tucker, P Craddock, Richard Dolphin,
Bob and Lesley Fawthrop, Mrs J Crawford, Hilary Bill, P J and S E Robbins, C J McFeeters, M
B P Carpenter, Alan and Marlene Radford, R H Sawyer, M A Watts, Roy Butler)

Whitbreads Tenants David and Glynis Best Real ale Meals and snacks (till 10pm)
(0772) 865235 Children in eating area of bar until 9pm Open 12–3, 6–11

HASLINGDEN (Lancs)   SD7823   Map 7

Duke of Wellington

Grane Road; B6232 signed from Haslingden centre – OS Sheet 103, map reference
767228

From the picnic-table sets outside this spacious pub there are views looking over to
the reservoirs nestling below the woods and sheep pastures of Rossendale; the
playground, fenced off in the garden, is notably well equipped and popular with
families; nice walks nearby. Inside, the softly lit main room, divided up by
balustered wood and black cast-iron screens, has lots of polished dark woodwork,
button-back pink cloth settees and slat-back chairs around its tables, the odd
button-back leather sofa, quiet country pictures on the muted pink-papered walls,
deco lamps, and bookshelves; part of the dining area is no smoking. Bar food
includes soup (95p), sandwiches (from £1.60), steak and kidney pie (£3.65),
Cumberland sausage and egg (£3.95), cold platters with salad (from around
£3.65), gammon with egg or pineapple (£3.95), and 8oz sirloin steak (£6.95); they
have a menu for the blind; service can be slow when it's busy (Sunday lunchtime,
say), but they do warn you. Well kept Boddingtons, Marstons Pedigree and
Whitbreads Trophy on handpump; fruit machine, video game, piped music and
quizzes. *(Recommended by Carol and Richard Glover, Mr and Mrs J H Adam, Dave and*
Kate Buckley, Len Beattie, Lee Goulding)

Whitbreads Manager Glyn Ferguson Real ale Meals and snacks (12–9.30; 10 Fri
and Sat) Restaurant Rossendale (0706) 215610 Children in restaurant Open
11.30–11; limited hours Easter weekend and 25 Dec

LIVERPOOL   SJ4395   Map 7

Philharmonic ★ £

36 Hope Street; corner of Hardman Street

Much of the craftsmanship in this opulent 19th-century gin palace is from summer work by the men who refitted the great liners in winter. At its heart is the mosaic-faced serving counter, from which heavily carved and polished mahogany partitions radiate under the intricate plasterwork high ceiling, dividing off cosy little cubicles from the echoing main hall. This is decorated with stained glass including contemporary portraits of Boer War heroes such as Baden-Powell and Lord Roberts, rich panelling, a huge mosaic floor, and copper panels of musicians in an alcove above the fireplace. The gents' is worth seeking out as more than a functional attraction – a remarkable period piece, all red marble and opulent glinting mosaics. Well kept Ind Coope Burton, Jennings Bitter and Tetleys Bitter and Mild on handpump, and some malt whiskies; fruit machine, piped music, and quizzes. Home-made bar food that includes sandwiches, and main courses like lasagne, scampi, curry, haddock and chilli con carne (all £2.95) is served in a splendid Grecian room decorated with half-naked art nouveau plaster goddesses reclining high above the squared panelling. There are two plushly comfortable sitting rooms, and a function room on the first floor. The pub's full name is the Philharmonic Dining Rooms. *(Recommended by Christopher Heathman, Andy and Jill Kassube, Carol and Richard Glover, Tony and Lynne Stark, Jim and Maggie Cowell, Kevin Fields, R Elliott)*

Tetley-Walkers (Allied)   Manager Phil Ross   Real ale   Lunchtime meals and snacks   Restaurant   Liverpool 051 709 1163   Children in restaurant   Metered parking nearby   Open 11–11 weekdays; 11–3, 6–11 Sat

LYTHAM (Lancs)   SD3627   Map 7

Captains Cabin £

A584 S of Blackpool; Henry Street – in centre, one street in from West Beach

There's quite a bit of stained glass decoration in the modest little Victorian-style bar here; in the solid wood screens which divide up the central area, and in the main windows, which have good freestyle stained inserts of fish and gulls. Also, well chosen pictures – including local boats – on the muted bird-of-paradise wallpaper, dark pink button-back plush seats and captains' chairs in bays around the sides, open fires, and a coal-effect gas fire between two built-in bookcases at one end. Good value, simple lunchtime bar food includes soup (85p), filled baked potatoes (from 90p), sandwiches (from £1.40, toasties from £1.70), and cold platters (from £2.30), with hot home-made daily specials like cottage pie and red cabbage (£1.95), chicken curry (£2.80) and lasagne (£2.95); the ham and beef are home-cooked. Well kept Boddingtons Bitter, Marstons Pedigree and Whitbreads Castle Eden and Trophy on handpump; two fruit machines, trivia, juke box, TV for special sporting events and piped music. *(Recommended by Peter Atkinson, Andrew Roberts, Graham Bush, F Teare, Simon Bates)*

Whitbreads   Manager John Rollo   Real ale   Lunchtime meals and snacks (not 25 or 26 Dec or 1 Jan)   Children in eating area during meal times   Open 11–11

MANCHESTER   SJ8398   Map 7

Lass o' Gowrie £

36 Charles Street; off Oxford Street at BBC

Popular with students (especially on Friday and Saturday nights) for its lively and friendly atmosphere and own-brewed beer. The mini-brewery is in the cellar – seats around a sort of glass cage in one part give a view of the brewing process of LOG35 and LOG42, malt-extract beers named for their original gravity (strength); the former is quite lightly flavoured and slips down very easily, the latter is meatier; there's also well kept Chesters Bitter and Mild on handpump. The tall and rather long bar has gas lighting, bare floorboards, big windows in its richly tiled arched brown facade, hop-sacks draping the ceiling, and walls mainly stripped back to varnished bricks; there are seats around lower tables on a cosier carpeted dais at one end, and quite high stools against ledges or higher tables. Good value bar food includes ploughman's, vegetarian dishes, quiche and chicken and ham pie (all £2.85); friendly, efficient service. The volume of the piped pop music really depends on the youth of the customers – so it may be at its loudest in term-time; fruit machine, video game and trivia. *(Recommended by Wayne Brindle, Caroline Wright, Steve Mitcheson, Anne Collins, Paul Evans, Brian and Anna Marsden, RT, Virginia Jones, Andy and Jill Kassube, Len Beattie)*

Own brew (Whitbreads)   Manager Joe Fylan   Real ale   Lunchtime meals and snacks   Manchester 061 273 6932   Children in small side room and raised area until 6pm   Open 11.30–11 weekdays; 11.30–3, 6–11 Sat; closed 25 Dec

Marble Arch £

73 Rochdale Rd (A664), Ancoats; corner of Gould St, just E of Victoria Station

The outstanding range of regularly changing beers on handpump here includes Fullers London Pride, Hydes Anvil, Marstons Pedigree, Moorhouses Pendle Witches Brew, Oak Wobbly Bob, Ruddles, Timothy Taylors Landlord, and rarities such as Goachers from Kent; there's also a good choice of bottled beers – such as Belgian Trappist beers – and a selection of country wines. A comfortable place for a chat, it's done out in Victoriana, with extensive marble and tiling (particularly the frieze advertising various spirits, and the chimney breast above the carved wooden mantlepiece), a sloping mosaic floor, rag-rolled walls, magnificently restored lightly barrel-vaulted high ceiling, and walls partly stripped back to the glazed brick. Bar food, served in the lounge extension at the back, includes filled barm cakes, a huge ploughman's or a daily vegetarian dish (£2.50), and hot dishes such as chicken and mushroom pie (£2.50) and curry (£3.50); bar billiards, dominoes, cribbage, pinball, fruit machine, and juke box. *(Recommended by Bill Ryan, Tony and Lynne Stark, Steve Mitcheson, Anne Collins, P Corris, R C Gandy; more reports please)*

Free house   Licensee Vance de Bechevel   Real ale   Meals and snacks (not Sat or Sun)   Children in eating area of bar   R & B or jazz some Thurs   Open 12–11; closed Sun and bank hol lunchtimes, and 25 and 26 Dec

Mark Addy 🅐 £

Stanley Street, Salford, Manchester 3; look out not for a pub but for what looks like a smoked glass modernist subway entrance

This very smart waterside place is attractively converted from waiting rooms for boat passengers and named after the man who rescued over fifty people from drowning in the canal – which in the 19th century was a sluggish open sewer. There's a series of barrel-vaulted brick bays with russet or dove plush seats and upholstered stalls, wide glassed-in brick arches, cast-iron pillars, and a flagstone floor. Bar food consists mainly of an incredible range of cheeses – 50 of them at any one time, from all over Britain and Europe; they come with granary bread (£2.30) and it's unlikely you'll be able to finish your helping – a doggy-bag is thoughtfully provided; there's also a choice of pâtés including a vegetarian one (£2.30), and soup in winter. Well kept Boddingtons and Marstons Pedigree on handpump, and quite a few wines; piped music; service stays efficient under pressure. The canalside courtyard has tubs of flowers around its tables, from which you can watch the home-bred ducks. They prefer smart dress. *(Recommended by Roy Cove, Dennis Jones, Virginia Jones, Keith Mills, Steve Mitcheson, Anne Collins, A M Neal,)*

Free house   Licensee Philip Mead   Real ale   Snacks (11.30–3, 4–9; not Sun evening)   Manchester 061 832 4080   Children in eating area of bar   Open 11.30–11

Royal Oak 🅐 £

729 Wilmslow Road, Didsbury, Manchester 20

Over the last 30-odd years, the enthusiastic landlord in this very busy pub has been tracking down cheeses and probably has the widest range you can find anywhere in the country; one reader says that try as he might he can't find a cheese that isn't stocked here. It's unusual to be served with less than a pound of cheese, even the rarer ones, with a substantial chunk of bread, salad and extras such as beetroot and pickled onions (£2.30; take-away bags provided); there are also pâtés. The bar is decorated with an interesting collection of theatrical handbills, porcelain spirit casks, coronation mugs, and old-fashioned brass anti-spill rims around the heavy cast-iron-framed tables; there's a quieter snug bar. Well kept Marstons Burton, Pedigree and Mercian Mild on handpump, and some sherries and ports from the wood; efficient, friendly service. There are some seats outside. (Recommended by Jim and Maggie Cowell, Pauline Crossland, Dave Cawley, Keith Mills, RT, Simon Turner, Simon Barber, Paul Evans)

Marstons   Tenant Arthur Gosling   Real ale   Lunchtime snacks (not Sat or Sun) Manchester 061 445 3152   Open 11–3, 5–11; 11–11 Sat; closed evening 25 Dec

Sinclairs Oyster Bar £

Shambles Square, Manchester 3; in Arndale Centre between Deansgate and Corporation Street, opposite Exchange Street

Split up into lots of snugs and (no smoking) dining areas, this welcoming, atmospheric pub has low ceilings, squared oak panelling, and traditional furnishings such as small-backed stools that run along a tall old-fashioned marble-topped eating (and no smoking) bar. The larger room upstairs has low old-fashioned wall settles, a scrolly old leather settee, pictures of old Manchester, and good lunchtime bar food such as sandwiches (from 95p), ploughman's, vegetarian or meaty lasagne or chilli con carne (£2.85), beef and oyster pie (£3.70), seafood platter (£3.85), and half-a-dozen oysters (£4.80); friendly service from neatly-uniformed barmaids. Very well kept Sam Smiths OB and Museum on handpump kept under light blanket pressure, chess, dominoes, cribbage, draughts, fruit machine, and piped music. There are picnic-table sets outside in the pedestrians-only square. (Recommended by Bill Ryan, Terry Buckland, Ian Phillips, Michel Hooper-Immins, Virginia Jones, BKA, Brian and Anna Marsden)

Sam Smiths   Manager Darren Coles   Real ale   Lunchtime meals and snacks (not Sun)   Manchester 061 834 0430   Children welcome   Nearby parking difficult   Open 11–11; closed 25 and 26 Dec

MELLOR (Gtr Manchester) SJ9888

Devonshire Arms ⊗

Longhurst Lane; follow Mellor signpost off A626 Marple–Glossop and keep on up hill

An engaging three-room pub with nice old-fashioned touches, obliging service and interesting food, up in the Pennine fringes of the conurbation's well-heeled outer suburbs (it welcomes walkers so long as they take their boots off). The unpretentiously welcoming little front bar has a couple of old leather-seated settles among other seats, lots of old local and family photographs, and a sizeable Victorian fireplace with a deep-chiming clock above it. A couple of small back rooms, attractively papered and with something of a period flavour, both have their own Victorian fireplaces – the one on the right including an unusual lion couchant in place of a mantelpiece. Distinctive home-cooked bar lunches put some readers in mind of small French brasseries: soups such as pea and ham with celery (£1.30), steamed fresh mussels in white wine, cream and garlic, chick-pea curry (£3.25), French bread with home-cooked ham (£3.25), gravadlax cured on the premises, fresh prawn sandwiches (£3.30), fresh sardines, smoked sausage or pasta shells (£3.35), ploughman's (£3.45), fresh crab salad, lamb or prawn curries, coq au vin or kidneys done well in red wine (£3.95), perhaps fresh oysters (£5.95 for six), and sweet crêpes (from £1.85). Robinsons Best and Best Mild on electric pump, a good collection of spirits including 50 malt whiskies, and good coffee (which comes with a little pot of fresh cream); quick friendly service, cribbage and dominoes; maybe unobtrusive piped radio. There are picnic-table sets out in front, and behind, where an attractively planted terrace leads back to a small tree-sheltered lawn.*(Recommended by Lee Goulding, Steve Mitcheson, Anne Collins, Keith Mills, R J August, Pauline Crossland, Dave Cawley, John and Celia Furnival)*

Robinsons Tenant Brian Harrison Real ale Meals and snacks (lunchtime) Manchester 061 427 2563 Trad jazz Thurs evenings Open 11–3, 5.30(7 Sat)–11; they may stay open longer in fine weather; closed evening 25 Dec

MERECLOUGH (Lancs) SD8332 Map 7
Kettledrum

302 Red Lees Road; from A646 Burnley–Halifax, quickest route is turn off between Walk Mill and Holme Chapel, signposted Over Town, Worsethorne; OS Sheet 103, map reference 873305

The ever-increasing and attractive collection of artefacts in the extended bar area consists of gruesome-looking knives by the dozen, wooden and copper masks, buffalo horns, and sparkling brass – shovels, knockers, measures, corkscrews, keys, scales, weights, spigots, fancy boot-horns, imps, toasting forks, and warming pans. Furnishings include some sensible angled and padded bottom-rests, tapestried wall seats, dimpled copper tables, and a solid-fuel stove. The gas-lit dining room is upstairs. Well kept Courage Directors, John Smiths Bitter and Theakstons Best, XB and Old Peculier on handpump; darts, fruit machine and piped music. A wide choice of food includes soup (£1.45), sandwiches (from £1.45), stuffed vine leaves (£2.95), omelettes (£3.35), ploughman's (£3.45), salads (from £3.50), chilli casserole, gammon with egg or home-made steak and kidney pie (£4), trout (£5.50), and children's dishes (from £1.65). Seats outside look over a low stone wall beyond the quiet road to Burnley and its surrounding moors. *(Recommended by Comus Elliott, Andy and Jill Kassube, Len Beattie, Dr Thomas Mackenzie; more reports please)*

Free house Licensee Roy Ratcliffe Real ale Meals and snacks (11.45–1.45, 6–10.30) Partly no smoking restaurant Burnley (0282) 24591 Children allowed away from main bar till 9pm Open 11–3, 5.30–11; closed evening 25 Dec

MIDDLETON (Gtr Manchester) SD8606 Map 7
Olde Boars Head

Just under 2 miles from M62 junction 19; A664 into Middleton (Long Street – pub on right)

Most of this beautifully restored building is Elizabethan, though parts date back to the 12th century. It's quaintly timbered and gabled and there's no end of faded oak beams and timbers, with some fine ancient door frames. A room on the left has standard lamps lighting the chairs and tables on its Turkey carpet, there's a spacious and rather grandly decorated sessions room at the opposite end, with a woodburning stove in its fine fireplace (and a little hatch to the servery, just about showing the top of the barmaid's head if you bend down enough), and two long front rooms comfortably fitted out with navy blue leatherette button-back built-in wall banquettes. A long central servery is backed by a flagstoned spinal corridor, leading out of a kitchen area with an open range in its massive chimney and hops strung from its high rafters. One of two small and cosily furnished parlours back here is named for Sam Bamford, a 19th-century weaver who was unjustly implicated in the events leading to the Peterloo massacre, and used to give readings of his pretty dire verse here. Simple bar food consists of soup (£1), sandwiches (from £1.30), a few hot dishes such as lamb stew, chicken and leek pie and lasagne (£3.10), puddings (£1.30), some vegetarian dishes and a bowl of chips (50p); the eating area is partly no smoking; well kept Lees Bitter and GB Mild on handpump; decently reproduced piped pop music; a warm, thoroughly pubby atmosphere, with good service. Picnic-table sets in a small sheltered back courtyard catch the evening sun; good parking (with TV surveillance). *(Recommended by M C Barres-Baker, Carol and Richard Glover; more reports please)*

Lees Manager Martin Reeves Real ale Meals and snacks (lunchtime) Manchester 061 643 3520 Children in eating area at lunchtime if eating Jazz 1st Thurs of month Open 12–3, 7–11; closed 25 Dec and lunchtime 1 Jan

NEWTON (Lancs)   SD6950 Map 7

Parkers Arms

B6478 7 miles N of Clitheroe

This is a lovely spot, and the black-and-white pub with its pretty window boxes is
a well run, friendly and homely place. The bar has red plush button-back
banquettes around dimpled copper tables on a flowery blue carpet, one or two
pictures on the white Anaglypta walls, and lots of copper and brass kettles,
candlesticks, and an urn on the neat stone mantlepiece. Beyond an arch is a similar
area with sensibly placed darts, pool, dominoes, fruit machine, video game and
discreet piped music; a black labrador may wander in – or escort you in friendly
fashion back to your car (and possibly bring you a stick to throw); this year he's
acquired a friend. Straightforward bar food includes soup (£1.20), sandwiches
(from £1.80), ploughman's (£2.75), pies and main meals (£4.50), and puddings
(£1.80); excellent service. Boddingtons and Flowers on handpump. There are well
spaced picnic-table sets on the big lawn, looking down towards the village's river,
and beyond to the hills. *(Recommended by Lee Goulding, G T Jones, P Devitt, Colin and
Caroline Maxwell, F and J Hamer, Len Beattie; more reports please)*

*Whitbreads   Tenant Henry Rhodes   Real ale   Meals and snacks   Restaurant
Slaidburn (020 06) 236   Children welcome   Open 11–3, 6–11; all day summer
Sundays; closed 25 Dec   Bedrooms; £17.50/£35*

RABY (Merseyside)   SJ3180 Map 7

Wheatsheaf

The Green, Rabymere Road; off A540 S of Heswall

Known locally as 'The Thatch', this timbered, 300-year-old alehouse is
traditionally furnished; the central room has an old wall clock and homely black
kitchen shelves, and a nice snug formed by antique settles built in around its fine
old fireplace. A second, more spacious room has upholstered wall seats around the
tables, small hunting prints on the cream walls and a smaller coal fire. Well kept
real ales on handpump such as Flowers IPA, Higsons, Ind Coope Burton, Tetleys,
Thwaites and Youngers Scotch and No 3, and there's a good choice of malt
whiskies. *(Recommended by D O'Hara, Mr and Mrs J H Adam, Christopher Heathman,
Tony and Lynne Stark, M J B Pearson; more reports please – the pub refuses to give us any
details)*

*Free house   Real ale   Lunchtime meals and snacks (not Sun)   Open 11.30–3,
5.30–10.30*

SLAIDBURN (Lancs)   SD7152 Map 7

Hark to Bounty

This popular old place is tucked away in a Forest of Bowland village; there are
high fells beyond the gently rolling wooded hills around here, and fly fishing can be
arranged on the nearby Stocks Reservoir. Inside, the comfortable and cosy lounge
bar has furniture ranging from an antique settee and a Victorian settle, to one or
two easy chairs and neat armed dining chairs; the cream walls are decorated with
big Victorian engravings, a few Victorian fashion plates, brass and copper over the
open fire, and local photographs. A wide range of good bar food includes
home-made soup, lunchtime sandwiches (not Sunday or bank holidays),
ploughman's (£3.45), Cumberland sausage with a tasty stuffing and apple sauce
(£3.90), salads, and good daily specials such as casserole (£4.75) or quarter of a
duckling with ginger (£4.80); Sunday roast lunch; professional service. The
restaurant has a small but praised menu. Well kept Theakstons Best and Old
Peculier and Youngers Scotch on handpump or electric pump; fruit machine and
piped music. There's lots of room to sit outside – on high days and feast days they
may even have a fairground organ. A steam traction rally is held annually on the
first weekend in June. *(Recommended by Ray and Gwen Jessop, Greg Turner, Robert and
Vicky Tod, A G Roby, Dr Keith Bloomfield, Dr T E Hothersall, Comus Elliott, Dave and Kate
Buckley, Mr and Mrs J E Rycroft, R D and H M Bromley, G Dobson)*

*Scottish & Newcastle   Manager Brian Hough   Real ale   Meals and snacks
Restaurant   Slaidburn (020 06) 246   Children welcome away from bar   Open
10.30–3, 6.30–11; 10.30–11   Bedrooms; £20S/£40B*

STALYBRIDGE (Gtr Manchester)   SJ9698 Map 7

Stalybridge Station Buffet £

This rather humble and very unpretentious working station buffet recalls the days
when there was still a third class on the railways. It's splendidly Victorian in a very
basic way with lots of railway memorabilia, including barge and railway pictures
set into the red bar counter, and more railway pictures and some old station signs
on the high walls; the beermats are interesting. Traditional cafe stand-bys are still
served – cheap snacks like delicious black-eyed peas (40p), hot or cold pies with
black peas (from 50p), sandwiches (60p), and tea made freshly by the pot. But
there's also very well kept Moorhouses Premier and three guest beers (almost
changing daily) from all over the country (including from home-brew pubs) on
handpump, and occasional farm ciders; trivia. Proceeds from a paperback library
on the piano beside the open fire go to a guide-dog charity. *(Recommended by Dennis
Jones, Michael Rooke, Gary Scott, Andy and Jill Kassube, P A Crossland, D A Cawley; more
reports please)*

*Free house   Licensee Ken Redfern   Real ale   Snacks   Children welcome   Folk
singers Sat evening   Open 12–3, 5(7 Sat)–11; closed Sun, Mon, and Tues lunchtime*

THORNTON HOUGH (Merseyside)   SJ3081   Map 7

Seven Stars

Church Road; B5136 in village centre

This is actually in an estate village built for Lord Leverhulme in the late 19th
century, and the Leverhulmes still live here. There's a firm emphasis on food, with
good service from uniformed waitresses: soup (95p), sandwiches (from £1.10),
ploughman's (£2.50), gammon (£3.75), a daily vegetarian dish (£4.25), gammon
(£4.25), and steaks (from £6.95); they also now do more specials – anything from
Turkish or Indian dishes to quail or local rabbit stew (around £3.50) and it's nice
to have a choice of potatoes; some of the tables are no smoking. Well kept
Flowers, Whitbreads Castle Eden and Thwaites on handpump, gentle piped music.
The two well kept bar rooms have cushioned wheelback chairs and button-back
wall banquettes, easy chairs, and a sofa by the fireplace; plastic plants hang along
the ceiling trusses, and there are framed accounts on the walls of local history.
Seats on the terrace and in the small garden look across to the neighbouring twin
churches. *(Recommended by Dave and Kate Buckley, Christopher Heathman, Mr M G Hart,
Christian Leigh, M J B Pearson, Alan and Marlene Radford, Drs M and K Parier, Mr and Mrs
J H Adam; more reports please)*

*Whitbreads   Mrs C E Nelson   Real ale   Meals and snacks   Liverpool 051 336
4574   Open 11–3, 5–11; closed 25 Dec*

TOCKHOLES (Lancs)   SD6623   Map 7

Rock

Village signposted from A666 S of Blackburn; OS Sheet 103, map reference 663233

Picture windows in the back dining area of this moorland pub have a fine view
over rolling well wooded pastures – and indeed as far as the coast some 20 miles
away, on a clear day. The two-room beamed bar is cosy, with brocaded wall
banquettes, moiré curtains, brass ornaments around the neat fireplace, old sporting
prints on the Regency-style papered walls, plates on a delft shelf. On the left by the
bar counter (which has unusually comfortable swivel bar stools) there's some dark
brown panelling. Bar food includes soup (£1.10), sandwiches (from £1.10),
ploughman's (£1.95), home-made steak pie (£3.45), roasts, gammon or chicken
baked in wine (£4.25), and puddings (from £1), cooked by the landlord's wife;

well kept Thwaites Bitter and Mild on handpump; unobtrusive piped music, darts, fruit machine, welcoming service. There are tables out on a small terrace. *(Recommended by John Fazakerley, Graham Bush, Bill Ryan)*

Thwaites   Tenants Dominic and Maureen Gallagher   Real ale   Meals and snacks (not Mon lunchtime, but all day Sun)   Children in two rooms away from servery   Open 12–2, 7–12 (supper licence); all day Sun; closed Mon lunchtime

Royal Arms

Village signposted from A6062 on S edge of Blackburn; though not signposted, good route on pretty moorland road about 1 1/2 miles N of Belmont, just past AA telephone box (and on opposite side of road) – this is then the first pub you come to

Chatty and friendly and popular with locals, the four old-fashioned little rooms of the bar here have rustic decorations on the panelling-effect walls, cushioned wall settles, and big log fires in handsome stone fireplaces. Well kept Thwaites Bitter and Best Mild on handpump and several malt whiskies, dominoes, fruit machine, and well reproduced easy-listening classics. Bar food includes sandwiches, soup, home-made steak and kidney pie, vegetarian dishes and curry. The views from the sheltered terrace are mainly of the woods in the surrounding rolling countryside, but if you look hard on a clear day you can make out Blackpool Tower. There's a play area in the garden, white doves in a dovecote, geese in the field behind, and a nature trail opposite. The local hunt meets in the car park. *(Recommended by Len Beattie, Ben Wimpenny, John Fazakerley, G T Jones, Denis Mann, Geoff Halson; more reports please)*

Thwaites   Tenant Peter Leighton   Real ale   Meals and snacks   (0254) 705373   Children welcome   Open 12–3, 6.30–11

UPPERMILL (Gtr Manchester)   SD9905   Map 7

Cross Keys   £

Runninghill Gate; from A670 in Uppermill turn into New Street, by a zebra crossing close to the chapel; this is the most practical-looking of the lanes towards the high moors and leads directly into Runninghill Gate, but is still steep and more than a mile long

The sporting connections here are strong; it's headquarters of the Oldham Mountain Rescue Team (newly equipped and decorated) and various outdoor sports clubs, they're annual sponsors of the road running or fell races in the first week in June and on the last Saturday in August (there are lots of colourful photographs of these among the interesting older prints on the walls), and the Saddleworth Clog and Garland Girls practise regularly here; new this year is the Gun Club with clay pigeon shooting every other Sunday at 10am. Tracks from behind the pub lead straight up towards Broadstone Hill and Dick Hill. Several connecting rooms of the bars have low beams, pews, settles, flagstones, and an original cooking range. Bar food includes soup (80p), sandwiches (from 80p, toasties from 90p), and a wide range of dishes such as liver and bacon casserole, Hungarian goulash, chilli con carne, and salads (all £3), with puddings like apricot crumble (from 90p). Well kept Lees Bitter and Mild on handpump; darts, dominoes, cribbage and fruit machine, and Bridge school Monday and Friday evenings and Saturday lunchtime. There's a side terrace and a stylish flagstoned back terrace with bright flowers sheltered by a dry stone wall; next to it are swings, a slide and a climbing frame. *(Recommended by Andy and Jill Kassube, Carol and Richard Glover, H K Dyson, Neil Barker, Roy Cove, P A Crossland, D A Cawley)*

Lees   Tenant Philip Kay   Real ale   Meals and snacks   Children welcome away from main lounge   Jazz and clog dancing Mon evenings, folk Weds evenings   Open 11–4, 6.30–11; open all day Sat and bank hols

WHARLES (Lancs)   SD4435   Map 7

Eagle & Child

Church Road; from B5268 W of Broughton turn left into Higham Side Road at HMS Inskip sign; OS Sheet 102, map reference 448356

Part of the landlord's fine collection of antique oak seats can be found in the L-shaped bar of this thatched country pub, especially round the corner past the counter where a beamed area has a whole group of them; one of the highlights is a magnificent, elaborately carved Jacobean settle which came originally from Aston Hall in Birmingham. There's also a carved oak chimneypiece, and a couple of fine longcase clocks. The plain cream walls are hung with modern advertising mirrors and some older mirrors, and there are exotic knives, carpentry tools and so forth on the plastered structural beams; even when it's not particularly cold, there should be a good fire burning in the intricate cast-iron stove. Well kept Boddingtons and Wadworths 6X on handpump and constantly changing guest beers; darts in a sensible side area; juke box, friendly ginger cat. One or two picnic-table sets outside. As we say, it's closed on weekday lunchtimes.
(Recommended by Graham Bush, Adrian Steen, Robert and Lesley Fawthrop, John Atherton, R Tomlinson, Simon Bates)

Free house   Licensees Brian and Angela Tatham   Real ale   No food   (0772) 690312   Open 7–11 (and 12–3 Sat; usual Sun hours)

WHEATLEY LANE (Lancs)   SD8338 Map 7
Old Sparrow Hawk

Towards E end of village road which runs N of and parallel to A6068; one way of reaching it is to follow Fence, Newchurch 1 3/4 signpost, then turn off at Barrowford 3/4 signpost

There are three stuffed sparrowhawks and an owl above the gleaming copper hoods of the log-effect gas fires in this bustling pub; also, studded leather seats, long button-back banquettes, dark oak panelling, stripped stonework, and an unusual stained glass ceiling dome in the big semi-circular bar; a small room leads off. Served from an efficient food servery, the food includes a good range of sandwiches (from £1.60, double deckers from £2.60; toasties from £1.80, steak £3.75), soup (£1.75), ploughman's (£2.10), and lots of attractively presented salads or cold plates including smoked or roast ham, roast meats and smoked salmon, and a range of at least five hot home-made daily specials such as chilli con carne and steak and kidney or chicken and leek pies (£4.50), and sirloin steak (£6.95). A mock-Tudor carvery serves good roasts (lunch, not Saturday, £9.95; dinner 3 courses £10.95) and has piped music. Well kept Bass, Bass Special and Mild on handpump and quite a few wines; good coffee. There are tables outside on the good-sized terrace, and views over to the moors behind Nelson and Colne.
(Recommended by Mike Tucker, Len Beattie; more reports please)

Bass   Tenant Don Butterworth   Real ale   Meals and snacks (11.30–11)   Restaurant (12–2.30, 4.30–9 Sun)   Burnley (0282) 64126   Children in eating area and restaurant   Open 11–11

WHITEWELL (Lancs)   SD6546 Map 7
Inn at Whitewell ★ ★ 🖙

Most easily reached by B6246 from Whalley; road through Dunsop Bridge from B6478 is also good

Praise from readers for this long, low stone inn has been particularly warm and enthusiastic this year. For the good, well prepared food, helpful young Australian staff, and superb views – one reader says there's a fine one from the garden looking across the river and down the valley; to reach it you walk through the bar and down a series of corridors (with strange objects like a stuffed fox vanishing into the wall). The bar itself, old-fashioned and country-house in feel, has antique settles, oak gateleg tables, sonorous clocks, old cricketing and sporting prints, log fires (the lounge has a very attractive stone fireplace), and heavy curtains on sturdy wooden rails; one area has a selection of newspapers, local maps and guide books. The public bar has darts, pool, shove-ha'penny, dominoes, and juke box, with a 1920s game-of-skill slot machine; there's a piano for anyone who wants to play. Lunchtime bar food includes soup (£1.30), sandwiches (from £2.50), smoked salmon and Coniston cold smoked trout mousse (£3.50), hearty Cumberland sausage casserole (£4), ploughman's (from £4.50), salads (from £5), steak and mushroom pie (£5.20), seafood pancake (£5.50), roast baby chicken (£6), home-made puddings (£2) and British hand-made cheese (from £2.50); in the evenings there's also braised leeks wrapped in ham (£4.50) and fisherman's pie (£5.60); they serve coffee and cream teas all day. Well kept Moorhouses Premier and Pendle Witches Brew on handpump. The inn also houses a wine merchant (hence the unusually wide range of wines available – the claret is recommended), an art gallery, and a shop selling cashmere, shoes and so forth, and owns six miles of trout, salmon and sea trout fishing on the Hodder; with notice they'll arrange shooting. The seats outside are in a pleasant suntrap. *(Recommended by Mrs R Heaton, Andy and Jill Kassube, Graham Bush, Mr and Mrs J H Adam, Greg Turner, Tessa Stuart, Michael and Joan Melling, WAH, Tony and Lynne Stark, John Watson, Jim and Maggie Cowell, Len Beattie, C F Walling, Douglas Cohen, Kathleen Morley, Mr and Mrs Harry McCann, John and Anne McIver, Andrew Stephenson, A M Neal)*

Free house Licensee Richard Bowman Real ale Meals and snacks (not Sat evening if a big function is on) Restaurant (not Sun lunchtime) Dunsop Bridge (020 08) 222 Children welcome Pianist Fri evening Open 11–3, 6–11 Bedrooms; £43B/£57B

YEALAND CONYERS (Lancs) SD5074 Map 7

New Inn ♀

3 miles from M6 junction 35; village signposted off A6 N

The Gilhams who made such a success of the Miners Arms at Mithian down in Cornwall, and then won brief months of glory (and a main entry) for the Stag Hunt in Ponsanooth there, have now turned up here. Already, the word is out locally about Mrs Gilham's good plain cooking and her husband's relaxed and good-humoured attention: people in the know are homing in so hungrily that if you want to eat there you really must book. Generously served, the food includes sandwiches (from £1.25), soup (£1.35), other starters (from £1.80), meaty lasagne (£2.95), salads (from £3.25), vegetarian lasagne (£3.50), plaice (£3.85), steak and mussel or pork and apricot pie, home-baked ham (£4.25), 12oz gammon (£5.45), trout (£5.95), steaks (from 8oz rump £6.95) and the odd special dish such as veal in tomato sauce with onions and mussels, served with a good choice of vegetables; puddings like home-made apple pie (£1.75). Well kept Hartleys XB on handpump, decent wines, a good choice of malt whiskies, piped light classics. There's a simply furnished little beamed bar on the left with a log fire in the big stone fireplace; on the right, they've converted what used to be a pool room into two communicating cottagey dining rooms with black furniture to match the shiny beams, and an attractive kitchen range with another winter fire. A sheltered lawn at the side has picnic-table sets among roses and flowering shrubs. *(Recommended by Rita Horridge, A B Clarke, Dorothy and David Young)*

Hartleys (Robinsons) Tenants Colin and Vicki Gilham Real ale Meals and snacks (not winter Mon evenings) Restaurant (0524) 732938 Children in restaurant if over 10 Open 11.30–2.30, 6–11

Lucky Dip

Besides the fully inspected pubs, you might like to try these Lucky Dips recommended to us and described by readers (if you do, please send us reports):

☆ **Adlington**, Lancs [5A Market St; SD5912], *White Bear*: Pretty stonebuilt village pub, small, quiet and attractively decorated, with cheap good food, quick friendly service, well kept Theakstons XB, Best and Old Peculier, open fire in one room, juke box in other, pool table in back room, children's play area in garden behind; parking difficult *(G T Jones, R J Yates, Debbie Jackson)*
Altrincham, Gtr Manchester [Stamford St;

SJ7788], *Malt Shovels*: Lively and spacious, with focal staircase, big side games room, good jazz most evenings, well kept Sam Smiths *(Bill Ryan)*; [Old Market Pl], *Orange Tree*: Cosy bar with side rooms, Watneys-related real ales and a guest beer such as Flowers; good value upstairs bistro *(Bill Ryan)*; [Tipping St], *Tatton Arms*: True local with basic decor, particularly well kept reasonably priced Boddingtons *(Bill Ryan)*

☆ **Ashton under Lyne**, Lancs [152 Old St; SJ9399], *Witchwood*: Refurbished but still unpretentious and friendly, popular for uncommonly wide choice of well kept real ales, which landlord is very knowledgeable about — on Tues for free live music — pop/rock Mon, soul Tues, rock Weds, pop Thurs, rock disco Fri, heavy metal Sat, 60s/70s rock Sun lunchtime, blues and rhythm-and-blues Sun evening; lunchtime sandwiches and hot snacks (not Sun), reasonable prices *(Adrian Steen, Dennis Jones)*

Ashton under Lyne [Mossley Rd], *Heroes of Waterloo*: Pleasant, clean and spacious, with good straightforward food from sandwiches up, good service *(Dennis Jones)*; [Kings Rd], *Oddfellows Arms*: Nice small pub with log fires and games room — darts, crib etc; friendly landlord, well kept Robinsons *(Ian Lees)*; *Red House*: Nice deco, good food and atmosphere *(Pauline Crossland, Dave Cawley)*

Aspull, Gtr Manchester [not far from M61 junction 6; SD6108], *Hare & Hounds*: Huge organ with lots of effects, gets very busy for sing-songs Weds, Fri, Sun and especially Sat; recently tastefully redecorated, with food lunchtime and evening, Greenalls Bitter, Mild and Original on handpump; bedrooms *(P Corris)*

Astley Green, Gtr Manchester [Higher Green Lane; off A580 E of Leigh; SJ7099], *Ross's Arms*: Very clean, with well kept Boddingtons, Holts, Jennings, Tetleys Mild and Bitter and Walkers, good range of very reasonably priced home cooked food, welcoming landlord *(John Scott)*

Audenshaw, Gtr Manchester [Audenshaw Rd (B6390); Guide Bridge; SJ8896], *Boundary*: Popular for good food — may have to wait for a seat *(P A Crossland, D A Cawley)*

☆ **Barnston**, Merseyside [Barnston Rd (A551); SJ2883], *Fox & Hounds*: Family-run country local with reasonably priced well presented good food, good atmosphere, friendly quick service even when crowded, well kept beer; bloomers hang over the range, jazz pianist Sun lunchtime, well kept Watneys-related real ales, pretty summer courtyard; by lovely wooded dell *(David and Rebecca Killick, Mr and Mrs J H Adam, Tony and Lynne Stark)*

Barrow, Lancs [Whalley Rd; SD7338], *Spread Eagle*: Comfortably refurbished, good friendly service, reasonable prices, spacious uncramped tables, good hot food — and a no smoking area *(J L and G M Chapman)*

☆ **Barrowford**, Lancs [Gisburn Road (A682); SD8539], *White Bear*: Cosy small-town pub, with wide choice of good bar food inc excellent sandwiches — popular for snacks served close to closing time; well kept Bass and Stones; children welcome *(Comus Elliott, Dr M A Thomas)*

Barton, Lancs [A6 Preston—Garstang; SD5137], *White Horse*: Cheerful landlord serves well kept Theakstons, wife does varied good simple food — best to arrive early weekend lunchtimes *(Jim Cowell)*

☆ **Bashall Eaves**, Lancs [SD6943], *Red Pump*: Beautifully placed, roomy, comfortable and warm, with friendly efficient service, reasonably priced good food (savoury pancake much praised), well kept ales, decent furniture and lovely views; busy weekend lunches *(G T Jones, F and J Hamer, Andrew Stephenson, KC, Dr P H Mitchell)*

Birkenhead, Merseyside [Claughton Firs, Oxton; SJ3289], *Shrewsbury Arms*: Atmospheric pub in villagey area, doing well under new licensee; friendly and bustling, well kept Whitbreads-related real ales with a guest such as Theakstons XB, bar food inc great double-deck toasties, big lounge, bar, terrace *(Tony and Lynne Stark, P Corris, Mr and Mrs J H Adam)*

Bispham Green, Lancs [Chorley Rd, off B5246 N of Parbold; SD4914], *Farmers Arms*: Pleasant and friendly with decent food, Burtonwood beers, several bars, family room and dining room; comfortable banquettes, mock timbering, usual bar food; children's play area; well placed for walks in the Wigan Alps area *(G T Jones)*

Blackburn, Lancs [Victoria St/James St — OS Sheet 103, map reference 683284; SD6828], *Annes*: Large pub with thorough-going Victorian decor, usual bar food, Theakstons Bitter and Old Peculier on handpump; piped music (loud when busy), open all day *(John Fazakerley)*

☆ **Blackpool**, Lancs [35 Clifton St, just behind Town Hall; SD3035], *St Martins Tavern*: Stylish cafe-bar with marble, columns, statues, lofty coffered ceiling, good swivel seats, solid ash bar counter in central sunken area, tasty reasonably priced home-made lunchtime food, espresso machine, rather assertive piped music; used to be a bank, now a popular evening meeting place; the star is for daytime (it's open all day) as young people and the video juke box dominate evenings — and it has no real ale *(Carol and Richard Glover, Wayne Brindle, LYM)*

Blackpool [Leamington Rd], *Raikes Hall*: Plush but traditional, big multi-level lounge bar with cosy end and drinking end; terrace overlooks own crown bowling green; summer barbecues, jazz Weds, well kept Bass and Stones, straightforward food *(Graham Bush)*; [204 Talbot Rd], *Ramsden Arms*: Notably warm pubby atmosphere with friendly licensee and well kept Jennings on handpump *(K Flack, Bill Ryan)*; [Whitegate Dr, Marton], *Saddle*: Refurbished 1991 though preserving some of the traditional features which made it special, inc all but one of the snugs; well kept Bass Mild and Special, good atmosphere *(Graham Bush)*; [Vicarage Lane/Cherry Tree Rd, Marton], *Welcome*: Large, friendly and lively family pub doing well under new regime, with well kept Burtonwood with a guest such as Hook Norton Old Hookey, wide choice of bar food piled really high, unusual conservatory bar, lounge, garden with good new fenced play area *(Graham Bush, Adrian Steen)*

Blacksnape, Lancs [Old Roman Rd; SD7121], *Red Lion*: Has been praised for well kept Burtonwood ales, generous helpings of standard bar food and interesting set lunches, but no recent reports *(News please)*

☆ **Bolton**, Gtr Manchester [Pool St; SD7108], *Howcroft*: Beautifully preserved friendly old local with lots of small, screened-off rooms, plenty of games inc pintable, darts, bar billiards, well kept Allied real ales, Addlestone's cider; bowling green; feels more like a country pub than its surroundings suggest *(Ben Wimpenny, Bill Ryan, Andrew Hazeldine)*

☆ **Bolton** [606 Halliwell Rd], *Ainsworth Arms*: Friendly and obliging unpretentious town pub, nicely decorated with side smoke room; with helpful attitude to wheelchairs, basic good value food in huge Yorkshire puddings, very quick service, particularly well kept Allied beers; busy evenings *(Keith Mills, Bill Ryan, Andrew Hazeldine)*

Bolton [Newport St], *Clifton Arms*: Friendly, handy for trains and buses, particularly well kept Moorhouses Premier and other beers such as Jennings and Tetleys *(Bill Ryan)*; [Bradshaw Rd], *Turton Heights*: Unusual modern pub with interesting decor, lively atmosphere, and reasonably priced food *(B Taylor)*; [Newport St], *York*: Pleasant bar with well kept Burtonwood and Forshaws, quite a few malt whiskies; handy for trains and buses *(Bill Ryan)*

☆ **Bolton by Bowland**, Lancs [SD7849], *Coach & Horses*: Delightful neatly kept village pub in lovely spot, comfortable and clean with coal fires and welcoming atmosphere, pleasantly untouristy traditional decor; well kept Whitbreads beers, good home-made bar food (not usually Tues) inc imaginative dishes; get there early weekends for a table; children may be allowed in dining room *(Dr Fuller, Jim and Maggie Cowell, Mrs J Crawford, Roy Cove)*

Brinscall, Lancs [58 School Lane; SD6221], *Oak Tree*: Village pub with well kept S & N beers, friendly efficient staff, good varied bar food *(Mr and Mrs L L Luck)*

☆ **Bromley Cross**, Gtr Manchester [Last Drop Village; Hospital Rd, just off A676 N of Bolton — OS Sheet 109, map reference 723141; SD7213], *Drop Inn*: Odd pastiche of old-world stone-and-cobbles village street complete with gift and tea shops, bakery etc — and this creeper-covered pub, spacious inside, with lots of beamery and timbering, reminiscent in mood of a big country-theme city pub, and heavy tables out on an attractive flagstoned terrace on the "High St"; popular one-price hot and cold buffet (till 5 Sun), Watneys-related real ales; bedrooms — all part of a big well equipped Rank hotel complex *(Dr and Mrs C D E Morris, Carol and Richard Glover, Jim and Maggie Cowell, BB)*

nr **Burnley** [Manchester Rd, Habbergham Eaves (A56 Burnley—Rawtenstall), a mile or so S; SD8332], *Bull & Butcher*: Plushly refurbished open-plan pub with decent food in barn buttery, family room with satellite TV etc, baby-changing facilities, play area outside; well kept Allied beers *(Carol and Richard Glover, George Day)*; [Habbergham Eaves, as above], *Waggoners*: Old-world, with fascinating bric-a-brac and brassware on walls, window sills and beams, good moorland views, well kept John Smiths and choice of wines; wide choice of good value simple food (not Tues evening) from sandwiches and baked potatoes to steak with speciality Cumberland sausage *(Carol and Richard Glover)*

☆ **Bury** [Nangreaves, off A56/A666 N; SD8115], *Lord Raglan*: Family-run 18th-century pub high on moors overlooking Bury, beams, pewter, brass, antique clocks, bric-a-brac, some old settles; back room with good valley views and huge open fire; Theakstons Best and Old Peculier, Youngers Scotch and No 3, interesting foreign bottled beers, bar food not cheap but good value, good polite efficient service, plainer larger dining room; opens 7.30 *(Carol and Richard Glover, Don Kirkpatrick)*

Bury [Rochdale Old Rd, Birtle], *Bird i' th' Hand*: Comfortable recently redecorated pub with panelling, two big open fires, good bar meals, Bass, no machines or music — except from antique penny polyphonium *(Carol and Richard Glover)*

Catforth, Lancs [SD4736], *Running Pump*: Lively local with well kept Robinsons in long narrow bar, plush lounge bar, pool room *(Graham Bush)*

Caton, Lancs [A683, E of M6 junction 34; SD5364], *Station*: Large, clean local with own bowling green, decent choice of generous good value food, well kept Mitchells; children welcome *(Andrew Hazeldine, Andy and Jill Kassube)*

Chadderton, Gtr Manchester [Hollins Rd; SD9005], *Bridgewater Arms*: Friendly staff and locals, and good Holts Bitter and Mild at low prices; in 1991 the original pub made way for a new motorway, being replaced by a fine new version just down the road *(Dennis Jones)*; *Whitegate*: Worth knowing for good food inc delicious help-yourself salads *(Pauline Crossland, Dave Cawley)*

Cheadle, Gtr Manchester [Manchester Rd, handy for M63; B5095 off Kingsway and Stockport Rd; SJ8688], *Ashlea*: Formerly the Railway, now refurbished as a comfortable Boddingtons Henry's Table family dining pub for Boddingtons, opp their catering HQ; decent food noon-10.30, comfortable tables in cosily divided areas, no-smoking area, conservatory extension *(John Gould)*; [1a Cheadle Rd (A5149)] *Village*: Boddingtons and good value food in attractive bar areas of hotel/restaurant/members' sports club complex, with plush buttery and comfortable conservatory *(Michael Sandy, Pauline Crossland, Dave Cawley)*

Chipping, Lancs [Windy St; SD6243], *Sun*: Simple stone local with three small snug rooms, open fire, well kept Boddingtons on handpump (an underground stream cools the cellar), bar food, pool, darts, papers and magazines; attractive village *(Andy and Jill Kassube, Graham Bush)*

☆ nr **Chipping** [Hesketh Lane Village; crossroads Chipping—Longridge with Inglewhite—Clitheroe — OS Sheet 103, map reference 619413], *Dog & Partridge*: Smartly genteel lounge bar in attractive countryside, easy chairs around low tables, log fire, generous home-made bar food (not Sat evening, Sun lunchtime), Tetleys; restaurant *(LYM)*

☆ **Chorley**, Lancs [Friday St, behind stn; SD5817], *Malt 'n' Hops*: Corner shop and house newly converted into warm, friendly and old-fashioned free house, very clean, comfortable and full of atmosphere; accent on wide range of ever-changing well kept real ales such as Hydes, Moorhouses Pendle Witches Brew and Timothy Taylors Landlord; bar food *(Comus Elliott, Jim and Maggie Cowell)*

Chorley [Bolton Rd — A6 S], *Yarrow Bridge*: Pub/restaurant, very busy weekends, with friendly staff, good reasonably priced bar snacks or restaurant meals, choice of beers; play area *(J McHugh)*

☆ nr **Chorley**, Lancs [White Coppice; 2 miles from M61 junction 8; signposted from A674 towards Blackburn; SD6118], *Railway*: Simple comfort, well kept Matthew Browns Bitter and Mild, bar food with half-price children's helpings; fine cigarette-card collection, Sat evening live entertainment (monthly in summer); on edge of North-West Pennine Recreational Park, with cricket on the green; may be closed winter lunchtimes, at least on Mon *(LYM)*

☆ **Churchtown**, Merseyside [off A565 from Preston, taking B5244 at Southport; SD3618], *Hesketh Arms*: Outstanding roast beef and Yorkshire pudding in attractively refurbished thatched pub; spacious bar keeping some partition walls for updated Victorian feel, other good freshly prepared food, Allied real ales on handpump from central servery, lively atmosphere; Weds jazz upstairs; in pretty village, close to botanic gardens *(Ian Phillips, Jim and Maggie Cowell, Graham Bush)*

☆ **Churchtown**, the different Lancs one [nr church, off A586 Garstang—St Michaels-on-Wyre; SD4843], *Punchbowl*: Cosy pub/restaurant in small and attractive peaceful village; stained glass, wood panelling, lots of stuffed animals in mock-Tudor beamed bar with friendly staff, reasonably priced good food, well kept Tetleys and Dark Mild, good fires; lavatory for disabled people *(Graham Bush)*

Clayton Green, Lancs [just off B5256, not far from M1 junction 29; SD5723], *Lord Nelson*: Friendly, busy 17th-century stripped-stone local, spaciously refurbished with decor reminiscent of lower deck of a ship of the line — lots of good naval prints; Matthew Browns beers, bar food *(Kathleen Morley)*

☆ **Clayton le Moors**, Lancs [Dunkenhalgh Hotel; ½ mile from M65 junction 7 —

A6185 then A678 towards Rishton — OS Sheet 103, map reference 741301; SD7430], *Dunk Inn*: Castellated Gothick house with substantial hotel accommodation in extensive grounds — and a properly pubby bar in its back stable block, with cosy barrel-vaulted alcoves (one with pool and darts), popular bar food (not Mon evening), CD juke box; live music Weds and Thurs, disco Fri-Sun; children in restaurant; bedrooms comfortable and well equipped *(Len Beattie, Mr and Mrs A Gray, LYM)*

☆ nr **Clitheroe** [Higher Hodder Bridge; nr Chaigley on old Clitheroe—Longridge high rd, parallel to B6243 — OS Sheet 103, map reference 699412], *Hodder Bridge*: Alone by the pretty River Hodder, with terraces looking down to the river — the hotel has its own fishing; panelled back lounge, bar food from sandwiches to steaks, generous Sun carvery, Watneys-related real ales on handpump, river-view restaurant; children welcome; bedrooms quiet and comfortable *(Len Beattie, LYM)*

Cowan Bridge, Lancs [Burrow-by-Burrow; A65 towards Kirkby Lonsdale; SD6477], *Whoop Hall*: Comfortably spruced-up and well laid out, with quick food buttery, well kept Tetleys and Youngers Scotch and No 3 on handpump, tables outside with play area; children allowed in eating area *(Andy and Jill Kassube, LYM)*

☆ **Croston**, Lancs [Westhead Rd; A581 Chorley—Southport — OS Sheet 108, map reference 486187; SD4818], *Black Horse*: Cheerfully take-us-as-you-find-us real-ale pub, with up to a dozen or more swiftly changing beers usually inc Black Country Milds, good relaxed atmosphere, good value bar food from sandwiches to steaks (huge cheap steak sandwich hotly tipped) served all day, small restaurant (closed Tues), darts, hexagonal pool table, cribbage, CD juke box, own bowling green; ambitious beer festivals *(Jim and Maggie Cowell, P Lloyd, Miss K Bamford, John Fazackerley, BB)*

Delph, Gtr Manchester [A62 — OS Sheet 109, map reference 980070; SD9808], *Cross Keys*: Friendly old-world atmosphere, log fire, good value bar food, Matthew Browns and Theakstons Best and Old Peculier; French licensees, good restaurant *(John Brooks)*

☆ **Denshaw**, Gtr Manchester [2 miles from M62 junction 2; A672 towards Oldham, pub N of village; SD9710], *Rams Head*: Comfortable moorland pub, part of a farm; small rooms with traditional settles, bric-a-brac on beams and panelling, big log fires; well kept Theakstons, Timothy Taylors and maybe a guest beer tapped from the cask, unobtrusive piped music, simple food Fri-Sun lunchtimes; lovely scenery, good walking; closed Mon-Thurs lunchtimes *(Gary Scott, H K Dyson, Steve Mitcheson, Anne Collins, Carol and Richard Glover, LYM)*

Denshaw, [off M62 junction 2; A672 towards Oldham, just N of village], *Black Horse*: Cosy, with plenty of brassware, good

Yorkshire puddings with roast beef, Bass (John Scott)

☆ **Diggle**, Gtr Manchester [Diglea Hamlet, Sam Rd; village signed off A670 just N of Dobcross; SE0008], Diggle Hotel: Three modernised open-plan rooms popular for above-average food from sandwiches to steaks, inc children's dishes; well kept Boddingtons, Oldham Bitter and maybe Mild, and Timothy Taylors Golden Best and Landlord, decent wines, good choice of malt whiskies, good coffee, soft piped music, welcoming service; rustic fairy-lit tables among the trees, nice spot just below the moors; opens noon (Steve Mitcheson, Anne Collins, Roy Cove, Jon Wainwright, Neil Barker, Pauline Crossland, Dave Cawley, BB)

Dunham Town, Gtr Manchester [OS Sheet 109, map reference 740881; SJ7488], Axe & Cleaver: Open-plan village pub with decent food; children in conservatory (John Watson)

Dunham Woodhouses, Gtr Manchester [B5160 — OS Sheet map reference 724880; SJ7288], Vine: Unusually well refurbished village pub, keeping old-world atmosphere and small separate rooms; food good under new landlord, handy for Dunham Massey Park and Hall (G T Jones)

☆ **Eccles**, Gtr Manchester [33 Regent St (A57 — handy for M602 junction 2); SJ7798], Lamb: Large splendidly Edwardian pub, etched windows, nice woodwork and furnishings, unusual bar counter; busy and down-to-earth, with well kept Holts; possibly the only pub around Manchester with a full-size snooker table (Steve Mitcheson, Anne Collins, P Corris, Michael Rooke)

Eccles, [133 Liverpool Rd — Patricroft, a mile from M63 junction 2], White Lion: Well kept Holts in big, busy three-room pub with etched windows and passageway servery (Steve Mitcheson, Anne Collins, Michael Rooke)

☆ **Entwistle**, Lancs [Overshores Rd, by stn; village signed off Blackburn Rd N of Edgworth — OS Sheet 109, map reference 726177; SD7217], Strawbury Duck: Lost in the moors, but with occasional trains from Blackburn and Bolton, this cosy beamed and flagstoned pub has bar food from sandwiches to steaks inc children's dishes (all day Sat and Sun), and real ales such as Boddingtons, Hartleys XB, Marstons Pedigree and Timothy Taylors Mild, Best and Landlord; good atmosphere, games room, restaurant, live music Thurs, tables outside; children till 8.30; closed Mon lunchtime; bedrooms (John Fazakerley, Ben Wimpenny, Brian and Anna Marsden, Carol and Richard Glover, Mr and Mrs S Turner, Dr and Mrs C D E Morris, Bill Ryan, LYM)

Euxton, Lancs [Runshaw Lane, Runshaw Moor; a mile from A49/B5252 junction; SD5519], Plough: Rural pub with sympathetic new extension, blackened beams, partitions and so forth; big sheltered back lawn with tables, small play area and chickens; well kept Youngers Scotch and IPA and limited choice of decent food (John Fazakerley)

☆ **Fence**, Lancs [2 3/4 miles from M65 junction 12 — follow Nelson, Brierfield sign, then right at roundabout, then right at traffic lights; in Fence turn right at T-junction, first left into Harpers Lane, OS Sheet 103, map reference 828376; SD8237], Harpers: Spaciously comfortable and handsomely modernised lounge bar with balustraded restaurant area (food all day Sun), friendly helpful staff, bar food from sandwiches to steaks, well kept Thwaites Mild and Bitter, decent choice of wines, piped music, thriving atmosphere; children in eating area (F and J Hamer, LYM)

☆ **Fence** [300 Wheatley Lane Rd], White Swan: About a dozen well kept real ales and good choice of whiskies in friendly and lively three-room village pub with simple comfortable furnishings, roaring fires, horsey decorations inc jockey's silks; pub may not open before 1pm weekdays (Andrew Stephenson, LYM)

Fleetwood, Lancs [Marine Hall, Esplanade; SD3247], Wyre: Part of Marine Hall exhibition centre, quiet, good views of beach, Morecambe Bay and boats and ships using docks; real ales such as Moorhouses Premier and Pendle Witches Brew, Timothy Taylors Landlord and two or three guests (Adrian Steen)

Freckleton, Lancs [off A584 opp The Plough; towards Naze Lane Ind Est, then right into Bunker St; SD4228], Ship: Roomy bar with big windows looking out over the watermeadows, food inc sandwiches, hot specials and salads (not Mon evening), well kept Boddingtons on handpump, tables outside; airy upstairs carvery and buffet; children provided for; oldest pub on the Fylde (Graham Bush, LYM)

Galgate, Lancs [A6 S of Lancaster; handy for M6 junction 33; SD4755], Plough: Good value fresh food inc sandwiches, filled baked potatoes and salads even in winter, cosy traditional bars, open fires, friendly efficient service, well kept Boddingtons, good coffee; open all day (I H Rorison, C C Kenny-Levick)

☆ **Garstang**, Lancs [on northbound section of one-way system; SD4845], Wheatsheaf: Good food inc notable specials (esp fish) in small and cosy pub, low beams and creaky ceiling-planks, gleaming copper and brass, little plush-cushioned black settles and dining chairs; warm atmosphere, good service (Jim and Maggie Cowell, BB)

Gathurst, Gtr Manchester [Gathurst Lane (B5206); not far from M6 junction 27, via Shevington; SD5407], Gathurst Station: Fairly new Whitbreads pub, ex-station — handsome sandstone building with railway memorabilia, window seats overlooking the still-working Southport line; nr canal, popular with young people (Susan Burton); [nr M6 junction 27; B5206 towards Orrell — OS Sheet 108, map reference 541074], Navigation: By bridge over Leeds—Liverpool canal, extended old building, good neo-Victorian refurbishment, interesting photographs of old canal scenes; Taylor Walker beers, standard food, well appointed dining room *(T Nott)*

☆ **Godley**, Gtr Manchester [signposted from A57, off Station Rd; SJ9595], *Godley Hall*: Well kept beer, cheap food and friendly licensees in lovely low-beamed character pub, plush seats, lots of brasses *(Dennis Jones)*

☆ **Goosnargh**, Lancs [pub signed from village, about 2 miles towards Chipping below Bleasdale Fell; SD5839], *Horns*: Homely and traditional old dining pub, five snug rooms all with open fires, antique chairs, gleaming brasses, intimate restaurant; wide range whiskies, Tetleys, well prepared food from sandwiches and other bar food to local game and fish, and popular roast duck dinners *(Graham Bush, Jim and Maggie Cowell, J A Boucher)*

Goosnargh, *Grapes*: Warm and cosy local with open fires, lots of little low-beamed rooms inc a billiards room, Tetleys beers, generous straightforward food, collection of water-jugs and old telephones *(Robert and Vicky Tod, Andrew Hazeldine)*

Grasscroft, Gtr Manchester [Oldham Rd; SD9704], *Farrars Arms*: Well kept Ushers and Ruddles, good choice of whiskies etc, log fires, pleasant atmosphere; food excellent, bar staff friendly *(Ian Lees)*

Greasby, Merseyside [Greasby Rd; off B5139 in centre; SJ2587], *Greave Dunning*: Genteel refurbishment and extension of 18th-century farm, lofty main lounge, upstairs food gallery, flagstoned locals' bar with cosy snugs leading off; Bass real ale, designer lace curtains *(E G Parish, Tony and Lynne Stark, LYM)*

Greenfield, Gtr Manchester [Grasscroft; SD9904], *Farrars Arms*: Comfortable and pleasant, with good Pennine views, Wilsons ales, choice of vegetarian food; nr stn *(Neil Barker)*

Hambleton, Lancs [OS Sheet 102, map reference 366429; SD3742], *Wardleys*: Originally a smugglers' pub, riverbank views, well kept Boddingtons and John Smiths on handpump, pleasant young staff, food such as pizzas and filled Yorkshire puddings; juke box, but nice atmosphere *(John Atherton)*

Haskayne, Lancs [Rosemary Lane; just off A567; SD3507], *Ship*: Busy canalside pub with very nautical theme — lots to look at; seats out by water, well priced food lunchtime and evening, family room *(P Corris)*

Haslingden, Lancs [Grane Rd (B6232); SD7823], *Holden Arms*: Large, recently refurbished country pub/restaurant with banquettes and pine chairs in flowery-curtained pastel bar, country-kitchen restaurant, wide choice of reasonably priced food inc bar snacks; well kept Boddingtons, fruit machine, juke box, trivia *(Anon)*

☆ **Hawk Green**, Lancs [SU9687], *Crown*: Spacious, clean and popular food pub (but

with drinking area too), lively atmosphere, well kept Robinsons, wide choice of food in bar and well laid out restaurant in barn extension, friendly waitresses *(Steve Mitcheson, Anne Collins, P Corris)*

☆ **Heaton with Oxcliffe**, Lancs [shd be signed Overton off B5273 Lancaster—Heysham; SD4460], *Golden Ball*: Fine isolated position on the River Lune, with antique settles and other traditional furnishings in little low-beamed rooms, good winter fires, Mitchells served from a hatch, reasonably priced food inc Italian dishes, evening restaurant; seats outside; children welcome; open all day Sat in summer *(Alison and Tony Godfrey, John Atherton, LYM)*

☆ **Heskin Green**, Lancs [Barmskin Lane; SD5315], *Brook House*: Pretty 17th-century Greenalls pub in Wigan Alps area, lots of character, friendly staff, generous food inc children's dishes in bar and restaurant *(G T Jones, D Bryan)*

Heswall, Merseyside [The Green, Rabymere Rd; SJ2782], *Wheatsheaf*: Caring staff, good food and service, delightful bars with open fires *(E G Parish)*

Heywood, Gtr Manchester [Pilsworth Rd; SD8612], *Three Arrows*: Open-plan spaciously rebuilt pub, old-world country-look in front, more modern plush-seated split-level back part; piped music, fruit machines; reasonably priced bar food and Lees ales *(Carol and Richard Glover)*

☆ **nr Heywood** [off narrow Ashworth Rd; pub signed off B6222 on Bury side of N Heywood], *Egerton Arms*: Alone by moorland church, with lovely views all around, especially from tables on terrace; comfortable sofas and easy chairs in plush lounge used mainly by people dining in the smart restaurant (huge steaks), more simply furnished bar with cosy coal fire even in summer, big-windowed small extension, good bar food from sandwiches up *(Carol and Richard Glover, BB)*

Hightown, Merseyside [Moss Lane; B5193 Liverpool—Southport, towards Little Crosby; SD2903], *Pheasant*: Well kept and pleasantly decorated up-to-date country pub, five spacious main areas, consistently good value food lunchtime and evening, Whitbreads real ales *(Vincent Ainsworth)*

☆ **Holden**, Lancs [the one up by Bolton by Bowland — OS Sheet 103, map reference 777494; SD7749], *Copy Nook*: Doing well under new regime, with friendly and helpful staff, good imaginative home-made food in bar and Thurs-Sat evening restaurant; Watneys-related beers *(F and J Hamer, J L and G M Chapman)*

Hornby, Lancs [SD5869], *Royal Oak*: Well kept beer, good range of cheap bar food, quick service *(Ray and Gwen Jessop)*

Hurst Green, Lancs [off B6243 Longridge—Clitheroe, towards Stoneyhurst Coll; SD6838], *Bayley Arms*: Attractive, with good value bar food *(G T Jones)*

Hutton, Lancs [Liverpool Rd; A59 on roundabout by Longton turnoff, just S of

Hutton; SD4826], *Anchor*: Large recently refurbished pub, popular for cheap Matthew Browns and Theakstons and smallish choice of good value food *(Jim and Maggie Cowell)*

Hyde, Gtr Manchester [Dukinfield; 50 yds from Lower Peak Forest Canal; SJ9497], *Globe*: Newly done up, with good value food, well kept beer *(Greenwood and Turner)*

Kirkham, Lancs [A583 Preston—Blackpool; SD4231], *Bell & Bottle*: Good spacious Brewers Fayre pub with cheerful, friendly service and Whitbreads-related real ales *(Ian D Coburn)*; [48 Preston St], *Stable*: Hartleys, Mitchells and Sam Smiths tapped from the cask, good range of bar snacks, attached restaurant, garden *(Jim Cowell)*

☆ **Lancaster** [Canal Side; parking in Aldcliffe Rd behind Royal Lancaster Infirmary, off A6 — cross canal by pub's footbridge], *Water Witch*: Nice waterside conversion of 18th-century barge-horse stabling, simple furniture, pitch-pine panelling, flagstones, stripped stone and rafters; real ales, bar food, lunchtime barbecues, games room, juke box; children allowed in eating areas, open all day Sat *(Jim and Maggie Cowell, Ray and Gwen Jessop, LYM; reports on new regime please)*

☆ **Lancaster** [Green Lane — heading N on A6, last turn on right leaving speed restriction], *Howe Ghyll*: Spacious former mansion in most attractive grounds on edge of town, well kept Mitchells real ales, efficient quick-service lunchtime food counter, games in public bar; children in family room *(LYM)*

Lancaster [Market Sq], *Blue Anchor*: Lots of atmosphere in several nautical-theme small rooms (same owners as Th'Owd Tithebarn at Garstang); straightforward inexpensive bar food, good upstairs restaurant *(Robert and Vicky Tod)*; [centre], *John of Gaunt*: Remarkable beermat collection; well kept Tetley *(Ray and Gwen Jessop)*; [Lower Church St], *Stonewell Tavern*: Well kept Thwaites Bitter and Mild, very generous if chippy lunchtime food inc several pies (not Sun); comfortably modern atmosphere though pub actually ancient, steps up to dining area where children allowed *(Jim and Maggie Cowell, LYM)*

Lathom, Lancs [SD4512], *Briars Hall*: Charming hotel conversion, beautiful carvings around bar, nice big rooms, Walkers Bitter and Mild, lovely inexpensive restaurant; bedrooms *(Comus Elliott)*; [Parbold Rd — turn after Ring o' Bells heading into Burscough], *Ship*: Lovely spot by well used canal, pleasant cottagey atmosphere, network of rooms with nautical bric-a-brac; nice food, wide choice of good beers *(Wayne Brindle)*

Lea Town, Lancs [Lea Rd; SD4731], *Saddle*: Straightforward country local with red plush banquettes, worth knowing for particularly well kept Thwaites; bar food evenings and all day Sun, CD jukebox not too loud, Fri karioke; small back garden with play area *(Graham Bush, John Atherton)*

Litherland, Merseyside [Sefton Rd; SJ3397], *Priory*: Modernised but cosy, with good value lunchtime food (inc Sunday roast), Ind Coope Burton and Walkers Mild, Bitter and Winter Warmer on handpump *(P Lloyd, Miss K Bamford, P Corris)*

Little Eccleston, Lancs [by toll bridge; off A586 Garstang—Blackpool; SD4139], *Cartford*: Busy Wyre-side pub, two of its three storeys set for dining — reasonably priced food till 10; well kept ales inc Boddingtons, Flowers and two guests (not cheap), quiet juke box, pool; small garden with play area; bedrooms *(Adrian Steen, Graham Bush)*

☆ **Littleborough**, Gtr Manchester [A58 towards Halifax, on right; SD9316], *Rake*: Three-room old-world pub, low beams, brasses, lovely old log-burning fire, partly panelled stripped stone, intimate dark alcoves and interesting niches with ancient monks' benches; easy to believe it's haunted *(Carol and Richard Glover)*

☆ **Liverpool** [Albert Dock Complex], *Pump House*: Fine waterside spot nr museums etc, cleverly converted with lots of polished dark wood, bare brickwork, several levels inc mezzanine and upper gallery with exposed roof trusses; marble counter with bulbous beer engines and brass rail supported by elephants' heads, tall chimney; wide choice of cheeses (very generous helpings), some hot food, friendly efficient service; dockside tables, boat trips in season *(Jim and Becky Bryson, E G Parish, John Fazakerley)*

☆ **Liverpool** [67 Moorfields], *Lion*: Splendidly preserved, with etched glass and serving hatches in central bar, unusual wallpaper, big mirrors, panelling and tilework, fine domed structure behind, well kept beer, cheap lunchtime bar food, well kept Walkers Bitter and Mild; can get crowded *(Jon Wainwright)*

☆ **Liverpool** [4 Hackins Hey, off Dale St], *Hole in Ye Wall*: Well restored 18th-century pub, several different areas in pleasant high-beamed panelled bar with well kept beer unusually fed by gravity via oak pillars from upstairs cellar; has been popular for friendly staff and lunchtime side food servery, but owners have been talking about redevelopment *(Jon Wainwright; news please)*

Liverpool [Albert Dock Complex], *Bar X*: Recent wild-west-style conversion with stone floors and polished panelling, reasonably priced bar food, well kept Wards; busy evenings *(Andy and Jill Kassube)*; [Ranelagh St, opp Central Stn], *Central Commercial*: Mahogany woodwork, sumptuous engraved glass, marble pillars and elaborately moulded domed ceiling in Victorian pub with attractively priced hot and cold buffet, well kept Ind Coope-related real ales, busy atmosphere; juke box may be loud evenings *(LYM)*; [13 Rice St], *Cracke*: Attractively basic students' pub with bare boards, walls covered with posters for local events and pictures of local buildings; largest room has unusual Beatles diorama; juke box and TV, simple sandwiches, well kept Marstons; sizeable garden *(Jon Wainwright, Tony and Lynne Stark)*; [25 Matthew St], *Grapes*:

Lively and friendly, with flagstones and open-plan but cottagey decor, well kept Boddingtons and Cains (new local brew from ex-Higsons brewery) on handpump, well priced lunchtime bar food; can get crowded Fri/Sat, and its Beatles associations are still remembered; open all day, closed Sun *(Andy and Jill Kassube, Peter Corris)*; [Dale St], *Rigbys*: Beamed and panelled character bar with real ale, said to be Liverpool's oldest pub; in same handsome Georgian building as Hole in Ye Wall and facing same future — see above *(Mr and Mrs A Robinson)*; [Roscoe St], *Roscoe Head*: Compact and often crowded, with good atmosphere, particularly well kept Jennings and Allied beers; active tie collection in lounge *(Andy and Jill Kassube)*

Longton, Lancs [Liverpool Rd; SD4726], *Golden Ball*: Well kept, with open fire, decent range of bar food, separate dining room, well kept Greenalls and quick, careful service *(D A Parker)*

Lydiate, Merseyside [Bells Lane; just off Southport rd; SD3604], *Running Horses*: Popular canalside pub with cosy and tastefully decorated lounge, consistently well kept Walkers, reasonably priced lunchtime food; family room, waterside terrace, garden with pets' corner *(P Corris)*

Lytham, Lancs [Church Rd; SD3627], *County*: Well kept Boddingtons in spaciously refurbished pub *(Simon Bates, Graham Bush)*; [Forest Dr], *Hole-in-One*: Well kept Thwaites in good modern local, comfortable two-room lounge, games bar *(Graham Bush, Simon Bates)*

☆ **Manchester**, [127 Gt Bridgewater St, Oxford St side], *Peveril of the Peak*: Homely survivor and unexpected in centre, with genuinely friendly local atmosphere in the three rooms looping around its central servery, lots of mahogany and stained glass, sturdy furnishings, interesting pictures; well kept Websters Yorkshire and Choice and Wilsons Original and Mild on handpump, cheap snacks (not Sun), pub games inc table football, seats outside, Mild-supping pub dog; children welcome; a nice pub, we wish we heard more of it *(Andy and Jill Kassube, Virginia Jones, Bill Ryan, LYM)*

☆ **Manchester** [Shambles Sq; behind Arndale off Market St in centre], *Old Wellington*: The only timber-framed building of its age to survive in the centre — flagstones and gnarled oak timbers, well kept Bass and Stones on handpump, oak-panelled bar; bar food (from noon, not Sun) with hot beef sandwiches a speciality, small upstairs Toby carvery (closed Mon-Weds evenings and all day Sun); often packed lunchtime *(Len Beattie, Terry Buckland, BB)*

☆ **Manchester** [Oldham St], *Dry 201*: More bar than pub, bare boards and pillars, minimalist decoration, up-to-date dance music loud but not overwhelming, well kept Marstons Pedigree, continental lagers, Russian vodkas, smart, designer-aproned staff; crowded with trendy customers *(Lee Goulding, Tony and Lynne Stark)*

☆ **Manchester** [50 Great Bridgewater St; corner of Lower Mosley St], *Britons Protection*: Fine tilework and solid woodwork in smallish rather plush front bar, attractive softly lit inner lounge with coal-effect gas fire, battle murals in passage leading to it; well kept though not cheap Ind Coope Burton, Jennings and Tetleys, popular at lunchtime for its simple well prepared food, quiet evenings; handy for GMEX centre *(Brian and Anna Marsden, Bill Ryan, Wayne Brindle, BB)*

☆ **Manchester**, [6 Angel St, off Rochdale Rd], *Beer House*: Up to ten changing well kept real ales, also farm ciders and good range of bottled foreign beers; lively atmosphere, simple inexpensive bar food, downbeat decor, juke box with good blues records; very popular lunchtime and early evening *(Brian and Anna Marsden, Andy and Jill Kassube, Alan Holden, Bill Ryan)*

☆ **Manchester** [East St; off Lower Mosley St], *Tommy Ducks*: Plush Victorian-style refurbishment with theatrical posters, mirrored walls and heavy swagged curtains, with usual weekday lunchtime bar food from sandwiches up, well kept Greenalls Local and Original on handpump, fruit machine, juke box, picnic-table sets outside; children in eating area, not evening; open all day weekdays *(Len Beattie, Brian and Anna Marsden, Wayne Brindle, LYM)*

☆ **Manchester** [682 Wilmslow Rd], *Station*: Character two-room pub full of railway memorabilia; well kept Marstons on handpump, friendly staff, back games extension, seats outside among lovely flowers *(Michael Cochrane, Lee Goulding)*

Manchester [Albert Hill Rd; off Wilmslow Rd, Didsbury], *Albert*: Traditional Hydes pub with three main rooms, big central area, smallish bar counter at far end; friendly service, well kept beer, cheap simple lunchtime food, low prices; really interesting cigarette cards and film-star photographs *(Michael Cochrane, RT)*; [Chapel St, Salford], *Cathedral Arches*: New pub reminiscent in style of the Mark Addy, in railway arches under old Exchange Stn, by R Irwell; good choice of Whitbreads-related ales and Marstons Pedigree, interesting renovation *(Brian and Anna Marsden)*; [86 Portland St], *Circus*: Two tiny panelled character rooms with well kept Tetleys; weekend evening opening 8 — so popular they may shut door when full *(Bill Ryan)*; [Kennedy St], *City Arms*: Well kept Ind Coope Burton, Jennings and Tetleys, popular bar lunches; quiet evening, may be closed much of weekend *(Bill Ryan)*; [41 Hilton St, off Newton St nr Piccadilly], *Crown & Anchor*: Well decorated, atmospheric pub with good choice of Whitbreads-related and other real ales such as Timothy Taylors Landlord on handpump, good value lunchtime food, efficient friendly service even when busy *(Brian and Anna Marsden, Bill Ryan, P Corris)*; [Oldham St], *King*: Not for the faint-hearted — boisterously entertaining mix of Mancunian characters in scrum of a long bar with good Tetleys (Lee Goulding); [4a Helmshaw Walk — nr Upper Brook St (A34), off Kincardine Rd/Whitekirk Cl], Kings Arms: Sparely but brightly refurbished Victorian pub worth tracking down for its Dobbins Mild, Bitter, Guiltless Stout and very strong Special; friendly staff, lunchtime food (Lee Goulding, Bill Ryan, Brian and Anna Marsden); [Droylsden], Moss: Family pub with good garden for children to play in, barbecues (Pauline Crossland, Dave Cawley); [52 Cross St], Mr Thomas Chop House: Gleaming tiles in small front bar, interesting food servery in long narrow bar behind, dining room beyond; very busy lunchtime for home-made chop-house food, esp pies and hot beef sandwiches (also served early evening); good choice of well kept real ales inc Boddingtons and Thwaites (Andy and Jill Kassube, Ian Phillips, Bill Ryan); [part of Piccadilly Hotel, Portland St], Portland Arms: Upmarket L-shaped bar on two levels, with alcoves and lots of polished wood and frosted glass; can be a crush at times; well kept Ind Coope Burton and Tetleys (Lee Goulding); [Honey St — off Red Bank, nr Victoria Stn], Queens Arms: Attractively renovated, cosy and welcoming, with well kept Theakstons, Timothy Taylors and several changing guest beers, simple lunchtime and evening bar food; bar billiards, good juke box, bottle collection; pleasant back garden sloping down towards the Irk Valley and its railway complex (P Corris, Bill Ryan); [Wilmslow Rd, Withington], Red Lion: Quaint, atmospheric front rooms, spacious two-level plusher back bar, food area (no food Sun evenings), well kept Marstons Pedigree, new conservatory partly encroaching on the pub's own bowling green (Bill Ryan, Gary Scott); [Trafford Wharf Rd], Samuel Platts: New pub/restaurant overlooking Manchester Ship Canal and modern Salford Quays development; bar, good first-floor grill room and circular restaurant built out over canal (J M Watson); [Kirk St, Gorton], Vale Cottage: Three cosy almost rural-seeming rooms, full of bric-a-brac, friendly welcome, well kept Watneys-related real ales, freshly squeezed orange juice, big helpings of reasonably priced bar food inc good value steak, nice tree-lined terrace; opens noon (Steve Mitcheson, Anne Collins, Pauline Crossland, Dave Cawley); [Liverpool Rd, Castlefield], White Lion: Well kept Boddingtons and Chesters on handpump, well priced good simple food, esp roast beef (Martin Newman)

☆ **Marple** [Ridge End; off A626 via Church Lane, following The Ridge signposts — OS Sheet 109, map reference 965867; SJ9588], Romper: Comfortable and busy old-world food pub with four softly lit knocked-through oak-beamed rooms, well kept real ales such as Tetleys, Theakstons Best and Old Peculier, Timothy Taylors Landlord and Wadworths 6X, helpful smiling staff, wide choice of good value food; tables outside; superb setting alone on

steep side of Goyt Valley above Peak Forest Canal; opens noon (RT, Pauline Crossland, Dave Cawley, Steve Mitcheson, Anne Collins, Bill Sykes, LYM)

☆ **Marple** [130 Church Lane; by canal, Bridge 2 — OS Sheet 109, map reference 960884], Ring o' Bells: Big friendly pub, comfortable but not elaborate, by Macclesfield Canal nr junction with Peak Forest Canal (16 locks, picturesque towpath walks); generous good value food served efficiently (it's becoming very much a dining pub), well kept Robinsons on electric pump, reasonable wine, lots of canal and barge pictures; small garden with summer barbecues and tables overlooking canal — but piped music even out here; children welcome (Pat and Tony Young, Steve Mitcheson, Anne Collins, Pauline Crossland, Dave Cawley)

Marple, Navigation: Good reasonably priced waitress-served food, well kept Robinsons; maybe brass band practice upstairs (Greenwood and Turner); Windsor Castle: Tasty hot beef muffins (all they do Sun lunch) (Pauline Crossland, Dave Cawley)

Marple Bridge, Gtr Manchester [SJ9689], Midland: Good food with lots of choice ordered from counter, very busy; play area (Pauline Crossland, Dave Cawley); Norfolk Arms: Good Sun lunch — very rare beef carved then further cooked to your liking on hot metal hob (Pauline Crossland, Dave Cawley)

☆ **Mawdesley**, Lancs [Bluestone Lane; Croston—Eccleston road, N of village — keep going! — OS Sheet 108, map reference 505164; SD4915], Robin Hood: Three open-plan well refurbished rooms with good atmosphere, popular for simple good value bar food inc children's helpings; well kept Whitbreads-related real ales on handpump with a guest such as Hartleys XB, quick friendly service, upstairs restaurant (Thomas Nott, Jim and Maggie Cowell, P Corris, F A Noble)

☆ **Middleton**, Gtr Manchester [Thornham Lane, Slattocks; track between A664 and A671 just S of M62 junction 20; SD8606], Tandle Hill Tavern: What's special here is the position — within the Manchester city limits yet isolated down a track through farmland and country park; actually part of a farm, with two snugly unpretentious rooms, coal fire; well kept Lees on handpump, snacks, low prices; darts, cribbage and highly competitive dominoes, benches out among ducks, ponies and ageing tractors — horses tethered outside may outnumber the cars; children welcome; closed winter weekday lunchtimes (Carol and Richard Glover, Comus Elliott, David Butcher, LYM)

Middleton, [Haigh Lane], Rose of Lancaster: Friendly post-war local with well kept very cheap Lees Bitter at 86p; lots of pine tongue-and-groove and tall, small pine-veneered tables; doll collection, big picture windows looking over fields to Rochdale Canal (currently being restored) and moors beyond (Brian Jones)

Moreton, Merseyside [Saughall Rd, Saughall Massie, off A553 towards Hoylake; SJ2588], *Saughall*: Large village local with two bars, family area and tables outside; friendly staff, well kept Whitbreads Castle Eden, good lunchtime food; quiet during week, lively weekends *(S Rushworth)*

Mossley, Gtr Manchester [Manchester Rd (A635 N); SD9802], *Roaches Lock*: Has been popular well laid-out stripped-stone free house with long bar, four well kept real ales, over a hundred whiskies, good value food and tables out by Huddersfield Canal; but changed hands and closed for refurbishment as we went to press *(News please)*

☆ **Mottram**, Gtr Manchester [off A57 M'ter—Barnsley; at central traffic lights turn opp B6174 into Broadbottom Rd; SJ9995], *Waggon*: Friendly and comfortable open-plan pub with brown furnishings, dimpled copper tables, big brass platters and a big central fire; well worth knowing for good value food such as steak pie, gammon and liver grill, mint-glazed lamb and massive puddings, served all through the day; well kept Robinsons Best and Best Mild on electric pump, good wheelchair access, picnic-table sets outside and a good play area *(Dennis Jones, Pauline Crossland, Dave Cawley, BB)*

Mottram, *Pack Horse*: Attractive, with low beams in back room, two-way stone fireplace with coal-effect gas fire, good food, friendly quick service *(Pauline Crossland, Dave Cawley)*

Newburgh, Lancs [SD4710], *Red Lion*: Friendly low-beamed village pub with cosy lounge bar, popular for good range of pleasantly presented bar food; pool and games room, well kept Burtonwood on handpump, separate upstairs restaurant, garden with swings; children welcome; bedrooms *(Comus Elliott)*

Oldham, Gtr Manchester [Hollins Rd; SD9305], *King George*: Good filling straightforward food *(Pauline Crossland, Dave Cawley)*

☆ **nr Oldham** [Grains Bar (A672/B6197); SD9608], *Bulls Head*: Gleaming brass and copper in snug two-room moorland pub with well kept Bass, Bass Special and Mild on handpump, good value evening food inc steaks, friendly staff; we have not heard whether the nostalgic singalongs have survived the recent departure of theatre-organist tenant Mr Wilson *(Dr Thomas Mackenzie, Pauline Crossland, Dave Cawley, LYM)*

☆ **Ormskirk**, Lancs [Burscough St; SD4108], *Buck i'th Vine*: Very pleasant old pub, lots of rooms, nooks and crannies, famous low "toffee-shop" serving window at bar — you have to stoop to order; good food (particularly chilli con carne, set lunch), well kept Walkers Bitter and Mild; live music and quiz some nights *(P Corris)*

Ormskirk [Heaton Bridge Rd — B5242, just off A59], *Heatons Bridge*: Clean and polished, lots of oak beams, brasses, old pictures and the like, two rooms off main semi-circular bar area, friendly landlady; nice spot by bridge over Leeds & Liverpool Canal, Tetleys on handpump *(Jeanne and Tom Barnes)*; [Narrow Moss Lane], *Kicking Donkey*: Picturesque and cosy local, very old core with stained glass and antique bar frontage, new part blended in quite well; three rooms each with coal fire, friendly, helpful staff, good value homely food, well kept Walkers, couple of fruit machines; nice tables out in front *(Keith Croxton, Carol and Philip Seddon)*

☆ **Oswaldtwistle**, Lancs [Haslingden Old Rd; A677/B6231; SD7327], *Britannia*: Solidly traditional old-fashioned furnishings and fittings inc log-burning ranges in friendly bar, Daniels Kitchen family restaurant, bar food from soup and lunchtime sandwiches to steaks with some emphasis on fresh fish, well kept Thwaites and Mild; suntrap back terrace and play area; food all day Sun; children in family room and restaurant *(Dave and Kate Buckley, LYM)*

Oswaldtwistle, [Haslingden Rd, Rams Clough], *Coach & Horses*: Stunning views from back windows; clean, bright and polished, with well kept beer, good food, nice landlord *(Comus Elliott)*

Parbold, Lancs [Alder Lane; SD4911], *Stocks*: Good bar food, efficient service, well kept Tetleys; very busy as evening wears on, quieter lunchtime *(Comus Elliott, A T Langton; reports on new regime please)*; [A5209], *Wiggin Tree*: Comfortable Brewers Fayre pub with magnificent view; has been praised for good friendly service, tasty reasonably priced food, well kept Whitbreads-related real ales, but no recent reports *(News please)*

Poulton le Fylde, Lancs [Ball St; SD3439], *Thatched House*: Recently refurbished open-plan local, lively, with well kept Boddingtons, good mix of customers, open fire, pool table, simple snacks; by pretty churchyard *(Graham Bush)*

Prescot, Merseyside [St James Rd; SJ4992], *Wellington*: Recently very tastefully converted, well kept real ale, good reasonably priced food, good staff *(Mr and Mrs A Robinson)*

Preston, Lancs [Mount St, off Fishergate; SD5329], *Hartleys*: New and magnificent, with high-quality interior inc wine bar, pub lunches, real ale *(Comus Elliott)*; [114 Church St], *Olde Blue Bell*: Good atmosphere in busy Sam Smiths pub, popular for well kept beer *(Graham Bush, Andy and Jill Kassube)*

Rawtenstall, Lancs [371 Bury Old Rd; A56 towards Edenfield — OS Sheet 103, map reference 803217; SD8123], *Whitchaff*: Large open-plan old-world pub with stripped stone, open fire, bric-a-brac, good food in bar and restaurant, tables outside *(Carol and Richard Glover)*

☆ **Ribchester**, Lancs [Church St; sharp turn off B6245 at Black Bull; SD6435], *White Bull*: Popular good value generous food inc particularly good black pudding starter, well kept Whitbreads-related real ales and good service even when busy, in comfortably and attractively refurbished village pub; porch supported by 1,900-year-old Tuscan pillars — the second-oldest component of any pub we know *(Len Beattie, David and Valerie Hooley, John Fazakerley, LYM)*

Ribchester [Main St (B6245)], *Black Bull*: Generous food and well kept Thwaites in unpretentious local opp good Museum of Childhood *(Hilary Bill)*

☆ **Riley Green**, Lancs [A675/A6061 — OS Sheet 103, map reference 622255; SD6225], *Royal Oak*: Cosy three-room pub with alcovey feel, particularly in end room on the right, stripped stone of considerable age, and low black beams; open fires, seats from high-backed settles to red plush armchairs, Turkey carpet, soft lighting, good range of bar food lunchtime and evening, Thwaites Bitter and Mild on handpump; can be packed weekends; interesting model steam engines *(P Corris, John Fazakerley, BB)*

Roby Mill, Lancs [not far from M6 junction 26; off A577 at Up Holland; SD5107], *Fox*: Nicely placed traditional two-roomed black and white pub, Greenalls ales, pool and darts; wide range of good value food in bar and restaurant *(P Lloyd, Miss K Bamford, Kathleen Morley)*

☆ **Rochdale**, Gtr Manchester [470 Bury Rd; A6222, junction with A6452 continuation — OS Sheet 109, map reference 881130; SD8913], *Cemetery*: Splendidly old-fashioned, with good bare-boarded parlour, two comfortable little Victorian-style lounges, tiled facade with etched windows, numerous bottled beers and over half-a-dozen well kept real ales inc one brewed for the pub; interesting mix of customers *(Steve Mitcheson, Anne Collins, N Burke)*

☆ nr **Rochdale** [Cheesden, Ashworth Moor; A680 towards Edenfield — OS Sheet 109, map reference 831161], *Owd Betts*: Isolated moorland pub with great views over Ashworth Reservoir and right across to Bury and beyond; lots of tables in three cosy low-beamed areas, dark oak settles, stripped stonework, brasses and china cabinet; friendly service, well kept Greenalls Bitter and Mild on handpump, good value bar food and family Sun lunches, open fires *(Carol and Richard Glover, Comus Elliott, Steve Mitcheson, Anne Collins, BB)*

☆ nr **Rochdale** [Oldham Rd, Thornham], *Yew Tree*: Cosy rooms with stripped stone walls and relaxed country atmosphere; well kept Sam Smiths, good value food in bar and Pullman railway-carriage dining room *(Alan and Marlene Radford, BB)*

☆ **Romiley**, Gtr Manchester [Stockport Rd (B6104); SJ9390], *Duke of York*: Friendly and old-fashioned, with lots of woodwork, some brasses, bar area opening into two smaller rooms, one up steps with creaky floorboards and hatch service, also back vaults bar — can get smoky when busy; bar food, John Smiths on handpump, low prices; good upstairs restaurant (not Suns in

Advent) *(Mr and Mrs Simon Turner, Pauline Crossland, Dave Cawley, RT)*

Sale, Gtr Manchester [Rifle Rd, nr M63 junction 8; SJ8092], *Jacksons Boat*: Country pub in Mersey Valley Country Park, with three distinctive open-plan areas inc alcovey bar with bare masonry and rafters, also conservatory; busy weekends, best enjoyed midweek; Tetleys real ale, occasional music/quiz nights, garden and play area; walks/boating/windsurfing nearby *(Lee Goulding)*; [Brooklands Rd], *Kilverts*: Well kept Watneys-related real ales in recently refurbished hotel bars, restaurant; bedrooms *(Bill Ryan)*

Salwick, Lancs [SD4532], *Windmill*: White-painted windmill conversion with decently priced food lunchtime and evening, Mitchells ESB on handpump, Bitter and Mild on electric pump, open fire in lounge; terrace with play area and pets' corner; fruit machines, juke box, furnishings could be more individual *(P Corris)*

Shaw, Gtr Manchester [Buckstones Rd (B6197); off A663 not far from M62 exit 21; SD9308], *Olde Black Ladd*: Black-and-white 18th-century beamed and timbered moorland pub overlooking mill towns, dark panelling, cosy little alcoves, old high-backed settles, plush banquettes and stools, log-effect gas fire in big fireplace, china on delft shelf, soft lighting, Vaux ales, reasonably priced bar lunches (not Mon), well priced Sun lunch, popular beamed evening restaurant (not Mon); warm welcome *(Carol and Richard Glover)*

Shevington Moor, Gtr Manchester [handy for M6 junction 27; SD5411], *Foresters Arms*: Recently extended and refurbished Greenalls pub, friendly staff, very popular for generous helpings of good cheap food in big dining area; very busy weekends; tables outside, open all day Weds-Sat and bank hols, food till 10, phone orders for lunch or takeaway if in hurry; real ales; children till early evening *(Susan Burton)*

☆ **Southport**, Merseyside [Seabank Rd; SD3316], *Windmill*: Good choice of well kept S & N real ales in spacious nicely kept pub with interesting bric-a-brac and old pictures on walls, good bar food inc fine steak sandwich, lunchtime and early evening; good spacious front garden suitable for children, with relayed juke box music *(D J Cargill, Richard A Bailey, Vincent Ainsworth)*

Southport [Bold St/Lord St], *Bold*: Popular and spacious lounge bar leading to front terrace, Tetleys real ales from long counter, good varied lunchtime bar food; bedrooms *(Vincent Ainsworth)*; [Lord St], *Scarisbrick*: Choice of several distinctive bars inc three dining bars, real ale bar with Boddingtons, Courage Directors, Tetleys, Theakstons and Wadworths 6X, lively big pool room with eight tables, video games; bedrooms *(Graham Bush)*

St Annes, Lancs [Church Rd; SD3129], *Victoria*: Well kept Boddingtons and Bass as guest in lofty-roomed local with lively lounge bar, public bar with pool table, pizza stall; originally designed by Mr Boddington the brewer as his own local *(F Teare, Graham Bush)*

Stalybridge, Gtr Manchester [Mottram Rd; SJ9698], *Hare & Hounds*: Decent relaxed pub with well kept Bass, good bar lunches *(Neville Kenyon, Roy Cove)*

☆ **Standish**, Gtr Manchester [4 miles from M6 junction 27; A5209, straight on into B5239 as you go through Standish, then at T-junction turn left into Worthington, then left into Platt Lane; SD5610], *Crown*: Chesterfields, armchairs, panelling, fresh flowers and an open fire in comfortable pub with wide range of good value bar food and well kept real ales such as Bass and Bass Mild and Boddingtons on rather splendid handpumps; decidedly nicer inside than you'd expect from outside; children allowed away from bar *(Comus Elliott, Wayne Brindle, R J Yates, J H M Broughton, Barry and Anne, LYM)*

Standish [closer to M6], *Beeches*: Recently refurbished and extended, with spacious modern two-level bar, partly flagstoned; wide range of reasonably priced food all day, wines good value too *(Harry Stirling)*

☆ **Stockport** [552 Didsbury Rd (off A5145), Heaton Mersey; SJ8691], *Griffin*: Busy local, particularly popular with real ale enthusiasts for remarkably cheap well kept Holts Bitter and Mild, in basic surroundings and thriving local atmosphere; four unpretentiously Victorian rooms off central servery with largely original curved-glass gantry, no piped music, basic lunchtime snacks; seats outside *(Michael Cochrane, RT, Pauline Crossland, Dave Cawley, BB)*

☆ **Stockport** [82 Heaton Moor Rd, Heaton Moor], *Plough*: Spacious comfortably refurbished pub with antique furnishings, bric-a-brac, polished wood, open fire, good bar food; well kept real ales can now run to quite an unusual range, such as Arrolls 80/-, Auld Reekie 80/-, Boddingtons, Hydes Anvil, Ind Coope Burton, Jennings, Robinsons, Robinwood Old Fart, Tetleys, Thwaites, Walkers Best *(RT, J C Gould)*

Stockport [Millgate], *Arden Arms*: Old-fashioned snug, several longcase clocks, traditional furnishings, bar area recently extended into ancient former kitchen; doing well under new landlord, with lunchtime bar food and well kept Robinsons *(Steve Mitcheson, Anne Collins, Steve Hampson)*; [Market Pl], *Bakers Vaults*: Good food and well kept Robinsons in good unpretentious town-centre local with evening live music; children welcome *(Peter Adcock, Steve Mitcheson, Anne Collins)*; [Brinksway Bridge], *Olde Woolpack*: Good range of well kept real ales inc interesting guest beers such as Exmoor Gold *(Keith Mills)*; [Little Underbank], *Queens Head*: Bustling atmosphere and reasonable bar food in long and narrow old lunchtime pub with quite a lot of seating in front bar, small snug, back dining area; well kept Sam Smiths on handpump, rare brass cordials fountain; the original gents' (still in use alongside the new

ones) is the smallest in Britain; no car park, may be bouncer *(Keith Mills)*; [14 Middle Hillgate], *Red Bull*: Substantial settles and seats, beams, flagstones, open fires, lots of pictures and brassware, traditional island servery; good value plain bar lunches (not Sun), well kept Robinsons Best and Best Mild — quiet lunchtime, can get crowded evening *(John Fazakerley, LYM)*

Strines, Gtr Manchester [SJ9786], *Sportsmans Arms*: Well kept Watneys-related beers with guests such as Everards Tiger and Timothy Taylors Landlord, good value meals and snacks till 10, small restaurant area, good views behind; can be quiet early evening *(Keith Mills)*

Summerseat, Gtr Manchester [Waterside Rd; nr M66 junction 1, via A56 towards Bury; SD7814], *Waterside*: Interesting conversion of 19th-century mill, huge split-level flagstoned space with heavy mill machinery, slow fans in vaulted brick ceiling, view from window tables of floodlit river which flows under building; other side overlooks viaduct with steam trains (station nearby); big well stocked bar, live music some nights; currently quite an in place *(Carol and Richard Glover)*

Tarleton, Lancs [70 Church Rd; off A59/A565 Preston—Southport; SD4420], *Cock & Bottle*: Pleasant village pub, reasonably priced bar snacks, well kept Thwaites *(Jim and Maggie Cowell)*

Tatham, Lancs [B6480; off A683 Lancaster—Kirkby Lonsdale; SD6169], *Bridge*: Two small, cosy rooms with well kept Mitchells, good value simple snacks; run by ex-QE2 bar steward *(Derek and Sylvia Stephenson)*

Timperley, Gtr Manchester [Bloomsbury Lane; SJ7988], *Quarry Bank*: Recently completely refitted and currently doing particularly well, with friendly atmosphere, cheap Hydes Bitter and Mild, food lunchtime and evening *(Bill Ryan)*; [Stockport Rd], *Stonemasons Arms*: Large modern-style pub with chesterfields, music, decent if pricey Ind Coope Burton, Jennings and Tetleys; food, coffee *(Bill Ryan)*

☆ **Tockholes**, Lancs [SD6623], *Victoria*: Good value bar food (not Mon evening) in cosily comfortable moorland pub with tables in snug alcoves, partly stripped stone walls, woodburning stove, well kept Matthew Browns and Theakstons, friendly service; Italian-oriented restaurant with midnight supper licence; children welcome *(Len Beattie, Bill Ryan, Greg Turner, LYM)*

☆ **Tockholes** [Brokenstones Rd, Livesey — towards Blackburn — OS Sheet 103, map reference 666247], *Black Bull*: Comfortably modernised and consistently welcoming food pub in good walking country, with good views from big windows; good straightforward bar food inc good home-made pizzas, well kept Thwaites Bitter and Mild on handpump, fine old slate-bed snooker table in side room, some seats outside; dogs allowed, and children at lunchtime (Len Beattie, LYM)

Town of Lowton, Gtr Manchester [OS Sheet 109, map reference 610962; SJ6096], *Travellers Rest*: Good food in admirable pub, very popular (G T Jones)

Two Mills, Merseyside [A540/A550; SJ3474], *Tudor Rose*: Extended and refurbished, bright, spacious and comfortable; good range of bar meals, cold table, restaurant, Boddingtons and Higsons real ales; bedrooms (Mr and Mrs J H Adam)

☆ **Uppermill**, Gtr Manchester [Runninghill Gate, nr Dick Hill; SD9905], *Church*: Well kept Theakstons and other real ales and small range of well prepared good hearty bar food served very generously in clean and comfortable partly stripped-stone old pub on steep moorland slope by isolated church; friendly helpful service, local drawings, annual gurning championship, carefully chosen piped music; downstairs restaurant (Pauline Crossland, Dave Cawley, Steve Mitcheson, Anne Collins, LYM)

Urmston, Gtr Manchester [Stretford Rd; SJ7695], *Lord Nelson*: Recently refurbished without losing its character; well kept cheap Holts on handpump, friendly atmosphere (Les Campbell); [Irlam Rd, Flixton], *Red Lion*: Converted back from 'sports' pub into traditional one with well kept Websters Choice and Wilsons, pool, and enthusiastic darts players (Les Campbell)

nr Waddington, Lancs [B6478 N — OS Sheet 103, map reference 719467; SD7146], *Moorcock*: Attractive old building with beams (some reproduction), and garden with fine views over Ribble Valley; large, enterprising choice of good food, Greenalls on handpump; bedrooms (G T Jones)

Weeton, Lancs [B5260; SD3834], *Eagle & Child*: Decent food in spacious well kept village local; tables outside (Simon Bates, F Teare)

Werneth Low, Gtr Manchester [Werneth Low Rd; from A560 Stockport Rd in Hyde take Joel Lane, turn right at top; SJ9592], *Hare & Hounds*: Large, popular hilltop pub in former farmhouse with lots of beams and stripped stone, good views; well kept Boddingtons, generous helpings of good value Henry's Table food in two eating areas (one no-smoking) (News please)

White Stake, Lancs [Wham Lane; not far from M6 junction 29; SD5126], *Farmers Arms*: Pleasant, extensive dining area done up in Victorian style with efficient service and largish choice of usual food; Whitbreads-related beers such as Boddingtons, Flowers IPA and Castle Eden, neutral piped music, fruit machines (John Fazakerley)

Whittle le Woods, Lancs [A6; not far from M61 junction 7; SD5721], *Sea View*: Recently extended, but still cosy and pleasant, with well kept Thwaites and bar food; though nearly 20 miles from the coast you can just make out the sea on a clear day, at least from over the road (Comus Elliott)

☆ **Wigan**, Gtr Manchester [Frog Lane; SD5805], *Old Pear Tree*: Friendly and cosy local not far from centre, with beams, brasses, old plates and pictures, and comfortable homely settees; well kept Burtonwood, wide choice of cheap lunchtime food inc vegetarian dishes (Susan Burton, Comus Elliott, Jim and Maggie Cowell)

Wigan [Springfield Rd], *Springfield*: Unspoilt large local with variety of rooms, good character, Walkers beer (J E Stanton); [New Market St], *Tudor House*: Old town-centre pub nr college and bus station, bare brick, beams, old plates, jugs and bottles, two big open fires, Bass and frequently changing guest ales, farm cider; bar food, and does breakfasts — open all day; jazz Thurs evenings; bedrooms (Susan Burton)

Wrea Green, Lancs [Station Rd; SD3931], *Grapes*: Large open-plan pub, recently refurbished and concentrating more on food under popular new licensees; Boddingtons beers, open fire, tables out overlooking village green, picturesque neighbouring church (Jon Wainwright, Graham Bush)

Wrightington Bar, Lancs [Moss/Lea Rd; B5250, nr M6 junction 27; SD5313], *Tudor*: Good choice of reasonably priced bar food inc vegetarian dishes, decent choice of wines, nicely set village (Jim and Maggie Cowell)

Leicestershire, Lincolnshire and Nottinghamshire

Pubs in this area tend to be good value. Drinks prices are on average rather below the national level, and food tends to be reasonably priced – with several pubs here gaining our new £ symbol for bargain meals or snacks. Several changes to note here include new managers at the Tom Hoskins in Leicester (besides the good beer from the adjacent brewery, they're doing low-priced food), and the Sir John Borlase Warren in Nottingham (some changes, but still delightfully chatty – and good value), and a new tenant at the Bull & Swan in Stamford (the home-cooked food under the new regime is proving popular). Entirely new to this edition of the Guide (or back after a break) are the cosy and interesting Black Horse at Donington on Bain (making the most of its Viking Way connections), the friendly Wishing Well at Dyke (decent low-priced food), the very welcoming Bell at Halton Holegate (a splendid village pub even if Sam's not doing her Smarties trick), the good value Square & Compass at Normanton on Trent (interesting beers and home cooking), the excellently run Muskham Ferry right on the Trent at North Muskham (very handy for the A1), and the stylish Peacock at Redmile in the Vale of Belvoir (particularly good food). Pubs currently on something of an upswing here include the Leagate at Coningsby (an interesting old Fenland place), the White Horse at Empingham by Rutland Water (good food and bedrooms), the Old Barn at Glooston (doing very well all round), the cheerful Bewicke Arms at Hallaton (another fine all-rounder), the very well run old Nags Head in Heckington, the proudly simple Cap & Stocking at Kegworth, the happy Three Horseshoes at Kibworth Harcourt, the Red Lion at Newton (superb food), the Market Hotel in Retford (decent food and marvellous beers), the friendly and relaxed King William up at Scaftworth, the civilised yet friendly old George in Stamford, the relaxed Cross Keys in Upton (lovely food), and the good value Olde Red Lion at Wellow (still the same friendly village pub – and still in the same family, despite new names on the door). In the Lucky Dip section at the end of the chapter, the Martins Arms at Colston Bassett, Five Bells at Edenham, Monkton Arms at Glaston, Plough at Horbling, Old White Hart at Lyddington and Kings Arms at Wing all currently look to be real comers, and others to note particularly (as with the above, most of them inspected by us) are the Tally Ho at Aswarby, Five Horseshoes at Barholm, Carpenters Arms in Boston, Finch Hatton Arms at Ewerby, George at Leadenham, Bull in Market Deeping, Nickerson Arms up at Rothwell, Black Horse at Sheepy Magna, White Swan at Sileby, Vine in Skegness, Bramley Apple in Southwell, Ram Jam at Stretton, French Horn at Upton, Star at West Leake and Rutland Arms at Woolsthorpe.

BOSTON (Lincs)   TF3244 Map 8

Eagle £

West Street; from centre towards railway station

Fairly regular mini beer festivals are held at this cheerful and simple corner pub with a dozen or more ales, jazz and barbecues; at other times there may be Adnams Mild, Bitter and Broadside, Marstons Pedigree, Timothy Taylors Landlord and always two guest beers on handpump; farm cider and country wines. The recently decorated plain L-shaped bar has red and black lino floor, workmanlike furnishings, darts, shove-ha'penny, cribbage, dominoes, fruit machine, trivia and juke box; lots of games teams and there's a fire in the small red plush lounge. Simple bar food includes filled jumbo rolls (from £1.15), home-made chilli con carne or pork chop cooked in traditional cider (£2.25); some seats outside. Local societies such as bee-keepers and fishing clubs meet here. *(Recommended by Andy and Jill Kassube, Michael Rooke; more reports please)*

Free house   Licensees Andrew Watson and Antony Eastwood   Real ale   Lunchtime meals and snacks (cold rolls only Tues)   Restaurant (functions only)   Boston (0205) 361116   Children in eating area between 11 and 3 only   Local folk club Mon and other live bands Sat   Open 11–2.30, 6(5 Thurs and Fri)–11; 11–11 Sat; closed evening 25 Dec

BURROUGH ON THE HILL (Leics)   SK7510 Map 7

Stag & Hounds

Village signposted from B6047 in Twyford, 6 miles S of Melton Mowbray

The little brewery just across the road which used to supply this friendly little village pub has now moved away. But the pub is still getting a beer brewed for them from another small brewery (Lloyds) – and selling it at a remarkably low price. They also keep up to eight other real ales; country wines. Popular bar food includes sandwiches (from £1), smoked mackerel in a stilton sauce (£2.95), omlettes or ploughman's (from £2.99), vegetable pie (£3.50), vegetable lasagne (£4.50), mixed grill (£4.99), bacon, apple and cider pie or fisherman's pie (£5.25), beef in one of the Parish ales (£5.99). Fruit and video machines, juke box; open fires and a friendly black cat. There are seats in the garden, with a children's play area; not far from *Good Walks Guide* Walk 112. *(Recommended by Michel Hooper-Immins, Mel and Phil Lloyd, Nigel Gibbs; more reports please)*

Free house   Licensees Peter and Sue Ierston   Real ale   Meals and snacks (till 10.30) Somerby (066 477) 375   Well behaved children welcome until 9.30   Live music Thurs   Open 12–2(3 Sat), 7–11; closed weekday lunchtimes in winter

COLEBY (Lincs)   SK9760 Map 8

Bell

Far Lane; village signposted off A607 S of Lincoln

This popular dining pub has a row of three communicating carpeted rooms with American and Canadian car licence plates above the bar, low black joists, pale brown plank-panelling, a variety of small prints, and open fires. The wide choice of bar food includes sandwiches (lunchtimes, not Sunday), home-made soup (£1.40), basket meals such as Lincolnshire sausage or chicken bites (from £2.95), grilled prawns (£3.30), grilled rainbow trout, breaded scampi or steak, mushroom and Guinness pie (£5.75) and steaks (from £8.45); children's menu. Well kept Courage Directors and Marstons Pedigree on handpump, decent wines; fruit machine, video game and faint piped music or juke box; service may be pushed when busy. There's a cosy and quite separate pool room, and a couple of picnic-table sets outside. *(Recommended by Dave Braisted, Andy and Jill Kassube; more reports please)*

Camerons   Tenant Mick Aram   Real ale   Meals and snacks (till 10)   Restaurant Lincoln (0522) 810240   Children welcome   Open 11.30–3, 7–11

CONINGSBY (Lincs)   TF2458 Map 8

Leagate £

B1192; off A153 NE of village

The small iron gantry outside the original roadside door here used to hold a lamp to guide travellers along the fenland path – this 16th-century inn is the last of the fenland guide houses to survive. Three separate cosy and softly lit areas are linked together around the corner bar counter, attractively furnished with a variety of tables and chairs including antique oak settles with hunting-print cushions and two great high-backed settles making a snug around the biggest of the fireplaces. Another fireplace has an interesting cast-iron fireplate depicting the Last Supper above it; there are heavy black beams supporting ochre boards, and a collection of game-bird decorative plates in one cabinet. Good value bar food includes nicely presented sandwiches (from 90p), soup (£1.20), garlic mushrooms (£1.70), burgers (from £1.80), Lincolnshire sausage (£2.75), ploughman's (£2.80), a good chilli con carne made with fresh chillis (£3.30), fresh fish or steak and kidney pie (£3.65), several fresh summer salads (£4), 6oz sirloin steak (£6.50); vegetarian dishes are usually available. Well kept Marstons Pedigree, Timothy Taylors Landlord and Whitbreads Castle Eden on handpump; piped jazz or pop music, fruit machine. The pretty garden has rustic seats and white modern furniture on the lawn, with more on a paved terrace and under a big yew tree; there's a play shoe and swings in an enclosed area, and beyond a rockery is their koi carp centre – they sell the fish. *(Recommended by P R Morley, Frank Cummins, Andy and Jill Kassube; more reports please)*

Free house   Licensee Ronald Dennison   Real ale   Meals and snacks (till 10 in evening)   Restaurant   Coningsby (0526) 42370   Children only if eating, up to 9pm   Open 11.30–2.30, 7–11

DONINGTON ON BAIN (Lincs)   TF2382 Map 8

Black Horse

Between A153 and A157, SW of Louth

Relaxed and chatty, this village pub has a good deal of character in its snug back bar, with cushioned seats by the log fire in the reconstructed brick inglenook, very low black beams, and antlers around the wall lanterns; a softly lit and heavily curtained inner room with pews and kitchen chairs has big murals of carousing Vikings. There's more room in the main bar area, which has some heavy-horse prints and harness, a very twisty heavy low beam under its ceiling joists, and a big woodburning stove; the public bar (another log fire) has a games room off, with darts, pool, dominoes, fruit machine, video game and juke box. Bar food includes home-made soup (£1.75), filled baked potatoes (from £1.75), ploughman's (£2.50), fresh cod (Friday and Saturday, £3.75), cottage pie (£3.50), a good steak and kidney pie with a huge puff pastry top (£3.95), vegetarian dishes such as courgette and tomato cheese bake (from £3.75), good gammon and egg (£4.75), steaks (from £5.95), a huge mixed grill (£9.25), children's dishes (£1.50) and specials such as smoked salmon roulade (£2.50) and turkey biriani (£4.95); pizzas are served till they close, and they do take-aways. Well kept Adnams Bitter and Broadside, Ruddles Best and Websters Yorkshire on handpump; maybe unobtrusive piped music. No dogs. There are heavy picnic-table sets in the back garden; summer barbecues. The bedroom block is new – so we haven't yet heard what it's like to stay in. *(Recommended by Jack and Barbara Smale, D Maplethorpe)*

Free house   Licensees Tony and Janine Pacey   Real ale   Meals and snacks   Restaurant   (0507) 343640   Children in eating area and restaurant   Open 11.30–3, 7–11(midnight supper licence)   Bedrooms; £25B/£35B

DRAKEHOLES (Notts)   SK7090 Map 7

Griff Inn 🛏

Village signposted from A631 in Everton, between Bawtry and Gainsborough

Around this civilised and much refurbished 18th-century inn are neatly landscaped gardens with tables which look out over the flat valley of the River Idle and a basin of the old Chesterfield Canal. The neat and carefully colour-matched main lounge bar has small plush seats around its tables, and little landscape prints on silky-papered walls; besides the main restaurant, there's a more airy brasserie-style summer restaurant and a cosy cocktail bar. A wide range of bar food includes soup (£1), sandwiches (from £1.80), ploughman's (from £2.60), salads (from £3.05), a choice of pies (from £4.25), seafood platter (£5.75) and fillet steak (£7); there are also vegetarian meals such as spicy vegetable casserole (£4.20), children's meals (£2.35), Sunday lunch (£4.25), and substantial breakfasts. Tetleys and Whitbreads Castle Eden on handpump; friendly and helpful service – they really put themselves out for guests; trivia and piped music. One bar is no-smoking. *(Recommended by Mr and Mrs B Yearley, Anthony Barnes, D L Parkhurst, David and Rebecca Killick, G D Stafford; more reports please)*

Free house   Licensees Michael and Barbara Edmanson   Real ale   Meals and snacks (till 10 evening)   No-smoking restaurant   Retford (0777) 817206   Children in eating areas   Open 12–3, 7–11; closed winter Mons (except for residents)   Bedrooms; £35B/£50B

DYKE (Lincs)   TF1022   Map 8
Wishing Well

21 Main Street; village signposted off A15 N of Bourne

Up at the dining end of the long, rambling front bar in this friendly village pub there is indeed a wishing well, as well as lots of heavy beams, dark stone, brasswork, candlelight and a cavern of an open fireplace. The carpeted lounge area has green plush button-back low settles and wheelback chairs around individual wooden tables. Well served, home-made bar food includes sandwiches (£1.25), ploughman's (£1.75), cottage pie (£2.75), roast beef with chips (£2.90), steak pie, prawn salad, lemon sole or scampi (£3.25); popular Sunday lunch (£7), huge puddings. Well kept Greene King Abbot, Ind Coope Burton and Tetleys on handpump. The quite separate public bar, smaller and plainer, has sensibly placed darts, pool, shove-ha'penny, dominoes, fruit machine and juke box. *(Recommended by M and J Back, M Morgan, Brian and Jill Bond, Anthony Barnes, Giles Quick, BKA)*

Free house   Licensee G R Jones   Real ale   Meals and snacks (not Sun evening)   Restaurant   Bourne (0778) 422970   Children welcome   Open 10.30–3, 6.30–11 (also supper licence); closed 25 Dec   Bedrooms; £16.50S/£27S

EMPINGHAM (Leics)   SK9408   Map 4
White Horse ⊘ ⇐

Main Street; A606 Stamford–Oakham

On the edge of Europe's largest man-made lake, with good water-sports facilities, this is a busy, extensively refurbished inn. The open-plan lounge bar has lovely flower arrangements, a big log fire below an unusual free-standing chimney-funnel, russet plush wall seats, and stools and armchairs with little silver scatter-cushions around dark tables; one side area is no-smoking. Bar food includes soups (£1.60), home-baked ham (£4.45), local Rutland cheese or pork pie and local ham with salad and pickles (£4.95), Rutland water trout (£6.55) and dishes of the day such as Cromer crab salad, garlic king prawns or 24oz T-bone steak; there is always a good selection of home-made sweets such as spotted dick and custard or jam roly poly; small helpings for children, fine breakfasts, lovely coffee and croissants from 8am and cream teas all year round. You can also choose from the à la carte restaurant menu (3 courses from £16). Friendly, efficient service; well kept Courage Best, Directors and John Smiths on handpump, and good wines; dominoes, fruit machine and piped music. Bedrooms include some in a delightfully converted back stable block away from the main road and a 4-poster honeymoon suite. Outside the inn are some rustic tables among urns of flowers – a popular stop for cyclists. *(Recommended by G E Rich, Anthony Barnes, John and Christine Simpson, M V and J Dixon,*

Gordon Theaker, Gwen and Peter Andrews, Andrew Morrissey, W H Bland, M Morgan, David Eversley, Tim and Lynne Crawford, Roy Butler, E J Cutting, David Eversley, David Oakes)

John Smiths (Courage) Lease: Roger Bourne Real ale Meals and snacks (till 10) Restaurant (closed Sun evening) Empingham (078 068) 221/521 Well behaved children allowed Open 11–11, open from 8am for breakfast etc; closed except for residents evening 25 Dec and 26 Dec Bedrooms; £25(£35B)/£35(£46B)

EXTON (Leics) SK9211 Map 8

Fox & Hounds

Signposed off A606 Stamford–Oakham

Remarkably imposing for a village inn, this friendly 17th-century place has an elegant high-ceilinged lounge bar with some dark red plush easy chairs as well as wheelback seats around lots of dark tables, hunting and striking military prints on the walls, brass and copper ornaments, and a winter log fire in a big stone fireplace. Good bar food includes soup (£1.60), sandwiches (from £1.50), ploughman's (from £2.50), lasagne, excellent chilli con carne, good chicken kiev, and home-made pies such as steak and kidney (£4.75) at lunchtime, with scampi or gammon (£5.65) and rump steak (£9) in the evenings. On Sundays at lunchtime there's a choice between ploughman's and a traditional roast lunch (£8.80). Well kept Marstons Pedigree and Sam Smiths OB on handpump, unobtrusive piped music. The lively and quite separate public bar has darts, pool, cribbage, juke box, fruit machine, and video game. There are seats among large rose beds on the well kept back lawn, overlooking paddocks. Rutland Water is about two miles away. Handy for Viking Way walkers. (Recommended by Dr Keith Bloomfield, D S and Mrs T M Beeson, Mayur Shah, David Oakes, Linda Dyrda)

Free house Licensee David Hillier Real ale Meals and snacks Restaurant Oakham (0572) 812403 Children welcome Open 11–2.30, 6.30(6.45 winter)–11; Bedrooms; £20/£34

GLOOSTON (Leics) SP7595 Map 4

Old Barn ★ ⊘ ⇌

From B6047 in Tur Langton follow Hallaton signpost, then fork left following Glooston signpost

Steep steps in this most attractively restored and carefully lit 16th-century pub lead down from the small and charming front restaurant with its attendant bar to the lower main bar behind it, which has pewter plates on a beam, stripped kitchen tables and country chairs on the green Turkey carpet, Players cricketer cigarette cards, and an open fire; up steps, a snug corner has easy chairs and attractive country prints. The choice of bar food has widened and now includes herb mushrooms on granary toast (£3.25), hot beef sandwich and baked potato (£4.50), home-made lasagne in onion gravy (£5.45), ham hock and mustard sauce or turkey and ham escalope (£5.50), rump steak (£6.95) and a selection of fresh fish such as sole fillets in banana and white wine sauce; vegetarians are catered for – especially if they ring ahead. Good breakfasts may include local ham. Three or four well kept real ales on handpump (from a wide choice) might include Adnams Broadside, Batemans XB, Greene King Abbot, Hook Norton Old Hookey, Jennings, Theakstons Best and XB, Thwaites, Wadworths 6X, Westmorland Cumberland and so forth; several foreign bottled beers. There are a few old-fashioned teak seats in front, with picnic-table sets by roses under the trees behind. The French-style shower-and-wash cabinets in the bedrooms please readers, but might perhaps suit best those with at least a modest degree of mobility. (Recommended by M V and J Dixon, Richard Fawcett, Mr and Mrs C H Garnett, A J and E M Watts, Susan and Nigel Siesage, Chris Raisin, W H Bland, Jill Hampton, Brian Metherell, L Walker, Phil Orbell, Mel and Phil Lloyd)

Free house Licensees Charles Edmondson-Jones and Stuart Sturge Real ale Meals and snacks (till 10) Fixed-price restaurant (not Sun evening) East Langton (085 884)

215   *Well behaved children allowed   Open 12–2.30, 7–11; closed Sun evening and Mon lunchtime   Bedrooms; £37.50B/£42.50B*

GRANTHAM (Lincs)   SK9135 Map 7

Beehive £

Castlegate; from main street turn down Finkin Street opposite the George Hotel

The inn-sign here is quite unique. It's a hive with live bees, mounted in a lime tree outside, and has been this friendly pub's sign since certainly 1830, and probably the eighteenth century – making this one of the oldest populations of bees in the world. An old rhyme mentions it:

> Grantham, now two rarities are thine:
>
> A lofty steeple and a living sign

The pub itself is pleasantly straightforward, and serves a good value basic ploughman's with cheese or ham (from £2 – or a small version from just £1.25); the present licensee's father has a fair claim to have invented the ploughman's lunch, serving it first under this name nearly 30 years ago. Other attractively priced bar food includes a wide choice of freshly cut sandwiches or filled baked potatoes (from £1.25), home-made chilli con carne (£2), half a pint of prawns with crusty bread (£2.55) and specials like home-made ratatouille tarts (£1.95) or home-made chicken and mushroom pancakes (£2.10) and puddings (from £1.35). Adnams Broadside, Southwold and a guest beer on handpump, under light blanket pressure; a few malt whiskies; dominoes, fruit machine, video game and good juke box. Live music two Sundays each month .*(Recommended by Dr T E Hothersall; more reports please)*

Free house   Licensee John Bull   Real ale   Meals and snacks (not evenings) Grantham (0476) 67794   Children in eating area   Open 11–3 (4 Sat), 5–11; (all day Fri); closed Sun lunchtime

GRIMSTON (Leics)   SK6821 Map 7

Black Horse

Village signposted off A6006 W of Melton Mowbray

A remarkable collection of memorabilia in this pretty flower-decked white house runs from the (signed) bat with which Joe Hardstaff scored 1750 runs for Notts and England in 1936 through interesting Larwood mementoes to Desmond Lilley's headband, and hundreds of Test and other cricketers' signatures on dozens of bats. More general virtues here include good freshly cooked bar food served with decent vegetables – the baby poussin (£4.95) is particularly recommended, and there's also home-made soup (£1.50), corn on the cob (£1.95), a selection of starters including pâté, prawn cocktail and crab cocktail (£2.60), a choice of salads (from £3.85), fresh haddock, plaice or scampi (£4.95), 8oz sirloin steak (£8.25), and home-made puddings (£2.05); well kept Marstons Pedigree on handpump; efficient service; and a good open fire. Furnishings are straightforwardly comfortable – built-in green plush wall seats and so forth, with neat tables; piped music. *(Recommended by Andrew Stephenson; more reports please)*

Free house   Licensees Bert and Doss Pooler   Real ale   Meals and snacks (12–1.30, 7–9.30; not Sun)   Melton Mowbray (0664) 812358   Open 12–2.30, 7–11; closed Sun evening and Mon (except bank hols)

HALLATON (Leics)   SP7896 (Map 5)

Bewicke Arms ★ ⊘

On good fast back road across open rolling countryside between Uppingham and Kibworth; village signposted from B6047 in Tur Langton and from B664 SW of Uppingham

Overlooking the village green where there are cheery traditional Easter Monday 'bottle-kicking' races (they actually use miniature barrels) and summer Morris dancing in summer, this thatched pub has a nice mix of customers and friendly, helpful staff. The unpretentious beamed main bar has two small oddly shaped rooms with farming implements and deer heads on the walls, pokerwork seats, old-fashioned settles (including some with high backs and wings), wall benches, and stripped oak tables, and four copper kettles gleaming over one of the log fires; the bottom room is no-smoking during the week. Bar food includes sandwiches (from £1.20), a huge crock of help yourself home-made soup (£1.75), ploughman's (£3.10), plaice (£4.10), haddock (£4.20), breaded scampi or half roast chicken (£4.80), grilled gammon served with pineapple or egg (£5.60), 8oz sirloin steak (£7.85), a choice of salads (from £4.60), popular puddings like excellent lemon cheesecake or pavlovas, and daily specials that change with the season such as Rutland trout; children's menu or small helpings of adult food. Bar meals can be booked on Saturday evening. Good friendly service. Very well kept Marstons Pedigree, Ruddles Best and County and Websters Yorkshire on handpump; coffee; darts, and a fruit machine in the side corridor; piped music. Picnic-table sets on a crazy-paved terrace behind the whitewashed pub look over the ex-stableyard car park to the hills behind. No dogs. (*Recommended by Rona Murdoch, Susan and Nigel Siesage, Brian and Jill Bond, Mel and Phil Lloyd, Chris Raisin, Philip Orbell, Mr and Mrs J Back, Andrew Stephenson, Mrs M Lawrence, Linda Dyrda, Robert Gower, George Atkinson*)

Free house   Licensee Neil Spiers   Real ale   Meals and snacks (till 9.45)   Restaurant   Hallaton (085 889) 217   Well behaved children allowed   Open 12–2.30, 7–11   Bedrooms; £25B/£39.50B; big self-catering flat for 8/10 people from £480 per week

HALTON HOLEGATE (Leics)   TF4165   Map 8
Bell

Frisby Rd; B1195 E of Spilsby

Warmly welcoming and unpretentious, this pretty tiled white pub opposite the village church shows on its inn-sign the Lancaster bomber which was flown by 44 and 207 Squadrons, stationed nearby. Inside, there are more aircraft pictures, mainly World War II; the bar has sturdy green plush wall seats and green leatherette stools around black tables, and open fires – one in a broad low fireplace. A wide choice of home-cooked bar food using local meat and fresh fish includes sandwiches (from £1.10), home-made soups (£1.10, a popular fish one £2), burgers (from £1.60), ploughman's (£2.95), pizza (£3.50), a lovely steak and mushroom pie with a rich wine sauce and puff pastry top (£4.50), lamb steaks (£4.50), a good curry (£5.25) and steaks (from £6.25), with puddings such as apple pie (£1.35) and vegetarian dishes; Sunday lunches. Well kept Batemans XB and XXXB and Old Mill on handpump; darts, shove-ha'penny, cribbage, dominoes, fruit machine, maybe piped music. If you have a tube of Smarties, you'll find out how Sam the friendly black labrador got her nickname – the Smartie Dog. (*Recommended by SS, Derek and Sylvia Stephenson*)

Free house   Licensee John Clayton   Real ale   Meals and snacks (till 10)   Restaurant   (0790) 53242   Children in eating area and restaurant   Open 11–3, 7–11; all day Sat

HECKINGTON (Lincs)   TF1444   Map 8
Nags Head

High Street; village signposted from A17 Sleaford–Boston

One reader who has been using this low, white-painted 17th-century village pub for 20 years feels it's now at its best. The left-hand part of the cosy two-room bar has a coal fire below the shiny black wooden chimney-piece in what must once have been a great inglenook, curving into the corner and taking up the whole of one end of the small room – it now houses three tables, one of them of beaten brass; on the right there are red plush button-back built-in wall banquettes, small spindleback chairs, a clock and an attractive bronze statuette-lamp on the mantlepiece of its coal fire, and a fruit machine; also, a lively watercolour of a horse-race finish (the horses racing straight towards you), a modern sporting print of a problematic gun dog, and newspapers and magazines set out to read. Good, well prepared bar food changes daily, and besides well filled sandwiches, might typically give a choice of liver and bacon (£2.95), bacon and cauliflower cheese (£3.25), avocado and prawn hot pot with garlic garnish (£3.50), moussaka or steak and kidney pie (£3.95), very good puddings and Sunday roast lunch. Well kept Ruddles Best and County and Websters Yorkshire on handpump, friendly, efficient service, and pool, shove-ha'penny, dominoes, video game and juke box. There are picnic-table sets in the garden behind. *(Recommended by Peter Race, John Evans, P R Morley, Andy and Jill Kassube, C Petts)*

Manns (Watneys)　Tenant Bruce Pickworth　Real ale　Meals and snacks (till 10) Sleaford (0529) 60218　Children in eating area lunchtime only　Open 11–3, 7–11 Bedrooms; £22S/£32S

HOSE (Leics)　SK7329　Map 7
Rose & Crown

Bolton Lane

Often from smaller breweries in the west country or up north as well as including more local heroes such as Batemans XXXB or draught Bass and Wadworths 6X this comfortably modernised village pub keeps an interesting range of around half-a-dozen, frequently changing real ales, all on handpump; quiet, homely service. A wide range of bar food includes filled rolls (from £1.10), ploughman's (from £3.50), vegetarian mushroom stroganoff (£4.25), home-made pies (£5.50), fresh seafood platter (£5.75), lots of steaks (from £6.55), good fresh salads including chicken and ham or trout (from £6.75), puddings such as cheesecake or apple pie and cream (from £1.95) and daily specials. The neat beamed lounge bar, separated into two areas by three broad steps, has green plush seats around dimpled copper tables. The simpler public bar has been redecorated and upgraded into a saloon; pool, cribbage, dominoes, a fruit machine and juke box. There are tables on a fairy-lit sheltered terrace behind the building and a fenced family area at the rear of the car park. Campers and caravanners are welcome. *(Recommended by A J and E M Watts, Tony and Lynne Stark, Jamie and Sarah Allan, Chris Raisin, R J Haerdi)*

Free house　Licensee Carl Routh　Real ale　Meals and snacks (till 10)　Restaurant (0949) 60424　Children welcome　Open 11.30–2.30, 7–11

KEGWORTH (Leics)　SK4826　Map 7
Cap & Stocking　★　£

Under a mile from M1 junction 24: follow A6 towards Loughborough; in village, turn left at chemists' down one-way Dragwall opposite High Street, then left and left again, into Borough Street

Each of the two determinedly simple front rooms here has a coal fire, and on the right there's lots of etched glass, big cases of stuffed birds and locally caught fish, fabric-covered wall benches and heavy cast-iron-framed tables, and a cast-iron range; the back room has French windows to the garden. Well kept and reasonably priced Adnams, Bass, Highgate Mild and a regularly changing guest beer on handpump; farmhouse cider. Very good value bar food includes filled cobs (from 55p), home-made soup (85p), burgers (from £1.50), ploughman's (from £1.95), good chilli con carne or vegetarian spaghetti (£2.55), Lancashire hot-pot (£2.95), and home-made specials (from £2.75); friendly atmosphere; dominoes and old juke box. There's a sheltered garden and terrace where they play boules and a quiz night Monday. *(Recommended by Andrew Morrissey, J Barnwell, Derek and Sylvia Stephenson, Mr and Mrs C H Garnett, JM, PM, Graham Bush, Andrew Stephenson, Wayne Brindle, Richard Sanders, Andy and Jill Kassube, C Petts)*

Bass　Lease: Bil Poynton, Managers Chris and Dominique Poulter　Real ale　Meals and snacks　Kegworth (0509) 674814　Children in one room till 9pm　Open 11.30–3, 6–11

KIBWORTH HARCOURT (Leics)   SP6894 Map 4

Three Horseshoes

Main Street; just off A6 in village centre

Well run and happy, this warmly welcoming cream-painted brick and slate house has a big open-plan bar with bays of comfortable tawny plush button-back built-in wall banquettes in the part by the serving counter, bookable tables set with wheelback chairs in two side areas, illustrated maps of hunting territory, and several elaborate table paraffin lamps converted to electricity. Bar food includes lasagne or moussaka (£4.75), home-made pies (£4.95), battered scampi or sole filled with crab meat (£5.95) and peppered steak (£8.50). Well kept Marstons Pedigree and Wrexham on handpump; piped music and a very friendly cat called Smoky. (*Recommended by Michael and Alison Sandy, Dr G Waring Taylor, John and Shirley Mason, H C Bassett*)

Free house   Licensee Barrie Sutton   Real ale   Meals and snacks (till 9.45; not Sun evening)   Restaurant (not Sun evening)   Leicester (0533) 793303   Children welcome   Open 11–2.30, 6.30–11

LAXTON (Notts)   SK7267 Map 7

Dovecote

Signposted off A6075 E of Ollerton

A window in the central room by the bar in this warmly welcoming redbrick house looks over the village to the church tower, and there are brocaded button-back built-in corner seats, stools and chairs, a coal-effect gas fire, and wild-rose wallpaper; it opens through a small bay which was the original entry into another similar room. Around the other side a simpler room with some entertaining Lawson Wood 1930s tourist cartoons leads through to a pool room with darts, juke box and fruit machine; also, cribbage and dominoes. Attractively presented home-cooked food includes sandwiches (from £2, chip buttie £1.10), soup (£1.50), ploughman's (£2.75), salads (from £2.75), steak and kidney pie (£4.75), lasagne (£4.95), several fish dishes from cod (£4.75) to fresh scampi (£6.65), gammon (£5.85) and puddings (from £1.60); well kept Mansfield Old Baily and Whitbreads Castle Eden on handpump; helpful service. There are white tables and chairs on a small front terrace by a sloping garden with a disused white dovecote. In a former stable block behind the pub is a walk-round visitor centre explaining the three huge medieval fields here, a unique survival. The unfenced and unmarked strips of farmland within the fields are individually owned, and photographs in the pub show the villagers meeting there for the Court Baron which still administers the system, and walking the fields on the original grassy sykes (with names like Honeyhole or Roebuck) which visitors too can use. (*Recommended by Norman and Barbara Wells, Alan and Eileen Bowker, Derek and Sylvia Stephenson, Colin and Mary Meaden*)

Free house   Licensees John and Elizabeth Waters   Real ale   Meals and snacks (till 10)   (0777) 871586   Children in eating area   Open 11–3.30, 6.30(4 Sat)–11

LEICESTER   SK5804 Map 4

Tom Hoskins £

131 Beaumanor Rd; from A6 at Red Hill Circle (huge roundabout N of centre) follow Motorway, Burton, Coventry sign into Abbey Lane (A5131), take second left into Wade St – pub on left at next crossroads

Converted from the brewery's former malt loft and decorated with old brewing equipment, the comfortable lounge here is a partly flagstoned and panelled room. The original and much plainer wood-floored tap room has a smokily masculine and chatty atmosphere, varnished pews around cast-iron-framed tables, and flagstones by the servery; Bitter, Penns, Churchills Pride and various guest beers on handpump; a range of malt whiskies; darts, shove-ha'penny, cribbage, dominoes, fruit machine and piped music. A small range of straightforward home-made lunchtime bar food includes filled rolls (from 90p), ploughman's or jumbo sausage, chips and peas or beefburger, chips and salad (£2.50) and dishes of the day such as lasagne, curries or hot pots. Beer prices are low and though it's part of the small Hoskins brewery, they also keep a changing choice of other brewers' real ales, too. Groups can arrange tours of the late Victorian brewhouse (£7 with meal). *(Recommended by Ian Phillips, Pete Storey; more reports please)*

Hoskins   Managers David and Angela Spiers   Real ale   Lunchtime meals and snacks (not Sun)   Leicester (0533) 611008   Occasional live entertainment   Open 11.30–3.30, 5.30(6 Sat)–11

LINCOLN   SK9872   Map 8

Wig & Mitre ★   ⊘

29 Steep Hill; just below cathedral

Served all day (with last orders around 11pm) and changed twice during that time, the food in this attractively restored, popular 14th-century place covers a remarkable range. Besides sandwiches (from £2) and all-day breakfast dishes (full fried breakfast £4.50) there is usually lobster bisque (£1.75), a choice of pâtés (from £3.50), main dishes like ratatouille with garlic toast (£3.50) braised lamb with tomatoes or roast chicken with brandy, cream and peppercorns (£4.95), beef braised in real ale (£5.25), supreme of cornish cod with herb and garlic crumbs on a parsley butter sauce (£7.50) and excellent puddings like chocolate roulade and tiramisu (£2.50). You can also choose from the less quickly changing restaurant menu, which includes more expensive dishes such as fillet of lamb topped with a fresh basil and chicken mousse baked in filo pastry or sautéed slice of calf's liver with a sauce of oranges and Dubonnet (£10.95) and fillet steak with mushrooms and onions (£13.50). A very wide though not cheap choice of wines by the glass, many more by the bottle, Sam Smiths OB and Museum on handpump, lots of liqueurs and spirits; freshly squeezed orange juice and good coffee; newspapers and magazines to read. The building is on two floors. Downstairs, the cheerful, simpler bar has pews and other more straightforward furniture on its tiles, and a couple of window tables on either side of the entrance; the upstairs dining room has settees, elegant small settles, Victorian armchairs, shelves of old books, and an open fire. It's decorated with antique prints and more modern caricatures of lawyers and clerics, and by the stairs you can see some of the original medieval wattle-and-daub; the oak rafters are exposed, too. Seats on the small sheltered back terrace. *(Recommended by John Evans, Phil Bryant, John and Joan Wyatt, Mr and Mrs P A Jones, Michael and Alison Sandy, ILP, BKA, Barry and Anne, Reg Nelson, Helen and Wal Burns, Andy and Jill Kassube, Sue Holland, Dave Webster, Jill Hampton, Brian Metherell, Paul McPherson, J R Smylie, David Shillitoe, BKA, Viv Middlebrook, Bryan Shiner, J M Watson)*

Sam Smiths   Lease: Michael and Valerie Hope   Real ale   Meals and snacks (8am–11pm)   Restaurant (8am–11pm Sun)   Lincoln (0522) 535190/537482/523705   Children in eating area and restaurant   Open 8–11, including Sun; closed 25 Dec

LYDDINGTON (Leics)   SP8797   Map 4

Marquess of Exeter

Village signposted off A6003 N of Corby

The comfortable easy chairs by the huge log fire in the rambling beamed lounge here are a lovely place to spend a few hours on a cold evening; the room is mainly carpeted, with flagstones by the serving counter, and leads off into various separate areas. Excellent value bar food, served by neatly uniformed welcoming staff, includes sandwiches (from £1.35), soup (£1.40), ploughman's (£3.75), four vegetarian dishes every day and steak (£8.25); home-made specials and puddings (£1.65). Well kept Batemans XXB, Ruddles Best and County and Theakstons XB on handpump, some malt whiskies; piped music. The charming village has long been owned by the Burghley family. *(Recommended by Neil Tungate, Brian and Jill Bond, Dr M V Jones, H D Spottiswoode, W H Bland, M C and S Jeanes)*

Free house   Licensees R M Morrell and L S Evitt   Real ale   Meals and snacks (till 10)   Restaurant (not Sun evening)   Uppingham (0572) 822477   Well behaved children in eating area of bar   Open 11.30–3, 6–11   Bedrooms; £53B/£67B, though prices are cheaper at weekends

MEDBOURNE   SP7993   Map 4

Nevill Arms

B664 Market Harborough–Uppingham

Surrounded by rolling countryside, this handsome stone-built, mullion-windowed pub has tables outside on the grass by the dovecote and village stream – and they may give you old bread for the noisy ducks. The main bar – through the arched doorway – has two winter log fires, chairs and small wall settles around its tables, and a lofty, dark-joisted ceiling. A spacious back room by the former coachyard has pews around more tables – much needed in summer. Excellent bar food includes sandwiches (from £1.20), home-made soup (£1.50), ploughman's (from £2.65), cod and chips or jumbo sausage (£3.25), seafood platter (£4.25) sirloin steak (£6.95) and puddings; dishes of the day like chicken in stilton and leeks, lamb and apricot casserole (£4.95) and very good lamb curry. Well kept Adnams Bitter, Hook Norton Bitter, Marstons Pedigree and Ruddles County on handpump; freshly squeezed orange juice; friendly service. Darts, shove-ha'penny, table skittles, hood skittles, cribbage, dominoes, fruit machine and piped music, with carpet bowls, Devil Among the Tailors, and Captain's Mistress available for organised functions. The pub dogs, not normally in evidence, include a stately great dane. *(Recommended by K H Frostick, Andrew Morrissey, Brian and Jill Bond, Rona Murdoch, D H Buchanan)*

Free house   Licensees E F Hall and partners   Real ale   Meals and snacks (till 10)   Medbourne Green (085 883) 288   Children welcome   Open 12–2.30, 6–11   Bedrooms; £40B/£50B

NEWARK (Notts)   SK8054   Map 7

Old Kings Arms   £

19 Kirkgate; follow To The Market Place signpost opposite Maltby agricultural engineers on A46

A stroll away from the castle ruins, this busy pub has a simply furnished bar with a vaulted ceiling, plain stripped deal tables, and traditional wall benches and so forth. Upstairs is an eating area which is open all day (from 9.30 for morning coffee; they also do afternoon teas till 5). Using free-range eggs, free-range, organically fed meat and poultry, and fresh (and sometimes organically grown) vegetables, the good home-made food includes sandwiches, soup (95p), ploughman's (from £1.80), two sizes of dishes like chilli con carne or lasagne (from £1.80), ratatouille (from £2.10), and chicken curry (from £2.80), salads (from £2.90), beef in Guinness (£3.30), 8–10oz steak (£5.50), and puddings such as fruit crumble or pie (80p); daily specials like nut roast, braised liver and onions, tuna and peanut risotto or pork in cider (all £3). Marstons Burton, Pedigree, Owd Rodger and Merrie Monk on handpump are notably well kept, and service helpful. Fruit machine, trivia and juke box (which can be loud). A small terrace has some tables and chairs. *(Recommended by Mr and Mrs P A Jones, Nigel Hopkins, Andy and Jill Kassube, T M McMillan; more reports please)*

Marstons   Tenant Christopher Holmes   Real ale   Meals and snacks (9.30–5)   Partly no-smoking restaurant   Newark (0636) 703416   Children in upstairs restaurant   Trad jazz Mon   Restricted nearby parking   Open 9.30–11 (9.30–3, 5.30–11 Sat; winter 9.30–3, 5–11)

NEWTON (Lincs)   TF0436 Map 8

Red Lion   ★   🚳

Village signposted from A52 E of Grantham; at village road turn right towards Haceby and Braceby; pub itself also discreetly signed off A52 closer to Grantham

People come from miles around to this quietly civilised village pub to enjoy the excellent, imaginatively displayed salads. You choose as much as you like, with six different types of fish such as fresh salmon, nine various cold meats, and pies; a small helping is £6.25, normal £7.25, and large £8.25, with children's helpings £2.50. The home-made soups are also very good (£1.65), as are the one or two local specialities such as stuffed chine of pork or spicy Lincolnshire sausages and the rich puddings; they'll do sandwiches. The communicating rooms have cream-rendered or bare stone walls covered with farm tools, malters' wooden shovels, a stuffed fox, stag's head and green woodpecker, pictures made from pressed flowers, a dresser full of china, and hunting and coaching prints; there are old-fashioned oak and elm seats, built-in cushioned wall benches, a Gothick carved settle, a stuffed rat hanging above the serving-counter, and even a penny-farthing cycle. Very well kept Batemans XXXB on handpump, good coffee and mints and good value champagne. Fresh flowers, unobtrusive but well reproduced piped music, friendly, relaxed service, and nice dogs. Pool, fruit machine and video game; during the day and at weekends two squash courts run by the pub can be used by non-members. The neat, well sheltered back garden has some seats on the grass and on a terrace; play area. There are pleasant walks in the surrounding countryside. *(Recommended by David and Ruth Hollands, Steve Dark, Tim and Lynne Crawford, Edward and Diane Everest, M J Morgan, Pete Storey, Neil and Angela Huxter)*

Free house   Licensee Graham Watkin   Real ale   Meals and snacks (till 10)   Sleaford (0529) 256   Children in eating area   Open 11–3, 6(7 Mon)–11(10.30 Mon); closed 25 Dec

NORMANTON ON TRENT (Notts)   SK7969 Map 7

Square & Compass

Signposted off B1164 S of Tuxford

This cosy village pub has big helpings of good value home-cooked specials such as celery and stilton soup (£1.20), devilled kidneys or chicken in whisky sauce (£3.50) and game pie (£4.25), besides regular dishes such as sandwiches, pâté made with local game, steak and kidney pie or barbecued spare ribs (£3.50), and Sunday lunches (two courses £5.50, three £6.50). There are some attractive farming photographs in the main part of the bar, which is divided by an enormous woodburning stove in a central brick fireplace, and has several more or less separate snug areas, alcoves and bays; furnishings are mainly dark green plush, with a flowery red carpet, red curtains and roughcast shiny cream walls; there's an attractive grandfather clock in one corner. The public side has pool, table skittles, dominoes and juke box. The two well kept real ales are changed frequently, and tend to come from interesting smaller breweries such as Exmoor, Robinwood or Moorhouses; friendly landlord. *(Recommended by Norman Edwardes, Derek and Sylvia Stephenson)*

Free house   Licensee Janet Lancaster   Real ale   Meals and snacks   Restaurant (0636) 821439   Children welcome   Open 12–2.30(3 Sat), 6–11   Family bedroom; £20B, plus £2 each breakfast

NORTH MUSKHAM (Notts)   SK7958 Map 7

Muskham Ferry

Ferry Lane; village signed off A1 N of Newark

Though so handy for the A1, this is a real haven of peace, a spreading big-windowed bar with shallow steps between its several levels, red plush button-back built-in wall banquettes and chairs, discreetly papered walls with some timbering, and small pictures – all neatly kept, light and airy. The view from the windows is of the River Trent, with cows in the fields beyond and a distant church tower. A back terrace has picnic-table sets under cocktail parasols (and summer barbecues), and leads past a border of lowering shrubs to a waterside lawn with boat swings, slides, a boot house and a beached clinker-built boat. The pub has good floating moorings, and its own fishing (35 pegs; they arrange fishermen's breakasts then lunch on club and match days). The landlord's Polish connections ensure a good range of vodkas (alongside John Smiths Magnet), and Polish wood-carvings and table-linen in the restaurant; soothing piped music, friendly efficient service. Bar food includes filled rolls (£1.20), steak sandwich (£1.95), home-cooked honey-roast ham salad (£2.85), omelettes (from £3.25), vegetarian dishes such as mushroom and nut fettucini (£3.95), haddock (£3.95) and a big mixed grill (£5.25); darts, pool, shove-ha'penny, skittles, dominoes, fruit machine and juke box in separate public bar. *(Recommended by PJP, Rona Murdoch)*

John Smiths (Courage)   Tenants Mario and Anne Paczesny   Real ale   Meals and snacks   Restaurant   Newark (0636) 704943   Children in eating area and restaurant   Open 11–3, 6.30–11

NOTTINGHAM   SK5640 Map 7

Fellows Morton & Clayton £

54 Canal Street (part of inner ring road)

The quietly friendly pubby atmosphere in this carefully converted former canal building appeals to shoppers and a wide mix of working people alike. It's a softly lit place, with screens of wood and stained glass, dark blue plush seats built into its alcoves, copper-topped tables, some seats up two or three steps in a side gallery, and bric-a-brac on the shelf just below the glossy dark green high ceiling. Cast-iron steps from the quarry-tiled glassed-in back area take you up to a big window where you can look into the brewery; it's here they produce their own delicious creamily malty, gently hopped Samuel Fellows and stronger Matthew Claytons – well kept on handpump, as are Boddingtons, Whitbreads Castle Eden and other guests (they also have decent wines). Very popular at lunchtime; good value bar food includes filled cobs (from 70p), home-made soup (90p), ploughman's (from £1.75), vegetarian dishes such as lasagne (from £2), home-made steak and kidney pie or curry (from £2.50), fish and chips (the house special, £3.25), and rump steak (£4.95); welcoming, quick service. Well reproduced nostalgic pop music, trivia, fruit machine and maybe newspapers on a rack. There's a terrace with seats and tables. The canal museum is nearby, and Nottingham station is just a short walk away. *(Recommended by D L Parkhurst, Dr Keith Bloomfield, BKA, Nick and Alison Dowson, Alan and Eileen Bowker, Wayne Brindle, Nigel Gibbs, Peter Griffiths, RJH, Richard A Bailey; more reports please)*

Own brew (Whitbreads)   Tenant Les Howard   Real ale   Lunchtime meals and snacks   Restaurant   Nottingham (0602) 506795   Children in restaurant   Open 11–11 (11–3.30, 6.30–11 Sat)

Olde Trip to Jerusalem ★   £

Brewhouse Yard; from inner ring road follow The North, A6005 Long Eaton signpost until you are in Castle Boulevard then almost at once turn right into Castle Road; pub is up on the left

Included above all for its curiosity value, this mainly 17th-century place has a unique upstairs bar: it's cut into the sandstone rock below the castle, and the walls, panelled at the bottom, soar steeply up into remote and shadowy heights, with cosy simply furnished hollowed-out side alcoves (it's often closed at lunchtime). The friendly downstairs bar is also mainly carved from the rock, with leatherette-cushioned settles built into the dark panelling, barrel tables on tiles or flagstones, and more low-ceilinged rock alcoves. Home-made bar food includes cobs and sandwiches (from 75p), filled baked potatoes (from £1.30), giant Yorkshire puddings with twelve different fillings such as beef and vegetables or pork and stuffing (£3.80), omelettes and daily specials. These caverns may have served as cellarage for an early medieval castle brewhouse which stood here, and they still keep the Kimberley Bitter, Classic and Mild, and Marstons Pedigree Bitter on handpump. Several whiskies and wines. Fruit machine, ring-the-bull; seats outside. *(Recommended by Nigel Gibbs, Mr and Mrs P A Jones, Wayne Brindle, Nick and Alison Dowson, Graham Bush, Helen and Wal Burns; more reports please)*

Hardys & Hansons   Managers Brian and Janet Palethorpe   Real ale   Lunchtime meals and snacks   Nottingham (0602) 473171   Open 11–3, 5.30–11 (11–11 Sat, winter 11–4, 6–11 Sat); closed 25 Dec

Sir John Borlase Warren £

1 Ilkeston Rd; Canning Circus (A52 towards Derby – pub faces you as you come up the hill from city centre)

This civilised, traditional pub has half-a-dozen chatty communicating rooms with pictures ranging from early humorous advertisements and Victorian sentimental engravings to the big chromolithograph of Queen Victoria's Diamond Jubilee procession or the various prints commemorating Sir John, who defeated an attempted French invasion of Ireland off Kilkenna in 1798; also, etched mirrors, engraved glass, comfortable parlourish seating, swirly Victorian acanthus-leaf wallpaper, dark brown Anaglypta dado, sturdy brass lamps, a delft shelf, and swagged russet curtains with net lower curtains in the three big bay windows. Good home-made bar food, from a counter in the downstairs room, includes filled cobs (from 90p), filled baked potatoes, ploughman's (from £2.05), chilli con carne and rice, mince or vegetarian lasagne (£2.65), steak and kidney pie (£2.80), chicken and mushroom pie (£2.95) and daily specials; Sunday lunch (£5.95). Cheap and well kept Greenalls Original, Shipstones Bitter and Tetleys Bitter on handpump; fruit machine, video game and piped music. No-smoking in eating area at lunchtime. The pub is attractively placed opposite Georgian almshouses and there are tables sheltering under an old tree behind. *(Recommended by Andrew Stephenson, Nigel Gibbs, Dr Keith Louden; more reports please)*

Shipstones (Greenalls/Allied)   Manager Donald Goudie   Real ale   Lunchtime meals and snacks   Nottingham (0602) 474247   Children in eating area   Open 11–11

OLD DALBY (Leics)   SK6723   Map 7

Crown ★ ⊘

By school in village centre turn into Longcliff Hill then left into Debdale Hill

There are no freezers, microwaves or chips in this rather smart ex-farmhouse, and the interesting, though not cheap, food might include soup (£2.50), sandwiches and rolls (from £2.50, sirloin steak in wholemeal roll £4.75), oven baked tomatoes stuffed with cheese, walnuts and sweetcorn, topped with thyme butter and served with melba toast (£4.95), peeled prawns in a Madras sauce served on wholemeal bread garnished with watercress and tomatoes (£5.75), a mixture of pulses in a hot chilli sauce baked in a whole pepper or very good Cumberland sausage with sage and onion sauce on a bed of red cabbage with potatoes (£6.50), black pudding and fried apple in a cream of mustard sauce with potatoes and side salad (£6.95), leg of lamb steak shallow fried and served with a raspberry sauce and vegetables (£7.95), whole lemon sole shallow fried in butter with lemon and garlic sauce and side salad or sirloin steak (£8.95); Sunday lunch; no credit cards. A wide range of real ales tapped from the cask includes Adnams Broadside, Badger Tanglefoot, Batemans XXXB, Exmoor Gold, Fullers London Pride, Kimberley Best, Marstons Pedigree, Merrie Monk and Owd Rodger, Theakstons Old Peculier, Thwaites Bitter, Timothy Taylors Landlord and Woodfordes Wherry and Baldric; reasonably priced wine selection; 20 malt whiskies and several brandies and Italian liqueurs served by staff wearing black-and-white uniforms and bow ties. The three or four little rooms have black beams, one or two antique oak settles, Windsor armchairs, easy chairs with Sanderson loose covers, hunting and other rustic prints, fresh flowers, and open fires. One room has darts, dominoes, and cribbage. Morris dancing once a year. There are plenty of tables on a terrace, with a big, sheltered lawn (where you can play boules and croquet) sloping down among roses and fruit trees. It can get very full (especially in the evenings and at weekends). *(Recommended by J Barnwell, Susan and Nigel Siesage, Nigel Hopkins, Karen and Graham Oddey, David and Rebecca Killick, Peter Barnsley, Sue Corrigan, L M Miall, Helen and Wal Burns, Philip Orbell, WTF, Mel and Phil Lloyd, Mr and Mrs G Gittings, Dr Keith Louden, A C and S Beardsley, Graham Bush, Linda Dyrda)*

Free house   Licensees Lynne Bryan and Salvatore Inguanta   Real ale   Meals and snacks (till 9.30; not Sun evening)   Restaurant (not Sun evening)   Melton Mowbray (0664) 823134   Children in eating area of bar   Open 12–2.30, 6–11

REDMILE (Leics)   SK8036 Map 7
Peacock ⊘

Off A52 W of Grantham at Belvoir Castle, Harlby, Melton signpost, then right at crossroads signposted Redmile

It's the food which fills this village house in the evenings and at weekends, yet there's still that easy mix of diners with drinkers which makes for a relaxed and easy-going atmosphere. The three beamed rooms of the bar have pews, stripped country tables and chairs, the odd sofa and easy chair, some stripped golden stone, old prints, chintzy curtains for the small windows, and a variety of wall and table lamps. They aim for a French flavour even with the generously served bar food, which includes a good few specials such as watercress soup (£1.55), rabbit pâté (£1.95), baked avocado and stilton (£3), chicken dijon or red mullet baked with tomato and basil (£4.95) and hare or veal casserole (£5.50), alongside lunchtime sandwiches (£1.80), poached eggs with mushrooms and bacon in red wine sauce (£2.30), seafood lasagne (£3.25), king prawns with garlic, parsley, white wine and cream (£5.75), sirloin steak (£7.25) and lots of puddings such as caramelised apple tart (£2); there's also a pretty little restaurant, reasonably priced. Well kept Bass, Greene King Abbot, Marstons Pedigree, Tetleys, Timothy Taylors Landlord and a weekly guest beer such as Ind Coope Burton on handpump, decent wines including fairly priced bottles, occasional special events such as cookery demonstrations or wine tastings. Open fires, darts, cribbage, dominoes, maybe unobtrusive piped music; there are tables outside, in a peaceful village setting. *(Recommended by S Wooler, Dr and Mrs A M Evans, Alan Tiplady)*

Free house   Licensees Celia and Colin Craword   Real ale   Meals and snacks (12–2.30, 6.30–10)   Restaurant   Bottesford (0949) 42554   Children welcome Open 12–3, 6–11

RETFORD (Notts)   SH7079 Map 7
Market

West Carr Road, Ordsall; follow Retford Leisure Centre sign off A620 W, then after West Carr Road Industrial Estate sign on your right take first left turning up track which – if you look closely – is signed for the pub; or, on foot, from Retford Rly Stn follow footpath under S of frontage, turn R at end; note that there is a quite separate Market Hotel in Retford itself

Named after the cattle market which had this site before the light industrial estate, this friendly, comfortable place has a long, cosy bar with green plush wall banquettes and dimpled copper or dark wood tables; pantiles over the bar servery, over the open fire at one end and over a little blue plush snug at the other; a spacious conservatory dining room opens off (it can get very warm on a sunny summer's day), and in turn gives on to a small terrace with white tables. A remarkable choice of fourteen well kept real ales on handpump runs to Adnams Best and Broadside, Bass, Everards Tiger, Mansfield Riding, Marstons Pedigree, Stones, Tetleys, Theakstons Best, Old Peculier and XB, Timothy Taylors Landlord, Whitbreads Castle Eden and Youngers No 3; farmhouse cider. A wide range of good home-cooked food gives real value – as does the service (they'll ask how hot you want your chilli, for instance); soup (£1), burgers (from £1.20), filled baked potatoes (from £1.65), quiches (£2.75), lasagne or moussaka (£3.10), pies such as steak and kidney and including one for vegetarians (from £3.20), fisherman's platter (£3.45), mixed grill (£4) and a good choice of steaks (from £6.95); children's menu; Sunday lunch. Theme nights like Bavarian or Italian every month. *(Recommended by John C Baker, Derek and Sylvia Stephenson, Mr and Mrs P A Jones, Michael Rooke, Andy and Jill Kassube; more reports please)*

Free house   Licensee Raymond Brunt   Real ale   Meals and snacks (till 10; 10.30 Sat/Sun)   Restaurant   Retford (0777) 703278   Children in restaurant   Occasional live entertainment   Open 11–3, 6–11; all day Sat

SCAFTWORTH (Notts)   SK6692   Map 7

King William

Village signposted (not prominently) off A631 Bawtry–Everton

A quiet and relaxing place to take a break from the A1, this friendly, family-run pub serves imaginative home-made bar food that includes soup (£1.50), very fresh prawns (£2.75 half pint helping, £5.50 pint), salads (£2.75), chilli con carne or sweet and sour fish (£4.85), a good many interestingly flavoured pies (you can choose between white or wholemeal pastry or a stuffing crumble topping) such as rabbit, tomatoes and mushrooms, chicken and mushroom, cod and prawns or vegetarian with a crispy cheese topping (all £5) and puddings like treacle tart or fruit pie (from £2.25); children's menu. Well kept Boddingtons, Everards Old Original, Marstons Pedigree and Whitbreads Castle Eden on handpump, over 52 malt whiskies, decent wines and an espresso coffee machine. The three connecting rooms of the bar have a pleasant variety of seats such as a sofa and high-backed settles, as well as plainer chairs around tables, hunting and other prints above the stripped dado, a wall filled with entertaining photographs, old farm tools, delft shelves of knick-knacks, and masses of brasses; in summer there are bunches of flowers, in winter generous open fires, and the end room is no-smoking. Shove-ha'penny, dominoes, cribbage, fruit machine, trivia and unobtrusive piped music. Down a corridor a clean, light and airy family room, with milk-churns as seats, leads through French windows to the sheltered garden. This runs down to the River Idle, with cows grazing beyond; it's sheltered and well planted with shrubs and young trees, with an increased number of well spaced tables, swings, slides, a climber, a covered barbecue area, and rooting chickens, preening peacocks, and maybe the friendly ginger cats. *(Recommended by Joy Heatherley, Gordon Pell, Mrs I L Phillipson, Mrs R M Morris)*

Free house   Licensee Michael Wright   Real ale   Meals and snacks (12–2.30, 7–10, but see opening hours below)   Doncaster (0302) 710292   Children in eating area of bar, in dining room and in games room   Morris men and mummers in summer and Boxing Day   Open 12–3, 6.30–11; closed lunchtimes Mon and Tues in summer and Mon-Wed lunchtimes in winter; open Bank Hol Mons; closed 25 Dec

SIBSON (Leics)   SK3500   Map 4

Cock

A444 N of Nuneaton

This rather smart, partly 13th-century timbered black-and-white pub shows its age in the unusually low doorways, ancient wall timbers, heavy black beams, and genuine latticed windows. The room on the right has seats built in to what was once an immense fireplace, with other comfortable seats around cast-iron-framed tables, and in the room on the left are country kitchen chairs around wooden tables. Good value bar food includes excellent sandwiches (from £1), home-made soup (£1.30), salads (from £3), a good home-made steak and kidney pie or lasagne (£4.35) and steaks (from £6.50), with children's dishes (£2.50) and specials – including a vegetarian dish of the day. Well kept Bass and M & B Brew XI on handpump; bar billiards, fruit machine and piped music. There are tables on the lawn behind. The restaurant (in a former stable block) is popular. They have a caravan field (certified with the Caravan Club). *(Recommended by Graham Bush, Dave Braisted, Graham Richardson, Mike and Wendy Proctor, Dorothee and Dennis Glover)*

Bass   Manager Graham Lindsay   Real ale   Meals and snacks (till 9.45; not Sun

lunchtime) Restaurant (not Sun evening) Tamworth (0827) 880357 Children in eating areas and games room Open 11.30–2.30, 6.30–11

STAMFORD (Lincs) TF0207 Map 8

Bull & Swan

High St, St Martins; B1081 leaving town southwards

Shallow steps and wooden partition walls in the cosy rooms of the comfortable bar create three levels in this old stone pub. There's a quiet, relaxed atmosphere, velvet-cushioned armchairs, low and heavy beams hung with lots of highly polished copper kettles and brassware, and log-effect gas fires. A wide choice of good bar food, all home-made, includes soup (95p), sandwiches (from £1.30), a choice of ploughman's (from £1.75), nice steak and kidney pie (£3.25), a good few puddings like apple pie and treacle pudding (from £1.20) and daily specials such as liver and onions (£3.95), Cromer crab salad or roast pork with apple sauce (£4.95) and veal (£5.50); 3-course fixed menu also available. Well kept Camerons Strongarm and Tolly Original; large selection of malt whiskies; pleasant service; unobtrusive piped music. There are tables in the coachyard behind. *(Recommended by T Mansell, Comus Elliott, Michael and Margaret Slater, John Evans, Dr M V Jones, Klaus and Elizabeth Leist, John Whitehead)*

Brent Walker Tenant David Wood Real ale Meals and snacks (till 10.15) Restaurant (not Sun evening) Stamford (0780) 63558 Children welcome Open 11–3, 6–11 Bedrooms; £31B/£38(£44B)

George ★ ★ ⊘ 🛏

71 High St, St Martins

There are several interesting and decidedly pubby bars in this elegant and beautifully preserved sizeable hotel. Though it's mainly Elizabethan it includes parts of a much older Norman pilgrims' hospice, and a crypt under the present cocktail bar may be more like 1,000 years old. A pair of front rooms are still named after the destinations of the coaches – twenty a day each way to London and York – which changed horses here in the 18th and 19th centuries; they have a medley of seats ranging from sturdy bar settles through leather, cane and antique wicker to soft settees and easy chairs. The refurbished central lounge has sturdy timbers, broad flagstones, heavy beams, and massive stonework. The nicest place for lunch (if it's not a warm sunny day) is the indoor Garden Lounge, with well spaced white cast-iron furniture on herringbone glazed bricks around a central tropical grove, and a splendidly tempting help-yourself buffet (from £9.50). Bar food includes soup (£3.25), Danish open sandwiches (from £5.95), lasagne (£6.45), gruyere cheese fritters with a spicy plum sauce, chicken and mushroom pie or fish and chips (£6.95), whole grilled plaice (£8.25), sirloin steak with baked potato and salad (£10.25) and puddings (£3.65). Well kept Adnams on handpump; the best drinks are the Italian wines, many of which are good value and they sell by the glass; freshly squeezed orange juice, filter, espresso or cappuccino coffee, and welcoming staff. The cobbled courtyard at the back is lovely in summer, with comfortable chairs and tables among attractive plant tubs and colourful hanging baskets; waiter drinks service. Besides the courtyard, there's a well kept walled garden, with a sunken lawn where croquet is often played. This is the headquarters of Ivo Vannocci's small but reliably good chain of Poste Hotels. *(Recommended by John Evans, Gary Scott, T Mansell, Peter Barnsley, Dr M V Jones, Margaret Dyke, Pete Storey, F Teare)*

Free house Licensees Ivo Vannocci and Chris Pitman Real ale Meals and snacks (till 11) Restaurant Stamford (0780) 55171 Children welcome Open 11–11 Bedrooms; £75B/£100B

SWITHLAND (Leics) SK5413 Map 7

Griffin

Village signposted from A6 Leicester–Loughborough

This chatty, unpretentious local has three modernised communicating rooms with beams, some modern panelling, carpet or parquet flooring, deep red plush seats, and chintz drapes in the windows. The end room is usually quietest and there's a nice children's room. Good home-made bar snacks done to order include cobs (80p), soup or toasties (£1.20), ploughman's (from £2.75), cottage pie with cheese topping, chips and veg (£3.65), a choice of salads with baked potato (£3.95), gammon steak, onion rings, grilled tomato, fried egg or pineapple, chips and peas (£4.15) and puddings; children's menu (£1.50). Well kept Adnams, Everards Beacon, Mild, Tiger and Old Original, and a guest beer on handpump. Dominoes, cribbage, fruit machine and piped music, with a skittle alley in the quite separate back Stable Bar. Handy for Bradgate Country Park, with walks in Swithland woods. *(Recommended by Susan and Nigel Siesage, Barry and Anne, Dave Braisted; more reports please)*

Everards   Tenants Norman and Brenda Jefferson   Real ale   Meals and snacks (not Sun)   Woodhouse Eaves (0509) 890535   Children in own room   Open 11–2.30, 6–11

TETFORD (Lincs)   TF3374 Map 8
White Hart

Village signposted from Greetham–Belchford road off A158 Horncastle–Skegness, and from Scamblesby–South Ormsby road between A153 and A16 S of Louth; inn near centre of this straggly village – OS Sheet 122, map reference 333748

Next to the primary school and a few yards from the church, this early 16th-century village inn has a cosily traditional red-tiled bar with a high-backed curved oak settle by a big brick inglenook fireplace hung with brass plaques and horsebrasses, china and pewter hanging from one black beam, hunting-print cushions on some settles, and slabby elm tables. A bigger extension opening off is more simply furnished with plenty of tables and chairs, and line ink drawings of the village. There's also a small, no-smoking snug. Reasonably priced home-made bar food includes soup, ploughman's, lasagne (£3.10), lamb cutlets, good pork chops with apple sauce, cottage or steak and kidney pies, grilled lemon sole and 8oz sirloin steak (£6); puddings like superb crumble. Well kept Batemans XB and XXXB, and Marstons Pedigree on handpump (the XXXB is under light CO2 blanket); quiet piped music. The sheltered back lawn has seats and swings, and the pub is near *Good Walks Guide* Walk 114. *(Recommended by Tim and Sue Halstead, Derek and Sylvia Stephenson, T Nott, Anthony Barnes, Sidney and Erna Wells, Robert Gower)*

Free house   Licensee Stuart Dick   Real ale   Meals and snacks (not Mon, except bank hols)   Tetford (0507) 533255   Children in eating area of bar and snug   Open 12–3, 7–11; closed Mon lunchtime (not bank hols)   Bedrooms; £23/£30

UPTON (Notts)   SK7354 Map 7
Cross Keys ★ ⊘

Main Street (A612 towards Southwell)

The summer hanging baskets outside this busy 17th-century pub are lovely and there is now a grassy area where children can play. The heavy-beamed bar rambles around a central two-way log fireplace and in and out of various alcoves, with decorative plates and metalwork in one corner, and lots of pictures from sporting cartoons to local watercolours. An extension room has carved pews from Newark church. Very good, generously served bar food includes home-made soup (£1.60), filled baked potatoes (from £1.85), savoury and sweet crêpes with fillings like creamed mushrooms or apple and raisin (from £2.50), potted shrimps (£3.25), excellent lasagne, lamb moussaka or fish pie (£4.25), a choice of salads (from £4.50) and chicken casserole or steak and mushroom pie (£4.50), as well as lunchtime sandwiches and ploughman's; home-made specials like rabbit and red pepper casserole and always vegetarian meals; inventive puddings; they don't do chips, and the menu changes day by day. The restaurant is in the old dovecote. Well kept Batemans XXXB, Boddingtons Bitter, Marstons Pedigree, Whitbreads Castle Eden and regular guest beers on handpump; efficient, friendly service.

Darts, dominoes and unobtrusive piped music; the dog's well behaved. *(Recommended by Dr Sheila Smith, Dr Keith Bloomfield, George Mitchell, Paul Harrop, Tony Gayfer, Andy and Jill Kassube, Derek and Sylvia Stephenson, Mike Tucker, Peter Burton, Mr and Mrs M O Jones, Maureen and Steve Collin, D P Ryan, Angie and Dave Parkes, George Mitchell, Miss Karen Ann Ross, Philip Wood, Helen and Wal Burns, H Lucas, Colin and Mary Meaden)*

Free house   Licensee Michael Kirrage   Real ale   Snacks (lunchtime) and meals (till 9.30 evening)   Restaurant (not Sun evening)   Southwell (0636) 813269   Children in new extension room lunchtime and early evening and in restaurant   Folk/roots music Sun evening Sept-May   Open 11.30–2.30, 6–11; closed evening 25 Dec

WALCOTE (Leics)   SP5683   Map 4

Black Horse ⊘

1 1/2 miles from M1 junction 20; A427 towards Market Harborough

The outstanding bar food in this unlikely-looking building is exclusively Thai – the landlady, who does the cooking, comes from Thailand. You can choose one of the half spicy and half savoury dishes such as strips of beef in oyster sauce or khao mu daeng (marinated pork – all £3.60), phat khing (stir-fry meat or prawn with ginger and onion or with garlic, chilli and special hot basil herbs, all from £3.60), a popular Thai mixed grill (£4.20), and various Thai curries such as kaeng pla (fish, £4.20) or kaeng kai (chicken, £4.80). A fine choice of drinks includes well kept Burton Bridge, Hook Norton Best and Old Hookey, Timothy Taylors Landlord, and guest beers on handpump, an eclectic range of bottled beers that runs to Singha from Thailand, and country wines. It's furnished with russet plush button-back built-in wall banquettes, cast-iron and other heavy tables, more booth-like seats at the side, and pale mates' chairs in an airier section up steps; dominoes and fruit machine; the atmosphere is quietly chatty, there's an open fire, and (for summer) seats out behind. Readers have been wondering if it's time for a bit of renovation. *(Recommended by Mr and Mrs B H James, PLC, Dick Brown, J D Cranston, John and Joan Wyatt, Jim Aitkenhead, Hilary Sargeant, Norman Clarke, Linda Dyrda)*

Free house   Licensee Mrs Saovanee Tinker   Real ale   Meals (till 9.30)   (0455) 552684   Children in eating area   Open 12–2.30, 6.30–11; closed Mon or Tues lunchtimes

WELLOW Notts   SK6766   Map 7

Olde Red Lion

Eakring Road; pub visible from A616 E of Ollerton

Windows in the low-beamed front room of this 16th-century place look out on a tremendously tall brightly spiral-painted maypole (where Spring Bank Holiday Monday celebrations take place). There are old-fashioned button-back built-in wall seats as well as captains' chairs and stools, all in red plush, around its dark cast-iron-framed tables, and beyond a snug little Turkey-carpeted drinking bar are two further rooms (the dining room is no-smoking). As the food has a great local reputation for value – a combination of low prices and big helpings – it's best to get here early if you want to eat: good doorstep sandwiches, vegetarian meals (from £2.95), steak and kidney pie (£3.25), lasagne (£4.95) and children's menu (£2.25 with dessert); bookings are recommended for the 3-course Sunday lunch (£6.95). Well kept Marstons Pedigree and Ruddles Best and County, and a few guest beers on handpump; quick service; dominoes and fairly unobtrusive piped pop music. An L-shaped strip of grass above the car park has picnic-table sets under cocktail parasols, and a set of swings. *(Recommended by T Henwood, Derek and Sylvia Stephenson, J M Watson; more reports please)*

Free house   Licensee Richard Henshaw   Real ale   Meals and snacks (till 10) Restaurant   Mansfield (0623) 861000   Children in eating area   Open 11.30–3.30(3 Sat), 5.30–11

WILSON (Leics)   SK4024   Map 7

Bulls Head

On side road Breedon on the Hill–Melbourne; village signposted from A453 Ashby de la Zouch–Castle Donington

Close to Donington race track, this well run and friendly country pub has a comfortably modernised, beamed bar with maroon plush banquettes and settles around neat black tables; cheerful, warm welcome, smart and efficient mature barmaids, and several quiet alcoves decorated with old sepia racing-car photographs and some striking modern prints of immensely magnified insects. Reasonably priced, popular bar food includes soup (£1), sandwiches (from £1.50), ploughman's (from £2.75), roast beef, Yorkshire pudding and vegetables (£5.25), a hot dish of the day (£4.50) and a wide choice of attractively presented salads from the buffet counter (from £3.75), including seafood such as dressed crab (£5), cold fresh salmon (£5.25) or freshly sliced smoked salmon (£5.50); very good Sunday lunch. Well kept Ind Coope Burton and Tetleys on handpump; table skittles.
(Recommended by P H Brown, Pete Storey, D L Smith; more reports please)

Ansells (Allied)   Tenant Michael Johnson   Real ale   Meals and snacks (till 10; not Sun or Mon evenings)   Derby (0332) 862644   Children in eating area   Open 11–2.30, 6–11

Lucky Dip

Besides the fully inspected pubs, you might like to try these Lucky Dips recommended to us and described by readers (if you do, please send us reports):

☆ **Alford**, Lincs [West St (A1004); TF4576], *White Horse*: Picturesque 16th-century inn, carefully restored over the years, and perhaps slightly further upmarket than our other entry here; plush beamed lounge with Bass and Batemans real ales, the best range of vodkas yet found in any inspected pub (the landlord comes from Poland), good range of well prepared reasonably priced bar food, popular communicating restaurant; comfortable and prettily furnished good value bedrooms *(Paulina Blowes, Andrew Morrissey, BB)*

☆ **Alford** [26 West St], *Half Moon*: Comfortable, spacious and clean 17th-century local with five well kept real ales such as Bass, Batemans XB, Darleys Dark Mild, Stones and Vaux Samson, good cheap food served quickly in main bar which angles back to games area, also simple dining area and more decorous recently refurbished lounge; nice fairy-lit back garden with barbecues (and maybe big st bernard); children welcome *(Keith and Aubrey Day, Derek and Sylvia Stephenson, BB)*

Allington, Lincs [SK8540], *Welby Arms*: Idyllic spot though nr A1; neat, clean and tidy, with well kept Courage and John Smiths, good simple food inc their own veg, civilised landlord *(Tony Gayfer)*

Appleby Magna, Leics [SK3109], *Appleby*: Civilised lounge, tables on terrace with pretty flowers; good waitress-served bar food *(Graham Richardson)*

Ashby Folville, Leics [SK7011], *Carrington Arms*: Spacious, comfortable bar in not over-done-up Edwardian pub; friendly landlord, good choice of well kept real ale inc Everards on handpump, reasonably

priced bar food inc proper omelettes *(John and Joan Wyatt, Dr and Mrs A K Clarke)*

Ashby Parva, Leics [off A426 N of Lutterworth; not far from M1 junction 20; SP5288], *Holly Bush*: Good recent refurbishment — well thought-out interconnecting big lounge; good range of beers inc a changing guest; superb cosy restaurant, food all home-cooked at keen prices, pleasant service; popular *(Ted George)*

Aslackby, Lincs [A15 Bourne—Sleaford; TF0830], *Robin Hood & Little John*: Timbered pub with brasses and potted plants, friendly, efficient service, Marstons and other beers and coffee; good varied menu, side restaurant area *(John Burgan, Hilary Irving)*

☆ **Aswarby**, Lincs [A15 Folkingham—Sleaford; TF0639], *Tally Ho*: Well kept country pub with two friendly rooms; country prints, big log fire and woodburning stove, oak beams, simple traditional furnishings; well kept Adnams, Batemans XB and a guest beer on handpump, straightforward bar food, welcoming service; tables and timber play fort on grass behind, by sheep meadow; bedrooms comfortable and well equipped, in neatly converted block behind *(BB)*

☆ **Aubourn**, Lincs [back st; SK9262], *Royal Oak*: Family-run country pub with two attractively decorated small lounge rooms, open fire, good generous standard food, well kept Batemans XB and XXXB, Sam Smiths, and a guest beer on handpump, friendly service, back games room; nice garden *(M and J Back, Derek and Sylvia Stephenson, Andy and Jill Kassube)*

Aylestone, Leics [Narrow Lane; SK5800], *Black Horse*: Tucked-away recently renovated local with friendly service, Everards beers and good atmosphere; back garden; parking may be very difficult *(Rona Murdoch)*

Bagthorpe, Notts [Upper Bagthorpe; 2 miles from M1 junction 27: A608 towards Eastwood, 1st right, right at T, 1st left; SK4751], *Shepherds Rest*: Traditional mining pub, isolated in pretty surroundings, with plenty of seats in big front garden; warm, welcoming and cosy inside, well kept Home ales *(Mr and Mrs P B Dowsett)*

☆ **Barholm**, Lincs [TF0810], *Five Horseshoes*: Well kept Adnams, Batemans and guest beers in homely easy-going village local, old-fashioned, clean and cosy, with old farm tools and vitrines of stuffed birds; fine piece of intricately carved Java teak forms bar canopy; tables in garden, with paddocks behind *(John Baker, M Morgan, LYM)*

☆ **Barrow upon Soar**, Leics [Mill Lane, off South St (B5328); SK5717], *Navigation*: Picturesque two-roomed extended split-level pub by Grand Union Canal, based on former barge-horse stabling, popular at weekends for good value straightforward lunchtime food; several well kept real ales, skittle alley, small back terrace by boat moorings *(P A and J B Jones)*

Barrow upon Soar, Leics [SK5717], *Soar Bridge*: Collection of old cast signs, local railway pictures and canal memorabilia; popular good value food, well kept Everards Beacon and Old Original, lots of country wines; short walk behind to river *(J and D Coates)*

Bassingham, Lincs [High St; SK9160], *Five Bells*: Warm, clean and friendly beamed pub with lots of brass and bric-a-brac, roaring fire, well kept Allied real ales, decent wine *(Andy and Jill Kassube)*

Belmesthorpe, Leics [Shepherds Walk; TF0410], *Bluebell*: Old-world pub with good choice of food under new landlord, inc well filled Yorkshire puddings; small dining room; well kept Bass and Marstons Pedigree on handpump *(M J Morgan)*

☆ **Bicker**, Lincs [A52 NE of Donnington; TF2237], *Red Lion*: Well kept Adnams Broadside, Bass, Ind Coope Burton, Tetleys and two guest beers on handpump in simply modernised 17th-century pub with masses of china hanging from bowed black beams, huge fireplace, bar food inc good mixed grill and inventive pancakes, tables on terrace and tree-shaded lawn; interesting area — formerly a sea inlet, with remains of Roman sea dykes *(D C Hawkins, LYM)*

Blaby, Leics [Church St; quite handy for M1 junction 21; SP5697], *Bakers Arms*: 15th-century pub tucked away in small side street — very popular; series of rooms with lots of low beams and nooks and crannies, decent food with reasonable prices, inc a vegetarian dish; some seating outside *(Rona Murdoch)*

☆ **Blidworth**, Notts [SK5956], *Bird in Hand*: Probably the best view in Notts over Sherwood Forest from friendly local with one comfortable U-shaped room and big garden; well kept Mansfield Riding and Old Baily on handpump, good cheap bar food; special welcome for wheelchair patients from nearby nursing home *(Derek and Sylvia Stephenson, Andy and Jill Kassube, Maureen and Steve Collin)*

Blyth, Notts [SK6287], *White Swan*: Clean and friendly, with big open fires in cosy lounge, good chatty atmosphere (no music); Boddingtons and Whitbreads Castle Eden and Trophy, wide range of decent bar food inc good fresh fish, helpful service *(Steve Taylor)*

☆ **Boston**, Lincs [Witham St; TF3244], *Carpenters Arms*: Traditional friendly bare-boards backstreet inn, vibrant with locals and young people (landlord's young too), well kept Batemans Mild and XB, enterprising home-cooked lunchtime food inc good cheap rolls; bedrooms reasonably priced *(Michael Rooke, Gary and Janet Amos)*

Boston [Horncastle Rd (B1183)], *Kings Arms*: Small redbrick town inn with light and airy front bar looking over road to canal and striking tall working windmill; neat smaller red plush back bar, well kept Batemans, fair-priced bar food; bedrooms modern and comfortable with cheery furnishings; good value *(Paulina Blowes, BB)*

☆ **Brandy Wharf**, Lincs [B1205 SE of Scunthorpe; TF0197], *Hankerin*: Riverside pub notable for remarkable choice of dozens of farm ciders (with summer 'Sydre Shoppe'); jovial licensee, standard choice of good cheap nicely served bar food inc good curry, unusual decor (perhaps not the main attraction); popular with boating people (good moorings, slipways); the buildings look lucky to have survived; closed Christmas, New Year and Mon winter lunchtimes *(Andy and Jill Kassube)*

☆ **Braunston**, Leics [off A606 in Oakham; SK8306], *Old Plough*: Good range of bar food in straightforward but clean and pleasant black-beamed pub with well kept John Smiths on handpump; seats in sheltered garden, some concentration on elegant back dining conservatory (where children allowed) *(CEP, RJH, LYM)*

Braunston, Leics [SK5717], *Blue Ball*: Perhaps Rutland's oldest pub, recently taken over by owners of Peacock at Redmile (see main entries), to be run on similar lines *(News please)*

☆ **Breedon on the Hill**, Leics [A453 Ashby—Castle Donington; SK4022], *Holly Bush*: Lovely old very low-beamed partly Tudor pub with interesting range of food in restaurant and (lunchtime only) bar, real ales such as Ansells, Ind Coope Burton and John Smiths; friendly welcoming landlord *(Gordon Theaker)*

Broughton Astley, Leics [Main St; SP5292], *Olde Bulls Head*: Village pub locally popular for good wholesome food, usual range from ploughman's to steaks; well kept Everards, very busy weekends, quieter midweek *(Celia Moore)*

Burbage, Leics [SP4294], *Cross Keys*: Well

kept Marstons in atmospheric building with open-fire snug and two bars around central servery; separate children's room in long garden with cricket pitch at end *(Graham Bush)*

Burgh le Marsh, Lincs [TO5065], *Fleece*: Very popular lunchtime for short choice of well presented cheap food from cobs to steak *(D Goodger); White Hart*: Pleasant local with well kept Batemans, good straightforward food (can be served in restaurant) *(Joan and Michel Hooper-Immins)*

Carlton on Trent, Notts [SK7964], *Great Northern*: Pub in long-closed station with railway memorabilia and good-humoured landlord; Inter-City trains belt past shaking the tables; good value standard bar food, quiet piped music, pool table, unusual beers and cider; family conservatory *(Michael Thomson, RAF)*

Castle Bytham, Lincs [SK9818], *Castle*: Doing well under current charming licensee, with consistently good bar food (not Tues) *(Mr and Mrs Frostick, Andy and Jill Kassube)*

Castle Donington [90 Bondgate (B6504); SK4427], *Cross Keys*: Has been praised for well kept Vaux Samson and Wards Best, attractive atmosphere and good fire, but no recent reports *(News please); [A453, S end], Nags Head*: Attractive decor, bar food from newly reworked kitchen, Marstons ales *(Dave Braisted)*

Catthorpe, Leics [just off A5 S of Gibbet Island; SP5578], *Cherry Tree*: Cosy, clean and tastefully furnished village pub with cheerful young licensees, well kept Bass, bar food, open fire; may be closed Mon-Thurs lunchtime *(Ted George)*

Claworth, Notts [High St; SK7388], *Blacksmiths Arms*: Interesting and popular old village local with well kept Bass and Tetleys, good value wines, country wines, and freshly squeezed orange juice; good straightforward bar food, good value back restaurant *(Mr and Mrs P A and J B Jones)*

☆ **Clipstone**, Notts [Old Clipstone; B6030 Mansfield—Ollerton — OS Sheet 120, map reference 606647; SK6064], *Dog & Duck*: Comfortably modernised and friendly three-roomed pub with good home-made hot meals and well kept Home ales; not far from Center Parc at Rufford; children's room *(Alan and Marlene Radford)*

Coleby, Lincs [SK9760], *Tempest Arms*: Genuine local with pleasant licensees, good choice of reasonably priced food served in bar, lounge or small dining room, well kept Marstons Pedigree *(M J Morgan)*

☆ **Colston Bassett**, Notts [SK7033], *Martins Arms*: Doing well since recent take-over by licensees of Crown at Old Dalby (see main entries); comfortable and homely seats, nice snug, murmur of conversation instead of piped music, open fire, conservative atmosphere; new kitchen doing similar food to the Crown inc decent sandwiches, good choice of well kept real ales such as Batemans XB, XXB and Mild, Marstons Pedigree and Exhibition *(Chris Raisin, Dr Keith Louden, Dr Keith Bloomfield, Simon Tormey)*

Congerstone, Leics [Bosworth Rd; SK3605], *Horse & Jockey*: Nicely modernised welcoming beamed pub with plush lounge, games in public bar, well kept Bass, good well presented bar food (not Weds); good restaurant (maybe Sat evening only, low season), playground; quite handy for Bridge 47 on Ashby Canal *(Mr and Mrs J D Cranston)*

☆ **Copt Oak**, Leics [nr M1 junc 22; A50 towards Leics, then B587; SK4812], *Copt Oak*: Well refurbished and spacious Marstons Tavern Table pub/restaurant, wide choice of reasonably priced decent generous food lunchtime and from 6pm, efficient friendly service, well kept real ale; 1920s decor, with lush green plants; pleasant surroundings, great views over Charnwood Forest *(C E Power, George Atkinson)*

☆ **Cottesmore**, Leics [Main St; SK9013], *Sun*: Very popular sensibly priced bar food in plushly modernised 17th-century pub with hot fire in stone inglenook, decent sporting prints, quiet side rooms; piped music, fruit machine, tables in garden; children welcome *(BB)*

Covenham St Bartholomew, Lincs [minor rd N of Louth; TF3395], *Plough*: Friendly and comfortable plush lounge, useful for the area, with wide choice of generous main dishes, Stones and Websters real ales; separate games and public bars, evening restaurant (also set Sun lunch) *(Mr and Mrs Back)*

☆ **Cropston**, Leics [15 Station Rd (B5328); SK5510], *Bradgate Arms*: Refurbished village pub with food (not Sun evening) in sunken dining area, good range of Hoskins real ales, interesting well kept guest beers and Weston's cider; family area, skittle alley, biggish garden *(Richard R Dolphin, Tim and Lynne Crawford, Joan and Michel Hooper-Immins)*

☆ **Diseworth**, Leics [street opp churchyard; nr East Midlands Airport, and M1 junction 23A; SK4524], *Plough*: Happy atmosphere in attractively extended pub with well kept Bass, good range of bar food, pleasant mix of locals and aviation people, aircraft pictures; weekday lunchtime closing 2.30 *(T Nott)*

Eastville, Lincs [TF4057], *Wheat Sheaf*: Enjoyable village pub with well kept Batemans and bar food *(John C Baker)*

Eastwood, Notts [A608/A610; SK4646], *Great Northern*: Recently re-opened with split-level partly open-plan layout and new carvery; well kept Hardys & Hansons ales on handpump, snooker table, garden and moorings by Erewash canal; not far from D H Lawrence Museum *(Alan and Eileen Bowker)*

☆ **Edenham**, Lincs [A151; TF0621], *Five Bells*: Busy but spacious modernised lounge with neatly ranged tables for wide choice of usual bar food; well kept Camerons Original and Strongarm and Tolly Best, friendly staff, log fire, piped music, lots of foreign banknotes, soft lighting; back restaurant/function room, tables in garden with good play area; children welcome *(Mr and Mrs J Barnes, Mr and Mrs Back, Brian and Jill Bond, LYM)*

Edith Weston, Leics [SK9305], *Wheatsheaf*: Worth knowing for position by Rutland Water; generous bar food, esp salads and ploughman's *(Margaret and Trevor Errington)*

☆ **Elkesley**, Notts [just off A1 S of Blyth; SK6975], *Robin Hood*: Tidy pub with good food inc imaginative specials in bar and restaurant, well kept Marstons Pedigree and Whitbreads Castle Eden, good service *(Gordon Smith, Andy and Jill Kassube)*

☆ **Elston**, Notts [A47 S of Lincoln; SK7548], *Coeur de Lion*: Pinnacles, domes, lancet windows, steep roofs, tall chimneys, elevated terraces; decorous panelled bar with soft russet plush seats, country prints and engravings, neatly uniformed careful staff; good bar food served under domed silver covers, decent spirits, free peanuts; two candlelit dining rooms, one upstairs with soaring pitched and raftered ceiling *(BB)*

☆ **Epperstone**, Notts [SK6548], *Cross Keys*: Particularly friendly pub with well kept Hardys & Hansons on handpump, copious helpings of good value bar food; in attractive bypassed village *(Derek and Sylvia Stephenson)*

☆ **Ewerby**, Lincs [TF1247], *Finch Hatton Arms*: Solid and substantial mock-Tudor pub, with neat red plush button-back seating, pegged rafters, delft shelf of china, some rustic bygones, efficient staff; good bar food from sandwiches up, well kept Stones Best and Wards Sheffield Best on handpump, coal fire, smart restaurant area, comfortable back locals' bar, a couple of rustic seats outside; bedrooms *(J D Maplethorpe, P R Morley, Andy and Jill Kassube, BB)*

Farnsfield, Notts [E end; SK6456], *Plough*: Welcoming local with good range of well prepared bar food at surprisingly low prices; Mansfield Riding and Old Baily on handpump, pleasant surroundings *(Alan and Eileen Bowker)*

Fleckney, Leics [7 High St; SP6493], *Old Crown*: Well run and friendly village pub, recently renovated, with lots of polished wood, cricket memorabilia; small range of good well prepared home-cooked bar food, Adnams and Everards ales, new dining room *(David Hollingworth, Rona Murdoch)*

Foxton, Leics [Foxton Locks; off A6 3m NW of Market Harborough, park by bridge 60 or 62 and walk — OS Sheet 141, map reference 691897; SP7090], *Bridge 61*: Flagstones, pine furniture, good atmosphere, good value food lunchtime and evening, canalia, Adnams, Everards Tiger and Old Original, games and family room; gift and provision shop next door — handy for boaters; nr start GWG113 *(P A and J B Jones)*

☆ **Glaston**, Leics [SK8900], *Monkton Arms*: Clean and pleasant bar with very wide choice of good generous well presented food, warm fire, friendly and informal

surroundings; well kept real ales inc Theakstons XB, good range of wines, attractive restaurant; new bedrooms, well equipped and comfortable *(M L Hooper-Immins, C E Power)*

Gotham, Notts [SK5330], *Star*: Comfortable and well run, with good welcome and good value food, though no real ale *(Pete Storey)*

☆ **Grantham**, Lincs [High St; SK9135], *Angel & Royal*: Unique 14th-century carved stone facade, interesting ancient oriel window seat in plush hotel bar on left of coach entry, massive inglenook in high-beamed main bar opp (has had spit-roasts); well kept Bass and occasional guest beers, bar food; THF, largely extended behind *(LYM)*

Grantham [Vine St], *Blue Pig*: Ancient, attractive half-timbered corner pub, with several cosy and atmospheric beamed drinking areas, lots of prints and photographs of old Grantham on the walls, pretty hanging baskets; has been popular for well kept Whitbreads-related real ales, quick generous bar food and friendly staff, but no recent reports *(News please)*

☆ **Great Casterton**, Lincs [village signed off A1; TF0009], *Crown*: High-backed booth seating in neat stripped-stone bar with good value home cooking, well kept Camerons and Tolly Original on handpump, log fire in inglenook; old-fashioned seats in pretty little garden opp attractive church; Post Office in car park *(BB)*

Great Glen, Leics [off A6 Leicester—Mkt Harboro; SP6597], *Greyhound*: Good food, rather original, from immaculate kitchen; well kept Tetleys *(A R M Moate)*

Greatford, Lincs [TF0811], *Hare & Hounds*: Cosy, comfortable and homely lounge with roaring fire, well kept Adnams Broadside, Charles Wells, Mansfield Riding and Websters Yorkshire, and widening choice of good properly cooked food (worth the wait); separate public bar *(Mr and Mrs J Back)*

☆ **Greetham**, Leics [B668 Stretton—Cottesmore; SK9214], *Wheatsheaf*: Good value bar food served till late evening in simply furnished L-shaped series of communicating rooms; coal fire, nautical charts, well kept Camerons Bitter and Strongarm Premium on handpump; pool and other games in end room, restaurant, tables on side grass *(BB)*

Halam, Notts [SK6754], *Waggon & Horses*: Well organised, popular and welcoming village pub with friendly landlord, Marstons Pedigree, good food at reasonable prices *(George Mitchell)*

Haltham, Lincs [off A163 Horncastle—Coningsby; TF2463], *Marmion Arms*: Small thatched pub, cosy and unpretentious but spotless, with well kept Shipstones, reasonably priced home-made food, friendly landlady, nostalgic piped pop; tables outside *(Terry Glendenning, D Maplethorpe)*

Harby, Leics [SK7331], *Bottle & Glass*: Well kept S & N beers, good value competently served bar food inc good choice of puddings; tables outside *(David and Ruth Hollands)*

☆ **Hayton**, Notts [Main St (B1403) — OS Sheet 120, map reference 728852; SK7384], *Boat*: Friendly and comfortable, with big log fire, good bar food, restaurant (booking essential), well kept Bass, Marstons Pedigree and other real ales; garden with play area and summer help-yourself barbecue; bedrooms in separate cottage block — good value, with good breakfasts; on quiet stretch of Chesterfield Canal (moorings) *(P A and J B Jones)*

Hinckley, Leics [Watling St (A5); SP4294], *Lime Kilns*: Real canalside pub recently refurbished to high standard, big waterside back garden with children's area, some moorings, good choice of reasonably priced food, Marstons Pedigree *(P A and J B Jones)*

☆ **Horbling**, Lincs [4 Spring Lane (off B1177); TF1135], *Plough*: Almost unique in being owned by Parish Council; cosy and friendly comfortable lounge with above-average carefully prepared food, well kept Greene King IPA and Abbot, Wards Sheffield Best and up to half a dozen guest beers, log fire; darts and other games in lively traditional inner public bar; children in eating area; bedrooms cheap but comfortable, with excellent breakfast *(Anthony Barnes, Nic James, LYM)*

☆ **Hough on the Hill**, Lincs [SK9246], *Brownlow Arms*: Attractive pub in peaceful picturesque village; sofas and comfortable chairs in relaxing lounge, separate bar, wide range of good value well cooked and presented food in bar and restaurant, friendly welcome, efficient service; closed weekday lunchtimes; good value bedrooms, good breakfasts *(Andy and Jill Kassube)*

Houghton on the Hill, Leics [Uppingham Rd (A47); SK6703], *Rose & Crown*: As a result of reorganisation by Bass the Vandellis, who gained this plush pub a main entry with their Italianate style and food to match, left in 1991 *(LYM)*

☆ **Hungarton**, Leics [SK6807], *Black Boy*: Consistently good reasonably priced food from filled cobs to grills in pleasant rustic local *(A R M Moate, A J and E M Watts)*

☆ **Illston on the Hill**, Leics [off B6047 Mkt Harboro—Melton; SP7099], *Fox & Goose*: A genuine original, packed with almost anything from skulls and stuffed animals to original McLachlan cartoons; well kept Adnams and Everards Tiger, good coal fires, weekend filled rolls; closed weekday lunchtimes *(LYM — more reports please)*

☆ **Ingham**, Lincs [High St; SK9483], *Inn on the Green*: Tastefully and comfortably modernised spacious beamed pub with good fire, lots of brass and copper, wide choice of quickly served good home-made food inc Sun lunch; upstairs dining room; on village green *(Gordon Pell, Andy and Jill Kassube)*

Kegworth, Leics [SK4826], *Anchor*: Three-roomed traditional local just over bridge from Kegworth Flood Lock — ideal for boaters; well kept Bass, bar snacks, good atmosphere; tables in forecourt *(P A and J B Jones)*; *White House*: On River Soar just outside village, country views; good value food inc bargain midweek suppers; moorings *(Jane Morrell)*

Kilby, Leics [off A50 S of Leicester; SP6295], *Dog & Gun*: Welcoming owners, good choice of good food fairly priced inc speciality plate-sized Yorkshire puddings and good fish; popular, can get busy — booking advised *(Elisabeth Kemp)*

☆ **Kilby Bridge**, Leics [A50 S of Leicester; SP6097], *Navigation*: Well kept and friendly low-ceilinged canalside pub, several rooms full of character, get there early for vast helpings of good Sun lunch; garden overlooking canal (by Bridge 87 of Grand Union Leicester arm), Ansells, Ind Coope Burton, Marstons Pedigree and Tetleys on handpump, great coffee; huge fish in tank in lounge; busy weekends *(P A and J B Jones, Mel and Phil Lloyd)*

☆ **Kimberley**, Notts [Station Rd; not far from M1 junction 26; SK5044], *Nelson & Railway*: Opp the Hardys & Hansons brewery, with Edwardian atmosphere in comfortable beamed bar, lounge and dining area, reasonably priced good bar food inc vegetarian dishes, well kept Hardys & Hansons Bitter and Classic on handpump, friendly welcome, good garden with swings; children in eating area; bedrooms *(Mel Landells, Alan and Eileen Bowker)*

Knipton, Leics [SK8231], *Red House*: Beautifully proportioned former hunting lodge looking over pretty village close to Belvoir Castle; orthodox bar furnishings, good value carefully prepared food, well kept Ind Coope Burton and Marstons Pedigree on handpump, unobtrusive piped music, friendly dogs; restaurant *(Dr Keith Bloomfield, BB)*

☆ **Lambley**, Notts [Church St; SK6245], *Woodlark*: Well preserved and interestingly laid out, cheerful welcome, with outstanding value cheap snacks, well kept Home ales, navy memorabilia, wide range of pub games inc pool room, table skittles and skittle alley; children in annexe *(BB)*

☆ **Leadenham**, Lincs [High St; A17 Newark—Sleaford; SK9552], *George*: Unpretentious bar with remarkable range of several hundred whiskies, good choice of wines by the glass inc their own direct German imports, well kept Greene King IPA, Ruddles County and Theakstons Old Peculier on handpump, and generous good value food; friendly service, side games room, piped music, restaurant; bedrooms plain but good value; good breakfasts, for non-residents too *(Col G D Stafford, Virginia Jones, Andy and Jill Kassube, LYM)*

☆ **Leicester** [Belgrave Gate (nr flyover)], *Black Swan*: Recently refurbished by Hoskins, with lots of pine furniture, sawdust on floor and little overt comfort — but pleasant atmosphere, welcoming licensees, full range of Hoskins ales and guest beers such as Camerons; two games machines, juke box, well cooked basic food; popular younger people evenings *(Joan and Michel*

Hooper-Immins, P A and J B Jones, Rona Murdoch, Comus Elliott)

☆ **Leicester** [Melton Rd (A607 N, corner of Gipsy Rd); edge of city], *Melton*: Large well run Asian-owned Victorian pub included for interesting back Simba grill (Thurs-Sun evenings, 7-11), where chef from Bombay cooks authentic tandoori and other food in front of you; no cutlery — use right hand for eating; well kept Marstons Burton, Pedigree and Border Mild on handpump *(P A and J B Jones)*

☆ **Leicester** [Charles St], *Rainbow & Dove*: Large pleasantly no-frills open-plan bar with full range of Hoskins beers and a guest such as Wadworths 6X kept well, straightforward weekday lunchtime bar food; popular with students, live music Sun evening, parking difficult *(Pete Storey, Graham Bush, Joan and Michel Hooper-Immins, Mel and Phil Lloyd)*

Leicester, [Welford Rd], *Bricklayers Arms*: Busy and lively, with well kept Shipstones, nice wood-partitioned snug, good value snacks, popular summer courtyard *(Graham Bush)*; [Silver St], *Globe*: Period features inc gas lighting, well restored woodwork and stone mullions, well kept Everards real ales with a guest beer such as Adnams or Eldridge Pope, rolls downstairs, simple well cooked hot lunchtime dishes upstairs, good mix of customers from mauve skinheads to business suits *(Andy and Jill Kassube, Graham Bush, BB)*; [Gypsy Lane], *Gypsy Lane*: Good relaxed ambience in spacious comfortably refurbished lounge of big 1930s pub, well kept Home Bitter and Mild on electric pump, good value lunchtime food *(P A and J B Jones)*; [London Rd], *Marquis Wellington*: Popular lunchtime rendezvous for the commercial sector, Everards beers with a guest eg Hook Norton Old Hookey, good soft rolls, well presented changing hot food, limited choice of evening pot meals; can be very crowded at peak times, but swift pleasant service *(Joan and Michel Hooper-Immins)*; [London Rd, opp Victoria Pk], *Old Horse*: Large Everards pub looking across to Victoria Pk, well kept ale on handpump, food bar inc Sun lunchtime, good atmosphere; conservatory, good-sized garden *(Graham Richardson)*; [Duns Gate (nr Polytechnic)], *Pump & Tap*: Plain tables, chairs and benches, lively young atmosphere, foreign bottled beers, well kept Allied ales, piped rock and jazz, occasional live bands *(Graham Bush)*; [216 Ayelstone Rd], *Sharpshooters*: Traditional pub with seven bars — the main one notable for its self-service beer engine; open fires and concrete floors *(Frazer Bird)*; [9 Welford Pl, corner Newarke St/Welford Rd], *Welford Place*: New venture by licensees of Wig & Mitre in Lincoln (see main entries), open all day for food in variety of styles (and degrees of formality) *(News please)*

Leicester Forest West, Leics [SK5001], *Bulls Head*: Well kept Everards and above-average food at attractive prices, in almost archetypal English inn *(Comus Elliott)*

☆ **Lincoln** [Union Rd; behind Castle], *Victoria*: Classic quaint Victorian backstreet local, a down-to-earth real ale drinkers' pub; two cosy and friendly rooms, Batemans, Timothy Taylors and several other changing real ales, country wines, cheap and cheerful bargain lunchtime food changing daily; can get crowded *(Virginia Jones, Derek and Sylvia Stephenson, Sue Holland, Dave Webster, P W Brindle, Andy and Jill Kassube, Reg Nelson, Michael Rooke)*

☆ **Lincoln** [Steep Hill], *Browns Pie Shop*: Not a pub, as you can get a drink only if you're eating — but it does have Everards Tiger and Ruddles Best and a good choice of wines, and is well worth knowing for the wide choice of food (which does include spectacular pies); comfortable seats, helpful staff, pleasant traditional atmosphere *(Mr and Mrs K J Morris, BKA, D L Parkhurst)*

☆ **Lincoln** [26 Broadgate], *Jolly Brewer*: Unusual art deco pub, with some items of special interest; thriving atmosphere, enthusiastic owners, good choice of real ales — Everards Tiger and Old Original, Home, McEwans; bar food; busy Sat night, quiet Sun lunchtime; good outside area *(P A and J B Jones, N J D Bodiam, Reg Nelson)*

☆ **Lincoln** [25 Lindum Rd, N of Bradgate], *Adam & Eve*: Large unspoilt pub, one of the oldest here, tucked behind cathedral; two busy, low-beamed atmospheric bars with curios and smart prints, good food *(BKA, Reg Nelson, P W Brindle)*

☆ **Lincoln** [Moor St (off A57 Sheffield rd nr racecourse)], *Queen in the West*: Pleasant back-street pub converted from farmhouse with military prints and miniatures in well decorated lounge, interesting sporting prints in public bar, welcoming atmosphere, well kept Marstons Pedigree, Theakstons XB and Old Peculier, Timothy Taylors Landlord, Wards Sheffield Best, reasonably priced simple home cooking *(BKA, Andy and Jill Kassube)*

Lincoln [2 Alfred St], *City Vaults*: Hatch service of particularly well kept Wards ales, inc Mild, in simple but welcoming backstreet local, a former police house; attractively restored tiled lounge, separate dining area; cheap nicely presented lunchtime food inc filled Yorkshire puddings, good atmosphere then, but can be taken over by young people evenings *(Sue Holland, Dave Webster, Andy and Jill Kassube, Reg Nelson, BB)*; [44 Bailgate], *Duke William*: Converted row of oak-beamed cottages close to cathedral with friendly weekday evening atmosphere (can be busier weekends), lunchtime bar food, restaurant; bedrooms *(Andy Kassube, Reg Nelson)*; [Waterside North], *Green Dragon*: Noble waterside Tudor pub — 16th-century carved facade gave its nickname the Cat Garret, and well worth a look for that *(P W Brindle, Reg Nelson, LYM)*; [Greetwell Gate], *Morning Star*: Well scrubbed comfortable ordinary pub with friendly atmosphere, well kept reasonably priced beer *(J D Maplethorpe, Andy and Jill Kassube)*;

[Brayford Pool], *Royal William IV*: Well kept Courage, hard-working landlord, wide choice of good reasonably priced food, waterside tables *(David and Ruth Hollands)*; [83 Westgate], *Strugglers*: Old-fashioned basic two-room local, unspoilt and friendly, with jolly atmosphere, good cheap Bass on handpump *(Sue Holland, Dave Webster, Andy and Jill Kassube, Virginia Jones)*

Lissington, Lincs [TF1183], *White Hart*: Character village pub with usual bar food, well kept Bass on handpump *(Andy and Jill Kassube)*

Littlethorpe, Leics [not far from M1 junction 21; off B4114; SP5496], *Plough*: Tastefully modernised, well kept 16th-century pub in quiet village with friendly, efficient staff and well kept Everards Tiger on handpump; good choice of bar food, separate small restaurant, good value Sunday lunch *(Paul and Margaret Baker)*

Long Sutton, Lincs [Main St; off bypass A17 Kings Lynn—Holbeach; TF4222], *Crown & Woolpack*: Generous good value bar food, well kept real ales such as Bass and Stones *(M and J Back)*

Long Whatton, Leics [SK4723], *Falcon*: Spacious and comfortable, with bric-a-brac and taxidermy, restaurant stepped up from lounge, and coffee lounge; has been popular for relaxing atmosphere, friendly efficient service, good bar food and well kept Everards Old Original and Tiger, but no recent reports *(News please)*

☆ **Loughborough** [canal bank, about 1/4 mile from Loughborough Wharf], *Albion*: Busy, welcoming, canalside local with friendly licensees, two rooms and central bar, white-washed walls, brasses and mirrors; changing well kept ales inc Milds, such as Banks's, Batemans, Hoskins & Oldfields and Sam Smiths, good value bar food, occasional barbecues; friendly staff; budgerigar aviary in big courtyard; children welcome *(P A and J B Jones, P W Brindle, Pete Storey, Andy and Jill Kassube)*

☆ **Loughborough**, Leics [The Rushes (A6); SK5319], *Swan in the Rushes*: No-frills town pub with outstanding range of well kept real ales inc lesser-known distant beers and several Milds, also good range of foreign bottled beers; good value straightforward bar food, open fire, three high-ceilinged rooms, some entertaining domestic strife cartoons, down-to-earth chatty atmosphere — popular with students *(D P Ryan, Andy and Jill Kassube, M L Hooper-Immins, Pete Storey, BB)*

Loughborough [centre], *Barley Mow*: Comfortable unpretentious pub with good value generous food, well kept Home ales on handpump, piped music, friendly *(M R Spells)*; [Hume St], *Cherry Tree*: Attractive, with good service and reasonably priced food inc excellent chips and bargain lunches *(J and D Coates)*

Low Marnham, Notts [SK8069], *Brownlow Arms*: Useful for area, with four rooms, pleasant food, friendly service, Boddingtons,

Moorhouses Pendle Witches Brew and two other ales, tables outside *(Anthony Barnes)*

☆ **Lyddington**, Leics [SP8797], *Old White Hart*: Well kept locally popular traditional village inn with smallish bar, adjoining eating area, good reasonably priced bar food, welcoming efficient staff; restaurant *(C E Power, Brian and Jill Bond)*

Manby, Lincs [TF3986], *Manby Arms*: Useful for the area, with vast choice of reasonably priced good food *(M J Whittemore)*

Mansfield, Notts [Woodhouse Rd; 1/4 mile out of town; SK5561], *Yew Tree*: Popular new landlord, well kept Camerons and Everards Old Original, regular quiz nights, occasional live music *(Kevin Rhodes)*

Maplebeck, Notts [signed off A616/A617; SK7160], *Beehive*: Snug little beamed village tavern, clean and tidy but basic, with plain traditional furnishings; tables on small terrace with grassy bank running down to small stream, open fire, Mansfield real ale on handpump; lovely rustic position *(LYM)*

Mapperley, Notts [Plains Rd; SK6043], *Travellers Rest*: Wide choice of decent but cheap food, no-smoking dining area, purpose-built annexe for family dining, play area *(T W Gooding)*

☆ **Mareham le Fen**, Lincs [A115; TF2861], *Royal Oak*: Pleasantly refurbished beamed pub with welcoming open fire, friendly staff; well kept Batemans XB, XXB and XXXB, decent coffee, limited but good bar food in small restaurant *(Michael Rooke, Derek and Sylvia Stephenson)*

Market Bosworth, Leics [1 Park St; from centre follow Leicester and Hinckley signs; SK4003], *Olde Red Lion*: Good range of Hoskins and guest beers in take-us-as-you-find-us town bar, generous inexpensive food (not Sun evening); bar billiards, piped music, tables and play area in sheltered courtyard, jazz 3rd Thurs of month; open all day; children welcome; bedrooms *(John Whitehead, Mike and Wendy Proctor, E J Alcock, LYM)*

☆ **Market Deeping**, Lincs [Market Pl; TF1310], *Bull*: Cheerful and lively atmosphere, quite a warren of low-ceilinged alcoves and little corridors inc interesting heavy-beamed medieval Dugout Bar; well kept Adnams, Everards Tiger and Old Original and a guest beer, good value bar food (not Sun or Mon evening), restaurant (not Sun evening — jazz then); seats in pretty coachyard; children in eating areas; open all day Fri, Sat; bedrooms *(M Morgan, LYM — more reports please)*

Market Harborough, Leics [High St; SP7388], *Three Swans*: Recently refurbished hotel bar with outstanding range of bar food served promptly in plush surroundings — anything from stilton ploughman's or canelloni to sole Mornay recommended; Ruddles Best on handpump; bedrooms *(Joan and Michel Hooper-Immins)*

Marston, Lincs [2 miles E of A1 just N of Grantham; SK8943], *Thorold Arms*: Straightforward pub with basic cheap food, well kept Batemans XXXB and welcome for children; but no news since 1991 closure for refurbishment *(Caroline Wright, Derek Patey)*

Mountsorrel, Leics [Loughborough Rd; SK5714], *Swan*: Former Courage pub reopened by Theakstons, log fires and red banquettes in two simple whitewashed bars, wide choice of wines by the glass, well kept XB, Old Peculier and maybe a guest beer; food adventurous and unusual if not cheap, big garden; bedrooms *(P A and J B Jones)*

☆ **Newark**, Notts [Northgate; SK8054], *Malt Shovel*: Welcoming and comfortably refurbished old-fashioned local, green-tiled outside, with well kept Timothy Taylors Landlord, Wards Sheffield Best and regular guest beers; good lunchtime hot dishes, thick crusty sandwiches and Sun lunches; nearby parking not easy *(Andy and Jill Kassube, Mr and Mrs P A Jones)*

Newark [Great North Rd, nr Trent Bridge], *Castle Barge*: Good for families, with good choice of bar food inc vegetarian dishes *(S Corrigan)*; [Gt North Rd, nr stn], *Midland*: Family atmosphere, good food at all times, competitive prices; handy for castle; bedrooms clean and good value *(D King)*

North Hykeham, Lincs [Lincoln Rd; SK9466], *Lincoln Green*: Large, popular pub with comfortable lounge, Home Bitter, good value lunchtime bar food generously served (not Sun) *(Andy and Jill Kassube)*

North Kilworth, Leics [4 1/2 miles from M1 junction 20; A427 towards Market Harborough; SP6183], *White Lion*: Clean and bright, with well kept Marstons Pedigree, friendly staff, decent generous food, pool, darts and dominoes; tables in garden *(A E Alcock, J P Cinnamond)*

North Luffenham, Leics [SK9303], *Fox & Hounds*: Village pub under very friendly new management, with good value food *(Margaret and Trevor Errington)*

Norton Disney, Lincs [Main St (off A46); SK8859], *St Vincent Arms*: Quiet little country pub with real fire, Adnams, Everards Old Original and guest beers on handpump, bar food, big back garden inc well equipped play area *(Andy and Jill Kassube)*

☆ **Nottingham** [18 Angel Row; off Market Sq], *Bell*: Quaint 15th-century central pub, three busy downstairs bars, low beams, timbers and panelling; interestingly raftered upstairs bar used as lunchtime family restaurant (food from filled cobs to steaks), with nice window seats; good value wines, half a dozen or more real ales from cellar 30 ft down in the sandstone; trad jazz Sun lunchtime (rolls only then), Mon and Tues evenings; friendly service, open all day weekdays *(Wayne Brindle, Dr Keith Bloomfield, Graham Bush, Richard A Bailey, Colin and Mary Meaden, Nigel Gibbs, LYM)*

☆ **Nottingham** [Mansfield Rd], *Lincolnshire Poacher*: Several basic but well refurbished bar areas inc large wood-floored front bar, small wood-panelled snug and conservatory; popular with real ale fans for particularly well kept Batemans, Marstons Pedigree and

other guest beers, good ciders, Continental lagers, lots of whiskies; bar food, young lively atmosphere evenings — as it's not big it can get crowded; open all day, tables in garden behind *(Derek and Sylvia Stephenson, Kevin Rhodes, Roger Taylor, Graham Bush, D P Ryan, Wayne Brindle, Richard Sanders, John L Laing)*

☆ **Nottingham** [40 Broad St; corner of Lower Parliament St, on inner ring rd], *New Market*: Austerely neo-classical facade and notably low prices for simple food and drinks inc Home Mild and Bitter and Youngers IPA and No 3 in perfect condition; comfortable back bar, utilitarian front one; children and dogs allowed *(Wayne Brindle, LYM)*

☆ **Nottingham** [Gt Northern Cl; just off London Rd (A60), opp junction with Station Rd], *Grand Central*: Imaginative conversion of two roomy railway-arch areas — one cocktailish, one pubbier with Ind Coope Burton and Tetleys on handpump; steps up to little row of snug booths in mock-up of Orient Express; bar food and rather elegant side dining area, some interesting cigarette cards, well reproduced pop music, good mix of ages; tables on tank-engine terrace *(BB)*

Nottingham [50 Upper Parliament St], *Blue Bell*: Friendly but busy with well kept Home and other S & N ales, good choice of wines and spirits, good value food; consistently warm welcome *(Russell Allen)*; [Lower Parliament St, nr ice rink], *Castle*: Good value food lunchtime and early evening inc imaginative specials, in modern but quite stylish pub with well kept Allied beers; friendly, quiet and relaxing at lunchtime *(Lee Goulding)*; [273 Castle Blvd, Lenton], *Grove*: Reputedly oldest pub in Lenton, with lots of brewery memorabilia, Home, Theakstons XB and a guest such as Felinfoel on handpump, simple well priced food *(D R Stephenson, Russell Allen)*; [Clumber St], *Lion*: Dating back to 14th century — manager may show you the ancient cock-fighting pit deep in the bowels of the building; fair choice of interestingly priced good food, consistently warm welcome *(Russell Allen)*; [Canal St], *Narrow Boat*: Well kept Shipstones, pin table in back bar, somewhat alternative clientele *(Graham Bush)*; [Mansfield Rd], *Peacock*: Pleasant old-fashioned alehouse with comfortable well kept lounge bar and unusual waiter-service public bar; reasonably priced good food, well kept Home ales, Theakstons XB and Old Peculier *(Russell Allen, Wayne Brindle)*; [Maid Marion Way], *Salutation*: Plush modern front, but attractive genuinely ancient beamed and flagstoned back part; Whitbreads-related real ales and Marstons Pedigree, reasonably priced bar food — inc snacks even late evening; can get smoky when it's crowded; the old rock cellars can be visited at quiet times by arrangement *(Wayne Brindle, Stephen and Alison Parker, BB)*; [Market Pl], *Talbot*: Good lively atmosphere in spacious unpretentious Yates Wine Lodge, efficient service, good value ports and other wines, mixed clientele *(Mr and Mrs P A Jones, Wayne Brindle)*; [402 Derby Rd], *Three Wheatsheaves*: Rambling old pub with flagstones, traditional furnishings, somewhat basic feel but good atmosphere; bar food, well kept Shipstones, summer lunchtime barbecues daily in big garden *(Andrew Stephenson, LYM)*; [Thurland St/Pelham St], *Thurland Hall*: Large imposing corner pub with original masonry and cut and etched windows, lofty decorative plaster ceiling, island bar, Bass; very busy Sat night *(Graham Bush)*; [Russell Dr, Wollaton], *Wheelhouse*: Good friendly busy pub, attractive games area, excellent restaurant with Italian and traditional English food *(Russell Allen)*

Oadby, Leics [Stoughton Pk Farm, Stoughton Rd; SK6200], *Cow & Plough*: Part of CWS's Stoughton Pk working farm with museums, animal pens, gardens, good cafe and this — with Hoskins Hob and Tom Kellys Stout, old church pews, fascinating pub memorabilia and enamel advertising signs *(P A and J B Jones)*; [18 New St], *Firemans*: New pub in residential area with lots of beers and very reasonably priced food inc French dishes; good long happy hour *(Frazer Bird)*

Oakham, Leics [Market Pl; SK8508], *Whipper In*: Attractive and well run old stone coaching inn with oak-beamed and panelled lounge with well kept Ruddles Best and County on handpump, but now primarily a restaurant (with good food); bedrooms *(Peter Barnsley, LYM)*

Oasby, Lincs [TF0038], *Houblon Arms*: Large and rambling, with lots of real beams, wood panelling and natural stone; well kept Batemans and Timothy Taylors (a pleasant surprise down here) *(John C Baker)*

Old Somerby, Lincs [SK9633], *Fox & Hounds*: Attractive pub with several rooms, has been popular for warm welcome, well kept real ales and good range of reasonably priced bar food; but no recent reports *(News please)*

Plumtree, Notts [just off A606 S of Nottingham; SK6132], *Griffin*: Generous good value straightforward food in clean pub with well kept beer; piped music has been rather pervasive *(E J Cutting, R J Haerdi)*

☆ **Potterhanworth**, Lincs [Cross St; TF0565], *Chequers*: Pleasant village pub, cheerful licensees, wide range of good value bar food, well kept Mansfield Old Baily; piano in lounge bar *(J D Maplethorpe, Andy and Jill Kassube)*

☆ **Preston**, Leics [High St; SK8602], *Fox & Hounds*: Well kept character 16th-century pub with nicely presented and generous good food inc three soups, lots of vegetarian dishes, bargain children's helpings; several real ales inc Adnams, chatty landlord, plenty of tables outside, friendly great dane; delightful stone village *(R Grey, S T L Coupland)*

Radcliffe on Trent, Notts [Main St; SK6439], *Royal Oak*: Cosy and friendly,

with Marstons Pedigree and Whitbreads Castle Eden, good value food — Italian cook specialises in pizzas, but good steak and kidney pie too *(Dr Keith Bloomfield)*

Ratby, Leics [Boroughs Rd; SK5105], *Plough*: Cheerful unpretentious village local with lively Fri night sing-alongs, well kept Marstons real ales, simple cheap lunchtime food and good play area in big back garden *(Janet and Paul Waring, LYM)*

☆ **Rothwell**, Lincs [Caistor Rd (A46); TF1599], *Nickerson Arms*: Good relaxed atmosphere in friendly and pleasantly decorated stone-built village local, good choice of well kept ales inc Batemans, Tetleys, Timothy Taylors Landlord and regular guest beers, simple but good weekday lunchtime bar food; children's room, tables outside *(Andy and Jill Kassube)*

Salmonby, Lincs [TF3273], *Crossed Keys*: Country local with simple but comfortable big-windowed lounge and larger dining area, pool and other games in public bar, Ruddles Best on handpump, unobtrusive piped pop music, cheap simple food, friendly staff, tables and play area in garden behind; bedrooms cheap, clean and comfortable, with big breakfasts *(BB)*

☆ **Saxilby**, Lincs [Canal Side (A57); SK8975], *Bridge*: Welcoming canalside pub with good home-made food from big hot-beef rolls and other bar dishes to restaurant steaks and seafood; good choice of well kept real ales such as Ansells Mild, Badger Tanglefoot, Marstons Pedigree and Ruddles Best and County, good well kept garden *(P A and J B Jones, J M Watson, Andy and Jill Kassube)*

☆ **Shackerstone**, Leics [SK3706], *Rising Sun*: Sleepy village atmosphere in well kept exceptionally clean local with panelled lounge, well kept Marstons Pedigree and Czech Budweiser on draught, restaurant in converted barn; nr steam railway centre; very busy at peak times *(P A and J B Jones, Graham Richardson)*

☆ **Shawell**, Leics [not far from M6 junction 1; village signed off A5/A427 roundabout — turn right in village; SP5480], *White Swan*: Oak panelling, royal blue upholstery, coal fire and two log-effect gas fires in bar, separate lounge and games room; good range of well kept real ales inc Adnams Broadside and Banks's, good well presented food (very popular for this at weekends), friendly staff *(Cdr Patrick Tailyour)*

☆ **Sheepy Magna**, Leics [Main St (B4116); SK3201], *Black Horse*: Decently kept village pub with generous helpings of good value bar food inc wide choice of cheeses for ploughman's; well kept Marstons Pedigree on handpump, games in lively public bar, family area, tables outside, plenty of parking *(Geoff Lee, Mr and Mrs J Back)*

Shireoaks, Notts [SK5580], *Hewitt Arms*: 17th-century former outbuilding of Shireoaks Hall, overlooks series of small lakes with Canada geese and fishermen; very good food, nice atmosphere *(Peter Burton)*

☆ **Sileby**, Leics [Swan St; SK6015], *White Swan*: Comfortable and welcoming book-lined dining lounge with generous helpings of interesting good value bar food (not Sun or Mon) inc home-made bread, good pies, casseroles and puddings, with a particularly wide evening choice; small tasteful restaurant; children's playroom in converted bowling alley at back, with closed-circuit TV *(Canon Stephen Jackson, Lucy Wright)*

☆ **Skegness**, Lincs [Vine Rd, Seacroft (off Drummond Rd); TF5660], *Vine*: Well run partly 17th-century hotel, with comfortable bar overlooking drive and own bowling green, juke box in further oak-panelled room, imposing antique seats and grandfather clock in Turkey-carpeted hall, porch with lots of signed photographs of entertainers who've stayed here; well kept Batemans XB and XXXB, good but limited bar food from dining room, tables on big back sheltered lawn with swings; friendly standard poodle called Gemma, whiskery tabby cat called Percy; bedrooms *(Dr Keith Bloomfield, BB)*

South Croxton, Leics [SK6810], *Golden Fleece*: Large, pleasant free house with good value food lunchtime and evening, good service, Ind Coope Burton, Marstons Pedigree and guests on handpump *(P A and J B Jones)*

☆ **South Luffenham**, Leics [10 The Street; off A6121 at Halfway House, then first right; SK9402], *Boot & Shoe*: Friendly village local with comfortable, rambling stripped-stone bar, good log fire, well kept Greene King Abbot and Tolly, no smoking eating area, also more upmarket evening restaurant (not Mon) run as quite separate operation; seats in neat small garden, pool in public bar; no dogs — friendly pub alsatian; children welcome; four simple bedrooms, sharing two bathrooms — good breakfasts *(Gwen and Peter Andrews, M and J Back, Michael Thomson, D P and M E Cartwright, LYM)*

☆ **South Luffenham** [Station Rd], *Run of the Mill*: Charmingly restored 16th-century watermill in seven acres, with excellent bars, good choice of bar food, restaurant *(Brian and Jill Bond)*

☆ **South Rauceby**, Lincs [Main St; TF0245], *Bustard*: Nice old stone building, neat and much modernised inside with red plush seating, bustard and other bird pictures, some bric-a-brac; appealing bar food from doorstep sandwiches using home-baked bread to steaks, with good choice of puddings; log fires, well kept Ruddles Best and County on handpump, maybe local Martins; pleasant piped music — operatic highlights and so forth; attractive sheltered garden *(P Williams, S Berrisford, Andy and Jill Kassube, Philip Harrison, BB)*

☆ **Southwell**, Notts [Church St (A612); SK6953], *Bramley Apple*: Comfortably and prettily refurbished on bramley apple theme, inc apple-and-blossom carpet; bar and restaurant sensibly divided by stained-glass screens; generous good value food such as roast beef carved from the joint, fresh fish,

ham and steaks, with help-yourself veg or salads; Batemans XB and Marstons Pedigree on handpump with an uncommon guest such as Big End Old Lubrication, welcoming service; big 3-D apple inn-sign *(Dr Keith Bloomfield, Derek and Sylvia Stephenson, George Mitchell, BB)*

☆ **Southwell**, *Saracens Head*: Interesting old THF hotel (where Charles I spent his last free night), with well kept John Smiths on handpump, straightforward bar lunches in character main beamed bar, pleasant staff; children in eating area or restaurant; bedrooms comfortable and well kept, though some are small and none are cheap (but no extra charge for room service) *(Andy and Jill Kassube, ILP, LYM)*

Spalding, Lincs [New Rd; TF2422], *Black Swan*: Large, comfortable town-centre pub, popular with locals on market day (Tues); good back restaurant with bar-priced food, friendly service *(Keith and Aubrey Day)*; [Barrier Bank, Cowbit; A1073 3 miles S], *Olde Dun Cow*: Bar meals and restaurant, pleasant service, good atmosphere; Batemans and Tetleys on handpump; good play area; bedrooms *(Alec Whitfield)*

☆ **Stamford**, Lincs [Broad St; TF0207], *Lord Burghley*: Well laid out and furnished town-centre pub with well kept Adnams, Fullers London Pride, Greene King Abbot and IPA and guests such as Elgoods or Marstons Pedigree, good choice of attractively priced bar food, small walled garden with summer barbecues; no dogs — except Jess, the huge pub dog *(Joan and Michel Hooper-Immins, Andrew Morrissey, Wayne Brindle)*

Stamford [All Saints St], *Albion*: Doing well under new landlord, with well kept Greene King IPA and Abbot on handpump, small cosy bar, long thin back lounge with good home-made food such as chicken and leek pie, toad-in-the-hole, trout; next to Steam Brewery Museum, open Weds-Sun Apr-Sept *(Colin and Mary Meaden)*; [High St, St Martins], *Anchor*: Well modernised old stone inn next to bridge, river views, good bar food, well kept Watneys-related ales; bedrooms *(T Mansell)*; [East St], *Dolphin*: Good value bar food, huge helpings, low prices, friendly atmosphere, lots of locals — may be packed Fri mkt day *(Margaret and Trevor Errington)*

☆ **Staunton in the Vale**, Notts [SK8043], *Staunton Arms*: Attractive open-plan refurbishment, with interesting partitions, raised dining area with good reasonably priced food; well kept Marstons Pedigree, Tetleys and guest beer such as Ringwood, good service *(Derek and Sylvia Stephenson)*

Stoke Golding, Leics [High St; SP3997], *Three Horseshoes*: Roomy and comfortable country local in attractive village by church, well kept Courage Directors and John Smiths on handpump, huge helpings of good reasonably priced food lunchtime and evening; 10 mins' walk from Ashby Canal, Bridge 25 *(P A and J B Jones, Andrew Mead)*

Stoney Stanton, Leics [Long St; SP4894],

Blue Bell: Comfortable and welcoming, with good food (not Sun under new licensees) and well kept Everards Tiger *(Mike Tucker)*; [Stoney Cove], *Cove*: Friendly modern pub at inland scuba centre, good reasonably priced snacks and meals, diving artefacts in bar, terraces look out over water; gets crowded weekend lunchtimes and Weds evenings when scuba diving on *(Dave Mead)*

☆ **Stragglethorpe**, Notts [off A52 Nottingham—Radcliffe-on-Trent;SK6437], *Shepherds*: Large thatched Brewers Fayre family pub-restaurant with usual food and Whitbreads beers; notable for splendid facilities for children — family room has railed-off play area well equipped with books and toys, garden has two separate good play areas, for different age-groups *(Roy Y Bromell, Graham Bush)*

☆ **Stretton**, Leics [Great North Rd (actually on A1); SK9416], *Ram Jam*: Civilised and unusual escape from A1: smart all-day continental-style snack bar from breakfast-time on, with good value well chosen and well prepared snacks, fresh-ground coffee, fresh-squeezed orange and so forth, friendly informal service; comfortably airy modern lounge bar — again, a civilised continental feel, not that of a traditional pub — with good choice of food served quickly from buffet counter, Ruddles Best and County on handpump, useful small wine list with some good odd-bin halves, teak seats on terrace; adjoining restaurant; bedrooms comfortable and well equipped *(Tony Bland, BKA, BB)*

☆ **Stretton** [village signed off A1], *Jackson Stops*: Idiosyncratic and informal, with homely furnishings and pleasant medley of rustic bric-a-brac, well kept Ruddles Best and County and Sam Smiths OB on handpump, decent wines, open fires, bar food *(P G Topp, A S Maxted, LYM)*

Sutton Bridge, Lincs [just off A17 Kings Lynn—Holbeach; TF4731], *Anchor*: Welcoming and useful for area, with decent freshly cooked food and well kept local beer *(Dr James Haworth)*

☆ **Sutton Cheney**, Leics [Main St — off A447 3 miles S of Mkt Bosworth; SK4100], *Royal Arms*: Attractive village pub with three smallish friendly low-ceilinged rooms around central bar, two open fires, well kept Marstons and Shipstones on handpump, wide choice of bar food (not cheap, but worth it) inc masses of changing specials; upstairs restaurant, family conservatory with wishing well, garden with children's play area; handy for Bosworth Field *(J Beeken, Mike and Wendy Proctor, Graham Richardson)*

☆ **Sutton Cheney** [Main St], *Hercules*: Wide range of frequently changing real ales inc rarities and one or two brewed for the pub, in cheerful refurbished bar; piped music, friendly licensees, dining area *(LYM)*

Sutton in Ashfield, Notts [Alfreton Rd; off M1 junction 28; SK5059], *Duke of Sussex*: Homely pub with well kept Hardys & Hansons on electric pump, good choice of meals and snacks inc Sun *(Joan and Michel Hooper-Immins, Angie and David Parkes)*

☆ **Sutton in the Elms**, Leics [Coventry Rd; B581/B4114 nr M69 junction 2 — OS Sheet 140, map reference 509937; SP5194], *Mill on the Soar*: Big bustling family place, conversion of substantial watermill — stripped brickwork, some rugs and carpet on the flagstones, brown beams and joists festooned with china and copper; no smoking conservatory, river views from upstairs restaurant, quickly served bar food until 10 (9.30 Sat), Everards and guest ales, lots of space and interest outside; children welcome; bedrooms in separate comfortably modern block *(David Williams, LYM)*

☆ **Tattershall Thorpe**, Lincs [TF2259], *Blue Bell*: Attractive outside and in, very friendly landlord, good value bar food *(Andy and Jill Kassube)*

☆ **Thurcaston**, Leics [Leicester Rd; SK5610], *Wheatsheaf*: Cosy and clean small-roomed village local, redecorated to move its appeal gently upmarket; well kept Everards Tiger, Old Original and a guest, interesting if not cheap food, garden with swing, well appointed skittle alley *(P A and J B Jones)*

Torksey, Lincs [Torksey Lock; SK8478], *White Swan*: Pretty and welcoming country pub with comfortably plush beamed and Turkey-carpeted main bar, friendly attentive service, decent piped music, decent bar food; large front terrace *(GB, CH)*

☆ **Tugby**, Leics [Main St; village signposted off A47 E of Leicester, bear right in village; SK7600], *Black Horse*: Good value home-made evening meals in cosy and attractively traditional small rooms of picturesque black-and-white thatched village pub, Ansells on handpump, friendly service, log fire; children welcome; closed lunchtime *(LYM)*

Tur Langton, Leics [off B6047; follow Kibworth signpost from village centre; SP7194], *Crown*: Well kept Bass, Marstons Pedigree and Shipstones in distinctive pub with attractive furnishings from an antique curved settle to chintzy easy chairs; tables on pleasantly planted terraces and in sheltered back courtyard; restaurant; closed weekday lunchtimes *(LYM)*

☆ **Upper Hambleton**, Leics [village signposted from A606 on E edge of Oakham; SK9007], *Finches Arms*: Dining pub with good choice of well prepared bar food from sandwiches up; built-in button-back leatherette banquettes and open fire in knocked-through front bar, velvet curtain to restaurant extension with picture windows, tables on gravel terrace looking down to Rutland Water; well kept Darleys Thorne, Wards Sheffield Best and Kirby and Vaux Samson on handpump *(M Morgan, BB)*

Uppingham, Leics [High St; SP8699], *Crown*: Though a hotel bar, atmosphere more that of a pub lounge — floral wallpaper over wooden dado, gas-type wall lamps, friendly service, wide choice of food, well kept Everards on handpump *(Brian Jones)*; [High St East/Market Sq], *Falcon*:

Quiet oak-panelled Tap Bar with log fire in big stone fireplace, large mullioned windows looking on to market square; Camerons Strongarm and Ruddles County and Best on handpump *(Brian Jones)*; [Market Sq], *Vaults*: Worth knowing for quickly served decent bar food, in long room with public area (darts, piped Radio 1) one end, lounge the other; bedrooms *(Geoff Lee)*

☆ **Upton**, Notts [A612; SK7354], *French Horn*: Neatly comfortable open-plan bar with generous helpings of home-made food inc interesting recipes and lots of good puddings; upstairs brasserie (not Sun evening), well kept John Smiths, good choice of decent wines by the glass, tables in pleasant surroundings outside; children welcome *(Mr and Mrs B H James, Andy and Jill Kassube, A J and E M Watts, LYM)*

Wainfleet, Lincs [High St; A52 Skegness—Boston; TF5058], *Angel*: Sturdy furnishings in neat lounge of this Bass outpost in Batemans territory, with friendly service, good value bar food from sandwiches though tasty omelettes or lasagne to steak, well kept real ale, snooker/children's room with video *(Derek and Sylvia Stephenson, LYM)*

Waltham on the Wolds, Leics [SK8024], *Marquis of Granby*: Pleasant local with very filling home-made food and satisfactory beer *(Mr and Mrs J M Elden)*; [A607], *Royal Horseshoes*: Sturdily furnished comfortable stone-built inn with help-yourself carvery/buffet and other bar food (cold buffet for residents only, Sun evening) — some cheaper snacks would be welcome; well kept John Smiths on handpump, decent wines, fair range of malts, piped music, three open fires, seats outside; children allowed in eating area; bedrooms *(G E Rich, LYM)*

Washingborough, Lincs [TF0270], *Ferry Boat*: Friendly village pub with reconstructed mill wheel; Watneys-related real ales, separate eating area with own bar and salad bar *(Andy and Jill Kassube)*

Wellingore, Lincs [High St; SK9856], *Marquis of Granby*: Attractive old pub in pretty village, welcoming service, good range of real ales on handpump, bar food inc particularly good value sandwiches, restaurant *(A G Roby)*

☆ **West Leake**, Notts [off A6006; SK5226], *Star*: Warmly welcoming traditional beamed and tiled bar with hunting trophies, sturdy furnishings and several cats, comfortable chairs and good log fire in partly panelled lounge, short choice of good value simple weekday lunchtime food, well kept Adnams and Bass; children in eating area *(Helen and Wal Burns, Andy and Jill Kassube, Dr Keith Louden, Pete Storey, LYM)*

☆ **West Stockwith**, Notts [SK7995], *Waterfront*: Well refurbished, in excellent waterside spot on basin between River Trent and Chesterfield Canal; particularly well kept beer, civilised landlord, interesting good value food; crowded summer evenings with jolly boating types *(P A and J B Jones, ILP)*

Whetstone, Leics [opp GEC works; off A426 S of Leicester, at Dog & Gun; SP5597], *Kaffir*: Very neat, spotless pub with central bar and several surrounding rooms; large eating area on left and two other interconnected rooms on right; generous helpings of good food; restaurant; lovely garden with plenty of toys *(Ted George)*

☆ **Whitwell**, Leics [A606 Stamford—Oakham; SK9208], *Noel Arms*: Engaging locals' bar with two tiny welcoming rooms of unpretentious but genuine character; also much more spacious and more orthodoxly plush and decorous back extension; wide choice of good waitress-served home-cooked food (till 10), afternoon teas (not Mon), Ansells and Ruddles Best and County, tables outside with occasional barbecues; children welcome; bedrooms *(W H Bland, LYM)*

Widmerpool, Notts [just off A46/A606 — 1st left off A606 towards Nottingham; SK6328], *Pullman Diner*: Completely redeveloped, with strong emphasis on food — generous helpings, reasonable choice and prices; Ruddles ales *(A C and S J Beardsley)*

Wigston, Leics [Oadby Rd; SK5900], *Firs*: Everards pub refurbished last year (mock bookcase, etc), popular for good choice of lunchtime hot food (be nice if they did more vegetarian and fish dishes); lots of space, uniformed bar staff; children allowed *(Rona Murdoch)*

Wilford, Notts [Main Rd; SK5637], *Ferryboat*: Clean traditional pub with genuine furnishings, two remote snugs, dining lounge with lofted roof and imposing fireplace; well kept Shipstones Bitter and Mild, tidy back terrace, garden with play area, view over river to Nottingham Castle *(Graham Bush)*; [Wilford Lane], *Maypole*: Recently refurbished, pleasant and comfortable, separate games area, very competitively priced good food, well kept Home beers *(Russell Allen)*

☆ **Wing**, Leics [Top St; signed off A6003 S of Oakham; SK8903], *Kings Arms*: Simple early 17th-century inn, carefully refurbished to make the most of the Rutland stonework and keep the coal fire and rare cash-register handpump set for well kept Bass, Hook Norton Best and Ruddles County; convivial atmosphere, wide choice of good generous home-cooked food; separate spacious restaurant, cottage to let; small but interesting medieval turf maze nearby *(P A and J B Jones, Brian and Jill Bond, LYM)*

☆ **Woodhouse Eaves**, Leics [off B591 S of Loughborough; SK5214], *Bulls Head*: Popular pub, nicely decorated and furnished, well placed in attractive village; hot and cold food display with wide and attractive choice, good table service by friendly staff *(J and B Grove)*

Woodhouse Eaves [Brand Hill; beyond Main St], *Wheatsheaf*: Open-plan country pub with good open fires, plush seating, well kept Ruddles, tables out in floodlit former coachyard *(T Nott, LYM)*

☆ **Woolsthorpe**, Lincs [the one nr Belvoir,

signed off A52 Grantham—Nottingham; SK8435], *Rutland Arms*: Quiet Vale of Belvoir setting by disused Grantham Canal for welcoming pub; smart, relaxed lounge with some high-backed settles, hunting prints and brasses, very popular midweek with older people; family extension with old furniture, open fire, video juke box, bric-a-brac on walls and windows; quite good range of reasonably priced bar food, well kept Whitbreads Castle Eden on handpump, two pool tables in annexe; play equipment on large lawn; also known as Dirty Duck *(Dr Keith Bloomfield, Gary Phillips)*

Woolsthorpe, *Chequers*: Very local but worth knowing for good value home-made food *(Mr and Mrs J M Elden)*

Worthington, Leics [Church St; off A447 and A453; SK4020], *Old Swan*: Village pub, recently refurbished but still with low beams and two large open fireplaces; friendly service, Ansells, Marstons and Ruddles beers, and big helpings of bar food; delightful tiled gents'; restaurant *(Jane Morrell, Dave Braisted)*

☆ **Wymondham,** Leics [Edmonthorpe Rd; off B676 E of Melton Mowbray; SK8518], *Hunters Arms*: Cosy foxhunting-theme pub with two bars, open fire, good value bar food, well kept Bass, Greene King IPA and Abbot; popular restaurant; run by Frenchman and English wife *(Ian Pendlebury, Dr Keith Bloomfield)*

Lincolnshire   *see* Leicestershire

Midlands
(Northamptonshire,
Warwickshire and West
Midlands)

The pubs in this area are among the best in Britain for giving you
value for your money. Drinks prices are noticeably lower than the
national average – particularly in pubs tied to the area's local and
regional breweries. In the Midlands these tend to show an even wider
price advantage over other pubs than elsewhere. Food prices also tend
to be low, with quite a number of bargain pubs. And, regardless of
price, food can sometimes be a special draw in the area's pubs – as it
is at the Bell at Alderminster (interesting freshly cooked dishes), the
Ferry at Alveston (a new entry, very promising indeed), the
charmingly informal Rose & Crown at Charlton, the popular and
civilised Falcon at Fotheringhay (imaginative cooking), the
surprisingly extensive yet interesting Snooty Fox at Lowick, the
attractively traditional Fleur de Lys by the canal at Lowsonford (very
good indeed for a chain pub), the Mill looking out over its millpond
just outside Oundle (another new entry), the Falcon at Priors Marston
(good wine, too, and a smashing landlord), the White Bear in
Shipston on Stour (very appealing to a wide mix of people), the
Griffin at Shustoke (notable for its beers, too), the Slug & Lettuce in
Stratford, the charmingly furnished Red Lion in Thornby (also new to
this edition – back in the Guide after a break), the Old Friar at
Twywell and the amazingly popular Pheasant at Withybrook – an
archetypal dining pub, where the food's definitely the main thing.
Some other pubs to note here include the idiosyncratic and appealing
Old Coach House at Ashby St Ledgers (getting better all round as its
newish licensees settle in), the Vine in Brierley Hill (a lovely example
of a basic Black Country pub, right by its brewery), the delightfully
unspoilt and traditional Case is Altered at Five Ways, the wildly
sloping Crooked House at Himley, the friendly Navigation by the
canal at Lapworth, the eccentric Little Dry Dock at Netherton, the
relaxed and historic Old Mint in Southam, the cheerful Garrick in
Stratford, the nice little Plough in Warmington, the well run Bell in
Welford on Avon, and the ancient Royal Oak at Whatcote – all doing
particularly well at the moment. Pubs in the Lucky Dip section at the
end of the chapter that also currently look to be really up and coming
include the Fox & Hounds at Clay Coton, Navigation at Cosgrove,
Rose & Crown at Ratley, Red Lion at Sibbertoft and Vane Arms at
Sudborough. The pubs in the Little chain are always worth a look,
and other Dip pubs to note particularly include the Greyhound and
Old Windmill in Coventry, Great Western at Deppers Bridge, Dun
Cow at Dunchurch, Plough at Eathorpe, Fox & Hounds at Great
Brington, Howard Arms at Ilmington, Saracens Head at Little

Brington, Napton Bridge at Napton, Abington Park in Northampton, Stags Head at Offchurch, Olde Crab Mill at Preston Bagot, Holly Bush at Priors Marston, Shakespeare in Stratford, Blue Boar at Temple Grafton and Shakespeare in Welford on Avon.

ALDERMINSTER (Warwicks)   SP2348   Map 4

Bell 🅟

A3400 Oxford–Stratford

Though this Cotswold pub is very popular for its interesting food, it's also a pleasant place just for a drink. The communicating areas of the spacious bar are stripped back to their original flagstones and wooden floors and have plenty of stripped slatback chairs around wooden tables, little vases of flowers, a panelled oak settle, small landscape prints and swan's-neck brass-and-globe lamps on the cream walls, and a solid fuel stove in a stripped brick inglenook. Using fresh produce (no fried food at all), the frequently changing menu might include soup such as bortsch, parsnip and orange or carrot and coriander (£1.95), various pâtés (£3.95), shrimps Phoebe (£4.25), crab and courgette au gratin (£4.50), seafood and mushroom scallop (£4.50), salads (from £5.75), and lots of changing specials such as the recommended marinated grilled cod (£6.95), crispy-topped lamb in cider, lamb and aubergine and lentil khoresh, chicken supreme in tarragon or beef and walnut casserole (all £7.25), rack of spare ribs (£7.95) and garlic king prawns (£8.50), with several puddings such as strawberry pavlova, banoffi pie and peach and almond tart (£2.75). Two course business lunch available weekdays (£5.50). Flowers IPA and Original on handpump, and a good range of wines (from Berry Bros & Rudd); good service; dominoes. There are tables under cocktail parasols on the sheltered grass, and a large car park; four miles from Stratford.

(Recommended by John Bramley, Mr and Mrs G J Rice, Sarah Bullard, Brian Skelcher, S V Bishop, John Whitehead, Mrs Simon Turner, John Knighton, C A Holloway, John Bowdler, Laurence Manning, Joy and Peter Heatherley; up-to-date reports please)

Free house   Licensees Keith and Vanessa Brewer   Real ale   Meals and snacks (12–2, 7–10)   Partly no smoking restaurant   Alderminster (0789) 450414   Children welcome   Open 12–2.30, 7–11; closed most evenings 26 Dec–3 Jan, inc 31 Dec

ALVESTON (Warwicks)   SP2356   Map 4

Ferry 🅟

End of village; off B4086 Stratford–Wellesbourne – OS Sheet 151, map reference 236565

The Russons who made a name for themselves at the Howard Arms in Ilmington have now settled in well here. It's a different style of building from their former pub. Though it too is old, it's less olde-worlde. Three rooms knocked into one long single bar have comfortable newish brocaded seating and a low-key decor – cream walls, fish prints, very clear lighting. This somehow seems to give the whole operation a more clearly defined sense of purpose and yet to allow for a very relaxed atmosphere – there's no sense of it being taken over by self-important routine lunchers, and everyone seems to be there to enjoy themselves. As before, the friendly staff are notably well trained, and all is neat and clean. But the main thing of course is the food. There's a good interesting choice, using all fresh produce bought daily, carefully cooked, attractively presented and generously served. It might include sandwiches (from £1.75), soup (£1.60), whitebait (£2.50), fried mushrooms, courgettes and cauliflower with tartare sauce dip (£2.75), vegetables in a nut and tomato bake (£3.75), a big filled Yorkshire pudding (£4.95), plenty of fish such as salmon with prawns in lobster sauce on pasta (£5.50), plaice (£5.75) or lemon sole (£6.50), Scotch steaks (from rump £6.50), and good home-made puddings like treacle sponge or banoffi pie (£1.85). Well kept Flowers IPA and Original, and a monthly guest beer (praise for them for getting this direct from the producer rather than through their tied brewery, and for charging less for it); a particularly good choice of wines by the glass, good coffee, no music or machines, log fire; get there early for a table. The pub's tucked away in an attractive spot, with a path leading off along the River Avon. *(Recommended by Mrs G Walsh, Philip and Trisha Ferris, S V Bishop, Peter Lloyd, John Bowdler, T Nott, Roy Bromell, W Lawrence)*

Flowers (Whitbreads)   Tenants David and Sarah Russon   Real ale   Meals and snacks (not Sun evening)   (0789) 269883   Children over 5 allowed   Open 11–2.30, 6–11; closed 25 Dec

ASHBY ST LEDGERS (Northants)   SP5768   Map 4

Old Coach House £

4 miles from M1, junction 18; A5 S to Kilsby, then A361 S towards Daventry; village is signposted left. Alternatively 8 miles from M1 junction 16, then A45 W to Weedon, A5 N to sign for village.

The hard-working and friendly licensees of this dark stone house are consolidating its appeal. Several comfortable, rambling little rooms have high-backed winged settles on polished black and red tiles, old kitchen tables, harness on a few standing timbers, hunting pictures (often of the Pytchley, which sometimes meets outside), Thelwell prints, and a big winter log fire. A front room has darts, pool, trivia and piped music. Good bar food, waitress served, includes sandwiches, home-made soup (£1.50), hamburgers (from £2.50), ploughman's (£2.95), chilli con carne (£2.95), lasagne (£2.95), all day breakfast (£3.25), trout (£4.50), halibut (£5.50), pork toppers (£5.50), salmon (£6.00), duck breast (£7.50), fillet steak (£9.25) and children's dishes (from 60p); daily cold buffet that includes beautifully rare beef and good ham salads, traditional Sunday lunch served in winter, barbecue every Saturday and Sunday lunchtime in summer. Well kept Everards Old Original and Tiger, Flowers Original and Marstons Pedigree on handpump (77 guest ales in April 1991). There are seats among fruit trees and under a fairy-lit arbour. All bedrooms have been upgraded. The attractive village is full of thatched stone houses, and has wide grass verges running down to the lane; the nearby manor house was owned by one of the gunpowder plotters. *(Recommended by KC, Geoff Wilson, Dennis Jones, Andrew Morrissey, Richard Dolphin)*

Free house   Licensees Brian and Philippa McCabe   Real ale   Meals and snacks Rugby (0788) 890349   Children allowed till 8pm   Open 12–2.30, 6–11   Bedrooms; £38B/£45B

ASTON CANTLOW (Warwicks)   SP1359   Map 4

Kings Head

This beautifully timbered, friendly village pub is not far from Mary Arden's house in Wilmcote – worth visiting in spite of the crowds. The carefully refurbished bar on the right has flagstones, an old-fashioned snug, and wooden settles around its massive central fireplace; the carpeted main bar has attractive window seats and Windsor chairs around its oak tables, with a longcase clock in the corner. A decent range of good home-made bar food includes sandwiches (from £1.60), ploughman's (£2.80–£3.10), scampi (£5.25), steak and kidney pie (£5.50), hake bake (£5.50), ham, mushroom and leek pie (£5.50). Puddings, pies and crumbles (£1.70–£2). Extended evening menu includes curries (£5.50-£6), steaks and gammons. Well kept Flowers IPA and Marstons Pedigree on handpump; dominoes, cribbage, fruit machine. You can sit outside on the sturdy teak seats in front decorated in summer with colourful hanging baskets below the wisteria that rambles along the warm red-tiled roof. *(Recommended by Mrs G Walsh, Hilary Aslett, H R Bevan, Brian Skelcher, Brian Jones)*

Flowers (Whitbreads)   Tenants Joe and Di Saunders   Real ale   Meals and snacks (till 1.45, not before 7.30 evenings, not Sun or Mon evenings)   Alne (0789) 488242 Children in area partly set aside   Open 11.45–2.30, 7.00–11

BERKSWELL (W Midlands)   SP2479   Map 4

Bear

Spencer Lane; village signposted from A452

In a pretty village, this big timbered dining pub has a bustling, friendly feel. On weekday lunchtimes there's a cold table with quiches, cold meats and cheese and help-yourself salads (£3.60), as well as rolls (from £1.10), and hot dishes such as steak and kidney or turkey and ham pie, lasagne, beef stroganoff or cod mornay (all £4.10). Ruddles Best and County on handpump; fruit machine and video game. Outside on the tree-sheltered back lawn are some tables and chairs. Children's bouncy castle at weekends. The cannon in front of the building is a veteran of the Crimean War; the church is well worth a visit. (*Recommended by M C Jeanes, Phil Clissitt, Ness Turner, Sheila Keene, H R Bevan, Graham Richardson, Brian Skelcher, R P Hastings; more reports please*)

Manns (Watneys)   Manager John D'Arcy   Real ale   Meals and snacks   Restaurant (not Sun evening)   Berkswell (0676) 33202   Children welcome   Jazz or folk Sun evening   Open 11–2.30, 6–11

BIRMINGHAM   SP0786   Map 4

Bartons Arms

2 miles from M6 junction 6; leave junction on A38(M) towards city centre but take first exit, going right at exit roundabout into Victoria Road, and left at next big roundabout into Aston High Street – A34 towards city centre; pub on the next corner at Park Lane (B4144); car park just past pub on opposite side of road; or take junction 7 of M6 – pub an unmissable landmark on A34 going N from town centre

As we go to press we hear that this landmark is likely to change hands, and perhaps breweries. So the practical details of food and drink will almost certainly change – it's had well kept Bass ales including M & B Mild, and the usual sorts of bar food at prices that would earn it one of our bargain food awards. But whatever happens, we wouldn't hesitate to recommend it as the grandest English example of Edwardian pub design. Easily recognised by its domed clock tower, this magnificent building has an eclectic series of rooms – from palatial salons to cosy snugs. These are strikingly decorated with richly coloured and painted elaborate tilework, there's lots of highly polished mahogany and rosewood, sparkling cut glass mirrors and stained glass, plush seating, heavy brass hanging lamps, and of course a full set of painted cut-glass snob screens – little swivelling panels that you open when you want a drink and shut when you want privacy. (*Recommended by Dr and Mrs C D E Morris, E J Alcock, Kevin Fields, Patrick and Mary McDermott, Len Beattie, Lynne Sheridan and Bob West; more reports please*)

See above   Real ale   Lunchtime meals and snacks (not Sat or Sun)   Children have been allowed lunchtime   Has been open 11.30–2.30(3 Sat), 6–11

BRIERLEY HILL (W Midlands)   SO9187   Map 4

Vine £

Delph Rd; B4172 between A461 and A4100, near A4100

Benefiting from being right next to the brewery, this lively and friendly Black Country pub serves very well kept and priced Bitter and Mild (dark, unusually full-flavoured with a touch of hops, and outstanding value) on handpump, with Delph Strong in winter. The front bar has wall benches and simple leatherette-topped oak stools, a snug on the left has solidly built red plush seats, and the back bar has brass chandeliers and more seats. Good, fresh snacks include old-fashioned sandwiches (from 90p), and marvellous-value salads (from £1.70). Darts, cribbage, dominoes, space game and trivia. (*Recommended by Dave Braisted, Comus Elliott, Brian Jones, J S Rutter, Michael Rooke, Kevin Fields, Matt Pringle; more reports please*)

Bathams   Manager Melvyn Wood   Real ale   Lunchtime snacks (not Sun)   Brierley

Hill (0384) 78293   *Children in own room   Rock or blues Sun, jazz or folk Mon
Open 12–4, 6–11 Mon-Thurs, 12–11 Fri and Sat*

CHARLTON (Northants)   SP5236 Map 4
Rose & Crown
Village signposted from A41 at W edge of Aynho, and from Kings Sutton

There's a convivial atmosphere and a jolly mix of customers in this neat thatched
stone pub. The beamed bar – mainly stripped back to carefully coursed masonry –
has a sofa and winged armchairs as well as seats that match the sturdy
country-kitchen tables, shelves of books by the big open fireplace, and some good
prints on the walls; the quiet collie is called Boltby. There's dominoes and also a
no-smoking lounge. Good bar food ranges from sandwiches (from £1.15), through
burgers (from £1.25), salads (from £4.50), lovely smoked salmon (£4), chilli con
carne or spaghetti bolognese (£4.75), Barnsley chop (£4.50) and fresh or smoked
haddock fillets (£5), to excellent Scottish steaks (from £8). The commendable
choice of real ales on handpump includes Bass, Flowers IPA and Original, Fullers
London Pride, Marstons Pedigree, Mitchells Bitter and ESB and Wadworth 6X;
also a vast range (60–70) of carefully chosen malt whiskies, good selection of
vintage ports including Grahams and Cockburns and a decent wine list with good
value house wines. There are a couple of picnic-table sets on a small front terrace
by the village lane, with a few more on gravel behind. *(Recommended by Sir Nigel
Foulkes, John Whitehead, C J Rosser, Elizabeth and Klaus Leist; more reports please)*

*Free house   Licensees Peter and Brenda Reeves   Real ale   Meals and snacks
(12.15–2.15, 7.15–9.30; not Sun evening, cold only Sun lunchtime)   Restaurant (only
buffet Sun)   Banbury (0295) 811317   Children allowed till 7.30 in small room away
from bar   Open 12–3, 5–11; Sat evening opening 6.30; closed 25 and 26 Dec
evenings   Bedrooms under construction*

CLIPSTON (Northants)   SP7181 Map 4
Bulls Head
B4036 S of Market Harborough

The atmosphere in this white-rendered, slate-roofed pub is very friendly and
relaxed, and though it's largely local in the evenings, there is a warm welcome for
visitors. The lounge bar is cosily divided into three snug areas leading down from
the servery and has a log fire, seats that are mainly comfortable and sturdy small
settles and stools upholstered in red plush, some harness and tools, and countless
coins glistening in the black beams; this continues an odd tradition started by US
airmen based nearby in World War II – they used to wedge the money waiting for
their next drink in cracks and crannies of the ancient woodwork. Decent bar food
includes sandwiches and other light snacks, with main dishes majoring on several
speciality pies eg Drunken Bull (£3.95); also lasagne, chilli and curry (all at £3.50)
and mixed grill (£4.50). Well kept Adnams, Ruddles Best and County, Theakstons
and Websters on handpump, and a very impressive choice of nearly 300 malt
whiskies. The long back games bar, lively in the evenings, has darts, pool, table
skittles, cribbage, pinball, dominoes, fruit machine and juke box. Outside, there
are a few white tables under cocktail parasols on the terrace that stretches back
beside it, with a barbecue. *(Recommended by M and J Back, David Butcher; more reports
please)*

*Manns (Watneys)   Leasehold: Colin and Jenny Smith   Real ale   Meals and snacks
(not Sun or Mon evenings)   Clipston (085 886)286   Children welcome   Occasional
discos, karaoki, live entertainment   Open 11.30–2.30, 6.30–11; closed 25 Dec
Bedrooms planned for 1992*

CRICK (Northants)   SP5872   Map 4

Red Lion

A mile from M1 junction 18; A428

Families looking for a relaxed refuge from the motorway can use a Perspex-roofed sheltered terrace in the old coach yard here, with lots of pretty summer hanging baskets; there are a few picnic-table sets under cocktail parasols on grass by the car park. Inside, it's pleasantly chatty (no piped music) with stripped stonework, soft lighting, and roaring log fires in winter (in summer the two ornamental stone fireplaces are bright with big copper dishes and brassware); it's quietest and snuggest in the inner part of the bar. Bar food includes gammon, scampi or trout (£5), steaks (from £7) and duck (£7.50) in the evening, with lunchtime sandwiches, ploughman's (£2), lasagne, steak and kidney pie and so forth (£3.50) and steak (£6.50); well kept Ruddles Best and Websters Yorkshire on handpump; hard to leave. *(Recommended by W J Wonham, K and G Jackson, David Gaunt; more reports please)*

Grand Met/Watneys   Leasehold: Tom and Mary Marks   Real ale   Meals and snacks (till 1.45; not Weds evening, not Sun)   Crick (0788) 822342   Open 11.30–2.30, 6.30–11

EAST HADDON (Northants)   SP6668   Map 4

Red Lion   ⇌

High St; village signposted off A428 (turn right in village) and off A50 N of Northampton

The walled side garden of this substantially built golden stone small hotel has lilac, fruit trees, roses and neat little flowerbeds, and leads back to the bigger lawn, where there are well spaced picnic-table sets; a small side terrace has white tables under cocktail parasols. A big copper beech shades the gravel car park. The civilised, panelled lounge bar – decorated in comfortably subdued colours – is well furnished with oak panelled settles, library chairs, soft modern dining chairs and a mix of oak, mahogany and cast-iron-framed tables, as well as recessed china cabinets, old prints and pewter; a couple of beams are hung sparingly with little kegs, brass pots, swords and so forth. There are sturdy old-fashioned red leather seats in the small public bar; well kept Charles Wells Eagle and Bombardier on handpump. Good bar food includes sandwiches (£1.90), stock pot and tomato soup (both £2.25), ploughman's (£3.50), and hot dishes such as mushroom and ham pancakes (£4.75), chilli con carne (£4.95), with a popular cold platter (£6.25). Extended evening menu includes Melton farmhouse pie (£4.50) and chicken, bacon and mushroom kebabs (£5.50), and a good choice of home-made puddings (all £2.75); attentive service. Bedrooms; excellent place to stay, with good breakfasts. *(Recommended by Keith Croston, J Barnwell; more reports please)*

Charles Wells   Tenants Mr and Mrs Ian Kennedy   Real ale   Meals and snacks (not over the Christmas period)   Pretty restaurant (evenings, Sun lunch)   Northampton (0604) 770223   Children in eating area and restaurant   Open 11–2.30, 6–11   Bedrooms; £35/£48

EASTCOTE (Northants)   SP6753   Map 4

Eastcote Arms £

Gayton Rd; village signposted from A5 3 miles N of Towcester

The conversation in this bustling country village pub may well be based on fishing, shooting and so forth – reflecting the wealth of pictures above the dark brown wooden dado which also include cricket and other sports, militia, and some related to the pub and its history. The traditionally furnished bar has two winter log fires, flowery curtains, and fresh flowers; dominoes and unobtrusive piped music. Good value food such as rolls (95p), soup (£1.25), very good big home-made pastie with gravy (£1.95), ploughman's (£2.75), and daily specials like lasagne (£2.95). Well kept Bass, Fullers ESB, Sam Smiths OB and a monthly changing guest beer such as Exmoor, Fullers Chiswick and Moorlands, as well as a fine fragrant beer brewed by Banks & Taylors especially for them (though now sold elsewhere too). There are picnic-table sets and other tables in an attractive back garden, with roses, geraniums and so forth around the neat lawn. *(Recommended by K H Frostick, Virginia Jones, Chris Aslett, Nick Dowson, Alison Hayward, R D and S A Mackay)*

Free house   Licensee Mrs Sheila Manning   Real ale   Lunchtime snacks (not Sun) (0327) 830731   Children in eating area   Open 12–2.30, 6–10.30(11 Fri and Sat, Sun 12–2,7–10); closed Mon lunchtime, except bank hols

FIVE WAYS (Warwicks)   SP2270 Map 4

Case is Altered

Follow Rowington signposts from A41 at junction roundabout with A4177 N of Warwick

What makes this delightful brick cottage special is the warmth of the welcome – from the landlady (probably sitting chatting to customers), and from the regulars themselves. The small main bar is very unspoilt and only has a few, sturdy and old-fashioned tables, with a couple of leather-covered sturdy settles facing each other over the spotless tiles; it's decorated with a fine old poster showing the Lucas Blackwell & Arkwright brewery (now flats), and a clock with its hours spelling out Thornleys, another defunct brewery. From here you reach the homely lounge (usually open only on Friday and Saturday evenings) through a door lit up on either side. A door at the back of the building leads into a simple little room, usually empty on weekday lunchtimes, with a rug on its tiled floor and a bar billiards table protected by an ancient leather cover (it takes pre-decimal sixpences). Well kept Ansells Mild and Bitter, Flowers Original, Ind Coop and Sam Smiths OB served by rare miniature pumps mounted on the casks that are stilled behind the counter. Behind a wrought-iron gate is a little brick-paved courtyard with a stone table under a chestnut tree. *(Recommended by Phil Bryant, Paul Evans, Gordon and Daphne, Mark Evans, Brian Jones, Karen Bettesworth, Chris Down, Judith Steinert; more reports please)*

Free house   Licensee Gwen Jones   Real ale   Snacks (lunchtime)   (0926) 484206 Open 11–2.30, 6–11(Closed evening 25 Dec)

FOTHERINGHAY (Northants)   TL0593 Map 5

Falcon ⊗

Village signposted off A605 on Peterborough side of Oundle

At lunchtime particularly, this attractive pub fills up very quickly with people keen to enjoy the good and imaginative bar food: home-made soups like French onion or iced gazpacho (£2.40), home-made pâtés like chicken or duck (from £2.50), excellent ploughman's (£2.50), lots of fish dishes such as home-made potted trout (£3.20) and smoked Scotch salmon (£4.20), steak and kidney pie (£4.10), cold local ham and turkey with salads (£5.50), rabbit in cider with apples and walnuts (£5.40), roast duckling with apple and rosemary stuffing (£6.40), roast rack of English lamb (£7); in summer you can eat on the terrace or in the neat garden under the trees; good service. The comfortable lounge has cushioned slatback armchairs and bucket chairs, antique engravings on its cream walls, a hum of quiet conversation, and winter log fires in stone fireplaces at each end. There is a simpler public bar which the landlord prefers to keep for the locals. Well kept Elgoods Bitter on handpump; darts, shove-ha'penny, cribbage and dominoes. The vast church behind is worth a visit and the site of Fotheringhay Castle is nearby (where Mary Queen of Scots was executed in 1587). *(Recommended by Mrs J A Blanks, Tom Evans, Paul and Margaret Baker, J P Cinnamond)*

Free house   Licensee Alan Stewart   Real ale   Meals (not Mon) and snacks (not Mon)   Cotterstock (08326)254   Children welcome   Open 10–3, 6–11

GREAT WOLFORD (Warwicks)　SP2434　Map 4

Fox & Hounds

Village signposted on right on A34 3 miles S of Shipston on Stour

A small tap room in this 16th-century pub serves Boddingtons, Flowers IPA, Marstons Pedigree, Wadworth 6X and Whitbreads Castle Eden on handpump, as well as quite a few malt whiskies and country wines; darts, shove-ha'penny, dominoes, chess, draughts, cards here, too. The old-fashioned open-plan bar is cosy, with flagstones, low beams, a pair of high-backed old settles and other comfortable armchairish seats around a nice collection of old tables, well cushioned wall benches and a window seat, and old hunting prints on the walls – which are partly stripped back to the bare stone. There's a large stone fireplace with a good winter log fire by the fine old bread oven, and classical piped music in the main bar. Bar food includes sandwiches, soup (£1.75), pâté (£2.30), garlic mushrooms (£2.50), ploughman's (£2.85), lasagne (£4.25), lamb's liver Italian (£5.25), chicken curry (£5.25), beef and mushrooms in beer (£5.95), sirloin steak (£7.25); the dining room doubles as the restaurant at weekends. On the terrace outside is a well. (*Recommended by Peter and Erica Davis, G P Beckett, JM, PM, Mrs Lili Lomas; more reports please*)

Free house　Licensees David and Joan Hawker　Real ale　Meals and snacks Barton-on-the-Heath (060 874) 220　Children in dining room　Jazz occasionally Sat lunchtime　Open 12–2.30(3 Sat), 7–11; closed Mon lunchtimes except bank hols

HIMLEY (W Midlands – though see below)　SO8889　Map 4

Crooked House ★ £

Pub signposted from B4176 Gornalwood–Himley, OS Sheet 139, map reference 896908; readers have got so used to thinking of the pub as being near Kingswinford in the Midlands (though Himley is actually in Staffs) that we still include it in this chapter – the pub itself is virtually smack on the county boundary

As a result of local mining, this pub is literally staggering. The walls and floors slope very steeply – even getting the doors open is an uphill struggle, and on one table a bottle on its side actually rolls 'upwards' against the apparent direction of the slope. For a 10p donation you can get a big ball-bearing from the bar to roll 'uphill' along a wainscot. There's still a room for locals with no food and the atmosphere throughout is very relaxed. At the back is a large, level and more modern extension with local antiques. Well kept cheap Banks's Bitter or Mild (on electric pump); dominoes, fruit machine and piped music. Bar food includes sandwiches, ploughman's (£2.40), home-made faggots (£2.55), home-made steak and kidney pie (£3.30). It can get busy if there's a local clay-pigeon shoot outside. The terrace is spacious. (*Recommended by Frank Cummins, Dr Paul Kitchener, Roger Huggins, Patrick and Mary McDermott, Matt Pringle, Audrey and Brian Green, Kevin Fields*)

Banks's　Manager Gary Ensor　Real ale　Lunchtime meals and snacks　(0384) 238583　Children in food area lunchtime only, no under 3s　Open 11–11; 11.30–2.30, 6–11 winter

KENILWORTH (Warwicks)　SP2871　Map 4

Virgins & Castle

High St; opposite A429 Coventry Rd at junction with A452

This pub has recently come under new management so food and drink may be altered. The entrance corridor in this old-fashioned town pub is flanked by a couple of simply furnished small snugs – one with flagstones and the other with rugs on its bare boards. Down a couple of steps, a large room has heavy beams, a big rug on ancient red tiles, and matching seat and stool covers; there's also a carpeted lounge with more beams, some little booths, hatch service, a good warm coal fire, darts, cribbage, dominoes, cards, video game and fruit machine (there's another in a lobby). Popular, good value bar food includes well filled sandwiches

(75p), ploughman's (£2.50), beef or roast chicken (£3.25), scampi or seafood platter (£3.95); well kept Davenports, Greenalls Original and Tetleys on handpump, and farm cider from the inner flagstones-and-beams servery. There are seats outside in a sheltered garden. *(Recommended by Brian Jones, Simon Collett-Jones, SJC, Graham Richardson, Brian Skelcher; more reports please)*

Davenports (Greenalls)   Manager Adrian Roberts   Real ale   Meals and snacks (12–2,6–8.30; not Sun evening)   Kenilworth (0926) 53737   Children in eating area of bar until 9   Open 11–2.30, 6–11

LANGLEY (W Midlands)   SO9788 Map 4

Brewery ★ £

1 1/2 miles from M5, junction 2; from A4034 to W Bromwich and Oldbury take first right turn signposted Junction 2 Ind Estate then bear left past Albright & Wilson into Station Rd

In this careful re-creation of a Victorian pub (the decor is, in fact, no older than 1984), the Parlour on the left has dining chairs or sturdy built-in settles around four good solid tables, plates and old engravings on the walls, a corner china cabinet, brass swan's-neck wall lamps, and a coal fire in a tiled Victorian fireplace with china on the overmantle. A red-tiled kitchen, divided off by shelves of Staffordshire pottery and old books, is similarly furnished, with the addition of lots of copper pans around its big black range. The more simple Tap Bar serves their own Entire – full-flavoured, quite strong and much loved by readers – as well as Bitter and Mild, both brewed up in Warrington. Simple bar food includes very good value doorstep sandwiches, cheese black pudding and onion double deckers (£1.20), tasty hot beef, pork or roast ham (£1.20-£1.30) and faggots (£1.20). Tractor seats in a back corridor give a view into the brewhouse (a charmingly think-small subsidiary of Allied Breweries, the Ind Coope empire) through a big picture window; darts, cribbage, dominoes and piped music. *(Recommended by Brian Jones, T Henwood, J S Rutter, John and Christine Simpson, Mike and Wendy Proctor)*

Holt, Plant & Deakins (Allied)   Manager Tony Stanton   Real ale   Snacks (not Sun) Birmingham (021) 544 6467   Children in eating area of bar at lunchtime only   Open 11–2.30, 6–11

LAPWORTH (Warwicks)   SP1670 Map 4

Navigation

Old Warwick Rd (B4439 Warwick–Hockley Heath)

Quiet most weekday lunchtimes and early evenings, this consistently friendly little pub really livens up later in the evening and at weekends – particularly in summer. The bustling flagstoned bar is decorated with brightly painted canal ware (you can buy horseshoes in this style here, in aid of cot death research), and cases of stuffed fish, and has newish high-backed winged settles, seats built around its window bay and a coal fire in its high-mantled inglenook. A second quieter room has tables on its board-and-carpet floor – and a dresser with dominoes, cribbage, solitaire and board games including chess. There are also trivia and fruit machines. Generous straightforward bar food, cheap for the area and pleasantly served, includes well filled cottage rolls (lunchtime, £1.20), lasagne, curries or steak and kidney pie (all at £3.95), lamb kebabs and barbecue sauce (£4.50), duck and orange sauce (£6.50); weather permitting, there is a Sunday summer barbecue. Parties can book a pig or lamb roast in the garden anytime during the summer. Well kept beers on handpump – Bass, M&B Brew XI and Mild, and a guest beer such as Timothy Taylors Landlord or Bathams Bitter; fruit machine. There are tables on a back terrace and sheltered canalside lawn, edged with flowers, with outside hatch service and lit at night. *(Recommended by Brian Jones, Lynne Sheridan, Bob West, J Barnwell, C H Stride, D P Cartwright)*

M&B (Bass)   Tenant Andrew Kimber   Real ale   Meals (not Mon evening) and snacks (not Mon evening)   Lapworth (0564) 783337   Children in eating area before 9pm

Open 11–2.30(3 Sat), 5.30(6 Sat)–11; maybe all day summer Sats if busy; closed evening 25/26 Dec

LITTLE COMPTON (Warwicks)   SP2630 Map 4

Red Lion 🛏

Off A44 Moreton-in-Marsh–Chipping Norton

Good bar food in this simple but civilised low-beamed Cotswold-stone inn is served in the dining area leading off the lounge and includes very good rolls filled with home-cooked ham (£2.25), ploughman's (from £3.35), celery, apple and prawn salad (£3.60), home-cooked ham with egg and chips (£4.05), chicken dish of the day (£5.65), fish dishes such as marinaded swordfish steak (£6.40), and lots of steaks (from 8oz rump £8.15). Current favourite specials are roast rack of lamb with redcurrant port and orange sauce (£8.95) and poached halibut with prawn and crab sauce (£9.15). The lounge has snug alcoves, a couple of little tables by the open fire, with a settee facing it, some window seats, and attractive etchings on the stripped stone walls. The plainer public bar has darts, cribbage, dominoes, fruit machine, juke box and Aunt Sally. Well kept Donnington BB and SBA on handpump and extensive wine list; piped music. In the garden there's a walled-off play area with climber, swings and tunnels made from giant piping. The bedrooms are good value. *(Recommended by Barry and Anne, VL; more reports please)*

*Donnington   Tenant David Smith   Real ale   Meals and snacks (not 25 Dec)
Restaurant   Barton-on-the-Heath (060 874) 397   Children in restaurant   Occasional live folk music   Open 11–2.30, 6–11   Bedrooms; £20/£32 (not 24–26 Dec, no under 8s)*

LOWICK (Northants)   SP9780 Map 4

Snooty Fox 🍸

Village signposted off A6116 Corby–Raunds

Good value, carefully cooked bar food in this imposing 17th-century inn includes spicy sausages (£3.50), lasagne (£4.75), crispy garlic chicken or Texas braised steak chilli (£5.95), rump steak (£6.50), English gammon (£6.95) and T-bone steak (£10.95). There is now a separate fish and shellfish menu with lots of fresh Whitby fish such as cod (£4.95), lobster, prawns and Scarborough haddock. Though you can eat anywhere, they may suggest you use the restaurant at the other end – similar in style, but more intimately lit. At lunchtime there is more choice at the lower end, including soup (£1.20) and pâté, ploughman's or cheese plate (£1.95). Well kept Adnams, Bass, Courage Directors, Marstons Pedigree, Ruddles Best and County and a changing guest beer from Yorkshire on handpump, with lots of malt whiskies, imported bottled/canned beers and carefully chosen wines (from a wide choice by the bottle, the bin-end burgundies tend to be particularly rewarding). Service is friendly and efficient, and they're good to children (with high chairs and so forth). The spacious two-room lounge has handsomely moulded dark oak beams, and stripped stone walls decorated with hunt caricatures, Monarch of the Glen lithographs and old prints of ornamental pheasants – there's a stuffed Lady Amherst's pheasant on the carved mantlebeam of the big stone log fireplace. Neat and attractive dining chairs are set around the well spaced tables – with plenty of space too along the formidable monumentally carved bar counter. The picnic-table sets softly floodlit on the front grass are very inviting on a warm evening. *(Recommended by Roy Bromell, Mr and Mrs M K Triebwasser; more reports please)*

*Free house   Licensees John and Linda Lewis   Real ale   Meals and snacks (till 10)
Restaurant (12–3, 7–11)   Thrapston (080 12) 3434   Children welcome   Open 11–3, 6.30–11*

LOWSONFORD (Warwicks)   SP1868   Map 4

Fleur de Lys ✇

Village signposted off B4439 Hockley Heath–Warwick; can be reached too from B4095 via Preston Bagot

At time of going to press Mr Pederson is leaving this pub for the Bear and Ragged Staff in Cumnor (see Main Entries, Oxfordshire). The new landlord, Mr Proctor, says there will be no major changes here. Down on the grass among tall weeping willows by the Stratford-upon-Avon Canal are picnic-table sets, with a very good safely fenced and well equipped play area. Inside, it's civilised and old-fashioned and the spreading bar has rugs on flagstones and antique tiles; it's at its most parlourish on the left, with a sofa and some bookshelves, and at its most dining-roomish down steps on the right, where there are flowers on polished tables, and cushioned plush button-back built-in wall banquettes. Elsewhere, most seats around the well spaced tables are brocade-cushioned mates', wheelback and dining chairs; the butter-coloured ceiling has lots of low black beams. Imaginative, changing bar food might include smoked haddock and leek crêpes (£2.95), crab, spinach and cream cheese strudel (£3.75), roast chicken breast stuffed with brie and honey (£6.95), swordfish and lemon pie (£6.75), calves livers (£7.75) and grilled lemon sole with walnut butter (£7.95). Extensive children's menu. Well kept Boddingtons, Flowers Original, Whitbreads Pompey Royal and Wadworths 6X on handpump, decent wines including good New World ones (lots by the glass), proper cider, several open fires, newspapers and magazines, piped trad jazz music; good staff. The family room is unusually elegant; plush dining chairs, and a red-ceilinged raftered upper gallery. This is now a Wayside Inn. (Recommended by Brian Jones, Phil Clissitt, Ness Turner, Lynne Sheridan, Bob West, Mayur Shah, Jonathan and Jane Hagger, A J Young, Daphne and David Carter, H R Bevan, Brian Skelcher, Wayne Wheeler, Ian Morley, D Swift, Laurence Manning, Mrs G Walsh, Frank Cummins, Roy Bromell, Mr and Mrs Simon Turner)

Whitbreads   Licensee Russell Proctor   Real ale   Meals and snacks (12–2.30, 6–9.30)   (0564) 782431   Children in family room   Open 11–11

NETHERTON (W Midlands)   SO9387   Map 4

Little Dry Dock

Windmill End, Bumble Hole; you really need an A-Z street map to find it – or OS Sheet 139, map reference 953881

Eccentric, lively and popular as ever, this tiny canalside pub – painted in red, white and blue, with a green-planked ceiling – has an entire narrow-boat somehow squeezed into the right-hand bar and used as the servery (its engine is in the room on the left). There's also a huge model boat in one front transom-style window, winches and barge rudders flanking the door, marine windows, and lots of brightly coloured bargees' water pots, lanterns, jugs and lifebuoys; piped music, fruit machine. High point of the menu is the Desperate Dan Pie, complete with horns (£4.65), with other generous food served from the end galley such as sandwiches (from £1.15), soup (£1.60), garlic mushrooms (£2.15), faggots and peas (£3.45), vegetarian/beef lasagne (£3.55/£3.75), home baked ham with parsley sauce (£4.25), rump steak (£6.95) and daily specials; traditional puddings include home-made bread and butter pudding and jam roly poly (both £1.60). They have their own Little Lumphammer ale as well as Holt, plant & Deakins Entire and Mild and their own wine, Chateau Ballykilferret. Others in Mr O'Rourke's small chain of Black Country pubs include main entries in Bewdley and Kidderminster (Hereford and Worcester), and several in the Lucky Dips. (Recommended by Peter Griffiths, Brian Jones, Comus Elliott, John and Christine Simpson, J S Rutter, Sue Holland, Dave Webster, Dr M A Thomas, A Parsons)

Free house   Manager Martin Corcoran   Real ale   Meals and snacks (11–2.30, 6–10; 12–2, 7–9.30 Sun)   (0384) 235369   Children welcome   Live Irish/folk entertainment Mon 8.30pm; special events throughout the year   Open 11–3, 6–11; 11–11 Sat

Old Swan £

Halesowen Road; A459 towards Halesowen just S of Netherton centre

This long-standing home-brew pub has changed hands yet again; this time it's been taken on by a local pub-owning company associated with Premier Midland Ales. The original bar is traditionally furnished, with mirrors behind the bar engraved with the swan design, an old-fashioned cylinder stove with its chimney angling away to the wall, and a lovely patterned ceiling with a big swan centrepiece. 'Ma Pardoe's Bar' itself is decorated with 1920s bric-a-brac, though fitted out very much in keeping with the rest of the building, using recycled bricks and woodwork, and even matching etched window panels. The home-brew is still good – fresh, fragrant and very cheap – and there's also Wiltshire Stonehenge, Old Grumble and Old Devil, a constantly changing guest beer and six fruit wines; darts, pool, cribbage, cards and piped music. Bar food includes big sandwiches (£1.65), faggots (£1.95), ploughman's (£2.25), Old Devil pie (£2.50), huge meat and vegetable pie (£3.50). There's a good car park at the back of the pub. *(Recommended by Sue Holland, Dave Webster, Michael Rooke, Patrick and Mary McDermott; more reports please)*

Own brew (Wiltshire)   Tenant Steve Yates   Real ale   Lunchtime meals and snacks (not weekends)   Dudley (0384) 253075   Children welcome   Live bands roughly once a fortnight   Open 12–2.30, 5.30–11 (all day Sat)

OUNDLE (Northants)   TL0487 Map 5

Mill

Barnwell Rd out of town; or follow Barnwell Country Park signs off A605 bypass

This tall stone mill, rebuilt in 1746 but dating from the early 16th century, has done well since its 1990 refurbishment as a pub. A rather dimly lit ground floor bar on the ground floor has red leatherette button-back built-in wall banquettes against its stripped-stone walls; on the way in a big glass floor panel shows the mill race below the building. Outside stairs take you up to the most popular part, the Trattoria, which has stalls around tables with more banquettes in bays, stripped masonry and beams, and a millstone feature; its small windows look down over the lower millpond and the River Nene. A very wide choice of good value bar food includes soup (£2.35), pizzas (from £2.75), whitebait (£2.95), ploughman's (from £3.25), satay (£3.55), burgers (£3.75), lasagne (£4.75), steak and kidney pie or lamb tikka kebabs (£5.95) and steaks (from 8oz, £7.95); all is kept very neat and clean. Bass on handpump; top-floor restaurant (more beams, and the corn hoist). There are picnic-table sets under cocktail parasols among willow trees by the pond, with more on side grass and some white cast-iron tables on a flagstoned terrace. *(Recommended by Mr and Mrs H M Ollis)*

Free house   Licensees Noel and Linda Tulley   Real ale   Meals and snacks (till 10) Restaurant   Oundle (0832) 272621   Children allowed, must not run around inside Open 12–3, 6.30(7 winter)–11

Ship £

West St

This is a friendly, chatty local in an elegant small town. The very heavily beamed lounge bar on the left is split into three rooms: up by the street there's a mix of leather and other seats including a very flowery piano stool (and its piano), with sturdy tables and a log fire in a stone inglenook; down one end a panelled no smoking snug has button-back leather seats built in around it. In between, well kept Bass, Batemans XXXB, Greene King IPA and Marstons Pedigree is served cheerfully and efficiently by the landlord and his son, and the atmosphere is warmly lively yet relaxing. Bar food includes soup (£1.20), ploughman's (£2), pâté (£2.25), smoked mackerel (£2.50), venison pie (£2.50), salads (from £3), with enormous Sunday lunches and summer lunchtime cold buffet (both £3.95); dominoes, maybe free Sunday nuts and crisps on the bar. The tiled-floor public side has darts, dominoes, juke box or piped music and fruit machine. A series of small sheltered terraces strung out behind has wooden tables and chairs, lit at night. Several of the bedrooms are in a new extension. *(Recommended by Dr and Mrs A K Clarke, Monica Darlington, David Brown, Nic James; more reports please)*

Free house   Licensee Frank Langridge   Real ale   Snacks (not Sun lunch) and meals (12–2, 7–10)   Oundle (0832) 273918   Children welcome   Live rock/dance bands winter Fri or Sat   Open 11–3, 6–11 (all day Sat)   Bedrooms; £27.50/£35(£45B)

PRIORS MARSTON (Warwicks)   SP4857   Map 4

Falcon

Hellidon Rd; village signposted off A425 Daventry Rd in Southam; and from A361 S of Daventry

It's the landlord's obviously welcoming attitude to all his customers that makes this handsome and neatly kept 17th-century pub so special. The main bar, with its civilised and relaxed atmosphere, rambles around into an L beyond the log fire in the big high-mantled stone fireplace, with well padded high-backed winged settles on its cheerfully patterned carpet; a couple of big framed mirrors alongside the country pictures give a feeling of extra space. One no smoking room. Well presented bar food in generous helpings includes sandwiches (£1.75-£3.45), barbecued smoked chicken wings (£4.75), 8oz burger (£4.75), lasagne (£4.75), scampi (£4.95), chilli con carne (£5.25), chicken and mushroom tagliatelle (£5.25), gammon and egg (£5.25), chicken teriyaki (£5.45), lamb kebabs (£5.55) and steaks (from £7.75); there's a choice of chips, new or baked potatoes. Well kept John Smiths, Moorhouses Pendle Witches Brew and Shepherd Neame Bishops Finger on handpump, good wine; cribbage, dominoes. *(Recommended by Mr and Mrs B J Twigger, David Elliott, Sylvia and Len Henderson, WHBM, Richard and Maria Gillespie, Lynne Sheridan, Bob West, Alexandra Gunther, Michael Schofield)*

Free house   Licensees Stephen and Jane Richards   Real ale   Meals and snacks (till 10)   Restaurant   Daventry (0327) 60562   Well behaved children allowed   Open 12–3, 7–11; closed evening 25 Dec

SAMBOURNE (Warwicks)   SP0561   Map 4

Green Dragon

A435 N of Alcester, then left fork onto A448 just before Studley; village signposted on left soon after

This pretty village-green pub with its shuttered and timbered facade serves good value bar food that includes sandwiches (from £1.15), home-made soup (£1.25), pâté (£2.25), ploughman's (from £2.90), omelettes (from £3.80), a fish dish of the day (£4.50), home-made steak and kidney pie (£4.90), gammon (£5.20), salads (from £5.20), and steaks (from £8.50). The modernised beamed communicating rooms have little armed seats and more upright ones, some small settles, and open fires; well kept Bass and M & B Brew XI on handpump; pleasant, attentive service. There are picnic-table sets and teak seats among flowering cherries on a side courtyard, by the car park. *(Recommended by E W Pitts, B T Smith, A J Woodhouse, S V Bishop; more reports please)*

M & B (Bass)   Leasehold: Phil Burke   Real ale   Meals and snacks (12–2, 7–10; not Sun)   Restaurant   Astwood Bank (052 789) 2465   Children welcome   Open 10.30–3, 6–11; closed evening 25 and 26 Dec

SHIPSTON ON STOUR (Warwicks)   SP2540   Map 4

White Bear

High Street

Though there are plans for the redecoration of the bar areas and bedrooms, the Robertses hope to keep the atmosphere in this fine old coaching inn very much as it is now – relaxed and friendly and popular with a wide range of locals and visitors. The narrow front bar on the left has massive stripped settles, attractive lamps on the rag-rolled walls, newspapers out for customers, and interesting pictures: charming pen and wash drawing of Paris cafe society, and sporting and other cartoons from Alken through Lawson Wood to bright modern ones by Tibb. The back lounge is more plainly furnished and decorated, with comfortable modern furniture, and big Toulouse-Lautrec and other prints of French music-hall life. A separate bar on the right has a woodburning stove in a big painted stone fireplace, with a fruit machine round at the back. Good, interesting food served in the bar and restaurant includes soups like cream of mushroom and coriander (£2), baked sardines (£2.95), lovely steak and kidney pie (£4.95), locally smoked sea trout (£4.95), warm salad of smoked chicken and grated ginger (£4.60), liver and bacon (£5.10), lemon sole (£6.50), roast rack of English lamb (£8.50), sirloin steak (£9), puddings such as rhubarb crumble or steamed treacle sponge and custard (£2.60), and British farmhouse cheeses; at lunchtime they do baguettes and a changing daily hot dish like savoury beef pancakes, lasagne verde or spagetti carbonara (all £3.50); decent breakfasts. Well kept Bass and Brew XI on handpump, with eclectically chosen wines – including up to 30 bin ends and good selection of ports; polite, knowledgeable service. Darts, shove-ha'penny, cribbage, dominoes and fruit machine. There are some white cast-iron tables in a small back yard, and benches face the street. *(Recommended by John Bowdler, Sheila Keene, S V Bishop, JM, PM, W H Bland; more reports please)*

M & B (Bass)   Leasehold: Suzanne Roberts   Real ale   Meals and snacks (6.30–9.30(10 Fri and Sat, not Sun evening)   Restaurant   Shipston on Stour (0608) 61558   Children welcome   Open 11–3, 6–11   Bedrooms; £35B/£47B

SHUSTOKE (Warwicks)   SP2290 Map 4

Griffin

5 miles from M6, junction 4; A446 towards Tamworth, then right on to B4114 and go straight through Coleshill; pub is at Furnace End, E of Shustoke

There's a good, friendly atmosphere in the low-beamed, L-shaped bar here, as well as an old-fashioned settle and cushioned cafe seats (some quite closely packed), sturdy elm-topped sewing trestles, lots of old jugs on the beams, and log fires in both stone fireplaces (one's a big inglenook). The good range of well kept real ales on handpump typically includes Adnams, Bathams, Brains, Bull Mastiff Son-of-a-Bitch, Marstons Pedigree, Theakstons Old Peculier and Wadworths 6X, all from a servery under a very low, thick beam; farm ciders also. Good value lunchtime bar food includes sandwiches, home-made steak and old ale pie or lasagne (both £3.80), mixed grill (£5.50); local fresh eggs, and leeks and cauliflower in season, for sale. The roomy conservatory is popular with families, there are old-fashioned seats and tables on the back grass, a children's play area, and the large terrace has plants in raised beds. *(Recommended by Len and Sylvia Henderson, Brian Jones, Alan and Eileen Bowker, T Henwood, J Harvey Hallam, M Rowlinson, J S Rutter, Derek and Sylvia Stephenson, Frank Cummins)*

Free house   Licensees Michael Pugh and Sydney Wedge   Real ale   Lunchtime meals and snacks (not Sun)   (0675) 81205   Children in conservatory   Open 12–2.30, 7–11

SOUTHAM (Warwicks)   SP4161 Map 4

Old Mint

Coventry Street; A423, towards Coventry

This 14th-century pub is named for the fact that in the Civil Wars it was used to melt down commandeered silver for coin to pay King Charles' troops before the Battle of Edge Hill. The interestingly-shaped, two-roomed bar has heavy beams, sturdy old seats and settles, masses of toby jugs behind the serving counter, an open fire, walls peppered with antique guns, powder flasks, rapiers, sabres, cutlasses and pikes, and two cosy little alcoves; darts, dominoes, fruit machine and piped music. Well kept Bass, Batemans Mild, Brains Bitter, Castle Eden, Flowers Original, Hook Norton, Marstons Pedigree, Wadworths 6X and regular guest beers on handpump; fruit and country wines include mead, parsnip and elderberry; friendly service. Bar food includes sandwiches, filled baked potatoes (from £1.80), filled Yorkshire puddings (from £2.50), cottage pie (£3.95), lasagne (£4.15), steaks (from £4.95) and three-course Sunday lunch (£6.95); pleasant, courteous service. Through the medieval arch of the back door there are tables and chairs in the sheltered, extended garden here, with more on the cobbles and laid bricks of a sheltered yard, which has clematis on a side wall and is fairy-lit at night. Permanent bouncy castle. *(Recommended by George Atkinson, D H Buchanan, Phil Clissitt, Ness Turner, J Barnwell, J E Stanton, William Rodgers, B R Shiner, A Parsons, Peter Watkins, Pam Stanley, Philip Orbell, T Nott)*

Free house   Licensee Geoffrey Wright   Real ale   Meals and snacks (12–2, 7–10) Restaurant (not Sun lunchtime)   Southam (092 681) 2339   Children welcome   Open 11–2.30, 6.30–11; 6 Fri,11–11 Sat

STOKE BRUERNE (Northants)   SP7450 Map 4
Boat

3 1/2 miles from M1 junction 15: A508 towards Stony Stratford, then Stoke Bruerne signposted on the right

The low-ceilinged and tiled-floor bar and taproom are the most atmospheric rooms in this old-fashioned place, well positioned by the Grand Union Canal; they're brightly painted with simple vignettes of barges and barge life and can be very busy. A spacious lounge at the back is perfectly comfortable though less special. Everards Old Original, Marstons Burton and Pedigree, Sam Smiths OB and Theakstons XB on handpump; dominoes, cribbage, fruit machine, piped music, and a separate alley for hood skittles. Sandwiches (£1.40; toasted £1.60), ploughman's (from £1.85), burgers (from £1.95), deep fried fish (from £3.30), home-made chilli con carne (£3.45), vegetarian lasagne or crumble (£3.85), home-made beef lasagne (£3.85), mini grill (£4.85) and sirloin steak (£7.45); there are also canalside tearooms. From tables outside by the neatly painted double locks you can watch the colourful narrowboats, and on the other side there's an interesting canal museum in a handsome row of 18th-century warehouses. A narrowboat is available for party or individual hire. *(Recommended by Tim and Sue Halstead, Monica Darlington, Mayur Shah, Carol and Richard Glover, Jim Aitkenhead)*

Free house   Licensee John Woodward   Real ale   Meals and snacks (11.30–2.30, 7–9.30; tearooms open 9.30–6)   Restaurant   (0604) 862428; not Sun evening Children in eating area, restaurant and tearooms   Cabaret Nov and Dec, local canal music throughout the year   Parking may be difficult at peak holiday times   Open 11–3, 6–11, maybe longer in afternoon if trade demands; all day Sat

STRATFORD UPON AVON (Warwicks)   SP2055 Map 4
Garrick

High Street; close to Town Hall

Before becoming a pub in the early 18th century, this elaborately timbered building was at one time the home of a Flemish weaver whose apprentice was the first person in Stratford to have the plague. The small and often irregularly shaped rooms have some walls stripped back to bare stone and others heavily plastered with posters, heavy wall timbers, high ceiling beams and long upholstered settles and stools made from barrels; the small dining room at the rear of the house centres on an open fire with a conical brass hood. Flowers IPA and Original on handpump, kept under light blanket pressure; a fruit machine and thoughtfully chosen piped music. Bar food includes ploughman's (£2.95), steak and kidney pie (£3.50), fried fillet of plaice (£3.50), scampi (£4.25), lasagne (£4.35), chicken casserole (£4.85), also various chef's specials (£3.95) and roast dinner on Sunday (£4.25); cheerful service. *(Recommended by Adrian Pitts, TBB, Frank Cummins, Sheila Keene, Carol and Mike Muston, Mr and Mrs J H Adam, Andy and Jill Kassube)*

Flowers (Whitbreads)   Manager P J Marsh   Real ale   Snacks (not Sun) and meals (12–2, 5–7; till 8 Sat, not Sun evening)   (0789) 292186   Children in dining room during food service hours   Nearby daytime parking difficult   Open 11–11

Slug & Lettuce ♀

38 Guild Street, corner of Union Street

Popular with theatre-goers – and later in the evening with younger customers – the bar here has pine kitchen tables and chairs on rugs and flagstones, a few period prints on stripped squared panelling, a newspaper rack, and a solid fuel fire; cribbage and dominoes. Well kept Ansells, Ind Coope Burton, Tetleys, and two other Ind Coope-related beers named for the pub, a decent wine list, and a good range of spirits. You can see some of the bar food being prepared at one end of the long L-shaped bar counter with such dishes as home-made celery and almond soup (£2), creamy garlic mushrooms (£3.75), black pudding topped with tomato, bacon and cheddar (£4.75), sautéed lamb's livers (£4.75), chicken breast baked with avocado and garlic (£8), salmon escalope (£8.50), beef and mushroom casserole (£8.50) and lovely puddings (from £2.75). The small flagstoned terrace at the back, floodlit at night, has lots of flower boxes and sturdy teak tables under cocktail parasols, with more up steps. *(Recommended by Mr and Mrs R Clifford, Ken and Barbara Turner, Brian Jones, Frank Cummins, R A Corbett, John Moate, Mr and Mrs G J Rice, Brian Skelcher, Len Beattie, T Nott)*

Ansells (Allied)   Manager Steve Sarton   Real ale   Meals and snacks (12–2, 5.30–9; 12–9 Thurs-Sat)   (0789) 299700   Jazz bands some summer Sun evenings   Open 11–11; closed 25 Dec

THORNBY (Northants)   SP6775   Map 4
Red Lion

Welford Road; A50 Northampton–Leicester

Very carefully chosen furnishings in this 17th century, cream-painted slated brick roadside pub include, for example, the lovingly polished big golden table that sits between a couple of pews in one of the bay windows, the deep leather armchairs and sofa in one of two smallish areas opening off, and the individual old-fashioned lamps. There are pewter tankards hanging from a beam, decorative plates densely covering the walls, china jugs and steins on a shelf and hanging over the bar, and logs burning in an open stove; shove-ha'penny, table skittles, cribbage, dominoes, piped music and friendly dogs. Good home-made bar food includes sandwiches (from £1.25), soup (£1.85), smoked salmon pâté (£2.35), ploughman's (£3.75), chilli con carne (£4.90), prawn and cauliflower gratinée (£5.25), prawn and smoked salmon salad (£5.75), fillet steak (£7.25) plus daily specials and traditional puddings. Well kept Marstons Burton and Pedigree plus guest beers such as Adnams and Hook Norton on handpump, decent wines, and good coffee; friendly service. There are some seats outside. *(Recommended by Irene and Derek Cranston, K H Frostick, Howard and Lynda Dix)*

Free house   Licensees Peter and Caroline Slater   Real ale   Meals and snacks (not Sun)   Small restaurant (not Sun)   Northampton (0604) 740238   Children in restaurant   Open 12–3, 7–11; closed Mon

THORPE MANDEVILLE (Northants)   SP5344   Map 4
Three Conies

In village, just off B4525 Banbury–Northampton

Pleasantly isolated, this friendly 17th-century village pub has a low-beamed lounge bar with tapestried built-in settles and spindleback chairs around tables on its patterned carpet, little hunting prints and polished brass on the walls (which are partly stripped back to golden stone), and horsebrasses around the open fireplace. Beyond the servery, the public bar has bigger pictures on its stripped stone walls, and a pool table. Popular home-made food includes good soup (£1.40), sandwiches (from £1.75), sausages (£2.50), ploughman's (£2.75), mushrooms in a garlic and cream sauce (£2.95), salads (from £3.50), chicken breast (£4.10), steaks (£6.25), daily specials such as steak and kidney pie or lasagne (from around

£3.50), and puddings like home-made ice creams, sherry trifle or chocolate éclairs (from £1.65). Well kept Hook Norton Best and Old Hookey on handpump and a good selection of wines and spirits. There are old-fashioned teak and curly iron seats on a lawn with a fruit tree; friendly cat. Close to Sulgrave Manor (George Washington's ancestral home) and Canons Ashby House (the Dryden family home). *(Recommended by Mrs G Walsh, John Whitehead, Tom Evans, Maysie Thompson, Ted George, Pete Storey, JM, PM; more reports please)*

Hook Norton   Tenants John and Maureen Day   Real ale   Meals and snacks (11.30–2.30, 6.30–9.30; not Sun evening)   Restaurant (booking Sun lunchtime) Banbury (0295) 711025   Children welcome   Open 11–3, 6–11

TWYWELL (Northants)   SP9478   Map 4
Old Friar

Village signposted from A604 about 2 miles W of Thrapston

Bustling and well run by hard-working staff, this food oriented pub has a good hot and cold carvery (£6.95), as well as sandwiches, soup (£1.65), oriental parcels (£3.10), coronation turkey (£3.40), lamb moussaka (£4.25), regularly changing vegetarian specials (£4.80), home-made pies (£5.50), chicken kiev (£7.50), steaks (from £8.45), Scotch salmon (£8.45), gammon steak (£9.45) and a children's menu. Most of the tables are set for eating and part of the dining area is no smoking. The bar is attractively furnished with plain wooden tables, tub chairs and settles; both the beams and the brick fireplaces have wooden carvings of friars. Well kept Ruddles Best and County, and Websters Yorkshire on handpump served from the brick bar counter; shove-ha'penny, cribbage, dominoes, fruit machine and piped music. No dogs; newly laid out garden with tables and children's play area. *(Recommended by George Atkinson, Mr and Mrs Brown, Maysie Thompson, John Whitehead, L Walker; more reports please)*

Grand Metl/Watneys   Licensee David J Crisp   Real ale   Meals and snacks Restaurant   Thrapston (080 12) 2625   Children welcome   Open 11–2.30(3 Sat), 6–11

WARMINGTON (Warwicks)   SP4147   Map 4
Plough

Village just off A41 N of Banbury

In autumn, this little golden ironstone pub is particularly pretty when the creeper that covers it turns crimson. The softly lit bar has a cosy atmosphere, with an old high-backed winged settle, leatherette-cushioned wall seats and lots of comfortable Deco small armed chairs and library chairs, and good winter log fires; on the walls, largely stripped back to the stone, there are old photographs of the village and locals. Well kept Hook Norton Best and Old Hookey, Marstons Pedigree on handpump, and several malt whiskies; darts, dominoes, fruit machine and faint piped pop music. Straightforward but generously served lunchtime bar food includes good minestrone soup, sandwiches, cottage pie (£3.50), flavoursome home-baked ham (£4.50), and home-cooked daily specials (from £3). Charles I marched through here towards Edge Hill with 18,000 men in October 1642, and some of those men are buried in the churchyard here. The village is most attractive. *(Recommended by George Atkinson, Sir Nigel Foulkes, M Rising, H R Bevan, C P Scott-Malden; more reports please)*

Free house   Licensee Mrs D L Willson   Real ale   Meals and snacks (12–2, 6–8) (0295) 89666   Children welcome   Open 12–3, 6–11; closed evening Dec 25

WELFORD ON AVON (Warwicks)   SP1452   Map 4
Bell

High Street; village signposted from A439

Convivial 17th-century pub with pleasant staff and decent food which is served in the nice light conservatory and beamed lounge bar. This bar is comfortable, with sober seats and tables to match the dark timbering, open fireplaces (one with a real fire, one with electric), and a low ceiling; the flagstoned public bar has another open fire. Bar food includes sandwiches, steak and kidney pie (£4.10), liver and bacon (£4.40), gammon and eggs (£4.65), cold Scotch salmon (£5.15) and chicken kiev (£5.45). Well kept Flowers Original and IPA on handpump; darts, pool, cribbage, dominoes, fruit machine, trivia, juke box and piped music; seats in the pretty garden area and back courtyard. The riverside village, with its church and thatched black and white cottages, is pretty. *(Recommended by Dave Braisted, J Barnwell, Sheila Keene, CEP, Mrs R Heaton)*

Whitbreads   Licensee Mike Eynon   Real ale   Meals and snacks (12–2.30, 7–10.30) Restaurant   Stratford-upon-Avon (0789) 750353   Children in centrally heated, furnished and enclosed terrace or restaurant if dining   Open 11–3, 6–11

WEST BROMWICH (W Midlands)   SP0091 Map 4
Manor House

2 miles from M6, junction 9; from A461 towards Wednesbury take first left into Woden Rd East; at T-junction, left into Crankhall Lane; at eventual roundabout, right into Hall Green Rd. Alternatively, 5 miles from junction 7.

Built for the Deveraux and de Marnham families in the 1300s, though a manor house was recorded on this site two centuries earlier. It's still a remarkable place: you enter through the ancient gatehouse, across the moat, and inside, the main bar is actually a great flagstoned hall, where massive oak trusses support the soaring pitched roof (the central one, eliminating any need for supporting pillars, is probably unique), and a fine old sliding door opens on to stairs leading up to a series of smaller and cosier timbered upper rooms, including a medieval Solar, which again have lovely oak trusses supporting their pitched ceiling beams; there are blue carpets, and plenty of tables, and upstairs comfortably cushioned seats and stools around small tables, with the occasional settle; a snug Parlour Bar is tucked in beneath the Solar. Well kept Banks's Bitter and Mild on electric pump; friendly service, piped music, trivia game, and fruit machines. Bar food, served from the left side of the main bar, includes steak and kidney pie or lasagne (£3.95) and chicken chasseur (£4); there are also banquets in the hall 3–4 times a year. A broad stretch of grass leads away behind the moat, towards the modern houses of this quiet suburb; a car park is sensitively tucked away behind some modern ancillary buildings. *(Recommended by Andrew and Ruth Triggs, Drs M and K Parier, Roger Huggins, J S Rutter, Len Beattie, Dr and Mrs C D E Morris)*

Banks's   Manager Robin Carter   Real ale   Meals and snacks (not Sun evening) Restaurant   Birmingham (021) 588 2035   Children in restaurant and eating area of bar   Open 11.30–2.30, 6–11(Sat 12–2.30, 7–10.30)

WHATCOTE (Warwicks)   SP2944 Map 4
Royal Oak

Village signposted from A34 N of Shipston on Stour; and from A422 Banbury–Stratford, via Oxhill

Built in 1168, this charming stone building was used by Cromwell in 1642 as temporary quarters, and the bread oven was removed to make an observation slit facing Edge Hill; there's a tradition that he came back here after the battle for drinks. Around 20–30 October the Sealed Knots re-enact the Battle of Edge Hill and come to the pub in period costume for lunch. The small rooms of the original bar have low ceilings, a miscellany of stools, cushioned pews and other seats, old local photographs, brasses, a sword, and a stuffed peewit on the walls, and coins, bookmatches and foreign banknotes on the beams behind the high copper bar counter; there's a huge inglenook fireplace with rungs leading up to a chamber on the right (originally either a priest's hiding hole, or a smoking chamber for hams). A larger, and less elaborately decorated bar is on the left. Well kept Marstons Pedigree and Whitbreads Castle Eden; darts dominoes, fruit machine and piped music; Shadow the german shepherd is friendly. A wide choice of bar food includes sandwiches (if they're not busy), home-made soup (£1.45), corn on the cob (£2), ploughman's (£3.30), tasty cold ham (£3.50), trout (£3.90), chicken kiev (£6.05), sirloin steak (£7.50) and imaginative specials such as vegetable lasagne (£4.65), game dishes in season (from £4.95), shark steak (£5), and chicken with leek and stilton (£6.15). The front terrace has some picnic-table sets, and there are more on grass at the side. *(Recommended by Sir Nigel Foulkes, H R Bevan, Mrs V A Middlebrook, Barry and Anne, P R Davis, C A Holloway, Frank Cummins, Wayne Brindle, John Bowdler, Brian Skelcher)*

Free house   Licensee Mrs Catherine Matthews   Real ale   Meals and snacks (12–2, 6–10.30)   (0295) 88319   Children in eating area   Open 10.30–2.30, 6–11

WITHYBROOK (Warwicks)   SP4384   Map 4
Pheasant

4 miles from M6, junction 2; follow Ansty, Shilton signpost; bear right in Shilton towards Wolvey then take first right signposted Withybrook – or, longer but wider, second right into B4112 to Withybrook

Very popular indeed, this bustling, well kept dining pub has a spacious lounge with a serving counter flanked by well polished rocky flagstones, lots of plush-cushioned wheelback chairs and dark tables on the patterned carpet, a few farm tools on its cream walls, and good winter fires; well kept and excellent value Courage Directors on handpump, with John Smiths on electric pump; trivia and fruit machines in the lobby, and piped music. Bar food includes sandwiches (from £1.25), soup (£1.20), a cheesy ploughman's (£3.75), omelettes (from £4.25), home-made lasagne, steak and kidney pie, fresh quiches or braised liver and onions (all £4.50), salads (from £4.95), vegetarian dishes such as pie (£4.50) or broccoli and walnut lasagne (£5.25), tasty seafood vol-au-vent (£5.50), chicken stuffed with lobster and prawns (£6.95), steaks (from £8.50), and puddings like Bavarian apple flan and lemon meringue pie (£1.85); Sunday lunch in restaurant (£9.50). There are tables under fairy lights on a brookside terrace, and the bank opposite is prettily planted with flowers and shrubs. The Ankor Morris Men come a few times a year. Parking can be difficult at busy times. *(Recommended by Dr Paul Kitchener, Harry Stirling, Geoff Lee, Olive Carroll, Brian and Genie Smart, Mike and Wendy Proctor, David and Sarah Gilmore, Dave Braisted, A Parsons, Tim Newell, Ken and Barbara Turner, Paul and Margaret Baker)*

Free house   Licensees Derek Guy, Alan and Rene Bean   Real ale   Meals and snacks (12–2, 6.30–10; not 25 and 26 Dec)   Restaurant   Hinkley (0455) 220480   Children in eating area and restaurant   Open 11–3, 6.30–11; closed evenings 25 and 26 Dec

---

Lucky Dip

Besides the fully inspected pubs, you might like to try these Lucky Dips recommended to us and described by readers (if you do, please send us reports):

Alcester, War [A433 towards Studley; SP0857], *Moat House*: Black and white timbered pub doing well under newish owners, with good atmosphere, log fires, well kept Banks's, Flowers IPA and Original and Marstons Pedigree; home-cooked good food, restaurant *(Brian Jordan)*
Amblecote, W Mid [Collis St; SO8985], *Robin Hood*: Cosy open-plan pub with good range of well kept ales such as Bathams, Hook Norton Old Hookey and guests, dining area with good value food inc good home-made curry *(John Tooth)*
☆ **Ardens Grafton**, War [on edge of village, towards Wixford — OS Sheet 150, map reference 114538; SP1153], *Golden Cross*: Over 200 dolls wearing costumes made by

landlady, in pleasant L-shaped room with generous helpings of good bar food, well kept Whitbreads-related real ales on handpump, warm welcome, efficient service, unobtrusive piped music, fruit machine; restaurant, seats outside *(E J Alcock, Mr and Mrs F Egerton)*
Arrow, War [A435 S of Alcester; opp gates of Ragley Hall; SP0856], *Arrow Mill*: Two very attractive bars — you can see the waterwheel in one; also pleasant courtyard and delightful grounds, with mill pool and R Arrow; well kept Watneys-related real ales, interesting food inc chicken casseroled with honey and walnuts, delicious home-made ice creams; moderate prices; bedrooms *(Robert and Vicky Tod)*

Ashton, Northants [SP7850], *Chequered Skipper*: Overlooking green of attractive village; four well kept ales, good reasonably priced bar food, friendly staff; on Nene Way footpath *(David Oakes)*

Avon Dassett, War [off A41 Banbury—Warwick; SO4049], *Avon*: Pleasant decor, friendly atmosphere, and good choice of tasty food *(D H Player)*

☆ **Badby**, Northants [village signposted off A361 Daventry—Banbury; SP5559], *Maltsters Arms*: Interesting character pub with good reasonably priced food in small cosy eating area with fire; darts, pool, skittles, nice licensees; well placed for walks on nearby Knightley Way *(David and Sue Elliott, George Atkinson)*

Badby, *Windmill*: Thatched inn with two connecting bars, flagstoned throughout, with Bass and Hook Norton real ales and decent house wines; primarily a hotel/restaurant now *(David and Sue Elliott, Ted George, LYM)*

Baginton, War [Coventry Rd; SP3474], *Oak*: Exceptionally wide range of bar food from salads to fresh lobster, inc lots of filled Yorkshire puddings; large, but right by Coventry Airport and can be very busy lunchtime; very large play area, good children's menu with free gifts *(Mr and Mrs B J Twigger, Roy Bromell)*

☆ **Balsall Common**, W Mid [SP2377], *Saracens Head*: Rambling 16th-century character pub, several interconnecting rooms some with beams and flagstones, good straightforward bar food, newspapers out to read, muted piped rock music, well kept Allied real ales, polite service, restaurant *(Brian Jones, Dr J A Benbow)*

☆ **Barnacle**, War [village signed off B4029 in Shilton, nr M6 junction 2; SP3884], *Red Lion*: Quiet pub with two rooms, one small, the other long with a leather bench seat around edge and collection of plates; Bass and M&B, good range of generous good value food (not Sun lunchtime); seats out in covered front area *(Geoff Lee, SJC)*

☆ **Barnwell**, Northants [TL0484], *Montagu Arms*: Popular old pub with low beams and flagstones in original core, well kept ales such as Greene King IPA, Marstons Pedigree and Charles Wells on handpump, simple reasonably priced but imaginatively presented lunchtime bar food inc good puddings, more extensive evening menu, restaurant; bedrooms and self-catering *(Mr and Mrs J Barnes)*

☆ **Barton**, War [pub signed off B4085; just S of Bidford-on-Avon; SP1051], *Cottage of Content*: Easy-going, with simple traditional furnishings in cosy flagstoned bar, solid fuel stove in inglenook, low black beams, good simple bar food from soup and sandwiches through home-made pies to lemon sole, roast beef and summer salmon, well kept Flowers IPA and Original on handpump, piped music, restaurant; picnic-table sets in front of the pretty house, touring caravan site with good play area behind; day fishing on River Avon here, though no nearby

moorings *(Phil Clissitt, Ness Turner, Dave Irving, BB)*

☆ **Bearley**, War [A34 N of Stratford; SP1860], *Golden Cross*: Popular and friendly pub/restaurant, lovely old timbered bar with open fireplaces, soft lighting, good generous bar food, well kept Flowers and other real ales, helpful staff; small restaurant *(Dr J A Benbow, A J Woodhouse, P Corris)*

☆ **Birmingham** [St Pauls Sq, Hockley], *Rope Walk*: Spacious new pub opp church and its attractive yard, next to Science Museum; expensive, detailed pastiche of Edwardian pub, lots of glass, wood and elegant period prints, snug with TV, two-level lounge with full range of well kept Banks's beers, good choice of food from separate servery; piped music, fruit machine, tiny outside verandah; open all day *(Ian Phillips, Colin Gooch)*

☆ **Birmingham** [Ravenhurst St; Camp Hill, by roundabout A41/Middle Ring Rd], *Brewer & Baker*: New pub done out in Black Country parlour style — quite successfully; small, with L-shaped lounge, darts in small back public area; can get quite busy lunchtimes but service friendly and quick; well kept Banks's Bitter and Mild on electric pump, cheap food from sandwiches and rolls to good value gammon and occasional daily specials; open all day *(Brian Jones)*

Birmingham [Stephenson St; in Midland Hotel, off New St], *Atkinson Bar*: Back bar of Midland Hotel with peaceful, subdued atmosphere and wide range of well kept beers on handpump *(Ann Griffiths, John C Baker)*; [Harborne Rd, Edgbaston], *Horts*: Useful for area, with wide choice of good value food and friendly service *(Anthony Sargent, Caroline Gant)*; [Aston St, nr Gosta Green triangle], *Sacks of Potatoes*: Refurbished pub popular with Aston students for well kept Bass, M&B Mild and Springfield on handpump, good varied cheap bar food *(Hilary Sargeant, N P Clarke, Gary Phillips)*

Bishops Tachbrook, War [SP3161], *Leopard*: Good bar meals, friendly Irish landlord, good atmosphere, children's playground *(Peter Castleton)*

☆ **Blakesley**, Northants [High St (Woodend rd); SP6250], *Bartholomew Arms*: Two pleasantly cosy beamed bars cluttered with nick-nacks, friendly staff, well kept Watneys-related real ales, cheap filled rolls and a few hot dishes, suntrap garden with summerhouse *(Nick Dowson, Alison Hayward, L Walker)*

Bodymoor Heath, War [Dog Lane; SP2096], *Dog & Doublet*: Canalside pub nr Kingsbury Water Park, which does not allow children in but has been popular for reasonably priced meals in separate dining room, and for its general character — beams, brasses, bargees' painted ware, well kept M&B, comfortable seats, several open fires, pleasant garden; but no recent reports *(News please)*

Brackley Hatch, Northants [SP6541], *Green Man*: Notably good play area inc wet-weather area in very big and sometimes noisy garden; beams and tasteful furnishings, open fires, Batemans, Marstons Pedigree and Websters Yorkshire, restaurant, conservatory; handy for Silverstone; bedrooms (Gwyneth and Salvo Spadaro-Dutturi)

Bretford, War [A428 Coventry—Rugby — OS Sheet 140, map reference 431772; SP4377], Queens Head: Roomy and airy two-bar pub with Watneys-related real ales on handpump, good cider, good range of generous bar food, darts and skittles; spacious family garden (Mike and Wendy Proctor, Chris Aslett)

☆ Brinklow, War [Fosse Way; A427, fairly handy for M6 junction 2; SP4379], Raven: Good spot at northern end of Fosse Way, ancient Roman rd from Bath to Lincoln; beams, cheerful staff, good choice of reasonably priced bar food inc vegetarian dishes, tables on raised lawn (Brian Barefoot, Geoff Lee, M A and W R Proctor)

Broom, War [SP0853], Broom Hall: Good choice of reasonably priced food, real ales, clean, comfortable and relaxing lounge bar, pleasant staff; bedrooms (JM, PM, H R Bevan)

Brownshill Green, W Mid [Wall Hill Rd/Hawkes Mill Lane; SP3082], White Lion: Bass pub with well kept beer, club and triple decker sandwiches, salads, chunky chips, grill room; popular with staff from nearby Jaguar works (E V Walder)

Bubbenhall, War [SP3672], Malt Shovel: Clean and tidy old-world pub with friendly staff, well kept Allied real ales, wide range of bar food, spacious garden, two bowling greens (Mr and Mrs B J Twigger)

Buckby Wharf, Northants [A5 N of Weedon — OS Sheet 152, map reference 607654; SP6065], New Inn: Simple food and well kept Marstons Pedigree in several friendly rooms radiating from central servery, hood skittles and other games, canalside terrace (Derek and Sylvia Stephenson, LYM)

☆ Bulwick, Northants [Main St; just off A43 Kettering—Duddington; SP9694], Queens Head: Beautiful 17th-century beamed stone pub, with genuine atmosphere, friendly landlord, well kept Batemans XXXB and two changing guest beers; cheap snacks, good value restaurant; no juke box (Nic James, Geoff Lee)

Chadwick End, War [A41; SP2073], Orange Tree: Well arranged and comfortable Whitbreads Brewers Fayre pub; Marstons Pedigree and Whitbreads-related real ales, well prepared standard bar food, piped music; no smoking family room with high chairs, children's food, games, even baby wipes (Mr and Mrs B J Twigger)

☆ Churchover, War [handy for M6 junction 1, off A426; SP5180], Haywaggon: Carefully modernised old pub on edge of quiet village in lovely countryside, with two small separate eating areas leading off bar, friendly pubby atmosphere, efficient staff, good range of beer inc Badger Best, Bass, Courage Best and Directors, Marstons, Ruddles County and regular guest beers,

good straightforward bar food (BB)

☆ Claverdon, War [SP1964], Red Lion: Clean and spacious back saloon (where children allowed) opening on to sheltered terrace, garden and play area; small plush front L-shaped lounge; popular for quickly served reliable food and well kept Flowers IPA and Original on handpump; open fire (Mrs R Heaton, BB)

☆ Clay Coton, Northants [off B5414 nr Stanford Hall; SP5977], Fox & Hounds: Friendly country pub, tastefully and comfortably furnished, with two log fires, well kept ales such as Batemans XXXB, Hook Norton, Jennings, Shepherd Neame Master Brew and Wadworths 6X, nice range of reasonably priced generous food inc good sandwiches in dining area; roaming dogs and cats, chatty licensees, interesting range of music — landlord chooses by clientele (George Atkinson, C E Power, Derek and Sylvia Stephenson)

☆ Coleshill, War [High St; not far from M6 junction 4; SP1989], George & Dragon: Well decorated and clean, with well kept M&B on handpump, good value bar food in dining lounge — may be packed Sat night, for remarkably cheap steaks (Brian Jones, E V Walder)

Collyweston, Northants [Main St; A43 4 miles SW of Stamford; SK9902], Cavalier: Much extended pub with interesting features, good range of quickly served meals and John Smiths, Ruddles Best and County and so forth on handpump; bedrooms (David Daws)

Corley Moor, War [Wall Hill Rd; SP2884], Red Lion: Extended pub with Watneys-related beers and good range of straightforward bar food from modern servery in new part (E V Walder)

☆ Cosgrove, Northants [Thrupp Wharf, towards Castlethorpe; SP7942], Navigation: Popular canal pub with good Grand Union moorings and spacious waterside garden with elevated verandah-terrace and play area; considerable concentration on beers, with well kept ales such as Adnams Broadside, Banks & Taylors, Bass, Hook Norton and Morlands, and decor inc masses of beer bottles, pump clips, cans and brewery mirrors; inexpensive good straightforward food, lots of dining tables in tidy lounge, coal-effect gas fires, pool and games in public bar; pleasant service (Dominic Woodfield, Michael and Alison Sandy, Derek and Sylvia Stephenson, BB)

☆ Coventry, W Mid [Spon St; SP3379], Old Windmill: Quaint and popular timber-framed 16th-century pub, all nooks and crannies, with fine ancient fireplace, good atmosphere, one of its small rooms with carved oak seats and flagstones; generous helpings of simple but extraordinarily cheap lunchtime food (chips and beans loom large) served quickly from the kitchen door, well kept Watneys-related real ales; very busy Fri and Sat evening, and still known locally as Ma Brown's (Geoff Lee, E V Walder)

☆ **Coventry** [Bond St, behind Coventry Theatre], *Town Wall*: Compact unspoilt Victorian pub, with original Atkinsons engraved windows, open fire in small T-shaped lounge, simple recently refurbished bar, tiny clubby snug and flower-filled back yard; new landlord settling in well, taking full advantage of guest beer rules — Hook Norton, Theakstons, Smiles etc, as well as farm ciders and perry and well kept Bass; generous good value home-cooked food; at lunchtime you draw a playing card — free meal for a joker *(Rob Weeks, Brian Randall)*

☆ **Coventry** [Sutton Stop, Aldermans Green/Hawkesbury; close to M6 junction 3, via Black Horse Rd off B4113 Coventry Rd], *Greyhound*: Good quickly served generous food at attractive prices inc particularly good pies in dining room, well kept Bass and Brew XI now on handpump, waterside tables in delightful garden by old cast-iron bridge at junction of Coventry and Oxford Canals, interesting collection of ties, odd little donkey-box (tiny snug); children welcome *(T R G Alcock, Rob and Gill Weeks, SJC)*

Coventry [252 Foleshill Rd], *Prince William Henry*: Very cheap good Indian food as well as some orthodox pubby dishes — cheap too; well kept Bass, wide range of customers; take-away service *(T R G Alcock)*; [Foleshill Rd], *Saracens Head*: Reproduction old-fashioned shopfronts as inside walls; simple inexpensive largely home-cooked food, friendly atmosphere, good pool table, juke box occasionally loud *(Anon)*; [Lockhurst Lane — Foleshill Rd, towards M6 junction 3], *Stag & Pheasant*: Friendly unpretentious Grand Met pub, good food served by cook from hotplates next to bar, picnic-table sets in garden *(Geoff Lee)*

Cradley Heath, W Mid [SO9486], *Black Country*: Nice old-fashioned drinking pub with well kept beers, usual bar food *(Comus Elliott)*; [St Annes Rd, Five Ways], *Sausage Works*: One of the smaller Little Pubs, plenty of mock sausages around the place and real ones in various guises on menu; well kept ales inc Lumphammer *(Brian Jones)*

Denton, Northants [SP8358], *Red Lion*: Small unpretentious pub in sleepy hollow of thatched stone houses, friendly atmosphere, obliging service, good snacks, Charles Wells beers, locals playing skittles *(George Atkinson, BB)*

☆ **Deppers Bridge**, War [SP4059], *Great Western*: Decorated in old GWR theme — lots of railway features and posters, even model railway around the ceiling; clean and comfortable family pub, with friendly efficient staff, unobtrusive piped music, well kept Allied beers on handpump, good choice of wines, good coffee, happy hours; extraordinarily wide choice of generous good value food inc vegetarian and children's dishes (high chairs, too), discount for regulars over 55; tiled terrace with plenty of seats and big play area; right by InterCity main line — can be a shock in the dark *(G H*

Gall, Roy Bromell, T R G Alcock, Mr and Mrs J Townsend, Mayur Shah, A E Alcock)

Dorridge, W Mid [Four Ashes Rd; SP1775], *Drum & Monkey*: Spacious and comfortable recently refurbished Millers Kitchen with good food inc well priced daily specials, well kept Greenalls Original and Davenports on handpump, friendly attentive service; no smoking dining area, big garden with play area *(J Barnwell)*

☆ **Dudley**, W Mid [Salop St, Eve Hill; SO9390], *British Oak*: Unpretentious place notable for its own good value beers and maybe cider, also Ansells, Tetleys and Wadworths on handpump, with a guest beer such as Boddingtons, and a good few whiskies, generous helpings of simple cheap food inc good value Sun roast; heady local atmosphere, piped music, fruit machine *(J S Rutter, Dave Braisted)*

☆ **Dudley** [Black Country Museum], *Bottle & Glass*: Friendly old-fashioned atmosphere in Victorian pub reconstructed in village of Black Country Museum (well worth a visit — also has working trams and trip up canal tunnel); well kept Hansons on handpump, good sandwiches; open lunchtime only *(News please)*

Dudley [Blowers Green Rd (A461/A454)], *Lamp*: Good choice of malt whiskies (bottle sales too) in Black Country drinkers' pub with well kept Bathams Mild and Bitter, good value food; good view from terrace *(Dave Braisted)*

☆ **Dunchurch**, War [very handy for M45 junction 1; SP4871], *Dun Cow*: Big central courtyard, pubby front bars (linked by hallway with settles and antiques), period atmosphere, heavy beams and panelling, prints and brasses, good fires in inglenooks, old-fashioned furnishings, panelling; good atmosphere, particularly in evenings, decent sandwiches and bar snacks, keg beers; bin-ends in courtyard wineshop; Tudor annex with bistro over road; bedrooms *(George Atkinson, Peter Holmes, LYM)*

Dunchurch [Daventry Rd], *Green Man*: Pleasant village local, friendly young licensees, dining area with home-cooked food, tables in garden; bedrooms, with big breakfasts *(Mr and Mrs R Berresford)*

☆ **Easenhall**, War [SP4679], *Golden Lion*: Good choice of good reasonably priced food in comfortable oak-beamed and carpeted bar with nice furniture inc cushioned old-fashioned settles; Flowers ales, log fires, good garden with swings and maybe a pet donkey; restaurant; bedrooms well equipped *(Geoff Lee)*

☆ **Eathorpe**, War [SP3868], *Plough*: Quietly traditional, just off Fosse Way; pronounced rugby theme, obliging landlady and friendly staff, well kept Ansells, good value food in bar, gigantic helpings of more challenging dishes in long, narrow restaurant very popular with locals — bookings advised weekends *(Roy Y Bramwell, Theo Schofield, Dr and Mrs A K Clarke, Mr and Mrs B J Twigger, Phil Bryant)*

☆ **Edge Hill**, War [SP3747], *Castle*: Notable

for terrific garden perched over steep slope of Edge Hill, with lovely views through the trees; and for the building itself, a battlemented folly of great potential; internally, the bar, like the turreted lavatories, is rather basic, with straightforward bar food and well kept Hook Norton real ales; particularly welcoming to children *(Derek and Sylvia Stephenson, LYM)*

☆ **Ettington**, War [A422 Banbury—Stratford; SP2749], *Chequers*: Simply furnished back lounge bar, spacious conservatory, tables outside and straightforward front bar with games and pool room; well kept real ales such as Adnams, M&B and Marstons Pedigree, wide choice of bar food; children if well behaved *(Andy and Jill Kassube, Frank Cummins, P R Davis, Mike and Wendy Proctor, LYM)*

Ettington [Banbury Rd (A422)], *Houndshill*: Well run and spotless, efficient barmaid who spelled out exactly what the wines were, good beer; decent bar food, restaurant, busy passing trade; children's play area in garden; bedrooms *(Sheila Keene, Roy Y Bromell)*

☆ **Farnborough**, War [off A423 N of Banbury; SP4349], *Butchers Arms*: Farmhouse-style main lounge bar with pews and stout deal tables, country furnishings in timbered and flagstoned extension, usual bar food, Flowers IPA and Original on handpump; play area on safely fenced front lawn, more tables on flower-edged lawn sloping up behind *(C Aydon, LYM)*

Farthingstone, Northants [SP6155], *Kings Arms*: Old-world pub full of atmosphere, pictures, nice home cooking, friendly service, well kept Hook Norton *(Comus Elliott, George Atkinson)*

Furnace End, War [SP2491], *Bulls Head*: Good village local, with friendly and interested landlord and good bar lunches *(Comus Elliott)*

Gaydon, War [B4451, just off A41 Banbury—Warwick; SP3654], *Malt Shovel*: Modernised pub with panelling, big stained-glass window over one raised end, friendly service, well kept Flowers IPA and Original, filter coffee, good value bar food with hefty helpings of chips; quite handy for M40 *(T F and V Marshall)*

Gayton, Northants [High St; SP7054], *Eykyn Arms*: Smallish, comfortable lounge, larger back public bar with table skittles; friendly landlord, well kept Charles Wells Eagle and Adnams Broadside *(Derek and Sylvia Stephenson, Nick Dowson)*

Gornalwood, W Mid [Summit Pl; just off B4176; SO9190], *Bush*: Holt Plant & Deakins pub done up in the style of inter-war living room with old electric fires; snacks, Hook Norton and Ruddles ales too, very low prices *(Dave Braisted)*

☆ **Great Brington**, Northants [SP6664], *Fox & Hounds*: Popular sandstone local, full of character, with open fire, cottage chairs on flagstone floor, low beams, separate games room with table skittles; Watneys-related beers, filled rolls and other bar snacks,

entertaining parrot; charming village nr Althorp House *(George Atkinson, Philip Orbell)*

☆ **Great Houghton**, Northants [up No Through Road just before the White Hart; SP7958], *Old Cherry Tree*: Cosy low-beamed old pub in quiet village spot, renovated but interesting, with single servery for two alcovey areas, well kept Charles Wells Eagle and Bombardier on handpump; good value bar food popular lunchtime with industrial estate businessmen, friendly staff *(Dr and Mrs A K Clarke, George Atkinson)*

Great Oxendon, Northants [SP7383], *George*: Civilised dining pub with no-smoking conservatory, restaurant, and consistently good, imaginative bar food; pleasant service, Adnams and other real ales, decent wines; popular with families weekends *(M Ruskin, George Atkinson)*

Greens Norton, Northants [SP6669], *Butchers Arms*: Large recently refurbished lounge, well kept Ruddles and Theakstons XB, emphasis on interesting good value food *(Gwyneth and Salvo Spadaro-Dutturi)*

☆ **Halesowen**, W Mid [Cowley Gate St; just off A458 to Stourbridge, at Cradley Heath — OS Sheet 139, map reference 941847; SO9683], *Little Chop House*: Formerly the Little White Lion, refurbished with more traditional pub style and atmosphere; good value freshly made bar food in massive helpings, consistently well kept Allied real ales inc Mild, and Little Lumphammer, good service; can get packed weekends *(Brian Jones)*

☆ **Hampton in Arden**, W Mid [High St; SP2081], *White Lion*: Attractive stuccoed village local, friendly and genuine, with small unspoilt public bar, cosy lounge and dining room at the back (not open weekday lunchtimes); well kept Bass, Brew XI and Mild on handpump, fairly limited range of prompt bar food inc lunchtime buffet and good filled baps, open fire; quite handy for National Exhibition Centre; children's room *(Audrey and Brian Green, Gwyneth and Salvo Spadaro-Dutturi)*

Hampton Lucy, War [SP2557], *Boars Head*: Pleasant, unspoilt village pub with log fire, brasses and friendly atmosphere; well kept Flowers, simple reasonably priced bar food and prompt service *(M Box, Vanessa and Peter Hurst)*

Harborne, W Mid [not far from M5 junction 3; SP0284], *Bell*: In Botanical Gardens area, with servery by passageway at foot of stairs, hatch-served inglenook snug, large, comfortable lounge, seats outside, wooden balcony overlooking bowling green; has been praised for well kept M&B Mild, reasonably priced lunchtime bar food, but no recent reports *(News please)*

Harbury, War [Chapel St; SP3759], *Gamecock*: Vast choice of well cooked good value food in small cheerful pub, very popular locally (booking advised); well kept beer, good reasonable wine *(Elisabeth Kemp)*

Harlestone, Northants [A428; SP7064], *Fox & Hounds*: Comfortable two-bar pub popular at lunch for good range of well presented reasonably priced food, consistently warm and welcoming atmosphere; Watneys-related real ales, good choice of wines, piped music, no dogs or children; nr Althorp House *(George Atkinson, Lyn and Bill Capper)*

☆ **Harpole**, Northants [High St; nr M1 junction 16; SP6860], *Bull*: Pleasant, clean and friendly pub with good choice of cheap food in generous portions; friendly, helpful service *(Virginia Jones)*

Harrington, Northants [off A508 S of Mkt Harboro; SP7779], *Tollemache Arms*: Small, well kept stone village pub, old beams, low doorways, open fire, nice mix of chairs and tables, soft lighting; lively country atmosphere, no music, well kept Charles Wells, good standard bar food *(Keith Croxton)*

Hawkesbury, W Mid [Aldermans Green; off Grange Rd; jnctn Coventry and N Oxford canals; SP3684], *Greyhound*: Booking essential for the Pie Parlour, comfortable banquettes and barrel chairs, lots of canalia and quite a private old-world atmosphere — several good home-cooked pies, pleasant service *(Irene and Derek Cranston)*

Hinton in the Hedges, Northants [SP5536], *Crewe Arms*: Well kept Hook Norton and guests such as Theakstons XB, big helpings of good value bar food, fine reasonably priced restaurant, friendly *(Douglas Reid)*

☆ **Hockley Heath**, W Mid [Stratford Rd; A34 Birmingham—Henley-in-Arden; SP1573], *Barn*: Beefeater motel with bustling, rambling bar/restaurant done out with beamery, bricks and tiles on various levels; decent standard range of food, well kept Marstons Pedigree and Whitbreads-related real ales on handpump, cheerful friendly service, genuine welcome for children; bedrooms satisfactory *(Dr R Fuller)*

Hockley Heath [Stratford Rd], *Wharf*: Spacious Chef & Brewer overlooking Stratford Canal, very popular for good value straightforward bar food in big helpings; four real ales, piped music, cheerful service, waterside garden and terrace, lavatory for disabled *(Ian Phillips, J Bramley, P M Elliott)*

☆ **Ilmington**, War [SP2143], *Howard Arms*: Warm and friendly atmosphere in handsome heavy-beamed golden stone village pub under new licensees, with polished flagstones, open fires (one in a big inglenook screened by a high-backed settle), promising choice of good interesting food in bar and elegantly redecorated restaurant booked out at weekends; well kept Flowers IPA and Original and Marstons Pedigree, attractive garden and village-green view *(Bob and Ann Westbrook, John and Celia Furnival, S V Bishop, E V Walder, LYM)*

Islip, Northants [just off M1/A1 link; SP9879], *Woolpack*: Old-style inn with shepherding theme — even lavatories labelled Rams and Ewes; good choice of bar food, restaurant, good attentive service, Riding ale and others; cream teas; bedrooms *(Hilary Aslett)*

☆ **Kenilworth**, War [Castle Hill; SP2871], *Clarendon Arms*: Long partly flagstoned bar and several small rooms in well refurbished old pub with Courage Directors, John Smiths and good food served for long hours in bar and upstairs dining room; opp castle *(Rob and Gill Weeks, A Parsons, Roger Braithwaite, David and Valerie Hooley)*

☆ **Kenilworth** [High St], *Clarendon House*: Painstakingly restored and interestingly decorated split-level hotel bar, partly panelled, with well kept Flowers IPA and Original and Hook Norton Best and Old Hookey, civilised atmosphere, friendly old english sheepdog; good value bar food, restaurant; bedrooms comfortable and good value *(Simon Collett-Jones, Mrs G Walsh, Brian Jones, Rob and Gill Weeks)*

Kilsby, Northants [handy for M1 junction 18; SP5671], *Red Lion*: Attractive building in beautiful thatched village, doing well under new landlord; lots of picnic-table sets on nice lawn, with unusual play houses and plans for pets' corner; one room set aside for wide choice of reasonably priced food inc good vegetarian dishes; Ruddles and Wadworths 6X, skittles evenings; popular but not too crowded *(Mrs R Heaton)*

Kings Hill, W Mid [160 Darlaston Rd; SO9896], *Three Crowns*: Warmly welcoming small terraced pub with even smaller pool/children's room; cheap pies and sandwiches, very cheap Bass Special, Highgate Mild and Springfield; juke box, darts, fruit machine *(P Roberts)*

Kingswinford, W Mid [Cot Lane; SO8888], *Park*: Friendly single-room local with well kept real ales such as Bathams, Holt Plant & Deakins Entire and Ind Coope Burton; no food evenings *(John Tooth)*

☆ **Ladbroke**, War [A423 S of Southam; SP4158], *Bell*: Pleasant surroundings, tables in garden, well kept Davenports and wide range of well served grilled and fried food, superb value for money; very busy at weekends *(Michael Brookes)*

Leamington Spa, War [SP3165], *Somerville Arms*: Good local with cosy lounge, well kept Ansells Bitter and Mild, Ind Coope Burton and Marstons Pedigree, friendly staff *(Graham Bush, SJC)*

☆ **Lilbourne**, Northants [Rugby Rd; 4 miles from M1 junction 18 — A5 N, then first right; SP5677], *Bell*: Spaciously clean and modern lounge bar well worth knowing as a motorway stopoff, with low-priced quickly served good value simple bar food, seats outside (and climbing frame); children welcome *(George Atkinson, LYM)*

☆ **Little Brington**, Northants [also signed from A428; 4½ miles from M1 junction 16; first right off A45 to Daventry; SP6663], *Saracens Head*: Old-fashioned village pub full of 1950s and other collectables, cosy seats by lounge fireside, games in big L-shaped public bar (log fire here too), tables in neat back garden overlooking quiet fields; friendly service and reasonably priced, well cooked and presented bar food, piano singalong Sat evening,

Watneys-related real ale; nr Althorp House *(George Atkinson, LYM)*

☆ **Long Itchington**, War [Church Rd; SP4165], *Harvester*: Clean pub with straightforward furnishings, well kept Hook Norton and Wadworths 6X on handpump, good value bar food, very reasonably priced meals in small, relaxed restaurant, friendly staff *(Ted George)*

☆ **Lower Boddington**, Northants [off A361 Banbury—Daventry — OS Sheet 151, map reference 481521; SP4852], *Carpenters Arms*: Warmly welcoming traditional country local, well kept Hook Norton beers, wide range of lunchtime bar food inc good fry-ups *(Joan and Michel Hooper-Immins)*

☆ **Lower Quinton**, War [off A46 Stratford—Broadway; SP1847], *College Arms*: Whitbreads pub attractively placed on village green, spacious open-plan lounge, unusual table in former fireplace, stripped stone walls, heavy beams, partly carpeted parquet floor; wide range of generous bar food, Flowers IPA and Original and Wadworths 6X on handpump, public bar with games *(Brian Skelcher, J Barnwell, W F C Phillips)*

☆ **Lye**, W Mid [Pedmore Rd; SO9284], *Shovel Inn*: Friendly refurbished town pub with good range of changing well kept real ales, good value home-cooked bar food inc good steaks; pleasant lounge, basic bar — small, can get very crowded *(Dave Braisted)*

Lye [Balds Lane], *Crown*: Interesting back-street pub, cheap lunches *(Dave Braisted)*

Marston St Lawrence, Northants [off A422 Banbury—Brackley; SP5342], *Marston*: Small, cosy and welcoming end-of-terrace local, brightly done-up, with good reasonably priced lunchtime and evening food inc ample sandwiches, well kept Hook Norton *(George Atkinson, J E Stanton, LYM)*

Meer End, W Mid [SP2474], *Tipperary*: Friendly and comfortable, with bar snacks, Davenports real ale, enormous goldfish in piano-aquarium, tables in garden *(Brian Skelcher, LYM)*

Middleton, War [OS Sheet 139, map reference 175984; SP1798], *Green Man*: Busy family pub with good value food inc ridiculously cheap steaks *(Hilary Sargeant, N P Clarke, E V Walder)*

☆ **Monks Kirby**, War [Bell Lane, just off A427 W of Pailton; SP4683], *Bell*: Good generous bar food with some emphasis on fish and Spanish dishes, in quiet open-plan beamed and timbered bar divided into separate areas, with slabbed and cobbled floor, woodburning stove; relaxed mainly Spanish service, restaurant, interesting wines *(Geoff Lee, Roy Bromell)*

☆ **Napton**, War [A425 Daventry—Leamington; SP4661], *Napton Bridge*: Well run, busy canal pub with well kept Davenports and particularly good plain but hearty food at reasonable prices inc genuine pasta specials (Italian landlady); former stable for bargees' horses is now a skittle alley *(WHBM, Cdr W S D Hendry)*

Napton on the Hill, War [Folly Lane; towards Priors Hardwick; by canal lock; SP4661], *Folly*: Free house converted from restored farmhouse, good choice of beers, good reasonably priced bar food, friendly staff and good landlord; busy weekends *(H R Bevan)*

☆ **Nassington**, Northants [Fotheringhay Rd; TL0696], *Black Horse*: Ambitious if not cheap food and well kept real ales such as Adnams, Greene King IPA and Wadworths 6X in two comfortable beamed dining rooms linked by bar servery, with striking stone fireplace, panelling from Rufford Abbey, easy chairs and small settees; children allowed in eating area; restaurant; seats on sheltered lawn *(Drs M and K Parier, LYM)*

☆ **Newbold on Avon**, War [SP4777], *Barley Mow*: Small, straightforward pub with pretty canalside terrace and garden; good value bar food from sandwiches to tender steaks inc children's dishes, well kept beer, good friendly service *(M Morgan, C H Stride)*

☆ **Newbold on Avon** [B4112], *Boat*: Plushly extended three-bar canalside pub with small but reasonable choice of good value food; Davenports Bitter and Mild on handpump, open fire between dining area and bar, table skittles, darts *(M Morgan)*

☆ **Newbold on Stour**, War [A34 Shipston on Stour—Stratford; SP2446], *White Hart*: Long beamed and tiled bar divided into areas by stub walls and log fire, big bay windows, roomy back bar with pool and so forth; bar food (not Sun evening, and not much that's cheap, though ploughman's is good value); Bass and maybe a guest beer; children welcome *(A C Morrison, Phil Clissitt, Ness Turner, LYM)*

Newnham, Northants [SP5859], *Romer Arms*: Own-brew beers from friendly, welcoming pub on village green with reasonably priced bar food and dining conservatory; good Sun roasts *(George Atkinson)*

Newton Regis, War [SK2707], *Queens Head*: In lovely village with traditional thatched cottages, duck pond etc; friendly atmosphere, good value food, lovely floral gardens *(Graham Richardson)*

☆ **Northampton** [Wellingborough Rd], *Abington Park*: Imposing and spacious Victorian own-brew pub nr Abington Park and Northants CC, with brewery tours by arrangement, and good choice maybe a Porter — they may give you free sips to try; several bars, lunchtime bar food, friendly helpful staff, restaurant *(Nigel Gibbs, Joan and Michel Hooper-Immins, George Atkinson)*

☆ **Northampton** [3 3/4 miles from M1 junction 15; A508, then A428 towards Bedford, then right just after roundabout], *Britannia*: Open-plan rambling riverside pub, beams, flagstones, stripped pine furnishings, Victorian-style decorations inc attractive 18th-century kitchen with original fittings; Watneys-related real ales, straightforward lunchtime bar food, carvery, conservatory; juke box (and gaming machines) may be loud, disco Sun, Tues, Thurs *(George Atkinson, Virginia Jones, Jim Aitkenhead, LYM)*

Northampton [11 Fish St], *Fish*: Central, bustlingly popular for good range of reasonably priced lunchtime food; bedrooms *(George Atkinson)*; [A428 N], *Fox & Hounds*: Good food in clean and tidy pub with efficient staff; rather pricey Watneys-related real ales *(Ted George)*

Nuneaton, War [Coton Rd; SP3592], *Rose*: Good choice of low-priced food from filled rolls and doorstep sandwiches through burgers, baked potatoes, omelettes and pizzas to fish and chargrills, well kept Marstons Pedigree on handpump, friendly atmosphere *(Mr and Mrs P A Jones)*

☆ **Offchurch**, War [off A425 Radford Semele; SP3565], *Stags Head*: 16th-century thatched dining pub with concentration on good varied food inc help-yourself salads and vegetarian dishes; helpful, efficient staff *(C H Stride, I H Rorison, Curt and Lois Stevens)*

☆ **Old Hill**, W Mid [Waterfall Lane; off Station Rd, between A4099 Gorstyhill Rd and A459 Halesowen Rd; SO9685], *Wharf*: Popular and chatty drinking pub, well kept — like its eight or so changing beers, often interesting ones; also sensibly priced bar food, seats in garden with good play area, pleasant canalside setting; children in family room; occasional live music *(J S Rutter, Brian Jones, LYM)*

☆ **Old Hill** [Waterfall Lane], *Waterfall*: Small, busy refurbished Black Country local worth knowing for its good range of beers inc Bathams; good value food, enthusiastic licensee *(T Henwood, Gareth Jones, Dave Braisted)*

☆ **Oldbury**, W Mid [Church St, nr Savacentre; SO9888], *Waggon & Horses*: Impressive tiled Edwardian bar with well kept ales inc Bathams, wide choice of food from hot pork sandwiches to frogs' legs, separate dining area, good service *(Hilary Sargeant, Norman Clarke, T Henwood, Gareth Jones)*

Oxhill, War [just S of A422; SP3145], *Peacock*: Worth knowing for good range of food *(M Joyner)*

Pailton, War [A427 Lutterworth—Coventry; SP4781], *Fox*: Good choice of bar food inc children's and vegetarian dishes, friendly quick service; bedrooms *(Geoff Lee)*; *White Lion*: Pleasant recently renovated village pub with wide range of food inc good lemon sole; friendly atmosphere, cheerful staff, play area in garden *(Roy Y Bromell, B R Shiner)*

☆ **Preston Bagot**, War [B4095 Henley-in-Arden—Warwick; SP1765], *Olde Crab Mill*: Comfortable old low-beamed and timbered pub with lots of nooks and crannies, three log fires, old prints and some interesting furniture inc carved settles; well kept Whitbreads-related real ales, usual bar food (not Sun evening), good service; seats outside, play area; children in own area; open all day *(C H Stride, H R Bevan, Kevin Fields, Ted George, LYM)*

Princethorpe, War [junction A423/B4453;

SP4070], *Three Horseshoes*: Very busy indeed for good value food *(Mr and Mrs B J Twigger)*

Priors Hardwick, War [SP4756], *Butchers Arms*: Spacious and well run old place with medieval oak beams, panelling, flagstones, antiques, log fire and country garden; now a good upmarket restaurant, and the inglenook bar is really just an adjunct *(J R and B Walker)*

☆ **Priors Marston** [from village centre follow Shuckburgh signpost, but still in village take first R by telephone box], *Holly Bush*: Rambling and unusual ancient golden stone house with interesting stripped-stone decor, oak beams, latch door, good log fire, friendly staff, well kept Marstons Pedigree and other real ales; darts and table skittles in side room, well cooked straightforward food *(G P Beckett, J D Maplethorpe, Mrs M Lawrence, R C Gandy, Peter Watkins, Pam Stanley, LYM)*

☆ **Pytchley**, Northants [SP8574], *Overstone Arms*: Delightful pub and garden in attractive countryside, friendly professional service, good changing choice of bar food in spacious lounge with dining area, Watneys-related real ales, games room *(Roy Y Bromell)*

☆ **Quarry Bank**, W Mid [High St; SO9390], *Church Tavern*: Pleasantly renovated homely pub with welcoming landlord, good value traditional Black Country bar food, reasonably priced well kept local Holt, Plant & Deakins beer *(Dave Braisted)*

☆ **Radford Semele**, War [A425 2 miles E of Leamington Spa — OS Sheet 151, map reference 343645; SP3464], *White Lion*: Good generously served cheap food inc speciality ploughman's in straightforward old pub, cheerful staff, Davenports ales, garden *(G H Gall)*

☆ **Ratley**, War [OS Sheet 151, map reference 384473; SP3847], *Rose & Crown*: Handsome old local of golden Hornton stone, nr lovely church in small sleepy village, with woodburning stove in flagstoned bar on right, big log fireplace in carpeted area on left, lots of cricket memorabilia, tables in small garden; very popular for wide and interesting range of real ales from smaller breweries, cosy atmosphere, and quickly served good food (not Sun or Mon evenings); has been closed Fri lunchtime and Mon in winter *(P R Davis, G Walsh, J E Stanton, Gordon and Daphne, Mark Evans, Ted George)*

☆ **Rockingham**, Northants [SP8691], *Sondes Arms*: Nice welcoming and civilised old pub with friendly service, good home-made food (sandwiches, mackerel bake, curries and puddings all praised) and well kept Charles Wells Bombardier and Eagle on handpump *(Anon)*

☆ **Rowington**, War [Finwood Rd; off B4439 N of Rowington, following Lowsonford sign; SP2069], *Tom o' the Wood*: Several comfortably modernised communicating rooms, well kept Whitbreads-related real ales on handpump, fruit machine, piped music, picnic-table sets on terrace and neat side lawn; bar food, handsome Elizabethan ceiling in upstairs restaurant, provision for children lunchtime; nice spot (Brian Jones, J Barnwell, H R Bevan, C E Power, LYM reports on new regime please)

Rowington [Old Warwick Rd], Cockhorse: Clean and attractive, currently doing well, with reasonably priced food, friendly staff, and tables outside — ideal for children, with big caged areas of birds, rabbits and guinea-pigs; dogs allowed (H R Bevan)

☆ Sedgley, W Mid [Bilston St (A463); SO9193], Beacon: Original Victorian fittings and furnishings in five distinct drinking areas, inc a family room, radiating from tiny serving area with hatches; well kept Holdens Special and M&B Springfield, their own interesting and potent Sarah Hughes Dark Ruby Mild brewed in a restored small tower brewery behind, and a guest beer that changes every second day; seats on terrace; good atmosphere, very mixed clientele (More reports please)

☆ Shuttington, War [SK2505], Wolferstan Arms: Attractively refurbished panoramic lounge and spacious restaurant with views over lake; nicely cooked reasonably priced straightforward food, pleasant waitress service, well kept Marstons Pedigree on handpump, tropical fishtank; popular with families at weekends; garden with children's play areas (Graham Richardson)

☆ Sibbertoft, Northants [SP6782], Red Lion: Small and welcoming, with limited but frequently changing menu concentrating on fish, steaks and old-fashioned puddings; well kept ales on handpump such as Adnams and winter Tally Ho, reasonable choice of realistically priced wine, friendly licensees, very civilised atmosphere (Harry Stirling, George Atkinson)

☆ Smethwick, W Mid [Waterloo Rd; A457/A4136/A4092; SP0288], Waterloo: Well worth a visit for the splendid Victorian tilework in the decidedly unpretentious public bar, and for the old-fashioned mosaic-floored tiled basement dining room, with good choice of steaks and vegetables, well served, from the open grill; cheap M&B and Springfield ales, separate plush lounge (LYM)

Smethwick [Uplands/Meadow Rd], Old Chapel: Small M&B beamed local, separate bars and lounges served from one counter; bright M&B Springfield and Brew XI on handpump, sandwiches inc hot pork, a few hot dishes (Frank Cummins)

Snitterfield, War [SP2159], Snitterfield Arms: Fairly big knocked-through U-shaped room with homely atmosphere, open fire, shelves of decorative plates; well kept Flowers Original and other Whitbreads ales, good range of bar food; popular with locals, walkers, businessmen and those from local gliding school; specially busy Sat evening for diners (Brian Jones)

Southam, War [A423 towards Banbury; SP4161], George & Dragon: Friendly welcome with good choice of food; garden with cages of rabbits, hens, birds and so forth (Anon)

Stockton, War [off A426 Southam—Rugby; SP4363], Barley Mow: Nice friendly clean pub with two-level lounge, well kept beer, and decent, well served food; upstairs restaurant serves only chargrilled meals, but of very high quality; high ceilings, wall plates and photos (Ted George)

Stonnall, W Mid [Main St; off A452; SK0503], Old Swann: Recently refurbished, but keeping its mock Tudor decor; now has Sam Smiths; varied well presented food lunchtime and early evening (Cliff Blakemore)

☆ Stourbridge, W Mid [Amblecote Rd (A491); SO8984], Moorings: Large, busy pub by canal spur, with good changing choice of real ales, fair choice of reasonably priced bar food, pleasant back terrace (E J Alcock, Dave Braisted)

☆ Stratford upon Avon, War [Chapel St; SP2055], Shakespeare: Not a place for your gardening gear — take your tweeds: stylish public rooms and accommodation based on handsome lavishly modernised Tudor merchants' houses, but inc comfortable Froth & Elbow bar with settles and armchairs, good choice of interesting and well kept Courage Directors and Hook Norton Best on handpump, bar food inc reliable cold table and hot dishes of the day, quick friendly service; tables in back courtyard, civilised tea or coffee in peaceful chintzy armchairs by blazing log fires; three mins' walk from theatre; bedrooms comfortable and well equipped, though not cheap — THF (David and Valerie Hooley, Frank Cummins, M A and C R Starling, Andy and Jill Kassube, Auriol and Paul McLoughlin, LYM)

☆ Stratford upon Avon [Southern Way], Black Swan: The Dirty Duck — neat 16th-century pub in delightful position with attractive terrace looking over the riverside public gardens; usual bar food at moderate prices, Flowers IPA and Original, signed RSC photographs, children allowed in restaurant; quietest during — rather than before or after — a performance at the nearby Memorial Theatre (Philip King, T Nott, Dr T W Hoskins, Jonathan and Jane Hagger, Gary Scott, LYM)

Stratford upon Avon [Rother St, opp United Reform Church; handy for Friday Mkt], Lamplighters: Long and spacious softly lit bar, log-effect gas fire, well kept if cold Tetleys; reasonably priced food, limited Sun (Lynne Sheridan, Bob West, Andy and Jill Kassube); [Sheep St], Rose & Crown: Two-level Chef & Brewer with upper eating area, Ruddles Best and County, good value roasts and other reasonably priced food (Roger Huggins); [Rother St], White Swan: Old-fashioned heavy-beamed bar with leather armchairs, ancient settles and fine oak panelling, with well kept Marstons Pedigree, Wadworths 6X and a guest beer, lunchtime bar snacks; a wall painting of Tobias and the Angel dates from 1560;

children in eating area; bedrooms — it's THF *(T C W Moody, Len Beattie, LYM)*

Stretton on Dunsmore, War [off A45; SP4172], *Leg of Mutton*: Spick and span unspoilt local of great character, with fancy tiled floor and grand piano in 1940s lounge, two darts boards, coal fire in small snug, unusual brass-foot tables, friendly staff, M&B Mild and Brew XI on handpump *(Ted George)*

☆ **Studley**, War [Icknield St Dr; left turn off A435, going N from B4093 roundabout; SP0763], *Old Washford Mill*: Pretty waterside gardens with good play area, by extensive and popular watermill conversion with old mill machinery, lots of different levels inc quiet alcoves, variety of catering, provision for children, real ales *(J Barnwell, LYM)*

Studley, *Barley Mow*: Toby Inn with good carvery — have to book Sun lunch; staff friendly and efficient, decent wines *(W H and E Thomas)*; [Alcester Rd (A435)], *Little Lark*: Another Little pub, with a newspaper theme *(Dave Braisted, E V Walder)*

☆ **Sudborough**, Northants [High St; SP9682], *Vane Arms*: Attractive and welcoming thatched inn in picturesque village, with inglenook fireplaces in comfortable main bar, particularly well prepared freshly cooked bar food, also seven to ten regularly changing well kept real ales, farm cider and a wide range of country wines; friendly landlord and staff, small public bar, small upstairs dining room; fine walking country; children welcome; luxurious bedroom block *(Ashley Jordan, Bob Allan, Michel Hooper-Immins)*

Sulgrave, Northants [Manor Rd; SP5545], *Star*: Old pub close to George Washington's ancestral home, with huge helpings of good food, esp steak and kidney pie, mixed grill and salmon dishes; friendly atmosphere *(C Wilson)*

☆ **Sutton Bassett**, Northants [SP7790], *Queens Head*: Enterprising bar food inc notable ploughman's and steaks, welcoming staff, four well kept real ales on handpump, upstairs restaurant *(George Atkinson, M B P Carpenter, Brian and Jill Bond)*

☆ **Temple Grafton**, War [a mile E, towards Binton; off A422 W of Stratford; SP1255], *Blue Boar*: Popular extended pub with softly lit stripped-stone bar, communicating dining room; good service even when crowded, consistently good reasonably priced bar food esp fresh fish, well kept Flowers, log fires, darts in flagstoned area; tables outside, parking can be difficult when busy *(Brian Skelcher, M S Hancock, S V Bishop, Peter Lloyd, John Bowdler, Margaret and Trevor Errington)*

Thorpe Waterville, Northants [A605 Thrapston—Oundle; TL0281], *Fox*: Big helpings of well prepared straightforward food at reasonable prices, coal fire, space for children, genial Irish landlord, real ales such as Adnams Broadside and Charles Wells *(Mr and Mrs J Back, Michael Back)*

☆ **Tipton**, W Mid [Hurst Lane, Dudley Rd; towards Wednesbury, junction A457/A4037 — look for the Irish flag; SO9592], *M A D O'Rourkes Pie Factory*: One of the liveliest and roomiest Little pubs, with a vivid meat-processing theme — all sorts of interesting ancient equipment, not to mention strings of model hams, sausages, pigs' heads and so forth; good value food inc traditional puddings, well kept Ind Coope-related real ales and their own Lumphammer, piped or live jazz or folk music; children welcome if eating *(J Overton, Comus Elliott, Brian Jones, Paul Denham, Nicola Brown-Denham, J S Rutter)*

☆ **Tipton** [Lower Church Lane, opp Police Stn], *Old Court House*: Well run but basic beer-lovers' local included chiefly for its half-dozen interesting real ales, often from distant small breweries; generous helpings of good value bar food *(Russell Allen)*

☆ **Titchmarsh**, Northants [village signed from A604 and A605, just E of Thrapston; TL0279], *Wheatsheaf*: Good value home-made bar food and Allied real ales in comfortably extended village pub with friendly service, pool room, restaurant; children allowed in eating areas; its restricted hours (has been closed Mon, and Tues-Fri lunchtimes) keep it local *(LYM)*

Tividale, W Mid [SO9890], *Boat*: Banks's beers, low-priced bar food, interesting canal photographs *(Dave Braisted)*

Towcester, Northants [Brackley Rd; SP6948], *Bull*: Reasonably priced bar food, quick friendly service; can be very busy, and popular with youngsters — music can be rather loud *(George Atkinson)*

☆ **Tredington**, War [SP2543], *White Lion*: Clean and comfortable pub, good food at attractive prices *(P R Davis)*

☆ **Upper Benefield**, Northants [SP9889], *Wheatsheaf*: Wide choice of interesting bar food, not cheap but good and generously served, in attractive and well run upmarket pub/hotel/restaurant; comfortable bedrooms *(Geoff Lee)*

☆ **Upper Braisles**, War [SP3039], *Gate*: Attractive low-beamed cottage-type village pub in pretty Cotswold hillside spot, genuine old-world atmosphere, pleasantly free from pretentious over-decoration (the locals' bar is bigger than the attractive lounge with its large fireplace); good generous straightforward bar food inc wide range of sandwiches, well kept Hook Norton, good service, genial landlord, extensive gardens with Wendy house; children if well behaved *(Sir Nigel Foulkes, R W Grey, Gwyneth and Salvo Spadaro-Dutturi)*

Walsall, W Mid [Birchills/Hollyhedge Lane; A454 towards M6 junction 10; SP0198], *Fourways*: Multi-roomed local, packed at peak times, with particularly well kept M&B Brew XI and Highgate Mild on handpump, live entertainment Sun evening, two darts boards, CD juke box, friendly customers, genial licensees, cheap cobs; children in side snug and back parlour *(P Roberts)*; [John St (properly the New Inn)], *Pretty Bricks*: Well kept Ansells and Ind

Coope Burton, good reasonably priced bar food (not Sun evening or Mon), good value Sun lunches, piped music *(Paul Noble)*; [behind Royal Hotel], *Walsall Arms*: Quaint old-fashioned pub being transformed by new licensees, well kept real ales such as Boddingtons and Marstons Pedigree, good atmosphere *(T Henwood)*

Warley, W Mid [Church St, Oldbury; SO9987], *Waggon & Horses*: Handsome well refurbished Edwardian tiled bar which has been popular for good range of well kept real ales, good bar food from sandwiches to steaks and friendly staff, but no recent reports *(News please)*; [Gorsty Hill Rd, Blackheath (A4099 not far from M5 junction 2)], *Beech Tree*: Restored Holt, Plant & Deakins pub with leather upholstery and case of old books; friendly service, good value food *(Dave Braisted)*

☆ Warmington, War [A41 towards Shotteswell; SP4147], *Wobbly Wheel*: Warm welcome, attractive lounge and bar, enterprising food, real ales, pleasant situation *(M Dolbear)*

☆ Warwick [Guy's Cliffe; A429 just N], *Saxon Mill*: Former mill building with wheel turning slowly below glass, mill race under glass floor-panel; a pine-clad and bookshelved Harvester family restaurant now, with beams, flagstones, open fires, Courage Best and Directors, gentle piped music; tables outside, summer weekend barbecues, play area; live music Tues, Thurs and Sun; open all day *(Miss R Murdoch, Auriol and Paul McLoughlin, LYM)*

☆ Warwick [11 Church St], *Zetland Arms*: Good value simple food, well kept Davenports on handpump, lively conversation around the bar but quieter areas too; delightful and well kept sheltered back garden *(R N Haygarth, LYM)*

Warwick [Smith St], *Roebuck*: Five real ales, good value food, nice friendly service; nr Castle *(Ralf Zeyssig)*

☆ Weedon, Northants [3 miles from M1 junction 16; A45 towards Daventry; on A5 junction; SP6259], *Crossroads*: Modern main-road hotel with surprisingly flamboyant decor in main bar, inc lots of bric-a-brac, counters made from antique mahogany chemist's-shop fittings; light and airy separate coffee parlour a useful all-day motorway break, also a restaurant; bar food rather pricey, well kept Bass and Watneys-related real ales, freshly squeezed orange juice; children welcome; bedrooms comfortable and attractive *(Robert Kimberley, R Elliott, Lynne Sheridan and Bob West, Philip Orbell, LYM)*

Weedon [Stowe Hill (A5, S)], *Narrow Boat*: Spacious terrace and big garden sweeping down to Grand Union Canal; pub has been revamped as Country Fayre dining pub — courteous prompt service and good value food, if not the atmosphere and Cantonese specialities it used to have *(W J Wonham, LYM)*

Welford, Northants [SP6480], *Shoulder of Mutton*: Friendly, well kept 17th-century

inn in lovely village, with simple food inc children's dishes, young efficient staff, Batemans XB and Ruddles Best ales, flowers on tables; piped music; good back play area *(Rona Murdoch)*

☆ Welford on Avon, War [Maypole; SP1452], *Shakespeare*: Comfortable, and very popular for food, with considerable concentration on this; well kept Flowers IPA and Marstons Pedigree on handpump, good range of wines, good service; exceptional garden with stunning displays of bedding plants and hanging baskets *(Brian Skelcher, J Barnwell)*

☆ West Bromwich, W Mid [High St; SP0091], *Old Hop Pole*: Cosy local with good atmosphere, interesting decor with lots of bric-a-brac, roaring fire in black-leaded grate, well kept Holt, Plant & Deakins ales, superb doorstep sandwiches — especially the local speciality, hot pork; Sun lunchtime popular with dominoes-players *(J S Rutter, Roger Taylor)*

West Bromwich, W Mid [High St — pedestrianised part], *Great Western*: Recently refurbished with good woodwork detailing on stained-glass screens; well kept Holt, Plant & Deakins, good choice of reasonably priced bar food; open all day *(Graham Richardson)*

West Haddon, Northants [about 3 miles from M1 junction 18; A428 towards Northampton; SP6272], *Sheaf*: Basic snug bar with pool table, comfortable upstairs lounge, good bar meals (maybe not Sat) and big candlelit restaurant; pool table in small cosy downstairs bar *(George Atkinson)*

☆ Weston, Northants [the one N of Brackley; SP5846], *Crown*: Good food and range of ales inc Hook Norton and Wadworths 6X in warmly welcoming and attractive flagstoned village pub with highwayman connections; handy for NT Canons Ashby and Sulgrave *(C A Gurney, George Atkinson)*

Wilbarston, Northants [SP8188], *Fox*: Good choice of good value bar food, small dining room (booking advisable), friendly local atmosphere, games room with darts, skittles and so forth; bedrooms *(Michael Andrews)*

☆ Willey, War [just off A5, N of A427 junction; SP4984], *Old Watling*: Neat, cosy and popular blend of polished flagstones, stripped masonry and open fire with modern comfort; big helpings of good value bar food, well kept Adnams, Banks's, Courage and John Smiths; big car park *(Dave Braisted, Ted George)*

Wilmcote, War [The Green; SP1657], *Swan House*: Peaceful country hotel, welcoming bar with terrace overlooking Mary Arden's house, good helpings of piping hot food in bar or restaurant, helpful staff, well kept Hook Norton Best and a guest such as Theakstons XB; bedrooms *(Joan and Michel Hooper-Immins, Mr and Mrs G W Olive)*

☆ Wixford, War [B4085 Alcester—Bidford — OS Sheet 150, map reference 085546; SP0954], *Fish*: Tastefully refurbished roomy L-shaped bar and snug, beams, polished panelling, carpets over flagstones, well kept Bass on handpump, reasonably priced bar food, pleasant, efficient service *(JM, PM)*

Wolvey, War [near M65 junction 1; SP4287], *Blue Pig*: A good Chef & Brewer, keeping its friendly old-world local atmosphere; reasonably priced bar food inc good chargrills, good mix of customers, friendly staff; busy weekends *(Geoff Lee, Comus Elliott, Ian Blackwell, Mr and Mrs B J Twigger)*

☆ **Wootton Wawen**, War [N side of village; SP1563], *Bulls Head*: 18th-century or older black-and-white pub with massive timber uprights and heavy low beams in L-shaped lounge, good bar food (may be a wait), friendly staff, popular restaurant; M&B Springfield and Brew XI, garden *(Nigel B Pritchard)*

Wordsley, W Mid [Cot Lane; SO8986], *Park*: Small but well laid out real ale pub with friendly atmosphere and well kept Ansells Mild, Bathams and Ind Coope Burton on handpump *(Keith Smith, Liz Window)*

☆ **Yarwell**, Northants [Main St; TL0697], *Angel*: Quaint and cosy old two-roomed village pub off the beaten track; well kept Youngers on handpump, notable food at reasonable prices (not Thurs), friendly and welcoming owners; children's room and garden with play area and maybe pets *(N W James)*

Norfolk

There's been something of an explosion of interest in Norfolk pubs recently. More than half the main entries here have found their way into the Guide in just the last couple of years or so, and this year's crop of new entries is full of interest. There's the Black Boys on the edge of Aldborough's fine cricket green (unpretentious, but very good food), the thriving Ratcatchers at Cawston (the only pub of that name we've ever come across – very popular for food, with prize-winning pies), the stylish and most unusual Saracens Head outside Wolterton Hall near Erpingham (already well on its way to a star award, though only recently opened by Iain Bryson, who has made the Red Lion at Upper Sheringham so popular for its enterprising food and relaxed atmosphere), the Tudor Rose in Kings Lynn (a classic old town pub, family-run and nice to stay at), the Red Lion at Stiffkey (another newly opened place) and the Chequers at Thompson (newly reopened after a long closure, with lots of antiques and interesting furniture). Other pubs currently on a winning streak here include the Kings Arms in Blakeney (a few popular changes since they've bought their freehold from the brewery), the Rose & Crown at Snettisham (gains a star award this year – and now has bedrooms), the Old Ram at Tivetshall St Mary (a spacious and enjoyable dining pub; among some other changes they have bedrooms now, too), and the lovely unspoilt Three Horseshoes at Warham (now under serious consideration for a star award). It has to be admitted that this is not a cheap area for pubs; prices of both drinks and food tend to be a little above the national average, though the interesting and friendly old Adam & Eve in Norwich is close to our "bargain" target. In the Lucky Dip section at the end of the chapter, current rising stars include the White Horse in Blakeney, White Horse at East Barsham, Reindeer in Norwich, Darbys at Swanton Morley and, particularly, Hare Arms at Stow Bardolph; other pubs to look out for here include the John H Stracey at Briston, Black Horse at Castle Rising, Crown at Colkirk, Bath House in Cromer, Feathers at Dersingham, Hill House at Happisburgh (or as the locals would have it Hazeborough), Marsham Arms at Hevingham, Nelsons Head at Horsey and Crown at Mundford.

ALDBOROUGH   TG1834 Map 8
Black Boys

Signposted off A140 S of Roughton

Tucked into the corner of the broad village green, this pretty little ochre pub could easily be just another local, with furnishings much as you'd expect – brocaded chairs, green leatherette button-back wall banquettes, cast-iron-framed tables, old local photographs, lots of fresh flowers. It's the food in the candlelit communicating back dining area which makes it special, all carefully cooked using fresh ingredients and served generously, including thick and nourishing winter soups (£1.50), sandwiches (from £2), local fish such as herrings, plaice or dabs (£4.75), free-range chicken or a genuine chilli con carne (£4.75), and a fine self-service cold table with good meats and salads and usually shellfish; they

generally have fresh lobsters in the evening (very popular then – booking
suggested). Vegetables are good, often unusual. Well kept Courage Directors,
Flowers Original and Tolly Original on handpump, decent wines, good coffee; log
fire, welcoming service, and a warm-hearted newfoundland called George; darts,
dominoes, dice, fruit machine. *(Recommended by Mr and Mrs J D Cranston, Gethin
Lewis)*

Brent Walker   Tenants Ian and Lynn Kew   Real ale   Meals and snacks   Cromer
(0263) 768086   Children allowed lunchtime and early evening   Open 12–2.30, 7–11

BLAKENEY   TG0243   Map 8

Kings Arms

West Gate St

This year, the licensees have bought the freehold of this bustling pub from the
brewery and although they are keeping the Ruddles County and Websters
Yorkshire on handpump, there will also be Marstons Pedigree and a monthly guest
beer; freshly squeezed fruit juice. They are also converting the upstairs into
self-catering accommodation. The three simply furnished, knocked-together rooms
are decorated with local artists' work and some interesting photographs of the
licencees' theatrical careers on the walls (a tiny art gallery is housed in what was
the telephone booth); one of the other small rooms (the family room) is
no-smoking – there are baby-changing facilities, too. The atmosphere is relaxed
and friendly and the staff are helpful and efficient. Tasty bar food at lunchtime
includes sandwiches (from £1.05; generously priced fresh local crab £2), lots of
filled baked potatoes (from £2), a wide choice of ploughman's (from £3.10; the
smoked mackerel is excellent), fresh local mussels (winter only, £3.60), locally
caught fresh haddock or cod or home-made curry (£4.10), fresh local crab (£4.25),
children's menu (£2.50), and puddings like home-made crumble (£2.05), with
evening salads (from £4.80, the seasonal local crab is lovely, £5.95) and grills
(from £5.60). Darts, dominoes and fruit machine. The large garden has lots of
tables and chairs and a separate, equipped children's area. *(Recommended by Derek
Patey, Norman Hill, Bill and Jane Rees, JMC, Gethin Lewis, Frank Davidson, P Craddock, D
Maplethorpe, Nigel Gibbs, Margaret Dyke, Margaret White, BKA)*

Free house   Licensees Howard and Marjorie Davies   Real ale   Meals and snacks
(served all day during school hols)   (0263) 740 341   Children welcome   Open
11–11   Self-catering accommodation available; £200 per week

BLICKLING   TG1728   Map 8

Buckinghamshire Arms ⌫

Off B1354 N of Aylsham

Though this handsome Jacobean inn has been redecorated this year, there have
been no major changes. It's friendly and welcoming and can get very busy, but the
staff remain helpful and seem to cope admirably. The small front snug is simply
furnished with fabric cushioned banquettes, some brass tack above the open fire,
and an antique seed-sowing machine in an alcove. The bigger lounge has neatly
built-in pews, stripped deal tables, and landscapes and cockfighting prints. Decent
bar food includes home-made soup (£1.50), sandwiches (from £1.65),
ploughman's (£3.25), home-made specials such as steak and kidney pie and meaty
or vegetarian lasagne (around £4.50), and home-made puddings (£1.80); decent
breakfasts. Well kept Adnams Best and Broadside, Woodfordes Wherry and a
guest beer on handpump. Picnic-table sets shelter under cocktail parasols on the
lawn (they serve food from an out-building here in summer), and there's a wide
stretch of neatly raked gravel between the inn and a splendid Dutch-gabled stable
block; climbing frame, slide and swing. Neighbouring National Trust Blickling
Hall is open from April to mid-October only, and closed Mondays and Thursdays,
though you can walk through the park at any time. *(Recommended by D L Smith, Syd*

and Wyn Donald, Derek Patey, David and Rebecca Killick, D Maplethorpe, Nick and Alison Dowson, Peter Burton, R C Vincent, P Thorogood, David Oakes)

Free house   Licensee Robert Dean   Real ale   Meals and snacks   Restaurant Aylsham (0263) 732133   Children in restaurant   Open 11–2.30, 6–11; closed 25 Dec   Three double bedrooms; £40/£50

BURNHAM THORPE   TF8541 Map 8
Lord Nelson

Village signposted from B1155 and B1355, near Burnham Market

Nelson actually gave a party here in 1793 and this delightfully unspoilt place has probably changed little since then. There's no bar counter – just a small room with well waxed antique settles on the worn red flooring tiles, a sheathed cutlass on one beam, and a cabinet of miniature bottles. Some 60 pictures connected with Nelson line the entrance corridor as well as the walls of the bar (though this is just part of the knowledgeable licensee's fine collection of over 200 items). Well kept Greene King IPA and Abbot is tapped from the cask in a back stillroom, and there's a delicious and extremely popular rum concoction called Nelson's Blood, made to a secret recipe by the landlord; they sell more proof-strength rum than anywhere else in Britain. The glasses are simply stacked by the spotless sink, separated off from the rest of the room by two high settle-backs; darts. You are asked not to smoke. Outside is a large play area. *(Recommended by Derek and Sylvia Stephenson, Robert Harman, Kevin Fields; more reports please)*

Greene King   Lease: Les Winter   Real ale   No food   (0328) 738241   Open 11.30–3, 7–11

CASTLE ACRE   TF8115 Map 8
Ostrich

Stocks Green; village signposted from A1065 N of Swaffham; OS Sheet 144, map reference 815153

This largely 18th-century ex-coaching inn has a lot of character and a good mix of locals and visitors in its back room: a very high pitched ceiling with exposed oak beams and trusses, an end wall with exposed sixteenth century masonry, and a good log fire. The L-shaped front bar has a huge old fireplace with a swinging potyard below its low mantlebeam (which may be used in winter for cooking soups and hams), straightforward furnishings, big photographs of the local sites on hessian walls, and a low ceiling. Decent bar food includes sandwiches (from £1; crab or smoked salmon £1.50), various basket meals (from £1.50), pizzas (from £1.70), a wide range of ploughman's (from £2.20), 3-egg omelettes (from £2.75), vegetarian dishes (£3), salads (from £4.30), local trout (£4.75), steaks (from £5.75), and daily specials such as kashmiri lamb in pitta bread, beef and oyster hotpot or seafood pancake. Well kept Greene King IPA, Abbot, Mild and Rayments on handpump; fruit machine, and picnic-table sets in the sheltered garden, where you can play boules. There's a Cluniac monastery in the village. *(Recommended by C T and J M Laffan, Neil Hardwick, Brenda Crossley, Andrew Morrissey, Charles Bardswell, Margaret Drazin, Derek Patey, Peter Griffiths, Tony and Lynne Stark, R P Hastings, P Thorogood, Derek Pascall, Nigel Gibbs)*

Greene King   Tenant Ray Wakelen   Real ale   Meals and snacks (till 10pm; not 25 Dec)   Swaffham (0760) 755398   Children in decent adjacent family room   Jazz every other Tues, Folk/Blues last Weds in month   Open 12–2.30, 7–11   Bedrooms; £15/£30

CAWSTON   TG1323 Map 8
Ratcatchers

Eastgate, S of village; heading N from Norwich on B1149 turn left towards Haveringland at crossroads ½ mile before the B1145 turn to Cawston itself

The L-shaped beamed bar is crowded with regulars in the evening, most drawn by the care the Charliers take over their food – meat hung specially for them by the local butcher, fresh fish several times a week from Lowestoft or Billingsgate, locally-grown vegetables, herbs from their own garden. The very wide choice, served in massive helpings, includes sandwiches (from £1.25), soup (£1.30), burgers (from £1.90), omelettes (from £2.75), lots of starters such as deep-fried camembert (£3.45), ploughman's (£3.55), vegetarian dishes and fish (from £4.05), chilli con carne and so forth (from £4.30), a variety of pies including a popular steak and kidney (£4.45), steaks (from 7oz rump £6.95) and children's dishes (from £1.70), with several specials such as herby pancakes with stilton, ham and orange (£4.95) or duck in orange, raspberry and elderberry sauce (£7.95); lots of puddings, and a popular Sunday lunch. Changing well kept real ales on handpump such as Bass and Greene King IPA or Adnams and Worthington BB, local country wines, open fires, darts, cribbage, maybe piped music; quieter and cosier candlelit dining room on the right. *(Recommended by P S Galbraith, Geoff Lee, Anthony Barnes)*

Free house   Licensees Eugene and Jill Charlier   Real ale   Meals and snacks (till 10.15)   Restaurant   (0603) 871430   Children in eating area and restaurant   Open 12–2.30, 7–11

ERPINGHAM   TG1631 Map 8

Saracens Head 🚫 🛏️

Address is Wolterton – not shown on many maps; Erpingham signed off A140 N of Aylsham, keep on through Calthorpe, then where road bends right take the straight-ahead turn-off signposted Wolterton

This distinguished late Georgian redbrick inn alone by the wall and trees of Wolterton Hall has recently been transformed into an unusually relaxed and civilised country pub, with simple yet stylish furnishings. The two-room bar on the left is not large, though its high ceilings and tall windows give a feeling of space. There are log fires, terracotta walls, a mix of seats from built-in leather wall settles to wicker fireside chairs, solid-colour carpets and curtains vaguely reminiscent of a shooting lodge (an illusion heightened by the sporting papers lying around), and flowers on the mantlepieces. Behind, it looks out on a charming old-fashioned gravel stableyard, with picnic-table sets and a couple of witty nudes. Good country food varies day by day and from lunchtime to evening, with rich soup (£1.85) and five or so other starters such as stilton and apple pâté or crisp-fried aubergine with garlic mayonnaise (£2.65); at lunchtime there is bread and a choice of cheeses (£2.75) with several hot dishes such as local rabbit braised in ale, cottage pie, tortellini with ham and tomato sauce, crispy sweetbreads, escalope of turkey with Pernod and cream, apricot-stuffed leg of lamb en croûte, roast guineafowl with sherry and lemon sauce (lunchtime prices mainly around £4.55, evening around £5.75). There's a pretty little four-table dining parlour on the right – cheerful nursery colours, another big log fire. Well kept Adnams Bitter and Broadside and Felinoel Double Dragon or a guest beer on handpump, decent whiskies and wines. *(Recommended by D J and J M Clifton, Dr and Mrs R G M Jones)*

Free house   Licensees Robert Dowson-Smith and Iain Bryson   Real ale   Meals and snacks   Cromer (0263) 768283   Well behaved children in eating area or dining parlour   Open 11–3ish, 6–11; closed 25 Dec   Bedrooms; £30B/£45B

HEMPSTEAD   TG1236 Map 8

Hare & Hounds

Towards Baconsthorpe – and actually closer to that village, though just inside the Hempstead parish boundary; village signposted from A148 in Holt; OS Sheet 133, map reference 115372

The two simple little bars in this small pantiled flint cottage have a casual mix of chairs and cushioned pews around plain deal or cast-iron-framed tables, pewter tankards hanging from one beam, several sets of Lawson Wood cartoons on the beige walls, dog-breed cigarette cards, earthenware flagons on the deep sills of the small windows, rugs on old red flooring tiles, and a big woodburning stove in the broad low-beamed fireplace below a pendulum clock. Bar food might include vegetarian parsley and watercress roulade, leek, bacon and potato bake, Normandy fish casserole, lamb biriani, beef bourguignonne, and game pie (all £4.25); well kept Adnams, Bass and Batemans on handpump, with a full-bodied and fragrantly fruity best bitter brewed for the pub by Woodfordes, guest beers, and decent wines. There are some picnic-table sets on the side grass, facing a pond and rockery; also a children's play area. (*Recommended by Anthony Barnes, Derek Patey, Frank Davidson*)

Free house   Licensee J M D Hobson   Real ale   Meals and snacks   Small children's room   Open 11.30–2.30(3 Sat), 7–11   Self-contained cottage for 5 £200pw

HUNWORTH   TG0635 Map 8

Hunny Bell

Village signposted off B roads S of Holt

This pub has been renamed this year – it used to be the Bluebell. The cosy L-shaped bar has Windsor chairs around dark wooden tables, comfortable settees (some of which are grouped around the log fire) and Norfolk watercolours and pictures for sale hanging above the panelling dado. Particularly well kept Woodfordes Wherry, as well as Adnams and Greene King Abbot. Generous helpings of good value bar food include sandwiches (from £1.40), home-made soup (£1.50), home-made pâté (£1.85), ploughman's (from £2.50), home-cooked ham and eggs or local sausages (£3.50), salads (from £3.75), steak and kidney pie (£4), gammon (£4.95), sirloin steak (£8), and a daily special such as rabbit pie or garlic ribs (£4). Darts, dominoes, cribbage and evening piped music. In good weather there's bar service to the tables under cocktail parasols on the back lawn where there are fruit trees – heavily laden in summer. They also own the Kings Head, Letheringsett. (*Recommended by Neil Hardwick, L W Baal, Norman Hill, F A Owens, Derek and Sylvia Stephenson, David Oakes, Laurie Walker, Mr and Mrs K H Frostick; more reports please*)

Free house   Licensee Sally King   Real ale   Meals and snacks   Restaurant   (0263) 712300   Children in eating area of bar   Open 11–3, 5.30–11

KINGS LYNN   TF6220 Map 8

Tudor Rose 🏠

St Nicholas St (just off Tuesday Market Place – main square)

Dating back to the 15th century, this has an attractive half-timbered facade with an interesting medieval oak studded door; some of the bedrooms have a pretty view of St Nicholas's Chapel. Both bars are chatty and well used by locals: the front one quieter and quite small and snug, with high beams, reproduction squared panelling and a big wrought-iron wheelrim chandelier; the quite separate back one more spacious, with sturdy wall benches, video games, fruit machine and piped music. Good value bar food, all home-made including the puddings, includes soup (£1.40), large home-baked rolls such as devilled ham or bacon and egg (£1.50), beef with dumplings (£3.50), dressed local crab (£3.95), strips of beef sautéed with mushrooms and onions, in a rich stock sauce, and vegetarian dishes. Well kept Adnams and Broadside, Bass and a guest beer such as Woodfordes Headbanger, a fine choice of whiskies and of rums, decent wines; friendly well trained staff, big open fire, no smoking upstairs raftered restaurant. Bedrooms are simple and modern but comfortable, with good breakfasts. (*Recommended by Mr and Mrs K E P Wohl, R C Vincent, Phil Bryant, Chris Vallely, Vanessa and Peter Hurst*)

Free house   Licensees Ian and Chris Carter   Real ale   Meals and snacks (maybe not Sun)   Restaurant   Kings Lynn (0553) 762824   Children in restaurant   Open 11–3, 5(5.30 Sat)–11   Bedrooms; £28.36B/£45

LETHERINGSETT TG0538 Map 8

Kings Head

A148 just W of Holt

There are lots of picnic-table sets on the surrounding spacious lawn here and park and paddock slope up beyond a post-and-rails fence. Inside, the main bar is decorated with lots of Battle of Britain pictures especially involving East Anglia, a panoramic view of Edward VII's first opening of Parliament, a signed John Betjeman poem, picturesque advertisements, and jokey French pictures of naughty dogs. There's also a small plush lounge, and a separate games room with darts, pool, shove-ha'penny, dominoes, cribbage, pinball (a rarity nowadays), fruit machines, and piped music. Reasonably priced bar food includes sandwiches (from £1.25, crab £1.75, evening toasties £2), ploughman's (£2.50), home-made pastie (£3.50), salads (from £3.75, local crab in season £3.95), home-cooked ham or steak and kidney pie (£3.95), a huge and tasty pork chop, steaks (from £7.25, evening only), a daily special, and vegetarian dishes. Well kept Adnams, Bass and Greene King IPA and Abbot on handpump and a dozen malt whiskies. Two decorative cats, no dogs. The church over the road has an unusual round tower, and nearby Letheringsett water mill is worth a visit. The licensee also owns the Hunny Bell at Hunworth. *(Recommended by L W Baal, R C Vincent, Derek and Sylvia Stephenson, Norman Hill, F A Owens, Charles Bardswell)*

Free house Lease: Thomas King Real ale Meals and snacks Restaurant Holt (0263) 712691; not Sun evening Children in eating area of bar during food serving times Country and Western Mon Open 11–3, 6–11

NORWICH TG2308 Map 5

Adam & Eve

Bishopgate; follow Palace Street from Tombland N of the Cathedral

First used as a refreshment house for the Cathedral builders, this pleasant old pub can get crowded, especially at lunchtime for its generous helpings of bar food: sandwiches, granary baps or filled French bread (from £1.35, excellent prawn £2.20), cheese and ale soup (£1.80), ploughman's (from £2.50), salads (from £2.60), shepherd's pie or vegetable curry (£2.90), fish or beef and mushroom pies (£3.40), puddings like home-made bread and butter pudding (£1.40), and daily specials. Ruddles Best and County, Websters Yorkshire and guest beers on handpump from a serving counter with a fine range of pewter tankards, several malt whiskies, and around 34 different wines (several by the glass); prompt, friendly service. The traditionally furnished bars have old-fashioned high-backed settles, one handsomely carved, cushioned benches built into partly panelled walls, and tiled or parquet floors. It's Norwich's oldest pub and parts of it date back to 1249; the snug is no-smoking at lunchtime. There are seats on the quiet terrace – pretty in summer with clematis and baskets of flowers. *(Recommended by David White, Mrs Richard Stewart, David and Rebecca Killick, R A Corbett, T K Baxter, Chris Vallely, Sidney and Erna Wells, Margaret White, Ian Phillips, Wayne Brindle, Audrey and Brian Green, J S Rutter)*

Grand Met/Watneys Lease: Colin Burgess Real ale Lunchtime meals and snacks Norwich (0603) 667423 Children in snug Open 11–11

REEDHAM TG4101 Map 5

Ferry ✿

B1140 Beccles–Acle; the ferry here holds only two cars but goes back and forth continuously till 10pm, taking only a minute or so to cross – fare £1.50, 10p passengers, 30p pedestrians

With its good moorings (the fee is refundable against what you buy in the pub), and solid tables spaced well apart on the neatly kept grass and looking out over the River Yare, this busy pub is much used by holidaymakers cruising the Broads.

Inside, the secluded and relaxing back bar has some traditional character, antique rifles, copper and brass, and a fine log fire. The long front bar has comfortable banquettes lining the big picture windows, robust rustic tables carved from slabs of tree-trunk, and video game and fruit machines. Generous helpings of good bar food include sandwiches (from £1.20), home-made soup (£1.60), ploughman's (£3.50), home-made steak and kidney pie (£5.60), trout fillets in prawn and parsley butter (£5.90), good beef curry, and puddings like good treacle tart (£2.10); children's dishes and arrangements for baby food (and changing facilities in the ladies' lavatory). Well kept Adnams Bitter and Woodfordes Wherry on handpump, quite a few malt whiskies; good cheerful service. Dominoes and piped music; showers in the lavatories for the boaters moored here. The woodturners shop next door is interesting. (*Recommended by P and J McComb, Andrew Morrissey, Steve Thomas, Dave Braisted, P S Vince, Gordon Theaker, Mr and Mrs P A Jones, T Nott*)

Free house Licensee David Archer Real ale Meals and snacks (till 10pm) Restaurant (0493) 700429 Children in sun lounge Open 11–3, 6.30–11; 11–2.30, 7–11 in winter

RINGSTEAD TF7040 Map 8

Gin Trap

Village signposted off A149 near Hunstanton; OS Sheet 132, map reference 707403

Lots of traps are used in decorating this friendly pub; there are a couple of man-traps hanging above the main door and many more in the very neatly kept open-plan bar – some are converted to electric candle-effect wall lights. Captains' chairs and cast-iron-framed tables sit on the green-and-white patterned motif carpet and there are copper kettles, carpenters' tools, and cartwheels, bottles hanging from the beams in the lower part of the bar, and toasting forks above an open fire (which has dried flowers in summer); the tortoiseshell cat is called Whisky. A small no-smoking room laid out for eating has quite a few chamber pots hanging from the ceiling and high-backed pine settles, and is bookable on Saturday evening. Well kept Adnams Bitter, Greene King Abbot and IPA, Woodfordes Nog and a beer brewed by Woodfordes for the pub on handpump; efficient staff; piped music. Good home-made bar food includes lunchtime sandwiches (£1.75), winter soup, ploughman's (£3), fresh plaice (£3.80), very good lasagne, steak and kidney pie or good home-cooked ham (£4.50), several steaks (from £7.25), puddings (£1.80), children's dishes (from £1.50), and daily specials such as good value liver and bacon and popular Norfolk pie; on Fridays they do fresh fish dishes. There are free nibbles on the bar counter on Sunday lunchtimes. The walled back garden has seats on the grass or small paved area and pretty flowering tubs. The pub is close to the Peddar's Way and hikers and walkers welcome (but not their muddy boots). There's an art gallery next door. (*Recommended by P and J McComb, Peter Griffiths, Colin and Mary Meaden, Phil Russell, TBB, Derek Patey, Margaret Bull, Charles Bardwell, Derek Pascall, Denise Plummer, Jim Froggatt*)

Free house Brian and Margaret Harmes Real ale Meals and snacks (not winter Sun evenings) (048 525) 264 Well behaved children in eating area of bar Occasional Morris Dancing Open 11.30–2.30, 6–11; closed evenings 25 and 26 Dec

SCOLE TM1576 Map 5

Scole Inn ★ ⇔

A140 just N of A143

This stately building with its magnificently rounded Dutch gables is one of only a handful of pubs or inns to have a Grade I preservation listing. The high-beamed lounge bar has a 17th-century iron-studded oak door, antique settles, leather-cushioned seats and benches around oak refectory tables on its Turkey carpets, a handsomely carved oak mantlebeam, and a big fireplace with a coat-of-arms iron fireback. In the bare-boarded public bar there's another good open fire, and stripped high-backed settles and kitchen chairs around oak tables.

Under the new licensee, the waitress-served bar food – popular with businessmen at lunchtime – includes home-made soup, sandwiches, good ploughman's, fresh spinach, mushroom, tomato and ham tagliatelle (£4.25), home-made steak and kidney pie and fresh fish dishes (£4.95) and puddings such as lovely syllabub. Well kept Adnams Best and Broadside on handpump, and over 30 malt whiskies; piped music (perhaps a bit of a false note here). The ladies' must be one of the only ones in the country with such a grand fireplace. *(Recommended by C C Cook, G M K Donkin, J Barnwell, Chris Vallely, George Atkinson, Tony and Lynne Stark, Gill and Doug Green, Mike and Jill Dixon and friends, WTF, J G Simpson, T Nott, P Thorogood, Simon Bates)*

Free house   Licensee Philip Hills   Real ale   Meals and snacks (12–2.30, 6–10) Restaurant   Diss (0379) 740481   Children welcome   Open 11–11   Bedrooms; £46B/£63.50B

SNETTISHAM   TF6834 Map 8

Rose & Crown ★

Old Church Rd; just off A149 in centre

Readers' comments on this pretty, early 14th-century white cottage have been particularly warm this year – it appeals to all sorts. The cosy locals' bar at the back has perhaps the nicest atmosphere, with tapestried seats around cast-iron-framed tables, and a big log fire. At the front is an old-fashioned beamed bar with lots of carpentry and farm tools, cushioned black settles on the red tiled floor, and a great pile of logs by the fire in the vast fireplace (which has a gleaming black japanned side oven). There's also an airy carpeted room with plush seats around tables with matching tablecloths, and pictures for sale on the wall, and an extensive family room with a clean Scandinavian look: bentwood chairs and tractor seats on its tiled floor, bare brick walls, and narrow-planked ceilings. Generous helpings of good, quickly served bar food include soup (£1.50), ploughman's (£2.95), open bap sandwiches (from £3.50; home honey roast ham or excellent rare topside of beef), savoury pancakes or vegetable curry (£5.75), salads (from £6.50), lamb chops with mint jelly (£7.25), steaks (from £3.95), puddings like home-made apple pie (£1.75), daily specials like steak and onion pie or rump steak in mustard and whisky sauce, children's menu (from £1.75), and barbecue menu (from £4.50). Adnams Bitter, Bass and a beer named for the pub on handpump, with freshly squeezed orange juice, own-label house wines, teas and coffee; friendly service, even when pushed; piped music in restaurant, and an old-fashioned penny slot game. Outside there are pretty hanging baskets and flowering tubs, picnic-table sets on a neat sheltered lawn and terrace, and a children's play area with a tree house, log cabin, climbing frame and swings. No dogs. *(Recommended by TBB, Nigel Gibbs, Charles Bardswell, Derek and Sylvia Stephenson, Jerry and Alison Oakes, Jim Froggatt, Denise Plummer, Neil Hardwick)*

Free house   Licensee Margaret Trafford   Real ale   Meals and snacks (till 10pm) Restaurant   Dersingham (0485) 541382   Children welcome (own room)   Occasional live entertainment   Open 11–3, 5.30–11; all day Sat; closed 25 Dec   Bedrooms; £25/£30(£40)

STIFFKEY   TF9743 Map 8

Red Lion

A149 Wells–Blakeney

Reopened in 1990 after 26 years as a private house, this has that studied casualness and careful rustic simplicity that now seems a hallmark of north Norfolk's best pubs. Three rooms have old flooring tiles or bare floorboards, open fires (a big log fire in the main room's large brick hearth, smaller tiled fireplaces in the flanking rooms), a mix of pews, small settles, built-in wooden wall seats and a couple of stripped high-backed settles, a nice old long deal table among quite a few others, oil-type or lantern wall lamps, a few beams – and a carefree, chatty atmosphere. Good bar food served generously includes sandwiches (from £1.70), soup (£1.95), soft herring roes (£1.95), hot local cockles (£2.50), ploughman's (£3.25), tagliatelle (£4.50), generous salads (£4.95), beef in Abbot ale, rabbit in port pie or crab and avocado bake (£5.25), local sea trout, grey mullet or plaice (£5.75), fresh scampi tails (£6.20) and children's dishes (£2.75). Well kept Greene King IPA and Abbot on handpump, Woodfordes Wherry tapped from the cask, friendly staff; games room, detached from the main building, with darts, pool, video game and juke box. The back restaurant leads into a conservatory, and there are wooden seats and tables out on a back gravel terrace, and on grass further up beyond. *(Recommended by Sarah King, Patrick Forbes, Peter Griffiths, TBB, Derek and Sylvia Stephenson, J E Romney)*

Free house   Licensees E A Carter and S L Doughty   Real ale   Meals and snacks   Restaurant   Fakenham (0328) 830552   Children in conservatory and games room   Open 11–2.30(3 Sat), 6–11

THOMPSON   TL9196 Map 5

Chequers

Griston Road; village signposted off A1075 Thetford–Watton; OS Sheet 144, map reference 923969

This long, low 14th-century thatched building was originally several cottages. The three main rooms, each with its own bar, have exposed beams, crooked oak wall timbers completely covered with original brass and copper artefacts, farming tools, Victorian corkscrews and boot-scrapers and so forth, uncommonly low doors and ceilings (one is only five feet high), genuinely old wheelback and spindleback chairs and round metal tables, a woodburning stove in one room, and a warm and relaxing atmosphere. At one end there's a dining bar with a high gabled ceiling and lots of antiques on the walls, hanging from the ceiling and in the inglenook fireplace; the small snug is a family room. Bar food can be eaten anywhere in the pub and includes burgers (from £1.20), soup (£1.25), sandwiches (from £1.25), filled baked potatoes (from £1.75), home-made mackerel pâté (£2), ploughman's (from £2.75), lasagne (£3.10), home-made steak and kidney pie or breaded cod (£3.50), salads (from £3.50), seafood lasagne (£3.95), steaks (from £6.75), and puddings (£1.55). Well kept Adnams, Bass, Greene King IPA and Worthington BB and guests like Batemans, Burton Bridge and Woodfordes; farm cider, coffee. There are benches outside, by flower tubs and wall baskets, and a large garden with picnic-table sets (a children's play area is planned); nearby there are plenty of good woodland walks. *(Recommended by Alan and Ruth Woodhouse, Pamela Goodwyn, Frank Davidson, Mr and Mrs Douglas Parker)*

Free house   Licensee Bob Rourke   Real ale   Meals and snacks (11–2, 6.30–10)   Casterton (0953) 83360   Children in eating area of bar   Open 11–3, 6–11

THORNHAM   TF7343 Map 8

Lifeboat ★

Turn off A149 by Kings Head, then take first left turn

One of the bars to the left of the door in this atmospheric pub has been extended into what was the old restaurant – a cosy beamed room with a huge fireplace; an adjacent room has a few tables, machine-tapestried walls, pews and a few wheelback chairs, a small brick fireplace and guns and swords on the walls; the new restaurant is underneath the new bedrooms and the kitchens have been remodelled. The chatty main bar has great oak beams hung with romantic antique lamps (which are still lit) and traps and yokes, low settles, window seats, pews, and carved oak tables on the rugs on the tiled floor, panelling, shelves of china, and masses of guns, swords, black metal mattocks, reed-slashers and other antique farm tools; no fewer than five fires – one with an elaborately carved wood overmantle. A simple conservatory (which is very popular with families) has benches and tables, an old-fashioned stove, a flourishing vine, and a food hatch. Bar food includes sandwiches (from £1.45), ploughman's (£3.50), cottage pie or curry (£4.95), fresh fish, scampi (£5.75), steaks (from £8.50), and children's dishes

Please use this card to tell us which pubs *you* think should or should not be included in the next edition of *The Good Pub Guide*. Just fill it in and return it to us – no stamp or envelope needed. And don't forget you can also use the report forms at the end of the *Guide*.

ALISDAIR AIRD

Your name and address (block capitals please)

☐ *Please tick this box if you would like extra report forms*

REPORT on *(pub's name)*

Pub's address:

☐ YES MAIN ENTRY ☐ YES *Lucky Dip* ☐ NO don't include

Please tick one of these boxes to show your verdict, and give reasons and descriptive comments, prices etc:

☐ Deserves FOOD award ☐ Deserves PLACE-TO-STAY award

REPORT on *(pub's name)*

Pub's address:

☐ YES MAIN ENTRY ☐ YES *Lucky Dip* ☐ NO don't include

Please tick one of these boxes to show your verdict, and give reasons and descriptive comments, prices etc:

☐ Deserves FOOD award ☐ Deserves PLACE-TO-STAY award

The Good Pub Guide

Freepost

London SW10 0BR

The Good
Pub Guide

(£2). Well kept Adnams Best, Greene King IPA, Abbot and Mild and two weekly guest beers and farm cider; good service. Shove-ha'penny and an antique penny-in-the-hole bench. Up some steps from the conservatory is a terrace with picnic-table sets, a climbing frame, and a slide. The pub – which can get very busy, even out of season – is near *Good Walks Guide* Walk 116. Large car park (which some readers feel obliterates the view of the marsh). They also own the Sculthorpe Mill at Sculthorpe near Fakenham. *(Recommended by Chris Vallely, Derek and Sylvia Stephenson, Jonathan Warner, Nora Casey, TBB, George and Mollie Dowglass, M J Morgan, Jim Froggatt, Denise Plummer, R E Horner, P Craddock, James Cane, Neil Hardwick)*

Free house   Licensee Nicholas Handley   Real ale   Meals and snacks (12–2.30, 7–10)   Restaurant   Thornham (048 526) 236   Children welcome   Open 11–11 Bedrooms; £35B/£60B

TITCHWELL   TF7543   Map 8

Manor Hotel 🛏

A149 E of Hunstanton

Relaxed and rather smart, this comfortable hotel looks over the salt marshes to the sea; the sunsets are said to be lovely. It's the central lounge which takes people's fancy: chintzy sofas, magazines, an open fire, and a good naturalists' record of the wildlife in the nearby RSPB reserve; a small bar opening off this has pretty patterned beige wallpaper, grey plush wall banquettes, small round tables, Impressionist prints, and another open fire. Another room – right over on the right – is rather like a farmhouse kitchen with pine furniture, a Welsh dresser with unusual mustards and pickles on it, and a collection of baskets and bric-a-brac; children are allowed in here. There's also a pretty restaurant with French windows that open on to a sizeable and sheltered neatly kept lawn with sturdy white garden seats. Bar food, served in the pine room, includes sandwiches, three local oysters grilled with cheese and white wine (£2.95), home-made vegetarian dishes, fillet of fresh salmon with hollandaise (£5.95), and half local lobster served with hot lemon butter (£8.95). Greene King IPA and Abbot on handpump. *(Recommended by Derek and Sylvia Stephenson, Jim Froggatt, Denise Plummer, Charles Bardswell, JMC, K F Templar; More reports please)*

Free house   Licensees G I and M M Snaith   Real ale   Meals and snacks   Restaurant Brancaster (0485) 210221   Children welcome   Open 12–2.30, 6.30–11   Bedrooms; £37B/£74B

TIVETSHALL ST MARY   TM1686   Map 5

Old Ram

Ipswich Rd; A140 15 miles S of Norwich

This big, enjoyable main-road pub has quite an emphasis on food: filled rolls (from £1.80), burgers (£3.50), ploughman's (£3.75), home-made aubergine and mushroom bake, excellent moussaka or steak and kidney pie (all £4.95), salads (from £4.95), jumbo-sized fresh cod fillet in home-made golden batter (£5.95), gammon and pineapple (£6.50), steaks (from £8.75), and formidable puddings (from £2.25). Well kept Adnams, Greene King Abbot, Ruddles County, Websters Yorkshire and a guest beer, decent house wines, several malt whiskies, good coffee, freshly squeezed orange juice; unobtrusive fruit machine, piped music. There are several individually refurbished areas; the spacious main room, ringed by cosier side areas, has standing-timber dividers, stripped beams and brick floors, a longcase clock, antique craftsmen's tools on the ceiling, and a huge log fire in the brick hearth; other rooms ramble off and there are pretty lamps and Sanderson fabrics. An attractive, intimate dining room with pews, an open woodburning stove and big sentimental engravings leads up to a gallery with Victorian copper and brassware and sofas for idle contemplation; another dining room is no-smoking. There are seats on the sheltered, flower-filled terrace and lawn behind. It can get very busy at weekends. No dogs. *(Recommended by Gill and Doug Green, Dr S R Dando, Mrs M E Beard, Edward and Jean Rycroft; more reports please)*

Free house   Licensee John Trafford   Real ale   Meals and snacks (from 7.30 for breakfast – for non-residents also – till 10pm); not 25 Dec   Pulham Market (0379) 676794   Children in eating area of bar   Open 11–11   Bedrooms; £40B/£60B

UPPER SHERINGHAM   TG1441 Map 8

Red Lion 🏮

B1157; village signposted off A148 Cromer–Holt, and the A149 just W of Sheringham

They keep quite the best range of malt whiskies we've come across in this area here (around 130), including a good few rarities; also well kept Adnams Bitter and Broadside and a guest like Youngs Special on handpump, and decent wines. The two quiet small bars are very simply furnished with stripped high-backed settles and country-kitchen chairs on the red tiles or bare boards, plain off-white walls and ceiling, a big woodburning stove, a rack of newspapers, and little bunches of country flowers. At its best, the often interesting home-made bar food is very good indeed: soup (£1.95), smoked mackerel pâté (£2.50), good lamb's liver and bacon, tasty spicy vegetable lasagne (£4.20), Cromer crab (£4.50; excellent baked crab £4.95), fresh salmon or very good home-baked hot glazed ham (which they then eat cold, £4.75), plaice or plump sole (from £4.75), and puddings like apple crumble or excellent bread and butter pudding (from £1.75). They do a winter three-course meal every Wednesday evening (£6.75), various feast evenings, and a traditional Sunday roast lunch (£4.75); dominoes and cards. There is sometimes an albino cockatiel in one room, and the atmosphere's good. Dogs welcome. *(Recommended by Peter Griffiths, L W Baal, R H Brown, Michael and Rachel Brookes, R A Palmer, Chris Vallely, Andrew Morrissey, David Lamb, John C Baker, Margaret Drazin, Mr and Mrs J D Cranston, Derek and Sylvia Stephenson)*

Free house   Licensee Iain Bryson   Real ale   Meals and snacks   Sheringham (0263) 825408   Children welcome   Open 11–3, 6–11   Bedrooms; £15/£30

WARHAM   TF9441 Map 8

Three Horseshoes

Warham All Saints; village signposted from A149 Wells-next-the-Sea–Blakeney, and from B1105 S of Wells

This is the friendly sort of pub where strangers talk to each other. Its two plain rooms are determinedly unspoilt and old-fashioned and have gas lighting (with an electric lamp for the darts), sturdy red leatherette settles built around the yellowing beige walls, stripped deal or mahogany tables (one marked for shove-ha'penny), an antique American Mills one-arm bandit still in working order (it takes the new 5p pieces), a big longcase clock with a clear piping strike, a Norfolk twister on the ceiling (you give it a twist and according to where it ends up you pay for the next round), a pianola, and a small but cheerful log fire. Particularly good value, freshly made bar food includes sandwiches (from £1.50), home-made soup (£1.60), cauliflower cheese (£2.50), local cockles in a cream and cider sauce (£2.70), huge double cheese ploughman's (£3.70), local sausages or an individual cottage roll filled with mince and baked (£4), local crab salad (£4.50), popular specials and especially good puddings like home-made fruit crumble (using their own fruit (£1.75). There are decent house wines and home-made lemonade as well as the well kept Greene King IPA on handpump and Abbot and Woodfordes Wherry tapped from the cask (also, tea or coffee). A separate games room has darts, pool, shove-ha'penny, cribbage, dominoes, fruit machine, video game and juke box, and one of the outbuildings houses a wind-up gramophone museum – opened on request. There are rustic tables out on the side grass, and the lavatories are outside. *(Recommended by Derek Patey, Charles Bardswell, Colin and Mary Meaden, TBB, Peter Griffiths, Derek and Sylvia Stephenson, J E Cooper)*

Free house   Licensee Iain Salmon   Real ale   Meals and snacks (12–2, 7–8.30; not Tues evening)   No smoking restaurant (not Sun evening)   Fakenham (0328) 710547 Children in restaurant and games room   Pianola every other Saturday night   Open 11–2.30, 6(7 in winter)–11   Bedrooms; £19(£21B)/£38(£42B)

WELLS NEXT THE SEA   TF9143 Map 8

Crown 🛏️

The Buttlands

Facing the long tree-lined central square of quiet Georgian houses, this inn has a front bar that's popular with locals and two quieter back rooms with some worthwhile pictures – including several big Nelson prints, maps showing the town in the eighteenth and nineteenth centuries, and interesting local photographs; roaring log fire. Waitress-served bar food includes sandwiches (from £1.25), soup (£1.60), ploughman's (£3), three-egg omelettes, vegetarian dish or ham and egg (£3.75), salads (from £3.75; crab £4.50), steak and kidney pie (£4.50), and rump steak (£10.50), with children's dishes (£2.50). Adnams, Marstons Pedigree and Tetleys on handpump; darts and piped music. A neat conservatory with small modern settles around the tables looks over the back garden. *(Recommended by Dr Keith Bloomfield, Phil Russell, Derek Patey, Peter Race, TBB, Denzil T Taylor, M Morgan)*

Free house   Licensee Wilfred Foyers   Real ale   Meals and snacks   Restaurant Fakenham (0328) 710209   Children in conservatory   Open 11–2.30, 6–11; closed evening 25 Dec   Bedrooms; £39(£46B)/£49(£56.50B)

WINTERTON-ON-SEA   TG4919 Map 8

Fishermans Return 🛏️

From B1159 turn into village at church on bend, then turn right into The Lane

Around 300 years old, this very friendly, pleasant brick inn is in a quiet village not far from a sandy beach. The white-painted, panelled lounge bar has a good, relaxed atmosphere and neat brass-studded red leatherette seats and a good winter log fire. The panelled public bar has low ceilings and a glossily varnished nautical air. There's also a separate serving counter in the back bar, which opens on to a terrace and good-sized sheltered garden; more seats face the quiet village lane. Good bar food includes toasted sandwiches (from £1.50), taramasalata with pitta bread (£2.50), ploughman's (£3), fish pie (£3.25), burgers (from £3.75), omelettes (from £4.25), seafood platter with their own special sauce (£4.75), and steaks (from £9), with seasonal daily specials like winter herrings or summer sea trout or crab, children's dishes (£2) and puddings like home-made spotted dick and custard (£1.60); excellent breakfasts. Well kept Adnams Bitter (Mr Findlay deserves praise for getting a different beer direct from the local brewery and selling it cheaper than his tied beers), and Ruddles Best and Websters Yorkshire on handpump, own label by the glass or bottle, malt whiskies and coffee; good service; darts, pool, fruit machine and piped music (CD). *(Recommended by Mr and Mrs Inman, L G and D L Smith, Derek and Irene Cranston, G T and J Barnes; more reports please)*

Manns (Watneys)   Lease: John Findlay   Real ale   Meals and snacks (11.30–2, 6 or 7–9; no food 25 Dec)   Winterton-on-Sea (0493) 393305   Children in dining room in winter and garden or family room in summer   Open 11–2.30, 6(7 in winter)–11 Bedrooms; £25/£40

Lucky Dip

Besides the fully inspected pubs, you might like to try these Lucky Dips recommended to us and described by readers (if you do, please send us reports):

Ashwellthorpe [B1135 SE of Wymondham; TM1497], *White Horse*: Comfortable small lounge with public bar and games room through short connecting passage; small choice of generously served, inexpensive, straightforward bar food and Watneys-related real ales on handpump; friendly licensees, prompt service *(Mr and Mrs J Back)*

Binham [TF9839], *Chequers*: Good friendly service and atmosphere, well kept beer, bar food inc very good ploughman's *(Revd L J and Mrs Melliss)*

☆ Blakeney [TG0243], *White Horse*: Doing well under dynamic new management, done up, with good food inc fresh fish in popular bar, friendly efficient service, good reasonably priced wines, Adnams and Ruddles on handpump; elegant new whitewashed restaurant; bedrooms *(P and J*

McComb, Christian Leigh, Gordon Wrigley, BKA)

Blakeney [The Quay], *Blakeney*: Well run hotel, good food and service; bedrooms very comfortable *(Mr and Mrs K J Morris)*; *Manor*: Hotel's public bar has attractive secluded courtyard with small pond and tables, wonderfully sheltered; good reasonably priced bar food, real ale *(Christian Leigh)*

☆ **Brancaster Staithe** [A149 Hunstanton—Wells; TF7743], *Jolly Sailors*: Interesting combination of upmarket atmosphere with stripped deal and other simple furnishings on old tiled floor of its three small rooms, well chosen decorations on rough white stone walls; can still hit it off with good food inc local winter mussels, well kept Greene King and decent wines, and at its best well worth knowing, with sheltered tables in nice garden, provision for children, attractive dining room, even a hard tennis court, and nearby NT dunes and salt flats; with more consistency would be an unqualified recommendation *(Charles Bardswell, Bev and Doug Warrick, Norman Hill, Hugh Stokes, LYM)*

☆ **Brandon Creek** [A10 Ely—Downham Mkt; TL6091], *Ship*: Good summer pub, in lovely spot on junction of the creek with the Great Ouse, tables out by the moorings; spacious bar with massive stone masonry in sunken area that used to be a forge, open fire one end, woodburner the other, friendly staff, Watneys-related real ales, usual bar food *(Frank W Gadbois, J P Cinnamond, LYM)*

Bressingham [A1066 Thetford—Diss; TM0781], *Garden House*: Cheerful, rambling sort of pub, with original beams in one part; well kept Adnams and Woodfordes Wherry on handpump, pool table and eccentric records on juke box; basic but popular bar food (not weekends), good generous restaurant; five mins' walk to Bressingham Gardens *(John Baker, David and Rebecca Killick)*

Brinton [TG0335], *Green Man*: Comfortably refurbished and friendly, with well kept beer and good food; smart pool table *(P Craddock)*

☆ **Briston** [B1354, Aylsham end of village; TG0532], *John H Stracey*: Wide choice of notable but reasonably priced bar food (Sun too) in attractive and spotless pub with nicely set out tables, friendly licensee, well kept real ales such as Ind Coope Burton and Ruddles County, perhaps one from a small local brewery; popular restaurant *(R C Vincent, Mrs R K Pugh, S Holder)*

☆ **Brundall** [Station Rd — OS Sheet 134, map reference 328079; TG3208], *Yare*: Busy, popular pub nr river; wattle hurdles on ceiling, navigation lamps, ship's curios, good photographs of boats; generous helpings of well presented pub food inc reliable crab salads, real ales such as Boddingtons, Sam Smiths and Woodfordes, splendid log fire; children's room *(T Nott)*

☆ **Burnham Market** [The Green (B1155); TF8342], *Capt Sir William Hoste*: On green

of lovely Georgian village, and under new licensees since end 1990 concentrating more on hotel side, with comfortable and attractive bedrooms; attractive bars with some interesting period features (though sadly the big window settle and table have gone, bar now has more small tables); real ales inc Woodfordes Wherry on handpump, friendly staff, food inc old favourites like very generous moules marinières and help-yourself salads *(Peter Griffiths, D W Featherstone, LYM; more reports on new regime please)*

Burnham Market, *Lord Nelson*: Exceptional cooking by landlord, esp fish such as sea trout and mullet; popular restaurant; bedrooms *(Charles Bardswell)*

☆ **Caistor St Edmunds** [Caistor Lane; TG2303], *Caistor Hall*: Quiet and comfortable pub/restaurant in lovely grounds; bar (counter an 18th-century shop front) leads into lounge looking on to sweeping mature lawns; original library, tables on terrace; bar food from good sandwiches up, decent wine *(Ian Phillips)*

Cantley [OS Sheet 134, map reference 380058; TG3704], *Cantley Cock*: Welcoming atmosphere, four real ales on handpump, good food *(MAC)*

Carleton St Peter [N of village; up track off lane Claxton—Langley Green, by River Yare — OS Sheet 134, map reference 350044; TG3402], *Beauchamp Arms*: Homely pub with armchairs, Woodfordes beers on handpump and good restaurant food; pool table; children's room *(MAC)*

☆ **Castle Rising** [TF6624], *Black Horse*: Well run and comfortable family pub, now a Whitbreads Beefeater — must be one of the friendliest; generous, wholesome and economical food, reliable; gets rather full at weekends *(Derek Pascall, J D Maplethorpe, Mr and Mrs K H Frostick, R C Vincent, Laurie Walker, Vanessa and Peter Hurst, M Morgan, C T and J M Laffan, Charles Bardswell)*

☆ **Cley Next the Sea** [The Green; nr church; TG0443], *Three Swallows*: Two-bar pub in quiet village nr bird-sanctuary salt marshes, with long, narrow Edwardian-style lounge, big garden; doing well under new management, with good imaginative home cooking, Wethereds *(R A Palmer, Christian Leigh, R P Hastings)*

Cley Next the Sea, *George & Dragon*: Three rooms, one with lively locals, one with tourists and bird watchers/walkers, one a restaurant/eating area with good choice of reasonably priced food; Greene King, garden over road; bedrooms *(Nigel Gibbs)*

☆ **Colkirk** [TF9126], *Crown*: Unpretentious but well furnished Greene King pub in pleasant village, good plain but tasty bar food presented well, friendly landlord, well kept IPA and Abbot on handpump, decent wines, good choice of other drinks; restaurant, own bowling green behind *(Gwen and Peter Andrews, Nora Casey, P Thorogood, Frank Davidson)*

Coltishall [TG2719], *Rising Sun*: Superb spot on pretty bend of River Bure; bar food,

Watneys-related real ales, waterside and other outside tables, family room *(LYM)*

☆ **Cromer** [Promenade; TG2142], *Bath House*: Welcoming inn below the cliff, down on the seafront; lots of dark wood, friendly staff, well kept Greene King Abbot and an interesting guest real ale such as Burton Bridge Porter on handpump; bar food from good sandwiches and ploughman's (lunchtime) through good range of salads to steaks, separate dining room; plenty of tables out on prom; bedrooms *(Michael and Alison Sandy, John and Bridget Dean, L G and D L Smith, Margaret and Roy Randle)*

Cromer [Tucker St; off A149; TG2142], *Red Lion*: Fairly dark locally popular Victorian bar divided into small comfortable areas by decorative glazed screens; big helpings of reasonably priced bar food, well kept Adnams, maybe rather obtrusive music; bedrooms *(Mr and Mrs K J Morris, R P Hastings)*

☆ **Dersingham** [Manor Rd (B1440 out towards Sandringham); TF6830], *Feathers*: Solidly handsome Jacobean sandstone inn with relaxed and comfortably modernised dark-panelled bars opening on to attractive garden with play area; well kept Charrington and maybe Adnams on handpump, pleasant service, reasonably priced bar food, restaurant (not Sun evening); can get very busy in season; children welcome; comfortable well furnished bedrooms *(Jack and Barbara Smale, LYM)*

☆ **Diss** [9 St Nicholas St; town centre, off B1077; TM1179], *Greyhound*: Handsome high moulded Tudor beams in welcoming and comfortably refurbished carpeted lounge, with big brick fireplace, well kept Watneys-related real ales, popular reasonably priced bar food, games in public bar; children in eating area *(K A V Read, LYM)*

☆ **Docking** [centre; TF7637], *Pilgrims Reach*: Pleasant and friendly pub with good food, Adnams and Everards real ales, tables in sheltered and attractive terrace garden; restaurant *(James Cane, Mr and Mrs D J Hancock)*

☆ **East Barsham** [B1105 3 miles N of Fakenham; TF9133], *White Horse*: Old building with recent sympathetic enlargement, above-average food inc local fish, well — even enthusiastically — kept beers such as Bass, Mauldons Suffolk Punch and Woodfordes Headcracker, big log fire; piped music; children welcome; bedrooms *(Derek and Sylvia Stephenson, John C Baker, Derek Pascall)*

East Dereham [High St; TF9913], *Bull*: Friendly, cosy and welcoming, various areas leading out of central serving area with central fireplace, good value food, Greene King ales, darts and other games, local old photographs *(Nigel Gibbs)*; *George*: Worth knowing for generous carvery eaten in bar or dining room, Watneys-related real ales; bedrooms *(Frank Davidson)*

☆ **East Harling** [High St; TL9986], *Swan*:

Quiet, comfortable and welcoming old-fashioned village pub with circular bar, tiled floor, low dark beams, lots of small pictures (mostly of ships); plush chairs and settles in lounge, pool table in separate alcove, well kept Watneys-related real ales, good home-cooked food, decent dining room *(K R Harris, Gwen and Peter Andrews)*

Erpingham [OS Sheet 133, map reference 191319; TG1931], *Spread Eagle*: Worth knowing for its full range of Woodfordes real ales (from Woodbastwick); usual food, terraced garden facing bowling green; children in games room *(Derek and Sylvia Stephenson)*

Fakenham [Market Pl; TF9229], *Crown*: Friendly unpretentious front bar in Elizabethan inn with dimly lit cosy front snug, nice carved oak furniture, well kept Greene King; interesting former gallery staircase now glassed in; bedrooms *(Derek Patey, LYM)*

Framingham Earl [B1332; TG2702], *Railway*: Well kept open-plan modern dining pub with character, friendly staff, well kept beer, good service, reasonably priced food *(C T and J M Laffan)*

Fritton [Beccles Rd (A143); TG4600], *Fritton Decoy*: Wide choice of good food — hot-pot and pies recommended; helpful cheerful staff, nice and warm, real ale, good atmosphere; opp country park *(Barbara and Mike Williams)*

Garboldisham [TM0081], *Fox*: Well kept real ale, big helpings of usual bar food — good value *(Frank Davidson)*

☆ **Great Cressingham** [OS Sheet 144, map reference 849016; TF8501], *Windmill*: Friendly and roomy but cosy beamed family pub, with three bars, conservatory, games room; good value food, quick service, Adnams, Batemans, Bass, Charrington, Sam Smiths and guest beers, huge log fireplace, lots of farm tools; well kept big garden, welcoming long-serving landlord *(R P Hastings, Charles Bardswell)*

Great Ryburgh [TF9527], *Boar*: Friendly, comfortable atmosphere, good food, well kept Adnams and Tolly *(Frank Davidson)*

Great Yarmouth [24 St Nicholas Rd; TG5207], *Tudor*: Well kept Greene King Abbot and Tetleys, good choice of locally popular bar food inc speciality pie, attractive garden *(Bill and Rosalie Link)*

☆ **nr Great Yarmouth** [St Olaves; A143 towards Beccles, where it crosses R Waveney — OS Sheet 134, map reference 458994], *Bell*: Attractive Tudor herringbone brickwork and heavy oak timbers (said to be oldest Broads pub); spacious and comfortably modernised inside, with efficient service, good bar food, Whitbreads-related real ales on handpump, games in public bar, two attractive open fires; barbecues and good children's play area in riverside garden with free moorings; children in restaurant *(A T Langton, LYM)*

☆ **nr Great Yarmouth** [Berney Arms Stn; 8-min train trip from Gt Yarmouth; OS Sheet 134, map reference 464049], *Berney Arms*: Only

safe mooring between Reedham and Gt
Yarmouth on River Yare, and accessible
only by water or by rail Gt
Yarmouth—Norwich; interesting building
with flagstone floors, woodburning stove,
fishing nets and lamps, settles made from
barrel staves; well kept Adnams and
Courage, decent straightforward bar food
inc good sausages, cheerful service; closed
winter; nearby windmill worth visiting
(MAC)

☆ **Hainford** [TG2218], *Chequers*: Attractive
thatched pub recently reopened (had been
closed since mid-80s fire); big airy bar area
and separate rooms, some for dining; well
laid-out gardens with shelters, seats and play
area, delightful setting; wide range of beers,
imaginative choice of well cooked and
presented food, pleasant staff *(G E Rich, Mr
and Mrs Nicholls)*

☆ **Happisburgh** [by village church; TG3830],
Hill House: Friendly atmosphere, well kept
Adnams, Greene King Abbot and
Woodfordes Wherry on handpump, well
presented, generous and reasonably priced
tasty bar food inc good crab sandwiches and
interesting salads; good restaurant for Sun
lunch; garden; children's room separate
from pub, well equipped with toys;
bedrooms *(Denzil T Taylor, P S Vince, Derek
and Sylvia Stephenson, T K Baxter, R H
Brown)*

☆ **Hethersett** [TG1505], *Kings Head*: Homely
and cheerful pub with enjoyable lunchtime
bar food, comfortable carpeted lounge,
friendly and courteous welcome, traditional
games in cosy public bar, attractive and
spacious back lawn; well kept
Watneys-related real ales *(LYM)*

☆ **Hevingham** [Holt Rd (B1149 N of
Norwich); TG1921], *Marsham Arms*:
Rambling and spacious modernised roadside
pub with particularly well kept real ales such
as Adnams, Bass, Greene King Abbot and
Woodfordes Wherry, country wines, wide
range of well prepared straightforward food,
double family room on right, tables in
garden behind; bedrooms in new motel wing
behind *(John Baker, BB)*

☆ **Heydon** [village signposted from B1149;
TG1127], *Earle Arms*: Flagstones, bare
boards, maybe a roll or basic sandwich, well
kept Adnams tapped from the cask and
served through a hatch — decidedly unsmart
and quite unspoilt (the plastic seats show
how unassuming the old-worldliness is);
bedrooms (cheap and simple); pub faces
interestingly untouched village green — and
still has stables in use behind *(Tony and
Lynne Stark, Derek Patey, LYM)*

☆ **Hillborough** [A1065; TF8100], *Swan*: Pretty
pink cottage pub, dated 1718, simple but
comfortable and welcoming, with obliging
staff, well kept Adnams, Batemans, Greene
King Abbot and IPA and Marstons Pedigree,
and good value simple food prepared to
order — so service can't be quick when it's
busy; tables on sheltered lawn *(Peter
Griffiths, Charles Bardswell)*

Hillington [TF7225], *Ffolkes Arms*: Large

and comfortable, with wide range of beers,
good carvery, good choice of bar food; new
very good bedrooms *(G E Rich)*

Hingham [TG0202], *White Hart*: Elegant
stuccoed Georgian facade with white hart
over handsome portico, in pretty village;
brightly renovated inside, with woodburning
stove in big brick fireplace; bar food *(Ian
Phillips, Frank Davidson)*

Holkham [A149 nr Holkham Hall;
TF8943], *Victoria*: Small and pleasantly
informal coastal inn by entry to Holkham
Hall, has been popular for bar food, Tolly
real ale, a welcome for children and good
position nr beaches and nature reserves; but
no reports since found closed earlier in 1991
(News please)

Holme Next the Sea [Kirkgate St; TF7043],
White Horse: Welcoming, down-to-earth
local with hearty, good value if rather basic
food from good crab sandwiches to super
steaks; gets busy *(Mr and Mrs B Foggitt,
Margaret Bull)*

Holt [White Lion St; TG0738], *White Lion*:
Georgian pub with friendly service, simple
food and well kept real ales in welcoming
small bar *(Neil Hardwick)*

Horning [TG3417], *Ferry*: Riverside Chef &
Brewer with well kept ales and friendly
service, even when busy *(Gethin Lewis)*

☆ **Horsey** [just visible down lane 'To The Sea'
from B1159 in S bends; TG4522], *Nelsons
Head*: Isolated pub, nr coast and actually
below sea level, which we've always thought
had great potential; the Whitbreads
leasehold's now been sold, and it's doing
well, with the bar extended, well kept
Adnams, friendly and welcoming service,
family room and garden *(Janet and David
Hampton, BB)*

Horstead [B1354 just W of Coltishall;
TG2619], *Recruiting Sergeant*: Limited
choice of good interesting food in bar and
restaurant, big open fire, brasses and
muskets on walls; friendly staff *(A Young)*

Ingham [TG3826], *Swan*: In old monastic
buildings next to church; six real ales, nice
food *(Richard A Bailey)*

Kings Lynn [Tuesday Mkt Pl; TF6220],
Maydens Heade: Popular town-centre pub
with home-cooked food inc self-service veg,
real ale; children in separate dining area *(R
C Vincent)*; [Gayton Rd], *Wildfowler*: Well
furnished Allied pub with reasonably priced
food, Ind Coope Burton and Tetleys real ales
(Patrick Godfrey)

Ludham [A1062; TG3813], *Kings Arms*:
Large and attractive, with big play area and
playroom, conservatory with generous
helpings of good value food inc children's
dishes; well kept beers inc Woodfordes
Wherry as well as Watneys-related ones *(P S
Vince)*

Marham [TF7009], *Fox & Hounds*:
Friendly family local, vivacious landlady,
Watneys-related ales, reasonably priced bar
food inc good speciality pizzas,
get-you-home service and pizza deliveries for
locals; children and dogs warmly greeted;
bedrooms reasonably priced *(Mr and Mrs K*

Roads)

☆ **Mundford** [Crown St; TL8093], *Crown*: Friendly small recently renovated village pub (originally ancient posting inn, rebuilt in 18th century), attractive choice of good value straightforward food, very welcoming staff, happy atmosphere, well kept real ale; charming village; bedrooms good *(E A George, Dr John Innes, Norman Hill, R P Hastings, Caroline Wright)*

Neatishead [Irstead Rd; TG3420], *Barton Angler*: Pleasant atmosphere in bar with good, reasonably priced food — well presented — and charming young owners; bedrooms excellent value, recently refurbished *(Anon)*; *White Horse*: Has been enjoyed as small, quiet and homely pub with lounge bar resembling one's own front room, Greene King ales, good reasonably priced home-cooked food and friendly service, but no recent reports *(News please)*

☆ **New Buckenham** [TM0890], *George*: Pleasant village-green pub with well kept Courage Directors, Greene King IPA and Tolly Original and small choice of generous food inc huge ploughman's, good steaks; dining room set out as restaurant; bar, lively games area with juke box *(Mrs J Back)*

Newton [A1065 by Castle Acre; TF8315], *George & Dragon*: Good choice of reasonably priced food, friendly staff, pleasant surroundings, well kept Watneys-related real ales, unobtrusive piped music; children in small restaurant area and games bar; small caravan site *(Bill and Wendy Burge, R P Hastings)*

☆ **North Creake** [TF8538], *Jolly Farmers*: Simple and unspoilt local, with good food, well cooked and genially served; Courage Best on handpump, Directors and Flowers Original tapped from the cask, attractive little restaurant *(Charles Bardswell, Bill Link)*

North Elmham [B1110 N of E Dereham; TF9820], *Kings Head*: Taken over 1991 by two ex-restaurateurs, welcoming and friendly, with good value generous food, Ruddles Best and County; bedrooms planned *(Anon)*

North Lopham [signed off A1066 Thetford—Diss; TM0383], *Kings Head*: Good basic food, open fire *(David and Rebecca Killick)*

☆ **Norwich** [10 Dereham Rd], *Reindeer*: Own-brew pub producing good cheap ales — you can see the brewery through back window; about five guest beers too, lively bare-boards-and-casks atmosphere, extension with dining area and tasteful kitchen serving big helpings of hearty food for wide range of tastes; thoughtful decor giving effect of age though pub is not old, friendly staff, occasional folk bands; not crowded outside University terms *(Frank W Gadbois, Alan Eardley, Maureen and Steve Collin, David White)*

Norwich [Tombland], *Edith Cavell*: Light and airy big-windowed former teashop, facing cathedral green; comfortable and friendly, with good value food (till 7); Watneys-related real ales, CD juke box loud

in evenings *(Wayne Brindle, Tony and Lynne Stark)*; [King St], *Ferryboat*: Traditional beamed old-fashioned front part, spacious raftered and flagstoned back area, former kitchen alcove complete with baking oven, well kept and attractively priced Greene King IPA and Abbot and Woodfordes, refurbished restaurant; slide and climbing frame in riverside garden with barbecue; children welcome *(MAC, LYM)*; [Timber Hill], *Gardeners Arms*: Spacious, with old beams and panels, Adnams, Tetleys and Woodfordes Best, bar food served in indoor garden, reasonable prices; piped pop music can be loud in evening; previously called the Murderers *(J McHugh, R P Hastings, Richard A Bailey)*; [Heigham St], *Gibraltar Gardens*: Well kept beer, good value food, excellent garden; good parking; children welcome *(Frank Davidson)*; *Rib of Beef*: Riverside pub, basic split-level interior full of students in term-time, splendid range of real ales inc Norfolk ones, farm cider, informative and friendly bar staff *(Richard A Bailey, Tony and Lynne Stark)* [centre], *St Andrews*: Well kept Adnams and Broadside, Badger Tanglefoot, Brains Mild and others; interesting bar with old pub signs and good line drawings; good food, bright back sunroom *(J V Cattell)*; [Newmarket St/Bury St], *Unthank Arms*: Refurbished old pub with good choice of wines by the glass, nice atmosphere, open fires, well kept real ales and good range of inexpensive food inc above-average steaks *(Anthony Barnes)*; [York St/Leicester St], *York*: Old pub not overly refurbished, with imaginative choice of good reasonably priced food, good range of beers, pleasant atmosphere *(Richard and Lorna Norton)*

Old Hunstanton [part of Le Strange Arms Hotel, Golf Course Rd; TF6842], *Ancient Mariner*: Interesting old bar with bare bricks and flagstones, several little areas inc upstairs room overlooking bar, usual food for large throughput of customers, well kept Adnams and Broadside, Bass and Charrington IPA; bedrooms *(Denise Plummer, Jim Froggatt, Charles Bardswell)*; [A149], *Lodge*: Bass, Greene King IPA, Abbot and Rayments Special on handpump in comfortable hotel bar with friendly staff, good value bar food; bedrooms *(Jim Froggatt, Denise Plummer)*; [A149], *Neptune*: Small no-nonsense local with Adnams, Greene King Abbot and guest beer such as Bass, straightforward bar food, restaurant, friendly staff *(Jim Froggatt, Denise Plummer)*

Poringland [The Street; B1332 5 miles S of Norwich; TG2602], *Royal Oak*: Friendly and neatly modernised, with wheelback chairs and leatherette banquettes in timber-effect bays, log-effect gas fire, well kept Adnams, Marstons Pedigree, Whitbreads Castle Eden and a guest beer, good wine list, locally popular bar food (some emphasis on this); open all day Sat, tables outside *(R A Gurney, K R and R E Roebuck, BB)*

☆ **Salhouse** [Bell Lane; TG3014], *Bell*: Pleasant and friendly, with well kept real ales and limited choice of inexpensive good food *(A T Langton, J H C Peters)*

Sculthorpe [A148 2 miles W of Fakenham; TF8930], *Sculthorpe Mill*: Beautiful surroundings and friendly atmosphere in riverside watermill converted by owners of Lifeboat at Thornham (see main entries), with similar restaurant — good, if not cheap; free shuttle bus runs between the two pubs; good choice of real ales *(Nic James)*

☆ **Sedgeford** [B1454, off A149 Kings Lynn–Hunstanton; TF7136], *King William IV*: Pleasant, well run pub with sensibly priced straightforward bar food, nicely cooked and presented and generously served; well kept Bass, Charrington IPA, Greene King Abbot and a guest on handpump, children allowed in lounge if eating; restaurant very busy weekends (best to book then) *(Derek and Sylvia Stephenson, Jim Froggatt, Denise Plummer)*

Sheringham [TG1543], *Two Lifeboats*: Well kept beer and good value food; bedrooms *(R P Hastings, Richard A Bailey)*

☆ **Smallburgh** [TG3225], *Crown*: Good atmosphere in small and friendly free house, very useful for the area, with good value home-made bar food using local ingredients and fresh veg; restaurant *(R C Watkins, Gethin Lewis)*

South Walsham [TG3713], *Ship*: Friendly landlord and staff, good home-cooked food, well kept Woodfordes Wherry *(John Tooth)*

Stanhoe [Main St (B1155); TF8036], *Crown*: Attractive L-shaped room, part partitioned, with bar in corner and pleasant low-key piped music; friendly helpful staff, properly cooked bar food, Elgoods Bitter and Mild *(M and J Back)*

Stoke Holy Cross [TG2301], *Kings Head*: Real pub with genuine welcome and food cooked by landlady with imagination and served in massive helpings; two bars — log fires in lounge and darts in public; very popular with locals *(Dr R Fuller)*

☆ **Stokesby** [TG4310], *Ferry House*: Traditional pub on River Bure with plenty of character, good service, generous helpings of good food, choice of real ales inc well kept Adnams Extra and Flowers on handpump; very popular with boating holidaymakers (free moorings); children welcome *(P S Vince, MAC)*

☆ **Stow Bardolph** [TF6205], *Hare Arms*: Pleasantly refurbished country pub opp Stow Hall, with good value quickly served interesting lunchtime bar food, a real cut above the area average; cheerful licensees, prompt courteous service even when busy, well kept Greene King IPA and Abbot, large open fire, plenty of tables around central servery, old-fashioned advertising signs, fresh flowers; separate elegant evening restaurant, big conservatory for children *(Dr John Innes, Mr and Mrs Clark, Derek and Sylvia Stephenson, Brenda Crossley, Anthony Barnes, Irene and Derek Cranston, Jon and Jane Fawbert)*

☆ **Stradsett** [A134/A1122; TF6604], *Fouldgate*: Long timbered bar with plenty of

tables and comfortable seats, big helpings of reasonably priced traditional pub food inc good salads, Watneys-related real ales on handpump, good white wine; pleasant, efficient staff, fresh flowers, juke box, big car park *(Gwen and Peter Andrews, Bill and Wendy Burge)*

☆ **Surlingham** [TG3206], *Coldham Hall*: Lovely waterside setting with attractive, well kept garden overlooking River Yare; generous helpings of good bar food (good value if not cheap), well kept beer and cider, friendly service, large main bar, pool table in smaller one, family room; free mooring if using pub *(J E Cooper, Janet and David Hampton)*

☆ **Surlingham** [from village head N; pub on bumpy track into which both village roads fork], *Ferry House*: Spaciously comfortable modernised bar with good views of the river (there's still a rowing-boat ferry); sensibly priced usual bar food and Sun roasts, Watneys-related real ales on handpump, homely atmosphere, traditional pub games, piped music, restaurant, free mooring for 24 hours; children welcome, with own menu; has opened 8pm winter *(David Oakes, Anthony Barnes, LYM)*

☆ **Sutton Staithe** [village signposted from A149 S of Stalham; TG3823], *Sutton Staithe*: The great attraction is the position, in a particularly unspoilt part of the Broads; little alcoves, built-in seats and an antique settle among more modern furnishings, well kept Adnams and sometimes other real ales tapped from the cask, usual bar food, restaurant; good nearby moorings; children allowed in eating areas; has been open all day summer; bedrooms *(M W Atkinson, MAC)*

☆ **Swanton Morley** [B1147, E end of village; TG0216], *Darbys*: Cosy beamed country pub, once a small row of cottages and now almost a museum of farm tools etc; welcoming village atmosphere, perfectly kept Adnams and Broadside, Woodfordes Wherry and guest beers, log fire, friendly staff and food way above average — especially baked crab and Sun roasts; children's room and play area *(John C Baker, Tony and Lynne Stark)*

☆ **Thetford** [King St; TL8783], *Bell*: Clean, tidy and pleasant beamed and timbered Tudor bar with Adnams and Greene King real ales and generously served bar food in THF hotel which is otherwise spaciously modern; bedrooms *(BB)*

☆ **Thetford** [White Hart St], *Thomas Paine*: Well kept Adnams and Tolly Original in friendly, spacious and comfortable hotel lounge bar, good value bar food from fine range of sandwiches to hot dishes; good service, small fire in big fireplace; children welcome; bedrooms *(Frank Davidson, BB)*

Thetford [Castle St], *Bridge*: Good lunchtime pub with Watneys-related real ales, cheerful service, good reasonably priced bar food inc lots of soups and pies; garden on river, play area, plenty of parking *(Frank Davidson, Mrs M E Beard)*

☆ **Thornham** [Church St; TF7343], *Kings Head*: Cosy old white-fronted pub converted from village cottages; two low-beamed attractive bars with lots of brass, darts in wider tiled part, narrower no-smoking part with carvery, tables and banquettes in well lit alcoves; big helpings of well presented good food, interesting landlord, friendly staff; real ales inc Greene King Abbot on handpump; nr GWG116; bedrooms *(Peter Griffiths, Mrs D K Rae, Gwen and Peter Andrews)*

Titchwell [A149; TF7543], *Three Horseshoes*: Friendly staff, well kept Bass and Greene King, decent specials and popular carvery in light and airy modern environment *(Charles Bardswell, George and Mollie Dowglass, Derek and Sylvia Stephenson)*

Upwell [TF5002], *Five Bells*: Good healthy food, Camerons, Greene King IPA and Abbot, Marstons Pedigree, and a good punch; waitress may be in Elizabethan dress *(E W Morgan)*

☆ **Walcott** [B1159, nr church; S of village — OS Sheet 133, map reference 359320; TG3632], *Lighthouse*: Friendly pub just outside village, well equipped family room, exceptional value food from sandwiches up inc summer evening barbecues and good children's menu, well kept Adnams and Allied real ales and their own very low-priced good Lighthouse Bitter, Addlestone's cider *(P S Vince, Mr and Mrs B J Twigger, David Oakes)*

Walpole Cross Keys [A17 8 miles W of Kings Lynn; TF5119], *Woolpack*: Attractive pub enlarged and modernised under friendly newish owners, with good choice of home-cooked food inc sandwiches, vegetarian dishes and children's meals; well kept Adnams and Broadside on handpump, efficient service, restaurant, large new family room, small garden with play area *(Derek and Sylvia Stephenson, G G Calderwood)*

☆ **Walsingham** [Common Place/Shire Hall Plain; TF9236], *Bull*: Well kept Watneys-related real ales, simple bar food, very friendly service and friendly company; a short walk from the shrine *(Canon Kenneth Wills)*

West Runton [TG1842], *Village Inn*: Beautifully placed in village, good food inc lunchtime cold table, well kept real ales on handpump, tables on front lawn *(Richard A Bailey)*

☆ **West Somerton** [B1159/B1152; TG4619], *Lion*: Warm and friendly welcome in airy and comfortable modernised pub with good value efficiently served bar food, well kept Greene King and guest real ales; handy for Martham Broad; children in family room *(LYM)*

☆ **Wighton** [TF9340], *Sandpiper*: Well-scrubbed modest country pub with well kept Tolly and guest beers, good bar food cooked to order, friendly hardworking licensees; games room; garden with play area and pretty views over the valley, animals on green opp; attractive village; children welcome; good value bedrooms *(Charles Bardswell, Derek Patey)*

Wiveton [TG0342], *Bell*: Popular old pub overlooking village green and church; much modernised inside with three well kept real ales and good straightforward bar food; tables out in front, more in attractive back garden *(R P Hastings, Frank Davidson)*

Wreningham [TM1598], *Bird in Hand*: Neatly extended and refurbished, with local bygones and Lotus car photographs (local company), good food at reasonable prices, Flowers, Marstons Pedigree and Woodfordes real ales, good service, pleasant surroundings *(Nigel Gibbs, John Whitfield)*

☆ **Wymondham** [Market Pl; TG1101], *Cross Keys*: Good value straightforward food inc very popular bookable Sun lunch, friendly staff and locals, good choice of real ales; bedrooms simple but clean and very reasonably priced *(Andrew Morrissey, Audrey and Brian Green, Mr and Mrs T F Marshall)*

Wymondham [Church St], *Green Dragon*: Unspoilt traditional pub with real ales tapped from casks behind bar, impressive bar food inc particularly good value specials; friendly service *(Geoff Wilson)*

Northamptonshire *see* Midlands
Northumberland *see* Northumbria

Northumbria (including Durham, Northumberland, Cleveland and Tyne & Wear)

A good clutch of new entries here this year is added evidence of how vigorously the area's pubs are thriving. They include the comfortable and well run Percy Arms at Chatton (a good example of that Northumbrian speciality, the village inn that's a popular eating place for people from miles around – and it's a comfortable place to stay); the ingeniously refurbished Wheatsheaf in Corbridge (another nice place to stay – and its bar is neatly divided between warm-hearted local and smart comfort); the Dipton Mill at Diptonmill (a wonderful little tucked-away country pub); the stylish General Havelock at Haydon Bridge (excellent food in attractive surroundings); and the friendly Bay Horse up at West Woodburn (taken well in hand by newish licensees, and attractively refurbished). Other pubs doing really well here at the moment include the Manor House at Carterway Heads (its small choice of imaginative food is catching wide attention, and the gradual refurbishment is working out well), the unpretentious Jolly Fisherman perched above the sea at Craster, the splendidly designed Shiremoor House Farm in New York (its separate family area is now open), the Cook & Barker Arms at Newton on the Moor (carefully refurbished under its hardworking licensees, and now doing bedrooms), the attractive old George at Piercebridge (another inn where gradual careful changes have been working out really well), and the vibrant Olde Ship at Seahouses (great fun, and a very proper pub). Things are stirring in the Lucky Dip section at the end of the chapter, too. The Plough near Berwick upon Tweed and the Kirk at Romaldkirk are both shining with current promise, and we'd put in a particular word too for the Lord Crewe Arms at Bamburgh, Sun at Beamish (or rather at the open air museum there), Milecastle at Haltwhistle, Northumberland Arms on Holy Island, Black Bull at Matfen, Teesdale Hotel in Middleton in Teesdale, and Seven Stars at Shincliffe. Prices of both food and drink are rather lower here than in the country at large – saving about 8p on each drink, typically.

BEAMISH (Durham)   NZ2254 Map 10
Shepherd & Shepherdess

By main gate of Open Air Museum

This slate-roofed white house is well managed and neatly refurbished. The spacious lounge has plush button-back built-in wall banquettes and small comfortable chairs on the carpet, a mural showing local places of interest above the substantial mahogany-fitted servery area, a spinning wheel in one corner, and lots of decorative plates and pleasant reproductions of Victorian pictures on the walls; there's an attractive Victorian fireplace. Bar food includes sandwiches, vegetarian dishes such as vegetable curry, cheese and broccoli lasagne or sautéed garlic mushrooms (£3), other dishes include lasagne, ham and mushroom pie or chicken curry (£3), breaded plaice (£3.25), steak and apple pie (£3.35), grilled trout (£3.85), and farmhouse grill or 8oz rump steak (£6.05). Well kept Vaux Samson and Wards Sheffield Best on handpump; fruit machine. There are tables outside. (*Recommended by Wayne Brindle; more reports please*)

Vaux   Manager William Dean   Real ale   Meals and snacks   (091) 3700 349 Children welcome   Open 11–11; 11–3, 6.30–11 in winter

BLANCHLAND (Northumberland)   NY9750 Map 10

Lord Crewe Arms

As early seekers of sanctuary must have done, one reader on a cold and snowy journey found this ancient inn a marvellous haven from the savage surrounding moorland – with today's comforts including huge log fires, big bowls of hyacinths and pot pourri, and cheerful local staff. Down in a crypt, one bar is simply furnished with pews against massive stone walls under a barrel-vaulted ceiling. Upstairs, the Derwent Room has low beams, old settles, and sepia photographs on its walls. There's also a priest's hole next to a striking thirteenth-century fireplace where the Jacobite Tom Forster (part of the family who had owned the building before it was sold to the formidable Lord Crewe, Bishop of Durham) is said to have hidden after escaping from prison in London, on his way to exile in France. Simple bar food includes soup (£1.50), filled granary rolls (from £2), ploughman's (£3.90), salads (from £3.95), grilled pork and apple burgers (£4.50), grilled lamb kebabs with barbecue sauce or breadcrumbed supreme of chicken with tagliatelle, crushed tomato and mozzarella cheese (£4.75) and king prawns sautéed with Worcester sauce and lemon juice (£6), with puddings (£1.50); Sunday lunch (£11.50) and afternoon teas with home-made cakes. Vaux Samson on handpump; darts. (*Recommended by Lynn Sharpless, Bob Eardley, Mike and Wendy Proctor, Wayne Brindle, SS, Nicky Moore, Sidney and Erna Wells, Simon Baker, David Oakes, Mrs S Mills*)

Free house   Licensees A S Todd and P R Gingell   Real ale   Lunchtime meals and snacks   Evening restaurant, though they do Sun lunch   Hexham (0434) 675251 Children welcome   Open 11–3, 6–11 (all day in summer if very busy)   Bedrooms; £65B/£88B

CARTERWAY HEADS (Northumberland)   NZ0552 Map 10

Manor House ⊘

A68 just N of B6278, near Derwent Reservoir

The food in this simple stone building is consistently imaginative, and though the menu is not huge it does change daily: sandwiches and soup, chicken liver pâté (£3.50), brie and smoked turkey (£3.75), warm courgette and cheese tart (£4.25), smoked cod gratin (£4.90), baked salmon with ginger and currants (£5.75), with puddings such as sticky toffee pudding (£1.90). The well kept ales change regularly and might include Centurion, Fullers London Pride or Ruddles on handpump, half-a-dozen malt whiskies, eleven wines and decent coffee. The lounge bar has been completely refurbished, and now has a woodburning stove in one corner which provides warmth in winter; the beamed locals' bar is furnished with pine tables, chairs and stools, old oak pews, and a mahogany bar. Darts, dominoes, and piped music. The evening restaurant has its own comfortable lounge, with sofas and so forth. Rustic tables out on a small side terrace and lawn have a pleasant view looking south over moorland pastures. (*Recommended by John Whitehead, Karen and Graham Oddey, Mike and Wendy Proctor, Margaret and Roy Randle, Bettina Hartas, Jerry and Alison Oakes, John Oddey, Lesley Jones, Geralyn Meyler, M B P Carpenter, Dr R H M Stewart*)

Free house   Licensee Anthony Pelly   Real ale   Meals and snacks (12–2.30, 7–9.30, 9 on Suns)   Restaurant   Consett (0207) 55268   Children in eating area until 8.30 Open 11–3, 6–11; closed 25 Dec

CHATTON (Northumberland)   Map 10

Percy Arms 🛏

B6348 E of Wooller

This solid stone inn, partly creeper-covered, has picnic-table sets on its small front lawn above the village road. Inside is clean, comfortable and spacious, with wooden wall seats upholstered in pale brocade, studded chairs and stools around the dark tables in the carpeted main lounge area, an armchair or two among other seats in a family area through a stone-faced arch, and round on the other side a similarly furnished tiled-floor section leading through to a stripped-stone restaurant. It's locally very popular for good value home-made food, including soup (95p) and several starters such as sweet pickled herring (£1.90), ploughman's (£2.45), fresh local cod (£3.20), steak and kidney pie (£3.60), home-cooked ham and other salads (from £3.60, local crab £3.95), a vegetarian dish (£3.80), steak sandwich (£3.85), evening gammon (done with brown sugar and crushed pineapple, £4.95) or local steaks (from £6.85) and children's dishes (£1.20). Well kept Theakstons XB on handpump, a good choice of malt whiskies, open fire, unobtrusive piped music; public bar with darts, pool, dominoes, fruit machine, video game and juke box. The inn has 12 miles of private fishing for residents (sea trout, salmon and stocked rainbow trout); also a holiday cottage. No dogs in public areas. (*Recommended by Jeanne and Tom Barnes, Dennis Heatley, Paul McPherson*)

Free house   Licensees Pam and Kenny Topham   Real ale   Meals and snacks Restaurant   Chatton (066 85) 244   Children welcome   Open 12–3, 6–11   Bedrooms £20B/£40B

CORBRIDGE (Northumberland)   NY9964   Map 10

Wheatsheaf 🛏

Watling St (former A69, just N of centre)

This pub, originally a farmhouse, was built in 1695, and still has many of its original features, although it no longer has the thatched roof. It's a proper pub, with a thriving atmosphere – particularly in the evenings. The lounge bar on the left has been stylishly refurbished with comfortable ribbed wall banquettes and cushioned chairs, pink patterned wallpaper above a darker toning dado and below a delft shelf packed with china, old-fashioned pictures, and roughened burnt orange paintwork between the beams. It opens through a chubby balustrade into a dining area with lots of little china bells on its delft shelf, and a similarly furnished conservatory section. A shame about the piped pop music in the public area – very chatty and engaging otherwise, with comfortable seats, a good local atmosphere, and boards up for the Corbridge Leek Club's weekly forecast tote. A good choice of reasonably priced bar food, at lunchtime includes soup (95p), ploughman's (£2.50), home-made vegetarian casserole (£3.25), salads (from £3.25), deep-fried scampi or home roast chicken (£3.50), home-made steak and mushroom pie (£3.95) and children's meals (all £2), while in the evenings a fuller menu offers a range of starters, such as soup (£1.10), and home-made pâté (£1.95), main meals such as a range of salads (£4.25), vegetarian meals such as nuts and vegetable fettucini (£4.50), and meaty dishes like beef madras curry or breaded lemon sole (£4.95); very generous Sunday lunches, well kept Samson and Wards on handpump, darts, dominoes, fruit machines, some picnic-table sets out on the side grass. The strange stones in the stable yard are probably of Roman origin – the chief figure is thought to represent the Roman goddess Ceres, the second, a corner stone wiith two heads facing in different directions, is probably the god Janus. (*Recommended by Andy and Jill Kassube, Bill and Sylvia Trotter, John Oddey*)

Vaux   Tenant Mr Gordon Young   Real ale   Meals and snacks   Corbridge (0434) 632020   Children in lounge area and separate restaurant   Live entertainment on Sat eves   Open 11–11   Bedrooms; £32B/£42B

COTHERSTONE (Durham)   NZ0119 Map 10

Fox & Hounds 🍸

B6277 – incidentally a good quiet route to Scotland, through interesting scenery

Overlooking a picturesque little village green, this thriving white-painted house has various alcoves and recesses in the beamed bar, comfortable furnishings such as thickly cushioned wall seats, local photographs and country pictures on the walls, and a winter open fire. Very popular home-made bar food is served in the L-shaped lounge bar. This might consist at lunchtime of open home-made rolls (from £2.25, prawn £3.95, hot steak roll £5.45) and ploughman's (from £3.50), starters such as home-made soup (£1.95) or cornet of smoked scottish salmon and greenland prawns (£4.75), main course dishes such as a wide choice of salads (from £5.45), home-made steak and kidney pie (£5.45), gammon (£6.75), steak (£8.95), and a big platter with steak, gammon, lamb cutlet and sausage (£9.95); daily specials include fresh fish dishes such as fresh halibut in creamy caper sauce or fresh salmon in orange, ginger and spring onion sauce (£8.95), and a vegetarian dish such as vegetarian crumble (£5.45); puddings might include hot treacle sponge and custard or white chocolate and bacardi cream crunch (£2.45); there's a children's menu (£2.25), or dishes can be served in smaller helpings, and a traditional Sunday lunch (£6.25); pleasant, willing service. The same menu – with the same prices – is used in the restaurant. Well kept John Smiths and Magnet on handpump, and over 50 wines. *(Recommended by Mrs J R Thomas, George Hunt, Kathryn Ogden, M V and J Melling, Roger Broadie, Simon Baker, Robert Kimberley, Ian and Penny Muir, Anthony Barnes)*

Free house   Licensees Patrick and Jenny Crawley   Real ale   Snacks (lunchtime, not Sun) and meals   Restaurant   Teesdale (0833) 50241   Children in eating area and restaurant   Open 11.30–2.30, 6.30–11   Bedrooms; £35B/£45B

CRASTER (Northumberland)   NU2620 Map 10

Jolly Fisherman   ★   £

Off B1339 NE of Alnwick

From the big picture window in the airy extension of this unpretentious place there are good sea views, and the atmospheric original bar (particularly the snug by the entrance) is popular with workers from the kippering shed opposite and the working harbour just below; it's close to a splendid clifftop walk – *Good Walks Guide* Walk 145 – to Dunstanburgh Castle. The pleasantly simple (and cheap) food includes burgers (90p), home-made pizzas (£1), and good local crab and salmon sandwiches (£1.25); obliging service. Well kept Wards Sheffield Bitter on handpump; darts, shove-ha'penny, dominoes, cribbage, juke box, fruit machine, trivia and space game. *(Recommended by T Nott, Mrs Pat Crabb, BKA, Michael Brookes, Wayne Brindle, Andrew Roberts, Frank Davidson, Hilary Bill, Helen and Roy Sumner, Mr and Mrs P R Lynch, Ann Marie Stephenson, Dr and Mrs Frank Rackow, David Oakes, Simon Baker, Linda Sewell, Derek Patey)*

Vaux   Lease: A George   Real ale   Snacks (available during opening hours)   (0665) 76461   Children welcome   Open 11–3, 6–11

DIPTONMILL (Northumberland)   NY9361 Map 10

Dipton Mill £

Off B6306 S of Hexham at Slaley, Blanchland and Dye House, Whitley Chapel signposts

Alone on a very quiet road by the tree-lined Dipton Burn, with easy-walking footpaths closeby, this small stone house has really come into the reckoning since the Brookers took it over a couple of years ago. Bar food is good, though limited to soup such as carrot and coriander or parsnip (£1.05), nicely presented sandwiches such as thick rare beef, or ploughman's, and salads, with a lunchtime hot dish such as home-made flan (£2.55), fish pie or chilli (£2.85), bacon chops in cider or beef and Guinness pie (£3.05) and puddings such as cheesecake or lemon meringue.

The homely and relaxed little bar has dark ply panelling, red furnishings and open fires; well kept Hadrian Gladiator, Theakstons Best, Yates Bitter and Premium and a guest beer on handpump (on our inspection visit, Butterknowle Festival Stout), quite a few malt whiskies, and tea, coffee or hot chocolate; notably friendly service; darts, bar billiards, shove ha'penny and dominoes. The garden, which may have barbecues on summer weekends, includes a sunken crazy-paved terrace by the restored mill stream, pretty plantings and aviaries with bantams and so forth. *(Recommended by Mrs Hazel Church, Mike and Wendy Proctor, John Oddey)*

Free house   Licensee Geoff Brooker   Real ale   Meals (lunchtime) and snacks   (0434) 606 577   Children in games room   Open 12–2.30, 6–11

DURHAM   NZ2743   Map 10
Shakespeare £

Sadler Street

Several small rooms link together in this cosy half-timbered pub – there's a busy, unpretentious main front bar, charming panelled snug, and further back room (popular with students). A good range of well kept real ales might typically include McEwans 80/-, Theakstons Best and XB and Youngers No 3, lots of malt whiskies, simple good value bar snacks such as good freshly made sandwiches and toasties (70p), and friendly efficient service. The pub is nicely placed on a pedestrians-only street between the old market square and the cathedral; you can hire boats on the river. *(Recommended by Gary Scott, Iain and Penny Muir, Barry and Anne, SJC, Ian and Sue Brocklebank)*

Scottish & Newcastle   Manager Mrs Karen Smurthwaite   Real ale   Snacks (not Sun)   Children welcome   Open 11–11; closed Sun 12–2

EGGLESTON (Durham)   NY9924   Map 10
Three Tuns ⊘

The friendly beamed bar of this peaceful stone-built country pub has old oak settles, one with amusingly horrific Gothick carving, as well as Windsor armchairs and the like, and a log fire. The Teesdale Room is used for bar meals – the best place to sit is by the big windows that look out past the terrace and garden to open fields and the Tees valley. A decent range of food includes home-made soup (£1.25), home-made steak and kidney pie (£3.95), fresh salmon steak (£4.95), mixed grill (£5.80), roast duck with orange sauce (£6.25) and puddings such as home-made Dutch apple pie (£1.60); snack meals served in the beer garden; Sunday lunch (booking essential); six decent house wines by the glass or carafe; attentive service; dominoes. There are some fine moorland roads – the B6282, B6278 and B6279 – closeby. *(Recommended by I H Rorison, M V and J Melling; more reports please)*

Free house   Licensee Peter Kirkman   Meals and snacks (not Sun evening)   Restaurant   Teesdale (0833) 50289   Children welcome, till 9pm   Open 11–3, 7–11

EGLINGHAM (Northumberland)   NU1019   Map 10
Tankerville Arms

B6346 NW of Alnwick

Lively and popular with locals, this long stonebuilt village pub has coal fires at each end, black joists, some walls stripped to bare stone and hung with brassware, and red plush banquettes and captains' chairs around cast-iron-framed tables on the Turkey carpet; there's a snug no-smoking area. Good, well presented bar food includes sandwiches, smoked fish or steak and kidney pies, tasty rabbit pie, gammon and peaches or fresh smoked trout and Aberdeen Angus steaks; good, friendly service. The restaurant has won recommendations in four publications. Tetleys and Stones on electric pump and decent wines chosen by a wine master; fruit machine, piped music and a no-smoking lounge. There are seats in the garden.

(Recommended by Geoff Wilson, Dr T H M Mackenzie; more reports please)

Free house　Licensee George Heydon　Real ales　Meals and snacks (11–2, 6–9.30)
Restaurant　Powburn (066 578) 444　Children welcome　Open 11–3, 6–11

GRETA BRIDGE (Durham)　NZ0813　Map 10

Morritt Arms ⇔

Hotel signposted off A66 W of Scotch Corner

The twin brothers who run this quiet hotel are keeping it impeccably clean and polished, with handsome flower arrangements everywhere. The Dickens Bar has sturdy green-plush-seated oak settles and big Windsor armchairs clustered around traditional cast-iron-framed tables, a lively, lifesize Pickwickian mural running right the way round the high-ceiling, and big windows that look out on the extensive lawn. The adjacent green bar has dark grey leatherette wall seats, a stag's head and a big case of stuffed black game; there's also a fine big model traction engine in one of the lounges. Well kept Butterknowle Conciliation on handpump; good open fires. A proper old shove-ha'penny board, with raisable brass rails to check the lie of the coins, and in the separate public bar, darts, dominoes and a juke box. Bar food includes soup (lunchtime, £1.50), sandwiches (evening), and ploughman's (£3.75), jumbo sausage with fried egg or home-made fish cake (£3.95), deep-fried kromeski with sweet and sour sauce (£4.25), home-cooked ham with two fried eggs (£5.50) and grilled rump steak (£10.85). In the nice garden are some picnic-table sets, teak tables in a pretty side area looking along to the graceful old bridge by the stately gates to Rokeby Park, and swings, slide and rope ladder at the far end. *(Recommended by Mrs R Heaton, I H Rorison, Kathryn Toledano, Simon Baker)*

Free house　Licensees David and John Mulley　Real ale　Meals and snacks (lunchtime; sandwiches and soup in evening)　Restaurant　(0833)27232　Children welcome, but 6-year-olds and under only till 7pm　Open 11–3, 6–11　Bedrooms; £45B/£68B

HAYDON BRIDGE (Northumberland)　NY8464　Map 10

General Havelock ⊘

A69 Corbridge–Haltwhistle

One of the most civilised pubs in the North of England, this village-terrace house has such a modest facade that it must escape the attention of all but the most knowledgeable, as they speed through on the trunk road. The attractively lit L-shaped bar is decorated in shades of green, and is at its best in the back part – stripped pine chest-of-drawers topped with bric-a-brac, colourful cushions on long pine benches and a sturdy stripped settle, interestingly shaped mahogany-topped tables, good wildlife photographs. The bar lunches are well above average: sandwiches (£1.35, open prawn sandwich £2.75), excellent soup (£1.45), savoury prawn dish (£2.30), ploughman's (£2.50), smoked cod done with cheese and mustard (£2.75), avocado with spiced prawns and mussels or a home-made terrine (£3.30), a fish dish such as fillet of plaice (£5.20), prawn salads, home-cooked meats with salad or roast sirloin with fresh vegetables (£5.75). Set evening meals, with a good choice of each of four courses, in a stripped-stone back dining room which overlooks the Tyne, are good value at £16, as are Sunday lunches (£9.75). Well kept Tetleys, decent wines, most agreeable service; they have no machines or background music but they do have darts. *(Recommended by M B P Carpenter, Dr R H M Stewart, Dr A U Callow)*

Free house　Licensees Ian and Angela Clyde　Real ale　Lunchtime bar meals and snacks　Restaurant (not Sun evening)　Hexham (0434) 684 283　Children welcome Open 11–2.30, 7–11; closed Mon and Tues, and 3 weeks in Jan, a week after Easter, first 2 weeks Sept

HEDLEY ON THE HILL (Northumberland) NZ0859 Map 10

Feathers

Village signposted from New Ridley, which is signposted from B6309 N of Consett; OS Sheet 88, map reference 078592

A proper rural atmosphere and a warmly individual welcome are what appeals most to readers here. The three well kept Turkey-carpeted bars have beams, woodburning stoves, stripped stonework, solid brown leatherette settles, and country pictures. Weekend lunchtime home-made bar food is good and might include sandwiches (£1), soup (£1.35), stilton baked potatoes (£1.95), fresh crab and mushroom ramekin (£2.95), home-cooked ham with soured cranberry sauce (£3.20), fresh salmon and spinach roulade (£3.35), smokies (£3.45) and various moussakas or casseroles (£3.50), with puddings (£1.25); at the moment they only do food at weekends but it is proving so popular that Marina Atkinson, who does all the cooking, is planning to extend both her range and times. Well kept Marstons Pedigree, Ruddles Best and a regular weekly guest beer on handpump, and around twenty-five malt whiskies; darts, shove-ha'penny, table skittles, dominoes and space game. *(Recommended by GB, Paddy Gascoigne, Beth Furniss, Simon Baker; more reports please)*

Free house   Licensees Marina and Colin Atkinson   Real ale   Snacks (Sat and Sun 12–3 and Sat 6–9, but see above)   (0661) 843 268   Children in eating area and family room   Open 6–11 weekdays; 12–3, 6–11 Sat

LONGFRAMLINGTON (Northumberland)   NU1301 Map 10

Granby 🕹 🛏

A697

Impressive helpings of well prepared enjoyable food served by smart, obliging and friendly staff is what draws people to this modernised 18th-century inn. From a wide range there might be soup (£1.35, not evenings), sandwiches (from £2.65, steak £3.10), moules marinières (£2.95), ploughman's (£3.90), home-made steak and kidney pie (£4.10), salads (from £5.40), grilled trout (£5.60), chicken kiev or grilled pork chop (£6.65), grilled prawns (£7.90), steak (from £8.25), duck with orange sauce (£8.35); puddings include apple pie and fresh cream or fresh cream sherry trifle (£1.55), freshly-made strawberry meringue with Jersey cream (£2.10) and hot black cherries with kirsch and fresh cream (£3.55); substantial breakfasts, with large kippers, for residents. The two rooms of the bar have red brocaded wall settles and stools around the white walls and in the bay windows, brown wooden tables, copper and whisky-water jars and ushers' lamps hanging from the black joists, a copper-covered little fireplace in one room, and faint piped music; they keep 27 malt whiskies. There are some picnic tables on the small front terrace. *(Recommended by D A Wilcock, Miss C M Davidson, Mr and Mrs J H Adam, Frank Davidson, RJH, R Johnstone)*

Bass   Tenant Anne Bright   Meals and snacks   Restaurant   (0665) 570 228 Children over 8 in lounge lunchtime only   Open 11–3, 6–11   Bedrooms; £24.75(£26.75B)/£49.50(£53.50B)

LONGHORSLEY (Northumberland)   NZ1597 Map 10

Linden Pub 🛏

Part of Linden Hall Hotel; down long drive (lots of sleeping policemen), and past the hotel itself

Set in the lovely grounds of the adjoining hotel (where there's a good outdoor games area), this airy and comfortable pub is a two-storey conversion of the stone granary. The red-carpeted bar has a remarkable collection of old enamel advertising signs, lots of light-coloured woodwork and bare stone, a log-effect gas fire in a large round central hearth and stairs to the partly no-smoking galleried upper part (not always open). The courtyard is to be revamped, new flagstones laid, and new wooden cask-type tables and seats added. With their lunchtime bar food, the licensees say they are trying to promote traditional northern dishes using fresh local produce, and the menu includes starters such as Northumbrian broth (£1.30), leek and potato pancake (£1.40), herring baked in Lindisfarne mead (£2.05), as well as Northumbrian rabbit casserole (£3.55), lamb's liver in onion sauce or Cumberland sausage in a hot-pot with fresh vegetables (£3.80), home-made steak and kidney pudding (£4.10), Kielder venison in a casserole with root vegetables (£4.95) and fresh river trout, coated in redcurrant and grilled in oatmeal (£5.95); they also offer filled baked potatoes (£1.45), sandwiches (from £1.60), salads (from £3.45), while vegetarian dishes are displayed on the blackboard and there's a selection of hot and cold puddings (from £1.50); helpful service. The ales, all on handpump, change regularly, at the time of going to press they had Theakstons Best, Old Peculier and Butterknowle Conciliation; darts, pool (both sensibly placed), dominoes, cribbage, fruit machine and piped music. Garden draughts are played out in the yard where barbecues are organised in good weather, and there is a play area by the pub. *(Recommended by Geoff Wilson, I H Rorison, Terry Glendenning, Mr and Mrs P Mackey, J H Tate)*

Free house   Licensees I M Moore and R W Tait   Real ale   Meals and snacks   Restaurant (jacket and tie)   Morpeth (0670) 516 611, Telex 538224   Children upstairs   Occasional live entertainment   Open 11–3, 6–11   Bedrooms; £89.50B/£110B

NEW YORK (Tyne & Wear)   NZ3370 Map 10

Shiremoor House Farm ★

Middle Engine Lane/Norham Road; from A1 going N from Tyne Tunnel, right into A1058 then next left signposted New York, then left at end of speed limit (pub signed); or at W end of New York A191 bypass turn S into Norham Road, then first right (pub signed)

Beautifully converted to preserve the origins of these former derelict farm steadings with warmly colourful farmhouse paintwork on the chunky bar counter and on some tables, conical rafters of the former gin-gan over the main bar's serving counter, gentle lighting picking up the surface modelling of the pale stone and beam ends, just a few farm tools, and good rustic pictures (mid-West prints, big crisp black-and-white photographs of country people, modern Greek bull sketches). It's well divided into separate areas, with a good variety of interesting and extremely comfortable furniture, and in one place a big kelim on the broad flagstones. The granary extension has now been opened, allowing children (high chairs, and bottle or baby food warmed on request). No music or games machines, so the atmosphere is very relaxed. Interesting bar food includes good soups (£1), starters such as garlic mushrooms (£1.80), main dishes such as steak and kidney pie (£3.75), various salads (£3.95), gammon and pineapple with ginger sauce (£4.50) and rump steak in a variety of sauces (£5.45); the lightly cooked vegetables keep their fresh taste, helpings are generous and the home-made puddings are tempting. Well kept McEwans 80/-, local Big Lamp Prince Bishops, Stones Best, Timothy Taylors Landlord and Theakstons Best and Old Peculier on handpump, decent wines by the glass, polite and efficient young staff. A separate bar serves the equally attractive rather smart restaurant. It's very popular, particularly at weekday lunchtimes. There are picnic-table sets on neat grass at the edge of the flagstoned farm courtyard, by tubs and a manger filled with flowers. *(Recommended by Michael and Rachel Brookes, John Coatsworth, Roger Bellingham, John Oddey, W H Bland, GB, Brian and Pam Cowling, GB)*

Free house   Licensees M W Garrett and C W Kerridge   Real ale   Meals and snacks (all day till 9.30pm)   Restaurant   (091) 257 6302   Children in separate family area Open 11–11

NEWCASTLE UPON TYNE (Tyne & Wear)   NZ2266 Map 10

Bridge Hotel £

Castle Square (in local A-Z street atlas index as Castle Garth); right in centre, just off Nicholas St (A6215) at start of High Level Bridge; only a few parking meters nearby, but evening parking easy

The atmosphere in this Grade II listed building is always lively – at lunchtime with business people and shoppers, and in the evening with the younger set (there's live music twice a week). The imposing, neatly kept Victorian lounge has high ceilings, a bar counter equipped with unusual pull-down slatted snob screens, decorative mirrors, brown leather banquettes and elegant small chairs on its rust carpet, and a massive mahogany carved fireplace. In the public bar, which has some cheerful stained glass, there's a good juke box, pool, dominoes, a trivia machine and fruit machine (with a second in the lounge lobby). Well kept McEwans 80/-, Theakstons Best and XB and a weekly guest beer on handpump; simple bar snacks include toasted sandwiches (70p) and stottie cakes with meat and salad (80p); friendly service. Some picnic-table sets on the flagstoned back terrace by the remains of the city wall look down over the Tyne and the bridges. The Thursday folk club here is one of the country's oldest. *(Recommended by Dave Braisted, Gareth and Kate Edwards, John Thorndike, Karen and Graham Oddey, Andy and Jill Kassube, Brian and Anna Marsden, Michael and Rachel Brookes, Simon Baker)*

Free house   Licensee Dave Shipley   Real ale   Snacks   (091) 2327780   Over 18s only   Blues club Tues, folk club Thurs   Open 11.30–3, 5.30 (6 Sat)–11; closed 25 Dec, 1 Jan

Cooperage £

32 The Close, Quayside; immediately below and just to the W of the High Level Bridge; parking across road limited lunchtime, easy evening

This wonky timbered Tudor house is one of Newcastle's oldest buildings. It's a popular place with locals and businessmen at lunchtime and students in the evening for its range of real ales. On handpump, these include regulars such as Ind Coope Burton (they are the second biggest seller of Burton ale in the country), Marstons Owd Rodger and Tetleys Bitter, as well as three guests from an extremely extensive list, like Ansells Mild, Benskins, Flowers Original, Friary Meux, Fullers ESB, Marstons Pedigree, or Timothy Taylors Landlord; also hand-pulled Addlestones and Coates farm cider. From a huge list of good value possibilities, they choose six items for their daily bar food menu: these might include soup (95p, seafood soup £1), fried whitebait with brown bread (£2.10), mushrooms and leeks in garlic butter with cauliflower cheese (£2.70), spicy meatballs with pasta shells (£2.95), black pudding, Northumbrian sausage, bacon and fried potatoes (£3), beef and beer pie or tandoori style chicken pieces (£3.35), prawns and seafood salad (£3.50) and beefsteak stroganoff and risotto (£4.50). The bustling bar has heavy Tudor oak beams and exposed stonework, and there's extra seating in the lounge area by the pool room; fruit and trivia machines and a juke box. *(Recommended by David and Rebecca Killick, E V Walder, Gareth and Kate Edwards, Dr T E Hothersall, Dave Whiteley, Andy and Jill Kassube, Brian and Anna Marsden, W H Bland, Simon Baker, Julian Holland)*

Free house   Licensee Michael Westwell   Real ale   Meals and snacks   Restaurant   Newcastle (091) 232 8286   Children in eating area of bar   Open 11–11; closed 25 Dec

Crown Posada

31 The Side; off Dean Street, between and below the two high central bridges (A6125 and A6127)

This is first and foremost a friendly, bustling city pub but it has a lot of architectural charm: a line of gilt mirrors each with a tulip lamp on a curly brass mount matching the great ceiling candelabra, Victorian flowered wallpaper above the brown dado (with its fat heating pipes along the bottom – a popular footrest when the east wind brings the rain off the North Sea), stained glass in the counter screens, and an elaborate coffered ceiling in cream and dusky pink. It's very long and narrow, making quite a bottleneck by the serving counter, and beyond that, a long soft green built-in leatherette wall seat is flanked by narrow tables. On weekday evenings you can find it quiet, with regulars reading the papers put out in the front snug. Well kept Hadrian Gladiator, Stones, Theakstons BB, and Timothy Taylors Landlord on handpump; lunchtime rolls and toasties (60p); friendly barmen, chatty customers; fruit machine. At night the pre-Raphaelite stained-glass windows catch the eye from across this steep street, and by day the golden crown adds grandeur to an already imposing carved stone facade. *(Recommended by John Thorndike, Gareth and Kate Edwards, Michael Brookes, Brian Marsden)*

Free house Manager Malcolm McPherson Real ale Snacks (lunchtime) 232 1269 Open 11–4, 5.30–11, Sat 12–4, 7–11

Tap & Spile

33 Shields Road, Byker; from central motorway (A6127(M)) take A193/A187 Wallsend road, then fork off left into Shields Road Shopping Centre

A wide and rapidly changing choice of interesting and well kept real ales from all over the country is served at attractive prices in this simply but comfortably furnished pub: Butterknowle Conciliation, Hadrian Gladiator and Camerons are the regulars with about nine others such as Badger Best, Bull Mastiff, Glenny Witney, Harviestoun Waverley, Mitchells ESB and Timothy Taylors Landlord, with Westons Old Rosie farm cider and country wines; if there's a distant beer you'd particularly like, they'll try to get it for you. The nicer room is at the back, and has a quiet, relaxed atmosphere, bare boards, big modern windows, stripped brickwork, sturdy built-in wall seats, stripped chairs, and even tractor seats around one corner table. There are lots of old brewery pictures, cases of taps and spiles, models of cask slings and so forth. The front bar has pool, darts and fruit machine. The bar food now only includes soup (80p) and sandwiches (75p-£1) and a hot dog machine (£1.30), but this might be extended to include ploughman's and baked potatoes. This is the model for other pubs in this growing small chain under the Camerons (now Brent Walker) umbrella. *(Recommended by Michael and Rachel Brookes, Gareth and Kate Edwards, John Thorndike, Julian Holland, W H Bland)*

Brent Walker Managers Kevin and Dina Watson Real ale Snacks (091) 276 1440 Open 11.30–3, 6–11; all day Fri, Sat

NEWTON ON THE MOOR (Northumberland) NU1605 Map 10

Cook & Barker Arms

Village signposted from A1 Alnwick–Felton

One reader felt the mixed grill he ate at this carefully refurbished pub was the best he'd had in years – and well worth his 30-mile trip. Other home-made lunchtime bar food (they don't serve evening bar meals, preferring to keep the place for drinkers only, then) includes sandwiches (from £1, popular open sandwiches like avocado and prawns and so forth from £4.05), while popular main dishes range from a warm salad of pigeon breast with a panache of five salad leaves (£3.95), to escalope of chicken with crayfish tail (£8.95). Well kept Theakstons Best and XB on handpump, and quite a few wines and whiskies; hardworking, friendly licensees. The long beamed bar has stripped, partly panelled walls, brocade-seated settles around oak-topped tables, paintings by local artists, brasses, a highly polished oak servery, and a coal fire at one end with a coal-effect gas fire at the other. What was the old storeroom now has tables, chairs and an old settle, and darts – it's popular with locals; there's also a games room with pool table, fruit machine, juke box and dominoes, and French windows from here lead to the terrace. The restaurant was a blacksmith's shop and dates in parts back to the 1700s. Please note they now do bedrooms. *(Recommended by Dave Whiteley, John Oddey, Ron and Marjorie Bishop; more reports please)*

Free house Licensees Lynn and Phil Farmer Real ale Lunchtime meals and snacks Evening restaurant Shilbottle (0665) 575 234 Children in eating area of bar and in pool room Open 11–3, 6–11 Bedrooms; £30B/£60B

PIERCEBRIDGE (Co Durham)   NZ2116 Map 10

George

B6275 over bridge just S of village

Attractively positioned on the alternative, scenic route between Scotch Corner and
Edinburgh, this busy inn has a fine garden that runs down to the River Tees.
Inside, the three bars have no less than five open fires in one room or another, solid
wood furniture, plates, pictures and old farming equipment on the walls, and
chesterfields in the lounge (which overlooks the river). Well worth a visit to the
Ballroom Bar – just that, a bar inside a fully-fitted ballroom (open only for special
functions or during barbecues). A wide choice of bar food includes breakfast, quite
a few starters like good soup, tuna and cucumber savoury or garlic mushrooms on
toast (all £1.55), vegetarian dishes such as stilton and mushroom tartlets, fruit,
vegetable and nut curry, or stroganoff (from £4.50), huge salads (all £4.50), quite a
few meaty dishes with wide selections of fish dishes (from £4.50), poultry (from
£4.95), and pork (from £5.50) with steaks (from £8.25); puddings such as
raspberry palmier pastry, lemon cheesecake and coffee sherry slice (all £1.55 and
served with whipped cream, grated chocolate and a wafer); good local vegetables,
and popular Sunday lunch; good, attentive service and piped music. John Smiths
and Websters Yorkshire on handpump, and decent wines; to save staff, they
actually close the bars in the afternoon, but continue to serve beers in the tea room.
They do weekend breaks (£170 per couple sharing a double room). This is said to
be where the clock *stopped short, never to go again, when the old man died.*
*(Recommended by J Barnwell, Murray Dykes, Robert Kimberley, Philip Harrison, Dr and Mrs
Frank Rackow, Simon Baker, John and Anne McIver, Dr R H M Stewart)*

*Free house Licensees Mr and Mrs Wain Real ale Meals and snacks (12–2, 6–9.30,
breakfasts and afternoon teas) Restaurant Piercebridge (0325) 374576 Children
welcome up to 8.30 but not in bars or main restaurant Open 11–11 Bedrooms;
£38B/48B*

ROMALDKIRK (Durham)   NY9922 Map 10

Rose & Crown ✪ ⌁

Just off B6277

This attractive and comfortable old coaching inn has undergone some redecoration
– the front hall has been refurbished, with a deep red carpet specially woven to
complement the woodwork and some of the bedrooms have also been redecorated.
The pub has a beamed, traditionally furnished bar with old-fashioned seats facing
the log fire, a Jacobean oak settle, cream walls decorated with lots of gin traps,
some old farm tools and black and white pictures of Romaldkirk at the turn of the
century, a grandfather clock, and lots of brass and copper. The Crown Room,
where bar food is served, has more brass and copper, original coloured etchings of
hunting scenes, and farm implements; the hall is hung with wine maps and other
interesting prints. They have introduced a new menu but continue to make their
own bread rolls for restaurant and bar; the sandwiches are served with coleslaw
and mushrooms marinaded in red wine (from £1.95), starters include home-made
soup (£1.50), home-made liver and brandy pâté (£2.95), and smoked Loch Fyne
salmon (£4.95), main dishes include ploughman's using local cheeses with
home-pickled onions and home-made tomato chutney (£3.50), fresh pasta tossed
in cream with peppers and mushrooms (£3.25), grilled Welsh rarebit made with
Theakston's ale (£3.50), locally smoked chicken with fresh herb sauce (£4.25),
gammon and pineapple (£4.95) and sirloin steak (£8.65), with puddings (all £1.95)
all home-made, except for the lemon cheesecake which is bought from a Cumbrian
farm with a Jersey pedigree herd; daily specials might include mussels with garlic
butter or baked with cream and Cotherstone chese (£2.95), sautéed Whitby woof
with prawns, brown butter and almonds (£5.50), strips of beef fillet with a brandy
and cream sauce (£7.50), and puddings such as hot sticky toffee pudding or
strawberry and almond tart; Sunday lunch (£9.75). Theakstons Best and Old
Peculier and Youngers No 3 on handpump; dominoes and occasional piped music.

The village is close to the Bowes Museum and the High Force waterfall.
(Recommended by Wayne Brindle, Alan and Ruth Woodhouse, M V and J Melling, Peter Barnsley, Simon Baker, J A Snell, Robert Kimberley, Andy and Jill Kassube, Mr and Mrs J F Stalley, K Leist)

Free house   Licensee Christopher and Alison Davy   Real ale   Meals and snacks Restaurant (not Sun evening)   Teesdale (0833) 50213   Children welcome   Open 11–3, 5.30–11; closed 25 and 26 Dec   Bedrooms; £45B/£63.50B

SEAHOUSES (Northumberland)   NU2232   Map 10

Olde Ship ★ ⊨

B1340 coast road

Throughout this busy but welcoming, harbourside inn the teak and mahogany woodwork, shiny brass fittings and small rooms make it feel almost more like a ship than a building – and many of the regulars are sailors. The floor of the saloon bar is scrubbed ship's decking, and the walls are packed with good sea pictures and ship's models, including a fine one of the North Sunderland lifeboat, finely polished brass and other ship's instruments and equipment given up by local sailors, and a knotted anchor made by local fishermen; the one clear window looks out over the harbour to the Farne Islands (the rest have stained-glass sea pictures). There is another low-beamed snug bar, and a family room at the back. An anemometer is connected to the top of the chimney. Popular bar food includes home-made soups such as vegetable (£1) or delicious crab (£1.50), filled rolls and sandwiches (beef stovies £3.50), ploughman's, and salads, with three or four lunchtime hot dishes, changing daily, like liver and onions, steak and kidney pie, fisherman's pie and fish stew (all £3.50); no chips, and various puddings (£1.25). The hotel dining room does a Sunday roast lunch (as well as good meals in the evening, when only sandwiches are served in the bar). Well kept Theakstons Best and XB on handpump, whiskies that include several malts, a hot toddy and mulled wine in winter, and some uncommon bottled beers. Open fire, dominoes, space game and trivia. Pews surround barrel tables in the back courtyard, and a battlemented side terrace with a sun lounge looks out on the harbour. You can book boat trips to the Farne Islands Bird Sanctuary at the harbour, and there are bracing coastal walks, particularly to Bamburgh, Grace Darling's birthplace.
(Recommended by T Nott, Gary Scott, Mike and Wendy Proctor, Janet Brown, Mrs Pat Crabb, Frank Davidson, Joy Heatherley, Lynn Sharpless, Bob Eardley, Klaus and Elizabeth Leist, Ken Armistead, John Atherton, BKA, Wayne Brindle, Tony and Lynne Stark, Andrew Morrissey, Robbie Pennington, E V Walder, Hilary Bill, Viv Middlebrook, Mr and Mrs P A Jones, Mrs E M Everard, W H Bland, Janet and Paul Waring, M and J Dixon, Mr and Mrs P R Lynch, Helen and Roy Sumner, Sidney and Erna Wells, Andrew and Michele Wells)

Free house   Licensee Alan C Glen   Real ale   Meals (lunchtime) and snacks (sandwiches only, evening)   Restaurant   (0665) 720 200   Children in small patio lounge until 8.30pm   Open 11–3, 6–11   Bedrooms; £28B/£56B

SEATON SLUICE (Northumberland)   NZ3477   Map 10

Waterford Arms ⊘

Just off A193 N of Whitley Bay

By midday, this comfortably modernised pub is packed with people who have come to enjoy the vast helpings of excellent local fish from the harbour just down the road. They are priced according to size – small, medium or large – and include lemon sole, cod or haddock (£4.25–£9.50); other food includes home-made soup (£1.35), sandwiches (from £1.40), sausage, mash and gravy (£3.65), leek pudding with mince or ploughman's (£4.53), home-made steak and kidney pie (£4.65), a generous seafood platter (£9.25), steaks (from £9.35), and puddings like home-made treacle or jam sponge (£1.65); for those in a hurry, it may be best to check how long the wait is likely to be; large breakfasts, with home-made jams, for residents. The bar has spacious green plush banquettes in its roomy bays, and bright paintings in one high-ceilinged room, and brown plush furnishings and a big children's rocking machine in another; cribbage, dominoes, a fruit machine and piped music, and one no smoking area. Well kept Vaux Samson and Lorimers on handpump; pool in the back lobby. *(Recommended by Dave Whiteley, E V Walder, Michael and Rachel Brookes, Mr and Mrs M O Jones, Iain and Penny Muir, R Johnstone, Barbara and Norman Wells, Richard Dolphin)*

Vaux   Tenant Mrs Patrica Charlton   Real ale   Meals and snacks   Children welcome   Tyneside (091) 237 0450   Open 11–3(3.30 Sat), 6.30–11   Bedrooms; £22.50S/£45S

TYNEMOUTH (Tyne & Wear)   NZ3468 Map 10

Tynemouth Lodge £

Tynemouth Road (A193); 1/2 mile W of Tynemouth Metro station

This clean and warmly friendly little pub has a good range of very well kept real ales on handpump: Bass, Belhaven 80/-, Ruddles County and Theakstons Best; Merrydown and Thatcher's ciders. They do good toasted sandwiches (85p, fresh seafood sandwiches from £1.20); free bar nibbles on Sunday lunchtimes. The bar has copper-topped cast-iron tables, and button-back green leatherette seats built against the walls (which have stylish bird-of-paradise wallpaper); there's a winter coal fire in the neat Victorian tiled fireplace; tables beyond the car park. The licensee also owns the Wolsington House in North Shields. *(Recommended by Brian and Anna Marsden; more reports please)*

Free house   Licensee Hugh Price   Real ale   Lunchtime snacks (11–3.30; not Sun) (091) 258 5758   Open 11–11 all year

Wooden Doll

103 Hudson Street; from Tyne Tunnel, follow A187 into town centre; keep straight ahead (when the A187 turns off left) until, approaching the sea, you can see the pub in Hudson Street on your right

On the walls of the three simply but comfortably furnished bars of this unassuming pub are photographs and paintings by local artists for sale; also, a couple of chesterfields, red plush seats and Formica-topped cast-iron tables, and a flame-effect gas fire. A good range of well kept real ales on handpump or tapped from the cask includes Arkells 80/-, Aylesbury, Falstaff Scotch, Ind Coope Burton, Tetleys, Timothy Taylors landlord, Theakstons Best and Old Peculier, Wards Sheffield Bitter, and Youngers No 3; happy hour 5.30–7pm. Home-made bar food includes filled baps, winter soup, vegetable lasagne or chilli con carne (£3), lasagne or chicken gratin (around £3.25), beef or lamb casseroles (£3.60), cod and prawn bake or cod mornay (£4), prawn or fresh salmon salad (£4.25), their special seafood platter (£5.25) and puddings like cherry pie or cheesecake. Dominoes, fruit machine, trivia, and piped music. From the covered glassed-in verandah there are fine views over the bustling boats and warehouses of the Shields Fish Quay immediately below, harbour derricks and gantries beyond, and then the sweep of the outer harbour with its long piers, headlands, and low Black Middens rocks. *(Recommended by Michael Brookes, David and Rebecca Killick, Linda Sewell, Brian and Anna Marsden, Dr T H M Mackenzie, Mr and Mrs Allan Chapman, Simon Baker)*

Free house   Licensee Mrs R A Holliday   Real ale   Meals and snacks (12–2, 6–9, Sat 8.30, not Sun eves)   (091) 257 3747   Children in eating area until 6.30   Live entertainment Weds, Thurs, Sat, Sun evening, classical quartet Sun evening   Open 11–11, winter 11–3, 5.30–11

WARENFORD (Northumberland)   NU1429 Map 10

Warenford Lodge 🍴

Just off A1 Alnwick–Belford, on village loop road

The uncommonly good and attractively presented home-made bar food here changes with the seasons, but might typically include starters such as home-made soup or chilled mango nectar with a hint of lime (£1.50), prawn fritters with oriental sauce, chicken liver pâté or cheese and asparagus savoury (£2.75), while main courses might include spaghetti bolognese or Goan-style vindaloo eggs with mango chutney (£3.75), deep-fried lambs' kidneys with fresh tomato sauce or spinach and pasta casserole (£4.20), home-cooked ham with pease pudding, smoked haddock vol-au-vent or Andalucian hot-pot (£4.50), a stew of venison and pork in red wine (£5.70), Northumbrian fish soup (£5.95), fresh salmon cutlet (£6.20), tiger prawn salad (£7.10) and sirloin steak (£10.50); puddings such as chocolate ice cream truffle, coffee and walnut gateau or blackcurrant and mint pie (all £2); decent selection of wines. Though it's quite old, the bar looks modern with cushioned wooden seats, a big stone fireplace, and some stripped stone walls; steps lead up to an extension which has comfortable easy chairs and settees around low tables, and a big woodburning stove. *(Recommended by T Nott, A J Powell; more reports please)*

Free house   Licensee Raymond Matthewman   Meals and snacks (not Mon, not Tues lunchtime Oct-Easter)   Evening restaurant   Belford (0668) 213 453   Children in restaurant   Open 12–2, 7–11; closed all day Mon and Tues lunchtime Oct-Easter

WEST WOODBURN (Northumberland)   NY8987 Map 8

Bay Horse

A68

Pretty, warm and welcoming, this 18th-century coaching inn has been pleasantly furnished and decorated by the present licensees. The bar is now open-plan with dark-stained wood, red plush banquettes, wheelbacks and tall bar stools, a new carpet, small pictures and black-and-white photographs on the cream walls, and a big horse collar over the good wood fire; nice chocolate-coloured labrador. Decent bar food includes starters such as home-made soup (80p), mushrooms with cream and garlic or deep-fried brie (£1.50), and main dishes such as burgers (from £2), stotties (£2.25), various home-made pizzas (£3.50, vegetarian pizzas £3.25), ploughman's (£3.75), lasagne or home-made steak and onion pie (£4.50), chicken kiev (£4.75), roast rack of lamb with hot honey dressing or grilled halibut with a creamy sauce (£5.50), vegetarian dishes (from £2) such as nut and pepper loaf or tagliatelle and puddings such as hot apple pie with custard (from £1.20); they do a children's menu (£1.50) or smaller helpings; Sunday roast lunch. There is just the one menu – you choose between bar and dining room. They now do Theakstons XB and boast a new pool room; darts, shove-ha'penny, fruit machine, space game and piped music. The neat garden, where there is a grassed children's play area and a large Roman marker stone, runs down under tall trees to the sizeable River Rede (good trout and salmon fishing). The modernised bedrooms are spick-and-span. They may be able to arrange riding for residents. *(Recommended by John Whitehead, Dr John Lawson, Stephanie Sowerby)*

Free house   Licensees John and Irenee Cowans   Real ale   Meals and snacks (open for morning coffee or tea before and during bar opening time)   Bellingham (0434) 270 218   Children welcome   Singer on Sat evenings, quiz Sun with prizes   Open 11–2.30, 6–11; Jan, Feb 11–2, 7–11   Bedrooms; £18/£32

Lucky Dip

Besides the fully inspected pubs, you might like to try these Lucky Dips recommended to us and described by readers (if you do, please send us reports):

☆ **Acomb**, Northumberland [NY9366], *Miners Arms*: Small, friendly old pub, charming character, huge open fire, welcoming licensee and locals; delicious food cooked to order, though following the local demand for chips (real ones) with everything; well kept real ales inc occasional festivals; children in dining room *(John Oddey)*
Allendale, Northumberland [NY8456], *Golden Lion*: Basic decor, well kept

changing real ales, and good food at low prices; same menu in bar or restaurant; children welcome *(Mel Landells)*
Alnmouth, Northumberland [Northumberland St; NU2511], *Red Lion*: Well kept McEwans 80/- and Theakstons Best, popular though not crowded, with an easy-going feel; some friendly regulars *(BKA)*
☆ **Alnwick**, Northumberland [Fenkle St; NU1913], *Market Tavern*: Not to

everyone's taste structurally, but a real local favourite, as the three bars (selling various well kept beers) lead on to a large, plain dining area where good food is served at ridiculously low prices (inc Sun lunch); play tree area at back *(P J and S E Robbins, Klaus and Elizabeth Leist)*

Alnwick [20 Bondgate Without], *Plough*: Well kept Vaux Samson, friendly locals and staff; good food from tandoori chicken to several Italian meals, with terrific veg — good value *(Stephen Williams)*; [Market St], *Queens Head*: Unpretentious, but roomy and dignified, with well kept Ind Coope Burton and very friendly helpful staff; bar food; bedrooms good value *(Neil and Angela Huxter, Paul McPherson)*

Anick, Northumberland [NY9665], *Rat*: Extensively refurbished by new owners, excellently kept real ales inc Ruddles, bar food inc interesting daily specials from hot counter; most attractively set out, but piped music *(John Oddey)*

☆ **Bamburgh**, Northumberland [NU1835], *Lord Crewe Arms*: Relaxing and comfortable old inn, beautifully placed in charming coastal village below magnificent Norman castle; back cocktail bar, with entertaining bric-a-brac and log fire, is the one to go for; generously served straightforward food in bar and grill room, good service, children in side bar; bedrooms comfortable, good breakfasts and dinners — it's a nice place to stay; dogs allowed *(Mrs S Major, Lynn Sharpless, Bob Eardley, Eric Dickinson, LYM)*

☆ **Barnard Castle**, Durham [Market Pl; NZ0617], *Golden Lion*: Warm and comfortable old pub with two sizeable bars, big helpings of good value, pleasantly served lunchtime food inc cheap but generous children's helpings and good filling home-made soup; friendly service even when busy, keg beers, children's room *(P J and S E Robbins, RAF)*

Barnard Castle, Durham [Harmire Rd; NZ0617], *Redwell*: Friendly staff, very pleasant big room, John Smiths Choice and Theakstons XB, and food such as local mushrooms in mustard sauce and good steak and kidney pie *(A J J Moulan)*

Beadnell, Northumberland [NU2329], *Craster Arms*: Lively atmosphere in lounge bar; also, pool room, keg beer, garden and good parking *(Graham Bush)*

☆ **Beamish**, Durham [far side of Beamish Open Air Museum — paid entry; NZ2254], *Sun*: The museum of which this is a part is great fun — covering a large area and served by its own steam railway and other antique transport, it recreates various periods of the area's past, mainly in Edwardian times; the pub itself, rescued from Bishop Auckland and rebuilt here, is a basic period piece, like the shops and offices in its cobbled street; well kept McEwans 80/- and Youngers No 3 on handpump, black pudding nibbles and filled barm cakes, and its two rooms have a real turn-of-the-century feel; it does get packed *(Andy and Jill Kassube, Gary Scott,*

Derek Patey, John Atherton, Margaret and Roy Randle, LYM)

☆ **Belford**, Northumberland [Market Pl; village signed off A1 S of Berwick; NU1134], *Blue Bell*: Comfortable, stylish and relaxing lounge; plentiful bar food inc children's dishes and cut-price OAPs' helpings, mainly in family bar in former stables, with harness, saddlery and so forth, Theakstons Best on handpump, darts, pool and piped music; pleasantly old-fashioned dining room overlooking attractive garden, which produces some of the vegetables and fruit they use — there may be a surcharge if you have bar food served out here; polite and friendly service; children in eating areas; comfortably refurbished bedrooms *(Helen and Roy Sumner, W T Aird, LYM)*

Belford [31 High St], *Salmon*: Recently refitted, light and airy with very decorative brocaded seat covers and embellishments, pleasant understated decor, relaxed and friendly atmosphere, Vaux ales, limited food; fine array of window boxes *(T Nott, LYM)*

Bellingham, Northumberland [NY8483], *Cheviot*: Lovely stone-built village; pub in centre, slightly raised from road; tables in front with view down street; stone frontage, two small bars cosy (if unmemorable); Whitbreads-related beers on handpump; bedrooms *(Graham Bush)*

Belsay, Northumberland [NZ1079], *Highlander*: Doing well under new manager, with good range of food in bar and restaurant, reasonable prices, cheerful welcome, well kept Youngers No 3 on handpump, blazing fire on cold days, and all spick and span *(John Oddey, Ann Marie Stephenson)*

☆ **Berwick upon Tweed**, Northumberland [West Allerdean; 5 miles S — B6354 towards Wooler — OS Sheet 75, map reference 965465; NT9646], *Plough*: Remote but comfortable and friendly country local by farm, chapel and sheep fields, with woodburning stove in understated traditional lounge up step from bar attractively decorated with farm tools, guns, jugs, brassware and so forth; pine-furnished dining room with reasonably priced but good standard food and small window giving magnificent views over to Cheviots; back bar with pool table, burmese cats, pleasant garden with splendid views and play area; Allied beers, very cheerful obliging service *(T Nott, Ian and Shirley Foster)*

☆ **Berwick upon Tweed** [Tweed St, nr rly stn], *Tweed View*: Former convent, with good bar food in lounge overlooking grand Tweed bridges — views from terrace too; bedrooms *(P J and S E Robbins)*

☆ **Berwick upon Tweed** [A1 N of town], *Meadow House*: Friendly atmosphere and good service in newly decorated and furnished big lounge bar with dark orange plush banquettes and wheelback chairs, very neat and clean; straightforward but good value bar food, well kept Vaux Lorimers

Best Scotch on handpump, tables outside
(Joy Heatherley)

Berwick upon Tweed [B6461 towards
Paxton — OS Sheet 75, map reference
959526], *Cantys Brig*: Good reasonably
priced food in upstairs dining room
overlooking Whiteadder River, tables out on
lawn running down to it; rather modern, but
nice *(Paul S McPherson)*; [Promenade, The
Spittal], *Galleon*: Small pub nr caravan site
with wide range of good value food,
pleasant service and good coffee; live music
Sat evening *(Mr and Mrs Taylor, Mr and Mrs
Morgan)*; [Spittal Rd, Tweedmouth], *Rob
Roy*: Quiet and pleasant, with well kept
cellar and good bar lunches and evening
meals — particularly good fresh seafood
straight off the boats docked opp *(Ian Scott
Watson)*

☆ **Billy Row**, Durham [Old White Lea, off
A689; NZ1638], *Dun Cow*: Cosy
old-fashioned front room with warming
range, comfortable wall settles, photographs
of long-gone and more recent local football
teams; bar in back room serving well kept
Camerons and Vaux Double Maxim,
friendly pub dog *(Ian and Sue Brocklebank)*

Bishop Auckland, Durham [Etherley Lane;
NZ2130], *Pollards*: Very popular, good
value bar food lunchtime and evening *(B
Wade)*

Boldon, Tyne & Wear [Front St (A184); E
Boldon; NZ3661], *Black Bull*: Open-plan
lounge bar with good-sized tables, pleasant
staff, well kept Vaux Samson, good whiskies
and decent lunchtime bar food; garden with
children's play area; shame about the music
(John Oddey)

☆ **Bowes**, Durham [NY9914], *Ancient
Unicorn*: Welcoming open-plan modernised
bar, good honest bar food, comfortable
bedrooms in well converted stables block, in
coaching inn with Nicholas Nickleby
connection; bedrooms comfortable *(Mr and
Mrs L G Smith, LYM)*

☆ **Byrness**, Northumberland [A68
Otterburn—Jedburgh; NT7602], *Byrness
Inn*: Particularly useful for the Pennine Way,
with big open fire in small rather dark but
cheerful bar, limited choice of nicely
prepared food, friendly cat; bedrooms *(John
Oddey)*

Causey Park Bridge, Northumberland [off
A1 5 miles N of Morpeth; NZ1894], *Oak*:
Good very reasonably priced bar food inc
outstanding steaks; small country pub with
well kept McEwans 80/- and Theakstons on
handpump; garden with ducks *(J F
Thompson)*

Chester le Street, Durham [Gt North Rd;
NZ2752], *Lambton Worm*: Affordable and
enjoyable, with reasonably priced good bar
meals and low-cost bedrooms *(Ian Robinson)*

Chollerford, Northumberland [NY9372],
George: Hotel in beautiful setting nr
Hadrian's Wall, with immaculate gardens
running down to Upper Tyne, and lovely
swimming pool; included here as its
Fisherman's Bar in what was the separate
original smaller stone inn has simple food,

Vaux Samson on handpump, pool, darts etc
(closed winter mornings), and there isn't
much competition locally; children
welcome; bedrooms comfortable *(Mr and
Mrs J H Adam, LYM)*

☆ **Coatham Mundeville**, Durham [part of
Hallgarth Hotel; from A1(M) turn towards
Brafferton off A167 Darlington rd on hill;
NZ2920], *Stables*: Converted from stone
outbuildings with high ceilings, lots of
seating, separate no smoking eating area
behind, good choice of well prepared bar
food and Sun lunches, well kept McEwans
80/- and Theakstons Best, Old Peculier and
XB; side conservatory for families;
bedrooms *(R J Walden)*

Coatham Mundeville [Brafferton Lane; off
A68, 1/4 mile from A1(M)], *Foresters Arms*:
Well kept John Smiths Magnet on
handpump, old-fashioned atmosphere, open
fire in bar and lounge, very friendly to
strangers; lunchtime bar food *(Tony Rae)*

Corbridge, Northumberland [Bridge End; S
of bridge — OS Sheet 87, map reference
998640; NY9964], *Lion of Corbridge*:
Friendly old creeper-covered building with
bar food served till quite late evening in
comfortable lounge bar; well worth
knowing for the newer hotel part behind,
with quiet and comfortable well equipped
bedrooms — good breakfasts, too *(BB)*

☆ **Cramlington**, Northumberland [NZ2777],
Plough: Large open-plan pub converted
from farm buildings, with original stone,
woodwork and impressive beams; wide
choice of real ales such as McEwans 80/- or
Youngers No 3, Marstons Pedigree and
Stones, good value bar food inc fine
freshly-made pizzas with thin bases and
thick toppings, friendly, helpful staff
(Graham and Karen Oddey)

Crook, Durham [off A68, W of Crook;
NZ1236], *Helm Park Hall*: Good bar food
and pleasant atmosphere, in lovely
surroundings; good views; bedrooms *(J H
Tate)*

☆ **Dunstan**, Northumberland [NU2520],
Cottage: Attractive layout, well stocked bar,
pleasant dining room and terrace, good
imaginative bar food with some
concentration on seafood, decent wines *(B
Isserlin)*

Durham [N of Nevilles Cross on A167],
Duke of Wellington: Wide choice of good
value bar food, big helpings, inc at least a
dozen vegetarian dishes; popular with
students, much refurbished refurbishment
has taken away its character; bedrooms
(Andy and Jill Kassube, John Watson); [Old
Elvet], *Dun Cow*: Cosy traditional
cottage-pub, popular esp lunchtime when
cheap pie and peas in demand; well kept
Whitbreads beers on handpump; lounge can
get crowded, esp evening; children welcome
*(Andy and Jill Kassube, Iain and Penny Muir,
LYM)*; [2 Sherburn Rd], *Queens Head*:
Friendly pub with Camerons and good
Marstons Pedigree, with comfortable
bedrooms and good breakfasts (but no
evening meals); staff and locals very friendly

(Steve Merson)

Eastgate, Durham [signposted from A689 W of Stanhope; NY9638], *Horsley Hall*: Old manor-house type with splendid views and period restaurant, also comfortable modern bar; has been praised for huge helpings of good value food but no recent reports *(News please)*

☆ **Egglescliffe**, Cleveland [NZ4214], *Pot & Glass*: Consistently warm and friendly welcome and excellently kept Bass, three cosy rooms with some slabby tree-trunk tabletops, stools and settles around panelled walls; lovely setting behind church, friendly helpful staff, good value food and well kept Bass; no music *(Ian and Sue Brocklebank, Dr M A Thomas, Richard Burt)*

☆ **Egglescliffe** [663 Yarm Rd (A67)], *Blue Bell*: Simple lunchtime bar food (not Sun) inc good sandwiches in spacious big-windowed bar, seats on terrace by goat-cropped grass sloping down to the River Tees with fine view of the great 1849 railway viaduct — it's the position that's the particular attraction; friendly service, restaurant; children welcome *(LYM)*

Ellingham, Northumberland [signed off A1 N of Alnwick — OS Sheet 75, map reference 167257; NU1726], *Pack Horse*: A lot of recent work on the external structure, but behind it is a pleasantly unspoilt smallish village pub with some character, lots of whisky-water jugs in front bar, standard food in small dining room, McEwans ales, pool table in back bar *(T Nott)*

Ellington, Northumberland [Main St (Cresswell Rd); off A1068 N of Ashington; NZ2892], *Plough*: Large old solid pub with front bar, and through a partition is a large, comfortable lounge and dining room; Vaux beers and wide choice of efficiently served straightforward food *(M and J Back)*

☆ **Elwick**, Northumberland [off A1/A19 just N of Belford; NU1237], *Spotted Cow*: Pleasantly placed on village green, old but refurbished pub with red plush lounge and separate dining room; wide choice of good value bar food from sandwiches or burgers to breaded plaice stuffed with crabmeat, Camerons Strongarm and Everards Old Original *(Dr Keith Bloomfield, W H Bland)*

Embleton, Northumberland [NU2323], *Dunstanburgh Castle*: Good dining room meals — game, fresh fish and so forth — in comfortable hotel attractively placed nr magnificent coastline; bedrooms *(Trudy and Malcolm Baker)*

☆ **Etal**, Northumberland [off B6354 SW of Berwick; NT9339], *Black Bull*: Pretty thatched pub in village by ruins of Etal Castle, good value straightforward food in modernised lounge (children allowed) well kept Lorimers Scotch and Wards Sheffield Best; helpful service, nice walks *(P J and S E Robbins, John Atherton, Mr and Mrs M O Jones, Wayne Brindle, Andy and Jill Kassube, Martin and Carol Fincham, LYM)*

☆ **Fir Tree**, Durham [A68 West Auckland—Tow Law; NZ1434], *Duke of York*: Plain but comfortable dining lounge

with decent solid furnishings, racing prints, delft shelf; wide choice of reasonably priced good bar food, Greenalls Original on handpump; cosy wing-chair bar on left leading into dining room; cheerful uniformed waitresses, children welcome, seats on grass between car park and paddock *(V R Flint, A J Powell, Mr and Mrs K Charlton, BB)*

☆ **Framwellgate Moor**, Durham [Front St; NZ2745], *Tap & Spile*: Refurbished pub run largely as free house, and like others under the same name most popular for its quickly changing choice of eight well kept real ales; simply but comfortably decorated series of four main rooms, one used for pool and fruit machines, another for board games; friendly atmosphere *(Maureen and Steve Collin, Iain and Penny Muir)*

Gateshead, Tyne & Wear [Eighton Banks; quite handy for A1(M); NZ2758], *Ship*: Very popular and comfortable open-plan pub with bar food (not Sun lunchtime — nibbles instead), great views, well kept Vaux Samson on handpump, good garden for children *(Michael and Rachel Brookes)*

Gosforth, Tyne & Wear [S Gosforth; NZ2568], *Millstone*: Promptly served good food from toasties to main dishes, well kept Bass *(Dave Whiteley)*

Grange Villa, Durham [NZ2352], *Highwayman*: Spacious, comfortable pub where families welcome; good value food inc cheap Sun lunch; efficient, friendly service *(Keith and Aubrey Day)*

Great Stainton, Durham [NZ3422], *Kings Head*: Has been popular for good value food and well kept Whitbreads Castle Eden in comfortable, friendly surroundings, but no recent reports *(News please)*

Great Whittington, Northumberland [NZ0171], *Queens Head*: Atractive clubby village local with warm welcome, well kept real ales and friendly natives; limited range of reasonably priced bar food, nicely cooked and presented *(John Oddey)*

☆ nr **Haltwhistle**, Northumberland [Military Rd; B6318 — OS Sheet 86, map reference 715660; NY7164], *Milecastle*: Interesting and generously served good value food inc superb pies such as turkey, ham and chestnut, in comfortably refurbished pub, lots of brasses in cosy, warm bar with good coal fire; welcoming service, Theakstons and Ruddles on handpump, local leaflets on mantlepiece; restaurant — best to book, very busy lunchtime *(Russell Hafter, A J and E M Watts, Mrs Wendy Loncaster, Graham Kirby, John Oddey)*

nr **Haltwhistle** [B6318 NE — OS Sheet 86, map reference 751668], *Twice Brewed*: Reopened after clean — almost clinical — refurbishment; Theakstons on handpump, good bar food, handy for walkers and the Wall *(John Oddey)*

☆ **Hexham**, Northumberland [Priestpopple; E end of main st, on left entering from Newcastle; NY9464], *County*: Reliably good straightforward bar lunches, friendly and considerate service *(Dr R H M Stewart,*

Mrs P Brown)

Hexham, Northumberland [Battle Hill; NY9464], *Tap & Spile*: Similar to others of the name — six well kept real ales inc comfortable and friendly ungimmicky surroundings *(W H Bland)*

High Coniscliffe, Durham [A67, W of A1; NZ2315], *Spotted Dog*: Popular Whitbreads house, good bar lunches and evening meals *(E Robinson)*

☆ **High Force**, Durham [B6277 about 4 miles NW of Middleton-in-Teesdale; NY8728], *High Force*: Handy for the moors (and England's highest waterfall, for which it's named), robustly basic masculine furnishings (it includes a mountain rescue post) and food from sandwiches to steaks (not winter Mon evenings); good range of malt whiskies, cheerful bar, friendly service; children allowed, though restricted evenings; bedrooms comfortable and clean *(I H Rorison, Helen and Roy Sumner, T N Brooke)*

☆ **Holy Island**, Northumberland [NU1343], *Northumberland Arms*: Carefully refurbished under current management, with pews around walls of spacious bar, comfortable tables and chairs, stripped floorboards, enormous log fire, welcoming licensees and staff; well kept Theakstons and McEwans on handpump, Youngers Scotch tapped from the cask, varied food with interesting starters inc whitebait and big helpings of main dishes such as trout, seafood platter, salads, steaks; pool room, dogs allowed; five reasonably priced bedrooms *(Francesca Lopez, Julian Holland, Mr and Mrs J H Adam, Janet Brown)*

Holy Island, *Lindisfarne*: Friendly very simple bar and restaurant, handy for good food even Sun evening; good service; bedrooms *(A D E Lewis, Janet Brown)*

Holystone, Northumberland [NT9503], *Salmon*: Comfortably furnished Coquet Valley local, good value simple food and lively pool room; in attractive countryside close to venerable Lady's Well *(Paul S McPherson, LYM)*

☆ **Horsley**, Northumberland [this is the one just off A69 Newcastle—Hexham; NZ0966], *Lion & Lamb*: Comfortable stone dining pub with open fire, well kept Whitbreads Castle Eden, decent wine and pleasant young staff; concentration now on the restaurant side, inc good Sun lunches, but bar snacks too *(Michael Brookes)*

Longbenton, Tyne & Wear [Front St; A191 towards Whitley Bay; NZ2769], *Ship*: Well run local with well kept McEwans 80/- and Theakstons Best on handpump, very friendly staff, front bar, sitting room with bell service (you ring for your pint); pub games *(Gareth and Kate Edwards, Michael Brookes)*

Longframlington, Northumberland [Wheldon Bridge; NU1301], *Anglers Arms*: Has been popular for imaginative lunchtime food inc fresh local fish, well kept Wards Sheffield Best, good service, but no recent reports *(News please)*

Longhorsley, Northumberland [A697 N of Morpeth; NZ1597], *Shoulder of Mutton*:

Big central bar with dining part at one end, friendly waitresses, and generous helpings of sandwiches and bar food *(Bob and Ann Westbrook)*

Lowick, Northumberland [OS Sheet 75, map reference 013396; NU0239], *Black Bull*: Better than average choice of food in dining room inc vegetarian dishes, pleasant village pub atmosphere, well kept McEwans on handpump, nice back snug *(T Nott, Mr and Mrs M O Jones)*

Maiden Law, Durham [A6067 N of Lanchester; NZ1749], *Three Horseshoes*: Nice looking pub with central bar, plush decor, dining areas on each side, and back lounge; Lorimers Best Scotch and Vaux Sampson, good value traditional pub food; piped music may be loud *(M and J Back)*

☆ **Marsden**, Tyne & Wear [signposted passage to lift in A183 car park, just before entering Marsden coming from Whitburn; NZ4164], *Grotto*: Notable for its unique and atmospheric position, partly built into cliff caverns: you take a lift down to the two floors — upper pink plush, lower brown varnish; Vaux Samson real ales, food in bar and restaurant; Gibberin' John the ghost is said to call the lift sometimes — pressing the button when no one's there *(Anon)*

☆ **Matfen**, Northumberland [NZ0372], *Black Bull*: A striking stone building by the green of an interesting out-of-the-way estate village; local eating-out atmosphere in extended Turkey-carpeted bar with Windsor chairs, plush banquettes and stools, copper-topped tables; efficient service, nicely presented good food — seafood pie, game pie, chicken with honey and almonds, day's specials and puddings all recommended; nice 1940s *Picture Post* photographs, well kept Theakstons Best and Youngers No 3 on handpump, efficient service, picnic-table sets outside; can be rather smoky, but with a little more atmosphere and character could easily be a main entry and is well worth knowing *(John Whitehead, Dr A U Callow, Mr and Mrs P G Endacott, John Oddey, BB)*

☆ **Middleton in Teesdale**, Durham [Market Pl; NY9526], *Teesdale*: Excellently kept John Smiths and Tetleys in beautifully warm and welcoming inn, well polished and brushed, with flowers, log fire and interesting and particularly well prepared reasonably priced bar food inc good sandwiches and an outstanding savoury cottage pie; very busy in summer; bedrooms well equipped and comfortable; bedrooms *(SS)*

Middleton St George, Cleveland [A67 Darlington—Yarm; NZ3412], *Fighting Cocks*: Newly refurbished, very welcoming, with marvellous quite unusual cooking by landlord's wife; good beer *(C A Holloway)*

☆ **Moorsholm**, Cleveland [A171 nearly a mile E of Moorsholm village turnoff; NZ6914], *Jolly Sailor*: Cosy little booths in long beams-and-stripped-stone bar with generous helpings of home-made bar food, good juke box, tables and play area looking out to the surrounding moors, restaurant; closed Mon lunchtime (except bank hols) and winter

weekday lunchtimes; children welcome
(LYM)

Morpeth, Northumberland [Wansbeck St;
NZ2086], *Joiners Arms*: Still proudly
old-fashioned and unspoilt despite some
recent renovation — still has a lamp post
holding up the ceiling, and stuffed birds
above the bar; little food but well kept Bass,
Timothy Taylors Landlord, Theakstons and
two guests on handpump; no juke box
(Terry Glendenning)

☆ **Newcastle upon Tyne** [High Bridge], *Duke
of Wellington*: Real ales inc Marstons
Pedigree, Tetleys and Timothy Taylors, and
good range of reasonably priced bar food, in
attractive softly lit horseshoe bar with
red-upholstered seats around small tables,
lots of 19th-century prints and documents,
many connected with the Iron Duke; open
all day, gets very lively on weekday evenings
*(Andy and Jill Kassube, Gareth and Kate
Edwards, Michael and Rachel Brookes, Julian
Holland, Ken Smith)*

☆ **Newcastle upon Tyne** [Broad Chare; by
river], *Baltic Tavern*: Spacious and
comfortably converted warehouse, lots of
stripped brick and flagstones or bare boards
(as well as plusher carpeted parts) in warren
of separate areas, good value bar food, well
kept Whitbreads Castle Eden and Durham
*(Michael and Rachel Brookes, Gareth and Kate
Edwards, LYM)*

Newcastle upon Tyne [High Bridge],
Bacchus: Comfortable traditional city bar,
can be very busy Thurs-Sun evenings;
lunchtime meals, well kept changing beers
such as Batemans XXX, McEwans 80/- and
Theakstons XB on handpump *(Michael and
Rachel Brookes, Gareth and Kate Edwards);*
[Clayton St W; Westmoreland Rd, nr
Central Stn], *Dog & Parrot*: Popular for the
beers which it brews here, so busy (often
with students); lots of space, loud juke box,
and maybe a November beer festival
*(Michael and Rachel Brookes, Gareth and Kate
Edwards);* [St Lawrence Rd, Byker; off
A186], *Free Trade*: Fairly basic split-level
pub popular with arts and music people —
often has live acts; beautiful river views, very
individual jazz and blues juke box,
uninhibited graffiti in lavatory; can be busy
evenings, pleasantly quiet lunchtime *(Michael
and Rachel Brookes);* [35 The Close],
Quayside: A good Beefeater — friendly, in
old building; pleasant outside on quay
between bridges across Tyne *(Dave Braisted);*
[Stowell St; also known as Darn Crook],
Rosies: Busy traditional pub with
Victorian/Edwardian theme, bicycles
hanging from ceiling, moving
Edwardian-dressed heads behind bar, well
kept beers such as Jennings and Tetleys on
handpump; juke box can be loud *(Michael
and Rachel Brookes)*

☆ **Newton**, Cleveland [A173; NZ5713], *Kings
Head*: Sprucely refurbished old pub with
lots of alcoves in nicely furnished spacious
lounge, good dining area with outside
terrace, well placed below Roseberry
Topping; has been praised for wide choice of

good value food and good service, but no
recent reports *(News please)*

☆ **Newton by the Sea**, Northumberland [The
Square, Low Newton; NU2426], *Ship*:
Unspoilt, idyllic spot in little cluster of
cottages around green, looking out to sandy
beach with lots of wildlife and sailing boats;
basic knocked-through bar, friendly, helpful
licensees, a wide choice of beers and local
seafood specialities inc good crab and
salmon sandwiches; good ploughmans and
soup too; keg Drybroughs, tea; children
welcome *(T Nott)*

Newton by the Sea [High Newton — OS
Sheet 75, map reference 235253], *Joiners
Arms*: In easy walking distance of best two
beaches in Northumberland; village focal
point, with pool and darts room as well as
bar and lounge/restaurant; popular good
food inc fresh fish, welcoming staff; music
may be loud; bedrooms good value and
clean *(Eric and Pauline Woolley)*

North Hylton, Tyne & Wear [Ferryboat
Lane; N bank of River Wear almost under
the A19 bridge — OS Sheet 88, map
reference 350570; NZ4057], *Shipwright*:
Old-world refurbished pub with river views,
has been popular for homely welcome and
wide choice of good value food, but no
recent reports *(News please)*

☆ **North Shields**, Tyne & Wear [New Quay;
NZ3468], *Chain Locker*: Nicely placed in
corner of recently restored Tyne pedestrian
ferry landing area, recently extended by
newish owners, with Watneys-related real
ales and three guest beers, good choice of
bar food from sandwiches up (not Sun
evening), nautical pictures and so forth,
open fire; subdued piped music, can be
smoky *(E V Walder, Brian and Anna Marsden,
Simon Baker, Michael and Rachel Brookes,
LYM)*

☆ **North Shields** [Burdon Main Row, off A187
Howdon Rd — by Appledore ship repair
yard], *Wolsington House*: Unspoilt
Edwardian docklands pub with thoroughly
masculine big lofty-ceilinged bar, family
lounge decorated in period style with two
coal fires (children allowed here), recently
stripped panelling, cheap bar food lunchtime
and early evening, well kept Hartleys XB,
Warsteiner real Pilsener, farm cider; open all
day, busy on free live music nights (most
nights inc Tues jazz) *(E V Walder)*

North Shields [Camden St], *Magnesia Bank*:
Free house with various real ales at
reasonable prices; friendly staff, affable
licensee, good bar food lunchtime and
evenings, occasional gourmet evenings; live
music Thurs, good atmosphere all round,
open fire; tables outside *(Roy and Nicola
Boyne)*

Otterburn, Northumberland [NY8992],
Tower: 1830s castellated mansion built
around original 13th-century Pele tower,
imposing but friendly, with armour,
crossbows, stuffed birds and so forth; a
former main entry, but now a private hotel
— still worth knowing for morning coffee or
afternoon tea with home-made biscuits in

plush lounge with lovely open fires, rather wildernessy stately grounds fun to explore; neat public bar, own fishing on 3 1/2 mile stretch of River Rede; bedrooms comfortable and good value, with good breakfasts *(Ian Robinson, LYM)*

Ovingham, Northumberland [NZ0964], *Bridge End*: 17th-century stone building tucked away nr green, blazing open fire, comfortable settles, beams, well kept Ind Coope Burton, friendly bar staff; usual pub food with emphasis on quantity *(John Oddey)*

Penshaw, Tyne & Wear [nr Monument; NZ3254], *Grey Horse*: Cosy though spacious, with low ceilings, nice decor, and welcoming atmosphere; good traditional bar meals *(Ken Smith)*

☆ **Rennington**, Northumberland [NU2119], *Horseshoes*: Clean and comfortable flagstoned pub, popular and welcoming, with happy and helpful staff, good helpings of reasonably priced freshly cooked straightforward food, S&N keg beers, friendly dogs, tables outside; attractive village well placed for coast *(P J and S E Robbins, Helen and Roy Sumner, C A Thomas, Dave Braisted, GB)*

☆ **Rennington** [Stamford Cott; B1340 NE of Alnwick], *Masons Arms*: Friendly family pub which has been open all day, and generally popular for generous helpings of quickly served bar food — a wider choice than usual, with more varied rich puddings; well kept Theakstons on handpump, homely but comfortable lounge bar decorated with heavy-horse photographs, piped music, games in public bar, tables on front terrace, cheery licensees; there have been mixed views on housekeeping standards, though most have found the bedrooms clean and tidy, with decent breakfasts *(John Atherton, T Nott, Dave Braisted, Helen and Roy Sumner, BKA, John Whitehead, LYM; reports on new regime please)*

☆ **Rochester**, Northumberland [A68 3 miles W of Otterburn; NY8398], *Redesdale Arms*: Convenient old coaching inn on the old hill road to Scotland, with well kept 80/-, friendly atmosphere and reasonably priced nourishing bar food inc good venison casserole; a good base for the Kielder Forest and Borders area — bedrooms good value *(Dennis Heatley, PLC, Bernard Phillips)*

☆ **Romaldkirk**, Durham [NY9922], *Kirk*: Friendly free house notable for outstanding imaginatively presented food, generously served and reasonably priced, with several beautifully kept real ales (some unusual), and admirable service; very attractive, with black oak and red covers, good open fire, spotlessly clean and comfortable *(SS, David and Christine Foulkes, M and J Back)*

Rothbury, Northumberland [NU0602], *Queens Head*: Stone-built village pub with comfortable and welcoming carpeted bars, limited choice of simple but very popular bar food from new chef; well kept Vaux Samson on handpump; good value bedrooms *(Mr and Mrs J H Adam, W H Bland)*

☆ **Saltburn by the Sea**, Cleveland [A174 towards Whitby; NZ6722], *Ship*: Magnificent position right on the beach (and Cleveland Way long-distance path) with splendid sea views from original nautical-style black-beamed bars and big plainer summer dining lounge; good range of speedily served bar food (poached cod recommended), cheerful friendly service, good evening restaurant (not Sun), children's room, seats on terrace by the beached fishing boats; busy at holiday times, no real ale; Jack the pub dog can open crisp packets neatly — he prefers beef flavour *(Walter and Susan Rinaldi-Butcher, Andrew Morrissey, Sue Corrigan)*

☆ **Seahouses**, Northumberland [NU2232], *Lodge*: Pleasant atmosphere and friendly staff in bar of Scandinavian-style hotel with nice atmosphere, specialising in seafood but inc particularly good ploughman's and other conventional bar food; keg beer, restaurant; bedrooms *(Lyn Sharpless, Bob Eardley, Frank Davidson)*

☆ **Shincliffe**, Durham [A177 a mile S of Durham; NZ2941], *Seven Stars*: Small but comfortably smart inn in attractive village, traditionally furnished in one half, with a remarkable fireplace in the other; friendly staff, amiable pug, quiet atmosphere, good substantial straightforward food in bar and restaurant, well kept Vaux ales; nice in summer, with some seats outside; nice bedrooms, substantial breakfasts (they don't let children stay) *(Andy and Jill Kassube, Maureen and Steve Collin, Iain and Penny Muir)*

Shincliffe, *Rose Tree*: Simple but clean and comfortable Vaux pub with good atmosphere and pleasant service; good prompt bar food, well kept Wards and Vaux Samson on handpump *(Iain and Penny Muir, Andy and Jill Kassube)*

☆ **Slaley**, Northumberland [NY9858], *Rose & Crown*: Cleanly refurbished and locally popular pub with good plain home-cooked bar food in tastefully railed-off eating area, and more upmarket evening menu; well kept McEwans 70/- and Youngers No 3, friendly landlord, efficient unobtrusive service; rather spartan decor *(John Oddey, Karen and Graham Oddey)*

☆ **South Shields**, Tyne & Wear [South Foreshore; beach rd towards Marsden; NZ3766], *Marsden Rattler*: A decided curiosity, made up of two railway carriages mounted on their tracks and joined by a bar, also a glass conservatory with plants; all-day tea, coffee and cakes, evening restaurant *(Andy and Jill Kassube)*

Spennymoor, Durham [Metal Bridge; B6291 1 1/2 miles past Thinford roundabout, towards Peterlee; NZ2834], *Wild Boar*: Newly refurbished country pub with good food in pleasant surroundings; good service, well kept Bass and Stones *(Andy and Jill Kassube)*

Stamfordham, Northumberland [NZ0872], *Bay Horse*: Large, clean, comfortable pub at end of green in attractive village; several recently redecorated areas, pleasant landlord, Flowers Original on handpump, good value food *(John Whitehead, Margaret and Roy Randle)*

☆ **Stannersburn**, Northumberland [NY7286], *Pheasant*: Friendly 17th-century pub in small scenic village with cosy bar — stone, panelling and beams, farm tools and harness on walls; Theakstons Best and XB and good value, well presented food; separate dining room; smallish but comfortable bedrooms in adjoining modern wing *(Lynn Sharpless, Bob Eardley, Andrew Triggs)*

☆ **nr Stannersburn** [Greystead; on Kielder Water rd from Bellingham, past Birks — OS Sheet 80, map reference 768856], *Blackcock*: Plain and unspoilt but comfortable country pub with welcoming atmosphere, well kept Boddingtons and Marstons on handpump, good cider, real fire in fine old black range, short choice of good lunchtime bar food — all home-cooked; within walking distance of Kielder Water; children welcome; well equipped bedrooms — there has been a possibility that this side will take over completely *(Mr and Mrs M O Jones, Caroline and Peter Warwick)*

☆ **Stannington**, Northumberland [NZ2279], *Ridley Arms*: Spacious open-plan bars with cosy furnishings, quiet lounge, particularly good food from efficient food counter, separate restaurant and pleasant bar; well kept Whitbreads Castle Eden; an excellent A1 stop-off *(Robert Hodgson, Dave Whiteley, LYM)*

☆ **Thro\pton**, Northumberland [NU0302], *Cross Keys*: Traditional stone-built three-bar village pub, handy for Cragside and Coquet Valley; open fires in cosy beamed main lounge, attractive garden with panoramic view over village to Cheviot, well kept Bass and a guest beer *(W H Bland, BB)*
Tynemouth, Tyne & Wear [NZ3468], *Park*: Three different bars, restaurant, bar food and friendly staff; lovely views; bedrooms excellent *(Ian Robinson)*

☆ **Upsall**, Cleveland [A171; NZ5616], *Cross Keys*: Good choice of S&N ales; fast, cafeteria-style food service of good value, well cooked meals inc good puddings, also salad and snack bar; children welcome at lunchtime *(E A Turner)*
Wall, Northumberland [NY9269], *Hadrian*: Friendly, attentive service and good helpings of imaginative, good food in Jacobean-style bars of 16th-century house, well run; prompt, willing and cheerful service, well kept Vaux beers; tables perhaps rather small and close, and piped music repetitive, but lovely views; bedrooms without private bathroom, not updated *(Miss S J Ebbutt, Mr and Mrs R Hepburn, Jean and Theodore Rowland-Entwistle, Margaret and Roy Randle, M V and J Melling)*
Wallsend, Tyne & Wear [NZ3066], *Rose*: Recently modernised and refurbished, very popular for wide range of bar food inc local stotties, and of real ales; pleasant staff, good reasonably priced small back restaurant *(Dave Whiteley)*

☆ **Warkworth**, Northumberland [23 Castle St; NU2506], *Hermitage*: Comfortable T-shaped bar downstairs, plush-seated restaurant up, huge helpings of food, veg properly lightly cooked; friendly, really trying to please; well kept Courage Directors, John Smiths and a guest such as Theakstons XB; picturesque village *(BKA, BB)*
Whalton, Northumberland [NZ1382], *Beresford Arms*: Good waitress-served food in pleasant bar or dining room inc range of proper pies with good veg; good service, Lorimers Scotch; in main street of very attractive village *(J H Tate, Geoff Wilson)*
Whitfield, Northumberland [off A686 SW of Haydon Bridge; NY7858], *Elks Head*: Lovely old hotel; free house; comfortable bedrooms *(Comus Elliott)*
Whitley Bay, Tyne & Wear [Sea Front; NZ3672], *Briar Dene*: Spotless, with bright decor and off-beat attraction; friendly efficient staff, several well kept real ales on handpump, wide range of good changing bar food, nicely cooked (particularly veg) and well presented *(John Oddey, Mrs R Sandford)*
Whitley Chapel, Northumberland [(closed for lunch weekdays Oct-Apr); NY9358], *Fox & Hounds*: Small, isolated country local with white walls, beams, blazing fire; interconnected rooms with a separate family room (with pool table); friendly licensees, Theakstons ales on handpump, limited range of decent bar food, homely atmosphere, popular with locals and walkers; picnic-table sets behind, backs on to open fields *(Mike and Wendy Proctor, John Oddey)*

☆ **Wooler**, Northumberland [Ryecroft Way (off A697)], *Ryecroft*: Busy lounge and conservatory-style bar in well run and friendly family hotel, locally popular for well kept real ales such as Caledonian, Marstons Pedigree and Yates; open fire, very good imaginative restaurant food; bedrooms comfortable and good value *(Andy and Jill Kassube, Paul S McPherson)*
Wooler [B6351 northwards], *Tankerville Arms*: Spacious south-facing lounge bar overlooking fields, log fire, public bar with darts, dominoes and pool, food from filled stotties amd ploughman's to steaks, with vegetarian and children's dishes; tables on lawn with play area; bedrooms *(Paul S McPherson)*
Yarm, Cleveland [High St; NZ4213], *Black Bull*: Spacious many-roomed pub looking good after recent refurbishment, popular with all ages; pleasant long grassy garden leading down to R Tees; Bass *(Dr M A Thomas); George & Dragon*: Included as the place where the Stockton & Darlington Railway Co first met, to start modern mass transport; comfortably modernised; quickly served bar food *(LYM); Ketton Ox*: Unpretentiously friendly local in ancient building (windowless upper floor once a cockpit); Vaux Samson and Wards on handpump, back pool room, fruit machines, no juke box; children welcome *(Dave Whiteley)*

Nottinghamshire *see* Leicestershire

Oxfordshire

One of the more expensive areas, this, with cheap pub food rare (the nice old Elephant & Castle at Bloxham is an outstanding exception), and drinks generally costing about 10p over the odds. Again, there's a shining exception: pubs tied to the local brewers Donnington and Hook Norton are decidedly cheaper than average, and Hook Norton beers tend often to be a bargain when they turn up in other pubs – they are not uncommon in the free trade. Another local brewer, Morlands, is expanding fast, having just bought a hundred or so pubs from Courage. A great many other changes here include new licensees for the Red Lion at Cropredy, the attractive Bear & Ragged Staff at Cumnor (they come from the Fleur de Lys up at Lowsonford in the Midlands, where they did very well indeed), the cheerful Wheatsheaf at East Hendred, the atmospheric King Charles Head in the woods at Goring Heath, the distinctive Three Tuns in Henley, the Old Swan at Minster Lovell (thorough-going refurbishments here), the Rose Revived in its lovely riverside position at Newbridge, and the remarkable Turf in Oxford. A substantial clutch of new entries, or pubs back in the Guide after an absence, includes the Red Lion at Adderbury (good all round), the friendly Fox at Bix, the very individual Duke of Cumberlands Head at Clifton (a French landlady), the Plough at Clifton Hampden (a Turkish landlord – tremendously helpful), the interesting Highwayman at Exlade Street (food till late), the well run Plough at Finstock, the beautifully placed Trout at Godstow, the immaculate Nut Tree at Murcott, the Bear (Oxford's oldest drinking house), and the very civilised Feathers in Woodstock; virtually all of these have good food, and several are comfortable places to stay in. Other pubs here of special note include the Lamb in Burford (wonderful atmosphere), the Falkland Arms at Great Tew (a perfect village pub), the King William IV at Hailey (a real rural museum), and the Lamb at Shipton-under-Wychwood (doing so well under its Italian licensees that it wins a star award this year). Some notable "comers" in the Lucky Dip section at the end of the chapter include the Romany at Bampton, Five Bells at Broadwell, White Horse at Duns Tew, Plough at Long Wittenham, Crown at Nuffield and North Arms at Wroxton, and others we'd pick out here include the Bull in Burford, Bell at Charlbury, Bell and Crown in Faringdon, White Horse at Forest Hill, Victoria Arms at Marston, White Hart at Nettlebed, Plough at Noke, Lamb at Satwell and Wykham Arms at Sibford Gower; there's a splendid choice in Oxford.

ADDERBURY   SP4635   Map 4

Red Lion 🛏

A423 S of Banbury

This pleasantly civilised 16th-century coaching inn, built in warm Hornton stone, has been carefully and attractively refurbished, keeping the lovely big inglenook in its right-hand bar. There are old prints on ochre walls, comfortable seats, heart-stirring quotations (*I like best the wine which is drunk at the cost of others –*

Diogenes). The left-hand bar is more for eating, with cosy floral tablecloths; it leads through to the comfortable and prettily decorated residents' lounge, and there's an attractive back dining room, partly no smoking. Good bar food, all home-made, includes proper crusty-bread sandwiches (from £1.95), soup (£1.95), ploughman's with home-made pickles (£3.95), Arbroath smokies (£3.75), liver casserole (£4.25), steak and kidney pie (£4.50), chicken done with a choice of interesting sauces (£7.50), a good choice of fresh fish (around £7.50) and lobster (£15), with traditional puddings (£2.25). Well kept Hook Norton Best, Websters Yorkshire and Wadworths 6X, and a guest changing twice a week such as Everards Tiger or Wiltshire Old Grumble, good changing wines by the glass (and a fine choice by the bottle); friendly landlord, good service; tables out on the well kept garden terrace. There may be unobtrusive piped music. *(Recommended by Gordon and Daphne, J E Stanton)*

Free house   Licensees Mark Cleaver and John Wilkinson   Real ale   Meals and snacks (not Sun evening)   Restaurant   (0295) 810269   Children in room on left and dining room   Open 11–11; closed evening 25 Dec   Bedrooms £35(£50B)/£55(£55B)

BECKLEY   SP5611 Map 4

Abingdon Arms

Village signposted off B4027

As we went to press the licensees told us that this pub was up for sale. The comfortably modernised simple lounge has cloth-cushioned seats built around the wall; a smaller public bar on the right has a couple of antique carved settles (one for just one person), and bar billiards; log fire, no music or games machines (they do have cribbage, dominoes, shove-ha'penny and bar billiards). Imaginative food in summer includes Greek salad with taramasalata (£4.25) and strips of rare beef or fresh Scotch salmon with mayonnaise (£6.25); in winter, there's a splendid bouillabaisse and chicken curry (£4.95) and rare roast beef (£6.40). Well kept Wadworths 6X and a guest beer such as Adnams Bitter on handpump, and decent wines. Service is usually friendly and efficient, but can seem low-key; there may sometimes be a wait for food. From a gently floodlit terrace and small formal flower-edged lawn just behind the stone-built pub, the garden drops quietly and spaciously away into the shadows of groves of fruit trees, willows and other shrubs and trees, with well spaced tables, a summer-house, a little tinkling fountain. *(Recommended by Sir Nigel Foulkes, Klaus and Elizabeth Leist, C Wilson, A T Langton, Margaret and Roy Randle, A M Ranklin)*

Free house   Licensee Hugh Greatbatch   Real ale   Meals and snacks (not Sun evening)   (086 735) 311   Open 10.30–2.30, 6.30–11; closed evening 25 Dec

BINFIELD HEATH   SU7478 Map 2

Bottle & Glass ★

Village signposted off A4155 at Shiplake; from village centre turn into Kiln Lane – pub at end, on Harpsden Road (Henley–Reading back road)

Even when this thatched, black-and-white timbered pub is very busy, service is quick and civilised. The well kept bar has very heavily scrubbed, ancient tables under the low beams, a bench built into black squared panelling, spindleback chairs, attractive flagstones, and huge logs in the big fireplace. The side room, similarly decorated, has a window with diamond-scratched family records of earlier landlords; Brakspears Bitter, SB and Old on handpump and quite a few malt whiskies. The good selection of bar food includes lunchtime sandwiches, pasta and prawns in cheese sauce or Cumberland sausage (£3.95), beef Oxford or steak and Guinness pie (£4.50), and avocado and prawns or smoked or grilled trout (£4.95). In the garden are some old-fashioned wooden seats and tables under little thatched roofs, and an open-sided shed like a rustic pavilion. *(Recommended by Simon Collett-Jones, TBB, Tony Bland, R K Sutton)*

Brakspears   Tenants Mike and Anne Robinson   Real ale   Meals and snacks (not Sun)   Henley-on-Thames (0491) 575755   Open 11–3, 6–11

BIX   SU7285 Map 2

Fox

Just off A423 Henley–Wallingford

The unusually warm and friendly welcome is really something special, in this immaculate creeper-clad brick pub. The attractively panelled beamed lounge has big log fires with armchairs making the most of them, and gleaming brasses. There's another log fire in the wood-floored farmers' bar, with darts and fruit machine. A good choice of bar food includes sandwiches (from £1.15), pasties (£1.75), their very popular soup (£1.85), ploughman's (from £2.75, a good ham version £3.35), pizzas (from £3.55), lasagne (£3.95), steak and kidney pie (£4.25) and good game specials in winter (around (£4.25). Sunday lunch is £4.25, and they don't do fried food or chips. Well kept Brakspears PA and Old on handpump, picnic-table sets in the good-sized garden behind. There's a much-used hitching rail for horses in the car park, and Ian Smith of Crocker End can be booked to bring you here by horse and cart; the friendly dog's called Henry. *(Recommended by Lyn and Bill Capper, Bill Ingham)*

Brakspears   Licensees Richard and Sue Willson   Real ale   Meals and snacks   Henley (0491) 574143   Open 11–3, 7–11; closed 25 and 26 Dec

BLOXHAM   SP4235 Map 4

Elephant & Castle £

Humber Street; off A361

The coach entry to this Cotswold stone pub is a very steep climb up through the building from the village street and the pretty neighbouring thatched cottages. An elegantly simple public bar has a striking 17th-century stone fireplace and a strip wood floor, and a comfortable lounge, divided into two by a very thick wall, has a good winter log fire in its massive fireplace; the atmosphere is relaxed and friendly. Remarkably good value food includes good sandwiches (from 60p), soup (75p), ploughman's (from £1.10), ham with eggs (£2), steak and kidney pie, lasagne, haddock or chicken (all £2.50), salads (from £2.50), excellent scampi (£2.60), and rump steak (£4.50). The beer is decently priced too – very well kept Hook Norton Best and Old Hookey on handpump; malt whiskies. Sensibly placed darts, dominoes, cribbage, a fruit machine, trivia and shove-ha'penny – the board is over a century old. In the flower-filled yard there's an Aunt Sally pitch, which they use just in the summer. *(Recommended by Bryan Wheeler, J E Stanton, Lyn and Bill Capper, Tom Evans, Marjorie and David Lamb)*

Hook Norton   Tenant Chas Finch   Real ale   Lunchtime meals and snacks (not Sun) Restaurant (not Sun)   Banbury (0295) 720383   Children in eating area of bar and in restaurant   Open 10–2.30, 6–11

BRIGHTWELL BALDWIN   SU6595 Map 4

Lord Nelson ⊗

Brightwell signposted off B480 at Oxford end of Cuxham or B4009 Benson–Watlington

This listed 17th-century building was closed in 1905 by the squire, and then became the village shop and post office, though the previous owners still renewed its licence each year. It's comfortably modernised, with wheelback chairs (some armed), country kitchen and dining chairs around the tables on its Turkey carpet, candles in coloured glasses, orange lanterns on the walls, and pretty fresh flowers. Nelson's presence is still very much felt – particularly in the bar on the left, where the plain white walls are decorated with pictures and prints of the sea and ships, there are some ship design plans, and a naval sword hangs over the big brick fireplace in the wall (which divides off a further room). The bar food changes daily and this menu covers both bar and restaurant (though in the evening the restaurant has its own menu): home-made soup such as cream of asparagus (£2.50), duck liver and pork pâté with Cumberland sauce (£3.25), garlic mushrooms with crispy bacon (£3.75), ploughman's (£3.95), popular and substantial lunchtime Welsh rarebit (£4.95), chicken curry (£6), steak and kidney pie simmered in Guinness and red wine (£6.95), wiener schnitzel (£7.95), peppered beef and strips of beef in creamy green peppercorn sauce (£8.50), and halibut with prawns and mushrooms in a creamy sauce (£10.25); some of the house favourites include duck in orange pie (£7.95) and casserole of monkfish, scallops and prawns (£8.50), and puddings such as a banana, cointreau and ice-cream concoction called Emma's delight or fruit crumble (£3.50); popular Sunday lunch; friendly waitress service. Tables are not bookable (except in the restaurant), so it's best to get here early at weekends. Brakspears PA on handpump, a decent wine list, including a good range of cheaper French wines and good coffee; piped music. There's a verandah at the front, and tables on a back terrace by the attractive garden or under its big weeping willow, beside the colourful herbaceous border. The village church is worth a look. *(Recommended by PLC, Sir Nigel Foulkes, Jeremy Isaacs, R K Sutton, Mrs H Jones, Jonathan Neil-Smith, R K Sutton, Joan Olivier)*

Free house   Licensees Peter Neal, Richard Britcliffe, Ann Neal   Real ale   Meals and snacks (till 10pm)   Restaurant (not Sun evening)   Watlington (0491) 612497 or 612330   Children by arrangement   Open 11.30–3.30, 6.30–11.20 (late supper licence); closed evening 25 Dec, all day 26 Dec

BURFORD   SP2512   Map 4

Lamb ★   ★   🛏

Sheep Street; A40 W of Oxford

It's the lovely restful atmosphere – especially in winter when the log fire is blazing under its elegant mantlepiece – that readers seem to enjoy most at this civilised 500-year-old Cotswold inn. The spacious beamed main lounge has oriental rugs on the wide flagstones and polished oak floorboards, distinguished old seats including a chintzy high winged settle, ancient cushioned wooden armchairs, easy chairs, and seats built into its stone-mullioned windows, and bunches of flowers on polished oak and elm tables. Also, attractive pictures, shelves of plates and other antique decorations, a grandfather clock, and a writing desk. The public bar has high-backed settles and old chairs on flagstones in front of its fire; the bedrooms are in similar style – simple, old-fashioned, chintzy. Well kept Wadworths IPA, 6X and winter Old Timer are dispensed from an antique handpump beer engine in a glassed-in cubicle, and well presented bar lunches, rotating on a daily basis, should typically include sandwiches (from £1.80, smoked salmon £3.95), home-made cream of cauliflower soup (£2.25), ploughman's (£3.95), pancake filled with mushroom, bacon and garlic in cream or sautéed chicken and duck liver (£4.25), fresh grilled sardines or provençale pork meatballs with pilaff rice (£5.25), sautéed king prawns in garlic butter (£5.50), and delicious puddings such as wild fruit bavarois or pear and apricot flan (£2.25); free dips at Sunday lunchtime; friendly, unobtrusive service. A pretty terrace leads down to small neatly-kept lawns surrounded by flowers, flowering shrubs and small trees, and the garden itself can be really sunny, enclosed as it is by the warm stone of the surrounding buildings. Dogs welcome. *(Recommended by J R Smylie, Ann Marie Stephenson, J and S Taylor, K and J O'Malley, S C N Jones, Dr and Mrs Frank Rackow, Michael Richards, Barbara Wensworth, Charles Turner, Steve Huggins, P Corris, H K Dyson, Laurence Manning, Alan Skull, Ruth and Andrew Triggs, Adam and Elizabeth Duff, J R Williams, Chris Raisin, Syd and Wyn Donald, J P Bowdler, Robert and Elizabeth Scott, Mr and Mrs G Turner, Brian Jones, P B Dowsett, Gordon and Daphne, Bev and Doug Warrick, John and Anne Mciver, Patrick Freeman, David and Jane Russell)*

Free house   Licensee Richard de Wolf   Real ale   Lunchtime bar meals and snacks (not Sun)   No smoking restaurant (not Sun evening)   Burford (099 382) 3155   Children in eating area of bar and lounges   Open 11–2.30, 6–11; closed 25 and 26 Dec   Bedrooms; £36(£55B)/£75B

Mermaid ✪

High St

Some parts of this popular dining pub date back to the 14th century and it was formerly known as the Three Pigeons. The attractive if rather dark flagstoned bar is long and narrow, with brocaded seats in bays around the single row of tables down one side – each softly lit by a red-fringed lamp. The inner end, with a figurehead over the fireplace and toby jugs hanging from the beams, is panelled, the rest has stripped stonework; bar billiards, shove-ha'penny, cribbage and dominoes. Bar food includes good sandwiches, lots of starters such as soup (£1.95), chicken wings with garlic and fresh ginger (£3.65), ploughman's (£2.95), Cumberland sausage with red cabbage (£3.95), smoked mackerel in cream cheese sauce (£4.95), over half-a-dozen vegetarian dishes such as vegetable hot-pot (£4.95), cottage pie (£5.65), fresh cod or beef sausages and mash (£5.95), gammon hot-pot (£6.95), steak and kidney pie (£7.95), seafood pancakes (£9.25) and steaks (from 8oz sirloin £10.95); vegetables are good. Well kept Morlands on handpump, and friendly and helpful service (food comes quickly, though there may be a wait at the bar). Out on the broad pavement of the famously picturesque sloping Cotswold street are picnic-table sets under cocktail parasols. *(Recommended by Vanessa and Peter Hurst, Brian Jones, Robert and Vicky Todd, P Corris, H K Dyson, Andrew and Ruth Triggs, Laurence Manning, Alastair Campbell, John Kimber, B Lambert, B Williams)*

Morlands   Tenant John Titcombe   *Real ale*   *Meals and snacks (12–2.30, 6–10)*
Restaurant   Burford (099 382) 2193   *Maybe no nearby parking*   *Open 11–11*

nr CHINNOR   SP7500 Map 4

Sir Charles Napier ✪

Spriggs Alley; from B4009 follow Bledlow Ridge sign from Chinnor; then, up beech wood hill, fork right (signposted Radnage and Sprigg Alley), then on right; OS Sheet 165, map reference 763983

From the outside this looks a plain and slightly dishevelled Chilterns pub; inside it's almost wholly dedicated to a stylish restaurant, though during the week, when it's quieter and there's more room in the original small front bar, you're more likely to find something cheaper to eat with a straightforward drink; the short menu includes soup such as ham and pea (£3.50), baked eggs with smoked salmon and cream (£4), mussels with wine, cream and shallots (£4.50), pasta carbonara (£4.50), Cumberland sausages with mustard sauce (£6.50), seafood rissotto (£5), roast chicken (£7.50), char-grilled cod with dill butter (£8) and braised Welsh lamb with caper sauce (£8.50). There are homely furnishings such as armchairs, narrow spartan benches by the wall, and highly polished tables on the plain wood block or tiled floor, with bare oak boards in the low ceiling, and a good winter log fire, which has gleaming copper pipes running from the back boiler; croquet and boules. Well kept Wadworths IPA tapped from the cask, champagne on draught, well chosen wines by the bottle, freshly squeezed orange juice, Russian vodkas and a few malt whiskies; piped music well reproduced by the huge loudspeakers; service is relaxed and friendly. The back restaurant is decorated with works by local artists – sketches of Francis Bacon by Claire Shenstone, commissioned by him to do his portrait, and sculpture by Michael Cooper; at weekends, there's little point coming here unless you do want a restaurant meal (which could easily cost you £50 a head); Sunday lunch, at around £25 a head, is distinctly fashionable – in summer it's served in the crazy-paved back courtyard with rustic tables by an arbour of vines, honeysuckle and wisteria (lit at night by candles in terracotta lamps). The croquet lawn and paddocks by the beech woods drop steeply away to the Chilterns. *(Recommended by Jim and Maggie Cowell, BKA, M A and C R Starling, Phil Bryant, A J Young; more reports please)*

Free house   Licensee Mrs Julie Griffiths   *Real ale*   *Lunchtime bar meals (not Sun or Mon)*   *Restaurant; not Sun evening*   Radnage (0494) 483011;   *Children welcome lunchtimes; in evenings if over 7*   *Open 11.45–3, 6.30–11 Tues-Sat; closed Sun evening and Mon*

CHRISTMAS COMMON   SU7193 Map 4

Fox & Hounds

Hill Rd from B4009 in Watlington; or village signposted from B480 at junction with B481

This unspoilt tiny cottage is in good Chilterns walking country and on one cream wall in the beamed bar on the left is a framed Ordnance Survey walker's map. Simple furnishings include three tables and wooden wall benches or bow-window seats, a little carpet down on the red-and-black flooring tiles, and two sturdy logs to sit on in the big inglenook – which has a fire burning even in summer; the room on the right is popular with locals and pretty much for drinking only; three cats and a friendly alsatian. Lunchtime food such as soup (£1; winter only), sandwiches (from £1), ploughman's (£2.50; summer only), sausage and eggs (£3.50) and they only do sandwiches on Sundays and Mondays; good coffee. Well kept Brakspears PA tapped from the cask in a back still room; shove-ha'penny, dominoes, cribbage. There are old-fashioned garden seats and sitting-logs by the roses and buddleia on the front grass beyond a small gravel drive, with picnic-table sets under a sumac beside the house. *(Recommended by TBB, Ian Phillips; more reports please)*

Brakspears   Licensee Mr K Moran   Real ale   Lunchtime snacks   (049 161) 2599 Children in games room off one bar   Open 12–2.30, 6–11

CLANFIELD   SP2801 Map 4

Clanfield Tavern

A4095 5 miles S of Witney

It's pretty in summer here, with tiny windows peeping from the heavy stone-slabbed roof and tables on a flower-bordered small lawn that look across to the village green and pond. Inside, several flagstoned, heavy-beamed and stone-walled small rooms lead off the main bar and are furnished with settles and various chairs and seats cut from casks, as well as brass platters, hunting prints, and a handsome open stone fireplace with a big log fire and 17th-century plasterwork panel above it; the restaurant is no smoking. Imaginative, home-made bar food includes sandwiches (from £1.40), soup (£1.60), ploughman's (£3), vegetable stroganoff (£4.25), burgers (from £4.25), and rump steak (around £6) and daily specials. Well kept Hook Norton Best, Morlands Bitter and Morrells Varsity on handpump, and quite a few bin end wines; chatty, friendly staff. Darts, dominoes, shove-ha'penny, cribbage, piped music, fruit machine and trivia, and there is a proper skittles alley. *(Recommended by Mr and Mrs P J Hardy, Jack and Barbara Smale, Mrs M E Lawrence; more reports please)*

Free house   Licensees Keith and Anne Gill   Real ale   Meals and snacks (11.30–2.30, 6–10)   Cottagey restaurant   Clanfield (036 781) 223   Children welcome   Open 11.30–2.30, 6–11   Bedrooms; £15/£30

CLIFTON   SP4831 Map 4

Duke of Cumberlands Head   🛏

B4031 Deddington–Aynho

Filthy ale and disgusting food is what they've been advertising here; surely running the risk of prosecution under the Trade Descriptions Act, as the truth is very different. Generous helpings of freshly home-made bar food include sandwiches on request (£1.20), ploughman's (£2.35), and interesting hot dishes that change day by day and might include steak and kidney pudding or ham and leek pie (£4.25), afelia (diced pork with coriander seeds, £4.50) and methi gosht (£4.75); there's some emphasis on fresh fish (from around £4.25). Besides well kept Hook Norton Best, Jennings, Ruddles Best, Wadworths 6X and a guest beer on handpump, there are four decent French wines by the glass and a good many interesting ones by the bottle (Mr Clark works also as a wine wholesaler). The spacious and simply but stylishly refurbished lounge has a lovely log fireplace and a thriving, buoyant atmosphere, and there's a cosy restaurant. Good service, neat housekeeping. There are tables (and an old cast-iron signpost) out in the garden by this thatched 16th-century stone pub; the canal's a short walk away. Bedrooms are in a new but sympathetic extension – you drive under it to park. *(Recommended by Prof J C Mann, Dr and Mrs James Stewart, John Whitehead, John and Joan Wyatt, Richard Gibbs)*

Free house   Licensees Marie-France and Graham Clark   Real ale   Meals and snacks Restaurant   (0869) 38534   Children away from bar till 8.30   Open 12–3, 6.30–11; closed 25 Dec   Bedrooms; £18S/£30S

CLIFTON HAMPDEN   SU5495   Map 4

Barley Mow

Back road S of A415 towards Long Wittenham

This ancient place is still – as Jerome K Jerome put it in *Three Men in a Boat* – very 'once-upon-a-timeyfied'. The well furnished lounge has low beams, antique oak high-backed settles, ship's timbers for its end wall, and old engravings on the walls. The black-flagstoned public bar is broadly similar, and the side family room has handsome squared oak panelling. Ruddles County, Ushers Best and Websters Yorkshire on handpump; fruit machine and background music. Decent bar food includes ploughman's (£2.25), salad bar (£4), daily specials, a roast of the day (£4.75), and puddings like apple or fruit pies (£1.75). The well tended, sheltered lawn has rustic seats, and the Thames bridge is nearby. *(Recommended by P Craddock, Mayur Shah, R A Corbett, R Tomlinson, R C Gandy, Marjorie and David Lamb; more reports please)*

Grand Met/Watneys   Manageress Margaret Welch   Real ale   Meals and snacks Restaurant; closed Sun evening   Clifton Hampden (086 730) 7847   Children in family room   Open 11–2.30, 6–11   Bedrooms; £36B/£56B

Plough

Mr Bektas, the quite extraordinarily obliging new Turkish licensee of this quaint little village pub with its steep thatched roof, may even wear tails. But the atmosphere is really relaxed and friendly. The cosy little bar – said to be haunted by a benign presence that neatly upturns empty glasses – has beams and panelling, black and red floor tiles, antique furniture, and attractive pictures; this leads to two lounge areas, and there's a new, no smoking restaurant. Fresh food is available all day, and as well as bar meals such as lasagne or mousaka (£4.95), kebabs (£5.95), smoked ham salad (£4.25), game or vegetarian pies, beef stroganoff and free-range chicken, they do sandwiches (£2.25) and soup (£2.45) and serve morning coffee and afternoon tea with muffins; no chips. Well kept Courage Best and Websters Yorkshire; even Turkish coffee as well as filter. There are some tables and seats outside. There are lots of free extras if you stay and indeed the room is free if you have a party of eight for a meal in the restaurant. *(Recommended by A T Langton, DCTF, Joan Olivier; more reports please)*

Free house   Licensee Yuksel Bektas   Real ale   Meals and snacks (served all day) Restaurant   (086 730) 7811   Children in no smoking family room   Open 11–11 One bedroom (4-poster); £49.50B/£64.50B

CROPREDY   SP4646   Map 4

Red Lion

Off A423 4 miles N of Banbury

In a lovely spot – just a short stroll from the Oxford Canal – this simply furnished place has high-backed settles under its beams, brasses on the walls, a fish tank, and a winter open fire. The good selection of drinks includes well kept Courage Best and Directors, Ruddles Best and County and John Smiths; darts, pool, dominoes, cribbage, fruit machine, and juke box. Bar food includes sandwiches (from £1.10), specials such as tagliatelli, chicken kiev, lasagne and chicken wings (all at £3.50) and steak (from £5.95), with puddings (from £1.75). Extended menu in evening.

Seats in the small back garden. The pub is opposite a raised churchyard. *(Recommended by TBB, Karen and Graham Oddey, Patrick and Mary McDermott; more reports please)*

Courage   Leasehold: John Dando   Real ale   Meals and snacks   Restaurant   (0295) 750 224   Children in separate restaurant and back room   Parking may be difficult in summer   Open 11–3.30, 6–11

CUMNOR   SP4603 Map 4
Bear & Ragged Staff

19 Appleton Road; village signposted from A420: follow one-way system into village, bear left into High St then left again into Appleton Road – signposted Eaton, Appleton

The comfortably rambling, softly lit bar in this largely 16th-century twin-gabled farmhouse has easy chairs, sofas and more orthodox cushioned seats and wall banquettes, and polished black flagstones in one part, with Turkey carpet elsewhere; it can get very busy at weekends. A good choice of food includes ploughman's (from £3.95), game meatballs with berries (£5.50), salmon and mango in filo pastry (£5.75) and beef and pigeon with dumplings (£5.95). Vegetarian dishes include goat's cheese in filo pastry or mushroom and pepper stroganoff (both £3.95); one of the eating areas is no smoking. Morrells, Graduate and Varsity on handpump, kept under a light carbon dioxide blanket, a decent wine list, cognacs and malt whiskies; friendly service. There's a children's play area, with a swing and climbing frame at the back by the car park. The building is named for the three-foot model of a Warwick heraldic bear which guards the large open fire; it's one of the 'Wayside Inns'. *(Recommended by John C Baker, Mr and Mrs D A P Grattan, Nigel Gibbs, Mike Tucker; more reports please)*

Morrells   Manager Simon Pedersen   Real ale   Meals and snacks (12–3, 6–10) Restaurant   Oxford (0865) 862329   Children in eating area of bar   Open 11–11

DORCHESTER   SU5794 Map 4
George 🛏

High St; village signposted just off A423 Maidenhead–Oxford

The comfortably old-fashioned bar in this 500-year-old building has a civilised atmosphere, cushioned settles and leather chairs, beams, a big fireplace, and carpet on the woodblock floor. Brakspears on handpump, good wine by the glass from an exceptional wine list. Lunchtime food includes home-made soup (£2.50), open sandwiches (£3.50), Cromer crab and mushroom bake (£3.95), salmon and spinach noodles with cheese sauce (£4.95), chicken in yoghurt and spices (£5.50), and home-made puddings (£2.50). There is a reduced menu on Sunday including traditional roast (£4.95). It was originally built as a brewhouse for the Norman abbey – which still stands opposite – before being used as a posting and then a coaching inn; close to *Good Walks Guide* Walk 96. *(Recommended by JMC, Peter Blood, Michael Richards, Simon Collett-Jones, Roger Bellingham; more reports please)*

Free house   Licensees Mark Stott and Brian Griffin   Real ale   Meals and snacks Restaurant   Oxford (0865) 340404   Children welcome   Open 11–3, 6–11; closed Christmas week   Bedrooms; £62B/£75B

EAST HENDRED   SU4588 Map 2
Wheatsheaf

Chapel Square; village signposted from A417

A wide mix of customers of all ages gather in this friendly 16th-century black and white timbered pub. At lunchtime, this is to enjoy the adventurous range of bar meals: mushroom fusilli (£2.50), curries (from £3.60), steak and kidney pie (£3.95), scampi or basque chicken (£6.95), pork calvados (£7.25), steaks (£9.95). There's more room for darts and Aunt Sally in the evening. The bar has some wall panelling, cork wall tiles, high-backed settles and stools around tables on quarry tiles by a log-burning stove, and a tiny parquet-floored triangular platform by the bar; low, stripped deal settles form booths around tables in a carpeted area up some broad steps. Well kept Morlands Bitter, Old Speckled Hen and Old Masters on handpump, a few malt whiskies and country wines; piped music, and maybe Bonnie, the golden labrador. Outside on the back grass area is a budgerigar aviary and play area for children with swings and so forth, colourful with roses and other flowers, conifers and silver birches. The nearby church is interesting – its Tudor clock has elaborate chimes but no hands. *(Recommended by A T Langton, Alex Waye, R and E Harfield, R C Watkins, P B Dowsett)*

Morlands   Tenants John and Maureen Donohue   Real ale   Meals and snacks (not Mon evening)   Restaurant   (0235) 833224   Children in eating area   Open 11–3, 6–11

EXLADE STREET   SU6582   Map 2

Highwayman   ⇌

Signposted just off A4074 Reading–Wallingford

This rambling low-beamed pub is largely 17th-century, though in part dates back another 300 years or so. Its unusual layout includes an interesting variety of seats around old tables and even recessed into a central sunken inglenook, in the two carpeted rooms of its bar. A wide choice of home-made bar food includes sandwiches (from £1.20), soup (£1.95), ploughman's (£3), tagliatelle (£4.95), steak and Guinness pie (£5.50), stir-fry chicken (£6.95), a big mixed grill (£7.95) and fresh fish such as lemon sole (£6.25) or salmon with prawn sauce (£7.20); puddings are £1.95, and they do Sunday lunch and occasional theme dinners. An airy conservatory dining room has now replaced the children's room that was demolished by the hurricane. Well kept Boddingtons, Brakspears, Wadworths 6X, Gibbs Mew Bishops Tipple and monthly guest beers such as Adnams; decent wines, winter mulled wine, lots of Pimmses in summer; subdued piped music, courteous and friendly service; tables out in the attractive garden. The friendly mongrel is called Willie. *(Recommended by Roderic Plinston, Lyn and Bill Capper)*

Free house   Licensees Carole and Roger Shippey   Real ale   Meals and snacks (till 10.30)   (0491) 682020   Children welcome away from bar   Open 11–3, 6–11; closed evening 25 Dec   Bedrooms; £50B/£58B

FERNHAM   SU2992   Map 4

Woodman   ★

A420 SW of Oxford, then left into B4508 after about 11 miles; village a further 6 miles on

At the heart of this friendly country pub is a big log fire that sometimes has a hot-pot simmering over it in winter; it's surrounded by an unusual collection of items such as clay pipes ready-filled for smoking, milkmaids' yokes, leather tack, coach horns, an old screw press, good black and white photographs of horses, and – over the bar – a collection of over a hundred hats. The heavily beamed rooms are furnished with cushioned benches, pews, Windsor chairs, and candle-lit tables made simply from old casks; there's another bar area in what was the barn. Bar food, served at your table, includes avocado or pâté (£2.30), chilli con carne, fisherman's pie or smoked haddock crumble (£4), home-made steak and kidney pie (£4.20), a choice of curries (£4.50), vegetarian and vegan dishes and various puddings such as apple crumble or pie and treacle tart (£1.80). Well kept Adnams Broadside, Fullers London Pride, Morlands PA, Old Speckled Hen and Old Masters and a guest beer tapped from casks behind the bar; regular OAPs get a very substantial discount; piped music, friendly dog and cats. *(Recommended by Robert Brown, Simon Reynolds, Marjorie and David Lamb, P A J Brown, W Bailey, Margaret Dyke, Gordon and Daphne, Margaret and Roy Randle, V Collman, Patrick Freeman)*

Free house   Licensee John Lane   Real ale   Meals and snacks (not Mon)   (036 782) 643   Children in eating area of bar   Open 12–2.30, 6.30–11

FINSTOCK   SP3616 Map 4

Plough 🛏

The Bottom; just off B4022 N of Witney

The long, rambling bar of this late 18th-century thatched pub is nicely split up by partitions and alcoves, and has a cosy feel under its low oak beams; up at the end by the servery its floor is tiled, elsewhere it's carpeted. Neatly refurbished, it's friendly, clean and comfortable, with an armchair by the open log-burning stove in the massive stone inglenook. Generous helpings of good value bar food include sandwiches (from £1.50), soup (£1.95), popular garlic mushrooms (£2.95), ploughman's (from £2.95), king prawns, a vegetarian dish or steak and kidney pie (£4.95), chicken tikka (£5.95), cantonese stir-fry (£6.95) and Sunday roast beef (evening too, £4.95), with bargain steaks on Wednesday evening, and specials including fish and game; there's a comfortable low-beamed stripped-stone dining room on the right. Well kept Adnams Broadside, Bass, Hook Norton Best and Ringwood Old Thumper on handpump, a decent choice of wines; maybe unobtrusive piped music; pleasant, flexible staff. A separate games area has darts, bar billiards, cribbage, dominoes, fruit machine and trivia. There are tables (and Aunt Sally) in the garden. The recently converted bedroom is comfortable and well equipped. *(Recommended by Sarah Bradbrook, M and Mrs J Back, Buck and Gillian Shinkman)*

Free house   Licensee Val Phillips   Real ale   Meals and snacks   (0993) 868333 Open 12–3, 6–11, all day Sat; closed evening 25 Dec   One bedroom; £32B/£45B

FYFIELD   SU4298 Map 4

White Hart

In village, off A420 8 miles SW of Oxford

The attractively large range of well kept real ales here changes from time to time, but usually includes Boddingtons Bitter, Gibbs Mew Bishops Tipple, Hook Norton, Morlands Original, Ruddles County, Theakstons Old Peculier and Wadworths 6X, with guest beers on handpump or tapped from the cask; Weston's cider. The main room is a hall with soaring eaves, huge stone-flanked window embrasures, and an attractive carpeted upper gallery looking down into it. A low-ceilinged side bar has an inglenook fireplace with a huge black urn hanging over the grate, and a framed history of the pub on the wall. The priests' room and barrel-vaulted cellar are dining areas. Bar food includes soup (£1.95), pâté (£2.75), ploughman's (from £2.95), tandoori chicken (£4.10), chilli (£4.50), vegetarian lasagne, pie or curry (£4.50), garlic king prawns (£4.95), steaks (from £7.50), daily specials such as venison in red wine (£6.95) and saddle of hare ((£7.95) and a selection of home-made puddings. Shove-ha'penny, dominoes, cribbage and fruit machine. A heavy wooden door leads out to the rambling, sheltered and flowery back lawn. *(Recommended by David Evans, Marjorie and David Lamb, P Craddock, Ted George, V Collman, Dr and Mrs A K Clarke, Jill Hampton, Brian Metherell; more reports please)*

Free house   Licensee John Howard   Real ale   Meals and snacks (12–2, 7–10) Restaurant   Oxford (0865) 390585   Children in four rooms   Open 11–2.30, 6.30–11; closed 25 and 26 Dec

GODSTOW   SP4708 Map 4

Trout

Follow Wytham signpost from roundabout at N end of Woodstock Road

It's the marvellous position that makes this pretty creeper-covered medieval pub special, with sturdy old tables on a lovely cobbled terrace by a stream clear enough to watch the plump trout, and peacocks in the grounds. The beamed main bar has cushioned old settles on the flagstones and bare floorboards, old Oxford views and sporting prints on the walls, and a weight-driven spit in front of its big stone fireplace. There is a separate beamed restaurant with a wide choice of good salads, and during the busier times a more modern extension bar is open for snacks such as ploughman's (from £3); hot dishes include curry, stuffed peppers and chicken cacciatore (all £4), barbecue at weekends. Well kept Bass and Charrington IPA on handpump; mulled wine and hot punch in winter, sangria, summer punch, Pimm's and champagne bar in summer. The present building replaced one destroyed by Cromwell in 1646, which had been set up in 1138 as a hospice for the nearby nunnery where Henry II's mistress Fair Rosamund was forced to drink poison by his wife Queen Eleanor. *(Recommended by David Evans, Robert Brown, Dr John Innes, Gordon and Daphne, R C Gandy; more reports please)*

Bass   Managers Gianni and Joe Cozzolino   Real Ale   Snacks and meals (not Sun evening unless weather good, then barbecue)   Oxford (0865) 54485   Children welcome   Open 11–3, 6–11 (11–11 Sat in summer)

GORING HEATH   SU6579   Map 2

King Charles Head

Goring Heath signposted off A4074 NW of Reading, and B4526 E of Goring

Small rooms ramble around a solidly built central servery in this warmly atmospheric brick cottage, with decorative plates and small country pictures on the white walls, comfortable floral-print wall banquettes and other seats, glossy plain tables, and logs burning in a back stove and the open fire on the right. The wide choice of well cooked and generously served food includes sandwiches (from £1), home-made soup (£1.75), ploughman's (£3.25), lasagne (£4.95), daily specials such as Cotswold chicken (£5.25), a good vegetarian selection including Covent Garden vegetable pie (£5.25), Sunday roast (£5.75) and puddings (from £1.75). Well kept Adnams Broadside, Brakspears PA and Mild, Flowers Original, Glenny Hobgoblin, Wychwood and Dr Thirstys, and Hook Norton Best on handpump; darts, cribbage, trivia game and fruit machine. A more modern back extension opens into the charmingly meandering garden, which blends into the surrounding tall beech woods; there are lots of tables under cocktail parasols on a terrace and on the grass, with a timber climber and tyre swings. The pub is within walking distance of Holly Copse and the Thames itself, by Mapledurham Country Park; it's close to *Good Walks Guide* Walk 98. *(Recommended by James Cane, Bob Timmis and others; more reports please)*

Free house   Licensee Bernard J Morris   Real ale   Snacks (not Sun lunch) and meals (0491) 680268   Children in eating area   Open 11–3, 6–11; closed 25 Dec

GREAT TEW   SP3929   Map 4

Falkland Arms ★ ★ ⌨

Off B4022 about 5 miles E of Chipping Norton

This is most people's idea of the perfect country pub – homely and full of atmosphere and set in a lovely village of golden stone thatched cottages surrounded by secluded wooded slopes. It's a Grade I listed building and the partly panelled bar has a wonderful inglenook fireplace, high-backed settles and a diversity of stools around plain stripped tables on flagstones and bare boards, one, two and three handled mugs hanging from the beam-and-board ceiling, dim converted oil lamps, and shutters for the stone-mullioned latticed windows. The bar counter, decorated with antique Doulton jugs, mugs and tobacco jars, always serves several reasonably priced and well kept guest beers, as well as the regular Badger Tanglefoot, Donnington BB, Hook Norton Best and Wadworths 6X; also country wines and farm ciders, hot punch in winter, clay pipes filled ready to smoke, some 50 different snuffs, and tankards, a model of the pub, and handkerchiefs for sale. Lunchtime bar food – naturally taking a back seat given the pub's tremendous appeal in other respects – is home-made and includes sandwiches (from £1), soup (£1.20), a range of ploughman's (from £2.80), pâté (from £3.20), and daily specials like vegetable lasagne or cod and prawn crumble (£4.50), breaded plaice (£4.80), gammon, pork and stilton hot-pot or lamb and apricot pie (all £5) and beef bourguignonne (£5.50); one room is no smoking at lunchtime; they use their own duck and chicken eggs for the Scotch eggs and bubble and squeak; friendly and cheerful service; darts, shove-ha'penny, dominoes, cribbage, and table skittles. The front terrace, with wooden seats among roses, doves cooing among the lumpy cushions of moss on the heavy stone roof-slabs, and maybe some ducks and geese wandering contentedly, can feel quite special. Note that as they can't do any 'improvements' to the building, the rather basic lavatories are a couple of doors down the lane. It does get very crowded indeed – especially at weekends. *(Recommended by Richard Carpenter, John and Joan Wyatt, Dr M V Jones, Carol and Mike Muston, Gary Scott, K and J O'Malley, Lynn Sharpless, Bob Eardley, John Bramley, Lee Goulding, Robert Gomme, J R Smylie, Dave Irving, Andy and Jill Kassube, P Craddock, J E Stanton, Andrew and Ruth Triggs, Pamela Sterling, Maysie Thompson, P and M Morey, Dr Michael Denton, Douglas Hain, John Bowdler, Bernard Phillips, Syd and Wyn Donald, Gordon and Daphne, Richard Houghton, Pete Storey, David Young, Diane Duane-Smyth, Chris Raisin, Tony and Lynne Stark, Ian Phillips, Paul Corbett, Kevin Myers, A M Kelly, Mrs S McGreevy, Dick Brown, Su and Andy Hill)*

Free house   Licensee John Milligan   Real ale   Lunchtime meals (not Sun or Mon) and snacks   Great Tew (060 883) 653   Children in eating area of bar   Folk music Sun evening   Open 11.30–2.30, 6–11; closed Mon lunchtime except bank holidays   Three bedrooms; £25S/£40S

HAILEY   SU6485   Map 2

King William IV   ★

Note – this is the hamlet of Hailey, near Ipsden (not the larger Hailey over in west Oxon); signposted with Ipsden from A4074 S of Wallingford; can also be reached from A423; OS Sheet 175, map reference 641859

A big collection of well restored brick implements, all with details of their age, use and maker covers the timbered bare brick walls in the beamed bar of this rustic pub: root cutters, forks, ratchets, shovels, crooks, grabbers, man-traps, wicker sieves, full-size carts, ploughs, and a pitching prong. The big winter log fire still has its original faggot oven, with good sturdy furniture on the tiled floor in front of it. Two broadly similar carpeted areas open off. Well kept and reasonably priced Brakspears PA, SB, XXXX Old and Mild tapped from casks behind the bar; farm ciders; popular filled rolls such as ham, cheese and pickle, and corned beef (from 55p – the only evening food), and pies, pasties or stilton ploughman's with home-made soup (from £3). The back lawn of this white house, which overlooks rolling pastures, has seats among smartly painted veteran farm equipment such as cake-breakers and chaff cutters. A friend of the landlord's operates horse and wagon rides from Nettlebed to the pub where you then have a ploughman's or supper and gently return through the woods and via Stoke Row back to Nettlebed (£8.50 a head; phone Ian Smith on 0491–641364); the pub's own Shire horse – popular with children – pulls a brewer's dray. *(Recommended by Keith and Sian Mitchell, David Warrellow, Bob Timmis, Simon Collett-Jones, Lyn and Bill Capper, Nick Dowson; more reports please)*

Brakspears   Tenant Brian Penney   Real ale   Snacks   (0491) 680675   Children in eating area at lunchtime   Open 11–2.30, 6–11

HENLEY-ON-THAMES   SU7682   Map 2

Three Tuns

5 Market Place

As we go to press we hear that the Knowles are moving on: it'll be interesting to see whether their replacement Mr Gladman shows more respect for the decimal system than their engaging pricing has done: soup (£1.04), sandwiches (from £1.19, two-rasher bacon, lettuce and tomato £2.09, hot salt beef £2.72), home-made chicken liver pâté (£2.06), ploughman's (from £2.40), vegetarian lasagne (£3.45), egg, bacon, sausage and tomato (£3.70), meaty lasagne (£3.84), a pie of the day (£4.15), gammon with egg or pineapple (£6.08), mixed seafood

(£6.33), and 6oz sirloin steak (£9). The traditional layout consists of two friendly small rooms opening off the long tiled and panelled corridor with several cast-iron, pre-nationalisation railway company notices on the walls. Notably cosy, the heavily beamed buttery has a central chimney and log-effect gas fire dividing off its back part; the panelled front public bar has dominoes, cribbage, shove-ha'penny and fruit machine. Well kept Brakspears PA and SB on handpump, with Mild and Old tapped from the cask, and reasonably priced doubles from an old-fashioned central servery; piped music. There's a small terrace at the back; close to *Good Walks Guide* Walk 68. *(Recommended by Ian Phillips, Mrs Richard Stewart, Simon Collett-Jones, Gary Scott, David Warrellow, R S Laws; more reports please)*

Brakspears   Real ale   Meals and snacks (10–9.30 Mon-Fri, noon–9 Sun)   Children in rear part of buttery   Open 10–11; closed evening 25 Dec

HENTON   SP7602 Map 4

Peacock

From B4445 SE of Thame, left on to B4009, village signposted on left after about 1 mile

From the courtyard in front of this courteously run house with its little goldfish pool and fountain, you make your way into a civilised and comfortable beamed bar, with plush wall banquettes and wheelback chairs or winged low settles and dining chairs around close-set tables, guns above the good log fire in its big brick fireplace, and a few swords on the wall. A wide choice of well served bar food includes soup (£2.25), sandwiches (from £2.25), vegetable curry (£5.95), chicken supreme (£5.95), home-made steak and kidney pie or grilled fresh sardines (£6.45) and several speciality seafood, duck and steak dishes – the restaurant area round on the left rather concentrates on these. Well kept Brakspears PA on handpump, winter mulled wine, smart and courteous measured service. There are peacocks around the quaint black and white thatched and timbered inn and its back bedroom block. *(Recommended by BKA, Richard Houghton; more reports please)*

Free house   Licensee Bert Good   Real ale   Lunchtime meals and snacks   Restaurant   Kingston Blount (0844) 53519   Children if eating, no under 5s   Open 12–3, 6–11   Bedrooms; £52B/£62B

nr HOOK NORTON   SP3533 Map 4

Gate Hangs High

Banbury Rd; a mile N of village towards Sibford, at Banbury–Rollright crossroads

Five miles south-west of this isolated country pub, are the Bronze Age Rollright Stones – said to be a king and his army who were turned to stone by a witch. It's a clean and welcoming place, with stools and assorted chairs on the carpet (some tables set for diners), joists in the long, low ceiling, a brick bar counter, and a gleaming copper hood over the hearth in the inglenook fireplace. The good choice of reasonably priced bar food, from a blackboard that changes daily, typically includes soup (£1.35), pâté (£2.70), lasagne or chilli con carne (both £4.50), lemon chicken or tuna tagliatelle (£4.75), home-cooked honeybaked ham (£4.95), chicken or beef curry or beef in Hooky beer (£5.50), navarin of lamb (£5.50), the ever popular steak and kidney pie (£5.95) and steak (£7.95); the emphasis tends to be on meals rather than snacks; good, friendly service. Well kept Hook Norton Best on handpump, dominoes. The broad lawn, under holly and apple trees, has swings for children to play on, and a view down over a plump quilt of rolling fields and pastures. *(Recommended by Sir Nigel Foulkes, Barbara M McHugh, Joy and Peter Heatherley, Frank Cummins, Alan and Julie Wear; more reports please)*

Hook Norton   Tenant Stuart Rust   Real ale   Meals and snacks (not Sun and Tues evenings)   Restaurant   Chipping Norton (0608) 737387   Children in restaurant   Open 11.30–3, 6.30–11

LITTLE MILTON   SP6100   Map 4

Lamb

3 miles from M40, junction 7; A329 towards Wallingford

In summer the quiet garden here comes into its own, with hanging baskets, tubs of flowers, roses, a herbaceous border, fruit trees, and swings. Inside the honey-coloured building, the little windows in the stripped stone walls of the beamed bar that are so low you have to stoop to look out; there are also lots of tables with wheelback chairs, and soft lighting. Bass, Ind Coope Benskins and Burton on handpump; fruit machine, piped music. Home-made food includes sandwiches (from £1.35), ploughman's with warmed bread (£2.75), ham or beef salad (£5.95), and hot main dishes such as venison in red wine (£5.85), guinea fowl (£6.75), and steaks (from £8.35); there are lots of puddings such as lemon charlotte (£1.85). *(Recommended by Mrs H Jones, David Evans, M A and C R Starling, Adrian Zambardino, Debbie Chaplin, Joan Olivier, A T Langton)*

Ind Coope (Allied)   Licensee David Bowell   Real ale   Meals and snacks (12–2.30, 7–10)   Great Milton (0844) 279527   Children welcome   Open 11–2.30, 6–11; closed evening 25 Dec

MAIDENSGROVE   SU7288   Map 2

Five Horseshoes ✪

W of village, which is signposted from B480 and B481; OS Sheet 175, map reference 711890

High up in the Chiltern beechwoods on a lovely common, this little 17th-century brick house is popular for its enterprising range of food. (The new conservatory dining area, due to open Easter 1992, should ease the queue for tables at the weekend.) This includes home-made stilton soup (from £2.50), ploughman's (from £3.30), baked potatoes with interesting fillings (from £3.95), deep fried mushrooms (£4.25), home-made pâtés like smoked trout or avocado and walnut (£4.50), shepherd's pie (£4.50), steak and kidney pie (£5.25), breaded prawns (£6.25), outstanding calf's liver (£6.95), pink trout in lobster sauce (£6.95), Scotch salmon (£7.25), king scallops (£7.50) and Scotch steak (from £9). Furnishings in the rambling bar are modern for the most part – wheelback chairs around shiny dark wooden tables – though there are some attractive older seats and a big baluster-leg table, as well as a good log fire in winter; the low ceiling in the main area is covered in bank notes from all over the world, mainly donated by customers. There's a separate bar for walkers where boots are welcome. Well kept Brakspears PA and SB on handpump and a decent wine list; courteous, helpful service. There are picnic-set tables on the sheltered lawn and under a fairylit Perspex arbour (where they hold summer barbecues). *(Recommended by Lyn and Bill Capper, Mrs R M Thomas, David Warrellow, Gordon and Daphne; more reports please)*

Brakspears   Tenants Graham and Mary Cromack   Real ale   Meals and snacks   Nettlebed (0491) 641282   Children in dining area   Open 11–2.30, 6–11

MINSTER LOVELL   SP3111   Map 4

Old Swan 🏠

Just N of B4047; follow Old Minster signs

Besides continuing its march up market (which we've already recorded) this ancient Cotswold inn has been so thoroughly immersed in refurbishment that it's hard for us to predict just how the atmosphere will settle down. Tending more towards hotel and restaurant than pub. But the smartly modernised and attractive low-beamed rooms opening off the small central bar have been very restful, and furnished and decorated with Liberty-print easy chairs, an antique box settle, Turkey carpets on the polished flagstones, good china in corner cupboards, and big log fires in huge fireplaces. Lunchtime set meal of one, two or three courses with a main course choice of, for example, poached salmon, breast of chicken or lamb kebab (£7.50-£11.50); well kept Morlands and Fullers London Pride on handpump pulled by a neatly dressed barman. The restaurant is housed in what used to be the brewhouse, and there's a medieval well on the way out to the garden – which has a lily pond, flowers and shrubs, and some shade from chestnut and sycamore trees for the seats on the neat lawn. *(Recommended by Lord Evans of Claughton, Laurence Manning, Mr and Mrs T A Towers, Andrew and Ruth Triggs, Tim and Sue Halstead, Pamela Sterling, B Lambert, B Williams, A T Langton, Ann Marie Stephenson, E G Parish, Jill Hampton, Brian Metherell, Richard Dolphin)*

Free house   Licensees Eric Roby, Sean Mitchell, Mark McGuire   Real ale   Lunchtime meals   Restaurant   Witney (0993) 774441   Children welcome   Open 11–11   Bedrooms; £117.50B/£138B

MOULSFORD   SU5983   Map 2

Beetle & Wedge ☆ ⇌

Ferry Lane; off A329, 1 ½ miles N of Streatley

Some of our most loyal readers feel that this riverside inn has, in the last couple of years, moved too far away from the feel of a real pub to count as a candidate for our *Guide* – even though they rate it highly as a hotel or restaurant. However, it's clear that other readers are perfectly happy to pay what amount to restaurant prices for the interesting food that is now served, not too formally, in this delightful spot by the Thames. The atmosphere is quite hotelish – not just in the lounge, but also in the pubby part in the Boathouse by the river, where there's a leisured, almost Edwardian feel – a mix of old chairs, some armchairs, bar stools, a ten-foot Edwardian sofa, polished wooden tables, oak saddle-beams, a tiled floor, and flint and brick walls, all done in a calming mixture of tortoiseshell, green and brown; you can also sit in the flagstoned conservatory. The range of bar food includes soup such as mushroom soup (£3.50), cod's roe pâté (£4.75), crispy duck with frisée salad or avocado salad with smoked chicken and prawns (both £4.95 or £7.95), ploughman's with local farm cheeses (£5.75), half dozen oysters (£6.95), calves' kidneys and black pudding with a green herb mustard sauce (£10.95), maybe whole red mullet with tomato and fennel (£11.95), sirloin steak (£12.95); there's a charcoal grill for steaks; bar food is served at dining tables which it is advisable to book, especially at weekends. Well kept Adnams Bitter, Badger Tanglefoot, and Wadworths 6X on handpump; an extensive wine list, freshly squeezed orange juice, friendly service. The waterside lawn, flanked by roses, has robustly old-fashioned garden furniture. Moorings are available at £15 per boat per night, refundable on food in the bar or restaurant, and rowing boats are available nearby; near the start of *Good Walks Guide* Walk 97. The Smiths recently sold the Royal Oak at Yattendon in order to concentrate on the Beetle and Wedge. *(Recommended by Mike and Alison Fenwick, Joan Olivier,GB, CH, W C M Jones, Steve Huggins, Hilary Roberts, Dick Brown, Kathy King, TOH)*

Free house   Licensees Richard and Kate Smith   Real ale   Meals and snacks (12.30–2, 7.30–10)   Restaurant   Cholsey (0491) 651381   Children welcome   Open 11.30–2.30, 6–11.30; closed 25 Dec   Bedrooms; £65B/£75B

MURCOTT   SP5815   Map 4

Nut Tree

Off B4027 NE of Oxford, via Islip and Charlton-on-Otmoor

Quiet and friendly during weekday lunchtimes, busier in the evenings and at weekends, this neat and welcomimg white thatched pub has a beamed lounge, done out in stylish shades of red, with fresh flowers on its tables (set for food), and a winter log fire; there's now a small back conservatory-style extension. The landlord is a master butcher and particularly proud of his Scotch steaks (from £10.20); other good home-cooked bar food includes sandwiches (from 85p), home-made soup (£2.10), giant sausages (£2.60), home-made 5oz burgers (£2.95), veal, ham and egg pie (£3.50), lots of starters such as garlic mushrooms (£2.50) or pâté (£3.10), good cold meat salads (£5.50), gammon, seafood platter or scampi

(£6.65), and daily specials such as fresh fish or beef provençale. Bass, Fullers London Pride and Wadworths 6X and guest beers on handpump or electric pump; there's also a fair number of malt whiskies, some interesting foreign bottled beers, and a wide range of wines by the bottle (there may be some bargains among the more superior clarets). Darts, shove-ha'penny, cribbage and dominoes, Sundays only. Outside there are ducks on a pretty front pond, trim lawns, and usually plenty of animals to see; also, ten gargoyles hanging in the garden – each carved into a magnificently grotesque form from a different wood. You can find nine of them in the walnut tree and one in a pillar overlooking the well. The pub's handy for walks through the boggy Otmoor wilderness. *(Recommended by Joan Olivier, Margaret and Roy Randle, Sir Nigel Foulkes, Marjorie and David Lamb)*

Free house   Licensee Gordon Evans   Meals and snacks (12–2, 6.30–9.30; not Sun) (086 733) 253   Children in one room if eating   Open 11–3, 6.30–11

NETTLEBED   SU6986 Map 2

Carpenters Arms

Crocker End; hamlet signposted from A423 on E edge of Nettlebed

In a quiet enclave of houses surrounded by woodland, this cottagey pub is popular for its bar food – they advise bookings at weekends. This includes home-made soup (£2.25), home-made pâté (£2.95), several ploughman's (from £3.25), smoked fish baked in cream and cheese (£3.25), prawn fritters in sweet and sour sauce (£4.95), home-cooked honey ham in Cumberland sauce (£5.25), home-made steak pie (£5.50) and breaded escalope with stilton butter (£6.75); at least two vegetarian main courses are always available; good puddings like bread and butter pudding soaked in whisky (£1.50); friendly service. The carpeted main room has burgundy upholstered dark small pews, wheelback chairs, and country pictures on the cream walls; the partly panelled side saloon bar has more wheelbacks and pews. The hooks on the ceiling here were originally used to hang up cooked pigs – regulars were handed a knife with their pint and helped themselves. Well kept Brakspears PA and SB on handpump; shove-ha'penny, dominoes, cribbage, and piped music; winter log fires. There are wooden tables and benches on the bright front terrace. *(Recommended by Jill Shepherd, David Warrellow, Mr and Mrs B J Twigger, Marjorie and David Lamb, John and Karen Day, C G and B Mason)*

Brakspears   Tenants David and Debbie Taylor   Real ale   Meals (not Tues) and snacks (12–2, 7–9.30, 10 Fri and Sat)   Nettlebed (0491) 641477   Open 11–3, 6–11

NEWBRIDGE   SP4101 Map 4

Rose Revived

A415 7 miles S of Witney

This large stone inn has a spacious garden with a long lawn, crazy-paved paths, weeping willows, and spring bulbs or a colourful summer herbaceous border; it's lit up at night by retired street lamps. There's a lot of Victoriana in the bar area (it's been used as a drinking house since the 18th century) – rose patterned wallpaper, rose pictures, polished flagstones, glass lamps, marble tables and so forth. In the dining room is a 16th-century stone fireplace – not always lit, even on a cold day – with an oak mantlebeam. The bar food includes soup (£1.35), pâté (£1.85), ploughman's (from £3.10), salads (from £4.35) and hot dishes such as lasagne or steak and kidney pie (from around £4.25); the area off here is no smoking. Morlands Original, Old Speckled Hen and Old Masters on handpump; fruit machine and piped music. *(Recommended by Robert Bland, D M and D E Livesley, Mr and Mrs D C Leaman, R C Gandy, Joan Olivier, A T Langton, Mr and Mrs P B Dowsett, W H Bland; more reports please)*

Morlands   Managers Andrew and Julia Dearie   Real ale   Meals and snacks all day Oxford (0865) 300221   Children welcome   Jazz Sun evening   Open 11–11 Bedrooms; £35(£40B)/£45(£50B)

OXFORD SP5106 Map 4

Bear

Alfred Street

This is the oldest drinking-house in Oxford (dating from 1242) and even the handpumps – serving well kept Ind Coope Burton and Tetleys – are over a century old. The four low-ceilinged and partly panelled rooms have traditional built-in benches and plain tables, a collection of 7,000 or so club ties, all neatly arranged behind glass (there are still regular additions), and an old-fashioned atmosphere that those who like call cosy, and those that don't call cramped; fruit machine. Good value home-made bar food includes good soup, sandwiches, home-made pâté, smoked mackerel (£1.75), omelettes, beef steak sandwich or ploughman's (all £2.60), vegetable risotto (£3.05), home-made lasagne (£3.55); friendly service. The menu says welcome in five languages, giving some idea of the customers, though in term time it gets very crowded with students from Oriel and Christ Church colleges, and often you'll find as many people drinking out on the street, by the tables on the side terrace. (*Recommended by S Corrigan, Wayne Brindle, Steve and Carolyn Harvey, Simon Collett-Jones, A J Young*)

Halls (Allied)   Manager Mike Halls   Real ale   Meals and snacks (12–2, 6–8.30) Oxford (0865) 244680   Nearby parking very limited   Open 12–11; closed 25 and 26 Dec and 1 Jan

Turf Tavern

Bath Place; via St Helen's Passage, between Holywell Street and New College Lane

Cut off from the modern bustle of the city by the high stone walls of some of its oldest buildings, including part of the ancient city wall, this rambling tavern has lots of dark beams, low ceilings with doors to match, and flagstoned or gravel courtyards. It's still much as Hardy described it when Jude the Obscure discovered that Arabella the barmaid was the wife who'd left him years before. Bar food includes sandwiches, home-made soup (£1.30), a good selection of vegetarian meals (from around £4), and beef and beer pie or lasagne (£4.25); you usually have to queue when it's busy and service is put under pressure; afternoon teas and sandwiches in summer. Well kept Archers Headbanger, Boddingtons, Brakspears Special, Flowers Original, Glenny Hobgoblin, Marstons Pedigree, Weathereds and Whitbreads Castle Eden on handpump, Merrydown country wines, mulled wine in winter; trivia machine. It's very close to the Bodleian and the Sheldonian theatre. (*Recommended by Nigel Gibbs, Paul Harrop, Steve and Carolyn Harvey, John and Joan Wyatt, Wayne Brindle, Mrs J Brown, Davis Fowles, Michael and Alison Sandy, Gordon and Daphne, John Hill; more reports please*)

Whitbreads   Manager William McSherry   Real ale   Meals and snacks (12–2.30, 6–9)~ Oxford (0865) 243235   Children welcome   No nearby parking   Open 11–11

PISHILL SU7389 Map 2

Crown

B480 N of Henley

Though this red brick and flint pub was largely rebuilt in the 15th century, records of a monastic building on this site go back to the 11th century, and the thatched barn they use for parties and functions is some 500 years old. The latticed-window bar, with its three fine fireplaces all blazing in winter, has an elegant corner cabinet of decorated plates, old photographs on the partly panelled walls in the front area, and a central black-beamed and red-and-gold carpeted part with little blocky country chairs and stools around wooden tables. The rear section is knocked-through, with standing oak timbers. Well kept Brakspears, Flowers Original, Fullers Chiswick, Greene King Abbot and Marstons Pedigree on handpump. Relatively expensive but good home-made bar food includes sandwiches (weekday lunchtimes only), filled baked potatoes, deep-fried mushrooms with a garlic dip or deep fried brie with apricot dip (all £3.50), tagliatelle with herb and mushroom sauce (£4.95), lasagne or steak, kidney and mushroom pie (£5.95) and various fish dishes. There are picnic table sets on the attractive side lawn. (Recommended by Phil Bryant, Jonathan Neil-Smith, Ian Phillips, D Mackay, P M Johnson, Richard Houghton, Tony and Lynne Stark, TBB; more reports please)

Free house   Licensee Jeremy Capon   Real ale   Meals and snacks (12–2, 7–10; not Sun or Mon evenings)   Restaurant   Turville Heath (049 163) 364   Children in restaurant Sun lunchtime only   Jazz Sun evening   Open 11.30–2.30, 6–11   Bedrooms in separate cottage; £65B

ROKE   SU6293 Map 2

Home Sweet Home

Village signposted off B4009 Benson–Watlington

The quietly welcoming main bar in this civilised dining pub is made up of two smallish, bare-boarded and stone-walled rooms with heavy stripped beams, leather armed chairs, just a few horsey or game pictures such as a nice Thorburn print of snipe, and big log fires – one with a great high-backed settle facing it across a hefty slab of a rustic table. On the right, a carpeted room with low settees and armchairs, and an attractive corner glass cupboard, leads through to the restaurant. It's here that the choice of home-made food is at its widest – and most exalted; however it is possible to eat in the bar from it. The vast bar menu ranges from sandwiches (from £1.40), soup (£1.60), ploughman's (from £2.55), lots of filled baked potatoes (from £2.65) and omelettes (£3.85), through burgers (from £3.25), salads (from £4.15), creamy baked prawns (£4.45) or ham and egg (£4.60), to good dishes of the day such as stuffed mushrooms with prawn and cream cheese salad, garlicky and herby chicken, turkey breast and a well flavoured game pie with very light pastry; they have a notable range of good vegetarian dishes (£1.85-£5.40); roast Sunday lunch. Well kept Brakspears and Courage Best on handpump, a good choice of malt whiskies, interesting wines; friendly service. The low-walled garden at the front of this thatched and tiled old house looks on to the quiet hamlet, and has lots of flowers around the tables out by the well. The licensees also run another of our main entries, the Old Boot at Stanford Dingley in Berkshire. (Recommended by H Wilkins, Margaret and Christopher Bond, Simon Collett-Jones, Geoffrey Medcalf, Richard Purser, Lyn and Bill Capper, TBB, Maureen Hobbs; more reports please)

Free house   Licensees Jill Madle, Peter and Irene Mountford   Real ale   Meals and snacks   Restaurant   Wallingford (0491) 38249   Well behaved children welcome Open 11–3, 5.30–11; closed evening 25 Dec

SHENINGTON   SP3742 Map 4

Bell

Village signposted from A422 W of Banbury

Served until late in the evening, the ever-changing, popular bar food in this 300-year-old pub might include sandwiches, fish stuffed cannelloni (£5.50), mustard rabbit (£5.75), pork chop in mushroom sauce (£5.95), cod in celery sauce or beef and orange casserole (£6.25), and duck breast in apricot (£8.25). Well kept Boddingtons Best and Hook Norton Best on handpump, and a good choice of wines from Berry Bros; friendly, prompt service. The heavy-beamed and carpeted lounge has tables with vases of flowers, brown cloth-cushioned wall seats and window seats, and old maps and documents on the cream wall; the wall in the flagstoned area on the left is stripped to stone and decorated with heavy-horse harness, and the right side opens into a neat little pine-panelled room (popular with locals) with decorated plates on its walls; darts, coal fire. The selection of animals includes two tortoiseshell cats (Myrtle and Mittens), a labrador called Katie and a west highland terrier, Lucy. The tables at the front look across to the green. (Recommended by Carol and Mike Muston, Frank Cummins, Peter Blood, J Bramley, Sir Nigel Foulkes, John C Baker, Mr and Mrs G J Rice, Sheila and Len Wallis, Joy and Peter Heatherley, Gordon and Daphne, N W Kingsley, Mrs Lili Lomas, Su and Andy Hill)

Free house   Licensees Jennifer and Stephen Dixon   Real ale   Meals and snacks (12–3,
7–11.30)   Restaurant   Edge Hill (0295 87274)   Children welcome   Open 12–3,
6.30–12 (supper licence); closed Sun evening   Bedrooms; £15(£18B)/£30(£36B)

SHIPTON-UNDER-WYCHWOOD   SP2717   Map 4

Lamb ★ 🧭 🛏

Just off A361 to Burford

Run by warmly friendly, helpful licensees, this rather smart old-fashioned inn
seems more popular than ever with both locals and visitors. The beamed bar has a
fine oak-panelled settle, long pews, a solid oak bar counter, and flowery curtains in
the small windows of the old partly bared stone walls; maybe newspapers to read.
Bar food includes a good summer cold buffet, home-made soup, duck and orange
pâté or buttered shrimps (£3), and main dishes such as gravadlax, vegetable tart or
smoked salmon (£5), roast garlic lamb, Cotswold pie or chicken with asparagus
and tarragon sauce (£6.50), poached salmon and shrimp sauce (£8.50), and
puddings such as treacle tart or tipsy-making trifle (£2.50); vegetables are well
presented, salads well dressed. Well kept Hook Norton Best on handpump; good
wines and several malt whiskies. In summer, you can sit at tables among the roses
at the back. The restaurant is no smoking. *(Recommended by Colin Pearson, H K*
Dyson, D I Baddeley, John Bramley, Andrew and Ruth Triggs, C J Colley, Charles Turner,
Adam and Elizabeth Duff, Sidney and Erna Wells, P B Dowsett, Mr and Mrs J W Gibson, A M
Ranklin, J R Smylie, A J Madel, Robin Hillman, Charles Bardswell)

Free house   Licensees Mr and Mrs L Valenta   Real ale   Meals and snacks (12–2,
7–10)   Restaurant; not Sun evening   (0993) 830465   Chidren in separate
restaurant   Open 11–2.30, 6–11; closed Mon   Bedrooms; from £48B/£68B

Shaven Crown

Parts of this large hotel are Tudor and it is said to have been used as a hunting
lodge by Elizabeth I. There's a magnificent double-collar braced hall roof and
lounge at the front with lofty beams and a sweeping double stairway down the
stone wall. A fine beamed bar has a relief of the 1146 Battle of Evesham, as well as
seats forming little stalls around the tables and upholstered benches built into the
walls. Beyond this bar is the courtyard garden, with its own lily pool, roses, and
old-fashioned seats set out on the stone cobbles and crazy paving. Decent bar food
includes soup (£1.65), smoked haddock mousse (£2.75), vegetarian nut and stilton
roast (£3.95), Babotie (£4.75), spinach and bacon lasagne (£4.95), lightly curried
prawns (£5.25), sirloin steak (£7.95), and puddings like treacle tart or summer
pudding (£1.65); good cream teas, even on a Sunday. Flowers Original and well
kept Hook Norton on handpump; the pub has its own bowling green.
(Recommended by Buck and Gillian Shinkman, Vanessa and Peter Hurst, Iain and Penny
Muir, H K Dyson, S V Bishop, David Lamb, Andrew and Ruth Triggs, Laurence Manning, Joy
and Peter Heatherley, Paul Harrop, Marjorie and David Lamb, Robert and Elizabeth Scott,
Tim Briely, Mrs Lili Lomas)

Free house   Licensees Trevor and Mary Brookes   Real ale   Meals and snacks
Restaurant   Shipton-under-Wychwood (0993) 830330   Children in restaurant and
eating area of bar   Open 12–2.30, 7–11   Bedrooms; £31B/£67B

SOUTH LEIGH   SP3908   Map 4

Mason Arms

Village signposted from A40 Witney–Eynsham

In a small village, this is a large, thatched pub with Cotswold stone walls and
sweeping lawns. The flagstoned lounge, separated into two halves by a
wrought-iron divider, has lots of brasses, built-in cushioned settles curving around
the corners, an open fire with stone hearth at one end, and a log-effect gas fire at
the other. Bar food includes home-made soup (£1.60), sandwiches (from £1.90),
ploughman's (£3.25), seafood or smoked bacon, chicken, ham and mushroom
pancake (£4.25), vegetable pasta (£4.45), salads (from £4.60), steak, kidney and

Guinness pie (£4.75), and steak (£8.25). Hook Norton Best and Sowlye on handpump, a good range of cognacs and malt whiskies, and lots of wines; friendly service. The pretty garden has peacocks and chickens – and there should be some Cotswold sheep in the small field by the car park; picnic-set tables shelter in a small grove. (Recommended by Joan Olivier, Bryan Wheeler, Andrew and Ruth Triggs, Mr and Mrs K Guyll, David Evans, TBB, Ian Phillips, Edward Hibbert)

Free house   Licensee Geoffrey Waters   Real ale   Meals and snacks (not Sun evening)   Restaurant (not Sun evening)   Shipton-under-Wychwood (0993) 702485 Children in restaurant   Open 11–2.30, 6.30–11; closed Mon (except bank hols) Bedrooms; £34.50B/£48.50B

STANTON HARCOURT   SP4105   Map 4

Harcourt Arms

B4449 S of Eynsham

It's best at the moment to think of this as very much a dining pub (though as we go to press the pub is up for sale, so a change is possible). Popular food includes sandwiches (from £1.50), soup (£1.95), home-made pâté (£2.25), ploughman's (from £3.50), burgers or home-made lasagne (£4.95), trout with orange butter (£5.25), vegetarian pasta (£5.50), steak and kidney pie (£5.50), and chicken tikka (£6.95); Sunday lunch (£9.50); maybe summer barbecues. Massive stone fireplaces dominate the three simply furnished old-fashioned dining areas, and there are framed Vanity Fair caricatures; around 100 wines; piped music. There are tables under cocktail parasols out in front, and in the back garden under the trees. (Recommended by JMC, Mr and Mrs Peter Woods, BKA, Mrs D M Hacker)

Free house   Licensee J Mouncey   Meals and snacks (12–2.30, 6–10)   Restaurant Oxford (0865) 881931   Children welcome   Open 11.30–3, 6–11

STANTON ST JOHN   SP5709   Map 4

Star

Pub signposted off B4027; village is signposted off A40 heading E of Oxford (heading W, the road's signposted Forest Hill, Islip instead)

A well refurbished, no-smoking extension is up a flight of stairs (but on a level with the car park) in this chatty, relaxed pub; there are rugs on flagstones, pairs of bookshelves on each side of an attractive new inglenook fireplace, old-fashioned dining chairs and an interesting mix of dark oak and elm tables, shelves of good pewter, terracotta-coloured walls with a portrait in oils, and a stuffed ermine. The original part centres on two little low-beamed rooms, one of which has ancient brick flooring tiles and the other, carpet and quite close-set tables. Badger Tanglefoot, Wadworths IPA, Farmers Glory and 6X on handpump, hot toddies and hot chocolate, country wines and Taunton Dry Cider; behind the bars is a display of brewery ties, beer bottles and so forth; shove-ha'penny, dominoes, cribbage, piped music, and Aunt Sally. Bar food includes sandwiches (from £1.45), soup (£1.70), half a pint of prawns or ploughman's (£2.95), home-made curries or chilli (£3.95), quiche (£4), specials such as beef and Guinness or bulghar wheat and walnut pie, cheese and tuna or seafood bake (all £4.25); a good choice of vegetarian dishes such as spicy vegetable crumble (£4.25); puddings such as giant chocolate éclairs and clotted cream (£1.95); the family room is no smoking. The walled garden has picnic-table sets among the rockeries, and swings and a sandpit. (Recommended by Joan Olivier, Marjorie and David Lamb, C Wilson, Bryan Wheeler, P Craddock, Sir Denis Wright, Edward Hibbert, John Day; more reports please)

Wadworths   Tenants Nigel and Suzanne Tucker   Real ale   Meals and snacks (12–2, 7–10)   (086 735) 277   Children in eating area and family room   Open 11–2.30, 6.30–11; closed 25 and 26 Dec

STEEPLE ASTON   SP4725   Map 4

Red Lion

Off A423 12 miles N of Oxford

On a summer's day, the suntrap front terrace, with its lovely flowers, is a marvellous place to relax – especially if you're escaping the M40. Inside this attractive village pub, the comfortable beamed bar has an antique settle and other good furnishings, dark hessian above its panelling, and a collection of rather crossword-oriented books. A decent choice of lunchtime bar food includes tasty stockpot soup (£1.20), sandwiches (from £1.40), ploughman's with local farm cheese and crusty bread (from £1.95), pâté or home-made taramasalata (£3.25), summer salads such as fresh salmon (around £4.50), and in winter varying hot-pots (around £3.50). Well kept Badger Tanglefoot, Hook Norton Best and Wadworths 6X on handpump, a choice of sixty or so malt whiskies, and around 100 good wines in the restaurant (they ship their own wines from France); friendly staff. *(Recommended by Tony and Lynne Stark, Bob Smith, Dr and Mrs James Stewart, Keith W Mills, Pete Storey, Jill Hampton, Brian Metherell, J Charles, V Collman, J P Cinnamond, John Bowdler, TBB, Gordon and Daphne)*

Free house   Licensee Colin Mead   Real ale   Lunchtime meals and snacks (not Sun) Restaurant (not Sun)   Steeple Aston (0869) 40225   Open 11–3, 6–11; closed 25 Dec evening

STOKE ROW   SU6784   Map 2

Crooked Billet

Newlands Lane; B481 N from Reading, village signposted on left at Highmoor Cross, after about 7 miles

Paul Clerehugh does the cooking in this food-oriented country pub, and depending on what fresh food they can get, the daily changing dishes might include soup such as vichyssoise (£2.80), adventurous starters like salad of wild mushrooms, green peppercorns and rabbit (£4), and main dishes such as baked red mullet (£6.95), calves' liver pan-fried in bacon (£8.50), chicken breast in hoi sin sauce and oyster mushrooms or fricassee of chicken (£8.95), salmon with white wine (£9.95) and lobster, crab and mussels for two (£20); puddings such as lemon cheesecake or treacle tart (£2.50). At the heart of the atmospheric bar is the little wood-panelled parlour with a big table under a single lamp hanging from the bowed beam and a log fire with an attractive rug in front of it; the public bar has a couple of scrubbed deal tables in front of a vast open hearth, and there's a second log fire in the renovated lounge. Well kept Brakspears PA, SB, and Old and Mild tapped from casks down six cellar steps and served through doorways, and a long list of wines chalked up on a board; dominoes and piped music. There are some plain benches at the front of the white stone building, and from the three-acre garden, with its picnic-table sets, you can walk straight into Chilterns beech woods. *(Recommended by TBB, Dick Brown, Jane and Calum, Joan Olivier, J Charles, David Warrellow, Gordon and Daphne, Nick and Alison Dowson)*

Brakspears   Tenant Paul Clerehugh   Real ale   Meals and snacks (12–2.30, 7–10) (0491) 681048   Children welcome   Open 12–3, 7–11; closed 25 Dec

SWINBROOK   SP2712   Map 4

Swan

Back road 1 mile N of A40, 2 miles E of Burford

Don't be put off by the uninviting 'no dogs', 'no boots', 'no children' signs – once inside, this quiet 400-year-old country pub is very friendly. The flagstoned bar has simple antique furnishings and a woodburning stove, there's a lounge area at the back, and a small dining room to the right of the main entrance; darts, shove-ha'penny, dominoes and cribbage. Lunchtime bar food includes sandwiches (from £1.60), ploughman's (from £2.50) and main dishes such as home-made steak and kidney pie (£4.50), lamb cutlets or scampi (£4.80), with evening dishes in the dining room including starters like whitebait (£2.30) or goat's cheese (£2.85), main dishes like trout (£5.40) and assorted puddings; Morlands Bitter and Wadworths 6X on handpump; old english sheepdog. There are old-fashioned benches outside by the fuchsia hedge, making the most of this idyllic spot. *(Recommended by H K Dyson, Marjorie and David Lamb, Mrs J Crawford, Mr and Mrs C G Finch, Roger Huggins, Gordon and Daphne, B Lambert, B Williams, John Kent, Elizabeth Lloyd, J Charles, EML, Mr and Mrs P B Dowsett)*

Free house   Licensee H J Collins   Real ale   Meals and snacks (12–1.30, 6.30–8.45; 7–8 Sun and Mon)   Dining room (not Sun evening)   Burford (0993) 822165   Open 11.30–2.30, 6–11

TADPOLE BRIDGE   SP3203   Map 4

Trout £

Back road Bampton–Buckland, 4 miles NE of Faringdon

As there are moorings for customers, this friendly Thames-side pub is popular with boating people. The small L-shaped bar has flagstones, attractive pot plants on the window sills and mantlepiece, and a good pubby atmosphere. A wide choice of promptly served bar food includes sandwiches (from 80p; toasted from £1.10), sausage and egg (£2.50), ploughman's (from £2.95), varying specials including pigeon hot-pot (£2.50), liver and bacon casserole, macaroni cheese or smoked mackerel (all £3), home-made chicken curry or steak and kidney pie (£4.50), steak (£9.50), and puddings such as rhubarb crumble or spotted dick (from £1.30); regular summer barbecues, pig roasts and barn dances and a garden hut selling soft drinks, ice creams and so forth. Archers Village, Gibbs Mew Salisbury and Chudleys, Hook Norton Best and Ringwoods Old Thumper on handpump; darts, dominoes, shove-ha'penny, piped music and Aunt Sally. The side lawn has small fruit trees, pretty hanging baskets, and flower troughs; you can also fish on a 2 mile stretch of the river (the pub sells day tickets), and there's a caravan and camping site for five. *(Recommended by David Lamb, Joan Olivier, EML)*

Free house   Licensees Mick and Maureen Bowl   Real ale   Meals and snacks   Dining room   Buckland (036 787) 382   Children welcome   Monthly jazz and country nights   Open 11–11 (11.30–3, 5–11 winter)   Bedrooms planned

WATLINGTON   SU6894   Map 4

Chequers ◎

2 ¼ miles from M40, junction 6; Love Lane – B4009 towards Watlington, first right turn in village

The low oak-beamed ceiling in the rambling bar here is darkened to a deep ochre by the candles which they still use, and there's a low panelled oak settle and character chairs such as a big spiral-legged carving chair around a few good antique oak tables, red-and-black shiny tiles in one corner, and rugs and red carpeting elsewhere; steps on the right lead down to an area with more tables. Bar food includes lunchtime toasted sandwiches, ploughman's (from £3.50), starters such as whitebait or butterfly prawns (£3.50) and main dishes like salmon and broccoli quiche or lentil and aubergine moussaka (£4.50), chilli con carne (£5.20), chicken curry (£5.50), gammon (£7), pork fillet in herbs and cream (£7.50), half duck (£8.50), veal T-bone valdostana (£8.80), and steaks (from £9.50). Brakspears PA and SB on electric pump, and a pale grey cat. The notably pretty garden has picnic-table sets under apple and pear trees, and sweet peas, roses, geraniums, begonias, as well as rabbits. The cheese shop in Watlington itself is recommended. *(Recommended by Maureen Hobbs, Ben Whitney, Pippa Redmond, Mike and Alison Fenwick, Neil and Anita Christopher, David Wallington, P C Russell, Henry Midwinter, Chris Raisin, Graham Doyle; more reports please)*

Brakspears   Tenant John Valentine   Real ale   Meals and snacks   Watlington (049 161) 2874   Open 11.30–2.30, 6–11

WOODSTOCK   SP4416 Map 4

Feathers 🍺 🛏

Market St

This is not a pub, but a fine traditional Cotswold hotel with beautiful furniture of all ages, and immaculate service. Our (perfectly valid) excuse for including it is the attractive old-fashioned garden bar at the back, becoming very popular with readers for good food and drink – at a price. It's an almost triangular room with a small bar in one corner, oils and watercolours on its green walls, stuffed fish and birds (with a live parrot somewhere offstage), a central open fire, and a gentle, even sedate, atmosphere; it opens on to a splendid sunny courtyard with attractive tables and chairs among geraniums and trees. The food changes day by day – on our test day last summer the shortish choice included chilled melon soup with peach champagne (£3.25), courgette soup with crispy bacon and croûtons (£3.50), game terrine (£3.75), cheese with home-baked walnut bread (£5), chicken casseroled with balsam vinegar (£5.25), lamb hot-pot or braised beef (£5.50), poached salmon (£6.75) and their summer favourite – delicious toasted marshmallow with soft fruits (£3.25); ingredients are first-class, deftly handled and imaginatively presented. Well kept (though costly) Wadworths 6X on handpump, Old Timer tapped from the cask in winter, a good choice of malt whiskies, proper Pimms, country wines and (the only place we've found it this year) home-made lemonade; maybe unobtrusive piped music. Get there early for a table; no dogs. *(Recommended by Robert and Vicky Tod, Laurence Manning, Brian Jones, Andrew and Ruth Triggs)*

Free house   General manager Tom Lewis   Real ale   Meals and snacks   Restaurant (0993) 812291   *Children in eating area   Open 11–2.30, 6–11   Bedrooms; £75B/£90B*

WYTHAM   SP4708 Map 4

White Hart

Village signposted from A34 ring road W of Oxford

David Mehsen – who took over this tall stone pub at the end of 1990 – believes he is Britain's only Jordanian licensee. It is still very much somewhere to eat, with an attractively presented and reasonably priced self-service cold table – very popular, particularly on a Sunday – ranging from salads to pies such as turkey and cranberry or chicken and ham (all £4.50), a summer lunchtime barbecue in the walled rose garden, with dishes such as lamb with rosemary (£6.50), and hot dishes in the evening such as chicken kiev (£6.35), red mullet in orange and thyme (£6), and salmon en croûte (£6.90); the area around the food servery is no smoking. The partly panelled, atmospheric bar has high-backed black settles built almost the whole way round its cream walls, wheelback chairs, flagstones, a shelf of blue and white plates, and a fine relief of a heart on the iron fireback; well kept Ind Coope Burton, Tetleys and Wadworths 6X on handpump. *(Recommended by H L Dyson, R Tomlinson, Charles Turner, Dick Brown, Joan Olivier, P J and M L Davies, Caroline Wright, P J Hanson, Jane Buerkett)*

Ind Coope (Allied)   Managers David and Nicki Mehsen   Real ale   Meals and snacks Oxford (0865) 244372   *Children in dining room and conservatory   Open 11–2.30, 6–11; all day Sat*

Lucky Dip

Besides the fully inspected pubs, you might like to try these Lucky Dips recommended to us and described by readers (if you do, please send us reports):

☆ **Abingdon** [St Helens Wharf; SU4997], *Old Anchor*: Tucked away by river, little front bar looking across Thames, flagstoned back bar with little shoulder-height serving hatch, bigger lounge and lovely little panelled dining room overlooking neat almshouse gardens; Morlands on handpump, usual range of bar food running up to steaks *(Ian Phillips, Jim and Maggie Cowell)*

☆ **Abingdon** [The Bridge], *Nags Head*: Friendly, with lovely views up Thames from tables on terrace; good bar food, well kept

Watneys-related real ales on handpump, free Sun bar nibbles; bedrooms comfortable and good value, with good breakfasts *(A L Willey)*

Adderbury, *White Hart*: Popular in previous editions, but now closed and seems unlikely to reopen *(LYM)*

Ardington [SU4388], *Blue Boar*: Pretty pub in well preserved small village; three traditionally decorated, low-beamed rooms, old-fashioned juke box and bar billiards; seats outside *(H M Skinner)*

☆ **Asthall** [just off A40 3 miles on Oxford side of Burford; SP2811], *Maytime*: Popular upmarket food pub in cosy old Cotswold-stone building with close-set tables in cosy lounge, airy new family conservatory, wide choice of food inc reasonably priced Sun lunch, Morrells and Wadworths 6X, prompt friendly service; in tiny hamlet — views of Asthall Manor and watermeadows from big car park; bedrooms set attractively around striking courtyard *(Sidney and Erna Wells, Buck and Gillian Shinkman, Mr and Mrs P B Dowsett, BB)*

☆ **Bampton** [Bridge St; SP3103], *Romany*: Wide choice of reasonably priced good food inc good value Sun lunch in stripped stone pub dating from 17th century, recently refurbished to include former barn behind, with bar on right, restaurant on left, children's room, panelling and big fireplaces; friendly, helpful service, well kept Archers, Hook Norton and generally an unusual guest beer, picnic-table sets and playthings in big back walled garden *(Marjorie and David Lamb)*

Banbury [Parsons St, off Market Pl; SP4540], *Reindeer*: Simple good value bar food, well kept Hook Norton and unobtrusive piped Radio 1 in traditional male-oriented bar of much-refurbished pub with long history; its 'gallows' inn-sign spanning street is one of only half a dozen left *(Neil Tungate, LYM)*

☆ **Barford St Michael** [Lower St; SP4332], *George*: Pretty thatched 17th-century pub, very pretty, with rambling comfortably modernised beamed bar, well kept real ales such as Adnams, Badger Tanglefoot and Wadworths 6X, good home-cooked bar food (not Mon evening), log fires, attentive service, Aunt Sally, blues band Mon. Lovely atmosphere, comfortable surroundings and good food; well kept real ales and attentive staff *(Beth Adair, Barry Spry, LYM)*

Barnard Gate [off A40 E of Witney; SP4010], *Boot*: Very popular ex-Morrells free house, formerly the Britannia, with bar food, restaurant, espresso coffee, friendly staff *(Joan Olivier)*

☆ **Begbroke** [A34 Oxford—Woodstock; SP4613], *Royal Sun*: Clean and attractively decorated open-plan stone-built pub with good choice of prompt reasonably priced food, Ind Coope Burton on handpump, friendly service, tables out on terrace and in small garden *(Joy and Peter Heatherley)*

☆ **Benson** [SU6191], *Three Horseshoes*: Friendly unspoilt local very popular for wide choice of good value food in generous helpings, good friendly service, well kept Brakspears and a weekly guest beer; big rather informal garden *(Paul and Geraldine Murphy, Gordon Theaker)*

☆ **Benson** [Brook St], *Farmers Man*: Good value food, pleasant atmosphere, well kept Brakspears (full range) and friendly efficient staff *(N S Holmes, Gordon Theaker)*

Blackthorn [SP6219], *Rose & Crown*: Old village pub with welcoming landlord, cheap bar food, well kept Morrells, many old enamel adverts *(Keith Stevens)*

☆ **Blewbury** [Chapel Lane; off Nottingham Fee — narrow turning N from A417; SU5385], *Red Lion*: Well kept Brakspears real ales and wide range of good bar food in downland village pub with beams, quarry tiles and big log fire — good atmosphere, friendly licensee; tables in pleasant back garden; children in small restaurant *(Robert Gomme, LYM)*

☆ **Broadwell** [SP2503], *Five Bells*: Small but comfortable beamed 16th-century coaching inn with well prepared prompt food under friendly new licensees, real ales such as Marstons Pedigree and Wadworths 6X, open fire; restaurant, big garden *(Joan Olivier, Marjorie and David Lamb, Roger Huggins, Tom McLean, Ewan McCall)*

Bucknell [handy for M40 junction 10; SP5525], *Trigger Pond*: Sizeable ironstone pub with good food, opp ancient pond, with terrace and garden *(Norman and Barbara Wells)*

☆ **Burcot** [SU5695], *Chequers*: Pretty black and white thatched pub with tables among roses and fruit trees on neatly kept roadside lawn; smartly comfortable lounge bar with pretty gallery, well kept real ales on handpump, good range of good value food, quick friendly service, piano Fri and Sat evenings; OK for wheelchairs, parking good *(Nick Holmes, David and Diane Livesley, BB)*

☆ **Burford** [High St; SP2512], *Bull*: Beamed and panelled reconstructed bar with good if somewhat hotelish atmosphere, wide range of food, well kept Ruddles Best on handpump, good choice of wines by the glass; comfortable settees as well as Windsor chairs and so forth, piped music, restaurant; children welcome; open all day (maybe winter afternoons for eaters only); bedrooms *(Andrew and Ruth Triggs, Brian Jones, George S Jonas, H K Dyson, LYM)*

☆ **Burford** [Witney St], *Royal Oak*: Lively, friendly and welcoming, with interesting choice of good generous food; spotlessly clean, not smoky, no music; well kept Wadworths Farmers Glory, lovely coffee *(Alan Skull, Mr and Mrs D G Jones)*

Burford [High St], *Highway*: Recommended in last edition as a pub, but they've now converted the front bars into a sewing shop; still worth knowing as a good value friendly B&B, original timbering in bedrooms *(Michael Player, Colin and Evelyn Turner)*; [just off main st], *Masons Arms*: Friendly and cosy family pub, decent sandwiches and other bar food, well kept Wadworths 6X *(J*

R Smylie, P Corris)

Caulcott [SP5024], *Horse & Groom*: Young and cheerful new manager is a good American-style cook; good log fire in one small bar with eating area off *(DCTF)*

Chalgrove [High St; SU6396], *Crown*: Friendly village local with cheap freshly cooked bar food, family room; big garden with play area, barbecues, boules pitch *(S Passey)*

☆ **Charlbury** [SP3519], *Bell*: Small 17th-century hotel, clean and smart, with spotless and attractive bedrooms, quiet and civilised flagstoned bar with stripped stone walls and enormous open fire, notable bar lunches (not Sun) inc interesting choice of dishes of the day and good sandwiches, well kept Wadworths real ales, efficient friendly service, decent restaurant; children in eating area *(Michael Lyster, Paul Harrop, Bridget Blythe, R N Haygarth, LYM)*

☆ **Chazey Heath** [Woodcote Rd; A4074 Wallingford—Reading; SU6977], *Pack Horse*: Well kept and attractive old pub with big log fire in simply furnished lounge bar, well kept Gales ales and country wines, good value home-cooked bar food, sizeable back garden with play area and fairy-lit barbecue terrace, family room *(B Colyer, BB)*

Chazey Heath [Woodcote Rd; A4074 Reading—Wallingford], *Pack Saddle*: Engagingly 1950s-ish pub with alligator skins, African spears and masks, old rifles, Spanish bullfighting pictures, tartan-blanket carpet, nostalgic pop music, cheery atmosphere, well kept Gales ales, country wines, basic food; pool in lounge bar *(BB)*

☆ **Checkendon** [OS Sheet 175, map reference 666841; SU6683], *Black Horse*: Great atmosphere in truly old-fashioned unspoilt three-room free house, well kept Brakspears tapped from the cask in a back room, unfashionable armchairs, friendly licensees; lunchtime opening can be erratic, antiquated gents' *(Col A H N Reade, Nick and Alison Dowson)*

☆ **Chipping Norton** [High St; SP3127], *Crown & Cushion*: Civilised and attractive bar with some stripped stone and flagstones, central flower-decked conservatory, well kept Donnington, Wadworths IPA and 6X and guest beers, bar food (may be restricted Fri/Sat evenings), subdued piped music, tables in sheltered garden with suntrap terrace; restaurant has been closed Sun lunchtime; children welcome; splendid if expensive bedrooms (also new swimming/sports complex) *(John C Baker, Andy and Jill Kassube, LYM)*

☆ **Chipping Norton** [High St], *Blue Boar*: Large, comfortable bar divided into several areas by arches and pillars; wide range of well priced food, Courage Directors and Marstons on handpump, good cider, pleasant atmosphere; big restaurant, long flagstoned back conservatory *(P R Davis)*

Chipping Norton, *Fox*: Good value bar food in comfortable old rambling lounge with Hook Norton real ales, antique oak settles, open fire; upstairs restaurant (can be used

for lunchtime bar food); children welcome; bedrooms *(Dave Braisted, LYM)*; [High St], *White Hart*: Cvilised, friendly bar in corner of hotel, with well kept real ales inc Glennys Wychwood; bar food; bedrooms *(John C Baker)*

Church Enstone [from A34 take B4030 turn-off at Enstone; SP3724], *Crown*: Cotswold stone inn in pretty village, attractive horseshoe bar, good atmosphere, friendly staff; Flowers Original and IPA, Hook Norton, bar food, restaurant; well appointed bedrooms, good breakfasts *(Lynn Sharpless, Bob Eardley)*

☆ **Crawley** [OS Sheet 164, map reference 341120; SP3412], *Lamb*: Splendid 18th-century pub with thick stone walls, low beams (some ornamental), heavy oak timbers and big inglenook fireplace, step up to two smaller areas for family meals; Witney Glenny and Hook Norton, Australian wines; wide choice of interesting bar food (not Sun evening), darts, quiet pop music; teetotal landlord drives locals home for donation to charity *(Frank Cummins)*

☆ **Crays Pond** [B471 nr junction with B4526, about 3 miles E of Goring; SU6380], *White Lion*: Low-ceilinged lounge, bar with open fire, darts and piped music, attractive conservatory; friendly licensee, well kept real ales, wide range of well presented bar food (not Tues evening), big garden with play area *(Barbara M McHugh)*

☆ **Crowell** [B4009, 2 miles from M40 junction 6; SU7499], *Catherine Wheel*: Old brick-and-flint pub with attractive oldish furnishings inc pews and a grandfather clock; nice welcome, good service, well kept Bass and ABC, pleasant locals *(R Houghton)*

☆ **Crowmarsh** [A423; SU6189], *Queens Head*: Good value straightforward bar food in spacious and friendly low-beamed bar dating to 13th century; open fires, Watneys-related real ales on handpump, decent wines, piped music; good French dishes in handsome galleried medieval-style restaurant (French licensees), garden *(Michael Mortimer)*

☆ **Deddington** [off A423 (B4031) Banbury—Oxford; SP4361], *Kings Arms*: Thriving, bustling atmosphere, black beams, stripped stone, prompt welcoming service, well kept Marstons Burton and Pedigree on handpump, interesting wine list, good variety of reasonably priced bar food inc children's helpings *(J Forster, Michael Player)*

Deddington [Oxford Rd (A423)], *Holcombe*: Decent food and well kept beer in pleasant and comfortable bar, though concentration on restaurant and hotel side — pleasant place to stay *(Richard Carpenter)*; [Market Pl], *Unicorn*: 17th-century inn with inglenook and Victorian fireplaces, home-made food in lounge and oak-beamed restaurant, family room with games area, tables in garden and brick-built coachyard; open for breakfast; bedrooms with satellite TV *(Reports please)*

☆ **Denchworth** [SU3791], *Fox*: Old thatched pub in quiet and pretty village, three low-ceilinged carpeted bars joined by archways, comfortable, clean and very warm, with log fires; pleasant and helpful landlord, quiet piped music, good popular food *(HNJ, PEJ, Mr and Mrs P B Dowsett)*

Dorchester [SU5794], *Fleur du Lys*: Attractive timbered building with friendly welcome, imaginative bar food, Brakspears and Morlands ales, morning coffee and old brick fireplace in moderate-sized bar with restaurant section; garden and car park through old coach arch *(Stan Edwards, Nigel Gibbs)*

Drayton [A422 W of Banbury; SP4241], *Roebuck*: Two small, nicely furnished bars with lots of local memorabilia, well kept Hook Norton, Ruddles, and some unusual guest beers, bar food inc interesting dishes; lovely exterior — old stone, hanging baskets and creepers *(Hilary Roberts)*

Drayton St Leonard [SU5996], *Catherine Wheel*: Friendly and attentive new licensees and reasonably priced varied food inc good toasties in recently refurbished pub — attractive furnishings, wood carvings by landlord *(Joan Olivier)*

Ducklington [21 Standlake Rd; off A415, a mile S of Witney; SP3507], *Bell*: Delightful thatched inn with well kept Courage Best on handpump, wide choice of good value food inc good sandwiches, good service *(A T Langton)*; *Strickland Arms*: Thatched 17th-century stone pub with low beams, large fireplace each end of bar and dining area, wide choice of food, tables in small courtyard *(Joan Olivier)*

☆ **Duns Tew** [SP4528], *White Horse*: Recently restored with lovely flagstones, old oak panelling on stripped masonry, ancient beams and enormous inglenook fireplaces — will be great when it all settles in; friendly staff, five real ales and good food in bar and restaurant — a window shows the food cooking; pretty village; bedrooms *(Jason Caulkin, C Aston, Robert Gomme)*

East Challow [On A417; SU3788], *Prince of Wales*: Used to be the Station Hotel by long-closed station, recently brought upmarket, with big helpings of nicely presented reasonably priced food, good service, nice furnishings, good range of beers *(HNJ, PEJ)*

☆ **Enstone** [SP3724], *Crown*: Stripped-stone beamed bar with log fire in brass-fitted stone fireplace, antique furnishings inc stone seats in latticed windows with velvet curtains; wide choice of good bar food, attractive dining area, friendly staff, well kept Hook Norton Best and Whitbreads on handpump; good value bedrooms *(John and Karen Day, Frank Gadbois)*

☆ **Enstone** [A34 Chipping Norton—Woodstock], *Harrow*: Pleasant and friendly 16th-century inn with public bar and much refurbished lounge, real ales and ciders, decent bar food *(Gordon Smith, Bernard Phillips, TOH)*

☆ **Eynsham** [Newlands St; SP4309], *Newlands*: Pleasant, friendly atmosphere in flagstoned inglenook bar with stripped early

18th-century pine panelling; good reasonably priced food inc produce from their own smokery at reasonable prices, Halls Harvest on handpump, decent wine, log fire, fairly unobtrusive piped music *(Edward Hibbert)*

☆ **Faringdon** [Market Pl; A420 SW of Oxford, then right into A417; SU2895], *Bell*: Interesting old bar with faded mural, hunting prints, handsome 17th-century inglenook; Badger Tanglefoot and Wadworths 6X, bar food served by neat waitresses, tables in cobbled back yard; children welcome; has been open all day Sat; bedrooms *(Mr and Mrs J H Adam, Robert Brown, Mr and Mrs P B Dowsett, Dr and Mrs M I Crichton, M B P Carpenter, Gordon and Daphne, LYM — more reports on new regime please)*

☆ **Faringdon** [Market Pl], *Crown*: Well kept real ales such as Hook Norton, Glenny Wychwood, Morlands and Theakstons, decent bar food, friendly staff, flagstones, panelling, varnished wooden tables and as a rule plenty of space, roaring log fires in winter and lovely courtyard for summer; children welcome; bedrooms *(Dr and Mrs B H Colman, Norman Hill, Patrick Godfrey, LYM)*

☆ **Fifield** [A424; SP2318], *Merrymouth*: Isolated stone inn, dating partly from 13th century, now back to its original name under new licensees (was Hunters Lodge for a while); bay-windowed flagstoned bar now knocked through into further area, open fires (may not be lit if quiet), Donningtons ales and a guest such as Banks's, bar food, piped music, tables on terrace and in back garden, restaurant *(Mr and Mrs P B Dowsett, LYM; more reports on new regime please)*

Filkins [village signed off A361 Lechlade—Burford; SP2304], *Five Alls*: Friendly welcome, good food inc unusual puddings; nr interesting working wool-weaving mill in splendid 18th-century barn; *(David Lamb)*; *Lamb*: Friendly welcome, popular with locals; good choice of generous and promptly served food *(David Lamb)*

☆ **Forest Hill** [B4027 just off A40 E of Oxford — turn off Eastbound only; SP5807], *White Horse*: Quiet and relaxed atmosphere in clean, friendly and well run village local with lots of china hanging from joists of small and simple lounge bar, dining room on left, some stripped stonework, good value interesting bar food (cooked to order, may be delays at busy times) from filled home-baked rolls (particularly popular with spicy sausages) to venison and steaks; well kept Morrells Bitter and Varsity, tables on small terrace; handy for Oxfordshire Way *(Mr and Mrs P B Dowsett, N Marsden, Margaret Dyke, BB)*

Frilford [Wantage Rd (A338); SU4497], *Ark*: Former restaurant, recently extended with pubby if somewhat upmarket atmosphere; real ale, good value bar meals, lovely garden — very popular *(Mr and Mrs P B Dowsett)*

Goring [SU6080], *Catherine Wheel*: Genuine and enjoyable pub, friendly licensee, good log fire at end of L-shaped bar *(Mike Tucker)*; [Manor Rd], *John Barleycorn*: Good food and service in old beamed pub with Brakspears beer, lots of old prints and dried flowers; 200yds from Ridgeway Long Distance Path; bedrooms *(Neil and Anita Christopher)*; [Cleeve — off B4009 about a mile towards Wallingford], *Olde Leatherne Bottle*: Overlooking quiet stretch of Thames from attractive unspoilt setting, this formerly unpretentious pub is now a good upmarket restaurant *(Mrs Helen Green, J M M Hill, LYM)*

☆ Great Milton [The Green; SP6202], *Bell*: Small, tastefully extended and really welcoming and well kept cottagey old country pub with good choice of well kept real ales inc Marstons Pedigree and unusual guests; good choice of home-made food, relaxed atmosphere *(Herr and Frau Peiffer, Richard Houghton)*

Great Milton [The Green], *Bull*: Whitewashed 16th-century stone local with big stone fireplace in cosy lounge, warm relaxing atmosphere, well kept Morrells, some emphasis on good varied bar food, restaurant; public bar with darts and fruit machine *(Richard Houghton, Susan and Nigel Siesage)*

☆ Henley [by the bridge; SU7882], *Angel*: Properly pubby bar with well kept Brakspears, nice atmosphere, decent food and friendly staff; superb river views from small intimate restaurant and waterfront terrace *(B R Shiner, Comus Elliott)*

☆ Henley [Riverside], *Little White Hart*: Friendly and unpretentious, in nice spot right on river, with good value food, well kept Brakspears and good atmosphere; bedrooms *(David Warrellow, Comus Elliott)*

Henley [Market Pl], *Argyll*: Well run pub with long tartan-carpeted lounge, Highland pictures; popular lunchtime food (only roasts Sun), well kept Morlands ales, seats on back terrace, handy parking behind; nr GWG68 *(LYM)*

☆ Highmoor [SU6984], *Dog & Duck*: Delightful small and cosy country pub with wide choice of food, well kept Brakspears, log fires; two low-beamed bars, back dining area, tables outside *(Joan Olivier)*

☆ Hook Norton, *Pear Tree*: The two small bars have been knocked together and there's some decent new furniture this year, with well kept Hook Norton ales from brewery a stroll away, open fire, and big garden with a children's play area; new tenants early summer 1991 though, and we wait to see how they'll settle in *(Robert Gomme, Joy and Peter Heatherley, Jonathan and Jane Hagger, Bob Timmis, Jim and Maggie Cowell)*

☆ Islip [B4027; SP5214], *Red Lion*: Wide choice of well presented good value food inc good Sun lunch, Halls ales and decent wine in cosy if not especially pubby bar; pleasant barn conversion behind, skittle alley and dining area; lavatories for the disabled *(H J Stephens, L M Miall, Robert M Deeley, Sir Nigel Foulkes, Marjorie and David Lamb)*

Kidmore End [signed from Sonning Common; SU6979], *New Inn*: Well kept Brakspears in two-bar village pub mixing traditional and modern, with carpet and some oak beams; friendly service, good food, pleasant atmosphere, maybe piped music *(Simon Collett-Jones, Phil Bryant)*

Langford [SP2402], *Crown*: Welcoming old country pub, clean and cosy, with log fires, barrel chairs, and lots of brassware, toby jugs and clay pipes; well kept Bass and Adnams or Hook Norton, notable range of whiskies for the area, wide choice of bar food from sandwiches to steaks, Sun lunches; dominoes and darts in snug, tables outside; closed Mon lunchtime *(Miss M Mutch, E L Calcutt)*

☆ **Letcombe Regis** [follow Village Only sign as far as possible; SU3784], *Sparrow*: Unpretentious almost spartan (though spotless) village-edge pub below prehistoric Segsbury hill-fort, relaxed if sometimes rather noisy atmosphere (shame about the piped music), well kept Morlands Bitter and Mild, simple cheap lunchtime food from soup and sandwiches to fry-ups (not Sun), obliging service; tables, swings and climbing-frame in safely fenced garden *(L Walker, LYM)*

☆ **Lewknor** [just off B4009; by M40 junction 6; SU7198], *Old Leathern Bottle*: Lovely beamed village pub, three small rooms (one for families, but separated only by standing timbers so that you still feel part of pub), thriving atmosphere, well kept Brakspears, good generous bar food, good service; tables in garden *(Dave Irving, L M Miall)*

Long Hanborough [B4095; SP4214], *Three Horseshoes*: Tidy Courage pub, good range of beers, very friendly landlord, superb flowering tubs and hanging baskets *(Patrick Godfrey)*

☆ **Long Wittenham** [SU5493], *Plough*: Unspoilt and cosy pub with rustic furniture in comfortable low-beamed lounge, pub games and occasional accordionist in public bar, inglenook log fires, welcoming landlord, good choice of reasonably priced prompt simple food inc fresh fish, Watneys-related real ales, pool and children's room; Thames moorings at bottom of long, spacious garden; bedrooms *(Mike Tucker, Marjorie and David Lamb, Maureen Hobbs)*

☆ **Long Wittenham**, *Machine Man*: On track parallel to High St and almost part of a farmyard, very simple single bar with good atmosphere, welcoming landlord; several changing well kept real ales, maybe home-made cider, bar food running up to steaks, Aunt Sally *(A T Langton, Richard Houghton, J M Potter)*

Longworth [SU3899], *Blue Boar*: Fairly old thatched pub with character and atmosphere; huge log and coal fires, pews, high-backed settles, warmly welcoming barmaid, generous helpings of reasonably priced quickly served food, piped music, friendly locals; Morrells keg beers *(Mr and*

Mrs P B Dowsett)

☆ **Lower Assendon** [B480; SU7484], *Golden Ball*: Unspoilt pub with well kept Brakspears, cosy and welcoming atmosphere, consistently good food inc fine home-made pies, log fire *(Richard Houghton, J M Potter)*

Marsh Baldon [the Baldons signed off A423 N of Dorchester; SU5699], *Seven Stars*: Was part of an old farm and has great friendly village atmosphere; one big L-shaped room, with interesting choice of reasonably priced food in big helpings, and good coffee; by green of attractive village *(Phil Bryant, Col A H N Reade)*

☆ **Marston** [Mill Lane, Old Marston — OS Sheet 164, map reference 520090; SP5208], *Victoria Arms*: Notable above all for its waterside position, with spacious terrace and attractive garden by River Cherwell; roomy single-floor extension with rugs on bare boards, wood and leather seats, Victorian prints and farm tools; original flagstoned and stone-built core now mainly an eating area (plenty of tables in main room and smaller ones, food generous and quick but not cheap); all the Wadworths real ales, and three guests such as Badger and Batemans; loudish piped music, children welcome; good play area, quay for punts *(Joan Olivier, Michael and Alison Sandy, Nigel Gibbs, Edward Hibbert, BB)*

☆ **Middle Barton** [SP4325], *Carpenters Arms*: Colour-washed, thatched village inn with open-plan bar, well kept Halls Harvest on handpump, friendly and obliging staff, good choice of reasonably priced lunchtime food served generously; bedrooms *(John and Joan Wyatt, Andy and Jill Kassube)*

Milton [off Bloxham Rd; the one nr Adderbury; SP4535], *Black Boy*: Cottagey free house with Courage, Morrells, Tetleys and others, food inc dozens of different sausages from around the world, new restaurant area, open fire; front and back gardens with barbecue and play area *(J E Stanton, Lyn and Bill Capper; reports on new management please)*

☆ **Nettlebed** [A423; SU6986], *White Hart*: Cosy leather easy chairs and other old-fashioned furnishings in rambling beamed bar with discreet atmosphere, good log fires and several snug areas; well kept Brakspears, piano some evenings, imaginatively presented food running to quail, duck and salmon in big dining room, also bar food inc sandwiches and home-made burgers; children welcome; bedrooms *(Roderic Plinston, Colin and Caroline Maxwell, Robert Timmis, LYM — more reports please)*

☆ **Newbridge** [A415 7 miles S of Witney; SP4101], *Maybush*: Low-beamed bar in small, unassuming Thames-side Morlands pub with pretty waterside terrace and moorings; good local atmosphere, good range of decent bar food, cheerful efficient service, interesting collection of old mangles and other machines; can be smoky *(Gordon Theaker, Mr and Mrs P B Dowsett, David Young, D A Wilcock, Miss C M Davidson, LYM)*

☆ **Noke** [signed off B4027 NE of Oxford; SP5413], *Plough*: This cheerful place has been very popular in the past for its friendly and unhurried atmosphere and generous helpings of simple food (not Weds evening), though we can't be sure from recent reports that this is still the case and would like more news; Courage real ales, tables in pretty garden, pleasant surroundings nr Otmoor; children if well behaved at kitchen end, some live music *(Mrs E Ellis, Marjorie and David Lamb, Margaret Dyke, Hazel J Church, Margaret and Roy Randle, Joan Olivier, TBB, C G and B Mason, LYM)*

☆ **North Leigh** [OS Sheet 164, map reference 384132; SP3813], *Woodman*: Friendly little single-room village free house with real ales such as Glenny Witney and Wychwood, Hook Norton Best and Wadworths 6X, wholesome food all freshly prepared and cooked (so you may have to wait for it), daily papers, big garden *(Iain and Penny Muir)*

North Newington [High St — just W of Banbury; SP4139], *Blinking Owl*: Formerly the Bakers Arms, now tastefully antiqued — bare stone walls etc; good choice of beers inc Halls, Ind Coope Burton, Tetleys and Wadworths 6X; friendly and comfortable, but may be smoky; bedrooms *(J E Stanton)*; [just W of Banbury], *Roebuck*: Free house with very friendly new ownership; well kept Morlands, open fires, fine dogs, and good food inc good Indian dishes from a brief but enterprising menu; play feature outside *(Margaret and Christopher Bond)*

☆ **Nuffield** [A423/B481; SU6687], *Crown*: Refurbished but keeping its character, with good reasonably priced food served quickly, well kept Brakspears, roaring winter log fires, welcoming newish licensees and prompt cheerful service; tables out on terrace and lawn; on Ridgeway Long Distance Path *(D Mackay, P M Johnson, Dick Brown, Jane and Calum Maclean, Nick and Alison Dowson, Neil and Anita Christopher)*

☆ **Oxford** [Binsey Lane; narrow lane on right leaving city on A420, just before Bishops Depository], *Perch*: Spacious thatched pub fronted by lovely riverside meadows; not too overmodernised, with bare stone walls, flagstones, high-backed settles as well as more modern seats, log fires, bar food, restaurant area, Arkells, Wadworths 6X and Allied real ales (drinks not cheap); big garden, play area, landing stage; piped music may be loud; no dogs; children allowed in eating area *(Phil Bryant, Andrew Triggs, Mrs Lili Lomas, John and Joan Wyatt, LYM)*

☆ **Oxford** [North Parade], *Rose & Crown*: Unspoilt traditional pub with simply furnished small rooms and authentic Oxford feel, but graduates not undergraduates; bar food from toasted sandwiches to exotic food with middle eastern specialities, three Sun roasts, well kept Allied ales, unusually good wine by the glass, pistachio nuts by the tumbler (half pint or pint); character landlord who can be very welcoming, plenty of reference books for crossword buffs, no piped music or machines; partly covered back walled courtyard very pleasant on summer evenings *(Jane Buekett, Richard Messer, TBB, Michael Lyster, BB)*

☆ Oxford [Holywell St], *Kings Arms*: A student favourite, very full and lively in term-time; big and basic, with one main room (talk of refurbishment), two more comfortably traditional and smaller ones at the back, no smoking coffee room just inside the Parks Rd entrance; beers mainly well kept Youngs now, dictionary provided for crossword buffs, decent bar food — no attempt to hurry you *(Liz and Ian Phillips, D L Evans, BB)*

☆ Oxford [14 Gloucester St, by central car park and Gloucester Green bus stn], *Oxford Brewhouse*: Big multi-level bar with medley of secondhand-looking chairs, pews and tables, stripped brickwork and woodwork, lots of well kept real ales, lively — even noisy — bustle in term-time, with piped music; bar food (not Sat or Sun evenings), seats in small courtyard, monthly live music, humorous service; children in upper levels *(Simon Collett-Jones, Steve Huggins, Paul Harrop, Jenny and Brian Seller, A W Dickinson, LYM)*

☆ Oxford [St Giles], *Eagle & Child*: Long and narrow, with two tiny panelled snugs either side of the entrance, each with its own fireplace; further tiny area on right just before bar (itself small); modern extension beyond bar with open ceiling joists, leading to no smoking conservatory and finally a small, pretty terrace; tends to feel least cramped early in the week out of term, with friendly old-fashioned feel, well prepared and reasonably priced basic bar food, well kept Allied ales and Wadworths 6X on handpump, piped classical music, newspapers provided *(Ian Phillips, P L Knight, BB)*

Oxford [39 Plantation Rd; 1st left after Horse & Jockey going N up Woodstock Rd], *Gardeners Arms*: Friendly open-plan pub with mock beams, old local photographs, antique plates and brasses, simple wooden furnishings, home-made bar food, garden room; Morrells real ales, darts, dominoes *(LYM)*; [101 St Aldates], *Old Tom*: Small attractive pub with food bar and garden; Morrells Varsity on handpump, friendly willing staff *(John and Joan Wyatt)*; [Broad St], *White Horse*: Small, busy one-roomed pub below street level, sandwiched between parts of Blackwells bookshop; lots of signed local team photographs, oars on exposed beams, other nick-nacks, well kept real ales, reasonable bar food, oak furniture *(Wayne Brindle)*

☆ Play Hatch [Foxhill Lane; SU7476], *Shoulder of Mutton*: Unspoilt little country pub with old-fashioned roses, real well, horses in meadows beyond, lovely oak settle snugly screening the fire, friendly locals, Courage beers *(Ian Phillips)*

Pyrton [SU6896], *Plough*: Surprisingly good choice of home-made food, not cheap but good value, in modest village local, with friendly welcome, Adnams, Brakspears and Fullers ales, unobtrusive piped music, no smoking area *(Marjorie and David Lamb)*

☆ Radcot [Radcot Bridge; A4095 2 1/2 miles N of Faringdon; SU2899], *Swan*: Unpretentious inn, delightful in summer for its riverside lawn, with Thames boat trips from pub's camping-ground opp — the boat has a powered platform to bring wheelchairs aboard; well kept Morlands Bitter, Best and Mild, log fire, straightforward food, piped pop music, pub games; children in eating area; bedrooms clean and good value, with hearty traditional breakfast *(LYM)*

Ramsden [SP3515], *Royal Oak*: Efficiently run recently refurbished 17th-century free house with Hook Norton real ale, wide range of good if not cheap food; cosy and comfortable with big cheery log fire; bedrooms in separate cottages *(Mr and Mrs P B Dowsett, Jim and Josephine Pocock)*

☆ Russells Water [up track past duck pond; village signposted from B481 S of junction with B480; SU7089], *Beehive*: Old-world pub with interesting decor and furnishings, big woodburning stove in inglenook, subdued red lighting, Brakspears, Flowers Original, Marstons Pedigree and Wadworths 6X, wide choice of home-made food (not Sun evening or Mon) inc popular Sun lunch; tables on rose-fringed terrace or under fairy-lit arbour, restaurant; children in family room *(R K Sutton, Mr and Mrs Graham Dyer, Nick and Alison Dowson, Tony and Lynne Stark, LYM)*

☆ Satwell [just off B481, 2 miles S of Nettlebed; follow Shepherds Green signpost; SU7083], *Lamb*: Sensitively refurbished 16th-century low-beamed farm cottage, very small (so can get cramped), with tiled floors, friendly licensees, huge log fireplace, well kept Brakspears, traditional games, bar food from sandwiches up *(Joan Olivier, David Warrellow, Nick and Alison Dowson, LYM)*

☆ Shilton [SP2608], *Rose & Crown*: Welcoming little stonebuilt village pub with good choice of well prepared straightforward food inc fine baked potatoes in dining lounge, well kept Courage Best and Directors, darts in traditional beamed public bar, tables in sizeable garden *(Joan Olivier, Marjorie and David Lamb)*

☆ Shiplake [A4155 towards Play Hatch and Reading — OS Sheet 175, map reference 746768; SU7476], *Flowing Spring*: Well kept Fullers ales and decent bar food from sandwiches and baked potatoes to attractively priced evening dishes such as beef and basil lasagne, in three cosy but unpretentious rooms of friendly, multi-level, countrified pub with open fires and floor-to-ceiling windows overlooking the water meadows; big attractive garden, occasional jazz and Morris dancing *(Ian Phillips, LYM)*

Shiplake Row [SU7578], *White Hart*: Nice location with open fields and good walks all round; friendly staff, well kept Brakspears and house wines, log fires, good fair-priced food (Mrs Caroline Gibbins)

☆ Sibford Gower [SP3537], Wykham Arms: Impressive food at reasonable prices in comfortable and well renovated thatched pub with low-beamed lounge (one table formed by glass over old deep well) and smaller bar; well kept Hook Norton, Flowers and Fremlins, decent wines, welcoming licensees and well trained staff; small lawn with tables, slide and swings; children welcome, with own menu (P and J Shapley, Joy and Peter Heatherley, Su Jones, Sir Nigel Foulkes)

☆ Sonning Common [Blounts Court Rd; just off B481 Reading—Nettlebed, NE of centre; SU7080], Butchers Arms: Well worth knowing for good garden, well equipped for families; in nice spot, with Brakspears real ales, bar food, restaurant; bedrooms (R K Sutton, LYM)

☆ Souldern [SP5131], Fox: Delightful beamed Cotswold stone pub in attractive village location, with well kept Hook Norton and other real ales, good value bar food, particularly good friendly German landlady; comfortable bedrooms, good breakfasts (Rich and Leslie Smith, John C Baker)

☆ South Stoke [off B4009 2 miles N of Goring; SU5983], Perch & Pike: Friendly pub with fish-painted plates and stuffed fish in low-beamed brick-floored bar, just a field away from Thames; home cooking with fresh herbs, well kept Brakspears, pub games, big lawn with play area, singing landlord Sat, maybe live music Thurs; no food Sun and Mon evenings winter, limited then in summer; fishing tickets; children in restaurant (Gordon and Daphne, Col A H N Reade, David and Diane Livesley, T Galligan, Keith and Sian Mitchell, LYM)

Sparsholt [SU3487], Star: Another real old village pub gone upmarket, two bars knocked together and nicely decorated and furnished — tables, Windsor chairs, matching upholstery etc, all well done; big garden good for families, new owners anxious to please; food very promising, inc good value ploughman's with excellent home-cooked ham (HNJ, PEJ)

Stadhampton [Thame Rd; SU6098], Crown: Straightforward pub with friendly and helpful staff, generous helpings of reasonably priced bar food (not Tues), also take-aways; pool, fruit machine, soft piped music, restaurant (Joan Olivier)

Stanton St John [B4027 skirting village; SP5709], George: Attractive Cotswold stone village pub, well kept Marstons Pedigree and Burton on handpump, friendly staff, lunchtime bar food from good sandwiches up; big garden (Joan Olivier)

☆ Steventon, Cherry Tree: Several well kept ales inc Hook Norton, Wadworths IPA and 6X, good value quickly served straightforward food, pleasant beams-and-brickwork decor; doing well under new management (M Morgan, HNJ, PEJ)

☆ Steventon [The Causeway; central westward turn off main rd — village signed off A34; SU4691], North Star: Unchanging village tavern, tiled passage leading to main bar with built-in settles forming snug, steam-engine pictures, interesting local horsebrasses; open fire in parlourish lounge, simple dining room; Morlands Mild, Bitter and Best straight from casks in a side taproom, cheap weekday lunchtime bar food, cribbage; tables on side grass (Gordon and Daphne, Phil and Sally Gorton, Martin Morris, LYM)

☆ Stonor [SU7388], Stonor Arms: Carefully refurbished upmarket village pub with flagstoned bar, open log fires and good individual bar food inc sophisticated dishes at appropriate prices; bedrooms (Harry Stirling)

☆ Sutton Courtenay [Appleford Rd (B4016); SU5093], Fish: Outstanding food, detailed and imaginative concentration on good fresh ingredients; not cheap, but undeniably good value considering the quality, and always inc a vegetarian dish though not listed on board; well kept Morlands and other beers, good wines, lovely nibbles; Sun lunchtime booked restaurant meals only (A T Langton, David Lamb, R C Watkins, Peter and Susan Maguire, Mrs S Boreham)

Swalcliffe [Bakers Lane; just off B4035; SP3737], Stags Head: Consistently friendly, with interesting reasonably priced food, popular Sun lunch, real ales such as Adnams, Hook Norton Best and Wadworths 6X on handpump, decent wine, very cosy atmosphere, lovely log fire, seats on front terrace and in attractive garden; picturesque setting (George Atkinson)

☆ Tackley [SP4720], Gardiners Arms: Popular pub with good atmosphere, friendly efficient service, comfortable lounge with coal-effect gas fire, well kept Allied real ales, efficiently served well presented good value bar food; public bar with darts and piped pop music, a few picnic-table sets on grass by car park; handy for Rousham House (Lyn and Bill Capper, Joan Olivier, Tim Brierly)

☆ Thame [Cornmarket; SP7005], Abingdon Arms: Small friendly free house with bare brickwork, old beams, open fireplace, nicely polished tables and truly warm welcome; newspapers and magazines in rack, Adnams and Theakstons real ales and good collection of bottled beers; good bar food with al dente veg. Nice and friendly old-world pub (Ian Phillips, Patrick Godfrey)

☆ Thrupp [SP4815], Boat: Friendly canalside local with Morrells ales, good reasonably priced food, most home-made, fresh and hot; warm and friendly, fairly comfortable, with lots of atmosphere, though may not appeal so much to non-smokers; canalside garden, pleasant surroundings, garden (Miss M James, A Clack, Comus Elliott, Sir Nigel Foulkes, TRA, MA)

Toot Baldon [village signed from A423 at Nuneham Courtenay, and B480; SP5600], Crown: Friendly village pub, enterprising newish young landlord, good promptly served reasonably priced food still inc the pub's spectacular 'Toot sweet', tables out on terrace *(Marjorie and David Lamb)*

☆ **Towersey** [down drive nr Chinnor Rd/Manor Rd crossroads; SP7304], *Three Horseshoes*: Warm and pleasant country atmosphere, with flagstones, old-fashioned furnishings and good log fire; well kept Allied and guest real ales, good bar food inc plenty for vegetarians, piped music, small restaurant, function room in medieval barn; biggish garden with playthings among fruit trees; children allowed at lunchtime *(Bryan Wheeler, MP, LYM)*

Wallingford [Thames St; SU6089], *Little House Around the Corner by the Brook*: Pews, old wooden tables and so forth in smallish wooden-floored bar, good range of quite imaginative food from soup to duck — light surcharge to eat in small restaurant; well kept local real ale, good bar games, outside stairway down to big pebbled terrace by stream *(Hilary Roberts)*

☆ **Wantage** [Mill St; past square and Bell, down hill then bend to left; SU4087], *Lamb*: Friendly and snugly comfortable family-run low-beamed and timbered pub with choice of attractively furnished seating areas, well kept Morlands, popular nicely presented freshly cooked bar food, good play area *(Barbara M McHugh, LYM)*

Wantage [Charlton Rd], *Lord Nelson*: Cosy and friendly, with attractive furnishings and well kept spacious garden; darts, fruit machine, juke box; Thurs evening raffle with free sandwiches *(H M Skinner)*

☆ **Warborough** [The Green South; just E of A329, 4 miles N of Wallingford; SU5993], *Six Bells*: Low-ceilinged thatched pub with particularly well kept Brakspears, country furnishings, big fireplace, antique photographs and pictures, fairly priced good simple bar food; tables in back orchard, cricket green in front, boules in summer; children in eating area *(Pat Jones, LYM)*

Wendlebury [a mile from M40 junction 9; signposted from A421 Bicester—Oxford; SP5619], *Red Lion*: Friendly old low-beamed pub with parquet floor, very reasonably priced food, games room with pool and fruit machine; big garden with play area, statuary and aviary inc waterfowl and peacocks *(Joan Olivier)*

West Hanney [SU4092], *Plough*: Popular and comfortable local with friendly service, wide range of bar food and Wadworths 6X *(R C Watkins)*

☆ **West Hendred** [Reading Rd; off A417 — OS Sheet 174, map reference 447891; SU4488], *Hare*: Generous helpings of good value food inc quite adventurous evening specials, and well kept Morlands, in civilised two-bar local with good welcome for strangers *(A T Langton, Sarah Bradbrook, R C Watkins, HNJ, PEJ)*

Wheatley [132 London Rd; SP5905], *Plough*: Friendly local, good value bar meals, farm cider, darts *(S Corrigan)*

Whitchurch [just over toll bridge from Pangbourne; SU6377], *Greyhound*: Small, friendly old pub, neat and interesting, with tasty, good value food, relaxed atmosphere, well kept Allied ales; close to Thames in pleasant village *(Neil H Barker, Mr and Mrs Skinner)*

Witney [17 High St; SP3510], *Royal Oak*: Cosy and welcoming, with log fire and good lunchtime bar snacks; busy on market days — Thurs and Sat *(J R Smylie, A T Langton)*

☆ **Woodstock** [A44 N; SP4416], *Black Prince*: Friendly and fairly small pub with ancient stone walls and furnishings to match, suit of armour in bar, swords on walls, dining room with bar food inc Mexican dishes and pizzas till late, well kept real ales such as Archers Village, Ringwood Old Thumper, Theakstons Old Peculier, Uley Old Spot, piped pop music (may be loud); outside lavatories, very basic but clean *(PLC, Richard Houghton, Margaret and Christopher Bond, Phil Bryant)*

Woodstock [Park St], *Bear*: Handsome and atmospheric partly medieval market-town hotel (THF), with easy chairs and hunting trophies in comfortable bar on right, well kept real ales, civilised if not cheap bar food, expert service; good bedrooms *(Comus Elliott, Ruth and Andrew Triggs)*; [Park St], *Vickers*: More restaurant than pub, but friendly and intimate, with superb snack lunches *(Ian Phillips)*; [Market St], *Woodstock Arms*: Tables under cocktail parasols in yard, good food, most friendly service; bedrooms *(Ian Phillips)*

☆ **Woolstone** [SU2987], *White Horse*: Partly thatched 16th-century pub in lovely isolated spot, almost clinically clean, but welcoming, with some concentration on quick food service; two big open fires in spacious beamed and partly panelled bar, well kept real ales such as Flowers and Wadworths 6X on handpump, very quiet during week but busy weekends; children allowed in side eating area; restaurant; handy for the White Horse; four bedrooms *(M J Dyke, Simon Reynolds, T Galligan)*

☆ **Wroxton** [Church St; off A422 at hotel – pub at back of village; SP4142], *North Arms*: Thatched stone pub in lovely village, tables on idyllically placed front garden, simple but comfortable modernised lounge; good value wholesome bar food, evening restaurant (not Mon); well kept Morrells Graduate on handpump, friendly staff, darts, dominoes, quiz evenings, summer folk music; the grounds of Wroxton College opp make a beautiful pre-lunch walk *(Peter Castleton, Miss L Y Taylor, Paul Corbett, I R Hewitt, LYM)*

Shropshire

A lot of pubs have been changing hands here; mostly the signs are good. There are new licensees at the friendly Hollyhead Inn in Bridgnorth (handy for the steam railway terminus), the interestingly furnished Crown at Hopton Wafers (a subtle change in character, but still well worth knowing for food and as a place to stay), the Green Dragon at Little Stretton (doing well), and the nicely placed Church Inn in Ludlow; also at two new main entries, the attractively traditional Red Lion at Llanfair Waterdine (in the Guide a few years back, under previous owners) and the good value Longville Arms at Longville – both these in their quite different ways are well worth considering as places to stay at. The county's two best pubs are both tucked away in marvellous countryside: the lovely Stables at Hope (excellent food, very friendly – it earns a star award this year) and the Wenlock Edge Inn up on Wenlock Edge (also excellent all round – and you can stay there). Pub food and drink is significantly cheaper in Shropshire than in England generally, with particular bargains being the food at the New Inn in its pretty riverside spot at Ironbridge, and at the Lion of Morfe out in the country at Upper Farmcote. The beers brewed in the splendid Victorian brewhouse at the Three Tuns in Bishops Castle are very attractively priced, too. A tale with many twists hangs over what until 1988 was the county's main beer, Wem. Until that year it was brewed in the town of that name. Then Greenalls of Cheshire, who'd bought the brewery, closed it and shifted production to another subsidiary of theirs, Davenports over in Birmingham. In 1989 they shut down Davenports and shifted the Wem brewing to yet another subsidiary, Shipstones in Nottingham. Now Greenalls have opted out of brewing altogether, and Wem is brewed by Allied, the national combine. So don't imagine from its name that Wem is still a local beer. In the Lucky Dip section at the end of the chapter, the Unicorn in Ludlow, Crown at Newcastle and Crown at Wentnor are currently on a decided upswing; and other pubs to note particularly in the Dip, most of them inspected by us, include the Railwaymans Arms in Bridgnorth, Feathers at Brockton, Crown at Claverley, Boat at Coalport, Sun at Corfton, White Hart at Ellesmere, Blacksmiths Arms at Loppington, Gaskell Arms in Much Wenlock (where there are two good main entries already), White Hart at Shifnal and Stiperstones at Stiperstones; there are several interesting pubs in Shrewsbury, and in Ludlow.

BISHOPS CASTLE   SO3289 Map 6
Three Tuns

Salop Street

The many-storied Victorian brick brewhouse across the yard from this unspoilt and family run pub is unique among pub breweries for its traditional tower layout, with the various stages of the brewing process descending floor by floor (it's a Grade I listed building). From it comes the good cheap XXX Bitter, Mild, an old-fashioned dark somewhat stoutish ale called Steamer and winter Old Scrooge; brewery tours can be arranged. The quaint public bar has a welcoming atmosphere, and home-made bar food includes soup (£1.25), baps, filled baked potatoes (from £1.25), burger (£2.75), ploughman's (from £3), ratatouille or cottage pie (£3.95), lasagne (£4.20), steaks (from (£8), and puddings like treacle tart (£1.25). Hall's and Weston's ciders; malt whiskies. Darts, dominoes and quoits. There's a garden and terrace, with a large selection of plants for sale. *(Recommended by Andy and Jill Kassube, Joy Heatherley, TOH, Dave Braisted, J Penford, Sue Holland, Dave Webster)*

Own brew   Licensee Dominic Wood   Real ale   Meals and snacks   (0588) 638797 Well behaved children welcome   Maybe disco/bands Fri evening   Open 11.30–3, 6.30–11; 11.50–5, 6.30–11 summer Fri, Sat and bank hols

BRIDGNORTH   SO7293 Map 4

Hollyhead 🛏

Hollybush Road; opposite station

A new licensee has taken over this cheerful pub and the real ales on handpump or tapped from the cask now include well kept Bass, Boddingtons, Flowers Ordinary, Marstons Pedigree and Wadworths 6X; fresh orange juice. The rambling areas of the lounge have oak beams and joists, new plush banquettes, wheelback chairs around sturdy dining tables, low chunky elm tables by the counter, one or two hunting prints, and logs burning in the big stone fireplace. A separate similarly furnished but smaller bar on the left has darts, cribbage, dominoes, fruit machine, piped music and satellite TV. Straightforward bar food such as filled rolls (70p), pork and pineapple curry (£3.20), chilli con carne or chicken (£3.50), steak and kidney pie (£3.75), plaice (£3.80), gammon (£4.75) and sirloin steak (£6.50). There are tables under cocktail parasols in a suntrap roadside courtyard, as well as brown-painted slatted railway benches – appropriate enough, with the headquarters of the Severn Valley steam railway across the road. Breakfasts are good. *(Recommended by A P Jeffreys, JM, PM, W H Bland; more reports please)*

Free house   Licensee Barry Goldsmith   Real ale   Meals and snacks (12–2, 6–8) Restaurant   Bridgnorth (0746) 762162   Children welcome (not too late)   Mon night disco   Open 12–2.30, 5.30–11; 11–11 Sat   Bedrooms; £18/£32

CARDINGTON   SO5095 Map 4

Royal Oak

Village signposted off B4371 Church Stretton–Much Wenlock, pub behind church; also reached via narrow lanes from A49

Popular for some miles around, this friendly old pub is in a lovely spot. Tables beside roses in the front court look over to hilly fields, and a mile or so away – from the track past Willstone (ask for directions at the pub) – you can walk up Caer Caradoc Hill which has magnificent views. Inside, there are rambling corners, low beams, old standing timbers of a knocked-through wall, hops draped along the bar gantry, a vast inglenook fireplace with its roaring winter log fire, cauldron, black kettle and pewter jugs, and gold plush, red leatherette and tapestry seats solidly capped in elm. Home-made lunchtime bar food includes sandwiches (£1.50; toasties £2.20), soup (£2), ploughman's (£2.90) and at least seven dishes – served without vegetables – such as macaroni cheese (£2.25), enjoyable fidget pie (£3.20), meaty or vegetarian lasagne (£3.75), steak and kidney pie (£4.50), with evening dishes like chicken (£4.80), gammon and egg (£5.90), and rump steak (£6.60); no chips at lunchtime. Well kept Ruddles County and Wadworths 6X on handpump, with Bass and Springfield, also on handpump, kept under light blanket pressure; darts, dominoes and cribbage in the main bar. One boxer is friendly, the other more stand-offish. *(Recommended by Denzil T Taylor, Mike and Carol Muston, Jenny Cantle, A P Jeffreys, Laurence Manning, Barry Gibbs, Helen and Wal Burns, Mike and Wendy Proctor, M Box, A G Roby, G T Jones, Paul McPherson)*

*Free house   Licensee John Seymour   Real ale   Meals and snacks (12–2, 7–8.30; not
Sun evening)   Children welcome lunchtime; only if eating in evening   Longville (069
43) 266   Open 12–2.30, 7–11; closed Mon Nov-Easter excluding school hols   One
self-contained double bedroom; £22S/£33S*

CLUN   SO3081 Map 6
Sun

High Street; B4368 towards Clunton

The beamed lounge bar in this small Tudor local has some attractive old tables,
one or two high-backed winged settles, built-in cushioned wall benches, a carved
antique oak armchair, and sturdy wall timbers. The L-shaped public bar has
traditional settles on its flagstones, an enormous open fire, and dominoes,
cribbage, chess, backgammon and piped music; there's a friendly Scotty dog (not
always around). Decent bar food includes sandwiches (from £1), home-made soup
(£1.50), ploughman's (£2.75), lasagne (£3.75), specials like shoulder of lamb with
garlic, cashew nut paella, wholewheat pancakes and Mexican beanpot (£5.75),
and puddings (£2). Well kept Banks's Bitter and Mild, Woods Special and up to six
guests like Adnams, Hook Norton, Timothy Taylors or Wadworths 6X on
handpump. The sheltered back terrace has tables among pots of geraniums and
other flowers. *(Recommended by John Evans, R and M Wallace, Susan and Nigel Siesage,
Andy and Jill Kassube, Joy Heatherley, David Fowles, Colin Laffan, Caroline and Colin, Sue
Holland, Dave Webster)*

*Free house   Licensee Keith Small   Real ale   Meals and snacks   Restaurant   Clun
(058 84) 277   Children in eating area of bar   Open 11–3 (4 Sat), 6–11   Bedrooms;
£18/£32(£36B)*

COALPORT   SJ7002 Map 4
Woodbridge

Turn off A442 S of Telford at Coalport 1/2, Broseley 3 signpost

An indication of this tall pub's age is that the present elegant bridge – of iron, not
wood – dates back nearly 200 years. The softly lit main bar has a big red cloth bow
window seat for the view with plenty of other seats below its joists and beams
(liberally hung with copper and brass bygones), and some carpeting on its quarry
tiles. There are Victorian prints, stuffed birds, old bottles and china, lots of modern
brass wall clocks, and a snug low-raftered back area with bookshelves and a coal
fire. A simple little side bar has the same view, as do the many tables on a side
terrace, with a barbecue. Decent bar food at lunchtime includes soup (£1),
sandwiches (from £1.30), burger or ploughman's (£2.50), a cold table or chilli con
carne (£3.50), home-made fish or beef, oyster and Guinness pies (£4), and daily
specials (around £3.50), with evening dishes like pizza (£2.50) and scampi (£3.50).
Courage Directors, John Smiths and a guest beer on handpump; darts, fruit
machine, rather loud piped pop music. This is a lovely spot above the River Severn
and the pub looks down over well spaced rustic benches on steepish waterside
lawns to the ash woods on the opposite bank. They now have seven pegs of coarse
river fishing – £2 a day. *(Recommended by J Penford, TOH; more reports please)*

*Courage   Lease: Sean Brennan   Real ale   Meals and snacks (12–2, 6–9.30)   No
smoking restaurant   (0952) 882054   Children in eating area of bar and in restaurant
Open 11–3, 6–11; all day Sat   Bedrooms; £15/£30; they plan to add bathrooms to the
rooms*

HOPE   SJ3401 Map 6
Stables ★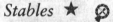

Drury Lane, Hopesgate; pub signposted off A488 S of Minsterley, at the Bentlawnt 3/4,
Leigh 1 3/4 signpost – then take first right turn

It's well worth going out of your way to find this delightful little cottagey pub. The welcome is warmly friendly, the atmosphere particularly homely, and the food very good indeed. The black-beamed L-shaped bar has comfortably cushioned or well polished wooden seats around attractive oak and other tables, hunting prints of varying ages and degrees of solemnity, well chosen china, and logs burning in the imposing stone fireplace; in a back room (with copper-topped cask tables) are some big prints of butterflies and herbs. Promptly served, the lunchtime home-made bar food changes day by day with excellent soup (£1.50), a mixture of three cheeses and pickles (£3.20), hot venison sausages with mustard mayonnaise (£3.50), cheesey tomato and aubergine bake (£4.50), creamy shropshire blue and mushroom crumble (£4.75), liver and bacon casserole (£4.90), spicy tandoori chicken (£5) and home-made puddings like bread and butter pudding or cherry and yoghurt mousse (£1.90; the home-made ice creams are highly recommended, too); evening dishes such as lovely asparagus (£2.85), dressed Cromer crab (£3), smoked haddock and prawn crumble (£4.95), rabbit casseroled with cider and mild mustard (£6.85) or fresh poached salmon with a light cucumber and dill sauce (£7.25); vegetables are fresh. On Thursday to Saturday evenings, the cottagey dining room is open (only four tables, so booking's worth while). Well kept Hancocks HB, Ind Coope Burton, Marstons Pedigree, and Woods Special on handpump, with Addlestones cider in summer, decent wines and spirits (they do a good kir, buck's fizz or black velvet, and Pimms), and half-a-dozen malt whiskies. On summer Sunday evenings when they have a boules knock-out they do barbecues with fresh sardines, grilled prawns and leg of lamb with fresh herbs and garlic; darts, shove-ha'penny, cribbage, dominoes; several cats (Winge is the characterful ginger tom) and Corrie and Kelly the gruffly friendly mother-and-daughter cream-coloured labradors. There's a lovely view from the front tables, over rolling pastures to the Long Mountain; behind, you look over the Hope Valley to the Stiperstones. A good place to take children at lunchtime. (*Recommended by A G Roby, A P Jeffreys, Paul S McPherson, Laurence Manning, Nora Casey, Bruce and Zoe Fraser, Andrew Stephenson, R C Morgan, Frank Cummins*)

Free house   Licensees Denis and Debbie Harding   Real ale   Meals and snacks (12–1.30, 7–8.30; not Mon)   Restaurant   Worthen (0743) 891344   Children in eating area of bar   Open 11.30–2.30, 7–11; 12–2, 7–11 in winter; closed Mon and 25 and 26 Dec

HOPTON WAFERS   SO6476   Map 4

Crown 🛏 🅿

A4117

This substantial and attractive creeper-covered stone building has a spreading bar with a large inglenook fire as well as a woodburning stove, various seats that include flowery cushions on the black settles, oil paintings, and maybe fresh flowers. Bar food includes sandwiches (from £1.70), soup (£1.75), ploughman's (£3.25), spinach and stilton or avocado and prawn pancakes (£3.75), tagliatelle with tomato and basil sauce (£4.25), salads (from £4.75), beef and mushroom pie in red wine (£5.25), lamb madras and poppadums (£5.50), smoked haddock and prawn gratin in a shellfish sauce (£6), steaks (£8.50), daily specials, home-made puddings, and children's meals (£2.50); it does get very busy. Well kept Bass, Boddingtons, Flowers Original and Marstons Pedigree on handpump, good house wines, and coffee. There are tables under cocktail parasols on the terraces and in the streamside garden, with plenty of tubs of bright flowers. It will be interesting to see if, as they settle in, the new licensees with their long experience in the hotel and catering trade succeed in retaining the welcoming atmosphere found here under their predecessors. (*Recommended by PLC, Mr and Mrs T A Towers, J G Quick, C J McFeeters, Dorothy and David Young, Hilary Sargeant, N P Clarke, J K Conneen, Mr and Mrs Frostick, B and M A Langrish, Paul Denham, Nicola Brown-Denham*)

Free house   Licensees John Price, T G Alexander   Real ale   Meals and snacks (till 10pm)   Restaurant; not Sun evening   Cleobury Mortimer (0299) 270372   Children in eating area of bar and in restaurant   Open 11–3, 6–11   Bedrooms; £35B/£55B

IRONBRIDGE   SJ6903 Map 4

New Inn £

Blists Hill Museum: follow brown museum signs from M54 exit 4, or A442; then Blists
Hill itself signposted

This unusual open-air museum is made up of the pub and other late Victorian
buildings – all formerly in Walsall. Obviously – the museum entrance fee is £4.50,
or £6 to include several other museums in the area – you wouldn't come here only
for the pub, but the whole site makes an appealing half-day visit, with shops, all
sorts of working tradesmen (tinsmith, cobbler, blacksmith, candlemaker among
others), sawmill, ironworks, tileworks and so forth. From most you can buy things,
using either modern money or Victorian pricing and money exchanged at the
bank. The tradesmen and "inhabitants" wear period clothes, and explain what
they're doing. The pub is a little red-brick corner building, very simple inside – gas
lamps, shiny black and brown paint, sawdust on the floorboards, rows of pewter
and china tankards, and virtually no ornamentation beyond a few period
advertisements; well kept Springfield Bitter and Highgate Mild on handpump, and
Bulmers cider; shove-ha'penny, alley skittles and table skittles. Upstairs is a
decorous club room (serving teas and snacks including excellent sandwiches,
home-made soup (£1.60), ploughman's with home-made apple chutney or
home-made pork pie (£2.60), vegetarian meals, a hot potted meal of the day or
chicken, leek and ham pie (all £3), and puddings like gooseberry and elderflower
fool (£2). The back yard has some slatted old benches with appropriate noises off –
the muted clatter of nearby iron and tin working, burbles from the pigeon coop,
and the excitement of the hens when one of the white-costumed girls from the pub
comes out to fling some greens over the wire. (Recommended by Julian Proudman, Mrs
Y M Healey, T Galligan, D W Crossley; more reports please)

M & B (Bass)   Licensee Brian Morris   Real ale   Lunchtime snacks and afternoon teas
(upstairs)   Restaurant   Ironbridge (0952) 586063   Children welcome   Open 11–5;
can be hired evenings; closed 25 and 26 Dec

LITTLE STRETTON   SO4392 Map 6

Green Dragon

Ludlow Road; village well signposted from A49

Popular with walkers, this creeper-covered white house has a new licensee. The
neatly kept carpeted lounge bar has green plush banquettes and stools around the
well spaced polished dark tables, and a relaxed atmosphere; welcoming coal fire.
Bar food now includes soup (£1.25), filled rolls or sandwiches (from £1.25),
ploughman's (£2.85), broccoli bake or home-made steak and kidney pie (£4.50),
steaks (from £5.10), halibut (£6.30), and puddings (£1.80). Well kept Ruddles Best
and County, Woods Parish and Websters Choice on handpump; dominoes. There
are picnic-table sets under cocktail parasols on the lawn of a prettily planted
garden. (Recommended by Graham Gibson, Dorothy and David Young, Mr and Mrs J H
Adam, P D Putwain, T Galligan, M Watson, Kevin Fields)

Free house   Licensee Jim Greenough   Real ale   Meals and snacks (not summer Sun
evenings)   Restaurant   Church Stretton (0649) 722925   Children welcome   Open
11–3.30, 6–11

Ragleth

Ludlow Road; village well signposted from A49

Close to Long Mynd (a spacious heather-and-bracken plateau owned by the
National Trust, with fine views) and near Good Walks Guide Walk 102, this
attractive pub is especially cosy in winter. There's a good fire in the comfortable
bay-windowed lounge bar, which also has an unusual curved corner, an
oak-topped bar counter, and built-in seats, and a huge inglenook fireplace in the
brick-and-tile-floored public bar; darts, fruit machine, juke box, maybe piped
music, and quiz nights. Reasonably priced, home-made bar food includes
home-made soup (£1.60), prawn sandwiches (£1.70), good cottage pie with red

cabbage (£3.25), delicious ploughman's (from £3.25), home-made vegetarian dishes, lasagne or chilli con carne (£4.35), puddings (£1.90), and Sunday roast (£8.25). Well kept Bass, M & B Brew XI and guest beers on handpump and house wines. Tables on the lawn (where there's a tulip tree) look across to an ancient-seeming thatched and timbered church (actually built in this century). *(Recommended by David Williams, Cyril Burton, G T Jones; more reports please)*

Free house   Licensees Harford and Marion Ransley   Real ale   Meals and snacks   Restaurant   Church Stretton (0694) 722711   Children in one bar   Occasional guitarist   Open 11–2.30, 6–11; maybe open all day Sat; closed 25 Dec

LLANFAIR WATERDINE   SO2476   Map 6

Red Lion 🛏

Village signposted from B4355; turn left after crossing bridge

The licensee of this fine old place is a firm believer in keeping his pub as a proper old-fashioned village tavern with no noisy machines or music and no children inside; and although they serve good, home-made food which can be eaten in the pub or small dining room (tables can be pre-booked) it is not a dining pub: sandwiches (from £1.10), home-made soup (£1.30), home-made chicken liver pâté (£2.85), ploughman's (£2.95), plaice (£3.50), evening grills, and daily specials like quiche, winter rabbit stew, turkey rissoles, vegetable curry and beef in red wine and garlic (from around £4). The rambling lounge bar has cosy alcoves, beams, easy chairs, some long, low settles and little polished wooden seats on its Turkey carpet, and a big open fire. The small black-beamed taproom has plain wooden chairs on its flagstoned floor, a woodburning stove, and table skittles, dominoes, cribbage, shove-ha'penny, and sensibly placed darts; quoits. Well kept Ansells Dark Mild and Marstons Pedigree on handpump; friendly service. There are seats on flagstones among roses by the quiet lane in front of the pub, with more on the grass at the back looking down over the River Teme (which is actually the border between England and Wales); a track, before you get to the main road, leads to a good stretch of Offa's Dyke and the long-distance walkway there. *(Recommended by A P Jeffreys, David Williams, Joy Heatherley, K and G Jackson)*

Free house   Licensee Mick Richards   Real ale   Meals and snacks (12–1.30, 7–9)   Knighton (0547) 528214   Open 12–2, 7–11; closed Tues lunchtime   Bedrooms; £20(£27.50B)/£33(£40B)

LONGVILLE   SO5494   Map 4

Longville Arms 🛏

B4371 Church Stretton–Much Wenlock

Very welcoming under its new owners, this big-windowed inn has two spacious bars. The left one is simpler, with sturdy elm or cast-iron-framed tables, leatherette banquettes and a woodburning stove at each end. The right-hand lounge has dark plush wall banquettes and cushioned chairs, with some nice old tables. A wide choice of good value home-made bar food includes soup (£1.10), filled baked potatoes (from £1.50), a ham and cheese toastie with a fried egg on top (£1.40), garlic mushrooms (£2.20), black pudding with a bacon roll and home-made chutney (£2.70), plaice or home-cooked meat salads (£3.40), lasagne (£3.70), gammon and egg (£3.90) and sirloin steak (£6.50), with dishes of the day such as duck or dressed crab, excellent puddings (£1.40) and children's dishes (from £1.35). Well kept Bass and Worthington BB on handpump; darts, bar billiards, cribbage, dominoes and fruit machine. There are picnic-table sets under cocktail parasols in a neat side garden, with a play area. Besides the good value bedrooms, there's a good self-contained flat in an adjacent converted barn. *(Recommended by R K Sutton, D O'Hara)*

Free house   Licensee Patrick Egan   Real ale   Meals and snacks (not Tues lunchtime)   Children welcome   Open 12–3, 7–11; closed Tues lunchtime   Bedrooms; £15S/£30S

LUDLOW   SO5173   Map 4

Church Inn 🛏

Church Street, behind town centre Buttercross

This Georgian-stuccoed inn opens behind on to a decorous walk by the red
sandstone church. Inside, the airy bar – divided into two by a stub wall – has
comfortably cushioned burgundy wall banquettes looping around the alcoves, and
cream walls hung with attractively engraved old song title-pages, botanical prints,
and paintings by local artists and so forth. Under the new licensees bar food
includes lunchtime sandwiches (from £1.50; toasties from £2) and ploughman's
(from £3), as well as soup (£1.30), quiche (£3.25), chicken curry (£3.50), trout,
lasagne or steak and mushroom pie (all £4.50) and rump steak (£6.95). Well kept
Ansells, Ruddles Best and County, Websters Yorkshire and a beer named for the
pub on handpump, with guest beers as well. *(Recommended by A G Riby, Denzil T
Taylor, Susan and Nigel Siesage, R and M Wallace)*

*Free house   Licensees Stuart and Brenda Copland   Real ale   Meals and snacks   No
smoking restaurant   Ludlow (0584) 872174   Children in eating area of bar and in
restaurant   Open 11–11   Bedrooms; £28B/£40B*

MUCH WENLOCK   SJ6200   Map 4

George & Dragon

High St

The biggest pub collection of water jugs in England – about a thousand – can be
found hanging from the beams in the front bar of this unpretentious town local;
there's also lots of bottle labels and beer trays, some George-and-the-Dragon
pictures, old brewery and cigarette advertisements, a few antique settles as well as
conventional furnishings, and a couple of attractive Victorian fireplaces (with
coal-effect gas fires). It can get smoky. At the back, the quieter snug old-fashioned
rooms have black beams and timbering, little decorative plaster panels, tiled floors,
a stained-glass smoke room sign, a big George-and-the-Dragon mural as well as
lots of smaller pictures (painted by local artists), and a little stove in a fat fireplace.
A good choice of bar food at lunchtime includes rolls and ploughman's,
home-made soup (£1.65), home-made pâtés (£2.50), lentils and vegetable bake or
fisherman's pie (£4), prawn provençale or beef and Guinness casserole (£4.25), and
home-made puddings; evening meals are served in Eve's Kitchen, with starters such
as avocado and bacon salad and main courses like monkfish roasted with garlic or
breast of chicken in local mead and cream (2 courses £11; 3 courses £13.50). Well
kept Hook Norton Best and guest beers on handpump; music from vintage
wireless. *(Recommended by Joy Heatherley, Paul Noble, Neil and Anita Christopher, Chris
Raisin; more reports please)*

*Free house   Licensee Eve Nolan   Real ale   Lunchtime meals and snacks (not Sun
evening)   Evening restaurant; closed Sun   Much Wenlock (0952) 727312   Older
children in restaurant if well behaved   Open 11–2.30, 6(7 winter)–11*

Talbot ⊘ 🛏

High Street

Several opened-together carpeted areas in this rather smart and very neatly kept
old pub have lovely flowers, comfortable green plush button-back wall banquettes
around highly-polished tables, walls decorated with prints of fish, and with shives,
tuts, spices and other barrel-stoppers, low ceilings, and two big log fires (one in an
inglenook). Good, attractively presented home-made bar food at lunchtime
includes soup (£1.50), filled baked potatoes (£2.95), ploughman's with two pâtés
and garlic sausage (£4.25), a pie suitable for vegetarians and vegans (£4.50),
delicious omelettes (from £4.50), very tasty home-made spicy pancake or haddock
fillet in lemon sauce (£4.75), special prawn salad (£5.25), daily specials such as
pork and apricot pie or liver and bacon casserole (around £4.75), and puddings
like bread and butter pudding (£2.25), with evening dishes like prawns in a mild

curry sauce (£3.25), lemon sole meunière (£7.75) and steaks (from £8.25); Sunday roast lunch; friendly service. Ruddles Best and Websters Yorkshire on handpump, good value wines, good coffee and tea; piped music. Through the coach entry, there are white seats and tables in an attractive sheltered yard. *(Recommended by A A Asbury, Ralf Zeyssig, Mike and Wendy Proctor, Colin Laffan, Mrs Y M Healey, Neil and Anita Christopher)*

Free house   Licensee Timothy Lathe   Real ale   Meals and snacks (not 25 Dec) Restaurant   Much Wenlock (0952) 727077   Well behaved children allowed (no babies or prams)   Open 10.30–2.30, 6–11; closed 25 Dec   Bedrooms; £30B/£50B

NORTON   SJ7200 Map 4

Hundred House ⊗ ⇔

A442 Telford–Bridgnorth

There are several more or less separate areas in this carefully refurbished pub with old quarry tiles at either end and modern hexagonal ones in the main central part – which has high beams strung with hop-bunches and cooking pots. Steps lead up past a little balustrade to a partly panelled eating area where stripped brickwork looks older than that elsewhere. Handsome fireplaces have log fires or working Coalbrookdale ranges (one has a great Jacobean arch with fine old black cooking pots), and around sewing-machine tables are a variety of interesting chairs and settles with some long colourful patchwork leather cushions. Food – served all day – starts with breakfast (from 8.30am, English £4.95) and includes afternoon tea (2.30pm–6pm, £1.95), as well as baps (from £1.25, bacon and mushroom £2.50), soup (£2), ploughman's (from £2.95), savoury pancake (£3.25), home-made lasagne (£5), grilled local gammon (£5.75), steak and kidney pie, goujons of fresh fish or vegetable and nut crumble with a cream and mint sauce (£5.95), puddings (£2.25), and children's dishes; maybe chutney for sale. If the restaurant is very busy on a Saturday night, they may well stop doing bar meals then, but would tell customers before they order. Well kept Brains Mild, Flowers Ordinary, Whitbreads Pompey Royal on handpump, with Heritage (light and refreshing, not too bitter) and the stronger Ailrics Old Ale at the moment brewed for them by a small brewery; over 50 wines. Shove-ha'penny, dominoes, cribbage, table skittles, and piped music; no dogs. Seats out in a neatly kept and prettily arranged garden which has an extensive herb garden to supply the kitchen; the licensees' own garden is open to those interested in gardens. The village bowling green is next to the inn. *(Recommended by Hazel Morgan, A P Jeffreys, J Roy Smylie, Wayne Brindle, J P Day, Kevin Fields, Mike and Wendy Proctor)*

Free house   Licensees Henry, Sylvia and David Phillips   Real ale   Meals and snacks (8.30am–10pm)   Restaurant   Norton (095 271) 353   Children in eating area of bar Open 11–11   Bedrooms; £59B/£69B

PULVERBATCH   SJ4202 Map 6

White Horse

From A49 at N end of Dorrington follow Pulverbatch/Church Pulverbatch signposts, and turn left at eventual T-junction (which is sometimes signposted Church Pulverbatch); OS Sheet 126, map reference 424023

Though plenty of local regulars crowd into this atmospheric pub there's a very warm welcome to strangers, too. There are black beams and heavy timbering in the several rambling but cosy areas, as well as unusual fabric-covered high-backed settles and brocaded banquettes on its Turkey carpet, sturdy elm or cast-iron-framed tables, and an open coalburning range with gleaming copper kettles; a collection of antique insurance plaques, big brass sets of scales, willow-pattern plates, and pewter mugs hang over the serving counter, and there's even a good Thorburn print of a grouse among the other country pictures. Well kept Flowers Original, Marstons Pedigree and a guest like Boddingtons on handpump, several decent wines by the glass, and 115 malt whiskies. Decent bar food includes sandwiches (their toasted roast beef and melted cheese is popular), tasty soup, omelettes, macaroni cheese (£2.85), shark steak and Arbroath pancake with smoked fish and shellfish (£4.85), a popular fry-up, and deep-fried jumbo prawns (£5.75). Darts, juke box, friendly efficient service. The quarry-tiled front loggia with its sturdy old green leatherette seat is a nice touch. The entrance is around the back of the pub. *(Recommended by Mrs P Langridge, Joy Heatherley, Janet Bord, Paul S McPherson, Colin Laffan, Brian and Anna Marsden)*

Whitbreads Lease: James MacGregor Real ale Meals and snacks (till 10pm) (0743) 73247 Children welcome Open 11.30–3, 7–11

UPPER FARMCOTE SO7792 Map 4

Lion of Morfe £

Follow Claverley 2 1/2 signpost off A458 Bridgnorth–Stourbridge

Perhaps the room with the most character here is the wallpapered public bar, popular with the strong-accented locals: wood-backed wall seats on the red tiles and a game trophy over the small coal fire; the carpeted pool room with its big black kitchen range is also much used. The brown-carpeted lounge bar – altogether smarter – has pink plush button-back built-in wall banquettes in curving bays, and a good log fire; it opens into the conservatory – no-smoking, with cushioned cane chairs around glass tables on the red-tiled floor. Attractively priced bar food includes sandwiches (from £1, steak £1.20), filled baked potatoes (£1.30), ploughman's (£2), salads (from £2.50), home-cooked hot dishes such as chicken curry with mango chutney or a vegetarian dish (£2.50), steak and kidney pie or chicken surprise (£2.60), lasagne (£2.75), deep-fried plaice (£2.95), and puddings (from £1), with evening dishes such as mushrooms in garlic (£2), tomato and herb quiche (£3.50), grilled trout (£5.50), and steaks (from £6.50); daily specials. Well kept, cheap Banks's Bitter and Mild on electric pump and Woods Special on handpump; darts, pool, dominoes and fruit machine on the public side; friendly service. There are picnic-table sets under cocktail parasols on a terrace, and a lawn spreading out into an orchard with a floodlit boules piste. *(Recommended by Dave Braisted; more reports please)*

Free house Licensees Bill and Dinah Evans Real ale Meals and snacks (not Sun) Claverley (074 66) 678 Children in eating area of bar Folk club Sat fortnightly Open 11.30–2.30(4 Sat), 7–11

WENLOCK EDGE SO5796 Map 4

Wenlock Edge Inn ★ ⊘ ⇌

Hilltop; B4371 Much Wenlock–Church Stretton, OS Sheet 137, map reference 570962

Readers' comments on this extremely friendly family-run inn remain consistently warm and enthusiastic. There's a lovely homely, chatty atmosphere in the two cosy low-ceilinged bar rooms (which have a door in between them). The one on the right has a big woodburning stove in its large inglenook, a shelf of high plates, and leads into a little dining room. The room on the left has pews that came from a Methodist chapel in Liverpool, a fine oak bar counter, and an open fire. The licensee's interested in local ghosts and chinese horoscopes. Using fresh ingredients, the very good home-made bar food includes soup (£1.75), prawn salad (£3.35 starter, £6.25 main course), steak and mushroom pie (£4.20), good ploughman's (£4.25), home-baked ham (£4.50), dishes of the day such as apricot and chicken quiche (£4.50), pork, chutney and apple pie (£5), rich beef cobbler (£5.90) or baked salmon (£6.25), evening rump steak (£7.75), and puddings like wonderful lemon pudding, fresh gooseberry cake or treacle tart (£1.90); no chips; excellent breakfasts (try the sausage). Well kept Robinsons, Ruddles Best, Thwaites and Websters Yorkshire and guests on handpump, interesting whiskies, decent wines by both glass and bottle, and no music – unless you count the deep-throated chimes of Big Bertha the fusee clock. There are some tables on a front terrace and the side grass. The building is in a fine position just by the Ippikins Rock viewpoint and there are lots of walks through the National Trust land that runs along the Edge. *(Recommended by Mr and Mrs C H Garnett, Anthony Barnes, Nigel Hopkins, Tony* and Lynne Stark, John Atherton, L T Parry, Jack and Barbara Smale, David Williams, Michael Badcock, A P Jeffreys, Christian Leigh, Cyril Burton, Gwen and Peter Andrews, Miss G Matthews, Mrs K Clark, Andrea McWilliams, Mike and Wendy Proctor, Mr and Mrs J M Elden, Paul McPherson, John and Christine Rees, M J Penford)

Free house   Licensee Stephen Waring   Real ale   Meals and snacks (not Mon except bank holidays)   Restaurant   Brockton (074 636) 403   Children in restaurant (not under 10 if after 8pm Sat)   Open 11.30–2.30(3 Sat), 6–11; closed Mon lunchtime except bank holidays; closed 25 Dec   Bedrooms; £28B/£40B

WHITCHURCH   SJ4947 Map 7
Willey Moor Lock

Pub signposted off A49 just under two miles N of Whitchurch

From the white tables under cocktail parasols on the terrace here you can watch the colourful narrowboats, and to get to the front door of this low fairylit pub, you have to cross the footbridge over the Llangollen Canal and the rushing sidestream by the lock; there's a children's play area with swings and slides. Inside, several neatly decorated carpeted rooms have low ceilings, a large teapot collection, a decorative longcase clock, a shelf of toby jugs, brick-based brocaded wall seats, stools and small chairs around dimpled copper and other tables, and two winter log fires. Popular, good value bar food includes winter home-made soup, good sandwiches, pastie (£3.25), cod (£4.25), seafood platter (£4.40), lasagne or home-made steak and kidney pie (£4.50), gammon (£6), steaks (from £6.25), puddings (around £1.50) and children's meals (£1.75); food stops one hour before closing, subject to seasonal variations. Well kept Marstons Pedigree and Theakstons Best and guest beers on handpump; fruit machine, piped music, and several dogs and cats. (*Recommended by R T and J C Moggridge, Laurence Manning, Carol and Richard Glover, Kate and Robert Hodkinson, Chris Raisin, Capt F A Bland*)

Free house   Licensee Mrs Elsie Gilkes   Real ale   Meals and snacks   Restaurant (0948) 3274   Children in eating area of bar and in restaurant   Open 12–3, 6(7 in winter)–11

WISTANSTOW   SO4385 Map 6
Plough ♀

Village signposted off A49 and A489 N of Craven Arms

The beers brewed here are among the best from any brewery – Woods Parish, Special, the strong Wonderful and the seasonal Christmas Cracker (the brewery is actually separate – an older building right by the pub). They keep two farm ciders, there's a fine display cabinet of bottled beers and 16 wines by the glass. The food is very popular, too. At lunchtime this includes sandwiches, home-made pâté or ploughman's with three English cheeses (£3.20), grilled sardines (£3.50), good steak and kidney pie (£3.95), grilled red mullet (£4.20) and chicken marsala (£5.20); in the evening there might be fresh salmon (£6.50), duck in orange sauce (£6.95), grilled red snapper (£7) and beef Wellington (£7.20); lots of genuinely home-made puddings. The decor of the high-raftered and brightly lit main lounge is rather a surprise for a Shropshire village pub and has numerous tables and chairs on the swirly-patterned carpet. The games area has darts, pool, fruit machine, video game and juke box; maybe piped music. There are some tables under cocktail parasols outside. (*Recommended by W F C Phillips, Mrs J Crawford, Denzil T Taylor, Joy Heatherley, Mr and Mrs J H Adam, Dr M Owton, Ian R Smith, Colin Laffan, John and Joan Wyatt*)

Own brew   Licensee Robert West   Real ale   Meals and snacks (not Mon evening except bank hols; not winter Sun evenings)   (0588) 673251   Children in eating area of bar lunchtime only   Open 11.45–2.30, 7–11

Lucky Dip

Besides the fully inspected pubs, you might like to try these Lucky Dips recommended to us and described by readers (if you do, please send us reports):

☆ **All Stretton** [SO4695], *Yew Tree*: Real ale inc bottled Worthington White Shield, good lunchtime bar food, no music, restaurant, friendly helpful service; lovely walks on Long Mynd nearby *(A G Roby, R and E Harfield)*

☆ **Aston Munslow** [OS Sheet 137, map reference 512866; SO5187], *Swan*: Ancient pub with several bars, log fires, pool room, well kept Bass and other real ales, good bar food, garden; lane beside leads to 12th-century White House (open summer) *(D W Crossley)*

Bishops Castle [High St — OS Sheet 137, map reference 324886; SO3289], *Boars Head*: Well modernised, nice old pub with pleasant atmosphere, real ale, and shortish choice of good well prepared food; busy Sat but they try to keep the dining area clear; bedrooms *(C T and J M Laffan, DC)*; *Castle*: Central but quiet, old stone-built house with tables out in front and big back garden; well cooked above-average food at reasonable prices, inc freshly cooked pasta; Weston's cider, good parking *(George Sayer)*

☆ **Bridgnorth** [Stn; A458 towards Stourbridge, opp the Hollyhead; SO7292], *Railwaymans Arms*: Great novelty value, part of Severn Valley steam railway terminus (car-parking fee is refundable against either your train ticket or what you spend in the pub); very basic re-creation of 1940s station bar, with simple snacks, coal fire, fine range of changing well kept real ales such as Bathams and Holdens Milds, Courage Best and Fullers ESB, some Polish and German bric-a-brac, seats out on platform; bustling summer daytime, quiet evening; children welcome *(E J Alcock, Graham Gibson, A P Jeffreys, LYM)*

☆ **Bridgnorth** [Old Ludlow Rd — B4364, a mile out], *Punch Bowl*: Panelled and beamed old-fashioned country pub, with superb views; good food in bar and restaurant, good range of real ales; service swift, efficient and courteous; very restful surroundings, nice atmosphere, armchairs *(P J Taylor)*

Bridgnorth [St Marys St, Central Ct], *Friars*: Flowers Original, good choice of malts, nice range of food; lounge bar and separate eating area *(A P Jeffreys)*

☆ **Brockton** [SO5894], *Feathers*: Country pub with wide choice of good well presented bar food inc children's dishes, warm welcome, and well kept real ales; huge set of bellows from local smithy as one table, pretty little covered back terrace *(Paul Denham, Nicola Brown-Denham, LYM)*

Broome [SO4081], *Engine & Tender*: Railway plaques, notices and other bric-a-brac, shelves filled with jugs, art deco bar frontage; well kept beer, good wine, popular food (best to book in restaurant) *(Denzil T Taylor)*

Broseley [Avenue Rd; SJ6802], *Foresters Arms*: Very welcoming family-run pub with good value home-made food *(G M K Donkin)*

☆ **Church Stretton** [High St; SO4593], *Wine Vaults*: Not a wine bar despite name; small very cosy front room, substantial back evening bar, reasonable food, comfortable furniture, delightful rural atmosphere, very welcoming landlady *(D J Penny)*

☆ **Claverley** [High St; off A454 Wolverhampton—Bridgnorth; SO7993], *Crown*: Ancient but comfortable pub with heavy beams, open fires, good home-made bar food (not Sun-Weds evenings), well kept Banks's, pleasant service, particularly good family garden with play area, summer children's bar and barbecues; dogs allowed, long Sat opening; lovely village; children allowed in eating area *(LYM)*

☆ **Coalport** [Salthouse Rd; nr Mawes Craft Centre — OS Sheet 127, map reference 693025; SJ6903], *Boat*: Simple and cosy waterside brick-built pub in quiet part of Severn Gorge, welcoming service, coal fire in lovely range, generous helpings of basic bar food, well kept Banks's on electric pump, darts; summer barbecues on tree-shaded lawn; watermarks on door show how flood-prone it is; easiest approach is by footbridge from china museum side as road itself is a rough track *(Julian Proudman, Jenny Cantle, BB)*

Coalport, *Shakespeare*: Simple cream-washed pub by road along Severn gorge, by pretty park; handy for china museum; Wem/Greenalls *(BB)*

☆ **Corfton** [B4368 Much Wenlock—Craven Arms; SO4985], *Sun*: Good value simple home cooking served till late inc children's dishes and bargain Sun lunch (especially cheap for children), in pleasant lounge bar and lively and cheery locals' bar; restaurant, tables on terrace and in good-sized garden with good play area inc retired tractor; piped music *(Mr and Mrs J Kirby, BB)*

Cressage [A458 Shrewsbury—Bridgnorth; SJ5904], *Eagles*: Friendly service, reasonably priced bar food, Wem beers *(Dave Braisted)*

Cross Houses [A458 Shrewsbury—Bridgnorth; SJ5407], *Fox*: Very pleasant roadside pub with bar meals and Wem Best *(Patrick Godfrey)*

☆ **Dorrington** [SJ4703], *Three Horseshoes*: Quite small spotless local, with M&B, Brew XI, food inc vegetarian dishes and stupendous ploughman's; tables on back lawn *(Mr and Mrs D Young)*

☆ **Ellesmere** [Birch Rd; SJ4035], *White Hart*: Ancient black and white pub, small and attractive, with homely atmosphere, warm and friendly welcome, good value, decent home-made food, well kept Marstons ales inc Border; some claim to be oldest pub in Shrops; a few mins' walk from canal *(Tracey*

Fairbanks, P Lloyd, Miss K Bamford, Chris Raisin)

Ellesmere [1 Birch Rd], *Millies*: A wine bar, but with real ale — and good food and service; intimate decor, china on walls, crystal in cabinet *(Carol and Richard Glover)*

Goldstone [Goldstone Wharf; SJ7128], *Wharf*: Well kept beers, good if not cheap food, friendly landlord, good service *(J R Jewitt)*

Hampton Loade [SO7586], *Lion*: Nice old pub, very busy in summer or when Severn Valley Rly has weekend steam spectaculars, quiet otherwise; good day-ticket fishing on River Severn *(S P Bobeldijk)*

Heathton [OS Sheet 138, map reference 813925; SO8192], *Old Gate*: Charming, with rooms on different levels, well kept Holt, Plant & Deakins ales, good choice of wines, wide choice of bar food, big garden *(Keith Smith, Liz Window)*

Hinstock [just off A41 9 miles N of Newport; SJ6926], *Falcon*: Friendly atmosphere and good reasonably priced lunches *(John Taylor)*

Ironbridge [Wharfage; SJ6704], *Malt House*: Large, long room with well kept Davenports and generous popular food; across road from Severn, with rather industrial view; useful for tourists *(Mrs Y M Healey)*

Lilleshall [just off A518 2 miles SW of Newport; SJ7315], *Red House*: Spacious, well equipped and popular, with well kept real ales, good lunchtime bar food, restaurant *(A T Langton)*

☆ **Linley** [pub signed off B4373 N of Bridgnorth; SO6998], *Pheasant*: Welcoming and relaxed country pub in lovely spot, with good honest food (not Sun if busy) maybe using their own free-range eggs, attractive prices, interesting choice of real ales *(A P Jeffreys, LYM)*

Little Wenlock [SJ6507], *Huntsman*: Free house with friendly licensee and bar staff, well kept Wem, good food in bar and restaurant inc Sun lunch *(Denzil T Taylor, M Joyner)*

☆ **Llanyblodwel** [village and pub signposted off B4396; SJ2423], *Horse Shoe*: Quaint black-and-white timbered Tudor inn in pretty spot by the River Tanat (where they have a mile of trout fishing), much enjoyed by readers who don't expect airs and graces; rambling low-beamed rooms, simple furnishings both traditional and more modern, limited choice of basic food from sandwiches to steaks, pub games, piped music, tables outside; the high-Victorian village church is well worth seeing; children in eating area till 9; two simple but cheap bedrooms *(Gordon and Daphne, LYM)*

☆ **Loppington** [signed off B4397 W of Wem; SJ4729], *Blacksmiths Arms*: Picture-postcard thatched pub with heavy beams, inglenook fireplace, country decorations and a couple of neatly comfortable side rooms; with good value home-made bar food, Bass on handpump, good choice of malt whiskies, pretty garden

with play area; children welcome; closed Mon lunchtime, restaurant *(Mike and Wendy Proctor, LYM)*

☆ **Ludlow** [Lower Corve St; off Shrewsbury rd; SO5175], *Unicorn*: Newly refurbished pub at quiet bottom end of handsome street, doing well under family who took over 1990 and already very popular evenings; most notable for generous helpings of well cooked traditional food lunchtime and evening in single spacious and nicely furnished room; log fire, Courage Directors and John Smiths on handpump, Weston's cider, piped music (very well known Vivaldi, Mozart etc — possibly not the place for it), some seats beyond car park by R Corve; restaurant (book Fri/Sat evening); children allowed *(HTBS, P J Taylor)*

☆ **Ludlow** [Lower Bridge St], *Wheatsheaf*: Good traditional atmosphere in attractively refurbished and tastefully furnished small 17th-century pub spectacularly built into medieval town gate; wide range of good bar food, well kept Bass, M&B and Ruddles County on handpump, choice of farm ciders, friendly owners; attractive oak-beamed bedrooms *(John and Bridget Dean, Julian Proudman, Helen and Wal Burns)*

☆ **Ludlow** [Bull Ring/Corve St], *Feathers*: Hotel with exquisitely proportioned and intricately carved timbered frontage, and Jacobean panelling and carving, period furnishings; for the decent bar food or a casual drink you may well be diverted to a humbler side bar; efficient pleasant service, well kept Flowers Original and Wadworths 6X; artistically presented food in restaurant; bedrooms comfortable; prices not for the faint-hearted *(Gwen and Peter Andrews, Iain and Penny Muir, LYM)*

Ludlow, *Blue Boar*: Cosy and attractively decorated pub which has been popular for good buffet and impressively big bedrooms, with good breakfasts, but no recent reports *(News please)*

Madeley [Coalport Rd; SJ6904], *All Nations*: Basic old-fashioned pub with remarkably cheap beer brewed on the premises — perhaps the cheapest pint in the country *(Comus Elliott)*

Market Drayton [A529, 2 miles S; SJ6734], *Four Alls*: Friendly 16th-century inn, tastefully extended and very comfortably furnished; Bass, extensive bar menu served 11-10, carvery and separate restaurant; open all day; convenient for Shropshire Union Canal *(Paul and Margaret Baker)*

☆ **Much Wenlock** [A458; SO6299], *Gaskell Arms*: Picturesque pub with good popular reasonably priced food in cosy relaxing lounge and restaurant; open fire, good service, well kept Courage Best and Directors on handpump, piped music, banknote collection; fruit machine in lobby *(P Corris, G M K Donkin, Chris Raisin)*

☆ **Munslow** [B4368 Much Wenlock—Craven Arms; SO5287], *Crown*: Attractive old building in pleasant countryside with variety of tables and chairs in split-level beamed lounge with flagstones, bare stone walls, bottle collection, original cupboards and doors; eating area around central bread oven chimney — generous helpings of decent home-made food; small snug; reasonably priced Bass, Marstons Mild and Wadworths 6X; sad about the piped pop music; open all day summer *(A P Jeffreys)*

Neen Sollars [SO6672], *Live & Let Live*: Beautifully placed interesting pub with good fairly priced food, comfortable furnishings, good service; pleasant tables outside *(Paul Denham, Nicola Brown-Denham)*

☆ **Neenton** [B4364 Bridgnorth—Ludlow; SO6488], *Pheasant*: Old cottagey building nicely placed in small village — bar, panelled lounge with open fire, small sitting room with armchairs, separate restaurant; well kept real ale, generous helpings of reasonably priced standard food *(A P Jeffreys, Brian Barefoot)*

Nesscliffe [A5 Shrewsbury—Oswestry; SJ3819], *Old Three Pigeons*: Friendly old coaching inn with Whitbreads-related real ales, coffee all day, wide choice of good bar food inc several fresh fish dishes, restaurant *(Gordon Theaker, J R Smylie)*

☆ **Newcastle** [B4368 Clun—Newtown; SO2582], *Crown*: Spacious and comfortable, with nicely presented good value food inc some interesting dishes and good set Sun lunch, friendly attentive licensees, wide choice of well kept beer; lounge, bar, games room, restaurant/eating area; tables outside, lovely quiet village on Offa's Dyke footpath, surrounded by attractive countryside *(J and R McFarlane, Dr M V Roman, A P Jeffreys)*

☆ **Newport** [SJ7519], *Bridge*: Small, friendly pub with decent bar food, restaurant, attentive staff; satisfactory bedrooms *(G B Pugh)*

Newport [Pave Lane (A41 S)], *Fox & Duck*: Friendly two-bar pub with wide choice of reasonably priced bar food, terrace, garden and paddock — good for families in summer; bedrooms with own bathrooms *(D L Williams)*

Picklescott [SO4399], *Bottle & Glass*: Attractive free house with Flowers beer and wide choice of decent, reasonably priced bar food; ample parking *(Mr and Mrs C Wyatt)*

☆ **Pipe Gate** [A51 Nantwich—Stone; SJ7441], *Chetwode Arms*: Friendly family pub, clean and comfortably refurbished, with wide choice of good bar food, attractively priced good carvery, evening restaurant; unusual real ales *(Mr Armitt)*

☆ **Shifnal** [High St; SJ7508], *White Hart*: Tastefully restored, comfortable and cosy village pub, notable for the quality of its well kept changing real ales; straightforward promptly served food *(Bob Alton, DC, Mr and Mrs J H Adam, Mike and Wendy Proctor)*

Shipley [A454 W of Wolverhampton; SO8095], *Fox*: Good bar food at low prices, Banks's ales, restaurant *(Dave Braisted)*

☆ **Shrewsbury** [Wyle Cop; follow City Centre signposts across the English Bridge], *Lion*: Imposing old THF coaching inn with cosy oak-panelled bar and sedate series of high-ceilinged rooms opening off; obliging staff, Bass under light carbon dioxide blanket, bar food — which may be served in the restaurant if it's not busy; children welcome; bedrooms comfortable *(LYM)*

☆ **Shrewsbury** [16 Castle Gates], *Castle Vaults*: Black and white pub with small, comfortable lounge, good range of real ales such as Border, Marstons Pedigree, Tetleys and Charles Wells Bombardier, decent wines; generous helpings of good value food in adjoining Mexican restaurant, roof garden; bedrooms good *(Graham Gibson, John Tooth)*

☆ **Shrewsbury** [New St; leaving centre via Welsh Bridge/A488 turn into Port Hill Rd], *Boat House*: Comfortably modernised pub worth knowing for its quiet Severnside position, with river views from long quiet lounge bar, tables out on sheltered terrace and rose lawn; Whitbreads-related real ales, usual bar food, afternoon teas, summer barbecues; open all day, by footbridge over to park *(A P Jeffreys, Brian Barefoot, LYM)*

Shrewsbury, *Heathgates*: Highly refurbished with plates and books for decoration, M&B beers and sound value food *(Dave Braisted)*; [Mardol; SJ4912], *Kings Head*: Welcoming 15th-century timber-framed pub, carefully restored; popular, esp lunchtime, and with younger people weekend evenings *(Denzil T Taylor)*

☆ **Stiperstones** [village signed off A488 S of Minsterley — OS Sheet 126, map reference 364005; SO3697], *Stiperstones*: Friendly little modernised lounge bar with leatherette wall banquettes, lots of brassware on ply-panelled walls, warm welcome, well kept Woods Parish on handpump, darts in plainer public bar, restaurant; at least in summer has been open all day, with good simple food inc some unusual dishes till 10; picnic-table sets outside; on GWG100 *(Paul S McPherson, R K Sutton, Denzil T Taylor, BB)*

☆ **Tong** [A41 towards Newport, just beyond village; SJ7907], *Bell*: Friendly staff, welcoming atmosphere, old-world stripped brickwork, big family room, small dining room, pleasant back conservatory, big garden with views of countryside nr Weston Park; busy at lunchtime for good choice of generous decent cheapish food inc cold table and good value Sun lunch; well kept Banks's real ales, unobtrusive piped music, no dogs; big car park *(T Henwood, Anthony Barnes)*

☆ **Upton Magna** [Pelham Rd; SJ5512], *Corbet Arms*: Big L-shaped lounge bar with armchairs by log fire, good range of popular reasonably priced food, well kept Banks's ales, darts and juke box in smaller public bar, friendly staff; handy for Attingham Park (NT), busy at weekends *(Mike Tucker)*

Wellington [Church St; SJ6611], *Charlton Arms*: Good lunchtime food in nicely furnished friendly inn with antique carved longcase clock, helpful staff; bedrooms comfortable *(M Joyner)*

☆ **Wentnor** [SO3893], *Crown*: Well kept and welcoming, popular for wide choice of well priced good food in bar and cosy and pleasant restaurant inc vegetarian dishes and good sausages made to landlord's recipe; decent wines, good coffee; bedrooms good value, caravan and camping facilities *(Denzil T Taylor, R and M Wallace, R K Sutton)*

☆ **Whitchurch** [St Marys St; SJ5341], *Old Town Hall Vaults*: Charming and friendly 18th-century pub with well kept Marstons Border Mild and Pedigree on handpump, good value home-cooked lunchtime and evening food, friendly staff, refined rather than hearty atmosphere; piped light classics (Sir Edward German was born here) *(Chris Raisin)*

Somerset and Avon

Pubs here tend to be very friendly; many of them have a great deal of character, often rubbed off on them over the centuries, and some are in lovely positions. But though it is the traditional old-fashioned charm that tends to show through most, there have been a good many recent changes. These include new licensees for the Square & Compass looking out over the countryside from its nice spot near Ashill, the Boars Head at Aust (doing very well, with good food – a remarkably fine break from the motorway), the Highbury Vaults in Bristol (a good value pub tied to Smiles the local brewer; notably cheap good food), the Poachers Pocket at Doulting (thriving with the change), and the White Hart at Trudoxhill (new licensees as proud as the old of its fine own brews). New main entries (or pubs back in these pages after a leave of absence) are the tiny little Coeur de Lion in Bath, the very traditional Old Green Tree there, the handsome and very individual Anchor by the river at Exebridge, the very unspoilt Rose & Crown at Huish Episcopi (amazing casks of cider), the interesting old Royal Oak tucked into the Brendon Hills at Luxborough (good all round), and the civilised and prettily placed Cotley Inn at Wambrook. In general food and drinks prices are around the national average. But on the food side a good few pubs stand out for combining quality with value: the George at Abbots Leigh (earning a food award this year; good use of herbs and spices), the homely little Malt Shovel at Bradley Green (very cheap), the Crown at Churchill (doing very well currently, with good beers too), the lovingly run Strode Arms at Cranmore, the Bull Terrier at Croscombe (good all round), the spotless New Inn at Dowlish Wake (the Swiss landlady does the cooking), the individual Haselbury Inn at Haselbury Plucknett, the Three Horseshoes at Langley Marsh (particularly good vegetarian dishes, too), the Notley Arms at Monksilver (only a superb landlord could cope so well with so much popularity), the busy Carpenters Arms at Stanton Wick, the cottagey little Rose & Crown at Stoke St Gregory, in marked contrast the big, well run Half Moon at Stoke St Mary, the Crossways at West Huntspill (though a dining pub it has a good deal of character) and the cheerful and relaxing Royal Oak at Withypool. Pubs in the Lucky Dip section at the end of the chapter which are currently on a decided upswing include the Crystal Palace in Bath, Carnarven Arms at Brushford and, particularly, City Arms in Wells; and others to note particularly (most inspected by us) are the New Inn at Blagdon, Raleghs Cross in the Brendon Hills, Red Cow at Brent Knoll, King William at Catcott, Ring o' Bells at Compton Martin, Bull at Hardway, Ring o' Bells at Hinton Blewett, White Hart at Littleton upon Severn, Queens Head at Milborne Port, Cottage at Nether Stowey, George at Nunney, Volunteer at Seavington St Michael, Crown at Tolldown, Red Lion at West Pennard and Burcott Inn at

Wookey. Bath and Bristol are rich hunting-grounds, too.

ABBOTS LEIGH (Avon)   ST5473 Map 2

George ✪

3 miles from M5 junction 19; Pill Road (A369 towards Bristol)

One reader thought the meal he and his wife had in this friendly and refreshingly unpompous place was the best pub food they could remember. Good value and home-made, it includes generous helpings of soups such as tomato and apple (£2.25), ploughman's with a good selection of cheeses (from £3.25), venus clams marinière (£3.25), baby squid salad (£3.45), up to fourteen main courses such as excellent steak and kidney pie, mushroom pie (£5.85), jhalfry curry puff (£6.25) and garlic chicken en croûte or fresh salmon and broccoli gratin (£6.25); good choice of vegetarian dishes, and puddings like chocolate Pithiviers, strawberry brûlée or chocolate-chip and sherry cake (£2.35); a tray of unusual bottled sauces includes fresh orange vinaigrette. Well kept Courage Best, Bitter, Directors and John Smiths, and a guest like Exmoor Gold, Fullers London Pride or Theakstons on handpump; obliging service. The single longish room has lots of harness and saddlery decorating the darkening cream walls, horsebrasses and some stirrups on the beams, brocaded cushions on the pews for tables along the walls, flowers in the windows, and a good log fire at either end; there are a couple more tables against the bar counter that lines most of the back wall; shove-ha'penny, cribbage, trivia and subdued piped music. A sheltered terrace and pretty walled garden has picnic-table sets; the two collies are called Eric and Ernie. The exit from the car park onto the fast main road can be a bit tricky. *(Recommended by Barry and Anne, D Godden, Tom Evans, D G Clarke, N Doncaster, Robert Gower)*

Grand Met   Tenants Mike and Elaine Meredith   Real ale   Meals and snacks (not Sat/Sun evening)   (0275) 372467   Children in eating area lunchtime only   Open 11.45(11 Sat)–2.30ish, 6(7 Sat)–11; closed 25 and 26 Dec

ALMONDSBURY (Avon)   ST6084 Map 2

Bowl

1 1/4 miles from M5, junction 16 (and therefore quite handy for M4, junction 20; from A38 towards Thornbury, turn first left signposted Lower Almondsbury, then first right down Sundays Hill, then at bottom right again into Church Road

Conveniently placed for a motorway break, this very popular and pretty white cottage has a long neatly kept beamed bar with blue plush-patterned modern settles and pink cushioned stools and mates' chairs, elm tables, and quite a few horsebrasses; the walls are stripped to bare stone and there's a big winter log fire at one end, with a woodburning stove at the other. Good home-made bar food includes sandwiches (£1.25; toasties from £1.30), Welsh rarebit (£1.65), soup (£1.75), crispy coated mushrooms and cauliflower (£1.95), burgers (from £2.35), ploughman's (£2.95), a good choice of salads and omelettes (from £3.75), celery and cashew nut risotto (£3.75), country lentil crumble (£3.65), spinach and mushroom lasagne or cottage pie (£4.25), chicken and vegetable curry (£4.65), steak and kidney pie (£5.65) and puddings (£1.85); grills and steaks Sunday evenings. Well kept Courage Bitter, Best and Directors, John Smiths Bitter and Wadworths 6X on handpump, some enterprising bottled beers, good value wines, freshly pressed fruit juices, tea or coffee; friendly service. Cribbage, dominoes, fruit machine and piped music. The little restaurant is very attractive. In summer the flowering tubs, hanging baskets and window boxes are lovely; the patio area at the rear overlooks a field and can be booked for private parties, and there are some picnic-table sets across the quiet road. The village church is next door. *(Recommended by D A Lloyd, Brian Jones, Peter and Rose Flower, Margaret Dyke, Mr and Mrs S Cowherd, Richard Parr, Stan Edwards, Carol Mason, Mark Jackson, Louise Mee, Gary Marchant)*

Courage   Tenant John Alley   Real ale   Meals and snacks (till 10)   Restaurant (not

Sun evening)   Almondsbury (0454) 612757   Children in eating area of bar and restaurant   Open 11–3, 6–11; closed 25 Dec   Bedrooms; £39.50B/£65B; cheaper weekend rates

APPLEY (Somerset)   ST0621   Map 1

Globe £

Hamlet signposted from the network of back roads between A361 and A38, W of B3187 and W of Milverton and Wellington; OS Sheet 181, map reference 072215

An entry corridor in this unspoilt 15th-century pub leads to a serving hatch where Boddingtons and Cotleigh Tawny (a local brew) are on handpump, also farmhouse cider made in a neighbouring village. The simple beamed front room has a relaxed, chatty atmosphere, benches and a built-in settle, bare wood tables on the brick floor, and pictures of magpies. The back room has a pool table, and yet another room has easy chairs and other more traditional ones. The dining room is no-smoking. Generous helpings of good value bar food include filled rolls (from 75p, the beef is especially recommended), a choice of ploughman's (from £3.35), seafood pancake (£4.35), lamb curry (£4.50) and lamb casserole (£5.10); good service. Darts, shove-ha'penny, alley skittles, fruit machine and trivia. The hilly pastures which surround this maze of twisting lanes are very pretty, and there are seats, climbing frame and swings outside in the garden; the path opposite leads eventually to the River Tone. *(Recommended by Katie Verner, Gordon Woodcock, Jon and Penny Barnes, R D Bowes, A Chadwick; more reports please)*

Free house   Licensees A W and E J Burt, R and J Morris   Real ale   Meals and snacks (till 10)   No-smoking restaurant (open Tues-Sat evenings; Sun lunchtime)   Greenham (0823) 672327   Children in eating area of bar and restaurant   Open 11–3, 6.30–11; closed Mon lunchtime, except bank hols

ASHCOTT (Somerset)   ST4337   Map 1

Ashcott Inn ⊘

A39 about 6 miles W of Glastonbury

Around ten different fresh fish dishes each day (from Brixham and Cornwall) are served then: monkfish and prawns with pine kernels and a walnut dressing, steamed brill on a red pepper coulis, turbot with a sauté of avocados and prawns, and plaice, lemon sole and so forth (from around £6); also, filled baps (from £1.25), a choice of hearty soups (£1.45), pizzas (from £2.75), ploughman's (from £2.85), ratatouille (£2.95), home-made cottage pie (£3.50), ham, egg and chips (£3.80), chicken lasagne or lamb curry (£4.95), creamy fish pie or steak and kidney pie (£5.25) and steaks (from £9.25); an interesting range of vegetarian dishes such as vegetable lasagne or stilton and broccoli bake, and puddings like steamed ginger pudding, treacle tart or home-made cheesecake (£2.35). Well kept Eldridge Pope Hardy and Marstons Pedigree on handpump, and quite a few wines. There are good oak and elm tables, some interesting old-fashioned seats among more conventional ones, beams, stripped stone walls, and a gas-effect log fire in its sturdy chimney; darts, shove-ha'penny, a fruit machine, alley skittles and piped classical music. Seats on the terrace, and a pretty walled garden. *(Recommended by S V Bishop, R W Stanbury, Ted George, Mrs D A Talbot, Tom Bowen, Brig J S Green; more reports please)*

Heavitree (who no longer brew)   Tenants Robert and Tess Porter   Real ale   Meals and snacks (12–2, 6.30–9.30)   Restaurant (closed Sun evening)   Ashcott (0458) 210282   Well behaved children allowed only if eating   Open 11–2.30, 5.30–11; closed Sun evening Sept-March

nr ASHILL (Somerset)   ST3217   Map 1

Square & Compass

Windmill Hill; turn off A358 at Stewley Cross Garage

Upholstered window seats in this pleasantly remote pub overlook the rolling pastures around Neroche Forest, and the cosy little bar has other comfortable seating (there's extra room for eating) and an open fire in winter. Well kept Bass, Exmoor Bitter and Gold on handpump; darts, cribbage, dominoes and piped music. Good bar food includes sandwiches (from £1.30), home-made soup (from £1.50), ploughman's or filled baked potatoes (from £2.25), home-made lasagne, scampi or honey-roasted ham with egg and chips (£3.95), vegetarian dishes (from £2.50), steaks (from £7.20) and good value daily specials such as excellent half duck. Outside on the grass there are picnic-set tables and a climbing frame. There's also a touring caravan site. New owners are likely to have taken over by the time this edition reaches the shops. *(Recommended by P H Brown, Derek Patey, Richard Dolphin)*

Free house   Real ale   Meals and snacks   Restaurant   Hatch Beauchamp (0823) 480467   Children in restaurant   Open 12–2.30(3 Sat), 7–11

AUST (Avon)   ST5789   Map 2
Boars Head

1/2 mile from M4, junction 21; village signposted from A403

An exceptional find for somewhere so close to the motorway, this friendly, small-roomed village pub has old-fashioned high-backed winged settles in stripped pine, well polished country kitchen tables and others made from old casks, big rugs on dark lino, some walls stripped back to the dark stone, decorative plates hanging from one stout black beam, and a log fire in the main fireplace. In another room there's a woodburning stove, and a third room has dining tables. Very popular bar food includes home-made soup (£1.10), sandwiches, ploughman's (£2.95), fish and chips or huge Yorkshire pudding filled with sausages in rich onion gravy (£3.95), spinach and mushroom lasagne or lentil crumble (£4.10), a tremendous spread of help-yourself salads (from £4.20), Scottish scampi, local rainbow trout, gammon steak or chicken chasseur (£4.75), steaks (£6.75), puddings like hot chocolate fudge cake, Belgian apple flan or sherry trifle (from £1.50), and daily home-made specials; Sunday lunch (children's helpings available); coffee. No-smoking near the eating area of the bar. Well kept Courage Best and Directors, and a guest beer on handpump; helpful service, even when busy. There's a medieval stone well in the pretty and sheltered garden, and a touring caravan site. *(Recommended by Dr M Owton, Dr K A and S F Louden, Drs M and K Parier, Dr R M Beard, TBB, John and Ruth Roberts, Barbara and Norman Wells, Charles Owens, Julian Proudman, D I Baddeley, Tom Evans, David Heath, Stan Edwards, M C Howells, William D Cissna, Jacqueline Davis, D G Clarke, Dr A J and M Thomasson)*

Courage   Tenant D R Poole   Real ale   Meals and snacks (till 10)   Pilning (04545) 2278   Children in eating area and family room till 9pm   Open 11–2.30, 6–11

BARROW GURNEY (Avon)   ST5367   Map 2
Princes Motto   £

Barrow Street; B3130 – linking A38 and A370 SW of Bristol

With a warm, chatty atmosphere, this is that rare sort of unpretentious and traditional local where strangers immediately feel they fit in. They specialise in Bass, but also do Boddingtons, Butcombe, Marstons Pedigree and Valances on handpump, with Bass and Wadworths 6X tapped from casks behind the bar. Good value bar snacks consist of filled rolls (70p), toasted sandwiches (£1.25) and ploughman's (from £2.10), and there may be nibbles. From the snug room by the bar, with a sentimental engraving of *Farewell to Nelson* over its log fire, steps lead up to an unusually long and narrow room behind. This has cosy winged high-backed settles at one end, and darts, shove-ha'penny, cribbage, and a fruit machine towards the other; there are lots of horsebrasses on the beams. Picnic-table sets on the back grass have rustic views; garden could perhaps do with some tidying up. *(Recommended by Mr Jennings, Steve and Carolyn Harvey; more reports please)*

Free house Licensees Paul and Doreen Bryant Real ale Lunchtime snacks (0275) 472282 Open 11–3, 6–11; closed 25 Dec

BATH (Avon)   ST7565 Map 2

Coeur de Lion

17 Northumberland Place; off High Street, by W H Smith

Standing in a flower-filled and flagstoned Georgian alley lined with small shops, this friendly and very pretty single-room pub has traditional furnishings, candles on each table, unusual ceiling lamps, and a stained-glass window. Well kept Boddingtons, Devenish Royal Wessex, Steam and Cornish Original, and Marstons Pedigree on handpump; farmhouse cider. Filled rolls (from £1.20) served at lunchtime. Table skittles, pinball and piped music. There are wooden benches outside; it's popular with tourists. *(Recommended by Andrew and Ruth Triggs, Wayne Brindle; more reports please)*

Devenish (Whitbreads) Tenant Mrs Frayling Real ale Lunchtime snacks (0225) 465371 Open 11.30–11

Old Green Tree

12 Green St

Away from the bustle, in a quiet street just up behind the GPO, this smart little oak-panelled pub is very traditional, except for a point which has appealed to a good many readers – the comfortable lounge on the left as you go in is no smoking. The main bar, not a lot bigger, can get quite busy, but service stays good, and there's no machine noise; it has a proper thriving old-fashioned feel, and the big skylight lightens things up attractively. The bar food, all home-made, is reasonably priced, a short choice that includes a good ploughman's and popular seafood avocado. Well kept Ruddles County, Ushers and local Smiles on handpump, with an eclectic choice of other drinks that include some uncommon wines – they do a good Pimms, and other cocktails. The lavatories, though good, are down steep steps. *(Recommended by Ted George, N G Bailey, Charlotte Thompson)*

Grand Met Real ale Meals and snacks (lunchtime) Open 11–3, 6–11

BATHFORD (Avon)   ST7966 Map 2

Crown ★ ∅

2 Bathford Hill; signposted off A363 Bath–Bradford-on-Avon

Spreading out from the central bar in this substantial pub are four or five carefully lit room areas with rugs on stripped and polished floorboards, prints, old photographs and mounted butterflies on the attractively decorated walls, china, stoneware and so forth on delft shelves, houseplants (even a sizeable palm), and a relaxed, pleasant atmosphere. There's a good variety of furnishings from sensible tables and chairs for people who want to eat to Lloyd-Loom-style chairs, large armchairs, and comfortable button-back leather settees. Bar food includes filled rolls (from £1.80), soup (£2.30), big toasted sandwiches and filled baked potatoes with unusual fillings like bacon and banana (from £3.10), ploughman's with good cheeses (£4.05), chicken satay (£4.65), steak, mushroom and ale pie (from £5.10), lentil nut casserole (£5.65), trout (£6.90), and chicken kiev (£8.25), nice puddings like Dutch brandy cake, toffee butterscotch pudding or meringue shells with clotted cream and hot butterscotch sauce (£2.85), specials such as seafood pancake or sausages in Yorkshire pudding; children's menu; Sunday lunch. Well kept Bass, Ruddles Best and Ushers Best, decent wines, non-alcohol cocktails, and good cafetiere coffee with fresh cream; rack of newspapers and lots of magazines, very unobtrusive piped music, good log fire; dominoes, cribbage and fruit machine. The no-smoking garden room on the left, with old nursery pictures among others, opens on to a terrace with tables under cocktail parasols; there's a small garden beyond its low retaining wall. *(Recommended by W F C Phillips, Pamela Sterling, June and Tony Baldwin, B and M A Langrish, Mrs Carol Mason, Michael Badcock, B R*

Woolmington, BKA, Mrs Joan Harris, Wayne Brindle, Caroline Raphael)

Ushers (Watneys)   Tenants Gregg and Angela Worrall   Real ale   Meals and snacks (not Mon lunchtime – except bank hols; till 9.30 Sun-Thur, 10 Fri/Sat)   (0225) 852297   Children in garden room and burgundy room   Magician Sun lunchtime Open 11–2.30, 6.30–10.30(11 Fri/Sat); closed 25 and 26 Dec

BRADLEY GREEN (Somerset)   SS0434   Map 1

Malt Shovel 🛏 £

Pub signposted from A39 W of Bridgwater, near Cannington; though Bradley Green is shown on road maps, note that if you're booking the postal address is Blackmoor Lane, Cannington, BRIDGWATER, Somerset TA5 2NE

This homely and friendly little country pub serves good value food that includes lunchtime sandwiches (from 90p, crusty French rolls from 95p), as well as curried vegetarian bake (£2.50), ploughman's (from £2.60), filled baked potatoes (from £2.75), lamb moussaka or pasta and spinach mornay (£3), smoked haddock cheesy bake or home-made steak and kidney pie (£3.50), salads (from £4), chicken and mushroom pie or gammon and pineapple or egg (£4.25), chicken kiev (£6.25) and steaks (from £6.95); also, starters and puddings; children's meals on request (£1.75); occasional summer barbecues. The main bar has photographs of boating scenes on the Bridgewater Canal, window seats, some modern elm country chairs and little cushioned casks, sturdy modern winged high-backed settles around wooden tables, and a black kettle standing on a giant fossil by the woodburning stove; there's also a tiny snug with red-hessian walls. Butcombe, Wadworths 6X and one guest ale on handpump; farmhouse cider; separate skittle alley. The family room opens on to the garden, where there are picnic-table sets (an adjoining field may be used by touring caravans). West of the pub, Blackmore Farm is a striking medieval building. Comfortable bedrooms. (*Recommended by R Tomlinson, Drs M and K Parier, Richard Gibbs, Caroline Raphael, Mr and Mrs J H Adam*)

Free house   Licensees Robert and Frances Beverley   Real ale   Meals and lunchtime snacks (not Sun evening Nov-Mar)   Restaurant (not Sun lunchtime)   Combwich (0278) 653432   Children in family room, eating area of bar and restaurant   Open 11.30–2.30(3 Sat), 6.30(7 winter)–11; closed 25 Dec   Bedrooms; £17.50(£28.50B)/£26(£36B); family room £40

BRISTOL (Avon)   ST5872   Map 2

Highbury Vaults £

St Michaels Hill, Cotham; main road out to Cotham from inner ring dual carriageway

Popular with students in term time (it's handy for the university), this is a classic corner pub and used to be the gaol, in early Georgian days, where condemned men ate their last meal (the bars can still be seen on the windows). There's a cosy and crowded front bar with the corridor beside it leading through to a long series of little rooms – wooden floors, green and cream paintwork, old-fashioned furniture and prints, including lots of period Royal Family engravings and lithographs in the front room. Bargain bar food may include hummus, vegetable curry, vegetable goulash, or a choice of pasta dishes (£1.80) or spicy bean lasagne, fish bake, chilli con carne or corned beef hash (£2). This is one of the handful of pubs tied to the local Smiles brewery, and has all their beers well kept on handpump at attractive prices, as well as Brains SA and interesting changing guests. Darts; friendly informal service. A nice terrace garden has tables built into a partly covered flowery arbour; not large, but a pleasant surprise for the locality. (*Recommended by Mr and Mrs C H Garnett, Barry and Anne, Paul Oakley, Drs M and K Parier, Michael Cochrane, Martin Smietanko, Samantha Taylor, David Warrellow, N Doncaster*)

Smiles   Manager Lloyd Fricker   Real ale   Meals and snacks (12–2, 5.30–8.30; not evenings Sat/Sun)   (0272) 733203   1950s disco Sun once a month   Open 12–11

CHURCHILL (Avon)   ST4560   Map 1

Crown

Skinners Lane; in village, turn off A368 at Nelson Arms

Readers really like this delightful, well run old cottage for its fine range of well kept real ales, decent lunchtime food, quick, friendly service and lovely quiet atmosphere (no piped music). The small and local stone-floored and cross-beamed room on the right has built-in wall benches, a wooden window seat, and an unusually sturdy settle; the left-hand room has a slate floor, and some steps past the big log fire in a big stone fireplace lead to more sitting space. As well as a nice light but well hopped bitter brewed for the pub by Cotleigh, there are often ten real ales including Bass, Butcombe, Cotleigh Tawny, Eldridge Pope Hardy, Greene King and Morlands Old Speckled Hen, all tapped from casks at the back; country wines. Bar food includes a good home-made soup (in winter, £2), sandwiches, wholesome ploughman's with real lumps of butter and a pickle tray, very good filled baked potatoes, tasty cauliflower cheese, honey-roast ham in French bread (£3.50), steak and kidney pudding (£3.75) and rare roast beef salads (£4.20). There are garden tables on the front and a smallish but pretty back lawn, and hill views; near the start of *Good Walks Guide* Walk 1. *(Recommended by Graham Bush, Romey Heaton, William Pryce, Steve and Carolyn Harvey, M Rowlinson, Drs M and K Parier, TBB, Jerry and Alison Oakes, Anthony Barnes)*

Free house   Licensee Tim Rogers   Real ale   Meals and snacks (not Sun)   (09340) 852995   Children in eating area   Open 11–3.30, 5.30–11

CLAPTON IN GORDANO (Avon)   ST4773   Map 2

Black Horse

4 miles from M5 junction 19; A369 towards Portishead, then B3124 towards Clevedon; in N Weston opp school turn left signposted Clapton, then in village take second right, maybe signed Clevedon, Clapton Wick

Tucked away down a country lane, this 14th-century flower-decked white house has a partly flagstoned and partly red-tiled main room with pleasant window seats, winged settles and built-in wall benches around narrow, dark wooden tables, amusing cartoons and photographs of the pub, a big log fire with stirrups and bits on the mantlebeam, and a relaxed, friendly atmosphere. A window in an inner snug is still barred from the days when this room was the petty-sessions gaol; high-backed settles – one a marvellous carved and canopied creature, another with an art nouveau copper insert reading *East, West, Hame's Best* – lots of mugs hanging from its black beams, and lots of little prints and photographs. There's also a simply furnished children's room, just off the bar, with high-backed corner settles and a gas fire; darts, dominoes, cribbage and table skittles. Bar food includes ploughman's (from £2.60), summer salads (from £3.50), and hot dishes such as beef cobbler (in winter), home-roasted ham, liver and bacon casserole and vegetable pie (all about £4); free roast potatoes on the bar Sunday lunchtime. Well kept Axminster Hardington and Courage Bitter, Best and Directors tapped from the cask; farmhouse cider. The little flagstoned front garden is exceptionally pretty in summer with a mass of flowers in tubs, hanging baskets and flowerbeds, and some old rustic tables and benches, with more to one side of the car park and in the secluded children's play area with its sturdy wooden climber, slide, rope ladder and rope swing. Paths from here lead up Naish Hill or along to Cadbury Camp. *(Recommended by Steve Huggins, Steve and Carolyn Harvey, Jon Wainwright, Drs M and K Parier, Genie and Brian Smart, David and Valerie Hooley, EML, D and B Carron, Jerry and Alison Oakes, Mr and Mrs P B Dowsett)*

Courage   Tenant Tom Shaw   Real ale   Lunchtime meals and snacks (not Sun) (0727) 842105   Children in family room   Live music/Quiz night alternate Mon evenings   Open 11–2.30, 6–11; closed 25 Dec

COMBE HAY (Avon)   ST7354 Map 2

Wheatsheaf ✿

Village signposted from A367 or B3110 S of Bath

Perched on the side of a steep wooded valley, this popular country pub has pleasantly old-fashioned rooms with old sporting and other prints, earthenware jugs on the shelf of the little shuttered windows, low ceilings, brown-painted settles, pews and rustic tables, and a very high-backed winged settle facing one big log fire. A wide choice of good food includes dishes like home-made soup (£2.25), ploughman's (£2.50, magnificent stilton £3), pork and cider pâté (£3), stuffed mushrooms with brie (£3.75), tasty vegetable crêpe with provençale sauce (£4), avocado and prawn platter or lasagne (£4.25), pigeon breast (£4.75), gammon steak with pineapple (£5), loin of pork (from £5.30), and specials like king prawns (£6.50), stuffed lemon sole (£8), Scotch salmon, whole fresh crab or lobster, duck breast and venison, with grouse in season, and puddings (from £2.25); summer barbecues. Well kept Courage Best and Hook Norton tapped from the cask; friendly staff (and dogs). There are tables on the spacious sloping lawn that look down past the enterprising plunging garden to the church and ancient manor stables. *(Recommended by Peter and Rose Flower, Dr Paul Kitchener, Tim and Sue Halstead, GB, Nigel Gibbs, Sandra Cook, Tony and Lynne Stark, Kevin and Tracey Stephens, Dr and Mrs R E S Tanner)*

Courage   Tenant M G Taylor   Real ale   Meals and snacks   Restaurant   Bath (0225) 833504   Children welcome   Open 11–3, 6.30–10.30(11 Sat)

CRANMORE (Somerset)   ST6643 Map 2

Strode Arms ★ ✿

West Cranmore; signposted with pub off A361 Frome–Shepton Mallet

This was built around 1400, first as a cottage and later extended to become a farmhouse selling cider. It's now a lovingly-run pub with charming country furnishings, a grandfather clock on the flagstones, newspapers to read, fresh flowers and pot plants, remarkable old locomotive engineering drawings and big black-and-white steamtrain murals in a central lobby, good bird prints, and pretty views through the stone-mullioned windows down to the village duckpond. Generous helpings of really good home cooking include sandwiches (from £1.05p), ploughman's (from £2.55), pancake filled with spinach (£2.65), filled baked potatoes (from £2.85), steak and kidney and other home-made pies, juicy ham and eggs or scallops with bacon (£3.85), sliced smoked duck breast (£4.95), ratatouille covered with breadcrumbs and topped with cheese and mushroom sauce (£5.35), avocado and seafood platter (£6.50), breast of chicken with cheese and a white wine sauce (£6.65), steaks (from £7.95), with game in winter; puddings such as home-made meringue with raspberries, bread pudding or treacle tart (from £1.40); daily specials and Sunday roast; coffee. Well kept Bunces Best, Wadworths IPA and 6X, and a fortnightly changing guest beer on handpump; an interesting choice of decent wines by the glass, and quite a few liqueurs and ports; efficient, friendly staff; good log fires (in handsome fireplaces). There's a front terrace with some benches and a back garden. On the first Tuesday of each month, there's a vintage car meeting. Handy for the East Somerset Light Railway. *(Recommended by Ted George, Mr and Mrs P B Dowsett, Dr F Peters, Dr J E Gore, Brig J S Green, R W Stanbury, S V Bishop, John and Joan Wyatt, Kevin and Tracey Stephens, M G Hart)*

Free house   Licensees Rodney and Dora Phelps   Real ale   Meals and snacks (till 10 Fri/Sat; limited Sun evening)   Cottagey restaurant (not Sun evening)   Cranmore (0749 88) 450   Children in restaurant   Open 11.30–2.30, 6.30–11; closed Sun evening Oct-Feb

CROSCOMBE (Somerset)   ST5844   Map 2

Bull Terrier ★ ◎ ⊨

A371 Wells–Shepton Mallet

Built in the last part of the 15th century and known as the Rose & Crown, this popular place was first granted a licence to sell alcohol in 1612. It changed its name in 1976 and this name has made it a regular calling place for bull terrier breeders and owners from all over the world. The lounge ('Inglenook') bar has attractively moulded original beams, cushioned wooden wall seats and wheelback chairs around neat glossy tables, pictures on its white walls, a log-effect gas fire in a big stone fireplace with a fine iron fireback, and a red carpet on its flagstone floor. A communicating ('Snug') room has more tables with another gas-effect log fire, and there's a third in the parquet-floored 'Common Bar', by the local noticeboard; there's also a family room. Wholesome bar food includes sandwiches (from £1.15; toasted from £1.40), soup (£1.60), basket meals (from £1.95), ploughman's (from £2.30), spaghetti bolognese (£3.50), salads (from £3.60), excellent home-made steak and kidney pie (£4.25), a choice of home-made vegetarian dishes like Indian spiced beans (£4.25) or Brazil nut loaf (£4.50), Barnsley chop (£5.75), trout and almonds (£5.25), steaks (from £8.95), and home-made specials like ginger chicken with noodles, red hot beef or lamb Shrewsbury; lovely puddings such as fudge cake with hot butterscotch sauce or Bavarian lemon torte. Very well kept Bull Terrier Best Bitter (a strongish beer brewed for the pub), as well as Badger Tanglefoot, Butcombe, Charles Wells Eagle, and Palmers on handpump; farmhouse cider, several whiskies and a decent choice of wines, both by the glass and by the bottle; they also have an off sales price list. Warm, courteous service; dominoes and cribbage. There's a two-mile footpath to Bishop's Palace moat in Wells. *(Recommended by Sumner L Hopkins, Mr and Mrs C H Garnett, Philip Orbell, A M J Chadwick, J and L, Jon Payne, Brian and Jenny Seller, D G and J M Moore, Roger Huggins, B and J Derry, K H Frostick, Duncan and Lucy Gardner, Brig J S Green, Mike Tucker, Dr F Peters, F E Bartholemew, J and L, Richard Dolphin, A M Kelly, Barry and Anne, J M and S A Smither)*

Free house   Licensees Stan and Pam Lea   Real ale   Meals and snacks (till 10 Fri/Sat evenings; not Sun evening or Mon Nov-Mar)   Wells (0749) 343658   Children in family room and restaurant   Open 12–2.30, 7–11; closed Mon Nov-Mar   Bedrooms; £20/£42B

DOULTING (Somerset)   ST6443 Map 2

Poachers Pocket

Follow Chelynch signpost off A361 in village, E of Shepton Mallet

It's worth getting here early if you want to enjoy the good and very popular food; this might include pâté (£1.60), sandwiches (from £1.35), ploughman's (from £2.40), home-made quiche (£3.50), cauliflower cheese (£3.60), home-cooked ham (£3.80), tasty home-made steak and kidney pie (£3.80), scampi (£3.95), and pan-fried steak (£5.50); the charcoal grill is now both lunchtime and evening and serves a selection of lamb cutlets or gammon steak and pineapple (£5.50), pork chops (£5.75) and steaks (from £6.75); puddings (from £1.40). Well kept Butcombe Bitter, Oakhill and Black Magic (a new one to us) on handpump; farmhouse cider. There are one or two settles, small wheelback or captains' chairs, some black beams, gundog pictures on the white walls, a crackling log fire in the end stripped-stone wall, flagstones by the bar counter (though it's mainly carpeted), and a lovely warm and friendly atmosphere; piped music. The extension has created a lot more bar space. *(Recommended by D S and Mrs T M Beeson, Tony and Lynne Stark, M J B Pearson, Dr F Peters, Klaus Leist; more reports please)*

Free house   Licensees Justine Tidmarsh aand Joanne Massey   Real ale   Meals and snacks (11.30–1.45, 6.15–9.45)   (074 988) 220   Children in family room   Open 11.30(12 Mon)–2.30, 6.15–11; closed evening 25 Dec

DOWLISH WAKE (Somerset)   ST3713   Map 1

New Inn ✪

Village signposted from Kingstone – which is signposted from old A303 on E side of
Ilminster, and from A3037 just S of Ilminster; keep on past church – pub at far end of
village

The Swiss landlady does the cooking in this spotlessly kept, friendly village pub. As
well as bar food that includes sandwiches (from £1.10), good ploughman's (from
£2), spicy sausage (£2.45), ham and egg (£2.65), omelettes (from £2.60) and
sirloin steak (£5.95), she's praised for dishes such as soft roes on toast (£2.75),
raclette, cheese and baked potatoes (£4.75), braised duck (£7.70), whole shoulder
of lamb (£10.75), and a choice of puddings like delicious apple and blackberry
pancake with blackberry ice cream; no credit cards. Well kept Butcombe,
Wadworths 6X and a guest beer on handpump; a decent choice of whiskies, and a
selection of Perry's ciders. These come from just down the road, and the thatched
16th-century stone cider mill is well worth a visit for its collection of wooden
bygones and its liberal free tastings (you can buy the half-dozen different ciders in
old-fashioned earthenware flagons as well as more modern containers; it's closed
on Sunday afternoons). Old-fashioned furnishings include a mixture of chairs,
high-backed settles, attractive sturdy tables, dark beams which are strung liberally
with hop bines, and a stone inglenook fireplace with a woodburning stove. Maybe
piped music, and in a separate area they have darts, shove-ha'penny, dominoes,
cribbage, table skittles as well as alley skittles and a fruit machine. In front of the
stone pub there's a rustic bench, tubs of flowers and a sprawl of clematis; the
pleasant back garden has flowerbeds and a children's climbing frame, and dogs are
allowed here. *(Recommended by Ted George, C P Scott-Malden, George Pugh, Bernard
Phillips, Robert and Vicky Tod, EML, Chris Raisin, David Shillitoe, Richard Dolphin, Mr and
Mrs B Dymott, Mr and Mrs G Turner)*

*Free house   Licensees Therese Boosey and David Smith   Real ale   Meals and snacks
(till 10)   Ilminster (0460) 52413   Children in family room   Open 11–2.30, 6–11;
may open all day Sat if trade demands*

DUNSTER (Somerset)   SS9943   Map 1

Luttrell Arms 🛏

A396

The back bar in this comfortably modernised THF hotel still has a pubby
atmosphere, as well as old settles and more modern furniture, bottles, clogs and
horseshoes hanging from the high beams, and a stag's head and rifles on the walls.
Ancient black timber uprights glazed with fine hand-floated glass, full of ripples
and irregularities, separate the room from a small galleried and flagstoned
courtyard. Bar snacks include sandwiches, a cold buffet, plaice and a speciality
mixed grill, as well as unusual evening meals; well kept Bass and Exmoor Bitter on
handpump. In the gardens there are cannon emplacements dug out by Blake in the
Civil War when – with Praise God Barebones and his pikemen – he was besieging
the Castle for six months. The town, on the edge of Exmoor National Park, is
pretty. *(Recommended by Jim and Maggie Cowell, Richard Gibbs, Mrs H M T Carpenter;
more reports please)*

*Free house (THF)   Real ale   Meals and snacks   Restaurant   Dunster (0643)
821555   Open 11–2.30, 6–11   Bedrooms; £59B/£118B*

EAST LYNG (Somerset)   ST3328   Map 1

Rose & Crown

A361 about 4 miles W of Othery

Warmly friendly and relaxed, this is a lovely place for a drink and a chat beside the
winter log fire in its modernised fine old stone fireplace; the open-plan beamed
lounge bar is traditionally furnished, and there's a stack of old *Country Lifes* on a

bow window seat by an oak drop-leaf table, a corner cabinet of glass, china and silver, a court cabinet, and well kept Butcombe, and Eldridge Pope Royal Oak and Hardy on handpump. Freshly prepared food includes good crusty sandwiches (from £1.10; steak £2.85), soup (£1.50), pâté (£1.95), ploughman's (from £2.35), ham and egg (£3.15), omelettes or salads (£4.25), scampi or trout (£4.95), mixed grill (£8.95), steaks (from £7.95) and very good duck (£9.25); also puddings (from £1.30) and coffee; piped music. The prettily planted back garden (largely hedged off from the car park) has picnic-table sets, and there's also a full skittle alley. *(Recommended by Richard Dolphin, Hilary Roberts; more reports please)*

Free house   Licensee P J Thyer   Real ale   Meals and snacks (till 10)   Restaurant (not Sun lunchtime)   Taunton (0823) 698235   Children in restaurant   Open 11–2.30, 6.30–11; Bedrooms; £30B/£50B

EXEBRIDGE (Somerset)   SS9224   Map 1

Anchor 🛏

B3222 S of Dulverton

A handsome three-arched stone bridge crosses the Exe at this peaceful spot; the river runs by the inn's sheltered lawn, which has well spaced picnic-table sets and old-fashioned teak seats. The main front bar is a companionable place, with some carpet on its floor tiles, individually chosen tables and seats such as a big winged settle and a nice old library chair among more orthodox furnishings, Cecil Aldin hunting prints and Exmoor pictures above the stripped wooden dado, some hunting trophies and a warm woodburning stove. Bar food includes good sandwiches (from £1.10, steak £3.25), home-made soup (£1.25), filled baked potatoes (from £1.95), pasties (£2.75), ploughman's (from £3), omelettes (from £3.25), steak pie or chicken and ham pie (£3.50), vegetarian dishes (£4.50), local trout (£4.95), 8oz rump steak (£7.95) and quite a wide choice of children's dishes (£1.50). There's a back games bar with pool and two fruit machines divided by a flexiwall from a lounge bar with button-back leather chesterfields, modern oak tables and chairs, and French windows to the garden, which has a play area. Well kept Ruddles County, Ushers Best and Websters Yorkshire (called "Doone" here) on handpump; alley skittles, trivia and piped light music, happy staff. The inn has fishing rights. *(Recommended by Gwen and Peter Andrews, J S Evans, R Gray)*

Free house   Licensees John and Judy Phripp   Real ale   Meals and snacks (till 10) Restaurant (not Sun lunchtime)   Dulverton (0398) 23433   Children in large family lounge   Open 11–2.30, 6(7 winter)–11   Bedrooms; £36B/£60B

FAULKLAND (Somerset)   ST7354   Map 2

Tuckers Grave £

A366 E of village

The flagstoned entry in this quite unspoilt and very friendly farm cottage (the smallest pub in the *Guide*) opens into a tiny room with casks of well kept Bass and Butcombe Bitter on tap and Cheddar Valley cider in an alcove on the left. Two old cream-painted high-backed settles face each other across a single table on the right, and a side room has shove-ha'penny. There's a skittle alley and tables and chairs on the back lawn. Food is limited to sandwiches (75p) and ploughman's (£2) at lunchtime. *(Recommended by Ted George, Mr Jennings, Bob Eardley, Roger Huggins, R W Stanbury, Jon Wainwright, Nick and Alison Dowson, Chris Newman, Deb Jay)*

Free house   Licensees Ivan and Glenda Swift   Real ale   Lunchtime snacks   Frome (0373) 834230   Children welcome   Open 11–3, 6–11

HASELBURY PLUCKNETT (Somerset)   ST4710   Map 1

Haselbury Inn ⊘

A3066 E of Crewkerne

There is now an even wider choice of bar food in this well kept and inviting place, including soup (£1.50), ploughman's with five cheeses (£3.20), home-made pâté (£3.50), good pasta dishes (£4), beef curry (£5), coq au vin (£8.50), a choice of fish such as plaice, local trout (£8.50), lobster, or large Dover sole (£12), charcoal-grilled steaks (from £8.50), guinea fowl (£7.50), and daily specials like moules marinières in season (£3.50) or Hungarian goulash (£3.50); also puddings such as apple strudel, home-made fruit pies, rich lemon crunch or treacle tart (from £2), and a barbecue menu. The neatly kept bar has a restrained collection of bric-a-brac on the rather lofty beams, plants in the windows, and fresh or dried flowers; one half has chintz armchairs and sofas around the fire and television set, and the other has candlelit wooden tables with unusually heavy red-cushioned cask seats – there's a fire down here, too; piped music. Well kept Butcombe Bitter, Exmoor Best, Smiles Best, Wadworths 6X and Charles Wells Bombardier, as well as a wide range of local beers and Hickelbury (brewed for them) tapped from the cask; a good choice of wines, country wines, freshly squeezed orange juice; espresso coffee. Evening meals in the attractive back restaurant should probably be booked on Fridays and Saturdays. There are picnic-table sets on the side grass. *(Recommended by Jamie and Sarah Allan, Mr and Mrs D V Morris, Mr and Mrs J R Hulley, Chris Raisin; more reports please)*

Free house   Licensee James Pooley   Real ale   Meals and snacks   No-smoking restaurant   Crewkerne (0460) 72488   Children welcome   Open 12–2.30, 7–11; closed Mon

HINTON ST GEORGE (Somerset)   ST4212   Map 1

Poulett Arms

Village signposted off A30 W of Crewkerne; and off Merriott road (declassified – former A356, off B3165) N of Crewkerne

The decorous atmosphere here is perhaps due to the emphasis on the handsome front dining lounge rather than the cosy little back bar. This larger room has maroon plush chairs (and a couple of high-backed settles), matching velvet curtains, big black beams, stripped masonry, an imposing stone fireplace, a few pistols and brasses, and two cosy smaller rooms opening off, one with a big disused inglenook fireplace. It can be very busy mid-evening. Good bar food includes sandwiches (from £1.50), home-made soup (£1.75), avocado mousse (£2.25), ploughman's (£2.75), lasagne (£3.95), particularly good steak and kidney pie (£4.25), trout (£5.25), steaks (from £7.95) and dishes of the day such as Cumberland sausage with egg and chips (£2.95), lamb Shrewsbury casserole (£3.95), rabbit casserole (£4.25), seafood salad (£4.50) or nut roast or chestnut patties in red wine (£5.75). Well kept Courage Best and Flowers Original on handpump; friendly welcome from the licensees – and from Burton, their cream labrador; fruit machine, cribbage, dominoes, maybe unobtrusive piped music. The prettily planted back garden has some white tables under cocktail parasols, near a real rarity – a massive pelota wall; there's also a skittle alley, with darts and table skittles. *(Recommended by Richard Dolphin, Chris Raisin, Nicholas Kingsley, Chris Heathman; more reports please)*

Free house   Licensee Ray Chisnall   Real ale   Meals and snacks   Crewkerne (0460) 73149   Children in family room   Open 11–3, 7–11

HUISH EPISCOPI (Somerset)   ST4326   Map 1
Rose & Crown

A372 E of Langport

For a long time in the main entries, this pub was "rested" last year – and readers immediately clamoured for its reinstatement, as a genuine rarity. It is after all remarkable to find such an accessible pub that's survived in such an untouched form. To get a drink, you just walk into the central flagstoned still room and choose from the casks of well kept Bass, Boddingtons and Butcombe or the wide choice of Somerset farm ciders and country wines which stand on ranks of shelves around it (prices are very low); this servery is the only thoroughfare between the casual little front parlours with their unusual pointed-arch windows and genuinely friendly locals. Food is simple and cheap: generously filled sandwiches (from £1), and ploughman's (from £2). There's a fruit machine in one of the front rooms, and shove-ha'penny, dominoes and cribbage. A much more orthodox big back extension family room has darts, pool, trivia and juke box; there's a skittle alley. Outside, there are tables and a lawn. George the dog will welcome a bitch but can't abide other dogs. A real ale festival is held in the adjoining field every September. *(Recommended by Steve and Carolyn Harvey, David Hunn; more reports please)*

Free house   Licensee Eileen Pittard   Real ale   Snacks   (0458) 250494   Children welcome   Open 11.30–2.30(3 Sat), 5.30–11; all day Fri and bank hols

KELSTON (Avon)   ST7067 Map 2
Old Crown
Bitton Road; A431 W of Bath

In one or other of the row of four small rooms in this carefully restored and genuinely preserved pub, you'll find beams strung with hops, lovely tableau photographs, interesting carved settles and cask tables on polished flagstones, candlelight, and logs burning in an ancient open range (there's another smaller, open range and a Victorian open fireplace – both with coal-effect gas fires). Well kept Axminster Hardington (summer only), Bass, Butcombe, Smiles Best, and Wadworths 6X and Old Timer (winter only) on handpump, also Mendip cider; no machines or music – just shove-ha'penny and dominoes. Lunchtime bar food includes home-made soup (£1.35), ploughman's (£2.95), a choice of salads (from £3.75), cottage pie (£3.95), spicy vegetarian casserole (£4.25), beef and Guinness casserole (£5.20) and steaks (from £8.30); also puddings like Dutch apple pie, crème de menthe sundae or chocolate profiteroles (£2.10). The neat, sheltered back garden has picnic-table sets under apple trees overlooking hills. The car park's over quite a fast road. *(Recommended by Steve and Carolyn Harvey, William Pryce, Roger Huggins, Tony Hodge, Lisa Wilson, J A Leeds; more reports please)*

Free house   Licensees Richard Jackson and Michael Steele   Real ale   Lunchtime meals and snacks (not Sun)   Restaurant Thurs-Sat evenings   Bath (0225) 423032 Children in restaurant if eating   Open 11.30–2.30, 5(5.30 winter)–11

KILVE (Somerset)   ST1442 Map 1
Hood Arms ⊘ ⇐
A39 E of Williton

Popular home-made food at lunchtime in this village inn includes sandwiches (from 90p), soup (£1.60), pâté or good ploughman's (£2.50), substantial salads (from £3), hot daily specials such as steak and kidney pie, chilli con carne, cauliflower, celery and stilton bake, chicken and broccoli au gratin, Brixham cod or lasagne (all £4.25), and tasty puddings like very good treacle tart (from £1.50); in the evenings the main bar takes on much more the style of a restaurant, with full meals. The straightforwardly comfortable and carpeted main bar has a woodburning stove in the stone fireplace (decorated with shining horsebrasses on their original leathers) and leads through to a little cosy lounge with red plush button-back seats. Well kept Boddingtons and Flowers Original on handpump, several malt whiskies, and they do tea and coffee; attentive service; dominoes, cribbage, alley skittles and gentle piped music. A sheltered back terrace, by a garden with a prettily planted old wall behind, has white metal and plastic seats and tables. *(Recommended by P A Devitt, Anthony Barnes, Peter Burton, Dr and Mrs Tanner, R and E Harfield, Mrs K J Betts, R Etherington, John and Joan Nash, Jim and Maggie Cowell, David and Valerie Hooley; more reports please)*

Free house   Licensees Robbie Rutt and Neville White   Real ale   Meals and snacks (12–2, 6.30–10)   No-smoking restaurant Weds-Sat evenings   Holford (027874) 210 Children over 7 in restaurant only   Open 11–2.30, 6–11; closed 25 Dec   Bedrooms; £33B/£56B

LANGLEY MARSH (Somerset)   ST0729   Map 1

Three Horseshoes ★ ◔

Village signposted off A361 from Wiveliscombe

Particularly good vegetarian dishes from a constantly changing and imaginative menu might include spinach parcels (£4.25) and courgette and mushroom bake or garlic mushroom pancakes (£4.50), with other good-value things such as baps (from £1.40), home-made soup (£1.50) ploughman's (from £2.85), a choice of salads or filled baked potatoes, pheasant and liver pâté (£2.50), garlic mushrooms (£2.60), excellent Somerset fish pie with perfect pastry or chicken and mushroom pie (£4.95), and pigeon breasts cooked in cider and cream or steak in oyster sauce (£5.25); most of the vegetables come from their garden (no chips or fried food), and the butter comes in little pots; puddings include good mincemeat, apple and brandy pancakes or cheesecake with cherry topping. The back bar has planes hanging from the ceiling, banknotes papering the wall behind the bar counter, low modern settles, polished wooden tables with plants, dark red wallpaper, a piano, and a local stone fireplace; the lively front room has sensibly placed darts, shove-ha'penny, table skittles, dominoes, cribbage, fruit machine and now bar billiards; separate skittle alley; piped music. Wide and often unusual, the range of real ales typically includes Badger Tanglefoot, Bass, and Palmers IPA, with continually changing guest ales like Harveys, Hook Norton, King & Barnes, Ringwood, Thwaites, Wadworths 6X or Youngs on handpump or tapped from the cask; they serve Perry's farmhouse cider from the cask. The pub alsatian is called Guinness. You can sit on rustic seats on the verandah or in the sloping back garden, with a climbing frame, swing and slide, and a view of farmland. In fine weather there are usually vintage cars outside. (*Recommended by C P Scott-Malden, Tim Gilroy, J Finney, Jim Baxter, P and J McComb, R A Riley, Alan Carr, A M J Chadwick, R W Stanbury, Adam and Elizabeth Gorb*)

Free house   Licensee J Hopkins   Real ale   Meals and snacks   Small restaurant Wiveliscombe (0984) 23763   Well behaved children allowed away from bar Singalongs Sat evenings and occasional spontaneous 'fiddle/squeeze box' sessions with local Morris Dancing musicians   Open 12–3, 7–11

LUXBOROUGH (Somerset)   SS9837   Map 1

Royal Oak ⇔

Kingsbridge; S of Dunster on minor rds into Brendon Hills – OS Sheet 181, map reference 983378

Tucked into a narrow pass of the Brendon Hills by the old coach road from Dunster, this has been a pub since the 17th century – and was built long before that. Its three rooms include flagstones in the front public bar, beams and inglenooks, a real medley of furniture, and good log fires, with a cosy dining room. But it's been the cheerful and enthusiastic young licensees that have really brought it into the reckoning in the last couple of years. Besides the buoyant atmosphere, they've brought good honest food such as huge sandwiches, good home-made soup with big hunks of bread and non-packet butter (£1.60), a pint of prawns (£2.85), gargantuan pasties (£3.25), ratatouille (£3.45), spicy Mexican beef (£3.65), lasagne or home-made pies (from £3.95), hearty beef stews (£3.95) served with up to four good fresh veg, home-cured ham with salad (£4.05) and specials such as chicken à la king (£4.25). Booking is recommended at weekends for the four-course evening meals. Well kept real ales such as Cotleigh Tawny and winter Reindeer, Eldridge Pope Royal Oak, Flowers IPA, Exmoor Gold and guest beers (often from afar) on handpump, decent wines by the glass and some remarkable ones by the bottle; pool, dominoes, cribbage, winter darts – no machines or music. Tables outside. (*Recommended by Bob Smith, Anthony Barnes, Mrs D M Everard, Michael Lloyd, Mrs J Bond*)

Free house   Licensee Robin Stamp   Real ale   Meals and snacks   (0984) 40319 Children in back bar and dining room   Quiz Tues, folk music Fri   Open 11–2.30, 6(6.30 winter)–11   Bedrooms; £19/£26

MONKSILVER (Somerset)   ST0737 Map 1

Notley Arms ★ ◎

B3188

It's not just the excellent food that draws people to this well run village inn (several readers say it's their favourite pub to eat in), but also the genuine warmth of the welcome and the way the licensee remembers you even if you're just an occasional visitor. The beamed and L-shaped bar has small settles and kitchen chairs around the plain country wooden and candle-lit tables, Old Master and other prints on the black-timbered white walls, a couple of woodburning stoves, and a relaxed atmosphere; dominoes, cribbage, trivia and alley skittles, well reproduced classical music, and a bright little family room; dogs welcome. Regular dishes on the ever-popular menu include soup (£1.25), sandwiches (from £1.35), filled baked potatoes (from £2.25, winter only), excellent ploughman's (from £2.60), pitta bread generously filled with bacon, mushroom and salad (£2.85), vegetarian dishes like curry or stuffed aubergines (from £3.50), home-made pasta (£3.75), a choice of salads including local cured ham (£4.75), delicious smoked mackerel (£4.95) or generous prawn mayonnaise (£5), superb Chinese-style red-roasted pork with stir-fry vegetables (£4.95), and correctly cooked vegetables; lots of interesting specials, and puddings like particularly good treacle tart (one couple say it's the best they've ever had) or home-made ice creams (from £1.75), and evening extras such as fresh local trout (£6.75) and 8oz sirloin steak (£7.75). Well kept Ruddles County, Theakstons Best and Ushers Best on handpump; country wines such as oak leaf or raspberry; efficient staff. The neatly kept cottage garden runs down to a swift clear stream. (*Recommended by PLC, Mr and Mrs R Gammon, Mr and Mrs W H Thomas, Mr and Mrs E Patterson, Pete and Mary Fintelley, Steve and Carolyn Harvey, Dr J E Gore, J D Cranston, A M J Chadwick, Mr and Mrs Morgan, Adam and Elizabeth Gorb, Richard Dolphin, PLC*)

Grand Met   Tenants Alistair and Sarah Cade   Real ale   Meals and snacks (not first two weeks of Feb)   (0984) 56217   Children in family room   Open 11–2.30, 6–11; closed 25 Dec

MONTACUTE (Somerset)   ST4916 Map 2

Kings Arms

A3088 W of Yeovil

This civilised early Georgian inn – with its handsome golden stone facade – is popular for its bar food: soup with home-made bread (£1), a generous buffet (£3.85 or £4.65), and daily specials such as steak and kidney pie, chicken chasseur or ham and asparagus bake (from £3.90); best to book for Sunday lunch (when people tend to dress smartly); no-smoking in the eating areas. Bass and a guest beer tapped from the cask, good wines and farmhouse cider; friendly and efficient service. The lounge bar is comfortably furnished with grey-gold plush seats, soft armchairs, chintz sofas, a high curved settle, and towards the front – where part of the walls are stripped back to the handsome masonry – plush seats around tables. The village includes the stately Elizabethan mansion of the same name, and behind the hotel the wooded St Michael's Hill is owned by the National Trust. (*Recommended by Major and Mrs E M Warrick, Mrs Joan Harris, JM, PM, Pamela Sterling, Dr and Mrs Frank Wells, D I Baddeley, Mrs A Crowhurst, Cdr G F Barnett, R W Stanbury*)

Free house   Licensee S D Price   Real ale   Meals (till 10)   No-smoking restaurant Martock (0935) 822513   Children in eating area   Open 11–3, 6–11; closed 25 Dec and 26 Dec   Bedrooms; £46B/64B

NORTON ST PHILIP (Somerset)   ST7755   Map 2

George ★

A366

Originally built to house merchants buying wool and cloth from the rich sheep-farming Hinton Priory at the great August cloth market, this historic building has been functioning as an inn for nearly 600 years – and is one of those rare pubs still opening at ten. There's a fine half-timbered and galleried back courtyard, with an external Norman stone stair-turret, massive stone walls, high mullioned windows, and simple furnishings: leather seats, square-panelled wooden settles, plain old tables, wide bare floorboards, and lofty beams hung with harness, copper preserving pans, and a magnificent pair of bellows; a long, stout table serves well kept Bass, and Wadworths IPA and 6X on handpump. Bar food includes filled rolls (£1.10), soup (£1.30), ploughman's (£3), filled baked potatoes (£2.55), lasagne (£3.25), a couple of daily specials such as crab pâté and salad, half roast chicken and chips, date and walnut quiche, or home-made steak and kidney pie (from £2.75); also puddings (from £1.20); tea and coffee. A panelled lounge is furnished with antique settles and tables. Off the courtyard is the cellar Dungeon Bar (opened only at busy times – weekends say), named to recall the men imprisoned there after the rebel Duke of Monmouth had been defeated. A stroll over the meadow behind the pub leads to an attractive churchyard around the medieval church whose bells struck Pepys (here on 12 June 1668) as 'mighty tuneable'. *(Recommended by Barry and Anne, Philip Orbell, J E Stanton, Mr Jennings, David Hunn, Janet Hill, Les Rae, Lynn Sharpless, Bob Eardley, Roger Huggins, Len Beattie, Tony and Lynne Stark, William Pryce, Tony Gayfer, R W Stanbury, D J Milner, W Bailey)*

Wadworths   Tenant M F Moore   Real ale   Meals and snacks (till 10)   Restaurant Faulkland (037 387) 224   Children in two separate rooms   Open 10–2.30, 6–11; 10–11 Sat

OLDBURY-UPON-SEVERN (Avon)   ST6292   Map 2

Anchor ⊘

Village signposted from B4061

A warm welcome (even when busy) and substantial good value food from a daily changing menu attract visitors and locals to this attractively modernised village pub. The comfortably furnished beamed lounge has a curved high-backed settle facing an attractive oval oak gateleg table, winged seats against the wall, easy chairs, cushioned window seats, and a big winter log fire. Bar food includes lasagne (£3.50), Yorkshire pudding filled with roast beef, chicken and mushroom pie or pork and ham pie (£3.95), fish pie (£4.10), chicken in white wine and stilton sauce (£4.25), locally made pork and garlic sausages (£4.50), particularly good charcoal grilled steaks (£6.95) and fresh Severn salmon (£7.45), also enterprising puddings such as gooseberry pie, fresh blueberry tart, macaroons soaked in brandy with chocolate sauce and fresh cream, blackcurrant supreme and so forth (from £1.55); friendly waitress service in no-smoking dining room; best to get there early if you want a seat. Bass tapped from the cask, with Butcombe, Marstons Pedigree and Theakstons Best and Old Peculier on handpump; over 70 malts, decent choice of good quality wines; darts, shove-ha'penny, dominoes and cribbage. You can sit outside in the garden in summer, and there's a donkey. St Arilda's church nearby is interesting, on its odd little knoll with wild flowers among the gravestones (the primroses and daffodils in spring are lovely), and there are lots of paths over the meadows to the sea dyke or warth which overlooks the tidal flats. *(Recommended by C H Stride, D A Lloyd, Charles Owens, Patrick Godfrey, J Warren, Margaret Dyke, Chris Newman, Deb Jay)*

Free house   Licensees Michael Dowdeswell and Peter Riley   Real ale   Meals Restaurant (not Sun evening)   Thornbury (0454) 413331   Children in dining room Open 11.30–2.30(3 Sat), 6.30(6 Sat)–11; closed evening 25 Dec

OVER STRATTON (Somerset) ST4315 Map 1

Royal Oak

Village signposted from former A303 Yeovil–Ilminster through Seavington St Michael, which itself is signposted off A303 at E end of new Ilminster bypass

A really nice place for a bar meal, this thatched dining pub: home-made soup (£1.80), pears with stilton (£2.80), filled baked potatoes (from £3), salads (from £4.05), deep-fried brie (£4.35), stuffed lemon sole (£4.85), vegetable samosas (£5.40), baked avocado and crab (£5.65), garlic-fried chicken (£7.10), venison with port and cranberries (£7.40), steaks (from £9.15) and fresh lobster (£15.20, when available); children's dishes (from £2). Well kept Badger Best and Tanglefoot, and Wadworths 6X on handpump; lots of malt whiskies and an extensive wine list. The cosy extended dark-flagstoned bars are simply but carefully furnished and decorated with scrubbed deal farmhouse kitchen tables, a mixture of similar or dining chairs, pews and settles, candles in bottles, plants in the windows, some hop bines, and a stuffed pheasant. The beams have been prettily stencilled with an oakleaf and acorn pattern, the walls are stripped to bare stonework or attractively ragrolled red, and log fires burn, even in summer. Lots of picnic-table sets on a floodlit reconstituted-stone terrace sheltered by the back wings of the building, with more on a further sheltered gravel terrace with a barbecue; the play area is large and well equipped – there's even a big trampoline. *(Recommended by WMS, A M J Chadwick, Major and Mrs E M Warrick, D I Baddeley, Cdr G F Barnett, Pat Woodward, R J Walden, Chris Raisin, David Wallington, Richard R Dolphin)*

Badger   Manageress Lyn Holland   Real ale   Meals and snacks (till 10)   Restaurant Ilminster (0460) 40906   Children in restaurant   Open 12–2.30, 7(6.30 Sat)–11

PORLOCK (Somerset) SS8846 Map 1

Ship ★ ⇌

A39

In little more than half a mile, Porlock Hill – at the foot of which this warmly welcoming, honest pub stands – climbs up more than 600 feet to the Exmoor plateau; there are good local walks. The characterful low-beamed front bar has an inglenook fireplace at each end, traditional old benches on the tiled and flagstoned floor, a sought-after window-ledge seat, and hunting prints on the walls. At the back, the carpeted lounge has plush red banquettes, a Gothic settle, and a chimney seat. Well kept Bass, Cotleigh Old Buzzard, Courage Best and a guest beer on handpump from an air-conditioned cellar; country wines (including local damson wine), choice of malt whiskies and Perry's cider. Bar food includes home-made soup (£1.50), ploughman's (from £2.50), main dishes such as good pheasant casserole, flavoursome trout with almonds, Somerset pork or Exmoor lamb casserole (£3.50) and seafood platter (£10.50); also children's menu; hearty breakfasts. Shove-ha'penny, dominoes, cribbage, bar billiards, fruit machine and video game; a separate pool room (which has sensibly placed darts too), and a full skittle alley. The extended garden (actually almost higher than the thatched roof) at the back of this partly 13th-century village cottage has lovely views of the sea and moor; there's also a children's play area. We should stress that the stay award is primarily for the charming *simplicity* of the bedrooms. *(Recommended by Chris Cook, Fleur Hitchcock, Ian McKay, Helen Roe, J L and J A Annandale, Jim and Maggie Cowell, BCM, Steve and Carolyn Harvey, Klaus Leist, Andrea and Guy Bradley, R Gray, Andy Hick, Carol Mason, W A D Hoyle, Vic and Reba Longhorn, Virginia Jones, G W Warren, David Young, I T and S Hughes, George Berry, Dr S E Martin, Dr L B Cook, R Etherington)*

Free house   Licensee C M Robinson   Real ale   Meals and snacks   Restaurant (not Sun lunchtime)   Porlock (0643) 862507   Children welcome   Morris dancing and occasional folk singers   Open 10.30–3, 5.30–11   Bedrooms; £16.50(£21B)/£33(£39B)

SHEPPERDINE (Avon)   ST6295   Map 4

Windbound

From B4061 just N of Thornbury turn off at Oldbury signpost, then right at
Shepperdine signpost, then next left into Shepperdine Lane; some maps and signposts
spell it Sheperdine

As well as seats up on the dyke, there are picnic-table sets among brightly coloured
summer flowers on the sheltered fairy-lit lawn outside this extended pub; also,
swings and slides. Inside, it's the spacious upper dining lounge that has the
extensive views over the Severn Estuary to the hills beyond; the downstairs bar –
below the level of the sea dyke – has dining chairs and straight-backed small settles
forming booths around the tables, one or two local watercolours and prints with
the wicker fish-traps on its walls, and a good winter fire. Hook Norton, Ind Coope
Burton, and Tetleys on handpump, farmhouse ciders such as Addlestones, and
quite a few sherries. Bar food includes soup (£1.20), sandwiches (from £1.20),
stuffed mushrooms (£2.55), ploughman's (from £2.95), a choice of salads (from
£3.85), plaice or vegetarian lasagne (£4.40), tagliatelli carbonara or chicken
enchilada (£5.40), roast duck (£6.75) and steaks (from £7.70), daily specials and
puddings (£1.75); children's menu (£1.95), Sunday lunch (£4.65, children's
£2.30); barbecues in fine weather. Darts, cribbage, dominoes, fruit machine, piped
music and a separate skittle alley. You can walk along the banks of the estuary to
Sharpness. *(Recommended by D A Lloyd, J R Jewitt, Gwen and Peter Andrews, Peter and
Rose Flower; more reports please)*

*Ansells (Allied)   Lease: Nigel and Josephine Wright   Real ale   Meals and snacks (till
10 Fri/Sat)   Restaurant   Thornbury (0454) 414343   Children in eating area and
restaurant   Occasional live entertainment   Open 11–2.30(3 Sat), 6.30(6 Sat)–11;
closed Mon lunchtime Jan-Easter*

SOUTH STOKE (Avon)   ST7461   Map 2

Pack Horse £

Village signposted opposite the Cross Keys off B3110, leaving Bath southwards – just
before end of speed limit

Clinging to the hillside down from the village centre, this 500-year-old pub has a
middle entrance corridor (still a public right of way to the church) which was used
for carrying the dead to the cemetery. This corridor also takes you to a central
space by the serving bar where you get your well kept Wadworths 6X on
handpump and a choice of ciders. The main room has a good local atmosphere, a
heavy black beam-and-plank ceiling, antique oak settles (two well carved),
leatherette dining chairs and cushioned captains' chairs on the quarry-tiled floor, a
cheery log fire in the handsome stone inglenook, some Royalty pictures, a chiming
wall-clock, and rough black shutters for the stone-mullioned windows (put up in
World War I). There's another room down to the left. Outstandingly good value
home-made bar food includes rolls (from 60p, home-baked cider ham 70p),
mouth-watering pasties or sausage plait (80p), several ploughman's (from £1.75),
fisherman's pie (£1.40) and steak pie, chips and peas (£1.85); friendly staff. Rather
fine shove-ha'penny slates are set into two of the tables, and there are darts,
dominoes, cribbage, fruit machine and piped music. There are children's swings in
the spacious back garden that looks out over the stolid old church and the wooded
valley. *(Recommended by M J B Pearson, Mr and Mrs Peter Woods, Roger Huggins, R W
Stanbury, Ron Gentry, Carol Mason; more reports please)*

*Courage   Tenant Colin Williams   Real ale   Meals and snacks   (0225) 832060
Children welcome   Open 11–4.30(3 winter), 6(7 winter)–11; 11–11 Sat*

STANTON WICK (Avon)   ST6162   Map 2

Carpenters Arms 🛏

Village signposted off A368, just W of junction with A37 S of Bristol

This very busy pub manages to combine a chatty pubby atmosphere with the demand for the wide choice of popular, good value food. On the right, the Coopers Parlour has red-cushioned wall pews around heavy tables, fresh flowers, one or two beams, and swagged-back curtains and houseplants in the windows; on the angle between here and the bar area there's a fat woodburning stove in an opened-through corner fireplace. The bar has stripped stone walls, wood-backed built-in wall seats and some red fabric-cushioned stools, a big log fire, and a prettily stocked aquarium. Diners are encouraged to step down into a snug inner room (lightened by mirrors in arched 'windows'), or to go round to the sturdy tables angling off on the right (where a pianist may be quietly vamping his way through the favourite standards five nights a week). Note that most of these tables get booked at weekends. The food ordering counter is round here: lots of starters like home-made soup (£1.50), grilled fresh sardines (£3.65) or devilled kidneys (£4.75), also interesting sandwiches (from £2.50, toasted fillet steak with onions and mushrooms £5.25), ploughman's (from £2.85), Welsh rarebit (£2.95), several vegetarian dishes such as ratatouille au gratin (£3.55), tagliatelli with asparagus and white wine sauce (£4.25) or onion tart (£5.25), deep fried plaice or scampi, or a choice of pies like creamy fish pie topped with potato or chicken and bacon (£5.95), salads (£6.25) and steaks (from £8.90); home-made puddings (from £2.25); tea and coffee. Well kept Bass, Butcombe, Theakstons and Wadworths 6X on handpump, and a good wine list, strong on medium priced well-made wines; efficient staff; cribbage, dominoes and trivia. The bedrooms are attractively furnished, and breakfasts are good. There are picnic-table sets on the front terrace. *(Recommended by P Devitt, Michele and Andrew Wells, Roger Huggins, William Pryce, Dr S E Martin, Dr L B Cook, Kevin and Tracey Stephens; more reports please)*

Free house   Licensee Nigel Pushman   Real ale   Meals and snacks   Restaurant (not Sun evening)   Compton Dando (0761) 490202   Children in eating area   Pianist 5 nights a week and Sun lunchtime   Open 11–11   Bedrooms; £42.50B/£49.50B

STAPLE FITZPAINE (Somerset)   ST2618 Map 1
Greyhound

Village signposted from A358 Taunton–Ilminster at Hatch Beauchamp; or (better road) from Shoreditch on B3170, just after crossing M5 S of Taunton

Over the last year or so we've detected signs of increasing enthusiasm, and perhaps increasing consistency, in readers' reports on this popular creeper-covered country pub. There are simple antique furnishings, flagstone floors, and log fires in attractive inglenooks. Wide choice of popular bar food includes home-made soup (£1.65), pâté or crusty mushrooms (£2.65), deep-fried brie (£2.75), lasagne (£4.25), spinach and cheese pancakes (£4.45), and evening charcoal grills like kebabs, gigot of lamb or trout (£6.45), medallions of pork (£6.95), and sirloin steak (£8.75), with home-made puddings such as treacle tart or elderflower fritters (£1.95), and profiteroles (£2.55); extra fish dishes on Friday evening; Sunday lunch. Well kept Boddingtons, Exmoor, Flowers IPA and Original, and Marstons Pedigree on handpump; lots of country wines and a fair number of malt whiskies. Darts, bar billiards, alley skittles and piped classical music. There are some seats outside in front of the pub among troughs of flowers, with more in the gravelled stable yard behind; also, a children's play area with a Wendy House and slide and a barbecue. Just to the south you can walk in the hillside woods of Neroche Forest, which has a signposted nature trail. *(Recommended by Maj and Mrs E M Warrick, Dr D M Forsyth, Maj H G Robertson, J and L, PLC, Patrick Young, Carol and Robin Tullo, T C W Moody, Mr and Mrs C Moncreiffe, Dr Keith Louden)*

Free house   Licensees Steven Watts and Mrs Audrey Watts   Real ale   Meals and snacks (till 10)   Restaurant (not Sun evening)   Hatch Beauchamp (0823) 480227   Children welcome   Jazz or Rythmn and Blues Thurs evenings, Folk 2nd and last Fri of month   Open 11–3, 5(5.30 Sat)–11

STOGUMBER (Somerset)   ST0937 Map 1

White Horse

From A358 Taunton–Williton, village signposted on left at Crowcombe

In a quiet conservation village and opposite the 12th-century red stone church, stands this consistently enjoyable little pub. The long room has old-fashioned built-in settles, a coal fire in cool weather, and settles and cushioned captains' chairs around the heavy rustic tables on the patterned carpet. Good, quickly served food includes sandwiches (from £1; toasted from £1.10), home-made vegetable soup (£1.40), burger (£1.60), salads or ploughman's (from £2.80), omelettes or vegetable casserole (£2.80), choice of meat, vegetable or fish lasagne (£3.60), lamb curry (£4), Somerset pork (£4.50), steak and kidney pudding (£5.10), chicken with peaches (£5.60), trout with almonds (£6.50) and steaks (£8.50); puddings such as walnut tart, steamed sultana sponge, home-made ice creams or apple crumble (from £1.20); three-course Sunday lunch; helpful, attentive service. Well kept Cotleigh Tawny and Exmoor on handpump, and farmhouse cider in summer. A side room has sensibly placed darts and a fruit machine; shove-ha'penny, dominoes, cribbage, video game and piped music, as well as a separate skittle alley. The garden behind is quiet except for rooks and lambs in the surrounding low hills. (*Recommended by K R Harris, Alan Carr, Gwen and Peter Andrews, David and Valerie Hooley; more reports please*)

Free house   Licensee Peter Williamson   Real ale   Meals and snacks (11–2, 6–10.30) Restaurant (not Sun evening)   Stogumber (0984) 56277   Children in restaurant Open 11–2.30, 6–11   Bedrooms; £25B/£35B

STOKE ST GREGORY (Somerset)   ST3527 Map 1

Rose & Crown 🏅 🛏

Woodhill; follow North Curry signpost off A378 by junction with A358 – keep on to Stoke, bearing right in centre and right again past church

Genuinely friendly to strangers, this 17th-century cottage is well known locally for generous helpings of particularly good value food, such as sandwiches (from £1.15), soup (£1.50), ravioli and garlic bread or pint of prawns (£3.35), omelettes (£4), other main dishes such as tandoori chicken (£4.95), stuffed plaice with prawns, seafood platter, grilled kidneys and bacon, or chicken casseroled in farm cider (all £4.95), steaks (from £7) and delicious mixed grill (£8.50); also home-made puddings with local clotted cream; excellent breakfasts. One small dining area is no smoking. Well kept Eldridge Pope Hardy and Royal Oak, and Exmoor on handpump; Taunton cider, decent wines; quick, courteous staff. The cosy and pleasantly romanticised stable theme includes stripped stonework, dark wooden loose-box partitions for some of the interestingly angled nooks and alcoves, lots of brasses and bits on the low beams and joists, and appropriate pictures including a highland pony carrying a stag. There's an 18th-century glass-covered well in one corner; unobtrusive piped classical music, dominoes, fruit machine and popular skittle alley. Under cocktail parasols by an apple tree on the sheltered front terrace are some picnic-table sets. (*Recommended by JM, PM, Miss K D Lambe, E H and R F Warner, Brett Williams, Derek Moore, Richard Dolphin, Graham Tayar, Kevin and Tracey Stephens, D E G and J E Dolling*)

Free house   Licensees Ron and Irene Browning   Real ale   Meals and snacks Restaurant   North Curry (0823) 490296   Children welcome   Open 10.30–2.30, 6–11   Bedrooms; £18.50/£35

STOKE ST MARY (Somerset)   ST2622 Map 1

Half Moon

2 3/4 miles from M5 junction 25; A358 towards Ilminster, then first right, then right in Henlade

The overall impression of this large and extensively modernised village pub is of clean, roomy comfort, with a warmly friendly atmosphere. Though it's open-plan, careful attention is given to each of its five neat main areas which are furnished and decorated with a good deal of character and individuality. A wide range of consistently good bar food includes soup (£1.25), sandwiches (from £1.25), starters such as breaded mushrooms with stilton sauce, fried Somerset brie, smoked trout pâté or vegetable pancake rolls (£1.95), also light basket meals (from £2.95), ploughman's (£3.25), salads (from £3.25), a choice of pies like steak and mushroom, ham and leek or lamb and apricot (from £4.25), several vegetarian dishes such as mushroom stroganoff, bean hot pot or vegetables topped with toasted almonds (£4.50), grilled fresh trout (£4.75), gammon steak (£4.95), very good lemon sole filled with smoked ham and cheese, or Barnsley chop (£5.50), steaks (from 8oz sirloin £6.95), a variety of children's dishes (from £1.75), good puddings like Dorset apple cake, chocolate fudge cake, treacle tart or excellent bread and butter pudding (from £1.30), lots of sundaes (£2.25); Sunday lunch; three areas, one no-smoking, are laid out as restaurant. Well kept Boddingtons, Flowers IPA and Marstons Pedigree on handpump; decent coffee; friendly and efficient staff. There are picnic-table sets on the well kept lawn, more tables on a small gravel terrace. *(Recommended by A M J Chadwick, John and Pat Smyth, Shirley Pielou, Mr and Mrs D V Morris, Mary Springer)*

Whitbreads   Tenant Pat Howard   Real ale   Meals and snacks (12–2, 6–10)
Restaurant   Taunton (0823) 442271   Children in eating area and restaurant   Open 11–2.30, 6–11

TORMARTON (Avon)   ST7678   Map 2
Compass

Under 1 mile from M4 junction 18; A46 towards Stroud, then first right turn

The lower bar of this well run and busy former coaching inn – with its glass cold food display cabinet – is more set out for eating and leads out to the nicest room, the light and spacious conservatory; this has orange or green garden chairs around wooden-slatted tables, flowers and shrubs, and a vigorous climbing vine. Popular with locals, the upper bar has stone walls, red plush chairs, red leatherette stools and cushioned settles. Bar food includes sandwiches (from £1.30), home-made soup (£1.65), ploughman's (from £3.15), a choice of salads served with a cottage loaf such as cheese flan, home-cooked ham, Cornish smoked mackerel, prawns or dressed crab (from £4.05, fresh poached salmon £6.65), filled baked potatoes (from £4.85) and main dishes such as lasagne (£5.10) and good seafood cassoulette (£5.30). Archers Village, Bass and Wadworths 6X on handpump, several malt whiskies and extensive wine list; darts, dominoes, cribbage, fruit machine and piped music. Outside, the crazy-paved terrace has bright flowers and some picnic-table sets. Badminton and Dodington are close by. *(Recommended by D A Lloyd, JM, PM, Martin and Gill Searle, Mrs M Price, Roger Huggins, Tom McLean, Ewan McCall, Len Beattie, John Fazakerley, Stan Edwards, Martin and Gill Searle)*

Free house   Licensee P Monyard   Real ale   Meals and snacks (11–10.30)
Restaurant (not lunchtime)   (0454) 218242   Children in eating area   Open 11–11
Bedrooms; £49.95B/£63.50B

TRISCOMBE (Somerset)   ST1535   Map 1
Blue Ball

Village (and pub) signposted off A338 Taunton–Minehead

The atmosphere in this cottagey little thatched country pub is particularly relaxed and unhurried out of season, and the neat brown-beamed bar has barely more than half a dozen tables – one tucked under the mantlebeam of what used to be a monumental brick and stone fireplace – sporting prints on the white walls, and piped light classical music. A new conservatory relieves the seasonal pressure on space; it can get very busy in summer. Quickly served bar food includes sandwiches (from £1.25, steak £3.75), good soups (£1.35), starters such as deep-fried brie with mango chutney (£1.80), ploughman's (£2.50), beef and stilton

pastie (£2.70), savoury pancakes (from £2.95), curried chicken livers (£3.20), Somerset pork casserole (£4.40), deep-fried stuffed plaice or beef goulash (£4.50), fillets of lemon sole with prawn and orange sauce (£4.80) and 8oz rump steak (£6.85); puddings include treacle tart or bread and butter pudding (£1.55) and sweet pancakes (more on the lines of flapjacks or giant dropscones than crêpes, from £1.70). Well kept Cotleigh Tawny, Exmoor and Tetleys on handpump, with another beer from those breweries, or Ansells, Benskins or Ind Coope as a guest beer; decent wines and coffee, polite service; dominoes (and there's a skittle alley). The two cocker spaniels Penny and three-legged Carver are often around. There are picnic-table sets on the narrow terraced lawns built into this steep and peaceful slope, looking across to the Brendon Hills. It's good walking country.
(Recommended by A M J Chadwick, PLC, Shirley Pielou, Dewi Jones, Gethin Lewis, Jon and Penny Barnes)

Free house   Licensee Gary Little   Real ale   Meals and snacks   (09848) 242   Well behaved children allowed in eating area till 9   Open 11–2.30, 6(7 winter)–11

TRUDOXHILL (Somerset)   ST7443   Map2
White Hart

Village signposted off A361 Frome–Wells

You can still visit the microbrewery at this busy, well kept and friendly pub and see where the strongly flavoured light Ash Vine Bitter, stronger mid-brown Tanker and new Challenger beers are brewed; they also have Bass; cheap Thatcher's farm ciders on handpump, and good country wines. The long, attractively carpeted, stripped-stone bar, really two room areas, has beams supporting broad stripped ceiling boards and a thriving, relaxed atmosphere. Mostly, it's table seating, with a couple of easy chairs by the big log fire on the right (there's a second at the other end), and some seats in the red velvet curtained windows. A very wide choice of popular bar food includes sandwiches (from £1), soup (£1.25), ploughman's (from £2.75), ham and egg (£3.75), stilton and celery pie or beef curry (£3.95), seafood platter (£4.50), 8oz rump steak (£6.95), dishes of the day such as turkey cordon bleu, and a bumper mixed grill (£7.95); puddings like fudge cake or fruit pie (from £1.50) and children's dishes (from £1.95); three-course Sunday lunch (£5.95); piped music. There are picnic-table sets on a sheltered side lawn. *(Recommended by Mr and Mrs D Hutchings, Nigel Gibbs, Sandra Cook, R and E Harfield, R W Stanbury, Andy Hick, Ted George)*

Own brew   Licensee Mr Rimmer   Real ale   Meals and snacks (till 10, 10.30 Sat)   Restaurant (not Sun evening)   (0373 836) 324   Children in eating area and restaurant   Open 12(11.30 Sat)–2.30, 7(6.30 Sat)–11

WAMBROOK (Somerset)   ST2907   Map 1
Cotley Inn

Village signposted off A30 W of Chard; *don't* follow the small signs to Cotley itself

Prettily placed outside the valley village and looking down on it, this stone-built country pub – in a lovely walking area – is named for the local hunt. It combines an unpretentious but civilised local atmosphere with a very wide range of good value food: good well garnished sandwiches (from £1.20), ploughman's or filled baked potatoes (from £2.40), starters like mushroom fritters (£2.95), and devilled lamb's kidney in port and cream (£3), omelettes and salads (from £3.95), good choice of vegetarian dishes such as mushrooms stuffed with spinach and cheese (£4.95), around ten fish courses like filleted plaice (£3.95) or seafood gratin (£6.75), and other dishes including chicken in stilton sauce, lots of meats from gammon with pineapple to sirloin steak (£9.20) and specials such as home-made curry (£5.50); puddings (£2); coffee and tea. The simple flagstoned entrance bar opens on one side into a small plush bar, with beyond that a two-room dining area. Well kept Boddingtons on handpump, good choice of wines; fruit machine, video game and piped middle-of-the-road music, various open fires; picnic-table sets out in the garden below, with a play area and goldfish pool. Quiet on weekday lunchtimes, it can be very busy at weekends. *(Recommended by K R Harris, W L B Reed, P R MacCrimmon)*

*Free house   Licensee D R Livingstone   Real ale   Meals and snacks (till 10)
Restaurant   (0460) 62348   Children in eating area   Open 11–2.30, 7–11
Bedrooms; £15B/£25B*

WELLOW (Avon)   ST7458 Map 2

Fox & Badger

Village signposted on left on A367 SW of Bath

This welcoming old stone-built pub has an attractively furnished flagstone-floored bar with seats built into snug alcoves, small winged settles with cushions to match the curtains, flowers on the tables, a handsome fireplace and a pleasantly chiming clock; there are three log fires in winter. Reasonably priced, wholesome bar food includes sandwiches such as hot lamb (from £1.10), ploughman's (£2.95), a choice of nine vegetarian meals, including vegan (from £3.50), tasty seafood lasagne (£3.95), home-made pies like steak, smoked haddock or country duck and cider (£4.60), lemony pasta with a sprinkling of prawns, chilli con carne, Cumberland sausage, fresh hot haddock bake, trout, steaks (£6.50) and so forth; Sunday lunch with a choice of three roasts (£3.95); summer barbecues in the courtyard. Well kept Butcombe Bitter, Ruddles Best and Ushers Best on handpump; decent choice of wines; friendly service. The cosy carpeted public bar has shove-ha'penny, table skittles, darts, dominoes, cribbage, trivia, fruit machine and piped music, there's also a free skittle alley. The inn-sign is rather striking, showing the two animals in Regency dress, and there is now a conservatory. *(Recommended by F R Hitchcock, Barry and Anne, Tony and Lynne Stark, Steve and Carolyn Harvey, Kevin and Tracey Stephens, M L Collier; more reports please)*

Ushers (Watneys)   Lease: Kevin and Maxine Spragg   Real ale   Meals and snacks (11–2, 6–9.30)   Restaurant   Bath (0225) 832293   Children welcome   Open 11–3, 6–11

WEST HUNTSPILL (Somerset)   ST3044 Map 1

Crossways ⚥

2 3/4 miles from M5 junction 23 (A38 towards Highbridge); 4 miles from M5 junction 22 (A38 beyond Highbridge)

Though this spacious, lively dining pub is very popular with visitors, it has a good, strong local following, too – especially for Sunday lunch. There are generous sandwiches (from £1.50), various home-made soups (£1.60), chicken liver pâté (£2.80), ploughman's (from £2.80), tasty prawns by the half-pint (£3.20), vegetarian curried nut roast (£3.80), quiches (from £3.90), home-made lasagne or home-baked steak and kidney pie or tasty lamb and apricot pie (£4.20), good grilled fresh trout or poached salmon (around £4.50), broccoli, chicken and ham mornay or super local faggots with marrowfat peas (£4.50), salads (from £4.50), excellent gammon with egg or pineapple (£5.50) and steaks (from £6.80). The home-made puddings are good and served with double cream – treacle tart, bitter sweet chocolate pudding or lemon cheesecake (all £1.80); children's menu (£1.60). Well kept Butcombe Bitter, Flowers IPA and Original, and Eldridge Pope Royal Oak on handpump, with a changing guest beer such as Cotleigh Old Buzzard, and good wines; friendly, prompt service. The main part of the bar has dining room chairs, a mixture of settles, seats built into one converted brick fireplace and good winter log fires in others. At one end there's more of a dining room, prettily decorated with old farm machinery engravings, Albert and Chic cartoons (chiefly about restaurants), and 1920ish hunting prints, as well as neat red seats, and a brass colonial fan in its dark ceiling (Friday and Saturday bistro menu here). The other end has an area with big winged settles making booths, and there's a family room with bamboo-back seats around neat tables; cribbage, pinball, dominoes, fruit machine and skittle alley. There are picnic-table sets among fruit trees in quite a big garden. Worth a detour from the motorway. *(Recommended by Stephen R*

Holman, S P Bobeldijk, Ted George, Les King, Tom Evans, J K Coneen, Mr and Mrs B J Twigger, F and J Sherwood, Robert and Vicky Tod, Gethin Lewis, W F Coghill, Richard R Dolphin, Peter Morwood, Diane Duane, Peter Watkins, Pam Stanley, W C M Jones, John and Pat Smyth, Lynne Sheridan, Bob West, Dr and Mrs K J Lower, Elisabeth Kemp, Drs M and K Parier, Mr and Mrs Peter Woods, Brian and Anna Marsden, Martin, Jane, Simon and Laura Bailey, Peter and Sue Darby)

Free house   Licensee Michael Ronca   Real ale   Meals and snacks   Restaurant (Fri/Sat only)   Burnham-on-Sea (0278) 783756   Children welcome   Jazz weekend in marquee in garden, 3rd weekend in Jun   Open 12–3, 5.30(6 Sat)–11   Bedrooms; £23.50B/£33.50B

WINSFORD (Somerset)   SS9034   Map 1

Royal Oak 🍺

In Exmoor National Park, village signposted from A396 about 10 miles S of Dunster

There are plenty of walks near this thatched Exmoor inn – up Winsford Hill for magnificent views for example, or over to Exford, and from the cushioned big bay-window seat in the cosy lounge bar you look across the road towards the village green and foot and packhorse bridges over the River Winn. Horsebrasses and pewter tankards hang from the beam above the attractively panelled bar counter, there are Windsor armed chairs and cushioned seats on the red carpet, and a splendid iron fireback in the big stone hearth (with a log fire in winter). Another similarly old-fashioned bar has good brass, copper, wall prints and darts. Home-made bar food includes soup (£1.50), sandwiches (£1.95), pasties (£2.50), filled baked potatoes (£2.75), ploughman's or chicken liver or smoked fish pâté (£3.95), chopped smoked bacon with button mushrooms and pasta shells in a cream sauce (£4.75), pies such as fish, chicken and leek, or steak and kidney (£5.75), sirloin steak (£8.95) and a choice of home-made puddings (£2.25); tea and coffee; big breakfasts. Well kept Flowers IPA and Original on handpump; friendly staff. *(Recommended by Rona Murdoch, Richard Gibbs, Klaus Leist, N W Acton, W A D Hoyle; more reports please)*

Free house   Licensee Charles Steven   Real ale   Meals and snacks   Restaurant (not Sun evening)   Winsford (064 385) 455   Children in back bar only   Open 11–2.30, 6–11   Bedrooms; £49.50B/£79B

WITHYPOOL (Somerset)   SS8435   Map 1

Royal Oak 🍺

Village signposted off B4233

This is a cheerful, bustling place in which to relax after enjoying some of the lovely walks around here. There are wooden benches and tables with parasols on the terrace, and just up the road, some grand views from Winsford Hill, with tracks leading up among the ponies into the heather past Withypool Hill. The River Barle runs through the village itself, with pretty bridleways following it through a wooded combe further upstream. For guests, they can arrange salmon and trout fishing, riding (stabling also), clay pigeon shooting, rough shooting, hunting, sea fishing from a boat and trips to see wild red deer. The cosy beamed lounge bar has a stag's head and several fox masks on its walls, comfortable button-back brown seats and slat-backed chairs, and a log fire in a raised stone fireplace; another quite spacious bar is similarly decorated. A wide range of good bar snacks includes sandwiches (from £1, giant filled rolls from £1.75, good steak and onions £3), filled baked potatoes (from £1.75), home-made soup (£1.70), ploughman's (from £2.80), good home-cooked ham (from £4; £4.75 with two eggs), two large sausages (a choice of pork and garlic, pork and herb, venison and bacon or spicy tomato – £5), good steaks (from £5.50) and large tasty Mediterranean prawns with garlic mayonnaise (£8.50); some good local cheeses. Well kept Exmoor and Ushers Best on handpump, fair number of vintage brandies, quite a few malt whiskies, and unusual wines. Shove-ha'penny, cribbage and dominoes; cheerful, pleasant service. *(Recommended by Mike Hallewell, Fleur Hitchcock, Ian McKay, Chris Cook, Mr and Mrs Morgan, Klaus Leist, T Galligan, R Gray, Mrs K J Betts, Anthony Barnes, W H Mecham)*

Free house   Licensee Michael Bradley   Real ale   Meals and snacks   Restaurant   Exford (064 383) 506   Children in restaurant   Occasional jazz or Country and Western Sun in winter   Open 11–2.30, 6–11; closed 25 and 26 Dec   Bedrooms; £30(£39B)/£50(£64B)

WOOLVERTON (Somerset)   ST7954   Map 2

Red Lion

A36, at N end of village on E side of road

Originally called the Woolpack, this attractively extended ex-farmhouse has beams, flagstones, old panelling, cushioned farmhouse chairs, and a winged high-backed settle by the big stone hearth with a log-effect gas fire. The main area has lots of comfortably cushioned seats around decent elm tables, and an expanse of parquet flooring with oriental-style rugs. Generous helpings of popular food include rolls (from £1.25), lots of interestingly filled baked potatoes (from £2.15, prawn, ham and asparagus £3.75), ploughman's (from £2.60), original salad bowls such as garlic croûtons, walnuts, ham and cheese or egg, tomato, smoked sausage, mushrooms and garlic croûtons (£4.15), or tuna, prawns, avocado, pineapple, sweetcorn and orange dressing (£4.30), chicken korma or a truly substantial seafood platter (£6.05), puddings and daily specials; you can eat outside, under the trees. Consistently well kept Bass, Wadworths IPA and 6X on handpump, several bottled beers; good service. *(Recommended by Mr Jennings, Susan Grossman, R W Stanbury, Tony and Lynne Stark, Len Beattie, Lynn Sharpless, Bob Eardley)*

Wadworths   Tenant Barry Lander   Real ale   Meals and snacks (till 10)   (0373) 830350   Children welcome   Open 11.30–11(10.30 Mon/Tues); closed 25 Dec; evenings 26 Dec, 31 Dec and 1 Jan

Lucky Dip

Besides the fully inspected pubs, you might like to try these Lucky Dips recommended to us and described by readers (if you do, please send us reports):

Ashcott, Som [High St; ST4337], *Ring o' Bells*: Comfortable village local with popular reasonably priced food inc vegetarian dishes *(G N V Green)*

☆ **Axbridge**, Som [The Square; quite handy for M5; ST4255], *Lamb*: Interesting rambling old place, just right for its position on the partly medieval market square, good value bar food, Butcombe and other real ales such as Wadworths 6X and Valances, plenty to look at, pub games inc alley skittles, pretty little garden with cockatiels; children in eating area till 9; bedrooms spacious, and in keeping with the old-world style *(Drs M and K Parier, J G Thorpe, LYM — more news please)*

Banwell, Avon [ST3959], *Ship*: Pleasant, with attentive friendly staff, good range of bar food, Courage, John Smiths and Wadworths real ale *(Mr and Mrs J H Adam)*

Batcombe, Som [ST6838], *Three Horse Shoes*: Well furnished and spacious beamed lounge with log fires, copper and brass; games room, small restaurant with comfortable minstrel's gallery; well kept Flowers Original, Marstons Pedigree and Oakhill on handpump, wide choice of reasonably priced food served with fresh veg, piped Radio 1, tables in walled garden; children welcome; two bedrooms *(Brian Chambers)*

☆ **Bath**, Avon [Abbey Green; ST7565], *Crystal Palace*: Thriving modernised Georgian pub in fine central leafy square, with well kept Eldridge Pope ales under light top pressure, straightforward bar food cooked to order, good service with plenty of staff; spacious and attractive sheltered courtyard, family area in large heated conservatory *(Tony and Lynne Stark, Neil and Anita Christopher, Michael and Alison Sandy, Wayne Brindle, Quentin Williamson, Alastair Campbell, LYM)*

☆ **Bath** [Mill Lane, Bathampton (off A36 towards Warminster or A4 towards Chippenham); ST7766], *George*: Photogenic canalside pub, busy but spacious, with wide choice of well cooked and quickly served food inc vegetarian dishes, friendly welcome, good log fires, well kept Courage Best and Directors; dining room leads directly off the canal towpath; family room, outside tables under cocktail parasols, garden bar; can be approached by peaceful 3-mile walk from centre; can get very busy at weekends *(Tony and Lynne Stark, Peter and Rose Flower, BB)*

☆ **Bath** [Lower Swainswick; Gloucester Rd (A46); ST7667], *Bladud Arms*: Friendly, simple and unassuming pub notable for its wide choice of pub games, modern and traditional, inc a skittle alley; good range of reasonably priced and well kept real ales such as Bass, Butcombe, Marstons Pedigree, Wadworths 6X and Whitbreads, good value plain lunchtime food (not Sun) *(Len Beattie, Roger Huggins, LYM)*

☆ **Bath** [The Paragon, junction with Guinea Lane], *Star*: Welcoming pub close to main shopping st, small rooms separated by glass and panelling, particularly well kept Bass tapped from the cask, fresh filled rolls, low prices, maybe locals playing cribbage at the back; popular with local cricket and rugby teams *(N Burke)*

Bath, [Bathampton, by toll bridge — OS Sheet 172, map reference 774669], *Bathampton Mill*: Beefeater in much altered mill building by weir with big gardens, landing stage, plenty of picnic-table sets among trees, play area; ducks and swans, view across to tollhouse on bridge and wooded hillside beyond; decent food, Marstons Pedigree, friendly service *(GB)*; [Newbridge; ST7265], *Boathouse*: Large new riverside pub on outskirts, rugs on wooden floor, riverside decorations; wicker furniture and potted plants in conservatory on lower level, several doors opening on to riverbank and garden area; big car park, nr new marina *(Peter and Rose Flower)*; [Combe Down; ST7662], *Cross Keys*: Popular with locals, Courage beers, efficient friendly service and good value food *(R Williams)*; [Lansdown Hill], *Farm House*: Landlord's big jolly personality imprinted on the pub — and its sign; well kept Wadworths beers, good jazz Tues, friendly locals *(F R Hitchcock)*; [North Parade], *Huntsman*: Popular old dining pub, open all day for wide choice of home-made hot and cold dishes, not cheap but good and often interesting; Eldridge Pope beers inc Royal Oak; nr Abbey, busy weekends *(Joan and Michel Hooper-Immins, Carol Mason)*; [42 Broad St], *Saracens Head*: Spacious beamed pub, perhaps Bath's oldest and no attempt to modernise, with good choice of good value food inc Sat cold table, several vegetarian dishes, fresh fish, old-fashioned puddings — big helpings; well kept Courage Best and Directors, quick service *(Dr and Mrs B D Smith, Andrew and Ruth Triggs)*

☆ **Bathford**, Avon [Kingsdown; pub actually just over the Wilts border — OS Sheet 173, map reference 809670; ST8067], *Swan*: Friendly and attractive, held by iron strap to hillside in beautiful countryside; with well kept Gibbs Mew beers, decent wines, wide choice of bar food inc interesting specials (weekend booking essential), log fire, gardens front and back *(B R Woolmington, Mr and Mrs R Vaughan, Anne Fleming)*

Bishops Hull, Som [ST2124], *Old Inn*: God value food inc Sun lunches, friendly service; spotless *(D S and T M Beeson)*

☆ **Bishops Lydeard**, Som [A358 towards Taunton; ST1828], *Kingfishers Catch*: Two neat little communicating rooms with wheelback chairs around dark shiny tables, mainly turquoise and blue decor, wide choice of good value honest food; while it

has a pub licence (and keg Eldridge Pope and lunchtime ploughman's) it's now really too much a cottagey restaurant to be a main entry, though well up to standard *(Shirley Pielou, LYM)*

☆ **Blagdon**, Avon [Church St; off A368; ST5059], *New Inn*: Two big log fires, interesting antique settles among more modern furniture, food from sandwiches to evening steaks, Bass and Wadworths IPA and 6X on handpump, nice view from picnic-table sets on back grass; only reason this is — we hope temporarily — relegated from main entries is lack of recent reports *(LYM — more news please)*

Blagdon, Avon [A368], *Live & Let Live*: Cosy and cheerful partly panelled back bar with log fire and sporting prints, generous bar food inc good value Sun lunch, well kept Courage Bitter and Best, sensibly placed darts, pool and other pub games; handy for fishing on Blagdon Lake; bedrooms *(Tom Evans, LYM)*; [away from main roads], *Queen Adelaide*: Quiet one-bar pub with plenty of tables, open fire, well kept Butcombe and a local beer brewed for the pub, small but good varied menu from sandwiches to steaks served lunchtime and right through evening; handy for fishing in Blagdon Lake which is overlooked from car park *(Brig J S Green)*; *Seymour Arms*: Pleasant family pub with Ansells and Ind Coope Burton tapped from casks behind bar, beer brewed for the pub by Churchill on handpump, interesting choice of food (somewhat restaurantish feel); well decorated, with lots of interesting antiques; good car park, steps down to pub *(Brian and Jenny Seller)*

☆ **Blagdon Hill**, Som [4 miles S of Taunton; ST2217], *White Lion*: Simple but pleasant village pub, gently refurbished, with good china ornaments, very pleasant service, and unexpectedly wide choice of good home-made food; good log fire *(Shirley Pielou, Mr and Mrs D V Morris)*

Bleadon, Som [ST3357], *New Inn*: Delightful little ancient inn with lovely flowers outside, enthusiastic service inside; Flowers tapped from the cask, bar food inc good value ham ploughman's *(Jenny and Brian Seller)*

☆ **Brendon Hills**, Som [junction B3190/B3224; ST0434], *Raleghs Cross*: Isolated but large roadside inn nearly 1,200 ft high, views to Wales on clear days; big light-hearted bar, plenty of tables outside, wide choice of honest straightforward food in big helpings (some tables no smoking), well kept Exmoor and Flowers Original, friendly staff, good walks, whippet races summer Sun; children in restaurant and family room, big play area; open all day summer; bedrooms *(U W Bankes, Keith Houlgate, LYM)*

☆ **Brent Knoll**, Som [2 miles from M5 junction 22; right on to A38, then first left; ST3350], *Red Cow*: Friendly spotless pub, attractively laid out, with well kept real ales inc Flowers IPA and Marstons Pedigree, good well priced food all week, quick service, well spaced tables, skittle alley, pleasant sheltered garden; notable lavatories *(M W Turner, Mr and Mrs B J Twigger, W F Coghill, John Hutson, BB)*

Bridgwater, Som [West Quay; ST3037], *Fountain*: Tastefully extended 18th-century pub on town bridge opp restored quay; friendly licensees, prints of old Bridgwater, and Flowers, Wadworths 6X and a guest beer on handpump *(BCM)*

☆ **Bristol**, Avon [St Thomas Lane, off Redcliff St/Victoria St], *Fleece & Firkin*: Lofty 18th-century wool hall stripped back to flagstones, basic furniture, guest beers and own-brewed ales such as the hefty Old Wolly — owned by Halls (Allied); lunchtime food (not Sun) inc gigantic filled baps, pleasant staff, live music Weds-Sat, lively Mon quiz night, children weekends *(R Houghton, Dr and Mrs A K Clarke, Michael Cochrane, LYM)*

☆ **Bristol**, [Lower Park Row], *Ship*: Busy atmosphere in low-ceilinged long and narrow bar mostly arranged in cubicles, featuring low dimly lit back balcony with timber and brass effect; nautical decor — ornaments, lots of naval pictures, mirrors, lamps and so forth; spiral stairs down to lower area with pool table, small lounge and small sunny terrace; up to half a dozen real ales such as Smiles and Wadworths 6X, reasonably priced food, rather loud but well reproduced piped music eg popular classics *(Tom Evans, Graham Bush)*

☆ **Bristol** [45 King St], *Old Duke*: Famous jazz pub, with Ellington inn-sign, ochre walls and ceiling festooned with jazz posters, saxophones etc; good bands (not free) every night and Sun lunchtime; usual pub furnishings, decent value simple food, well kept Courage Best and Directors on handpump; in attractive cobbled area between docks and Bristol Old Vic, gets packed evenings *(Roger Taylor, N Doncaster, D P Ryan, Barry and Anne, Tony and Lynne Stark, Nigel Gibbs, Sandra Cook, BB)*

☆ **Bristol** [between Sion Pl and Portland St, Clifton; ST5673], *Coronation Tap*: Small low-ceilinged local notable for its fat casks of farm ciders (also Courage Best and Directors, no spirits or wines); limited reasonably priced lunchtime bar snacks (not Sun) *(Roger Taylor, Wayne Brindle, Mr and Mrs C H Garnett, Carol Mason, R W Stanbury, LYM)*

Bristol [off Boyce's Ave, Clifton; ST5673], *Albion*: Friendly and unpretentiously old-fashioned pub with unusual flagstoned courtyard off cobbled alley, well kept Courage ales tapped from the cask *(Roger Taylor, Mr and Mrs C H Garnett, LYM)*; [Philip St, Bedminster; ST5670], *Apple Tree*: Reputedly the smallest pub in Bristol; basic place with an accent on cider — real one-off *(Dr and Mrs Tony Clarke)*; [Wellington Hill W, Henleaze; ST5876], *Beehive*: Big 1930s pub with Courage and Smiles beers, bar food, skittle alley, children's area, and extensive garden with play area *(Drs McCarthy and Mutch)*; [21 Alfred Pl,

Kingsdown], *Bell*: Well run by two warmly welcoming girls, good atmosphere, good home-made food in pottery bowls, well kept Butcombe and Watneys-related real ales, traditional furnishings *(Charlotte Thompson)*; [Prince St], *Bristol Clipper*: Decidedly sports-oriented, with keen landlord, well kept Courage, all sorts of mice — china, fluffy, metal *(Dr and Mrs A K Clarke)*; [17-18 King St], *Naval Volunteer*: Busy daytime, more relaxed evening, good choice of bar food, well kept real ales such as Bass, Butcombe, Marstons Pedigree and local Smiles, nice atmosphere, open fire, attractive prices *(Jim Cowell, Roger Taylor, Tony and Lynne Stark)*; [Weston Rd (A370 towards Weston-super-Mare)], *New Inn*: Good value fish dishes, good coffee, no piped music *(Anon)*; [Lower Guinea St, Bathurst Basin — follow General Hospital sign from inner ring rd], *Ostrich*: Straightforward Courage pub included for its good dockside position, with waterside seats *(N Doncaster, LYM)*; [Merchants Rd], *Pump House*: Smartly converted imposing dockside building, charcoal-grey brickwork, tiled floors, high ceilings, well kept Bass, decent wines, lunchtime bar food, waterside tables *(Gwen and Peter Andrews, LYM)*; [68 Prince St], *Shakespeare*: Elegant Georgian house nr docks, popular for good value bar lunches, busy early evening too; pleasant partly panelled bar with big windows, rugs on bare boards, open fire, appropriate old prints; fine staircase to upper room, tables out on flagstones of iron-railed terrace; well kept Courage Best and Directors, John Smiths and a guest such as Wadworths 6X on handpump *(J R Carey, BB)*; [different one on Victoria St, between shopping centre and rly stn], *Shakespeare*: Useful for reasonably priced meals and snacks; Bass and Courage, pleasant staff *(Carol Mason, Dr and Mrs A K Clarke)*; [Old Market St], *Stag & Hounds*: Recently reopened, with well kept beers inc Marstons Pedigree; flagstones, well in upper bar *(Dr and Mrs A K Clarke)*; [57 Whiteladies Rd, Clifton; ST5773], *Vittoria*: Small lively place, good food inc excellent burgers *(Barry and Anne)*; [Narrow Quay], *Waterfront*: Relaxing early evening, busier later and lunchtime, well kept Flowers and Smiles, bar food — choice wider at lunchtime *(Jim Cowell)*

☆ **Brushford**, Som [SS9225], *Carnarven Arms*: Sporting hotel with own stabling, fishing and shooting, also fine full-sized billiards table, heated swimming pool and tennis court; well kept bar with friendly staff, Cotleigh Tawny, occasional guest beers, wide range of spirits and liqueurs, notably good food in popular buttery bar, quieter smaller side bar; homely comfort in bedrooms *(P M Bisby, P Spence)*

☆ **Bruton**, Som [High St; ST6834], *Castle*: Good solid food value — particularly inc well presented Indian food with proper side dishes, changing choice of well kept real ales, skittle alley with striking mural of part of town, tables in sheltered back garden;

welcoming, with courteous service, but can
get very full; children in eating area and
skittle alley *(LYM)*

Buckland Dinham, Som [A362
Radstock—Frome; ST7551], *Bell*: Spotless
and attractive old pub, usual food very well
cooked, cheerful staff *(John and Pat Smythe)*

☆ **Butleigh**, Som [ST5233], *Rose & Portcullis*:
Welcoming old pub with pleasant
atmosphere, good food in bars and
restaurant, well kept Courage Directors *(Cdr
G F Barnett)*

Carhampton, Som [A39
Williton—Minehead; ST0042], *Butchers
Arms*: Well kept Watneys-related real ales,
and Harriers SPA; friendly staff, family
room and garden well equipped for children;
reasonably priced food, good on quantity
and quality with alternatives to chips,
children's dishes, restaurant *(Keith Houlgate,
Steve and Carolyn Harvey)*

☆ **Catcott**, Som [signed off A39
Street—Bridgwater; ST3939], *King William*:
A shame we don't hear more of this
enjoyable cottagey pub, traditional
furnishings, big fireplaces, good food from
sandwiches to veal or duck (till 10),
interesting decor, Bass, Eldridge Pope and
Palmers real ale, Wilkin's farm cider, skittle
alley in big back extension; children
welcome *(Ted George, LYM)*

Chapel Allerton, Som [ST4050],
Wheatsheaf: Good local with pleasant
atmosphere and reliable food inc good
sandwiches *(M P Furmston)*

Charfield, Avon [ST7191], *Pear Tree*:
Warmly welcoming local doing well under
new landlord, with well kept beer and lots of
pub teams — cribbage, darts, pool and so
forth *(Peter and Rose Flower)*

Charlton Adam, Som [just off A37 about 3
m N of Ilchester; ST5328], *Fox & Hounds*:
Partly 16th-century pub with big family
room and well equipped play area, has been
popular for wide choice of good freshly
cooked reasonably priced food inc children's
menu, but no recent reports *(News please)*

Charlton Horethorne, Som [ST6623], *Kings
Arms*: Small, very friendly pub doing well
under new licensees, with good food and
friendly and efficient service; well kept
Eldridge Pope beer *(John and Joan Nash)*

☆ **Chiselborough**, Som [signed off B3165
between A3088 and A30, W of Yeovil;
ST4614], *Cat Head*: Old-fashioned pub with
flagstones, big woodburner and civilised
furnishings, kept spotlessly by new licensees,
with Gibbs Mew real ales and a skittle alley;
but we've had no reports since the kitchens
closed for refurbishment — news please *(Mr
and Mrs G Turner, Major and Mrs E M
Warrick, Chris Raisin, LYM)*

Clevedon, Avon [The Beach; ST4071],
Moon & Sixpence: New, beautifully
decorated pub, upstairs balcony room on
two levels overlooking sea, good choice of
good food, quick helpful service, two real
ales; children allowed on ground floor
(Graham Woods)

Cold Ashton, Avon [A420

Bristol—Chippenham just E of A46;
ST7572], *White Hart*: Very spacious pub
dating back several centuries, with various
rooms, well kept beers, bar food *(Patrick
Godfrey)*

☆ **Combe Florey**, Som [off A358
Taunton—Williton, just N of main village
turn-off; ST1531], *Farmers Arms*: Neatly
restored thatched and beamed pub with
wide choice of food pleasantly served, good
winter log fire, well kept Bass; popular in
summer, with plenty of tables outside
(Shirley Pielou, BB)

Combe St Nicholas, Som [ST3011], *Green
Dragon*: Pleasant service and good
reasonably priced food under new licensees;
well kept Bass *(John and Joan Nash)*

Combwich, Som [Ship Lane; ST2542], *Old
Ship*: Nicely decorated and renovated old
pub with reasonably priced good food —
steaks popular with locals *(BCM)*

☆ **Compton Martin**, Avon [A368; ST5457],
Ring o' Bells: Attractively placed country
pub with well kept real ales such as
Butcombe, Exmoor, Marstons Pedigree and
Wadworths 6X, good bar food, generous
Sun lunch, reasonable prices; snug
traditional area with inglenook log fire, rugs
and flagstones, opening into extensive
carpeted part with lots of tables — cool and
spacious in summer; cigarette card collection
in public bar with darts and fruit machine,
family room with rocking horse, table
skittles and toys, good-sized garden with
fruit trees, swings, climber and slide *(Tom
Evans, William Pryce, Revd L J & Mrs Melliss,
Peter Adcock, Jon Wainwright, LYM)*

Congresbury, Avon [St Pauls Causeway; off
main rd; ST4363], *Old Inn*: Friendly
low-ceilinged local with open fire, real ales
such as Bass, Marstons Pedigree, Smiles and
Wadworths 6X, and very cheap food — 8oz
steak £3.60 *(Craig Gerrard Williams, Rita
Ashley, Dr and Mrs A K Clarke)*

Corfe, Som [ST2319], *White Hart*: Well
kept Exmoor, Wadworths 6X and
Whitbreads-related ales, very warm
welcome *(Richard Dolphin)*

Coxley, Som [ST5344], *Pound*: Busy and
lively local atmosphere, dark and cosy, with
various bar games and interesting
bric-a-brac on walls *(Phil Gorton)*

Creech Heathfield, Som [Monkton; nr M5
junction 25; ST2827], *Crown*: Comfortable
and welcoming local doing well under new
landlord, well kept Cotleigh as well as
Watneys-related real ales *(Richard Dolphin)*

Cross, Avon [A38 Bristol—Bridgwater,
junction A371 — OS Sheet 182, map
reference 420549; ST4155], *New Inn*:
Good, friendly pub, Flowers ale, wholesome
reasonably priced food in generous helpings,
crack football team, fine views; games room
upstairs *(Jenny and Brian Seller)*

Culbone Hill, Som [A39 W of Porlock;
SS8247], *Culbone*: Low building, spotless,
with friendly service, Bass and other real
ales, wide range of reasonably priced food
(Bob Smith)

☆ **Ditcheat**, Som [village signed off A37 and

A371 S of Shepton Mallet; ST6236], *Manor House*: Welcoming relaxed atmosphere in neat and simple communicating rooms, flagstones in public bar, unusual arched doorways, close-set tables, good attractively priced bar food; well kept Butcombe on handpump, open fires if cold; skittle alley, white rabbits by tables on back grass; attractive frontage, good views on way down from Pye Hill on A37 *(Ted George, BB)*

☆ **East Coker**, Som [ST5412], *Helyar Arms*: Tastefully extended oak-beamed pub with pleasant staff, good range of real ales, interesting range of good food — especially fish; nicely decorated, attractive setting *(Dr W M Owton, R Boyd McMurrick)*

☆ **East Harptree**, Som [ST5655], *Waldegrave Arms*: Good food with proper veg in dining room and pleasant lounge with lots of nooks and crannies, welcoming service, separate locals' bar popular with young people; decent wine, good coffee *(E H and R F Warner, Kevin and Tracey Stephens, Marjorie and David Lamb)*

Enmore, Som [ST2434], *Tynte Arms*: Low beams, open fires, pleasant dining areas; well kept Whitbreads-related real ales, wide choice of bar food, reasonable prices, friendly service; restored well in car park wall *(Shirley Pielou)*

☆ **Evercreech**, Som [A371 Shepton Mallet—Castle Cary; ST6438], *Pecking Mill*: Comfortable low-ceilinged stone-walled pub with ornate solid fuel stove, long- barreled rifles and harness on walls, well kept real ales, good value bar food, restaurant, friendly staff; seats outside *(BB)*

☆ **Exford**, Som [B3224; SS8538], *White Horse*: Country-kitchen furnishings in open-plan bar of three-storey Exmoor village inn with hunting prints and trophies, several real ales such as Bass, Cotleigh Tawny, Exmoor Bitter and Gold and Worthington on handpump, log fire, good value bar food, friendly efficient staff; peaceful village; children in eating area; open all day summer; bedrooms comfortable; dogs allowed *(Mr and Mrs P A Jones, Mr and Mrs B Dymott, LYM)*

Exford, *Crown*: Traditional old pub despite its pink and orange paintwork; big yet cosy bar with well kept local ales, pine furniture, log fire, good bar food, jovial landlord; attractive streamside garden, peaceful village *(Fleur Hitchcock, Ian McKay, T Galligan)*

Flax Bourton, Avon [A370 Bristol—Weston-super-Mare; ST5069], *Jubilee*: Popular two-level bar/lounge with good food inc lovely puddings, good log fires, well kept beers, big car park; bedrooms *(Ian Phillips)*

☆ **Freshford**, Som [OS Sheet 172, map reference 790600; ST7859], *Inn at Freshford*: Picturesque three-storey stone building with comfortably modernised carpeted bar, lots of pictures, plates and rustic bygones, stone serving counter with built-in old bread oven; helpful staff, good

range of simple but good bar food in big helpings, imaginative good value restaurant; well kept Watneys-related real ales, separate pool room, picnic-table sets on secluded sloping back lawn with shrubs; quiet countryside by old stone bridge over the Avon, footpath walks *(Ron Gentry, BB)*

☆ **Glastonbury**, Som [High St; ST5039], *George & Pilgrims*: Rambling medieval building most notable for its magnificently restored carved stone frontage — much more straightforward inside, though the front bar has a big open fire and 15th-century traceried stained-glass bay window; bar food, consistently well kept Bass, interesting local sweet wine, children in buffet and good upstairs restaurant; good clean bedrooms *(Steve Thomas, Mrs K J Betts, Robert and Elizabeth Scott, Tony and Lynne Stark, Carol Mason, LYM)*

☆ **Glastonbury** [27 Benedict St], *Mitre*: Good proper pub with straightforward lounge, welcoming landlord, good food with interesting specials, real ale, decent garden; children allowed *(Malcolm Ramsay)*

Glastonbury [43 High St], *Beckets*: Wadworths on handpump, good interesting bar food, attractive garden with big fig tree *(John and Joan Wyatt)*

Hanham, Avon [ST6472], *Chequers*: Comfortable, popular for riverside position, bar food *(N Doncaster)*; *Lock & Weir*: On the river, quite tucked away but popular on sunny days, with seats out by the water; small, low-ceilinged pub, bar food *(N Doncaster)*; [Lower Hanham Rd], *Queens Head*: Large updated pub with accent on food; very friendly, well kept Courage *(Dr and Mrs A K Clarke)*

☆ **Hardway**, Som [off B3081 Bruton—Wincanton at Redlynch; pub named on OS Sheet — OS Sheet 183, map reference 721342; ST7234], *Bull*: Pretty pub alone in pleasant countryside nr Alfred's Tower on the Somerset plains; comfortable bar, open fire, well kept Butcombe and Wadworths 6X on handpump, farm cider, good value imaginative and satisfying home-made food inc lots of vegetarian dishes in character dining room (book, or get there early), cheerful efficient licensees; nice outside area, handy for Stourhead Garden *(Caroline Gibbins, B and D Carron, Mrs J Gardner, John and Joan Nash, R J Entenman)*

Hewish, Avon [nr M5 junction 21; A370 towards Congresbury; ST4064], *Full Quart*: Clean, pleasant and well furnished, with good atmosphere, attentive staff, good range of beers — Bass, Butcombe, Worthington; food well cooked and presented *(K R Harris)*

☆ **Hillesley**, Avon [ST7689], *Fleece*: Attractive pub in small Cotswolds village with well kept Marstons Pedigree and Whitbreads-related real ales, decent wines and interesting collection of malt whiskies; basic old-fashioned bar, busy lounge, friendly service, bar food, no smoking dining room; beautiful surrounding countryside, close to Cotswold Way; bedrooms *(John and*

Joan Wyatt)

☆ **Hillfarance**, Som [ST1624], *Anchor*: Popular local with good range of bar food in two good eating areas and small restaurant, speedy friendly service, good beers, children's play area in garden; lovely rural position *(Shirley Pielou)*

☆ **Hinton Blewett**, Avon [village signed off A37 in Clutton; ST5957], *Ring o' Bells*: Peaceful low-beamed stone-built village local with good value home cooking (not Sun evening), well kept Wadworths Devizes and 6X on handpump, friendly service, simple furnishings; pleasant view from tables in sheltered front yard, pretty flowers in summer — outside and in; children welcome *(Drs M and K Parier, Kevin and Tracey Stephens, Jon Wainwright, Tony and Lynne Stark, LYM)*

☆ **Hinton Charterhouse**, Avon [B3110; ST7758], *Stag*: Attractively furnished ancient pub with good range of well kept real ales such as Bunces Best, Gibbs Mew Salisbury, Marstons Pedigree and Smiles Exhibition, log fire, often enterprising freshly cooked food at a price but usually worth it, in bar's stripped-stone eating area and restaurant; no piped music; children allowed in well thought out eating area, away from bar but not isolated; tables outside, has been open all day *(Tony and Lynne Stark, Lynn Sharpless, Bob Eardley, LYM)*

Hinton Charterhouse, *Rose & Crown*: Friendly atmosphere in comfortable panelled bar areas, well kept Bass, Marstons Pedigree and Wadworths 6X, restaurant *(Lynn Sharpless, Bob Eardley, Tom Evans)*

Hinton Dyrham, Avon [nr M4 junction 18; A46 towards Bath, then 1st right; ST7376], *Bull*: Pretty, small village pub doing well under new young couple, varied bar food pleasantly priced, public bar with oak and elm settles, log fire, friendly atmosphere, good beer *(B Haskins)*

☆ **Holton**, Som [ST6827], *Old Inn*: Friendly 16th-century inn with beams, ancient flagstones, log fire, masses of keys hanging over bar; good service, friendly atmosphere, real ales and ciders, usual bar snacks and various cooked dishes; can fill up early; tables on terrace, restaurant — best to book for Sun lunch *(Lt Cdr G J Cardew)*

Holywell Lake, Som [off A38; ST1020], *Holywell*: Village pub with above-average decor, log fire, small dining room; tables in peaceful garden; has been popular for good value interesting food, but no recent reports on new regime *(News please)*

☆ **Howley**, Som [ST2609], *Howley Tavern*: Country pub with atmosphere; Exmoor real ale, farm cider, good choice of malts and cognac; good value bar food cooked to order, vegetarian specialities; staff courteous and efficient, intimate restaurant area and away from bar area; big garden overlooking hills; bedrooms *(Dave and Kate Buckley)*

Knapp, Som [ST2925], *Rising Sun*: 16th-century pub with stripped beams and stonework, has been praised for good

enterprising home-made food and well kept Bass and Exmoor, but no recent reports *(News please)*

☆ **Littleton upon Severn**, Avon [ST5990], *White Hart*: Carefully extended flagstoned and panelled pub in isolated village with hatch service of well kept ales inc Smiles, Long Ashton farm cider, good busy atmosphere (esp Weds jazz night), limited choice of generous good food, various games inc table football, genial bar staff, log fires; garden *(Dr and Mrs A K Clarke, Dr K A and S F Louden, Steve and Carolyn Harvey)*

☆ **Litton**, Som [off A39 Bath—Wells; ST5954], *Olde Kings Arms*: Atmospheric 15th-century pub with friendly, helpful service, big helpings of reasonable food, two big open fires, well kept Butcombe, Wadworths 6X and another ale tapped from the cask; pleasant terrace and lovely streamside garden with swings and slides; very quiet midweek lunchtime, but can get busy; in unspoilt setting at bottom of tiny valley next to old cottages and interesting little church *(GB)*

Locking, Avon [ST3760], *Coach House*: Lots of features, warm and friendly, accent on food *(Dr and Mrs A K Clarke)*

☆ **Long Sutton**, Som [A372 E of Langport; ST4625], *Lime Kiln*: Friendly pub with generous helpings of good food, well kept Palmers, reliably good service; bedrooms good and spacious, in modern extension above new restaurant *(Roy Bromell, Sarah Haines)*

Lopen, Som [Lopen Head; ST4214], *Poulett Arms*: Straightforward but spotless roadside pub with really good value generous food (prepared to order; not quick); warm welcome, well kept Bass and guest beer *(Richard Dolphin)*

Lydford on Fosse, Som [A37/B3153; ST5531], *Cross Keys*: Interesting pub which has been praised for good freshly cooked food, well kept real ales and spotless housekeeping, but no recent reports *(News please)*

Mark, Som [ST3747], *White Horse*: Old-world dining pub dating back to 17th century, with roomy attractive bars and large, pleasant garden; has been very popular for home-cooked food and well kept Whitbreads-related real ales, but no reports since recent change of ownership and kitchen refurbishment *(News please)*

☆ **Marshfield** [A420 Bristol—Chippenham; ST7773], *Lord Nelson*: Wide choice of fresh home-made bar food from well filled French sticks to porbeagle shark, well kept ales such as Butcombe, Courage Directors, Marstons Pedigree, Smiles and Wadworths 6X, and choice of places to sit from locals' games bar through smarter one with view of deep well in cellar to ex-stables restaurant done out as cobbled lamplit street with tables in old carriages or repro Victorian railway carriages; beams, open fires, good atmosphere, tables in small courtyard; now has bedrooms in cottage annexe *(Carol Mason, Peter and Rose Flower)*

Marshfield, *Catherine Wheel*: Old pub with superb log fires, occasional barbecues, impromptu music most Thurs; new licensees – who made the Salutation nr Castle Combe very popular – planning new kitchen, transformation of parlour into eating area, five bedrooms; one to watch *(Peter and Rose Flower)*; [A420], *Crown*: Wide choice of good quick cheap food till 10.30, inc children's dishes and Sun roasts; Ushers beers, live music Tues, Sat, Sun, upstairs games room, tables in courtyard *(Peter and Rose Flower)*

☆ **Midford**, Avon [ST7560], *Hope & Anchor*: Welcoming local with comfortable L-shaped open-plan bar, wide range of well kept real ales such as Bass, Butcombe, Fullers and Wadworths 6X, good moderately priced food inc popular Sun lunch (booking advised), quick pleasant service, restaurant; passage under road to derelict canal, also good walks along disused railway line through beautiful countryside *(Roger Huggins, M J B Pearson)*

☆ **Milborne Port**, Som [A30 E of Sherborne; ST6718], *Queens Head*: Good coaching-inn atmosphere in beamed lounge with plentiful good value genuine food, friendly service, good choice of well kept real ales and farm ciders, games in public bar, skittle alley, quiet restaurant; tables in sheltered courtyard and garden with unusual playthings; children welcome (except in bars); three cosy bedrooms — good value *(E Mitchelmore, Mr and Mrs T A Towers, LYM)*

☆ **Milton Clevedon**, Som [High St (B3081); ST6637], *Ilchester Arms*: Friendly three-storey early 17th-century pub with homely and comfortable beamed and stripped-brick lounge bar; rustic bric-a-brac, old-fashioned gas-style lamps in wall alcoves, wide choice of reasonably priced food, well kept Palmers and Wadworths 6X, friendly landlord, piano, smaller restaurant bar; lovely hill views from garden and from conservatory with hanging plants; no food Sun, closed Mon lunchtime *(Brig J S Green, Mike Tucker)*

☆ **Minehead**, Som [Harbour; SS9746], *Old Ship Aground*: Seaside yachting pub by lifeboat station, old-world but comfortably modernised and extended, with decent bar food all day, Watneys-related real ales, friendly atmosphere, tables on terrace; preserved Victorian pleasure steamers to Wales and North Devon outside in summer *(John Feehan, Diane Barnes)*

Minehead [Esplanade], *Hobby Horse*: Good value food inc low-priced lunchtime special, very substantial mixed grill, popular Sun lunch; well kept Flowers Original *(D S and T M Beeson)*

☆ **Monkton Combe**, Avon [ST7762], *Wheelwrights Arms*: Wide choice of fine bar food from good sandwiches to quite elaborate evening dishes, in small inn well placed in lovely surrounding countryside; friendly and attractively laid out bar with lots of other bric-a-brac, big open fire, tiny darts room at end, fruit machine, quiet piped music; Adnams, Flowers IPA and Original; bedrooms comfortable and well furnished, across narrow car-park lane; bedrooms *(Dr F Peters, LYM)*

☆ **Montacute**, Som [ST4916], *Phelips Arms*: Particularly good relaxing atmosphere in spacious room with friendly service, good choice of decent low-priced food; lovely setting in delightful village *(Joan Harris, Mrs A Crowhurst, Steve Thomas)*

☆ **Nether Stowey**, Som [Keenthorne — A39 E of village; not to be confused with Apple Tree Cottage; ST1939], *Cottage*: Warm and cheerful, with big helpings of good value simple bar food, well kept Flowers Original on handpump, friendly service; comfortable dining lounge with woodburning stove, aquarium, interesting pictures; games room with two pool tables, juke box and machines (children allowed here); skittle alley, tables on terrace *(WHBM, J and L, Lynne Sheridan and Bob West, LYM)*

North Curry, Som [Queens Sq; ST3225], *Bird in Hand*: Good atmosphere, pleasant and helpful staff, bar food inc good filled baked potatoes; decor on the modern side *(Mrs S M Judge)*

North Perrott, Som [ST4709], *Manor Arms*: Attractively and comfortably refurbished, with helpful and friendly new licensees, varied choice of good home-made food in bar and restaurant, garden with adventure play area *(Clem Stephens)*

North Wootton, Som [ST5641], *Crossways*: Good value food in big pub; bedrooms *(Richard Dolphin)*

Norton Fitzwarren, Som [ST1925], *Victory*: Locally popular open-plan, barn-like building with well kept local beers, good well cooked standard food inc some vegetarian *(R A Riley)*

☆ **Nunney**, Som [Church St; village signed off A361 Shepton Mallet—Frome; ST7345], *George*: Extensive rambling and much modernised open-plan bar with stripped stone walls, good log fire, four well kept changing real ales such as Butcombe and Websters Yorkshire on handpump, decent wines and good choice of other drinks, generous helpings of good value food from good sandwiches up in bar and restaurant, afternoon teas; rare 'gallows' sign spanning road, in quaint village with stream (vociferous ducks) and ruined castle; bedrooms quiet, clean and well equipped *(Dr and Mrs A K Clarke, Mrs Joan Harris, GB, Nigel Gibbs, Sandra Cook, Tony and Lynne Stark, Ron Gentry, BB)*

☆ **Panborough**, Som [B3139 Wedmore—Wells; ST4745], *Panborough*: Carefully reconstructed 17th-century village pub with friendly atmosphere in several clean, comfortable and attractive rooms, main one with inglenook, beams, lots of brass and copper; good range of generous bar food, efficient service, real ales; very popular weekends; skittle alley, small restaurant, tables in front terraced garden *(Jenny and Brian Seller)*

☆ **Pennsylvania**, Avon [4 miles from M4

junction 18 — A46 towards Bath; ST7373], *Swan*: Fine old unspoilt village inn formed from row of stone cottages stepped downhill, doing well under new landlord, with five well kept real ales inc Smiles, bar food, log fires, good service, lovely atmosphere; children welcome in dining area *(Comus Elliott, Mr Jennings, Stan Edwards)*

Pensford, Avon [A37 S of Bristol; ST6263], *Rising Sun*: Old village pub with good bar food cooked to order (so don't be in too much of a hurry); pretty country location, tables in garden *(D J Brighouse)*

Pitminster, Som [OS Sheet 193, map reference 219191; ST2118], *Queens Arms*: Small, unpretentious old country pub in quiet village; huge helpings of good value food in nice dining room, good choice of changing well kept real ales, friendly family service *(Richard Houghton, A M J Chadwick)*

☆ **Polsham**, Som [A39 N of Glastonbury; ST5142], *Camelot*: Peaceful, very friendly and well staffed 200-year-old inn, though thoroughly up-to-date with large children's area, big terrace and conservatory looking out to fields as well as spacious carpeted bar areas and restaurant; very varied menu, Palmers and a local beer brewed for the pub; bedrooms *(Brig J S Green, Dr and Mrs A K Clarke)*

Porlock Weir, Som [separate from but run in tandem with neighbouring Anchor Hotel; SS8547], *Ship*: Sadly this ancient little inn in its spectacular spot by the peaceful harbour has had a bad fire, destroying its thatch and old-fashioned internal decor; the separate front Mariners Bar has less atmosphere *(LYM)*

Portishead, Som [ST4777], *Royal*: Solid Victorian pub, popular in summer for superb location at confluence of Avon and Severn estuaries; well kept Bass, nourishing old-fashioned well priced food *(Tom Evans)*

☆ **Priddy**, Som [from Wells on A39 pass hill with TV mast on left, then next left — OS Sheet 183, map reference 549502; ST5450], *Hunters Lodge*: Very unassuming, basic and rather spartan isolated inn, much enjoyed by walkers, potholers, and others who like things simple and down-to-earth; good range of well kept real ales such as Badger, Bass, Butcombe and Oakhill Farmers tapped from casks behind the bar, log fire, flagstones; simple very cheap bar food such as faggots with bread, tables in garden; bedrooms clean and adequate for their low price *(William Pryce, Brian and Jenny Seller, R K Sutton, Jon Wainwright, LYM)*

☆ **Priddy**, Som [off B3135], *New Inn*: Good low-cost food, particularly the specials, in busy and cheery former farmhouse on quiet village green — probably the pub to choose here if you want more cosseting than the Hunters Lodge; good log fire in lovely fireplace, low beams, horsebrasses and so forth; well kept Eldridge Pope Royal Oak and Wadworths 6X, good local cider, efficient and friendly service; bedrooms comfortable and homely *(Andy Hick, Jenny and Brian Seller, Mr and Mrs D Darby)*

Priddy, *Queen Victoria*: Pleasant country inn with interesting bric-a-brac around well stocked bar, good choice of well kept ales inc Wadworths Farmers Glory, reasonably priced standard food, nice country atmosphere; lovely garden for children across rd; popular in summer *(Jenny and Brian Seller, D Price)*

Redhill, Avon [ST4963], *Bungalow*: Rather cosy if slightly odd architecturally, in rather out-of-the-way setting; friendly staff, pub games, well kept Wadworths *(Dr and Mrs A K Clarke)*

☆ **Ridgehill**, Avon [off B3130 2 miles S of Winford; ST5462], *Crown*: Lively at weekends, with well kept Wadworths real ales, good sensibly priced food in bar and restaurant, log fires, country views, tables in small back garden *(D G and J M Moore)*

☆ **Rudge**, Som [just off A36; ST8251], *Full Moon*: Unspoilt and old-fashioned, with massive flagstones in entrance hall, well kept Butcombe, better-than-average food inc great doorstep sandwiches and children's dishes *(John C Baker)*

☆ **Seavington St Michael**, Som [signed from E side of A303 Ilminster bypass; ST4015], *Volunteer*: Wide choice of reliably good value food using fresh and often local ingredients in comfortable much modernised pub with well kept Badger beers, good local Perry's cider, friendly service, restrained decor *(Bernard Phillips, Phil and Sally Gorton, John and Pat Smyth)*

Shepton Mallet, Som [Downside, off A37 N; ST6244], *Downside*: Attractive homely 18th-century beamed country pub with wide choice of generous good value home-made food, cosy fire; pleasant garden with flowers, window boxes and tubs, aviary *(Mr and Mrs Jack Crookes, Mrs L S Richard)*; [in town], *Thatched Cottage*: Attractive, clean and well kept, with friendly, relaxing atmosphere and good reasonably priced food *(Mrs B A Blatch)*

Shipham, Som [ST4457], *Star*: Tiny inn notable for exceptionally good freshly cooked food, changing daily, with daily deliveries of mouthwatering Cornish fish, and thick and succulent unfrazzled gammon with peaches and pineapple; exemplary chips, prices very fair for the uncommon quality *(Mrs E M Astley-Weston)*

☆ **Somerton**, Som [Church Sq; ST4828], *Globe*: Popular tastefully refurbished local, comfortable and friendly, good value lunchtime bar food, well kept Bass, lots of flat-irons; big garden with terrace, skittle alley *(Ian Phillips)*

☆ **Somerton** [Church Sq], *White Hart*: Smart, clean and well run, with well kept Courage Best and Directors, good value bar food inc children's helpings in two small eating rooms and airy, spacious and well furnished family room *(Mr and Mrs A Smith)*

Stratton on the Fosse, Som [A367 towards Radstock, at B3139; ST6550], *White Post*: Limited choice of good value well prepared food in popular local — clean and comfortable, with good welcome, Ushers ale

(K R Harris, David Lamb)

☆ **Taunton**, Som [Middleway, Wilton], *Vivary Arms*: Good interesting range of home-made fresh lunchtime bar food from sandwiches up, with particularly good soup and fish *(Shirley Pielou, Maj S C Thompson)*

Taunton [Magdalene St], *Masons Arms*: Comfortable and welcoming old-fashioned pub, well carpeted and intelligently lit; well kept Exmoor, healthy and wholesome good value bar food; bedrooms good value *(David and Valerie Hooley)*

☆ **Tickenham**, Avon [B3130 Clevedon—Nailsea; ST4571], *Star*: Impressive choice of good generous food in spacious, light and airy dining lounge, quick and cheerful service, pine furniture, good range of beers, decent wine, piped music *(R Combes, Tom Evans, F J Willy)*

Timsbury, Avon [North Rd; B3115; ST6658], *Seven Stars*: Cheerful and brightly lit village pub with big woodburning stove, cheap well kept Courage Best and Directors, well reproduced juke box, pub games *(LYM)*

☆ **Tintinhull**, Som [Farm St; village signed off A303; ST4919], *Crown & Victoria*: Good range of bar food (not Sun) from sandwiches to steaks, real ales such as Butcombe and Youngs Special, Burrow Hill farm cider, big log fire, some easy chairs and other old-fashioned seats among more modern ones, bar billiards, skittles and other games, tables in big garden with goldfish pool and play area; children in eating area *(M D Hare, A M Kelly, LYM)*

☆ **Tockington**, Avon [ST6186], *Swan*: Attractive and spacious stone-built timbered pub in quiet village; wide choice of good food from sandwiches to steaks, with some more unusual dishes, in bar or dining room; well kept Courage Best and Directors, tables in garden *(M G Wadsworth, Stan Edwards)*

☆ **Tolldown**, Avon [under a mile from M4 junction 18 — A46 towards Bath; ST7577], *Crown*: Useful motorway stop, with generous helpings of straightforward bar food served efficiently in heavy-beamed stone pub with no smoking area, well kept Wadworths IPA, 6X and winter Old Timer on handpump, friendly staff, good garden with play area, dominoes, darts and fruit machine, open fires; children in eating area and restaurant; bedrooms *(Gary Marchant, John Knighton, Joan and Michel Hooper-Immins, Barry and Anne, JM, PM, LYM)*

Tormarton, Avon [ST7678], *Portcullis*: Big three-room bar, busy at weekends (when piped music may be loud), big helpings of reasonably priced beers, seven draught beers, boules pitch *(Peter and Rosemary Woods)*

Trull, Som [ST2122], *Winchester Arms*: Doing well under current regime, with attractively served if not particularly cheap largely home-cooked food; small dining area, good tables in attractive unassuming garden — very peaceful *(Shirley Pielou)*

☆ **Upton**, Som [OS Sheet 181, map reference 006293; SS9928], *Lowtrow Cross*: Isolated but very welcoming country inn with well kept Cotleigh Tawny, nice low-beamed bar with enormous inglenook, simple good value bar food, skittle alley, provision for children *(LYM)*

☆ **Upton Cheyney**, Avon [signed off A431 at Bitton; ST6969], *Upton*: Spaciously refurbished creeper-covered stone village pub with splendid Avon Valley views from rather ornately elegant plush bar with well kept Bass and Wadworths 6X, good reasonably priced home-cooked bar food (not Sat evening, Sun or Mon); restaurant; closed Sun evening, Mon. Good food such as lamb stew (though served with chips) and asparagus and ham pancake; good house wine and coffee, pleasant staff *(E H and R F Warner)*

☆ **Upton Noble**, Som [ST7139], *Lamb*: Small, comfortable village local with great views, stripped-stone lounge and small restaurant, well kept beer and good value bar food, Sun roasts; big garden, closed Mon *(Brian Chambers, Ted George)*

Vobster, Som [Lower Vobster; ST7049], *Vobster*: Spacious and comfortable, with tables outside, in good walking area; has been praised for well kept Bass, Ushers and Wadworths, generous helpings of good value food and friendly staff, but no recent reports *(News please)*

Wanstrow, Som [A359 Frome—Bruton; ST7141], *King William IV*: Neat tidy pub — open all day — with hanging baskets and window boxes, dining area and skittle alley; very friendly service, extensive, reasonably priced menu inc children's dishes, Butcombe, Courage Directors and Wadworths 6X, Thatcher's *(Bill and Ruth Gascoyne)*

☆ **Waterrow**, Som [A361 Wiveliscombe—Bampton; ST0425], *Rock*: Welcoming pub prettily placed in small valley village, with log fire and a modicum of copper and brass in smallish bar; couple of steps up to civilised lunchtime dining room with dark polished tables, doubling as smart evening restaurant; good range of beers, decent coffee, wide choice of food from breakfast through bar snacks and meals to full dinners; good value bedrooms with own bathrooms *(Michael and Alison Sandy, D C and R J Deeming, Gwen and Peter Andrews)*

Wedmore, Som [ST4347], *George*: Traditional furnishings in interesting stripped-stone bar of rambling coaching inn with real ale, bar food, lively locals' bar, sheltered lawn; bedrooms *(Gwen Cranfield, LYM)*

Wellington, Som [Hockholler; A38 3 miles E; ST1320], *Blackbird*: Friendly pub with well kept Ushers, well presented straightforward bar food and service with a smile; restaurant *(R K Harris)*

☆ **Wells**, Som [nr St Cuthberts Church; ST5545], *City Arms*: Very promising indeed; attractively converted early 18th-century building with outstanding food at reasonable prices in big L-shaped bar and upstairs restaurant, with well stocked bar and friendly service; already so popular with locals that it can be hard to get a table *(John Calvert, Miss R Halling, Graham Patrick)*

☆ **Wells** [High St], *Star*: Attractively old-fashioned bar, part no smoking, off narrow cobbled yard (tables under the hanging baskets), with beams, dark panelling, cosy atmosphere of shoppers dropping in, bar food such as steak and kidney pie, ham and egg, salads, steak, well kept real ales such as Bass and Butcombe or Wadworths 6X on handpump, piped music, fruit machine; gingham-tablecloth dining room leads off; steak restaurant; bedrooms comfortable, with appropriate furnishings inc four-posters *(Andy Hick, M K C Wills, P and R Woods, Janet Hill, Les Rae, BB)*

☆ **Wells** [St Thomas St], *Fountain*: Friendly and comfortable, very popular locally for good value food pleasantly served; well kept Courage Directors, farm cider, piped music; restaurant, Sun lunches *(I B Maw, P and R Woods)*

☆ **Wells** [Market Pl], *Crown*: Good atmosphere in pleasant old multi-level coaching inn nr cathedral, with interesting William Penn connection; magnificent fireplace behind bar, well kept Wadworths ales tapped from the cask, good choice of food from separate servery, efficient helpful service *(P and R Woods, T Nott)*

Wells [High St], *Kings Head*: Old Courage pub with deal tables in flagstoned front bar, two-level main bar area beyond; good lunchtime food and Courage Best and Directors on handpump; attracts young people in evening, with loud music then *(P Corris, K W J Wood)*; [outside], *Pheasant*: Promising under pleasant new licensees, with wide-ranging ambitious food *(M P Furmston)*

West Bagborough, Som [ST1633], *Rising Sun*: Pleasant quiet little place in tiny Quantocks village with short choice of fresh generously served food eg ham and egg or shepherd's pie, well kept Exmoor and Oakhill Farmers, unobtrusive piped music, darts, table skittles, big log fires *(Dr and Mrs B D Smith)*

☆ **West Buckland**, Som [nr M5 junction 26; A38 Wellington—Taunton; ST1720], *Blackbird*: Friendly and homely partly 16th-century inn, clean and quiet, with good value home-cooked food from sandwiches up inc good Sun lunch, well kept Watneys-related real ales, skittle alley, pleasant garden with unusual statue; restaurant; bedrooms good value and well equipped, with good breakfasts *(Audrey and Roger Adcock, Mr and Mrs B J Twigger)*

☆ **West Harptree**, Avon [B3114, out of village towards Chew Lake; ST5657], *Blue Bowl*: Popular and well run dining pub with wide choice of good value meals inc massive range of puddings; lots of bookable tables in a row of communicating rooms, with good atmosphere and attractive family room; well kept Courage Best and Directors and John Smiths on handpump, tables out on terrace and safely fenced lawn, surrounded by fields; bedrooms comfortable and good

value, with good breakfasts *(Mrs M Mills, BB)*

West Hatch, Som [Slough Green, which is signed off A380 and B3170; ST2720], *Farmers Arms*: 16th-century, with beams and open fires, well kept Exmoor and Whitbreads-related real ales on handpump, good range of food priced to include soup and main course in bar or dining room, also Sun lunch; skittle alley, games area with darts and bar billiards, children's room, live music Fri/Sat; garden with play area; children in children's room and restaurant *(Richard Dolphin)*

☆ **West Pennard**, Som [A361 E of Glastonbury; ST5438], *Red Lion*: Welcoming efficient service and wide choice of bar food inc good children's menu in neat dining areas opening off small flagstoned and black-beamed core, with log fire in big stone inglenook, another in stripped-stone family area); Ash Vine (carrying the pub's name), Badger Tanglefoot and Butcombe on handpump, maybe piped radio; bedrooms comfortable and well equipped, in neatly converted side barn *(John and Pat Smyth, BB)*

Weston in Gordano, Avon [B3124 Portishead—Clevedon; ST4474], *White Hart*: Attractive furnishings in cheerful and cosy village pub inc some fine small settles, no smoking restaurant area, family room, good bar food, Courage ales, garden with play area *(Joan Olivier)*

☆ **Weston Super Mare**, Avon [seafront, N end; ST3261], *Claremont Vaults*: Friendly, comfortable and plushly decorated, well kept Bass and Charrington from central servery, good choice of lunchtime bar food, helpful staff, relaxing atmosphere, piped music; evening live music in season; good views of sea, the piers and Brean Down *(Peter Woods, P Corris, E H and R F Warner)*

Weston Super Mare [Lower Church Rd], *Regency*: Comfortable and spacious, with civilised atmosphere and smartly dressed customers, good value lunchtime food inc well presented sandwiches, French sticks and cod or plaice; Bass, Butcombe and Wadworths 6X, pool room, seats out in front *(Nigel Gibbs)*; [Upper Bristol Rd], *Windsor*: Friendly service and good reasonably priced daily specials *(S G Gunn)*

Wheddon Cross, Som [junction A396/B3224, S of Minehead; SS9238], *Rest & Be Thankful*: Modern comfortable furnishings in two-room bar with log fire, aquarium and piped music, usual bar food inc children's dishes, well kept Watneys-related real ales, also tea, hot chocolate and so forth; communicating games area, skittle alley, buffet bar *(LYM)*

☆ **Wick**, Avon [ST7072], *Rose & Crown*: Beautiful old-world 18th-century building in attractive spot, good traditional food, first-class service; very popular, kept clean *(Dr F Peters)*

☆ **Widcombe**, Som [OS Sheet 193, map reference 222160; ST2216], *Holman Clavel*: Comfortably modernised Whitbreads pub named after its massive holly chimney-beam, good food, helpful service, nice country atmosphere; handy for Blackdown Hills and Widcombe Bird Garden *(BB)*

Williton, Som [ST0740], *Egremont*: Friendly old coaching inn, good staff, generous reasonably priced food *(Joan Olivier)*; [A39], *Foresters Arms*: Straightforward well organised pub with good beer and a real welcome for children *(C J Parsons)*

Winsley, Avon [B3108 W of Bradford-on-Avon; ST7961], *Seven Stars*: Stripped stonework and snug alcoves, with Watneys-related real ales, reliable reasonably priced food, decent piped music, tables in garden; attractive village *(Mrs E M Astley-Weston, Mrs Joan Harris)*

☆ **Winterbourne Down**, Avon [Down Rd, Kendleshire; just off A432 Bristol—Yate, towards Winterbourne; ST6679], *Golden Heart*: Beams, open fires, inglenook and good atmosphere, with limited choice of good cheap food, friendly staff, pleasant country view from restaurant; children's room, good gardens front and back, play area *(M A Watts, Dr K A and S F Louden)*

☆ **Wookey**, Som [B3139; ST5245], *Burcott Inn*: Unspoilt local, friendly and bustling, with scrubbed wood tables, well kept real ales inc Butcombe on handpump, good German lager and choice of wine, good bar food inc interesting specials and doorstep sandwiches, open fires, attentive friendly service, cottagey back restaurant (children allowed here), walled garden *(Richard Houghton, Phil and Sally Gorton, John Fazakerley)*

Wookey Hole, *Wookey Hole*: Family pub useful for its location, with Courage ales, no-nonsense bar food at realistic prices, unpretentious dining room; bedrooms *(Jenny and Brian Seller)*

Worle, Avon [Ebdon Rd; ST3562], *Nut Tree*: Well appointed, with substantial good value snacks and main dishes, good choice of well kept real ales such as Brains SA, Theakstons, Youngers Scotch *(A M Kelly, N J Mackintosh)*

☆ **Wrington**, Avon [High St; 2 1/2 miles off A370 Bristol—Weston, from bottom of Rhodiate Hill; ST4662], *Plough*: Friendly, rural atmosphere, wide choice of tasty home-made food, good service, well kept beer *(Dr and Mrs A K Clarke)*

Staffordshire *see* Derbyshire

Suffolk

A good clutch of new entries here, or pubs back in the Guide after a break, are the Queens Head at Blyford (doing well under its newish licensee; good food), the civilised and spacious Trowel & Hammer at Cotton (Greek-run, with some Greek dishes), the Old Chequers at Friston (a very interesting new place, with really good food), the well restored Angel in Lavenham (good food, a nice place to stay), the unassuming yet rewarding Brewers Arms tucked away at Rattlesden, and the most engaging Cat & Mouse near Wetheringsett – hard to track down but well worth the effort if you like beer, cider, country wines, animals, or just plain honest friendliness. Among other pubs here, ones currently doing particularly well include the Butt & Oyster near Chelmondiston (with its good river views), the cheerful and obliging Bell at Cretingham (decent food, good for families), the friendly Ship at Dunwich (good fresh fish), the relaxed Victoria at Earl Soham (good beers brewed here), the Beehive at Horringer (notable food, very friendly), the Swan at Hoxne (earning a food award this year), the Kings Head in Orford (good local fish, again), the Plough in a lovely quiet spot at Rede (splendid daily specials), the civilised Crown at Southwold (fine food and wines), the elegant yet relaxed Angel at Stoke by Nayland (another with really good food), the friendly Gardeners Arms at Tostock (an exemplary village pub) and the Crown at Westleton – extending itself, but still doing well. Among the Lucky Dip entries at the end of the chapter, pubs currently moving smartly up the charts include the Queens Head at Bramfield, Greyhound at Chevington, Black Lion at Glemsford, Crown at Hartest, Fox at Pakenham and White Horse at Whepstead; we'd also pick out for attention the Ship at Blaxhall, Masons Arms in Bury, Affleck Arms at Dalham, Kings Head at East Bergholt, Queens Head at Erwarton, Plough & Sail at Snape and Black Horse at Thorndon. All the Southwold pubs listed are good; we'd rate this small, quiet seaside town as among the very best places for pubby explorations. Prices of both food and drink in the county are very much in line with the national average.

BLYFORD   TM4277 Map 5

Queens Head

B1123

The food in this friendly thatched 15th-century village pub is very good. At lunchtime it includes sandwiches (from £1.40), home-made quiche or ploughman's (£3.50), moussaka (£4.45), vegetarian pasta, and steak and kidney pie (£4.75); in the evening it's more elaborate with guinea fowl in raspberry and redcurrant sauce (£5.50), quails stuffed with pâté and mushrooms (£6.50), fresh trout with kiwi and strawberry sauce (£6.55) and half a duckling or whole lobster. Well kept Adnams Bitter, Mild and Broadside on handpump, and local James White draught cider. The attractively furnished, low-beamed bar has some antique settles, pine and oak benches built into its cream walls, heavy wooden tables and stools, and a huge fireplace with good brickwork. There are seats on the grass outside, and a small village church opposite. *(Recommended by C C Cook, Mrs H Fuller, Nick Dowson, A T Langton, Klaus and Elizabeth Leist)*

Adnams   Tenant Jonathan Matthews   Real ale   Meals and snacks   Blyburgh (050 270) 404   Children in eating area of bar   Open 11–3, 6.30–11; closed 25 Dec

nr CHELMONDISTON   TM2037   Map 5

Butt & Oyster

Pin Mill – signposted from B1456 SE of Ipswich

There are lovely views out over the River Orwell and the wooded slopes beyond from the many solid tables and chairs by the water and from the seats in the big bay window of this old bargeman's pub. The small, half panelled smoke room is decorated with model sailing ships and has high-backed and other old-fashioned settles on the tiled floor; spare a glance for the most unusual carving of a man with a woman over the mantlepiece. Good, popular bar food includes sandwiches (from £1; not on Saturday or Sunday lunchtimes when there's a buffet), ploughman's (from £2.50), home-made pies and quiches (from £3.75), salads (from £4), and home-made daily specials like lamb casserole, seafood provençale or mushroom tagliatelle (around £4.50). Tolly Original, Mild and winter Old Strong on handpump, with Bitter tapped from the cask; winter darts, shove-ha'penny, dominoes and shut-the-box. A good time to visit the pub would be when the annual Thames Barge Race is held (end June/beginning July). *(Recommended by Nick and Alison Dowson, Norman and Barbara Wells, Gwen and Peter Andrews, JF, Mrs P J Pearce)*

Tolly (Brent Walker)   Tenants Dick and Brenda Mainwaring   Real ale   Meals and snacks (till 10pm in summer; not 25 Dec)   (0473) 780764   Children in two separate rooms   Occasional piano   Open 11–11; 12–3, 7–11 in winter; closed evening 25 Dec

CHELSWORTH   TL9848   Map 5

Peacock ★ 🛏

The Street; B1115

It's the building itself that is so special here: an elegantly restored 14th-century inn with a large beamed bar divided into several areas by a partly open timbered partition and with a splendid stone inglenook fireplace. The cosy inner lounge has some exposed Tudor brickwork and is decorated with local paintings which are for sale (there is a craft shop behind the garden). Straightforward bar food includes sandwiches (from £1.50), ploughman's (£2.60), game pâté (£2.50), quiche or hand-raised game pie (£4.50), seafood lasagne (£5.50) and puddings (£2.50), with evening extras such as gammon (£5), chicken kiev (£6.75) and steaks. Well kept Adnams Bitter, Greene King IPA and Abbot and Mauldons Bitter on handpump, country wines and fresh orange juice; sometimes there are nibbles such as stuffed olives or nuts on the tables; darts, cribbage, and maybe a friendly jack russell. Just over the bridge is the rich parkland of Chelsworth Hall. *(Recommended by Bill and Jane Rees, Frank W Gadbois, Prof S Barnett, Nick Dowson, Mr and Mrs J M Elden, J P Cinnamond, John Evans, Barbara and Norman Wells, R C Gandy)*

Free house   Licensees L R Bulgin and A F Marsh   Real ale   Meals and snacks (till 10pm)   Restaurant   Bildeston (0449) 740758   Children in eating area   Jazz Fri evening   Open 11–3, 6–11; closed 25 Dec   Bedrooms; £22/£40

CLARE   TL7645   Map 5

Bell

Market place

The rambling lounge bar in this attractive timbered hotel has splendidly carved black beams, panelling and woodwork around the open fire, armchairs on the green carpet and local notices on the hessian walls. Another room leads off, and to eat you go through to the Leggers Bar with masses of prints – mainly to do with canals – on its walls: food here includes soup (£1.50), pizzas (from £3.50), omelettes (from £4), curries (from £4.25), liver and bacon or lasagne (£4.50), gammon (£4.95), and steaks (from £6.50); toasted sandwiches in the comfortable lounge bar. A comfortable, light and airy conservatory has sofas and armchairs prettily covered in a burgundyLaura Ashley paisley. Well kept Greene King IPA and Abbott and Nethergate Bitter and Old Growler on handpump; fruit machine, trivia and piped music. There's a back terrace and attractive garden. Several other striking buildings in the village include the remains of the priory and the castle (which stands on prehistoric earthworks). *(Recommended by A D Atienza, R A Corbett, Margaret Drazin, J P Cinnamond, Derek and Sylvia Stephenson; more reports please)*

Free house   Licensees Brian and Gloria Miles   Real ale   Meals and snacks Restaurant (not Sun evening)   Clare (0787) 277741   Children welcome   Open 11–11   Bedrooms; £38.50(£44.50B)/£56.50(£61.50B)

COTTON   TM0766 Map 5
Trowel & Hammer

Mill Rd; just off B1113 N of Stowmarket

Partly thatched and partly tiled, this white house has neat climbers on trellises, and picnic-table sets in a pretty back garden with a pool. Inside, the spreading red-carpeted lounge has wheelback and one or two older chairs and settles around a variety of tables, lots of dark beamery and timber baulks, lantern lights, a big log fire and at the back an ornate woodburning stove; the windows have elaborately pelmeted and swagged velvet curtains. It all adds up to a relaxed and comfortable feel. Well kept Adnams, Flowers IPA and Greene King IPA and Abbot on handpump, welcoming service. The food, generously served and good value, includes Greek dishes among more usual things: hummus, taramasalata, kebabs, moussaka and a popular kleftiko cooked with plenty of oregano (£4.75). *(Recommended by L W Baal, Mr and Mrs A Albert)*

Free house   Licensees George Kattos and Chris Frydas   Real ale   Meals and snacks (till 10.30)   Open 11.30–2.30, 6.30–11

CRETINGHAM   TM2260 Map 5
Bell

This is a cheerful and popular old pub – originally built as a manor house in the 16th century and converted later into four cottages; it became a pub in 1967. Families are made very welcome (well behaved children get an ice lolly) and there's a special family room, children's menus or an extra plate and a secluded play area with play-frame and their own tables and chairs. The comfortably modernised lounge bar has exposed beams, standing timbers of a knocked-through wall, a large old fireplace, and a wall tapestry. Well presented, good bar food includes soup (£1.65), open baps (from £1.95), burgers (from £2.95), local sausages (£3.25), fruity vegetarian curry or home-made steak and kidney pudding (£3.95), home-cooked ham (£4.75), spare ribs (£5.25), fresh fish of the day, steaks (from £8.45), and children's dishes (£2.65); popular Sunday roast lunch and summer barbecues; they do a take-away service for food and beer which is popular with local golfers. Well kept Adnams Best, Greene King IPA, Tetleys and a regular guest beer on handpump, and several malt whiskies; piped jazz. The quarry-tiled public bar has darts, trivia, shove-ha'penny, dominoes and cribbage. On the sheltered grass in front there are rustic tables and seats, with more on another lawn by rose bushes and a fine old oak tree on the corner. The local harriers meet here each New Year's Day. *(Recommended by Brian and Fran Bannatyne-Scott, Gordon Leighton, David Cardy, Nick Dowson)*

Free house   Licensees Ron and Sheila Blackmore   Real ale   Meals and snacks (till 10pm)   Restaurant   Earl Soham (0728) 685419   Children welcome   Regular live music – jazz and Spanish evenings   Open 11–2.30, 6–11; maybe open all day July/August; 11.30–2.30, 6.30–11 in winter

DUNWICH TM4770 Map 5

Ship

On a sunny Sunday you may find quite a queue waiting for this atmospheric inn to open. The main bar has cushioned wall benches, pews and captains' chairs and wooden tables with candles on the tiled floor, a dusky ochre ceiling, and a woodburning stove (cheerfully left open in cold weather). Reasonably priced, tasty, home-made bar food at lunchtime includes lovely soup (£1.10), ploughman's or cottage pie (£3), lasagne (£3.50), and excellent fresh local fish such as plaice (£3.75), with evening dishes like garlic mushrooms (£2.75), home-made pâté (£3), hot home-cooked ham with peach and brandy sauce (£6.50), fish of the day or sirloin steak (£7.25), and vegetarian dishes. Well kept Adnams Bitter, Broadside and Old, and Greene King Abbot on handpump at the handsomely panelled bar counter. The public bar area has darts, dominoes, cribbage, fruit machine, video game, trivia and piped music. The conservatory has bunches of grapes on the vine, there's a well kept garden with an enormous fig tree, and a sunny back terrace. On current form this pub seems clearly in the running for a star award – we'd be glad of your views on this. *(Recommended by Dr M Bailey, Mark Sargeant, Gwen and Peter Andrews, Mr and Mrs F E M Hardy, David and Katharine Cooke, Alison and Tony Godfrey, Mrs S Burrows-Smith, Klaus and Elizabeth Leist, A T Langton, C J Parson, Nick and Alison Dowson, Derek and Sylvia Stephenson)*

Free house   Licensees Stephen and Ann Marshlain   Real ale   Meals and snacks (not 25 Dec)   Evening restaurant   Westleton (072 873) 219   Children welcome (not in Ship Bar)   Open 11–3, 6–11 (winter evening opening 7); closed evening 25 Dec Bedrooms; £18/£36

EARL SOHAM SM2363 Map 5

Victoria ★

A1120 Stowmarket–Yoxford

The very good home-brewed beer in this relaxed and friendly little pub includes Victorian Bitter, a mild called Gannet, and a stronger ale called Albert (you can visit the brewery); (they do a take-away service too). The furnishings are nicely chosen – kitchen chairs and pews, plank-topped trestle sewing-machine tables and other simple country tables with candles, tiled or board floors, stripped panelling, an interesting range of pictures of Queen Victoria and her reign, a piano, and open fires. Reasonably priced, the good home-made food includes sandwiches (under £1), home-made soup (£1.35), ploughman's (from £2.25), proper home-made burgers, fine undyed kippers, delicious chilli con carne (£2.95), vegetarian lasagne (£3.45), and pork with apple and cider or beef curry (£4.15). Darts, cribbage, cards and backgammon; seats out in front and on a raised back lawn. The pub is close to a wild fritillary meadow at Framlingham and a working windmill at Saxtead. *(Recommended by Andrew Morrissey, Nick Dowson, John C Baker, John Whitehead, Klaus and Elizabeth Leist, Comus Elliott, Gwen and Peter Andrews)*

Own brew   Licensees Clare and John Bjornson   Real ale   Meals and snacks   (0728) 685758   Children in back bar only   Impromptu folk music Tues and Fri evenings Open 11.30–2.30(3 Sat), 5.30–11

FRAMLINGHAM TM2863 Map 5

Crown 🛏

Market Hill

Perhaps the best place to sit in the cosy bar of this bustling, friendly little black-and-white Tudor inn is at the old windows overlooking the unusual sloping triangular market place (market day is Saturday, when nearby parking may be difficult). This room is popular with locals: high heavy beams, one or two settles (including an antique carved one), dark green plush armed seats, and a log fire. The comfortable lounge has wing easy chairs beside the fire, and there are more seats in the hall. Bar food includes sandwiches or filled baked potatoes (from £2.50), vegetarian risotto or canelloni (£4.25), and a daily special like steak and kidney pie or moussaka (£4.25). Adnams on handpump; piped music. Coaches once clattered through what is now a prettily planted flagstoned courtyard (with a cheerful winter flowering cherry). *(Recommended by D S Cottrell; more reports please)*

Free house (THF)   Managers Mrs Scougal and Mr Manby   Real ale   Meals and snacks   No smoking restaurant   Framlingham (0728) 723521   Children in lounge   Open 10.30–2, 6–11   Bedrooms; £67.95B/£100.90B

FRAMSDEN   TM1959 Map 5

Dobermann

The Street; pub signposted off B1077 just S of its junction with A1120 Stowmarket–Earl Soham

Kept spotlessly clean, this relaxed and welcoming thatched pub has very low, pale stripped beams, photographs of and show rosettes won by the owner's dogs on the white walls, and a central fireplace that divides the room into two – its log fire open to both sides. On one there's a big sofa (a favourite with Lottie, the tabby cat), a couple of chintz wing armchairs, and by the big window a refectory table. The other side has a mix of chairs, plush-seated stools and winged settles around polished rustic tables. Popular bar food includes sandwiches (from £1.15, maybe hot beef £1.70), home-made soup (£2.25), sausage in a basket (£2.50), ploughman's (from £3.80), home-made chicken and mushroom or steak and kidney pies (£6.25), gammon, sausage and egg (£6.50), popular chicken breast St Etienne (£7.75), and trout in wine and almonds (£8.25). Well kept Adnams Bitter, Felinfoel Double Dragon, Greene King IPA and Abbott and Rayments on handpump, with a decent choice of spirits and malt whiskies; piped music. They play boules outside, where there are picnic-table sets by trees, a fairy-lit trellis, and pretty hanging baskets and window boxes. *(Recommended by Patrick and Patricia Derwent, L W Baal, John Whitehead, Alison Hayward, Nick Dowson)*

Free house   Licensee Susan Frankland   Real ale   Meals and snacks (11.30–2, 7–9.45)   Helmingham (0473) 890 461   Open 11.30–2.30, 7–11   Bedroom; £15/£30

FRISTON   TM4160 Map 5

Old Chequers ✏

B1121 SE of Saxmundham; and village signposted off A1094

David Grimwood made a name for himself with the White Horse at Easton, turning it into a delightful combination of studied rustic simplicity with innovative food. His new pub, on a larger scale, is as rewarding. A small red-carpeted area by the bar, with a woodburning stove and stripped brickwork, opens on the left into an airy and spacious room decorated in cool greens and cream, with another big woodburner in one stripped wall, and well spaced chairs and country-kitchen tables (with fresh flowers) in pale wood; there are shelves of preserves, chutneys, grissini and so forth for sale. As before, food is the main interest, though one doesn't feel at all out of place dropping in for a drink; besides well kept Adnams Bitter and Broadside, a guest bitter such as Ridleys and a guest strong ale such as Felinfoel Double Dragon, they keep good malt whiskies, a decent choice of wines by the glass, and an excellent choice of bottles in the £6–£10 range, eclectic and thoughtful, with a few half-bottles. Food is carefully cooked using good fresh ingredients. A shortish lunchtime choice might include cider-baked ham, ratatouille crumble, baked cod and steak and kidney pie (£5.95), served quickly from a hot buffet with help-yourself vegetables. The wider evening choice might include watercress soup (£2.50), mussels (£3.25), pâté (£3.50), baked local crab (£3.95), rabbit in filo pastry with sage mousse (£8.95), steaks (from £9.75) and roast guineafowl (£9.25), with puddings such as caramelised oranges (£2.50). Service is considerate and attentive, and the atmosphere relaxed and enjoyable; no music or machines. There are a few picnic-table sets in the small back yard. *(Recommended by Brenda Crossley, Heather Sharland)*

Free house   Licensee David Grimwood   Real ale   Meals (not Sun evening)   Snape
(072 888) 270   Children allowed Sun lunchtime in eating area   Live music Sun
evening   Open 11.30–3, 6.30–11

HORRINGER   TL8261 Map 5

Beehive

A143

The friendly licensees were celebrating their sixth year here as we went to press and
are still enjoying running this busy pub as much as ever. The little rambling rooms
have stripped panelling or brickwork, some very low beams in some of the furthest
and snuggest alcoves, carefully chosen dining and country kitchen chairs, one or
two wall settles around solid tables, picture-lights over lots of 19th-century prints,
and a woodburning stove; there's a couple of quiet dogs including an aloof borzoi
(who becomes less aloof when the After Eights appear with the coffee). Very good,
often unusual food includes home-made soup (£1.50), sandwiches (from £1.50),
ploughman's or home-made taramasalata with hot pitta bread (£2.95), a peppered
salami omelette (£3.25), honey-roast goose breast thinly sliced and served with its
own dressing or tortellini with a ricotta and tomato filling and cream sauce
(£3.95), local ham carved from the bone (£4.95), a plate of exceptionally presented
hors d'oeuvres (£5.50), chicken fillets in a creamy curry sauce or pork steak
marinaded in fresh oranges, garlic and rosemary (£6.95), lovely puddings, and
specials such as grilled puff mushrooms with a warm yoghurt and tarragon sauce
(£2.95), local venison sausages cooked in a rich claret sauce (£4.95), and stir-fry
Australian pink prawns and noodles with stick vegetables (£6.50). Well kept
Greene King IPA and Abbot on handpump and decent house wines. A most
attractively planted back terrace has picnic-table sets, with more seats on a raised
lawn. (Recommended by M J Brooks, Gwen and Peter Andrews, David Shillitoe, J J Gower,
John C Baker, A D Atienza, M Rising, John Matthews)

Greene King   Tenant Gary Kingshott   Real ale   Meals and snacks (not Sun evening)
Horringer (0284) 735260   Children welcome   Open 11.30–2.30, 7–11

HOXNE   TM1777 Map 5

Swan

Off B1118; village signposted off A140 S of Diss

Even at busy times when customers crowd in to enjoy the good home-made bar
food at this Grade II* listed, carefully restored late 15th-century inn, the staff
remain as efficient and friendly as ever. The front bar has two solid oak bar
counters, heavy oak floors, and a deep-set inglenook fireplace with an armchair on
either side and a long bench in front of it; you can see the ancient timber and
mortar of the walls. A fire in the back bar divides the bar area and snug, and the
dining room has an original wooden fireplace. Bar food includes burgers (from
£1.05), sandwiches (from £1.30), ploughman's (from £2.25), a choice of omelettes
(£2.75), tasty pancakes filled with mushrooms and cheese (£3.25), gammon
(£3.80), plate of salamis with black olives (£3.95), excellent scampi (£4.30),
wonderfully tender rump steak (£7.25), daily specials such as courgette and
rosemary soup (£1.30), nut and herb loaf with tomato sauce or stuffed mussels
(£2.75), chicken casserole with anchovies and olives (£4.25) and cod and prawn
gratinée (£4.95). Well kept Adnams tapped from the cask and Greene King Abbot
on handpump with winter Old and Tally Ho kept under light blanket pressure,
decent wines, and half-a-dozen malt whiskies; pool, shove-ha'penny, cribbage, and
juke box. The pub is close to the site of King Edmund's Martyrdom on 20
November 870. The extensive lawn behind the building is used for croquet – a nice
place to sit in summer on the hand-made elm furniture, sheltered by a willow and
other trees and its shrub-covered wall; if you are eating outside, rather than use a
Tannoy, they press a buzzer and then prop up scoreboard-type numbers on the
roof to indicate your ticket number. (Recommended by Gwen and Peter Andrews, John C
Baker, William and Alison Trelawny, A D Atienza, Nick and Alison Dowson)

Free house   Licensees Tony and Frances Thornton-Jones   Real ale   Meals and snacks (not Sat and Sun evenings or Sun lunch)   Restaurant Weds-Sat evenings   Hoxne (037 975) 275   Well behaved children allowed   Open 12–2.30(3 Sat), 5.30–11; closed 25 Dec

HUNDON   TL7348 Map 5
Plough

Brockley Green; on Kedington road, up hill from village

This extended and modernised pub still has a double row of worn old oak timbers to mark what must have been the corridor between the two rooms of the neatly-kept and friendly carpeted bar; there are low side settles with Liberty-print cushions, spindleback chairs, and sturdy low tables on the patterned carpet, lots of horsebrasses on the beams, and striking gladiatorial designs for Covent Garden by Leslie Hurry, who lived nearby, on the bare brick walls. Decent bar food includes sandwiches or filled French bread (from £1.50), home-made soup (£1.75), ploughman's (£2.95), mushrooms stuffed with stilton and garlic and deep fried (£2.95), tortellini with ricotta cheese in a cream sauce (£3.95), ham and cauliflower cheese (£4.25), scrambled eggs with lamb's kidneys (£4.75), seafood bake (£5.25), game or steak pie (£5.75), and puddings (from £1.95). Well kept Greene King IPA, Nethergate and a guest beer on handpump, and freshly squeezed orange; cheerful piped music. There's a terrace with pergola and ornamental pool and a garden. It's also a certified location for the Caravan Club, with a sheltered site to the rear for tourers. *(Recommended by Gwen and Peter Andrews, JM, PM, John C Baker)*

Free house   Licensee David Rowlinson   Real ale   Meals and snacks   Partly no-smoking restaurant (not Sun evening)   Hundon (0440) 86789   Children welcome   Jazz Sun, piano in restaurant Fri   Open 11–11; 11–3, 7–11 Sats; 12–2.30, 5–11 in winter   Bedrooms; £35B/£50B

IXWORTH   TL9370 Map 5
Pickerel

Village signposted just off A143 Bury St Edmunds–Diss

Leading off the central servery are several small rooms with moulded Elizabethan oak beams, panelling that varies from ancient to 18th-century, attractive brickwork, cushioned chairs and pews, and big fireplaces. The pretty two-roomed dining room has stripped pine tables and dressers, stripped pine dado, blue patterned wallpaper and a high shelf of plates, and there's a small back sun lounge facing a sway-backed Elizabethan timbered barn across the old coach yard. Under the new licensee the bar food includes filled French bread (from £1.25), mushroom and nut stroganoff (£4.80), poussin or Pickerel pie (£4.95), and swordfish or chicken tikka masala (£5.50); winter Sunday lunch (from £4.95). Well kept Greene King Abbot and IPA and Rayments on handpump; fruit machine, juke box and piped music. On a goodish stretch of grass under a giant sycamore are some picnic-table sets. *(Recommended by James and Hilary Barber, Brenda Crossley, David and Rebecca Killick, Roxanne Chamberlain, A D Atienza, R M Savage, Maureen and Pat Campbell, John Baker, Charles Bardswell, David Cardy)*

Greene King   Lease: Vella Galea   Real ale   Meals and snacks (not Sun evening or all day Mon)   Restaurant (not Sun evening)   Pakenham (0359) 30398   Children in family room   Jazz and folk evenings planned   Open 11–2.30(3 Sat), 6–11 Bedrooms; £25/£35

KERSEY   TL9944 Map 5
Bell

Village signposted off A1141 N of Hadleigh

Doors off a worn brick-tiled corridor in this fine timbered building open into a bar and lounge which are divided by a brick and timber screen decorated with copper and brassware. The low-beamed public side has simple seating on its tiled floor and a log fire, and the lounge side has comfortable red plush button-back banquettes, latticed windows, and a swirly red carpet. Bar food includes sandwiches (from £1.25), home-made soup (£1.70), ploughman's (£2.95), salads (from £3.75, dressed Cromer crab £5.25), omelettes (£4.25), lasagne or fruit and vegetable kebabs (£4.75), daily fish dishes, lemon chicken (£5.25), home-made steak and kidney pie (£5.45), 10oz gammon steak (£5.95), steaks (from £6.95), and puddings (£1.95). When booking a 3-course meal between November and February they offer a free return coach trip for groups of 38 or more (within 30 miles); not Christmas Day or Boxing Day. On a rotational basis, the three handpumps here may serve Adnams Best, Batemans XXXB, Boddingtons, Brains SA, Felinfoel Double Dragon, Mansfield Old Baily, Mauldons Mild, Rayments, Sam Smiths and Tolly Mild; around a dozen malt whiskies; dominoes, cribbage, trivia, cards and piped music. Out on the sheltered back terrace and under a fairy-lit side canopy, there are white cast-iron tables and chairs. They are listed as a certified location for the Caravan Club (up to 3 units). *(Recommended by Paul S McPherson, Prof S Barnett, Gwen and Peter Andrews, Barbara and Norman Wells, John Evans)*

Free house   Licensees Alex and Lynne Coote   Real ale   Meals and snacks Restaurant   Ipswich (0473) 823229   Children with parents who are eating in eating area of bar and in restaurant only if bar eating area is full   Open 11–3(5 summer Sats), 6–11; winter evening opening 7; closed evening 25 Dec and all day 26 Dec   Bedrooms; £17.50/£40B

LAVENHAM   TL9149   Map 5

Angel 🏆 🛏

Market Pl

The green-carpeted main bar of this recently carefully renovated Tudor inn feels very up-to-date on the right, with piped light classics (unless Mr Whitworth himself happens to be playing Chopin), lots of shelves of readable books, blonde furniture including heavy kitchen tables and chairs; one table shaped like a piano-top occupies a bay window, with a nice polished wooden seat running around it to look out on the little market square of this pretty village, and its Guildhall (NT). The open-plan area loops around the servery to a more softly lit dark-beamed part on the left, with some sofas and mates' chairs around darker tables. There is a big log fire in the inglenook, under a heavy mantlebeam. The changing bar food is carefully home-cooked, using fresh largely local ingredients. Besides lunchtime sandwiches (from £1.95) and ploughman's (£2.95), it might include carrot and lentil soup (£1.95), several starters such as garlic mushrooms (£2.75) or warm chicken liver salad (£3.75), seafood pancakes (£3.25), vegetable lasagne (£4.25), steak and kidney pie (£4.95), grilled trout (£6.25) and lamb chops (£6.95), with good puddings (£2.25); in the evenings there are also more expensive richly textured main dishes, such as baked fillet of sole with prawn sauce (£7.95). Well kept Nethergate, Ruddles County and Websters Yorkshire on handpump, quite a few malt whiskies, decent wines by the glass and a good choice by the bottle; a back games area has bar billiards, lots of board games, cribbage, bridge on Thursday, dominoes, fruit machine and trivia. The big ginger cat is called Dilly, the one without a tail is Stumpy. There are picnic-table sets out in front, and white tables under cocktail parasols in a sizeable sheltered back garden; it's worth asking if they've time to show you the interesting Tudor cellar. *(Recommended by Frank W Gadbois, Brian and Genie Smart, John Bowdler, John C Baker, Ann and John Cox, Gwen and Peter Andrews, M Bates, Mr and Mrs J R M Deakin, Mrs C M John, R J Nelson, Sally Ann Lomax, Richard Joyce, G A Cape)*

Free house   Licensees Roy and Anne Whitworth, John and Val Barry   Real ale Meals and snacks   Restaurant   Lavenham (0787) 247388   Children in eating area Classical piano   Open 11–3, 6–11   Bedrooms; £25.30B/£40.50B

LAXFIELD   TM2972 Map 5

Kings Head

Behind church, off road toward Banyards Green

A new licensee has taken over this thatched Tudor pub. The old-fashioned front room has a high-backed built-in settle on the tiled floor and an open fire, and a couple of other rooms have pews, old seats, scrubbed deal tables, and some interesting wall prints. Bar food now includes sandwiches (from £1.20), ploughman's (£2.80), vegetarian dishes (from £2.40), and steak and kidney pie or lasagne (£3.60); oak-smoked kippers on Friday evening. Well kept Adnams Bitter and Broadside, Bass, Brains, and Wadworths 6X tapped from the cask, local cider and some country wines. Going out past the casks in the back serving room, you find benches and a trestle table in a small yard. From the yard, a honeysuckle arch leads into a sheltered little garden and the pub's own well kept and secluded bowling, badminton and croquet green; occasional Morris dancers on summer weekends. (*Recommended by Nick Dowson, Anthony Barnes, Frank Gadbois; more reports on the new regime, please*)

Free house   Licensee E MacLeod   Real ale   Meals and snacks   Restaurant (bookings only)   Ubbeston (0986) 798395   Children welcome   Regular folk and blues bands Open 11–3, 6–11; closed 25 Dec   Bedrooms; 25B/£50B

ORFORD   TM4250 Map 5

Jolly Sailor ★

This pub stands by a busy little quay on the River Ore, opposite Orford Ness and close to marshy Havergate Island, where avocets breed. Several cosy rooms are served from counters and hatches in an old-fashioned central cubicle. The main room has an uncommon spiral staircase in the corner and is warmed in winter by a good solid fuel stove, another has a flagstoned floor, and a small room is popular with the dominoes and shove-ha'penny players; often, seats are pews. The dining room is no smoking. There are some curious stuffed 'Chinese muff dogs', about half the size of a chihuahua – said to be Tudor, though no one's sure, and a collection of military badges/shields. Well kept Adnams Bitter on handpump; shove-ha'penny, dominoes, fruit machine, and piped music. Bar food includes sandwiches, ploughman's or smoked mackerel (£2.30), scampi (£3.50), steaks (£6.50) and a daily special such as fresh local cod (when available) or beef and vegetable or cottage pies (£2.50); good breakfasts. Tables and chairs in the big garden which also has a children's play area. At weekends, the big car park is often given over to activities such as car boot sales, though the consequent street parking is not popular with locals. There's a caravan for rent. (*Recommended by Tim Barrow, Sue Demont, Derek Patey, Heather Sharland, Caroline and Colin, John Baker, Comus Elliott, Richard Gibbs, Nigel Gibbs, WTF*)

Adnams   Tenant Patrick Buckner   Real ale   Meals and snacks (11.45–1.30, 6.30–8.30)   Orford (0394) 450243   Children in dining room if eating   Live music some Sat evenings   Open 11–2.30, 6–11   Bedrooms; £16/£30

Kings Head 🅰

Front Street

Very good fresh fish in the friendly bar of this nice old pub might include breaded plaice or cod in batter (£3.50), wing of skate (£5.20), whole Orford crab or monkfish and lobster soufflé (£5.75), delicious home-made fish pie (£5.80), whole grilled lemon sole (£6.20), fillet of brill (£6.75), locally-caught lobster (from £7.95), and whole Dover sole (£8.95); also, home-made soup (£1.95), home-made pâté (£2.85), ploughman's (from £2.90), locally grown samphire (£3.85), chicken and pasta (£5.25) and evening steaks (from £8.50); good breakfasts often include grilled sole or poached whiting. Note though that they don't do sandwiches. Well kept Adnams Bitter, Broadside, Mild and winter Old and Tally Ho on handpump, and quite a few wines; fruit machine and trivia. There are cigarette cards, pictures and models of wild birds on the walls of the bar, carved black oak beams, one or two fine old wooden chairs, comfortable blue leatherette seats and cushioned wall benches grouped around the low tables, and an open fire. The pub is by the historical church and there are views from the well restored keep of the nearby 12th-century castle. *(Recommended by P Craddock, Katharine and David Cooke, J V, Heather Sharland, WHBM, C T and J M Laffan, Caroline and Colin, Richard Gibbs, Nigel Gibbs, Jane Buekett, Jamie Lyons, Ruth Harrison)*

Adnams Tenant Alistair Shaw Real ale Meals and snacks Restaurant (not Thurs, not Sun evening) Orford (0394) 450271 Children in restaurant Open 11–11; 11–2.30, 6–11 in winter (though still open all day Sat) Bedrooms; £22/£36

RAMSHOLT TM3141 Map 5
Ramsholt Arms

Village signposted from B1083; then take turning after the one to Ramsholt Church

Surrounded by quiet pine woods, this beautifully placed pub is quite isolated by an old barge quay on the River Deben which winds past to the sea. The uncarpeted riverside bar has been refurbished with comfortable banquettes and chairs, and there's a good winter log fire. The engine bar has a big picture window, some neatly nautical woodwork, tide tables and charts, and simple dark oak brocaded seats on the plain carpet. Well kept Adnams Bitter and guest beers on handpump, and several wines and malt whiskies; bar food includes sandwiches, ploughman's and evening burgers (from £3.25), dressed Cromer crab (£3.95), gammon (£4.95), and steaks (from £7.55). Sensibly placed darts, dominoes, fruit machine, and piped music. The riverside terrace bar is a splendid place on summer afternoons – excluding Sundays. *(Recommended by Gill and Doug Green, Gwen and Pete Andrews, P Craddock, Drs M and K Parier)*

Free house Licensees M E Lomas and N S Girling Real ale Meals and snacks Woodbridge (0394) 411229 Children in dining room Steep longish walk down from car park Open 11–11 Bedrooms; £25/£50

RATTLESDEN TL9758 Map 5
Brewers Arms

Signposted on minor roads W of Stowmarket, off B1115 via Buxhall or off A45 via Harleston

Tucked away in a quiet village, this 16th-century pub has been reopened after careful refurbishment. The small but lively public bar on the right has pool, cribbage, dominoes and fruit machine. On the left, the pleasantly simple beamed lounge bar has horsebrasses, and individually chosen pictures and bric-a-brac on the walls. It winds back through standing timbers to a partly flint-walled area that opens on to a garden edged with bourbon roses, with a boules pitch. Besides sandwiches, the good bar food, using local fresh ingredients, changes day by day, and might typically include mushroom and celery soup (£1.50), two or three starters such as hummus with pitta bread (£1.95), and half a dozen or so main dishes such as pasta (from £3.60), spicy nut loaf with watercress sauce (£4.20), Turkish lamb or a good fish pie (£5.20) and steak and Guinness pie (£5.45), with a few puddings (from £1.95). Well kept Greene King IPA, XX Mild and Abbot under light carbon dioxide blanket on handpump, decent wines (if you want a half bottle they may let you have a whole one and charge just for what you drink), a good selection of spirits; very welcoming atmosphere. *(Recommended by Simon Reynolds, Gethin Lewis)*

Greene King Tenant Ron Cole Real ale Meals and snacks (not last week June/1st week July) (0449) 736377 Well behaved children allowed Occasional folk music Open 12–2.30(3 Sat), 7–11

REDE   TL8055 Map 5

Plough 🏮

Village signposted off A143 Bury St Edmunds–Haverhill

One reader regularly does an 80-mile round trip to enjoy the peaceful, welcoming atmosphere and very good home-made food in this this pretty pink-washed, partly thatched pub. It's the dishes of the day which earn our food award, and on a typical day, they might be osso buco (£5.50), lovely Hungarian-style venison (£5.95), whole spring chicken stuffed with garlic and herbs (£6.50) and turbot with asparagus and hollandaise sauce (£6.95); puddings like excellent lemon crush pie, and lovely strawberry and raspberry mousses. They do a lot of game in season, such as roast partridge or pheasant casserole. There is a wide choice of other hot bar dishes, ploughman's and salads (outstanding beef and Cromer crab), and the little evening restaurant does things like moules au gratin, chicken stuffed with crab meat and swiss cheese, poached salmon, and steaks; attentive, caring service; decent wine. The simple and traditional cosy bar has decorative plates on a delft shelf and surrounding the solid fuel stove in its brick fireplace, copper measures and pewter tankards hanging from low black beams, and red plush button-back built-in wall banquettes; fruit machine, unobtrusive piped music. In front of the building are some picnic-table sets, with more in a sheltered cottage garden behind; it's a lovely quiet spot, with not much sound beyond the birds in the aviary (and the surrounding trees) or the burbling white doves in the dovecote. (*Recommended by Gwen and Peter Andrews, A D Atienza, N Holmes, Brenda Crossley, Mr and Mrs D E Milner, N S Holmes, Frank W Gadbois*)

Greene King   Lease: Brian Desborough   Meals and snacks (not Sun evenings) Evening restaurant (though they do Sun lunch)   Hawkedon (028 489) 208   Children in eating area of bar   Open 11–3, 7–11

SIBTON   TM3669 Map 5

White Horse

Halesworth Road; village signposted from A1120 Peasenhall–Yoxford

This pleasant and attractively laid out 16th-century inn has lots of tack, horsebrasses and plates on the walls, cushioned settles and little red plush armchairs, a big rug on the black and red tiled floor, and a woodburning stove. Five steps take you up past an ancient partly knocked-through timbered wall into a carpeted gallery with comfortable armed seats around rustic tables. Bar food includes sandwiches, soup (£1.20), ploughman's (£1.90), lasagne (£3.60), curry (£3.95), rump steak (£5.95), and a daily special. Well kept Adnams Bitter and Broadside on handpump; darts, shove-ha'penny, dominoes, cribbage and piped music. Out in the big garden are tables under cocktail parasols, a children's play area and space for caravans. (*Recommended by Peter Burton, Klaus and Elizabeth Leist; more reports please*)

Free house   Licensees Tony and Fay Waddingham   Real ale   Lunchtime meals and snacks (not Sun or Mon)   Restaurant   Peasenhall (072 879) 337   Children in eating area of bar and in restaurant   Open 11.30–2.30, 7–11; closed Mon lunchtime except bank hols   Bedrooms; £16S/£30S

SNAPE   TM3959 Map 5

Golden Key ★ 🏮

Priory Lane

At the serving end of the low-beamed stylish lounge here is a winter open fire, an old-fashioned settle curving around a couple of venerable stripped tables and a tiled floor, and at the other end there are stripped modern settles around heavy Habitat-style wooden tables on a Turkey carpet, and a solid fuel stove in the big fireplace; the cream walls are hung with pencil sketches of customers, a Henry Wilkinson spaniel and so forth. A brick-floored side room has sofas and more tables. Home-made food includes soup, open rolls (from £2.25), ploughman's (from £2.95), smoked haddock or spinach and mushroom quiche or steak and kidney pie (£4.95), and roast beef and Yorkshire pudding or steak, venison and mushroom pie (£5.50). Well kept Adnams Bitter and Broadside on handpump, with Old ale and Tally Ho in winter, and local cider and malt whiskies; pleasant staff. The small and sheltered pretty front garden has white tables and chairs on the gravel, and a lovely mass of summer flowers. (*Recommended by C C Cook, Gwen and Peter Andrews, Gordon Leighton, John Bowdler, J P Cinnamond, J A Gifford, Derek Patey, Jamie Lyons, Ruth Harrison, Derek and Sylvia Stephenson*)

Adnams   Tenants Max and Susie Kissick-Jones   Real ale   Meals and snacks   Snape (072 888) 510   Open 11–3, 6–11, with afternoon and evening extensions during Aldeburgh Festival

SOUTHWOLD   TM5076   Map 5

Crown ✏ 🛏

High Street

The elegant main bar in this well run place has a stripped curved high-backed settle and other dark varnished settles, a mix of kitchen pine tables and kitchen chairs on the blue patterned carpet, yellow walls with some tooth-and-egg plasterwork, large beams, a carefully restored and rather fine carved wooden fireplace, pretty fresh flowers, a big Act of Parliament clock, and a few bar stools; the small restaurant with its white cloths and pale cane chairs leads off. The bar food is really special and from a menu that changes daily, this might include starters like cream of leek and potato soup with croûtons (£1.75), excellent soft roes, roast quail on a black cherry sauce (£3.60), lovely fresh Cromer crab with lime mayonnaise (£4.50), wonderful mixed hors d'oeuvres (£5.25), main courses such as baked aubergine stuffed with vegetables (£5.25), good steamed wing of skate with pernod butter (£6.75), beef, wild boar and pheasant casserole (£6.80), and panfried loin of pork with apricot and cream (£7), and puddings like tia maria cheesecake with coffee sauce, crème brûlée or hot bread and butter pudding with cream (£2.75); cheeses are carefully chosen, and breakfasts are good. The 20 wines by the glass or bottle are kept perfectly on a cruover machine and chosen monthly and are always interesting, often with a common theme running through; they also have the full range of Adnams wines by the bottle (over 250) which you can get from the cash and carry by the mixed dozen round the corner; the Adnams Bitter, Broadside, winter Old and Tally Ho (Christmas only) on handpump are in superb condition – it's the nearby Adnams brewery's flagship; tea, coffee and herbal infusions; staff are friendly and helpful, even when under pressure. The smaller back oak-panelled locals' bar has more of a pubby atmosphere, red leatherette wall benches and a red carpet. Shove-ha'penny, dominoes and cribbage. There are some tables in a sunny sheltered corner outside. (*Recommended by D D Collins, N Patton, Tony and Lindsay Gray, Harry McCann, Brian and Fran Bannatyne-Scott, Richard Goss, Mrs M E Springer, John Molyneux, Shirley Pielou, Chris Vallely, Tim Barrow, Sue Demont, Gwen and Peter Andrews, Robert Gomme, SJC, Audrey and Brian Green, Alison and Tony Godfrey, Martin Richards, Patrick Young, T Nott, K A V Read*)

Adnams   Manager Anne Simpson   Real ale   Meals and snacks   No smoking restaurant   Southwold (0502) 722275   Children in eating area of bar   Open 11–3, 6–11; closed second week Jan   Bedrooms; £33B/£52B

STOKE BY NAYLAND   TL9836   Map 5

Angel ✏ 🛏

B1068 Sudbury–East Bergholt; also signposted via Nayland off A134 Colchester–Sudbury

Though this very popular dining pub is elegant and rather smart, the atmosphere is relaxed and friendly. To enjoy the very good, often enterprising bar food it's best to get there early or book a table in advance: gazpacho (£2), brie in filo pastry or curried lamb parcels (£3.75), Mediterranean-style salad or mushroom stuffed

snails (£3.95), a vegetarian dish such as cottage cheese and spinach tartlet (£4.95),
sauté of liver and bacon (£5.25), mixed fish hors d'oeuvres (£5.75), griddled fresh
fish like skate, plaice, mackerel or trout (from £6.75), medaillons of pork (£6.95),
and lovely puddings (from £2.45); vegetables are crisply cooked and full of
flavour. The main bar area has handsome Elizabethan beams, some stripped
brickwork and timbers, a relaxed mixture of furnishings including wing armchairs,
mahogany dining chairs, and pale library chairs which, like the tables, are lightly
stained to bring out the grain, local watercolours and older prints, attractive table
lamps, and a huge log fire. Round the corner is a little tiled-floor stand-and-chat
bar – with well kept Adnams Bitter, Greene King IPA and Abbot and Nethergate
Old Growler on handpump, decent house wines and good coffee. One room has a
low sofa and wing armchairs around its woodburning stove, and Victorian
paintings on the dark green walls. There are cast-iron seats and tables on a
sheltered terrace. (*Recommended by Vicki and Jeremy Elden, J S Evans, Paul S McPherson,
Mrs V Middlebrook, Gwen and Peter Andrews, Margaret Drazin, Hope Chenhalls, Wm H
Mecham*)

*Free house   Licensee Peter Smith   Real ale   Meals and snacks   Restaurant (not Sun
evening)   Colchester (0206) 263245   Open 11–2.30, 6–11; closed 25 and 26 Dec and
1 Jan   Bedrooms; £38.50B/£51.25B*

SUTTON   TM3046 Map 5
Plough

B1083

This tiled white house is popular with locals and servicemen from the nearby US
bases. The cosy little front room has button-back wall banquettes, and there's a
more spacious room round the side. Good bar food includes sandwiches (from £1),
cold buffet (from £1.60), ploughman's (from £3), steak and kidney pie or lasagne
(£3.75), gammon (£3.95), and lots of fresh local fish dishes. Courage Best, Tolly
Bitter and Mild and Websters Yorkshire on handpump; darts, pool, dominoes,
cribbage, fruit machine, video game, juke box in the public bar and piped music in
the restaurant. There are picnic-table sets in front and more by the fruit trees.
(*Recommended by David Cardy; more reports please*)

*Brent Walker   Tenant Mike Lomas   Real ale   Meals and snacks (not Sun evening)
Restaurant (not Sun evening)   Shottisham (0394) 411785   Children welcome   Open
11–2.30, 6.30–11*

TOSTOCK   TL9563 Map 5
Gardeners Arms

Village signposted from A45 and A1088

You're always sure of a warm welcome in this pretty sand-coloured pub – and
good, popular food, too. The lounge bar has low heavy black beams, lots of what
used to be called carving chairs (dining chairs with arms) around the black tables,
and a nice villagey atmosphere. The bar food includes tasty home-made soup
(£1.30), sandwiches (from £1.30; toasties from £2.10), ploughman's with
home-made granary rolls (from £2.60), home-made vegetarian pizza (£3.35),
salads (from £4.10), gammon and egg (£4.30), with supper dishes (bookings only)
like ratatouille with peanuts and cheese topping (£2.30), poached salmon steak
with home-made mayonnaise (£6.60) and sirloin steak (£7.95); daily specials such
as a fine vegetable curry, and puddings (£1.80). Very well kept Greene King IPA
and Abbot and Rayments on handpump. The lively tiled-floor public bar has darts,
pool, shove-ha'penny, dominoes, cribbage, juke box, and fruit machine. There's a
terrace and a sheltered lawn – a lovely place to sit at picnic-set tables among roses
and other flowers, and watch the local team playing steel quoits on the pitch.
(*Recommended by Brian Jones, Richard Fawcett, A D Atienza, Charles Bardswell, John Baker*)

*Greene King   Tenant Reg Ransome   Meals and snacks (not Mon or Tues evenings or
Sun lunchtime)   Restaurant; Sun opening 8–10pm   Beyton (0359) 70460   Children in
eating area of bar   Open 11–2.30, 7–11*

WALBERSWICK   TM4974   Map 5
Bell

Just off B1387

Not far from the harbour and beach, this busy local has a rambling oak-beamed bar with curved high-backed settles on well worn flagstones, tankards hanging from oars above the bar counter, tiles and flooring bricks, and a woodburning stove in the big fireplace; to one side is a more conventionally comfortable area decorated with local photographs; maybe two friendly bull-mastiffs. Bar food includes winter soup, sandwiches (from £1.20), ploughman's (from £2.70), good local fish with chips (£4), and summer salads (from £4, fresh Cromer crab £5). Well kept Adnams Bitter, Broadside and Extra on handpump. Darts, cribbage, dominoes, and fruit machine. A sizeable lawn with seats and tables among roses and other flowers is sheltered by a hedge from the worst of the sea winds. Most of the bedrooms look over the sea or the river. *(Recommended by Gwen and Peter Andrews, Mayur Shah, Anthony Barnes, John Townsend, A T Langton, SJC, Charles Bardswell, D J Milner)*

Adnams   Tenant Mark Stansall   Real ale   Meals and snacks (lunchtime)   Evening restaurant   Southwold (0502) 723109   Children in small room off bar   Occasional folk evenings   Open 11–3.30, 6–11   Bedrooms; £20(£25S)/£40(£50S)

WESTLETON   TM4469   Map 5
Crown 🏆 🛏️

On B1125 Blythburgh–Leiston

Some changes to this well kept village inn this year include a new kitchen and lavatories (with disabled and baby-changing facilities), and a new, separate reception area created from the old kitchen. The comfortably furnished bar has a growing collection of old photographs and postcards of Westleton, farm tools, pews, stools and settles, a couple of crab pots at one end, and a good open fire in winter; there's also a smart no smoking dining conservatory. Good bar food includes sandwiches (from £1.50), home-made soup (£1.90), ploughman's (from £2.85), salads (from £3.75), home-made quiche (£4.15), cauliflower and stilton pie (£4.35), tasty fresh-caught local fish such as cod, haddock, plaice and lemon sole (from £4.35), home-made steak and kidney pie (£4.75), good duck, venison, pork and port pie (£4.85), walnut and cashew paella (£5.75), sirloin steak (£7.45), puddings such as raspberry and apple or rum and raisin puddings (£2.15), a decent children's menu (from 90p), and Sunday roast beef (£5.45); good breakfasts; courteous staff. Well kept Adnams Bitter, Broadside and winter Old, Charles Wells Bombardier and Greene King Abbot on handpump, a decent, well-priced wine list, around 50 malt whiskies, James White cider, and coffee. Dominoes, shove-ha'penny, table skittles, cribbage, and piped music. There's an extensively landscaped garden (ramped for disabled people), and a terrace, barbecue area and outside bar, which is floodlit at night. Good walks nearby (the 'Westleton Walks') – perhaps over to our Lucky Dip entry at Eastbridge. Minsmere bird reserve is only a couple of miles away. *(Recommended by Gwen and Peter Andrews, Gill and Doug Green, Mrs Hilarie Taylor, John Bowdler, David Cardy, Richard Fawcett)*

Free house   Licensees Richard and Rosemary Price   Real ale   Meals and snacks Evening restaurant   Westleton (072 873) 777 or 273   Children allowed anywhere except bar   Open 11–2.30, 6–11; closed 25 and 26 Dec   Bedrooms; £43.50B/£59.95B; some have jacuzzis and 4-posters

WETHERINGSETT   TM1465   Map 5
Cat & Mouse

Pages Green; Wetheringsett signposted off A140 just S of Brockford; then turn right at Mickfield, Debenham signpost, left at Aspall, Debenham signpost, then left at cat and mouse picture; OS Sheet 155, map reference 145652

Wholly delightful, this rural retreat is a bit reminiscent of Old MacDonald; beyond the tables in its nice undeveloped garden is a paddock with several goats, two donkeys, hens, chickens, turkeys, maybe a couple of loquacious geese, and Toddles the Shetland pony. In summer there is a weekend barbecue and soft drinks bar outside. Inside doesn't let you down. The simple beamed tap bar with its tiled floor and green-tiled open fire opens into a big, comfortably haphazard sort of room, with a couple of easy chairs, a remarkable amount of bric-a-brac including lots of soft toys, books, a woodburning stove, a pool table at the far end, various cats (Ethel, Jasper, Woodforde, Herbert, Marmalade and Wadworth) and probably a dog or two (Millie, Holly or Alice). There's another smaller but similar room on the left. They keep a splendid range of real ales in top condition, ten on handpump and at least a couple more tapped from casks behind the bar. On our inspection visit the choice actually ran to Adnams Best and Broadside, Bass, Boddingtons, Brakspears PA, Charrington IPA, Fullers London Pride, Marstons Pedigree, Mitchells Mild and ESB, Nethergate and Old Growler, Theakstons Old Peculier, Tolly Mild, Woodfordes Wherry, Worthington BB. They also have a fine range of country wines, and four farm ciders such as Potmere, James White's Suffolk and Wilkins'; darts, shove-ha'penny, cribbage, dominoes, trivia, maybe radio. Food is restricted to chunky doorstep sandwiches and maybe other snacks, freshly made and good, such as Welsh rarebit; they have a notable range of crisps and so forth. What a friendly place. *(Recommended by John C Baker, David and Rebecca Killick, Gwen and Peter Andrews)*

Free house Licensees Roy and Anne Booth Real ale Lunchtime snacks Open 11–3, 5–11; all day summer

---

Lucky Dip

Besides the fully inspected pubs, you might like to try these Lucky Dips recommended to us and described by readers (if you do, please send us reports):

Aldeburgh [Crabbe St; TM4656], *Cross Keys*: Busy low-ceilinged 16th-century pub with a woodburner each side of the massive chimney dividing its two bar areas, plain furnishings, straightforward bar food, well kept Adnams ales (the full range), traditional bar games and fruit machine, tables on back gravel which opens on to promenade and beach; nr start GWG120; children may be allowed in to eat if it's wet *(G and M Stewart, LYM)*

☆ **Aldringham** [TM4461], *Parrot & Punchbowl*: Special virtue is wide choice of good wines by the glass, also good food and well kept Flowers IPA and Original in three-level beamed pub with steps down to food servery; piped music, dining-room meals Fri/weekend — when booking essential; garden with swings and tables under cocktail parasols; handy for Aldeburgh Festival *(J H Walker, C J Parsons, BB)*

Badingham [TM3068], *White Horse*: Old-fashioned, with neat bowling green, well kept Adnams, cheapish bar food inc summer lunchtime cold buffet, vegetarian and children's dishes as well as usual pub food; nice rambling garden *(LYM; reports on new licensee please)*

☆ **Bardwell** [The Green; TL9473], *Six Bells*: 16th-century free house with log fires, wide choice of food cooked to order inc fresh fish specialities (rather expensive), well kept Adnams and Tolly Original, extensive wine list, restaurant; games evening Sun, folk music weekly; garden with play area; newly converted bedrooms/flatlets *(Mr and Mrs Naworynsky, Charles Bardswell)*

☆ **Barton Mills** [A11; TL7173], *Bull*: Rambling partly candlelit bar with big fireplaces, beams, panelling, antique prints; well kept Adnams, Bass, Charrington IPA or Worthington BB and a guest beer, decent wines, reasonably priced standard bar food inc good cold pies and help-yourself salads usefully served noon-10 (not Sun) from smallish food counter down steps; generally friendly welcome and good service, piped music, grill room; children allowed in eating area, open all day; bedrooms (maybe due for some refurbishment) *(J P Cinnamond, George Atkinson, John Day, John Whitehead, Jack Taylor, Norman Hill, LYM; more reports please)*

Beck Row [A1101 W of Mildenhall; TL6977], *Smoke House*: Decent bar snacks in elegant surroundings with lots of good antiques; modern hotel/motel complex; keg beers *(Frank W Gadbois)*

☆ **Bildeston** [TL9949], *Crown*: Welcoming courteous service, well kept Adnams, Greene King IPA, Marstons Pedigree and Nethergate on handpump, decent food from sandwiches up, in comfortable well furnished lounge with open fire; busy restaurant; Tudor building, said to be haunted; pleasant garden; bedrooms *(Gwen and Peter Andrews, Simon Reynolds, E A George)*

☆ **Blaxhall** [off B1069 S of Snape; can be reached from A12 via Little Glemham; TM3657], *Ship*: Thriving local atmosphere in low-beamed traditionally furnished public bar with log fire, pool table etc; generous bar food in unassuming dining lounge, well kept Tolly and Marstons Pedigree on handpump, piped music; closed Mon lunchtime, no food Mon evening, except bank hols; children in eating area; two bedrooms *(Jane Buekett, LYM)*

☆ Blundeston [from B1074 follow Church Lane, right into Short Lane, then left; TM5197], *Plough*: Smartly modernised old country pub which was the home of Barkis the carrier in *David Copperfield*; bar food, real ales; handy for Jacobean Somerleyton Hall *(A T Langton, LYM)*

☆ Blythburgh [A12; TM4575], *White Hart*: Well appointed high-throughput open-plan dining pub in lovely position opp grand church, with spacious lawns looking down on the tidal marshes; lovely Elizabethan beams and woodwork, fine Stuart staircase, big open fires (one fireplace very ancient), well kept Adnams Bitter, Broadside and winter Old, decent wines; children in eating area and restaurant, open all day Fri/Sat *(M Morgan, J P Cinnamond, T Nott, Mrs P J Pearce, LYM)*

☆ Boxford [Broad St; TL9640], *Fleece*: Partly 15th-century pink-washed pub doing well under entertaining new licensees, back from the Far East; cosy panelled bar on right, more spacious and airy lounge bar with wonderful medieval fireplace, armchairs and some distinctive old seats among more conventional furnishings; unpretentious atmosphere, good home cooking, well kept Tolly *(Paul S McPherson, Prof S Barnett, LYM)*

☆ Bramfield [A144; TM4073], *Queens Head*: Handsomely refurbished high-beamed hall-house, clean and pleasant, doing well under new licensees; good freshly cooked food inc enterprising specials as well as standard dishes in bar and restaurant, Adnams Bitter, Old and Broadside on handpump, big log fire *(Nick Dowson, Alison Hayward, Barbara and Mike Williams, JV)*

Brampton [A145 S of Beccles; TM4382], *Dog*: Pleasant small pub — light, clean and not smoky; public bar with darts, lounge and family room; licensees warmly welcoming; food generous, good value and varied, Adnams, live music most Suns *(M Mouat)*

☆ Brandeston [back rd Wickham Market—Earl Soham; TM2460], *Queens Head*: Good value home-made food in spacious open-plan country pub, partly panelled and divided into bays, with brown leather banquettes, pews and other seats; well kept Adnams on handpump, helpful staff, family room, big neat garden with good play area; caravan/camp site behind; good value bedrooms *(Comus Elliott, Noel and Mo Tornbohm)*

Brantham [junction A137/B1080; TM1033], *Bull*: Pleasant pub with decent-sized reasonably priced helpings of good food *(Gill and Doug Green)*

Bures [TL9033], *Eight Bells*: Very pleasant

old-fashioned pub with good well served food in simple but attractive bar *(N S Holmes, Prof S Barnett)*; [Station Hill], *Swan*: Friendly 15th-century village local with unspoilt public bar, bar food inc some imaginative home-made dishes, log fires *(Richard Goss)*

☆ Bury St Edmunds [Whiting St; TL8564], *Masons Arms*: White weatherboarded pub, useful for filling and quickly served lunch in busy but comfortable and relaxing dining lounge which incorporates former next-door cottage, divided from it by standing timbers; well kept Greene King IPA, friendly service, wall decorated with interesting folk remedies, jazz Sun night *(Ian Phillips, Mrs P J Pearce, K A V Read, Wayne Brindle, Mark Blackburn)*

☆ Bury St Edmunds [Traverse, Abbeygate St], *Nutshell*: Included as one of the smallest pubs in the country — probably the smallest of all, inside; friendly and cosy, with well kept Greene King IPA and Abbot on handpump, odd bric-a-brac from old banknotes to skeleton foot and mummified cat; attractive corner facade *(R C Gandy, Nigel Gibbs, Nick and Alison Dowson)*

Bury St Edmunds [Angel Hill], *Angel*: Thriving country-town hotel with particularly well kept Adnams and good atmosphere in relaxed Regency bar, good too for coffee and tea; prices keep clientele extremely select; bedrooms comfortable *(John Baker, Peter Burton)*; [Crown St], *Dog & Partridge*: Very popular and atmospheric, well renovated by Greene King — lots of stripped stone and panelling, original windows, leading nicely into conservatory *(Wayne Brindle)*; [Station Hill], *Linden Tree*: Well renovated, with obligatory Greene King conservatory restaurant; very family-oriented, lovely garden; concentration on food, good but not cheap *(Wayne Brindle)*

Butley [TM3651], *Oyster*: Partly 15th-century, with several small rooms, informal furniture, friendly welcome, good service, Adnams and generous food inc good game pie; relaxed atmosphere, pleasant outside area *(John Whitehead)*

Buxhall [Mill Green; village signed off B1115 W of Stowmarket, then L at Rattlesden sign; TM0057], *Crown*: Tucked-away country pub with snug little bar and side room, games in separate public bar, restaurant; bar food, Adnams Broadside and Greene King IPA, open fires, jazz twice a month; children allowed if eating *(Gethin Lewis, LYM)*

☆ Chevington [TL7860], *Greyhound*: Wide choice of good authentic curries in big helpings as well as usual steaks, burgers and so forth; enormously welcoming woodburner, humorous landlord, helpful polite staff, comfortable surroundings, interesting memorabilia, particularly well kept Greene King IPA; restaurant, garden with good facilities for children *(John C Baker, Barbara and Mike Williams)*

☆ Clare [Callis St; TL7645], *Cock*: Friendly

pubby atmosphere, straightforward comfort in lower bar, some brass on walls and above fireplace, plainer public bar, evening restaurant down some steps; well kept Adnams, well served wholesome food inc Thurs fish and chips to eat there or take away, plus half-price pint while you wait; piped music, open all day Sat *(Gwen and Peter Andrews, Capt John W Behle, Frank Gadbois)*

Clare [Nethergate St], *Seafarer*: Tidily decorated L-shaped bar with wide choice of bar food, real ales inc Nethergate, good small wine list, tables in garden; bedrooms *(Nigel Gibbs, Paul S McPherson, LYM)*

Clopton Corner [Crown Hill; TM2254], *Crown*: Clean, comfortable bar and pleasant, friendly landlord; good value standard bar food well cooked and presented *(R D Norman)*

Coddenham [1 1/4 miles E of junction A45/A140; TM1354], *Dukes Head*: Simple stripped-pine village pub with seats in steep garden behind, and three bedrooms, which has been enjoyed for well kept Tolly, good helpings of interesting fresh food, welcoming service (and pin-table in public bar); but no recent reports *(News please)*

☆ Dalham [TL7261], *Affleck Arms*: Good atmosphere in friendly and attractive thatched village pub by stream with ducks, log fire in cosy low-beamed locals' bar, more comfortable and intimate rambling dining bar on right; straightforward food, some tables outside; nice village *(Frank W Gadbois, LYM)*

Debenham [High St; TM1763], *Red Lion*: Nice pub with very friendly staff, well kept Tolly, decent food; attractive lounge with fine 16th-century plaster ceilings *(David and Rebecca Killick, BB)*

Earl Soham [A1120 Yoxford—Stowmarket; TM2363], *Falcon*: Good value local inn with hearty breakfast cooked by very friendly landlord; Adnams and Wethereds; bedrooms simple but clean and cheap *(Andrew Morrissey, Comus Elliott)*

☆ East Bergholt [Burnt Oak — towards Flatford Mill; TM0734], *Kings Head*: Clean and attractive beamed lounge with comfortably chintzy sofas, interesting china, brasses, farm tools, photographs and so forth (besides the Constable prints you'd expect); good food at very reasonable prices inc interesting dishes, friendly quick service, well kept Tolly Bitter, Original and XXXX on handpump, decent coffee, piped classical music (but juke box in plain public bar); lots of room in pretty garden, masses of flowers inc flower-decked haywain *(Audrey and Brian Green, Bill and Jane Rees, Gwen and Peter Andrews, L G and D L Smith)*

East Bergholt, *Red Lion*: Wide choice of very generous food inc particularly good pies and ploughman's; pleasant atmosphere, well kept Ruddles and cider *(Mrs C M John)*

☆ Eastbridge [TM4566], *Eels Foot*: Simple local well placed for Minsmere bird reserve, Sizewell pebble beach and heathland walks; crisp varnish, red leatherette, bright carpet

or linoleum, well kept Adnams, hefty helpings of basic home-made bar food (no winter evening meals); tables on quiet front terrace, children in eating area; pretty village, at start of GWG122 *(S Corrigan, Gwen and Peter Andrews, LYM)*

Eriswell [TL7278], *Chequers*: Slightly smartened up but a genuine local with extremely welcoming and efficient service, wide choice of decent pub food *(The Shinkmans)*

☆ Erwarton [TM2134], *Queens Head*: Wide choice of good home-cooked food served cheerfully in unassuming 16th-century country pub with simple old-fashioned furnishings; well kept Tolly (inc Mild and XXXX), picture window with fine view over the fields to red-sail barges on the Stour estuary, modern restaurant; seats in orchard behind *(L W Baal, LYM)*

Exning [TL6165], *Wheat Sheaf*: Attractive, unusual and spacious old Greene King pub on quiet street with huge bar areas, friendly atmosphere and good-sized lawn with picnic-table sets and boules *(Frank W Gadbois)*; *White Horse*: Attractive corner pub with well kept Marstons Pedigree and Whitbreads-related real ales on handpump, friendly service, good daily specials; two dining rooms, tables in courtyard *(Frank W Gadbois)*

☆ Felixstowe Ferry [TM3337], *Ferry Boat*: Well kept Tolly real ales, decent simple bar food and good atmosphere in neatly kept 17th-century pub nr sand dunes, Martello Tower and harbour *(Comus Elliott, LYM)*

☆ Glemsford [Lion Rd (B1065 N); TL8247], *Black Lion*: Notable for wide choice of decidedly good food cooked by obliging young landlord's German wife, from ploughman's through smoked tuna or sturgeon to fondues, seafood mornay and locally reared beef; pleasant bar, Greene King IPA and Abbot, good service, small restaurant; bedrooms *(Paul S McPherson, Dr M G Kelvin, N S Holmes)*

Great Barton [TL8967], *Flying Fortress*: Well kept Adnams, Greene King and Mauldons, competent friendly service and good freshly prepared bar food (currently a Chinese chef) in former farmhouse HQ of USAF support group, on north edge of former Rougham airfield — the original for the film *Twelve O'Clock High* *(John C Baker)*

☆ Great Glemham [between A12 Wickham Mkt—Saxmundham and B1119 Saxmundham—Framlingham; TM3361], *Crown*: Unspoilt old pub with beamed lounge rambling around central chimney with big log fire on one side, woodburner on the other; friendly landlord, well kept Adnams and Greene King beers, decent wines and whiskies, welcoming service, limited choice of straightforward bar food, not Mon evening, maybe quiet piped music; seats on neat lawn; children allowed in eating area and restaurant; has been open all day Sat; comfortable, with big brass beds but steep stairs *(Gwen and Peter Andrews,*

Brian MacIvor, Dr R Fuller, B and J Derry, Caroline and Colin, Mr and Mrs C H Garnett, LYM)

Great Waldingfield [TL9143], *Swan*: Small country local, unchanged for years; scrubbed wooden tables, well kept Greene King ales, no food *(D A Parker)*

☆ **Grundisburgh** [TM2250], *Dog*: Elegant period pub, carefully extended, with pleasant staff, good bar food and good range of well kept beers *(L W Baal, E B Warrington)*

☆ **Hartest** [B1066 S of Bury; TL8352], *Crown*: Greene King pub, taken over 1991 by the Ashworths who had made the Plough at Coton (Cambs) a popular main entry for its food; neatly renovated, with good reasonably priced food, well kept real ale, house wine well above average; a tick for the good car park and lavatories, too *(E A George)*

☆ **Haughley** [Station Rd; by level crossing towards Old Newton; TM0262], *Railway*: Congenial country pub, friendly and relaxed, with plain traditional furnishings and old-fashioned popular good value food (not Mon pm); log fire, well kept Greene King IPA with Adnams and Woodfordes Wherry as regular guests, lots of labrador pictures; children in neat back room *(John C Baker, BB)*

☆ **Haughley** [centre], *Kings Arms*: Lots of dark tables in beamed lounge, log fire, wide choice of good value bar food from sandwiches to tender steaks, well kept Greene King ales, good service and atmosphere, maybe loud but well reproduced piped pop music; pool and other games in comfortable saloon; tables and play house on back lawn *(G R Prest, BB)*

Hepworth [A143 Bury—Diss; TL9874], *Duke of Marlborough*: Beer well kept by an enthusiast— Adnams, Ridleys, ever-changing guests; food too *(John C Baker)*

☆ **Hitcham** [The Street; B1115 Sudbury—Stowmarket; TL9851], *White Horse*: Good, friendly local with obliging service, well kept Greene King Abbot and outstanding food in bar and restaurant *(James and Hilary Barber, T Gondris)*

Holbrook [Ipswich Rd; TM1636], *Compasses*: Very welcoming, log fire, garden with children's play area, good value popular food in bar and restaurant, well kept Tolly *(Mr and Mrs A Albert)*

Hollesley [TM3544], *Fox*: Remote but welcoming village pub with comfortable bar, full of foxes (stuffed, ornaments or pictures); has been popular for wide choice of well presented good food, but no recent reports *(News please)*

☆ **Huntingfield** [TM3374], *Huntingfield Arms*: Good range of bar food, Adnams real ale, friendly staff, handsome sectioned-tree-trunk tables and matching hard chairs; restaurant; on attractive village green *(Jane Palmer, Nick Dowson, Alison Hayward)*

Ipswich [Woodbridge Rd; TM1744],

Golden Key: Greene King pub with real ales on handpump, live Irish folk music first Thurs of month, tables in garden behind *(Tina Hammond)*; [Nacton Rd], *Thresher*: Greene King pub with Mild and Bitter on handpump, famous for games such as quoits and shove-ha'penny; farm tools around lounge *(Tina Hammond)*; [Spring Rd], *Trafalgar*: Tetleys, Theakstons, a beer called Baldrick after the landlord's dog (brewed by Mauldons) and two guest beers; free pint for first person to find small ceramic frog hidden here each day *(Tina Hammond)*

☆ **Lavenham**, *Greyhound*: Refreshingly unspoilt and simple despite the tourists, with heavy-beamed narrow lounge, more austerely furnished public bar with polished tables and matching settles, and back dining area (decent food from soup to steaks); well kept Greene King IPA and Abbot on handpump, friendly staff; busy at weekends *(Gwen and Peter Andrews)*

☆ **Lavenham** [TL9149], *Swan*: Handsome and comfortable Elizabethan hotel, with in its heart a pubby little bar, popular among locals, with leather seats on its tiled floor, well kept Nethergate and Ruddles County, maybe a dog, and plenty of USAF memorabilia inc pilots' signatures on wall; spacious overflow into numerous communicating but cosy seating areas and alcoves with beams, timbers, armchairs and settees; bar food, afternoon teas and so forth, lavishly timbered restaurant, seats in well kept garden, friendly and helpful staff; a magnet for American and other tourists; children welcome; pleasant if pricey bedrooms *(John Evans, Maysie Thompson, LYM)*

Levington [Gun Hill; TM2338], *Ship*: This has been engagingly traditional, with several rooms inc a no smoking area, lots of sailing-barge and other nautical memorabilia, a view of the distant water from its front benches, well kept Tolly and interesting home-made food inc meats smoked here; but the tenant who has given it so much atmosphere left in 1991 — after we went to press, so we do not yet have any information on the new regime *(LYM; news please)*

☆ **Lidgate** [TL7257], *Star*: Attractive old tiled-floor building doubling as village post office, partly an old cottage and hardly smart, with welcoming landlord, wide choice of reasonably priced bar food inc home-made specials, magnificent log fire with winter Sun spit-roasts, indoor summer barbecue, Greene King IPA and Abbot under light pressure; lovely garden; children welcome *(Gwen and Peter Andrews, Anthony Johnson)*

☆ **Lindsey Tye** [TL9843], *Red Rose*: Pink-washed pub with plenty of tables in part-tiled part-carpeted bar, open fire, unobtrusive piped music, oak beams and exposed masonry, rows of hanging jugs, wide choice of reasonably priced food, well kept Adnams, Greene King IPA and Mauldons on handpump, good coffee,

friendly landlord *(Gwen and Peter Andrews)*
Little Bealings [Sandy Lane; TM2347],
Admirals Head: Very varied menu from
Italian chef — outstanding bread and butter
pudding *(L W Baal)*
Little Glemham [TM3458], *Lion*: Most
hospitable rural pub with good food *(Mr and
Mrs F E M Hardy)*
☆ **Long Melford** [TL8645], *Crown*: Friendly
service and good bar food from big filled
rolls and ploughman's through plenty of
vegetarian dishes full of seasonal vegetables
to gammon and so forth, in comfortable and
quietly kept small inn with pastel decor,
rugwork 'pictures', easy chairs and sofas as
well as smaller chairs and cushioned pews;
good choice of real ales such as Adnams,
Greene King IPA, Mauldons and
Nethergate, morning coffee, afternoon tea,
tables in walled garden with play area,
restaurant open all day Sun; children
welcome — nicely furnished back family
room; bedrooms *(John C Baker, Prof Barnett,
Gwen and Peter Andrews, LYM)*
Long Melford, *Bull*: Fine black and white
building, originally a medieval manorial hall
and an inn since 1580, in beautiful village;
handsome and interesting recently stripped
woodwork and timbering, large log fire,
old-fashioned and antique furnishings;
tables set out for bar food in spacious back
room, more in central courtyard, good real
ales; service can be leisurely; bedrooms
either entertainingly ancient or very
comfortably modern *(Barbara and Norman
Wells, JF, R M Savage, P Meacock, David
Cardy, John Evans, LYM)*; [Hall St], *George
& Dragon*: True village local, well
patronised, with friendly effective service
and decent basic food inc chips in enormous
quantity; well kept beer, good wines, regular
live music from blues to folk; garden with
summer barbecues; bedrooms simple and
comfortable *(Richard Goss, J S Evans)*
Lound [Yarmouth Rd; TM5099], *Village
Maid*: Imaginative menu with lots of game
in season, fresh fish, and lovely puddings;
overlooks village pond; wonderful licensees
(Mr and Mrs D E Milner)
Lowestoft [151 High St; TM5492], *Crown*:
Attractive pub brewing its own good Scotts
beers, good honest food inc fresh fish *(N A
Gammon)*; [29 St Peters St], *Triangle*:
Friendly atmosphere, darts and pool, well
kept Rayments and Woodfordes NOG,
good choice of strong lagers *(N A Gammon)*
Market Weston [TL9877], *Mill*:
Comfortable and friendly, well prepared
traditional bar food with some original
dishes, well kept real ale inc Nethergate, the
landlord's favourite here *(John C Baker)*
☆ **Martlesham** [off A12
Woodbridge—Ipswich; TM2547], *Black
Tiles*: Well kept and spacious roadhouse
with quickly served fairly priced home-made
food from lots of sandwiches, soup or a
choice of ploughman's through steak and
kidney pie and so forth to steaks, well kept
Adnams Bitter and Broadside, garden tables;
children allowed in restaurant; has been

open all day *(Derek Patey, LYM)*
☆ **Mendham** [TM2782], *Sir Alfred Munnings*:
Cheery atmosphere in big open-plan bar of
inn under promising new regime, with well
kept Adnams, Charles Wells Bombardier
and a weekly summer guest beer, bar food
inc good value ploughman's and fresh
mackerel served by neat waitresses,
unobtrusive piped music, restaurant;
children welcome, bedrooms, swimming
pool for residents *(LYM)*
☆ **Mildenhall** [Main St; TL7174], *Bell*: Classy
old inn with good choice of good bar food in
pleasant and spacious open-plan bar, lounge
and attractive dining room; quick friendly
service, Adnams IPA and Greene King on
handpump, old photographs; bedrooms
(Frank W Gadbois)
Mildenhall [Main St], *White Hart*: Good
choice of bar meals in back carvery; keg
beers; bedrooms *(Frank W Gadbois)*
☆ **Newmarket** [High St; TL6463], *Rutland
Arms*: Georgian hotel with well spaced
tables in elegant and gracious two-room bar,
good mix of customers, well kept Adnams
Bitter on handpump, cheerfully pubby
atmosphere; tucked-away fruit machine;
good service, restaurant; handy for National
Museum of Horseracing; bedrooms good
value — the ones overlooking the lovely
cobbled yard are very quiet *(Gwen and Peter
Andrews)*
☆ **Newmarket** [High St], *White Hart*:
Comfortable central hotel with racing
pictures and open fire in spacious lounge,
bar food not cheap but reliable, well kept
Tolly, friendly staff, solid back cocktail bar,
restaurant; children welcome; bedrooms
(LYM)
Orford [TM4250], *Froize*: In old house with
woodburning stove, games room,
straightforward bar food, tables in garden;
pony-trekking, room for campers and
caravans; bedrooms *(Richard Gibbs)*
☆ **Pakenham** [signed off A1088 and A143 S of
Norwich; TL9267], *Fox*: Village pub doing
well under new regime, with good food inc
lots of vegetarian dishes, fresh fish and fine
chilli, relaxed atmosphere, well kept Greene
King XX, IPA and Abbot, cheerful quick
service; beamed lounge with attractive
Skegness advertising posters and so forth,
flame-effect gas stove, games room; small
neat dining room (listed former reading
room); tables in streamside garden with
ducks; children now welcome *(John C Baker,
Mr and Mrs J Barnes, Charles Bardswell, M J
Brooks, BB)*
Red Lodge [A11 Newmarket—Thetford;
TL6970], *Red Lodge*: Comfortable stone
pub with Greene King ales and reasonably
priced lunchtime and evening meals *(Nigel
Gibbs)*
☆ **Risby** [a mile off A45 at Risby turnoff;
TL7966], *White Horse*: Free house tastefully
renovated under new regime, with personal
effects inc photographs and antiques;
beautiful dining room, friendly staff,
Mauldons, Tetleys and a guest real ale on
handpump; good food; very useful break

from A45 *(Frank W Gadbois, LYM)*

☆ **Saxtead Green** [B1119, opp windmill; TM2665], *Volunteer*: Light and airy lounge bar with reliable and popular bar food (they make their own pasties), Tolly ales, spotless housekeeping; games in simpler public bar, plenty of tables on pretty back terrace with small rockery pool; lovely setting, across green from windmill; children allowed in corner bar *(Nick Dowson, Alison Hayward, LYM)*

☆ **Snape** [The Maltings; TM3959], *Plough & Sail*: Right by Snape Maltings so can get very full when there are concerts; but carefully modernised, with deliberately rather spartan tiled-floor decor in two areas off narrow serving part, with alcoves, coveted fireside settles, sturdy tables and pale country-kitchen chairs, small restaurant leading off; well kept Adnams Bitter and Old, interesting and individual home-cooked bar food changing twice a day, welcoming efficient staff, lively atmosphere, tables outside; the Maltings also has quite an elaborate crafts/plants/kitchenware complex *(Heather Sharland, Derek and Sylvia Stephenson, John C Baker, BB)*

☆ **Snape** [B1069], *Crown*: Cheery pub, pleasant and relaxed, with civilised customers, well kept Adnams, no piped music, good food running up to pheasant and lobster; front room supposed to be the model for the Boar in Britten's *Peter Grimes*; tables in sizeable garden; bedrooms well equipped *(John Whitehead, LYM)*

☆ **Southwold** [Blackshore Quay; from A1095, right at Kings Head — pass golf course and water tower; TM5076], *Harbour*: Friendly if somewhat rough-and-ready waterside pub among the small black fish-sheds; tiny low-beamed front bar, upper back bar with lots of nautical bric-a-brac — even ship-to-shore telephone and wind speed indicator; fish and chips served in newspaper, other basic bar food (not Tues or Thurs evening, cold things only Sun lunchtime; at peak holiday times the system can tend to seize up for a while — or they may opt out of food altogether); well kept Adnams Bitter and Broadside, darts, tables outside with play area and animals — can be a bit untidy out here, and the hens and gulls leave their mark *(D J and K Cooke, Mr and Mrs F E M Hardy, LYM)*

☆ **Southwold** [42 East St], *Lord Nelson*: Very low-ceilinged wood-panelled tiled-floor local, small and well placed nr sea — so can get crowded, but stays cheerful and pleasant, with well kept Adnams Mild, Bitter, Broadside and Old on handpump, good lunchtime food, sheltered back garden *(Mr and Mrs P A Jones, Mr and Mrs F E M Hardy, Caroline and Colin, Robert Gomme, BB)*

☆ **Southwold** [Market Pl], *Swan*: Comfortable back hotel bar with leather banquettes and good prints, chintzy and airy calm front lounge, short daily choice of good bar food, efficient uniformed service, well kept Adnams and Broadside on handpump and the full range of their bottled beers, also

decent wines and malt whiskies; ambitious restaurant; well renovated bedrooms inc garden rooms where (by arrangement) dogs can stay too *(Mr and Mrs P A Jones, T Nott, LYM)*

☆ **Southwold**, *Kings Head*: Clean, efficient, comfortably modernised and relatively spacious open-plan pub, lots of maroon and pink plush, with good food, especially seafood, well kept Adnams, decent house wines and efficient, friendly staff; children welcome — comfortable family/games room with well lit pool table; decent bedrooms in house owned by pub across road *(Gordon Theaker, L G and D L Smith, W J Wonham, John and Bridget Dean, BB)*

☆ **Southwold** [7 East Green], *Sole Bay*: Cheerful and delightfully relaxed backstreet Victorian local, just across rd from the brewery (and the lighthouse sharing its name), moments from the sea; low-priced simple lunchtime food esp local sprats (not Sun) and particularly well kept Adnams, tables on side terrace and in yard *(Mr and Mrs P A Jones, Anthony Barnes, LYM)*

☆ **Southwold** [South Green], *Red Lion*: Well kept Adnams ales, good range of snacks and salads (seafood recommended) in pale-panelled bar a bit away from the crowds, with fine views over green from big windows, ship pictures, brassware and copper, elm-slab barrel tables; friendly local atmosphere, welcoming family room and summer buffet room, tables outside; right by the Adnams retail shop; bedrooms *(Gwen and Peter Andrews, Robert Gomme, BB)*

Spexhall [Stone St; TM3780], *Huntsman & Hounds*: Very pleasant rural spot; splendid food *(Mr and Mrs F E M Hardy)*

☆ **Sproughton** [Old Hadleigh Rd — from A45 Claydon interchange go through village then left down unmarked dead end; TM1244], *Beagle*: Well kept Adnams, Greene King IPA and Abbot and Mauldons in tastefully if plushly converted row of timber-framed cottages with back conservatory; popular at lunchtime for good genuine food *(John C Baker)*

☆ **Stoke by Nayland** [TL9836], *Crown*: Spacious and well kept series of comfortably modernised room areas, very wide choice of good value popular bar food inc children's dishes in spotless flock-wallpaper dining lounge, well kept Tolly on handpump, restaurant (open through Sun afternoon); lovely garden with good play area, big car park; bedrooms *(Jane Palmer, LYM)*

Stoke by Nayland [TL9836], *Black Horse*: Village local with generous, interesting and reasonably priced food cooked to order, inc fresh fish; good choice of beers inc Adnams and guests *(P and J McComb)*

Stowmarket [Station Rd, by church; TM0458], *Queens Head*: Quiet and clean with pleasant staff and reasonably priced bar food, inc daily specials; nr E Anglian Museum of Rural Life *(Margaret and Trevor Errington)*

Stradbroke [Wilby Rd; TM2374], *Ivy House*: Friendly and hospitable, wide choice of good food inc home-made dishes, interesting vegetarian ones and Sun roast lunch; several real ales; bedrooms *(Miss M Foulger, Miss J Gilbey)*

Stradishall [A143; TL7452], *Cherry Tree*: Small country pub notable for unusually spacious informal garden, with very well spaced tables and sizeable pond — friendly ducks and ducklings, moorhens, a side hen run; two small low-beamed bars have big fireplaces and traditional furniture; bar food, Greene King beers under pressure *(BB)*

Sudbury [Acton Sq; TL8741], *Waggon & Horses*: Town-centre local with splendid, traditional atmosphere; comfortable old chairs, good snacks, lively company; Greene King beers, traditional games *(Richard Goss)*

☆ **Thorndon** [off A140 or B1077, S of Eye; TM1469], *Black Horse*: Dark beams, standing timbers, stripped brick and ancient flooring tiles in relaxed and individual pub with lots of interest, good range of attractively priced bar food, well kept Adnams Broadside, Courage Best and Wadworths 6X, Sun lunch in stables restaurant, tables on spacious lawn with country views; well behaved children in eating areas *(Nick Dowson, Alison Hayward, LYM)*

☆ **Thornham Magna** [Finningham Rd; off A140 S of Diss; TM1070], *Four Horseshoes*: Bustling and spacious dining pub spreading through attractive very low-beamed thatched country inn; food has been very popular indeed with readers, but the owners (who supplied much of their needs from their own butcher's and greengrocer's shop, and their market garden) sold towards the end of 1990, and we are waiting to see how things settle down with the new regime; several real ales, tables on sheltered terrace and lawn, a welcome for children, restaurant, occasional live entertainment and comfortable good value bedrooms *(LYM)*

Thurston [Barrells Rd; village signed from A1108 N of Norton, then turn left by S-bend by Bayer Experimental Farm, then first right — OS Sheet 155, map reference 939651; TL9365], *Black Fox*: Landlord here is to real ale what a top sommelier is to wine — particularly well kept Adnams, Greene King IPA and Abbot, Mauldons and at least two guest beers a week tapped from barrels in back room and served in gently redecorated parlour; thriving atmosphere, open fire, darts room, frequent sing-songs *(John C Baker)*

Tunstall [TM3555], *Green Man*: Good value food and well kept Tolly in comfortable and airily modern village inn; pool, juke box and fruit machine in smaller bar; bedrooms *(Chris Fluck, BB)*

Ufford [Lower Street; TM2953], *White Lion*: Well kept Tolly and good reasonably priced home-cooked food in basic, clean, small and friendly pub; open central fireplace, jazz Thurs *(Dr M Bailey)*

☆ **Wenhaston** [TM4276], *Star*: Good reasonably priced food, well kept Adnams, freshly squeezed orange juice and kindly landlord in small village local with suntrap lounge, games in public bar, tables on sizeable lawn *(Rob Harrison, LYM)*

West Row [TL6775], *Judes Ferry*: Worth knowing for riverside position, with barbecue in big garden, tables by water *(Frank Gadbois)*

☆ **Westleton** [TM4469], *White Horse*: Friendly pub with well kept Adnams, good well presented reasonably priced bar food inc a children's menu, garden with climbing frame; has been open all day at least in summer, handy for Minsmere RSPB reserve *(Gill and Doug Green)*

☆ **Whepstead** [Rede Rd; off B1066 S of Bury; TL8358], *White Horse*: Well restored country pub with roaring log fire in beamed Turkey-carpeted lounge and eating area, welcoming atmosphere, well kept Greene King IPA, good range of unusual bar food inc specialities cooked by landlord's Malaysian wife; Sun free nibbles on bar; pool in quarry-tiled public bar, picnic-table sets in side orchard *(E B Warrington, John Baker, BB)*

☆ **Woodbridge** [Market Sq; TM2749], *Kings Head*: Good atmosphere in spacious bar with blazing inglenook log fire, scrubbed hardwood tables and chairs, well kept Tolly on handpump, good basic bar food, no loud music *(Chris Fluck, Robert Gomme)*

Woodbridge [Melton Rd N; TM2749], *Coach & Horses*: Was Chef and Brewer, now under new licensees; trying hard — friendly service, quite varied menu inc good set meals with good fresh veg; good choice of beers *(Bill and Wendy Burge)*; [off Market Sq], *Olde Bell & Steelyard*: Unusual old-world pub with steelyard still overhanging the street; more straightforward inside, but has well kept Greene King IPA and Abbot on handpump *(Chris Fluck)*; [Seckford St], *Seckford Arms*: Inside various bric-a-brac inc Mexican carvings, well kept beer inc Crouch Vale Paul's Preference specially brewed for landlord's son — who cooks good food inc real curries, proper tortillas and genuine chilli sauce; children welcome in garden lounge; very promising *(John Baker)*

Woolpit [The Street; TL9762], *Bull*: Sensibly refurbished without being spoilt; the restaurant bar's recently been done up a lot, with good cooking by new young couple; bedrooms *(Charles Bardswell)*

Yoxford [OS Sheet 156, map reference 395690; TM3968], *Griffin*: Pleasant, friendly pub with 13th-century origins — landlady happy to talk about the village over a cheap cup of coffee *(Mrs P J Pearce)*

Surrey

This is the most expensive area in the country, outside London: drinks prices run at around 20p more each than the national average, and on average a main dish such as steak and kidney pie now costs £4.50 in a Surrey pub – half as much again as the £3 target we set in our national search for bargain pub food. So it's a relief to find at least one really good pub here – the friendly Cricketers in Dorking – serving substantial main dishes for £3 or less (and cheap sandwiches, too). If one pub can do it, why not more? Allowing for the area's generally high price levels, we can pick out a good few other pubs here that are well worth knowing for food at sensible prices: the Cricketers on its pretty green near Cobham (back in these pages after a break), the busy and cheerful Woolpack at Elstead, the Woodcock at Felbridge with its intriguing mix of spartan and sumptuous, the nice little White Horse at Hascombe, the unpretentious King William IV at Mickleham (notable vegetarian specialities), the Fox Revived at Norwood Hill (hearty helpings), the friendly old Cock in its pretty position at Headley (another new entry), the attractive Kings Head in Shepperton, and the cheerful and busy Fox & Hounds in Walton on the Hill. Other good pubs to note particularly here include two with remarkably good choices of wine by the glass, the Plough at Blackbrook (it also makes its own country wines) and the stylish Squirrel at Hurtmore (a new entry, and a comfortable place to stay); also, the charmingly unspoilt King William IV at Albury Heath, the neatly kept Donkey with its pretty garden at Charleshill, the White Bear at Fickleshole and White Lion at Warlingham (both places bursting with far more character than you'd expect for the outer fringes of London's suburbs), the Punch Bowl near Ockley (friendly new young licensees), the very individual Skimmington Castle on Reigate Heath, the carefully modernised but palpably ancient White Horse at Shere, the dark and cosy Three Horseshoes at Thursley, and the unspoilt Scarlett Arms at Walliswood, which earns a star award this year. In the Lucky Dip section at the end of the chapter, pubs currently on the up-and-up include the Dukes Head at Beare Green, Harrow at Charlton, Thurlow Arms at Cox Green, Stag at Eashing, Hare & Hounds in Lingfield, Black Swan at Martyrs Green and Cricketers Arms in Ockley. We'd also make special note of the Abinger Hatch on Abinger Common, Blue Bell at Batts Corner, William IV just outside Bletchingley, Queens Head at East Clandon, Plough at Effingham (an almost classically reliable Dip), Parrot at Forest Green, Inn on the Lake in Godalming, Olde Six Bells in Horley, Seven Stars (and possibly Plough) at Leigh, Onslow Arms at West Clandon, Lincoln Arms in Weybridge, Half Moon at Windlesham and Wotton Hatch at Wotton; each of these (most of them inspected by us) is very rewarding in its own particular way.

ALBURY HEATH   TQ0646 Map 3

King William IV

Little London; off A25 Guildford–Dorking to Albury, first left to Albury Heath; go over railway and take first left to Peaslake, then right towards Farley Green; OS Sheet 187, map reference 065468

In the neat little garden in front of this unspoilt family-run pub are some picnic-table sets under umbrellas and old cast-iron garden furniture. Inside, three warmly friendly, chatty small rooms are linked together. The main bar has a big chunky elm table with a long pew and a couple of stools, beams in the low ochre ceiling, an enormous basket of dried flowers in the big brick fireplace (with a log fire in winter), several horse bits, traps and old saws, and an ancient baboon dressed in a jacket and hat in one corner; a tiny room leading off one end has an L-shaped elbow rest with a couple of stools in front of it, a table and settle, and darts, and up a few steps at the other end of the main bar is a simple dining room with gingham-clothed tables, two glass cases with stuffed owls and a piano. Good home-made food includes sandwiches (from £1.40), soups like ham and lentil or stilton and celery (£1.60), generous ploughman's (from £3), home-cooked ham, egg and chips (£3.40), pot-roast pigeon (£3.80), steak and kidney pie (£4), beef and venison pie (£4.20), roast pheasant (£4.50); and lovely puddings like treacle or butterscotch tart, chocolate roulade or crumbles (£1.85); Sunday roast lunch; a fresh seafood evening on the first Saturday of the month, and a whole spit-roasted lamb or pig on the third Saturday of the month. Well kept Benskins, Courage Best, Greene King Abbot, Sam Smiths OB and Tetleys on handpump; farmhouse cider; the friendly alsatian is called Major. *(Recommended by Phil and Sally Gorton, Mayur Shah, Ian and Liz Phillips, Graham Pettener, J P Berryman)*

Free house   Licensees Mike and Helen Davids   Real ale   Snacks (not Sun lunchtime) and Meals (12–2.30, 7–10)   Restaurant (Weds-Sat evenings)   (048641) 2685 Children welcome   Open 11–3, 5.30–11

BETCHWORTH   TQ2049 Map 3

Dolphin

The Street; A25 W of Reigate, village signposted on left after 2 1/2 miles, at Buckland

Relaxed and friendly, this pleasant village pub still has log fires in each bar, and gas lighting, and under the new regime seems to be attracting a better than ever mixture of locals and visitors. The front room of this listed building has kitchen chairs and plain tables on the 400-year-old scrubbed flagstones, and the carpeted back saloon bar is black-panelled with robust old-fashioned elm or oak tables and a sonorous longcase clock. An increased range of good bar food includes home-made soup (£1.45), sandwiches (from £1.50), ploughman's (from £2.45), whitebait (£2.50), a choice of salads or quiche with baked potato (from £3.65), vegetable lasagne (£4.05), steak and kidney pie (£4.60), daily specials and puddings like apple pie, pancakes or fudge cake (from £1.65). Well kept Youngs on handpump; efficient service; darts and fruit machine. There are some seats in the small laurel-shaded front courtyard and picnic-table sets on a lawn by the car park, opposite the church. *(Recommended by John Pettit, R C Vincent, Doreen and Reg Tickner, Michael Thomson, TBB, D J Penny, Richard Houghton, D Swift)*

Youngs   Managers George and Rose Campbell   Real ale   Meals and snacks (till 10) Betchworth (073 784) 2288   Open 11–3, 5.30–11

BLACKBROOK   TQ1846 Map 3

Plough ⊘

On byroad E of A24, parallel to it, between Dorking and Newdigate, just N of the turn E to Leigh

Notably well kept King & Barnes Sussex, Broadwood, Festive and Old Ale (in winter) are kept on handpump in this popular white-fronted pub, and there are 14 wines by the glass, including a wine of the month, vintage port by the glass, and good country wines (the Damson is recommended). Excellent bar food in generous helpings is also quite a draw: imaginative specials such as chicken and prawn jambalaya, cockles, mussels and prawns in calvados sauce, chicken and asparagus with mushroom and white wine sauce or stuffed poussin; permanent menu includes ploughman's (from £2.65), basket meals like Cumberland sausage or seafood platter (from £2.85), salads (from £3.65, fresh prawn £6.25), fillet of plaice or ham steak (£4.25), ratatouille niçoise (£4.45), lasagne (£4.65), prawn curry (£5.25) and steaks (£8.75); pleasant, friendly staff. Part of the airy saloon bar is no-smoking and there are fresh flowers on the tables, with more on the sills of the large windows (that look out onto woods and open fields). Down some steps, the public bar has brass-topped treadle tables, quite a formidable collection of ties as well as old saws on the ceiling, bottles, flat irons, piped music; Tess the black labrador puts in an appearance after 10pm. You can sit outside on the grass or a small terrace at the back (which in summer is full of tubs of flowers), or at the front under the pretty hanging baskets; there's a sizeable garden. Just south is a good stretch of attractive oakwood with plenty of paths – and a big pond. *(Recommended by Mrs V Middlebrook, D S and Mrs T M Beeson, John Pettit, Wendy McCaw, Peter Griffiths, D J Penny, TOH, Trevor and Helen Dayneswood, DWAJ, Jenny and Brian Seller, Carol and Mike Muston, Heather Sharland, Klaus and Elizabeth Leist)*

King & Barnes   Tenant Robin Squire   Real ale   Meals and snacks (not Mon evening)   Dorking (0306) 88603   Only children over 14 in bar (must be eating) Open 11–2.30, 6–11(winter 10.30 if weather poor); closed 25, 26 Dec and 1 Jan

CHARLESHILL   SU8944 Map 2

Donkey

On B3001 Milford–Farnham; as soon as you see pub sign, turn left

The two little bars in this early 18th-century cottage are both neatly kept. The saloon is bright and cheerful with prettily-cushioned built-in wall benches and wheelback chairs, and there are lots of polished stirrups, bits, lamps, watering cans, scales and so forth. The lounge bar has similar seating as well as a lovely old high-backed settle and a couple of unusual three-legged chairs, lots of highly polished horsebrasses, a longcase clock, some powder pouches, swords on the walls and beams, and maybe Fred, the engaging west highland white. Popular home-made bar food includes sandwiches (from £1.50, toasted prawn and cheese £2.20), soup (£1.50), filled baked potatoes (winter only, from £2.20), ploughman's (£2.75), steak and kidney or chicken and ham pie (£4.50), and specials like a platter of salamis and sausages (£3.75), spiced beef pasta bake (£4.50), vegetarian broccoli, walnut and mushroom crumble or leek and stilton tart; delicious home-made puddings such as lemon and syrup tart or gooseberry pie (£1.80); friendly service. Well kept Morlands Old Masters and Original on handpump; country wines; piped music. A no-smoking conservatory with blond wheelback chairs and stripped tables, fairy lights and some plants, has sliding doors into the garden. This is very pretty, with bright flowerbeds, white garden furniture, a tiny pond, an aviary with cockatiels, a big fairy-lit fir tree, and a children's play area with swings, slide and roundabout. *(Recommended by P A Barfield, Lyn and Bill Capper, Carol and Mike Muston; more reports please)*

Morlands   Tenant John Foskett   Real ale   Meals and snacks (not Sun evening) Elstead (0252) 702124   Children in conservatory lunchtimes   Open 11–2.30, 6–11

CHIDDINGFOLD   SU9635 Map 2

Swan

Petworth Road (A283 S)

The walls in the comfortable and spacious bar of this tile-hung pub are hung with a good many hunting, shooting and fishing pictures and objects, and there are good winter log fires, as well as darts, bar billiards, shove-ha'penny, cribbage, dominoes, fruit machine and piped music. Friary Meux, Ind Coope Burton and King &

Barnes Susex on handpump. Bar food includes sandwiches (from £1.20), soup (£1.50), filled baked potatoes or omelettes (from £1.95), herby grilled sardines (£3.25), ploughman's (from £3.50), good steak and kidney pie (£4.25), tasty steaks (from £6.50) and puddings (from £1.50). Some seats outside. *(Recommended by Graham Pettener, Adrian Pitts; more reports please)*

Ind Coope (Allied)   Manager Paul Edwards   Real ale   Meals and snacks (till 10) Restaurant   Wormley (0428) 682073   Children welcome   Open 11–3, 6–11

CHIPSTEAD   TQ2757   Map 3
Well House

3 miles from M25, junction 8; A217 towards Banstead, turn right at second roundabout following Mugswell, Chipstead signpost; can also be reached from A23 just W of Coulsdon

This cottagey-looking country pub does indeed have a well – it's on the sheltered back terrace (proceeds to charity); the garden, lively with birds and colourful with flowers in summer, has an old yew coppice with taller trees behind. Inside, the central room (mainly used for standing) has a few tables and wheelback chairs, big low 14th-century beams, and inglenook fireplaces; a quieter room has many more tables and tapestried seats, and there are darts in the side room. Bar food includes sandwiches, ploughman's (£2.50), fish, chips and peas (£3.95), home-made cheese and asparagus quiche or steak pie (£4.25). Bass and Charrington IPA and guests like Batemans Victory, Fullers ESB or Marstons Pedigree on handpump; friendly service; darts, cribbage, dominoes and fruit machine. *(Recommended by D J Jeffery, Graham Pettener, Kristine and Peter Guest, R Bennett, C P Scott-Malden, E G Parish)*

Charringtons (Bass)   Tenant W G Hummerston   Real ale   Lunchtime meals and snacks (not Sun)   (0737) 832233   Children in eating area   Open 10.30–2.30, 5.30(6 Sat)–11

COBHAM   TQ1060   Map 3
Cricketers

Downside Common; from A245 on Byfleet side of Cobham follow Downside signpost into Downside Bridge Rd, follow road into its right fork – away from Cobham Park – at second turn after bridge, then take next left turn into the pub's own lane

Plenty of tables and chairs outside this busy country pub look over the broad village green, and the garden is neat and charming, with standard roses, dahlias and other bedding plants, urns and hanging baskets. There are simple, traditional furnishings, some very old standing timbers, beams (a few are so low they have crash-pads on them), places where you can see the wide oak ceiling boards and ancient plastering lathes, horsebrasses and big brass platters on the walls, and a good winter log fire. Good bar food includes sandwiches, home-made quiche (£3.50), risotto or vegetable pasta (£3.95), steak and kidney pie (£4.15), fresh poached trout (£4.75) and fresh seafood salad (£4.95). Well kept Ruddles Best and County, and Websters Yorkshire on handpump; friendly service; dogs welcome. *(Recommended by C P Scott-Malden, TBB, Adrian Zambardino, Debbie Chaplin, John Pettit, Mr and Mrs G Turner, Richard Carpenter)*

Watneys (Courage)   Lease: Brian Luxford   Real ale   Meals and snacks (till 10) Restaurant (not Sun evening)   Cobham (0932) 62105   Children in stable bar   Open 11–2.30, 6–11

COLDHARBOUR   TQ1543   Map 3
Plough

Village signposted in the network of small roads around Abinger and Leith Hill, off A24 and A29

This pretty black-shuttered white house keeps a good range of well kept real ales on handpump – typically Adnams Broadside, Badger Best, Batemans Mild and XB,

Chudleys Local Line, Gibbs Mew Bishops Tipple, Ringwood Old Thumper and Theakstons Old Peculier; country wines and farmhouse cider. The two bars have stripped light beams and timbering in the warm-coloured dark ochre walls, with quite unusual little chairs around the tables in the snug red-carpeted room on the left, and little decorative plates on the walls and a big open fire in the one on the right – which leads through to the restaurant. Decent home-made bar food includes ploughman's (£2.95), baked potatoes (£3.25), toad-in-the-hole (£4.50), beef stew, chicken and leek or steak and kidney pie and vegetarian tagliatelle or celery, garlic and mushrooms in a cream sauce (£5.25). The games bar on the left has darts, pool, cribbage, shove-ha'penny, dominoes, and piped music. Outside there are fine views, either from the picnic-table sets by the tubs of flowers in front or from the peaceful garden, with its terrace, fish pond with waterlilies, and more picnic-table sets; walkers are welcome. Dogs are allowed if on a lead, but not in the restaurant. *(Recommended by Peter Barnsley, Jenny and Brian Seller, Ian Phillips, Maureen Preston, D J Penny)*

Free house   Licensees Richard and Anna Abrehart   Real ale   Meals and snacks   Restaurant (not Sun evening)   Dorking (0306) 711793   Children in family room, eating area of bar and restaurant   Quiz night Weds   Open 11.30–3, 6–11; 11.30–11 Sat (winter 11.30–3, 6–11); closed evening 25 Dec; Bedrooms; £17.50/£35

COMPTON   SU9546 Map 2

Harrow 🏠

B3000

This is a rather smart, well kept dining pub (with prices to match) fairly close to the North Downs Way. Often unusual, the bar food includes sandwiches such as smoked turkey and avocado (£3.75), curries, pastas and fresh fish (from £6), home-made pies with fresh vegetables (£7) and seafood platter including smoked salmon and prawns (£8.50). Well kept Friary Meux Bitter, Ind Coope Burton and Tetleys on handpump. The main bar has interesting racing pictures below the ancient ceiling – mostly portraits of horses, jockey caricatures and signed race-finish photographs. Opening off here are more beamed rooms with latched rustic doors, and nice touches such as brass horse-head coat hooks, photographs of the area, and a bas relief in wood of the pub sign; trivia and piped music. You can sit outside in summer, round by the car park but looking out to gentle slopes of pasture. In the pretty village the art nouveau Watts Chapel and Gallery are interesting, and the church itself is attractive; Loseley House is nearby too. *(Recommended by Adrian Zambardino, Debbie Chaplin, Carol and Mike Muston, John and Karen Day, Mrs K J Betts, R Gray, Peter and Susan Maguire, M B Porter, Capt F A Bland, Mr and Mrs J H Adam, Mrs J A Blanks)*

Ind Coope (Allied)   Lease: Roger and Susan Seaman   Real ale   Meals and snacks (till 10)   (0483) 810379   Children in eating area   Open 11–3, 5.30(6 Sat)–11; Bedrooms; £25S/£40S

DORKING   TQ1649 Map 3

Cricketers £

81 South Street; from centre follow signs to Horsham (A2003)

Exceptionally good value home-made food in this friendly town pub includes sandwiches and rolls (from 90p), filled baked potatoes (from £2.25), ratatouille (£2.80) and beef en croûte, beef and vegetable pie or gammon steak (£2.90); well kept Fullers Chiswick, ESB and London Pride on handpump. The comfortably modernised, attractive bar has well cushioned sturdy modern settles, library chairs around cast-iron-framed tables, stripped-and-sealed brick walls decorated with Spy cricketer caricatures and other cricketing pictures, and a central servery with a big modern etched-glass cricketers mirror; there's a log-effect gas fire, darts, cribbage, dominoes, and piped music. Up steps at the back there's a very pretty little sheltered terrace, interestingly planted with roses, a good red honeysuckle, uncommon shrubs and herbaceous plants, and gently floodlit at night. Patience does pay off in the nearby car park. (*Recommended by John Pettit, Tony Bland, TBB, James A Gear, S J Rice, D J Penny; more reports please*)

Fullers Tenant Iain Anderson Real ale Meals and snacks (not Sun) Dorking (0306) 889938 Nearby daytime parking difficult Open 11–3, 5.30–11

ELSTEAD SU9143 Map 2

Woolpack ✦

The Green; on B3001 Milford–Farnham

There's plenty of room to enjoy the ambitious range of interesting bar food – that readers suggest is better than ever – in this bustling, cheerful pub. Chalked up on a big board near the food servery, this might include filled baked potatoes (from £3), mushrooms in herb and garlic butter (£3.50), baked goat's cheese with garlic and chives or hot camembert with mango liqueur sauce (£3.95), home-made pies such as smoked cod and prawn or chicken and ham (£5.95), delicious lamb with Roman sauce, beef, orange and Guinness casserole, chicken in whisky, ginger and red peppers, chicken tikka or pork steak in thyme, schnapps and apricot sauce (£6.50), tuna steak in rich herb and tomato sauce (£8.25), and lovely puddings like crème brûlée, chocolate and fruit scrunch or choux ring filled with cream and bananas; vegetables are good – beetroot in creamy sauce, leeks with crunchy topping and cheesy potatoes; Sunday lunch. Well kept Friary Meux, Ind Coope Burton and Shepherd Neame tapped from the cask; quite a few wines by the glass and bottle. The long, airy main bar has a couple of high-backed settles with weaving shuttles and cones of wool above them, window seats and spindleback chairs around plain wooden tables, a small brick fireplace at one end with copper pans on the mantlepiece and some pretty china on a shelf above it, and another little fireplace at the other end; the large dog basket tucked into a corner is for Megan the golden retriever. Leading off here is a big room decorated with lots of country prints, a weaving loom, scales, and brass measuring jugs; the fireplace with its wooden pillars and lace frill is unusual. In the family room there are nursery-rhyme murals and lots of dried flowers hanging from the ceiling, and a door that leads to the garden with picnic-table sets and a children's play area. (*Recommended by W A Gardiner, Lyn and Bill Capper, Father Robert Davies, Mr Turrall-Clarke, Mr and Mrs J H Adam, Peter Burton, Michael and Harriet Robinson, Carol and Mike Muston*)

Friary Meux (Allied) Lease: Jill and Kevin Macready Real ale Meals and snacks (till 9.45) Restaurant Elstead (0252) 703106 Children in eating area and family room Open 11–2.30, 6–11; closed 26 Dec

FELBRIDGE TQ3639 Map 3

Woodcock ✦

A22 N

The busy little flagstoned entrance bar in this spacious and plush roadhouse opens on the left into a quieter carpeted room with interesting prints on the walls, oriental screens, a stuffed bird of paradise, unusual furniture from heavily upholstered chairs to finely lacquered oriental benches, occasional tables (maybe with copies of *Vogue*), attractive table lamps – and lots of candles, in wall sconces and on tables. A handsome black spiral staircase leads up from here into the high eaves, where an almost entirely candlelit gallery has low stools and sprawly cushions around a couple of low tables at one end, a fanciful crowd of decorative fans and parasols, and a flamboyant dressing-table which houses, among lots of other bird images elsewhere, the only woodcock in the place – but this one's a delicate skeleton. This in turn opens into a lovely old-fashioned Victorian dining room with just one long, handsome table, used for bar meals (or you can book the whole room – a nice place for a private party of a dozen or so). On the right of the downstairs core, a few steps take you into a sumptuous Victorian parlour area filled with thickly cushioned chairs, settees and chaises-longues that would do credit to any seraglio; beyond that yet more candles glitter and flicker in the inviting restaurant. Bar food veers firmly towards fish, delivered fresh from Argyllshire – deep fried whitebait (£3.25), grilled giant prawns with garlic butter (£6.40) or a plate of mixed shellfish (£7.50); there's also sandwiches (from £1.35, fillet steak £4.55), soup (£1.85), avocado with fruits, nuts and crunchy salad (£3.15), ploughman's (from £3.75), specials like fresh roes on toast (£3.95), grilled plaice (£5.95) and charcoal grilled rump steak (£8.95); a 3-course table d'hôte menu can be arranged at the price of your choice. Well kept Greene King Abbot, Harveys, Ringwood Old Thumper and Wadworths 6X; relaxed atmosphere and friendly service. There are tables under cocktail parasols on the flagstones of a sunken front courtyard. *(Recommended by Alan Skull, BHP, L M Miall)*

Free house   Licensee Valerie Jones   Real ale   Meals and snacks (till 10)   Restaurant East Grinstead (0342) 325859   Children in eating area and restaurant   Open 11.30–11.30   Bedrooms; l£35(£55B)

FICKLESHOLE   TQ3860   Map 3
White Bear

Off A2022 Purley Road just S of its junction with A212 roundabout; at The Willows follow Addington Court Golf Club signpost into Featherbed Lane and keep on

It's a real surprise to find this whitewashed country pub on London's southern outskirts. There's a big play area and a walk-through paddock with hens, ducks, geese and white doves, pheasants and rabbits in big pens, and a Nubian goat; other paddocks have a donkey, ponies and sheep. Inside, several rambling, partly 15th-century, dimly lit rooms range from very cosy to quite spacious, with low and heavy black beams, quarry tiles and oak parquet, polished flagstones, bay windows inset with stained-glass panels, and an attractive variety of seating including some antique settles; decorations include china on delft shelves through halberds and pikes to a handsome Act of Parliament clock. Open fires, solid fuel stoves and a good mix of customers. Bar food includes soup (£1.10), sandwiches (£1.50), ploughman's (£2.50), a vegetarian dish (£3.80), daily roast (£4.50) and specials like home-made steak pie, lasagne or Lancashire hot-pot (£3.80). Well kept Charringtons IPA, Fullers London Pride and ESB, and John Smiths on handpump. Fruit machine, video game and piped music. *(Recommended by Tony and Lynne Stark, Jenny and Brian Seller, Helen and Wal Burns, Ian Phillips, Maureen Preston, P Thorogood)*

Free house   Licensee Barrie Clarke   Real ale   Meals and snacks   (0959) 73166 Children welcome   Jazz night (Wed)   Open 11–3, 6–11 (11–11 Sat)

HASCOMBE   TQ0039   Map 3
White Horse

On B2130 S of Godalming

This friendly rose-draped pub is popular for its interesting range of bar food: huge sandwiches (from £1.75), lovely home-made soup (£2), whitebait (£2.95), home-made meaty burgers or swordfish steak (£4.75), fresh, interesting salads with vegetables like mangetout or avocado (from £4.55, prawn £6.50), poussin dijonnais (£5.95) and tasty home-made puddings like treacle tart or fruit crumbles (from £2.50); best to get there early at lunchtime (especially Sunday). Well kept Friary Meux Bitter, Fullers London Pride and Ind Coope Burton on handpump; quite a few wines. You can eat in a cosy inner beamed area with quiet small-windowed alcoves and a woodburning stove, or the light and airy extension. Darts, fruit machine and piped music. There are some tables in several places outside – on a little patio by the porch at the rose-draped front, in a bower and under a walnut tree. The National Trust's Winkworth Arboretum, with its walks among beautiful trees and shrubs, is nearby. *(Recommended by Michael and Harriet Robinson, Tessa Stuart, P A Barfield, Jenny and Brian Seller, T Galligan, Phil and Sally Gorton, Carol and Mike Muston; more reports please)*

Friary Meux (Allied)   Tenant Susan Barnett   Real ale   Meals and snacks (till 10) Restaurant (not Sun evening)   Hascombe (048 632) 258   Well behaved children Open 11–3, 5.30(6 Sat)–11; closed 25 Dec

HEADLEY   TQ2054 Map 3

Cock

Church Lane; village signposted off B2033 SE of Leatherhead

In an attractive setting, with tables and chairs outside giving pleasant views over rolling horsey countryside, this dates back to Tudor times. The main bar is attractively simple, with pews forming booths around its tables, and a good log fire; it pays to get there by 12.30 at lunchtime. On weekdays there's an overflow into an attractively spare dining area with well spaced tables (this functions as a restaurant, Friday to Sunday). Sensible-sized helpings of all home-cooked bar food include filled French sticks (from £1.60), good soup (£1.60), ploughman's (from £2), lasagne (£3.25), salads (around £3.50), steak and kidney pie (£4), specials such as sweet and sour chicken or Cumberland sausage (around £4) and steaks (from £6.50), with puddings such as apple pie (£1.50); there are Sunday nuts and cocktail biscuits on the bar counter. Well kept Friary Meux Best, Ind Coope Burton and Tetleys on handpump, a good choice of wines, cheerfully efficient service, maybe unobtrusive well reproduced piped music. The public end has darts, pool, cribbage, chess, fruit machine and trivia. It's a good walking area. *(Recommended by Jane Palmer, Jenny and Brian Seller, Adrian Zambardino, Debbie Chaplin, Giles Quick)*

Allied   Manager Ian Winfield   Real ale   Meals and snacks   Leatherhead (0372) 377258   Children welcome   Live music 3rd Thurs of month   Open 11–2.30, 6.30–11; closed 25 Dec

HURTMORE   SY9545 Map 2

Squirrel

Hurtmore Rd; just off A3 nr Godalming, nestling under E embankment just by Hurtmore/Shackleford turn

The L-shaped bar of this carefully refurbished pub is spacious and comfortable, with pale country-kitchen tables and chairs, some stylish sofas matching the curtains, and a fresh, airy decor – far from olde-worlde, but very much alive. Besides well kept Ruddles Best and County and Websters Yorkshire, they have an excellent choice of some two dozen or more wines by the glass – and may even give you a free tasting. A good range of home-cooked bar food includes soup (£1.95), sandwiches (from £2.50), potted shrimps or a choice of ploughman's (£3.25), grilled sardines (£3.50), filled baked potatoes (from £3.50), omelettes (£4.75), chilli con carne (£4.95) and a variety of things to cook yourself on a sizzle-stone, with kebab vegetables (from £7.95); at one end the bar leads into a restaurant with a no smoking area, and there's a comfortable new conservatory. Unobtrusive piped music, no machines; friendly service; facilities for the disabled. There are picnic-table sets out in front, and under cocktail parasols in a spacious garden with a play area. The bedrooms are in a recently converted 17th-century cottage row; weekend bargains. *(Recommended by GSS, John Evans)*

Grand Met   Lease: David and Jane Barnes   Real ale   Meals and snacks (12–2.30, 6.30–10.30)   Restaurant   (0483) 860223   Children in eating area and conservatory   Open 11–3, 6–11   Bedrooms; £45S/£50S

LALEHAM   TQ0568 Map 3

Three Horseshoes

Junction 1 of M3, then W on A308; village signposted on left on B377

There's been a tavern here since the 13th century, and when it became fashionable with Edward VII (as Prince of Wales), Lily Langtry, Jenny Lind and W S Gilbert, it was just an old stone-flagged country tavern. The facade is still almost hidden by wisteria, hanging baskets and cartwheels, but inside it's now comfortably modernised. The open-plan bar is furnished with comfortable burgundy plush seats on the red carpet, lots of big copper pots and pans hanging from beams, interesting cock-fighting prints on the red walls, and blacksmith's tools hanging over the main fireplace. One small alcove has high-backed settles, and there's a conservatory. Popular and highly praised bar food includes an excellent choice of sandwiches (from £1.25, prawn with asparagus £2.35), soup (£1.75), ploughman's (£3.25), a wide range of huge baked potatoes with hot or cold fillings (from £3.50, prawns £4.75), salads (from £5.25), a selection of daily specials such as pork in cider and cream (£4.25), lamb and cherry casserole (£4.50), steak and oyster pie or rump steak (£7.50), and puddings like sherry trifle, chocolate fudge cake or hot waffles and maple syrup (from £1.50); they may also prepare dishes on a more individual basis on request. Well kept Fullers London Pride, Ruddles Best and County, Websters and a guest beer on handpump; regular real ale weeks with different beers on each day; decent wines, country wine and farmhouse cider; piped music. There are plenty of tables in the garden; the lane opposite leads down to a stretch of the Thames popular for picnics and sunbathing. *(Recommended by R A Corbett, Liam Devlin, Mike Rising, TOH, Ian Phillips, Peter Griffiths, Richard Carpenter)*

Watneys Tenant Philip Jones Real ale Meals and snacks (noon–9 Mon-Sat, 12–2 Sun) Restaurant Staines (0784) 452617 Children in conservatory Open 11–11

MICKLEHAM TQ1753 Map 3

King William IV

Byttom Hill; short but narrow steep track up hill just off A24 Leatherhead–Dorking by green-painted restaurant, just N of main B2289 village turnoff; OS Sheet 187, map reference 173538

Just far enough off the A24 to avoid intrusive traffic noise, this relaxed, unpretentious pub – a steep climb up – has a popular summer garden, mainly brick-tiled, with crazy paving in front, then grass below, and plenty of tables (some in a wooden open-sided shelter). A path leads straight up into the open country. The snug plank-panelled front bar looks down the hill, and there's a rather more spacious quite brightly lit back bar with kitchen-type chairs around its cast-iron-framed tables; decent log fires. Good value bar food now tends to specialise much more for vegetarians, with at least six tasty vegetarian dishes such as courgette and mushroom ratatouille, tostados with spicy tomato and bean sauce, aubergine moussaka or huge mushrooms stuffed with cheese, onion and garlic (£3.95); there's also sandwiches, filled baked potatoes, ploughman's, jumbo sausage in French bread (£2.95) and steak and kidney pie cooked in Guinness (£4.65). Well kept Adnams, Badger Best, Boddingtons and Wadworths 6X on handpump; friendly service; darts sensibly placed in one corner, shove-ha'penny, cribbage, dominoes, unobtrusive nostalgic piped pop music, and a serviceable grandfather clock. *(Recommended by Phil and Sally Gorton, VL, Adrian Zambardino, Debbie Chaplin, R E Horner, John Kimber, John Pettit, Jane Palmer, TOH, D J Penny, Mrs K J Betts, Roger Taylor, Carol and Mike Muston)*

Free house Licensee J E Beynon Real ale Lunchtime meals and snacks Restaurant (not Sun evening) Leatherhead (0372) 372590 Children in eating area of bar and restaurant Occasional folk/country groups in summer Open 11.30–2.30, 6–11 (winter 12–2.30, 7–10.30)

NEWDIGATE TQ2042 Map 3

Surrey Oaks

Parkgate Road; A24 S of Dorking, then left on to unmarked road signposted for Beare Green – go through that village and take first left fork

In the much older part on the right of this tiny country pub, there's a little snug beamed room by a coal-effect gas fire, then a real open fire in a standing area with unusually large flagstones. The main lounge has rustic tables lit by lanterns hanging low from fairy-lit lowered beams and tapestried seats in little partly curtained booths. A separate games room has a well lit pool table, darts, shove-ha'penny, dominoes, cribbage, a fruit machine, video game, and juke box. Decent bar food includes sandwiches (from £1.25), home-made soup (£1.75), ploughman's (£2.45), filled baked potatoes (£2.60), salads (£2.75), cannelloni, lasagne, moussaka or chilli con carne (£3.50), an interesting selection of vegetarian dishes such as butter bean and vegetable au gratin or good mung bean and mushroom biriani (£4), and puddings (£1); their own free-range duck, hen and goose eggs are for sale at the bar. Friary Meux, Ind Coope Burton and Youngs Bitter on handpump. The substantial, pretty garden outside has a large terrace, a rockery with illuminated pools, fountains and waterfall, and a flock of pure white doves; they also have sheep, a calf, and an aviary of budgerigars, and all sorts of fowls – the source of the eggs. *(Recommended by Alec Lewery, TOH, John Pettit, C T H Wickham; more reports please)*

Ind Coope (Allied)   Tenant Colin Haydon   Real ale   Meals and snacks (till 10) Restaurant (not Sun evening)   Newdigate (0306 77) 200   Children welcome   Live entertainment Sun evening   Open 11–2.30(3 Sat), 6–11

NORWOOD HILL   TQ2343 Map 3
Fox Revived

Leigh–Charlwood back road

This bare-boarded country cottage – popular with Gatwick staff – has a front area with decorative mugs on the beams, chairs, cushioned pews and an attractive high-backed settle, kitchen tables, and shelves of books; the back dining area is similarly furnished, and has a woodburning stove in a central brick hearth, a mix of photographs in one alcove, and a pleasantly relaxed atmosphere. Opening off of this is a double conservatory with its own stove, cane chairs and tables on shiny brown tiles, and some big plants. Well kept Friary Meux Bitter, Harveys Best Bitter and Ind Coope Burton on handpump, decent wines; daily newspapers. Quickly and cheerfully served, the hearty heaps of good food might include jumbo sausages (£2.50), pasta with bolognese sauce (£4.50), steak and kidney pie (£4.95), lamb curry or a hefty half-shoulder of lamb (£7.95) and seafood platter (£12.95). Good Sunday roast and tasty puddings. Shove-ha'penny, table skittles, cribbage and dominoes. Spread well through the big garden are lots of picnic-table sets, and there's a retired tractor among the weeping willow, apple and other trees; it backs onto paddocks. Note that they don't allow any children under 14. *(Recommended by Jenny and Brian Seller, Ian and Wendy McCaw, D J Penny)*

Ind Coope (Allied)   Tenant Gary Kidd   Real ale   Meals (till 10)   (0293) 862362 Open 11–2.30(3 Sat), 5(6 Sat)–11

nr OCKLEY   TQ1439 Map 3
Punch Bowl

Oakwoodhill (some maps and signposts spell it Okewoodhill); village signposted off A29 S of Ockley

The homely bar in this partly tile-hung old house with its heavy Horsham stone slab roof, has big dark polished flagstones, lots of beams, some timbering, an antique settle among simpler country seats and scrubbed deal tables, and an inglenook fireplace with huge logs on the vast round hearth. Shove-ha'penny, cribbage, dominoes, Scrabble, chess, trivial pursuit, shut-the-box, fruit machine and juke box. Well kept Adnams Broadside, Badger Best and Tanglefoot, and Wadworth's Farmers Glory and 6X; a good choice of malt whiskies. Bar food includes sandwiches (from £1.25), soup (£1.75), egg and chips (£2.05), ploughman's (£3.15), huge burgers (£3.95), stuffed plaice (£3.95) and local trout or sliced duck breast and orange sauce (£8). You can sit outside on the several terraces with fields, oak trees and woods stretching away on all sides. The new people are young and friendly; before moving here, they gave the Dog & Duck at Outwood its distinctive, relaxed style. *(Recommended by John Whitehead, David Hunn, Edward Burlton Davies, D J Penny, Jenny and Brian Seller, M Rising, TOH, M C Howells)*

Badger   Manager Amanda Munro   Real ale   Meals and snacks (noon till 10) Oakwood Hill (0306) 79249   Children in dining area   Open 11–11

OUTWOOD TQ3245 Map 3

Bell

If you want a table in this popular dining pub, it's best to book in advance, especially in the evening (when drinking-only space is limited). The carpeted front bar has elm and oak tables and chairs (some in Jacobean style), low beams, and a vast stone inglenook fireplace; there's another lounge bar at the back. Bar food includes sandwiches (from £2), filled baked potatoes (from £2.95), ploughman's (£3.15), and main dishes such as steak and kidney pie, English rack of lamb, char-grilled sirloin or rump steak or daily roast (£5.65), fillet steak topped with stilton (£9.70) and daily specials; all-year barbecue, outdoors in good weather. Well kept Harveys Best Bitter, Pilgrims Progress, Youngs Special and three guests on handpump; large range of liqueurs; piped music. In summer, the well-managed garden is a peaceful place to sit among flowers and shrubs on the sheltered lawn and look past its bordering pine trees to the fine view over rolling fields, dotted with oak trees and woods. *(Recommended by Richard Houghton, David and Debbie, R E Horner, R Bennett, P Thorogood, Raymond Palmer, M Rising, K Leist, A J Young, Lyn and Bill Capper, Mrs J A Blanks, J H Bell, Dick Brown, D J Penny, Jerry and Alison Oakes)*

Free house Licensees Harry Pam and John Lane Real ale Meals and snacks (till 9.30) (0342) 842989 Children welcome Occasional live entertainment (Sun evening) Open 11–2.30, 6–11; closed 25 Dec, 26 Dec

Dog & Duck

From A23 in Salfords S of Redhill take Station turning – eventually after you cross the M23 the pub's on your left at the T-junction; coming from the village centre, head towards Coopers Hill and Prince of Wales Road

There's a friendly, relaxed atmosphere in the spaciously rambling bar areas here, as well as a good log fire, comfortable settles, oak armchairs and more ordinary seats, ochre walls, stripped dark beams, rugs on the quarry tiles, and newspapers to read. Well kept Badger Best and Tanglefoot, Everards Old Original and Tiger and Wadworths 6X on handpump; darts, shove-ha'penny, ring-the-bull, cribbage, dominoes, Scrabble, backgammon, chess, trivia and unobtrusive piped music. A wide range of bar food includes sandwiches (from £1.25), soup (£1.75), a choice of ploughman's (£3.15), salads (from £3.95, dressed crab £6.50), fish and chips (£4.10), ham and eggs or chicken curry (£4.25), vegetarian dishes like cheese, leek and potato pie, vegetable stroganoff or vegetable lasagne (£4.60), home-made steak and kidney pie or scampi (£5.10), filled plaice (£5.25); Sunday roast lunch. There is another huge fireplace in the restaurant area which leads off the bar. Picnic-table sets under cocktail parasols on the grass outside look over a safely fenced-off duck pond to the meadows. The village, with its old windmill, is worth the walk. *(Recommended by Sue Corrigan, Raymond Palmer, TOH, David and Sarah Gilmore, WFL, A J Young)*

Badger Manager Stephen Slocombe Real ale Meals and snacks (noon–10pm) Restaurant Smallfield (0342) 842964 Children in restaurant Quiz night (Sun) Open 11–11

PIRBRIGHT SU9455 Map 2

Royal Oak

Aldershot Rd; A324S of village

Handy for Bisley Camp, this pleasant, neatly kept old pub has a rambling series of side alcoves, heavy beams and timbers, ancient stripped brickwork, and gleaming brasses set around the big low-beamed fireplace; it's furnished with wheelback chairs, tapestried wall seats and little dark church-like pews set around neat tables. Lunchtime bar food includes soup (£1.25), sandwiches (from £1.50; toasted £1.95), a choice of ploughman's (from £2.95), salads (£4.75), hot dishes such as chilli con carne, lasagne, fish pie or moussaka (all £4.85), daily specials, including a vegetarian dish, and puddings; Sunday lunch. Well kept Badger Best, Brakspears, Flowers Original, Marstons Pedigree, Whitbreads Castle Eden and a guest; several malt whiskies; they do coffee. In summer the neat gardens are a mass of colour. *(Recommended by Richard Houghton, TBB, Col G D Stafford, Alan Skull)*

Whitbreads   Managers Annette and Anthony Woodbine   Real ale   Lunchtime meals and snacks   Restaurant (12–3, 7–10.30 Sun only)   (0483) 232466   Children in small bar on Sun   Open 11–11

PYRFORD LOCK   TQ0458 Map 3
Anchor

Lock Lane; service road off A3 signposted to RHS Wisley Gardens – continue past them towards Pyrford

The lovely position by the River Wey Navigation is the main draw here – it's especially popular in summer when you sit at the picnic-table sets on the big terrace and watch the canal boats go through the locks. Inside, the open-plan bar, partly carpeted and partly brick-floored, has big picture windows and comfortable furnishings; upstairs is full of narrow-boat memorabilia and is mainly reserved for parents with small children. Bar food includes basket meals (from £2.35), ploughman's (£3.25), a choice of salads (from £3.25), home-made steak and kidney pie or home-made cheese and onion quiche (£3.95) and scampi or gammon steak (£4.50); daily vegetarian special (from £3), children's menu (from £1.80) and puddings (from £1.50); coffee. Courage Best and Directors, and John Smiths on handpump; lots of bustle and noise from the Tannoy system. Friendly, efficient staff; fruit machine, piped music. Close to the Royal Horticultural Society's Wisley Garden. *(Recommended by Roger Danes, Neil H Barker, Rob and Gill Weeks, RJS, R N Haygarth, TBB, Michael and Alison Sandy, WTF, Roger Huggins, Ian Phillips, S Bentley, Cdr W S D Hendry, Mayur Shah)*

Grand Met   Manager Stephen Kerrawn   Real ale   Meals and snacks (12–2, 6–9; not Fri, Sat and Sun evenings, not evenings in winter)   (0932) 342507   Children in own first-floor room overlooking canal   Open 11–3, 6–11; 11–11 Sat (winter 11–3, 6–11)

REIGATE HEATH   TQ2349 Map 3
Skimmington Castle ★

3 miles from M25 junction 8: through Reigate take A25 Dorking (West), then on edge of Reigate turn left past Black Horse into Flanchford Road; after ¼ mile turn left into Bonny's Road (unmade, very bumpy track); after crossing golf course fork right up hill

Surrounded by wooded countryside reached from here by winding paths, this popular old cottage makes the most of its position with a crazy-paved front terrace and tables on the grass by lilac bushes, and more tables at the back with good views over the meadows and the hillocks. The bright main front bar leads off from a small central serving counter with dark simple panelling and a collection of oddly shaped pipes (and a skull among them) dangling over it. There's a miscellany of chairs and tables, shiny brown vertical panelling decorated with earthenware bottles, decorative plates, brass and pewter and a brown plank ceiling. The back rooms are partly panelled too – cosy, with old-fashioned settles and Windsor chairs; one has a big brick fireplace with its bread-oven still beside it. A small room down steps at the back has video games, darts, shove-ha'penny, cribbage and dominoes. Friary Meux Best, Ind Coope Burton and Shepherd Neame Old on handpump, and Addlestones draught cider; the stuffed fox leering out of the crisp packets is commonly known as Derek; there's also a stuffed badger. Bar food includes local sausages (35p), soup (£1.05), sandwiches (from 95p, cream cheese and prawn with walnuts £1.55), basket meals (from £1.55, scampi £3.80), ploughman's (from £1.85), vegetarian mushroom and nut fettucini or country lentil crumble (£3.40), salads (from £4.60, smoked salmon £6.60), gammon steak with egg (£5.20), steaks (from £8.70) and daily specials. Big back car park. *(Recommended by Gary Scott, Graham Pettener, Adrian Zambardino, Debbie Chaplin, Simon Collett-Jones, D J Penny, Peter Griffiths, Nigel Gibbs)*

Ind Coope (Allied)   Tenants Andrew and Ann Fisher   Real ale   Lunchtime meals and snacks   (0737) 243100   Children in small back room until 9   Open 11–3(2.30 winter), 5.30–11

SHEPPERTON   TQ0867   Map 3
Kings Head
Church Square; E side of B375

As parking is not very easy nearby, this attractive pub, in the quiet old square, doesn't get too crowded at lunchtime. The atmospheric small rooms have dark panelling, oak beams, and oak parquet flooring, and one has an inglenook fireplace; Courage Best, Wadworths 6X and Youngs Special on handpump. Large helpings of good, plain food include sandwiches (from £1.50), tasty Welsh rarebit to a secret recipe (£3), jumbo sausages (£3.45), Shepperton pie (£3.20) or chilli con carne (£3.50), steak and kidney pie (£4.35), and scampi (£7.25); pleasant service. Darts (winter only), fruit machine and juke box. The conservatory has detachable outer walls, removed in summer to give an airy covered area merging with the pretty terrace. The pub looks across to the brick and flint church. *(Recommended by Tom Thomas, E G Parish, Ian Phillips, Mayur Shah; more reports please)*

Courage   Tenant David Longhurst   Real ale   Meals and snacks (till 10) Restaurant   Walton-on-Thames (0932) 221910   Children welcome   Disco Tues Open 11–3, 5.30–11; 11–11 Sat

SHERE   TQ0747   Map 3
White Horse
Village signposted on right on A25 3 miles E of Guildford

Careful restoration has made the most of this interesting half-timbered pub, and the open-plan main lounge bar has genuinely ancient features: massive beams, a huge inglenook fireplace, uneven floors – there are no foundations, just salvaged ships' timbers plunged into the ground some 600 years ago – antique oak wall seats, and old manuscripts on the walls; there's some elegant Tudor stonework in a second inglenook fireplace through in the Pilgrim's Bar. It can get very busy at weekends. Quickly served bar food includes sandwiches, beef Wellington, gingered beef casserole, honeyed chicken, aubergine bake or bacon, avocado and spinach salad (£4.50) and stuffed local trout (£4.95). Ruddles Best and County, and Websters Yorkshire on handpump. There are seats outside on a sunny cobbled courtyard among carefully planted troughs of flowers and bright hanging baskets; good walking in the beech woods on the road north towards East Clandon. The village is pretty. *(Recommended by Robert Danes, Mayur Shah, Robert and Elizabeth Scott, Mark Porter, Dick Brown, D J Penny; more reports please)*

Grand Met   Manager M J Wicks   Real ale   Meals and snacks (not Sun evening) (048 641) 2518   Children in eating area   Nearby parking may be difficult   Open 11.30–2.30(3 Sat), 6–11

THURSLEY   SU9039   Map 2
Three Horseshoes
Just off A3 SW of Godalming

The dark, cosy bar of this distinctly civilised, tile-hung stone pub has fine old country furniture, including lovingly polished elm tables, and some Brockbank cartoons (he lived here). Bar food changes pretty much every day, typically including sandwiches (from £1.85), ploughman's (£3), starters such as soup, devilled mushrooms or brie wedges (from £1) and main dishes like steak and kidney pie, fresh fish, veal stroganoff, trout, steaks or Hungarian goulash (from £4.75). Gales BBB and HSB on handpump; country wines; piped music in restaurant only. There are tables outside on a big roundel of grass under pine trees at the front, with summer barbecues; the back garden is now open to the public. *(Recommended by Dr Paul Kitchener, Phil and Sally Gorton, Alan Skull, Jane Clayton; more reports please)*

Gales   Tenants Mr Snedden and Mr Mallett   Real ale   Meals and snacks (till 10) Restaurant   Elstead (0252) 703268   Children welcome   Open 11–3, 5.30–11; 11–11 Sat; closed evening 25 Dec

WALLISWOOD   TQ1138 Map 3

Scarlett Arms ★

Village signposted from Ewhurst–Rowhook back road; or follow Oakwoodhill signpost from A29 S of Ockley, then follow Walliswood signpost into Walliswood Green Road

This red-tiled white building was once a pair of labourers' cottages and the old small-roomed layout has been carefully preserved: three communicating rooms have heavy black oak beams in the low brown ceiling, deeply polished flagstones, simple but perfectly comfortable benches, high bar stools with backrests, trestle tables, country prints, and welcoming log fires – one is an inglenook; darts, cribbage, dominoes and a fruit machine in a small room at the end. Well kept King & Barnes Bitter, Broadwood, Festive, Mild and winter Old on handpump. Good, reasonably priced bar food includes sandwiches (from £1.20, toasties from £1.30), ploughman's (from £2.10), salads (from £2.75), a bowl of chilli con carne (£2.90), breaded plaice or tasty ham and eggs (£3.60), home-made daily specials (good steak and kidney pie), and puddings (from £1); attentive, friendly licensees. There are old-fashioned seats and tables with umbrellas in the pretty garden.

(Recommended by C P Scott-Malden, Edward Burlton Davies, Doreen and Reg Tickner, D Hughes, Norman Foot, Mr and Mrs Woodger, Richard Houghton, D J Penny, Barbara M McHugh, Stephen Goodchild, Paul Sexton, Sue Harrison, R Caldwell,)

King & Barnes   Tenants David and Pat Haslam   Real ale   Meals and snacks   (030 679) 243   Open 11–2.30, 5.30–11; closed 25 Dec

WALTON ON THE HILL   TQ2255 Map 3

Fox & Hounds ⌀

Walton Street

A wide choice of popular bar food in this bustling, cheerful pub includes generous helpings of pâté (£2.25), avocado and prawns (£3.25), popular chargrilled burgers (from £3.50), chilli con carne (£3.95), a very good continental platter of meats, hams, cheeses and fresh fruits, vegetarian bake (£4.25), chicken and ham or steak and kidney pie (£4.50), gammon or prawn curry and a good choice of steaks; at lunchtime they add good sandwiches (from £2), ploughman's (£2.25), and sausages; there are good value specials such as tasty daily roasts, tagliatelle with a spicy cheese sauce, or pork escalope done with brandy and mushrooms (from £4.75), and puddings like delicious lemon meringue pie (£2); capable, friendly service. The restaurant area, over on the left of the serving counter, has a separate menu. Bass, Charrington IPA and Highgate Mild, and well kept Wadworths 6X on handpump, with a decent choice of wines. There are low ceilings, some dark panelling, armed chairs and tables spread around the central bar, and though the various areas open into one another, it's cosy and friendly, with three good coal fires; fruit machine. Some rustic picnic-table sets on a back terrace – but if children want to run around, they're supposed to go instead to a freer area beyond the car park, with a timber climber and swing. *(Recommended by Dr and Mrs R Hodrinson, R E Horner, John Molyneux, TOH, Mrs J A Blanks, TBB, Gary Scott)*

Bass   Tenant J Hawkins   Real ale   Meals and snacks (noon–9.30)   Restaurant (0737) 812090   Open 11–11

WARLINGHAM   TQ3658 Map 3

White Lion

B269

The cosy heart of this unspoilt old pub is a fine Tudor fireplace, more or less enclosed by high-backed settles, and there's a friendly warren of black-panelled rooms with lots of nooks and crannies, wood-block floors, extremely low beams, and deeply aged plasterwork. Good value home-made bar food, served in the bigger, brighter room at the end of the building, includes sandwiches (from £1.40, filled French bread from £1.90), filled baked potatoes (from £1.45), steak and kidney pie, curry and rice, or chicken kebabs (£3.50). Bass, Charrington IPA, and Youngs Special on handpump. A side room with some amusing early 19th-century cartoons has darts and fruit machine; piped music in eating area. The well kept back lawn, with its rockery, is surrounded by a herbaceous border. *(Recommended by Dr and Mrs A K Clarke, John Molyneux, Graham Pettener, Peter Griffiths, Sandra and Dave Price)*

Charringtons (Bass)   Manager Ian Andrews   Real ale   Lunchtime meals and snacks
Warlingham (0883) 624106   Children in eating area   Open 11–3, 5.30(6 Sat)–11

Lucky Dip

Besides the fully inspected pubs, you might like to try these Lucky Dips recommended to us and described by readers (if you do, please send us reports):

☆ **Abinger Common** [Abinger signed off A25 W of Dorking — then right to Abinger Hammer; TQ1145], *Abinger Hatch*: Its position nr church in a clearing of the rolling woods, with attractive garden areas by duckpond, wins many friends (and crowds on fine weekends) for this plainly furnished pub with its heavy beams, flagstones and big log fires; half a dozen changing well kept real ales on handpump such as Badger Best and Tanglefoot, Gibbs Mew Bishops Tipple, King & Barnes and Wadworths 6X, with their strengths chalked up; country wines, limited range of usual bar food, restaurant; provision for children *(Peter Barnsley, Dr B A W Perkins, Roy McNeill, John Pettit, LYM)*

☆ **Addlestone** [off A317 into Weybridge industrial estate; left over bridge then first right — pub with about 1/2 mile on left; TQ0464], *Pelican*: Comfortably modernised canalside pub, busy at lunchtimes, with well kept Watneys-related real ales on handpump, good choice of lunchtime food, large coal-effect fires, waterside views from big conservatory, own moorings; children welcome *(Ian Phillips, Cdr W S D Hendry)*

Addlestone [New Haw Rd; corner A318/B385], *White Hart*: Cheerful local with attractive waterside garden, good value simple food, well kept Courage, quick service, darts, bar billiards, juke box *(LYM)*

☆ **Albury** [TQ0547], *Drummond Arms*: Nicely refurbished, with wide choice of good value food inc Sun roast and decent sandwiches served quickly, Courage, Harveys Sussex and Festive, pretty garden with tables under cocktail parasols by river; attractive and interesting village *(J and H Dwane, Jenny and Brian Seller)*

Ashtead [48 The Street (A24); TQ1858], *Leg of Mutton & Cauliflower*: Deceptively large, low-beamed pub with surprisingly antipodean clientele (even has Christmas lunch on August Bank Hol); good value food from separate pantry, Bass and Charrington IPA on handpump, no smoking back bar, darts and pintable in side bar, barbecues in nice garden behind *(Adrian Zambardino, Debbie Chaplin, Chris Fluck)*

Bagshot [56 High St; SU9163], *Three Mariners*: Welcoming and comfortable, with upper gallery, separate pool/darts/music area, and extension into former adjoining warehouse — beams, some flagstones, carpet, mix of kitchen-style chairs; wide choice of good food from separate lunchtime servery, Courage ales, courteous service; thriving lunchtime, quieter evenings *(Dr M Owton, Ian Phillips, Simon Collett-Jones)*

Banstead [TQ2559], *Mint*: Popular and roomy, with chamber-pots and big jugs hanging from ceiling; no food Sun, clean lavatories, one real ale *(Jenny and Brian Seller)*; [High St, off A217], *Victoria*: Good food inc good choice of fresh sandwiches in spacious well laid out lounges and attractive small conservatory; good service, well kept Courage ales; said to have sold ales since 1799 *(E G Parish)*; [High St], *Woolpack*: Spacious lounge with comfortable no smoking area, John Smiths Magnet on handpump with Tues discount, rather good range of relatively cheap bar food well cooked and presented, good service by extremely pleasant staff *(John Pettit, E G Parish)*

☆ **Batts Corner** [off A325 S of Farnham at Halfway House, Bucks Horn Oak, towards Rowledge, but bear off left after 3/4 mile — OS Sheet 186, map reference 820410; SU8240], *Blue Bell*: Civilised interestingly extended country pub, kept spotless, with wide choice of well kept real ales such as Adnams, Ballards and Brakspears tapped from the cask, quick service, traditional games (darts could be better placed), simple bar food inc good substantial sandwiches; extensive garden with rolling views and good facilities for children — nowhere for them inside though *(Alan Skull, Richard Houghton, Derek Patey, LYM)*

☆ **Beare Green** [A24 Dorking—Horsham; TQ1842], *Dukes Head*: Attractive roadside pub with popular food from good sandwiches and baked potatoes to steaks, obliging staff, good atmosphere, well kept Allied real ales, garden *(D J Penny, Jenny and Brian Seller, Stephen Goodchild, TOH, LYM)*

☆ **Betchworth** [TQ2049], *Red Lion*: Pleasant and friendly atmosphere in large, popular bar, extensively fairy-lit with chamber-pot collection and polished copperware above panelled dado; wide choice of generous food inc particularly good puddings, well kept Bass, friendly staff; plenty of tables in rose-trellised garden with play area; can book squash court *(John Pettit, TOH)*

☆ **Bletchingley** [Little Common Lane; 3 miles

from M25 junction 6; off A25 on Redhill side of village], *William IV*: Good choice of reasonably priced bar food (lunchtime, not Sun) in country local, prettily tile-hung and weatherboarded, with well kept Bass, Charrington IPA and a guest such as Harveys, charming bar staff; darts, dominoes, cribbage and fruit machine in back bar, seats in nice garden with summer barbecues (Sat evening, Sun lunchtime) *(J T Charman, LYM)*

☆ **Bletchingley** [11 High St; 2 1/2 miles from M25 junction 6, via A22 then A25 towards Redhill; TQ3250], *Whyte Harte*: Low-beamed mainly open-plan bars with old prints, big log fire in inglenook fireplace, plush settles, rugs and parquet, home-made bar food from sandwiches to steaks, well kept Allied real ales and fair range of wines, seats outside; has been open all day Sat; children in dining room; bedrooms *(Dr M I Crichton, W J Wonham, David Shillitoe, LYM)*
Bletchingley [A25, Redhill side], *Red Lion*: Heavily modernised Tudor pub, with log fire, cosy atmosphere and warm welcome; fair range of very fairly priced bar food, small restaurant area *(M D Hare)*
Bramley [High St; TQ0044], *Jolly Farmer*: Cheerful and lively Watneys pub with two log fires, very wide choice of well presented good bar food, beer mats on ceiling, big restaurant; quite handy for Winkworth Arboretum and Loseley House; bedrooms *(LYM); Parrot*: Clean, modernised pub with efficient service, restrained piped music, Watneys-related real ales and reasonable, straightforward food; decent garden beside Wey Navigation *(Ian Phillips)*

☆ **Brockham** [Brockham Green; TQ1949], *Royal Oak*: Relaxed and welcoming small local with open fire, good standard bar food, well kept Gales HSB and Ind Coope Burton, attentive staff, ring the bull; pleasant outlook over green, tables with tablecloths on enclosed lawn with play area, more out on green; be prepared for children (and dogs) at weekends *(J S Evans, Jenny and Brian Seller, John Pettit, John Evans)*

☆ **Brook** [A286 — OS Sheet 186, map reference 930380; SU9337], *Dog & Pheasant*: Pleasant atmosphere in busy and friendly character pub attractively placed opp cricket green, with polished walking-sticks decorating low beams; well kept Allied real ales, good choice of reasonably priced food lunchtime and evening, shove-ha'penny; seats in garden, front and back; handy for Witley Common Nature Reserve *(Phil and Sally Gorton, John Pettit, J G Francis)*

☆ **Charlton** [off B376 Laleham—Shepperton; TQ0869], *Harrow*: Delightful thatched building, maybe 17th-century, tastefully refurbished without detriment to overall character — a real oasis in an urban desert, still with a pump feeding stone trough in former cattle sheds; well kept Watneys-related real ales, food choice not large but generous, inc interesting dishes and good puddings (tables can be booked); very

friendly staff, plenty of seats inside and out *(Genevieve Clarke, Ian Phillips)*
Chelsham [Limpsfield Rd; TQ3659], *Hare & Hounds*: Much improved recently — must be a prize pub for its floral decorations; friendly atmosphere, good bar food at reasonable prices *(W J Wonham)*

☆ **Chertsey** [London St (B375); TQ0466], *Crown*: Lively congenial atmosphere and fast friendly (mainly antipodean) service in big Victorian-style pub, open-plan but still with the feel of separate bars; well kept Youngs, good reasonably priced food in back food area, restaurant, lovely big garden behind back with masses of roses, pond, parakeet and budgerigar aviaries; exemplary lavatories *(Richard Houghton, Ian Phillips)*

☆ **Chertsey** [Ruxbury Rd, St Anns Hill (nr Lyne)], *Golden Grove*: Good choice of generous reasonably priced home-cooked lunchtime food in pine-tabled eating area, well kept Allied and Gales real ales, open-plan but with a two-bar feel and lots of bare wood; unusually big garden with dogs (and a white goat tethered out of reach), play area, wooded pond — nice spot on edge of St Anns Woods *(Ian Phillips, Richard Houghton)*
Chertsey [Guildford St (A317)], *Kings Head*: Good value food and warmly welcoming staff in straightforward pub; open all day *(Chris Fluck)*

☆ **Chiddingfold** [A283; SU9635], *Crown*: Famous old inn with ancient panelling, fine carving, massive beams and tapestried restaurant; also reasonably priced bar food, several Whitbreads-related real ales and others such as Courage or Wadworths; not perhaps as consistent as it might be but always worth a visit — and the surroundings are nice; staff can be very helpful; children allowed in some areas; has been open all day; bedrooms comfortable *(Gwen and Peter Andrews, Margot Styles, John Coatsworth, Robert and Elizabeth Scott, LYM)*
Chobham [Windsor Rd; SU9761], *Cricketers*: Good home-cooked food, friendly landlord, well kept Courage Best and Directors and Wadworths 6X *(G V Price)*; [High St, 4 miles from M3 junc 3], *Sun*: Low-beamed lounge bar with big inglenook fireplace, good choice of bar food, Courage beers, restaurant *(Ian Phillips, LYM)*; [High St], *White Hart*: Nice beamed pub next to cricket pitch; well kept Courage beers *(Dr and Mrs A K Clarke)*

☆ **Cobham** [Pains Hill/Byfleet Rd; TQ1158], *Little White Lion*: Comfortable and friendly cottagey pub almost opp entrance to 18th-century Parishill Park (and by giant new Sainsburys); two or three intercommunicating bars, well kept real ales, good food from sandwiches to steaks even Sun lunchtime; a few tables in small front garden *(Ian Phillips, John Pettit)*
Cobham [Plough Lane], *Plough*: Comfortably modernised low-beamed lounge bar, nice little snug with darts and old deal panelling, reasonably priced straightforward popular food, well kept

Courage real ales, traditional games in public bar, seats outside the pretty black-shuttered brick house; cheerful, and in the evening popular with young people *(Ian Phillips, LYM)*

☆ **Compton** [Withies Lane; SU9546], *Withies*: Smart and busy dining pub with immaculate garden, good civilised atmosphere in attractive beamed bar with settles and inglenook, some good well presented lunchtime bar snacks, well kept Bass, decent wines, quick service; prices not low; children in restaurant *(John Evans, Mrs J A Blanks, Col G D Stafford, Mrs Hilarie Taylor, LYM)*

☆ **Cox Green** [Baynards Station Yard; Baynards Lane (W off B2128 just N of Rudgwick) — OS Sheet 187, map reference 076349; TQ0934], *Cox Green*: Tucked away in super spot on Downs Link footpath, interesting place with fascinating bric-a-brac on walls and ceiling, well kept real ales such as Badger, King & Barnes Broadwood and Marstons Owd Roger, good range of food and friendly staff; busy weekends (when service can slow); pool, fruit machines, good parking *(Jenny and Brian Seller, Douglas Reid)*

☆ **Cranleigh** [Smithwood Common — OS Sheet 187, map reference 053410; TQ0638], *Four Elms*: Welcoming beamed pub facing big green and overlooking North Downs, with warm welcome, good atmosphere and service, good bar food (not Sun), central open fire; seats and summer barbecues in back garden, good walks *(Jenny and Brian Seller)*

Dorking [West St; TQ1649], *Olde House At Home*: Now Youngs, well furnished, with pleasant atmosphere, tables on concrete back terrace, food; parking limited *(D J Penny)*; [Horsham Rd], *Queens Head*: Now Fullers, with all their beers, informal decor, open all day; parking limited *(D J Penny)*; [West St], *Star*: Now Greene King, with well kept Abbot in small bar; parking limited *(D J Penny)*

☆ **Dunsfold** [TQ0036], *Sun*: Good atmosphere, friendly staff and decent choice of good bar food (not cheap) in elegantly symmetrical 18th-century pub overlooking attractive green; well kept Allied real ales, helpful service, comfortable seats, log fires, and beams; separate cottage dining room; children welcome *(Doreen and Reg Tickner, LYM)*

☆ **Eashing** [Eashing Lane; SU9443], *Stag*: Attractive 17th-century riverside pub with original beams, wattle and daub walling and several traditionally furnished interconnecting rooms; well kept Allied real ales, good range of bar food from sandwiches to steaks inc children's dishes and Sun roasts, log fire, friendly efficient service, no piped music (but fruit machine); small garden, big car park *(Lyn and Bill Capper, Ian Phillips, J G Francis)*

☆ **East Clandon** [TQ0651], *Queens Head*: Traditionally furnished half-timbered pub with big inglenook fireplace, fine old elm bar counter, relaxed atmosphere and tables outside; useful range of straightforward bar

food, well kept Allied real ales, decent house wines, friendly staff, piped music *(John Evans, Ian Phillips, John Pettit, TOH, LYM)*

☆ **Effingham**, [Orestan Lane, TQ1253], *Plough*: Civilised if not cheap commuter-belt pub, particularly popular with older people; consistently imaginative choice of non-chip food at prices that are relatively very low for the area — get there early for a table; well kept Youngs, log fires, pleasant staff, tables in garden with play area; convenient for Polesdon Lacey; no dogs, children or sleeveless T-shirts allowed inside *(TOH, John Pettit, C P Scott-Malden, Mr and Mrs W B Barnes, WFL, Edwina Vardey, K Flack)*

Ellens Green [TQ1035], *Wheatsheaf*: Very clean and well kept rather modern-feeling pub, popular with regulars for full lunches — good choice inc specials such as roast lamb with all the trimmings; also evening meals *(John and Heather Dwane)*

Englefield Green [Northcroft Rd; SU9970], *Barley Mow*: Courage pub worth knowing for its pleasant position overlooking cricket green, also tables out in nice back garden; usual bar food, darts, machines, CD juke box *(David Fowles, Mayur Shah)*; [Wick Lane], *Sun*: Pleasant cottagey pub with newish conservatory full of horseshoes, saddles, boots and so forth; interesting, moderately priced food, well kept Courage beers, and small garden with picnic tables and big aviary along one side; very handy for Savill Garden *(Ian Phillips, Richard Houghton)*

Epsom [on green; TQ2160], *Cricketers*: Totally refurbished over the past couple of years — perhaps a little overdone; on a green overlooking pond — best location in Epsom; bar billiards, lunchtime and evening food *(Giles Quick)*; [Dorking Rd], *Magpie*: Well kept Courage ales, good beef sandwiches and other snacks *(T and A Kucharski)*; [West St], *Marquis of Granby*: Comfortable and very popular, with good value bar food, especially sandwiches inc formidable hot salt beef ones; attractive wooden ceiling in bar, fresh flowers in lounge, well kept ales, friendly landlord and staff *(John Pettit, Chris Fluck)*

☆ **Esher** [82 High St; TQ1464], *Albert Arms*: Good range of real ales (not cheap) and decent French regional wines in lively Victorian pub/bistro with good value bar food inc interesting pâtés and well kept cheeses, friendly service *(Tony and Lynne Stark, LYM)*

☆ **Esher** [High St], *Bear*: Very civilised, spacious and sedate, ideal for older people with several elegant, relaxed rooms and lots of different-sized tables; good choice of standard well prepared food, open fire, no piped music, friendly staff *(Miss Clare Crameri, Ian Phillips)*

Esher [West End La, off A244 towards Hersham, by Princess Alice Hospice], *Prince of Wales*: Comfortable and spacious, with wide choice of bar food, coal-effect gas fire, Watneys-related real ales, piped music; tables on good-sized lawn *(Mrs A Crowhurst,*

Ian Phillips)

Ewell [High St; TQ2262], *Green Man*:
Roomy and comfortable two-bar pub with
reasonably priced food from corner servery
in connected eating area; darts, fruit
machines and quiet piped music; friendly
service; handy for riverside walks *(John
Pettit)*; [Kingston Rd], *Jolly Waggoners*:
Long bar with comfortable seating, friendly
good service, Courage ales, and fair choice
of good value, well cooked food *(DJ)*

☆ **Ewhurst** [Pitch Hill; a mile N of village on
Shere rd; TQ0940], *Windmill*: Hillside
country pub given its star rating for the
spacious series of lawns dropping down
below, and the marvellous views to the
south; smart and spotless inside, with
expensive bar food and well kept real ale
such as Badger Tanglefoot and Courage in
what's now more an opened-out modern bar
than the two-room pub it used to be;
concentration on light and airy conservatory
restaurant; handy for good walks (and on
GWG55) *(Liz and Ian Phillips, D J Penny,
Stephen Goodchild, Michael Badcock, WFL,
Mayur Shah, LYM)*

Ewhurst [The Street; TQ0940], *Bulls Head*:
Particularly well kept gardens, with neat
lawn and flower beds, clean tables; big
village pub with Friary Meux Best, King &
Barnes and Tetleys on handpump, food
good if not cheap; at start of GWG55 *(Jenny
and Brian Seller)*

Farleigh [bus route 403 from Croydon;
TQ3659], *Harrow*: Quite atmospheric
converted barn with tasteful brickwork,
farm tools and so forth, extension, big
garden; popular with younger people in
evening, popular for food at lunchtime *(Neil
Barker)*

Farncombe [Catteshall; outskirts of
Godalming; SU9844], *Ram*: Good ciders
(and beer and spirits too now), reasonably
priced food inc good ploughman's, rooms
that are cool and old without being shabby,
lots of space in big shaded garden with
pretty flowered terrace and barbecue; has
been very firmly shrugging off its former
studenty character *(Mrs Hilarie Taylor, Peter
Barnsley)*

Farnham [A31/A324/A325; up lane into
roundabout on W side — OS Sheet 186,
map reference 855474; SU8446], *Shepherd
& Flock*: Hidden in a cluster of houses in
dell well screened from roundabout traffic,
on Pilgrim Way; good atmosphere, well kept
beer, good food (especially chips), and
altogether very well run *(KC)*

☆ **Forest Green** [nr B2126/B2127 junction;
TQ1240], *Parrot*: Attractively placed by
cricket pitch in nice countryside, rambling
and quaint inside, with all sorts of parrot
designs, well kept real ales inc Courage Best
and Directors and their own Parrot (from
Courage too) on handpump, good often
interesting food (many tables reserved,
giving it something of a restaurant feel in the
evening); plenty of space outside, children
welcome, generally cheerful staff (mainly
young Australians); open all day *(Roy*

*McNeill, Doreen and Reg Tickner, T Galligan,
LYM)*

☆ **Frensham** [A287 Farnham—Hindhead —
OS Sheet 185, map reference 848421;
SU8341], *Mariners*: Small, cosy and busy
bar with wide choice of pizzas and other
dishes, well kept beer, prompt friendly
service; children allowed in pew-seat
restaurant with marine decor; occasional
jazz, handy for Frensham ponds; bedrooms
(KC)

Friday Street [TQ1245], *Stephen Langton*:
Doing well under new management, with
super log fire, warm welcome for all, good
friendly service, well kept beer, good
restaurant; on GWG52 *(Ian Phillips)*

☆ **Godalming** [Ockford Rd; junction
Portsmouth Rd (A3100) and Shackstead
Lane; SU9743], *Inn on the Lake*: Relaxed
atmosphere, well kept Whitbreads-related
and guest real ales, comfortable decor and
furnishings, nicely presented bar food, log
fire and friendly staff with a real welcome
for families; good though not cheap
restaurant with indoor fishpond and grand
piano, good choice of wines; tables out in
lovely garden overlooking lake, summer
barbecues; bedrooms *(John and Heather
Dwane, Jim and Maggie Cowell, J E Newman,
Christian Menzies, Mrs J A Blanks, John and
Karen Day)*

Godalming [High St (A3100)], *Kings Arms
& Royal*: Substantial 18th-century coaching
inn with good value lunches in busy but
friendly warren of little partitioned rooms
and rather splendid Tsar's Lounge; lively
atmosphere, nice service, interesting history;
bedrooms *(K and E Leist, BB)*; [High St, top
end], *Richmond Arms*: Unpretentious but
friendly and comfortable pub on two levels
(approached from two streets); very good
bar food with unusual features — eg
cauliflower cheese topped with bacon and
served with huge wedge of home-baked
brown bread *(Ian Phillips)*

☆ **Godstone** [128 High St; under a mile from
M25 junction 6, via B2236; TQ3551], *Bell*:
Spacious beamed and partly panelled main
bar of quite some character, with big fires at
each end, comfortable and individual seats;
also smaller timbered bar set out more for
eating; well kept Allied real ales on
handpump straightforward lunchtime bar
food, more main dishes and grills evening,
restaurant; prices high; good garden for
children; bedrooms *(E G Parish, Roger
Taylor, LYM)*

Gomshall [Station Rd; A25
Dorking—Guildford; TQ0847], *Black
Horse*: Whitbreads have now turned this
former popular main entry into a Mulligans
Fish Restaurant *(LYM)*

☆ **Guildford** [Quarry St; SU9949], *Kings
Head*: Lots of beams and stripped
brickwork, lovely big inglenook, spacious
banquettes, intimate nooks and crannies,
subdued piped music, well kept Courage
Best and Directors, decent wines, good range
of good value food, especially pies and
ploughman's, seats in back courtyard *(Ian*

Phillips, Ian and Wendy McCaw, Simon Collett-Jones, Mark Porter)

Guildford [80 Sydenham Rd], *Rats Castle*: Friendly atmosphere, attractive decor, wide range of moderately priced food, good varied entertainment inc music, comedians and CD juke box; garden, terrace, and summer barbecues; bedrooms good, clean and comfortable *(Rachael Moore, Ian Phillips)*; [2 Quarry St], *Star*: Recently tastefully refurbished, with lots of woodwork, arches and comfortable seats; daily papers set out, Allied real ales *(Phil and Sally Gorton, Matt Pringle)*; [High St], *Three Pigeons*: Panelling, bare boards, repro 19th-century plaster ceiling, winding stair up to two-level plusher upstairs bar; stuffed birds, barrels, and chests, Liberty-style decor, Allied beers, good value food *(Matt Pringle, Ian Phillips)*

Hambledon [SU9638], *Merry Harriers*: Cosy and homely country pub, with lovely inglenook log fire, well kept Allied real ales, welcoming landlord, wide choice of good freshly cooked food inc sandwiches, filled baked potatoes, steak and kidney pie and scampi at very reasonable prices; impressive collection of chamber-pots hanging from beams, lovely inglenook fireplace *(Mr and Mrs M Wilkinson, Phil and Sally Gorton)*

Haslemere [B2131 Liphook rd; SU9032], *Crowns*: Has gone back to its old name of Crown & Cushion, and Brenda Heath who made it very popular for interesting food has now moved to the Red Lion at Fernhurst *(LYM)*;

Hersham [67 Molesey Rd; TQ1164], *Barley Mow*: A Watneys Country Carvery dining pub, but cottagey and largely unspoilt with beams and comfortable modern kitchen chairs; limited choice of decent food inc great hot bacon baguette, pleasant atmosphere *(Ian Phillips)*; [Queens Rd], *Bricklayers Arms*: Friendly atmosphere in well kept and clean pub with good value bar food and decent wines *(Ian and Wendy McCaw)*

Holmbury St Mary [TQ1144], *Kings Head*: Quietly spacious pub in beautiful spot on the Greensand Way, with friendly staff, half a dozen well kept real ales on handpump, sensible helpings of reasonable food, big garden *(Jenny and Brian Seller)*; *Royal Oak*: Pleasant spot by green and church; log fire in old brick fireplace, Friary Meux Best, good value bar food *(Dave Braisted)*

☆ **Horley** [Church Rd; quite handy for M23 junction 9, off Horley turn from A23; TQ2842], *Olde Six Bells*: Heavy-beamed open-plan bar, part of which was probably a medieval chapel, with spacious new conservatory and raftered upstairs food area (usual bar food, and more elaborate evening dishes); friendly unpretentious local atmosphere and little play on the building's undoubted history; Bass and Charrington IPA on handpump, open all day weekdays; children in restaurant *(David and Sarah Gilmore, Lesley Sones, Geralyn Meyler, Howard and Lynda Dix, LYM)*

Horley, *Game Bird*: Extraordinary decor ranging from bicycle wheels through stuffed birds to partly-clad mannequins beckoning from balcony; central bar made of bricks and barrel staves, surrounded by half a dozen side alcoves with games; Allied ales, good bar food at lunchtime, snacks evening (when there may be a DJ and staff may dress up; children and dogs in garden only *(Cdr W S D Hendry)*

Horsell Common [A320 Woking—Ottershaw; SU9959], *Bleak House*: Good nicely presented food (choice wider in summer than in winter), decent, friendly staff, good range of reasonably priced wines *(Ian Phillips)*

Irons Bottom [Irons Bottom Rd; off A217; TQ2546], *Three Horseshoes*: Simple friendly country pub, changing well kept real ales, inexpensive and freshly cooked straightforward bar food, no piped music, tables outside *(WFL)*

☆ **Kenley** [Old Lodge Lane; left (coming from London) off A23 by Reedham Stn, then keep on; TQ3259], *Wattenden Arms*: Friendly country pub, though actually within London's boundary (by long tradition we list it here under Surrey); cosy and genuine, with dark panelling, traditional furnishings, firmly patriotic decor, well kept Bass and Charrington IPA on handpump, big helpings of reasonably priced bar food (not Sun — and no children); prompt service, crisp-loving cat, seats on small side lawn; good car park *(Ian and Wendy McCaw, Adrian Zambardino, Debbie Chaplin, LYM)*

☆ **Kingswood** [Waterhouse Lane; TQ2455], *Kingswood Arms*: Popular, spacious bar, open-plan yet divided into alcoves, and light and airy conservatory dining extension — refreshingly non-smoky; wide choice of good value food, quickly served; Watneys-related real ales, massive rolling garden with play area *(R Bennett, Adrian Zambardino, Debbie Chaplin)*

Knaphill [Robin Hood Rd; SU9658], *Robin Hood*: 1920s cottage-style pub with bar, lounge, and family areas, even though open-plan; interesting Basingstoke canal photographs, straightforward decor, nice atmosphere and pleasant staff; pricey Courage beer and good value food; pretty hillside garden *(Ian Phillips)*

☆ **Laleham** [The Broadway; TQ0568], *Feathers*: Beamed lounge with red gingham tablecloths at lunchtime, generous helpings of imaginative bar food inc fine well filled baps, steak sandwiches and good value hot dishes, well kept Courage Best and Directors; tables outside; live music Thurs evening *(Ian Phillips, Mrs Shirley Mackenzie)*

☆ **Leatherhead** [Chessington Rd; A243 nr M25 junction 9 — OS Sheet 187, map reference 167600; TQ1656], *Star*: Busy and friendly, with some emphasis on generously served if not cheap food lunchtime and evening, running up to popular chargrilled steaks; winter log fire, choice of real ales, good service *(John Pettit, Adrian Zambardino, Debbie Chaplin, John Pettit)*

☆ **Leigh** [S of A25 Dorking—Reigate;
TQ2246], *Seven Stars*: Pretty country pub
with flower-filled garden, quiet and friendly
inside, horse-racing pictures, inglenook
fireplace, bar food all week, Allied real ales,
maybe summer Sun barbecues; darts alley in
public bar, friendly landlord; no children
*(Jenny and Brian Seller, D J Penny, A Gordon,
LYM)*

☆ **Leigh** [village green; S of A25
Reigate—Dorking], *Plough*: Pretty
weatherboarded cottage with extremely
low-beamed lounge, good bow-windowed
seat in bar, bar food, King & Barnes real
ales, pretty garden; was a great pub under its
former tenants, the Walkers, who left
summer 1990 *(Graham Pettener, D J Penny,
LYM; news of new regime please)*

Limpsfield Chart [TQ4251], *Carpenters
Arms*: Under new management but bar food
still good; prompt and friendly service,
delightful setting with lovely walks, within
easy reach of Chartwell; has been much
modernised *(W J Wonham)*

☆ **Lingfield** [Haxted Rd; TQ3843], *Hare &
Hounds*: Quiet and homely unspoilt country
pub with friendly locals, landlord who does
much of the cooking — very wide range of
imaginative, reasonably priced food such as
cassoulet, curry, fish, rabbit; walkers (and
followers of nearby clay-pigeon shooting)
asked to leave their wellies in the porch; nr
Haxted Mill *(E G Parish, Neil H Barker,
BHP)*

Lingfield, *Old Cage*: Well preserved late
16th-century pub run by nice people; good
beer, decent food, and a lively atmosphere
(especially before race meetings) *(Klaus and
Elizabeth Leist)*

☆ **Little Bookham** [Little Bookham Street;
TQ1254], *Windsor Castle*: Pleasant dining
area in lounge bar of well extended Chef &
Brewer family dining pub, good choice of
hot and cold dishes inc ploughman's, sturdy
roasts, and children's helpings, friendly staff,
well kept Watneys-related real ales, tables in
huge garden with terrace and popular
children's play area *(Mr and Mrs S Cowherd,
D P Wilcox)*

Lower Bourne [SU8544], *Spotted Cow*:
Attractive rural pub with Courage ales, wide
changing choice of good food, efficient
service, well kept beer, pleasant lunchtime
clientele *(Mr and Mrs Foreman)*

☆ **Martyrs Green** [Old Lane; TQ0957], *Black
Swan*: Pleasant woodland pub, currently
doing well; extensively enlarged, handy for
RHS Wisley Gardens, with fine range of a
dozen or so real ales inc Badger Tanglefoot,
Ringwood Old Thumper and Theakstons
Old Peculier; bar food inc lunchtime
sandwiches — not cheap but good, and
served with salad — such as hot beef and
prawns with seafood, good separate
restaurant, log fire; can get crowded with
young people evenings, piped pop music
may be loud; tables in garden with play
area *(Jenny and Brian Seller, WFL, Mike
Rising, Nick Dowson, John Pettit)*

☆ **Merstham** [Nutfield Rd; off A23 in
Merstham, or follow Nutfield Ch,
Merstham 2 signpost off A25 E of Redhill —
OS Sheet 187, map reference 303514;
TQ2953], *Inn on the Pond*: Lots of tables in
engagingly furnished and decorated back
family conservatory, sheltered back terrace;
front area rambles around central fireplace,
with settles, pews, shelves of old books,
decent prints; half a dozen well kept real ales
on handpump, good choice of hot and cold
bar food with big crusty sandwiches, good
vegetarian dishes, daily specials and Sun
morning breakfast; rather pervasive piped
radio; views over scrubland (and the small
pond and nearby cricket ground) to the
North Downs *(BB)*

☆ **Mickleham** [Old London Rd; TQ1753],
Running Horses: Particularly friendly staff
who really make you feel at home (walkers
welcome, too) in pleasant pub with
widening choice of bar food in glazed-over
restaurant area; well kept Allied real ales
and Gales HSB; attractive village nr Box Hill
(Jenny and Brian Seller, John Kimber)

☆ **Mogador** [from M25 up A217 past 2nd
roundabout, signed off; edge Banstead Hth;
TQ2452], *Sportsman*: Low-ceilinged
18th-century pub with interesting layout, in
quiet country setting on edge of Walton
Heath; half a dozen well kept ales inc
Courage Directors and King & Barnes, good
if not cheap food every lunchtime and
evening; darts, bar billiards; dogs welcome if
not wet or muddy, seats out in front and on
lawn behind *(C P Scott-Malden, John Pettit)*

Oatlands [Anderson Rd, just off main
Walton—Weybridge rd; TQ0965], *Prince of
Wales*: Civilised, warm, pleasant and
comfortable pub, with several well kept
changing real ales, good service, good bar
food, popular restaurant; HQ for local
rowing clubs, very busy evenings; Sun free
bar nibbles *(R Houghton)*

☆ **Ockley** [Stane St (A29); TQ1439],
Cricketers Arms: Flagstones, low oak beams
and shinily varnished pine furniture in
15th-century stone village pub currently on
the up, with good simple generous bar food,
well kept real ales such as Badger Best and
Fullers London Pride, country wines,
friendly staff, inglenook log fires, quiet piped
music, darts area, small attractive dining
room decorated with cricketing
memorabilia; seats in back garden with duck
pond and play area, roses around the door
*(D J Penny, TOH, Stephen Goodchild, Richard
Houghton, Mr and Mrs R P Begg, John Pettit)*

Ockley [Stane St (A29)], *Kings Arms*:
Country pub under new licensee, tastefully
refurbished with tables around half-circle
bar, good generous bar food, Fullers and
Youngs ales, small restaurant *(DJ)*

☆ **Oxted** [High St, Old Oxted; TQ3951],
Crown: Stylish Elizabethan pub with classic
Victorian panelling in upper bar, good range
of well kept ales eg Adnams and local
Pilgrims Progress, wide choice of
particularly good value bar food inc
interesting dishes and good veg, cosy
restaurant — a good lunch pub, with

friendly efficient staff; can get crowded with young people and loud music evenings; children welcome weekends, nearby parking virtually impossible *(Andy and Jill Kassube, W J Wonham, Jenny and Brian Seller)*

☆ Oxted [towards Broadham Green], *Hay Cutter*: Country pub extended and refurbished but still cosy, with good choice of bar food (not Sun), well kept Allied real ales, friendly if not brisk service, skittle alley, picnic-table sets in garden; on Greensand Way *(W J Wonham, Jenny and Brian Seller)*

Oxted [High St, Old Oxted], *Old Bell*: Attractive pub with popular Chef & Brewer food inc all-day Sun carvery; friendly welcome, comfortable seating, garden *(E G Parish)*

Puttenham [Seale Lane; SU9347], *Good Intent*: Long open-plan local running from traditional bare public side through to cosy saloon area with big open fire; individual character, Courage ales with a well kept guest such as Adnams, good sustaining food priced reasonably, prominent pool table *(Phil and Sally Gorton)*; [Hook Lane; just off A31 Farnham—Guildford], *Jolly Farmer*: Clean and comfortable Victorian-cottage-theme rooms, some concentration on Harvester restaurant but bar food too, inc a good choice of ploughman's; well kept Courage Best and Directors; picnic-table sets by car park; children welcome *(Lyn and Bill Capper, Ian and Wendy McCaw, LYM)*

Ranmore Common [nr Dunley Hill Farm; towards Effingham Forest, past Dogkennel Green — OS Sheet 187, map reference 112501; TQ1451], *Ranmore Arms*: Country pub attached to big house which seems involved in caravans and car repairs or salvage; warm and friendly, with good food, wide range of well kept ales and lots of outside seating; barbecues in summer, especially Sun lunch; huge log fire in winter, with oil stove for the farther end of the bar *(Ian Phillips, WFL)*

Redhill [St Johns; TQ2650], *Plough*: Small and welcoming, with good feel — open fires, genuine old-world ambience; well kept Ind Coope Burton and Gales HSB, reasonably priced food such as steak and kidney pie and lentil crumble, friendly efficient staff, interesting bric-a-brac *(Jenny and Brian Seller, Ian M Baillie)*

☆ Ripley [High St; TQ0556], *Ship*: Small and busy but comfortable 16th-century local with low beams, flagstones, cosy nooks, window seats and log fire in vast inglenook on left; welcoming atmosphere, efficient service, well kept Courage Best and Directors and John Smiths on handpump, wide choice of reasonably priced bar food from sandwiches up, small upstairs games room with pool and cribbage; interestingly converted courtyard garden *(Ian Phillips, Sandra and Dave Price)*

☆ Ripley [Newark Lane, Pyrford Rd], *Seven Stars*: Typical 1940s open-plan brick pub with lots of red leatherette stools and brocaded banquettes, piped music, darts and fruit machines discreetly tucked round a corner; worth knowing for big helpings of good value generous bar food (evening choice more limited, and music may be more prominent); good friendly service, lots of tables in spacious garden, nr River Wey *(R N Haygarth, Ian Phillips)*

Ripley [High St], *Anchor*: Beamed Tudor inn with many small rooms and a lot of potential; Ind Coope related ales, locally popular bar food, tables in coachyard *(Mike Rising, E G Parish, LYM)*

Row Town [off Addlestone—Ottershaw rd, sharp left past church up Ongar Hill — OS Sheet 176, map reference 036633; TQ0363], *Cricketers*: Good bar food and Watneys-related real ales in unpretentious, creeper-covered pub with big woodburner, a few picnic-table sets outside *(Ian Phillips, Mike Rising)*

Rowledge [Cherry Tree Rd; SU8243], *Cherry Tree*: Delightful, friendly country pub; good Courage beer, food impressive and not too expensive, restaurant area off bar, big garden; very popular, handy for Birdworld and Alice Holt Forest *(Klaus and Elizabeth Leist, Norman Foot)*; [OS Sheet 186, map reference 822434], *Hare & Hounds*: Clean, with good beer, good food (inc good pizzas) and prize-winning garden *(Mr and Mrs Foreman)*

☆ Runfold [B3000, off A31 just E of Farnham; SU8747], *Jolly Farmer*: Comfortable and well run trunk-road pub with popular bar food and well kept Courage real ales; garden a relative haven, given its position, with good adventure playground; children in restaurant; no dogs *(Mr and Mrs Foreman, Mark Porter, LYM)*

Runfold [A31 Farnham—Guildford], *Princess Royal*: Reliably good value food, served so generously that one never seems to have room for a pudding *(G M K Donkin)*

Send [TQ0155], *New Inn*: Warm and friendly, with coal fire, interesting canal photographs, Allied real ale, good straightforward food; seats on lawn separated from canal by gravel track *(Ian Phillips, Mr and Mrs Ken Woolcott, Cdr W D S Hendry)*

Shamley Green [B2128 S of Guildford; TQ0343], *Red Lion*: Handsome settles and other country furniture, antique clocks and interesting pictures, well kept Allied real ales tapped from casks behind the bar, bar food; lovely views over cricket green *(Jenny and Brian Seller)*

☆ Shepperton [Shepperton Lock, Ferry Lane; turn left off B375 towards Chertsey, 100 yds from Square; TQ0867], *Thames Court*: Impressive 1930s riverside pub with lots of quiet nooks and corners, panelled walls, soft lighting, roomy mezzanine and striking upper gallery looking out on to Thames and moorings; relaxed atmosphere, spotless housekeeping, well kept Bass and Flowers IPA, bar food inc Sun hot roast, children in eating area (where there may be a queue); pleasant service, seats out under willow by water, more in big side garden *(Mrs A*

Crowhurst, Chris Fluck, Dr and Mrs R B Crail, E G Parish, Ian and Liz Phillips)

☆ **Shepperton** [Russell Rd], *Red Lion*: Attractive if sometimes busy Thames-side pub dating back to 17th century, dripping with wisteria; plenty of tables on terrace among fine displays of shrubs and flowers, more on lawn over road with lovely river views and well run moorings; good reasonably priced well presented bar food, restaurant, well kept Courage Best and Directors, friendly licensees *(Michael Pritchard, E G Parish)*
Shepperton, *Bull*: Reasonably priced good straightforward food *(Mrs Shirley Mackenzie)*; [47 Upper Haliford Rd], *Goat*: Attractive Watneys Country Carvery, with comfortable leather armchairs and settee, several nooks and alcoves; quick, pleasant service, atmosphere nicely pubby despite leaning towards dining facilities *(E G Parish)*; [Russell Rd], *Ship*: Good river views, helpful young manager, spacious bars, very reasonable bar food, well kept Flowers on handpump, live music Fri *(E G Parish)*

☆ **South Godstone** [Tilburstow Hill Rd; TQ3648], *Fox & Hounds*: Very cosy and friendly atmosphere in truly old-fashioned but comfortably modernised low-beamed pub; well kept Friary Meux Best, good bar and reasonably priced bar snacks; old prints, some high-backed settles, relaxing garden *(W J Wonham, BHP)*
South Holmwood [Horsham Rd; A24 northbound S of Dorking; TQ1744], *Hollys*: Was Holly & Laurel, renamed after Buddy; completely renovated 1990 with very spacious back bar, much of it conservatory-like, formally dressed staff, King & Barnes ales, limited choice of interesting wine-bar-like food inc children's helpings, big back garden, front restaurant; open all day inc Sun *(D J Penny)*

☆ **Staines** [Moor Lane, The Hythe; south bank, over Staines Bridge; TQ0471], *Swan*: Pleasant Thames-side setting, with sycamore-shaded river terrace partly sheltered by upper balcony; both big bars have good river views; well kept Fullers real ales, usual bar food (snacks only, evening), open fireplaces, piped music, restaurant; busy with young people Fri and Sat evenings; children in eating area, open all day summer; bedrooms *(Cdr W D S Hendry, Mayur Shah, Ian Phillips, Andrew Cooke, Hazel R Morgan, LYM)*

☆ **Staines** [124 Church St], *Bells*: Attractive and pleasantly decorated local, comfortable and compact around central fireplace, welcoming atmosphere, well kept Courage Best and Directors, wide range of constantly changing good value bar food inc Sat; darts and cribbage *(Ian Phillips)*
Staines [46 Church St], *Cock*: Friendly, comfortable and welcoming town pub with real ale and open fire *(Neil H Barker)*; [Leacroft], *Old Red Lion*: Old-world 17th-century beamed pub overlooking green; warm welcome, well kept beer, wide

choice of bar food, prize-winning floral displays and lots of charity events *(Ian Phillips)*

☆ **Stoke d'Abernon** [Station Rd (off A245); TQ1259], *Plough*: Homely and comfortable pub with reasonably priced good sensible bar food in airy conservatory eating area; well kept Watneys-related real ales, big window seats, coal fire, helpful staff, sizeable garden *(Ian Phillips, BB)*
Sunbury [Green St, Lower Sunbury; nr start of M3; TQ1068], *Admiral Hawke*: Consistently good value no-nonsense cooking inc good Sun lunch; friendly service, staff eager to please, comfortable seats in small lounges, warm and cosy, with well padded banquettes *(E G Parish)*; [Staines Rd W/Chertsey Rd], *Black Dog*: Attractively pubby, with bric-a-brac galore such as brasses, old pipes, nearly 1000 key-rings hung from ceiling; good fresh sandwiches, obliging landlady, well kept Charrington IPA on handpump, comfortable seating — one alcove has Concorde seats *(E G Parish)*; [Thames St], *Flower Pot*: Attentive landlord, ample helpings of good medium-priced bar food, evening bistro, half a dozen real ales on handpump; comfortable, open all day May-Oct *(E G Parish)*; [French St], *Jockey*: Lively little Charrington local with bags of character and pianola *(Ian Phillips)*; [64 Thames St], *Magpie*: Lovely spot on Thames, with moorings and river terrace; friendly, with well kept beer, decent bar food, helpful staff, unsmart early 60s decor; restaurant and food counter at street level, stairs down to bar and snug; open all day; bedrooms *(Ian Phillips, E G Parish)*; [Staines Rd W; nr Sunbury Cross], *Prince Albert*: Exceptionally well run, with several alcoves in interesting well furnished bar, one with a settee, and unusual individual shelf-tables; good fresh sandwiches, Watneys-related ales on handpump, cheerful friendly staff *(E G Parish)*

☆ **Sutton** [B2126 — this is the Sutton near Abinger; TQ1046], *Volunteer*: Lovely quiet setting, with plenty of well spaced tables in good-sized garden (Tannoy food announcements); good value food served promptly, warm welcome, well kept Allied and Gales real ales; attractive decor, artefacts and military paintings in cosy low-beamed traditional bar *(Trevor and Helen Dayneswood, Jenny and Brian Seller)*
Tadworth [Box Hill Rd; TQ2256], *Hand in Hand*: Roomy country pub handy for Box Hill — popular in summer; extended bar with iron scrollwork, brassware, paintings, relaxed atmosphere, well kept Courage, good simple bar food, Sun lunch, friendly service, fruit machine; big garden sheltered by shrubs and trees, with well spaced tables *(John Pettit)*

☆ **Thames Ditton** [Queens Rd; TQ1567], *Albany*: Clean and spacious, with well kept Bass on handpump, three real fires, wide range of good lunchtime bar food in big helpings, friendly staff; attractive Thameside terrace and lawn overlooking

Hampton Court grounds; restaurant; busy in summer *(P Gillbe, TOH)*

☆ **Thorpe** [Thorpe Green; TQ0268], *Rose & Crown*: Well kept rose-covered pub on one of Surrey's largest village greens, with tables among flowers on grass outside; Courage ales and good home-cooked bar food lunchtime and evening, pleasantly busy atmosphere and good staff; play area *(Mayur Shah, Mike Rising)*

Thorpe [Ten Acre Lane], *Red Lion*: Mellow brick pub, relaxing and civilised; small back terrace leading to orchard with picnic-table sets, swings and slide; well presented standard Whitbreads menu; nr Thorpe Park (theme park and stately home) *(Ian Phillips)*

☆ **Tilford** [SU8743], *Barley Mow*: Friendly pub in beautiful spot by village cricket green, with riverside garden; quarry-tiled floor, wall benches, scrubbed tables, open fire in big inglenook, curved bar counter, darts and table skittles; good food and service in small back eating area, well kept Courage ales *(Phil and Sally Gorton, G and M Stewart)*

Virginia Water [Christchurch Rd (B389); TQ0067], *Trottesworth*: Comfortable and friendly, with tempting carvery and buffet in spacious, attractive and friendly restaurant — good choice and quality, reasonable prices, some Portuguese dishes *(Clem Stephens)*

Walton on Thames [50 Manor Rd; off A3050; TQ1066], *Swan*: Pleasant riverside pub with fine views of Thames from spacious garden area with summer barbecues; good bar, cheerful and lively atmosphere, friendly staff and good choice of reasonably priced food *(Miss Clare Crameri, Adrian Zambardino, Debbie Chaplin)*; [Sunbury Lane], *Weir*: Well run pub in attractive position beside Thames opp Lower Sunbury weir; well kept Courage beers on handpump, good choice of bar food inc sandwiches *(R B Crail)*

☆ **Walton on the Hill** [Chequers Lane; TQ2255], *Chequers*: Well laid out series of mock-Tudor rooms rambling around central servery, dark ochre walls, dark beams, copper-topped tables, tapestry banquettes, flowers and tropical fish; efficient good value lunchtime food bar, popular though not cheap restaurant, well kept Youngs real ale, friendly service, terrace and neat garden with good summer barbecues; traditional jazz Thurs; children in restaurant *(Barbara M McHugh, Richard Houghton, Adrian Zambardino, Debbie Chaplin, LYM)*

Walton on the Hill [inn signed down dirt track, N end], *Bell*: Cheerful two-bar pub with well kept Bass, Charrington IPA and a guest beer, bar food, pub games, good mix of customers; woodland all round *(Gary Scott)*; [Deans Lane], *Blue Ball*: Friendly welcome and well kept Courage in pub with two separate smallish eating rooms, one set more as restaurant with fresh flowers and lovely log fire; good food from 11, not Sun evening *(DWAJ)*

☆ **Warlingham** [Farleigh Rd; TQ3658], *Harrow*: Sandwiches, ploughman's and four

or five beautifully cooked and presented piping hot traditional dishes with a couple of puddings (lunchtime, not Sun), in delightful stripped-flint barn bar with well spaced seating, raised no smoking area, rustic decoration inc an owl high in the rafters; separate locals' bar, tables on lawn, open fields behind *(Jane Palmer, M Desphond)*

☆ **West Clandon** [TQ0452], *Onslow Arms*: Rambling beamed country pub, pricey, often busy but well laid out, with comfortable seating in nooks and corners, open fire, soft lighting, lots of brass and copper, thick carpets, friendly customers; wide choice of well kept real ales inc Brakspears, Courage Directors and Youngs, good straightforward bar food from small servery, stylish restaurant (popular Sun lunches), efficient service, great well lit garden; children welcome *(D J Penny, Mayur Shah, J S Evans)*

☆ **West Clandon** [Clandon St], *Bull*: Increasingly popular small country pub with comfortably modernised but cosy split-level bars, friendly staff, well kept beers, decent wine, big helpings of good value home-cooked lunchtime food (Sun roasts if booked); get there early for a table; convenient for Clandon Park, good walking country *(John Pettit, Ian and Wendy McCaw)*

West Molesey [Island Farm Rd; off Molesey Rd Weybridge—Molesey; TQ1367], *Surveyor*: Modern estate pub with partitioned-off public bar and partly separate eating area; well kept, if rather pricey, Fullers ales, good value lunchtime food, good service, darts; open all day *(Richard Houghton)*

☆ **Weybridge** [Thames St; TQ0764], *Lincoln Arms*: Large oldish pub on river road, popular for bar lunches; comfortably refurbished and extended, with Ushers and other real ales, log-effect gas fires at either end, genuinely welcoming staff, good mix of customers, unobtrusive piped music; picnic-table sets on back lawn, other tables on little green in front *(Cdr W D S Hendry, Ian Phillips, Dr and Mrs R B Crail)*

☆ **Windlesham** [Chertsey Rd], *Brickmakers Arms*: Small, friendly country pub with well kept Courage, good separate restaurant, upstairs room with baby alarm, newspapers on Sun; new garden behind with boules and summer barbecues *(Dr M Owton)*

☆ **Windlesham** [Church Rd; SU9264], *Half Moon*: A proper pub, straightforward but very pleasant (and very popular), with up to ten or so real ales, straightforward lunchtime food and good Sun lunches, thriving atmosphere, cheerful quick service even when busy, interesting WWII pictures; huge attractive garden overlooking nearby church and paddock *(Richard Houghton, Dr R Fuller, G V Price)*

☆ **Witley** [Petworth Rd (A283); SU9439], *White Hart*: Largely Tudor, with good oak furniture, pewter tankards hanging from beams, inglenook fireplace where George Eliot drank; Watneys-related real ales, traditional games, unobtrusive piped music, straightforward bar food; children in restaurant and eating area, seats outside, playground; village church well worth a visit *(LYM)*

Woking [right off Goldsworth Rd towards St Johns; TQ0159], *Bridge Barn*: Large Beefeater worth knowing for canalside position (lots of waterside tables) and interesting layout — restaurant up in barn rafters, flagstoned bars below; very welcoming *(Mr and Mrs W H Crowther)*; [12 Chertsey Rd, nr stn], *Old Stillage*: Cosy beamed town pub popular with businessmen and shoppers for good choice of food in separate dining area, very efficient friendly service, several real ales inc Marstons Pedigree, Wadworths 6X and Websters Yorkshire; piped music *(Richard Houghton, Simon Collett-Jones)*

Wonersh [The Street; TQ0245], *Grantley Arms*: Half-timbered 16th-century pub with good food *(D R Bettison)*

Wood Street [White Hart Lane; SU9550], *White Hart*: Attractive building and setting, welcoming warm feel with big central log-effect gas fire, good varied beers such as Brakspears, Courage Directors and Flowers, good value bar food — soup, sausage and chips and delicious cold puddings recommended; restaurant *(Carol and Mike Muston, Dr and Mrs R B Crail, Adrian Zambardino, Debbie Chaplin)*

Worplesdon [take Worplesdon Stn rd from Guildford—Woking rd; SU9753], *Jolly*

Farmer: Fine range of about eight well kept real ales — at a price — inc rarities here, in simply furnished L-shaped beamed bar of isolated country pub; piped music, welcoming staff, big sheltered garden *(M B Porter, LYM)*

☆ **Wotton** [A25 Dorking—Guildford; TQ1247], *Wotton Hatch*: Busy little traditional low-ceilinged front bar with open fire, handsome old-world cocktail bar, traditional games and fruit machine in tiled-floor public bar, well kept Fullers real ales on handpump, bar food, good carvery restaurant — primarily a dining pub Sun lunchtime; attentive staff, tables with play area in sizeable neat garden; children allowed in restaurant *(S Corrigan, Gwen and Peter Andrews, D J Penny, LYM)*

☆ **Wrecclesham** [Bat & Ball Lane; Boundstone — off Upper Bourne Lane, itself off Sandrock Hill Rd; SU8245], *Bat & Ball*: Seven frequently changing real ales in fine condition, Sun bar nibbles, very young but good staff; cosy old main bar with family extension, spacious terrace and gardens *(Richard Houghton, Steve Huggins)*

Wrecclesham [Sandrock Hill Rd], *Sandrock*: Good range of real ales mostly from smaller breweries all in top condition, in simply converted regulars' pub with buzz of conversation in main room; games room and garden *(David Fowles)*

Sussex

Prices here have inched up even more than in most other places this last year, making Sussex pubs almost as costly as those in Surrey (and noticeably more expensive than those just over the border in Kent). Sadly, pubs tied to the area's local breweries charge only a couple of pence or so less for drinks than other pubs here; not as wide a margin as usual. However, there are undoubted compensations. This area does have a remarkably high concentration of really good country pubs – and in a good many of them, the food's well worth paying for. For this we'd single out the pretty little Rose Cottage at Alciston, the Fountain at Ashurst (its short and simple choice just right for a pub), the George & Dragon at Burpham (its enterprise and imagination earning it a food award this year), the Bell in the charming village of Burwash (doing very well this year), the unpretentious Elsted Inn at Elsted (a new entry this year) and the interesting old Three Horseshoes there, the very civilised Griffin at Fletching (a nice place to stay at – and this year it wins a star award for its all-round excellence), the bustling Anchor at Hartfield (back in these pages after quite an absence, with bedrooms now), the George & Dragon at Houghton (doing very well under a new licensee), the rambling and friendly Juggs at Kingston near Lewes, the handsome Lickfold Inn at Lickfold, the Halfway Bridge at Lodsworth (inventive if not cheap), the cheerful and bustling Star at Normans Bay (another new entry), the Jack Fullers at Oxleys Green (a charming dining pub), the nice old Chequers at Rowhook (it's on particularly good form, earning a food award this year), the Golden Galleon at Seaford (doing very well indeed under its Italian landlord), the White Hart at Stopham (good fish in the restaurant), the charming Bull just outside Ticehurst (another pub that's currently on a winning streak) and the very popular New Inn in Winchelsea. The Six Bells at Chiddingly stands out for low prices – a very fine pub, all round. Changes to note include a new manager winning praise at the fine old Star in Alfriston, and new licensees at the Fox Goes Free at Charlton (some changes on the food side), the tucked-away Royal Oak at Chilgrove, the George & Dragon in its splendid garden near Coolham, the fine old Bull in Ditchling, the Shepherd & Dog just below the Downs at Fulking, the Richmond Arms at West Ashling (if anything, determined to beat the former owner's record for introducing new beers), and the interesting Dorset Arms at Withyham. The delightful Gribble at Oving has finally got its own microbrewery on stream; we happened to telephone them to check some factual details on the day Reg's Tipple was first ready for tasting, and the landlady was so excited she could scarcely speak to us. The Three Cups at Punnetts Town, an archetypal country local formerly tied to Courage, has just won its independence – which seems to have given it a splendid new lease of life. Several other pubs back in these pages after quite a break are the Black Rabbit in a lovely spot on the edge of Arundel (much reworked and improved since we last saw it, under a different brewery), the Old

House At Home at Chidham (with a wider appeal nowadays), and the Ram at West Firle (doing very well indeed under its current regime). Among the Lucky Dip entries at the end of the chapter, the Bridge at Amberley, Sussex Ox at Berwick, White Harte in Cuckfield, Coach & Horses at Danehill, Blacksmiths Arms at Donnington and Hurdlemakers at East Dean have all been moving sharply into the frame in the last few months. Others we'd pick out as notable include the Black Horse at Binstead, Hatch at Colemans Hatch, Lamb and Pilot in Eastbourne, New Inn in Hurstpierpoint, Lewes Arms in Lewes, Crow & Gate at Poundgate and Horseguards at Tillington. There's quite a choice in Brighton – and at Alfriston.

ALCISTON　TQ5103　Map 3

Rose Cottage ⊘

Village signposted off A27 Polegate–Lewes

Even regulars sometimes crack their heads on the low beams of this tiled white wisteria-covered cottage – but rate that a small price to pay for good helpings of well prepared home-cooked food. They are licensed to deal in game (as well as selling local eggs), so this can work through into the menu, with rabbit pie a special favourite. Other dishes include wholesome soup, good ploughman's (£2.95; they also do soup and ploughman's together, £3.95), cold gammon and egg (£3.50), big salads (from £4, prawn with avocado £5.80), lasagne (£4.25), barbecue ribs, excellent home-made pie and home-made quiche, good stuffed pork, and steaks (from £7.95); in the evening there are extras like whitebait (£2.65), smoked salmon cornet (£4.25), scampi (£4.95), and half a roast duckling (£8.50). Get there early for one of the half-dozen tables with their cushioned pews in the relaxed and friendly little bar under quite a forest of harness, traps, a thatcher's blade and lots of other black ironware, with more bric-a-brac on the shelves above the dark pine dado or in the etched glass windows. There is a lunchtime overflow into the restaurant area. Service is pleasant and efficient. Well kept Harveys (sold as Beards) and Ruddles Best on handpump (Harveys under light pressure); Merrydown cider; log fires, in the mornings a talking parrot, piped music. There are some seats under cover outside, and a small paddock has a goat, chickens and duck-pond. If you fancy your long-rope skipping prowess, don't miss Good Friday lunchtime. *(Recommended by Mrs K J Betts, N Patton, Howard and Lynda Dix, W J Wonham, Mr and Mrs D W Fisher, Tony Gayfer, Miss P A Barfield, John Beeken, Mike and Joyce Bryant, Nigel Gibbs, Jenny and Brian Seller, Lesley Sones, Geralyn Meyler)*

Free house　Licensee Ian Lewis　Real ale　Meals and snacks (till 10)　Small evening restaurant (not Sun)　Alfriston (0323) 870377　Children in eating area and restaurant　Open 11.30–2.30, 6.30–11

ALFRISTON　TQ5103　Map 3

Star ⟻

Several unique antiquities make a visit to this 15th-century inn a must for lovers of pub rarities. Its facade is studded with curious medieval carvings, mainly religious (Battle Abbey had it built as a guest house for pilgrims), and the wooden pillar in the heavy-beamed bar was once a sanctuary post – holding it gave you the protection of the Church against even the highest temporal authority. Elegant furnishings include a heavy Stuart refectory table with a big bowl of flowers, antique Windsor armchairs worn to a fine polish and a handsome longcase clock; the fireplace is Tudor. Lunchtime food includes home-made soup (£1.25), sandwiches (from £2.50), ploughman's (from £3.50), a mixed meat salad or home-made dishes of the day such as chicken casserole or good steak and kidney pie (£3.50); puddings (from £1.40); on Sunday there's a buffet in the bar, full lunch in the restaurant. Bass and John Smiths on handpump, English wines (drinks prices are very reasonable, considering the old-fashioned service and style of the place). Bedrooms are in a comfortably up-to-date back part that you'd scarcely guess at from the ancient front inn. *(Recommended by D A Wilcock, Miss C M Davidson, Harry McCann, Alec Lewery, WHBM)*

Free house (THF)   Manager James Stewart   Real ale   Lunchtime meals and snacks   Restaurant   Alfriston (0323) 870495   Children welcome   Open 11–11   Bedrooms; £73B/£101B

ARUNDEL   TQ0107   Map 3

Black Rabbit

Mill Road; keep on and don't give up!

Reopened in 1990 after changing hands and extensive renovation, this has one of the most charming locations in Sussex. It's the lovely waterside position which makes it really worth knowing – idyllic in summer, with tables over the service lane in sheltered paved areas beside a peaceful stretch of the River Arun, looking over the bird-reserve marshy water meadows towards what is one of the best views of the Castle. There are more tables under a verandah. Inside, big windows give an airy feel to the long smart bar, with a help-yourself food bar and restaurant at its far end. Well kept Badger Best and Tanglefoot on handpump or electric pump. Lunchtime food includes filled baked potatoes (from £2.50), jumbo sausage (£3.25), quiche (£3.75), salads (from £4.25), and daily specials such as lasagne, steak and mushroom pie, chicken curry or vegetable stir-fry (£4.95); in the evening there are basket meals like prawns, crab claws or chicken (from £3.25) or an à la carte menu. The bar lounge and top restaurant area are no-smoking. Good service; neat lavatories. There's ample mooring, and boat trips to and from Arundel during lunchtime. *(Recommended by WFL, MCG, Gwen and Peter Andrews, Mayur Shah, Alec Lewery, Marie Enright)*

Badger   Manager Martin Earp   Real ale   Meals and snacks   Restaurant   Arundel (0903) 882828   Children in eating area of bar and restaurant   Open 11–11, (winter 11–3.30, 6.30–11)

ASHURST   TQ1716   Map 3

Fountain

B2135 N of Steyning

In contrast to so many publicans who crowd their menus with almost everything the catering salesmen can dream up, the Caines concentrate on getting a short and simple choice of home-cooked food just right – still good value, though prices have gone up since they bought the freehold (it was a Whitbreads tenancy). Recent tips have included interesting soups (£1.80), filled baked potatoes (evenings only, from £2.95), pâté (£2.95), sausages and mash (winter only, £3.25), ploughman's (from £2.75), pizza (£2.95), sausage curry (£3.25), cheese and broccoli flan (£3.95), steak and kidney pie (£4.50) and steaks (evenings only); the quiches and flans are consistently good; also puddings like apricot crumble (£1.75). A particular plus point is that they have not turned this ancient place into a quasi-restaurant; it's still very much a pub, with a charmingly unspoilt tap room on the right: scrubbed 16th-century flagstones, a couple of high-backed wooden cottage armchairs by the log fire in its brick inglenook, two antique polished trestle tables, a friendly pub dog, and well kept real ales such as Batemans XXXB, Flowers Original, Fremlins and Marstons Pedigree, with a regular guest beer tapped from the cask. A bigger carpeted room (no dogs here) has country-kitchen chairs, settles and stools around its tables, corner cupboards, a woodburner, and shove-ha'penny, dominoes and cribbage; cheerful service. Booking is advisable for their candlelit suppers. A gravel terrace has picnic-table sets by an attractive duckpond, and there are swings and a see-saw (and weekend barbecues) in a garden with fruit trees and roses. *(Recommended by Peggy and Mike Woodger, Frank Cummins, Mayur Shah, TOH, R Houghton; more reports please)*

Free house   Licensee Maurice Caine   Real ale   Meals and snacks (not Sun or Weds evenings)   (0403) 710219   Children in eating area lunchtime only   Open 11–2.30, 6–11; closed evening 25 and 26 Dec

nr BILLINGSHURST   TQ0925 Map 3
Blue Ship

The Haven; hamlet signposted off A29 just N of junction with A264, then follow signpost left towards Garlands and Okehurst

Tucked away down a quiet lane, this is included for its resolute refusal to follow the stampeding herd of pubs rushing to turn themselves into conservatory-bedecked restaurants. It is very much an unspoilt country pub, from the tangle of honeysuckle round the door, through the brick-floored front bar with its low beams, inglenook fireplace and corridor to a couple of other simple rooms, to the fact that it still runs its own shoot. Good home-made bar food includes sandwiches, ploughman's, cottage pie (£3.50), cod or plaice (£3.75), lasagne (£4.15), steak and kidney pie or scampi (£4.65), and puddings like fruit crumble or treacle tart (£1.80). Well kept King & Barnes Bitter tapped from the cask. A games room has darts, bar billiards, shove-ha'penny, cribbage, dominoes and fruit machine. Plenty of tables outside, and the remote spot, make it a great summer pub; it can get crowded with young people at weekends. *(Recommended by Mr Cowell, Paul Smith, David and Sarah Gilmore; more reports please)*

King & Barnes   Tenant J R Davie   Real ale   Meals and snacks (not Sun or Mon evenings)   (0403) 822709   Children in eating area and games room   Open 11–3, 6–11

BLACKBOYS   TQ5220 Map 3
Blackboys

B2192, S edge of village

With the Weald Way crossing the Vanguard Way nearby, this 14th-century weatherboarded house is particularly popular in summer – when the gardens come into their own. There's masses of space outside, with rustic tables in the back orchard, some seats overlooking the pretty front pond, a play area with a challenging wooden castle and quite a few animals, and a barn with a big well equipped playroom. Inside, a string of old-fashioned and unpretentious little rooms, with dark oak beams, bare boards or parquet and masses of bric-a-brac and antique prints, have a lot of atmosphere: one reader who knew it from 40 years ago when his father was a licensee found not much changed, but delighted in a novel version of ring-the-bull – ring-the-stag's-nose. Good waitress-served food includes open sandwiches (from £2.25), soup (£1.75), steak sandwich (£2.95), ploughman's with good home-cooked ham (£3.25), seafood pancakes (£4.95), summer crab salad (£6.95) or lobster salad (£7.95), steaks (from £7.50) and daily specials like turbot (£7.50), with winter game such as pheasant braised in calvados and cider (£6.95). Well kept Harveys Armada and BB on handpump; welcoming service, a good inglenook log fire, and darts, shove-ha'penny, dominoes, table skittles, cribbage, fruit machine, space game, and juke box. *(Recommended by B R Shiner, Jenny and Brian Seller, Alan Skull, Caroline Wright, M Rising, Mike and Joyce Bryant)*

Harveys   Tenant Patrick Russell   Real ale   Meals and snacks (12–2.30, 6.30–10.15) Restaurant   Framfield (0825) 890283   Children in eating area and restaurant Occasional Morris dancers and singers   Open 11–3, 6–11; 11–11 Sat; closed evening 25 Dec

BURPHAM   TQ0308 Map 3
George & Dragon 🏮

Warningcamp turn off A27 outside Arundel, then keep on up
Nothing much beyond the ticking of a clock to disturb the peace of this airy and

spaciously comfortable open-plan lounge. Food served efficiently by friendly staff
includes home-made soup (£2.25), sandwiches (from £1.90), filled baked potatoes
(from £2.90), ploughman's (from £3), gammon steak with pineapple (£6.85),
chicken breast stuffed with garlic (£6.95), unusual vegetarian specials and
inventive dishes of the day including maybe avocado and fresh crab (£3.95),
home-made fish cakes (£4), fresh skate or pork kebabs (£5.95), or fresh salmon
(£6.95), and a good selection of home-made puddings (£2.35); Sunday lunch
(£14.50); well kept Adnams, Courage Directors, Harveys, Ruddles and two weekly
changing guest real ales, decent choice of wines; coffee, immaculate housekeeping.
There are tables outside: bright with window-boxes, the pub fits well into this
charming hill village of thatch and flint. The partly Norman church has some
unusual decoration, and there are good downland walks nearby, with spectacular
views down over Arundel Castle and the river. *(Recommended by David Hunn, Iain and
Penny Muir, E G Parish, P A Barfield, P Gillbe, D C Horwood, Michael Player; more reports
please)*

*Free house Licensees George and Marianne Walker Real ale Meals and snacks (not
Sun evening) Restaurant Arundel (0903) 883131 Well behaved children in eating
area and restaurant Open 11–3, 6–11; longer on bank hols; closed evening Sun (2 Jan
– Easter)*

BURWASH   TQ6724   Map 3

Bell ★

A265 E of Heathfield

From the churchyard opposite, this mainly 17th-century pub, covered in flowers in
summer, looks a delight; and it earns special praise for the way that it serves fine
food in the genuine atmosphere of a warmly friendly village local (not a restaurant
masquerading as a pub). The L-shaped bar on the right has an armchair by its big
log fire (two fires if it's cold), all sorts of ironwork, bells and barometers on its
ochre Anaglypta ceiling and terracotta walls, and well polished built-in pews
around tables; the Victorian night-watchman arcade machine is fun. Food includes
sandwiches (from £2.75), chicken tikka which can make a starter for two or a light
main course, (£2.85), broccoli and cheese in pastry (£5.20), steak, kidney and
mushrooms in ale (£5.40), lamb steak in mushroom sauce (£5.50), curry (from
£5.50), chicken and avocado (£6.95), chicken Wellington (£7.20), huge mixed grill
(£9.20), with lots of fresh Hastings fish such as grilled sea bream (£6.50), fresh
dressed crab (£6.75), grilled plaice (£6.90), scallops and prawns in cream and
brandy (£7), skate (£7.35); also puddings like splendid treacle sponge and custard.
The room on the left is broadly similar, but quieter (and greener). Well kept
Badger, Gales BBB, Harveys and Mitchells ESB on handpump, Taunton cider,
respectable house wines; friendly and efficient service; shove-ha'penny,
ring-the-bull and toad-in-the-hole; maybe unobtrusive piped music; seats out in
front. The village is very pretty, and near Batemans (Kipling's home); *Good Walks
Guide* Walk 67 starts close by. Nearby parking may be difficult. The bedrooms
(oak beams, sloping floors) can be recommended, but the bathroom is shared.
*(Recommended by Neil Barker, Geoff and Julie Bond, D J Milner, J P Cinnamond, Ron
Tennant, Dr P D V Gwinner, C R and M A Starling, Giles Quick, Mike and Joyce Bryant,
Michael Bourdeaux)*

*Beards (who no longer brew) Tenant David Mizel Real ale Meals and snacks (not
Sun evening) Restaurant (not Sun evening) Burwash (0435) 882304 Children in
restaurant Traditional jazz last Sun of month Open 11–2.30, 6–11 Bedrooms;
£25/£35*

BYWORTH   SU9820   Map 2

Black Horse

Signposted from A283

The austere feel, particularly in the front bar, fits well with the pub's 15th-century
origins, built as it was on the site of a friary: stripped pews, scrubbed tables, bare

floorboards, candles in bottles, just a few sepia photographs in the back rooms. By contrast, the garden is almost opulently lush in high summer, just right for a leisurely lunch. At the top, tables on a steep series of grassy terraces, sheltered by banks of flowering shrubs, look across a drowsy valley to swelling woodland; a small stream runs along under an old willow by the more spacious lawn at the bottom. A wide choice of bar food includes good French onion soup (£2.30), ploughman's (from £3.20), shepherd's pie (£3.75), salads (from £3.90), scallops in garlic (£4.10), lamb's kidneys in sherry or beef curry (£5.85), sweet and sour chicken (£6.25), monkfish in cream of mustard sauce or poached salmon (£6.85), steaks (from £9.50), vegetarian dishes available on request, also puddings such as apple flan or treacle tart (£2.50). Well kept Ballards, Courage Directors and Youngs on handpump; friendly service; darts. *(Recommended by Mrs J Silverstein, John Whitehead, G S B G Dudley, Alec Lewery, Marie Enright, John and Heather Dwane, Ian and Wendy McCaw, Peter Woods, Hope Chenhalls, T Galligan, Mrs Lili Lomas)*

Free house   Mr and Mrs P Hess   Real ale   Meals and snacks (12–1.45, 7–9.45) Restaurant   Petworth (0798) 42424   Children in restaurant if well behaved   Open 11(11.30 winter)–2.30, 6(6.30 winter)–11

CHARLTON   SU8812 Map 2

Fox Goes Free

Village signposted off A286 Chichester–Midhurst in Singleton, also from Chichester–Petworth via East Dean

This was just the Fox until it was bought from Watneys and set "free" in 1985: it's hard to judge whether the warm and relaxed atmosphere is the result of nearly 500 years as a pub, or simply of the cosy series of separate rooms. The main one has a big brick fireplace and partly carpeted brick floor, elm benches built against its yellowing walls and a small but entertaining hat collection; a nice little low-beamed snug has a sturdy elm settle and a second big inglenook fireplace, and there are more tables in a no-smoking, country-style extension which serves as an eating area. Bar food includes good home-made soup (£2), rolls (from £1.60), filled baked potatoes (from £2.75), ploughman's (from £3), steak and mushroom pie, chicken kiev, plaice, curry or scampi (all £3.95), specials like lobster, crab, shark or salmon steaks, and puddings such as apple and blackcurrant pie or passion cake (£1.80). Well kept beers include Adnams, Ballards Wassail, Greene King Abbot, King & Barnes Festive and Ringwood Old Thumper on handpump and under light pressure; good range of country wines; they also have darts, dominoes, cribbage, fruit machine and trivia. Tables among fruit trees in the back garden look up to the Downs, and there's a safe children's play area with sandpit and swings; the barbecue area can be booked. Handy for the Weald and Downland Open Air Museum. *(Recommended by Klaus and Elizabeth Leist, Jim and Becky Bryson, Viv Middlebrook, David Hunn, T Galligan, Mrs Lili Lomas, Margaret and Roy Randle, Mr Cowell, Dr B A W Perkins, Jacqueline Davis, E G Parish, Dr A M Rankin, Grace and Michael Kirby, Peter Burton, Jerry and Alison Oakes)*

Free house   Licensee Gil Battley   Real ale   Meals and snacks (11.30–2.30, 7–10.30 Mon-Sat, till 9 Sun)   Restaurant   (024 363) 461   Children in stable bar and restaurant   Open 11–2.30(3 Sat winter), 6(7 winter)–11; all day Sat in summer; Bedrooms; £25/£35

CHIDDINGLY   TQ5414 Map 3

Six Bells ★ £

Village signed off A22 Uckfield–Hailsham

If we gave prizes for pubs with that happy knack of getting all sorts to mix really happily, from pensioners to punks, from burly fellers on big quackers or chopped hogs to chaps under Lanchesters, from Brighton students to Glyndebourners – this idiosyncratic low-beamed country pub would certainly be well in the running. Well sited where the Weald Way crosses the Vanguard Way, it gets a good few walkers too. The style and furnishings conjure up Portobello Road, Camden Passage and the Brighton Lanes: an attractive mix of lots of old pictures, interesting bric-a-brac, pews and antique seats, even a working pianola in one bar, and a fine collection of enamelled advertising signs in the gents'. The home-made food is consistently good value; dishes in favour recently include bargain French onion soup (60p), cheesy garlic bread (£1.30), beef and vegetable or shepherd's pie (£1.60), meat or vegetarian lasagne (£1.70), steak and kidney pie (£1.75), ploughman's or filled baked potato (£2.25), huge salads (from £2.50), spicy prawns (£3.25), spare ribs in barbecue sauce (£3.30), and generous puddings like banana splits, treacle pie (£1.30) and spicy pears Mexicana (£3.25). Well kept Courage Best and Directors on handpump, with Harveys tapped from the cask in winter; farmhouse cider, and a good log fire; dominoes and cribbage. Outside at the back, there are some tables beyond a goldfish pond; the church opposite has an interesting Jeffrey monument. Weekends are lively (delightfully so, say readers – the music is well segregated in the barn). *(Recommended by Klaus and Elizabeth Leist, Jenny and Brian Seller, Simon Velate, Win and Reg Harrington, John Beeken; more reports please)*

Free house   Licensee Paul Newman   Real ale   Meals and snacks (11.30–2, 6–10) (0825) 872227   Small children's room   Live bands Fri, Sat and Sun evenings, jazz Sun lunchtime   Open 10–2.30, 6–11; closed Mon except bank hols

CHIDHAM   SU7903 Map 2
Old House At Home

Cot Lane; turn off A27 at the Barleycorn pub

Though one or two readers hark wistfully back to this pub's former life as a brew-it-yourself alehouse, there's no doubt that its current concentration instead on a wide range of food from good sandwiches (from £1.10), through lots of family dishes such as chicken morsels (£3.60), fisherman's pie (£3.95), roast rib of beef (£5.50), to fresh salmon with asparagus (£6.75), is bringing it many more new friends down these quiet country lanes. Part of a peaceful cluster of farm buildings, it's quite handy for good walks by Chichester harbour, and in summer has a couple of picnic-table sets on its terrace, with many more in the garden behind. Inside, the timbered and low-beamed bar is busy and very friendly, with Windsor chairs around the tables, long seats against the walls, a welcoming log fire and maybe a large friendly dog; well kept real ales such as Badger Best, Morlands, Ringwood Best and Old Thumper with a guest beer on handpump. *(Recommended by A G Roby, Mr Cowell, Gethin Lewis, BCM, Col G D Stafford)*

Free house   Licensee Terry Brewer   Real ale   Meals and snacks (12–2, 6.30–9.30) Restaurant   (0243) 572477   Children welcome   Open 11.30(12 Sat)–2.30(3 Sat), 6–11

CHILGROVE   SU8214 Map 2
Royal Oak

Hooksway, which is signposted down track off B2141 Petersfield–Chichester – we list it instead under nearby Chilgrove as few maps show Hooksway itself; OS Sheet 197, map reference 814163

Suiting its sleepy surroundings tucked away in an unspoilt valley, this rustic white cottage has plain country-kitchen tables, sturdy leatherette wall benches and huge log fires in the two cosy rooms of its partly brick-floored beamed bar. Home-made bar food includes chicken and chips (£3.60), pizza (£3.70), meat or vegetarian lasagne (£3.85), steak and kidney pie (£4.10), gammon, egg and chips (£4.25) and venison pie (£4.30). Well kept Gibbs Mew Bishops Tipple and Salisbury, King and Barnes Festive, Ruddles Best and County, and Websters on handpump; sensibly placed darts, shove-ha'penny, cribbage, dominoes, fruit machine, trivia and piped music. There are rustic seats on a sunny front terrace and on the grass of the pretty garden, with some play equipment for children and a pony-paddock alongside. *(Recommended by Philip and Trisha Ferris, J E Newman, Mrs Lili Lomas, Alan Skull, Brian Cheshire; more reports please)*

Free house   Licensee D Jeffery   Real ale   Meals and snacks (till 10)   Restaurant (not

Sun evening)   East Marden (0243 59) 257   Children in eating area of bar and extension   Jazz night last Fri of month   Open 11–2.30, 6–11; 11–11 Sat; closed Mon Oct–March   Bedrooms; £16B/32B

nr COOLHAM   TQ1423 Map 3
George & Dragon

Dragons Green; pub signposted off A272 between Coolham and A24

There's quite a sparkle to the massively beamed and timbered bar in this interesting 16th-century country pub, with its unpretentious old-fashioned furnishings and enormous inglenook fireplace. Home-cooked bar food includes sandwiches (from £1.10), ploughman's (from £2.65), quiche and salads (£3.45), ham and egg (£4), home-made steak and kidney pie (£4.80), and cold topside of beef with pickles (£4.60); daily specials such as vegetarian and vegan dishes and an extended winter menu that may include fresh salmon, stuffed chicken or duck. Well kept King & Barnes Broadwood, Sussex and Festive on handpump; darts, bar billiards, shove-ha'penny, cribbage, dominoes, fruit machine and piped music; can get busy. The big grassy back garden has been kept beautifully even through the droughts, with lots of rustic tables and chairs well spaced among fruit trees, shrubs and lovely flowers. *(Recommended by WHBM, John Whitehead, Pam Hall, Phil Bryant, Mr and Mrs R P Begg)*

King & Barnes   Licensee Colin Hood   Real ale   Meals and snacks   (0403) 741 320   Children welcome   Open 11–2.30, 6–11

COWBEECH   TQ6114 Map 3
Merrie Harriers

Village signposted from A271

Over the last few years emphasis has increasingly been put on food here, especially now that a back conservatory dining room (with waitresses as well as decor in Victorian style) has joined the busy but comfortable dining lounge. Lunchtime food includes home-made soup (£1.75), sandwiches (from £1.80), filled cottage rolls (from £1.95), ploughman's (from £3.25), vegetarian quiche (£3.95), salads (from £5), steak and kidney pie (£6), grilled lemon sole (£7.50) and puddings like apple pie or summer pudding; good crispy vegetables. The evening choice includes dishes such as trout (£6), mixed grill (£7.75) and steaks (£8). Well kept Flowers Original, Harveys and a guest on handpump; good choice of wines; friendly and efficient service, Sunday bar nibbles. There is still a beamed and panelled public bar, with a traditional high-backed settle by the brick inglenook, several friendly cats, and darts, shove-ha'penny, dominoes and cribbage. There are rustic seats and a swing in the terraced garden. *(Recommended by Geoff and Julie Bond, Colin Laffan, Dr B A W Perkins, Mike and Joyce Bryant; more reports please)*

Free house   Licensees G M and B J Richards   Real ale   Meals and snacks (not Sun evening)   Hailsham (0323) 833108   Children in conservatory   Open 11–2.30, 6.30–11; closed Mon from 25 Dec to Easter

nr DALLINGTON   TQ6619 Map 3
Swan 🖝

Wood's Corner; B2096 Heathfield–Battle, E of Dallington

It's the home-made specials which gain most approval from readers in this friendly and unassuming place, with its bar billiards table happily taking up the most prominent corner of the simple but comfortable main room to prove it's still a proper pub: besides sandwiches and vegetarian dishes (£3.95), there might be beef stew with dumplings or chicken, ham and mushroom pie (£4.95), steak and kidney pudding (£5.95), and puddings like treacle tart, bread and butter pudding or apple and blackcurrant pie (£1.75). Well kept Adnams, Harveys, and Marstons Pedigree on handpump; decent house wines, a good log fire; shove-ha'penny, chess, trivia and unobtrusive piped music. There's an overflow into a small but airy picture-window back dining room. From the picnic-table sets in the neatly kept back flower garden (and the back bedroom – the front one overlooks the road) you can see from this high ridge of the Weald to Beachy Head. Good woodland walks nearby. *(Recommended by Colin Laffan, K Smurthwaite, K Soutter, David Fowles, David Gaunt, Chris Dyer-Smith, A C Earl, S J A Velate, J M Shaw, Mike and Joyce Bryant)*

Free house   Licensee John Blake   Real ale   Meals and snacks   Brightling (042 482) 242   No smoking restaurant (not Sun evening)   Children in bar lobby area and restaurant   Occasional folk nights   Open 11.30–3, 6.30–11   Bedrooms; £17/£35

DITCHLING   TQ3215 Map 3

Bull 🛏

2 High St; B2112, junction with B2116

Get there just after weekday opening time and, alone in the heavily beamed main bar, you can easily imagine yourself slipping back a century or two, when those handsome tables, chests and settles of oak, elm and mahogany were a little younger, and the longcase clock had chimed perhaps a million fewer hours than it has now. As it fills up, though, it loses nothing in character, staying friendly and relaxed, with no games or piped music. Bar food includes sandwiches (from £1.50), ploughman's (from £3), home-made steak and kidney pie (£5), steaks (£9.50), fresh fish when available, and home-made fruit pies and crumbles (£1.60) – we've yet to see how it's received under the new regime. Flowers Original, Marstons Pedigree, Whitbreads Best and Pompey Royal on handpump; relaxed atmosphere. A separate Turkey-carpeted corner bar has simpler, neater furnishings; three inglenook log fireplaces. There are picnic-table sets on a back suntrap terrace and in a good-sized pretty garden looking up to Ditchling Beacon, and the charming old village is a popular base for the South Downs Way and other walks. *(Recommended by A W Woods, Phil Bryant, Paul Evans, David and Fiona Easeman, Patrick Godfrey)*

Whitbreads   Tenant R G Forty   Real ale   Meals and snacks   (0273) 843147 Children in eating area   Open 11–2.30, 6–11   Bedrooms; £30.50B/£42.50B

EASEBOURNE   SU8922 Map 2

Olde White Horse ⊗

A272, just N of Midhurst

The change of brewery tie (it was Allied) seems scarcely to have affected this popular place – a food pub, but still with a good local feel, the Leech and other sporting prints in its neat and friendly little modernised lounge reminding you that around here "local" means polo, shooting or racing parties, as well as the atmosphere you'd more readily associate with the darts, dominoes, cribbage and juke box in the separate tap room or the bigger public bar. The imaginative food is largely prepared to order by the landlady, with careful use of herbs, reduced wine sauces and so forth, so there may be a wait; but good value makes it worth while. Besides sandwiches (lunchtime only, not Saturday or Sunday), recent tips – served with a good choice of fresh vegetables – include fresh fish (Fridays, and summer Tuesdays) soufflé omelettes using local free range eggs (from £4.95, filled with lemon sole fillet, crab meat, scallop and prawns in a brandy sauce £5.45), pies including steak and kidney with oyster (Friday, £4.75) and a choice of game dishes in season; also ratatouille in home-made cheese pastry case (£2.45), spiced lamb with almonds and yoghurt (£4.95) and steaks (from £5.65). Luscious puddings such as chocolate rum pancakes and profiteroles (from £1.75), and the regular three-course special meals can be memorable; good service. Well kept Greene King IPA, Abbot and occasionally XX on handpump, a few malt whiskies, and around 40 wines by the bottle; a small log fire. There are tables out in a courtyard, with more on the sheltered well kept back lawn. *(Recommended by Phil and Sally Gorton, Mrs W Lait, Mrs B M Blackman, Mrs J A Blanks, Ian and Wendy McCaw, Mr and Mrs Bob Gollner, James and Gillian Moller, J A Boulton; more reports please)*

Greene King   Tenants Alan and Christine Hollidge   Real ale   Meals and lunchtime snacks   Restaurant   Midhurst (0730) 813521   Children over 5 in restaurant   Open 11–2.30, 6–11; closed evening 25 Dec

ELSTED   SU8119 Map 2

Elsted Inn

Elsted Marsh; off A272 about 2 miles W of Midhurst, and on the Midhurst side of Elsted

A cheerful sight on the road at night – really in the middle of nowhere since Beeching closed the railway it was built for – this little pub has two small bars, with an open fire in the Victorian fireplace, simple country furniture on wooden floors, local photographs on the cream walls, and a warm and friendly atmosphere; there's a good welcome for children, too. Good bar food using a good deal of fresh local produce includes sandwiches (from £1.50), baked potatoes with lots of fillings (from £2.60), twelve spicy snails (£4.75), vegetarian bake (£5), charcuterie, curry, lasagne, bacon and sausage pudding, rabbit pie or local pigeon in red wine (all £5), steak and kidney pudding (£6.50), fresh fish at weekends, and superb home-made ice cream (£1.50) and puddings (£2.25); there's a separate cottagey candlelit dining room; they do small helpings for children. When Ballards was the house brew (it's now brewed a couple of miles away) Mr Horton was the head brewer – he certainly knows how to keep the full range of Ballards which is stocked here; also Marstons Pedigree and two or three guest beers, such as Mitchells, Everards Tiger and Tetleys, on handpump, and decent wines. Darts, dominoes, shove-ha'penny, cribbage, backgammon. There are tables out in a sizeable enclosed garden. *(Recommended by Andy and Jill Kassube, Dr R Fuller, HEG; more reports please)*

Free house   Licensees Tweazle Jones and Barry Horton   Real ale   Meals and snacks (12–2.30, 7–10)   Restaurant   (073 081) 3662   Children in eating area and saloon bar   Open 11–3, 5.30–11 (6 Sat); closed evening 25 Dec

Three Horseshoes ★ Ⓟ

Village signposted from B2141 Chichester–Petersfield; also reached off A272 as above

There's no doubting the rustic charm of this Tudor drovers' inn, with its cosy little rooms, enormous log fires, antique furnishings, ancient beams and flooring, attractive prints and photographs, and night-time candlelight. On top of that, it scores well for an inventive choice of both food and drinks. The food changes regularly and wins praise for the home-made soups like tomato and celery (£2.25), generous ploughman's with a good choice of cheeses (£3), baked potatoes with interesting fillings (from £3.75), hot-pot (£4.25), excellent rabbit pie in cider (£5.25), local dressed crab (£4.95), steak and kidney pie in Guinness (£5.25), whole plaice (£5.50), chicken tandoori (£4.95), garlicky giant prawns (£6.75), steak (£7.50) and even lobster, with succulent puddings like delicious treacle tart; high chairs and half-helpings for children; summer weekend barbecues. The pretty little dining room has a set evening menu on winter Fridays and Saturdays, but otherwise serves the same food as the bar. Well kept changing ales tapped from the cask might include Adnams, Ballards Best and Wassail, Badger, Batemans, Brakspears, Buckleys, Fullers London Pride, Gales HSB, Wadworths 6X and Charles Wells; farmhouse cider, a decent choice of wines by the glass, country wines, summer Pimms; dominoes, cribbage, backgammon and shut-the-box; friendly, obliging service. There are picnic-table sets in a prettily planted and well kept sizeable garden with a lovely view of the Downs, and a pets' corner with ornamental fowl. *(Recommended by Phil Bryant, David Hunn, Mrs V Middlebrook, Jacqueline Davis, Norman Foot, S L Hughes, Bev and Doug Warrick, K Leist, Paul and Margaret Baker, John and Chris Simpson, Roy McIsaac, Mrs L Lomas, Malcolm and Hilary Leeves, Annie Taylor, Mrs C M Chapman, Graham and Glenis Watkins; more reports please)*

Free house   Licensees Ann and Tony Burdfield   Real ale   Meals and snacks (till 9.45)   Partly no-smoking restaurant   Harting (0730) 825746   Children (over 2) in eating area   Live entertainment Midsummer's Eve   Open 11–3, 6–11; closed evening 25 Dec   Bedrooms planned summer 1992; £40B/(£25)£50B

FLETCHING   TQ4223 Map 3

Griffin ★ 🔊 🛏

Village signposted off A272 W of Uckfield

How nice to find an honest and extremely civilised old country inn that relies for its considerable appeal on its own natural qualities, the enthusiasm of its staff, and genuine attention to the detail of pleasing customers, rather than the common current A-B-C formula – Add-on Beams and Conservatories. This approach shows particularly in the bar food. Besides a couple of unusual soups (£2.25), ploughman's (£3.25), filled baguettes (£3.50), home-made pizza with smoked fish and anchovy topping, roquefort and walnut terrine or several interesting quiches (£3.95), fresh sardines with herb stuffing (£4.25), steak and Guinness pie (£5.50) and chargrilled steaks (from £7.95), this treats fresh – often local – produce with imagination, to give eight or so specials such as crispy chicken in soy sauce or grilled guineafowl drumsticks in peach sauce (£3.95), linguine with ham and mushroom sauce (£4.25), pork and pepper kebabs, chicken tikka or cappilletti bolognese (£4.95), salmon fishcakes with lemon and dill mayonnaise (£5.50), poached salmon (£6.25), Mediterranean fish casserole or fried trout with almonds (£6.50) and puddings such as home-made treacle tart, queen of puddings or fresh fruit meringue (£2.95). The restaurant menu now merges with the bar menu on Monday-Friday evenings. Readers particularly enjoy the theme nights, with the friendly staff acting more gallic than garlic and Gaulloises on Beaujolais Nouveau night for instance. The beamed front bar has a cosy and relaxed 1930s feel – straightforward furniture, squared oak panelling, some china on a delft shelf, a big corner fireplace, and a small bare-boarded serving area off to one side. Well kept Harveys BB, King & Barnes and Badger Best and Tanglefoot on handpump; over 60 good wines. A separate public bar has darts, pool, fruit machine, video game and juke box. Picnic-table sets under cocktail parasols on the back grass have lovely rolling Sussex views; there are more tables on a sheltered gravel terrace, used for dining on warm evenings. Three of the four attractively individual bedrooms have four-posters; the village is on the edge of Sheffield Park. *(Recommended by Andy and Sue Tye, Prof J R Leigh, Miles Kington, Bill Sykes)*

Free house   Licensees Nigel and David Pullan   Real ale   Meals and snacks Restaurant (not Sun evening)   Newick (082572) 2890   Children welcome   Piano Fri/Sat evenings, Sun lunchtime   Open 11.30–3, 6–11; afternoon opening by arrangement; closed 25 Dec   Bedrooms; £25(£45B)/£40(£50B)

FULKING   TQ2411 Map 3

Shepherd & Dog

From A281 Brighton–Henfield on N slope of downs turn off at Poynings signpost and continue past Poynings

At weekends this charmingly refurbished and extended but still smallish pub in its choice spot below a magnificent sweep of the downs attracts such flocks of customers that a queue tends to build up even at the efficient food servery. So it pays to get there early, particularly if you want one of the favoured seats, by the big log fire in winter or the bow windows in summer. The partly panelled bar has decorations that recall its days as a downland shepherds' refuge, and furnishings are either stoutly rustic or antique. In summer the garden's a real bonus: a series of prettily planted grassy terraces, some fairy-lit, with a little stream running down to feed a big stone trough, and an upper play lawn sheltered by trees. Food includes sandwiches (from £1.70, smoked salmon £2.70), a wide choice of ploughman's (from £3.30), with evening dishes like vegetarian pancakes (£4.50), home-made lasagne (£4.75), salmon and cream pie (£5.05), half an oak-smoked chicken (£5.25), home-made beef and Guinness pie (£5.45), lamb kebab (£5.65), and sirloin steak (£6.50); also daily specials and home-made puddings, perhaps a barbecue on Sunday evening. Harveys, Ruddles County, and Websters Yorkshire on handpump; good service, toad-in-the-hole. A path leads straight up to the South Downs Way (if you fancy a longer walk than the one back to your car parked down the lane). *(Recommended by Terry Buckland, Frank Cummins, Paul Evans, M C Howells, Frank Gadbois, Gwen and Peter Andrews, Father Robert Davies, Alan Skull, Dr T W Hoskins, Simon Reynolds, Mike and Joyce Bryant, Edward Burlton Davies; more reports please)*

Phoenix (Watneys)   Lease: Mrs J A Thomson and N Hazel   Real ale   Meals and snacks   (0273) 857382   Open 11–2.30, 6–11

GUN HILL   TQ5614   Map 3

Gun   🍺

From A22 NW of Hailsham (after junction with A269) turn N at Happy Eater

Readers who've been coming for years reckon that currently this interesting 15th-century tiled and timbered pub is on quite an upswing – though some of the good value food is still cooked on a venerable Aga in one corner; you have to get there early to be sure of the full choice, which besides soup might include good local sausages, lamb and apricot pie or turkey, ham and leek pie or smoked haddock pasta (£4.50), fillet steak Wellington (£6.50), and lots of rich puddings. It has quite a warren of rooms and alcoves, and in the evening it pays to know your colour-coding: the flowery curtains are for windows, but the red ones may hide yet another room. There are oak beams and panelling, an attractive variety of furnishings (though preponderantly table-based – this is very much a dining pub), brasses, copper, pewter, and several open fires, one in a fine inglenook. Well kept Charrington IPA and Larkins Sovereign on handpump, a good choice of wines by the glass, and country wines; friendly service, with a good mix of ages among the many customers (they're kind to small children). The pretty house is covered with clematis, honeysuckle and hanging baskets, and there are plenty of flowers (and fairy-lit trees) in its big well hedged garden, which has sensibly placed swings. *(Recommended by N Patton, P Gillbe, G Carter, M A and C R Starling, Simon Velate, Colin Laffan, Mike and Joyce Bryant)*

Free house   Licensee R J Brockway   Real ale   Meals and snacks (12–2, 6.30–10) Children in eating area and family room   Chiddingly (0825) 872361   Open 11–3, 6–11; closed 25 and 26 Dec   Bedrooms; £22(£27B)/£27(£32B)

HALNAKER   SU9008   Map 2
Anglesey Arms

A285 Chichester–Petworth

Even on a race day (when it's particularly important to book – Goodwood's only half a mile away) they cope really well here, creating order out of what might elsewhere be chaos. But popularity all year gives them plenty of practice. It's the right-hand bar where they normally serve food, though on an anonymous inspection visit one busy evening they managed to find us seats at the counter in the friendly left-hand public bar, with its darts, dominoes, cribbage, fruit machine, backgammon, chess, shut-the-box and even yatzee – engrossed in a fine dressed crab with good mayonnaise (£5.20) and a juicy steak (from £6.25) we never found out how to play that. Round on the right is stripped pine, flagstones, candles and modern paintings, with another carpeted dining room beyond. Generously served food includes sandwiches (from £1.65), omelettes (from £1.75), toasties (from £1.75), ploughman's (£2.95), salads (from £4.50), fry-up (£4.30), and Mediterranean prawns (£6.75), with home-made dishes of the day such as crab pâté (£2.50), home-made quiche (£4.50), lobster (from £7.50) when available, apple pie or treacle tart with custard (£2.25), and Sunday roast lunches; vegetables are extra, and they hint that service is not included (a hint that in our view should fall on deaf ears – tipping is not a tradition in pubs). Well kept Friary Meux, Harveys and Ind Coope Burton on handpump, and quite a few wines, especially from Northern Spain. There are picnic-table sets on a side lawn, with more tables by a fig tree in a sheltered back garden. The Weald and Downland Open Air Museum is nearby. *(Recommended by W C M Jones, J H L Davis, R T and J C Moggridge; more reports please)*

Friary Meux (Allied) Tenants C J and T M Houseman Real ale Meals and snacks (till 9.45; not Sun) Restaurant Chichester (0243) 773474 Children in restaurant Open 11–3, 6–11; closed 25 Dec

HARTFIELD   TQ4735   Map 3

Anchor 🏮

Church Street

There's a thriving atmosphere of contented enjoyment in the heavy-beamed bar which rambles informally around the cheerful central servery. The tables with their cushioned chairs and wall seats are set out in a way that lets you have a quiet tete-a-tete without ever feeling cut off (the evening seafood restaurant is used as a lunchtime overflow if the bar is full). There are old advertisements and little country pictures above the brown-painted dado, houseplants in the brown-curtained small-paned windows. Generously served bar food includes soup (£1.75), sandwiches (from £1.30, toasties from £1.50), ploughman's (from £2.25), pâté (£2.75), salads (from £3.25), chilli con carne (£4.50) and sirloin steak (£9.25), though the emphasis is on seafood – crab sandwiches (£2.50), fresh plaice (£3), crab and prawn curry (£4.75), skate with capers (£6), and a giant seafood salad (£32 for two); puddings (from £1.25) and children's meals (£2.50). Very well kept Adnams, Flowers Original, Fremlins, King & Barnes Bitter, Marstons Pedigree and Whitbreads Pompey Royal on handpump; warm woodburner; friendly quick service. Darts in a separate lower room; cribbage, dominoes, and unobtrusive piped music. A front verandah gets packed on warm summer evenings, and there are some seats outside behind. This pub is near the start of the *Good Walks Guide* Walk 62. *(Recommended by Patrick Godfrey, Michael Quine, N Patton, Paul Sexton, Sue Harrison, Mrs C Hartley, Richard Gibbs, Colin Laffan)*

Free house   Licensee Ken Thompson   Real ale   Meals and snacks (12–2, 6–10) Restaurant (not Sun)   Hartfield (089 277) 424   Children in eating area and small games room   Open 11–11; Bedrooms; £30S/£35S

nr HEATHFIELD   TQ5920   Map 3

Star

Old Heathfield – head East out of Heathfield itself on A265, then fork right on to B2096; turn right at signpost to Heathfield Church then keep bearing right; pub on left immediately after church

Snugged below the handsome Early English tower of the church, this late 14th-century pilgrims' inn is so tucked away that only those in the know track it down. Even so, get there early at weekends for a good place in the L-shaped beamed bar – maybe a window seat, or in cold weather one of the two tables by the log fire in the huge inglenook. In summer, it's the gently sloping garden that's most in demand, with imaginatively planted and neatly kept flowerbeds, and a peaceful outlook over rolling oak-lined sheep pastures; Turner painted this view, from behind the village. Food is brought out to the well spaced tables here, including soup (£1.95), ploughman's (£3.25), omelettes (£3.75), good home-cooked ham and eggs (£3.95), salads (from £5.50), steak and kidney pie (£5.95), sirloin steak (£9.25) and daily specials; the puddings such as apple pie or banoffi (from £1.50) are particularly favoured, as is the Sunday roast lunch (£5.95). There's a hedged-off children's play area with a peak-time soft-drinks kiosk, and a floating population of rabbits and birds – maybe even an owl and a couple of peacocks. Well kept Gales HSB, King and Barnes and Ruddles Best on handpump, with Harveys (which they get direct from the brewery and price more cheaply than the tied-supply beers) and good value wines; friendly staff and atmosphere; darts, dominoes and maybe unobtrusive piped music, mainly classical. No dogs; the pub has its own. *(Recommended by J E Hilditch, Prof A N Black, M C Howells, Jean and Rowland Theodore-Entwistle, Mike and Joyce Bryant; more reports please)*

Grand Met   Tenants Chris and Linda Cook   Real ale   Meals and snacks (not Sun evening)   Partly no-smoking restaurant (Fri/Sat evening, Sun lunchtime)   Heathfield

(0435) 863570   Children in eating area and restaurant   Occasional live entertainment   Parking can be difficult (if so, park beyond church and walk through churchyard)   Open 11–3, 6–11

HOUGHTON   TQ0111 Map 3
George & Dragon

B2139

Though its origins go back some 700 years, the half-timbered front part is mainly Elizabethan, with its handsome heavy oak beams and formidable fireplace. Over the last few years the old-fashioned and spotless bar has picked up quite a few points of interest, from a clockwork roasting-spit motor to gourds given a glowing patina by rubbing with goosefat. Tables, some of them attractive antiques, spread down into a back extension which takes off some of the pressure on wet days; there are also some tables out on a pretty back terrace and sloping lawn, with wishing well, walnut tree (bearing well, these last warm summers) and gentle, extensive views of the Arun valley. Bar food includes home-made soup (£1.95), good sandwiches (from £1.15, steak £3.95), mushroom and ham tagliatelli or vegetarian lasagne (£3.95), varied fresh salads such as avocado and prawns (£6.95), fresh local trout (£7.75), and tempting puddings (£1.95). Well kept Courage Directors, Eldridge Pope Best, and Theakstons Best on handpump; Sussex pressed apple juice and country wines. To reach the South Downs Way, turn left off the side road to Bury. *(Recommended by Jenny and Brian Seller, Dr A M Rankin, John Whitehead, M M Badcock, Harriet and Michael Robinson, WFL, K Leist, R Gray, Trevor and Helen Dayneswood, TOH, D C Horwood)*

Free house   Licensee Alan Birkbeck   Real ale   Meals and lunchtime snacks   Partly no-smoking restaurant   (0798) 831559   Children welcome   Open 11–2.30(3 Sat), 6–11

KINGSTON NEAR LEWES   TQ3908 Map 3
Juggs

The Street; Kingston signed off A27 by roundabout W of Lewes, and off Lewes–Newhaven road; look out for the pub's sign – may be hidden by hawthorn in summer

Pleasantly unpretentious, this 15th-century rose-screened former farm cottage has a rambling beamed bar with the most interesting medley of furnishings and decorations – particularly the pictures – we've come across in any Sussex pub. In summer, it's well worth staying inside long enough for your eyes to accommodate to the relative dimness for a good look, though most people are all too quickly tempted out to the sunny brick front terrace with its many close-set rustic teak tables and benches. A neatly hedged inner yard has more under cocktail parasols, and there are two or three out on grass by a timber climber and commando net. Though the choice of bar food is not in itself unusual, and chips figure quite prominently, the quality of the home cooking is well above average – close to award level. It includes open sandwiches, taramasalata, ploughman's, an enterprising vegetarian dish or sausages (£2.75), pitta bread with grilled ham, tomato, mushrooms and cheese or chicken tikka (£3.75), sirloin steak (£5.95), a dish of the day such as a particularly good crab salad, puddings (from £2.25 – the summer pudding is highly praised) and children's helpings; there's a small no smoking dining area. At Sunday lunchtime the choice is limited to cheese or pâté. Particularly well kept Harveys, and King & Barnes Broadwood and Festive on handpump; helpful, welcoming service; log fires, darts, shove-ha'penny. It's worth getting there early at weekends or holiday times. *(Recommended by C R and M A Starling, Alec Lewery, Marie Enright, Mike Rising, Neil Barker, Hon Mrs A M Viney, Prof S Barnett, P A Barfield)*

Free house   Licensee Andrew Browne   Real ale   Meals and snacks (12–2, 6–9.30; limited Sun lunchtime)   Restaurant (not Sun lunchtime)   (0273) 472523   Children in two family areas   Open 11–2.30, 6–11; closed evening 25 Dec, 26 Dec and evening 1 Jan

LICKFOLD   SU9225 Map 2

Lickfold Inn 🅠

In summer the interesting well planted garden with its several separate seating areas (and its own bar and barbecue) has its charm, and the setting's particularly attractive then too, with good woodland walks nearby. But it's in winter that the bar itself is undoubtedly at its best, as its central feature is the enormous brick fireplace which divides it into two – and that's brought to life by the big winter log fires that in summer have been replaced by extra tables. At any time you can enjoy the antique furniture including elegant Georgian settles, heavy Tudor oak beams, handsomely moulded panelling, and ancient herringbone brickwork under rugs. Changing home-made bar food might include sandwiches (from £1.95), ploughman's (£2.75), lasagne or steak and mushroom pie (£4.85), half shoulder of lamb (£6.50), guinea fowl (£7.50), duck in orange sauce (£8), and puddings such as home-made ginger pear dumplings or treacle tart (£2.25); good Sunday roast lunches. Well kept Adnams, Badger Best and Tanglefoot, Ballards, Fullers ESB and London Pride, and Hook Norton Old Hookey on handpump; good coffee. *(Recommended by Richard Houghton, Mike Rising, A Sharp, Mrs L Davey, Mrs Lili Lomas)*

Free house   Licensees Ron and Kath Chambers   Real ale   Meals and snacks   (0798) 5285   Open 11–3, 6–11, all day Sat in fine weather; winter 11–2.30, 6.30–10.30 Mon-Thurs; closed Mon evenings in winter

LITLINGTON   TQ5201 Map 3

Plough & Harrow

Off A27 Lewes–Polegate, after Alfriston turn (or can be reached from Alfriston); also signed off A259 E of Seaford

Summer keeps this extended flint pub so busy (get there early for a seat, particularly on weekend lunchtimes) that it can serve a variety of six real ales in peak condition in any one week, rotating them to include Adnams Best, Badger Best and Tanglefoot, Brakspears, Charles Wells Eagle, Everards Tiger, Felinfoel Double Dragon, Greene King Abbot, Harveys BB, Larkins Best, Mitchells ESB, Wadworths 6X and Youngs Special. There's also a decent choice of wines by the glass – again, kept fresh by the demand. The small but comfortable beamed and lattice-windowed front bar leads back to a newer eating area done up as a dining car, with steam railway models, pictures and memorabilia, and a back lawn has rustic seats by a kaleidoscope of clematis, with a children's bar and aviary, and charming views across the Cuckmere Valley to nearby Alfriston. Consistent home-made bar food, served both inside and outside, includes sandwiches (from £1.50, toasties from £2.60), soup (£1.95), ploughman's (from £3.20), giant sausages (£3.65), quite a few salads (from £4.30, crab £7.65), steak and kidney pie (£4.95), scampi (£5.90), charcoal-grilled steaks (from £7.75) and specials like vegetarian dishes, quiches and pies; there may be delays at busy times. Darts, shove-ha'penny, dominoes, cribbage and evening piped music. *(Recommended by A L Willey, Gwen and Peter Andrews, Jane Palmer, M Box; more reports please)*

Free house   Licensees Roger and Christine Taylor   Real ale   Meals and snacks (till 10)   Restaurant   Alfriston (0323) 870632   Children in restaurant   Live music Fri evening   Open 11–2.30(3 Sat), 6.30–11

LODSWORTH   SU9223 Map 2

Halfway Bridge ★ 🅠

A272 Midhurst–Petworth

This rambling building has clearly been serving travellers down the main road (which used to run right by the door, but now bypasses the gently sloping garden) for centuries: in the last three years its cottagey rooms have been brought sympathetically up to date – and decidedly up market. This shows in the inventive home cooking, which besides sandwiches (choice of white or brown bread) runs from stilton and courgette pasta (£3.95) through steak, kidney and Guinness pie

(£5.95) to a good choice of fish dishes such as trout and almonds (£6.50), grilled whole plaice (£6.95), lemon sole (£7.95), salmon with mint and cucumber mayonnaise (£8.50) and huge grey mullet (£8.95), also lamb in red wine, rosemary and redcurrants (£4.95) and half a roast duck with orange and sherry sauce (£7.95); there's a good choice of fresh vegetables and home-made puddings, Sunday roasts such as beef, pork or chicken (from £4.95) – it gets busy at weekends so booking is advisable. The three or four comfortable rooms that loop around the central servery have attractive fabrics for their wood-railed curtains and pew cushions, with other furnishings running through good oak chairs and an individual mix of tables (many of them set for dining) to a dresser and longcase clock down steps in a charming country dining room; log fires include one in a well polished kitchen range. Well kept Boddingtons, Flowers Original, Fremlins, Fullers London Pride, Marstons Pedigree and Whitbreads Strong County on handpump; civilised family service. There are tables and chairs on the new back patio. *(Recommended by John Gillett, Ian and Wendy McCaw, John and Heather Dwane, W K Struthers; more reports please)*

Free house   Licensees Sheila and Edric Hawkins   Real ale   Meals and snacks Restaurant   Lodsworth (07985) 281   Children over 10 in restaurant   Open 11–2.30, 6–11(10.30 winter); closed winter Sun evening

LURGASHALL   SU9327   Map 2

Noahs Ark

Village signposted from A283 N of Petworth; OS Sheet 186, map reference 936272

The churchyard opposite makes this a delightfully peaceful spot – the unusual oak-built verandah or cloister running down the sunny side of the church is said to have been for people walking from the far side of the parish to have their lunch in after service, so that they didn't have an excuse to visit the alehouse. Nowadays, they'd have a hard time resisting the lure of the inviting log fires (one in a capacious inglenook) in winter, and the vivid hanging baskets in summer; there are usually fresh flowers inside the two clean and simply but attractively furnished little rooms. Good bar food includes sandwiches, toasties such as bacon and mushroom (£1.95), lasagne or moussaka (£3.25), chicken tikka (£3.50), English lamb cutlets (£4.50), and calves' liver and bacon (£4.75). Greene King IPA and Abbot on handpump (this is one of the pubs just sold to Greene King by Allied); friendly service. Sensibly placed darts and bar billiards, also shove-ha'penny, dominoes, and cribbage. Rustic seats and tables outside overlook the secluded village green. *(Recommended by Dr P H Mitchell, Ian and Wendy McCaw, Mrs Lili Lomas; more reports please)*

Greene King   Tenant Ted Swannell   Real ale   Meals and snacks (till 10, not Sun) Restaurant (not Sun)   (0428) 78346   Children in family room and restaurant   Open 11–2.30(3 Sat), 6–11

MAYFIELD   TQ5827   Map 3

Rose & Crown   ★   🛏

Fletching Street; off A267 at NE end of village

Roaring fires, a good pubby atmosphere and friendly staff make this pretty weatherboarded 16th-century inn a companionable place; its two cosy little front rooms have low beam-and-board ceilings, some panelling and a handsome inglenook, and there's a quieter side dining room. Besides rustic tables out among hanging baskets and flower tubs on the front terrace, there are several picnic-table sets in the quiet and attractive back garden. Bar food includes home-made soup (£1.95), rolls (from £2.25), Florida prawns (£2.95), ploughman's (from £2.95), baked potatoes (from £3.25), fish pie (£4.75), char-grilled gammon, steak and ale pie or Yorkshire beef in real ale (all £4.95), lamb fillets with redcurrants and rosemary, and beef Wellington (£7.95); also home-made puddings such as a light lemon bavarois or apple and blackberry pie (£2.20). The small central servery stocks a commendable run of well kept guest beers such as Badger Tanglefoot,

Exmoor Gold, King & Barnes, Moorhouses Pendle Witches Brew, Morrells
Graduate, Shepherd Neame, Tetleys and Youngs Special, as well as the regular
Adnams Best and Harveys Best on handpump; quite a few malt whiskies, and
several wines by the glass; darts, bar billiards, shove-ha'penny, dominoes and
cribbage, piped music at lunchtime; at weekends the bar may stay busy till late, but
the rooms are very pretty. *(Recommended by D H K Reakes, Miranda Goddard, Mr and
Mrs Peters, J L and J A Annandale, Gwen and Peter Andrews, P Bell, Mrs C Hartley, Hazel
Morgan, Mike and Joyce Bryant; more reports please)*

*Free house   Licensee Peter Seely   Real ale   Meals and snacks   Restaurant   Mayfield
(0435) 872200   Children in eating area and restaurant   Open 11–3, 6–11
Bedrooms; £44.50B/£61B*

MIDHURST   SU8821   Map 2

Spread Eagle 🛏

South St

Cheerful lunchtime bar food such as home-made soup (£1.75), sandwiches (from
£1.30, toasties 30p extra), filled French bread (from £2), filled baked potatoes
(from £2.55), ploughman's (£2.95), decent salads (from £3.75), and specials like
fish pie, lasagne, or coq au vin (£4.25) is carefully presented by courteous staff in a
neatly modernised and surprisingly airy barrel-vaulted cellar "Coal Hole" bar,
with big oak cask seats or brocaded settles on its tiles. But it's the spacious
massively beamed and timbered lounge which gets most attention, with its
dramatic fireplace, imposing leaded-light windows looking out on the most
attractive part of this old town, and handsome yet quite unpretentious old
armchairs and settees spread among the rugs on the broad-boarded creaking oak
floor. Badger Best on handpump, not cheap but well kept; shove-ha'penny,
dominoes, trivia and piped music; though they don't have crisps there may be bar
nibbles. The restaurant is good. *(Recommended by David and Ruth Hollands, GB, Phil
and Sally Gorton, TBB, Ian Phillips, Jacqueline Davis, E G Parish, Sidney Wells)*

*Free house   Licensee George Mudford   Real ale   Lunchtime meals and snacks
Restaurant   Midhurst (0730) 816911   Well behaved children welcome   Open
11–2.30, 6–11; closed evening 25 Dec   Bedrooms; £70B/£80B*

NORMANS BAY   TQ6805   Map 3

Star

Signposted off A259 just E of Pevensey; and from Cooden, off B2182 coast road W out
of Bexhill

In what used to be a particularly isolated part of the Pevensey Levels, with boat
access to the sea which is only minutes away, this is said to date back to an early
15th-century cottage for workers on the nearby sluice, and was a smugglers' inn
for some two or three centuries from around 1550 – there was a pitched battle
here between smugglers and excisemen in 1822. There's now little echo of those
hard days in what's become a spaciously modernised family pub, with comfortably
cushioned seats spreading over the carpet of a brick-pillared partly timbered dining
lounge, and a cheerful and lively atmosphere. An efficient food bar serves a wide
choice of good value food, in helpings so generous that not only do they hand out
doggy bags, but they even warn you on the menu of the things that might defeat
even a smuggler-sized appetite; readers particularly like the half-dozen or more
vegetarian dishes such as tomato and courgette pie (all £3.25) and fresh local fish
like cod (£4.75). Other dishes include a dozen or more starters such as soup
(£1.95), ploughman's (from £2.95), burgers, with plenty of main dishes such as
ham and eggs or scampi (£4.55), half a roast chicken with jumbo sausage (£5.75),
spiced pheasant in prunes (£6.95), and 8oz rump steak (£8.50); children's dishes,
masses of puddings – people especially like their waffles. Well kept Bass, Harveys,
Charles Wells Bombardier and a beer named for the pub on handpump, with lots
of foreign bottled beers, good country wines (the local apple is recommended);
piped music, games in the children's room; friendly staff, coping admirably even

when busy. There are tables on a small front terrace, with more in a hawthorn-sheltered streamside garden with a play area. Paths inland quickly take you away from the caravan sites into marshy nature reserve. *(Recommended by Clem Stephens, Colin Laffan, David Gaunt, Alec Lewery, Marie Enright)*

Free house   Licensee Francis Maynard   Real ale   Meals and snacks (till 10)   (0323) 762648   Children in own room   Jazz Tues evening and Sun lunchtime   Open 11–3, 6–11

OVING   SU9005   Map 2

Gribble ★

Between A27 and A259 just E of Chichester, then should be signposted just off village road; OS Sheet 197, map reference 900050

Though this lovely old thatched cottage got its licence only a decade or so ago, it looks and feels as if it's been a pub for centuries, with its heavy beams and timbering, old country-kitchen furnishings and pews, big log fire, lively atmosphere and charming service. On the left, a family room with pews provides perhaps the biggest no-smoking area we've so far found in a Sussex pub; shove-ha'penny, dominoes, cribbage, and fruit machine, and a separate skittle alley. Besides good well kept Gribble Ale and Reg's Tipple (now brewed in their own microbrewery), there's Badger Best and Tanglefoot, Gales HSB and Palmers on handpump, country wines, Inch's farm cider. Home-cooked bar food includes good sandwiches (from £1.45, toasties 20p extra, toasted steak £3.35), soup (£1.30), ploughman's with five different cheeses or ham or burgers including a vegetarian one (from £3.05), cottage pie (£3.35), ham and eggs (£3.60), salads (from £4.05, Selsey crab £5.40), big fresh trout (£5.50, mainly Friday), sirloin steak (£8.15), puddings like apple and blackberry pie (from £1.95), and a choice of Sunday roasts (£5.35). A good customer-oriented practice here is their policy of serving some dishes in smaller, cheaper helpings for less hungry people. A small open-sided barn opens on to a garden with rustic seats among apple trees. *(Recommended by David Hunn, Alan Skull, Pamela Harris, Harry McCann, BHP, Lyn and Bill Capper, John Evans, Alec Lewery, Marie Enright, Jenny and Brian Seller, Dr A M Rankin, Trevor and Helen Dayneswood, Mrs Lili Lomas, R Gray, Richard Houghton)*

Own brew (Badger)   Manager James Wells   Real ale   Meals and snacks (12–2, 6.30–9.30, not Sun evening)   (0243) 786893   Children in family room   Open 11–2.30, 6–11

OXLEYS GREEN   TQ6921   Map 3

Jack Fullers ✑

Follow Brightling signposts from Robertsbridge (off A21 N of Hastings); or take Brightling road off B2096 just W of Netherfield, then fork right at Robertsbridge, Mountfield signpost; or turn off Brightling road 50 yds from church

Very much a dining pub, this is best known now for its massive piping hot meat puddings and pies (most around £4.95) such as gammon and onion, steak or steak and kidney, chicken and sweetcorn or halibut and prawn. Other food includes specials such as salmon mousse or roast local pheasant, and regulars like beef stew with dumplings or vegetarian lasagne – though vegetarians often put together a meal of some of the many inventive separate vegetable dishes such as excellent honeyed carrots (£1.10, generous helpings). It can be quite a struggle to save room for one of the old-fashioned steamed puddings such as spotted dick (£2.25), or the formidable ice creams. Prices are higher in the evenings and on Saturdays. Two rooms loop around the servery, with white and gingham cloths and fresh flowers on good sturdy tables; the part furthest from the entrance, with excellent fireback and dogs in its big main fireplace, is the nicer. Candlelit and packed with happy people at night, it can be very quiet on weekday lunchtimes. Well spaced tables in the beautifully kept and interesting garden give fine views over part of the unspoilt Robertsbridge Estate. Well kept Harveys and Brakspears; there are decent spirits and French wines, and a quite remarkable collection of English ones – including up to a dozen by the glass; 30 malt whiskies, freshly squeezed orange juice; table tennis in summer. As we've said before, this is definitely a pub that grows on one; repeat visits make clear the landlord's genuine considerateness, underlying what can first strike you as a rather abstracted air. *(Recommended by Alec Lewery, Marie Enright, Mark Martin, M J Harper; more reports please)*

Free house   Licensees Shirley and Roger Berman   Real ale   Meals   Restaurant (not Sun evening)   Brightling (042 482) 212   Children welcome   Open 12–3, 7–11; closed Mon and occasionally Sun evening

nr PUNNETTS TOWN   TQ6220 Map 3
Three Cups

B2096 towards Battle

In an area where so many good pubs now firmly major in food, it's a great relief to find this genuinely traditional place – a real country local of the best sort. It does indeed serve food, but without making it a dominant feature; honest value, too, from sandwiches or filled baked potatoes (from £2.50), through prize-winning local giant sausages (£2.95), cottage pie (£3.50) or lasagne (£3.75, vegetarian £3.50), half a roast chicken (£6.75), to trout or 8oz steak (£7.25). What counts for most, though, is the welcoming atmosphere of the long very low-beamed bar, with enormous logs amounting almost to trunks of wood smouldering at one end, attractive panelling, and comfortable seats, including some in big bay windows overlooking a small green. Well kept Courage Best and Directors, King & Barnes, Shepherd Neame, John Smiths and Youngs on handpump; piped music. A back family room has darts, table skittles, shove-ha'penny, dominoes and cribbage; it leads out to a small covered terrace, with seats in the garden beyond – where there are chickens and bantams, a safe play area, and no less than three boules pitches. Space for five touring caravans. Good walks from here, on either side of this high ridge of the Weald. *(Recommended by Mrs P Brown; more reports please)*

Free house   Licensees Leonard and Irenie Smith   Real ale   Meals and snacks   (0435) 830252   Children in eating area of bar and family room   Open 11–3, 6.30–11

RIPE   TQ5010 Map 3
Lamb

Signposted off A22 Uckfield–Hailsham at Golden Cross; and via Chalvington from A27 Lewes–Polegate

The interesting prints, many of them antiques, and the nostalgic song-sheet covers make it fun to wander through the various snug rooms that ring the island serving bar. The furnishings too seem lovingly collected, a motley mix of church pews, 18th-century oak settles and stripped deal, red hessian and pastel velvet – though the dominant impression is of shiny stripped pitch-pine. Home-made bar food includes good sandwiches (from £1.50, toasties from £1.60), soup (£1.50), ploughman's (from £2.95), ham and two eggs, tagliatelli, omelettes, meaty or vegetarian lasagne or shepherd's pie (all £3.95), salads (from £3.95), steak and mushroom pie or chicken and leek pie (£4.25), and a good choice of children's dishes (£2.50); there's a no smoking area, and a snugly pretty brick-floored back dining room. Well kept Courage Best and Directors, King & Barnes Broadwood, Rayments and John Smiths on handpump; there are several open fires, some attractive Victorian fireplaces, and the atmosphere is warm and lively; friendly service; darts, shove-ha'penny, cribbage, dominoes, fruit machine, video game, juke box, maybe piped music, and toad-in-the-hole. The sheltered back garden has rustic tables and picnic-table sets under cocktail parasols, with a climber and swings. *(Recommended by John Beeken, Mr and Mrs A Albert; more reports please)*

Free house   Licensees P A Wilkins, J R Bentley   Real ale   Meals and snacks (11–2, 6–9.30)   Restaurant   (0323) 811280   Well behaved children welcome   Open 11(12 Sat)–3, 6–11

ROGATE   TQ5529   Map 3

White Horse

A272 Midhurst–Petersfield

Early on a weekday, before it fills up, there's a faintly theatrical feel to this rambling old oak-beamed village local, an air of something waiting to happen: will Miss Marple step down to the rush-matting dining area and shake her head significantly at the big fish in the aquarium, or pull down one of the leather-bound books, or pick out a flower to sniff? Will Lord Peter Wimsey saunter over the flagstones to warm himself at the generous log fire? But the livelier evening bustle quickly puts that sort of nonsense out of your head, so that you can concentrate on realities like the changing choice of bar food such as sandwiches (from £1.70), ploughman's (from £2.75), omelettes (from £2.95), vegetarian dishes (made to order £4.50), lasagne (£4.95), beef in peppers or ale, steak and kidney pie or curry (all £5.25), lamb cutlet (£5.75), children's menu (from £2.50), also good puddings. The staff are friendly, and the Ballards, Flowers Original, Marstons Pedigree, and Gales HSB on handpump are well kept; fruit machines, well reproduced piped pop music. Some tables shelter out behind; the noises off come from a nearby aviary. *(Recommended by K Leist; more reports please)*

Free house   Licensees Sheila and Jack Cowlam   Real ale   Meals and snacks (11–2.30, 6–11)   Restaurant   (0730) 821333   Children welcome   Occasional live entertainment Sun   Open 11–2.30, 6–11; may open all day Sat

ROWHOOK   TQ1234   Map 3

Chequers ⊘

Village signposted from A29 NW of Horsham

Readers reporting on this pub invariably pick out the tasty home-made food for special mention: though helpings may not be large, well presented lunchtime dishes people have recently singled out from the wide choice include the home-made soups (£1.95), bacon, lettuce and tomato French bread sandwich (£2.95), stilton ploughman's (£3.25), steak and kidney pie or sauté of chicken liver with red wine (£5.25), tagliatelli with smoked salmon and cream cheese (£5.50), mushrooms and crispy bacon sautéed in garlic butter with cheese and cream and topped with fresh crumb gratin (£4.75), home-baked honeyed ham, and puddings (£1.95). In the evening there may be chicken satay (£4.50), chicken breast baked with avocado and garlic or garlicky king prawns (£7.25) and steaks (from £9, fillet £10.50), and they do traditional Sunday lunches; best to book at weekends. People are surprised to find a pub at this Surreyfied tip of the county with such a pleasantly rustic and unyuppy atmosphere: an inglenook log fire in the snugly unpretentious beamed and flagstone front bar, an unfussy low-ceilinged lounge, friendly service; darts, shove-ha'penny, dominoes and cribbage, and boules in the garden. Well kept Flowers Original, Marstons Pedigree and Whitbreads Strong Country on handpump, choice of a dozen wines sold by the glass; piped music. A sunny little front terrace borders the quiet lane, and there are a good few more tables in a peaceful and prettily planted side garden and on another crazy-paved terrace; children's play area. It can get very busy at peak times. *(Recommended by TOH, John Bowdler, John and Heather Dwane, M G Richards, Angela and Colin Smithers, Norman Foot, Peter Griffiths, Mike and Joyce Bryant)*

Whitbreads   Tenant Gyles Culver   Real ale   Meals and snacks   (0403) 790480   Children in overflow eating area   Occasional jazz outside in summer   Open 11–3, 6–11

RYE   TQ9220   Map 3

Mermaid

Mermaid St

The ancient timbered inn with its sign hanging over the cobbled street is one of the classic images of this charming town, such a rewarding place for a day trip. And a day trip here would scarcely be complete without a drink in the civilised little bar right at the back. A picture on the wall shows it some 70 years ago – and shows that even the detail of its furnishings has scarcely changed since. Unusual intricately carved antique seats include one in the form of a goat, the fireplace is big enough to hide a whole gang of smugglers, and there's plenty to peer at. Bass and Charringtons IPA on handpump, and their own house wines, ports and sherries. In the main part of the inn you'll find fine panelling, other woodwork dating back some five centuries (the cellars are even older), and rare frescoes; readers have enjoyed the restaurant, where there's a salad buffet (about £7). There are seats on a small back terrace. *(Recommended by Mike Rising, JM, PM, Tony and Alison Sims, Edward Burlton Davies; more reports please)*

Free house   Licensee M K Gregory   Real ale   Restaurant   Rye (0797) 223065 Children in restaurant   Open 11–3, 6–11, all day Fri/Sat in summer; closed Sun evening in winter   Bedrooms; £57.20B/£88B

nr SCAYNES HILL   TQ3623   Map 3
Sloop

Freshfield Lock; at top of Scaynes Hill by petrol station turn N off A272 into Church Lane, follow Freshfield signpost

Doing particularly well at the moment – and very busy at weekends – this consistently friendly pub serves generous helpings of good well presented changing bar food such as filled warm cottage loaves (from £2.25), winter soups (£2.95), filled baked potatoes (from £3.25), garlic pâté (£3.95), ploughman's (from £3.95), a choice of vegetarian dishes like tagliatelli with courgettes, mushrooms and onions, seasonal vegetables in a cream sauce or cauliflower florets in breadcrumbs, interesting quiches (all £5.95), scampi (£6.95), pasta, steaks, and a huge mixed grill, also children's dishes. The long saloon bar has comfortable sofas, armchairs, and cushioned banquettes, and there are plenty of tables out in the attractive and sheltered garden, in a lovely spot by what used to be the Ouse Canal, with a children's climbing frame, and more benches in the old-fashioned brick porch. Well kept Harveys and guest beers on handpump; an excellent choice of country wines; piped music. The basic but airy public bar has a small games room – sensibly placed darts, pool, dominoes, cribbage and fruit machine. The Bluebell Line steam railway is nearby, and the pub is quite handy for Sheffield Park. *(Recommended by John Beeken, Alec Lewery, Marie Enright, Miss P M Hayes, W G Harvey, Paul Evans, Dr Keith Bloomfield, Edward Burlton Davies, Roy Wilson, Terry Buckland)*

Beards (who no longer brew)   Tenants David and Marilyn Mills   Real ale   Meals and snacks   Restaurant   Scaynes Hill (0444) 831219   Children in eating area   Open 11–11

nr SEAFORD   TV4899   Map 3
Golden Galleon

Exceat Bridge; A259 Seaford–Eastbourne, near Cuckmere

Though it gets lots of customers in summer this copes well with them; there's little feeling of crowdedness, and the food has quite an individual flavour, with Italian touches reflecting the young licensee's origin (his wife's English). As we go to press they are in the process of buying the pub from the brewery. Good home-cooked bar food includes starters like tonno e fagioli and a good few others such as an Italian seafood salad, sweet-cured herrings or pâté (all around £2.60-£3), fresh local fish (from £4.95), a couple of specials such as lasagne (£4.95) or spaghetti carbonara (£5), scampi (£5), chicken in tomato and ginger sauce (£6.75), gammon (£6.50), pork tenderloin (£7.50) and steaks (from 8oz sirloin £8.95), with a good help-yourself salad counter (from £3.50), and half-portions of most things for children. The position's a big draw in fine weather, with plenty of seats on the terraces and grass of the sloping garden, and views of Beachy Head and the Cuckmere estuary. Well kept Harveys Armada, Courage Best and Directors on handpump, freshly squeezed orange juice; particularly good friendly service, piped music. Half the Turkey-carpeted bar/dining area with its neat rows of tables is no smoking; high trussed and pitched rafters give this an airy feel. One nice little side alcove is snugged in by an open fire. Outside, a good many well spaced tables on the sloping grass give view out past the road to Beachy Head on the right, with the Seven Sisters Country Park just over the nearby Cuckmere River; it's a ten-minute easy walk down to the beach, and there are walks inland to Friston Forest and the Downs. (*Recommended by C T and J M Laffan, P Gillbe, Mr and Mrs Russell Bathie, Elaine Sinclair, Lesley Jones, Geralyn Meyler*)

Courage   Tenant Stefano Diella   Real ale   Meals and snacks (12–2, 6–9)   Seaford (0323) 892247   Open 11–2.30, 6.30–11

SIDLESHAM   SZ8598 Map 2
Crab & Lobster

Off B2145 S of Chichester, either Rookery Lane N of village (on left as you approach) or Mill Lane from village centre

Well liked for its evocative position well away from the main tourist places, this has a back garden filled with sweet peas, gladioli, snapdragons, roses and so forth, looking across a meadow to the coastal bird-reserve flats and silted Pagham Harbour. The ochre-walled bar is straightforward and traditional, with a good log fire and wildfowl and marine prints; there's also a plusher side lounge. Simple food at sensible prices includes crab or prawn sandwiches, garlic prawns or steak and kidney pie (£4.50), Selsey crab (£5.20), and home-made puddings; the seafood is particularly good. Well kept GBB, HSB and BBB on handpump, Gales old country wines and a decent choice of other drinks. (*Recommended by BHP, P Devitt, J F Reay, Dr P H Mitchell, Mrs J A Blanks, Roger Taylor, M Morgan, Dr J D Bassett, Paul and Margaret Baker*)

Gales   Tenant Brian Cross   Real ale   Meals and snacks (not Sun evening)   (0243) 641233   Open 11–2.30, 6–11

STOPHAM   TQ0218 Map 3
White Hart

Just off A283 towards Pulborough

There's been some sort of building here for as long as the graceful bridge nearby – not far short of 700 years – and the bypass has brought back something of the tranquillity of the past. The three present cosy and comfortable beamed rooms are quite a draw in their own right, but the main focus of attention for most people is the good food. It includes home-made soup (£1.45), sandwiches (from £1.10, smoked salmon £2.20), baked potatoes (from £2.50), various platters (from £2.95), spicy sausages (£2.95), home-made fresh pasta dishes (£3.75), home-made fish pie (£4.25), and children's dishes (£1.50); the beamed and candlelit restaurant serves a splendid range of fresh fish. Well kept Flowers Original and Marstons Pedigree on handpump, and decent wines; darts, shove-ha'penny, cribbage, dominoes, fruit machine, and piped music, and they hold special event evenings. There are tables on the lawn across the road, with a play area, and tree-lined grass walks down by the meeting of the Arun and Rother rivers. (*Recommended by P Gillbe, Iain and Penny Muir, Charles Turner, John Knighton, Mr and Mrs G Turner, Mrs Lili Lomas, Mrs Joan Harris*)

Whitbreads   Tenant Bill Bryce   Real ale   Meals and snacks   Restaurant (not Sun evening)   Pulborough (079 827) 3321   Several live entertainment evenings   Children welcome   Open 11–3(3.30 Sat); 6.30–11; winter evening opening 7

nr TICEHURST   TQ6830 Map 3
Bull ✪

Three Legged Cross; coming into Ticehurst from N on B2099, just before Ticehurst village sign, turn left beside corner house called Tollgate (Maynards Pick Your Own may be signposted here)

Doing particularly well at the moment, this 14th-century country pub has a very friendly feel, with its beams and roaring log fire. The food's good, too. At lunchtime it includes home-made stilton soup (£1.35), sandwiches (from £1, hot gammon £1.30, tasty steak £3), good ploughman's (£2.75), sardine and salad platter (£2.85), moules marinières or lamb's liver and bacon (£3.50), help yourself buffet (£3.75), pork chop and stilton in port (£3.95), popular steak and kidney pie (£4.50), gammon steak with mustard and demarara glaze (£4.25), 12oz rump steak (£7.95), and home-made puddings like apple strudel, summer pudding or hokey-pokey ice cream with honeycombe in it (£1.95). In the evenings (when they prefer bookings), they do more elaborate meals. Service is friendly and efficient; two well kept Harveys beers and three other such as Morland Old Speckled Hen, Timothy Taylors Landlord or Ringwood – and they make a good pot of tea. The part where seats go first is the original low-ceilinged core, where small flagstoned, brick-floored or oak parquet rooms run together, with heavy oak tables, seats of some character, and the big focal fireplace (which the soft grey tabby heads for). A larger, more modern room is light and airy; darts, dominoes and cribbage. The pretty garden is sheltered by fruit and other trees, including a weeping willow by a pool. Children can escape to a big playing field, and maybe a bouncy castle. *(Recommended by Klaus and Elizabeth Leist, Tom and Mary Farr, Mrs Christina Hartley, Mr and Mrs David Bing, R Houghton, Caroline Hall, R C Morgan, M C Howells, Maysie Thompson)*

Free house   Licensee Josie Wilson-Moir   Real ale   Meals and snacks (not Sun evening)   Restaurant   Ticehurst (0580) 200586   Children welcome   Open 11–3, 6–11

WEST ASHLING   SU8107   Map 2

Richmond Arms

Mill Lane; from B2146 in village follow Hambrook signpost

A new regime here, but the pub's crusade for real ales is still being carried on – a continuous search for new real ales to add to the several hundred which in the few years we've known it have passed through that imposing line of ten handpumps. A typical selection might include Brakspears PA, Harveys XX, King & Barnes Festive, Timothy Taylors Landlord and Thwaites. The furnishings fit in well – the main room's dominated by the central servery, and has a 1930s feel, with its long wall benches, library chairs, black tables and open fire. There's a good range of no-nonsense food, such as sandwiches (croque monsieur £3), excellent ploughman's, and 6oz steak sandwich (£4.99), there are filled baked potatoes (from £3.30), home-made chilli con carne, curry, lasagne, tuna or cottage pie (all £3.80), and steak pie (£3.95). Attentive, friendly service even when it's busy (weekends, say). Bar billiards, shove-ha'penny, dominoes, cribbage, and trivia and fruit machines in games room. The old skittle alley doubles as a function and family room. There's a pergola, and some picnic-table sets by the car park. *(Recommended by John and Christine Simpson, Phil and Sally Gorton, Derek and Sylvia Stephenson, David and Sarah Gilmore, Mrs Lili Lomas, M Morgan, Richard Houghton)*

Free house   Licensees Bob and Christine Garbutt   Real ale   Meals and snacks (0243) 575730   Children in skittle alley   Open 11–3, 5.30–11; all day Sat in summer

WEST FIRLE   TQ4607   Map 3

Ram 🛏

Signposted off A27 Lewes–Polegate

The current licensees have settled in well at this 17th-century village inn – very welcoming indeed, with various well brought up dogs and cats. Improvements have concentrated on the accommodation side (and the lavatories), and what changes there have been in the bars have not affected their unspoilt appeal – chiefly more (and more comfortable) seating, softer lighting in the front area, and a no smoking rule for the snug. Bar food, though, has become a good deal more attractive than the nice enough hearty walkers' fare the inn was known for previously. It now majors on local produce, including free range eggs and poultry: game soup (£2.25), open sandwiches week days only (from £2.95), ploughman's (from £3.25), pizzas (£3.95), salads (from £6.25), rabbit hot-pot (£6.35), beef and Guinness pudding (£6.65) and home-made puddings such as pecan pie and bread pudding (£2.75). Well kept Harveys BB and Charrington IPA and a guest beer on handpump, decent wines (including a dry white produced locally), particularly good coffee; good log fire, darts, shove-ha'penny, dominoes, cribbage and toad-in-the-hole. There are tables in a spacious walled garden behind. Nearby Firle Place is worth visiting for its collections and furnishings. The pub is handy for a particularly fine stretch of the South Downs, and for Glyndebourne. *(Recommended by N Patton, Tony Gayfer, Lynne Sheridan, Bob West, Dr Keith Clements, John Kimber, J W Deane, Dr C S Shaw, Giles Quick, Lesley Sones, Geralyn Meyler)*

Free house   Licensees Michael Wooller and Margaret Sharp   Real ale   Meals and lunchtime snacks   (0273) 858222   Children in snug bar   Traditional folk music every 2nd Mon   Open 11.30–2.30, 7–11; 11.30–3, 6–11 Sat (7 in winter)   Three good value bedrooms; £23/£40(£50S)

WEST HOATHLY   TQ3632 Map 3
Cat

Village signposted from either A22 or B2028 S of East Grinstead

This is a peaceful and very pretty spot – very photogenic too, with the old tiled pub and even older church pairing well. Inside looks good, too, with ancient carving around the inglenook on one side of the massive central chimney separating off the area with the food servery, hefty blocks of stone masonry, some beams and panelling, even some traces of wattle and daub plaster. Nicely presented, if rather pricey, home-made bar food from a menu that changes daily may include soup (£1.75), sandwiches (from £1.95), smoked salmon pâté (£4.55), pie of the day or mushroom and bacon (£5.25), chicken livers with chipolatas (£6.50), kidneys in red wine (£6.95), chicken curry (£7.45), salmon or crab salad (£7.95), fresh haddock (£8.75), steak au poivre (£12.95) or whole lobster (£15.95). Well kept Adnams BB and Harveys BB on handpump; friendly and willing service, decent wines. Seats among the roses out in front catch the sun; the pub is near the start of the *Good Walks Guide* Walk 64. *(Recommended by Tom Thomas, the BGs, Robert A Anderson, David and Sarah Gilmore, Peter Hall, T Galligan)*

Beards (who no longer brew)   Tenant G Burillo   Real ale   Meals and snacks (not Sun evening)   Restaurant   (0342) 810369   Children in restaurant   Open 11–2.30, 6–11

WINCHELSEA   TQ9017 Map 3
New Inn   🛏

Just off A259

Full of folk enjoying good value food, this 18th-century pub has an interesting set of rambling communicating rooms, with a comfortable variety of wall banquettes, settles and dining chairs around good sturdy tables, and a mix of bric-a-brac and interesting old photographs and other pictures on walls painted a deep and relaxing terracotta colour. Masses of hop bines hang from the beams. Good, hearty bar food includes sandwiches (not Sunday lunchtime or bank holidays), home-made soup (£1.95), garlic mushrooms (£2.95), ploughman's (from £2.75), home-cooked ham and egg (£3.95), salads (from £3.95), steak and kidney pie with good thick fluffy pastry (£5.50), and steaks (from £8.95); children's meals until 7.30pm (from £1.75), daily specials like local plaice, trout or skate (£5.50), lemon sole (£6.95) or Dover sole (£7.95) or home-made pies, and puddings like home-made trifle or bread and butter pudding; friendly, efficient waitress service. Well kept Courage Best and Directors and Youngs Special on handpump, decent wines by the glass, and around 10 malt whiskies; good log fires. A quite separate public bar has darts, well lit pool, cribbage, fruit machine, and unobtrusive piped music. There are picnic-table sets and swings in a sizeable neatly mown orchard. Some of the pretty bedrooms look across to the church among the lime trees opposite – particularly pretty in spring, with daffodils then drifts of bluebells. *(Recommended by Michael Bourdeaux, David Gaunt, Dave Braisted, H Crookston, W J Wonham, K J Betts)*

Courage Leasehold: Richard Joyce Real ale Meals and snacks (12–2, 6.30–9.30) Rye (0797) 226252 Children in no-smoking family area Open 11–2.30, 6–11; closed 25 Dec and evening 26 Dec Bedrooms; £23/£29

WINEHAM TQ2320 Map 3
Royal Oak

Village signposted from A272 and B2116

One of the prettiest pubs in the county, this ancient tiled and timbered cottage changes scarcely at all year by year – though Mr Peacock has taken advantage of the legislation to liberalise the brewery tie by buying in BB direct from Harveys in Lewes, besides the Whitbreads Strong Country and Pompey Royal that he's always kept so well, tapped from casks in a still room on the way back through to the small snug. As this implies, the layout and style is commendably traditional, with very low beams above the serving counter decorated with ancient corkscrews, horseshoes, racing plates, tools and a coach horn, basic old-fashioned furniture, logs burning in an enormous inglenook. Darts, shove-ha'penny, dominoes, cribbage; a limited range of bar snacks: sandwiches (from £1), home-made soup in winter (£1.50). There are wooden tables by the well on the neat front lawn; on a clear day see if you can catch a glimpse of Chanctonbury Ring from the window in the gents' – something readers of the *Guide* have been arguing about year after year. *(Recommended by R A Corbett, Phil and Sally Gorton, T Buckland)*

Whitbreads Tenant Tim Peacock Real ale Snacks (available throughout opening hours) (0444) 881252 Children in family room Open 11–2.30, 5.30–11; 11–3, 6–11 Sat; closed evening 25 Dec

WITHYHAM TQ4935 Map 3
Dorset Arms

B2110

Deep in Sackville-West country, this is a good deal older than its white Georgian facade implies. It's unusual in that you have to go up a short flight of outside steps to enter the beamed L-shaped bar, which rewards you for the climb with a splendidly welcoming atmosphere; there are sturdy tables and simple country seats on its wide polished oak floorboards, and a good log fire in the stone Tudor fireplace. Good bar food includes sandwiches (from £1), huge filled rolls (£1.50), ploughman's (£2.50), popular fresh plaice or trout or smoked trout salad (£6.50), and Scotch smoked salmon (£9.50), with daily specials such as steak and kidney pie, jumbo sausage and egg, braised steak or venison (from £4); on Sunday lunchtimes and Tuesday they only do rolls and ploughman's (though the restaurant does Sunday lunches £7.75). Well kept Harveys BB, PA and XX on handpump, a good relaxed atmosphere; darts, dominoes and cribbage; tables on the raised brick terrace outside. *(Recommended by N Patton, Mike and Joyce Bryant; more reports on new regime please)*

Harveys Tenant Mr Young Real ale ¯Meals and snacks Restaurant (not Sun evening) Hartfield (0892) 770278 Children in restaurant and eating area of bar Open 11–11 weekdays; 11–3, 6–11 Sat

Lucky Dip

Besides the fully inspected pubs, you might like to try these Lucky Dips recommended to us and described by readers (if you do, please send us reports):

☆ **Adversane**, W Sus [TQ0723], *Blacksmiths Arms*: Attractive old beamed pub, well kept and spacious but cosy, with good value though not cheap varied choice of food, friendly service; restaurant *(Ron Gentry, Norman Foot)*

☆ **Alfriston**, E Sus [TQ5103], *Market Cross*: Also known as the Smugglers — low beams, cutlasses over the big inglenook, white-painted panelling, cosier side room, back conservatory, generous bar food from sandwiches to steaks (snacks only, Sun lunchtime), well kept Courage Best and Directors, good choice of wines by the glass, friendly staff, children allowed in eating area and conservatory, tables in garden; charming village *(Iain and Penny Muir, M J D Inskip, LYM)*

☆ **Alfriston** [High St], *George*: Long, spacious and well decorated heavily beamed bar dominated by huge fireplace — inn first licensed in 1397; wide choice of good bar food, good friendly service, King & Barnes Festive and Watneys-related real ales on handpump; bedrooms well regarded *(Alec Lewery, John Beeken, Mike Rising)*

Alfriston, *Deans Place*: Reasonably priced drinks, good bar food and pleasant staff in pleasant lounge and bar of beautiful old hotel appealing to the middle-aged; spacious old-fashioned gardens, swimming pool and tennis court; no dogs; good walks in every direction *(Romey Heaton)*; [Tye Green], *Wingrove*: On edge of picturesque green; good beer and food in very pleasant surroundings *(Alan Skull)*

☆ **Amberley**, W Sus [off B2139; TQ0212], *Black Horse*: Welcoming and unusual village pub, up a flight of steps, its beams festooned with sheep and cow bells and other Downland farm equipment; flagstones, well kept Allied real ales, wide choice of home-cooked bar food from ploughman's to steaks, garden; children in eating area and restaurant, occasional folk music *(P A Barfield, P and J M Lewis, Iain and Penny Muir, LYM)*

☆ **Amberley** [Houghton Bridge], *Bridge*: Doing well under new regime, well run busy but friendly free house with consistently good value food emphasising fresh produce, also fish and superb steaks; choice of well kept real ales; tables in tranquil garden with R Arun meandering nearby; bedrooms *(Iain and Penny Muir, P Gillbe, Mr and Mrs P E Hallam)*

☆ **Angmering**, W Sus [TQ0704], *Spotted Cow*: Cheerful landlord, good range of drinks inc wines at reasonable prices; food above average, attentively served, roomy garden with good separate play area; dogs allowed, at start of lovely walk to Highdown hill fort *(H C Clifford)*

Angmering [The Square], *Lamb*: Friendly, with well kept Allied beers, good choice of

reasonably priced food all home-made *(P Gillbe)*

Apuldram, W Sus [Birdham Rd; SU8403], *Black Horse*: Comfortably modernised 18th-century pub with Allied ales on handpump, wide range of straightforward food from sandwiches to steaks at sensible prices; helpful friendly staff, juke box *(Peter Ames)*

☆ **Ardingly**, W Sus [B2028 2 miles N; TQ3429], *Gardeners Arms*: Warm and pleasant atmosphere, no music, in attractive old-world bar with inglenook fireplace; simple range of good value food individually cooked and well presented from sandwiches up, with good specials; King & Barnes Festive, Theakstons and Watneys-related real ales on handpump; plenty of space on big lawn, handy for Borde Hill and Wakehurst Place *(Norman Foot, M Hunt, Tom Rhys)*

☆ **Ardingly** [Street Lane], *Oak*: Clean and pleasant beamed 14th-century pub with wide choice of good food at reasonable prices inc delicious puddings, Watneys-related and guest real ales, antique furnishings and lovely log fire in magnificent old fireplace; bright and comfortable restaurant, friendly efficient service; pool table in public bar *(Mrs Blanks, Phil Bryant, Audrey and Brian Green)*

Ardingly [College Rd], *Avins Bridge*: Rather elegant pub with well kept King & Barnes, good bar snacks and friendly staff; well furnished bars and garden *(John Kimber)*

☆ **Arlington**, E Sus [Caneheath; TQ5407], *Old Oak*: Pleasant country free house with changing real ales such as Badger, Charles Wells and Harveys tapped from the cask, good reasonably priced food; friendly staff, restaurant (busy Sun, no food Mon), pleasant garden; children tolerated, handy for Bluebell Walk *(Nigel Gibbs, N Patton)*

☆ **Arlington**, *Yew Tree*: Welcoming, neatly kept and comfortably modernised village local with big garden, usual bar food priced reasonably and well presented, Harveys on handpump, subdued piped music; restaurant *(J Beeken, BB)*

☆ **Arundel**, W Sus [High St; TQ0107], *Swan*: Several real ales, friendly staff and wide range of popular bar food in red plush bar; children in eating area; open all day; bedrooms comfortably refurbished *(D C Horwood, Norman Foot, Mrs Richard Stewart, Sandra Kempson, LYM)*

Arundel [High St], *Norfolk Arms*: Comfortable genuinely old hotel with good food and service, good snacks and Whitbreads real ale in public bar, also hotel bar and lounge; restaurant, ample parking under coach arch *(D C Horwood)*; *White Hart*: Jovial landlord, interesting though not cheap changing guest real ales in two cosy lounges with old settles and ancient books;

reasonably priced fresh food, comfortable dining area *(Iain and Penny Muir)*

Barcombe, E Sus [TQ4114], *Anchor*: Remote, idiosyncratic inn worth knowing for charming gardens and boating on very peaceful river; sandwiches in small regulars' bar, restaurant *(LYM)*

☆ **Barns Green**, W Sus [TQ1227], *Queens Head*: Old pub in pretty village, pleasantly modernised with one big but cosy bar, several fires inc huge one in inglenook, wide choice of food on several separate blackboards, piped music, fruit machine; well kept Whitbreads-related real ales, live music evenings, benches in front by quiet road, garden behind *(Norman Foot)*

☆ **Battle**, E Sus [25 High St; TQ7416], *George*: Friendly welcome in lovely old well run coaching inn with L-shaped bar, part pine-panelled and with pine counter, upmarket atmosphere, well kept Harveys on handpump, good lunchtime bar food inc sandwiches, a daily hot dish and good cold table in restaurant, good teas, well kept Harveys; no music; bedrooms *(Prof S Barnett, J A H Townsend)*

Battle [High St], *1066*: Wide range of particularly well kept real ales, generous good food, prompt waitress service, friendly bar staff, oak beams, open fire, friendly great dane; nr abbey *(Jenny and Neil Spink)*

☆ **Beckley**, E Sus [TQ8523], *Rose & Crown*: Character coaching inn with real ales such as Fremlins, Harveys, King & Barnes Bitter and winter XXXX and Marstons Pedigree on handpump, good bar food just right for hungry walkers, welcoming staff *(Dr B A W Perkins, AMC)*

☆ **Berwick**, E Sus [Milton Street, which is signed off A27 SIZE6$\frac{1}{4}$ mile E of Alfriston roundabout; TQ5105], *Sussex Ox*: Marvellous play area inc two-storey wooden house, by big lawn outside country pub just below Downs; can get very busy (and noisy in family room), but good atmosphere and well kept Adnams and Harveys, with the food side coming on strongly (taken over by Browns restaurant, Brighton); pleasantly simple country furniture to match the brick floor and woodburning stove; lots of good walks *(R Heaton, John Beeken, Lesley Sones, Geralyn Meyler, LYM)*

Berwick [by stn], *Berwick*: Family pub with attractive Perspex-roofed garden bar, good choice of food and real ales; good children's playground behind *(Neil H Barker, LYM)*

Bexhill, E Sus [nr stn; TQ7407], *Castle*: Lively young person's pub, lots of fish dishes *(Alec Lewery, Marie Enright)*; [Polegate rd, W], *Denbigh*: Attractive, nicely placed pub with small bar and dining area; good bar food inc Sun lunch, cheerful landlord, well kept Courage beers on handpump; children welcome in dining area *(Alec Lewery)*; [A259 W, nr Cooden], *Lamb*: Recently refurbished and much enlarged dining pub with inviting open fire in snug original core, extension into former barn; good choice of generous food with changing specials such as fresh skate or pheasant casserole; well kept

Harveys *(Alec Lewery, Marie Enright)*; [Cooden Beach Hotel], *Sovereign*: Fine choice of lunchtime food (may stop as early as 12.45 Sun) in self-contained bar of hotel, popular with locals; warm and comfortable with well kept Harveys, more space in no smoking area than in smoking part, good service; bedrooms *(Alec Lewery, Marie Enright)*; [Egerton Park Rd], *Traffers*: Well kept real ales such as Harveys and King & Barnes, upstairs restaurant *(Geoff and Julie Bond)*

Billingshurst, W Sus [High St; A29; TQ0925], *Olde Six Bells*: Partly 14th-century flagstoned and timbered local with well kept King & Barnes real ales, decent wines, friendly welcome, food, inglenook fireplace, pretty roadside garden; gets very busy evenings, particularly Fri/Sat *(P Thorogood, J S Evans, LYM)*

☆ **Binstead**, W Sus [Binstead Lane; about 2 miles W of Arundel, turn S off A27 towards Binstead — OS Sheet 197, map reference 980064; SU9806], *Black Horse*: Unpretentious pub in quiet country lane, clean and polished, with big helpings of reasonably priced bar food inc some unusual dishes, well kept Gales, sensibly placed darts, welcoming landlord, rack of tourist information; sheltered back garden with views over meadows towards coast; bedrooms *(Dr A M Rankin, David Hunn, Sion Hughes)*

☆ **Birdham**, W Sus [B2179 a mile S of village; SU8200], *Lamb*: Comfortable and spotless, lots of small friendly rooms, good range of well kept ales inc Harveys, King & Barnes, Tetleys, good reasonably priced choice of wines, interesting fairly priced food, more choice evenings and weekends; lots of tables out in front and in sheltered back garden — good for children *(Peter and Susan Maguire)*

Blackham, E Sus [A264 towards East Grinstead; TQ4838], *Sussex Oak*: Superbly positioned pub with flowering tubs, hanging baskets and window boxes; spotless carpeted interior, promising bar menu, Fremlins and Whitbreads on handpump, pleasant service; attractive restaurant *(E G Parish)*

☆ **Bodiam**, E Sus [TQ7825], *Curlew*: Well kept Adnams and King & Barnes on handpump, sensibly priced decent wines, good choice of bottled beers, wide range of generous food inc interesting daily specials in L-shaped bar and back dining area *(Patrick Young)*

☆ **Bodle Street Green**, E Sus [off A271 at Windmill Hill; has been shut Mon Oct—Easter, opens 7pm; TQ6514], *White Horse*: Unassuming country pub, clean and well run, with good value generous straightforward food in simply modernised welcoming bar; well kept Harveys and King & Barnes Sussex and Festive on handpump, decent wines and malt whiskies, open fires, bar billiards, darts, cheery piped music; some tables outside — a helpful touch for walkers is the OS map framed outside *(Alan Skull, BB)*

Bognor Regis, W Sus [Steyne St; SZ9399], *Lamb*: Small, unpretentious pub converted from fishermen's cottages with beams from drawbridge of Arundel Castle; friendly, efficient licensees, Flowers beer and home-cooked, individually prepared and reasonably priced food; homely atmosphere, log fire; children in restaurant *(Cdr William Tegg)*; [12 High St], *William Hardwicke*: Nice atmosphere, wide choice of good, reasonably priced lunchtime food *(Mrs S Stewart)*

☆ **Bosham**, W Sus [High St; SU8003], *Anchor Bleu*: Lovely sea and boat views from waterside pub with usual bar food, well kept beer, low beams, open fires and distinct maritime feel; some tables outside, in attractive unspoilt village; friendly staff, can get very busy *(Margaret and Roy Randle, Graham and Glenis Watkins, LYM)*

Bramber, W Sus [TQ1710], *Castle*: Popular, with friendly helpful staff, good range of bar snacks (free Sun nibbles), Bass and Charrington IPA on handpump, pleasant back garden *(Jenny and Brian Seller)*

☆ **Brighton**, E Sus [Castle Sq; TQ3105], *Royal Pavilion*: Sizeable place, with all sorts of different moods in well laid out series of rooms attractively done up for successful old-fashioned look, inc intimate candlelit winebar area (good big glasses), more open space with choice of real ales, generous central food bar and popular first-floor nightclub *(Alec Lewery, Marie Enright, LYM)*

☆ **Brighton** [15 Black Lion St], *Cricketers*: Warm, friendly old-fashioned atmosphere and idiosyncratic decor inc lots of crushed velvet, old record sleeves, stuffed grizzly bear and musical instruments; 1930s and 1940s gramophone, well kept Ruddles County; just in from seafront *(Mark Dickens, Neil Barker, BB)*

☆ **Brighton** [100 Goldstone Villas, next to Hove Rly Stn], *Hedgehog & Hogshead*: Big and airy, first of a small new chain by the team who developed the Bruce's Brewery Firkin pubs and strongly reminiscent of them; brews its own very palatable Brighton Breezy, and strong Hogbolter; food generally tasty, music sometimes loud *(Lesley Sones, Geralyn Meyler, Alan Skull)*

Brighton [The Lanes], *Bath Arms*: Pretty stonebuilt pub, basic bar with open fire, bookshelves, Watneys-related real ales and malty own-brewed Bathwater; pleasant atmosphere, friendly service *(Neil Barker)*; [New Rd, off North St, by Theatre Royal], *Colonnade*: Unusual, original theatre bar (though most certainly a pub), richly decorated with velvet and mirrors; interesting theatre posters and photos from 20s to 80s; everything on slightly small scale, inc tiny front terrace; nice atmosphere, very friendly staff; spoilt only by high-tech cigarette machine *(Neil Barker)*; [Palace Pier], *Horatios*: Large, unusually plush bar nr end of pier with sea views, reasonable range of lagers, live music; a cut above most pier bars *(Neil Barker)*; [13 Marlborough Pl], *King & Queen*: Genuinely old, with medieval-style lofty and spacious main hall, straightforward decent food, well kept beer, pool table, good jazz most evenings (when parking tends to be difficult), aviary in flagstoned courtyard *(Andrew Cooke, LYM)*; [George St], *Kings Arms*: The feel of a country pub; food lunchtime, live music (usually one-man bands) Fri-Sun evenings *(Alec Lewery, Marie Enright)*; [Trafalgar St], *Lord Nelson*: Good value unpretentious home cooking, good choice of well kept beers inc Harveys, farm cider, truly pubby atmosphere *(Alec Lewery, Peter Barnsley)*; [68 Queens Rd (nr stn)], *Queens Head*: Twelve real ales on handpump, simple good value food lunchtime and evening, lively yet welcoming, traditional decor with Victorian mirrors *(Lee Goulding, Peter Barnsley)*; [Queens Rd], *Royal Standard*: Small bar also nr stn, with lots of real ales inc several guests tapped from the cask in separate small room called the Vestry *(Patrick Godfrey, D J Penny)*; [Hove St, Hove], *Ship*: Pub-hotel in good part of Hove just off seafront; clean and well looked after, good atmosphere, good home-cooked food at pub prices; well regarded by all, especially the retired *(John Blake)*

☆ **Bucks Green**, W Sus [TQ0732], *Fox*: Old-world village pub recently taken over by new tenants and refurbished; well kept King & Barnes, good varied and well presented food in good helpings inc good value Sun lunch *(Mr and Mrs R P Begg, Roy Wilson)*

☆ **Bucks Green**, *Queens Head*: Old-world village free house with well kept Badger, Courage Directors and King & Barnes; big pleasantly decorated single bar with log fires, nice atmosphere, amiable landlord and wide choice of good value food inc some enterprising specials *(Mrs J A Blanks)*

☆ **Burwash**, E Sus [TQ6724], *Rose & Crown*: Timbered and beamed local tucked away down side street in quaintly restored village, with wide choice of real ale such as Bass, Charrington IPA and Shepherd Neame, decent wines, good log fire, friendly atmosphere, quite enterprising bar food, restaurant; tables on quiet lawn; nr start GWG67 *(Neil H Barker, BB)*

Burwash, *Bear*: Friendly, roomy pub with relaxing atmosphere, promising menu, and nice fire; open all day; bedrooms *(Neil H Barker)*

☆ **Burwash Weald**, E Sus [A265 two miles W of Burwash; TQ6624], *Wheel*: Good inglenook log fire in long open-plan carpeted room with green plush button-back banquettes along wall, lots of brasses on its five black beams, nicely framed old local photographs; decent bar food, well kept Harveys and Ruddles Best and County, games bar up a step or two behind, tables outside; lovely walks in valley opp; in summer 1991 turned itself into a lottery, £100 tickets with a chance of winning the pub *(BB)*

☆ **Bury**, W Sus [A29 Pulborough—Arundel; TQ0113], *Black Dog & Duck*: Pretty flint-walled village pub, homely ancient front snug seating about twelve people, bigger back public bar with original flagstones, fruit machine, bar billiards, no music; well kept Gales and Watneys-related ales on handpump, generous bar food (not Sun or Weds evenings) in small dining room, very friendly landlord, Gales HSB, small pleasant garden; in good walking country *(Alan Skull, R Bennett, Jenny and Brian Seller, Iain and Penny Muir)*

☆ Chalvington, E Sus [village signed from A27 and A22; then follow Golden Cross rd — OS Sheet 199, map reference 525099; TQ5109], *Yew Tree*: Isolated country local nicely stripped down to bricks and flagstones inside, with elm seats built into the walls, low beams and inglenook fireplace; straightforward bar food (not Sun), well kept Harveys and Fremlins; popular with young people Fri and Sat evenings; attractive little walled terrace, and extensive grounds inc own cricket pitch *(Dr B A W Perkins, N Patton, BB)*

☆ Chelwood Gate, E Sus [A275 S of Forest Row; TQ4129], *Red Lion*: Good quickly served bar food, well kept King & Barnes and Watneys-related real ales on handpump, green plush furnishings, small coal fire, lacy-tablecloth dining room on left; delightful big sheltered garden with well spaced sheltered tables and barbecue; children welcome *(BB)*

Chichester, W Sus [St Martins St; SU8605], *Hole in the Wall*: Large popular pub with old beams, good open fire, well kept Flowers Orginal, Whitbreads real ale, well priced food inc children's dishes, restaurant; staff pleasant and cheerful *(NEB, WA)*; [St Pauls St], *White Horse*: Friendly staff in pleasant pub with nice choice of food inc burgers, sausages, quite a few vegetarian dishes; small suntrap garden *(Alec Lewery, Marie Enright)*

☆ Cocking, W Sus [A286 Midhurst—Chichester — OS Sheet 197, map reference 878179; SU8717], *John Cobden*: Welcoming low-beamed three-roomed 18th-century pub with well cushioned settles and other seats, open fire, generous helpings of good value bar food, well kept Ballards Best and Wadworths 6X, friendly staff; piped music; shut Mon lunchtime *(Jenny and Brian Seller)*

☆ Colemans Hatch, E Sus [signed off B2026; or off B2110 opp church; TQ4533], *Hatch*: Basic but welcoming rustic pub with lunchtime sandwiches, cheese rolls and home-made pies, pub games, well kept Larkins and Harveys BB on handpump, no juke box, Ashdown Forest views from tables on bluff of grass by quiet lane; outside lavatories; very busy summer weekends *(Jenny and Brian Seller, Richard Gibbs, Comus Elliott, LYM)*

☆ Compton, W Sus [SU7714], *Coach & Horses*: Friendly Spanish licensees in spotless free house; walkers welcome in traditional public bar, second beamed bar by good restaurant, well kept changing real ales such as Adnams on handpump *(Paul and Margaret Baker)*

☆ Copsale, W Sus [TQ1725], *Bridge*: Clean and comfortable country local with King & Barnes, good value standard food (not Tues evening), warm welcoming atmosphere *(Iain and Penny Muir, M Hunt)*

☆ Cousleywood, E Sus [TQ6533], *Old Vine*: Busy but attractive low-beamed lounge bar with Fremlins on handpump, good coffee, wide choice of good bar food in small bistroish dining area inc large puddings trolley, good value restaurant, efficient service *(R and S Bentley)*

Cowfold, W Sus [Mockbridge; TQ2122], *Bull*: Recently refurbished, with lots of country bygones on walls and ceiling; good fresh pasta and pizzas, separate dining room, well kept King & Barnes, friendly young barmaids, garden *(Terry Buckland)*

Crawley, W Sus [High St; TQ2636], *George*: Old-world hotel bar, very popular for lunchtime buffet and short choice of hot dishes; friendly staff; bedrooms *(Alec Lewery)*

☆ Cripps Corner, E Sus [TQ7721], *White Hart*: Comfortable, roomy and pleasantly redecorated, with good food at reasonable prices (not Sun evening), pleasant atmosphere and staff, several well kept beers, sensibly priced wines, fairly discreet piped music; garden *(Tom and Mary Farr, J H Bell)*

☆ Cuckfield, W Sus [TQ3025], *White Harte*: Popular medieval pub by lychgate to church, very simple, with cosy little comfortably modernised but old-world bars, roaring log fire in inglenook, friendly licensees and good value lunchtime food, particularly the cheap specials inc a vegetarian one (which go by 1.30ish); well kept King & Barnes real ales, keen darts teams *(Terry Buckland, Gwen and Peter Andrews, W J Wonham, LYM)*

Cuckfield, [South St; TQ3025], *Kings Head*: Good mix of young and old in bar, pleasant staff, well kept if not cheap King & Barnes, secluded garden; live music weekends; restaurant run under separate franchise, food itself most enjoyable but rather expensive *(Terry Buckland)*

Dale Hill, E Sus [by Dale Hill golf club; junction A268 and B2099; TQ6930], *Cherry Tree*: This previously recommended pub closed late 1990 *(News please)*

☆ Danehill, E Sus [School Lane; off A275 opp the former Crocodile; TQ4027], *Coach & Horses*: Gently updated pub in attractive spot, with pews in pleasant lounge, friendly young licensees, reliably well kept Harveys, a weekly changing guest beer such as Exmoor, decent house wine and good value home made bar food in dining extension — formerly a small stables *(Alan Skull, Ron Gentry, S D Sizen)*

☆ Dell Quay, W Sus [SU8302], *Crown & Anchor*: Modernised 15th-century pub on site of Roman quay, yacht-harbour views from bow window and garden; bar food, evening restaurant with grills and fish; log fire, plenty of tables outside overlooking water, Watneys-related real ales *(Dr A M*

Rankin, BB)

Devils Dyke, W Sus [TQ2511], *Devils Dyke*:
Recently rebuilt as Whitbreads Brewers
Fayre pub, standard food inc decent specials,
helpful friendly staff, pleasant spacious
decor; but it's mainly the staggering view
night and day which earns a listing for this
pub perched on the Downs above Brighton
*(Alec Lewery, Marie Enright, Phil Bryant,
LYM)*

Ditchling, E Sus [High St; TQ3215],
Sandrock: Good value food, all
home-prepared, inc Sun lunches; Harveys
and Watneys-related beers, open all day Fri
and Sat, friendly landlady *(David L Brown)*

☆ **Donnington**, W Sus [Selsey Rd (B2201);
SU8502], *Blacksmiths Arms*: Doing well
under very welcoming new owner,
completely renovated, with attractive new
dining room extension, nice atmosphere in
both bars, good choice of conventional food,
well kept real ales such as Badger, Bass and
Ringwood Old Thumper, good house wine,
attentive service; occasional live music,
garden *(N E Bushby, W Atkins, Mrs Joan
Harris)*

☆ **Duncton**, W Sus [set back from A285 N;
SU9617], *Cricketers Arms*: Lovely pub full
of cricket memorabilia with jovial licensee
and pub labrador called Cricket; several
attractive rooms on different levels, original
home-cooked food and Sun lunch, quickly
served and good if pricey; well kept Allied
and King & Barnes real ales, nice
atmosphere *(Harriet and Michael Robinson,
Tim and Sue Halstead)*

☆ **Eartham**, W Sus [SU9409], *George*: Country
pub with cosy, uncluttered and restful
lounge, and bar with games area; six well
kept real ales, reasonably priced and
generously served bar food, swift and
courteous service; separate restaurant *(Mrs
Lili Lomas, David Hunn, John Beeken, Iain
and Penny Muir)*

East Ashling, W Sus [SU8207], *Horse &
Groom*: Specialises in good seafood inc well
cooked whitebait, good crab and prawns;
obliging service, good coffee, tables outside
(Dr Sheila Smith)

☆ **East Dean**, W Sus [village signed off A286
and A285 N of Chichester — OS Sheet 197,
map reference 904129; SU9013],
Hurdlemakers: Formerly the Star & Garter,
under friendly new ownership, with a much
wider range of real ales than before, and
considerable emphasis on food from
sandwiches to trout and roasts, with good
nursery puddings; atmosphere and staff very
pleasant; charmingly placed by peaceful
green of quiet village below South Downs,
with rustic seats and swing in pretty walled
garden, and handy for South Downs Way,
with pleasant walk to Goodwood *(Grace and
Michael Kirby, T W Hall, LYM)*

East Hoathly, E Sus [TQ5216], *Foresters
Arms*: Very pleasant, unpretentious and
homely pub with attentive licensees; bar
decorated with brass and copper
breweriana, Harveys Sussex and Mild ales,
plenty of bites on bar Sun lunchtime, decent

good value food *(Jenny and Brian Seller)*

East Wittering, W Sus [Church Lane/Piggery
Hall Lane; SZ7997], *Thatched Tavern*:
Under new management, and very popular
for food from sandwiches to steaks, esp
good value Sun lunches — tables in dining
extension often fully booked weekends; Ind
Coope beers *(N E Bushby)*

☆ **Eastbourne**, E Sus [The Goffs, Old Town;
TV6199], *Lamb*: Interesting oak-beamed
Tudor building with several low-ceilinged
rooms off central oval bar, roaring log fire,
friendly welcome, Harveys Best, Armada
and Old on handpump, good changing
range of reasonably priced food; well placed
by parish church, a mile from seafront so
quieter than more touristy pubs *(Joan and
Michel Hooper-Immins, Iain and Penny Muir,
John Beeken)*

☆ **Eastbourne** [Holywell Rd, Meads; just off
front below approach from Beachy Head],
Pilot: Comfortable, with friendly licensees,
good variety of promptly served food, real
ales, attractively homely bars — another
that's escaped the tourists *(Roy Wilson, E G
Parish)*

Eastbourne [Terminus Rd], *Terminus*:
Friendly, old-fashioned and busy
town-centre pub with popular lunchtime
food and well kept Harveys; tables and
chairs out in pedestrian precinct *(Alan Skull);*
[Latimer Rd], *Victoria*: Just behind eastern
part of Esplanade, with big semi-circular
bar, high ceiling and wonderful atmosphere;
lots of young people enjoying the Harveys
Old and BB; no food; if evening piped music
gets too loud, escape to small back bar *(Joan
and Michel Hooper-Immins)*

Eastdean, E Sus [signed off A259
Eastbourne—Seaford; TV5597], *Tiger*:
Pretty tiled pub, low-beamed and
old-fashioned inside, on lovely sloping green
lined with cottages, by lane down to the sea
(and on GWG60); has been a popular main
entry in previous editions, with well kept
Courage, a good choice of wines by the
glass, and decent bar food; but the tenant
expects to leave as we go to press, and the
building's future as a pub is in some doubt
(LYM — news please)

Falmer, E Sus [Middle St; TQ3508], *Swan*:
A pub for committed real ale hunters, with
about eight well kept; good value simple
lunchtime food, too *(Alan Skull)*

Faygate, W Sus [Wimland Rd; TQ2134],
Frog & Nightgown: Tiny cosy and friendly
pub, one of the smallest you'll ever see, with
bird prints and pink decor; friendly dog, nice
scenery *(Edward Burlton Davies)*

Felpham, W Sus [102 Felpham Rd; just E of
Bognor; SZ9599], *George*: 17th-century
coaching inn of considerable character with
Allied ales, wines by the glass and extensive
lunchtime menu with evening extras; large,
well kept garden with fish pond; smart
customers; children welcome *(Cdr William
Tegg)*

Fernhurst, W Sus [A286 towards Midhurst;
SU9028], *Kings Arms*: Attractive pub in
pleasant setting with extensive lunchtime

menu and well cooked, well presented food; good beer *(Mrs Joan Harris)*

☆ **Findon**, W Sus [TQ1208], *Gun*: Large helpings of good standard food, well presented with fresh veg though not cheap, friendly service, and well kept Marstons Pedigree and Whitbreads-related real ales on handpump in comfortably modernised straightforward if low-beamed pub with attractive sheltered lawn, in quiet village below Cissbury Ring *(P A Barfield, Jean and Theodore Rowland-Entwistle, Alan and Ruth Woodhouse, LYM)*

☆ **Fittleworth**, W Sus [Lower St (B2138); TQ0118], *Swan*: Attractive 15th-century Chef & Brewer doing well under new manager, with big inglenook log fire in comfortable lounge, collections of wooden truncheons and of bottle-openers, usual bar food from sandwiches up inc children's dishes but little vegetarian food, friendly service, piped music (even in gents'); landscapes by Constable's brother George in attractive panelled side room; Watneys-related real ales, games inc pool in public bar, well spaced tables on big sheltered back lawn, good walks nearby; open all day Thurs-Sat, children in eating area; bedrooms *(Jenny and Brian Seller, D C Horwood, Alec Lewery, Marie Enright, Mrs Lili Lomas, LYM)*

Fletching, E Sus [TQ4223], *Red Lion*: Good country pub which hasn't gone out of its way to be odiously and unnaturally countrified; good simple food, huge garden *(R Tomlinson)*; *Rose & Crown*: Beams, log fires and inglenooks, food in bar (from sandwiches to steaks) and restaurant all prepared to order from fresh ingredients, real ales, well kept garden *(More reports please)*

Framfield, E Sus [The Street; B2012 E of Uckfield; TQ5020], *Hare & Hounds*: Roomy old country pub with exposed beams, capable and friendly licensees, varied menu *(Mr and Mrs I W Stapleton)*

Funtington, W Sus [SU7908], *Fox & Hounds*: Old pub extended into attractive, comfortable dining room, with generous helpings of good well cooked (if not cheap) food using fresh ingredients, and delicious puddings; welcoming helpful licensees and staff *(Y M Healey)*

Hammerpot, W Sus [A27 4 miles W of Worthing; TQ0605], *Woodmans Arms*: Comfortable and welcoming, with low ceilings, interesting prints, horsey bric-a-brac, well kept Allied real ales, massive helpings of usual pub food; seats outside *(Michael Bechley)*

☆ **Handcross**, W Sus [Horsham Rd; TQ2529], *Royal Oak*: Well kept King & Barnes and Watneys-related real ales and willing and friendly staff combine to make this relaxing and enjoyable; well cooked straightforward bar food served quickly and generously, spotless housekeeping, lightly themed rooms (aircraft, Churchill); if you feel poor, ask for method of payment — one reader was offered cash, card or washing-up *(K Baxter,*

Terry Buckland, DJ)

Handcross [High St], *Fountain*: Homely and comfortable two-bar pub, short walk from Nymans Garden (NT) and open all day, some snacks through afternoon; limited range of beers, sensibly priced straightforward bar food; darts and pool table, quiet piped music *(John Pettit)*

☆ **Hartfield**, E Sus [A264; TQ4735], *Haywaggon*: Warm welcome, oak beams, good food in clean bar and attractive good-value restaurant (good value set dinners), quick and attentive service; nr start GWG62 *(Colin Laffan)*

Hastings, E Sus [Old Harbour; TQ8109], *Dolphin*: Pleasant bar, Watneys-related ales, good value locally caught fish, tables out overlooking harbour *(Geoff and Julie Bond)*; [14 High St, Old Town], *First In Last Out*: Worth knowing for the keen-priced beers brewed on the premises, esp its fine strong Cardinal; food lunchtime, small back courtyard *(David and Fiona Easeman)*

Heathfield, E Sus [Horam Rd; TQ5821], *Prince of Wales*: Good well kept beer, wide choice of good cheap food, pleasant staff *(P Gillbe)*

☆ **Henfield**, W Sus [TQ2116], *George*: Spacious old-world pub with friendly staff, big helpings of decent bar food, well kept Gales HSB and Ushers Best; restaurant; pretty village *(Dr P H Mitchell, Mrs C M John)*

☆ **Hermitage**, W Sus [36 Main Rd (A259); SU7505], *Sussex Brewery*: May be packed weekends, for Hermitage, Warrior and Wyndhams brewed here, with guest beer such as Badger; basic sawdust-floor bar with simple rustic decor, no machines or piped music (may be pianist), log fire, cheerful staff; fair-priced food from sandwiches up, inc fine sausages and fresh local seafood (may take time but worth the wait); small garden *(Richard Houghton, J F Reay)*

☆ **Heyshott**, W Sus [SU8918], *Unicorn*: Friendly welcome and helpful service in small pub with nice local atmosphere in L-shaped bar; well kept beer, bar food, restaurant, garden with barbecue; in attractive country at foot of Downs; children allowed *(Ian and Wendy McCaw, JSE)*

Holtye, E Sus [A264 East Grinstead—Tunbridge Wells; TQ4539], *White Horse*: Harry Pam and his son who have made a great success of the Bell at Outwood (gaining it a starred main entry) are now operating here — unpretentious old village pub, with lots of fresh fish (and some meat) in spacious if rather plain dining room, pet fish swimming under its glass floor of dining room *(Anon)*

Horsham, W Sus [centre; TQ1730], *Bear*: Friendly small town pub with good atmosphere, tasty bar snacks and well kept King & Barnes *(Neil H Barker)*; [Tower Hill, S towards Worthing], *Boars Head*: Comfortable free house with three bars, well kept Eldridge Pope and Wadworths 6X, good variety of bar food, terrace *(Norman Foot)*; [Bearsden, Warnham Rd — A24, some way N], *Dog & Duck*: Attractive cottage-type King & Barnes pub, food lunchtime and evening, very pleasant service break *(E G Parish)*; [31 North St], *Hurst Arms*: Food good, pub has a lot of charm for a town one *(Phil Bryant)*; [Carfax], *Stout House*: Good little King & Barnes local — very basic and untrendy; good beer, filled rolls *(D J Penny)*

☆ **Hurstpierpoint**, W Sus [High St; TQ2716], *New Inn*: Old-fashioned local with good warm atmosphere in charming quiet traditional back room, bar billiards in panelled snug, separate simpler front public bar (can be noisy, with piped music and young people), well kept Bass and Charrington IPA; increasingly popular for good if not cheap bar food, good value dining room, tables in garden *(Mr Turrall-Clarke, John Molyneux, LYM)*

Icklesham, E Sus [TQ8816], *Queens Head*: Old beamed country pub with farm tools, splendid view over Brede to Rye, small garden; has been popular for good value home-cooked bar food inc children's dishes, John Smiths and other real ales, farm cider, country wines, but no recent reports *(News please)*

☆ **Isfield**, E Sus [TQ4417], *Laughing Fish*: Welcoming newish landlord in simply modernised Victorian village local with well kept Adnams and Harveys Best, PA and Old on handpump, reasonably priced straightforward bar food; tables in small garden with enclosed play area; children welcome *(John Beeken, Alec Lewery, Alan Skull, N Patton)*

Keymer, W Sus [TQ3115], *Thatched*: Unusual arc-shaped pub in scenic spot, friendly staff, well kept Harveys, reasonable food, small back garden with tame rabbits *(Alec Lewery, Marie Enright)*

☆ **Kirdford**, W Sus [TQ0126], *Foresters*: Well run flagstoned bar with bench seats and tables, lounge with stools, upholstered benches and tables, third room suitable for families; well kept King & Barnes, nice atmosphere, limited choice of simple but genuinely home-cooked bar food, quick service; restaurant *(John and Heather Dwane, J H Bell)*

Kirdford [opp church], *Half Moon*: Pleasant flagstoned bar with wide choice of food, good service and pleasant atmosphere; well kept Whitbreads-related real ales; good restaurant *(Norman Foot)*

☆ **Lambs Green**, W Sus [TQ2136], *Lamb*: Attractive country pub with warmly welcoming, relaxed atmosphere in beamed plush bar, cosy though extended; open fire, wide choice of quickly served generous food (inc good value Sun roast), several well kept real ales such as Badger Best, Gales HSB, King & Barnes and Ruddles County; big glass-walled garden room, interesting outside facilities *(John Kimber, David and Sarah Gilmore, BB)*

☆ **Lavant**, W Sus [SU8508], *Royal Oak*: The unassuming decor doesn't prepare you for the outstanding food, imaginative and varied (though not cheap); two log fires, friendly welcome, well kept beer tapped from the cask *(Mrs Yvonne Healey, J H L Davis)*

Lavant, [Midhurst Rd (A286)], *Hunters*: Bright, attractive and roomy, with wide choice of attractively presented and reasonably priced bar food inc some exotic dishes; well kept beer, nice atmosphere, pleasant restaurant, large, pretty garden; bedrooms *(Dr P H Mitchell)*

☆ **Lewes**, E Sus [Castle Ditch Lane/Mount Pl; TQ4110], *Lewes Arms*: Nice old-fashioned town local, little changed in 20 years, with wall benches, bare boards, big bow window overlooking street, no tourists, no concessions to 1990s; cosier back bar, separate games room with pool; well kept Harveys the main attraction, food very basic but cheap; tucked behind castle ruins *(Phil and Sally Gorton, David and Fiona Easeman, John Beeken, J S Rutter, Alan Skull, N Patton)*

☆ **Lewes** [22 Malling St], *Dorset Arms*: Friendly, comfortable and spotless refurbished 17th-century pub with good bar food, especially fresh fish Fri lunchtime, and well kept Harveys — it's within sight of the brewery; civilised atmosphere, restaurant, outside terraces; children in well equipped annexe next to main bar; bedrooms *(Alec Lewery, Marie Enright, Alan Skull, T Darling)*

☆ **Lindfield**, W Sus [98 High St (B2028); TQ3425], *Bent Arms*: Fascinating place, you need a long time to take in all the interesting furnishings and bric-a-brac, from chinoiserie longcase clock to Afghan Wars wheel-mounted cannon — beef cooked on a spit driven by a model steam-engine (lunchtimes, not Weds or Sun), other bar food from sandwiches to game casserole, friendly waitresses (but specials may start to run out from 12.30, so get there early); well kept Gales HSB, King & Barnes and maybe Whitbreads Pompey Royal on handpump; attractive garden; children in restaurant and eating area; bedrooms *(Mrs J A Blanks, LYM)*

☆ **Littlehampton**, W Sus [Wharf Rd; westwards towards Chichester, opp rly stn; TQ0202], *Arun View*: Attractive 18th-century inn built out on to harbour edge, with extensive views of river — busy here with seagoing vessels; comfortable banquettes, accurate drawings of barges and ships worked into counter-top, Whitbreads-related real ales on handpump, wide choice of reasonably priced decent bar food, restaurant (wise to book), flower-filled terrace; summer barbecues evenings and weekends; bedrooms *(E G Parish, P Gillbe)*

Lodsworth, W Sus [SU9223], *Hollist Arms*: Generous helpings of good food in small bar with well kept King & Barnes, decent wines; games room with pool, good mix of customers *(W K Struthers)*

☆ **Lower Beeding**, W Sus [TQ2227], *Crabtree*: Large pub with public bar, snug and inglenook back bar; well kept King & Barnes, good bar food, attractive dining room, attentive welcoming service *(Stephen Goodchild, Norman Foot)*

Lyminster, W Sus [Lyminster Rd; TQ0204],

Six Bells: Good pub with above-average food, all home-made using fresh veg; well kept Allied beers *(P Gillbe)*

☆ **Mayfield**, E Sus [TQ5827], *Middle House*: Old-world Elizabethan hotel with attentive staff; chatty bar with lots of locals, well kept Harveys and usually an interesting guest beer on handpump, darts and fruit machines at one end, wide choice of decent food, not cheap, inc lots of different ploughman's and maybe a spit-roast over the open fire; separate morning coffee/afternoon tea area with log-effect gas fire in ornate fireplace, big reddish leather chesterfield, armchairs; pretty back garden with log house, slide, dovecot, picnic-table sets and pleasant views; bedrooms *(Keith Stevens, BB)*

☆ **Midhurst**, W Sus [opp Spread Eagle; SU8822], *Bricklayers Arms*: Very small pub dating back to around 1600, two cosy bars with sturdy old oak tables and chairs, bar food inc wonderful fresh egg, bacon and sausage sandwiches and hearty Bricks Brunch with slabs of home-cooked ham, egg, sausage and chips; also more usual pub food, and good range of puddings; well kept beer, pleasant service, 'young' atmosphere *(Mrs V Middlebrook, K Leist)*

☆ **Midhurst** [Petersfield Rd (A272 just W)], *Half Moon*: Popular, cheerful and friendly; wide range of good bar food from sandwiches up, at reasonable prices, restaurant *(G M K Donkin, Jim and Becky Bryson)*

☆ **Midhurst** [South St/Market Sq], *Swan*: Popular town pub with oak-beamed lounge and lower more refurbished public bar, three well kept Harveys real ales on handpump, wide and interesting range of bar food, pleasant service, small restaurant; open all day; parking may be difficult; bedrooms *(Peter Ames, Richard Houghton, Ian Phillips)*

Midhurst [A286 towards Chichester], *Royal Oak*: Pleasant old-world atmosphere (it is genuinely old underneath), good staff, two superb log fires, Ind Coope Burton, Ringwood Old Thumper and Tetleys, usual bar food inc Sun lunches and children's dishes; barbecues in the fine extensive garden surrounding it; children in restaurant area *(N E B and W A Bushby, LYM)*

☆ **Newhaven**, E Sus [West Quay; follow West Beach signs from A259 westbound — OS Sheet 198, map reference 450002; TQ4502], *Hope*: Nice spot just out of town, with big windows looking out on the neck of the busy harbour, and upstairs conservatory room for even better view; well kept Flowers Original and Whitbreads Pompey Royal on handpump, unfussy decor with some simple nautical touches, darts and pool in the airy public bar, tables out on terrace by water *(Lesley Jones, Geralyn Meyler, BB)*

Newick, E Sus [A272; TQ4121], *Bull*: Good pub in small village, very clean and friendly; well kept beer, good choice of reasonably priced good food in generous helpings *(P Gillbe)*

☆ **Nuthurst**, W Sus [off A281 at Monks Gate 2 miles SE of Horsham; TQ1926], *Black Horse*: Black-beamed country pub with flagstones and inglenook, several real ales, usual bar food from open sandwiches to steaks, streamside back garden with barbecues summer Sun evenings, maybe live music Mon evening; children in eating area *(Katharine Cowherd, Norman Foot, Win and Reg Harrington, LYM)*

☆ **Nutley**, E Sus [A22; TQ4427], *William IV*: Spacious pub with big log fires, has been popular for friendly welcome, wholesome generous bar food, well kept King & Barnes and Ushers Best and decent wines, but no recent reports *(News please)*

Offham, E Sus [A275 N of Lewes; TQ4012], *Blacksmiths Arms*: Warm welcome in comfortable pub with log fire in big stone fireplace, well kept Harveys Best and Shepherd Neame on handpump, good honest home cooking, obliging landlord; may be very quiet weekday lunchtimes *(John Beeken, Ronald Hallett)*

Pease Pottage, W Sus [by M23 junction 11; TQ2533], *James King*: Interesting pub, handy for M23 *(Phil Bryant)*

☆ **Pett**, E Sus [TQ8714], *Two Sawyers*: Good village pub with friendly staff, good range of great value waitress-served bar food, well kept beer *(Alec Lewery, Marie Enright)*

☆ **Petworth**, W Sus [A283 towards Pulborough; SU9721], *Welldiggers*: Smart low-ceilinged food pub very popular for its good value restaurant-style meals — hardly a place for just a drink; plenty of tables on attractive lawns and terraces *(David Hunn, LYM)*

Petworth [Angel St], *Angel*: Friendly efficient service, reasonably priced food, well kept beer, a nice pub to take children to; bedrooms expensive for what they are *(R T and J C Moggridge)*

Plumpton, E Sus [Ditchling Rd (B2116); TQ3613], *Half Moon*: Popular pub with attractive rustic tables and benches on front terrace, and on back lawn looking towards South Downs, with play things inc tractors and other farm gear; prompt friendly service, well kept Harveys, King & Barnes and Ruddles County on handpump, speciality ploughman's and other reasonably priced bar food inc baked potatoes (not Sun evening), log fires and woodburner; walkers welcome — take boots off; nice painting of dozens of regulars over servery; evening restaurant *(John Beeken)*

Polegate, E Sus [A27; TQ5805], *Old Polegate Station*: Beefeater unusual for being in renovated station; usual food and drink, more the feel of a restaurant *(Alec Lewery, Marie Enright)*

☆ **Poundgate**, E Sus [A26 Crowborough—Uckfield — OS Sheet 199, map reference 493289; TQ4928], *Crow & Gate*: Good atmosphere in beamed bar with big copper-hooded fireplace, pleasant helpful staff, very large helpings of food in bar and separate restaurant (massive choice), well kept Charrington IPA on handpump, sensible prices *(Paul Norton, Jenny and Brian Seller, Pauline Hayes, Bill Harvey)*

☆ **Poynings**, W Sus [TQ2612], *Royal Oak*: Almost opp start of Devils Dyke climb, with decorative beams, stone fireplaces, two woodburning stoves, central servery, pleasant bar staff, well kept King & Barnes Festive and Watneys-related real ales on handpump, good varied bar food from sandwiches up inc good fish; picnic-table sets on attractive raised lawn with play area *(Frank Cummins)*

Rake, W Sus [A3 S of Liphook; SU8027], *Flying Bull*: Well kept Eldridge Pope Hardys and Royal Oak in friendly local with big helpings of good cheap food; part of bar is actually in Hants *(David White)*; *Sun*: Good well presented food in bar and restaurant at reasonable prices, Gales BBB and HSB and Wadworths 6X not so cheap *(David White, Ian Phillips)*

☆ **Ringmer** E Sus [outside village; A26 Lewes—Uckfield, S of Isfield turnoff; TQ4412], *Stewards Enquiry*: Tastefully refurbished old-world beamed pub with good choice of food inc vegetarian dishes, fish and steaks as well as quicker things; good courteous service, reasonable prices, three well kept real ales; some outside tables, play area *(Colin Laffan, Mary and Peter Clark, A L Willey, Brian Seabrook)*

☆ **Ringmer** [off A26 N of Lewes, just N of village turn-off], *Cock*: Civilised and softly lit heavily beamed bar with good inglenook log fire, good waitress-served bar food freshly prepared to order, well kept Ruddles Best and County and King & Barnes on handpump, good choice of wines inc monthly specials; eclectic and enjoyable piped music, one lounge no smoking, restaurant; seats out on good terrace and in attractive fairy-lit garden; well behaved children allowed *(John Beeken, Tony Gayfer, LYM)*

☆ **Ringmer** [B2192, in village], *Anchor*: Warm, friendly welcome in pretty pub facing green in well tended big garden, with side pigeon loft and play area; bays of comfortable banquettes in attractive main room, brocaded upholstery in comfortable dining room, good choice of fairly priced food and of wines, King & Barnes and Watneys-related real ales; children's play area; bedrooms *(C Pilbeam, Joan and Rowland Bodger)*

Rotherfield, E Sus [TQ5529], *George*: Attractive village pub with hanging baskets and window boxes, real ales on handpump and home-cooked food at well spaced tables; pool table in one bar *(E G Parish)*

☆ **Rudgwick**, W Sus [Church St; TQ0833], *Kings Head*: Character and atmosphere in attractively refurbished pub backing on to lovely old church in small pretty village; very popular for wide choice of generously served good straightforward home-made food at reasonable prices, well kept Whitbreads-related real ales, no piped music; helpful, cheerful service — generally antipodean or S African *(Stephen Goodchild, Mr and Mrs R J Foreman, Dr B A W Perkins, Carol and Mike Muston, D J P Dutton)*

☆ **Rushlake Green**, E Sus [signed off B2096; TQ6218], *Horse & Groom*: Old country pub overlooking quiet village green, beamed and timbered dining area on right with big log fire; well kept Harveys and King & Barnes, bar food, attractive decor, tables on front lawn; children in eating area and restaurant; has been open all day Sat *(Mr and Mrs Clark, Dr B A W Perkins, LYM)*

Rusper, W Sus [village signed from A24 and A264 N and NE of Horsham; TQ2037], *Gate*: Quaint little country pub with well kept King & Barnes Sussex on handpump, varied if not cheap food, very friendly, helpful staff with some tables under overhanging trees *(Alec Lewery)*; *Plough*: Generous collection of real ales in 17th-century pub with big inglenook in very low-beamed but smartly refurbished partly panelled bar; civilised if not cheap bar food, fountain in back garden, pretty front terrace; children welcome *(LYM)*; [Friday Street, Great Benhams], *Royal Oak*: Interesting food, well kept King & Barnes, good service *(Norman Foot)*

☆ **Rye**, E Sus [Gun Garden; off A259; TQ9220], *Ypres Castle*: Good position up the hill towards the tower, with view over Rother river-mouth from bar and picnic-table seats on big lawn; friendly, with well kept Whitbreads-related real ales, old yachting magazines, local events and art exhibition posters, bar food, piped music *(Dave Braisted, Edward Burlton Davies, Alan Skull, Phil and Sally Gorton)*

Rye [Ferry Rd], *Crown*: Good value bar food, freshly prepared when ordered, and well kept real ales *(Mr and Mrs B J Twigger)*; [Military Rd], *Globe*: Pleasant atmosphere, decent bar food inc good sandwiches and ploughman's, kind service, well kept Courage Directors *(Edward Burlton Davies)*; [Landgate], *Queens Head*: Friendly old pub with good food inc fresh local fish, Courage ales; bedrooms *(Edward Burlton Davies)*; [East St], *Union*: Good sound split-level dining pub, with good range of relatively modestly priced bar food, quick service, real ales such as Flowers, Larkins and Ruddles, fresh flowers; children particularly welcome, with a table of games *(David and Diana Livesley, Keith Widdowson, Dave Braisted, Edward Burlton Davies)*

Rye Harbour, E Sus [TQ9220], *William the Conqueror*: Big beamed lounge, attractively furnished and clean, with plenty of seating around wooden tables on nice carpet, Courage and Watneys-related real ales on handpump, good range of bar food inc good value sandwiches, neat restaurant; no music or machines in lounge, separate public bar with pool and fruit machines; well placed on undeveloped harbour edge *(Harry McCann, BB)*

☆ **Sedlescombe**, E Sus [TQ7718], *Queens Head*: Attractive and spotless traditional country local on pretty village green, with three distinct areas giving chatty bar and quieter corners; big inglenook log fire, Doulton toby-jugs, hunting prints, Flowers on handpump, decent coffee, plain lunchtime bar food inc some freshly-made sandwiches, garden *(E G Parish, WHBM)*

☆ **Selsfield**, W Sus [Ardingly Rd; B2028 N of Haywards Heath, nr West Hoathly (its postal address); TQ3434], *White Hart*: Good friendly atmosphere, dark oak beams and timbers, big log fire dividing bar in two, well presented bar food, well kept Gales, King & Barnes Sussex and Broadwood and Tetleys; barn restaurant, picnic-table sets on side lawn above steep wooded combe; handy for Wakehurst Place and Ingwersen's nursery; on GWG64; children welcome *(Norman Foot, John Pettit, Alan Skull, LYM)*

☆ **Shipley**, W Sus [TQ1422], *Countryman*: Two-bar Whitbreads pub with well kept Flowers and Marstons Pedigree, wide choice of good value bar food, restaurant, tables in pleasant garden *(Norman Foot)*

☆ **Shoreham by Sea**, W Sus [Upper Shoreham Rd; TQ2105], *Red Lion*: Lovely old pub with low beams, prompt service by welcoming staff, Watneys-related ales, decent wines, big helpings of good value unfussy bar food, Sun lunch, pretty sheltered garden; river walks, good South Downs views *(S L Hughes)*

☆ **Shortbridge**, E Sus [Piltdown — OS Sheet 198, map reference 450215; TQ4521], *Peacock*: Attractive old pub with big inglenook fireplace, Turkey rugs on oak parquet, heavy beams in ochre ceiling, timbered walls, soft lighting, room on left set more for eating (usual bar food, from sandwiches up), real ales such as Courage Directors, Flowers Original, Harveys Best and Larkins on handpump; sizeable garden with playhouse *(John Beeken, BB)*

Shripney, W Sus [London Rd (A29); SU9302], *Robin Hood*: Well kept Gales HSB, friendly efficient service, reasonably priced well cooked food (mostly in restaurant) *(R T and J C Moggridge)*

☆ **Slinfold**, W Sus [The Street; TQ1131], *Kings Head*: Comfortable two-bar pub with good choice of cheap honest food served generously, separate dining room and children's room, well kept Marstons and Whitbreads-related real ales, tables in big garden, big car park; four bedrooms *(Norman Foot, Mr and Mrs R J Foreman, Stephen Goodchild)*

Sompting, W Sus [TQ1605], *Gardeners Arms*: Friendly welcoming pub with generous helpings of good value lunches, Gales HSB and Watneys-related real ales *(Nigel Gibbs)*

South Harting, W Sus [SU7819], *Coach & Horses*: Recently refurbished, former family room now more part of main bar; log fire in main bar (flame-effect gas in family area), lots of bric-a-brac, warm welcome and good home-cooked food; friendly locals; garden, terrace, climbing frame and trampoline; good views of South Downs *(A J Blackler)*

☆ **South Harting**, W Sus [B2146; SU7819], *White Hart*: Busy, friendly old pub with lots of polished wood, big log fire, attentive licensees and staff, good generous

above-average home-cooked food with crisp fresh veg; separate public bar for locals and young people; well kept Ind Coope Mild, decent coffee; pretty village *(Mary Springer, Dr P H Mitchell)*

☆ **Steyning**, W Sus [41 High St; TQ1711], *Chequer*: Old-fashioned timber-framed coaching inn, probably Tudor behind its 18th-century facade, a warren of small, interconnecting rooms with open fires, friendly welcome, decent food; Whitbreads and Marstons Pedigree on handpump *(Phil and Sally Gorton)*

Steyning [High St], *Star*: Welcoming, good value bar food, drinks attractively priced *(Dave Braisted)*

☆ **Stoughton**, W Sus [signed off B2146 Petersfield—Emsworth; SU8011], *Hare & Hounds*: Much modernised 17th-century brick-and-flint pub in heart of South Downs, pine cladding, red leatherette, big open fires in dividing chimney, an airy feel; good home-cooked bar food (served soon after opening), changing well kept real ales such as Boddingtons, Fullers London Pride, Gales and Greene King Abbot, friendly young staff, winter restaurant, back darts room, pretty terrace; children in eating area and restaurant; nr start GWG56 *(Richard Houghton, LYM)*

☆ **Tillington**, W Sus [village signed off A272 Midhurst—Petworth — OS sheet 197, map reference 962221; SU9621], *Horseguards*: Perched above village lane, with lovely view from bow window; very much a dining pub now, with ambitious dishes (particularly in the evening) and civilised, unhurried atmosphere, but well kept real ales such as Badger Best and Wadworths 6X too — and the bar still has darts; good coffee, no piped music, tables outside; bedrooms *(Mrs Lili Lomas, Lyn and Bill Capper, D J Cooke, R G and S Bentley, LYM)*

☆ **Tismans Common**, W Sus [TQ0732], *Mucky Duck*: Oak beams, timbers and flagstones in cheery well run country pub with good choice of standard home-cooked bar food, well kept King & Barnes and Tetleys, lively evening atmosphere, play area and garden seats *(R Caldwell, LYM)*

☆ **Trotton**, W Sus [A272 Midhurst—Petersfield; SU8323], *Keepers Arms*: Straightforwardly furnished L-shaped bar angling around into restaurant area, in beamed and timbered tile-hung pub standing on a little rise — country views from its latticed windows and from teak tables on a narrow terrace; real ales such as Badger Best, Ballards and King & Barnes Festive on handpump, decent spirits, lots of non-alcoholic drinks, quietly chatty atmosphere, decent straightforward food cooked nicely and served quickly, piped music some evenings (not lunchtime) *(Lyn and Bill Capper, BB)*

☆ **Turners Hill**, W Sus [East St; TQ3435], *Crown*: Bookshelves-and-Staffordshire-china dining pub, pictures inc Victorian oils, low settees as well as tables with dining chairs, open fire, steps down to bookable dining area with lofty stripped beams and pitched rafters; well kept Allied ales, wide choice of quickly served bar food, soft piped music; tables in garden, and in front; handy for Wakehurst Place, and Standen (NT); two bedrooms *(Robert and Elizabeth Scott, John Pettit, BB)*

Uckfield, E Sus [High St; TQ4721], *Olde Maidens Head*: Hotelish though not upmarket bar of some potential, two parquet-floored rooms separated by staircase, comfortable straightforward furnishings, decent beer, good range of food (no sandwiches), piped music, dining room *(Patrick Young, Michael Quine, BB)*

☆ **Upper Dicker**, E Sus [TQ5510], *Plough*: Welcoming three-room country pub, wide choice of well prepared bar food, Watneys-related and King & Barnes real ales, good homely atmosphere — busy in the evenings; log fire, friendly staff; children's swings in big garden *(E G Parish)*

☆ **Walberton**, W Sus [Yapton Lane; B2132, just off A27 Arundel—Chichester — OS Sheet 197, map reference 975067; SU9705], *Royal Oak*: Very big helpings of freshly made very varied food in spick and span bar and restaurant, friendly management, Watneys-related real ales, good range of wines at good prices, bar billiards; garden with play area *(Mrs S Stewart, TOH, Grace and Michael Kirby)*

☆ **Warbleton**, E Sus [TQ6018], *Warbil in Tun*: Wide choice of food in friendly country dining pub, with pleasant and efficient staff; cosy beamed L-shaped bar with plum-coloured seating, big log fire, well kept Flowers IPA and Harveys on handpump *(J H Bell)*

☆ **Warnham**, W Sus [Friday St; TQ1533], *Greets*: Charming 15th-century rambling pub, beautifully restored, with uneven flagstones and inglenook fireplace; friendly atmosphere, well kept Flowers and Whitbreads Strong County, palatable wines, wide choice of food inc unusual specials and delicious puddings *(Mrs J A Blanks)*

☆ **Washington**, W Sus [just off A24 Horsham—Worthing; TQ1212], *Frankland Arms*: Roomy and welcoming, with wide range of enjoyable food specialising in pies, luscious gateaux, several real ales, decent

house wines, pleasant, efficient staff; big bar, smaller dining area, games area with pool and darts; tables in garden *(Mrs J A Blanks, Alec Lewery)*

☆ **West Marden**, W Sus [B2146 2 miles S of Uppark; SU7713], *Victoria*: Pleasant rustic surroundings, well kept Gibbs Mew, decent house wines, constantly changing good home-made food inc generous ploughman's and interesting hot dishes, quick friendly service, restaurant; best to book Fri/Sat *(D D Ash)*

Wilmington, E Sus [TQ5404], *Wilmington Arms*: Bright and tidy, with good value burgers and very cheerful staff *(Alec Lewery, Marie Enright)*

☆ **Wisborough Green**, W Sus [TQ0526], *Three Crowns*: Comfortable and spotless recently refurbished bar and adjoining dining rooms with oak beams, brick walls, parquet and carpeted floors; well kept Allied real ales, wide choice of reasonably priced bar food inc good Sun roast, good service by pleasant young staff *(C T and J M Laffin)*

Wivelsfield Green, E Sus [TQ3519], *Cock*: Wll kept ales, good value home cooking *(Ron Gentry)*

Worthing, W Sus [Arundel Rd; A27 W; TQ1402], *Coach & Horses*: 300-year-old coaching inn, very much a friendly local with lots of its original character, run by champion ex-boxer Terry Spinks and family; good lunchtime food in pleasant, well furnished dining area with boxing and other memorabilia; also a cosy back room and well kept garden with lots of tables; well kept Allied ales *(John and Vi Collins)*; [Broadwater Green], *Cricketers*: Very comfortable pub, nice staff and good food *(Elaine Sinclair)*; [80-82 Marine Parade], *Wine Lodge*: Roomy seafront pub with pleasant staff, mixed clientele, Ruddles or Youngers IPA, wine from the barrel, good reasonably priced bar food generously served; quiet at lunchtime, but has two pool tables and can get packed Fri/Sat evenings, with disco-type music *(S P Loraine)*

Yapton, W Sus [Maypole Lane — OS Sheet 197, map reference 977042; SU9703], *Maypole*: Welcoming out-of-the-way two-bar free house with half a dozen real ales inc Mild, good food *(Iain and Penny Muir)*

Wiltshire

This county now has a goodly number of really nice atmospheric pubs that have struck a good balance between the demands of the dining side and the importance of preserving a properly genuine pubby atmosphere. Licensees who have been outstandingly successful at this are Chris and Jenny Phillips, who have in the last decade reorganised or even started from scratch four pubs all of which – at least in their time there – have struck a particular chord with readers. These have admittedly been over in Gloucestershire: but their very latest venture is here in Wiltshire – the interesting and attractive White Hart at Ford. We won't be at all surprised if this becomes one of the county's star pubs in the next few months. Another new venture here, currently doing well, is the Barford Inn at Barford St Martin, taken in hand by another experienced landlord, and its traditional qualities underlined by careful restoration; it too is currently gaining warm approval from readers. Other changes here include a friendly new landlord at the Maypole at Ansty (named for England's tallest, just outside), a new manager at the ancient Waggon & Horses at Beckhampton (bringing in changes on the food side), the Dove at Corton's escape from its previous tie to Watneys/Grand Met (a fine little pub, free now to break further ground on the food side), considerable alterations to the fabric of the Crown at Everleigh (the charm of the building itself, and its friendly atmosphere, have not been damaged), new landladies for the Royal Oak at Great Wishford (doing very well since their alterations), a new couple at the enjoyable old George & Dragon at Potterne (with its unique internal shooting gallery), and new licensees for two Salisbury pubs, the companionable Avon Brewery and the much grander Kings Arms – both doing well. Other pubs here that are currently doing particularly well include the Three Crowns at Brinkworth (engaging combination of innovative cooking with the relaxed atmosphere of a village pub), the Red Lion at Castle Eaton (good food, a lovely Thamesside garden), the unspoilt yet spick-and-span Horseshoe at Ebbesbourne Wake, the very civilised Lamb at Hindon (so popular for its food), the atmospheric old George in Lacock, the Suffolk Arms in Malmesbury (a fine all-rounder), the Silver Plough at Pitton (really good if not cheap food; lots of interesting bric-a-brac), the lovely old Haunch of Venison in Salisbury, the Barge at Seend (now the canal's been reopened it's even better), and the thriving Royal Oak at Wootton Rivers (good food). Five of the Lucky Dip entries at the end of the chapter have recently started coming in for a lot of praise: the Red Lion at Axford, Quarrymans Arms at Box, White Hart at Castle Combe, Sun in Marlborough and Wig & Quill in Salisbury. Devizes (the home of Wadworths brewery) and Salisbury (Gibbs Mews' base) both have a good few pubs well worth trying. In general, prices in the area are close to the national average – if anything, a trifle higher than average.

ALVEDISTON   ST9723 Map 2

Crown 🛏️

Village signposted on left off A30 about 12 miles W of Salisbury

There seems to be more of an emphasis on food now in this magnificently thatched inn, with dishes like soup (£2), trout, cod, plaice or scampi (from £3.50), salads or spaghetti carbonara (£3.95), steak and kidney pie or gammon (both £4.95) and specials such as mussels and escargot (£5), or pork fillet in stilton and cream sauce (£6.95), as well as sandwiches (from £1.80), cheeseburgers (£3) and good ploughman's (from £3.25). Fullers London Pride, John Smiths, Ringwoods Fortyniner and Wadworths 6X on handpump. The two open-plan low beamed rooms are comfortably furnished in greens, pinks and browns, brocaded seats, and there's a fire at one end; friendly, cheerful service, darts and piped music. The dining extension opens on to the garden and there's also a family room; the siamese cat is called Su-Ming, the springer spaniel, Henry, and the terrier, Crumpet. On different levels around a thatched white well, the attractive garden is nicely broken up with shrubs and rockeries among neatly kept lawns; it faces a farmyard with ponies and other animals, and there's a children's play area. *(Recommended by Bridget Williams, Darren Peisley, Jerry and Alison Oakes, K Swann, Maj Andrew Scott, Lyn and Bill Capper, Stan Edwards, Andrew and Marguerite Scott, Richard Fawcett)*

Free house   Licensee Mrs Mary Moxam   Real ale   Meals and snacks   Salisbury (0772) 780335   Children welcome   Pianist Fri and Sun evening   Open 12–2.30, 6–11   Bedrooms; £35B/£55B

ANSTY   ST9526 Map 2

Maypole

Village signposted from A30 Shaftesbury–Salisbury

During the last century, this white-shuttered brick and flint building was the ale or beer house for the workers on the estate. The dark green hessian walls of the bar are hung with old local photographs, drawings and hunting prints, and there are spindleback chairs, cushioned wall seats and winged settles around tables on the Turkey carpet. The licensee is most friendly and attentive, and popular bar food includes sandwiches (from £1.75, prawn mayonnaise £2.50), filled baked potatoes (from £2.75), ploughman's (from £2.95), basket meals (from £3.50), lasagne (£3.95), salads (from £3.75, topside of beef £4.95), seafood platter (£4.95), breaded chicken with cream cheese and pineapple filling (£5.95), gammon steak with egg or pineapple (£6.25), trout (£7.25), steaks (from £9.45), and enterprising puddings. Well kept Butcombe, Fullers London Pride and Wadworths 6X on handpump, decent wine list. There are seats in front and in the back garden. The maypole in front of the pub is England's tallest – 96 feet. The pub is near *Good Walks Guide* Walk 34. *(Recommended by Richard Gibbs, Mayur Shah, Jerry and Alison Oakes, Mr and Mrs B E Witcher, J Lyons, R Harrison, Roy McIsaac, R W Stanbury; more reports please)*

Free house   Licensees Brian and Pat Hamshere   Real ale   Meals and snacks (not Sun evening in winter or Mon)   Restaurant (not Sun evening)   Tisbury (0747) 870 607 Children over 5 in eating area and restaurant   Open 11–2.30, 6.30–11; closed Mon, except bank holidays (they then close the next day)   Bedrooms; £23B/£40B

BARFORD ST MARTIN   SU1531 Map 2

Barford

Junction A30/B3089

Refurbished and renamed, this pub is doing well under the new licensee whose previous pub was the Scott Arms in Kingston. The original front bar in this friendly and comfortable inn, with its dark squared oak panelling, cushioned wall benches, dark seats and tables, and big log fire in winter, is warmly welcoming; soft piped music. Food is served in both bars and includes home-made soup (£1.45), pâté (£2.55), ploughman's (from £2.30), filled jacket potatoes (from £2.45), salads (from £3.20), vegetarian dishes such as spinach and mushroom lasagne (£4.50), scampi (£4.75), chicken, ham and mushroom pie (£5.60), escalope of veal (£6.50), 8oz sirloin steak (£8.40) and daily specials; well kept Badger Best on handpump, country wines and extensive wine list. One bar is no smoking. *(Recommended by Anthony Barnes, Mr and Mrs D J Rutter, R H Inns, Sandy Muirhead; more reports please)*

Badger   Leasehold: Phil Stansfield   Real ale   Meals and snacks   Restaurant Salisbury (0722) 742242   Children welcome   Open 11–2.30, 6.30–11

BECKHAMPTON   SU0868   Map 2

Waggon & Horses

A4 Marlborough–Calne; OS Sheet 173, map reference 090689

This attractive old thatched ex-coaching inn was a welcome sight to coachmen coming in from what was notorious as the coldest stretch of the old Bath road. The open-plan bar is still welcoming with its beams in the shiny ceiling where walls have been knocked through, with an old-fashioned high-backed settle on one side of the room and a smaller one opposite, red cushioned Windsor chairs, leatherette stools, and comfortably cushioned wall benches. Bar food includes home-made soup (£1.75), lots of sandwiches (from £1.40, roast beef £1.60), home-made pâté (£2), ploughman's (from £3.10), vegetable lasagne or moussaka (£3.95), salads (from £4.10), plaice (£4.25), gammon with pineapple (£6.25), steaks (from £8.75), and puddings like home-made fruit pie (£1.75); there is an extended evening menu; children's helpings on request. Well kept Badger Tanglefoot, Wadworths IPA, 6X, Farmers Glory and in winter Old Timer on handpump; lots of whiskies; darts, dominoes, fruit machine and CD juke box. Silbury Hill – a prehistoric mound – is just towards Marlborough, and Avebury stone circle and the West Kennet long barrow are very close too. *(Recommended by Lyn and Bill Capper, M M Badcock, A T Langton, Marjorie and David Lamb, Martin and Gill Searle)*

Wadworths   Manager Kevin Keeling   Real ale   Meals and snacks (12–2, 7–10; 9.30 Sun)   Avebury (067 23) 418   Children in side lounges   Open 11–3, 6.30–11 (6 Sat)

BERWICK ST JOHN   ST9323   Map 2

Talbot

Village signposted from A30 E of Shaftesbury

Well run and friendly, this simply furnished village pub has a single long bar with cushioned solid wall and window seats, spindleback chairs and a comfortable kitchen armchair (at the other end of the room there's a high-backed built-in settle), heavy black beams and cross-beams, nicely shaped with bevelled corners, and a huge inglenook fireplace with a good iron fireback and bread ovens. Decent bar food includes soup (£1.95), lunchtime sandwiches (from £2.65) or ploughman's (£3), basket meals (from £3.75), macaroni with cheese and bacon (£4.95), steak and kidney pie, popular curry or lasagne (£5.25), with evening steaks (gammon £7.50, 10oz T-bone £9.50). Adnams, Bass, Badger and Wadworths 6X on handpump. Table skittles, cribbage, dominoes, fruit machine and piped music. Some tables on the back lawn, with swings for children. *(Recommended by Brian Chambers, H D Wharton, Mr and Mrs D R H Dean, Mr and Mrs B E Witcher)*

Free house   Licensees W A and R H Rigby   Real ale   Meals and snacks (not Sun) Restaurant   (0747) 828222   Children in eating area of bar at lunchtime   Open 11.30–2.30(3 Sat), 7–11(6.30 Sat) nr BRADFORD-ON-AVON   ST8060 Map 2

Cross Guns

Avoncliff; pub is across footbridge from Avoncliff Station (first through road left, heading N from river on A363 in Bradford centre, and keep bearing left), and can also be reached down very steep and eventually unmade road signposted Avoncliff – keep straight on rather than turning left into village centre – from Westwood (which is signposted from B3109 and from A366, W of Trowbridge); OS Sheet 173, map reference 805600

Becoming more of a stylish restaurant – with reserved seats and table lights – than the old-fashioned pub it used to be, this busy place has low 17th-century beams, rush-seated chairs around plain sturdy oak tables, stone walls, and a large ancient fireplace with a smoking chamber behind it. Good bar food includes sandwiches (from 75p), home-made pâté (£1.60), ploughman's (from £2), home-made steak and kidney pie (£3.65), various fish dishes including crab salad (£3.30), trout (£3.65) and enjoyable lemon sole (£4.65), and steaks (from £5.20); well kept Badger Tanglefoot, Ruddles Best and County, Smiles Best and Exhibition, and Ushers Best on handpump. Darts, fruit machine and piped music. In summer the floodlit and terraced gardens are quite a draw – they overlook the wide river Avon and a maze of bridges, aqueducts (the Kennet & Avon Canal) and tracks winding through this quite narrow gorge. Though a lot of walkers stop here, muddy boots are not allowed. *(Recommended by Peter and Rose Flower, Jerry and Alison Oakes, Martin and Gill Searle, Mr and Mrs W S Kennedy, B R Woolmington, Roger Huggins, Tony and Lynne Stark, P and R Woods, Ian and Debby Mullins)*

Free house   Licensees Dave and Gwen Sawyer   Real ale   Meals and snacks (12–2, 6.45–10)   Bradford on Avon (022 16) 2335   Children welcome before 8pm   Open 11–3, 6.30–11   Bedrooms; £16B/£32B

BRINKWORTH   SU0184 Map 2

Three Crowns 🏮

The Street; B4042 Wootton Bassett–Malmesbury

Alongside more unusual dishes such as crisp-flavoured vegetarian crêpes (£6.50), lamb and mint pie (£6.95), excellent seafood pie, guineafowl (£8.75), locally smoked chicken in a dijon mustard and cream sauce (£8.95), venison medallions with green peppercorns and redcurrant jelly flamed in brandy with cream (£9.45), monkfish done with prawns and scampi in a vermouth sauce (£9.50), baked bream or a prize-winning dish of sautéed scallops wrapped in bacon and served with a Benedictine cream sauce (£9.95), and a tender and unusual duck flavoured lightly with fresh strawberries (£11.45), this busy, friendly little pub gives equal attention to humbler, pubbier things: at lunchtime excellent double-decker rolls (from £1.40), fine ploughman's (from £4 – not cheap, but a collossal helping) and interesting filled baked potatoes (from £4). Main dishes include an excellent steak and kidney pie done with Guinness (£6.50), steaks (from £10.45) and rack of lamb (£9.95); occasional pig roasting in the garden. Besides well kept tied beers – Bass Special and Wadworths 6X – they have very good value Archers Village on handpump, decent spirits and wines including some useful bin-ends. The small L-shaped bar with its easy-going, villagey atmosphere rambles around the servery giving a series of quiet enclaves. A conservatory extension in the same style is planned. Two of the tables are gigantic forge bellows, others are stripped deal, with green-cushioned big pews and blond chairs. The plaster's been partly stripped away from the masonry; there are big landscape prints and other pictures, some horsebrasses on the dark beams, a dresser with a collection of old bottles, log fires, and discreet piped music; on the right there are sensibly placed darts and a fruit machine. The garden stretches around the side and back, with well spaced tables, a good climber and maybe a summer skittle alley; it looks over a side lane to the village church, and out over rolling prosperous farmland. *(Recommended by Nick and Alison Dowson, Jane and Steve Moor, Comus Elliott, Peter and Rose Flower, Mr and Mrs Peter Woods, E U Broadbent, David and Christine Foulkes, Mr and Mrs P B Dowsett, Mr and Mrs T F Marshall)*

Whitbreads   Leasehold: A Windle   Real ale   Meals (12–2, 6.30–9.30) and lunchtime snacks   (066 641) 366   Children in eating area of bar   Open 10–2.30(11–3 Sat), 6–11

CASTLE EATON   SU1495 Map 2
Red Lion

The Street; village signposted off A419 Swindon–Cirencester

On the Thames Path walk, halfway between Lechlade and Cricklade, stands this unpretentious village local. The small, unchanging lounge on the right has simple chairs around a few tables on the parquet floor, a brown dado, big fireplace (log fires throughout the winter). On the left a little carpeted snug leads through into a games bar with darts, pool, dominoes, shove-ha'penny, juke box (strong on 60s/70s), space game and fruit machine. A limited bar menu includes sandwiches (from £1.10), filled rolls (from £1.10), very filling soups such as chicken and ham (£2.60), potted shrimps (£2.90), home-made hot-pot (£2.95) and bangers and mash (£3.30), venison goulash (£3.90), but given 24 hours' notice they'll cook much more ambitiously – pigeon hot-pot (£5.30), roast gammon knuckle (£5.60), pheasant casserole (£8.95) or wild duck (£9.80); and will try to do anything you ask for. Well kept Courage Best and Directors on handpump, quietly friendly licensees. The big garden along the bank of the fledgling upper Thames is lovely, with carefully tended flowers, well spaced picnic-table sets among lots of willows and poplars, lighting by old streetlamps, and a neat boules pitch – no dogs. *(Recommended by Ewan McCall, Tom McLean, Roger Huggins, David Backhouse, Jenny and Brian Seller)*

Courage   Tenant Tony Beare   Real ale   Meals and snacks served throughout opening hours   Cirencester (0285) 810280   Children if eating   Open 12–3, 6–11, but may open longer on good afternoons

CHICKSGROVE   ST9629 Map 2
Compasses

From A30 5 1/2 miles W of B3089 junction, take lane on N side signposted Sutton Mandeville, Sutton Row, then first left fork (small signs point the way to the pub, but at the pub itself, in Lower Chicksgrove, there may be no inn sign – look out for the car park); OS Sheet 184, map reference 974294

The big garden and the flagstoned farm courtyard outside this charming inn are peaceful places to sit. Inside, there are old bottles and jugs on the beams above the roughly timbered bar counter, farm tools, traps and brasses hanging on the partly stripped stone walls, and high-backed wooden settles forming snug booths around tables on the mainly flagstone floor. The good choice of home-made bar food includes ploughman's, sweet cured herring or deep fried camembert (£3.50), chestnut, mushroom and claret pie or vegetarian goulash (£4.50), chicken with mushroom and white wine sauce (£6.50), duck oriental (£7.95); Sunday roasts with a choice of beef, lamb, chicken or duck (£5.50). Well kept Adnams, Wadworths 6X, Bass and a guest such as Fullers on handpump; darts, shove-ha'penny, table skittles, dominoes, cribbage and piped music. *(Recommended by Maureen and Steve Collins, Roy McIsaac, Gordon and Daphne, WHBM, Brian Chambers, Jerry and Alison Oakes, Mrs J A Gardner, Barbara M McHugh; more reports please)*

Free house   Licensees Andrew and Linda Moore   Real ale   Meals and snacks Restaurant; reservations recommended Sun   Fovant (072 270) 318   Children in eating area   Open 12–3.30, 7–11   Bedrooms; £15B/£30B

CORTON   ST9340 Map 2
Dove ★ ⊘

Village signposted from A36 at Upton Lovell, SE of Warminster; this back road on the right bank of the River Wylye is a quiet alternative to the busy A36 Warminster–Wilton

Though you can still enjoy the good bar snacks or a quiet drink at lunchtime here, the emphasis in the evening is very much on inventive restaurant dishes. The lunchtime snacks include home-made soup (£2.50; summer gazpacho £3.50), pâté or good ploughman's (£4.25), half pint of prawns (£4.75), with more main dishes such as lasagne, chicken braised in cider or roast lamb (£4.95) and salmon, trout, rib of beef or steak and kidney pie (£5.25); puddings such as home-made ice creams (from £2.50). The neatly kept and attractively furnished bar has cushioned brick side benches, red bentwood cane chairs on the brick-tiled floor, a cane settle with colourful cushions by a pretty little chest-of-drawers in an alcove under the stairs, and a rug in front of the small log fire. Courage and Ushers Best on handpump and good wines including some New World ones. There are rustic seats on the grass behind the stone building, which has dovecots by the climbing roses on its walls, as well as a barbecue area and a children's bar and play area. *(Recommended by Jerry and Alison Oakes, T Nott, Dr T Morgan, J M Guyer, W K Struthers, Mr and Mrs D V Morris, Jane and Steve Moor, FG, JG)*

Free house   Licensee Stuart Broadbent   Real ale   Meals and snacks (12–3, 7–10; not Sun evening except on bank hols)   Restaurant; closed Sun evening   Children welcome   Andy Dickins Jazz Band in garden occasionally   Open 11–3.30, 6–11; 11–11 Sat   Bedrooms; £25B/£50

DEVIZES   SU0061 Map 2

Bear 🛏

Market Place

In 1772 this country inn was run by the father of Thomas Lawrence who was described as 'the only man upon the road for warm rooms; soft beds; and Oh; prodigious! – for reading Milton'. It's still a fine place to stay, and the big main bar, leading off the central hall, has big winter log fires, black winger wall settles, muted red button-back cloth-upholstered bucket armchairs around oak tripod tables, old prints on the walls, and fresh flowers. The Lawrence Room, down some steps from the main bar and separated from it by an old-fashioned glazed screen, is in a traditional style, with dark oak-panelled walls, a parquet floor, shining copper pans on the mantlepiece above the big open fireplace, and plates around the walls; food served here includes salads such as turkey and ham pie with cranberry topping or daily hot dishes such as chicken tikka or braised beef in real ale (all around £3.60), mixed grill (£4.75), and steaks (from £6.50). Quick snacks such as a good range of sandwiches or rolls (from £1.20, vegetarian wholewheat crispbread sandwich £1.50, roast sirloin of beef with horseradish £1.95, smoked salmon with capers £3.35, steak £3.60), and ploughman's (from £1.90) are served from the bar, with a wider choice ordered from the Lawrence Room waitress in the evening; part of the restaurant is no smoking. The Wadworths IPA and 6X on handpump, served from an old-fashioned bar counter with shiny black woodwork and small panes of glass, is consistently well kept; it's brewed in the town, and from the brewery you can get it in splendid old-fashioned half-gallon earthenware jars; freshly squeezed orange juice, freshly ground coffee, Sunday roast lunches, and afternoon teas; helpful service. *(Recommended by Martin and Gill Searle, Gwen and Peter Andrews, William Rodgers, D I Baddeley, A R Sayer, David Backhouse; more reports please)*

Wadworths   Tenant W K Dickenson   Real ale   Meals (10–2.30, 7–9.30) and snacks Restaurant; closed Sun evening   Devizes (0380) 722444   Children in eating area and restaurant   Open 10–3, 6–11 Mon to Wed, all day Thurs to Sat; closed 25 and 26 Dec Bedrooms; £35B/£50B

EBBESBOURNE WAKE   ST9824 Map 2

Horseshoe

On A354 S of Salisbury, right at signpost at Coombe Bissett; village is around 8 miles further on

This old-fashioned and delightfully simple village local has a beautifully kept bar with lanterns, farm tools and other bric-a-brac crowded along its beams, an open fire, fresh garden flowers, and a marvellously friendly atmosphere. Simple bar food consists of sandwiches (from £1.30), trout pâté (£4.25), and ploughman's (£2.90) with other hot dishes such as home-made steak and kidney pie (£4.95) and lemon sole with crabmeat (£5.75); Sunday lunch (£6.25). Well kept Adnams Broadside, Batemans, Ringwood Best, Wadworths 6X and a guest drawn straight from the row of casks behind the bar; farm cider and malt whiskies, darts and piped music. The pretty little garden has seats that look out over the small, steep sleepy valley of the River Ebble. A pets' corner in a paddock at the bottom of the garden houses a Vietnamese Pot-Bellied pig, two goats and a donkey. Booking is advisable for the small restaurant. *(Recommended by Jerry and Alison Oakes, Paul and Elizabeth Wright, WHBM, Gordon and Daphne, Mrs J A Gardner, Roy McIsaac, JM, PM, R W Stanbury, Sidney Wells; more reports please)*

Free house   Licensees Anthony and Patricia Bath   Real ale   Meals and snacks (not Mon evening)   Restaurant (evenings and Sun lunchtime only)   Salisbury (0722) 780474   Children in restaurant   Open 11.30–2.30, 6.30–11; winter opening 11.30–2.30, 7–11 (6.30 Sat)   Bedrooms; £20B/£32B

EVERLEIGH   SU2054 Map 2

Crown

A342 SE of Devizes and Upavon

The extensive alterations to this fine 17th-century building with its twin 18th-century wings have been sensitively carried out to keep the relaxed and friendly atmosphere intact. The opened out bar area has a variety of furniture from wood and leather rocking chairs to comfortable old velvet armchairs, there are fresh flowers, watercolours and oils on the walls for sale, and an open fire. Home-cooked bar food includes a substantial soup (£2.25), filled home-baked rolls (from £2.25, sirloin steak £4), ploughman's (from £3), with a daily selection of dishes such as quails' eggs with celery salt (£3.50), hot peppered mackerel with horseradish (£3.25), cheese herbies (£3.50), and vegetarian dishes (from £3.50); specialities are seafood in summer and game in winter. Well kept Bass, Wadworths 6X and John Smiths Bitter on electric pump. The spacious walled garden is safe for children; fishing can be arranged for residents. Part of the restaurant – with its sweeping mahogany staircase – is no smoking. *(Recommended by Gordon and Daphne, June and Tony Baldwin, David Backhouse, HNJ, PEJ)*

Free house   Licensee Mrs Jacki Chapman   Real ale   Meals and snacks (12–2, 6.45–11)   Restaurant   Collingbourne Ducis (026 485) 0229   Children over 5 in restaurant   Pianist in restaurant Fri and Sat evening, Sun lunchtime; monthly restaurant dinner dance   Open 11–3, 6–11   Bedrooms; £35B/£50B

FORD   ST8374 Map 2

White Hart 🛏

A420 Chippenham–Bristol; follow Colerne sign at E side of village to find pub

Just as this edition went to press the White Hart was being taken over by Chris and Jenny Phillips, who have a remarkable record (which can be traced through the pages of our previous editions) for giving almost a magic touch to the four Gloucestershire pubs we've seen them move through (though not all have kept up the Phillipses' standards. From 1981 to 1983 they were at the Boat at Redbrook; then came the Green Dragon near Cowley, the Seven Springs at Coberley and, most recently, the Kilkeney Inn. So we expect great things here. They've got fine material to work with. The cosy bar has heavy black beams supporting the white-painted boards of the ceiling, tub armchairs around polished wooden tables, small pictures and a few advertising mirrors on the walls, gentle lighting and a big log-burning stove in the ancient fireplace (inscribed 1553). Even as we went to press the food was showing their influence, including soup (£1), sandwiches (from £1), ploughman's (£2.75), seafood terrine (£3.50), diced beef and ale pie, lamb with sweet pepper sauce or smoked trout (£3.95), rack of lamb (£6.50), home-made puddings (£1.95) and daily specials; hearty breakfasts. Well kept Badger Best and Tanglefoot, Bass, Fullers ESB and London Pride, Greene King Abbot, Hook Norton, Marstons Pedigree, Theakstons and Wadworths 6X on handpump; country wines. In summer, you can drink outside at the front of the ivy-covered and L-shaped stone building, and there's another terrace behind by a stone bridge over the By Brook; secluded swimming pool for residents. *(Recommended by Roger Huggins, Martin and Gill Searle, W Bailey, Audrey and Brian Green, M C Howells, P B Rea, Tim Locke, P and R Woods, Nick Dowson, Alison Hayward, A R Sayer)*

Free house   Licensees Chris and Jenny Phillips   Real ale   Meals and snacks Restaurant   Castle Combe (0249) 782213   Children in annexe   Jazz Tues evening Open 11–3, 6–11; 11–11 Sat   Bedrooms; £43B/£59B

GREAT WISHFORD   SU0735   Map 2

Royal Oak

In village which is signposted from A36

The beamed main bar in this renovated village pub has cushioned pews, small seats and some easy chairs on the bare boards, tapestry curtains, and in winter a log fire at each end; a lounge area has some fishing paraphernalia and there's a cheery family area with sturdy bleached wood tables; darts and a trivia game. A wide and varying choice of bar food includes sandwiches, ploughman's (from £2.75), regular dishes such as chilli con carne, lasagne and chicken curry (all at £4.95), beef bourguignonne (£5.25), a large selection of fish dishes including trout or American catfish (both £5.25), fillet of plaice with prawns in white wine sauce or salmon (both £5.95), steaks (from £5.95) and a comprehensive vegetarian menu. Ruddles County and Ushers Best and a guest beer on handpump, and country wines. The garden behind is now a car park but there are tables on the front lawn. *(Recommended by Mrs Richard Stewart, Stan Edwards, Roy McIsaac, Robert and Vicky Tod; more reports please)*

Ushers (Watneys)   Lease: Sue Wheeler and Sue Lowe   Real ale   Meals and snacks (12–2, 7–9.45)   Restaurant   Salisbury (0722) 790 229   Children in eating area of bar   Open 11–3, 6.30–10.30; Fri and Sat evenings close 11

HIGHWORTH   SU2092   Map 2

Saracens Head 🛏

Market Place

The central chimney block in the big beamed lounge bar of this handsome old brick-faced inn stops it being wholly open-plan and the original decor of the four separate rooms is still obvious. So, with timbered walls covered with pictures and decorative china here, easy chairs by a window looking into the courtyard there, and more formal tables and settles in another oak-panelled area, there's a pleasantly airy and relaxed feel – helped by the absence of piped music. A wide choice of good value straightforward bar food includes soup (£1.45), various starters such as Scandinavian spring roll (£1.70), ploughman's (from £2.85), several grills (around £3), and conversely several weight watcher meals (around £2), lots of vegetarian dishes such as lasagne, pizza and cauliflower cheese (from £3), basket meals such as fish and chips (£2.90), and more substantial things running up to gammon and egg (£6.75) and sirloin steak (£9.75). Well kept Arkells BB on handpump; good friendly service; fruit machine. There are a few tables in the sheltered courtyard. The small market-place which the inn faces is most attractive. *(Recommended by David Backhouse, Nigel Gibbs, Sandra Cook)*

Arkells   Tenant Roy Bennett   Real ale   Meals and snacks   Restaurant (not Sun evening)   Swindon (0793) 762064/762284   Children in eating area of bar   Open 11–11; Sat 11–2.30, 6–11; closed 25 Dec   Bedrooms; £41.50B/£54B

HINDON   ST9132 Map 2

Lamb ★ ⊘

B3089 Wilton–Mere

Several readers have commented that while the very good bar food in this civilised village pub is not cheap, the quality (and quantity) of the dishes make it seem good value. The varying menu typically includes sandwiches, venison and pigeon terrine (£3.50), fresh mussels or wild boar sausages (£4.25), home-made game pie or duck casserole (£4.25), salmon and broccoli bake (£6.25), and fish such as baked salmon (£6.25) and Dover sole (£10.95); sustaining, good value Sunday lunch. The really long bar is split into several areas: one end in the lower part has a window seat with a big waxed circular table, spindleback chairs with tapestried cushions, a high-backed settle, brass jugs on the mantlepiece above the small fireplace, and a big kitchen clock, and the middle – and main – part has a long polished table with wall benches and chairs, and a big inglenook fireplace. Up some steps, a third, bigger area has lots of tables and chairs. Well kept Hook Norton, Wadworths 6X and Youngs IPA on handpump and large choice of malt whiskies; service is friendly and helpful, the restaurant is no smoking. Shove-ha'penny; no dogs. There are picnic-table sets across the road (which is a good alternative to the main routes west). *(Recommended by John Evans, TBB, T Nott, G M Pearce, J S Evans, E V Walder, Richard Gibbs, S J Rice, R C Vincent, A R Tingley, J J Elkerton, Andrew Fowles, John Widdess, Colin Laffan, W A Gardiner, Robert and Vicky Tod, S V Bishop, John Townsend, Patrick Young, James Cane, Gordon and Daphne, Dr and Mrs Tanner)*

Free house   Licensees A J Morrison and J Croft   Real ale   Meals and snacks (12–2, 7–10)   Restaurant   Hindon (074 789) 573   Children in eating area   Open 11–11   Bedrooms; £38B/£50(£60B)

KILMINGTON   ST7736 Map 2

Red Lion

Pub on B3092 Mere–Frome, 2 1/2 miles S of Maiden Bradley

This splendid local – popular with farmers and businessmen – has a curved high-backed black settle and red leatherette wall and window seats on the flagstones, photographs on the beams, a deep fireplace with fine old iron fireback and a second large brick fireplace, both with log fires in winter. A newer area has a large window and is decorated with brasses, a large leather horse collar and hanging plates. Bass under light blanket pressure and Butcombe Bitter on handpump, with quickly changing guest beers; sensibly placed darts, dominoes, shove-ha'penny and cribbage. Bar food includes soup (£1.10), baked potatoes (from £1), toasties or sandwiches (from £1.75), ploughman's (from £2.60), salads (£2.75), hot dishes such as meat or vegetable lasagne, steak and kidney or chicken and mushroom pie (£3.25), with, in the evenings, gammon steak (£3.95) and sirloin steak (£6.60). The black labrador is called Lady. Picnic-table sets in the large garden overlook White Sheet Hill (riding, hang gliding and radio-controlled gliders), and can be reached by a road at the side of the pub. Stourhead Gardens are only a mile away. *(Recommended by Roger Huggins, S V Bishop, Jerry and Alison Oakes, Michael and Harriet Robinson; more reports please)*

Free house   Licensee Chris Gibbs   Real ale   Meals and snacks (not Mon and Tue eves or 25 Dec)   Maiden Bradley (098 53) 263   Children in eating area till 9   Occasional singer/guitarist   Open 11–3, 6.30–11; only 9–10.30pm 25 Dec   Bedrooms; £16/£32

LACOCK   ST9168 Map 2

George

This notably friendly 14th-century place has been licensed continuously since the 17th-century, when it was known as The Inn. The atmospheric bar has a low beamed ceiling, upright timbers in the place of knocked-through walls making cosy corners, armchairs and windsor chairs, seats in the stone-mullioned windows and flagstones just by the bar; the big central fireplace with its roaring log fire has a three-foot treadwheel set into its outer breast, originally for a dog to drive the turnspit. Well kept Wadworths IPA, 6X, and Farmers Glory on handpump. Bar food includes sandwiches (from £1.25), home-made soup (£1.75), tasty Wiltshire ham, home-made dishes such as steak and kidney or cheese and onion pie, faggots or vegetarian dishes such as mushroom moussaka or spinach, mushroom and blue cheese crumble, excellent fresh crab salad, and evening grills such as fresh trout or steaks; darts, shove-ha'penny, cribbage, local radio music at lunchtime. There are picnic-table sets with umbrellas in the back garden, and a bench in front that looks over the main street. *(Recommended by Malcolm White, T Nott, G M Pearce, Christopher Heathman, Michael Manser, Klaus and Elizabeth Leist, E V Walder, Roger Huggins, Tom McLean, Ewan McCall, Lyn and Bill Capper, Robert and Vicky Tod, Nick Dowson, Alison Hayward)*

Wadworths Tenant John Glass Real ale Meals and snacks (12–2, 7–10) Restaurant Lacock (024 973) 0263 Children welcome Open 10–3, 5.30–11

Red Lion

High Street; village signposted off A350 S of Chippenham

New licensees have taken over this tall, red brick Georgian inn and early reports suggest that little has changed. The long, busy bar has a good pubby atmosphere, partly panelled walls hung with plates, oil paintings, Morland prints, and tools, a high ceiling hung with branding irons, and stuffed birds and animals; it's divided into separate areas by cart shafts, yokes and other old farm implements, and the old-fashioned furniture includes a mix of tables and comfortable chairs, Turkey rugs on the partly flagstoned floor, and a fine old log fire at one end. Well kept Wadworths IPA, 6X, and Farmers Glory on handpump; good wine by the glass; darts. Popular bar food, from a blackboard that changes daily, includes Mediterranean prawns in garlic (£3.85), giant sausages (£4.65), Lacock beef pie (£5.50), spicy lamb or turkey and apricot pie (£5.70), Wiltshire duck with orange and brandy sauce (£6.80); prices may be slightly higher in the evening; good breakfasts. They serve morning coffee from 10am, and an old stable block is used for teas, with fresh home-made scones. The pub is close to Lacock Abbey and the Fox Talbot Museum. *(Recommended by Richard Gibbs, June and Tony Baldwin, Jane and Steve Moor, Norman Hill, Martin and Gill Searle, T Nott, Gethin Lewis, Nick and Alison Dowson, Sandra Kempson, John and Joan Wyatt, R W Stanbury, Hugh Saddington)*

Wadworths Manager Clive Hurrell Real ale Meals and snacks (12.15–2.15, 6.30–9.30) Lacock (024 973) 0456 Children welcome Open 11–3, 6–11; winter opening 11–2.30, 6–11; closed 25 Dec Bedrooms; £32/£40(£50B)

nr LACOCK ST9367 Map 2

Rising Sun ★

Bowden Hill, Bewley Common; on back road Lacock–Sandy Lane

It's rare to find somewhere that's popular with locals of all ages and where strangers feel immediately at home – but this welcoming little country pub does just that. There's an L-shaped series of three simply furnished rooms; the end one has a big case of stuffed birds, a stuffed badger, a grandfather clock, some old woodworking planes, a shotgun on the wall and a few country pictures; the middle one has a mix of old chairs and a couple of basic kitchen tables on the stone floor, flowery cushioned wall benches, antlers on the wall, and dried flowers and plants in the windows, and the third has a Victorian fireplace and sensible darts area. Well kept Moles PA, Bitter, 97 and Landlords Choice (brewed by Moles to the landlord's recipe) and Wadworths 6X on handpump, with several uncommon guest beers and Long Ashton cider; friendly service. Home-made bar food includes generous toasties and sandwiches (£1.60), smoked trout pâté (£2.55), Wiltshire sausage or macaroni cheese (£3.35), lasagne (£3.95), coronation chicken (£4.25) and steak and kidney pie (£4.60). Darts, dominoes, shove-ha'penny, cribbage and other card games; there's two gordon setters and a tabby cat. One of the best places to sit is on the two-level terrace outside, from where you can enjoy the magnificent view (especially at sunset) looking out over the Avon valley, some 25 miles or so. *(Recommended by Rodney Middleton, Jerry and Alison Oakes, Simon Reynolds, Christopher Heathman, Martin and Gill Searle, Robert Brown, Roger Huggins, Tom McLean, Ewan McCall, Norman Hill, Peter Woods, R and E Harfield, Derek and Sylvia Stephenson, David and Christine Foulkes, Nick and Alison Dowson, Bev and Doug Warrick, Richard Houghton, Tony and Lynne Stark)*

Free house   Licensees Roger and Laura Catte   Real ale   Lunchtime meals and snacks (not Mon or Sun)   Children welcome   Open 12–2.30 (11–3 Sat), 7–11; closed Mon lunchtime

LIMPLEY STOKE   ST7760 Map 2

Hop Pole

Coming S from Bath on A36, 1300 yds after traffic-light junction with B3108 get ready for sharp left turn down Woods Hill as houses start – pub at bottom; if you miss the turn, take next left signposted Limpley Stoke then follow Lower Stoke signs; OS Sheet 172, map reference 781610

This friendly little cream stone-built pub – dating back to 1350 – has its name deeply incised in the front wall. The dark-panelled room on the right has red velvet cushions for the settles in its alcoves, some slat-back and captains' chairs on its turkey carpet, lantern lighting, and maybe a log fire. The spacious left-hand Avon Bar (with an arch to a cream-walled inner room) also has dark wood panelling, and a log-effect gas fire; the lounge is no smoking. Bar food includes rolls, soup (£1.30), pâté (£2.25), salads (from £3.75), steak and ale pie (£4.50), fresh trout (£5.90) and vegetarian dishes such as cracked wheat and walnut casserole (£4.90); in the evening there are extra dishes such as lemon sole (£7.50), chicken filled with smoked salmon wrapped in pastry (£7.75) and steaks (from £7.25); roast Sunday lunch (£5.50); lunchtime help-yourself buffet operates on Sunday from Easter to September; children's menu (from £1). Bass, Courage Best and John Smiths, Wadworth 6X and Wiltshire Old Grumble on handpump; malt whiskies; darts, dominoes, fruit machine and piped music The large garden has a summer weekend barbecue. *(Recommended by Ian Phillips; more reports, please)*

Courage   Tenants Susan and Howard Roberts   Real ale   Meals and snacks (12.30–2, 7–9.30; not Sun evening)   (0225) 723134   Children in eating area   Open 11–2.30(3 Sat), 6–11 (winter 11.45–2.30, 6.30–11)

LOWER WOODFORD   SU1235 Map 2

Wheatsheaf

Leaving Salisbury northwards on A360, The Woodfords signposted first right after end of speed limit; then bear left

When this 18th-century building was a farm, what is now the extensive dining bar was the barns and stables. The two main areas are linked by a miniature footbridge over a little indoor goldfish pond, and there are various rambling side areas: attractive William Morris wallpaper, cushioned wall seats, and sturdy pale varnished tables and chairs on parquet or brown carpet. The snug separate Cabin Bar, with cask seats and an inglenook log fire, has cribbage, dominoes and a fruit machine. A substantial choice of bar food includes a good few vegetarian dishes such as mushroom and nut fettucini (£4), as well as home-made soup (£1.30), ploughman's (from £2.35), filled baked potatoes (from £2.75), salads (from £3.25), local ham (£4.40), steak and kidney pie (£4.50), gammon (£4.95), veal or trout (£5.20) and steaks (from 8oz rump or sirloin, £7.15); children's dishes (£1.55) and daily specials. Well kept Badger Best and Tanglefoot and Charles Wells Eagle on handpump, and a good open fire. The big walled garden has picnic-table sets, a climber and swings, and is surrounded by tall trees. *(Recommended by Mike Rising, W F C Phillips, Adrian M Kelly; more reports please)*

Badger   Tenants Peter and Jennifer Charlton   Real ale   Meals and snacks (12–2, 7–10)   (0722) 73203   Children in eating area   Open 11–2.30, 6.30(6 Sat)–11(10.30 winter)

MALMESBURY ST9287 Map 2

Suffolk Arms

Tetbury Hill; B4014 towards Tetbury, on edge of town

A good choice of well prepared, home-made bar food in this cosy and friendly pub includes sandwiches (from £1.65), ploughman's (from £2.85), smokie (£3.05), grilled sardines or crab au gratin (£3.25), salads (from £3.95), steak and kidney pie (£4.95), good steaks (rump £7.95) and vegetarian dishes such as beany cheese hot-pot or vegetable pie (£4.25); puddings (from £2.25). Consistently well kept Badger Tanglefoot, Wadworths IPA and 6X on handpump; very pleasant bar staff in long aprons. The softly lit, knocked-through bar has comfortable seats such as a chintz-cushioned antique settle, sofa and easy chairs, captains' chairs, and low Windsor armchairs, and there are copper saucepans and warming pans on the stripped stone walls; a stone pillar supports the beams, leaving a big square room around the stairs which climb up apparently unsupported. There's also a lounge. The neat lawns outside have some seats. *(Recommended by Mayur Shaw, Pamela Stirling, Marjorie and David Lamb, Roger Huggins, Comus Elliott, Mr and Mrs Peter Woods, Hilary Roberts, R W Stanbury, Mr and Mrs Evelyn Cribb, Chris and Linda Elston)*

Wadworths Tenant John Evans Real ale Meals and snacks (12–2, 7–10; 9.30 Sun) (0666) 824323 Children over 10 in eating area Open 11–2.30, 6–11

NORTON ST8884 Map 2

Vine Tree

4 miles from M4 junction 17; A429 towards Malmesbury, then left at Hullavington, Sherston signpost, then follow Norton signposts; in village turn right at Foxley signpost, which takes you into Honey Lane

Three smallish rooms open together here, with plates, small sporting prints, carvings, hop bines, a mock-up mounted pig's mask – a game involves knocking coins off its nose and ears – lots of stripped pine, candles in bottles on the tables (the lighting's very gentle), and some old settles. Well kept Bass, Wadworths 6X, a guest beer such as Greene King Abbott or Marstons Pedigree and a beer brewed for them by a Mr Kemp, as well as decent wines. Home-made bar food includes soup (£2.95), snails in wine and garlic butter (£3.25), ploughman's (from £2.50), filled baked potatoes (from £3.50), chilli con carne (£3.95), burgers and nutburgers (£4.35), steak and kidney pie, swordfish pie or lasagne (£4.95), beef kebabs (£6.50), giant prawns (£8.50) and steaks from 10oz rump (£8.50) to 30oz whoppers (£21.50); puddings are all home-made and include lemon crunch, trifle and rhubarb and peach pie (from £1.95). There are picnic-table sets under cocktail parasols in a vine-trellised back garden with young trees and tubs of flowers, and a well fenced separate play area with a fine thatched fortress and other goodies – they have stables at the back. *(Recommended by Nick and Alison Dowson, Chris and Linda Elston, D Godden; more reports please)*

Free house Licensees Ken Camerier and Pete Draper Real ale Meals and snacks (12–2, 6.30–10) Restaurant (0666) 837654 Children in eating area of bar and restaurant Open 12–2.30, 6.30–11; closed Tues

PITTON SU2131 Map 2

Silver Plough ★ 🅟

Village signposted from A30 E of Salisbury

Decidedly somewhere to enjoy a meal in civilised comfort – though they do do a properly simple ploughman's with a handsome choice of cheeses (£3.65) and soup; most of the dishes are substantial and strong on style – for example fresh Dorset mussels or marinated Orkney herring (£4.35), fresh pasta with smoked chicken and thyme (£5), home-made fish pie (£6.25), fresh tuna or grilled hake (£12.25) and sliced duck breast (£14.25); set dinner (£16.45); their particular strengths are fresh fish and seafood, and game in season. Well kept Bass, Courage Best, Eldridge

Pope Dorchester, Wadworths 6X and Farmers Glory on handpump, decent wines, good country wines, and a worthy range of spirits. The comfortable front bar has black beams strung with hundreds of antique boot-warmers and stretchers, pewter and china tankards, copper kettles, brass and copper jugs, Toby jugs, earthenware and glass rolling pins, painted clogs, glass net-floats, and coach horns and so forth; seats on the Turkey carpet include half-a-dozen red-velvet-cushioned antique oak settles (one elaborately carved beside a very fine reproduction of an Elizabethan oak table), and the timbered white walls are hung with Thorburn and other gamebird prints, original Craven Hill sporting cartoons, and a big naval battle glass-painting. The back bar is broadly similar, though more restrained, with a big winged high-backed settle, cased antique guns, substantial pictures, and – like the front room – flowers on its tables. The separate skittle alley has a fruit machine, maybe unobtrusive piped music. There are picnic-table sets and other tables under cocktail parasols on a quiet lawn, with an old pear tree. *(Recommended by JMC, John and Christine Simpson, Celia and David Watt, WHBM, James Cane, Gordon and Daphne, Joan and John Calvert, T Galligan, Maysie Thompson, Jim and Maggie Cowell, Simon Reynolds, Jerry and Alison Oakes; more reports please)*

Free house Licensees Michael Beckett, Paul Parnell and Charles Manktelow Real ale Meals and snacks Restaurant Farley (072 272) 266 Well behaved children in skittle alley Open 11–3, 6–11; closed 25 Dec

POTTERNE ST9958 Map 2

George & Dragon 🛏

A360 beside Worton turn-off

You can still see the fireplace and old beamed ceiling of the original hall in this much restored 15th-century thatched cottage. Furnishings include old bench seating and country-style tables, there are banknotes from around the world, box matches, and colourful toby jugs, and a traditional atmosphere. The new licensees have changed the menu and specialise in home-made crêpes with savoury fillings (around £3.95), as well as sandwiches (from £1.25), ploughman's (from £2.50), steaks (from £5.25), mixed grills (£7.50), vegetarian dishes such as spinach and mushroom lasagne plus a vegan special; well kept Wadworths IPA and 6X on handpump. A separate room has pool and fruit machine; also, darts, shove-ha'penny, dominoes, and cribbage, and there's a full skittle alley in the old stables. Through a hatch beyond the pool room there's a unique indoor .22 shooting gallery (available under licence to visiting rifle clubs). A museum of hand-held agricultural implements has been opened at the pub. There's a pleasant garden and a suntrap yard with a grapevine. *(Recommended by Jerry and Alison Oakes, Barry and Anne, Gwen and Peter Andrews, Mr and Mrs A Smith, David and Christine Foulkes, Mr and Mrs Peter Woods; more reports please)*

Wadworths Tenants Richard and Paula Miles Real ale Meals and snacks (not Mon) Devizes (0380) 722139 Children in eating area of bar Open 12–2.30, 6.30–11 Bedrooms; about £25B/£35B

RAMSBURY SU2771 Map 2

Bell

Village signposted off B4192 (still shown as A419 on many maps) NW of Hungerford, or from A4 W of Hungerford

Well presented, popular bar food in this neat, civilised pub, brought to your table by pleasant waitresses, has included home-made soup, filled baked potatoes, ploughman's, home-made pâté, Cumberland sausages with bubble and squeak, beef curry, beef and ale or fish pie, steak sandwich, and delicious puddings. Recently new owners have taken over, and though there have not yet been changes in this (as we go to press), we can't rule them out; but prices here are fair. Well kept Marstons Burton and Pedigree, Wadworths IPA and 6X and a monthly guest on handpump. The two bar areas – separated by a chimney breast with a woodburning stove – have polished tables, fresh flowers, and window settles in two sunny bay windows (one with Victorian stained glass panels). There are picnic tables on the raised lawn. Roads lead from this quiet village into the downland on all sides. (*Recommended by GB, CH, Mr and Mrs W S Kennedy, Mr and Mrs P B Dowsett, David Backhouse, Mr and Mrs R Onslow, C A Gurney, Gordon and Daphne, G B Pugh, D G Clarke; reports on new regime please*)

Free house   Real ale   Meals and snacks (not Sat evening)   Restaurant   Marlborough (0672) 20230   Children in room between bar and restaurant and in eating area   Open 11–3, 6–11

SALISBURY   SU1429   Map 2

The pubs mentioned here are all within a short stroll of one another. The George, which used to be one of the country's finest old inns – Shakespeare probably performed in its yard – has now been rebuilt as a shopping arcade, but its facade is still well worth a look, and an upstairs coffee shop gives some idea of what it used to be like inside

Avon Brewery £

Castle St

The narrow garden here runs down to the River Avon where there are ducks and swans, and is marvellous on warm nights with seats among the fruit trees, roses and hops. Inside, the long narrow bar has a very companionable atmosphere (there's a library of reference books should you need back-up in a discussion) and is divided by little balustered partitions; attractive decorations include lots of pictures (often patriotic or military), framed ensigns, cigarette cards, decorative china and frilly wall-lamps. Lunchtime bar food is good: sandwiches (from 90p), hot dogs (£1.15), filling soups (£1.20), hot dishes such as hot beef in bread, pork steak in white wine or devilled pork chop (all £3). Well kept Eldridge Pope Dorchester, Hardy and Royal Oak and a guest on handpump; hospitable service. Darts, dominoes, cribbage, a rack of newspapers and classical piped music. The bar broadens out at the back, with darts and a dainty Victorian fireplace. The facade, all mosaic tilework and elegant curves, makes it one of the city's prettiest pubs. (*Recommended by Mr and Mrs A P Reeves, David Nutt, Joan and Michel Hooper-Immins*)

Eldridge Pope   Lease: Brendan O'Malley   Real ale   Meals and snacks (12–2.30, 5–8; not Sun evening)   (0722) 327280   Children in eating area   Open 11–11

Haunch of Venison ★

1 Minster Street, opposite Market Cross

An old-fashioned – and as far as we know unique – pewter bar counter in this thoroughly ancient and atmospheric place has a rare set of antique taps for gravity-fed spirits and liqueurs. There are massive beams in the ochre ceiling, stout red cushioned oak benches built into its timbered walls, genuinely old pictures, a black and white tiled floor, and an open fire; a tiny snug opens off the entrance lobby. A quiet and cosy upper panelled room has a small paned window looking down onto the main bar, antique leather-seat settles, a nice carved oak chair nearly three centuries old, and a splendid fireplace that dates back some 600 years. In 1903 workmen found a smoke-preserved mummified hand holding some 18th-century playing-cards in here; it's now behind glass in a small wall slit. Well kept Courage Best and Directors and Wadworths 6X on handpump; over 100 malt whiskies. Bar food, served in the lower half of the restaurant, includes sandwiches (from £1.15, toasties 20p extra), home-made soup (£1.30), baked potatoes (from £1.85), ploughman's (from £2.45), home-made pies such as game, ham and mushroom or steak and kidney (from £2.25), savoury pancakes (£4), daily specials such as macaroni cheese, good chicken curry or peppered beef (£2.75), and puddings such as apple pie (£1.35); attentive and friendly service. Parts of this building date back to about 1430, when it was the church house for the church of St Thomas, just behind. (*Recommended by Nick and Alison Dowson, Ian Phillips, JM, PM, Simon Reynolds, Adam and Elizabeth Gorb, Jerry and Alison Oakes, Gordon and Daphne, Gordon Mott*)

Courage   Licensees Antony and Victoria Leroy   Real ale   Meals and snacks (12–2, 6–10; not Sun evening in low season)   Restaurant (not Sun evening in low season) Salisbury (0722) 322024   Children in upper room   Nearby parking may be difficult Open 11–11

Kings Arms 🛏

St John Street; the main one-way street entering city centre from S

As well as Tudor timbering, this creaky old inn has fireplaces of the same Chilmark stone as the Cathedral, and so may be as old as it. The dark-panelled bars have red leatherette benches built around their walls: one has attractive Windsor arm chairs under its heavy beams, with carving around its fireplace and door; the other, more local, has darts, cribbage, dominoes, fruit machine, trivia game and piped music. The panelling in the heavily beamed restaurant, which has snug high-backed settles, is considerably older. Well kept Whitbreads Strong Country and Flowers on handpump; hospitable staff. Bar food includes soup (£1.50), sandwiches (from £1.25), ploughman's (from £3), filled jacket potatoes (from £1.50), plaice or cod (£3.25), scampi or home-made steak and kidney pie (£3.45). *(Recommended by Dr and Mrs R B Crail, Mrs Richard Stewart, Judith Pickett, Gordon Mott)*

Whitbreads   Manageress Bryony Lee Rippon   Real ale   Meals and snacks (12–2, 6–9.30)   Restaurant   Salisbury (0722) 327629   Children welcome   Open 11–3, 6–11   Bedrooms; £37B/£55B

SEEND   ST9461 Map 2

Barge

Seend Cleeve; signposted off A361 Devizes–Trowbridge, between Seend village and signpost to Seend Head

Now that the Kennet and Avon Canal has been reopened after 40 years of restoration, the picnic-table sets among former streetlamps in the neat waterside garden here let you watch passing barges and other boats as well as the occasional kingfisher. Inside, the strong bargee theme is perhaps at its best in the intricately painted Victorian flowers which cover the ceilings and run in a waist-high band above the deep green lower walls; more bargee paintwork includes some milkchurn seats among a distinctive mix of other attractive seats, including the occasional small oak settle among the rugs on the parquet floor. There are big sentimental engravings, a well stocked aquarium, a pretty Victorian fireplace, big bunches of dried flowers, crushed red velvet curtains for the big windows, and a friendly, relaxed atmosphere. Good bar food includes soup (£1.35), pâté (£2), ploughman's (from £2), open sandwiches (£2.55), pizzas (£4.95), steak and kidney or chicken and ham pie (£5.50), with daily specials and children's menu (£1.75); well kept Wadworths IPA and 6X on handpump, with Old Timer and mulled wine in winter, plus a guest beer such as Adnams or Badger Tanglefoot; fruit machine. The neat waterside garden, with moorings by a humpy bridge, has picnic-table sets among former streetlamps; besides a busy bird table, nice touches include the weatherdrake, the good inn sign, and attractively tiled lavatories. *(Recommended by W F C Phillips, Marjorie and David Lamb, Mr and Mrs P B Dowsett, Mrs Pat Crabb, June and Tony Baldwin, WHBM, Mr and Mrs W S Kennedy, Jane and Steve Moor, C T and J M Laffin, Mr and Mrs Peter Woods, B R Woolmington, Gwen and Peter Andrews, Mr and Mrs D A P Grattan, Neil and Anita Christopher, Martin and Gill Searle)*

Wadworths   Tenant Christopher Moorley Long   Real ale   Meals and snacks (12–2, 7–9.30; evening food till 10 Fri and Sat)   (0380) 828230   Well behaved children allowed   Open 11–2.30, 6–11

SEMLEY   ST8926 Map 2

Benett Arms 🛏

Turn off A350 N of Shaftesbury at Semley Ind Estate signpost, then turn right at Semley signpost

This late 18th-century village inn, across the green from the church, has two relaxed and cosy rooms separated by a flight of five carpeted steps; there are one or two settles and pews, deep leather sofas and armchairs, hunting prints, carriage lamps for lighting, a pendulum wall clock, and ornaments on the mantlepiece over the log fire. Down by the thatched-roof bar servery, the walls are stripped stone; upstairs, there's hessian over a dark panelling dado. Good bar food includes home-made soup (£1.95), ploughman's (£2.95), local ham and egg (£3.75), omelette or lasagne (£3.95), home-made steak and kidney pie (£4.25), freshwater trout (£4.50), gammon with pineapple (£4.95), scampi (£4.90), and home-made puddings such as apple crumble or chocolate mousse with rum (£1.95); children's menu; Sunday roasts; good breakfasts. Gibbs Mew Salisbury and Bishops Tipple on handpump, kept under light blanket pressure, good house wines, and a wide range of spirits; dominoes, cribbage and piped music. There are seats outside. Well behaved dogs welcome. *(Recommended by Rod Middleton, Roger and Deborah Dawes, P R Morley, David Lamb, Sandra Kempson, Bernard Phillips, John and Christine Simpson, Mrs J A Gardner, S V Bishop, TBB)*

Gibbs Mew   Tenant Joe Duthie   Real ale   Meals and snacks (12–2, 7–10) Restaurant   East Knoyle (074 783) 0221   Children welcome   Open 11–2.30, 6–11; closed 25 and 26 Dec   Bedrooms; £26B/£40B

UPAVON   SU1355   Map 2

Antelope ⊘ ⊨

3 High St; village on junction A345/A342

This pleasing old brick-built house in the village centre has an attractively simple lounge bar with wall settles around dark tables, stools at the long bar counter, an interesting antique wheel-driven water pump at one end, a good winter log fire at the other, and a little bow-windowed games area with darts, bar billiards, cribbage and dominoes. Bar food includes sandwiches, local ham and eggs (£3.75),lots of home-made pies such as steak and kidney or pork, apple and cider (£4.65), and pheasant and venison (£6.95), fish such as local trout (£5.95), with home-made puddings like banoffi pie (£1.95); good breakfasts. Bass, Wadworths IPA and 6X on handpump; courteous, friendly staff. Outside there are hanging baskets and a vine, and a pets' corner with goats, rabbits and guinea pigs. *(Recommended by P Hamlin, L Walker, Chris Humphreys, June and Tony Baldwin, Harry Stirling, Kev and Caron Holmes, Jerry and Alison Oakes, David Backhouse, S Watkins, J H Walker)*

Wadworths   Licensees Mervin and Sandy Parish   Real ale   Meals and snacks Restaurant   Stonehenge (0980) 630206   Children in eating area of bar and restaurant   Open 11–3, 6.30–11   Bedrooms; £20/£32.50

WOOTTON RIVERS   SU1963   Map 2

Royal Oak ⊘

Village signposted from A346 Marlborough–Salisbury and B3087 E of Pewsey

Though this prettily thatched pub is very popular for its good food, it hasn't lost sight of its true identity as a pub, with well kept Wadworths 6X tapped from the cask, Badger Best and Tanglefoot on handpump, decent wines (running up to some very distinguished vintage ones), and a relaxed, friendly atmosphere. The L-shaped dining lounge has slat-back chairs, armchairs and some rustic settles around good tripod tables, a low ceiling with partly stripped beams, partly glossy white planks, a woodburning stove, discreetly colourful plates, small mainly local prints, drawings, watercolours and photographs. The timbered bar on the right is comfortably and similarly furnished, though with fewer tables, and has a small area with darts, pool, dominoes, cribbage, fruit machine and juke box. Bar food includes lots of specials like deep fried stilton with cranberry sauce (£3.75), smoked duck breast with kiwi fruit (£4.25), pan-fried mackerel with gooseberry sauce (£5), particularly good home-made steak and kidney pie (£6), and pork in green pepper sauce (£7.50), with regular dishes such as soup (£1.25), lunchtime sandwiches (£1.25; open from £2) or ploughman's (from £2.25), basket meals (from £2), a good choice of salads (from £2.75; seafood £8.75), and fish dishes such as local pink trout (£5.75), chicken kiev (£7.50) and lots of steaks (from £8.75; T-bone £10.25); puddings (£2.50); they take table bookings, and people may be quite smartly dressed; courteous service. There are tables under cocktail parasols in the back gravelled yard, by the car park. The thatched and timbered village is very attractive. (*Recommended by June and Tony Baldwin, R T and J C Moggridge, Peter and Rose Flower, Robert and Vicky Tod, Gwen and Peter Andrews, Frank Gadbois, Mayur Shah, Michael and Rachel Brookes, Jane and Steve Moor, Martin and Gill Searle, David and Ruth Shillitoe, A R Sayer, John Hill, R and E Harfield, David Backhouse*)

Free house   Licensees John and Rosa Jones   Real ale   Meals and snacks (not Sun evenings Oct–Jun, nor 26 Dec)   Burbage (0672) 810322   Children welcome   Open 11–3(3.30 Sat), 6(7 winter)–11   Bedrooms (in adjoining house); £22.50S/£30(£35B)

Lucky Dip

Besides the fully inspected pubs, you might like to try these Lucky Dips recommended to us and described by readers (if you do, please send us reports):

☆ **Aldbourne** [The Green (off B4192); SU2675], *Blue Boar*: Pretty little Tudor village tavern with genuine atmosphere in spick and span bar, well kept Wadworths IPA and 6X on handpump (Ringwood Old Thumper tapped from the cask in winter), some food, stuffed boar's head over attractive inglenook fireplace, just a few seats, obliging landlady; picnic-table sets overlooking green and 14th-century church, charming village (*Mr and Mrs P B Dowsett, David Backhouse*)

☆ **Aldbourne**, *Crown*: Quickly served reasonably priced standard bar food and well kept Watneys-related ales on handpump in friendly, spacious and civilised local with huge log fire, quiet piped music, helpful licensee; clean and well kept, with interesting collections, piped music; tables under cocktail parasols in pleasant courtyard (*A Y Drummond, Mr and Mrs P B Dowsett, David Backhouse*)

Ashton Keynes [SU0494], *Plough*: Worth knowing for good value food inc no-hurry Sun lunch in eating area through sliding doors off small lounge; well kept Whitbreads-related real ales, log fires, garden with play area (*Mr and Mrs P B Dowsett, David Backhouse, Roger Huggins*); *White Hart*: Renovated pub popular for very generous bar food; log fires; skittle alley, pleasant sheltered garden (*Mr and Mrs P B Dowsett*)

Atworth [Bath Rd (A365); ST8666], *White Hart*: Pleasant spot, friendly landlord and reasonable food; bedrooms (*Dr and Mrs A K Clarke*)

Avebury [A361; SU0969], *Red Lion*: Comfortable thatched Whitbreads pub, much modernised and a bit stereotyped, but worth knowing for its position right in the heart of the stone circles; well kept real ales, food (*David Backhouse, LYM*)

☆ **Axford** [SU2370], *Red Lion*: Friendly flintstone pub in attractive village, all fresh and clean; lovely Kennet valley views, well furnished pine-panelled, wood-floored beamed bar; well kept Archers Village, Marstons Pedigree and Wadworths 6X,

quick but friendly service, well presented simple but thoughtful bar food, fine restaurant; quiet piped music, quick service; sunny tables in garden; bedrooms (*HNJ, PEJ, A Y Drummond, David Backhouse, T Muston*)

☆ **Badbury** [very near M4 junction 15 — A345 S; SU1980], *Plough*: Well kept Arkells BB, BBB and Kingsdown on handpump, wide choice of food, friendly landlord, sunny village looking beyond the road to the Vale of the White Horse (*David Backhouse, Mr and Mrs F Hardy*)

☆ **Biddestone** [The Green; ST8773], *White Horse*: Friendly and busy local overlooking duckpond in picturesque village; good generous bar food, Courage ales, small carpeted rooms running one into another, shove-ha'penny, darts and table skittles; tables in garden; bedrooms (*C G Barnett, Jane and Steve Moor*)

☆ **Blunsden** [SU1593], *Cold Harbour*: Reliable and respectable Chef & Brewer, well kept Watneys-related real ales, tables out on terrace, good play area (*Mr and Mrs P B Dowsett, David Backhouse, P and R Woods, Dave Irving*)

☆ **Box** [Box Hill; off A4 just W of Box; ST8268], *Quarrymans Arms*: Unspoilt pub up on a hill in middle of nowhere, two small rooms knocked together, very rewarding home-cooked food inc Sun lunch, good range of real ales, very friendly staff and atmosphere, quarrying memorabilia, superb views, small garden; children really welcomed; two bedrooms (*Peter and Rose Flower, Mr Jennings, Gillian Savitz*)

☆ **Bradford Leigh** [B2109 N of Bradford; ST8362], *Plough*: Pleasant free house with Bass, Wadworths 6X and Worthington, decent cider, good choice of well cooked food, quick service; nice seats outside (*B R Woolmington, Jan and Ian Alcock*)

☆ **Bradford on Avon** [Silver St; ST8261], *Bunch of Grapes*: Big helpings of good interesting reasonably priced food and wide range of well kept and attractively priced beers — usually Smiles, with several guests from small breweries — in spotless converted shop on two levels in picturesque steep street; friendly atmosphere, good service *(Derek and Sylvia Stephenson, R W Stanbury, John and Joan Wyatt, B R Woolmington)*

Bradford on Avon [Masons Hill], *Dandy Lion*: Newly opened, formerly a restaurant; well done pastiche, popular with young people *(Dr and Mrs A K Clarke)*; *George*: Superb canalside position means some commercialism to cope with the crowds, in very pretty pub with fast efficient service even when very busy; bar food inc good generous and imaginative ploughman's; children's garden room, two gardens *(Michael and Harriet Robinson)*

Broad Chalke [SU0325], *Queens Head*: Lovely pub with delicious, unusual food and friendly welcome; pretty courtyard, good coffee; bedrooms *(Michael and Harriet Robinson)*

☆ **Broad Hinton** [High St; off A4361 about 5 miles S of Swindon; SU1076], *Crown*: Spacious, comfortable open-plan bar with good value straightforward home-cooked bar food, attractive restaurant, well kept Arkells BB, BBB and Kingsdown, attentive landlord, cheerful piped music, unusual gilded inn sign; bedrooms *(David Backhouse, June and Tony Baldwin, LYM)*

Brokenborough [ST9189], *Rose & Crown*: Quaint little country pub with cosy lounge and separate bar, well kept Ruddles on handpump, friendly staff, usual bar food *(Roger Huggins, Dr and Mrs A K Clarke)*

☆ **Bromham** [ST9665], *Greyhound*: Good atmosphere in two attractively lit bars with lots of interesting bric-a-brac, blazing log fires, even a well; imaginative well cooked and presented generous bar food inc lots of fish, well chosen real ales, friendly landlord; skittle alley, pool and darts; big garden, small intimate restaurant *(Mrs D C Starkey, Jane and Steve Moor)*

Bromham [A342], *Oliver Cromwell*: Good value quickly served home-cooked bar food, Sun lunch in restaurant, friendly landlord *(S Watkins)*

☆ **Broughton Gifford** [ST8763], *Fox & Hounds*: Traditional timbered pub, welcoming licensee, well kept Watneys-related real ales, helpful staff and good varied bar food *(B R Woolmington)*

Broughton Gifford [ST8763], *Bell on the Common*: Lovely old pub with traditional old English furnishings; two bars with separate dining room, children welcome; good meals *(Renna and Gerard Grieu)*

Bulford [Crown St; SU1643], *Rose & Crown*: Friendly Chef & Brewer with deep leather seats and well kept Ruddles; generally quite lively *(Dr and Mrs A K Clarke)*

Burton [ST8179], *Old House At Home*: Dining pub worth knowing for ambitious choice and big helpings; attractive food area, log fire, well kept Wadworths *(Jane and Steve Moor)*; [B4039], *Plume of Feathers*: Good choice of changing food in small, cosy pub, inc good range of curries and spicy dishes;

very relaxing atmosphere; bedrooms *(Jane and Steve Moor)*

Bushton [SU0677], *Trotting Horse*: Character pub with notable food, well kept Ind Coope Burton, Tetleys, Wadworths 6X and guest beer on handpump, wide choice of malt whiskies, caring licensees; bedrooms *(David Backhouse, Steven Saltzman)*

☆ **Castle Combe** [signed off B4039 Chippenham—Chipping Sodbury; ST8477], *White Hart*: Pretty stone-built pub with log fire in beamed and flagstoned main bar, useful family room; settling down well now under new management, nice atmosphere building up, warm welcome, good food inc super soups and home-cured gammon, well kept Wadworths, chatty locals; occasional live music Fri; on the tourist track, and a popular call for the Japanese from Honda in Swindon; children's room *(Peter and Rose Flower, E V Walder, William Rodgers, Barry and Anne, Tony Gayfer, A R Sayer, LYM)*

☆ **Castle Combe**, *Castle*: Old-world country inn in beautiful village, reopened early 1991 under friendly new ownership, with nicely furnished bars, clean and attractive, food virtually all day from breakfast on, cellar games room, tables out on terrace; bedrooms competitively priced *(Peter and Rose Flower)*

☆ **nr Castle Combe** [The Gibb; B4039 Acton Turville—Chippenham — OS Sheet 173, map reference 838791], *Salutation*: Well restored old dining pub with well kept Flowers and raftered restaurant; has been very popular for wide range of good bar food, but we've had no reports since new licensees 1991 *(Jane and Steve Moor, Pamela Sterling; news please)*

☆ **Charlton** [B4040 towards Cricklade; ST9588], *Horse & Groom*: Quiet and civilised pub of character, with welcoming log fire, agreeable and relaxing decor, well kept local real ales, potent cider, decent wines, good bar food, restaurant (good Sun lunch), tables outside; piped music, closed Sun evening, Mon *(June and Tony Baldwin, Tom McLean, Roger Huggins, Ewan McCall, J R Smylie, D Irving, Chris and Linda Elston, E V Walder, LYM)*

Charlton [A342 W of Upavon; SU1156], *Cat*: Free house with nice views to the north; very comprehensive menu, two bars, restaurant *(Patrick Godfrey)*

Cherhill [SU0370], *Black Horse*: Well kept Courage beer and guest, wide choice of meals and snacks, friendly atmosphere; children welcome *(Jim and Pauline Howell)*

☆ **Chilmark** [B3089 Salisbury—Hindon; ST9632], *Black Dog*: Friendly licensees settling down well in comfortably modernised 15th-century pub in attractive village; horsebrasses, equestrian plates, armchairs by the log fire in the lounge, fossil ammonites in the stone of another bar, and games in third bar; well kept Courage Best and Directors on handpump, good fresh food inc interesting cheese dishes from their own goats (not Mon evening); children allowed in low-key separate dining room;

interesting links with Massachusetts (*J Whitley, Robert and Elizabeth Scott, D P Pascoe, Mrs Richard Stewart, LYM*)

Chippenham [Market Pl; ST9173], *Rose & Crown*: Low-beamed Tudor pub with pleasant atmosphere, clean; helpful staff, Ushers ales, food not expensive (*K R Harris*)

Colerne [High St; ST8171], *Six Bells*: Pleasant local with good food, choice of beers and friendly landlord; skittle alley, video games, sensible piped music, folk club Thurs (*Dr and Mrs A K Clarke*)

☆ **Coombe Bissett** [Blandford Rd (A354); SU1026], *Fox & Goose*: Spacious and very clean open-plan pub by green of delightful village, with rustic wooden refectory-style tables, coal fires, old prints, hanging chamber-pots and classical piped music; Watneys-related real ales, good coffee, friendly service, good choice of standard food with tempting interesting specials in bar and evening restaurant; tables in garden with play area; good access for wheelchairs; children catered for; play area in garden (*Tim Brierly, Stephen Goodchild, Andrea and Guy Bradley, Dr and Mrs R E S Tanner*)

☆ **Corsham** [A4, Pickwick; ST8670], *Two Pigs*: Real old-fashioned drinkers' pub with several changing well kept real ales, very friendly character landlord, super funky decoration, good atmosphere and service; parking a problem, no under-21s (*Roger Huggins, Peter and Rose Flower, Dr and Mrs A K Clarke*)

Corston [A429, N of M4 junction 17; ST9284], *Radnor Arms*: Straightforward pub worth knowing for good home-made food, Flowers IPA and Original, and log fires (*P Saville*)

Cricklade [SU0993], *Kings Head*: Small and friendly, with well kept Whitbreads PA on handpump, good sherry, popular food, good service (*P and R Woods, David Backhouse*)

Crudwell [A429 N of Malmesbury; ST9592], *Plough*: Recently renovated, welcoming, lively, busy; small rooms joined by judicious knocking through, raised eating area adjoining main room in converted barn behind; well kept Whitbreads-related real ales, appealing garden (*Roger Huggins, Tom McLean, Ewan McCall, Dave Irving, B R Woolmington*)

☆ **Dauntsey** [Dauntsey Lock; A420 — handy for M4 junctions 16 and 17; ST9782], *Peterborough Arms*: Very friendly, with good range of good value, generous and often imaginative food, half a dozen real ales, pool, skittle alley, garden with play area; nice location by old Wilts & Berks Canal (*P and R Woods, EML*)

☆ **Derry Hill** [ST9570], *Lansdowne Arms*: Busy but friendly atmosphere in intimate Victorian bar with good choice of bar food inc good home-made pies, very friendly staff, well kept Wadworths inc Farmers Glory and Old Timer, good range of country wines, open fire; lots of strange articles on walls and ceilings; restaurant, garden for children; nr Bowood House (*Jane and Steve Moor, Mr and Mrs D A P Grattan, Dr V Randle*)

☆ **Devizes** [Long St; SU0061], *Elm Tree*: Great bar food in 16th-century pub with well kept Wadworths IPA and 6X on handpump, friendly service from Big John and wife, wide choice of fresh bar food; bedrooms (*Frank Gadbois, David Backhouse*)

☆ **Devizes** [Monday Mkt St], *White Bear*: 15th-century, with beams, antiques, lots of atmosphere, well kept Wadworths IPA, 6X on handpump, good food; good big bedrooms (*Frank Gadbois, David Backhouse*)

Devizes [Market Pl], *Black Swan*: Pleasant comfortable town-centre pub with well kept Wadworths; bedrooms (*Tom McLean, Ewan McCall, Roger Huggins, David Backhouse*); [New Park St], *Castle*: Outstanding, clean, well priced lunchtime food, immaculate bar areas, friendly service; Wadworths and other ales (*Anon*); [Maryport St], *Three Crowns*: Long, low and dark, with friendly atmosphere and well kept Wadworths IPA and 6X on handpump; seats in small sheltered yard (*David Backhouse, BB*)

☆ **Dinton** [SU0131], *Penruddocke Arms*: Spacious and comfortable country pub, welcoming atmosphere, well kept real ales, country wines, reasonably priced good bar food, welcoming landlord, good pub games in public bar (*J M Watkinson, LYM*)

☆ **East Chisenbury** [SU1452], *Red Lion*: Unspoilt and basic country village pub with settles forming old-fashioned snug around huge log fire — sad they no longer keep real ale, but still a fine survivor; play area on lawn (*LYM*)

☆ **Easton Royal** [SU2060], *Bruce Arms*: Another fine old unspoilt pub, nicely basic; one room with elderly easy chairs and amaryllis plants, another just benches and tables; well kept Whitbreads Strong Country (*JM, PM, David Backhouse*)

☆ **Enford** [SU1351], *Swan*: Thatched village local with big log fireplace in comfortable bar, second bar serving as lunchtime family room, several well kept local ales on handpump, food, relatively cheap; tables outside, play area (*David Backhouse, Richard Houghton*)

☆ **Farleigh Wick** [A363 Bath—Bradford; ST8064], *Fox & Hounds*: Old low-beamed stone pub with quiet welcoming rambling bar, clean and neat, highly polished old oak tables and chairs; interestingly but not excessively decorated with rural objects and prints; food decidedly above average, using local ingredients, great garden; can get packed weekends (*GSB, John and Bridget Dean*)

Fovant [A30 Salisbury—Shaftesbury; SU0128], *Cross Keys*: Relaxing 15th-century pub with antique seats and tables, open fire, wide range of tasty, low-priced bar food, good wines, restaurant, afternoon teas; bedrooms (*Paul Corbett*)

Giddeahall [A420 Chippenham—Ford; ST8574], *Crown*: Interesting rambly bar with character furnishings, all sorts of points of interest; real ales such as Butcombe, Marstons Pedigree and Wadworths 6X; two successive recent changes of management have been something of an obstacle to real continuity of purpose, though we hope things are settling down — lots of potential *(David Lamb, LYM — more reports please)*

☆ **Great Bedwyn** [SU2764], *Cross Keys*: Spacious old village pub with comfortable chairs and settles, friendly locals, pleasant, helpful bar staff; well kept Ma Pardoes, Wiltshire Stonehenge, Old Grumble and Old Devil on handpump, very wide choice of generous food quickly served; pool table, occasional juke box — can be lively evenings; bedrooms *(HNJ, PEJ, David Backhouse)*

☆ **Ham** [SU3362], *Crown & Anchor*: Neat and smart timbered 18th-century bar with well kept Hook Norton Best and Wadworths 6X on handpump, small restaurant with good range of standard pub food, pleasant friendly staff *(Stan Edwards, David Backhouse)*

☆ **Hannington** [SU1793], *Jolly Tar*: Smartly refurbished village local with good value honest straightforward food at low prices; big log fire and beams with ships' crests in lounge on right — mix of stripped stone and flock wallpaper; well kept Arkells BB, BBB and Kingsdown, no music or machines; games bar; upstairs grill room; good robust play area in biggish garden, tables out in front too; skittle alley; pretty village *(David Backhouse, Mr and Mrs P B Dowsett, BB)*

Hawkeridge [ST8552], *Oak Tree*: Particularly good bar food, especially fish, and well kept beers *(B R Woolmington)*

☆ **Heddington** [ST9966], *Ivy*: Lovely thatched village pub with woodburner in good inglenook fireplace of simple low-beamed bar, timbered walls, well kept Wadworths real ales tapped from the cask, limited bar food such as rolls or pies, children's room; seats outside the picturesque house; ideal for walkers *(Roger Huggins, LYM)*

Heytesbury [High St; ST9242], *Angel*: Beautiful little coaching inn doing well under new regime, with good home-made innovative pub food, superb service, very friendly staff; restaurant; comfortable bedrooms *(J M Guyer)*; [High St], *Red Lion*: Also doing well under new regime, comfortable high-backed settles in rustic alcoves, small dining room; well kept Gibbs Mew and Salisbury Best, wide choice of reasonably priced food, good value wine by the bottle; lovely, large, well-tended garden sloping down to bank of river Wylye; play area; bedrooms excellent *(Mrs P M Woodger)*

Highworth [Swindon St; SU2092], *Jesmond House*: Good rather hotelish bar with friendly licensee and well kept Archers Best and ASB on handpump; bedrooms *(David Backhouse)*

☆ **Hindon** [ST9132], *Grosvenor Arms*: Old pub refurbished with bookcases and so forth, open fires, Watneys-related and other real ales, shortish choice of good home-cooked food, fruit machine; nice terrace *(Barbara M McHugh, Richard Gibbs, Brian Chambers)*

Holt [ST8662], *Old Ham Tree*: Popular local, relaxed and welcoming, with Marstons Pedigree, Wadworths 6X and other real ales, good food in small but well appointed dining room, friendly staff; nr NT 'Garden of Mystery' — The Courts *(B R Woolmington, Tom Evans)*

☆ **Honey Street** [SU1061], *Barge*: Welcoming unspoilt canalside pub with well kept Courage Best and Directors on handpump, pleasant pictures, standard bar food inc good sandwiches, log fires; dogs allowed, garden; bedrooms *(David Backhouse, Michael and Harriet Robinson, A Y Drummond)*

☆ **Horningsham** [by entrance to Longleat House; ST8141], *Bath Arms*: Comfortable old inn in pretty village, modernised without being spoilt; good interesting food, pleasant service, well kept Bass, Wadworths 6X and three other real ales; bedrooms well equipped, clean and comfortable *(John C Baker, Maysie Thompson)*

Kington Langley [ST9277], *Plough*: Attractive, with most welcoming barman; no food Sun or Mon *(Anon)*

Kington St Michael [ST9077], *Jolly Huntsman*: Good welcome, decent house wine, relaxed atmosphere, good fresh-cooked food *(Barry Gray, William D Cissna)*

☆ **Lacock** [ST9168], *Carpenters Arms*: Several rambling cottagey areas in carefully contrived pastiche of old-fashioned pub, with interesting mix of furnishings and decorations; quickly served good standard bar food (no sandwiches), well kept Watneys-related real ales, friendly service, restaurant, children in eating area; has had jazz Mon; bedrooms *(Mr and Mrs D A P Grattan, Roger Huggins, Tom McLean, Ewan McCall, Mr and Mrs F E M Hardy, Robert Brown, Dr and Mrs A K Clarke)*

Landford [Hamptworth; village signed down B3079 off A36, then right towards Redlynch; SU2519], *Cuckoo*: Unaffectedly rustic and welcoming thatched cottage, well kept real ales such as Adnams Broadside, Badger Best and Tanglefoot, Bunces Best, Wadworths IPA and 6X and a monthly guest, cheap filled rolls, pies and pasties; impromptu folk music Fri and maybe Sat and Sun; children in small room off bar; tables in garden with bantams and big play area, a very peaceful spot *(WHBM, LYM)*

☆ **Liddington** [a mile from M4 junction 15; just off A419; SU2081], *Village Inn*: Comfortable and well furnished quiet village pub, friendly owners, well kept Fullers ESB, Marstons Pedigree, Wadworths 6X, Whitbread IPA and guest beers on handpump, Bulmers Traditional cider tapped from the cask, consistently good home-cooked lunchtime bar food, log fire; bedrooms simple but clean *(Peter Woods, K R Harris, David Backhouse, L G and D L Smith)*

Little Bedwyn [off A4 W of Hungerford — OS Sheet 174, map reference 294657; SU2966], *Harrow*: Has been well worth knowing for good home cooking, neatly unpretentious surroundings and several real ales; but for most of 1990 it was closed on weekday lunchtimes, then more recently has been found more thoroughly closed *(Jerry and Alison Oakes, LYM — news please)*

Little Cheverell [Low Rd; B3098 Westbury—Upavon, W of A360; ST9853], *Owl*: Good home cooking — soups, curries and pies all recommended *(G M K Donkin)*

☆ **Lockeridge** [signed off A4 Marlborough—Calne just W of Fyfield — OS Sheet 173, map reference 148679; SU1467], *Who'd A Thought It*: Friendly and relaxing if not throbbing with atmosphere, plush seats around pine and wood-effect tables in three carpeted rooms around small bar, friendly landlord, ten or so good reasonably priced dishes of day, well kept Badger Tanglefoot, Wadworths IPA, 6X and in winter Old Timer, log fire; family room, back garden with children's play area; handy for Avebury *(HNJ, PEJ, Jane and Steve Moor, David Backhouse)*

☆ **Lower Chute** [the Chutes signed via Appleshaw off A342 2 1/2 miles W of Andover; SU3153], *Hatchet*: Neatly kept and increasingly upmarket but friendly low-beamed thatched pub with huge log fire, good range of real ales such as Adnams, Bass, John Smiths and Wadworths 6X; the generally good quickly served bar food runs from baked potatoes, cheese and ham toasties, crab bake and so forth to considerably more expensive dishes — there's also a restaurant; seats on terrace and lawn; children in restaurant *(Gordon and Daphne, William Rodgers, Laurie Walker, Lynda Cantelo, PEJ, HNJ, LYM)*

☆ **Malmesbury** [Abbey Row; ST9287], *Old Bell*: Sensitively redecorated old hotel looking across churchyard to Norman abbey, traditionally furnished, with Edwardian pictures and recently uncovered early 13th-century hooded stone fireplace; pub part has two good fires, cheerful and helpful long-serving barmaid, good range of usual pub food, Ushers Best and Wadworths 6X on handpump, attractively old-fashioned garden; bedrooms *(Michael Richards, LYM)*

Malmesbury [High St], *Smoking Dog*: Cosy and unpretentious inside; good choice of real ales, log fires, small garden *(Chris and Linda Elston)*

Manton [High St; SU1668], *Up The Garden Path*: Modernised village local up steep path, friendly staff with relaxing atmosphere; very mixed clientele; popular eating area, games room; well kept Archers BB, Hook Norton Best and a guest beer such as Wadworths 6X on handpump *(David Backhouse, David and Christine Foulkes, Jane and Steve Moor, Derek and Sylvia Stephenson, Richard Houghton)*

Market Lavington [B3098 towards Upavon; SU0154], *Green Dragon*: This rambling early 17th-century pub was run for many years with a great deal of panache by the Godbolts, with good home cooking using fresh ingredients, well kept Wadworths and a wide range of wines in old-fashioned

surroundings with an interesting mix of individual furnishings; sadly, they've decided to leave just before this edition comes out — so we can't tell yet what will happen here *(LYM — news please)*

☆ **Marlborough** [High St; SU1869], *Sun*: Attractively furnished, friendly 16th-century pub doing well under new French licensees, really good food now; good lively atmosphere in bar on right with black panelling, heavy sloping beams, big fireplace, well kept Watneys-related real ales; plainer lounge on left, seats in small sheltered back courtyard; simple bedrooms *(Drs G N and M G Yates, David Backhouse, LYM)*

☆ **Marlborough** [High St], *Wellington Arms*: Thriving atmosphere in cosy well run pub with lots of commemorative and decorative mugs hanging from ceiling, newspapers on canes, steps down to eating area with wide range of good bar food from soup, good crab pâté and ploughman's to steaks; well kept Marstons Pedigree and Whitbreads Strong County on handpump, tables in courtyard; bedrooms *(Col G D Stafford, David Backhouse, BB)*

☆ **Marlborough** [High St], *Green Dragon*: Good town pub with well kept Wadworths 6X and IPA on handpump, wide choice of well prepared lunchtime bar food; bedrooms *(David Backhouse)*

Marlborough [The Parade], *Lamb*: Good lively atmosphere in town-centre local with separate pool room and well kept Wadworths IPA and 6X tapped from the cask under light blanket pressure *(David and Christine Foulkes, David Backhouse)*; [111 High St], *Royal Oak*: Watneys Country Carvery with very reasonable prices and good quick service; booking advised *(H H Denman)*

☆ **Marston Meysey** [SU1297], *Spotted Cow & Calf*: Picturesque stone pub, once a farmhouse, with good low-priced straightforward food, welcoming landlord, well kept Flowers IPA, Wadworths 6X and guest beer on handpump, raised stone fireplace; fruit machine and piped music may be rather intrusive; spacious garden, pleasant setting *(Simon Reynolds, Ewan McCall, Tom Mclean, Roger Huggins, E V Walder, David Backhouse, Mr and Mrs P B Dowsett)*

Melksham [Forrest Rd; ST9063], *Pig & Whistle*: Comfortable, rather smart and friendly family pub *(Dr and Mrs A K Clarke)*

☆ **Mere** [Castle St; ST8132], *Old Ship*: Interesting 16th-century building with open fire in cosy, friendly hotel bar, obliging service, spacious separate bar across coach entry divided into cosy areas by standing timbers and so forth, log fire here too, bar games; standard bar food, Badger Best under light blanket pressure; timber-walled restaurant; children allowed in eating area; bedrooms *(Roy McIsaac, Brian Chambers, Tony and Lynne Stark, Robert and Elizabeth Scott, Barbara M McHugh, LYM)*

Milton Lilbourne [SU1860], *Three*

Horseshoes: Fiendly service, good reasonably priced meals *(H H Denman)*

Monkton Farleigh [OS Sheet 173, map reference 804654; ST8065], *Kings Arms*: Friendly and welcoming, Courage and Wadworths 6X, farm cider; food ample, good and home-made; dogs allowed *(Roger Cunningham, Deborah Frost)*

☆ **Netherhampton** [SU1029], *Victoria & Albert*: Small and spotless low-beamed bars with antique furnishings on polished flagstones, well kept Watneys-related real ales, good choice of wines, good bar food cooked by the landlord; maybe unobtrusive piped music, fruit machine in side room; nice long garden behind with own serving hatch *(Jerry and Alison Oakes; more reports please)*

Newton Toney [off A338 Swindon—Salisbury; SU2140], *Malet Arms*: Friendly, warm and cosy country pub, with good range of reasonably priced food, well kept Wadworths 6X and Watneys-related real ales, open fire, beams, and brasses; stream outside *(Daniel Moate, R Elliott)*

☆ **Nunton** [SU1526], *Radnor Arms*: Quaint and rustic spacious beamed room with cheerful and efficient service, good wine list, good varied reasonably priced food (more elaborate in the evenings), well kept Badger ales, lavatory for disabled people; large attractive garden, quiet spot *(Roy McIsaac, Viv Pyne)*

Odstock [SU1526], *Yew Tree*: Thatched pub with low padded beams; strong accent on food; friendly; well kept Wadworths 6X *(Dr and Mrs A K Clarke)*

Ogbourne St George [A345 Marlborough—Swindon; SU1974], *Old Crown*: Attractively comfortable and clean with friendly service, Wadworths 6X and Worthington BB, decent range of bar food inc good ham *(C W and D I Morley)*

☆ **Pewsey** [A345 towards Marlborough; SU1560], *French Horn*: Good canalside food-oriented pub with very good daily specials, friendly and welcoming staff, well kept Wadworths IPA, 6X and in winter Old Timer on handpump, striking elm furniture, open fires, games in public bar; can get crowded weekends *(JM, PM, Dr and Mrs R E S Tanner, David Backhouse, P and R Woods)*

Purton [High St; SU0887], *Angel*: 18th-century pub with spacious beamed bars and well kept Arkells Bitter and BBB on handpump *(David Backhouse, Dr and Mrs A K Clarke)*

☆ **Salisbury** [Harnham Rd — at southernmost ring rd roundabout (towards A354 and A338) an unclassified rd not signed city centre leads to pub], *Rose & Crown*: Worth a visit for the view — almost identical to that in the most famous Constable painting of Salisbury Cathedral; elegantly restored inn with friendly beamed and timbered bar, popular simple bar food (snacks only, Sun — when the restaurant does good generous lunches), Watneys-related real ales, charming Avonside garden, picture-window bedrooms in smart modern extension as well

as the more traditional ones in the original building *(Roy McIsaac, LYM)*

☆ **Salisbury** [New St], *Wig & Quill*: 16th-century building (former shop) with wonderful low beams, ornate rugs, subtle lighting, real fire, worn leather chairs, stuffed birds and low arches to connecting rooms — good traditionally basic town pub with Wadworths 6X and up to four or five guest beers sold by the jug, interesting long summer drinks, usual bar food — locally popular for this, with very little smoking; open all day, dogs allowed, nice courtyard behind *(Ian, Wendy and James Phillips, Dr and Mrs R B Crail, T Nott, Dr and Mrs A K Clarke)*

☆ **Salisbury** [Milford St], *Red Lion*: Hotel with mix of antique settles, leather chairs and modern banquettes in small two-roomed panelled bar, spacious old-fashioned hall with interesting furnishings inc clock with skeleton bellringers; well kept Watneys-related real ales and a guest beer, lunchtime bar food, medieval restaurant, loggia courtyard seats; children in eating areas; bedrooms comfortable — a nice place to stay *(Jerry and Alison Oakes, LYM)*

Salisbury [Sunnyhill Rd], *Butt of Ale*: Fine 1960s estate pub — light and airy with friendly staff and well kept Eldridge Pope *(Dr and Mrs A K Clarke)*; [Ivy St/Catherine St], *Cloisters*: Tavern Fayre pub done up to look old and homely, with low beams, spacious seating; useful for well kept local beers, good choice of food, all-day opening *(Dr and Mrs A K Clarke)*; [New St], *New Inn*: No smoking throughout this creaky-beamed ancient timbered pub concentrating on good choice of genuine food carefully prepared and presented, well kept Badger beers *(Celia and David Watt, BB)*; [Market Pl], *Wiltons*: Newly refurbished, warm atmosphere; obliging staff, wide choice of good bar food, home-made bread, vegetarian dishes, good coffee, well kept beers, good beaujolais; restaurant *(Peter and Susan Maguire)*

Sandy Lane [A342 Devizes—Chippenham; ST9668], *George*: Rather a splendid Georgian building overlooking a small but serene green just off the main road, this has housed an enjoyable and homely pub with well kept Wadworths, largely home-made food and log fire; but as we went to press the tenants told us that the landowner was planning to take it back into his own estate, and there was some talk of its becoming a small hotel *(LYM — news please)*

☆ **Seend** [ST9461], *Bell*: Spotless and welcoming traditional country pub with small lounge and bar, well kept beer and good freshly cooked food changing daily; well kept Wadworths IPA and 6X; children in dining area; good sloping garden, not far from canal *(Angus and Rosemary Campbell, Mrs E M Astley-Weston, Peter Woods, B R Woolmington, Tim and Ann Newell)*

☆ **Sherston** [B4040 Malmesbury—Chipping Sodbury; ST8585], *Carpenters Arms*: Cosy and friendly village pub with scrubbed floors and tables, open fire, area set aside for eating — unusual food running to good local game dishes; well kept Whitbreads-related ales tapped from the cask, secondhand books, welcoming staff, piped radio; tables in garden *(Roger Huggins, Tom McLean, Ewan McCall, Dave Irving, Pamela Sterling)*

☆ **Sherston** [Church St; B4040 Malmesbury—Chipping Sodbury — OS Sheet 173, map reference 854859], *Rattlebone*: Pretty 17th-century beamed and stone-walled pub with big stone fireplace in spacious dining room, good choice of standard bar food, well kept changing real ales such as Bass and Butcombe on handpump, games bar/skittle alley with CD juke box; pebbled terrace, attractive walled back garden; has been open all day Sat *(Roger Huggins, Mr and Mrs Peter Woods, Pamela Sterling, D Lloyd-Jones)*

Stapleford [Warminster Rd (A36); SU0637], *Pelican*: Long, narrow roadside pub with accent on food; good choice of real ales, friendly landlord *(Dr and Mrs A K Clarke)*

☆ **Stibb Green** [SU2363], *Three Horseshoes*: Old-world beams and inglenooks in lovely little pub with well kept Wadworths, farm cider, particularly good food and friendly landlord *(David Backhouse, Dr and Mrs A K Clarke)*

☆ **Stourton** [Church Lawn; follow Stourhead signpost off B3092, N of junction with A303 just W of Mere; ST7734], *Spread Eagle*: Included chiefly for its lovely setting at head of Stourhead Lake, and popular with mostly older customers; old-fashioned furnishings, Bass and Charrington IPA under light blanket pressure, straightforward bar food inc self-service buffet, restaurant, benches in back courtyard; bedrooms spacious and comfortable, with good residents' lounge; a National Trust pub *(Tony and Lynne Stark, M J Joyner, Robert and Elizabeth Scott, J M M Hill, Derek Patey, Gwen and Peter Andrews, John and Betsey Cutler, Marjorie and David Lamb, LYM)*

☆ **Stratton St Margaret** [A420 out of Swindon; SU1787], *White Hart*: Spaciously modernised and welcoming pub with plush lounge, popular lunchtime for quickly served plentiful hot bar food; well kept Arkells BB and BBB on handpump *(David Backhouse, Mr and Mrs Peter Woods)*

☆ **Swindon** [Prospect Hill; SU1485], *Beehive*: Quaint and lively little simply furnished up-and-down pub, quite a social centre in the evening, with lots of interesting characters as customers; poetry readings, live Irish folk music, well kept Morrells on handpump, filled rolls and limited range of lunchtime hot food *(Brian Jones, W Bailey, David Backhouse)*

Swindon [Emlyn Sq], *Glue Pot*: Street-corner local worth knowing as tap for Archers Brewery — well kept Village, Best, ASB and guest beer on handpump, good value straightforward lunchtime food *(David Backhouse, Tom McLean)*; [Fleet St], *Mail Coach*: Well kept Courage real ales on handpump, low beams, high-backed

back-to-back settles, back conservatory and nice terrace *(Roger Huggins, David Backhouse)*; [Newport St], *Wheatsheaf*: Big pub with wood-floored public bar and new back lounge extension; welcoming landlord, good service, good value food and well kept Wadworths IPA, 6X, Farmers Glory and in winter Old Timer on handpump *(David Backhouse, Brian Jones)*

☆ **Teffont Magna** [ST9832], *Black Horse*: Good food with interesting specials and puddings in pretty pub with comfortable and welcoming lounge; well kept real ales, good value wines, very pleasant service, more basic public bar; in attractive village *(E H and R F Warner, LYM)*

Tisbury [Station Rd; ST9429], *South Western*: Bright and airy bar and games room, friendly barmaids, well kept Wiltshire beers from the nearby brewery, good low-priced food — plaice and local ham and egg recommended; good cheap coffee *(Bernard Phillips)*

Upton Lovell [ST9440], *Prince Leopold*: Accent on food; amusing cartoons by friendly local artist *(Dr and Mrs A K Clarke)*

☆ **Wanborough** [2 miles from M4 junction 15; Callas Hill, B4507 towards Bishopstone; SU2083], *Black Horse*: Cheerful, unpretentious two-bar country pub, lounge doubling as homely Mon-Sat lunchtime dining room; generous good value honest food (snacks only, Sun lunchtime) from good sandwiches and feast of a ploughman's up, well kept Arkells BB and BBB on handpump, Kingsdown tapped from the cask in winter, friendly staff, piped music; adventure playground, aviary, pets' corner and fine views from the garden; children very welcome *(Virginia Jones, Mr and Mrs B E Witcher, Dr Robert Sherriff, David Backhouse, Mr and Mrs P B Dowsett)*

☆ **Wanborough** [Foxhill; from A419 through Wanborough turn right, 1 1/2 miles towards Baydon; SU2381], *Shepherds Rest*: Remote pub where Ridgeway crosses Roman rd, with two pool tables in bright and airy basic public bar, lots of tables in low-beamed lounge with hunting prints and brasses, lively atmosphere, good value plentiful food, well kept Marstons Pedigree and Flowers IPA and Original on handpump; can get very busy, dining room decor not inspiring; garden with play area; walkers welcome, camping *(D W Backhouse, Roger Huggins, Tom McLean, Ewan McCall, Dave Irving, Neil and Anita Christopher, Peter Woods)*

Wanborough [Burycroft, Lower Wanborough], *Cross Keys*: Small bar with comfortable atmosphere, well kept Whitbreads-related real ales, bar food inc good toasties, shove-ha'penny, more secluded side area *(David Backhouse, Roger Huggins, Tom McLean, Ewan McCall, Dave Irving)*; [High St], *Plough*: Thatched pub opened up inside around big central feature fire, rough wooden tables, dim lighting give rather a barn-like feel; Archers, Flowers Original and Wadworths 6X kept well, farm ciders, good bar lunches, pleasant landlord

(David Backhouse, Tom McLean, Simon Reynolds)

Warminster [Mkt Pl; ST8744], *Old Bell*: Old-world country-town hotel handy for stn and shops, with good service, decent bar food, good choice of wines; restaurant *(T Nott)*

☆ **West Dean** [SU2527], *Red Lion*: Unaffected country inn, in lovely setting, with tree-sheltered village green running down to fresh and pretty stream-fed duckpond; simple lounge with easy chairs and open fires, games inc pool in small plain back bar, well kept Whitbreads-related real ales, pleasant atmosphere, good value straightforward bar food inc Sun carvery; tables outside; part of the pub actually over the Hants border; bedrooms *(Ken and Barbara Turner, R A Corbett, LYM)*

Westbrook [A3102 about 4 miles E of Melksham; ST9565], *Westbrook*: Unpretentious little cleanly renovated pub with friendly staff, relaxed atmosphere and good range of home-cooked food inc mild curries and vegetarian dishes; Watneys-related real ales on handpump, piped music; may be crowded *(Jane and Steve Moor, LYM)*

Westbury [Market Pl; ST8751], *White Lion*: Genuine locals' pub with a lot of atmosphere *(Dr and Mrs A K Clarke)*

☆ **Westwood** [off B3109 S of Bradford-on-Avon; ST8059], *New Inn*: Cheerful little pub doing well under newish licensee, with several small rooms knocked into one, lots of beams and brasses, pleasant efficient staff, well kept Ushers, good fire, surprisingly wide choice of good value hot, plentiful and home-cooked food — ham and egg the popular favourite; no smoking in cellar bar *(Mrs E M Astley-Weston, Mrs D C Starkey, Mr and Mrs John Goodacre, Joan Olivier, B R Woolmington)*

Whaddon [ST8761], *Three Crowns*: Good meals *(S Watkins)*

Whitley [ST8866], *Pear Tree*: Reopened 1991 after restoration; good food, not over-priced, unusual beers; popular for lunch *(B R Woolmington)*

☆ **Wilcot** [SU1360], *Golden Swan*: Ancient steeply thatched village inn, very picturesque, with rustic tables on pretty front lawn; friendly atmosphere in two small rooms with lots of china jugs and mugs

hanging from beams, well kept Wadworths IPA and 6X and in winter Old Timer on handpump; bar food, dining room, simple bedrooms *(David Backhouse, BB)*

☆ **Winterbourne Monkton** [A361 Avebury—Wroughton; SU0972], *New Inn*: Small and friendly village local with well kept Adnams, Wadworths 6X and a guest such as Archers on handpump; wide choice of good bar food, full meals in separate restaurant; comfortable bedrooms in adjacent converted barn, with good breakfasts *(David Backhouse, Caroline Black and Roger Sealey)*

☆ **Woodborough** [Bottlesford — OS Sheet 173, map reference 112592; SU1059], *Seven Stars*: Thoughtfully restored small rooms, pleasant atmosphere, interesting food at slightly upmarket prices, well kept Wadworths 6X and a guest beer on handpump *(David Backhouse, Mr and Mrs F Hardy)*

Wootton Bassett [Swindon Rd; A420 towards M4 junction 16; SU0682], *Sally Pusseys*: Pleasant Arkells pub named for former landlady; good choice of food *(Dave Braisted)*

☆ **Wroughton** [A4361 — handy for M4 junction 16; SU1480], *White Hart*: Thatched pub, formerly a blacksmith's, with big old stone fireplace in spacious smartly kept L-shaped beamed lounge; good choice of straightforward bar food, well kept Badger Tanglefoot, Wadworths IPA, 6X and winter Old Timer on handpump, welcoming service, lively public bar and skittle alley *(Peter Woods, David Backhouse, LYM)*

Wroughton [High St], *Carters Rest*: Has been basic pub popular with real ale fans for ten well kept guest beers, but bought by Archers 1991 — promise of wider appeal, with guest beers still, friendly new licensees, good comprehensive range of food, talk of redecoration *(Mr and Mrs Peter Woods)*

☆ **Wylye** [just off A303/A36 junction; SU0037], *Bell*: Village local, recently become a free house, clean and comfortable, with friendly staff, decent choice of reasonably priced good food, Gibbs Mew, Wadworths and country wines in beamed front area with some stripped masonry, log fire in huge stone inglenook; bedrooms *(LYM; more reports on new regime please)*

Yorkshire

One of Britain's great value areas for pubs, Yorkshire benefits from
drinks prices that are well below the national average; now, a
Yorkshire pint costs around 30p less than a London one. Pub food
prices are on the low side, too – and that's even before you take into
account the fact that Yorkshire helpings tend not to be modest. Some
pubs here are indeed real bargains from the food point of view – the
Falcon up at Arncliffe (cheap snacks for hungry walkers), the
unpretentious and friendly Crown at Bolton Percy (good cheap Sam
Smiths, too), the Garden Gate in Leeds (lovely Victorian tiling),
Whitelocks there (a classic city pub, civilised yet full of life), the Will's
o' Nat's at Meltham (a new entry – a fine country pub), the Mount
Skip near Midgley (wonderful views), the Fat Cat in Sheffield (it's just
opened its own microbrewery) and the Frog & Parrot there
(particularly good fish – and they brew their own beers, too), the
Angel & White Horse in Tadcaster (a handsome tap for the Sam
Smiths brewery, whose dray horses can be seen from the pub), the
interesting Staff of Life on the edge of Todmorden (a lot of Indian
food at the moment), and the pleasantly traditional Tap & Spile in
York (another newcomer to the Guide). We've mentioned two new
entries here: others are the Crab & Lobster at Asenby (really good
food in entertainingly individual surroundings – a very good
discovery), the Blue Lion at East Witton (another place with really
good food, in a pub that's just been very carefully refurbished, gaining
a great deal of charm in the process), the Cover Bridge not far outside
East Witton (a pub that by contrast takes pride in not changing from
one decade to the next – very enjoyable), the nice little Sandpiper in
Leyburn (good all round), and the Hole in the Wall in York (a useful
addition to that city's string of fine pubs). Changes afoot in other
pubs include considerable development in the hotel side of the Kings
Arms in Askrigg (the bar has by no means suffered), the Buck at
Buckden's increasing concentration on its virtues as a place to stay
(perhaps a mixed blessing in some ways), new licensees discernably
raising the quality – already high – of the food in the Fauconberg
Arms at Coxwold, new licensees also doing well at the White Lion at
Cray, the Old Hall at Heckmondwike suddenly earning particular
approval from readers, new owners opening up the Shoulder of
Mutton at Kirby Hill a bit, the people who took over the Queens
Arms in Litton last year making improvements to the building itself
and to the food, quite a bit of work on the bar and dining room of the
Buck at Thornton Watlass (currently doing very well indeed in
readers' ratings), and a new restaurant for the George & Dragon at
Wentworth. Pubs doing really well at the moment include the friendly
very personally run Malt Shovel at Brearton (it wins a food award
this year), the Abbey Inn in its lovely setting at Byland Abbey (nicely
furnished, with very enjoyable cooking by the landlord's Norwegian
wife), the Fox & Hounds at Carthorpe (this happy dining pub also
gains a food award this year), the Angel at Hetton (imaginative food,

*exceptionally friendly and hard-working staff), the very civilised
Black Bull at Moulton (not a pub for torn jeans), the Nags Head at
Pickhill (good food, currently doing very well all round), the friendly
Kings Arms in its fine position at Redmire (good home-made food,
nice people), the White Horse at Rosedale Abbey (another pub in a
lovely spot — and they've been working hard on getting everything
right), and the interesting Old Hall at Threshfield (a nice place to eat
— but very much a proper pub, too). In the last few months, often
under new or newish licensees, several pubs in the Lucky Dip section
at the end of the chapter have begun to attract a lot of interest, among
them the White Swan at Ampleforth, Old Hill at Chapel le Dale,
Bryherstones at Cloughton Newlands, Farmers Arms at Muker, Kings
Arms at Reeth, Boars Head at Ripley, Water Rat in Ripon, Castle
Arms at Snape, Old Silent at Stanbury and Wombwell Arms at Wass;
good news too is that that old favourite the Malt Shovel at
Oswaldkirk seems to be coming back on form.*

ALDBOROUGH (N Yorks)   SE4166 Map 7

Ship 🛏

Village signposted from B6265 just S of Boroughbridge, close to A1

A nice mix of locals and visitors fills the neatly kept, heavily beamed bar in this
friendly fourteenth-century pub; also, some old-fashioned seats around heavy
cast-iron tables, sentimental engravings on the walls, and a coal fire in the stone
inglenook fireplace. A quieter back room (decorated with ship pictures) has lots
more tables. Good home-made bar food includes soup (£1.15), sandwiches (from
£1.30, open sandwiches from £2.30), good ploughman's (£3.25), salads (from
£3.25), Yorkshire pudding with meat and onion gravy (£3.95), steak and kidney
pie (£4.25), fresh cod in batter (£4.40), gammon with egg (£5.95), and steaks
(from £6.50); Sunday roast lunch. Well kept John Smiths, Tetleys and Theakstons
on handpump, and some malt whiskies; dominoes, shove-ha'penny, trivia, and
piped music; summer seats on the spacious grass behind. The ancient church is
across the lane and beyond it is the Roman town for which the village is famous.
*(Recommended by Mrs V Middlebrook, Tony Gayfer, Barry and Anne, Paul and Janet
Waring, GB, J A Gifford, John N Skeldon, David Boyd, J D Andrews, David and Rebecca
Killick)*

*Free house   Licensee Duncan Finch   Real ale   Meals and snacks; Sun evening
restricted to sandwiches   Restaurant   (0423) 322749   Children by prior
arrangement   Open 12–2.30(3 Sat), 5.30–11   Bedrooms; £29S/£40S*

ARNCLIFFE (N Yorks)   SD9473 Map 7

Falcon £

Off B6160

A small servery at the back of this friendly walkers' pub taps the Youngers ales
from the cask, and there's hatch service to a couple of functional little rooms with
heavy settles and cast-iron tables, some old humorous sporting prints, and a fire (if
you're lucky enough to get near it); there's also a homely front lounge, and an airy
conservatory-room behind. The dining room is no smoking. Simple bar food
includes baked potato with cheese (90p), soup (£1), pie and peas (£1.20),
sandwiches (from £1.20) and good ploughman's (£2.50); enormous breakfasts;
winter darts, dominoes. The pub is set at the head of a long village green, is on
Good Walks Guide Walk 151, and stands right by a bridleway leading up to
Malham Tarn and beyond. *(Recommended by Neil and Angela Huxter, Andy and Jill
Kassube, Lee Goulding; more reports please)*

*Free house   Licensee Robin Miller   Real ale   Lunchtime snacks   Arncliffe (075 677)
205   Well behaved children in conservatory (lunchtime only)   Open 12–3, 6.30–11 in
summer; 12–2, 7–11 in winter; closed winter Thurs evenings   Bedrooms; £20/£40
(may not be available in winter)*

ASENBY (N Yorks)   SE3975 Map 7

Crab & Lobster ★ ✿

Village signposted off A168 – handy for A1

A real find, this: excellent if pricey food and good wines in engagingly idiosyncratic
surroundings, with a relaxed and informal atmosphere. The old thatched pub
which readers may have known as the Shoulder of Mutton has been transformed
inside into a rambling L-shaped bar cosily cluttered with an interesting jumble of
seats from antique high-backed and other settles through settees and wing
armchairs heaped with cushions to tall and rather theatrical corner seats and even
a very superannuated dentist's chair; the tables are almost as much of a mix, and
the walls and available surfaces are quite a jungle of bric-a-brac, with standard and
table lamps keeping even the lighting pleasantly informal. Perhaps the most
attention-grabbing decoration though is the writing chalked over all the dark
beams and joists – a tantalising choice of food including five soups such as
asparagus or crab bisque (from £2.50), stuffed mushrooms (£3.50), black pudding
with caramelised apple (£3.95), boudin blanc, roquefort and walnut salad (£4.50),
tomatoes baked with basil and garlic or baked avocado with stilton, celery and
walnuts (£4.50), smoked prawns or mussels mouclade (£4.75), chicken and
chestnut sausages and mash or croustades of wild mushrooms (£4.95), avocado,
prawn and crab salad (£5.50), six oysters, roast beef or smoked salmon (£5.95),
liver and bacon (£6.50), pasta with bacon and queen scallops (£7.50), steaks,
paella or curried seafood cassoulet (£7.95) and lemon sole or giant prawns in
bacon (£8.95). Cooking is precise, using absolutely fresh ingredients, presentation
is modern (large plates, pretty detailing, fresh herb garnishes, pools of sauces), and
their bread is full of flavour; if you're really hungry ask to be pointed towards
something substantial. They do sandwiches, and a good choice of puddings served
with a genuine crème anglaise (£2.95) includes a superb though very rich white
chocolate truffle-cake maybe with strawberry coulis. Theakstons Best and
Youngers Scotch and No 3 on handpump, good wines by the glass, with interesting
bottles (plenty under £10), well reproduced though not unobtrusive piped music
(jazz, Paul Simon, nightclub piano). There are rustic seats on a side lawn, and out
on a front terrace by tubs of flowers; summer barbecues Friday and Saturday
evenings and Sunday lunchtime, running to tiger prawns, lobster and suckling pig
(£9.50 including strawberries and cream). *(Recommended by Viv Middlebrook, Gill and
Neil Patrick, Peter Race, P H and E Gallagher, David Watson)*

*Free house   Licensees David and Jackie Barnard   Real ale   Meals and snacks (till
10pm; not Sun evenings)   Restaurant   (0845) 577286   Children in eating area of bar
and in restaurant   Open 11.30–3, 6.30–11; closed Sun evenings*

ASKRIGG (N Yorks)   SD9591 Map 10

Kings Arms ✿ 🛏

Village signposted from A684 Leyburn–Sedbergh in Bainbridge

Continuing developments at this former Georgian manor house will include this
year a separate hotel entrance, reception area, two lounges (one is no smoking), a
new grill room, new bedrooms, and off-street parking for residents. The very
high-ceilinged central room has a homely, friendly atmosphere, an attractive
medley of furnishings that includes a fine sturdy old oak settle, nineteenth-century
fashion plates, a stag's head, hunting prints, and a huge stone fireplace; a curving
wall with a high window shows people bustling up and down the stairs and there's
a kitchen hatch in the panelling. The small low-beamed and oak panelled front bar
has been refurbished, there are period furnishings, some side snugs, and a lovely
green marble fireplace; all the bars have photographs of the filming of James

Herriot's *All Creatures Great and Small* (the inn itself, in the series, is the Drovers Arms). A simply furnished flagstoned back bar has yet another fire, and a fruit machine; also, darts, shove-ha'penny, dominoes, and cribbage. Bar food includes lovely home-made soup (£1.75), well presented open sandwiches (from £1.75), filled baked potatoes (from £2.10), first-class ploughman's (from £3.50), tasty steak and kidney or chicken, ham and mushroom pies (£4.75), gammon and egg (£4.95), rump steak (£7.95), and lots of home-made puddings like poached pear with a ginger and apricot sauce or bramble and apple pie (from £2); daily specials such as smoked prawn salad (£3.75), fricassée of seafood with Chinese noodles (£4.95), poached sea trout or beef stroganoff (£5.50), and whole grilled Dover sole (£15.25). Well kept Ind Coope Burton, McEwans 80/-, Tetleys Bitter and Youngers No 3 on handpump, freshly squeezed orange juice, quite a few malt whiskies, an award-winning wine list (including interesting champagnes), and filter, espresso and cappuchino coffee, and tea; pleasant, helpful staff. The two-level courtyard has lots of tables and chairs. *(Recommended by Mrs R Heaton, Adam and Elizabeth Gorb, Ian Louden, Tim Bishop, John and Helen Thompson, Mrs S M Judge, P R Morley, A P Jeffreys, Roy and Nicola Boyne, Kelvin Lawton, George Hunt, Kathryn Ogden, Mike and Wendy Proctor, Mr and Mrs M O Jones, Bob Smith, Sidney and Erna Wells, Barbara and Ken Turner, John Fazakerley, Brian and Genie Krakowska-Smart, J E Rycroft, Paul McPherson)*

Free house   Licensees Raymond and Elizabeth Hopwood   Real ale   Meals and snacks   Partly no smoking restaurant   Wensleydale (0969) 50258   Children in eating area of bar and in grill room   Open 11–4, 6.30–11; 11–11 Sat   Bedrooms; £35B/£55B

AUSTWICK (N Yorks)   SD7668   Map 7

Game Cock 🛏

Just off A65 Settle–Kirkby Lonsdale

The atmosphere in this prettily placed inn is especially warm and welcoming – the sort of place where strangers easily get into conversations with one another. The beamed and simply furnished but cosy back bar has well made built-in wall benches and plain wooden tables, a few cockfighting prints on the butter-coloured wall, and a good winter fire. Bar food includes soup (£1.15), sandwiches (from £1.30), popular potato skins with stilton and port dip, crispy crab and vegetable parcels (£2.60), pork satay (£2.90), Cumberland sausage with gravy (£3.20), jumbo cod (£3.90), gammon with egg or pineapple (£5.35), and sirloin steak (£8.75). Well kept Thwaites on handpump; darts and dominoes. There are some seats in a glass enclosed sun loggia, and outside – where there's also an equipped children's play area. Above the green pastures around this quiet village of rose-covered stone houses rise the crags and screes of the Dales National Park and the Three Peaks. *(Recommended by P R Morley, WAH, Michael Simmonds, Mel Landells, Andy and Jill Kassube, Robert and Vicky Tod, Derek and Sylvia Stephenson, Mrs Hilarie Taylor, David Warrellow, Dr Thomas Mackenzie, G Dobson, A McK, Alan and Ruth Woodhouse, Mike and Wendy Proctor, A T Langton, Simon Bates)*

Thwaites   Tenant Jack Kenyon   Real ale   Meals and snacks (not Mon evening in winter)   Restaurant   Clapham (046 85) 226   Children in restaurant   Open 11–3.30(5 Sat), 6.30–11   Bedrooms; l£32

BINGLEY (W Yorks)   SE1039   Map 7

Brown Cow

Ireland Bridge; B6429, just W of junction with A650

Handy for the flights of locks on the Leeds and Liverpool canal and just below the old stone bridge over the River Aire is this quiet, friendly pub. The carpeted open-plan main bar is divided into smaller and snugger areas, with a high shelf of toby jugs under the dark ceiling, lots of pictures and some brass on the partly panelled walls, and comfortable easy chairs and captains' chairs around the black tables. They specialise in large Yorkshire puddings – served either with beef, stew or Yorkshire sausage (from £1.30). Other home-made bar food includes soup

(90p), sandwiches (from £1.10), a brunch (around £2), ploughman's (£2.75), lasagne (£3.25), and steaks (from £5.25). Well kept Timothy Taylors Best, Ram Tam and Landlord on handpump; coffee served all day; fruit machine, quiz nights, and piped music. Below a steep bluebell wood is a sheltered corner terrace behind with tables and chairs – some of them sturdy pews. There are several antique shops in the town. *(Recommended by Dave and Carole Jones, WAH, Andy and Jill Kassube, Dr and Mrs I C Jones, J E Rycroft, Reg Nelson, Brian Jones, Barbara Wensworth; more reports please)*

Timothy Taylors　Tenant Mrs Wheelhouse　Real ale　Meals and snacks (lunchtimes Mon–Fri and Sun)　Restaurant　Bradford (0274) 569482　Children in eating area and small snug　Traditional jazz Mon　Open 11.30–3.30, 5.30–11

BLAKEY RIDGE (N Yorks)　SE6799　Map 10

Lion 🛏

From A171 Guisborough–Whitby follow Castleton, Hutton le Hole signposts; from A170 Kirkby Moorside–Pickering follow Keldholm, Hutton le Hole, Castleton signposts; OS Sheet 100, map reference 679996

The moorland views in virtually every direction from this mainly sixteenth-century pub are spectacular – at 1325 feet above sea level, it's said to be the fourth highest inn in England. The characterful rambling bars have a few big high-backed rustic settles around cast-iron-framed tables, lots of small dining chairs on the Turkey carpet, a nice leather settee, beams, dim lamps, and stripped stone walls hung with some old engravings and photographs of the pub under snow (it can easily get cut off in winter – but there are good fires). What characterises the food here is the generous helpings: soup (£1.10), sandwiches (from £1.35), ploughman's (£3.55), steak sandwich (£2.75), home-made steak and mushroom pie, vegetarian dishes or home-cooked ham and egg (£4.45), steaks (from £6.95), puddings (£1.55), children's menu (£2.55) and Sunday roasts; good breakfasts. Well kept Tetleys and Theakstons Best, Old Peculier and XB on handpump and organic wines; dominoes, fruit machine and piped music. During the late nineteenth century coal-mining days, the mine here was linked to the railway at Rosedale by a tramway that ran within yards of the pub – it's now the course of the Cleveland Way, Coast to Coast path and Lyke Wake walk. *(Recommended by John Burgan, Hilary Irving, J White, John and Christine Simpson, Len Beattie, Anthony Sargent, Caroline Gant, PLC, Ian and Susan Brocklebank, John and Helen Thompson, Ian and Jill Johnson, Jill Hampton, Brian Metherell, Brian and Anna Marsden, Sidney and Erna Wells, Tim and Lynne Crawford)*

Free house　Licensee Barry Crossland　Real ale　Meals and snacks (noon till 10pm) Restaurant (food served all day Sun)　Lastingham (075 15) 320　Children welcome Open all day　Bedrooms; £15.50(£18B)/£36(£42B)

BOLTON PERCY (N Yorks)　SE5341　Map 7

Crown £

Signposted with Oxton from Tadcaster – first real right turn after crossing the bridge, heading out from centre on York road

It's not surprising that the cheap Sam Smiths OB on electric pump in this tiny, unpretentious pub is in tip-top condition – the brewery is just over three miles away. The two simply furnished, friendly rooms are decorated with brass ornaments, a delft shelf of fox-hunting plates and a big print of shire horses; the three dogs are called Teal (the spaniel) and Coot and Gipsy (the labradors). Freshly made, good value bar food includes soup (90p), sandwiches (from 95p, toasties from £1.05), burgers (£1.50), filled Yorkshire pudding (from £2.25), ploughman's (£2.95), home-made steak and kidney pie or kebabs (£2.95), children's menu (£1.25), and there are summer barbecues on Saturday evenings. Darts and dominoes. Outside, the biggish terrace (with ornamental pheasants in a row of pens beside it) has picnic-table sets among fruit trees, and a very long wooden cat-walk footbridge that snakes out over a slow dark stream and its bordering nettle flats. The landlord runs the village cricket team and another team in York. *(Recommended by John C Baker, Ben Wimpenny; more reports please)*

Sam Smiths   Licensees Geoff and Angela Pears   Real ale   Meals and snacks (not Mon or Tues)   (0904) 84255   Children welcome   Open 11.30–2.30, 6.30–11; 10–3, 6–11 Sat

BREARTON (N Yorks)   SE3261   Map 7

Malt Shovel ✪

Village signposted off A61 N of Harrogate

The wide choice of very good home-made food in this friendly, family-run, sixteenth-century village pub might include vegetable samosas (£3.60), spicy bean pot (£3.85), good spinach and mushroom or meaty lasagne (£3.90), ham salad (£3.95), roast ham with parsley sauce or tasty nut roast with tomato and mint sauce (£4.05), really fresh haddock in batter (£4.75), Trinidad prawn curry (£5.10), fresh salmon with cucumber mayonnaise (£6.10), and puddings like banana caramel pie or treacle tart. They have decent wines, and well kept Big End Piston (local), Old Mill Traditional, Tetleys Bitter, Theakstons Best and XB, and guest ales on handpump. Radiating from the attractive linenfold oak bar counter, the several rooms have heavy beams, an ancient oak partition wall, both real and gas fires, sewing-machine and other tables, plush-cushioned seats, and lively Nigel Hemming hunting prints; shove-ha'penny, darts, cribbage, dominoes, and piped music. If the cat who makes friends with you isn't Harry, William, Thomas, Charlie or Sooty, it'll be Scraggs from over the road. There are tables behind, with Saturday summer barbecues, on the terrace and the grass leading to a discreet little caravan site; exemplary lavatories. *(Recommended by Viv Middlebrook, G Dobson, Peter Race, Andy and Jill Kassube, Tim and Ann Newell, Michael Rooke)*

Free house   Licensee Leigh Parsons   Real ale   Meals and snacks (not Sun evening, not Mon)   (0423) 862929   Well behaved children allowed   Open 12–3, 6.45(6.30 Sat)–11; closed Mon, except bank hols

BUCKDEN (N Yorks)   SD9278   Map 7

Buck

B6160

This busy pub has changed hands yet again and seems to be moving more into the hotel mood – the bedrooms have been recently upgraded and the atmosphere is perhaps less obviously aligned with walkers' needs than in most pubs in the valley. The modernised and extended open-plan bar has local pictures, hunting prints, willow-pattern plates and the mounted head of a roebuck on the mainly buttery cream walls (one by the big log fire is stripped to bare stone), and upholstered built-in wall banquettes and square stools around shiny dark brown tables on its carpet – though there are still flagstones in the snug original area by the serving counter. Popular bar food includes home-made soup (£1.50), giant Yorkshire puddings filled with rich onion gravy or home-made smooth chicken liver pâté with cream, brandy and garlic (£2.80), mushroom and nut fettucini (£3.50), omelettes (from £4.20), steak and mushroom pie or haddock (£5.50), gammon steak (£6), steaks (from £8.20), and mixed grill (£8.70 – to suit the heartiest appetite); traditional Sunday lunch. Well kept John Smiths, Tetleys Bitter, Theakstons Old Peculier and a guest beer such as Malton on handpump served by uniformed staff; good choice of malt whiskies and decent wines. Darts, cards, dominoes, cribbage, and occasional piped music. Seats on the terrace and beyond the sloping car park in the shelter of a great sycamore have good views of the surrounding moors. *(Recommended by Mr and Mrs R Clifford, Andy and Jill Kassube, D Goodger, Mrs R Hecton, J E Rycroft, Geoff and Julie Bond, G T Jones, Robert and Vicky Tod, Janet and Paul Waring, Mr and Mrs M Cockram, Jon and Jacquie Payne, Mr and Mrs K H Frostick; more reports on the new regime, please)*

Free house   Licensees Mr and Mrs Roy Hayton   Real ale   Meals and snacks   No smoking evening restaurant (mainly for residents)   Kettlewell (075 676) 227   Children

*in room away from bar and in restaurant   Winter quiz evenings, karaoke, and country
& western music   Open 11–11   Bedrooms; £30B/£60B*

BURNSALL (N Yorks)   SE0361 Map 7
Red Lion

B6160 S of Grassington, on Ilkley road; OS Sheet 98, map reference 033613

The lively main bar in this pretty stone-built pub has flowery-cushioned sturdy
seats built in to the attractively panelled walls (decorated with pictures of the local
fell races), Windsor armchairs, rugs on the floor, and steps up past a solid fuel
stove to a back area with sensibly placed darts (dominoes players are active up
here, too). The carpeted front lounge bar, which is served from the same
copper-topped counter through an old-fashioned small-paned glass partition, has a
coal fire. At lunchtime bar food includes sandwiches (from £1.20), ploughman's
(from £2.90), home-cooked cold ham (£3.30), steak and potato pie (£3.50), and
trout (£3.90), with evening soup (£1.20), home-made liver pâté (£2.20), and steak
(£6.50). Well kept Tetleys and Theakstons on handpump. White tables on the
front cobbles look over the quiet road to the village green (which has a tall
maypole) running along the banks of the River Wharfe. *(Recommended by John and
Christine Simpson, Derek Patey, Charles and Dorothy Ellsworth, Mrs S Mills, Greg Turner,
Virginia Jones, J E Rycroft, H K Dyson, Andrew Triggs, Andy and Jill Kassube)*

*Free house   Licensee Patricia Warnett   Real ale   Snacks   No smoking restaurant
Burnsall (075 672) 204   Children welcome until 9pm   Open 11.30–3(2.30 winter),
6–11   Bedrooms; £25.30(£25.30S)/£39.60(£50.60B)*

BYLAND ABBEY (N Yorks)   SE5579 Map 7
Abbey Inn ✿

The Abbey has a brown tourist-attraction signpost off the A170 Thirsk–Helmsley

Though this out-of-the-way pub is very much somewhere to go to enjoy Mrs
Handley's cooking, the atmosphere in the rambling series of rooms is relaxed and
pubby. There are oak and stripped deal tables, settees, carved oak seats, and
Jacobean-style dining chairs on the polished boards and flagstones, some discreet
stripping back of plaster to show the ex-abbey masonry, big fireplaces, decorative
bunches of flowers among the candles, various stuffed birds, cooking implements,
little etchings, willow-pattern plates, and china cabinets. In a big back room an
uptilted cart shelters a pair of gnomelike waxwork yokels, and there are lots of
rustic bygones. Bar food brought to your table by neat waitresses might include
lovely sandwiches (£2.25), home-made pâtés or chicken coronation (£3.60),
ploughman's (£4), Abbey platter (£4.50), home-made pies like steak and kidney or
chicken and leek (£5.25), breast of chicken with tarragon sauce (£6), fillet of pork
in dijon mustard sauce (£6.50), puddings like excellent sticky toffee or bread and
butter puddings (£2.25), and roast Sunday lunch (from £5.50). Well kept Tetleys
Bitter and Theakstons Best on handpump, interesting wines, and inoffensive piped
music; friendly landlord. No dogs. There's lots of room outside in the garden and
the setting opposite the Abbey ruins is spectacular. *(Recommended by H K Dyson, G
Dobson, Laurence Manning, Viv Middlebrook, WAH, Peter Burton, Andrew and Ruth Triggs,
Mr and Mrs Peter Crane, Richard Gibbs, Mary and Lionel Tonks, Mr and Mrs M Cockram,
Andy and Jill Kassube, Patrick Clark)*

*Free house   Licensees Peter and Gerd Handley   Real ale   Meals and snacks (not Sun
evening, not Mon)   (03476) 204   Children welcome   Open 11–2.30, 6.30–11; closed
Sun evening and all day Mon*

CADEBY (S Yorks)   SE5100 Map 7
Cadeby Inn ★

3 miles from A1(M) at junction with A630; going towards Conisbrough take first right
turn signposted Sprotbrough, then follow Cadeby signposts

Warmly welcoming, this bustling ex-farmhouse has its serving bar in the main lounge at the back: comfortable seats around wooden tables, a high-backed settle made in the traditional style to fit around one stone-walled alcove, an open fire in the big stone fireplace, caps of all seventeen County Cricket Clubs, a stuffed fox and pheasant, some silver tankards, and lots of house plants. There's a quieter front sitting room, and decently out of the way, a fruit machine (they also have a separate darts room, an old each-way horse racing machine, shove-ha'penny, dominoes, cribbage, and quiz evenings). Good bar food includes a good lunchtime salad bar, generous carvery or gammon steak (all £4.25), as well as soup and sandwiches, home-made steak and kidney pie (£3.45), and sirloin steak; their traditional Sunday lunches are exceedingly popular. Well kept Courage Directors, Ind Coope Burton, John Smiths Magnet, Sam Smiths and Tetleys Bitter on handpump, attractively priced, and over 200 malt whiskies. There are seats in the front beer garden where they hold summer barbecues. *(Recommended by Anthony Barnes, Barry and Anne, A and J Jackson, Andy and Jill Kassube, Paul Mellors, ILP, Richard Cole, Mary and Lionel Tonks, David and Christine Foulkes, T Nott, Barbara and Norman Wells, Michael and Alison Sandy)*

Free house   Licensee Walter William Ward   Real ale   Meals and snacks (till 10pm) (0709) 864009   Children in eating area of bar till 8.30pm   Open 10.30–3, 5–11; all day Sat

CARTHORPE (N Yorks)   SE3184   Map 10

Fox & Hounds 🛇

Village signposted from A1 N of Ripon, via B6285

Food is a main focus of attention in this pretty little extended village house. In the bar, it includes stilton and onion soup (£1.85), several starters or snacks such as duck liver pâté in port jelly (£2.95), curried vegetable pancake (£3.25), whole fresh dressed crab (£4.95), main courses like steak and kidney pie (£4.95), medium hot chicken curry (£5.25), fillet of salmon with hollandaise sauce or halibut with mustard sauce (£6.95), rack of English lamb (£7.45), half duckling with orange and apple sauce (£7.95), and home-made puddings (from £1.95). They use local fish according to season and local meat and cheeses, and devote a good deal of care to their wines, with a wide choice by the bottle and half-bottle, decent wines by the glass, and some interesting bin-ends; well kept John Smiths on handpump; coffee. The cosy, L-shaped bar has a couple of nice seats by the larger of its two log fires, dark red plush button-back built-in wall banquettes and chairs, blue patterned wallpaper with matching curtains on brass rails, plates on stripped beams, and some limed panelling; there are quite a few mistily evocative Victorian photographs of Whitby. An attractive high-raftered restaurant leads off with lots of neatly black-painted farm and smithy tools. Quick happy service, inoffensive piped music, exemplary lavatories. *(Recommended by Alan and Ruth Woodhouse, Ian Richard Smith, Tim and Sue Halstead, Mr and Mrs F S Stabler, H Bramwell)*

Free house   Licensee Howard Fitzgerald   Real ale   Meals and snacks (not Mon) Restaurant   Thirsk (0845) 567433   Children in eating area of bar lunchtime and until 8.30pm   Open 12–2.30, 7–11; closed Mon and first week of the year from Jan 1

COXWOLD (N Yorks)   SE5377   Map 7

Fauconberg Arms ★   🏠

Named after Lord Fauconberg, who married Oliver Cromwell's daughter Mary, this well kept and civilised old stone inn has a lounge bar made up of two cosy and comfortably furnished knocked-together rooms. There are cushioned antique oak settles, including one that's handsomely carved and another curved to fit the attractive bay window, an oak porter's chair, Windsor armchairs, matting on the flagstones, gleaming brasses on one beam, and an unusual arched stone fireplace which has a winter log fire and is filled in summer with lots of copper and horsebrasses; some of the furniture has squirrels carved into it. Under the new licensee bar food now includes home-made soup (£1.75), sandwiches (from £1.95;

smoked salmon and cream cheese £3.25), deep-fried puff pastry parcels filled with creamy garlic mushrooms (£2.95), hot buttered potted shrimps (£3.25), home-made vegetarian nutty loaf or home-made steak, kidney and oyster pie (£4.95), salads (from £4.95), home-made moussaka with Greek yoghurt and cheese sauce (£5.35), fresh seafood strudel (£5.95), pan-fried lamb with apple, mint and rosemary gravy (£6.55), and puddings such as peach brandy egg custard or ginger raspberry trifle (£2.50); children's menu (from 95p), and Sunday roast beef (£4.95 – lots of other things then as well); decent breakfasts. On the face of it, all this seems to match the high standards set by the previous owners – we look forward to reports from readers confirming this. Well kept Tetleys Bitter and Mild and Theakstons Best on handpump, lots of wines, vintage champagnes and draught cider. At the back, the locals' spacious public bar has darts, dominoes, trivia and piped music. The broad, quiet village street is pretty, with tubs of flowers on its grass or cobbled verges and the pub is close to Shandy Hall, the home of Laurence Stern the novelist. *(Recommended by Andrew and Ruth Triggs, Andy and Jill Kassube, Greg Turner, Ian and Sue Brocklebank, Laurence Manning, H K Dyson, Mary and Lionel Tonks, Barbara M McHugh, Mr and Mrs M Cockram, Nick and Alison Dowson, Peter Burton, David and Rebecca Killick)*

Free house Licensee Robin Jaques Meals and snacks Restaurant Coxwold (03476) 214 Children welcome Open 11–3, 6–11 Bedrooms; £24(£26S)/£40(£45S)

CRACOE (N Yorks) SD9760 Map 7

Devonshire Arms

B6265 Skipton–Grassington

In the middle of this small Dales village and popular with readers for its warm, friendly atmosphere, stands this neatly kept, attractive stone pub. Solidly comfortable furnishings include green plush cushioned dark pews, built-in wall settles and sturdy rustic or oak tripod tables, as well as low shiny black beams supporting creaky white planks, polished flooring tiles with rugs here and there, and gleaming copper pans round the stone fireplace; above the dark panelled dado are old prints, engravings and photographs, with a big circular large-scale Ordnance Survey map showing the inn as its centre. Good bar food includes good soup (£1.65), decent sandwiches (from £1.75), sausage and mash (£3.85), stuffed pears (£3.90), delicious scrambled egg done with smoked salmon (£4.50), cheese platter (£4.80), fresh haddock (£4.70), steak and kidney pie (£4.95); huge breakfasts; well kept Youngers Scotch and No 3 on handpump, decent coffee, and attentive service. A fruit machine is tucked discreetly away by the entrance; darts, maybe unobtrusive piped music. There are picnic-table sets on a terrace flanked by well kept herbaceous borders. *(Recommended by G Dobson, Andy and Jill Kassube, C E Hall, WAH, D Goodger, Michael and Joan Melling, John and Barbara Moss, H K Dyson, Len Beattie, W Marsh, Mr and Mrs J E Rycroft)*

Youngers (S & N) Lease: Morris Jaques Real ale Meals and snacks Restaurant (not Sun evening) Cracoe (075 673) 237 Children welcome until 9 Open 11–3, 6.30–11; closed 25 Dec Bedrooms; £18/£36

CRAY (N Yorks) SD9379 Map 7

White Lion ★

B6160, Upper Wharfedale N of Kettlewell

New licensees have taken over this friendly little stone-built pub and have made a few changes to the menu: excellent value parsnip and apple soup with croûtons, sandwiches, large Yorkshire pudding with onion gravy (£1.85), locally-made Cumberland sausage (£3.80), home-made steak and kidney pie or battered haddock (£3.95), scampi (£4.40), Kilnsey trout (£6.50), and sirloin steak (£8.95). The simply furnished bar has seats around tables on the flagstone floor, shelves of china, iron tools and so forth, a high dark beam-and-plank ceiling, lovely winter open fire, and a traditional atmosphere; it's especially cheerful and lively on

Tuesday evenings – which is the local dominoes night. The dining room is no smoking. Well kept Moorhouses Premier and Pendle Witches Brew, Theakstons Best and Youngers Scotch on handpump; dominoes, ring the bull and piped music. There are picnic-table sets above the very quiet, steep lane, and great flat limestone slabs (pleasant to sit on) in the shallow stream which tumbles down opposite. The pub is the highest in Wharfedale (1,100 feet up by Buckden Pike) and the surrounding countryside is superb. *(Recommended by P R Morley, B C Armstrong, Andy and Jill Kassube, Mr and Mrs R Clifford, R J August, Barbara and Mike Williams, Geoff and Julie Bond, P Corris, A M Neal, Lee Goulding, J and K O'Malley)*

Free house   Licensees Frank and Barbara Hardy   Real ale   Meals and snacks Kettlewell (075 676) 262   Children welcome   Limited parking   Open 11–11 Bedrooms; £25.50S/£40S

CRAYKE (N Yorks)   SE5670   Map 7

Durham Ox

Off B1363 at Brandsby, towards Easingwold

At one end of the old-fashioned lounge bar in this distinctive inn is an enormous inglenook fireplace with winter log fires (flowers in summer); also, antique seats and settles around venerable tables on the flagstoned floor, pictures and old local photographs on its dark green walls, a high shelf of plates and interestingly satirical carvings in its panelling (which are Victorian copies of medievel pew ends), and polished copper and brass. Some of the panelling here divides off a bustling public area with a good lively atmosphere and more old-fashioned furnishings; above the Victorian fire grate is a written account of the local history dating back to the 12th century, and on the opposite wall, a large framed print of the original famous Durham ox; friendly dog and cat. Darts and fruit machine. Bar food includes sandwiches (£1.50, double deckers £2), fresh grilled haddock (£3.75), lasagne (£3.80), curry (£4.25), gammon (£5.25), chicken breast with stilton (£6.20), and puddings (£1.75). Well kept Tetleys and Theakstons Best, XB and Old Peculier on handpump. The tale is that this is the hill which the Grand Old Duke of York marched his men up; the view from the hill opposite is wonderful. *(Recommended by Anthony Barnes, Roger Bellingham, Tim and Sue Halstead, Mary and Lionel Tonks, Simon J Barber, Virginia Jones, JM, PM; more reports please)*

Free house   Licensee Ian Chadwick   Real ale   Meals and snacks   Restaurant Easingwold (0347) 21506   Children in restaurant and eating area of bar   Open 12–3, 7–11   Bedrooms; £20/£30

EAST WITTON (N Yorks)   SE1586   Map 10

Blue Lion ♦

A6108 Leyburn–Ripon

Dropping in on the off-chance to see what had happened to what used to be a remarkably preserved unspoilt little tavern until it closed on the death of its landlady a couple of years ago, we were delighted to find that it's been transformed into a stylish and civilised dining pub while losing none of its distinctive character. The partition making a narrow entrance hall has been taken down, giving one big squarish room. But the ham-hooks in the high ceiling are still there (decorated now with dried wheat, teazles and so forth), as are the high-backed antique settles (joined now by old Windsor chairs and round tables), the flagstones have been softened by Turkey rugs, the delft shelf has been filled with appropriate bric-a-brac, and the walls have been sensitively decorated with a couple of prints of the Battle of Omdurman, hunting prints, sporting caricatures and other pictures. Besides sandwiches and soup (£1.75), a wide choice of enterprising home-made bar food might include leeks cooked with local cheese and bacon (£2.55), fresh asparagus (£2.75), salmon ravioli (£2.95), tagliatelle (£4.25), chargrilled herring or pork and sage meatballs (£4.50), grilled turbot or salmon stuffed with spinach in dill sauce (£5.25), wild boar (£7.95) and steaks (from £7.95). Well kept Theakstons Best, XB and Old Peculier and Youngers Scotch on handpump, decent wines, country wines (try sparkling gooseberry with a little cassis) and old English liqueurs; log fire, daily papers. Picnic-table sets on the gravel outside look beyond the stone houses on the far side of the village green to Witton Fell. *(Recommended by M J Brooks, Edward Parkinson, Mel Landells)*

Free house   Lease: Paul Klein   Real ale   Meals and snacks   Restaurant (closed Mon)   Wensleydale (0969) 24273   Children welcome   Open 11–3, 6.30–11; 11–11 Sat   Bedrooms; £30B/£50B

nr EAST WITTON (N Yorks)   SE1586 Map 10
Cover Bridge

A6108 a mile N

Very unpretentious and homely, with lots of red-cushioned seats crowded into the friendly little locals' bar on the left – where two elderly housekeepers' chairs share the broad space under a fine arched stone chimney-piece with an old-fashioned grate complete with side kettle-rests; try not to tread on the plump collie cross who may be asleep in the shadows by the serving counter. The room on the right, no bigger, has attractive pews, unusual black cast-iron stools, a piano and a nice Victorian fireplace: it leads out into a biggish rather rough-hewn country garden – a nice spot, by a small river and steep stone bridge, with summer barbecues. Generous bar food includes sandwiches (£1.50), home-made soup (£1.75), ploughman's (£3.50), salads (from £3.50), a special such as mince-filled Yorkshire puddings (£3.95), trout (£4.50), lasagne, steak pie or bacon chop (£4.75), ham and eggs (£6.50) and steaks (from £7.50); well kept Theakstons Best on handpump; darts, dominoes. *(Recommended by Nick and Alison Dowson; more reports please)*

Free house   Licensees Jim and June Carter   Real ale   Meals and snacks (till 10pm; not 25 Dec)   Restaurant   (0969) 23250   Children welcome   Open 10.30am–11pm Bedrooms; £20B/£36B

CROPTON (N Yorks)   SE7588 Map 10
New Inn

Village signposted off A170 E of Pickering

Close to Cawthorn Roman camps and the North Yorkshire Moors National Park, this comfortably modernised village inn brews its own robustly flavoured beer – Two Pints, Special Strong and Sconesby Stout; it is brewed using locally-grown malt barley and uses Kentish hops and natural finings (no added sugar). They also keep Tetleys Bitter on handpump. The airy lounge has an aquarium let into one wall, green plush seats, copper and brassware, and a small open fire; the no smoking family conservatory downstairs has sturdy cast-iron-framed tables and plush seats, and big french windows opening on to a neat terrace and garden with pond. Substantial helpings of good value bar food include lunchtime sandwiches, home-made soup (£1.65), ploughman's (£2.95), steak and mushroom pie, smoked haddock and broccoli, lentil lasagne and vegetarian nut roast (around £4.25), and 9–10oz sirloin steak (£7.50); they start serving early in the evening – popular with older people in the neighbourhood. There's an elegant Victorian-style small restaurant in burgundy plush. Friendly service; darts, dominoes, fruit machine, pool room, and piped music. Comfortable, good value bedrooms. *(Recommended by John and Christine Simpson, Mary and Lionel Tonks, Tim and Lynne Crawford)*

Own brew   Licensee Michael James Lee   Real ale   Meals and snacks   No smoking restaurant   Lastingham (07515) 330   Children in family room and in restaurant Open 11–3, 5.30–11; 12–2.30, 7–11 in winter; closed evening 25 Dec   Bedrooms; £19B/£39B

EGTON BRIDGE (N Yorks)   NZ8105 Map 10
Horse Shoe 🛏

Village signposted from A171 W of Whitby; via Grosmont from A169 S of Whitby

One reader thinks the best way to reach this beautifully placed pub is to park by the Roman Catholic church, walk through the village and cross the River Esk by stepping stones. The bar is furnished with high-backed built-in winged settles, wall seats and spindleback chairs around the modern oak tables, the walls are decorated with a big stuffed trout (caught near here in 1913), a fine old print of a storm off Ramsgate and other pictures, and there's a log fire. Well kept John Smiths, Tetleys and Theakstons on handpump, and a weekly guest beer. Darts, dominoes, cribbage and piped music. Good bar food with daily specials includes home-made soup (£1.70), lunchtime sandwiches (from £1.95), ploughman's (£3.95), vegetable or meaty lasagne (£4.85), home-made steak and kidney pie (£4.95), chicken kiev (£5.35), grilled gammon with egg or pineapple (£5.50), Japanese prawns with garlic dip (£5.95), and steaks (from £8.20); children's dishes (£2.50). On a quiet terrace and lawn beside a little stream with ducks and geese are some comfortable seats, and a footbridge leads to the tree-sheltered residents' lawn which runs down to the river. (*Recommended by Ian and Susan Brocklebank, Mary and Lionel Tonks, J S M Whitaker, C J McFeeters, Mike and Wendy Proctor; more reports please*)

Free house   Licensees David and Judith Mullins   Real ale   Meals and snacks (not 25 Dec)   Restaurant   Whitby (0947) 85245   Children in eating area of bar   Open 11.30–3.30, 6.30–11; closed evening 25 Dec   Bedrooms; £26(£28B)/£36(£42B)

Postgate 🖛

Village signposted from A171 W of Whitby; via Grosmont from A169 S of Whitby

This friendly pub is named after Father Nicholas Postgate, hanged, drawn and quartered at York 300 years ago for baptising a child into the Roman Catholic Church. The well kept and carpeted lounge bar has upholstered modern settles and seats in a sunny window, Windsor chairs, a high shelf of cups and bottles, and an open fire. Good, home-made food from the daily changing menu might include sandwiches, liver and onion casserole (£3.75), steak and mushroom pie (£4.25), rabbit pie (£4.50), 16oz sirloin steak (£7.70), and home-made puddings. Camerons Lion and Strongarm, Courage Directors and Tolly Cobbold on handpump. The public bar has darts (one ladies' team as well as three men's), dominoes (Monday evening), cribbage, and trivia. Seats and big umbrellas on a sunny flagstoned terrace look down the hill – this steep twisty valley of the lovely River Esk is one of the prettiest parts of the moors. Salmon or trout fishing can be arranged, as can boat fishing. (*Recommended by Peter Burton, David and Rebecca Killick, Paul McPherson; more reports please*)

Camerons   Lease: David Mead   Real ale   Meals and snacks   Restaurant   Whitby (0947) 85241   Children welcome   Occasional folk nights for charity   Open 11–11; 11–3, 6–11 in winter   Bedrooms; £18/£30

ELSLACK (N Yorks)   SD9249   Map 7
Tempest Arms

Just off A56 Earby–Skipton; visible from main road, and warning signs ¹/₄ mile before

The licensee of this eighteeenth-century pub flies the English flag, the Union Jack, the French tricolour, and the EEC flag. The many tables are spread carefully through a series of quietly decorated areas and there are small chintz armchairs, chintzy cushions on the comfortable built-in wall seats, quite a bit of stripped stonework, and a log fire in the dividing fireplace. Using fresh produce, the bar food includes home-made soup (£1.60), sandwiches (from £2.25, 6oz steak £4.25), chicken liver and duck pâté (£2.95), home-cured gravadlax (£3.75), vegetarian dishes (£4), lamb's liver with a Dubonnet sauce (£4.30), cold seafood platter (£5), fresh fish dishes, prize-winning black pudding with mustard and apple purée (£5.25), home-made steak, kidney and mushroom pie (£5.60), and sirloin steak (£7.75); cheerful and helpful staff. Well kept Tetleys Mild and Bitter, Thwaites Bitter and Youngers Scotch on handpump, good French house wines by the glass or bottle, and malt whiskies; darts, dominoes, fruit machine and piped music. Tables outside are largely screened from the road by a raised bank. (*Recommended by Greg Turner, J Fenlon, Charles and Dorothy Ellsworth, Syd and Wyn Donald, I H Rorison, Keith Croston, Geoff and Julie Bond, Roy and Nicola Boyne, WAH, Len Beattie, Bev and Doug Warrick, Dr Thomas Mackenzie, Ben Wimpenny; more reports please)*

Free house   Licensee Francis Boulongne   Real ale   Meals and snacks (11.30–2.15, 6.30–10)   Restaurant   Earby (0282) 842450   Children welcome until 8.30pm Open 11.30–3, 6.30(7 Sat)–11; closed evening 25 Dec   Bedrooms; £39.50B/£47B

GOOSE EYE (W Yorks)   SE0340 Map 7

Turkey

High back road Haworth–Sutton-in-Craven, and signposted from back roads W of Keighley; OS Sheet 104, map reference 028406

Interestingly placed in an ex-milling village at the bottom of a steep valley, this friendly, cosy pub has various refurbished snug alcoves with brocaded upholstery, and walls covered with pictures of surrounding areas. Generous helpings of value-for-money food include winter soup, sandwiches, cheese and onion quiche (£3.40), fillet of breaded haddock (£3.60), chicken breast (£4), steaks (from £5.20; 32oz £13), daily specials like filled Yorkshire puddings (from £3) or chilli con carne (£3.50), and puddings (from £1.40). Tetleys, Ind Coope Burton and Gooseye Bitter (brewed by a local man) on handpump. A separate games area has darts, dominoes, fruit machine, trivia, and juke box. *(Recommended by Peter Race, W A Harbottle, H K Dyson, Andy and Jill Kassube, Stephen Blencowe)*

Free house   Licensee Harry Brisland   Real ale   Meals and snacks (not Mon evening) (0535) 681339   Children in eating area of bar   Open 12–3, 5.30–11; 12–5, 7–11 Sat; closed Monday evening

HARDEN (W Yorks)   SE0838 Map 7

Malt Shovel

Follow Wilsden signpost from B6429

This handsome dark stone building is in a lovely spot by a bridge over Harden Beck and the big garden is open to the public. The three rooms (two small and one with oak-panelling, a beamed ceiling, and an open fire) are spotlessly clean and carefully kept, with red plush seats built into the walls, kettles, brass funnels and the like hanging from the black beams, horsebrasses on leather harness, and stone-mullioned windows; one room is no smoking at lunchtime. Simple bar food includes sandwiches (from £1.20; steak £2.05), ploughman's, giant Yorkshire puddings, and omelettes. Well kept Tetleys Bitter on handpump, and efficient service; dominoes. From the other side of the bridge you can walk upstream beside the river. *(Recommended by W A Harbottle, J E Rycroft, T Nott, Ben Wimpenny, Andy and Jill Kassube, Andrew and Ruth Triggs; more reports please)*

Tetleys (Allied)   Managers David and Dee Biggs   Real ale   Meals and snacks (12–2, 6–8)   (0535) 274724   Children in eating area of bar at lunchtimes only   Occasional ceilidh/folk evenings   Open 12–2.30, 5.30–11; 12–11 Sat

HAROME (N Yorks)   SE6582 Map 10

Star ★

2 miles south of A170, near Helmsley

In a quiet village, this picturesque thatched pub has a friendly atmosphere, cushioned old settles and heavy, deeply polished dark rustic tables on the Turkey carpet, a few ancient bottles and glass net floats hanging from the dark bowed beam-and-plank ceiling, a glass cabinet holding képis, fine china and Japanese dolls, and a copper kettle on the well polished tiled kitchen range (with a ship in a bottle on its mantelpiece); the fox mask with little spectacles and a lacy ruff now also has a pipe. Since our last edition, the chef has moved to the White Swan in Ampleforth and lunchtime home-made bar food here now includes sandwiches (from £2), a daily special (from £4.95), and puddings like bread and butter pudding (£1.95); there's a coffee loft up in the thatch. Well kept Tetleys, Timothy Taylors Landlord and Theakstons Old Peculier on handpump; darts, dominoes, Scrabble, Monopoly, and classical piped music. On a sheltered front flagstoned terrace there are some seats and tables, with more in the garden behind which has an old-fashioned swing seat, fruit trees and a big ash. *(Recommended by Laurence Manning, WAH, Caroline Wright, Peter Race, Andrew Morrissey, John and Christine Simpson, Bob Smith, H K Dyson, David and Ruth Hollands, Mark Porter, W C M Jones, Brian and Anna Marsden, Anthony Sargent, Caroline Gant, Andrew and Ruth Triggs, Anne Marie Stephenson, Fiona Mutch, J P Cinnamond, Margaret and Roy Randle)*

Free house   Licensee T E Blackburn   Real ale   Lunchtime meals and snacks Evening restaurant (they do Sun lunch)   Helmsley (0439) 70397   Children welcome Open 12–3, 6.30–11; closed evening 25 Dec

nr HARROGATE (N Yorks)   SE3155   Map 7
Squinting Cat

Whinney Lane, B6162 W of Harrogate; turn at traffic lights down Pannel Ash Rd; at roundabout near sports centre, bear right along Whinney Lane; pub on left after about ³/₄ mile; OS Sheet 104, map reference 296517

The rambling rooms in the original part of this very popular and friendly eighteenth-century pub have dark oak panelling, beam and plank ceilings, some copper warming pans and horsebrasses, and a stained-glass cat worked into a latticed bow window. The barn-like beamed extension has pine chairs and tables in one part with re-covered armchairs in another, York stone walls (re-fashioned from an old railway bridge) hung with pictures, old grain sacks, barrels, and bottles, and nautical wooden pulley systems radiating out from a minstrel's gallery complete with boat. Bar food includes home-made soups such as stilton and onion (from £1.50), sandwiches (from £2; hot roast beef £3.25), home-made pâtés (from £2.25), winter pies and casseroles, a cold carvery with home-cooked meats (from around £3.75), home-made pasta dishes (£3.95), and curry (£4.25). Well kept Tetleys Mild and Bitter on handpump; attentive service; piped music, dominoes and fruit machine. There are tables outside. The North of England Horticultural Society's fine gardens on the curlew moors at Harlow Car are just over the B6162. *(Recommended by Mr and Mrs C H Garnett, Andy and Jill Kassube, Mr and Mrs B Foggitt, Genie and Brian Smart, H K Dyson, Mike Tucker, Gwen and Peter Andrews, Mary and Lionel Tonks, David and Rebecca Killick, Carol and Richard Glover, Steve and Carolyn Harvey)*

Tetleys (Allied)   Manager David Funnell   Real ale   Meals and snacks   Harrogate (0423) 565650   Children welcome   Occasional jazz   Open 11.30–3, 5.30–11; closed 25 Dec

HATFIELD WOODHOUSE (S Yorks)   SE6808   Map 7
Green Tree

1 mile from M18 junction 5: on A18/A614 towards Bawtry

Even when this neatly kept old pub is busy, there's plenty of space in the comfortably modernised series of connecting open-plan rooms and alcoves: brown leatherette seats and Windsor chairs around the tables, an expanse of Turkey carpet, fresh flowers and a warm atmosphere. Good, reasonably priced bar food includes soup (£1.10), sandwiches (from £1.25; the open-prawn is recommended, £3.20), very good ploughman's (£2.75), home-made steak and kidney pie (£3.60), salads (from £3.60), fresh haddock or plaice from Grimsby (from £3.75), broccoli and cream cheese pie (£3.90), grilled gammon (£3.95), steaks (from £4.65), and puddings like home-made fruit pie (£1.40); carvery (Tuesday to Friday £4.25) and Sunday lunch; you can eat in the garden. Well kept Darleys and Vaux Samson on handpump; prompt service; piped music. *(Recommended by ILP, Dr K Bloomfield, T Nott, Genie and Brian Smart; more reports please)*

Wards (Vaux)   Tenant Trevor Hagan   Real ale   Meals and snacks (12–2.30, 6.30–10; not 25 Dec)˜ Restaurant (evenings and Sun lunch)   Doncaster (0302) 840305   Children in eating area of bar   Open 11–3, 6–11   Bedrooms; £25S/£35S

HEATH (W Yorks)   SE3519   Map 7
Kings Arms

Village signposted from A655 Wakefield–Normanton – or, more directly, turn off to the left opposite Horse & Groom

It's hard to believe that this characterful old pub is in the industrial heartland of West Yorkshire. The dark-panelled original bar has a fire burning in the old black range (with a long row of smoothing irons on the mantlepiece), plain elm stools and oak settles built into the walls, some heavy cast-iron-framed tables on the flagstones, and a built-in cupboard of cut glass. A more comfortable extension (with a fitted red carpet, even) has carefully preserved the original style, down to good walnut-pegged oak panelling (two embossed with royal arms), and a high shelf of plates; there are also two other small flagstoned rooms and another with its own bar. Good bar food includes Yorkshire pudding and gravy (£1.20), sandwiches (from £1.25, the ham is good), soup (£1.40), excellent cheese and pickle platter (£2.50), omelettes (from £2.75), salads (from £3), beef pie or vegetarian bake (£3.25), daily specials like Somerset beef (£3.50), home-made puddings (from £1.50); the tables are cleared and cleaned promptly. As well as Clarks Bitter and Hammerhead, they also serve guests like Tetleys Bitter and Timothy Taylors Landlord on handpump, and tea or coffee; dominoes, and Tuesday evening quizzes. Picnic table-sets along the front of the pub face the village green and there are several more on a side lawn. *(Recommended by Andy and Jill Kassube, T Nott, Dave and Carole Jones, Ian Robinson, Anthony Barnes, Frank Cummins, Roger Huggins, G R Prest, Maureen and Steve Collin, Michael Rooke)*

Clarks   Manager John Radley   Real ale   Meals and snacks (not Sun or Mon evenings)   Gas-lit restaurant (not Sun evening)   Wakefield (0924) 377527   Children in eating area of bar until 8.30   Occasional Morris Dancers   Open 11.30–3, 6–11; closed evening 25 Dec

HECKMONDWIKE (W Yorks)   SE2223   Map 7
Old Hall

New North Road; B6117 between A62 and A638; OS Sheet 104, map reference 214244

By an open space above the town and dating back to 1470, this fine old manor house has been thoughtfully restored. The walls are brick or stripped old stone (with pictures of Richard III, Henry VII, Katherine Parr and Priestley), there are lots of oak beams and timbers, and latticed mullioned windows with worn stone surrounds. Snug low-ceilinged alcoves lead off the central part with its high ornate plaster ceiling, and an upper gallery room, under the pitched roof, looks down on the main area through timbering "windows". Comfortable furnishings include cushioned oak pews and red plush seats, some with oak backs, on a sweep of Turkey carpet (there are flagstones by the serving counter). Good waitress-served bar food includes sandwiches (from £1.30), soup (£1.35), pâté (£1.55), scampi (£3.60), steaks (from £7.15), and daily specials like filled Yorkshire pudding or lasagne (from £3.45); nice puddings. Well kept Sam Smiths OB on handpump; unobtrusive piped music, Tuesday evening music quiz, and Thursday evening general knowledge quiz. This was once the home of the Nonconformist scientist Joseph Priestley. *(Recommended by Roger Bellingham, Andy and Jill Kassube, H K Dyson, Anthony Barnes, Mr and Mrs B Hobden, T Nott, Ben Wimpenny, Mary and Lionel Tonks)*

Sam Smiths   Manager Thomas Hancock   Real ale   Meals and snacks   York (0924) 404774   Children in separate area of bar   Open 11–2.30, 6–11; will stay open longer in afternoon if trade demands

HELMSLEY (N Yorks)   SE6184   Map 10
Feathers

Market Square

Though the main inn (with its own comfortable lounge bar) is a handsomely solid 3-storey stone block, the adjoining, atmospheric pub part is much lower and a

3-storey stone block, the adjoining, atmospheric pub part is much lower and a good deal older, with heavy medieval beams and dark panelling, unusual cast-iron-framed tables topped by weighty slabs of oak and walnut, a venerable wall carving of a dragon-faced bird in a grape vine, and a big log fire in the stone inglenook fireplace. Good value, well prepared bar food includes soup (£1.50), sandwiches (from £1.65), ploughman's (£2.50), sausage and egg (£2.65), good garlic mushrooms (£2.70), home-made quiche or lasagne (£4.25), salads (from £4.75), fresh Scarborough haddock in batter (£4.95), home-made steak pie (£5), gammon with egg or pineapple (£5.75), steaks (£8.95), daily specials such as Cumberland sausage (£4.25), sweet and sour prawns (£5), and roast duckling (£7.50), and puddings. Well kept Tetleys and Theakstons Best and Old Peculier on handpump, large choice of wines chalked on a blackboard, and some malt whiskies. Darts, dominoes, fruit machine, and piped music. There's an attractive back garden. Rievaulx Abbey (well worth an hour's visit) is close by. *(Recommended by WAH, Mrs S Mills, Greg Turner, Derek Patey, John and Helen Thompson, K J Betts, Mark Porter, Sidney and Erna Wells, H K Dyson, Peter Race, Sue Corrigan, Tim and Lynne Crawford, Tim Locke, Barbara and Norman Wells)*

Free house   Licensee Jack Feather   Real ale   Meals and snacks   Restaurant (not Sun evening)   Helmsley (0439) 70275   Children in eating area of bar but in small lounge between bars when busy   Open 10.30–2.30, 6–11; 10.30–11 Fri and summer Sats; closed 25 Dec   Bedrooms; £22(£26.50B)/£44(£53B)

HETTON (N Yorks)   SD9558   Map 7

Angel ★ ⊘

Just off B6265 Skipton–Grassington

The consistently good and imaginatively presented food here continues to delight readers. And despite the efforts of the very friendly, hard-working uniformed staff, this means that unless you arrive early you may have a long wait ahead of you. Dishes might include home-made soup with croûtons (£1.95) or terrific provençal fish soup with aioli (£2.45, lunchtime sandwiches, farmhouse cheeses (£2.75), fresh spinach noodles in a garlic and basil sauce and fresh parmesan (starter £2.95, main course £4.85), smoked fish platter (starter £3.80, main course £6.50), their own home-cured and air dried beef (£3.95), fillet of baby cod with bearnaise sauce (£4.50), avocado and smoked chicken salad (£4.85), brochette of pork (£5.25), breast of chicken stuffed with prawns and smoky bacon (£5.85), calves' liver with a Dubonnet sauce (£7.75), and very good puddings like crème brûlée, sticky toffee pudding or summer pudding (from £2.75); also, daily fresh fish specials such as scallops baked with garlic and gruyere cheese (starter £3.85, main course £5.25), popular hot, poached salmon (£5.95), their award-winning fisherman's pot with five Mediterranean fish (£8.95), and superb seafood platter (£13.95). Well kept Theakstons Bitter and XB, Timothy Taylors Landlord, and Youngers Scotch on handpump, a decent choice of wines by the glass or bottle (chalked up on a blackboard, and often bin-ends), and quite a few malt whiskies. The four rambling rooms have lots of cosy alcoves, comfortable country-kitchen chairs or button-back green plush seats, Ronald Searle wine snob cartoons and older engravings and photographs, standing timbers and panelling, and some beams; there are log fires, a solid fuel stove, and in the main bar a Victorian farmhouse range in the big stone fireplace. Darts and dominoes. Sturdy wooden benches and tables are built on to the cobbles outside this pretty house. *(Recommended by Paul and Janet Waring, Wyn and Syd Donald, Alan and Lesley Holden, Viv Middlebrook, E A George, Mr and Mrs C W Rudman, Michael and Joan Melling, Paul S McPherson, Tim and Sue Halstead, Ray and Gwen Jessop, Geoff and Julie Bond, Olive Carroll, Peter Burton, Len Beattie, G D Collier, Margaret White, Mr and Mrs M Cockram, J E Rycroft, Gwen and Peter Andrews, Neville Kenyon, Olive Carroll)*

Free house   Licensee Denis Watkins   Real ale   Meals and snacks (till 10pm)   Partly no smoking restaurant   Cracoe (075 673) 263; not Sun evening   Children welcome Open 12–2.30, 6–10.30 (till 11 Fri and Sat); closed evenings 25 and 26 Dec and 1 Jan

HUBBERHOLME (N Yorks)   SD9178   Map 7

George ★

Village signposted from Buckden; about 1 mile NW

This was J B Priestley's favourite pub and the two small and well kept flagstoned bar-rooms (refurbished this year) have dark ceiling-boards supported by heavy beams, walls stripped back to bare stone and hung with antique plates, seats (with covers to match the curtains) around shiny copper-topped tables, and an open stove in the big fireplace. The dining room is no smoking. Hearty helpings of food for the cheerful walkers who crowd in at lunchtime include soup, delicious hefty warm rolls filled with big slices of juicy fresh ham, cheese or bacon (around £2.20), pâté (£2.60), steak and kidney or turkey and mushroom pies with lovely crusts (£4), and evening dishes like salmon in asparagus sauce or venison in red wine and port sauce (£7.50), steaks, and a 1 *SIZE*6¹/₂lb barnsley chop (£8). Very well kept Youngers Scotch and No 3 on handpump, 20 malt whiskies, and quite a few wines; darts, dominoes and cribbage. The inn looks out on a lovely swirly stretch of the River Wharfe where they have fishing rights; they still let riverside land in aid of a church charity, and when they do (on the first Monday of the New Year), there's a licensing extension till nearly midnight. Seats and tables look up to the moors which rise all around. *(Recommended by G T Jones, P R Morley, Jim and Maggie Cowell, Carol and Richard Glover, Paul Perry, Andy and Jill Kassube, Paul S McPherson, Neil and Angela Huxter, Phil Clissitt, Ness Turner, J White, Theo Schofield, Mary and Lionel Tonks, Gwen and Peter Andrews, Helen and Wal Burns, Lynne Sheridan, Bob West, Ian Whitlock, J E Rycroft, J and K O'Malley, Mr and Mrs K H Frostick)*

Free house   Licensees John Fredrick and Mrs Marjorie Forster   Real ale   Meals and snacks   Kettlewell (075 676) 223   Children in eating area of bar   Open 11.30–3, 7(6.30 Sat)–11; closed evening 25 Dec   Bedrooms; £36

KILBURN (N Yorks)   SE5179   Map 7

Forresters Arms 🛏

Signposted from A170 E of Thirsk

Most of the sturdy yet elegant furniture (usually oak) in this ex-coaching inn has the trademark little carved mouse sitting, standing or running in some discreet corner of the piece – the Thompson furniture workshop is next door. That's also the source of the fine bar counter and the great slab shelf along the wall of the inner room – lights beneath it throw the stripped stonework into striking relief. This inner room has tables for people eating; the smaller outer bar's chairs are much more for sitting and chatting by the log fire in its unusual rounded stone chimney-breast. Well kept John Smiths and Tetleys Bitter on handpump, coffee and tea, and popular bar food that includes sandwiches (from £1.15), home-made soup (£1.30), ploughman's (£2.85), vegetable grill (£3.10), chicken curry or battered haddock (£3.95), home-made steak and kidney pie (£4.40), gammon steak (£4.75), steaks (from £6.95), puddings (£1.60), and children's meals (£2.05). Darts, cribbage, dominoes, fruit machine, video game and piped music. White tables on the terrace in front of this stone and brick building look across to pretty village gardens, which are interspersed with planked oak trunks weathering for the furniture workshop. Dogs welcome (James Herriot is in fact their vet). *(Recommended by H K Dyson, Stephanie Sowerby, N S and J Dury, N P Hodgson, Andrew and Ruth Triggs, G Dobson, Jenny Cantle; more reports please)*

Free house   Licensee Peter Cussons   Real ale   Meals and snacks   Restaurant   Coxwold (03476) 386   Children welcome   Open 11–11   Bedrooms; £32B/£46B

KIRBY HILL (N Yorks)   NZ1406   Map 10

Shoulder of Mutton

Signposted from Ravensworth road about 3 ¹/₂ miles N of Richmond; or from A66 Scotch Corner–Brough turn off into Ravensworth, bear left through village, and take signposted right turn nearly a mile further on

The licensees who have taken over this friendly pub since our last edition have refurbished the bedrooms and front bar and have opened a stone archway between the lounge and public bar: plush wall settles around simple dark tables, local turn-of-the-century photographs of Richmond, and an open stone fireplace. Decent bar food includes lunchtime sandwiches (from £1.20), lasagne or steak and mushroom pie (£3.60), haddock (£4.10), panfried trout (£4.95), crispy roast duck (£6.95), and steaks; good, ubobtrusive service. Well kept John Smiths, Ruddles County, Theakstons Best and Websters Choice on handpump; darts, dominoes, fruit machine around the back, and piped music. The yard behind has picnic-table sets and fine views. The church clock opposite has an unusually tuneful bell. *(Recommended by H S Harries, Mr and Mrs Bill Muirhead, Mrs R Heaton; more reports please)*

Free house   Licensee Geoffrey Gore   Real ale   Meals and snacks (not Mon lunchtime)   Restaurant   Richmond (0748) 82772   Children in eating area of bar until 8.30pm   Sing-along Mon evening   Open 12–3, 7–11; closed Mon lunchtime Bedrooms; £25(£25B)/£33(£39B)

LANGTHWAITE (N Yorks)   NZ0003 Map 10
Red Lion

Just off the Arkengarthdale road from Reeth to Brough

This homely and unpretentious little pub is in a delightful spot – footpaths from here thread their way along the Arkle beck and up the moors on either side. It's kept spick and span, and has comfortably cushioned wall seats, flowery curtains, a few decorative plates on a delft shelf, a fox mask, and a beam-and-plank ceiling (if you think that one's low, try the burrow-like side snug). They also have carved horn beakers, signed copies of books by Herriot (the BBC filmed the bar for an episode in the *All Creatures Great and Small* series) and Wainwright, Ordnance Survey maps, and local paintings and books on the Dales for sale; this is one of the few places where you can buy the Hill Shepherd book by the Forders; dominoes. Bar food, country wines and Merrydown cider, tea and coffee. There are some picnic-table sets out in the tiny village square. *(Recommended by Paul S McPherson, J A Snell, Mr and Mrs R Clifford, Gordon Theaker, Mrs R Heaton, Anthony Barnes)*

Free house   Licensee Mrs Rowena Hutchinson   Lunchtime meals and snacks (not 25 Dec)   Well behaved children in snug at lunchtime   Open 10.30–3, 6.30(7 in winter)–11

LASTINGHAM (N Yorks)   SE7391 Map 10
Blacksmiths Arms

Off A170 W of Pickering at Wrelton, forking off Rosedale rd N of Cropton; or via Appleton and Spaunton; or via Hutton-le-Hole

The countryside all around this cosy little village pub is lovely and there are tracks through Cropton Forest. Inside, the comfortable bar has cushioned Windsor chairs and traditional built-in wooden wall seats, an attractive cooking range with swinging pot-yards, some sparkling brass, oak beams, and a good winter fire; piped music. Bar food includes sandwiches, popular filled Yorkshire puddings (from £2.95), steak and kidney pie (£3.95), vegetarian dishes, and steaks. A simply furnished dining area opens off the main bar, and serves traditional Sunday roasts. Well kept Ruddles Best and County, Websters Yorkshire and two weekly guests on handpump; good range of malt whiskies. They've converted part of the cellar into a new pool and games room: darts, dominoes, and fruit machine. Good wheelchair access. *(Recommended by H K Dyson, John and Christine Simpson, Andy and Jill Kassube, Eileen Broadbent, Tim and Lynne Crawford)*

Free house   Licensees Mike and Sheila Frost   Real ale   Meals and snacks (served all the time they are open)   Restaurant   Lastingham (075 15) 247   Children in eating area of bar   Open 11–11   Bedrooms; £16.50/£33

LEDSHAM (W Yorks)   SE4529   Map 7
Chequers
A mile off A1 N of Pontefract

Small, individually decorated rooms in this smart but busy creeper-covered village pub open off an old-fashioned little central panelled-in servery and have low beams, lots of cosy alcoves, and log fires. Decent, nicely presented bar food includes soup (£1.05), sandwiches (from £1.60; steak £3.25), ploughman's with two cheeses and an apple (£2.75), tasty scrambled eggs and smoked salmon (£3.25), lasagne (£3.60), gammon and eggs (£4.70). Well kept John Smiths, Theakstons Best and Youngers Scotch and No 3 on handpump; dominoes. A sheltered two-level terrace behind the house has tables among roses and is popular with families and their dogs. *(Recommended by Mrs M Inman, Syd and Wyn Donald, Andy and Jill Kassube, Brian Jones, J D Andrews, Ben Wimpenny, Tim and Sue Halstead, Dr and Mrs Frank Rackow, Mike and Wendy Proctor)*

Free house   Licensee Chris Wraith   Real ale   Meals and evening snacks Restaurant   (0977) 683135   Children in eating area of bar lunchtime and early evening   Open 11–3, 5.30–11; 11–11 Sat; closed Sun

LEEDS (W Yorks)   SE3033   Map 7
Garden Gate ★ £
37 Waterloo Road, Hunslet; leaving Leeds centre on A61, turn right at traffic lights signpost 'Hunslet Centre P, Belle Isle 1 1/2, Middleton 3', take first right into Whitfield Way, first left into Whitfield Drive, then first right and park at rear of pub

Four old-fashioned rooms in this handsome, marvellously preserved Victorian building are linked by a high cool corridor with a tiled floor, deep-cut glass, and mahogany panelling. The finest, on the left as you enter, has a mosaic floor and a lovely free-flowing design of tiles coloured in subtle tones of buff, cream and icy green: the bar counter itself, the front of which is made from elaborately shaped and bowed tiles, has hatch service to the corridor too. Perfectly kept Tetleys Bitter and Mild on handpump – the brewery is just up the Hunslet Road; farm cider. Sandwiches (from 70p), snacks (from £1.50), lasagne or Yorkshire pudding filled with savoury mince (£2.50), and roasts (from £2.75); pleasant staff; darts, pool, dominoes (very popular here), cribbage, fruit machine and juke box. It's very much a working men's pub and is surrounded by a modern development. *(Recommended by Pete Storey, Andy and Jill Kassube, Mr and Mrs Simon Turner, Tim Halstead, Matt Pringle; more reports please)*

Tetleys (Allied)   Tenant B Baraud   Real ale   Snacks (served all day)   (0532) 700379   Children in lounge and games room   Open 11–11

Whitelocks ★ £
Turks Head Yard; gunnel (or alley) off Briggate, opposite Debenhams and Littlewoods, park in shoppers' car park and walk

Hardly changed since 1886, this bustling and splendidly preserved city-centre tavern has a long, narrow and wonderfully atmospheric old-fashioned bar. The fine bar counter is decorated with polychrome tiles, and there are stained-glass windows and grand advertising mirrors, with red button-back plush banquettes and heavy copper-topped cast-iron tables squeezed down one side. Good, reasonably priced lunchtime bar food includes bubble and squeak (60p), sausages (65p), home-made Scotch eggs (70p), sandwiches or Yorkshire puddings (£1), home-made quiche (£1.20), very good meat and potato pie (£2), and jam roly poly or fruit pie (75p); when it gets busy you may have to wait for your order, though the staff are very cheerful and pleasant. Well kept McEwans 80/- and Youngers IPA, Scotch and No 3 on handpump; quiz evenings every Tuesday in top bar. At the end of the long narrow yard another bar has been done up in Dickensian style. *(Recommended by Andrew Roberts, Dr M A Thomas, Andy and Jill Kassube, John Thorndike, Reg Nelson, Pete Storey, J E Rycroft, Mr and Mrs Fraser, Virginia Jones, Drs M and K Parier, Ben Wimpenny, Michael Rooke)*

Youngers (S & N)   Manager Julie Cliff   Real ale   Meals and snacks (11–7.30; not Sun evening)   Restaurant   Leeds (0532) 453950; not Sun evening   Children in restaurant   Open 11–11

LEVISHAM (N Yorks)   SE8391 Map 10
Horseshoe

Pub and village signposted from A169 N of Pickering

Families, plentiful dog owners and walkers crowd here on warm days to enjoy meals served at the picnic tables on the attractive village green. Inside this well kept and friendly pub the refurbished bars have brocaded seats, a log fire in the stone fireplace, and bar billiards, dominoes and piped music. Popular bar food includes soup (£1.45), sandwiches (from £1.60), ploughman's (£3.05), salads (from £3.60), steak and kidney pie or fresh Whitby haddock (£4.15), chicken curry (£4.35), tasty gammon and egg (£4.70), good fresh local trout (£5.45), steaks (from £5.80), puddings (£1.95), and children's menu (£1.95). Well kept Malton, Tetleys Bitter, Theakstons Best and guest beers on handpump, a good range of malt whiskies, wines by the glass, and coffee; service is pleasant, quick and efficient. Three to five times a day in spring and autumn, and seven times in summer, two steam trains of the North Yorks Moors Railway stop at this village. *(Recommended by N H White, Tim and Sue Halstead, Anthony Sargent, Caroline Gant, A M Neal, John and Christine Simpson, Eleanor Wallis, Walter and Susan Rinaldi-Butcher)*

Free house   Licensees Roy and Marjorie Hayton   Real ale   Meals and snacks Restaurant   Pickering (0751) 60240   Children in eating area of bar   Open 11–3, 6–11   Bedrooms; £20/£40B

LEYBURN (N Yorks)   SE1191 Map 10
Sandpiper

Market Place – bottom end

Clear of the main bustle, this pretty little stone cottage with white cast-iron tables among the honeysuckle, climbing roses, cotoneaster and so forth on the front terrace certainly lives up to its promise inside. The very neatly kept low-beamed bar just has seven tables, even including the back room up three steps – where you'll find attractive Dales photographs, toby jugs on a delft shelf, and a collection of curious teapots. Down by the servery there are stuffed sandpipers, more photographs and a woodburning stove in the stone fireplace. There's also a neat dining area on the left: food includes soups such as watercress (£1.50), sandwiches (£1.50), home-made chicken liver and pork pâté (£2.75), haddock (£3), chicken nuggets (£3.50), a choice of ploughman's (£3.25) and meat salads (£3.75), with dishes of the day such as big filled Yorkshire puddings (£3.50) and braised liver and onions (£3.75), and evening dishes such as beef curry (£6.25), gammon and egg or salmon (£6.95) and steaks (from £8); roast sirloin of beef Sunday lunchtimes. Well kept Theakstons Best and Websters Yorkshire on handpump, with Ruddles Best kept under light blanket pressure; around 60 malt whiskies, bin-end wines, friendly service, maybe a friendly pub dog. There are more tables in the back garden. *(Recommended by B and J Derry, Mr and Mrs D C Leaman, Mr and Mrs R Clifford)*

Free house   Licensees Peter and Beryl Swan   Real ale   Meals and snacks (not Sun evening or all day Mon in winter)   Evening restaurant   Wensleydale (0969) 22206 Children in snug if well behaved   Open 11–2.30(3 Fri and Sat), 6.30–11; closed Sun evening and all day Mon in winter

LINTHWAITE (W Yorks)   SE1014 Map 7
Bulls Head ⊘

31 Blackmoorfoot; from A32 Huddersfield–Marsden turn off opp Coach & Horses – road leads straight up to pub; or from Marsden turn off B6107 towards Blackmoorfoot

Popular with locals, cyclists and walkers, this cheerful, dark stone pub serves very fairly priced, imaginative food; changing from day to day, this might include sandwiches (the Yorkshire pudding one is delicious), baked avocado with sherry and Brazil nut stuffing or upside-down vegetable cake (£3.50), black pudding and apple tartlet with wholegrain mustard sauce or baked peppers stuffed with cauliflower cheese and ham (£3.75), punjabi baked cod with ginger and chilli or baboutie (African spiced meat loaf with apple, apricot and nuts, £3.90), and Thai-style beef curry with oranges and cashews or tagliatelle with prawns in lemon and vodka sauce (£4); quick, efficient service. Mondays is their steak 'n' bake night (now copied by several dozen other pubs in the area). Well kept Boddingtons Bitter and Mild and Stones on handpump, and quite a few malt whiskies. The two unassuming communicating rooms are furnished with sturdy brown-plush-upholstered wall benches and stools around cast-iron-framed tables; the room on the right has Victorian-style wallpaper and a Victorian fireplace, and the one on the left has views from its back windows over Linthwaite to the moors beyond, and a stone fireplace. Well reproduced, unobtrusive piped music, and fruit machine. There are picnic-table sets in front of the dark stone pub. *(Recommended by Roy Cove, Frank Cummins, Mr and Mrs R Clifford, H K Dyson, Robert and Lesley Fawthrop, Robert Gartery, Dave and Carole Jones, Barbara and Mike Williams, T Nott, Neville Kenyon, Ben Wimpenny)*

Free house Licensees Stephen and Brenda Head Real ale Meals and snacks (all day Mon-Fri; 11–3, 6.30–10 Sat) (0484) 842715 Children in eating area of bar till 8pm Open 11–11; 11–4, 6.30–11 Sat

Sair

Hoyle Ing, off A62; as you leave Huddersfield this is one of the only left turns in Linthwaite, and the street name is marked, but keep your eyes skinned for it – it burrows very steeply up between works buildings; OS Sheet 110, map reference 101143

There's a happy, chatty atmosphere in the quaint cluster of rooms in this breezily rough-and-ready pub: pews or smaller chairs, bottle collections, beermats tacked to beams, rough flagstones in some parts and carpet in others, and several big stone fireplaces. The remarkable range of very well kept, home-brewed ales includes the pleasant and well balanced Linfit Bitter, Mild and Special, Old Eli, Leadboiler, a Christmas Ale that has a habit of turning up at the most unseasonable times and the redoubtable Enochs Hammer. There's even stout (English Guineas), a Hoyleingerbrau lager, a low-alcohol real ale, and a cider called Causeway Sider; they may provide lunchtime sandwiches. The room on the right has darts, shove-ha'penny and dominoes. There's a half-timbered cat mansion for the four cats with lots of rooms and toy mice and birds. The view down the Colne Valley is very striking. *(Recommended by H K Dyson, Andy and Jill Kassube, M J Cochrane, Andrew Roberts, P Corris, Matt Pringle, Ben Wimpenny, Maureen and Steve Collin, Michael Rooke)*

Own brew Licensee Ron Crabtree Real ale Children in three rooms away from the bar Open 7–11 only on weekdays, 12–4 too Sat and bank hols; otherwise closed weekday lunchtimes

LITTON (N Yorks) SD9074 Map 7

Queens Arms 🏠

From B6160 N of Grassington, after Kilnsey take second left fork; can also be reached off B6479 at Stainforth N of Settle, via Halton Gill

Some changes to this friendly seventeenth-century inn this year include extending the restaurant and the addition of bathrooms to some bedrooms. The choice of reasonably priced bar food has been widened too: lunchtime sandwiches (from £1.60) or ploughman's (£2.85), pork sausage and gravy (£2.95), broccoli and cheese bake (£3.65), home-made chicken and mushroom or rabbit pies (£3.95), gammon and egg (£4.20), cold ham or beef and pickle (£4.25), and sirloin steak (£8.50), with evening extras such as home-made soup (£1.35), crevettes (£3.50), and a massive grill (£10.50); good breakfasts. Well kept Youngers Scotch on handpump, tea, coffee and hot chocolate. The main bar on the right has stools around cast-iron-framed tables on its stone and concrete floor, a seat built into the stone-mullioned window, a large collection of cigarette lighters, a brown beam-and-plank ceiling, stripped rough stone walls, and a good coal fire. On the left, the red-carpeted room has another coal fire and more of a family atmosphere with varnished pine for its built-in wall seats, and for the ceiling and walls themselves; darts, dominoes, shove-ha'penny, cribbage, and piped music. A track behind the inn leads over Ackerley Moor to Buckden and the quiet lane through the valley leads on to Pen-y-ghent. *(Recommended by Phillipa and Andrew Williams, George Hunt, Kathryn Ogden, P R Morley, Andy and Jill Kassube, Robert and Vicky Tod, Ruth Humphrey, Major E G Cox, TRA, MA, Roger Etherington, P Corris, A M Neal, Tim and Sue Halstead, Neil and Angela Huxter)*

Free house   Licensees Eric and Kaye Davidson   Real ale   Meals and snacks (11–3, 7–11)   Arncliffe (0756) 77208   Children welcome   Open 11–3, 7–11; usually all day Sat; closed Mon evening in winter   Bedrooms; £18/£32(£39B)

MASHAM (N Yorks)   SE2381 Map 10

Kings Head 🛏

Market Square

This is a lovely village and the tall handsome stone inn faces the broad partly tree-shaded market square. The two opened-up rooms of the neatly kept, spacious lounge bar have green plush seats around heavy cast-iron-framed tables on the patterned carpet, a big War Department issue clock over the imposing slate and marble fireplace, which is decorated with four tall brass coffee-pots (usefully, they serve coffee before the bar opens), a dark green ceiling, and a high shelf of Staffordshire and other figurines. Home-made bar food includes sandwiches (lunchtime) or home-made soup (from £1.10), Yorkshire pudding with onion gravy (£1.25), ploughman's or vegetarian dish of the day (£2.95), steak and kidney (£3.25), Old Peculier casserole (£3.50), chicken kiev (£3.65), and daily specials like curries, rice and pasta dishes. Well kept Theakstons Best on handpump, with XB and Old Peculier kept under light blanket pressure in winter; fruit machine, dominoes, piped pop music. The hanging baskets and window boxes are most attractive and there are picnic-table sets under cocktail parasols in a partly fairy-lit coachyard. *(Recommended by James and Libby Cane, Andy and Jill Kassube, Rona Murdoch, Eileen Broadbent, G Dobson; more reports please)*

Theakstons (S & N)   Manager Colin Jones   Real ale   Lunchtime meals and snacks Evening restaurant   Ripon (0765) 689295   Children in eating area of bar and in restaurant   Open 11–11   Bedrooms; £38.50B/£55B

White Bear ★

Signposted off A6108 opposite turn into town centre

This busy pub is part of Theakstons old stone headquarters buildings and the brewery is on the other side of town – tours can be arranged at the Theakstons Brewery Visitor Centre (0765 89057, extension 4317, Weds-Sun). The Theakstons Best, XB and Old Peculier on handpump are, not surprisingly, very well kept. The traditionally furnished public bar is packed with bric-a-brac: copper brewing implements, harness, pottery, stuffed animals – including a huge polar bear behind the bar – foreign banknotes, and even an electric shock machine that's supposed to help rheumatism (though it's not always working). A much bigger, more comfortable lounge has a Turkey carpet. Bar food includes sandwiches (from £1), curries or trout (£3.95), seasonal game dishes like pigeon, rabbit, pheasant and venison (around £4.55), and daily specials like home-cured smoked bacon with an egg (served in a cob, £1.50) or chicken korma; no chips. Shove-ha'penny, dominoes, cribbage, fruit machine and CD juke box. In summer there are seats out in the yard. *(Recommended by H K Dyson, Andy and Jill Kassube, Mr and Mrs R J Foreman, John and Christine Simpson, A M Neal, J D Andrews, J E Rycroft, M Hudson, Nick and Alison Dowson)*

Theakstons (S & N)   Tenant Neil Cutts   Real ale   Meals and snacks (not Sat or Sun evenings)   Ripon (0765) 689319   Children welcome   Live music Sat evenings   Open 11–11   Two bedrooms; £20/£30

MELTHAM (W Yorks)   SE0910 Map 7
Will's o' Nat's £

Blackmoorfoot Road; off B6107

Quite alone in a fine spot up on the moors, this solidly traditional place has a wide choice of good value food such as home-made soup (85p), sandwiches (from £1.10, hot ones £1.50, maybe fresh salmon £2.10), pear and cottage cheese salad (£1.55), giant sausages (£2.15), ploughman's (from £2.50), haddock or steak and kidney pie (£2.85), tagliatelle with ham, mushrooms and chicken (£2.95), braised steak (£3.85), garlic butterfly prawns (£4.05), succulent gammon with two eggs (£4.25), scampi (£4.35) and steaks (from £5.50), with children's dishes (£1.40) and several puddings (from £1.35) such as a good treacle tart served with a big jug of fresh cream. By the bar there are heavy wooden wall seats cushioned comfortably in pale green corduroy around heavy old cast-iron-framed tables; the cream walls have lots of old local photographs (for once interesting enough to be well worth a look), and a large attractive pen and wash drawing of many local landmarks, with the pub as its centrepiece. A slightly raised dining extension at one end, with plenty of well spaced tables, has the best of the views. Well kept Tetleys and Mild and Theakstons Best on handpump, a good collection of malt whiskies, dominoes, fruit machine, piped music, and excellent friendly service – the landlord keeps a careful but entirely unobtrusive eye on everything. There are some picnic-table sets on the back lawn (food is not served out here at weekends or on bank holidays). *(Recommended by H K Dyson, A Triggs, Pauline Crossland, Dave Cawley)*

Tetleys (Allied)   Lease: Kim Schofield   Real ale   Meals and snacks (till 10pm; not 25 Dec or bank hol evenings)   Restaurant   Huddersfield (0484) 850078   Children welcome until 9pm   Open 11.30–3(3.30 Sat), 6(6.30 Sat)–11; closed evening 25 Dec

nr MIDGLEY (W Yorks)   SE0326 Map 7
Mount Skip £

Village signposted from Hebden Bridge; or from A646 W of Halifax go straight through village, keeping on high road; OS Sheet 104, map reference 007272

The view from here is quite outstanding and there are high walks nearby on Midgley Moor and Crow Hill. Inside, the modernised bar has a warm fire, copper-topped tables and so forth, and windows well placed for the view. Generous helpings of good value bar food include sandwiches, filled Yorkshire puddings (from £1.50), locally-made pork and leek sausage (£1.90), steak and mushroom pie (£2.85), vegetarian dishes (£3), and 20oz T-bone steak (£7.75). Well kept Tetleys and Timothy Taylors Bitter, Landlord and Golden Best on handpump; darts, pool, dominoes, fruit machine, video game, trivia, and piped music. *(Recommended by C and L H Lever, A M Neal, Mrs J Keen, Jean and Edward Rycroft; more reports please)*

Timothy Taylors   Tenants Stephen and Gail Farrell   Real ale   Meals and snacks   Restaurant   Halifax (0422) 842765   Children in family room and in bar at lunchtime and early evening   Open 12–3(4 Sat), 7–11; 12–2, 7–11 winter weekdays; closed Mon lunch Oct-Easter and Tues lunch Jan-Easter

MOULTON (N Yorks)   NZ2404 Map 10
Black Bull ✿

Just E of A1, 1 mile S of Scotch Corner

This decidedly civilised, well run place has an antique panelled oak settle, an old elm housekeeper's chair and built-in red-cushioned black settles and pews around the cast iron tables (one has a heavily beaten-copper top), silver-plate Turkish coffee pots and so forth over the red velvet curtained windows, copper cooking utensils hanging from black beams, dark grey carpet squares, and a huge winter log fire; decorations include three nice Lionel Edwards Hunting prints, an Edwardian engraving of a big hunt meet, and a huge bowl of flowers. A nice side dark-panelled seafood bar has some high seats at the marble-topped counter. Bar snacks (you must search out someone to take your order – the bar staff just do drinks) includes excellent smoked salmon: sandwiches (£2.25), pâté (£3.25), and smoked salmon plate (£5.25); they also do a very good home-made soup served in lovely little tureens (£1.75), mushrooms in garlic butter (£2), lovely fresh plump salmon sandwiches (£2.25), avocado and prawns (£3.25), memorable seafood pancakes (£3.75), and Welsh rarebit and bacon (£4.25). In the evening, you can also eat in the polished brick-tiled conservatory with bentwood cane chairs or in the Brighton Belle dining car. Tetleys and Theakstons on handpump, good wine, a fine choice of sherries, and decent coffee. Service can seem a little unbending to first-time visitors, but most people quickly come to appreciate the dry humour and old-fashioned standards. There are some seats under trees in the central court. *(Recommended by SS, Paul S McPherson, M V and J Melling, Mrs K J Betts, Hilary Bill, Geoff and Julie Bond, Leith Stuart, W H Bland)*

Free house   Licensee Audrey Pagendam   Real ale   Lunchtime bar meals and snacks (not Sun)   Restaurants (not Sun)   Barton (0325) 377289   Children over 7 welcome Open 12–2, 6.30–11; closed 24 Dec–1 Jan

NEWTON ON OUSE (N Yorks)   SE5160   Map 7
Dawnay Arms

Village signposted off A19 N of York

On the right-hand-side of the entrance to this Grade II listed building is a comfortable, spacious room with a good deal of beamery and timbering and green plush wall settles and brown plush chairs around wooden or dimpled copper tables. To the left is another airy room with red plush button-back wall banquettes built into bays and a good log fire in the stone fireplace. Popular bar food includes home-made soup (£1.35), sandwiches (£2.50, this includes chips), ploughman's (£3.95), vegetarian mushroom and nut fettucini or chilli (£4.50), fisherman's platter (£4.75), lots of steaks (from £7.95), and daily specials like fillet of pork normandy with an apple and cider sauce or chargrilled swordfish with herb butter and prawns (£6.75), roast duckling with a cherry and cointreau sauce (£7.25), and fillet of salmon with a lobster and white wine sauce (£7.50). Well kept John Smiths, Tetleys and Theakstons on handpump, decent house wines and good sherry; alcove with darts, fruit machine and trivia; maybe unobtrusive piped music. The Ouse swirls past the moorings at the bottom of the neatly kept lawn, and there are picnic-table sets and other tables on the terrace, with a children's play-house and see-saw. *(Recommended by Andy and Jill Kassube, Roger Bellingham, Tim and Anne Halstead; more reports please)*

Free house   Licensees John and Angela Turner   Real ale   Meals and snacks (12–2, 6.45–9.45; not Mon lunchtime)   Restaurant Linton-on-Ouse (034 74) 345   Children in eating area of bar and in restaurant   Trad jazz Thurs evenings   Open 11.30–2.30(3 Sat), 6.30–11; closed Mon lunchtime

NUNNINGTON (N Yorks)   SE6779   Map 7
Royal Oak

Church Street; at back of village, which is signposted from A170 and B1257

The carefully chosen furniture on the Turkey carpet in this friendly pub includes kitchen and country dining chairs or a long pew around the sturdy tables, and a lectern in one corner. One of the walls is stripped back to the bare stone to display a fine collection of antique farm tools, the high black beams are strung with earthenware flagons, copper jugs and lots of antique keys, and there are open fires. It's the home-made daily specials that receive the most praise: ham and mushroom pasta, steak and kidney casserole with herb dumpling (£5.50), breast of chicken in orange and tarragon, and seafood crumble. Other good food includes home-made soup (£1.60), sandwiches, good ploughman's (£3.75), salads (from £3.95; seafood hors d'oeuvres £4.50), meaty or vegetarian lasagne or chicken curry (£4.50), gammon and egg (£5.75), sweet and sour battered prawns (£5.95), and steaks (from £6.50). Theakstons Bitter on handpump, with Old Peculier kept under light top pressure. Near the car park there are a couple of tables on a little terrace with a good view. Handy for a visit to Nunnington Hall (National Trust). (*Recommended by W H and E Thomas, H K Dyson, Ruth and Andrew Triggs, J A Snell, Jan and Ian Alcock, D E Nicholls, Peter Race, Barbara and Ken Turner; more up-to-date reports please*)

Free house   Licensee Anthony Simpson   Real ale   Meals and snacks (not Mon) Restaurant   Nunnington (043 95) 271   Children over 5 welcome   Open 11.45–2.30, 6.30–11; closed Mon

nr PATELEY BRIDGE (N Yorks)   SE1966 Map 7
Half Moon

Fellbeck; B6265 3 miles E

It's been the welcoming atmosphere that has lifted this pub out of the ordinary, and though Mr Crosby's son-in-law has just taken over the management, Mr Crosby himself will still be around. The spacious open-plan bar has light-wood country kitchen chairs and a spread of russet plush button-back built-in wall banquettes around decent wooden tables, a delft shelf on the cream walls, and some easy chairs and a big sofa by the entrance, near a fat free-standing woodburning stove; the dog is called Maurice. Well kept Theakstons Best, Timothy Taylors Landlord and Youngers Scotch on handpump; big helpings of simple but properly home-cooked bar food such as sandwiches (the wensleydale cheese ones are good), home-made soup (£1.20), omelettes, haddock, cod or home-made steak and kidney pie (£3.55), pork chop (£3.95), fresh chicken kiev (£4.35), gammon (£4.95) and sirloin steak (£6.65). A back area has darts, pool, dominoes, fruit machine, and piped music; there's a caravan park behind the pub. The bedrooms are in well equipped modern chalets. (*Recommended by A and J Jackson, Mr and Mrs J H Adam, R Etherington, Derek Patey, Andy and Jill Kassube, Phillipa and Andrew Williams, Janet and Gary Amos, Barbara and Mike Williams, D A Wilcock, Miss C M Davidson, David and Rebecca Killick, Steve and Carolyn Harvey*)

Free house   Licensees Colin and Tracy Sidley   Real ale   Meals and snacks Harrogate (0423) 711560   Children welcome   Open 11–11   Bedrooms; £25B/£36B

PENISTONE (S Yorks) Map 7
Cubley Hall

Mortimer Road; outskirts, towards Stocksbridge

The spreading bar in this former country house has plenty of red plush chairs, stools and button-back built-in wall banquettes, panelling or red and gold flock wallpaper, an elaborately plastered pink and cream ceiling, mosaic tiling or Turkey carpet, and a vast brass chandelier. Leading off this spacious main area are two snug rooms and a side family sun lounge which gives a nice view beyond the neat tree-sheltered formal gardens to pastures in the distance; there's a second children's room, too. One room is no smoking. A wide choice of good value bar food served efficiently by neat waitresses includes noted chip butties (90p), home-made soup (£1.05), sandwiches (from £1.15, steak £1.75), meaty or vegetarian lasagne (£3.45), salads (from £3.95), omelettes (from £4.05), plaice (£4.25), steaks (from £5.50), puddings (£1.50), and children's menu (£2.35); specials such as cubley pie, hot and spicy ribs or tuna bake, and Sunday lunch (£4.25, children £3.20). Well kept Ansells Bitter, Arrols 80/-, Ind Coope Burton and Tetleys on handpump, lots of malt whiskies and other spirits, a fair choice of wines, and good coffee; cribbage, dominoes, fruit machines, trivia, and piped music. There's a function room in a converted barn with exposed oak beams, stone walls and arches, half-panelled walls, and real ales. Out on the terrace are some tables and the attractive garden has a good children's play house. (*Recommended by Andy and Jill Kassube, Derek and Sylvia Stephenson, Michael Rooke*)

Free house   Licensee John Wigfield   Real ale   Meals and snacks (till 10pm)   (0226)
766086   Children in two rooms for them   Jazz/folk/blues – no set dates   Open 11–3,
6–11

PICKHILL (N Yorks)   SE3584 Map 10

Nags Head 🏅

Village signposted off A1 N of Ripon, and off B6267 in Ainderby Quernhow

One reader speaks for many when she says she feels this friendly pub deserves a
special award for all-round enjoyment. And the food certainly comes in for strong
praise, with a changing choice of about twenty dishes. Depending wholly on what
looked good – maybe only a couple of helpings of some things (but their definition
of a helping is pretty massive) – this might include home-made soup (£1.50), wild
boar terrine (£3.45), fresh squid and octopus salad (£3.60), hot roast sirloin beef
sandwich (£3.75), vegetarian lasagne (£4.50), steak and kidney pie (£4.75),
smoked halibut with lumpfish roe and lime (£5.25), beef curry masala (£5.75),
hare fillets with thyme and redcurrants (£7.50), rump steak with three pepper
sauce (£8.50), and grilled whole Dover sole (£12.75); they will do sandwiches, and
breakfasts are huge. Well kept Theakstons Best, XB and Old Peculier, Youngers
Scotch and IPA and a beer brewed only a mile away called Hambleton Bitter on
handpump; over 40 malt whiskies, French farm ciders, and over 100 decent wines,
including some by the glass. The busy tap room on the left is comfortably
furnished with red plush button-back built-in wall banquettes around dark tables,
the beams are hung with jugs, coach horns, ale-yards and so forth, and there are
masses of ties hanging as a frieze from a rail around the red ceiling. One table's
inset with a chessboard, and they also have darts, shove-ha'penny, dominoes,
cribbage, a silenced fruit machine and faint piped music in here, with pool in a
separate room. A smarter bar with deep green plush banquettes and a carpet to
match has pictures for sale on its neat cream walls. *(Recommended by P R Morley, J
and K Craddock, Viv Middlebrook, John C Baker, Joy Heatherley, J Barnwell, M Hudson, W
H Bland, Tim and Sue Halstead)*

Free house   Licensees Raymond and Edward Boynton   Real ale   Meals and snacks
(12–2, 6–10)   No smoking restaurant (not Sun evening)   Thirsk (0845) 567391
Well behaved children allowed in eating area   Open 11–3, 5–11; 11–11 Sat
Bedrooms; £30B/£42B

RAMSGILL (N Yorks)   SE1271 Map 7

Yorke Arms 🛏

Take Nidderdale rd off B6265 in Pateley Bridge; or exhilarating but narrow moorland
drive off A6108 at N edge of Masham, via Fearby and Lofthouse

This was the shooting-lodge of the Yorke family's Gouthwaite Hall, which now
lies drowned under the nearby reservoir named after it. The carefully refurbished
bars have two or three heavy carved Jacobean oak chairs, a big oak dresser laden
with polished pewter and other antiques; the public bar has been opened up; open
log fires. Bar food includes soup (£1.55), sandwiches (from £1.80, open from
£2.80), filled baked potatoes (from £2.55), ploughman's (from £3.50), mini grill
(£4.35), salads (from £4.50), seafood pasta in white wine sauce (£4.95), pan fried
trout with almonds and grapes or Nidderdale lamb chops (£5.25), sirloin steak
(£7.50), and puddings (from £1.95). The inn's public rooms are open throughout
the day for tea and coffee, and shorts are served in cut glass. Dominoes and
cribbage. You can walk up the magnificent if strenuous moorland road to
Masham, or perhaps on the right-of-way track that leads along the hill behind the
reservoir, also a bird sanctuary. *(Recommended by Paul S McPherson, Nick Emberley, J E
Rycroft; more reports please)*

Free house   Licensees Peter and Pauline Robinson   Lunchtime bar meals and snacks
No smoking restaurant   Harrogate (0423) 755243   Children in eating area of bar and
in restaurant   Open 11–11   Bedrooms; £30B/£42B

REDMIRE (N Yorks)   SE0591 Map 10

Kings Arms

Wensley–Askrigg back road: a good alternative to the A684 through Wensleydale

All that a country village pub should be – cheerfully friendly staff (both to locals and visitors, even on a busy Saturday night), very good food, well kept beer, a relaxed, unassuming atmosphere and a lovely position. The neatly kept and simply furnished bar has a long soft leatherette wall seat and other upholstered wall settles, red leatherette cafe chairs or dark oak ones, round cast-iron tables, and a fine oak armchair (its back carved like a mop of hair); lots of interesting photographs include those of local filming for *All Creatures Great and Small*, old local scenes (including folk-singers recording here in three-piece suits), of the licensee's RAF squadron, and of his steeplechasing friends such as John Oaksey. Popular, home-made bar food includes sandwiches, very good soup (£1.55), excellent pâté in lovely brown terrine pot (£2.95), decent pasties, very good omelettes (£3.45), meaty or good vegetarian lasagne (£4.55), grilled local trout (£4.75), good steak and kidney pie (£4.95), venison in red wine (£7.45), and steaks (from £8.45); Sunday roast lunch (£4.25, best to book). Well kept John Smiths and Theakstons Best with guests like Tetleys, Theakstons XB and Websters Yorkshire on handpump, 53 malt whiskies, and good Rombouts coffee. The pit bull terrier is called Bess. Darts (under fluorescent light at one end), pool, dominoes, and piped music. There are tables and chairs in the pretty garden, which has a superb view across Wensleydale; fishing nearby. Handy for Castle Bolton where Mary Queen of Scots was imprisoned. *(Recommended by Mr and Mrs R Clifford, John Fazakerley, John and Helen Thompson, M V Melling, Mike and Wendy Proctor, C and V Lindsay, H Bramwell, Julian Yorke, Mrs T Wattison-Ridge, Sidney and Erna Wells, Mrs R Heaton, Stephanie Sowerby)*

Free house   Licensee Roger Stevens   Meals and snacks   Restaurant   Wensleydale (0969) 22316   Children in eating area of bar and in restaurant   Sing-alongs every fourth Fri   Open 11–3, 6–11   Two bedrooms; £17/£28

RIPPONDEN (W Yorks)   SE0419 Map 7

Old Bridge 🏰

Priest Lane; from A58, best approach is Elland Road (opposite Golden Lion), park opposite the church in pub's car park and walk back over ancient hump-backed bridge

Mr Beaumont has run this carefully restored and well kept medieval house for 28 years and there's a very relaxed, welcoming atmosphere in its three communicating rooms, each on a slightly different level. Comfortable furnishings include oak settles built into the window recesses of the thick stone walls, antique oak tables, rush-seated chairs, a few well-chosen pictures and a big woodburning stove; some of the plasterwork has been stripped away to show the handsome masonry, and ceilings have been removed to show the pitched timbered roof. On weekday lunchtimes, there's a popular cold meat buffet which always has a joint of rare beef, as well as spiced ham, quiche, Scotch eggs and so on (£6.50, with a bowl of soup and coffee). In the evenings, and at lunchtime on Saturdays (when you may have to wait some time for your food), good tasty filling snacks include mushrooms parisienne (£2.50), steak and kidney pie (£3.95), and sticky toffee pudding (£1.75), with frequently changing specials like delicious smoked haddock pancakes or ham shank and peas (£2.50); they will cut fresh sandwiches (£1.80). Well kept Ruddles Best, Timothy Taylors Bitter and Mild and Whitbreads Castle Eden on handpump. The pub has a good restaurant, across the very pretty medieval bridge over the little river Ryburn. *(Recommended by Mary and Lionel Tonks, Mr and Mrs J E Rycroft, Andy and Jill Kassube; more reports please)*

Free house   Licensee Ian Beaumont   Real ale   Meals and snacks (not Sun) Restaurant (not Sun)   Halifax (0422) 822295   Children in eating area of bar   Open 11.30–4, 5.30–11

ROBIN HOODS BAY (N Yorks)   NZ9505 Map 10

Laurel

Village signposted off A171 S of Whitby

Right in the heart of one of the prettiest and most unspoilt fishing villages on the North East coast, this cosy white pub has a good local atmosphere. The friendly beamed main bar is decorated with old local photographs, Victorian prints and brasses, and has an open fire. Well kept John Smiths, Malton Double Chance, Theakstons Old Peculier and a couple of guest beers such as Adnams Best or Timothy Taylors Landlord on handpump; darts, shove-ha'penny, table skittles, dominoes, and cribbage. In summer, the hanging baskets and window boxes are lovely; *Good Walks Guide* Walk 160 is closeby. The self-catering flat above the bar is enticing, and there's also a cottage. Please note, they don't do food. *(Recommended by John and Chris Simpson, Andy and Jill Kassube, Brian Barefoot, Mike and Wendy Proctor; more reports please)*

Free house   Licensee Martin Tucker   Real ale   Whitby (0947) 880400   Children in family room   Open 11.30–3, 6.30–11

ROSEDALE ABBEY (N Yorks)   SE7395 Map 10

Milburn Arms ⇐

The easiest road to the village is through Cropton from Wrelton, off the A170 W of Pickering

New licensees have taken over this popular eighteenth-century pub. The traditionally furnished main bar has banquette seating (the engravings and sporting prints have gone), and well kept Theakstons Best, XB and Old Peculier and Youngers Scotch and No 3 on handpump, around 20 malt whiskies, over 60 wines (5 by the glass) kept fresh by a vacuum system, and fresh ground coffee. Decent food includes good granary buns (from £1.35), home-made soup or pâté (from £1.50), ploughman's and vegetarian chilli and lasagne (from £3.95), mariners hot-pot, home-made steak and kidney or rabbit pies, pheasant casserole, chicken forrester, seafood tagliatelle and sirloin or gammon steaks (from £4.95), and puddings like sticky toffee pudding (from £1.75). Sensibly placed darts, winter pool table, shove-ha'penny, dominoes, cribbage, trivia, fruit machine, and piped music. There are picnic-table sets on the terrace and in the garden area. The steep surrounding moorland is very fine. *(Recommended by John and Christine Simpson, S Mills, Jeremy and Vicki Elden, BKA, H K Dyson, P G Topp, Tim Gilroy, John and Joan Wyatt, Mr and Mrs Peter Crane, Brian and Anna Marsden; more reports please)*

Free house   Licensee Terry Bentley   Real ale   Meals and snacks   No smoking restaurant   Lastingham (075 15) 312   Well behaved children welcome until 8.30pm Open 11.30–3, 6.30–11; all day summer Sat   Bedrooms; £44B/£64B

White Horse ⇐

Above village, 300 yards up Rosedale Chimney Bank – the exhilarating 1-in–3 moorland road over Spaunton Moor to Hutton-le-Hole

Views of the high surrounding countryside from the the picnic-table sets on the stone front terrace are marvellous (the inn itself has 11 acres) and the windows of the cosy beamed bar share the same views. There are captains' chairs, red plush cushioned pews salvaged from a church in Wakefield, wooden tables, a welcoming log fire and fox masks, a stuffed heron and peregrine falcon, various antlers and horns, and a reindeer skin. Good, generously served bar food includes home-made soup (£1.55), sandwiches (from £1.50), macaroni cheese with mushrooms (£2.99), mushrooms filled with cream cheese and chives or Whitby haddock in a creamy sauce (£3.60), ploughman's (from £3.60), filled Yorkshire puddings (£4.10), salads (from £4.60), home-made pies (£4.90), two local woodpigeon cooked in a game sauce (when available, £6.60), and barbecue spare ribs (£5.60), with children's dishes (£2.60), puddings like fruit pies or treacle pudding (£1.99), and Sunday roast lunch. Well kept Tetleys and Theakstons on handpump, good choice of malt whiskies and quite a few wines; friendly service. Darts, dominoes, cribbage, and piped music. *(Recommended by John and Christine Simpson, M J Morgan, Bob and Lesley Fawthrop, BKA, Tim Gilroy, Jill Hampton, Brian Metherell, Tim and Lynne Crawford)*

Free house   Licensees Howard and Clare Proctor   Real ale   Meals and snacks (12–2, 7–10)   Restaurant   Lastingham (075 15) 239   Children in bar if eating till 8.30   Open 12–3, 6.30–11; all day Sat; closed evening 25 Dec   Bedrooms; £40B/£60B

SAWLEY (N Yorks)   SE2568   Map 7

Sawley Arms

Village signposted off B6265 W of Ripon

Interesting home-made food in this decidedly civilised place includes soups such as celery and apricot, fennel or mushroom with cumin, all made with proper stock, good sandwiches, ham, spinach and almond pancake (£3.20), good ravioli, splendid salmon mousse or tasty ham and celery pâté, fresh daily fish dishes or steak pie with a fine buttercrust pastry (around £4.90), salads, steaks, and puddings like amaretti schokoladentorte (£3.50); there may be a bit of a wait at peak times. Decent house wines (the beers are keg) and courteous service. Comfortable furnishings in the series of small and cosy Turkey-carpeted rooms range from small softly cushioned armed dining chairs and greeny gold wall banquettes to the wing armchairs down a couple of steps in a side snug; also, log fires, unobtrusive piped piano music, and an engaging burmese cat; a small area is reserved for non-smokers. The pub is handy for Fountains Abbey (the most extensive of the great monastic remains – floodlit on late summer Friday and Saturday evenings, with a live choir on the Saturday). An attractive and carefully kept small award-winning garden has some white ornamental tables – no dogs. *(Recommended by H Bramwell, WAH, I H Rorison, Geoff and Julie Bond, Neville Kenyon, J D Andrews, Syd and Wyn Donald, Gwen and Peter Andrews, Mr and Mrs M Cockram, Mrs V Middlebrook)*

Free house   Licensee Mrs June Hawes   Real ale   Meals and snacks (not Sun evening, not Mon, except bank hols)   Restaurant   Ripon (0765) 620642   Children over 9 in restaurant   Open 11.30–3, 6.30–11; closed Mon, except bank hols

SAXTON (N Yorks)   SE4736   Map 7

Greyhound

Village signposted off B1217 Garforth–Tadcaster; so close to A1 and A162 N of Pontefract

The companionable locals' favourite place in this wonderfully unspoilt village pub is the cosy and chatty taproom on the left, with a cushioned window seat by the mouth of the corridor as well as other simple seats, a coal fire burning in the Victorian fireplace in the corner, ochre Anaglypta walls and a dark panelled dado; an etched glass window looks into the snug with its sturdy mahogany wall settle curving round one corner, other traditional furniture, fancy shades on the brass lamps, and browning Victorian wallpaper. Down at the end of the corridor is another highly traditional room, with darts, shove-ha'penny, table skittles, cribbage, dominoes, and cards. Well kept Sam Smiths OB and Museum tapped from casks behind the counter. The pub – next to the handsome church – is bright in summer with a climbing rose, passion flower and bedding plants, and there's a couple of picnic-table sets in the side courtyard. Close to Lotherton Hall Museum. *(Recommended by Brian Jones, Andy and Jill Kassube, Matt Pringle; more reports on the new regime, please)*

Sam Smiths   Real ale   Sandwiches (lunchtime, not Sun)   (0937) 817202   Children in two areas away from bar   Morris Dancers in summer   Open 11–3, 6–11; all day Sat

SETTLE (N Yorks)   SD8264   Map 7

Royal Oak 🔎 🛏

Market Place; town signposted from A65 Skipton–Kendal

Welcoming, helpful staff serve a wide choice of good value bar food in this well
kept and substantial low stone inn: soup (£1.55), sandwiches (from £1.90, open
ones from £2.20, hefty French bread from £3.55), shepherd's pie (£3.50), salads
(from £3.90), half a dozen vegetarian dishes such as home-made vegetable curry
(from £2.70), lamb stew with dumplings (£4.45), smoked seafood pancake
(£4.75), steak and kidney pie (£5.20), children's dishes (£2.50) and good puddings
(hot tip is a puff pastry and raisins concoction they serve hot with cream and call
Fat Rascals – £1.85). Well kept Boddingtons, Flowers IPA and Whitbreads Castle
Eden on handpump. The ground floor is virtually one huge room, yet enough walls
have been kept to divide it into decent-sized separate areas. Throughout there's
dark squared oak or matching oak-look panelling, with a couple of elegantly
carved arches and more carving above the fireplaces. Plenty of tables (some
dimpled copper, but most wood) are spread over the flowery maroon carpet; lights
vary from elaborate curly brass candelabra through attractive table lamps and
standard lamps with old-fashioned shades to unexpectedly modernist wall cubes.
There's a pleasantly relaxed atmosphere. Some road noise (absurdly heavy quarry
lorries cut through the attractive small town – they should certainly be kept out).
*(Recommended by Mrs J Crawford, Wayne Brindle, Jacquie and Jon Payne, M J Whitehouse,
Peter Race, C A Holloway, J E Rycroft)*

*Whitbreads   Tenants Brian and Sheila Longrigg   Real ale   Meals and snacks (till 10)
Restaurant   Settle (0729) 822561/823102   Children welcome   Open 11–3, 6–11;
11–11 Sat; closed evening 25 Dec   Bedrooms; £39B/£68.25B*

SHEFFIELD (S Yorks)   SK3687   Map 7

Fat Cat £

23 Alma St

On September 21 1990, the first independent Sheffield brewery this century was
formerly opened here and called Kelham Island Brewery (after the nearby
Industrial Museum) – there's Kelham Island Bitter and they hope to introduce a
couple of others as well. There's also a wide range of other well kept real ales and
foreign bottled beers (particularly Belgian ones): Marstons Pedigree, Merrie Monk
and Owd Rodger, Timothy Taylors Landlord, Theakstons Old Peculier, and five
interesting guest beers on handpump; country wines, several organically grown
wines and farm cider. Cheap bar food includes sandwiches (from 45p; granary
sticks 90p), soup (£1), good vegetarian chilli, ploughman's, pork and pasta
casserole, spinach and mushroom lasagne or cauliflower in mustard sauce (all
around £2), and Sunday lunch (£2.50; vegetarian alternative £2.20); efficient
service, cribbage, dominoes. The two small downstairs rooms have simple wooden
tables and grey cloth seats around the walls, with a few advertising mirrors and an
enamelled placard for Richdales Sheffield Kings Ale; the one on the left is
no-smoking and both have coal fires. Steep steps take you up to another similarly
simple room (which may be booked for functions) with some attractive prints of
old Sheffield; there are picnic-table sets in a fairylit back courtyard. *(Recommended
by John and Helen Thompson, Matt Pringle, A M Neal, Frazer and Louise Smith, Steve
Mitcheson, Anne Collins)*

*Own brew   Licensee Stephen Fearn   Real ale   Meals and snacks (lunchtime)   (0742)
728195   Children allowed upstairs if not booked, lunchtime and until 8   Open 12–3,
5.30–11*

Frog & Parrot

Division Street, corner of Westfield Terrace

The atmosphere here is chatty and relaxed and furnishings include high stools at
elbow-height tables, bare boards, a lofty brown ceiling and huge windows, though
one side (with an old neatly blacked kitchen range in a brick chimney-breast) is

carpeted, and an area up a few steps (refurbished this year) has Victorian brewery-theme memorabilia and blue and cream brocaded button-back built-in wall banquettes. Up here, you can see down into the basement brew house where they produce the pub's speciality – Roger and Out, a hefty 1125OG ale (at nearly 17% alcohol about five times the strength of an ordinary bitter), which they sell in 1/3 pint glasses, restricting customers to one pint a session. The other beers here are Old Croak (by contrast very light and easy-to-drink), Reckless and Conqueror, with occasional commemorative strong ales, and a guest such as Boddingtons; tea and coffee served all day. Bar food includes sandwiches, giant Yorkshire puddings (£1.45), corned beef pie (£2.75), pork in cider (£3.05), chilli con carne (£3.25), and broccoli and cheese flan (£3.50). Pinball, fruit machine, video game, trivia, juke box and piped music. *(Recommended by Dennis Jones; more reports please)*

Own brew/Whitbreads   Manager Steve Cheetham   Real ale   Meals and snacks (served all day)   Sheffield (0742) 721280   Open 11–11; closed Sun lunchtime

SICKLINGHALL (N Yorks)   SE3648 Map 7
Scotts Arms

Leaving Wetherby W on A661, fork left signposted Sicklinghall

Some sense of the original rooms of the more-or-less open plan bar in this stone village pub is kept with stubs of the old dividing walls left standing and there are seats built into cosy little alcoves cut into the main walls. There's a curious sort of double-decker fireplace with its upper hearth intricately carved, a big inglenook fireplace, and on a shelf in the corner of the bar is a working model of a two-foot high traditional Scotsman constantly raising and lowering his glass. Popular bar food includes good home-made soup (£1.45), sandwiches (£1.55), hot beef and onion bun (£3.50), ham and pineapple salad (£4.25), steak and kidney pie (£4.45), scampi (£4.75), and home-made puddings (£1.75). Well kept Theakstons Best, XB, Old Peculier and Youngers IPA and No 3 on handpump; darts, dominoes, fruit machine, video game, juke box and unobtrusive piped music, and down steps a separate room has pool and another fruit machine. There are tables outside in summer, and a children's play area with slide, climbing frame and wooden animals. *(Recommended by Syd and Wyn Donald, Robert and Lesley Fawthrop, T Nott, David Oakes, GB, Mrs V Middlebrook, Tony and Penny Burton, Andy and Jill Kassube; more reports please)*

S & N   Manager Carl Lang   Real ale   Meals and snacks (not 25 Dec)   Restaurant   Wetherby (0937) 582100   Children in eating area of bar and restaurant   Open 11.30–3, 5.30–11

SOWERBY BRIDGE (W Yorks)   SE0623 Map 7
Moorings

Off Bolton Brow (A58) opposite Java Restaurant

This attractively converted ex-canal warehouse overlooks the basin where the Rochdale and Calder & Hebble Canals meet and there are tables out on a terrace with grass and small trees. Part of the canal has been reopened and there's a circular walk, and other old canal buildings house a boat chandlery and canal hire company. The spacious beamed bar has big windows, bare floorboards, stone walls, a grain hopper, grain sacks and old pulley wheels; there's an eating area up some steps. The lounge bar is pleasantly furnished with rush-seated stools, tile-top tables and fabric-covered seats built against the stripped stone walls (which are decorated with old waterways maps and modern canal pictures), and the big windows and very high ceiling give a relaxed and airy atmosphere. A lobby leads to a no smoking family room alongside, similarly furnished. Good, reasonably priced bar food includes home-made soup, filled granary cobs (from £1.90), mushrooms stuffed with ham and cheese (£2.55), tandoori chicken (£2.75), help-yourself salads (from £3.15), aduki bean casserole (£4.25), breaded pancake filled with scallops, prawns, mushrooms and asparagus spears or steak and kidney cooked in Murphy's Irish Stout (£4.95), hot chilli crunch (£5.50), gammon steak (£5.90), steaks (from £8.20), puddings (from £1.50), and children's meals (in the family area, £1.80); service does get pushed when busy. Besides well kept Moorhouses Bitter, McEwans 80/-, Theakstons XB, Youngers Scotch and a regularly changing guest beer and Liefmans Kriek (Belgian cherry beer) on handpump, there is a range of 30 foreign bottled and canned beers, and they import more than 40 Belgian bottle-conditioned real ales (there's a menu with full descriptions), and Dutch Lindeboom; also, over 90 malt whiskies (including 7 Irish), reasonably priced house wines, and cocktails – including children's specials; they do tea and coffee. Dominoes and piped music. (*Recommended by D Swift, Keith W Mills, WAH, Mr and Mrs C H Garnett, Steve and Maureen Collins, Andrew and Ruth Triggs, Mr and Mrs P A Jones, P A Crossland, Andy and Jill Kassube, Syd and Wyn Donald, David Oakes, Michael Rooke*)

Free house   Licensees Ian Clay and Andrew Armstrong   Real ale   Meals and snacks Restaurant   Halifax (0422) 833940   Children in family room till 8.30   Open 11.30–3, 5(6 Sat, 7 Mon)–11; closed 25 Dec

STANSFIELD MOOR (W Yorks)   SD9227 Map 7
Sportsmans Arms

Hawks Stones, Kebcote; on the old packhorse road between Burnley and Hebden Bridge, high above Todmorden; OS Sheet 103, map reference 928273

Built around 1660 and originally a farm, this lonely but very welcoming place has fresh flowers in the stone hearth and on some of the tables, some dark squared panelling, stone-mullioned windows with pot plants on the stone sills, a few toby jugs and other decorative china on a high shelf, beams hung with mugs and horsebrasses, and swords, knives, assegais, and heavy-horse harness. A comfortable mix of old and new furnishings includes big heavy russet plush settles facing the open fire in the back area, with mustard-coloured leatherette seats elsewhere; piped music. The colour photographs of show horses and of a pony and trap are a clear clue to the licensee's interests; the pub is the headquarters of the Calder Valley Driving Club (horses). Good quality bar food includes sandwiches (from £1.10), steak pie, lasagne or gammon (£3.75), trout or salmon (£4.95), and steaks (from £6.25). Well kept Websters Yorkshire on handpump, with quite a few decent malt whiskies; darts, pool, fruit machine, video game, and juke box in a separate bar. Walkers welcome and dogs too, if on a lead. They hold a clay pigeon shoot in the field twice a week. (*Recommended by Carol and Richard Glover, Len Beattie; more reports please*)

Free house   Licensee Jean Greenwood   Real ale   Meals and snacks (till 10pm) Evening restaurant (they do Sunday lunch)   Todmorden (0706) 813449   Children welcome   Open 7–11 (closed Mon-Fri lunchtimes); 12–3, 7–11 (midnight supper licence) Sat

SUTTON (S Yorks)   SE5512 Map 7
Anne Arms £

From A1 just S of Barnsdale Bar service area follow Askern, Campsall signpost; Sutton signposted right from Campsall

An interesting and profuse collection of ornaments in this cosy creeper-covered stone house consists of latticed glass cases thronged with china shepherdesses and the like, a throng of toby jugs collected over many years, oak dressers filled with brightly coloured plates, fruit plates embossed with lifesize red apples, lots of colourful five-litre and smaller Bavarian drinking steins, and wooden figures popping out of a Swiss clock when it chimes the quarter-hours. A separate room is filled with brass and copper, and there's a Victorian-style conservatory. Generous helpings of remarkably good value, home-made food include a fresh roast every day, their speciality rabbit pie, braised pork chops with apple sauce and stuffing, poached salmon, fresh haddock, Barnsley chops with mint sauce (all £3), and puddings like home-made fruit pies (£1). John Smiths Magnet on handpump; fruit machine, and piped music. One reader was startled to find they would not take a cheque – even with a banker's card. (*Recommended by W C M Jones, Mrs R M Morris, Mrs B Y Lockwood, Mr and Mrs D W Fisher, Wayne Brindle; more reports please*)

*John Smiths (Courage)   Tenants John and Irene Simm   Real ale   Meals and snacks
(not Sun)   (0302) 706500   Children in conservatory   Open 11.30–3, 6–11*

SUTTON HOWGRAVE (N Yorks)   SE3279   Map 7

White Dog

Village signposted from B6267 about 1 mile W of junction with A1

This delightful cottage, standing at the end of a little farming hamlet, has two main rooms furnished with comfortably cushioned Windsor chairs and flowers on the polished tables. On one side of the black-beamed bar there's an open kitchen range with a welcoming fire in cool weather; friendly cat. Good bar lunches include French onion soup (£1.50), sandwiches (from £1.50), mariners hot-pot (£3.50), omelettes and salads (from £4.25), chicken casserole or fillet of plaice (£4.75), lamb casserole (£5.10), venison pie (£5.50), and puddings (£1.95); small selection of New World wines. In summer, the upper windows are almost hidden by the flowers in the window boxes and two clematis, and there are picnic-table sets among flowerbeds on the grass. (*Recommended by George Kovacs, Peter Race, Penny Webster, Fiona Mutch, Graham and Karen Oddey, Syd and Wyn Donald, J E Rycroft*)

Free house   Licensees Basil and Pat Bagnall   Lunchtime meals and snacks (not Sun evening or all day Mon)   No smoking restaurant (Tues-Sat evenings, bookings only) Melmerby (076 584) 404   Children in restaurant at licensees' discretion   Open 12–2.30, 7–11; closed Sun evening, all day Mon, 23 Dec – 2 Jan

TADCASTER (N Yorks)   SE4843   Map 7

Angel & White Horse £

1 Bridge Street

The open-plan series of rooms in this atmospheric pub have fine oak panelling with unusually well made solid furniture to match, photographs of past brewery workers, and above a handsome stone fireplace a striking oil painting of a dappled grey shire horse. It's the tap for the Sam Smiths Brewery, and from the bar you can see the team of grey shire horses peering out of their stalls across the neat yard. They do brewery tours at arranged times: Tadcaster (0937) 832225. Remarkably cheap and well kept Sam Smiths OB and Museum. Good value bar food includes sandwiches (from £1.25), filled baked potatoes (£1.65), roast beef with Yorkshire pudding (£2.95) and daily specials like chicken, ham and mushroom pie (£2.85); darts and piped music. (*Recommended by Jan and Ian Alcock, Andy and Jill Kassube, Maureen and Steve Collin, Eileen Broadbent, T Nott; more reports please*)

Sam Smiths   Manager Joanne Williams   Real ale   Lunchtime meals and snacks Restaurant   Tadcaster (0937) 835470   Children in restaurant at lunchtime   No nearby daytime parking   Open 11–3, 5.30–11; 11–11 Sat

THORNTON WATLASS (N Yorks)   SE2486   Map 10

Buck 🅟 🛏

Village signposted off B6268 Bedale–Masham

With warmly friendly licensees, very good food and comfortable bedrooms, it's not surprising that this peaceful country pub is so popular with readers. The pleasantly traditional right-hand bar has been revamped this year – the handsome old-fashioned wall settles have been re-upholstered, a new brick fireplace has been installed, a new carpet laid, a fine mahogany bar (which was being thrown out of a pub in Somerset) added, and new wall lights added; also, cast-iron-framed tables, a high shelf packed with ancient bottles, and several mounted fox masks and brushes (the Bedale hunt meets in the village). A new entrance into the old dining room has been made and ceiling beams and wall panelling have given the room a more traditional feel; large prints of old Thornton Watlass cricket teams have been hung on the walls. At lunchtime, bar food includes home-made soup (£1.40), home-cooked beef or ham in crusty French bread (from £1.70), scrambled egg and smoked salmon (£1.85), home-made pâté or a small lasagne (£2.60), aubergine and tomato charlotte or leek and mushroom pie (£4.25), lunchtime platters (£3.50), superb lasagne or delicious fresh Whitby cod (£4.50), and pork fillet and creamed mushrooms (£6.25), with evening dishes like grilled lamb chops (£4.75), mixed grill (£5.50), and grilled salmon (£6.25); smaller helpings for OAPs and children (the tagliatelle with mushrooms and bacon is good); well kept Tetleys Bitter, Theakstons Best and XB and a guest beer on handpump, and around 45 malt whiskies. A bigger plainer bar has darts, pool, and dominoes. The low stone building looks past a grand row of sycamores to the village cricket green (they have a team), and has two quoits pitches in the garden (with league matches on summer Wednesday evenings, practice Sunday morning and Tuesday evening); the front part of the garden has been re-rendered and the hanging baskets are lovely; trout fishing on the Ure, and an equipped children's play area. *(Recommended by Bob Smith, Allen Sharp, Allan Clarke, Viv Middlebrook, Mick Hall, Mr and Mrs D C Leaman, Kelvin Lawton, D S and Mrs T M Beeson, Jack and Barbara Smale, Janet and Gary Amos, Ian Ornes, James Cane, John and Christine Simpson, Mary and Lionel Tonks, Stephen and Alison Parker, J Leslie Anthony, Janice Diamond, Angela Lockett, Richard Gibbs, J D Andrews, H Bramwell)*

Free house   Licensees Michael and Margaret Fox   Real ale   Meals and snacks (11.30–2, 6.30–9.30; not 25 Dec)   Restaurant   Bedale (0677) 22461   Well behaved children welcome (not late in evening); not in function room Sat or Sun evenings Organ singalong and dancing Sat, country and western or 60s-type singer Sun evening Open 11–2.30(3 Sat), 6–11, all day for cricket matches and so forth; midnight supper licence Sat   Bedrooms; £25S/£40S

THRESHFIELD (N Yorks)   SD9763   Map 7

Old Hall ✪

B6265, just on the Skipton side of its junction with B6160 near Grassington

Huge helpings of imaginative bar food here change daily and use fresh, seasonal ingredients: hot beef sandwich (£1.65), smoked seafood platter (starter £3.50, main £5.95), mussels baked in garlic breadcrumbs and cheese (£3.65), peach and prawns in a spicy mayonnaise (£2.75), late breakfast (the home-made sausages are lovely), lamb's liver and onion with Yorkshire pudding or tagliatelle verde with mixed vegetable sauce (all £4.95), steak pie or seafood lasagne (£5), wild boar and pheasant pie (£5.25), very popular individual lamb joint in mint and redcurrant sauce (£6.95), 14oz steaks (£8.50), and puddings like lemon and lime tart or her hot chocolate fudge cake (£1.75). Well kept Theakstons Best, Timothy Taylors Bitter and Landlord and Youngers Scotch on handpump. The three communicating rooms have simple, cushioned pews built into the white walls, a tall well blacked kitchen range, a high beam-and-plank ceiling hung with pots, and unfussy decorations such as old Cadburys advertisements and decorative plates on a high delft shelf. Darts, dominoes, tucked away fruit machine, maybe piped pop music. A neat side garden, partly gravelled, with young shrubs and a big sycamore has some tables and an aviary with cockatiels and zebra finches. This is, of course, a fine base for Dales walking and the inn is on *Good Walks Guide* Walk 150. Please note that they no longer do bedrooms. *(Recommended by Jim Cowell, Prof S Barnett, Viv Middlebrook, G Dobson, Fred Walmsley, Andy and Jill Kassube, Joan and John Calvert, Graham Bush, Margaret White, Gwen and Peter Andrews, Syd and Wyn Donald, A M Neal, Jane Buekett)*

Free house   Licensees Ian and Amanda Taylor   Real ale   Meals and snacks (till 10pm; not Mon from 2nd week in Jan–Easter)   Restaurant   (0756) 752441   Children in eating area and conservatory   Open 11–3, 5.30–11

nr TODMORDEN (W Yorks)   Map 7

Staff of Life   £

Burnley Road, Knotts; A646 out of centre – after the built-up area ends with an imposing mill and viaduct, keep eyes skinned for car park on right, which is 90 yards' walk from pub itself

On the right as you come out of Todmorden you pass this warmly welcoming and cheerful pub's own brewery (though it's run separately); interesting and well kept, the beers include delicately hopped Robinwood Bitter, XB and – nothing delicate about this one – Old Fart; they also have guest beers such as Timothy Taylors Bitter and Landlord; also, farm ciders, malt whiskies, fruit wines and Belgian bottled beers. On the left, a two-level simply furnished lounge has Turkey carpet on its flagstones, seats including a colourfully upholstered wall settle, bedpans, giant mounted insects, a reindeer's head over the open fire, and lots of stripped stonework. The bar on the right has lots of bedpans on its mainly plastered walls, some horsebrasses on the beams, and a coal fire. Very good value freshly cooked bar food includes sandwiches (from 95p), basket meals (from £1.65), fiery kebab in pitta bread (£1.95), lentil cheese bake (£2.45), chicken, lamb or vegetable curries (from £2.50), home-made lasagne (£2.75), gammon and eggs (£4.75), a huge mixed grill (£5.75), and steaks (from £5.95); the upstairs restaurant specialises in fish; coffee and tea. Darts, dominoes and juke box. There are picnic-table sets and a couple of rustic benches on a flagstoned roadside terrace. *(Recommended by Lee Goulding, Andy and Jill Kassube, Barbara Wensworth, Steve and Maureen Collins, Andrew Stephenson, Michael Rooke)*

Free house   Licensee Freddie Sleap   Real ale   Meals and snacks (till 10pm; not Mon lunch)   Restaurant (not Sun)   Todmorden (0706) 812929   Children in eating area of bar until 8.30   Open 12–3, 7–11; closed Mon lunchtimes   Bedrooms; £18B/£30B

WATH-IN-NIDDERDALE (N Yorks)   SE1467   Map 7

Sportsmans Arms ⊘ ⌨

Nidderdale rd off B6265 in Pateley Bridge; village and pub signposted over hump bridge on right after a couple of miles

Though this friendly seventeenth-century country place is more of a hotel than a pub and the bar has elegant curtains and fabrics in pinks and blues, it is very much somewhere where people can – and often do – drop in just for a drink. It would be a great pity, however, to miss trying the excellent food (no deep-frying and only fresh produce used); at lunch in the bar this might include a selection of fresh fish such as moules marinières (£3.50), fresh dressed crab (£3.75), Scarborough woof sautéed in butter with prawns, almonds and capers (£5.80), scallops tossed in garlic butter and glazed with mozzarella or fresh monkfish in a grape and mushroom sauce (£6.50), fresh local trout cooked in brown butter with roasted almonds and capers (£5.95), and whole grilled lemon sole with prawn and parsley butter (£7.50); also, home-made soup (£1.80), chicken liver pâté or locally-made or continental cheese ploughman's (£3.20), prawns in wholemeal bread with a tomato flavoured mayonnaise (£4.95), breast of local chicken sautéed and served with garlic butter (£5.90), and puddings like crème brûlée or chocolate roulade (£2.50) and a tremendous range of 18 cheeses (many local); 3-course restaurant Sunday lunch. To get the best of the young chef's excellent cooking, you should really stay overnight and enjoy a good leisurely dinner. There's a very sensible and extensive wine list, good choice of malt whiskies and attentive service; open fire, dominoes. Benches outside. *(Recommended by Tim Gilroy, Syd and Wyn Donald, I H Rorison, John and Christine Simpson, WAH, Peter Race, J K Percival, Geoff and Julie Bond, Janet and Gary Amos, Mrs K J Betts, Joy Heatherley, Fiona Mutch, Joan and John Calvert)*

Free house   Licensee Ray Carter   Lunchtime bar meals and snacks   Evening restaurant (not Sun evening)   Harrogate (0423) 711306   Children welcome   Open 12–3, 7–11   Bedrooms; £27(£29S)/£45(£48B)

WELBURN (N Yorks)   SE7268   Map 7
Crown & Cushion

Village signposted from A64 York–Malton

This pleasant old stone pub has two connecting lounge bar rooms with little pictures between strips of black wood on the cream walls, high shelves of plates, a growing collection of nearly 700 water jugs, wheelback chairs and small cushioned settles around wooden tables, and open fires in winter. Bar food includes soup (£1.70), sandwiches (from £1.55), ploughman's (£3.20) salads (from £4.30, the ham roasted in cider is good), steak and kidney pie (£4.15), pork and pineapple curry (£4.30), breaded haddock (£4.60), steaks (from £8.50) and daily specials on a blackboard; Sunday roast (£5.95). Well kept Camerons Bitter and Strongarm on handpump. Darts, dominoes and fruit machine and juke box in the public bar; piped music. The neatly landscaped back garden has a terrace with tables and chairs. Castle Howard and Kirkham Abbey are closeby. *(Recommended by Mr and Mrs Peter Crane, Anne Phelan, Jean and Edward Rycroft, Robert Kimberley, Tim and Sue Halstead; more reports please)*

Brent Walker   Tenant David Abbey   Real ale   Meals and snacks (not Mon lunchtime in winter; lunchtime food service may stop promptly at 1.30)   Restaurant   Whitwell on the Hill (065 381) 304   Children in eating area of bar and restaurant   Open 11.30–2.30, 6.30(7 in winter)–11; closed Mon lunchtime in winter

WENTWORTH (S Yorks)   SK3898   Map 7

George & Dragon

3 miles from M1 junction 36: village signposted from A6135; can also be reached from junction 35 via Thorpe; pub is on B6090

A wide range of well-kept ales here includes Ind Coope Burton, Oak Wobbly Bob and a beer brewed for them by Oak called Dragon's Blood, Timothy Taylors Bitter and Landlord, Tetleys Bitter and three different guest beers each week on handpump; also Westons cider. The pleasantly rambling bar has an assortment of old-fashioned seats and tables, blue plates on the walls, and steps that split the front area into separate parts; there's also a lounge (back by the little games room) with an ornate stove. Bar food includes sandwiches (from £1), meat and potato or turkey and venison pies (£3.50), vegetarian dishes, and very good Sunday roast lunch (£3.95). Dominoes, cards, fruit machine, video game and piped music. There are benches in the front courtyard. *(Recommended by Ian Robinson, Mary and Lionel Tonks, Andrew Turnbull, M C Howells, Andy and Jill Kassube, Derek and Sylvia Stephenson, David Warrellow, Michael Rooke; more reports please)*

Free house   Licensee Steve Dickinson   Real ale   Meals and snacks (not Sun evening)   Restaurant   (0226) 742440   Children in eating area of bar at lunchtime   Open 12–3, 7–11

WIDDOP (W Yorks)   SD9333   Map 7

Pack Horse

The Ridge; from A646 on W side of Hebden Bridge, turn off at Heptonstall signpost (as it's a sharp turn, coming out of Hebden Bridge road signs direct you around a turning circle), then follow Slack and Widdop signposts; can also be reached from Nelson and Colne, on high, pretty road; OS Sheet 103, map reference 952317

Considering its isolation high up on the moors, this friendly, traditional walkers' pub is remarkably popular. There are window seats cut into the partly panelled stripped stone walls that take in the view, sturdy furnishings, and warm winter fires. Good, straightforward bar food includes sandwiches (from £1.20, open sandwiches on French bread from £2.50), cottage hot-pot (£2.95), ploughman's (£3.25), salads (from £3.75), home-made steak and kidney pie (£4), giant prawns (£5.50), steaks (from £5.95), and specials such as curry, vegetable lasagne or beef in ale; lots of fancy puddings. Be prepared for a wait on summer weekends, when it's crowded. Well kept Ruddles Best, Theakstons XB, Thwaites Bitter and Youngers IPA on handpump, and 78 single malt whiskies. There are seats outside. *(Recommended by Lee Goulding, D Swift, Andy and Jill Kassube, Len Beattie, Simon Bates, Michael Rooke; more reports please)*

Free house   Licensees Ron Evans and Andrew Hollinrake   Real ale   Meals and snacks (till 10pm; not winter Mon or Tues evenings, see note below)   (0422) 842803   Children welcome until 9pm   Open 12–3, 7–11; closed weekday lunchtimes from end Sept-Good Fri (except Christmas holiday period)

WIGHILL (N Yorks)   SE4746 Map 7

White Swan ★

Village signposted from Tadcaster; also easily reached from A1 Wetherby bypass – take Thorpe Arch Trading Estate turnoff, then follow Wighill signposts; OS Sheet 105, map reference 476468

The star is for the homely and unspoilt feel in the several little rooms here, though this can take a knock or two if the tiny front locals' bar is so crowded (as it often is at weekends) that you can't get in. Apart from this cosy room there's a plainer one opposite with lots of racing prints, a small lobby that's also a favoured place for locals to gather, and a back bar with a mix of old chairs and tables, and lots of decorative plates and sporting prints on the wall; a dining room leads off this; open fires in most rooms. Lunchtime bar snacks include giant rolls filled with rare beef, prawns or ham (from £2.60), home-made steak pie (£3.60), and lasagne or chilli con carne (£3.20); evening dishes range from fisherman's pot (£3.20) to duckling (£8.75) and fillet steak (£10.50). Well kept Stones, Tetleys, Theakstons and Youngers on handpump; dominoes, cards and piped music. There's a terrace overlooking the garden where there are lots of seats. (*Recommended by H K Dyson, Andy and Jill Kassube, Steve and Carolyn Harvey, T Nott, Mr and Mrs M Cockram, Ruth Humphrey, TBB, J C Proud, Mrs B Y Lockwood, Tim and Sue Halstead, GB*)

Free house   Licensee Mrs Rita Arundale   Real ale   Lunchtime meals and snacks (evening meals only Fri and Sat)   (0937) 832217   Children in two family rooms Open 12–3, 6–11; closed 25 Dec evening

WINKSLEY (N Yorks)   SE2571 Map 7

Countryman

Village signposted off B6265 W of Ripon

Down stairs from the car park, the stone-walled and heavily beamed main bar of this civilised and welcoming 18th-century pub has red plush seats, dimpled copper tables, a good log fire even in summer, a rack of newspapers and relaxing piped music. It can get busy in summer, though it's much more of a warm-hearted local in winter – when the crack darts teams return to the fray. Good bar food in generous helpings includes soup (£1.10), sandwiches (from £1.35), vegetarian chilli (£2.95), salads (from £3.25), lasagne (£3.95), home-made steak and kidney pie (£4.25), charcoal-grilled steaks (from £6.75), daily specials like pork Devonshire (£4.95), lamb Shrewsbury (£5.75), and half duckling à l'orange (£7.50), and tasty puddings; well kept Theakstons Best and Old Peculier and Websters Yorkshire on handpump, decent whiskies, good coffee, tea. A simple, cheerful and spacious upstairs family room has pool, dominoes, video game, juxe box, and another log fire, and there are some picnic-table sets on a small fairylit front terrace, with more behind. Fountains Abbey and Studley Royal are closeby. (*Recommended by Tim Baxter, D Lermon, H Bramwell*)

Free house   Licensees Mark and Linda James   Real ale   Meals and snacks Restaurant   Ripon (0765) 658323   Children in family room   Open 12–3, 6.30–11; closed Mon from Nov to end Feb and Mon lunchtimes all other times

WORMALD GREEN (N Yorks)   SE3065 Map 7

Cragg Lodge

A61 Ripon–Harrogate, about half way

There are over 800 malt whiskies housed in this comfortably modernised dining roadhouse, including a dozen Macallans going back to 1937 (£2.30 – a remarkable bargain, smooth as silk yet glowing with deep character). They have 16 price bands, between 80p and £7, depending on rarity – with a 17th 'by negotiation' for their unique 1919 Campbelltown. Not being too single-minded, they also have well kept Tetleys Bitter and Theakstons Best, XB and Old Peculier on handpump, several distinguished brandies, and mature vintage port by the glass; pleasant staff.

The big open-plan bar has horse brasses and pewter tankards hanging from side beams, a dark joist-and-plank ceiling, Mouseman furniture as well as little red plush chairs around dark rustic tables, and a coal fire; part of the eating area is no smoking. Truly home-made food at lunchtime includes soup (£1.10), sandwiches (from £1.35), game and liver pâté (£1.70), ploughman's (£2.80), curry or home-made steak and kidney pie (£3.30), vegetarian dishes (£3.60), salads (from £3.60), lamb cutlets (£3.90), gammon with glazed peach (£4.45), steaks (from £6.60), and a daily roast; in the evenings, there's a larger, more elaborate menu (main courses from around £5.65). Home-made puddings such as cheesecake (£1.70), children's meals (from £1.50), and morning coffee and snacks from 10am. There are picnic-table sets under cocktail parasols on the side terrace, with more in a sizeable garden and pretty hanging baskets in summer. *(Recommended by Mr and Mrs C H Garnett, Greg Turner, Paul S McPherson, Peter Burton, John Munro, Dr T H M Mackenzie, Mike Tucker, Andy and Jill Kassube)*

Free house   Licensee Garfield Parvin   Real ale   Meals and snacks (11.30–2, 6–9.30; till 10 Fri and Sat)   Restaurant   Ripon (0765) 677214   Children in eating area of bar and in restaurant   Open 11–2.45, 6–11   Bedrooms; £25B/£41B)

YORK (N Yorks)   SE5951   Map 7

Black Swan

Peaseholme Green; inner ring road, E side of centre; the inn has a good car park

This surprisingly uncommercialised 15th-century building has a warmly chatty, black-beamed back bar with wooden settles along the faded cream walls, some cushioned stools and copper-topped tables, and a throne-like cushioned seat in the vast brick inglenook, where there's a coal fire in a grate with a spit and some copper cooking utensils; the fish above the door in the opposite corner was caught in 1942. With its little serving hatch, the cosy panelled front bar is similarly furnished but smaller and more restful. The crooked-floored hall that runs along the side of both bars has a fine period staircase (leading up to a room fully panelled in oak, with an antique tiled fireplace). Good bar food served by cheerful staff includes home-made soup (£1.40), attractively presented sandwiches (from £1.40), ploughman's (£3), a generous helping of excellent home-made filled Yorkshire pudding (from £1.70), home-made steak and onion pie, lasagne or curry (£3.50), a roast (£3.75), a vegetarian dish, and puddings such as treacle sponge or apple crumble (£1.90). Well kept Bass and Stones and a guest beer on handpump, and country wines; dominoes, fruit machine and maybe faint piped Radio 2. The timbered and jettied facade and original lead-latticed windows in the twin gables are very fine indeed. *(Recommended by Ben Wimpenny, Mr and Mrs C H Garnett, Brian Jones, Brian and Anna Marsden)*

Bass   Manager Joseph Cahill   Lunchtime meals and snacks   York (0904) 625236   Children in eating area of bar   Folk Thurs evening, Jazz Sun lunchtime   Open 11–11   Bedrooms; £20B/£40B

Hole in the Wall

High Petergate

By no means a hole in the wall, this is spacious enough to be relatively uncrowded for a pub so handy for the Minster – though it does get busy in the evening. Beams, stripped stone, Turkey carpet, red plush seating, prints, paintings and plates, a couple of open fires, piped music; generous helpings of decent inexpensive food include two bread cobs, grated cheese and side salad (£1.90), ploughman's (£2.25), steak and kidney pie or haddock (£3.35), scampi (£3.60), and 4oz sirloin steak sandwich (£3.95), with puddings like apple pie (from £1.15). Well kept Mansfield Riding and Old Baily; very friendly staff. Fruit machine, juke box and piped music. *(Recommended by Anne Phelan, Bernard Phillips, Ian Baillie, Roger Bellingham, Roger Taylor)*

Mansfield   Manager F Somerset   Real ale   Meals and snacks (noon–8 weekdays, till 6 Sat)   York (0904) 634468   Open 11.30–11

Kings Arms

King's Staithe; left bank of Ouse just below Ouse Bridge; in the evening you should be able to get a parking space right outside, turning down off Clifford Street; otherwise there's a 1/4 mile walk

Very popular in the evenings – especially in summer and on bank holidays – this white painted, black beamed riverside pub is included mainly for its position. It gets flooded so often that its 'cellar' is above ground in an adjacent building which used to be a mortuary; a painted board by the entrance to the pub shows how high the floods have been. There are cushioned stools and wall benches around wooden tables, good thick cushions on stone window seats that look out over the river, bare brick and stone walls, bowed black beams, and flagstones; a cosier area up a step at the back on the left has a few prints of Charles I, Edward VI, and Henry VIII. Bar food includes sandwiches, ploughman's, steak and kidney pie (£3.50), and roast beef and Yorkshire pudding (£3.80); fruit machines, trivia, loud CD juke box (very popular with young people). There's a row of black-painted picnic-table sets on the cobbled riverside terrace. *(Recommended by Laurence Manning, H K Dyson, Ben Wimpenny, Brian Jones, Wayne Brindle, F Teare, E H and R F Warner)*

Sam Smiths   Manager I C Webb   Meals and snacks (12–2, 5.30–8.30; not Sat evenings)   York (0904) 659435   Open 11–11

Olde Starre

Stonegate; pedestrians-only street in centre, far from car parks

Right in the busy town centre, this is one of York's most touristy pubs and is at its most appealing at lunchtime (in the evening it tends to be popular with York's younger drinkers and the juke box may be louder then, too). The main bar, with its large servery running the length of the room, has green plush wall seats, some diagonal beams on the cream-papered walls, and a large leaded window with red plush curtains at the far end. Several other little rooms lead off the porch-like square hall – one with its own food servery, one with panelling and some prints, and a third with cream wallpaper and dado. Well kept Ruddles Best and County and Websters Yorkshire on handpump; fruit machine and CD juke box. Bar food includes sandwiches (from £2.10), Scottish haddock or ploughman's (£3), steak and kidney pie, mince and vegetable pie or lasagne (£3.25), lamb in cider, a vegetarian dish or sweet and sour pork (£3.60), and Sunday roast beef (£4.50); salad and pudding bar, children's menu (£1.65). *(Recommended by Mrs Richard Stewart, Wayne Brindle, Andy and Jill Kassube, F Teare, Hazel R Morgan, Bernard Phillips)*

Websters (Watneys/Courage)   Managers Bill and Susan Embleton   Real ale   Meals and snacks (11.30–3, 5.30–8; not Sun evening, not Fri or Sat)   York (0904) 623063   Children in own rooms   Occasional karaoke   Open 11–11 Mon-Thurs; 11–3, 7–11 Fri and Sat

Tap & Spile £

Monkgate

A good example of the small chain of pubs with this name: decently made traditional furnishings, brewery memorabilia, and above all a good choice of changing real ales – well kept Hadrian Gladiator, Old Mill Traditional and Stocks Horizontal and maybe Fullers, Hartleys XB, Jennings, Mitchells ESB, Moorhouses Pendle Witches Brew andWadworths 6X; fruit wines. It has a big split-level bar with bare boards, green leatherette wall settles right around a big bay window, with a smaller upper area with frosted glass and panelling; newspapers to read, shove-ha'penny, table skittles, dominoes, fruit machine and piped music; quiz night Monday. Simple cheap bar food includes sandwiches (from £1.20), ploughman's (from £2.60), Yorkshire pudding with mince or giant sausage (£2.70) and lasagne or chilli con carne (£2.85). There are a few picnic-table sets outside. *(Recommended by Russell and Christina Jones, Mr and Mrs C H Garbett)*

Brent Walker   Manager Andrew Fairbotham   Real ale   Lunchtime meals and snacks (11.30–2)   York (0904) 656158   Children in top room   Open 11.30–3, 5.30–11   Bedrooms; £30/£30

Lucky Dip

Besides the fully inspected pubs, you might like to try these Lucky Dips recommended to us and described by readers (if you do, please send us reports):

☆ **Aberford**, W Yor [Old North Rd; best to use A642 junction to leave A1; SE4337], *White Swan*: Major Whitbreads refurbishment of early 18th-century coaching inn, rather well done, with standard bar food extended to dishes such as venison, exotics and huge steaks and mixed grills; Whitbreads-related drinks — very popular; bedrooms (*T Nott, Andy and Jill Kassube*)

Aberford, *Arabian Horse*: Beamed local with blazing winter fires, comfortable feel, Theakstons real ale (*T Nott*)

Addingham, W Yor [SE0749], *Craven Heifer*: Modernised in pleasing way, dark green plush, lots of pictures, Ind Coope Burton, Tetleys and Websters Green Label Mild; standard bar food, log-effect gas fire in snug (best place to mitigate piped music); steep steps from car park (*Gwen and Peter Andrews, A and J Jackson, Prof S Barnett, Geoff and Julie Bond*)

Ainthorpe, N Yor [NZ7008], *Fox & Hounds*: 16th-century, lovely dark old room with oak beams, horsebrasses, log fires and homely atmosphere; well kept Theakstons, reasonably priced bar food, friendly cat, outside tables; bedrooms (*Eileen Broadbent, Ian Tysh*)

☆ **Almondbury**, W Yor [bear left up Lumb Lane; village signposted off A629/A642 E of Huddersfield — OS Sheet 110, map reference 153141; SE1615], *Castle Hill*: High above Huddersfield on site of prehistoric hill fort, with very spacious grounds and terrific views of the moors dwarfing the mill towns; lots of coal fires in rambling partly panelled bar, stripped stonework, sturdy traditional furnishings; has had well kept Timothy Taylors Best and Landlord and Tetleys, simple bar food (not Sun-Tues evenings), popular Sun lunch, but up for sale summer 1991 (*Carol and Richard Glover, LYM; news please*)

☆ **Ampleforth**, N Yor [SE5878], *White Swan*: Roomy, well kept and friendly, recently expanded and refurbished and doing particularly well, with newish chef, wide choice of good varied bar food from soup and well filled sandwiches to pheasant casserole or roast guineafowl; in attractive village (*Patrick Clarke, Mark Porter*)

Appleton Roebuck, N Yor [SE5542], *Shoulder of Mutton*: Straightforward pub/steak bar with incredible value food (*Tim and Sue Halstead*)

☆ **Appletreewick**, N Yor [SE0560], *Craven Arms*: Very pleasant country pub, lovely views across Wharfedale from outside tables, two cosy bar rooms and small separate dining rooms, roaring fires (one in old iron range), attractive settles and carved chairs, interesting decorations, fine relaxed atmosphere; friendly staff, well kept Tetleys, Theakstons XB and Old Peculier and Youngers Scotch on handpump, generous helpings of freshly prepared food at reasonable prices; convenient for walkers (*Margaret White, Wayne Brindle, Tim Baxter, Bridget Hill, Tony and Penny Burton*)

☆ **Appletreewick**, *New Inn*: Splendidly basic stone pub in superb spot, with lovely views; simple good food, cheerful welcome, well kept S&N beers, splendid collection of bottled foreign beers, pub games; garden (*Andy and Jill Kassube, Peter Race, LYM*)

Askwith, W Yor [3 miles E of Ilkley; SD1648], *Black Horse*: Tastefully redecorated, with more emphasis on food and families; rugged stone exterior with good views of Wharfedale, popular for good lunchtime cold buffet plus the usual range; Watneys beers on handpump (*Andy and Jill Kassube, Paul S McPherson*)

Atley Hill, N Yor [B1263 NE of Catterick Bridge, off A1; NZ2902], *Arden Arms*: Good food (especially in restaurant — eg duck with honey sauce) in pub stepped up hill; pleasant atmosphere, real ale (*Will Pascall*)

☆ **Aysgarth**, N Yor [SE0088], *George & Dragon*: More hotel than pub, pleasant atmosphere in spacious attractive lounge divided into nooks and crannies; well kept Websters Yorkshire, good value bar food inc interesting vegetarian dishes, seafood and Sun roast; friendly staff, a welcome for dogs, separate pool area; bedrooms (*S V Bishop, Robert and Vicky Tod*)

☆ **Bainbridge**, N Yor [A684; SD9390], *Rose & Crown*: Antique settles and other old furniture in beamed and panelled front bar, recently refurbished public bar, bar food from sandwiches and good ploughman's to steaks, John Smiths, Theakstons and Youngers Scotch, big wine list; games, juke box or piped music; overlooking lovely village green; restaurant; children welcome; bedrooms comfortable; open all day Sat (*J C Proud, J E Rycroft, Robert and Vicky Tod, Mr and Mrs M D Jones, H K Dyson, LYM*)

☆ **Bardsey**, W Yor [A58; SE3643], *Bingley Arms*: Ancient pub and decorated to look it, full of interest and atmosphere; very wide range of reasonably priced bar food, picturesque restaurant, charming terrace (*Tony and Penny Burton, Paul and Janet Waring, J N Skeldon*)

Barkisland, W Yor [Saddleworth Rd, Dean Hd; SE0416], *Brown Cow*: Clean, with cheap snacks and meals, darts, pool and so forth, extensive country view from front bay window, back garden with play area; lovely outing in summer, isolated in winter (*Paul Lightfoot*); *Fleece*: Good choice of real ales in comfortable character moors-edge pub with wide choice of bar food — open till small hours; CD juke box in small cellar wine bar, bar billiards, piano restaurant, maybe disco/bar (*BB*)

Barnsley, S Yor [Sheffield Rd; start of A61,

nr roundabout edge of centre; SE3406], *Manx Arms*: Pleasant, popular partly open-plan town-centre pub, very wide range of real ales, also farm ciders; lunchtime meals (not Sun) *(Michael Rooke, W P P Clarke)*

☆ **Beck Hole**, N Yor [OS Sheet 94, map reference 823022; NZ8202], *Birch Hall*: Really unspoilt and unusual, incorporating the village shop, with ancient picture on outside wall; keg beer and other drinks, sandwiches and hot pies served through a hole in the wall into small room with very simple furniture; lovely spot by bridge over river in beautiful steep-valley village; up some steep steps at the side is a little garden with a nice view — lovely on a sunny afternoon; nr Thomason Fosse waterfall, steam railway and delightful gentle walk (GWG159) on old railway track to Goathland *(Ian Clayton, Hilary Thorpe)*

Beckwithshaw, N Yor [Church Row; SE2753], *Smiths Arms*: Pleasant Watney's Country Carvery dining pub, bar food too *(J E Rycroft, Andy and Jill Kassube)*

Biggin, N Yor [SE5435], *Blacksmiths Arms*: 18th-century beamed and flagstoned pub which has been popular for good value food and John Smiths ale, but lease sold free of tie earlier in 1991 and no news since *(Reports please)*

Bingley, W Yor [Otley Rd, High Eldwick; SE1240], *Dick Hudsons*: Comfortable, with lovely moors views; good place to finish a walk; popular for food, but not cheap, and food service may slow; simple family room *(A and J Jackson, J E Rycroft, Roy Cove, Robert and Lesley Fawthrop, Reg Nelson)*

Birchencliffe, W Yor [Halifax Rd; nr M62 junction 24; SE1118], *Grey Horse*: Small village pub with well kept Bass and Stones, coal fire, good lunchtime food, welcoming atmosphere and very friendly landlord; has been open all afternoon *(S Rushworth)*

☆ **Birstwith**, N Yor [SE2459], *Station*: Welcoming atmosphere in interesting stone-built old railway hotel tucked away deep in a picturesque valley; smartly modernised but cosy lounge, good value bar lunches, well kept Tetleys, nice china, friendly staff; attractive hanging baskets and tubs in summer *(Andy and Jill Kassube, Tim and Ann Newell)*

Bishop Monkton, N Yor [off A61 Harrogate—Ripon; SE3366], *Lamb & Flag*: Pleasant pub in pretty village *(Tim and Sue Halstead)*

Boroughbridge, N Yor [Horsefair; SE3967], *Crown*: 17th-century coaching inn on Great North Road, good value food in hotel bar, bedrooms good value too *(W T Aird)*

☆ **Bradfield**, S Yor [Strines Reservoir; signed from A616 W of Stocksbridge, and A57 Sheffield—Ladybower — OS Sheet 110, map reference 222906; SK2692], *Strines*: Very relaxed take-us-as-you-find-us atmosphere in isolated moorland pub of great antiquity, where landlord works a thriving hill sheep farm; three rooms downstairs (one candlelit), open fires,

hunting pictures, lots of stuffed animals, wide choice of bar food from sandwiches up (not Sun evening, except residents), upstairs restaurant; Whitbreads Castle Eden on handpump, decent wines and malt whiskies; children welcome; open all day — unless snowed in; bedrooms *(Ben Wimpenny, Dave Braisted, Robin and Christine Harman, Steve Mitcheson, Anne Collins, LYM)*

☆ **Bradford**, W Yor [Preston St (off B6145); SE1633], *Fighting Cock*: Basic traditional alehouse with hard benches and bare floors, but pleasant atmosphere, ten or more well kept real ales inc many guests, farm ciders, some foreign beers, coal fires, legendary doorstep sandwiches, good chilli con carne and pies; interesting customers, live jazz Mon; not the kind of place to take your mother *(Barbara Wensworth, T Nott, Reg Nelson, Keith Adams, Bill Ryan)*

☆ **Bradford** [Kirkgate/Ivegate], *Rams Revenge*: Relaxed and unpretentious pub formed from several different buildings on site of former city gate; old pews, wooden floor, seats in upper gallery, fascinating old clock from the former gate house in back room, fine old Bradford prints; well kept Clarks, Theakstons and guests such as Moorhouses Pendle Witches Brew on handpump, lunchtime bar food, folk music *(Mr and Mrs P A Jones, Reg Nelson, Bill Ryan)*

☆ **Bradford** [Barkerend Rd; up Church Bank from centre, on left few hundred yds past cathedral], *Cock & Bottle*: Notable Victorian decor in well preserved small rooms, good value cheap lunchtime snacks, unusually well kept Tetleys real ales, live music Fri and Sat evenings; down-to-earth atmosphere, no frills *(LYM)*

Bradford, [Westgate], *Beehive*: Renovated and now a free house, with pleasant traditional decor, several rooms, wide range of well kept beers *(Bill Ryan)*; [Heaton Rd], *Fountain*: Very popular; welcoming efficient landlord, well kept beers and good food, from good sandwiches up; can get crowded lunchtime *(J E Rycroft)*; [28 Kirkgate], *Shoulder of Mutton*: Notably good garden for a city pub — real suntrap; cosy inside, with cheap fresh food (not Sun), well kept and well priced Sam Smiths *(John Thorndike, Andy and Jill Kassube, Bill Ryan)*

☆ **Bramham**, W Yor [The Square; just off A1 2 miles N of a64; SE4243], *Red Lion*: Good food, well kept beers and attractive seats and decor in comfortable and warm former coaching inn, consistently well run *(K H Frostick, Brian and Genie Krakowska-Smart)*

Bramhope, W Yor [SE2543], *Fox & Hounds*: Popular two-bar Tetleys pub with well kept Mild and Bitter, good hot and cold food, efficient landlord; children welcome; has been open all day *(John C Gould)*

Brighouse, W Yor [Brookfoot; A6025 towards Elland; SE1524], *Red Rooster*: Beer lover's pub, with good real ales inc Exmoor Gold, Moorhouses Pendle Witches Brew, Old Mill, Timothy Taylors Landlord; knowledgeable friendly landlord, brewery memorabilia, real fire, homely atmosphere

(Andy and Jill Kassube)

☆ **Burnlee**, W Yor [Liphill Bank Rd; just off A635 Holmfirth—Manchester — OS Sheet 110, map reference 131078; SE1307], *Farmers Arms*: Classic smallish stone-built pub on narrow back rd, attractive, popular and friendly; well kept Timothy Taylors Landlord, Tetleys and guest beers, cheap lunchtime and evening bar food inc huge Yorkshire pudding sandwiches, homely decor; children welcome *(Michael Rooke, Andy and Jill Kassube, W P P Clarke, Andrew Roberts)*

☆ **Calder Grove**, W Yor [just off M1 junction 39; A636 signposted Denby Dale, then first right into Broadley Cut Rd; SE3116], *Navigation*: Well kept Tetleys and simple food in profusely decorated canalside pub with tables outside — attractively placed for a pub so nr the M1 *(LYM)*

Carlton, N Yor [Coverdale; SE0684], *Foresters Arms*: Smallish pub with tremendous atmosphere and good food *(Paul S McPherson)*

Carperby, N Yor [a mile NW of Aysgarth; SE0189], *Wheatsheaf*: Good friendly atmosphere, well kept Theakstons and Websters Yorkshire, bar food inc good sandwiches and ploughman's; not the cheapest pub in the area *(Gordon Theaker)*

☆ **Chapel le Dale**, N Yor [SD7477], *Old Hill*: Roaring log fire in cosy back parlour, bar packed with pot-holers and walkers, stripped stone walls with potholing pictures and memorabilia of the Settle railway line and its viaduct, flagstone floors, old woodwork and partitions with waggon wheels; well kept Theakstons Bitter, XB and Old Peculier on handpump; popular food in separate room inc good home-made Old Peculier pie; pity about the juke box; children welcome; bedrooms warm, basic but well furnished, good bathroom with high-pressure shower, good breakfast *(Michael Simmonds, HKD, David Warrellow, LYM)*

Chapeltown, S Yor [107 Station Rd; SK3596], *Commercial*: Old style blue-collar pub with decent Wards, Batemans and others; good value food — beef and beer pie, Sun lunch; pool table *(John Cattell)*; [Station Rd, Warren], *Norfolk Arms*: Very welcoming pub and licensees; good Wards; black pudding on bar Sun lunchtime; pool table *(John Cattell)*

Cleckheaton, W Yor [Whitechapel Rd; nr M62 junction 26; SE1825], *Brown Cow*: Large old pub by church, popular for food inc good hot roast beef sandwiches with chips and home-made curries; Boddingtons, Tetleys and Whitbreads Trophy on handpump *(Andy and Jill Kassube)*

Clifton, W Yor [Westgate; off Brighouse rd from M62 junction 25; SE1623], *Black Horse*: Smart village inn, good food in bar (wide choice, very popular lunchtime and weekends) and restaurant (weekend booking recommended, good service); cosy oak-beamed drinking areas, well kept Whitbreads beers; bedrooms comfortable *(Andy and Jill Kassube)*; [just off M62, junction 25; A644 Huddersfield Rd], *Old Corn Mill*: Renovated corn mill with attractive, smart furnishing, very popular with families on summer weekends; Tetleys beer, good choice of bar food from sandwiches with hot fillings up; huge car parks *(H K Dyson, Andy and Jill Kassube)*

Cloughton, N Yor [N of village; TA0096], *Hayburn Wyke*: On former Scarborough—Whitby rly line, by rugged cliffs; formidable helpings of good food inc huge steaks and legendary Sun carvery, reasonable prices, well kept John Smiths and Theakstons, log fire, character restaurant, friendly and obliging licensees; bedrooms well equipped, with huge breakfasts *(Stephen Fox)*

☆ **Cloughton Newlands**, N Yor [TA0196], *Bryherstones*: Cosy pub with lovely warm welcome, in delightful surroundings; delicious bar food (best chips in many a day), pleasant staff, well kept Youngers *(Ian and Joan Jagor, Harry Blood, Andy and Jill Kassube)*

Colden, W Yor [Jacks Bridge; Heptonstall—Burnley; SD9628], *New Delight*: Pleasant, ideally placed for walkers, cheap food lunchtime and evening, small games room, Tetleys *(Paul Lightfoot)*

☆ **Constable Burton**, N Yor [SE1791], *Wyvill Arms*: Comfortably converted and attractively decorated farmhouse with elaborate stone fireplace and fine plaster ceiling in inner room; good value bar food, well kept Theakstons, obliging service *(LYM)*

☆ **Cridling Stubbs**, N Yor [between junctions 33 and 34 of M62 — easy detour; SE5221], *Ancient Shepherd*: Has been quiet and comfortable refuge from M62/A1/A19, with well kept real ales such as Marstons Pedigree and Whitbreads Castle Eden and Trophy on handpump, popular food in bar and restaurant, and polite service *(Bob Smith, Andy and Jill Kassube, T Nott, M J Cochrane, Dr James Haworth, R A and B F Harrison, LYM; but we've heard little since thorough internal refurbishment — news please)*

Dacre Banks, N Yor [SE1962], *Royal Oak*: Peaceful old stone and panelled villlage pub just above River Nidd; stylishly decorated, with good food inc big Nidderdale trout, steaks, salads, Sun lunches; Tetleys and Youngers Scotch on handpump; bedrooms *(Andy and Jill Kassube)*

Dalehouse, N Yor [Dalehouse Bank; off A174 at Staithes; NZ7818], *Fox & Hounds*: Cosy and warming, busy local front bar, side room with food inc good value Sun lunch, quieter family room at back; friendly welcome and service, well kept Tetleys and Theakstons XB *(Ian and Sue Brocklebank)*

Dalton, N Yor [between A19 and A168, S of Thirsk; SE4377], *Jolly Farmers of Olden Times*: 18th-century beamed pub, consistently welcoming, wide range of bar food, good value Sun lunch, well kept Websters and guest beers *(Andy and Jill Kassube)*

Dalton on Tees, N Yor [NZ3008], *Chequers*: Well kept John Smiths Magnet and guest beer, good generous food inc Sun lunch, good service, attentive owners *(Tony Rae)*

☆ **Danby Wiske**, N Yor [off A167 N of Northallerton; SE3499], *White Swan*: Cosy little pub in the middle of nowhere, handy for walkers on coast to coast footpath; very friendly licensees, good choice of good value food inc free range eggs from own chickens; bedrooms cheap and comfortable *(Andrew Ellis, Len Beattie)*

Deepcar, S Yor [Manchester Rd; SK2898], *Royal Oak*: Recently refurbished with good food and Tetleys and Stones on handpump *(John Cattell)*

Doncaster, S Yor [St Sepulchre Gate West; Cleveland St; SE5703], *Corner Pin*: Good traditional well priced pub food (hot sandwiches and rabbit pie particularly popular), well kept John Smiths and Magnet; handy for stn *(Andy and Jill Kassube)*; [Market Pl], *Masons Arms*: Traditional pub popular with market traders and locals, well kept Tetleys, good atmosphere, friendly welcome; comfortable without being plush *(Andy and Jill Kassube)*; [Frenchgate, edge of central pedestrian precinct], *White Swan*: Front room so far below counter level that you need a high reach for your well kept Wards Sheffield Best; snacks *(BB)*

☆ **Dunford Bridge**, S Yor [Windle Edge Lane; off A628 — OS Sheet 110, map reference 158023; SE1502], *Stanhope Arms*: In a smashing spot tucked below the great dam of Winscar Reservoir up on dramatic moors, this friendly place has a comfortable rather restaurant-like high-ceilinged lounge bar, a little copper-tabled snug and a plain pool room (with fruit machine) radiating from the central servery; decent food from sandwiches and baked potatoes to scampi and gammon, afternoon teas summer Suns, well kept John Smiths and Magnet on handpump; warm welcome for families, sizeable garden; bedrooms *(W P P Clarke, Andy and Jill Kassube, A G Roby, BB)*

East Keswick, N Yor [Main St; SE3644], *Duke of Wellington*: Big ornate Victorian dining room (no booking) with good value straightforward meals and snacks, generously served (not Mon) *(Tony and Penny Burton, Mr and Mrs M Cockram)*

☆ **East Layton**, N Yor [A66 not far from Scotch Corner; NZ1609], *Fox Hall*: Cosy booths around panelled bar, sporting prints, more open back part with big south-facing window, bar food from sandwiches to duck and steak, well kept Theakstons Best with wider summer choice, good range of malt whiskies and wines; games room, juke box, piped music; tables on back terrace; evening restaurant, Sun lunches; children and well behaved dogs welcome; bedrooms comfortable, good breakfasts *(H K Dyson, H S Harries, LYM)*

☆ **East Marton**, N Yor [A59 Gisburn—Skipton; SD9051], *Cross Keys*: Interesting and comfortable old-fashioned furnishings in nicely decorated pub with ample choice of bar food, interesting evening restaurant, well kept Watneys-related beers, friendly helpful staff, open fires, children's area (where the food counter is); tables outside, handy for the Leeds & Liverpool Canal *(Brian Jones, Paul and Janet Waring, Simon Bates, LYM)*

☆ **Egton**, N Yor [NZ8106], *Wheatsheaf*: Popular village local catering for shooting parties; well kept Theakstons Best and McEwans 80/- on handpump, decent bar food throughout opening hours, evening restaurant, good family service; bedrooms pretty *(Eileen Broadbent, Brian and Genie Smart)*

Egton, *Horseshoe*: Warm welcome and good open fire in low-beamed moorland village pub popular for grills and so forth *(LYM)*

☆ **Embsay**, N Yor [Elm Tree Sq; SE0053], *Elm Tree*: Good bar food inc giant Yorkshire puddings with various fillings, in open-plan beamed village pub with brasses, old-fashioned prints and log-effect gas fire; friendly staff, locals' area with pool table, darts, fruit machine, dominoes and TV; well kept Whitbreads ales, juke box; busy weekends *(Mr and Mrs J E Rycroft)*

Emley, W Yor [Church St; SE2413], *Green Dragon*: Opp church, comfortable and well furnished, clean and tidy, good value food most evenings and Sun lunchtime; wide range of beers *(Paul Lightfoot)*

Eppleby, N Yor [off B6274 N of Richmond; NZ1813], *Travellers Rest*: Airy bar and separate dining room, Vaux Sampson on handpump and good English food such as big trout and gammon; also Chinese food Fri evening *(A J J Moulam)*

☆ **Escrick**, N Yor [E of A19 York—Selby — OS Sheet 105, map reference 643425; SE6343], *Black Bull*: Unchanged for some years, with cheerful fire, quickly served straightforward bar food, pleasant dining room; comfortable bedrooms *(Roger Bellingham, T Nott)*

Esholt, W Yor [Main St; just off A6038 Shipley—Otley; SE1840], *Commercial*: Usual bar snacks inc ploughman's, pies etc, popular restaurant (booking recommended), well kept Whitbreads Castle Eden; can be crowded with lunchtime tourists; aka the Woolpack, Beckindale, in TV's *Emmerdale Farm* *(Andy and Jill Kassube)*

☆ **Fadmoor**, N Yor [SE6789], *Plough*: Hearty little pub overlooking quiet village green, cheery landlady, spick and span bar with whitewashed walls, crackling open fire and simple old furnishings; Tetleys and Websters Yorkshire, usual bar food with plenty for vegetarians; Sun lunchtime only sandwiches, soup or full Sun lunch; restaurant like a little private dining room; stunning location, easy parking; comfortable bedrooms *(Viv Middlebrook, LYM)*

Farndale East, N Yor [Church Houses; next to Farndale Nature Reserve; SE6697], *Feversham Arms*: Small pub in beautiful valley next to Farndale Nature Reserve, good walking country; sandwiches, ploughman's, Cumberland sausage and chips all recommended; friendly service, open fire, coffee and tea as well as beer; restaurant *(John and Helen Thompson, Mr and Mrs Peter Crane)*

Farnham, N Yor [opp church; SE3461], *Crown:* Enthusiastic current licensees, Tetleys, Theakstons and lots of wines by the glass, lunchtime food inc sandwiches, ploughman's, pies, more elaborate evening dishes from filled Yorkshire pudding to halibut or salmon, puddings inc lots of home-made ice creams; live jazz Sun, pianist some nights *(Viv Middlebrook)*

☆ **Farnley Tyas,** W Yor [OS Sheet 110, map reference 165128; SE1612], *Golden Cock:* Smart plush dining pub more like a comfortable city bar in style; has been popular for bar and restaurant food inc Sun lunch, with well kept real ales, decent wines; reports on new regime please *(Frank Cummins, Andy and Jill Kassube, ILP)*

Felixkirk, N Yor [SE4785], *Carpenters Arms:* Comfortable 17th-century free house with good if not cheap bar food; restaurant *(Andrew and Ruth Triggs)*

Flixton, N Yor [A1039 W of Filey; TA0479], *Fox & Hounds:* Good food, good beer *(D J Bennett)*

☆ **Follifoot,** N Yor [OS Sheet 104, map reference 343524; SE3452], *Lascelles Arms:* Small, cosy, quiet and welcoming, with many cosy nooks and blazing fires; generous helpings of simple, tasty and inexpensive bar food, well kept Sam Smiths OB, friendly staff *(Dr K A and S F Louden, Ian Richard Smith)*

Follifoot, *Radcliffe Arms:* Well run, with attractive bar, friendly pleasant atmosphere and short choice of good food, good value *(J E Rycroft)*

☆ **Galphay,** N Yor [SE2573], *Galphay Inn:* Good atmosphere, log fire and singing landlord in dining pub with beautifully cooked food in huge helpings, eg chicken breast stuffed with prawns, lamb in honey and rosemary, dreamy home-made puddings — a queue at 7 for tables, maybe a note on the door by 8 saying no more; efficient welcoming staff, two bars; decent house wine, Tetleys and Czech beer; an all-round pleasurable place if low on beams and horsebrasses *(Mrs V Middlebrook, H Bramwell)*

Garforth, W Yor [41 Selby Rd; SE4033], *Gaping Goose:* Very busy, three rooms inc thriving games room, great mix of customers, well kept Tetleys; brasses and oak beams *(M J Cochrane)*

☆ **Gargrave,** N Yor [A65 W of village; SD9354], *Anchor:* Extensive canalside art deco Chef & Brewer, worth knowing as useful family pub with superb play area and waterside tables; usual bar food inc good puddings served all day at least in summer, pleasant competent service, Marstons Pedigree and Whitbreads-related real ales, prominent piped music; economically run

bedrooms in modern wing *(Gwen and Peter Andrews, Dr M A Thomas, Denzil T Taylor, Mr and Mrs Peter Nelson, LYM)*

Gargrave, [Church St/Marton Rd], *Masons Arms:* Friendly and impressively well run, between river, church and open country; Boddingtons and Whitbreads Castle Eden on handpump, lavish helpings of good value quick bar food inc good vegetarian choice, copper-canopied log-effect gas fire serving two open plan bar areas *(D W Stokes, Bill Sykes)*

☆ **Gayles,** N Yor [NZ1207], *Bay Horse:* Much done-up open-plan bar in friendly farm pub with small open fires, well kept McEwans 80/-, Newcastle Exhibition and Youngers Scotch on handpump, darts, good value straightforward food inc good home-cooked ham and Sun lunch; closed Weds; children welcome *(J A Snell, BB)*

Gildersome, W Yor [SE2429], *Griffin:* Well cooked food such as ham and egg, steak pie, Yorkshire puddings and sandwiches *(Wyn and Syd Donald)*

☆ **Goathland,** N Yor [opp church; NZ8301], *Mallyan Spout:* Comfortable traditional Spout Bar with well kept Malton Bitter, wide varying choice of above-average imaginative bar food, good popular restaurant, cheerful service; nr GWG159; splendid view from big garden behind; children allowed away from bar; bedrooms *(Frank Davidson, Dr and Mrs A K Clarke, Brian and Anna Marsden)*

Golcar, W Yor [Scapegoat Hill; off A62 (or A640) up W of Huddersfield; SE0915], *Scapehouse:* Doing well under new owner, very old-world, with magnificent views over Colne valley; Tetleys and Timothy Taylors on handpump; bar food from sandwiches to lots of steaks *(H K Dyson)*

Gomersal, W Yor [Little Gomersal; SE2026], *Wheatsheaf:* Village pub very popular for good value early evening food inc good home-made pies, haddock, steak with plenty of extras, and good sandwiches and burgers; well kept Tetleys, very warm welcome *(Andy and Jill Kassube, Ian W Robinson)*

Grange Moor, W Yor [A6142 Huddersfield—Wakefield; SE2216], *Kaye Arms:* Wide range of bar food from interesting soups, good beef sandwiches or ploughman's with home-made chutney to steaks; lots of whiskies *(D A Wilcock, Miss C M Davidson)*

☆ **Grantley,** N Yor [off B6265 W of Ripon; SE2369], *Grantley Arms:* Attractive beamed stone pub in quiet Dales village, cosy coal fires; locally popular for good plain bar food inc pies, steaks and a superb mixed grill, Tetleys and Theakstons on handpump, restaurant; if they're busy you may be asked to give up your table when you've eaten *(Andy and Jill Kassube, PJP)*

☆ **Grassington,** N Yor [Garrs Lane; SE0064], *Black Horse:* Good value traditional home-cooked bar food and well kept Tetleys and Theakstons Bitter and Old Peculier in busy but comfortable open-plan modern bar with darts in separate back room, open fires, friendly staff, sheltered terrace, small but attractive restaurant; bedrooms good value; nr start GWG150 *(H K Dyson, Andrew Triggs, Tim and Lynne Crawford, Dick Brown, BB)*

☆ **Grassington** [The Square], *Devonshire*: Pleasant and popular, interesting big pictures, attractive ornaments, open fires, good window seats overlooking sloping village square; Youngers Scotch and No 3 on handpump, good range of food in separate eating area and well furnished dining room, friendly staff and quick service; nr start GWG150; bedrooms reasonable, good breakfasts *(Andrew Triggs, H K Dyson, LYM)*

☆ **Great Ayton**, N Yor [High Green; off A173 — follow village signs; NZ5611], *Royal Oak*: Friendly old bar with huge inglenook, beam-and-plank ceiling, aged partly panelled stone walls, traditional furnishings inc antique settles, pleasant views of elegant village green from bay windows; tables in longer room for wide range of generously served food from sandwiches to steaks, well kept Theakstons XB and Youngers No 3 on handpump; service generally friendly; children in eating areas; bedrooms *(Andrew Morrissey, GB, LYM)*

☆ **Great Broughton**, N Yor [High St; NZ5405], *Wainstones*: Well kept Bass and Stones on handpump and fine home-made bar food inc Sun lunches in smartish hotel bar; efficient service, good restaurant; bedrooms *(Roger A Bellingham, E J Cutting)*

Great Broughton, *Jet Miners*: Busy village pub with good Theakstons XB on handpump, substantial bar meals *(Len Beattie)*

Great Ouseburn, N Yor [SE4562], *Crown*: Surprisingly atmospheric with heavy beams and open fire, and popular for its food (nothing too ambitious — steaks etc) and range of beers, inc Timothy Taylors Landlord; certainly worth an inspection *(Tim and Sue Halstead)*

☆ **Grenoside**, S Yor [Skew Hill Lane; 3 miles from M1 junction 35 — OS Sheet 110, map reference 328935; SK3394], *Cow & Calf*: Good high settles in the several rooms of this neatly converted farmhouse, friendly and entertaining landlord, attractively priced home-cooked weekday bar food, well kept Sam Smiths on electric pump; pleasant out in the walled yard, with animals wandering around outside, and splendid views of Sheffield; children in family area, with children's shop in farmyard *(LYM)*

☆ **Grewelthorpe**, N Yor [SE2376], *Hackfall*: Simple L-shaped lounge with brocaded mates' chairs around brown tables, Theakstons Best and XB on handpump, fruit machine, piped pop music, decent bar food; pool in public bar, couple of tables in small back garden; bedrooms warm and cosy *(H Bramwell, BB)*

☆ **Gristhorpe**, N Yor [off A165 Filey—Scarborough; TA0982], *Bull*: Spacious open-plan low-beamed bar with cushioned banquettes, lots of sporting pictures and village scenes; good value bar food inc lunchtime cold buffet; games area; well kept Youngers Scotch and No 3 *(LYM)*

☆ **Gunnerside**, N Yor [SD9598], *Kings Head*: Classic Dales pub with seats out by pretty bridge, reasonably priced good home-cooked food; popular with locals, but strangers welcomed; well kept Theakstons Old Peculier *(Mrs R Heaton, Jacquie and Jon Payne, KC)*

Haigh, S Yor [M1 junction 38, just off exit roundabout; SE2912], *Old Post Office*: Former PO with pleasant bars upstairs and down, good range of imaginative food inc giant Yorkshires very generously filled with roast beef, pork and stuffing, steak and onions, well kept Tetleys and Whitbreads Castle Eden; avoid the Sun car boot sales *(Hilary Sargeant, N P Clarke)*

☆ **Halifax**, W Yor [Paris Gates, Boys Lane — OS Sheet 104, map reference 097241; SE0924], *Shears*: Superbly unspoilt, tucked away down narrow cobbled alleys, shut in by towering mills and the bubbling Hebble Brook; very dark inside, with decor reflecting sporting links with local teams, also collection of pump clips and foreign bottles; well kept Marstons Pedigree, Timothy Taylors Landlord and unusual guest beers, good food from hot-filled sandwiches to home-made pies, curries, casseroles etc, at keen prices, consistently warm welcome *(Michael Rooke, Andy and Jill Kassube)*

Halifax [Bulls Green], *Plummet Line*: Large Victorian corner hotel recently cheerfully refurbished; mainly open-plan with some partitioned areas, stained glass and mahogany, and plenty of tables; efficient, friendly service, well kept Tetleys on handpump, good choice of food inc sandwiches from separate servery; bedrooms *(D Swift)*

☆ **Hardrow**, N Yor [SD8791], *Green Dragon*: Worth knowing for its right of access to Britain's highest single-drop waterfall (have to pay to see it); spacious bar with big helpings of quickly served good value basic food, well kept Theakstons, good pickled eggs, beamed snug bar with coal fire in old iron range, friendly staff; fruit machines, bar billiards and small juke box in beamed public bar; reasonable range of bar food; tourist prices; children welcome; on GWG147; bedrooms, self-catering units *(Pauline Crossland, Dave Cawley, C and V Lindsay, Janet and Gary Amos, WAH, Mel Landells, LYM)*

Harecroft, W Yor [B6144 Bradford—Haworth; SE0835], *Station*: Nice quiet comfortable two-room pub with real fires and particularly well kept Whitbreads Castle Eden and Trophy *(Bill Ryan)*

Harewood, W Yor [SE3245], *Harewood Arms*: Recently redecorated in comfortable homely style, good sandwiches and bar food in pleasant surroundings, friendly and helpful staff *(Mrs S Mills)*

☆ **Harrogate**, N Yor [1 Crescent Rd; SE3155], *Hales*: Popular and atmospheric unspoilt 18th-century town local close to pump rooms, with gas lighting, comfortable seats, well kept Bass and Stones, simple good value lunchtime bar food; entertaining quiz nights Tues *(Andy and Jill Kassube)*

Harrogate [31 Tower St], *Tap & Spile*: Deliberately basic, traditional three-room pub with wooden floors, stripped stonework; lunchtime food such as sandwiches and home-made pies; Camerons and several regularly changing beers *(Andy and Jill Kassube)*

☆ **Hartoft End**, N Yor [SE7593], *Blacksmiths Arms*: Spaciously extended modernised bars and lounges in attractive surroundings at the foot of Rosedale; nicely furnished, good service, imaginative food — light lunch of soup, sandwiches and an apple, celery and nut crunch; well kept Tetleys on handpump, log fires; bedrooms *(Barbara and Ken Turner)*

☆ **Hartshead**, W Yor [15 Hartshead Lane; not very far from M62 junction 25; SE1822], *Grey Ox*: A bit isolated in winter, but comfortable, with huge helpings of well cooked food running up to hefty steaks; well kept Watneys-related real ales, cosy armchairs by fire, garden with good views and play area *(Alistair Wood, Andy and Jill Kassube)*

Hawes, N Yor [High St; SD8789], *Board*: Welcoming Marstons pub, lounge with open fire, fruit machine and juke box; nice dining room (children allowed if eating) with prints, delft shelf of old bottles and plates; reasonably priced lunchtime and evening food, well kept Marstons Pedigree on handpump; nr start GWG147 *(P Corris, John Fazakerley, Mr and Mrs M D Jones)*; [High St], *Crown*: Bright by comparison, bar and stone-pillared lounge with beams, cottage furniture, hunting prints, brassware, stuffed pheasant and open fire, and attractive, more rustic tap room with bar billiards, more prints and stuffed birds, and open fire; good popular range of quickly served food inc big baps and vegetarian dishes, well kept Theakstons on handpump; children's room *(John Fazakerley, Mel Landells, Gwen and Peter Andrews, C and V Lindsay)*; [High St], *White Hart*: Pleasant bar with well kept Ind Coope Burton and Marstons ales, straightforward bar food, and friendly, efficient bar staff; children only in plainly furnished dining room; bedrooms *(C and V Lindsay, John Fazakerley, Mr and Mrs C R Douglas)*

☆ **Haworth**, W Yor [Main St; SE0337], *Fleece*: Friendly flagstoned village pub with well kept Timothy Taylors Landlord and Ram Tam, good wholesome lunchtime food inc marvellous range of filled good value Yorkshire puddings; real fires, great 'alternative comedy' Brontë room, piped disco/pop music *(Charles Hall, Michel Hooper-Immins, Mrs M J Fraser)*

☆ **Haworth** [Sun St], *Old Hall*: Friendly and atmospheric 16th-century village pub, reputedly haunted; two-room panelled high-ceilinged bar, adjoining Tudor Room, generous good reasonably priced food in bar and restaurant, good service, well kept Bass, Stones and Tetleys, inoffensive piped music; five mins from centre; bedrooms *(C F Walling, Charles Hall)*

Haworth [Main St], *Black Bull*: Smartly redone warmly comfortable Brewers Fayre family pub, with wide choice of standard food, friendly staff and Whitbreads Castle Eden and Trophy; used to be Branwell Brontë's main drinking place; bedrooms good *(Mrs M J Fraser, Dennis Jones, David and Christine Foulkes)*; [Main St], *Kings Arms*: Nice cosy pub with well kept Allied real ales and a fortnightly guest, good bar meals, and Sun lunch *(J V Cattell)*; [West Lane], *Old White Lion*: Three bars, cosy restaurant with good vegetarian dishes; comfortable bedrooms — well priced weekend breaks all year *(C F Walling)*; [out on Bingley Rd; turn off A629 in Cross Roads, up Lees Moor towards Harden — OS Sheet 104, map reference 054381], *Quarry House*: Converted former farmhouse on high moors, almost more of a restaurant but has small bar with well kept Bass, good bar food inc notable soups, good steak sandwiches, pies and puddings, friendly staff; cricket ground next door *(Andy and Jill Kassube, WAH)*; [Main St], *White Lion*: Friendly and atmospheric, with reasonably priced bar food and well kept Websters Yorkshire *(Len Beattie)*

Hebden Bridge, W Yor [Keighley Rd; A6033, on right towards Keighley; SD9927], *Nutclough House*: Interesting range of beers inc Robinwood and Thwaites; very cosy, with attractive food, good games room; bedrooms *(Maureen and Steve Collin, D Swift)*; [Thistle Bottom], *Stubbings Wharf*: Warm and friendly with cheap, wholesome food and good Boddingtons *(Robert Gartery)*

☆ **Helmsley** [Market Sq], *Crown*: Good friendly atmosphere in simple but pleasant beamed front bar rambling back to bigger central dining bar with wide choice of good value bar food (and afternoon teas); friendly and efficient service, good choice of well kept beers, roaring fires, tables in sheltered garden behind with conservatory area; bedrooms nice *(H K Dyson, M J Morgan, Sidney and Erna Wells, Derek Patey, JM, PM)*

☆ **Helmsley**, N Yor [Market Pl; SE6184], *Black Swan*: Striking Georgian house and adjoining Tudor rectory included primarily as a place to stay; beamed and panelled hotel bar with well kept real ale, attractive carved oak settles and Windsor armchairs; cosy and comfortable lounges with a good deal of character; charming sheltered garden; bedrooms particularly well equipped and comfortable, but expensive — one of THF's nicest inns *(H K Dyson, BB)*

☆ **Helmsley** [B1257], *Feversham Arms*: Comfortable and cosy bars in pleasant, efficient and welcoming hotel with well kept Youngers and good bar food inc good omelettes and superb seafood served by smart waitresses; real ale; bedrooms comfortable *(M J Morgan, Walter and Susan Rinaldi-Butcher)*

☆ **High Hoyland**, S Yor [Bank End Lane — OS Sheet 110, map reference 273101; SE2710], *Cherry Tree*: Attractive stone-built village pub with food and well kept John Smiths on handpump in clean bar, small popular restaurant (best to book, esp Sun lunch), friendly staff; lovely views of Cannon Hall Country Park from front *(W P P Clarke, Paul Lightfoot)*

☆ **Holmfirth**, W Yor [known as the Nook; SD1508], *Rose & Crown*: Like entering a time-warp: very basic furnishings, flagstones, low beams, open fires and a barman who can't be hurried as he deals with his 11 well kept real ales; fruit machine, video game, riverside garden *(Michael Rooke, Alastair Campbell)*

Holmfirth [Liphill Bank Rd], *Farmers Arms*: Popular pub with good cheap bar food lunchtime and evening inc big filled Yorkshire puddings; good choice of real ales inc Timothy Taylors and guests *(Andy and Jill Kassube)*; *Huntsman*, *Old Bridge* and *Victoria* also worth knowing for food *(Pauline Crossland, Dave Cawley)*

☆ **Honley**, W Yor [SE1312], *Coach & Horses*: Imaginative bar food, good value from sandwiches and ploughman's up, with friendly service *(John and Jane Horn, Ben Wimpenny)*

Horbury, W Yor [Westfield Lane (B6128); SE3018], *Old Halfway House*: Large family pub, spacious garden with play area, some barbecues *(Paul Lightfoot)*

Hornby, N Yor [NZ3505], *Grange Arms*: Pleasant neatly refurbished white-painted pub with well kept beer, bar food inc decent lunchtime sandwiches, friendly landlord *(John and Joan Wyatt)*

Horsehouse, N Yor [Coverdale rd Middleham—Kettlewell; SE0481], *Thwaite Arms*: Unspoilt, simple country pub with log fire in oak-beamed main bar, John Smiths and Theakstons Best and Old Peculier, and well cooked, traditional food in quiet dining room; garden, camping field; bedrooms *(David Daws)*

Horton in Ribblesdale, N Yor [SD8172], *Crown*: Cheerful, welcoming bar with low ceiling, dark wood, brasses and good fire; bar food, well kept Theakstons; try to chat with elderly gent who though drinking nothing is welcome in bar with his dog who eats coal; bedrooms *(Anon)*

☆ **Hovingham**, N Yor [SE6775], *Worsley Arms*: Good value bar food inc superb ploughman's in comfortable lounge with settees and low tables, Tetleys and Theakstons on handpump in neat, plain but well kept locals' back bar with darts and lots of Yorkshire cricketer photographs, especially of 1930s and 40s; nice tables out by stream; pleasant bedrooms, swifts and house-martins nesting under the eaves — a nice place to stay *(Paul McPherson, BB)*

Hudswell, N Yor [NZ1400], *George & Dragon*: Cosy cottage-style free house,

tranquil and relaxing, with simple unpretentious decor, open fire in small snug bar with hatch service, lots of sporting prints and decorative plates; plentiful good value home-cooked straightforward food evenings and Sun lunchtime, John Smiths Magnet and Websters Choice on handpump, panoramic Swaledale views from little back terrace; service extremely friendly *(Liz and Martin Phillips)*

☆ **Hunton**, N Yor [SE1992], *Countrymans*: Nicely refurbished stripped-stone pub with open fire, no smoking areas, friendly atmosphere, well kept John Smiths, Theakstons and Youngers No 3, substantial straightforward food, good welcoming service — handy for the Dales; live music Sun; well equipped bedrooms *(Mr and Mrs C G Crowther, G W H Kerby)*

☆ **Hunton**, [Leyburn Rd], *New Inn*: Good food inc wide range of vegetarian and German dishes, welcoming local atmosphere, decent wines *(Gill and Neil Patrick)*

Ilkley, W Yor [Ben Rhydding; SE1347], *Wheatley Arms*: Well kept Tetleys on handpump, wide choice of interesting home-made food inc Sun roasts *(Martin and Carol Fincham)*

☆ **Ingbirchworth**, S Yor [Welthorne Lane; off A629 Shepley—Penistone; SE2205], *Fountain*: Neatly kept Wayfarer Inn, with plush spacious lounge, comfortable family room, quite snug front bar, open fires; consistently good bar food, well kept Tetleys and Mild on handpump, well reproduced pop music, pleasant staff, tables outside with play area *(Mr and Mrs R Shaw, Michael Rooke, BB)*

Ingleby Cross, N Yor [NZ4501], *Blue Bell*: Cosy and friendly country local with well kept beer and interesting bar food; simple but good bedrooms in converted barn *(John Burgan, Hilary Irving)*

Ingleton, N Yor [SD6973], *Craven Heifer*: Pleasant pub with lounge and public bars, well kept Thwaites, reasonable range of usual food; children in lounge *(Mel Landells)*; *Wheatsheaf*: Friendly pub with long bar serving particularly well kept Theakstons XB; handy for Ingleborough *(Len Beattie)*

☆ **Jackson Bridge**, W Yor [Scholes Rd; SE1607], *White Horse*: Character low-ceilinged small-roomed pub with friendly landlord, pool room looking out on to charming waterfall and ducks behind, well kept Bass, basic home cooked bar food inc filled Yorkshire puddings served in flat-cap plates, till about 1.30; lots of *Days of Summer Wine* photographs, coffee from 9am *(P A Crossland, D A Cawley, Alastair Campbell)*

☆ **Keighley**, W Yor [Church Green, North St; SE0641], *Grinning Rat*: Busy real ale pub with bare wooden/flagstoned tap room popular with young people and hikers, and basic lounge; extensive range of ales such as Moorhouses Pendle Witches Brew, Timothy Taylors Landlord, Theakstons XB and Old

Peculier, strong farm ciders and interesting bottled beers; good cheap pizzas, CD juke box *(Mel and Phil Lloyd, Charles Hall)*

Kettlesing, N Yor [A59; SE2256], *Bull*: Long circular bar with pool table, darts and juke box; well kept John Smiths Magnet, decent food with daily specials, friendly staff; morning coffee; live entertainment Weds *(Gwen and Peter Andrews)*; [signposted 6 miles W of Harrogate on A59], *Queens Head*: Good local pub nestling in picturesque village, lovely open fires, well spaced tables, food all home-made, from just a starter and pudding (ample helpings of treacle tart, jam roly-poly and so forth) to good scampi, duckling, steaks and pies *(Viv Middlebrook)*

☆ **Kettlewell**, N Yor [SD9772], *Bluebell*: Strong local flavour and busy, lively atmosphere in quaint but unpretentious knocked-through bar with snug areas and flagstones; friendly helpful staff, decent food, Theakstons Best and Old Peculier, Youngers Scotch and No 3, pool room, piped music, children's room, tables on good-sized back terrace; nr start GWG151; bedrooms *(David Oakes, Pauline Crossland, Dave Cawley, Phil Clissitt, Ness Turner, LYM)*

☆ **Kettlewell**, *Kings Head*: Lively and cheerful local away from the tourist centre, cheap food (straightforward, but imaginatively prepared and presented), well kept Tetleys and Timothy Taylors; pool room, bedrooms *(Dick Brown, G T Jones, Gordon L Smith, BB)*

☆ **Kettlewell**, *Racehorses*: Relatively sedate open-plan hotel bar, comfortable and well furnished, with well kept real ales, good bar food inc decent sandwiches, pleasant helpful staff; nr start GWG151; bedrooms *(Joan and John Calvert, J B Lewis, Mr and Mrs J H Adam, S V Bishop, Tony and Penny Burton, G T Jones, LYM)*

Kilnhurst, S Yor [1 Hooton Rd; 5 miles from M18 junction 1: B6090 nr hump-backed bridge; SK4697], *Ship*: Old coaching inn with good home-made lunchtime bar food, evening restaurant, well kept Whitbread Castle Eden and a guest like Marstons Pedigree on handpump *(K J Keegan)*

☆ **Kilnsey**, N Yor [Kilnsey Crag; SD9767], *Tennant Arms*: Spacious beamed and flagstoned inn with open fires (one fireplace made from an ornate carved four-poster), well kept Tetleys and Theakstons Best and Old Peculier, good value bar food inc local trout, piped music, friendly service and atmosphere; weapon collection, maps and stuffed or skeleton animals and fish; views over spectacular Kilnsey Crag from restaurant, nice spot by River Wharfe; on GWG150; comfortable bedrooms all with private bathrooms *(Len Beattie, Wayne Brindle, Dick Brown, G T Jones)*

☆ **Kirkby Overblow**, N Yor [SE3249], *Star & Garter*: Popular cosy local with welcoming landlord, generous helpings of good value standard bar food, dining room for evening meals; well kept Camerons and Everards *(Syd and Wyn Donald, Robert and Lesley Fawthrop)*

☆ **Kirkby Overblow**, *Shoulder of Mutton*: Landlord adds lots of warmth to lovely old pub in picturesque village, good food inc lots of specials and good value steaks (sandwiches only, Sun); two open fires, several wines by the glass, Tetleys and other beers *(Viv Middlebrook)*

☆ **Kirkham**, N Yor [Kirkham Abbey; SE7466], *Stone Trough*: Quaint inn with small, cosy rooms, beams and interesting features, particularly good bar food, log fires, warm welcome, well kept real ales such as Timothy Taylors Landlord and Youngers No 3; restaurant has oak tables and old-fashioned kitchen range with fire; pool room; good outside sitting area with views, good walks *(J C Proud, I S Morley, D E Nicholls)*

☆ **Knaresborough**, N Yor [High Bridge, Harrogate Rd; SE3557], *Yorkshire Lass*: Big pub-restaurant, its lively decoration an acquired taste; good food (especially loaf-sized Yorkshire puddings, also more exotic dishes), comfortable dining room, friendly licensees and staff, well kept Watneys-related real ales and fine riverside position, close to Mother Shipton's Cave with picturesque views from terrace; mellow live music Fri and Sat, monthly dress-up theme nights, daily newspapers, courtesy bus for customers; bedrooms well equipped and good value *(Bob Easton, Beryl and David Bowter, Tim and Ann Newell, Fiona Mutch)*

Langsett, S Yor [SE2100], *Waggon & Horses*: Busy pub with good if rather limited food, Bass and Stones ales *(Dave Braisted)*

Leavening, N Yor [SE7963], *Jolly Farmers*: Well kept Ind Coope Burton, Timothy Taylors and Tetleys, good bar food with lots of fresh veg in separate dining room; friendly licensees; good bedrooms *(Frank Gadbois)*

☆ **Leeds**, W Yor [Hunslet Rd], *Adelphi*: Well restored Edwardian woodwork, glass and tiling in several rooms; particularly well kept Tetleys (virtually the brewery tap), good lunchtime bar food at reasonable prices, live jazz Sat *(Andy and Jill Kassube, Dr and Mrs A K Clarke)*

☆ **Leeds** [Kirkgate, by indoor mkt], *Duck & Drake*: Cavernous no-frills city-centre pub for real ale fans, with over a dozen different beers from all over the country, quick enough turnover to keep them fresh; bustling, friendly atmosphere, limited range of good value bar food, open fire, good service *(Pete Storey, Matthew Redman, David Oakes)*

☆ **Leeds** [86 Armley Rd, by Arkwright St], *Albion*: Fascinating architecture — the original for the 00-gauge model railway pub; a Tetley Heritage Inn, two pubs knocked together in the 1920s, three well restored rooms, separate pool room, well kept Tetleys from superb brass handpumps *(Matt Pringle, Dr and Mrs A K Clarke)*

☆ **Leeds** [9 Burley Rd, junction with Rutland St], *Fox & Newt*: Cheerfully done up with bright Victorian-style paintwork, dark

panelling, bare floorboards, lots of
entertaining nick-nacks, well reproduced but
not obtrusive piped music or juke box, and
reasonably priced lunchtime bar food; main
draw is the range of beers brewed on the
premises (a What The Butler Saw machine
shows the microbrewery); open all day;
children welcome (John Thorndike, LYM)

☆ Leeds [Gt George St], *Victoria*: Well kept
Tetleys, friendly smart bar staff, interesting
mix of customers, wonderful big mirrors
with etched Queen Victorias, impressive
lamp stands extending from the bar which
has unusual elephants' trunks supporting its
brass rail (Michael Rooke, Reg Nelson, Pete
Storey, David Oakes)

Leeds [Great George St], *George*: Good
central well preserved Tetleys drinking pub,
welcoming and lively, at its best during the
week (Comus Elliott, Reg Nelson); [Merrion
Centre], *Pig & Whistle*: Large pub at base of
an office block with well kept pleasant
Camerons on handpump, very reasonable
lunchtime food and friendly staff; can get
busy at lunchtimes and weekend evenings
(John Thorndike); [alley off Briggate, opp
Dixons], *Ship*: Good pubby atmosphere,
every inch lined with custom-framed ship
prints and photographs; well kept Tetleys,
simple lunchtime food; music can be loud
(Dr M A Thomas); [Kirkstall Rd (A65)],
Vesper Gate: On N side of Kirkstall Abbey
ruins, modernised Victorian pub with big
semi-circular bar, good Bass and Stones ales
and wide choice of varied food (popular at
lunchtime); children in family room (A J
Woodhouse)

☆ Leyburn, N Yor [Market Pl], *Golden Lion*:
Calm refuge from the bustling search for
car-park spaces in the market place outside
— two comfortable bay-windowed rooms
knocked together, light squared panelling,
armchairs, china on delft shelf, pale country
tables and chairs in airy eating area with
log-effect gas fire, good value
straightforward bar food, evening
restaurant; good beer brewed to their own
recipe in Harrogate as well as Theakstons,
popular for coffee too; helpful service, tables
out in front; open all day, dogs allowed;
bedrooms good value — especially the
bargain breaks (John Fazakerley, Rita
Horridge, Mr and Mrs M O Jones, Mr and Mrs
D C Leaman, DP and ME Cartwright, Ray and
Gwen Jessop, Paul S McPherson, BB)

☆ Linton, W Yor [SE3947], *Windmill*:
Polished charm, generous helpings of good
bar food and pleasant atmosphere in
carefully preserved small rooms with
antique settles, oak beams, longcase clock,
well kept Youngers Scotch and No 3 —
where the Leeds millionaires go for Sun
sherry, not so upmarket weekdays; tables in
pleasant garden (Tim and Sue Halstead, Ben
Wimpenny, J E Rycroft, LYM)

☆ Linton in Craven, N Yor [B6265
Skipton—Grassington, forking right;
SD9962], *Fountaine*: Glorious surroundings
— neat green running down to little stream,
ancient buildings; and well kept Theakstons

Best, Youngers Scotch and a guest beer,
good range of reasonably priced bar food;
traditional pub recently carefully extended
and now deceptively large, with interestingly
furnished little rooms, open fires, friendly
atmosphere, darts, dominoes, cribbage and
ring-the-bull, fruit machine; children
allowed away from bar (R J August, Andy
and Jill Kassube, Paul Perry, Paul S
McPherson, M V and J Melling, C E Hall,
LYM; more reports please)

Lockton, N Yor [A169 N of Pickering;
SE8490], *Fox & Rabbit*: Family pub nicely
placed on the edge of the moors, well kept
real ales, good value straightforward food,
seats outside and in sun lounge; children's
room (Eileen Broadbent, LYM)

Lofthouse, W Yor [383 Leeds Rd; SE3326],
Gardeners Arms: Nicely appointed, friendly,
well kept Tetleys, lots of dray horse pictures
(Dr and Mrs A K Clarke)

Long Preston, N Yor [A65 Settle—Skipton;
SD8358], *Maypole*: Goes back to 1600s
though main room is Edwardian in style,
with open fire, well kept real ales such as
Boddingtons, Whitbreads Castle Eden and
Trophy and Timothy Taylors Landlord,
wide choice of reasonably priced good
straightforward food inc Sun lunch (Bill
Sykes, Andy and Jill Kassube)

Luddenden Foot, W Yor [Burnley Rd;
SE0424], *Coach & Horses*: Bar food from
burgers to steaks most evenings and
lunchtimes, big open bar with
red-upholstered seats and carpet and a
couple of cosy bay-windowed alcoves,
friendly efficient service (Paul Lightfoot)

Lumbutts, W Yor [Mankinholes Rd;
SD9523], *Shepherds Rest*: Two pleasant
bars, one at back with good views from
tables by picture window; reasonably priced
food lunchtime (Sat only, winter) and
evenings, friendly staff, good service; ideally
placed for walkers, nr Stoodley Pike
monument (Paul Lightfoot)

☆ Malham, N Yor [SD8963], *Buck*: The grand
scenery nr Malham Cove and Gordale Scar
enhances this, the most prominent pub in the
village; busy hikers' bar, spacious lounge
bar, children's area off, well kept
Theakstons Best, XB and Old Peculier, usual
food inc decent ploughman's; nr start
GWG152, on Pennine Way; good value
comfortable bedrooms (Sidney and Erna
Wells, N F Calver, Ben Wimpenny)

Malham, N Yor [SD8963], *Lister Arms*: Large stonebuilt pub
doing well under new management, good
food in bar and restaurant, well kept beer
inc Timothy Taylors; bedrooms (Prof S
Barnett)

Mankinholes, W Yor [SD9523], *Top Brink*:
Lively moorland village pub, quite close to
Pennine Way and nice walks to nearby
monument on Stoodley Pike; has been
popular for friendly atmosphere and good
steaks (midnight licence extension), but no
recent reports (News please)

Marsden, W Yor [Manchester Rd;
Standedge; SE0412], *Great Western*: High
on moors opp small reservoir; slightly

old-fashioned decor, clean, with warm friendly atmosphere; delicious home cooking inc big filled Yor puddings, haddock and plaice evenings and Sat lunchtime, Tetleys *(Paul Lightfoot)*

Marton, N Yor [SE4263], *Apple Tree*: Spotlessly clean with helpful Scots landlord and good choice of real pub food; wider choice in restaurant *(W H and E Thomas)*

Marton cum Grafton, N Yor [signed off A1 3 miles N of A59; SE4263], *Olde Punch Bowl*: Comfortable and spacious open-plan heavy-beamed lounge bar well divided by timbers, with neat groups of tables and open fire; Tetleys and Youngers IPA, Scotch and No 3, generous helpings of good straightforward lunchtime bar food, restaurant; games and juke box in public bar, space for caravans; ; children welcome *(Andy and Jill Kassube, LYM)*

Masham, N Yor [Silver St; linking A6168 with Market Sq; SE2381], *Bay Horse*: John Smiths, Theakstons Old Peculier, XB and Best on handpump, good value if chippy bar food, good friendly service, chatty parrot *(T Preston, Mr and Mrs Hart)*

Menston, W Yor [129 Bradford Rd; A65/A6038; SE1744], *Fox*: Old coaching inn, now a Beefeater but good reasonably priced bar food as well as steaks, well kept Timothy Taylors Landlord and Best; nice surroundings *(Andy and Jill Kassube)*

☆ **Mexborough**, S Yor [S of A6023: follow 'waterbus' signs; SE4800], *Ferry Boat*: Old-fashioned with some traditional furnishings, lively friendly atmosphere, good welcome, well kept real ales inc Bass Special and Theakstons, bar food inc filled Yorkshire puddings, hot meal sandwiches, good pie; nr Aire & Calder Navigation canal *(Mrs M Lawrence, LYM)*

Micklebring, S Yor [SK5295], *Plough*: Well kept John Smiths, cosy bar, winter fire, popular bar food; wide views *(Paul Cartledge)*

☆ **Middleham**, N Yor [SE1288], *Black Swan*: Cheerful local atmosphere and wide choice of filling bar food from good sandwiches and lunchtime ploughman's upwards in heavy-beamed bar with stripped stonework, very sturdy furniture inc high-backed settles built in by big stone fireplace, well kept Theakstons Best, XB and Old Peculier on handpump, maybe piped pop music, separate dining room, tables on cobbles outside and in sheltered back garden; charming village; bedrooms *(Jean and Edward Rycroft, Julian Yorke, Peter Race, P H Brown, H Bramwell, C and V Lindsay, BB)*

Middleham, *Richard III*: Licensees have worked hard to renovate this pub; Theakstons beer and good food; good value bedrooms *(R Groves)*

Middlesmoor, N Yor [up at the top of the Nidderdale rd from Pateley Bridge; SE0874], *Crown*: The great attraction is the position high in Nidderdale; many small rooms, good pub food, dearer but imaginative dishes inc Nidd trout, veal and pork with unusual sauces in dining room

furnished like 1920s living room; extensive wine list; bedrooms *(H Bramwell)*

Mirfield, W Yor [Dunbottle Lane; SE2019], *Dusty Miller*: Modernised, tastefully restored, popular with families for good well priced food; well kept Bass *(Andy and Jill Kassube);* [Stennard Lane, just off A644 towards Dewsbury], *Ship*: Large pub by R Calder, now a Roast Inn with well priced bar food inc good home-made pies, restaurant with good value carvery, Whitbreads-related real ales *(Andy and Jill Kassube);* [105 Leeds Rd (A62), Mirfield Moor], *White Gate*: Recently tastefully renovated, popular at lunch for reasonably priced sandwiches, filled Yorkshire puddings, pies etc; well kept Bass, Bass Light and Stones, popular Mon quiz night *(Andy and Jill Kassube)*

☆ **Muker**, N Yor [B6270 Swaledale rd; SD9198], *Farmers Arms*: Utterly unpretentious local in beautiful valley village with very friendly landlord, genuine and cosy atmosphere, well kept John Smiths and Theakstons, good cider, simple but well prepared bar food, good service; nr start GWG148 *(George Hunt, Kathryn Ogden, WAH, Adam and Elizabeth Gorb, Gordon Theaker)*

Netherton, W Yor [SE1213], *Beaumont Arms*: Pleasant friendly local, good range of cheap, good food and real ale on handpump *(A G Roby)*

☆ **Newholm**, N Yor [signed off A171; NZ8611], *Beehive*: Long pub with low black beams, snug rooms, well kept McEwans 80/- and Theakstons Bitter and Old Peculier, good value food inc local seafood in bar and upstairs restaurant; seats outside *(I H Rorison, Mike and Wendy Proctor, M J Morgan, Margaret and Roy Randle, Mr and Mrs Peter Crane, LYM)*

Norland, W Yor [Moorbottom Rd; coming from Halifax, about a mile past village; SE0723], *Moorcock*: Very clean, bar food inc speciality big beef and onion Yorkshire pudding sandwich, amusing landlady, restaurant *(Paul Lightfoot)*

☆ **Nosterfield**, N Yor [B6267 Masham—Thirsk; SE2881], *Freemasons Arms*: Slightly smarter than usual for the area, with fire in centre of open-plan bar and dining area, Theakstons real ales, unusual country wines, friendly youngish staff, usual food but using fresh local produce — good value; tables outside, very pleasant surroundings; children welcome *(H Bramwell, W B and G Gray)*

Nun Monkton, N Yor [off A59 York—Harrogate; SE5058], *Alice Hawthorn*: Modernised beamed bar with dark red plush settles back-to-back around dimpled copper tables, good value food, friendly service, open fire in big brick fireplace, keen darts players; on broad village green with pond, near River Nidd *(Jean and Theodore Rowland-Entwistle, BB)*

☆ **Ogden**, W Yor [Keighley Rd; SE0631], *Causeway Foot*: Friendly and well kept pub with tasty and wholesome bar food inc lovely fresh sandwiches (well worth the wait if service slows when busy); spacious bar with dance floor for weekly discos; by Ogden reservoir, being developed as country park with surrounding moor and woodland *(Paul Lightfoot, Syd and Wyn Donald)*

Ogden, [Keighley Rd (A629)], *Goose:* Good value bar food lunchtime and evening, friendly service, beers inc Samuel Websters, two spacious and attractive bars *(Paul Lightfoot)*

☆ **Oldstead,** N Yor [SE5380], *Black Swan:* Friendly new licensees, beautiful surroundings with pretty valley views from two big bay windows and picnic-table sets outside; good interesting keenly priced food in bar and restaurant, well kept John Smiths, Tetleys and Theakstons Bitter and Old Peculier on handpump, good log fire, plate collection, maybe piped music; children welcome; recently refurbished bedrooms in comfortable modern back extension *(R A Clements, David and Tessa Garwood, H K Dyson, Andrew and Ruth Triggs, BB)*

☆ **Osmotherley,** N Yor [The Green; SE4499], *Golden Lion:* Good range of medium-priced very good bar food and well kept John Smiths in very friendly family-run pub, a base for the Dirgers (those who've done the gruelling 44-mile Lyke Wake Walk which starts here); popular Sun lunchtimes *(Andrew Morrissey, E A Turner)*

☆ **Osmotherley,** *Three Tuns:* Small, pleasant pub in honeypot village, well kept McEwans 80/-, Theakstons Old Peculier and Youngers No 3 in clean and tidy simple bar, notably good food in back restaurant — big helpings, very good value *(Ruth and Andrew Triggs, E J Cutting, Walter and Susan Rinaldi-Butcher)*

Ossett, W Yor [Densbury Rd; SE2820], *Red Lion:* Popular for meals — tables to be booked for Sun lunch; clean and tidy; good value hot food and well kept beer; friendly service; comfortable chairs *(A and J Jackson)*; [Owl Lane], *Royal Oak:* Small cosy local by fields on outskirts, alcoves at far end of main room, small games room, Wilsons and other ales *(Paul Lightfoot)*

☆ **Oswaldkirk,** N Yor [signed off B1363/B1257 S of Helmsley; SE6279], *Malt Shovel:* Distinctive ancient building, a former small manor house, with interestingly decorated rooms leading off small heavily beamed traditional bar; well kept Sam Smiths, big blazing open fires in stone fireplaces, generous helpings of straightforward freshly cooked bar food from sandwiches up, friendly staff, piped music, period garden; children welcome; big bedrooms with lovely views, huge breakfasts *(D M and D E Livesley, JM, PM, WAH, John and Chris Simpson, Celia and Gordon Christie, Hilary Bill, Virginia Jones, Andrew Morrissey, Brian and Anna Marsden, A M Neal, J E Rycroft, Paul McPherson, LYM)*

Otley, W Yor [Newall with Clifton; off B645 towards Blubberhouses, a mile N; SE2045], *Spite:* Comfortably modernised pub which has had good food inc good

ploughman's, and particularly well kept Websters Yorkshire and Choice, with log fire and neat well lit rose garden; we've heard too little since it changed hands in 1990 to be sure about its status now, and hope for more news from readers *(Richard Cole, Andy and Jill Kassube, LYM)*

Overton, W Yor [204 Old Rd; SE2617], *Reindeer:* Attractive and spacious free house, good views from back conservatory and terrace, cheap tasty food evenings (not Sun) and Sun lunch, friendly staff; Tetleys, juke box; handy for Mining Museum *(Paul Lightfoot)*

☆ **Oxenhope,** W Yor [off B6141 towards Denholme; SE0335], *Dog & Gun:* Busy pub with plenty of character and atmosphere, well kept Timothy Taylors Landlord and Tetleys on handpump, good bar food inc sandwiches at reasonable prices and good value Sun lunches; bistro-style restaurant *(Geoff and Julie Bond, J E Rycroft)*

☆ **Oxenhope,** W Yor [A6033 Keighley—Hebden Bridge; SE0335], *Waggon & Horses:* Good range of beers and reasonably priced food in moorside pub with wonderful views; pleasant simple decor, fleeces on stripped stone walls *(Geoff and Julie Bond, LYM)*

Patrick Brompton, N Yor [SE2291], *Green Tree:* Public bar, nicely furnished lounge other side of entrance porch; John Smiths and Theakstons on handpump; blackboard menu from ploughman's to steak, extensive wine list, waitress service; busy summer Sats *(M and J Back)*

☆ **Pickering,** N Yor [Market Pl; SE7984], *White Swan:* Inviting small and quiet plush hotel bar, friendly staff and locals, good chip-free bar food, well kept Camerons Bitter and Strongarm; good restaurant with remarkable choice of St Emilion clarets — a house speciality; a good place to stay *(Brian and Anna Marsden, A and J Jackson, Paul McPherson, Bob and Lesley Fawthrop)*

☆ **Pickering** [Market Pl], *Bay Horse:* Cosy red plush bar with red curtains, old-fashioned prints, watercolours and horsey bric-a-brac, heavy beams, big fire, well kept Camerons Bitter, Strongarm and Premium on handpump, above-average bar food from ploughman's through steak and kidney pie to steaks (not Fri or Sat evenings); bigger public bar behind, restaurant upstairs *(Eileen Broadbent, WAH, Brian and Anna Marsden, BB)*

Pickering [A169 towards Malton], *Bulls Head:* It's the food in this straightforward roadside pub that draws people; outstanding value, substantial helpings *(Roy Cove)*

Pudsey, W Yor [SE2233], *Beulah:* Clean, well kept and popular, with lovely plain food inc good prawn sandwiches and hot varied dishes *(Syd and Wyn Donald)*; [Swinnow Rd], *Britannia:* Old stone pub, very tastefully modernised, very popular for big helpings of early evening food running up to very big mixed grill, with puddings such as good trifle; good value — get there early; John Smiths and Magnet on handpump *(Andy and Jill Kassube)*

Raskelf, N Yor [SE4971], *Three Tuns*: Well kept Theakstons XB in vibrant and friendly local, plentiful food *(Jacquie and Jon Payne)*

☆ Reeth, N Yor [Market Pl (B6270); SE0499], *Kings Arms*: 18th-century oak-beamed free house by wide sloping green of old-world village — a lovely spot; recently refurbished as dining pub, with homely welcome, pine pews around lounge walls, log fire in big stone inglenook, quieter room behind, well kept Theakstons (and tea or coffee), also John Smiths and Tetleys; good reasonably priced food, obliging service; children very welcome; bedrooms — we have not yet had reports on these *(Adam and Elizabeth Gorb, Gordon Theaker, Jacquie and Jon Payne, John Fazakerley)*

Reeth, *Black Bull*: On same green, with beamed L-shaped bar, well kept McEwans 80/- and Theakstons Best, XB and Old Peculier, reasonably priced bar food; children allowed till 8.30, public bar with pool and other games; bedrooms pleasant with good facilities, good breakfasts *(John Fazakerley, Penny Webster, Mike and Wendy Proctor, LYM)*

☆ Richmond, N Yor [Finkle St; NZ1801], *Black Lion*: Cosy and welcoming pub with dark decor, lots of separate rooms, well kept Camerons Strongarm and Everards Old Original on handpump, no smoking lounge, good generous bar food (salads, chicken pie, casseroles, game and steaks all recommended); bedrooms reasonably priced *(Andy and Jill Kassube, Len Beattie)*

☆ Ripley, N Yor [off A61 Harrogate—Ripon; SE2861], *Boars Head*: Long flagstoned bar in beautiful old building, newly opened as hotel; notable wines by the glass inc a 1er cru Chablis, bar food such as Yorkshire pudding with Old Peculier casserole, steak sandwich, Welsh rarebit, pasta with cream cheese and garlic, vegetarian lasagne, smoked haddock and spinach bake, and puddings clearly from the good restaurant's kitchen; Theakstons real ale; bedrooms *(Viv Middlebrook)*

☆ Ripon, N Yor [Bridge Lane; off Bondgate Green (itself off B6265); SE3171], *Water Rat*: Relatively new riverside pub, already a favourite for its attractive decorations, charming terrace, cathedral view and huge helpings of notable bar food inc wide vegetarian choice, filling soups, fresh fish, big steaks; good choice of real ales inc Big End, Marstons Pedigree, Old Mill and guests *(Isolde King, Andy and Jill Kassube)*

Ripon [Boroughbridge Rd, nr racecourse], *Blackamoor*: Doing well as an eating place under newish landlord, Bass and Stones on handpump, great food at moderate price *(Bill Link)*

Roberttown, W Yor [just off A62; SE1922], *Star*: Smart little pub, locally popular for good value home-made bar food and daily carvery; good service, Stones on handpump *(Andy and Jill Kassube)*

☆ Robin Hoods Bay, N Yor [King St, Bay Town; NZ9505], *Olde Dolphin*: Interesting 18th-century inn on several levels, part being restored; friendly service, well kept Courage and good food inc quite a few local seafood specialities at very reasonable prices; nr sea front in attractive little town; dogs welcome in bar if well behaved, some live entertainment in winter; bedrooms basic but very cheap *(WAH, Mike and Wendy Proctor, Len Beattie, Andy and Jill Kassube)*

Robin Hoods Bay [The Dock, Bay Town], *Bay*: Main attraction is its beach location; friendly and busy, with warm fire, welcoming staff, good bar food inc good steaks at moderate prices, well kept Camerons and Everards; long walk back up to village car park; bedrooms *(Mike and Wendy Proctor)*

☆ Runswick Bay, N Yor [NZ8217], *Royal*: Lovely views down over fishing village and bay from big-windowed plain front lounge (with fishtank) and terrace; cheerful and lively atmosphere, well kept John Smiths, welcoming staff, nautical back bar; limited choice of bar food inc local fresh fish, in very generous helpings *(Prof S Barnett, Mike and Wendy Proctor, LYM)*

Saltergate, N Yor [A169 N of Pickering; SE8594], *Saltergate*: Classic Yorkshire moorland pub close to scenic Hole of Horcum, and surrounded by bleak heather moors; two rooms, spartan bar with centuries-old, ever-burning fire and wildlife sketches; austere atmosphere; family room with pool and moorland views; home-cooked, cheap bar meals, keg beers; customers mainly walkers; seats outside *(Lee Goulding)*

☆ Scarborough, N Yor [Cambridge Terrace; TA0489], *Cask*: Decent choice of real ales in lively conversion of big Victorian house, quite a rabbit-warren of interconnecting rooms, lots of panelling — some carved, lots of bric-a-brac hanging from ceiling inc gas mask, china bedpans etc; lively but well behaved young clientele, well kept Tetleys, Theakstons Old Peculier, Youngers Scotch and No 3 and changing guest beers, good choice of bottled beers, good value home-cooked food 11-2 and early evening, juke box *(Mr and Mrs M Phillips, LYM)*

Scarborough [opp harbour], *Golden Ball*: Old seafront pub with fruit machines and TV in smallish panelled bar, upstairs bar overlooking harbour and passing holidaymakers; well kept Sam Smiths, children's room; can get very crowded *(Colin and Mary Meaden)*; [Vernon Rd], *Hole in the Wall*: Basic beer drinkers' pub with good, well kept beers, good welcome and mix of customers; no piped music *(Phil and Sally Gorton)*; [St Marys St], *Leeds Arms*: Well kept, cheap Bass on handpump; interesting interior, in old town *(David and Ruth Hollands)*; [North Marine Rd], *North Riding*: Much used by locals — a corner pub behind quieter North Beach, with traditional public bar and plush lounge; cheap bar meals such as Yorkshire pudding with hot-pot or beef curry; keg Camerons; welcome haven from fish-and-chip holiday bars *(Joan and Michel Hooper-Immins)*

☆ **Scawton**, N Yor [SE5584], *Hare*: Low and pretty pub, much modernised, with a couple of cosy settees, simple wall settles, stools, little wheelback armchairs and wood-effect or trestle tables, and inoffensive piped music; cheerful welcome, well kept Theakstons Best, XB and Old Peculier and McEwans 80/- on handpump, decent straightforward food from sandwiches to big steaks; pool table up steps, seats outside, nice inn-signs; handy for Rievaulx *(Nick Dowson, Alison Hayward, BB)*

Scorton, N Yor [B1263 Richmond—Yarm; just outside village; NZ2500], *St Cuthberts*: Welcoming staff, well kept Theakstons on handpump, wide choice of good food, esp whitebait and fish platter, with children's helpings of all dishes; nr Catterick racecourse *(Martin and Carol Fincham)*

☆ **Seamer**, N Yor [Main St; TA0284], *Copper Horse*: Wide range of generously served good bar food inc good ploughman's, sandwiches, fine fresh fish and meat dishes, some starters big enough for main courses, in white-painted old pub in pretty village; beams, brasses, bare stone, part wood-floored and part carpeted, with gold plush bar stools and wooden chairs around cast-iron-framed tables; well kept Websters Yorkshire, very friendly service, restaurant *(Dr Thomas Mackenzie, Viv Middlebrook)*

Settle, N Yor [SD8264], *Golden Lion*: Bright red plush in cheerful high-beamed bar with enormous fireplace, bar, well kept Thwaites ales, games in lively public bar, horses still stabled in coachyard; bedrooms *(LYM)*

Sheffield [Globe Works, Penistone Rd], *Ratteners Rest*: In basement of restored 1825 cutlery factory, named for 1840 saboteurs active here; flagstones, comfortable sofas, unusual artefacts inc scythes, knives and butter churn; good value home-made bar food, Tetleys and Theakstons on handpump, interesting visitor centre and cutlery shop upstairs; children in separate dining area; open all day *(Gill Burley)*; [Charles St, handy for stn], *Red Lion*: Busy, well run, refurbished open-plan town pub, very clean and comfortable; efficiently served standard bar food (not Sun) with orders called over Tannoy, well kept Wards beers, small conservatory, pleasant landlady *(T Nott, Pete Storey)*; [86 Brown St], *Rutland Arms*: Good local atmosphere in comfortably refurbished pub full of china, brass and plates, well kept Ind Coope Burton, Tetleys and Youngers No 3, well prepared reasonably priced lunchtime food, exemplary lavatories; delightful hanging baskets and window-boxes; handy for rly stn and Polytechnic *(Alan and Heather Jacques, Dr P Johnson)*

☆ **Shelley**, W Yor [Roydhouse; SE2112], *Three Acres*: Good range of real ales in pleasant pub with emphasis on wide choice of nicely presented good food; restaurant, pleasant attentive staff, pianist playing light music; bedrooms *(Roger A Bellingham, Mrs M*

Whiteley)*

☆ **Skipton**, N Yor [Canal St; from Water St (A65) turn into Coach St, then left after canal bridge; SD9852], *Royal Shepherd*: Nr canal (and centre) with big bar, snug and dining room with open fires and old pictures of town and canal, tables outside, games and juke box; children allowed in dining room lunchtime; good reasonably priced, nicely presented straightforward food, quick service and Hartleys XB and Whitbreads-related real ales, unusual whiskies, good mix of lunchtime customers *(Derek and Sylvia Stephenson, WAH, Barbara and Mike Williams, Adam and Elizabeth Gorb)*

Skipton [Market Pl], *Black Horse*: Old coaching inn opp Skipton castle; good choice of meals in bar and dining area, well kept beers on handpump; popular with pot-holers and climbers; huge open fire in winter attracts market shoppers for coffee *(Jim and Maggie Cowell)*

☆ **Slingsby**, N Yor [Railway St; SE7075], *Grapes*: Straightforward but popular good value food and well kept Camerons in stone-built village local, quiet and clean, with cast-iron-framed tables on patterned carpet, children in room off bar, friendly service; tables in garden behind *(J and D Coates, BB)*

☆ **Snape**, N Yor [SE2784], *Castle Arms*: Comfortable and homely, with cosy inglenooks and open fires, and enterprising food in attractive small dining area; friendly licensees — and now has real ale, and wide choice of reasonably priced wines by the bottle; pleasant village *(Kelvin Lawton, H Bramwell, I H Rorison)*

☆ **Sowerby**, W Yor [Steep Lane; SE0423], *Travellers Rest*: Surrounded by fields and farms, overlooking Calderdale Valley (view at night particularly beautiful); several cosy and spotless little rooms, open fire, reasonably priced good food such as hot beef sandwich or big filled Yorkshire puddings; spotless, with friendly service; garden *(Mrs Marjorie Donchey, P N Lightfoot)*

☆ **Soyland**, W Yor [OS Sheet 110, map reference 012203; SE0423], *Blue Ball*: Unspoilt but adequately comfortable moorland pub, good range of consistently well kept Theakstons and Timothy Taylors ales and guest beers; straightforward bar food; music room with piano and organ; bedrooms *(Michael Rooke)*

Speeton, N Yor [B1229 — OS Sheet 101, map reference 140746; TA1575], *Honeypot*: New purpose-built roadhouse close to the spectacular RSPB trails along Bampton Cliffs, useful as a family refreshment stop, with straightforward bar food, Watneys-related real ales, friendly staff, piped music, fine Wolds views, well-designed children's play area *(Anthony Sargent, Caroline Gant)*

☆ **Sprotbrough**, S Yor [Lower Sprotbrough; 2 3/4 miles from M18 junction 2; SE5302], *Boat*: Nice spot by River Don for busy but spacious ex-farmhouse with three interestingly furnished areas, big stone fireplaces, latticed windows, dark brown beams, bar meals rather than snacks; piped music can be rather obtrusive; well kept Courage Directors and John Smiths Bitter and Magnet, farm cider; big sheltered courtyard, river walks; restaurant (Tues-Sat evening, Sun lunch); open all day summer Sats *(Paul Mellors, GSB, Andy and Jill Kassube, ILP, K Leist, Wayne Brindle, LYM)*

☆ **Stainforth**, N Yor [B6479 Settle—Horton-in-Ribblesdale;SD8267], *Craven Heifer*: Small cosy village pub with friendly licensees, log fire, reasonably priced bar food inc well filled sandwiches, well kept Thwaites on handpump, useful for this Upper Ribblesdale walking area; bedrooms excellent value *(John and Dee Morrison, RAF, Andy and Jill Kassube)*

☆ **Staithes**, N Yor [NZ7818], *Cod & Lobster*: Superb waterside setting for friendly local in unspoilt fishing village under dramatic sandstone cliff; well kept Camerons; parking nearby difficult, and the walk up to the top car park is quite steep *(Mike and Wendy Proctor, Eileen Broadbent, LYM)*

☆ **Stanbury**, W Yor [SE0037], *Old Silent*: Popular moorland village inn near Haworth, small rooms packed with bric-a-brac, four real ales, food in bar and restaurant served till late in the evening; friendly newish licensees have now settled in well; good hill views, tables on attractive terrace; bedrooms old-fashioned but well equipped *(Anthony Barnes, Geoff and Julie Bond)*

Stanbury [OS Sheet 104, map reference 008371], *Wuthering Heights*: Clean and very friendly, with good landlord, good value food (esp Yorkshire pudding with onion gravy) and well kept Tetleys on handpump; Thurs quiz night; bedrooms *(Peter and Bridgett Kitson)*

☆ **Starbotton**, N Yor [B6160 Upper Wharfedale rd N of Kettlewell — OS Sheet 98, map reference 953749; SD9574], *Fox & Hounds*: Prettily placed little Upper Wharfedale village inn, updated and brought rather upmarket (not all who knew it before approve of the changes) — but still has flagstones, beams, big log fire, lunchtime bar food such as sandwiches, soup and Yorkshire puddings, evening meals (no smoking dining room); well kept Theakstons Best, XB and Old Peculier and Youngers Scotch, board games, dominoes; children allowed in small side room, lunchtime; bedrooms; closed Tues lunchtime and Mon in winter *(Mr and Mrs K H Frostick, Andy and Jill Kassube, Carol and Richard Glover, J E Rycroft, Mary and Lionel Tonks, LYM)*

☆ **Staveley**, N Yor [signed off A6055 Knaresborough—Boroughbridge;SE3663], *Royal Oak*: Prettily laid out beamed and tiled-floor pub with broad bow window and tables on front lawn; good service, friendly atmosphere, very reasonably priced food *(Peter Burton, LYM)*

Staxton, N Yor [TA0279], *Stirrup*: Small pub with good licensees, well kept Tetleys and Youngers, good range of bottled beers,

good food inc soup, sandwiches, ploughman's and home-cooked hot dishes *(J E Rycroft)*

Stillington, N Yor [SE5968], *White Bear*: Clean village pub with pleasant old-world surroundings, friendly staff and efficient service; amazingly good value 3-course meals Mon-Thurs between 5.30 and 7; good value at other times as well *(Mr and Mrs W Davies)*

Stokesley, N Yor [1 West End; NZ5209], *White Swan*: Free house with vast range of beers, guests every two weeks, such as Batemans XXXB, Fullers ESB, Marstons Pedigree, Premier Maidens Ruin, Robinwood Old Fart and Whitby Wobble; simple country place with food limited to pizza, no music *(E J Cutting)*

☆ **Stutton**, N Yor [SE4841], *Hare & Hounds*: Old stone-built pub with old-world low-ceilinged lounge and comfortable restaurant; well kept and priced Sam Smiths OB on handpump, decent wine, generous bar food (inc Yorkshire pudding with lots of dishes) — if tables are full they take your name at the bar so there's a strict rota; children allowed if eating *(Andy and Jill Kassube, J G Thorpe, T Nott)*

Summer Bridge, N Yor [junction B6451/B6165; SE2062], *Flying Dutchman*: Named, not after the operatic mariner, but a racehorse who won his owner 2000 gns in 1851; racing prints on walls, carpeted lounge with upholstered chairs and wall settles, and piped folk music; general knowledge quiz Thurs evening; well kept Sam Smiths OB on handpump and bar food inc good giant Yorkshire pudding with beef and gravy; roast Sun lunch; back garden; bedrooms *(Frank Cummins)*

☆ **Sutton under Whitestoncliffe**, N Yor [A170 E of Thirsk; SE4983], *Whitestonecliffe*: Beamed roadside pub with Theakstons and Watneys-related real ales on handpump, good value bar meals (can be eaten in restaurant) inc fresh fish, good puddings; good service, open fire in main bar, back games room with pool; bedrooms *(Andrew and Ruth Triggs, H K Dyson, Mr and Mrs F W Sturch)*

☆ **Tan Hill**, N Yor [Arkengarthdale (Reeth—Brough) rd, at junction with Keld/W Stonesdale rd; NY8906], *Tan Hill*: Included for its remarkable very remote position completely isolated (and often snowbound) on the moors — Britain's highest pub, and a haven for walkers on the Pennine Way; basic furnishings, no mains electricity (the juke box is powered by a generator), flagstone floors, two big fires, Theakstons Best, XB and Old Peculier, cheery food, games room, occasional singalong accordion sessions; housekeeping can be rather rough-and-ready, can get very crowded if not fine — plenty of room outside; children welcome; bedrooms basic *(Paul McPherson, Mrs R Heaton, Anthony Barnes, LYM)*

☆ **Thirsk**, N Yor [Market Pl; SE4382], *Golden Fleece*: Popular bar in attractive and comfortable THF hotel well used by locals, with well kept real ales, good reasonably priced bar food, eager young staff; pianist Sun lunchtime, violinists Thurs and Fri evenings; can get rather cramped; comfortable bedrooms *(Peter Race)*

Thixendale, N Yor [SE8461], *Cross Keys*: Small, warm and peaceful, two real fires, Tetleys and Youngers Scotch on handpump, good food from well filled sandwiches up, lunchtime and evening; handy for Wolds Way *(Steve White)*

Thornton in Lonsdale, N Yor [SD6976], *Marton Arms*: Over a dozen real ales on handpump, such as Dent, Fullers, Hartleys and Theakstons — real care taken over them; good pizzas, burgers, specials and other food, attractive Dales setting; bedrooms *(Peter Barnsley)*

Thornton le Clay, N Yor [SE6865], *White Swan*: Good value well presented food inc good Sun lunch in welcoming and attractive L-shaped room with central bar, brasses, tankards and corn dollies hanging from rafters; relaxed atmosphere, good value bar food inc Sun roast lunch; no smoking area *(Barbara and Ken Turner)*

☆ **Thruscross**, N Yor [signed from A59 Harrogate—Skipton at Blubberhouses, or off B6255 Grassington—Pateley Bridge at Greenhow Hill; OS Sheet 104, map reference 159587; SE1558], *Stone House*: Moorland pub with beams, flagstones, stripped stone, dark panelling and good fires; straightforward bar food from sandwiches to steaks, Tetleys Mild and Bitter, traditional games, sheltered tables outside; restaurant (not Sun evening); has been open all day; children welcome *(Simon Bates, LYM)*

☆ **Thurlstone**, S Yor [OS Sheet 110, map reference 230034; SE2303], *Huntsman*: Well run old stone-built pub with well kept Wards and maybe other real ales on handpump, friendly atmosphere, lunchtime bar food *(Michael Rooke)*

Tosside, N Yor [SD7755], *Dog & Partridge*: Friendly comfortable village pub, home-cooked food, rustic tables *(Mrs J Crawford)*

☆ **Ulley**, S Yor [Turnshaw Rd; 2 miles from M1 junction 31 — off B6067 in Aston; SK4687], *Royal Oak*: Friendly and popular stone-built country pub with stable-theme beamed lounge, family room, big garden; well kept Sam Smiths OB on handpump, good food seven days *(WAH)*

☆ **Upper Poppleton**, N Yor [A59 York—Harrogate; SE5554], *Red Lion*: Attractive and spotless old-world bars and dining areas, with warm atmosphere, dark and cosy, quiet and friendly — popular with older people and businessmen; good lunchtime bar food from sandwiches through good vegetarian dishes to roast beef and Yorkshire pudding; pleasant garden; bedrooms in extension *(F J Robinson, Roger Bellingham, James Newton)*

Upper Poppleton [The Green, off A59 York—Harrogate], *White Horse*: Lovely

setting in charming village, hotel with friendly, relaxed atmosphere, good bar staff, no delays no matter how busy, good choice of beers (Bass particularly well kept) on handpump, good value food; bedrooms very comfortable and good value, with a kitchen for guests and good breakfasts *(G A Bailey)*

Wainstalls, W Yor [Lower Saltonstall — turn off opp Crossroads Inn; SE0428], *Cat i' th' Well*: Small, very cosy and spotless, with many interesting ornaments and pictures, pleasant garden with play area; next to waterfall in quiet countryside below steep hill *(Paul Lightfoot)*; [Mt Tabor Rd — take Pelton New Rd out of Halifax], *Crossroads*: In tiny village overlooking Calder Valley, quiet, with friendly atmosphere, live entertainment some nights, reasonable prices *(P N Lightfoot)*

☆ **Wakefield**, W Yor [77 Westgate End], *Beer Engine*: Great atmosphere in basic pub done out with flagstone floors, wood-backed wall seats, fires in Victorian cast-iron fireplaces, old brewery mirrors, real gas lighting — some fittings rescued from defunct pubs; well kept Old Mill, Tetleys, Timothy Taylors Landlord and Ram Tam on handpump, Marstons Owd Rodger tapped from the cask and other guest beers, good value lunchtime bar food Fri and Sat (closed lunchtime Sun-Thurs); darts, fruit machine, loud juke box, TV in third room; seats out in pleasant area behind *(W P P Clarke, Andy and Jill Kassube, Michael Rooke)*

Wakefield [Westgate], *Henry Boons*: Brewery tap for adjoining Clarks Brewery, main bar full of breweriana, side room papered with local newspaper cuttings, library for customers, tables with inlaid chess boards (pieces available); lots of character with cubby holes and wooden floor; guest beers too, food in back room, live bands some evenings; very much a young person's place now *(Mr and Mrs P A Jones, Andrew Roberts)*

☆ **Warthill**, N Yor [village signed off A64 York—Malton and A166 York—Great Driffield; SE6755], *Agar Arms*: Welcoming and prettily placed pub opp duckpond, famous for its steaks, all sorts and sizes, with other dishes inc lunchtime sandwiches and children's dishes; softly lit and nicely decorated, with open fires and well kept Sam Smiths on electric pump *(BB)*

☆ **Wass**, N Yor [SE5679], *Wombwell Arms*: Former 18th-century granary, just attractively renovated by new owners, with well kept guest beers and fine choice of interesting wines by glass and bottle in small, friendly and cosy bar; superb imaginative food such as beef with orange and brandy or venison with redcurrants; clean and well kept yet informal and intimate; bedrooms comfortable, great value *(Chris and Dawn Waldron, Richard Gibbs)*

Weaverthorpe, N Yor [SE9771], *Star*: Neat litle village inn with front lounge, main back lounge, small pool room, restaurant and open fires; has been praised for well kept Tetleys and Theakstons Bitter and XB, extensive range of upmarket food inc pheasant and so forth, good value bedrooms and friendly licensees, but no recent reports *(News please)*

☆ **Wentworth**, S Yor [3 miles from M1 junction 36; signed off A6135; SK3898], *Rockingham Arms*: Comfortably furnished main bar with coal fires, hunting pictures and copper-topped tables, good bar food from sandwiches through filled Yorkshire puddings up (not Sun evening), well kept Theakstons and Youngers on handpump; separate lively Barn Bar with live music Weds-Fri, tables in attractive garden with own well kept bowling green; has been open all day; bedrooms *(LYM)*

☆ **West Burton**, N Yor [on green, off B6160 Bishopdale—Wharfedale; SE0186], *Fox & Hounds*: Unspoilt, simple local doing well under friendly newish licensees; small bar with extension, homely welcoming atmosphere, well kept Theakstons on handpump, generous wholesome home-cooked bar food inc children's dishes, good service from friendly staff, residents' dining room; in idyllic Dales village along long green; good bedrooms *(Helen and Tom Atkins, Mr and Mrs A E Woodward)*

West Tanfield, N Yor [A6108 N of Ripon — OS Sheet 99, map reference 268788; SE2678], *Bruce Arms*: Traditional village pub with mixture of old-fashioned seats around the log fire in its snug front bar, arch to back bar, short choice of good bar food from sandwiches through cottage pie or ham and eggs or steak (the ploughman's has been good), well kept John Smiths and Theakstons Best and XB, darts, fruit machine, tables outside (the stables are still in use); restaurant; no bar food Mon, closed Mon lunchtime exc bank hols; children welcome lunchtime *(Frank Cummins, LYM)*

☆ **West Witton**, N Yor [A684 W of Leyburn; SE0688], *Wensleydale Heifer*: Clean and comfortable lounge and two snug bars, good log fire, pleasant decor, interesting prints, chintz-upholstered furniture — more the feel of a hotel than a pub; pleasant service, well kept John Smiths, good helpings of carefully prepared food inc interesting dishes in stall-style separate bistro or restaurant; attractive bedrooms *(Paul McPherson)*

Whiston, S Yor [Turner Lane; nr M1 junction 33; SK4590], *Golden Ball*: Cosy, with low beams, well kept Tetleys, reasonably priced bar food, good back restaurant *(Paul Cartledge)*

☆ **Whitby**, N Yor [Bagdale; off Stn Sq opp Pannett Pk; NZ9011], *Bagdale Hall*: Handsome medieval manor newly converted to restaurant and hotel, not a pub but included for its good bar lunches — also a good place to stay; Camerons real ale, good choice of spirits, fine restaurant *(Dave Buckley)*

☆ **Whitby** [Flowergate], *Little Angel*: Clean and friendly local with boating-theme decoration, welcoming licensees, well kept Tetleys, generous helpings of good reasonably priced food; service quick even if busy, children allowed if well behaved *(WAH, Eileen Broadbent, Mrs R M Morris)*

Whitby [off West Cliff], *Granby*: Clean and well kept traditional Camerons pub with dimpled copper tables, flock wallpaper, Victorian photographs, hexagonal ceiling design with mirror centrepiece, public bar up a few steps; friendly service, generous helpings of good value food lunchtime and evening seven days, piped music; children welcome *(Colin and Mary Meaden)*; [nr West Cliff], *White House*: Modern, lots of knick-knacks such as aeroplane propeller, plates, plants and so forth; well kept Bass and Stones bitter, good sandwiches as well as other food, comfortable seating; restaurant *(G T Jones)*

Wigginton, N Yor [Plainville Lane; off B1363 York—Helmsley; SE5958], *Jacobean Lodge*: Lovely secluded country-style inn with tables on lawn, friendly service, good home-cooked inexpensive food, open fires, oak beams, pool room; bedrooms pleasant *(James Newton)*

☆ **Wigglesworth**, N Yor [SD8157], *Plough*: Pleasant and well run country inn attracting most people for its highly regarded barn/conservatory restaurant, good food in bar too; lots of little rooms surrounding bar area, some smart and plush, others spartan yet cosy; well kept Flowers IPA and Hartleys XB, good friendly service; seats outside, with views of rolling hills; bedrooms good and well equipped, with big breakfasts *(Lee Goulding, G W H Kerby)*

Wooldale, W Yor [SE1509], *Wooldale Arms*: Friendly little free house in small village with well kept Lorimers Scotch and Wards Best, and two others in rotation on handpump; comfortable and popular *(Andrew Roberts)*

Wortley, S Yor [A629 Sheffield—Huddersfield; SK3099], *Wortley Arms*: Carefully and very recently refurbished old coaching inn with Youngers and Theakstons XB and Old Peculier all on handpump; restaurant; bedrooms *(J V Cattell)*

☆ **York**, N Yor [26 High Petergate], *York Arms*: Many-roomed pub just down from Minster, warm, friendly and relaxed; entrance nearest Minster leads into snug little basic panelled bar with a large refurbished no smoking lounge on right; second entrance further down opens into second cosier partly panelled lounge full of old bric-a-brac, prints, brown-cushioned wall settles, dimpled copper tables and an open fire; well kept Sam Smiths OB and Museum, good value food lunchtime and early evening from soup and well filled crusty sandwiches to Yorkshire puddings, cheerfully efficient service, no music, open all day *(Vincent Ainsworth, Tony Bland, Lee Goulding, H K Dyson, BB)*

☆ **York** [Walmgate], *Spread Eagle*: Narrow, popular pub with main dark vault and two cosier rooms leading off; lots of old enamel adverts and prints on walls, good regularly changing range of well kept real ales such as

Timothy Taylors and Caledonian 80/-, good bar food inc huge chip butties and luscious Yorkshire puddings served 12-8, friendly staff, good atmosphere, juke box *(Lee Goulding, Mr and Mrs C H Garnett, BB)*

☆ **York** [Micklegate], *Walkers*: Unusual layout, front mainly a comfortable eating area — good generous food, very prompt; long bar at back, with beautifully kept Theakstons; friendly service, lively but civilised atmosphere *(Ben Wimpenny)*
York [55 Blossom St], *Bay Horse*: Rambling-roomed and staunchly traditional Victorian, low beams, old prints, tiled fireplace, still-intact bar hatches, buttoned leather settles and so forth — nothing posey about it, very much a well used local, though popular with young people *(Dr and Mrs A K Clarke, LYM)*; [Goodramgate], *Cross Keys*: Large, rambling town pub with very friendly bar staff and well kept Bass on handpump *(R P Taylor)*; [23 Market St], *Hansom Cab*: Comfortable, with well kept Sam Smiths on handpump, good appetising food *(Alastair Campbell)*; [7 Stonegate], *Punchbowl*: Black and white timbered pub with a couple of wood-panelled bars, photographs of old York and unobtrusive piped music; well kept Bass and Stones on handpump, jazz Thurs *(Brian Jones)*; [Merchantgate, between Fossgate and Piccadilly], *Red Lion*: Low-beamed rambling rooms with some stripped Tudor brickwork, relaxed old-fashioned furnishings, well kept John Smiths real ale, bar snacks and summer meals, tables outside, good juke box or piped music *(LYM)*; [High Petergate — ie a different pub], *Red Lion*: Ideally placed almost next to Abbey; well kept Sam Smiths OB, interesting customers in evenings *(Roger Taylor)*; [18 Goodramgate], *Royal Oak*: Small and compact black-beamed pub, plenty of charm and atmosphere in traditional, cosy rooms with prints, old guns and swords, friendly and welcoming helpful staff, consistently well kept Camerons and Everards Old Original, bar food (till 7.30) inc good roast beef and massive ploughman's *(Vincent Ainsworth, Melvyn Payne, BB)*; [Monkgate/St Maurices Rd], *Russells*: Monk Bar of this hotel very new and trying very hard; well furnished, if a little overdone, with very helpful barman; well cooked bar food; bedrooms *(Roger Bellingham)*

London

London

In London, at least towards the centre, pubs in general have a captive audience – or rather two captive audiences. On the one hand are people working close by a pub, who flood into it during lunch to grab something to eat and drink, or maybe drop in for a quick one before the journey home. On the other hand are the visitors to London, who aren't likely to come back to the same place again much. A pub has to be really very bad indeed to deter the first group of people from using it. And a pub that relies on visitor or tourist trade doesn't have to worry very much about pleasing its tourist customers – as they are not likely to be coming back to that area anyway. This contrasts strongly with country areas, where pubs rely more and more on attracting regularly returning customers from outside their immediate localities – if they are not good, they'll soon be without customers. It's our theory that this is why London does not have more really good pubs. There are some – this would be a really empty chapter if there weren't. But only a few are so distinguished that they deserve to be singled out specially. Among them we'd include the Black Friar in EC4 (for its remarkable decoration, a tribute to the enthusiasm people used to put into building pubs at the start of this century), the Cittie of York in WC1 (tremendously alive – a pub that's both very large and very individual), the Lamb in WC1 (old-fashioned architecture – snob screens and all – but very much not a pub that's letting time slip by it), the Princess Louise in WC1 (flamboyant gin palace), and the Red Lion in Waverton Street, WI (a shining example of how a pub doesn't need to be gimmicky to be good). All these are in central London; in the north, we'd add Crockers in NW8 (another flamboyant piece of Victoriana); in the south, the George of Southwark in SE1 (the only ancient coaching inn to have survived, at least in part, so close to the centre); in the west, the Dove on the river in W6; and in the east, Hollands (E1) as a reminder that what matters most in a pub is the devotion of the people running it. Part of the appeal of virtually all of these is in their connections with the past. Some newcomers have made their mark in a different way. In particular, we'd single out three small chains that are doing a good deal to set standards for London pubs. The Page pubs (the Front Page in SW3, Sporting Page in SW10, both main entries, and now the Racing Page in Richmond, in the Lucky Dip section at the end of the chapter) show that food in London pubs does not have to be dull – yet they are very much pubs, rather than dining places. Hardly a chain as they are at the moment only a pair, the Alma in SW18 and Coopers Arms in SW3 are alternative examples of this approach, though perhaps they emphasise the pubby side more than the food side. Then there is the Wetherspoons chain, flourishing in north London and beginning to spread into other parts (we have in the main entries the White Lion of Mortimer in N4 and Moon Under Water in Barnet, and several examples in the Lucky Dip section); the Wetherspoons approach shows how much can be done by making value for money the essential factor. Which brings us to another point

*about London pubs – their normally cavalier attitude to giving value.
Our price survey suggests that at the time this book comes out the
average price of a pint of beer in London will be £1.50. Typically,
London pubs now charge about 20p more a pint than pubs elsewhere,
and about 30p more than pubs in the cheapest areas. What came to us
as even more of a surprise, however, was the result of our check on food
prices, using steak and kidney pie as a yardstick. On this measure, food
in London pubs turns out to be cheaper than the national average.
Following this up with spot checks on other London pub food prices, we
find that this is indeed the case. Food prices in London pubs have in this
last year risen less than elsewhere; so London can now be counted as
relatively good value for pub food – if not exactly as the gastronomic
capital of the pub world.*

CENTRAL LONDON

Covering W1, W2, WC1, WC2, SW1, SW3, EC1, EC2, EC3 and EC4 postal districts
*Parking throughout this area is metered during the day, and generally in short supply
then; we mention difficulty only if evening parking is a problem too*

Antelope (Belgravia) Map 13

Eaton Terrace, SW1

Though this pleasantly old-fashioned pub can get crowded in the evening, at
lunchtime it's quiet and peaceful with plenty of standing room round the central
bar servery; old and modern settles in the front part, and the side room houses the
fruit machine. The small downstairs ante-room is no smoking at lunchtime. Bar
food downstairs includes smoked salmon mousse or mushrooms in cream, garlic,
wine and herbs (£3.25), 12oz baked stuffed trout, whole roast baby poussin or
beef casserole with dumplings (all £7.85), and puddings like home-made fruit
crumble (£2.85). The upstairs restaurant is open for evening meals Tuesdays to
Fridays. Well kept Adnams, Benskins, Ind Coope Burton, Tetleys, Wadworths 6X
and an Allied beer named for Nicholsons on handpump; 36 bin-end wines in the
restaurant. There are a couple of long seats outside in the quiet street (though you
are no longer allowed to drink out here). *(Recommended by Andrew Morrissey, Ralf
Zeyssig, Tony and Lynne Stark, Mrs S Mills, Dr and Mrs A K Clarke, Andy and Jill
Kassube)*

*Benskins (Allied)   Manager Geoff Elliott   Real ale   Meals and snacks   Restaurant
(071) 730 7781   Children in eating area of bar and in restaurant   Open 12–11*

Argyll Arms (Oxford Circus) Map 13

18 Argyll St, W1; opp tube side exit

Despite the rapid turnover of Oxford Street shoppers, this traditional place still has
a friendly atmosphere and efficiently welcoming staff. The most unusual part is the
three cubicle rooms at the front of the pub – all oddly angular, and made by
wooden partitions with frosted and engraved glass. A long mirrored corridor leads
to the spacious back room, with the food counter in one corner; the blackboard
menu includes good sandwiches (from £1.50; club sandwich £3.25), ploughman's
(£3.50), steak and mushroom or cottage pies or whole avocado and tuna salad
(£3.95), lamb and apricot or beef and venison (£4.25), and roast beef (£4.95).
Adnams Southwold, Boddingtons, Tetleys Bitter and Wadworths 6X on
handpump; two fruit machines, piped pop music. The quieter upstairs bar, which
overlooks the busy pedestrianised street, is divided into several snugs with
comfortable plush easy chairs; swan's neck lamps, and lots of small theatrical

prints along the top of the walls. A penned area outside has elbow-height tables. *(Recommended by John Fazakerley, Lee Goulding, Ian Phillips, Peter Griffiths, Gary Scott, Prof S Barnett)*

Nicholsons (Allied; run as free house)   Managers Mike and Sue Tayara   Real ale   Meals and snacks (11–9; not Sun)   Restaurant   071 734 6117   Children in eating area of bar and in restaurant   Open 11–11; closed Sun

Black Friar (City) Map 13

174 Queen Victoria Street, EC4

Justly famous, this busy pub has an inner back room with some of the best fine Edwardian bronze and marble art-nouveau decor to be found anywhere. It includes big bas-relief friezes of jolly monks set into richly coloured Florentine marble walls, an opulent marble-pillared inglenook fireplace, a low vaulted mosaic ceiling, gleaming mirrors, seats built into rich golden marble recesses, and tongue-in-cheek verbal embellishments such as Silence is Golden and Finery is Foolish. In the front room, see if you can spot the opium smoking-hints modelled into the fireplace. Bar food includes filled baked potatoes (from £1.50), French bread or ploughman's (from £1.95), a varied cold buffet (around £3.95), and two daily hot specials such as beef in red wine or cranberry lamb stew (around £3.85). Well kept Bass, Marstons Pedigree, Tetleys and an Allied beer named for Nicholsons on handpump; fruit machine. There's a wide forecourt in front, by the approach to Blackfriars Bridge.*(Recommended by Peter Griffiths, Brian Jones, David Hunn, G D Collier, Jamie Lyons, Ruth Harrison, Prof S Barnett, David Fowles, Dr J C Harrison)*

Nicholsons (Allied)   Manager Mr Eales   Real ale   Lunchtime meals (11.30–5; not Sat or Sun) and snacks (not Fri evening, not Sat or Sun)   Children in eating area of bar Open 11.30–10 weekdays; closed weekends and bank hols

Cittie of Yorke (Holborn) Map 13

22 High Holborn, WC1; find it by looking out for its big black and gold clock

The bar counter in this ancient place is the longest in Britain, with vast thousand-gallon wine vats (empty since prudently drained at the start of the Second World War) above the gantry, and a cat-walk running along the top of them. If you get there early enough (it can get packed at lunchtime and in the early evening, particularly with lawyers and judges), you can bag one of the intimate old-fashioned and ornately carved cubicles; there's an unusual big stove – uniquely triangular, with grates on all three sides, and big bulbous lights hanging from the extraordinarily high raftered roof. A smaller, comfortable wood-panelled room has lots of little prints of York and attractive brass lights. There's a lunchtime food counter in the main hall with more in the downstairs cellar bar: ploughman's (£3.25), filled baps (£2), salads (£4.25), and chilli con carne, curry, lasagne, and daily specials like pasta dishes or chicken and broccoli pie (all £3.75). Sam Smiths OB and Museum on handpump; friendly service; darts, fruit machine and piped music. The ceiling of the entrance hall has medieval-style painted panels and plaster York roses. *(Recommended by John Evans, Mrs S Mills, J E Stanton, Peter Griffiths, Wayne Brindle, Andy Hick, Andy and Jill Kassube, Simon Collett-Jones)*

Sam Smiths   Manager Stuart Browning   Real ale   Meals and snacks (12–2.30, 5.30–11)   Well behaved children welcome if sitting   Open 11.30–11 weekdays; 11.30–3, 5.30–11 Sat; closed Sun

Coopers Arms (Chelsea) Map 12

87 Flood St, SW3

Under the same management as the Ship and the Alma in Wandsworth (see South London), this spacious open-plan pub is interestingly furnished and has a relaxed, friendly atmosphere. Rush-seated chapel chairs, kitchen chairs and some dark brown plush chairs sit on the dark-stained floorboards, there's a mix of old tables, and LNER posters and maps of Chelsea and the Thames on the fresh ochre walls, a very big railway clock, vases of pretty flowers, a pre-war sideboard and dresser, a fireplace with dried flowers, and tea-shop chandeliers. Food at lunchtime might include spanish omelette (£3.50), beef and pasta or chicken and courgette pies (£4), and chicken waldorf salad (£4.25), with evening nibbles on toast such as scambled eggs, wild mushrooms or smokcd salmon (from £1.50); cheeses and cold pies are laid out on a chunky pine table, and they do Sunday brunch. Well kept Youngs Bitter and Special on handpump, and several wines by the glass; a huge waterbuffalo head dominates the bar area; chess. *(Recommended by Richard Gibbs, Mrs S Mills)*

Youngs Tenant Charles Gotto   Real ale   Meals and snacks (not Sat or Sun evening) 071 376 3120   Well behaved children allowed   Open 12–11

Cross Keys (Chelsea) Map 12

Lawrence St, SW3

This popular and friendly Victorian pub has tables in a pretty little sunny back courtyard planted with creepers and tubs of brightly coloured flowers. Inside, several interconnecting little rooms radiate off the walk-around island serving counter with military prints, a set of Cries of London prints and photographs of old London on the red or cream walls, high ceilings, and an open fire in winter. Good value food includes sandwiches, seven salads, and home-made hot dishes like sausage and mash (£2.75), steak en croûte (£4), and fresh poached salmon (£4.50). Well kept Courage Best and Directors on handpump, good mulled wine, a fine range of Irish whiskeys, a proper Pimms, and quick and efficient service; shove-ha'penny, dominoes, and fruit machine. *(Recommended by Wayne Brindle, Robert and Elizabeth Scott, Patrick Stapley, Richard Gibbs)*

Courage   Licensee Arthur Goodall   Real ale   Meals and snacks (not Sun)   071 352 1893   Children in eating area   Open 11–11

Front Page ✪ (Chelsea) Map 12

35 Old Church Street, SW3

Big blackboards at either end of this light and airy popular pub list the good value and nicely presented food: good soup of the day (£2.50), chicken liver pâté (£3.50), sausage and mash (£4.25), steak sandwich (£4.70), warm chicken and avocado salad (£4.80), smoked salmon with scrambled eggs (£5), salmon fish cakes with hollandaise sauce (£5.70), and puddings like baked bananas (£3). Well kept Ruddles County and Websters Yorkshire and a guest like Boddingtons on handpump; decent wines; quick, pleasant service. There are pews and benches around the panelled walls, heavy wooden tables, a wood-strip floor, big navy ceiling fans, huge windows with heavy navy curtains, and an open fire in one cosy area; lighting is virtually confined to brass picture-lights above small Edwardian monochrome pictures. Fruit machine. Outside, there are big copper gaslamps hanging above pretty hanging baskets. They are gradually expanding so keep your eyes open for 'Page' pubs – and they have the Chequers at Well (see Hampshire main entries). *(Recommended by Wayne Brindle, Simon Richards, Mrs S Mills, Dr John Innes)*

Courage   Lease: Peter Stevens and Patrick Coghill   Real ale   Meals (12–2.15, 7–10.15)   Children in eating area of bar   071 352 0648   Open 11–3, 5.30(6 Sat)–11; closed 24–26 Dec

George (West End) Map 13

55 Great Portland Street, W1

Dozens of 'George' pot tankards belonging to regulars (it's popular with BBC workers) are hung around the bar in this solid place. Also, comfortable red plush high chairs at the bar, captains' chairs around traditional cast-iron-framed tables, heavy mahogany panelling, deeply engraved mirrors, equestrian prints, and etched windows. Bar food includes sandwiches, quiche or Balmoral pie (£2.40), ploughman's or taramasalata with pitta bread (£3.25), and specials such as steak and kidney or beef in Guinness pie, sweet and sour pork and lamb casserole (all £4.50), and roast Sunday lunch (£5.50). Well kept Greene King Abbot, IPA and Mild and Rayments on handpump. They do guided tours of the cellar. *(Recommended by Lee Goulding, John Fazakerley, Simon Collett-Jones; more reports please)*

Greene King   Manager Harry Medlicott   Real ale   Meals and snacks   071 636 0863   Open 11–11 weekdays; 11–8 Sat

Glassblower (Piccadilly Circus) Map 13

42 Glasshouse Street, W1

A wide range of real ales on handpump in this vibrant pub includes Brakspears PA and SB, Greene King Abbot and IPA, Ruddles Best and County, Rayments and Websters Yorkshire, and Scrumpy Jack cider. The main bar has lots of untreated rough wooden beams with metal wheel-hoops hanging on them, plain wooden settles and stools, and sawdust on gnarled floorboards. An enormous copper and glass gaslight hangs from the centre of the ceiling, flickering gently, and there are more gaslight-style brackets around the walls, as well as lots of beer towels, framed sets of beer mats and bottle tops. Food includes sandwiches, fresh and very popular fish and chips (£3.85), ploughman's and home-made daily specials (£4.35). Fruit machine, video game, trivia, pinball, juke box and piped music. There are hanging flower-baskets outside. *(Recommended by Prof S Barnett, Wayne Brindle, Iain and Penny Muir, John Fazakerley, M B Porter, Simon Collett-Jones)*

Grand Met   Manager Ronan McLister   Real ale   Meals and snacks (11.30–3; not Sun)   071 734 8547   Children in eating area of bar   Rock/comedy duo Sat evenings Open 11.30–11; closed Sun morning and 25 Dec

Bunch of Grapes (Mayfair) Map 13

Shepherd Market, W1

Bang in the bustle of Shepherd Market, this very busy pub has a cosy and relaxed little alcove at the back, and the main area has a traditional and old-fashioned style of decoration. Bar food includes sandwiches (from £1), ploughman's (£2.25), steak and kidney pie, plaice and daily specials (£2.50), and steak (£4.85). Well kept Adnams, Boddingtons, Brakspears, Sam Smiths and Wethereds on handpump; fruit machine and juke box. *(Recommended by Tony and Lynn Stark, John Fazakerley, JM, PM, Mrs S Mills)*

Free house   Licensees Mr and Mrs Lewis   Real ale   Meals and snacks (12–3, 7–10) Restaurant   071 629 4989   Children welcome   Singing duo Mon evening   Open 11.30–11; 11.30–3, 7–11 Sat; closed 25 and 26 Dec

Grenadier (Belgravia) Map 13

Wilton Row, SW1; the turning off Wilton Crescent looks prohibitive, but the barrier and watchman are there to keep out cars; walk straight past – the pub is just around the corner

Proud of its connection with Wellington, whose officers used to use it as their mess, this tucked-away little pub has a cramped front bar with a few stools and wooden benches, a shelf, and a rare pewter-topped bar counter. It's popular with a wide variety of customers, and serves well kept Ruddles Best and County, and Websters Yorkshire on handpump – or if you'd prefer it they will shake you a most special Bloody Mary. A corner snack counter serves very reasonably priced lunchtime food such as ploughman's (£3.95), and hot dishes like sausage and beans (£4.40) and scampi (£4.90). *(Recommended by Jamie Lyons, Ruth Harrison, Karen and Graham Oddey; more reports please)*

Watneys (Grand Met)   Licensee Peter Martin   Real ale   Lunchtime meals and snacks   Intimate candlelit restaurant   071 235 3074   Children in restaurant   Open 12–3, 5–11; closed 24, 25, 26 Dec and 1 Jan

Lamb ★ (Bloomsbury) Map 13

94 Lamb's Conduit Street, WC1

The pub like the street is named for the Kentish clothmaker William Lamb who brought fresh water to Holborn in 1577. All the way around the U-shaped bar counter there are cut-glass swivelling 'snob-screens', as well as traditional cast-iron-framed tables with neat brass rails around the rim, and on ochre panelling lots of sepia photographs of 1890s actresses; a small room at the back on the right is no-smoking. Good bar food includes sandwiches (£1.15, not Sun), ploughman's (£2.50), quite a few salads, as well as hot dishes such as home-made pies or steak and kidney pudding (£3.75), and daily specials like spinach and prawn crêpe or pork in cider casserole; Sunday carvery in restaurant (£3.75). Consistently well kept Youngs Bitter and Special on handpump, with Warmer in winter; prompt service, and a good mix of customers. There are slatted wooden seats in a little courtyard beyond the quiet room which is down a couple of steps at the back; dominoes, cribbage, backgammon. *(Recommended by SJC, Peter Griffiths, Brian Jones, Michael and Alison Sandy, Wayne Brindle, Joel Dobris, Andy and Jill Kassube)*

Youngs   Manager Richard Whyte   Real ale   Meals and snacks (11.30–10)   071 405 0713   Children in eating area of bar   Open 11–11; closed evening 25 Dec

Lamb & Flag (Covent Garden) Map 13

33 Rose Street, WC2; off Garrick Street

This busy, friendly pub was once known as the Bucket of Blood from the bare-knuckle prize-fights held here. It is still much as it was when Dickens described the Middle Temple lawyers who frequented it when he was working in nearby Catherine Street – low ceiling, high-backed black settles and an open fire. The upstairs Dryden Room tends to be less crowded. There's a choice of ten well kept cheeses and eight pâtés, served with hot bread or French bread, as well as pasties, quiche, steak and kidney pie, roast beef baps (Mon-Fri), shepherd's pie, chilli con carne or curry. Very well kept Courage Best and Directors and John Smiths on handpump, and some malt whiskies. Darts in the small front public bar. Dryden was nearly beaten to death by hired thugs in the courtyard outside. *(Recommended by Karen and Graham Oddey, Gary Scott, Peter Griffiths, A Y Drummond, Peter Maden, Hilary Robinson, David Shillitoe)*

Courage   Lease: Adrian Zimmerman   Real ale   Meals and snacks (11.30–5 downstairs, not Sun evenings)   071 497 9504   Open 11–11; closed 25 and 26 Dec and 1 Jan

Museum Tavern (Bloomsbury) Map 13

Museum Street, WC1

Karl Marx is fondly supposed to have had the odd glass here after the British Museum, opposite, had shut him out for the night. It's an old fashioned place with high-backed benches around traditional cast-iron pub tables, old advertising mirrors between the wooden pillars behind the bar, an 'Egyptian' inn sign, and gas lamps above the tables outside. Bar food, served all day, includes sandwiches, a range of salads (from £3.25), hot dishes such as steak and kidney or shepherd's pies (£4.75), and puddings (£1.70). Well kept Brakspears PA and SB, Greene King IPA and Abbot, Rayments, Ruddles County and Websters Yorkshire on handpump, a wide range of wines by the glass, and malt whiskies; fruit machine. *(Recommended by Prof S Barnett, Ralf Zeyssig, Dr and Mrs A K Clarke, David Hunn, Peter Griffiths, Joel Dobris)*

Grand Met   Managers John and Carmel Keating   Real ale   Meals and snacks (11–10)   071 242 8987   Open 11–11; closed evening 25 Dec

Nags Head (Belgravia) Map 13

53 Kinnerton St, SW1

Tiny low-ceilinged mews pub near Belgrave Square and Knightsbridge with a small, panelled old-fashioned front area and a wood-effect gas fire in an old cooking range; a narrow passage leads down steps to an even smaller back bar with comfortable seats; piped music, a 1930s What-the-butler-saw machine and one-armed bandit that takes old pennies. Benskins and Youngs pulled on attractive 19th-century china, pewter and brass handpumps; freshly squeezed orange juice. Food includes sandwiches, cauliflower cheese (£2.85), filled baked potatoes (£2.95), quiche of the day or ploughman's (£3.50), calves' liver and onion (£3.75), and steak and mushroom pie (£3.75); 50p service charge in the evening, when it can get crowded. *(Recommended by Richard Gibbs, Gordon B Mott, John Fazakerley; more reports please)*

Benskins (Ind Coope) Tenant Kevin Moran Real ale Meals and snacks (11–9.30) 071 235 1135 Children in eating area Open 11–11

Old Coffee House (Soho) Map 13

49 Beak Street, W1

Even though this pub is small you can often find somewhere to sit. It's piled high with bric-a-brac and downstairs is a busy jumble of stuffed pike, stuffed foxes, great brass bowls and buckets, ancient musical instruments (brass and string sections both well represented), a good collection of Great War recruiting posters, golden discs, death-of-Nelson prints, theatre and cinema handbills, old banknotes, even a nude in one corner, and doubtless lots more that we failed to spot. Upstairs, the food room has as many prints and pictures as a Victorian study. Lunchtime bar food includes sandwiches, filled baked potatoes (from £1.70), ploughman's and salads (from £2), burgers (£2.50), home-made specials like beef stew and dumplings, chicken tikka masala or vegetarian special (£3.50), and puddings (£1.35). Well kept Ruddles Best and County and Websters Yorkshire on handpump. *(Recommended by Wayne Brindle, John Fazakerley, Peter Maden, Hilary Robinson)*

Watneys (Grand Met) Lease: Barry Hawkins Real ale Meals and snacks (lunchtime; not Sun) 071 437 2197 Children in upstairs food room Alternative comedy planned upstairs on Tues evenings Open 11–11

Ye Olde Mitre £ (City) Map 13

Ely Place, EC1; there's also an entrance beside 8 Hatton Garden

With its nice homely atmosphere, it can be hard to realise you are so close to Holborn and the edge of the city. The dark panelled small rooms have antique settles and big vases of flowers; an upstairs room, mainly used for functions, doubles as an overflow at peak periods. Good bar snacks include a good selection of sandwiches such as ham, salmon and cucumber or egg mayonnaise (from 85p, toasted £1); well kept Friary Meux, Ind Coope Burton and Tetleys on handpump, reasonably priced for the area. There are some seats with pot plants and jasmine in the narrow yard between the pub and St Ethelreda's church. *(Recommended by T Nott, Matt Pringle, Simon Collett-Jones, M B Porter, John Evans, Andy Hick, Andy and Jill Kassube, Joel Dobris)*

Taylor-Walker (Allied) Manager Don O'Sullivan Real ale Snacks (all day) 071 405 4751 Open 11–11; closed Sat, Sun, bank hols

Orange Brewery (Pimlico) Map 13

37 Pimlico Road, SW1

This lively and friendly pub has been refurbished this year – the bar has new furniture on its carpeted floor, though the sepia photographs, decorative Victorian plates, and stuffed fox above the nicely tiled fireplace, have remained. The cheery Pie and Ale Shop (open all day in summer) has lots more sepia photographs on the dark stained plank-panelling, plain wooden tables and chairs on pretty black and white tiles, and a shelf full of old flagons and jugs above the counter where they serve a range of home-made food: sandwiches (from £1.75; hot salt beef £2.65), ploughman's (£3.60), quiche (£4), and Sunday roast (£6.25). As well as a couple of guest beers on handpump they brew over 300 gallons a week in the cellars – SW1, a stronger SW2, Pimlico Light and Pimlico Porter, and new this year, Victoria lager. Piped music. There are seats outside facing a little concreted-over green beyond the quite busy street. *(Recommended by Andrew Hazeldine, Lee Goulding, David Hunn, Andrew Morrissey, Wayne Brindle, Roger Taylor)*

Own brew (though tied to Clifton Inns, part of Watneys) Licensee Bernadette Cloran Real ale Meals and snacks (12–9.30) 071 730 5984 Children in eating area Open 11–11

Princess Louise (Holborn) Map 13

208 High Holborn, WC1

Considering how expensive Thai restaurants can be, it's worth coming to this old-fashioned gin-palace for the food alone. Cooked by a Thai couple, it's spicy and authentic and served at lunchtime and in the evening (£3.50 per dish); they also do sandwiches (from £1.50). The elaborate decor includes etched and gilt mirrors, brightly coloured and fruity-shaped tiles, and slender Portland stone columns soaring towards the lofty and deeply moulded crimson and gold plaster ceiling; the green plush seats and banquettes are comfortable. The magnificent gents' is the subject of a separate preservation order. People cluster around the enormous island bar servery, eager for the fine range of regularly changing real ales, well kept on handpump. These include Bass, Brakspears, Eldridge Pope Hardy, Darleys Thorne, Vaux Samson, Wards Best and a beer brewed for the pub; several wines by the glass – including champagne; quick, Antipodean staff in white shirts and red bow ties. *(Recommended by Stephen R Holman, Peter Griffiths, Prof S Barnett, Michael and Alison Sandy, Tony and Lynne Stark, T K Baxter, Neil Barker, Andy Hick, Roger Taylor, Dr J C Harrison, Andy and Jill Kassube, Dr and Mrs A K Clarke, Wayne Brindle)*

Free house   Licensee Ian Phillips   Real ale   Meals and snacks (not weekends) Restaurant   071 405 8816   Jazz Sat evening   Open 11–11; 12–3, 6–11 Sat

Red Lion (Mayfair) Map 13

Waverton Street, W1

This stylish Mayfair pub has a little L-shaped bar with small winged settles on the partly carpeted scrubbed floorboards, London prints below the high shelf of china on its dark-panelled walls, and an atmosphere almost like that of a civilised country pub. Good food includes sandwiches, Cumberland sausage, duck and venison pie or stuffed cabbage leaves (£4.25); they home-cook all their meats; unusually for the area, food is served morning and evening seven days a week. Greene King IPA, Ruddles Best and County and Websters Yorkshire on handpump. It can get crowded at lunchtime. In the gents' there's a copy of the day's *Financial Times* at eye level. *(Recommended by John Fazakerley, Wayne Brindle, Tom Thomas, JM, PM, Andy and Jill Kassube, Freddy Costello)*

Watneys (Grand Met)   Manager Raymond Dodgson   Real ale   Meals and snacks (12–3, 6–10)   Restaurant   071 499 1307   Children in eating area of bar and in restaurant   Open 11.30–11; 11.30–3, 6–11 Sat

NORTH LONDON

Parking is not a special problem in this area, unless we say so

Crockers ★ (Maida Vale) Map 12

24 Aberdeen Place, NW8

This pub's Victorian nickname – Crocker's Folly – came after its builder miscalculated where the entrance to Marylebone Station would be; he built it hoping to cash in on floods of customers from the new railway – missing them by half a mile or so. The architecture is really fine, and the ceiling in the main room is possibly the most elaborately moulded of any London pub: marble pillars support arches inlaid with bronze reliefs, there's a sweeping marble bar counter, and a vast pillared marble fireplace with a log-effect gas fire; part of this room is no smoking. A row of great arched and glazed mahogany doors opens into a similarly ornate but more spacious room; furnishings are soft and comfortable. A wide range of real ales includes Arkells Kingsdown, Boddingtons, Brakspears, Eldridge Pope Hardy, Marstons Pedigree, Rayments, Vaux Samson, Wards and a beer named after the pub; also Weizenbier from Wards – the only beer in the country brewed from wheat rather than barley. Bar food at lunchtime ranges from sandwiches and home-made Scotch eggs, through ploughman's, to three hot dishes such as steak and kidney pie, beef in horseradish and cheese sauce and lamb chops in mint (£3.45); in the evening they do vegetarian dishes and rump steaks (£6.20); Sunday lunch (£3.95). Darts, bar billiards, cribbage, dominoes, fruit machine, space game, trivia and juke box are in a less opulent room; also piped music. The pub is not far from Regents Canal towpath. *(Recommended by Tony and Lynne Stark, Wayne Brindle, Gary Scott, Edward Burlton Davies, Neil Barker, GB, CH)*

Free house Licensee David Toft Real ale Meals and snacks (12–2.30, 6–9.45) 071 286 6608 Children in eating area of bar Occasional piano player Daytime parking meters Open 11–11 Bedrooms planned

Holly Bush (Hampstead) Map 12

Holly Mount, NW3

The atmospheric front bar here has real Edwardian gas lamps, a dark and sagging ceiling, brown and cream panelled walls (which are decorated with old advertisements and a few hanging plates), and cosy bays formed by partly glazed partitions. The more intimate back room (named after the painter George Romney) has an embossed red ceiling, panelled and etched glass alcoves, and ochre-painted brick walls covered with small prints and plates. Bar food includes ploughman's, pasties, home-made sausage and apple, scouse and vegetable pies, and quiches. Benskins, Ind Coope Burton, Tetleys and Youngs on handpump; darts, shove-ha'penny, cribbage, dominoes, fruit machine, and video game. *(Recommended by Mrs S Mills, Tom Thomas, Neil Barker, Wayne Brindle, Andy Hick, Mike Tucker)*

Taylor-Walker (Allied) Manager Peter Dures Real ale Meals and snacks 071 435 2892 Children in coffee bar 60s live music Weds evening, jazz Thurs evening Nearby parking sometimes quite a squeeze Open 11–3(4 Sat), 5.30(6 Sat)–11

Moon Under Water (Barnet) Map 12

148 High Street, Barnet

This busy town pub has a long and very narrow wood-panelled bar, lots of mirrors, an Anaglypta ceiling, some stuffed fish in glass cases, and a print of, literally, the moon under water; in the main part there's no room for tables, just tall wheelbacks and an elbow shelf opposite the serving counter. The front area is wider, with square tables, wheelbacks and an old-fashioned street lamp by the glass front. The more spacious back area has a conservatory feel, with a glass roof with plants hanging down and attractive blue and white tiling set high up in the walls; seating is homely – mainly plain wooden tables with stools and more wheelbacks, and there are lots of bookshelves with an eclectic range of paperbacks (including some Orwell); swan's neck lamps throughout; three fruit machines and a video game (all completely silent). The range of beers on handpump changes pretty much every week: Courage Directors, Eldridge Pope Royal Oak, Greene King Abbot and IPA, Marstons Pedigree and Theakstons XB, with one bargain at under a pound, usually Youngers Scotch. Bar food includes sandwiches, ploughman's, quiche, pizzas, chicken, lasagne and steak and mushroom pie. Picnic-table sets in the garden area at the back. This is one of Wetherspoons' rapidly expanding chain of pubs (see also the White Lion of Mortimer, in this chapter), and there are actually three more with this pub's name – in Enfield, Colindale and Lordship Lane in Tottenham. *(Recommended by Chris Fluck, Hugh Jones, R McIntosh; more reports please)*

Free house Licensee Kevin Rees Real ale Meals and snacks 081 441 9476 Open 11–11

Olde White Bear (Hampstead) Map 12

Well Road, NW3

In a nice part of Hampstead, this neo-Victorian pub has a dimly-lit main room with lots of Victorian prints and cartoons on the walls, wooden stools, cushioned captains' chairs, a couple of big tasseled armed chairs, a flowery sofa (surrounded by the excrescences of an ornate Edwardian sideboard), and a tiled gas-effect log fire with a heavy wooden overmantle. A small central room – also dimly lit – has Lloyd Loom furniture, dried flower arrangements and signed photographs of actors and playwrights. In the brighter end room there are cushioned machine tapestried ornate pews, marble topped tables, a very worn butcher's table and dark brown paisley curtains. Bar food includes sandwiches, filled baked potatoes (£2.10), salads (from £2.75), and home-made dishes such as curries (£3.15), moussaka (£3.80), and steak and kidney pie (£4). Adnams Best, Ind Coope Burton and Tetleys Bitter on handpump with guests like Greene King Abbot, Marstons Pedigree and Wadworths 6X, a decent range of malt whiskies, and winter mulled wine. Video game, trivia, quiz night (first Monday of the month) and piped music. *(Recommended by Wayne Brindle; more reports please)*

Ind Coope   Manager David Booker   Real ale   Meals and snacks   071 435 3758 Children lunchtime if eating   Quiz nights first Mon of the month   Open 12–3(4 Sat), 5.30(6 Sat)–11

Spaniards Inn (Hampstead) Map 12

Spaniards Lane, NW3

This civilised ex toll house is very popular with walkers from the Heath. The attractive main bar area (lit by candle-shaped lamps in pink shades in the evening) has genuinely antique winged settles, open fires, and snug little alcoves in the low-ceilinged oak-panelled rooms; the upstairs bar is quieter. Daily changing bar food includes sausage and chips (£2), ploughman's (from £2.50), vegetable lasagne (£4), shepherd's pie (£4.25), and chicken chasseur (£4.50). Bass, Charrington IPA, Fullers London Pride, Highgate Mild and Stones on handpump; piped music. The attractive sheltered garden has slatted wooden tables and chairs on a crazy-paved terrace which opens on to a flagstoned walk around a small lawn, with roses, a side arbour of wisteria and clematis, and an aviary. The pub is named for the Spanish ambassador to the Court of James I who is said to have lived here. *(Recommended by Gary Scott, Ian Phillips, Mrs S Mills, Tony and Lynne Stark)*

Charringtons (Bass)   Manager P A Rendall   Real ale   Meals and snacks (12–3, 6–9.30)   081 455 3276   Children in eating area of bar and in upstairs bar   Open 11–11

Waterside Inn ✪ (Kings Cross) Map 13

82 York Way, N1

A big plus here is the outside terrace which overlooks the Battlebridge Basin. Inside, the busy bar is done out in traditional style, with latticed windows, stripped brickwork, genuinely old stripped timbers in white plaster, lots of dimly lit alcoves, spinning wheels, milkmaids' yokes, horsebrasses and so on, with plenty of rustic tables and wooden benches. Boddingtons and Greene King Abbot on handpump, as well as wines on draught; fruit machine, video game, trivia, and juke box. Decent bar food includes filled rolls, ploughman's (£3.25), filled baked potatoes (£3.50), salmon fishcakes (£3.75), spinach lasagne or steak and mushroom pie (£3.95), smoked chicken salad or game pie (£4.75), and poached salmon (£5.25). *(Recommended by Gary Scott, Neil Barker, Joel Dobris; more reports please)*

Whitbreads   Manageress Ann Edmunds   Real ale   Meals and snacks (all day; not Sun evening)   071 837 7118   Children in eating area of bar   Open 11–11; 12–3, 7–11 Sat; closed 25 and 26 Dec and 1 Jan

White Lion of Mortimer (Finsbury Park) Map 13

127 Stroud Green Road, N4

Even at its busiest, this spacious place manages to keep its easy-going atmosphere. The carved island servery runs the length of the bar, which has cream tilework at the front, lion pictures on the partly panelled walls, and a medley of old tables. The cooking implements down the left-hand side contrast with the horse harness and farm tools on the right, which also has a public telephone with an old copper fireplace as its booth. Some alcoves have an old cast-iron fireplace and plush settees, and there's a relaxing conservatory area at the back, with hanging ivy plants, and a small fountain outside its door. A particular virtue is the emphasis on real ale; the range changes frequently, always with one beer offered at a price few other London pubs could match – Youngers Scotch at 99p, say; there's also

typically Greene King IPA and Abbot, Rayments and Theakstons XB and Old
Peculier; country wines and farm cider. Bar food includes large granary baps
(£1.50), ploughman's (£2.30), burgers (from £2.75), plaice or shepherd's pie
(£3.10), chilli con carne or vegetable lasagne (£2.75), daily specials (£3.20), and
Sunday roast (£3.95); dominoes, fruit machine, video game. There are some
cast-iron tables on the pavement outside. Other Wetherspoons pubs include the
Moon Under Water in Barnet. *(Recommended by Gary Scott, Andy Hick, Alan Skull,
Mugs Vernon, M B Porter)*

*Free house   Licensees Andrew Winter, D J Kitching   Real ale   Meals and snacks
(12–10; not Sun evening)   071 281 4773   Open 11–11*

SOUTH LONDON

Parking is bad on weekday lunchtimes at the inner city pubs here (SE1), and at the
Orange Tree in Richmond; it's usually OK everywhere in the evenings – you may again
have a bit of a walk if a good band is on at the Bulls Head in Barnes, or at the Windmill
on Clapham Common if it's a fine evening

Alma (Wandsworth) Map 12

499 York Road, SW18

There's a thriving atmosphere in this stylish place, authentically done out as a
French cafe-bar. Lots of ochre and terracotta paintwork, gilded mosaics of the
Battle of the Alma, an ornate mahogany chimneypiece and fireplace, bevelled
mirrors in a pillared mahogany room divider, pinball and table footer, and a mix
of chairs around cast-iron-framed tables; the popular dining room has a fine
turn-of-the-century frieze of swirly nymphs. Service is careful and efficient, even
when it's very full – which it often is. Besides Youngs Bitter and Special on
handpump from the island bar counter, there are usually decent house wines, good
coffee, tea or hot chocolate, newspapers out for customers, and bar food that
includes soup and a sandwich, croque monsieur (£2), moules marinières or
calamaris (£3.95), eggs and bacon, sausages, lamb chops, and steak. A thriving
local atmosphere. The pub is under the same management as the Ship at
Wandsworth (see below). *(Recommended by Andy and Jill Kassube, Mrs S Mills,
Caroline Hall, Richard Gibbs)*

*Youngs   Tenant Desmond Maddon   Real ale   Meals and snacks (12–2.30, 7–10.30;
not Sun evening)   Restaurant   081 870 2537   Children welcome   Open 11–3, 5–11;
11–11 Sat*

Anchor (South Bank) Map 13

34 Park St, Bankside, SE1; Southwark Bridge end

This was probably where Pepys went to watch the Great Fire burning London:
'one entire arch of fire above a mile long, the churches, houses, and all on fire at
once, a horrid noise the flames made, and the cracking of houses at their ruine'.
There's still a lot of atmosphere these days, and even when it's invaded by tourists
it's usually possible to retreat to one of the smaller rooms. The rambling series of
rooms have creaky boards and beams, black panelling, and old-fashioned
high-backed settles as well as sturdy leatherette chairs. Bar food includes
sandwiches, pasties (£1.60), ploughman's (£3), daily specials such as sweet and
sour chicken and chilli con carne (£4.30), and Sunday roast beef. Courage Best and
Directors, Larkins and Wadsorths 6X on handpump, and a fair selection of wines
by the glass and bottle; darts, bar billiards, fruit machine, video game, trivia, juke
box, and piped music. A terrace overlooks the river. *(Recommended by Gary Scott,
Wayne Brindle, Jan and Ian Alcock, Jamie Lyons, Ruth Harrison; more reports please)*

*Free house   Licensee Brian Redshaw   Real ale   Meals and snacks (11.30–3, 5–9)
Restaurant   071 407 1577   Children in eating area of bar   Open 12–3.30, 7–10.30;
11.30–11 Sat*

Angel (Rotherhithe) Map 12

101 Bermondsey Wall East, SE16

The interesting location and splendid river views are the main draw here. Upstream you can gaze on Tower Bridge and the City, and the other way is the Pool of London. The bare-boarded balcony, on timber piles sunk into the river, is lit by lanterns at night. Bar food includes baps (from £1.30), giant sausage (£2.50), ploughman's (£2.70), pork and chestnut pie (£3.15), and Sunday roast beef (£4.95); Courage Best and Directors, Larkins and Wadworths 6X on handpump; fruit machine, piped music. Pepys bought cherries for his wife at the jetty here. *(Recommended by Ian Phillips, Neil Barker; more reports please)*

Free house (THF)   Licensee Steven Meakin   Real ale   Lunchtime meals and snacks Restaurant   071 237 3608   Children in eating area of bar   Open 11–3, 5.30–11

Bulls Head (Barnes) Map 12

373 Lonsdale Road, SW13

The big draw to this riverside pub, just across from the Thames flood wall, is the live music – top-class modern jazz groups every evening, and weekend lunchtime big band sessions (practice on Saturday, concert on Sunday). Though admission to the well equipped music room is £3 to £7 the sound is perfectly clear – if not authentically loud – in the adjoining lounge bar. Alcoves open off the main area around the efficient island servery, which has Youngs Bitter and Special on handpump; darts, Scrabble, chess, cards, fruit machine and video game in the public bar. Bar lunches include soup (£1.30), sandwiches (from £1.50; hot roast meat £2), a pasta dish or home-baked pie (£3.10), and carvery of home-roasted joints (£3.30). *(Recommended by R Houghton, Graham Bush, Mrs S Mills)*

Youngs   Tenant Dan Fleming   Real ale   Lunchtime meals and snacks   Evening restaurant (they do Sun lunch)   081 876 5241   Children in eating area of bar and in restaurant   Jazz nightly and Sun lunchtime   Nearby parking may be difficult   Open 11–11

Crown & Greyhound (Dulwich) Map 12

73 Dulwich Village, SE21

Handy for walks through the park, this grand pub has lots of mahogany, etched glass and mirrors inside, with dark green velvet curtains swagged over the big windows looking out on the village road. The most ornate room is on the right, with its elaborate ochre ceiling plasterwork, fancy former gas lamps, Hogarth prints, good carved and panelled settles and so forth. It opens into the former billiards room, where kitchen tables on a stripped board floor are set for the food, which includes doorstep sandwiches and toasties (from £1.95), filled baked potatoes (£2), curry or vegetarian lasagne (£4.25) and help-yourself salads. A central snug leads on the other side to the saloon – brown ragged walls, upholstered and panelled settles, a coal-effect gas fire in the tiled period fireplace, and Victorian prints. A big two-level back terrace has a good many picnic-table sets under a chestnut tree, with summer weekend barbecues. Fairly quiet on weekday lunchtimes, it can be very busy in the evenings. Well kept Ind Coope Burton, Tetleys and Youngs on handpump; fruit machines, video game, and piped music. *(Recommended by E G Parish, JF, Mrs J A Blanks)*

Tetley-Walkers (Allied)   Managers B P Maguire, Charles Counsel   Real ale   Meals and snacks (12–2.30, 5.30–9; not Sun evening)   Restaurant   081 693 2466   Children in restaurant   Open 11–3.30, 5.30–11; 11–11 Fri and Sat

George ★ (Southwark) Map 13

Off 77 Borough High Street, SE1

This historic place is in fact the only coaching inn in London to survive intact, with its tiers of open galleries looking down on the cobbled courtyard; these days it's carefully preserved by the National Trust. The row of ground-floor rooms and bars all have square-latticed windows, black beams, bare floorboards, some panelling, plain oak or elm tables, old-fashioned built-in settles, a 1797 'Act of Parliament' clock, dimpled glass lantern-lamps and so forth. It does of course attract quite a stream of tourists, and we'd recommend as the safest refuge from them the simple room nearest the street, where there's an ancient beer engine (currently not in use) that looks like a cash register. Boddingtons, Greene King Abbot and Fullers London Pride on handpump, and mulled wine in winter; video game and trivia. Bar food includes sandwiches, and home-made steak and mushroom pie and home-cooked gammon (£4). A splendid central staircase goes up to a series of dining rooms and to a gaslit balcony. Jugglers, acrobats, conjurers, animal-trainers, musicians and even Shakespeare's strolling players used to perform here when Southwark was London's entertainment centre; this tradition is maintained in summer, when there may be Morris men dancing or players from the nearby Globe Theatre performing in the courtyard. *(Recommended by David Bell, Neil Barker, Ian Phillips, John Whitehead, Dr S D Paige, Gary Scott, D J and P M Taylor, Mr and Mrs J M Elden, Comus Elliott, Roger Bellingham, P Thorogood, Brian Jones, Wayne Brindle)*

Whitbreads   Manager John Hall   Real ale   Meals and snacks (not Sat and Sun evenings)   Restaurant   071 407 2056   Children in eating area of bar   Nearby daytime parking difficult   Globe Players, Morris dancers and Medieval Combat Society during summer   Open 11–11 (12–3, 6–11 Sat); closed 25 & 26 Dec

Horniman (Southwark) Map 13

Hays Galleria, Battlebridge Lane, SE1

Above the bar in this ambitiously-designed waterside pub is a set of clocks made for Frederick Horniman's office, showing the time in various places around the world. The bar itself is spacious, elegant and neatly kept; the area by the sweeping bar counter is a few steps down from the door, with squared black, red and white flooring tiles and lots of polished wood. Steps lead up from here to various comfortable carpeted areas, with the tables well spread so as to allow for a feeling of spacious relaxation at quiet times but give room for people standing in groups when it's busy. From some parts there are good views of the Thames, HMS *Belfast* and Tower Bridge, as there are from the picnic-table sets outside. Bar food includes filled baps (£1.95), ploughman's (£3.20) and hot dishes such as steak and kidney pie (£4.15). Well kept Adnams, Tetleys, Wadworths 6X, Youngs Special and a beer named for the brewery on handpump, and there's a tea bar serving coffee, chocolate and other hot drinks, and Danish pastries and so forth; a hundred-foot frieze shows the travels of Horniman's tea. Fruit machine, bar billiards, video machine, maybe piped music. The pub is at the end of a visually exciting development, several storeys high, with a soaring glass curved roof, and supported by elegant thin cast-iron columns; various shops and boutiques open off. *(Recommended by Gary Scott, Mr and Mrs J M Elden, Wayne Brindle, Richard Gibbs; more reports please)*

Nicholsons/Taylor Walker (Allied)   Manager Mr Hastings   Real ale   Bar meals and snacks (lunchtime)   Restaurant   081 407 3611   Children in eating area and restaurant   Live music every 2 months   Open 11–11; Sat closing 10 (6 winter), Sun 6; closed evenings 24 and 31 Dec and all day 25 and 25 Dec

Market Porter (Southwark) Map 13

9 Stoney Street, SE1

As we went to press, this lively pub was hoping to start brewing their own beer again (though they weren't sure whether they would be brewing here or somewhere else). As well as their own brews, they keep Adnams Mild, Boddingtons, Felinfoel Double Dragon, Greene King IPA, Marstons Pedigree and Youngs PA. The main part of the long U-shaped bar has rough wooden ceiling beams with beer barrels balanced on them, a heavy wooden bar counter with a beamed gantry, cushioned bar stools, an open fire with stuffed animals in glass cabinets on the mantlepiece, several mounted stags' heads, and 20s-style wall lamps. Green and brown cushioned captains' chairs sit on the patterned green and brown carpet. Bar food includes bacon sandwich (£1.50), steak sandwich (£2.50), ribs (£3), lasagne (£3.50), curry or steak and kidney pie (£3.75), and sweet and sour turkey (£3.75); darts, fruit machine, pinball, and piped music. A small partly panelled room has leaded glass windows and a couple of tables. *(Recommended by John Whitehead, Comus Elliott; more reports please)*

Own brew   Licensee Andrew Bishop   Real ale   Lunchtime meals and snacks Restaurant (not Sun evening)   071 407 2495   Children in eating area of bar and in restaurant   Open 11–11 (11–3, 7–11 Sat)

Mayflower (Rotherhithe) Map 12

117 Rotherhithe Street, SE16

This carefully restored 18th-century pub takes its name in honour of the Pilgrim Fathers' ship which sailed from here in 1611: one side room has a set of pictures showing the way it would have been built and there's a model of the *Mayflower*. The rather dark old-fashioned main bar has black ceiling beams, dark panelled walls, latticed windows, and high-backed winged settles and wheelback chairs around its tables. Decent bar food includes tasty smoked salmon bagels as well as rolls (£2.10), salads (£4), steak in ale or vegetable pies (£4.95), sausages (£5), and lots of daily specials. Well kept Bass and Charringtons IPA and a guest such as Fullers or Stones on handpump, and nine wines by the glass; fruit machine, juke box. The wooden jetty outside feels very close to the Thames of days gone by, with its heavy piles plunging down into the water, converted high old warehouse buildings on either side and lighters swinging on their moorings. *(Recommended by Jenny and Brian Seller, Roger Huggins; more reports please)*

Charringtons   Manager David Pascoe   Real ale   Meals and snacks   071 237 4088 Children in eating area of bar   Open 12–3, 6(6.30 Sat)–11

Olde Windmill (Clapham) Map 12

Clapham Common South Side, SW4

This year the bar area in this large Victorian inn has been refurbished, the food area expanded, a new conservatory/family area added and more bedrooms are planned. Bar food includes sandwiches (from £1.20), filled baked potatoes or ploughman's (from £2.50), salads (from £3.50), and home-made daily specials such as curry, chilli con carne, pies and pasta dishes. Youngs Bitter and Special on handpump; fruit machine and video game. There are courtyards at each end with picnic tables, and one has a colonnaded shelter and tubs of shrubs. The inn can get packed in summer, when it seems to serve not just the pub but half the Common too. *(Recommended by Greg Parston; more reports please)*

Youngs   Manager Richard Williamson   Real ale   Meals and snacks (not Sun evening)   Restaurant (mainly for residents; closed Sun)   Children in restaurant   Open 11–11; may close winter afternoons   Bedrooms 081 673 4578; £33S/£42S

Phoenix & Firkin ★ £ (Denmark Hill)

5 Windsor Walk, SE5

This attractively renovated, palatial Victorian building has a vast lofty pavilion of a bar; the bar counter itself is made from a single mahogany tree, and there's solid wooden furniture on the stripped wooden floor, paintings of steam trains, old seaside posters, Bovril advertisements, old-fashioned station name signs, plants, big revolving fans, and a huge double-faced station clock, originally from Llandudno Junction, hanging by chains from the incredibly high ceiling. At one end there's a similarly-furnished gallery, reached by a spiral staircase, and at the other arches lead into a food room; fruit machine; piped music. The building spans the railway cutting, and you can feel it throb when trains pass underneath. In the evenings it can get packed with a good mixed crowd. Straightforward food includes big filled baps, ploughman's, and a daily hot dish such as trout, beef bourguignonne or duck à la crème (£2.95). The beers include Phoenix, Rail and Dogbolter on handpump, as well as two weekly guest beers kept under light blanket pressure. Outside there are some tables and chairs with parasols, and the steps which follow the slope of the road are a popular place to sit. *(Recommended by Jamie and Ruth Lyons, Sue Corrigan; more reports please)*

Own Brew   Licensee Carl Flynn   Real ale   Meals and snacks   081 701 8282

Children in eating area of bar   Live music Mon evening   Open 11.30–11

Ship 🚫 (Wandsworth) Map 12

41 Jews Row, SW18

Always popular (it gets packed in summer), most of the main bar here is in a conservatory style, with only a small part of the original ceiling left. It's light and airy with a relaxed, chatty atmosphere, wooden tables (one a butcher's table), a medley of stools and old church chairs, and two comfortable leatherette chesterfields on the wooden floorboards; one part has a Victorian fireplace, a huge clock surrounded by barge prints, and part of a milking machine on a table, and there's a rather battered harmonium, old-fashioned bagatelle, and jugs of flowers around the window sills. The basic public bar has plain wooden furniture, a black kitchen range in the fireplace and darts, pinball and a juke box. Youngs Bitter and Special on handpump. Bar food uses mostly free-range produce and might include sandwiches, wild mushroom omelette (£4), sausages with stilton sauce, smoked salmon fishcakes with scrambled eggs or fresh mussels in garlic butter and wine (£4.50), and a good summer barbecue from the charcoal barbecue counter on the extensive terrace; changing daily, this includes burger, sausages or chicken, Mediterranean prawns, lamb steak or kingfish, seafood kebab and sirloin steak. The terrace is on two levels, partly cobbled and partly concrete, with picnic-table sets, pretty hanging baskets, brightly coloured flowerbeds, small trees and its own summer bar. A Thames barge is moored alongside and can be used for private parties, although she may sail along the East and South coasts during the summer months. *(Recommended by Hazel Morgan, Mrs S Mills, Andy and Jill Kassube, Richard Gibbs, Greg Parston, Ian Phillips)*

Youngs   Licensee Charles Gotto   Real ale   Meals and snacks (12–10)   081 870 9667   You may have to park some way away   Open 11–11

White Swan (Richmond) Map 12

25/26 Old Palace Lane

It's particularly pleasing to find such a warmly friendly, almost villagey pub in London. There are copper pots hanging from the dark beamed ceiling in the open-plan bar, old prints of London and china plates on the walls, captains' chairs, dark wood tables and plush banquettes on the green and terracotta patterned carpet. The good range of bar food includes sandwiches (from £1.30), and salads or hot dishes like fish pie, vegetarian pasta, chilli con carne or lasagne (all £3.25). Courage Best and Directors on handpump; fruit machine. An attractive place to sit in summer is the conservatory, looking on to the paved garden with its climbing plants, flowering tubs, flowerbeds and wooden tables and benches; summer barbecues out here on Tuesday and Thursday evenings. *(Recommended by J E Stanton, J M Foulds, Andrew Morrissey, Wayne Brindle, Miss D Baker, M E A Horler)*

Courage   Tenant Harry Savage   Real ale   Meals and snacks (12–2.30, 5.30–10.30)   081 940 0957   Children in conservatory till 9   Open 11–3, 5.30–11; 11–4, 6–11 Sat

WEST LONDON

During weekday or Saturday daytime you may not be able to find a meter very close to the Anglesea Arms or the Windsor Castle, and parking very near in the evening may sometimes be tricky with both of these, but there shouldn't otherwise be problems in this area

Anglesea Arms (Chelsea) Map 13

15 Selwood Terrace, SW7

Always bustling with well-heeled young people, this welcoming pub keeps a good range of ales on handpump: Adnams, Boddingtons Bitter, Brakspears SB, Eldridge Pope Hardy, Greene King Abbot, Theakstons Old Peculier and Youngs Special. The bar has central elbow tables, leather chesterfields, faded Turkey carpets on the

EC4

[Old Mitre Ct], *Clachan*: Tasteful Scottish "transplant" nr Barts; quiet, well refurbished *(Dr and Mrs A K Clarke)*

[St Andrews Hill; off Queen Victoria St], *Cockpit*: Friendly little pub, a must for Guinness-lovers, with very long-serving Irish landlord — and no juke box or fruit machine *(David Hunn)*

☆ [6 Martin Lane], *Old Wine Shades*: More wine bar than pub, and packed with City types, but worth knowing as one of very few buildings to have escaped the Great Fire of 1666, and much as when Dickens used it as a tavern — heavy black beams, dark panelling, old prints, subdued lighting, old-fashioned high-backed settles, antique tables and dignified alcoves; good value weekday lunchtime traditional bar snacks, good wines, smart dress only; open weekdays 11.30-3, 5-8 *(G D Collier, LYM)*

☆ [off 145 Fleet St; shuts 9pm and weekends], *Olde Cheshire Cheese*: A piece of national pub history, little 17th-century rooms, bare boards, steep stairs, crackly old varnish (and great cellar vaults predating the Fire of London), and surprisingly untouristy; Sam Smiths have closed it for extensive building work inc an extension towards Fleet Street, planning the work closely in line with the original style and character, and hope to reopen in summer 1992; will be open all day *(Simon Collett-Jones, Mary and James Manthei, Jamie Lyons, Ruth Harrison, David Hunn, Matt Pringle, LYM)*

[2 3/4 Watling St], *Pavilion End*: Good beer and jolly atmosphere — it does look like a cricket pavilion *(LEE)*

SW1

☆ [Victoria St], *Albert*: Splendidly redecorated and harmonious Victorian exterior, psychologically dwarfing the much bigger bleak cliffs of modern glass around it; imposing inside, gleaming with polished mahogany, original gas lamps and engraved windows; quiet evenings and weekends; popular for decent bar food served quickly even when packed with civil servants; Watneys-related real ales; portraits of former Prime Ministers upstairs, Division Bell in restaurant *(R Lester, John Whitehead, BB)*

☆ [104 Horseferry Rd], *Barley Mow*: Comfortable and well kept pub, handy for Royal Horticultural Society's Halls in Vincent Sq, with Watneys-related real ales, good value efficient self-service food counter with three or four hot dishes and wide range of salads, friendly staff, a few pavement tables in side street *(John Fazakerley, BB)*

[62 Petty France], *Buckingham Arms*: Congenial Youngs local, big but narrow bar widening at the back where the food counter is — can be a squeeze to get in; unusual long side corridor fitted out with elbow ledge for drinkers; cheerful efficient service; good cheap food from ploughman's to pies and fish and so forth; Youngs Bitter *(Ian Phillips, Mike Tucker, LYM)*

[63 Eaton Terr], *Duke of Wellington*: Friendly Whitbreads pub in elegant street not far from house where Mozart lived; real ales, good value snacks *(Mrs S Mills)*

[20 The Broadway], *Feathers*: A Scotland Yard local, popular too with civil servants, quite spacious, with upstairs dining area; well kept Bass, Charrington IPA and Youngs Special on handpump, friendly service; opp St James's Park stn *(Robert Lester, BB)*

[Chesham St], *Lowndes Arms*: Friendly and efficient staff, good atmosphere, delicious lunchtime food, pretty terrace, real ale *(Robert Hodgson)*

☆ [58 Millbank], *Morpeth Arms*: Handy for the Tate, well kept Youngs, bar food, good service even when busy; seats out on Millbank and quiet less sunny side street; said to be haunted *(John Fazakerley)*

☆ [153 Knightsbridge], *Paxtons Head*: Splendid Victorian pub — some of its mirrors and glass salvaged from the Crystal Palace he designed; stylish pale green button-back plush chairs, spacious bar with central servery, cellar bar, upstairs crystal wine bar with good food — surprisingly calm and unhurried despite being so handy for Hyde Park and Knightsbridge, quiet music *(Ian Phillips, Dr and Mrs A K Clarke)*

☆ [Duke of York St], *Red Lion*: Tiny pub gleaming with magnificent mirrors, glass-dropper chandeliers, cut and etched windows, splendid mahogany; sandwiches, rolls, sausages and hot meals, well kept Ind Coope Burton, Taylor-Walker, quick friendly Australian service; gets crowded easily *(Ian, Liz and Wendy Phillips, LYM)*

[48 Parliament St], *Red Lion*: Ornate pub nr Houses of Parliament, with Division Bell — used by MPs and Foreign Office staff; Allied real ales on handpump, good range of snacks and meals; also cellar bar and upstairs restaurant *(R Lester, BB)*

☆ [Belgrave Mews West; behind German Embassy, off Belgrave Sq], *Star*: Real institution of a place, in quietly evocative mews position; small entrance bar with separate counter serving good value food lunchtime and evening; arch to side room with swagged curtains in tall windows, lots of dark mahogany, stripped mahogany chairs and tables, heavy upholstered settles, globe lighting, raj fans; back room similar but also has button-back green plush built-in wall seats; well kept Fullers Chiswick, London Pride and ESB; not too crowded lunchtime, can get packed evenings though even then upstairs — with settles, bookshelves, fire — is usually quieter; and the atmosphere is always good *(Mike Tucker, John Whitehead, Roger Taylor, John Fazakerley, Dave Gardiner, Brian Jones, BB)*

[Kinnerton St], *Turks Head*: Pleasant little pub with mock library and good roaring fire in raised lounge area, comfortably lived-in but clean and tidy; small food counter *(Ian Phillips)*

[39 Dartmouth St], *Two Chairmen*: Packed at lunchtime for good freshly cut meat sandwiches and well kept Watneys-related real ales, refurbished in old-fashioned style, in pretty Georgian street near St James's Park *(John Whitehead, BB)*

[9 Storeys Gate], *Westminster Arms*: Real ales such as Adnams, Arkells, Brakspears and Marstons Pedigree in small, friendly panelled pub, attractively refurbished 1991 to give a bit more space; popular with MPs (has Division Bell) and civil servants; food upstairs, cellar wine bar next door; now has clock instead of inn-sign *(R Lester, LYM)*

SW3

[17 Mossop St], *Admiral Codrington*: Attractive old-fashioned pub, wooden floor, conservatory-style back bar, unobtrusive piped music, good atmosphere, restaurant *(Mrs S Mills)*

[207 Brompton Rd], *Bunch of Grapes*: Splendid Victorian pub with some robust wood carving and effusive Victorian decoration; friendly *(Dr and Mrs A K Clarke)*

[298 Kings Rd], *Cadogan Arms*: Rough timber baulks, red-bulbed lanterns, impression of intimacy, well kept Watneys-related real ales, friendly atmosphere, good Chef & Brewer lunchtime and evening *(JB, RB, BB)*

☆ [197 Kings Rd], *Henry J Beans*: Not a traditional pub, but this spacious bar has — at a price — a splendid range of whiskies, other spirits and bottled beers, and good value burger-style bar food; well spaced tables, fine collection of enamelled advertising signs, and the biggest sheltered courtyard garden of any central London pub we know (was a bowling green); open all day; the branch in Abingdon Rd W2 is run on similar lines; provision for children *(P A Devitt, LYM)*

[50 Cheyne Walk], *Kings Head & Eight Bells*: Its position by garden just over busy road from Thames, nr Albert Bridge, lifts this nice traditional pub out of the ordinary *(Robert and Elizabeth Scott, Mrs S Mills, BB)*

[9 Phene St; corner Oakley St], *Phene Arms*: Outstanding garden — well worth knowing in summer; Allied beers, usual food *(C Aston)*

[86 Fulham Rd], *Rose*: Charming traditional mahogany-and-mirrors decor, with particularly attractive lighting; pleasant staff, small but good choice of bar food, well kept Fullers, theatrical connections *(Stephen R Holman, BB)*

W1

☆ [41 Mount St], *Audley*: Spacious and well kept Mayfair pub with heavily ornamented mahogany panelling, generous (if pricey) helpings of food; upstairs restaurant, basement wine bar; choice of well kept real ales *(Prof S Barnett, LYM)*

[Gresse St], *Bricklayers Arms*: Sam Smiths pub with downstairs bar, comfortable upstairs lounge, unobtrusive piped music, vaguely bricklaying decor *(T Nott)*

☆ [15 Bruton Lane; off Berkeley Sq], *Brutons*: Stylish — undoubtedly more wine bar than pub, but does have Courage Best and Directors and Websters Yorkshire on handpump; specialises in restaurant seafood showing considerable imagination, and attractively priced for the area; stained-wood booths on the left, small raised front dining area marked off by wood and glass partition, interesting prints on pink ragged-look walls, service by waistcoated waitresses, good wines, lively piped music *(BB)*

[17 Denman St], *Devonshire Arms*: Young, helpful and friendly staff, decent real ale and bar food; pub refurbished to seem old-world *(Dr and Mrs A K Clarke)*

☆ [18 Bateman St; corner of Frith St], *Dog & Duck*: Enchanting little real Soho pub, all wood, glass and superbly lively tiles, mosaic and mirrors, showing dogs and ducks; busy but not uncomfortable, well kept Tetleys and Ind Coope Burton on handpump *(LYM)*

[94A Crawford St], *Duke of Wellington*: Consistently excellent, always good service and friendly welcome, interesting decor, notably well kept Bass; comfortable *(Stephanie Adam, BB)*

[45 Harrowby St], *Duke of York*: Cosy two-bar pub decorated with Welsh Rugby shirts, bustling at lunchtime; food inc good turkey pie with generous veg, well kept Charrington IPA *(Tony Tucker, Dr and Mrs A K Clarke)*

[1 D'Arblay St], *George*: Unpretentious and friendly, with interesting mirrors and well kept ales inc Marstons Pedigree *(Dr and Mrs A K Clarke)*

☆ [30 Bruton Pl], *Guinea*: Partly 15th-century oak-panelled mews pub, smartly dressed customers overflow into the quiet mews; a long-standing part of traditional Mayfair, and well kept Youngs — if you can get near enough to order *(Ian Phillips, LYM)*

☆ [2 Shepherd Mkt], *Kings Arms*: Lively, with stripped-down decor of bare wood and rough concrete, dim upper gallery; a Chef & Brewer with mainly Watneys-related real ales but also well kept Wadworths 6X too; CD juke box may be loud, and some evenings they allow only couples inside; bar food all day *(Ian Phillips, Andy and Jill Kassube, JM, PM, LYM)*

[174 Tottenham Ct Rd; corner Capper St], *Mortimer Arms*: Refurbished Taylor Walker pub with small square bar at front and longer one at back; comfortable, padded new furniture, tastefully done in subdued colours, a lot of patterned fabrics — oriental designs on the curtains — and numerous prints, inc some modern ones; lunchtime food display, friendly bar staff, well kept Friary Meux, Tetleys and Burton on handpump *(Dr and Mrs A K Clarke)*

[183 Tottenham Court Rd], *New Inn*: Posh stripped-pine pub with accent on lunchtime food *(Dr and Mrs A K Clarke)*

[Wigmore St; corner with St Christopher Pl], *Pontefract Castle*: Rather better than many themed pubs, with good Pontefract pictures — though more Plantagenet and less Boycott might please some; open spiral staircase, feeling of space, decent furnishings, piped music not too loud *(T Nott)*

[118 Marylebone High St], *Prince Alfred*: Busy well refurbished pub, friendly service, good choice of well kept beers; interesting facade, good furnishings *(Dr and Mrs A K Clarke)*

☆ [Kingly St], *Red Lion*: Smartly modernised and relaxing two-storey pub, recently refitted so that its Twenties-Tudor panelling now forms a small front snug; well kept Sam Smiths OB and Museum, realistically priced upstairs food bar (grandfather clock on the oak stairs); music may be loud in the evening *(Ian Phillips, Michael and Alison Sandy, LYM)*

[Newman St/Eastcastle St], *Rose & Crown*: Good range of Sam Smiths beers, a decent London pub *(T Nott)*

[5 Charles St], *Running Footman*: Small and often crowded, but doesn't feel uncomfortable; staff efficient *(Neil Barker)*

☆ [Langham Pl; take express lift in far corner of hotel lobby], *St Georges Hotel*: One of the finest views in London from the Summit Bar, which has floor-to-ceiling picture windows looking out over the city to the west (the gents', facing the other way, also has a splendid view); comfortable well spaced settees, low gilt and marble tables, properly mixed cocktails (not cheap), abundant good nibbles, and good fresh sandwiches and other bar food; usually a pianist at the grand piano (not Sun); adjoining restaurant; bedrooms *(Lee Goulding, LYM)*

☆ [Poland St], Star & Garter: Unspoilt, very friendly little Soho local with well kept Courage Best and Directors, handy for Oxford Street *(LYM)*

☆ [1 Portman Mews S], *Three Tuns*: Interestingly refurbished, with lots of nooks and crannies, well kept beer, quick service *(Dr and Mrs A K Clarke, Virginia Jones)*

[8 Mill St], *Windmill*: Youngs pub with well kept Special, usual food in lower-level back food area, windmill prints, wall banquettes *(John Fazakerley)*

W2
[Hammersmith Rd], *Harvey Floorbangers*:

Spacious, with unusual and tasty choice of bar and restaurant food; good mix of seating from recline-in-comfort to sensible eating, wonderful flower arrangements *(Daphne Carter)*

[132 Edgware Rd], *Old English Gentleman*: Good example of the modern type of mock-old-world pub *(Dr and Mrs A K Clarke)*

[London St; quite nr Paddington Stn], *Sawyers*: Interesting panelled and galleried pub with lots of brewing memorabilia, Watneys-related real ales, adequate food, attentive service *(J V Dadswell)*

[66 Bayswater Rd], *Swan*: Touristy pub worth knowing for its courtyard with tree-shaded tables looking across busy road to Kensington Gardens; well kept Watneys real ales, busy food bar; interesting room on right with lofty vaulted ceiling and lantern roof, quiet room at back *(LYM)*

WC1
[New Oxford St; other entrance top Shaftesbury Ave], *Crown*: Good range of beers inc Adnams, Boddingtons, Ind Coope Burton and guests, good choice of lunchtime food, friendly young staff, comfortably padded banquettes and stools; tables and benches out on paved triangle at top of Shaftesbury Ave can be very pleasant in summer; open all day *(Andy and Jill Kassube, Andy Hick)*

[31 University St], *Jeremy Bentham*: Well managed Chef & Brewer popular with research students *(T Nott)*

[2 New Oxford St], *Oarsman*: Jolly pub, well renovated, with well kept Theakstons; formerly the Oxford & Cambridge *(Dr and Mrs A K Clarke)*

☆ [Queens Sq], *Queens Larder*: Small and friendly pub with good choice of well kept real ales inc Timothy Taylors and Wethereds, good value food in charming upstairs corner dining room, pleasant seating outside overlooking secluded square *(John Whitehead, LYM)*

[Judd St; nr St Pancras Stn], *Skinners Arms*: Lots of glass, brass and polished wood in Greene King outpost with well kept IPA, Abbot and Rayments Special, smiling attentive service, wide choice of food lunchtime and evening; peaceful lounge, lively public bar with pool *(Joan and Michel Hooper-Immins)*

☆ [63 Lambs Conduit St], *Sun*: Pleasantly spartan bare-boards pub with about 10 well kept ales from changing range, cellar tours for groups, informal friendly and efficient service, decent straightforward food, tables on pavement in pedestrian area *(Richard Houghton, Joel Dobris)*

[2 Theobalds Rd], *Yorkshire Grey*: Open-plan basic pub with good beers brewed on the premises — an interesting range; decent food, friendly polite service, typical London atmosphere, pavement tables *(Richard Houghton, Joel Dobris)*

WC2

☆ [St Martins Lane], *Chandos*: Comfortable upstairs area with open fires serving good home-cooked food all day, in quite an oasis for this area; panelling downstairs, with bare boards, Dutch wall tiles, lots of alcoves — and charm, despite getting crowded; well kept Sam Smiths OB and Museum *(Andy and Jill Kassube, Dr and Mrs A K Clarke, Steve Thomas, John Baker)*

[Lisle St/Wardour St], *Falcon*: Small and lively, with lots of mirrors and fireplaces at each end of dark panelled bar, steep stairs to lounge; homely and friendly, with Watneys-related real ales *(R Lester)*

[Long Acre], *Freemasons Arms*: Popular local, straightforward-seeming yet rewarding, with reasonable choice of food inc filled baked potatoes (not Sun), well kept Sam Smiths OB and Museum, acceptable wine; pleasant upstairs with warm gas fire *(Steve Thomas)*

[Cambridge Circus], *Marquis of Granby*: Fine place to watch the world go by, cosy and full, with friendly — even laddish — staff; winter hot toddies, and attractive range of real ales at very high prices *(Peter Griffiths)*

[10 James St], *Nags Head*: Useful for Covent Garden, U-shaped servery with food counter, pleasant friendly service, etched brewery mirrors, red ceiling, mahogany furniture, some partitioned booths; McMullens *(Andy and Jill Kassube, Simon Collett-Jones)*

[30 Lisle St], *Polar Bear*: Large open-plan pub with trendy Venetian blinds, Bass and Charrington IPA on handpump, useful for cinema and theatre *(R Lester)*

☆ [90 St Martins Lane], *Salisbury*: Authentic floridly Victorian interior, changing little over the years, with glistening big mirrors and cut glass, brass lamps, sumptuous plush banquettes and long red velvet curtains; good food (confined to right-hand side evening), well kept Allied real ales on handpump, decent white wine, no smoking area, acceptable piped music, pleasant staff; close to theatres and antiquarian bookshops *(Simon Collett-Jones, Ian Phillips, Gwen and Peter Andrews, BB)*

☆ [53 Carey St], *Seven Stars*: One of the very rare London pubs without machines or music — and it's not been rebuilt since 1710; lots of character, small cluttered layout, friendly staff *(Gilbert C Johnson, Dr and Mrs A K Clarke)*

[10 Northumberland St; Craven Pl], *Sherlock Holmes*: Lots of convincing Sherlock Holmes memorabilia (with a replica of his sitting room, closed Sun, and some good original cartoons); busy lunchtime, but reasonable quickly served

food, well kept real ales such as Wethereds *(BB)*

[66 Long Acre], *Sun*: Small, narrow pub with lots of heavy gilt framing, red plush seating and a high ceiling; cosier, semi-circular area with a couple of tables at far end; Watneys-related beers, thoughtful service, piped Radio 2, pleasant atmosphere; surprisingly has delicious reasonably priced Sun roast lunches — children allowed in dining room *(The Shinkmans, BB)*

NORTH LONDON

N1

☆ [4 Compton Ave, off Canonbury Lane], *Compton Arms*: Open all day, this diminutive pub tucked away in a narrow back street has the atmosphere of a country pub — small low-ceilinged rooms with their assorted unpretentious furniture, a little tree-shadowed courtyard garden, and friendly service; bar food is served all day (not Sun), with well kept Greene King IPA and Abbot and Rayments BBA; only an absence of reader reports keeps this attractive place out of the main entries this year *(LYM)*

☆ [60 Copenhagen St], *George IV*: Stripped woodwork, pine furniture and masses of old Burnley photographs — it was designed as a replica of a Northern pub; lunchtime bar food inc big sandwiches (not Sun), well kept real ale, conservatory area, French windows to terrace and garden with play area; handy for Regents Canal towpath *(LYM)*

☆ [87 Noel Rd], *Island Queen*: Good unusual home cooking and a friendly welcome for families in friendly big-mirrored pub handy for Camden Passage antiques area, well kept Bass and Charrington IPA, pool in back room, good juke box, tables out in front; upstairs dining room *(LYM)*

[Canonbury St; junction with Marquess Rd], *Marquess Tavern*: Large Youngs pub with comfortably plush domed back room, front bar with attractively stripped half-panelling, relaxed atmosphere, good value food inc salads, toasted sandwiches and hot dish of day, well kept real ales *(BB)*

N6

☆ [77 Highgate West Hill], *Flask*: Partly early 18th century, with old-fashioned features like the little sash-windowed bar servery, panelling, high-backed carved settle; this snug area has been closed on recent lunchtimes though; the upper bar near the dining area, with a new salad bar, is more straightforward; standard pub food, Allied real ales and Youngs on handpump, well behaved children allowed; spacious front courtyard popular in summer *(Robert Lester, LYM)*

NW1

[Camden High St], *Bucks Head*: Friendly

young trendy customers in convivial and sympathetically refurbished big room with oak tables and wooden benches, good lunchtime food, well kept Watneys-related real ales, quick staff; handy for Camden market *(Jonathan Warner, Simon Tormey)*

[383 Euston Rd], *Green Man*: Neat and clean if big and busy refurbished pub, with very friendly helpful staff; handy for the Royal College of Physicians *(Dr and Mrs A K Clarke)*

[49 Regents Park Rd], *Queens*: Typically Victorian — mahogany, stained-glass windows, secluded corners; Bass beers, reasonable food *(Mike Tucker, BB)*

[59 Parkway], *Spread Eagle*: Very pleasant, with no music, well kept Youngs, friendly service, reasonably priced food, civilised atmosphere — chat, newspaper and book reading *(Simon Tormey, Mike Tucker, BB)*

[26 Tolmers Sq], *Square*: Modern pub with well kept Youngs; friendly, with nice atmosphere *(Dr and Mrs A K Clarke)*

[Marylebone Stn], *Victoria & Albert*: Good traditional railway bar, with well kept Arkells and Bass *(Neil Barker)*

NW3

[14 Flask Walk], *Flask*: Snug Hampstead local, popular with actors and artists for 300 years *(BB)*

☆ [32 Downshire Hill], *Freemasons Arms*: Spacious garden right by Hampstead Heath with good arrangements for serving food and drink outside; skittle alley (one of only three in London) and unique lawn billiards court; good comfortable seating inside, well spaced tables in inner lounge, usual bar food inc Sun roast beef (no smoking eating area, at lunchtime), Bass and Charrington IPA; open all day summer *(Michael and Alison Sandy, LYM)*

[2a South Hill Park], *Magdala*: Good local atmosphere in panelled lounge bar, good choice of real ales with occasional guests, cosy log fire *(Jonathan Warner, BB)*

[79 Heath St], *Market*: Pleasant atmosphere, wooden floor, amazing candle effects, good if not cheap food; formerly the Nags Head, reopened in this more-bar-than-pub guise late 1990 after changing hands for nearly £1 million *(Jonathan and Polly)*

[97 Haverstock Hill], *Sir Richard Steele*: Cosy, with lots of atmosphere, interesting bric-a-brac and wooden floors; candlelit at night *(Jonathan Warner)*

NW6

☆ [West End Lane], *Arkwrights Wheel*: Imaginative new pub, already feeling quite authentic, with lots of wood, bricks, brass, bottles and bright architectural ideas — pleasant rustic impression, no junk; lighting particularly good; welcoming landlord, formerly popular at the Clifton, NW8, good food and drinks, good friendly young staff *(GB,*

CH)

NW8

☆ [96 Clifton Hill], *Clifton*: In a quiet residential area, with attractive layout and decor, elegant wallpaper, panelling and lamps, antique prints, impression of series of small rooms; conservatory, leafy front terrace; open all day Fri, Sat, provision for children; has been among the most popular pubs in London, for relaxed countryfied atmosphere, decent home cooking, and well kept Allied ales, and still has its firm supporters, though not everyone would agree it still has its edge *(Gary Scott, Joel Dobris, Tony and Lynne Stark, LYM; more reports on current regime please)*

[11 Alma Sq; off Hill Rd], *Heroes of Alma*: Good value freshly cooked food and well kept Watneys real ales in friendly little unaffected Victorian local with tables outside *(A M Kelly, LYM)*

[2 Allitsen Rd; on corner of Townsend Rd], *New Inn*: Really good value lunchtime food such as salads, fish and chips and cheap steak, in clean well kept pub with John Smiths and other beers; not too crowded, no juke box, and decorated much as you might expect for St Johns Wood *(Dr and Mrs A K Clarke)*

☆ [23 Queens Grove], *Rossetti*: Good range of reasonably priced hot and cold lunchtime food inc daily hot specials in unusually Italianate pub with lots of marble and open space, stairway up to cocktail bar and restaurant with mainly Italian food, no piped music or fruit machines, well kept reasonably priced Fullers London Pride and ESB; friendly service, food well priced for London *(LYM)*

Barnet

[133 East Barnet Rd], *Alexandra*: Fairly small, with well kept prize-winning garden; Fullers ESB on handpump, weekday lunchtime food, friendly landlord *(Chris Fluck)*

[Barnet Rd (A411); nr Hendon Wood Lane], *Gate at Arkley*: Civilised and well run pub with comfortable seats, good log fire in winter and lovely secluded garden for summer; good choice of food from sandwiches to hot dishes, and a better choice of whiskies than usual around London *(BB)*

☆ [High St], *Mitre*: Small-roomed friendly tavern, the taproom area of what was an extensive 17th-century inn with Dickens connections; well kept Benskins Best, Ind Coope Burton and Tetleys on handpump, food even on Sun, usually uncrowded; no piped music *(M B Porter, LYM)*

Cockfosters

[nr Trent Pk], *Cock*: Well kept Ind Coope Burton, good food, lots of room, friendly staff; garden bar *(Patrick Vaughan)*

Enfield

[5 The Town], *George*: Much-modified former coaching inn with mock-Elizabethan black and white frontage — passage to back bar used to be the coach entry; Bass and Charrington IPA on handpump, old local postcards, good Toby grill-restaurant upstairs *(Neil Barker)*

☆ [Whitewebbs Lane; A10 from M25 junction 25, right at 1st lights, right at left-hand bend], *King & Tinker*: Good food specialising in huge filled rolls, in pleasant pub of real character, with lots of old local photographs and good garden; well kept Allied real ales and several guests such as Adnams, Greene King IPA and Abbot and Marstons Pedigree kept well, decent wines by the glass, welcoming staff coping very well even if busy; occasional Morris men *(Gwen and Peter Andrews, Roger and Carol Chisnall, Joy Heatherley)*

☆ [Chase Side], *Moon Under Water*: Carefully refurbished free house with splendid range of cheap well kept real ales such as Brains, Greene King Abbot, Marstons Pedigree, Wadworths 6X and — at bargain price — Youngers IPA; good food, comfortable civilised surroundings *(R McIntosh, Robert Lester)*

Robin Hood: Pleasant McMullens family pub, wide choice of food, good staff, large attractively laid out garden with impressive focal weeping willow *(Gwen and Peter Andrews)*

Harrow

☆ [30 West St], *Castle*: Unspoilt inn in picturesque part, classic lively traditional bar, sedate and civilised lounge with open fires, wall seats, variety of prints; good service, well kept Fullers, lunchtime food (just toasties weekends), maybe Sun seafood nibbles; nice garden with chatty caged birds *(Lee Goulding, Philip Harrison)*

Harrow Weald

☆ [Old Redding; off A409 — OS Sheet 176, map reference 144926], *Case is Altered*: Notably unspoilt country setting, with peaceful views from very extensive sloping garden (excellent for children); inside, the atmosphere's more villagey than you might expect from London's suburbs, with a low ceiling, wooden wall benches, old-world prints, well kept Benskins Best and Ind Coope Burton on handpump, friendly service, bar food from sandwiches and cheap burgers to big steaks (only snacks weekends, no food Sun evening); children welcome until 9 *(Michael and Alison Sandy, Tony and Lynne Stark, Kathy Holt, LYM)*

☆ [Brookshill], *Hare*: Particularly good value generous bar lunches inc fine open sandwiches, ploughman's and imaginative hot dishes, quickly and pleasantly served; comfortable bar with good atmosphere;

space somewhat limited inside, but nice garden *(A C Morrison)*

New Barnet

☆ [13 East Barnet Rd; A110 nr stn], *Railway Bell*: Transformed by Wetherspoons into civilised free house with no machines or piped music, well kept Greene King IPA and Abbot, Marstons Pedigree, Youngs and Youngers Scotch at relatively low prices, good hot and cold food, good service, plenty of room; lots of railway memorabilia, garden bar *(Patrick Vaughan, David Fowles, Richard Houghton)*

Pinner

[Waxwell Lane], *Oddfellows Arms*: Comfortable, with darts, usual bar food lunchtime and evening, Greene King Abbot, Tetleys and Youngs; garden behind *(Nigel Gibbs)*

South Harrow

[3 Shaftesbury Parade; Shaftesbury Ave/Ridgeway], *J J Moons*: Well decorated Wetherspoons pub, was a shop; fine friendly service, nice atmosphere, friendly regulars, clean lavatories, well kept changing real ales, good range of lunchtime food *(R Houghton)*

SOUTH LONDON
SE1

[Upper Ground; by Blackfriars Bridge], *Doggetts Coat & Badge*: Magnificent Thames views from comfortable three-level modern pub handy for South Bank arts complex *(Neil Barker, BB)*

☆ [Bankside], *Founders Arms*: Notable for the almost unobstructed view over the Thames of St Pauls, from the spacious glass-walled modern bar and the big waterside terrace; Youngs Bitter and Special on handpump, green plush banquettes, elbow-rest screens *(Roger Huggins, Neil Barker, LYM)*

☆ [47 Borough Rd], *Goose & Firkin*: The first Firkin pub, brewing Goose, Borough and Dog; handy for War Museum, bare and basic in Firkin style, with assorted tables and chairs on bare boards; reasonably priced food inc giant baps *(Matt Pringle, LYM)*

☆ [5 Mepham St], *Hole in the Wall*: A dog-eared charm about this railway-arch pub with Waterloo trains shaking its ceiling; remarkable choice of well kept real ales at low prices, cheap bar food, basic furnishings, very mixed clientele, busy early Fri evening *(A W Dickinson, Simon Collett-Jones, A J Brown, LYM)*

☆ [St Mary Overy Wharf; off Clink St], *Old Thameside*: Dark floorboards, bare yellow brickwork and hefty timbers in main river-view bar, dark beams, pews and flagstones in more intimate candlelit lower bar; well kept Boddingtons, Courage Directors, Flowers and another real ale, good generously filled baps etc upstairs, more choice downstairs; charming waterside terrace by schooner docked in landlocked inlet; views across to the Monument and overweening modern City developments *(Comus Elliott, LYM)*

SE3

[1a Eliot Cottages], *Hare & Billet*: Nicely placed opp pond, lovely views, but high prices; comfortable Victorian-style refurbishment, Whitbreads-related and guest real ales, food such as ploughman's, sausage and mash, turkey and ham pie, beef stew, meat salads *(R N Haygarth, BB)*
[Prince of Wales Rd], *Princess of Wales*: Recently renovated Village Inn, with big back conservatory and lots of terrace seating, also some front tables looking out over the heath; comfortable, with efficient obliging service, food such as ploughman's, chicken and broccoli bake and filled baked potatoes; closes 4, pleasant views *(Ian Phillips)*

SE10

☆ [Lassell St], *Cutty Sark*: Attractive white-painted pub looking over Thames to Docklands, with big upper bow window jettied out over the road; evocative decor of flagstones, rough brick walls, wooden settles, barrel tables, large and elaborate central wooden staircase, narrow opening to tiny side rooms, low lighting, open fires — you half expect the next customers to be the Pirates of Penzance; large food area serving omelettes, steak and kidney pie and so forth, with amazing seafod Sun bar snacks; well kept Bass, small upstairs restaurant; jazz some nights, occasional Morris men *(Brian and Jenny Seller, K Flack)*
☆ [52 Royal Hill], *Richard I*: Quiet and friendly haven with no gimmicks or music; though it's now under management after the tenant's retirement, it's doing well under the current regime, with a good range of food inc sausages in French bread, good toasted sandwiches and ploughman's, well kept Youngs; no-nonsense atmosphere, white plastic seats in substantially reworked back garden *(Robert Gomme, Adrian Pitts, Andrew Cooke)*

SE16

☆ [118 Lower Rd], *Prince of Orange*: Famous for different good jazz acts each night and weekend lunchtimes, with simple but good value food (especially pizzas), several Watneys-related real ales, fine collection of jazz photographs in one of the two smaller rooms off the main simply furnished bar; children allowed in eating area; open evenings, and Sun lunchtime *(LYM)*

SE19

☆ [41 Beulah Hill], *Beulah Spa*: Large extensively renovated pub, with most

impressive entrance; popular and well appointed Toby carvery and bars, good bar meals, well kept Charrington IPA on handpump, plenty of picnic-table sets in garden *(E G Parish, Mrs J A Blanks)*

SE25

[2 Penge Rd], *Goathouse*: Spacious and comfortable Fullers pub, not too modern, warm atmosphere *(Adrian Zambardino, Debbie Chaplin)*

SE26

[Sydenham Rd], *Golden Lion*: Eye-catching red-painted outside, with white seats on attractive front forecourt and more tables in pleasant white-trellised back shrub garden; well managed, with reasonably priced bar food and well kept Courage Directors on handpump *(E G Parish)*

SW4

[38 Old Town], *Prince of Wales*: Piled high with flags and bric-a-brac, always something new to see; good range of well kept Whitbreads-related real ales, good value, well cooked, simple lunchtime dishes, friendly and occasionally jokey staff; can get very crowded *(Peter Griffiths, Jonathan Warner)*

SW8

[St Stephens Terr; off S Lambeth Rd], *Royal Albert*: Whitbreads pub with book-lined walls, armchairs, sofas, tables of varying heights, clever lighting, good range of real ales such as Flowers IPA, Greene King Abbot, Marstons Pedigree and Wethereds, video juke box (reasonable volume); quiet back terrace *(Tim Barrow, Sue Demont, BB)*

SW9

[261 Brixton Rd], *Old White Horse*: Large and friendly, with famous cabaret room winter Fris; lunchtime meals, evening snacks, Allied real ales, darts and space game *(Steve Rogerson)*
[90 Stockwell Rd], *Plough*: Live jazz or R&B Tues-Sun, with midnight licence Tues-Sat; well kept Watneys-related real ales, friendly public bar with pool table; 3 mins from Stockwell tube *(Steve Rogerson)*

SW11

☆ [60 Battersea High St], *Woodman*: Busy local with lots of prints and a stag's head in its little panelled front bar, long Turkey-carpeted room decorated with dried flowers, baskets, a boar's head and even an aged wheelbarrow; brocaded stools and chairs, some big casks, log-effect gas fires; well kept Badger Best and Tanglefoot, Wadworths 6X and guest beers on handpump, good service and atmosphere, bar billiards, darts and trivia machine at one end, picnic-table sets on raised terrace with barbecue area; not to be confused with the Original Woodman next door *(Nick and Alison Dowson, J Hampton, B Metherell, Richard Houghton, BB)*

SW12

[97 Nightingale Lane], *Nightingale*: An old friend, deservedly popular, some extension behind, gallery of guide-dog pictures on one wall, barman copes with even the liveliest crowd; well kept Youngs, generous bar food (not Sun) *(Hazel Morgan, BB)*

SW13

[2 Castelnau], *Red Lion*: Fine well restored Victorian pub with impressive decor, three separate areas, efficient welcoming service, well kept Fullers Chiswick, London Pride and ESB; big garden *(R Houghton)*
[7 Church Rd], *Sun*: Country-style pub in town overlooking duckpond, well kept interconnecting bars around central servery, various rooms and snugs; very busy evenings and lunchtimes, good choice of beers, good food *(Nigel Gibbs, Iain Hewitt, Jonathan and Polly, BB)*

SW14

[216 Upper Richmond Rd], *Hare & Hounds*: Good well run pub with well kept Youngs, variety of good reasonably priced food *(P Gillbe)*

SW15

☆ [8 Lower Richmond Rd], *Dukes Head*: Grand and spacious Youngs pub very popular for its super position on Thames (at Boat Race start point); two bars, big dining area, good freshly cooked lunchtime food, well kept Youngs; lavatories below street level, parking can be difficult *(Ian Phillips, Simon Collett-Jones, R Houghton, BB)*
[Wildcroft Rd], *Green Man*: In popular spot on the edge of Putney Heath, with cosy main bar, quiet sitting room, friendly atmosphere, well kept Youngs Bitter and Special; simple bar food; popular, but never seems overcrowded, with tables in front and pretty, sheltered garden behind taking overflow; barbecues, play area *(Ann Marie Stephenson, LYM)*
[122 High St], *Spotted Horse*: Comfortably carpeted open-plan bar with island servery, well kept Youngs, good service, lunchtime food, relaxing evening atmosphere *(R Houghton)*

SW16

☆ [151 Greyhound Lane], *Greyhound*: Handsome main bar on right, middle bar with local ice-hockey team souvenirs, well equipped games bar on left; spacious and attractive family conservatory, sizeable garden beyond; meals and snacks throughout day till 10, and up to half a dozen beers brewed here inc unusual recipes — despite the price of these (not as cheap as own-brews tend to be), it all adds up to a very attractive picture, and only a run of recent management changes leaves us in some uncertainty about whether a main entry is still in order *(Neil Barker, Andrew Cooke, Andy and Jill Kassube, R Houghton, LYM)*

SW17

[Bellevue Rd], *Hope*: Opp Wandsworth Common, open all day (even does breakfasts); well kept Ind Coope Burton on handpump, wide choice of imported lagers, bar food inc enormous ploughman's with three different cheeses *(C J Parsons)*

SW19

☆ [Camp Rd], *Fox & Grapes*: Well run and spacious, with huge beams in high ceiling of main bar, dark wooden furniture on patterned carpet; friendly staff, good choice of fresh-cooked food, with big ploughman's, enjoyable seafood surprise, main dishes served with lots of vegetables; well kept Courage and John Smiths; not at its best on a Saturday evening, crowded Sun lunchtime — unless it's fine enough to sit out on Wimbledon Common *(Brian and Jenny Seller, Ann Marie Stephenson, Robert Hodgson, BB)*
☆ [6 Crooked Billet], *Hand in Hand*: Picturesque old pub with tables out on the grass at the edge of Wimbledon Common; cheerful U-shaped bar serving several small areas, some tiled, others carpeted, inc useful family room; well kept Youngs, reasonable choice of food from good ploughman's to steaks, real log fires, darts *(Ian Phillips, Iain Hewitt)*
[Coombe Lane (A238)], *Raynes Park*: Friendly contrasting bars — comfortably modern public, bookshelf saloon, Watneys-related real ales *(Robert Lester)*

Bexley

[Black Prince Interchange, Southwold Rd (A2)], *Black Prince*: Reliably welcoming, food decent if not cheap; warm and comfortable, preserving its original atmosphere though now part of a hotel complex; bedrooms *(E G Parish)*

Biggin Hill

[Jail Lane], *Old Jail*: Doing well under new management, well kept pub with delightful atmosphere (but mind your head), friendly prompt service, good helpings of reasonably priced bar food, restaurant; visitors welcome at Foal Farm opp *(W J Wonham)*

Bromley

[Gravel Rd], *Bird in Hand*: Simple well established Courage pub with well kept beer and short choice of cheap food inc a good special — popular at lunchtime with older people; friendly atmosphere, quiet garden

(Robert and Fiona Ambroziak)

Chislehurst

[Royal Parade], *Bulls Head*: Well kept Youngs Bitter and Special in two big bars, one with high-backed armchairs and big winter fire; pleasant staff, generous helpings of straightforward bar food, spacious back carvery; tables in garden, nr pleasant nature reserve; open nearly all day, closed 4-5 *(Adrian Pitts, M E A Horler)*

Croydon

[Laud St], *Bulls Head*: Very comfortable and friendly, handy for High St; opens 7 Sat *(Neil Barker)*

[Junction Rd; off Brighton Rd], *Crown & Sceptre*: Small, friendly one-bar pub, clean and nicely furnished, tropical fish above fireplace, old brewery advertisements, well kept Fullers, big front beer garden, small back terrace, some floral decoration *(M Desmond, Neil Barker)*

[Morland Rd], *Joiners Arms*: Almost enough brass to rival the Seven Stars down at Penryn in Cornwall; dimly lit and comfortable, beautifully kept, with good short choice of bar food (not Sun), well kept Allied beers, tables in pretty creeper-clad courtyard *(Brian and Jenny Seller, Neil Barker, Ian Phillips)*

[1 Sheldon St], *Royal Standard*: Small basic corner local worth knowing for well kept Fullers, unusual terrace on other side of the quiet rd; handy for High St *(Neil Barker)*

☆ [Upland Rd; off Brighton Rd], *Woodman*: Almost a country pub in town, relatively big frontage adorned with greenery and flowers, subdued lantern lights, lots of prints, posters, London General Omnibus Co prospectus, football shirts and so forth on walls and ceiling, jug collection, unusual longitudinal seating, seats outside *(Neil Barker)*

Cudham

[Cudham Lane], *Blacksmiths Arms*: Real old cottage atmosphere, with window boxes, two or three log fires; clean and well run, with good promptly served bar food, morning coffee too; nice walks and riding nearby *(W J Wonham)*

Farnborough

[High Elms], *Two Badgers*: Free house with delightful first-floor bar giving superb views over parkland and golf links, good bar food, wide range of drinks *(W J Wonham)*

Keston

[Westerham Rd], *Keston Mark*: Attractively redecorated, with good atmosphere; open all day *(E G Parish)*

Kew

[Kew Green], *Kings Arms*: Clean and well ordered, with good helpings of nicely cooked food — fetch it yourself when they call your number; Fullers London Pride and Wadworths 6X on handpump; handy for Kew Gdns, cricket on green *(Jennifer and Brian Seller)*

Kingston

[2 Bishops Hall; off Thames St — down alley behind W H Smiths], *Bishop out of Residence*: Spacious semi-circular bar with double row of banquettes facing river, Edwardian-style wallpaper, Coronation curtains; modern, but well kitted out to take advantage of Thames and bridge views, second bar upstairs (quieter, when young people and loud music downstairs) with terrace with small cast-iron chairs and tables, picnic-table sets by riverside walk; Youngs real ales, good value bar food inc sandwiches, ploughman's and hot dishes such as chilli or plaice segments; tables on terrace; handy for central Kingston *(Michael and Alison Sandy)*

☆ [Canbury Gdns; Lower Ham Rd], *Boaters*: Good river views from comfortable banquettes inside and floodlit tables in garden, real ales inc Courage Directors, John Smiths and guests such as Wadworths 6X, reasonable food *(Ian Phillips)*

[88 London Rd; corner Albert Rd], *Flamingo Brewery*: Large bare-boards pub with lots of tables around edges, snugs and corners, plenty of standing room too; three good real ales brewed on the premises, with guest beer, good value bar food inc cheap Sun lunch, efficient service; disco Fri, Sat night sing-songs; children's room with adventure play area and view into brewery, seats on terrace *(Ian Phillips, Richard Houghton)*

☆ [Portsmouth Rd], *Harts Boatyard*: Vast Beefeater, but full of character — endless boating paraphernalia, boathooks, bottom-boards, formers, jigs, frames, rudders, tillers, even whole boats overhead and serving as seats (some parts of the building are genuinely very old); two shaded balconies overlooking Thames and Hampton Court grounds, seats out in sun, upstairs steak house, lunchtime bar food, Flowers IPA on handpump; dinghy chandlery at river level *(Ian Phillips)*

[13 Bloomfield Rd; just S of Polytechnic, E of B3363], *Spring Grove*: Large open-plan local with several distinct areas, well kept Youngs, warm atmosphere (gas fires), pleasant service — clean pub *(R Houghton)*

Richmond

[5 Church Ct; alley by Owen Owen], *Angel & Crown*: Rather plain, but well kept Fullers, good choice of hearty bar meals, friendly and efficient service by informally dressed staff, relaxed atmosphere *(R Houghton)*

☆ [Upper Ham Rd], *Hand & Flower*: Watneys pub with smart tiled verandah opening into very sheltered pretty garden, banks of greenery and an alternative grotto, waterfall and pond; spacious and comfortable lounge leading to lower snugs and eating area with coal-effect gas fire and china on walls; piped pop music; public bar's beams festooned with soccer programmes *(Ian Phillips)*

[345 Petersham Rd; Ham Common], *New Inn*: Busy well organised refurbished local, friendly staff, good home-made food, log fire, good staff; can get rather crowded *(P Gillbe)*

[45 Kew Rd], *Orange Tree*: Interesting main bar with fine plasterwork, big coaching and Dickens prints, fine set of 1920s paintings; open all day, with theatre club upstairs, well kept Youngs beers, friendly service, and has been popular for original food (also served all day, not Sun evening) in spacious and attractive cellar bar; but there have been changes on the food side, and this edition went to press before it was clear how things would turn out; pleasant tables outside *(R Houghton, A W Dickinson, Wayne Brindle, David Fowles, Michael and Alison Sandy, LYM; news please)*

[28 The Green], *Princes Head*: Large open-plan pub nr theatre, nice mixed clientele, friendly service, Fullers *(R Houghton)*

☆ [Duke St], *Racing Page*: Formerly Cobwebs, recently done up and reopened as latest link in the small chain that includes the Front Page and Sporting Page in Chelsea; well kept Watneys-related real ales, decent wines, interesting food, much as them *(Mr and Mrs R J Foreman)*

[130 Richmond Hill], *Roebuck*: Quaint if not necessarily genuine interior, very comfortable, with superb view and good lunchtime food inc particularly well filled rolls, appetising salads, home-made pies *(Ian Phillips, I Kelly)*

☆ [Petersham Rd], *Rose of York*: Well furnished, clean and spacious panelled pub overlooking Thames, with softly lit corners, well kept Sam Smiths, good choice of ample lunchtime food, reasonably priced; efficient service from smart staff, discreet alcove for darts and pool; pleasant location, esp in summer, with extended garden *(TBB, John Whitehead, Ian Phillips, P Gillbe)*

[17 Parkshort; just tucked away from shopping centre], *Sun*: Delightfully traditional pub on quiet street; entrances from front or via alleyway opp Richmond stn; sporting pictures in front bar, bar billiards in attractive long back room with tables, well kept Fullers; tables among flowers outside; Fullers beers *(Peter Griffiths, David Hunn)*

[Petersham Rd], *Three Pigeons*: Large river-view pub with several real ales, bar food, restaurant *(M E A Horler)*

[12 Water Lane], *Watermans Arms*: Nice friendly atmosphere and very helpful licensees in small two-bar local with fresh flowers, Youngs beer; handy for Thames, nearby parking unlikely *(R Houghton)*

☆ [Cholmondeley Walk; riverside], *White Cross*: Busy yet civilised and relaxing — especially on the banquettes around those big tables in the deep bay windows that overlook the Thames and Richmond Bridge not far from Quinlan Terry's pastiche; recently extensively refurbished, but no music, machines or other gimmicks; reasonably priced lunchtime bar food, friendly service; spacious upstairs family dining room with river-view balcony, tables outside with summer garden bar *(Ian Phillips, Prof S Barnett, Neil Barker, Mayur Shah, Chris Ralph, William Robinson)*

Thornton Heath

[Bensham Gr; corner Beulah Rd], *Lord Napier*: Youngs pub with well kept real ales, popular new landlord, jazz all week in big room off bar *(Neil Barker)*

West Wickham

[Pickhurst Lane], *Pickhurst*: A Watneys Country Carvery dining pub, consistently popular for good value Sun lunches (must book in summer — when children like the big garden); nice atmosphere *(E G Parish, Ian Phillips)*

☆ [High St], *Swan*: A picture of rustic tranquillity, overlooking village cricket green and ancient church; attractive and spotless, particularly well kept Courage Best, reasonably priced wines, delightfully good value ploughman's, locally popular first-floor restaurant *(E G Parish, Jenny and Brian Seller)*

WEST LONDON
SW6

[577 Kings Rd], *Imperial Arms*: Spacious and comfortable, with consistently good food inc brilliant hot salt beef sandwich; well kept beer (its pricing encourages upmarket clientele); handy for Christopher Wrays *(JBM, P C Russell)*

[871 Fulham Rd], *Pitcher & Piano*: Bright, clean, modern, young design, simple menu of snacky food, good wine list, great music *(R Tomlinson)*

SW7

☆ [2 Ennismore Mews], *Ennismore Arms*: Small, friendly and civilised mews pub, handy for Harrods and V & A but tucked away from the scrum in a lovely quiet spot; Watneys-related real ales and decent food, inc Sun lunch, reasonably priced for the area; approaching by Holy Trinity Brompton puts you in a properly countryfied mood *(E Spencer, Neil Barker, BB)* [127 Gloucester Rd; opp Hereford

Squ], *Hereford Arms*: Good range of beers inc Brakspears, Charles Wells Bombardier and Greene King Abbot, good Antipodean staff, busy atmosphere *(Nick and Alison Dowson)*

[44 Montpelier Sq], *King George IV*: Quiet pub, good value considering its convenience for Knightsbridge *(Liz Phillips)*

W4

☆ [72 Strand on the Green], *Bell & Crown*: Big riverside Fullers pub with well kept beer and simple good value food inc interesting choice of cheap lunchtime sandwiches; good warm atmosphere *(Tony and Lynne Stark, BKA, Ray and Gwen Jessop)*

☆ [27 Strand on the Green], *City Barge*: Partly 15th-century, picturesque and right on the river, though at lunchtime the attractive original core can be used only if you are eating here; its two ageing front rooms by the river are a good deal more atmospheric if less comfortable than the airy upper New Bar with all its maritime signs and bird prints; lunchtime bar food (not Sun), Courage Best and Directors, back conservatory, blazing winter fires *(BKA, Ray and Gwen Jessop, Andrew Cooke, R Bennett, J Hampton, B Metherell, LYM)*

[Burlington Lane; Hogarth Corner, A4], *George & Devonshire*: Spacious and popular old-style Fullers pub with Chiswick, London Pride and ESB and good choice of reasonably priced bar food *(Pat and Derek Westcott)*

[185 Chiswick High St], *George IV*: Spacious, clean pub with exceptionally friendly staff, nice atmosphere, real fire; good traditional food, particularly the three Sun roasts carved by the landlord in the bar; well kept Fullers Chiswick, London Pride and ESB; popular with OAPs lunchtime, busier evening *(Dennis Owen, Samantha Prior, Richard Fathers)*

W5

☆ [Elm Grove Rd; by Warwick Dene], *Grange*: Well kept Watneys-related real ales, food inc popular Sun roast lunch, small lounge, quite separate public bar, bigger lounge on higher level and conservatory with own bar (leading to back terrace with tables) *(Philip Harrison, Ben Wimpenny)*

W6

☆ [2 South Black Lion Lane], *Black Lion*: Very comfortable and cosy, with friendly, efficient staff, nice oil of A P Herbert over fireplace, photographs of Thames barges, tie collection over bar and so forth; good doorstep sandwiches, also hot dishes inc good value curries Weds evening; healthy mix of customers, easy atmosphere, popular with families for Sun roast beef; Watneys-related beers *(BB)*

[Lower Mall], *Blue Anchor*: Good, honest riverside pub, very popular in summer; well kept Courage from lovely brass pumps, good value food — big rolls, steak and kidney pie — rather nautical flavour, with oars and so forth around the panelling *(Jamie Lyons, Ruth Harrison, Chris Fluck)*

[57 Black Lion Lane], *Cross Keys*: Well kept simple backstreet local not far from Thames, modernised open-plan bar, good friendly atmosphere, Fullers beers in top condition, good service *(R Houghton, BB)*

☆ [25 Upper Mall], *Old Ship*: Riverside pub, more spacious than its rivals, with three comfortably refurbished bar areas, a clutter of nautical memorabilia, sizeable side terrace, reasonably priced straightforward snacks and (not Sun) lunchtime bar meals, well kept Watneys real ales *(Edward Burlton Davies, Wayne Brindle)*

[Goldhawk Rd; junction Stamford Brook Rd], *Queen of England*: Spacious, with comfortable seating inc great armchairs; real ale, friendly staff, not too crowded even Fri or Sat evening *(Neil Barker)*

W7

[Green Lane, Hanwell], *Fox*: Friendly traditional local, in quiet spot nr Grand Union Canal *(Neil Barker)*

W8

☆ [1 Allen St; off Kensington High St], *Britannia*: Unchanging peaceful comfort, with helpful and charming landlady, good beer and good fresh home-cooked food at reasonable prices; no music, attractive indoor 'garden' *(Prof S Barnett, BHP, Leigh Mellor)*

☆ [9 Kensington Church St], *Churchill Arms*: Great Fullers local with long-serving spirited Irish landlord and traditional swinging snob screens; crowded for TV sportscasts, especially rugby internationals, but escape into quieter parts possible even then; consistently well kept ale, lots of brass jugs, Churchill portraits; delicious reasonably priced bar food cooked by Thai chef, charming Thai staff; light and airy family conservatory with landlord's butterfly collection, no music *(Ian Phillips, Leigh Mellor, Tony and Lynne Stark)*

[40 Holland St], *Elephant & Castle*: Basic small two-bar open-plan pub with polished floors, friendly staff, Bass and Charrington IPA on handpump, good pizzas (busy at lunchtime); seats on small terrace with hanging baskets *(Samantha Prior, Richard Fathers)*

☆ [23a Edwardes Squ], *Scarsdale Arms*: Well kept Watneys-related real ales and decent wines in partly gaslit Chef & Brewer done up in old-fashioned style with winter fires in spacious bar; tree-shaded front courtyard, meals and snacks (not Sun), children in eating area *(LYM)*

[13 Uxbridge St], *Uxbridge Arms*: Small

backstreet local with real village feel, consistently well kept Boddingtons, Brakspears and Wethereds, good choice of bottled beers *(Tony and Lynne Stark)*

☆ [114 Campden Hill Rd], *Windsor Castle*: Mr Owen who as tenant had run this pub with such distinction for 25 years, keeping a remarkable country atmosphere in its series of small traditional rooms, was sadly given notice by his brewery in 1991, and it is to become a Charrington managed house; it may still be worth knowing, given its distinctive old-fashioned layout (if they don't knock it all into one) and particularly for its remarkably large tree-shaded terrace *(LYM)*

W9

☆ [6 Warwick Pl], *Warwick Castle*: Unspoilt traditional high-ceilinged Victorian pub with quiet and friendly atmosphere, bar food inc good value Sun lunch, well kept Bass and Charrington IPA, benches out by quiet lane; close to Little Venice *(Nicky Moore, LYM)*

W11

[179 Portobello Rd], *Duke of Wellington*: Good choice of ales (Greene King Abbot as well as Bass, Charrington IPA and so forth), usual bar food, pleasant staff, relaxing atmosphere *(Stephen R Holman)*

☆ [54 Ladbroke Rd], *Ladbroke Arms*: Pleasantly refurbished with red and green banquettes, and open fire in upper room; food now the main attraction under new landlord, up to restaurant standard, with interesting and sometimes unusual home cooking; Watneys-related real ales, with a guest such as Eldridge Pope *(Patrick Young)*

W12

☆ [172 Uxbridge Rd; by Wood Lane/Shepherds Bush Green], *Moon on the Green*: Fine Victorian pub newly refitted by Wetherspoons, comfortable, attractive and friendly, with two bars, one below ground level; five real ales changing weekly — notably low drinks prices inc a bargain beer; varied reasonably priced food, good service *(R Houghton, Layne Hudes, Craig Kalpakjian)*

W14

☆ [187 Greyhound Rd], *Colton Arms*: Remarkably village-like atmosphere, helped by the dark wood, high-backed settle and indivual decorations, not to mention the attractive little rose-arbour garden; Watneys-related real ales — ring bell for service *(BB)*

[247 Warwick Rd], *Radnor Arms*: Recently refurbished basic open-plan pub with very pleasant service and atmosphere, full range of Everards beers in top condition *(R Houghton)*

[160 Warwick Rd], *Warwick Arms*: Open-plan, but otherwise a fine example of a London pub; friendly regulars (some playing darts or bridge), service fast, friendly and courteous, Fullers beers in top condition from elegant Wedgwood handpumps *(R Houghton)*

Brentford

☆ [Brook Rd], *Griffin*: Lively traditional local, pleasant well organised service, Fullers beers, bustling confiding atmosphere — strangers don't feel out of place; ebullient French landlady who observes French festivals appropriately; good red wines; parking may be difficult *(Caroline Black, Roger Sealey, R Houghton)*

[3 High St], *O'Riordans*: Good choice of well kept real ales inc Flowers and Wadworths 6X, good cheap home-made food, pleasant service, lots of bric-a-brac, nice atmosphere; parking may be difficult *(R Houghton, Mark Blackburn)*

[107 Ealing Rd], *Princess Royal*: Two tastefully refurbished bars with Victorian windows, pleasant service and locals, Fullers beers, disco music Fri *(R Houghton)*

Cranford

[123 High St; Cranford Lane off A312], *Queens Head*: Large three-bar pub with local atmosphere and good spread of ages in evening, more airport workers at lunchtime when there's a good choice of food; well kept Fullers Chiswick, London Pride and ESB, efficient service, warm atmosphere *(R Houghton)*

Hampton

☆ [8 Thames St], *Bell*: On busy rd, but next to church, with fine views of Thames and Ham meadows from lounge, tables on terrace under chestnut; newly refurbished, spaciously open-plan divided into comfortable areas by balustrades — fresh and brisk feel, but welcoming, with speedy polite uniformed service; good bar food inc sandwiches, quiche, fresh salads, sensibly priced daily specials such as gammon and lasagne; one regular in her 90s has been coming by bus from Hanworth for lunch at least once a week for longer than she can remember *(Ian Phillips, E G Parish)*

☆ [70 High St], *White Hart*: Good range of changing well kept and competitively priced real ales inc unusual ones from small, distant breweries, lunchtime filled rolls and chippy food, friendly service, nice log fire, soft lighting; atmosphere of this beer-drinkers' pub building up as evening progresses; seats out on small front terrace, not far from Thames, easy parking *(Dr M Owton, Ian Phillips, Richard Houghton)*

Harefield

[Hill End Rd; lane to Springfield Lock, just N of hospital], *Plough*: Pleasant atmosphere, no music, welcoming landlord and staff, good service; worth knowing for the nine or so well kept real ales, such as Brakspears, Fullers London Pride, Greene King Abbot, Marstons Pedigree and changing guests *(R Houghton)*

[Church Hill/Harvil Rd], *White Horse*: Old cottage-type pub, not spoilt by overmodernisation, with well kept Allied real ales and a guest beer such as Adnams or Youngs, popular for good cheap food *(J E Stanton)*

Hatton

☆ [Green Man Lane; 30 yds from A30 crossroads at Bedfont], *Green Man*: Cosy low ceilings and alcoves, genuinely old (and genuinely once a highwaymen's lair); lunchtime food inc good big ploughman's, lots of salads, good choice of hot dishes; popular with airport staff *(Mayur Shah, Ian Phillips)*

Hounslow

[121 Bath Rd], *Queen Victoria*: Small one-bar local, very welcoming to all, with nice friendly atmosphere, popular lunchtime food; Fullers ales *(Richard Houghton)*

Isleworth

[183 London Rd], *Coach & Horses*: Open-plan suburban pub to note for particularly well kept Youngs *(R Houghton)*

[Church St], *London Apprentice*: Long famous for its pretty Thames-side position, this spaciously comfortable Chef & Brewer pub does get very popular in summer and on winter weekends, especially with younger people; several Watneys-related real ales, young friendly staff, help-yourself salads and daily roast, upstairs restaurant (open all afternoon Sun); children welcome; open all day *(LYM)*

[407 London Rd], *Rising Sun*: Smallish Fullers pub with well kept beer, pleasant friendly service, relaxing atmosphere — no loud music; island servery in single bar area *(R Houghton)*

[1 Swan St], *Swan*: Open-plan town local with good service, pleasant landlord, well kept Fullers Chiswick, London Pride and ESB; all age groups, proper pub atmosphere; parking not easy *(R Houghton)*

Longford

[M4 junction 14; A3113, then left into A3044, then right at roundabout into Bath Rd], *White Horse*: Small and quaint, with brasses on low black beams, fireplace between the two areas, comfortable seats, pot plants in windows, cosy atmosphere; good lunchtime bar food, efficient friendly service, Courage real ales, Cockspur rum on optic, fruit machine, piped music, Barn annexe, tables outside, open all day; popular with airport staff *(Mayur Shah)*

Northwood

Gate: Old-style pub, recently tastefully refurbished, with homely, welcoming atmosphere, pubby food, real ales such as Adnams, Greene King, Ind Coope Burton and Wadworths 6X *(Nigel Gibbs)*

[Rickmansworth Rd], *True Lovers Knot*: Plenty of seats in pleasant recently built conservatory-style extension, helpful service, generous helpings of reasonably priced lunchtime bar food with wider evening choice — well worth knowing for the area *(A C Morrison)*

Norwood Green

☆ [Tentelow Lane (A4127)], *Plough*: Warm and friendly atmosphere — amost that of a country pub, with two log fires, even a venerable but still active bowling green dating to 14th century; fairly compact and does get crowded weekends, but good service, well kept Fullers Chiswick, London Pride and ESB, good value bar food from sandwiches to gammon and egg or savoury omelette *(Tom Evans, Richard Houghton)*

Osterley

☆ [Windmill Lane; B454, off A4 — called Syon Lane at that point], *Hare & Hounds*: Suburban pub with soft lighting, busy but relaxed atmosphere, reasonably priced straightforward bar lunches, Fullers Chiswick, ESB and London Pride, piped music; good mature garden, nr Osterley Park *(A C Morrison, Jonathan Warner)*

Teddington

[58 Broad St], *Hogarth*: Small well run Fullers pub, comfortable and relaxed, with pleasant service, well kept real ales, many old photographs *(R Houghton)*

Twickenham

☆ [Cross Deep], *Popes Grotto*: Spacious and solid well run suburban pub with balustraded outer area overlooking stroll-around central core; helpful staff, good value lunchtime bar food from sandwiches to carvery, well kept Youngs real ale, good range of other drinks, games in public bar; tables in own garden, and attractive public garden opp (closed at night) sloping down to Thames; children in eating area *(LYM)*

[The Green], *Prince Blucher*: Busy open-plan local with plenty of efficient friendly staff, well kept Fullers ESB and London Pride, real pub atmosphere in open-plan bar *(R Houghton)*

☆ [Riverside], *White Swan*: Family pub resolutely preserving its idiosyncratic atmosphere, steps up from elegant waterside road, with pleasant balcony overlooking river; plain and simple, blazing fire, wholesome lunchtime food — enjoyed best if you're not in a rush, odd dining tables and chairs, minimal decor (style may not appeal to everybody, and the front bar's refurbishment is slightly out of keeping with the older elements); riverside garden, can be very crowded some evenings *(Ian Phillips, Roger Taylor, Neil Barker, LYM)*

Uxbridge

[Windsor St], *Metropolitan*: Between-wars suburban pub, Allied real ales with a guest such as Youngs, mixed clientele, quiz nights *(Nigel Gibbs)*

[Hillingdon Hill], *Red Lion*: Quiet and friendly 16th-century low-ceilinged pub with period decoration; good choice of beers inc Fullers ESB, good lunchtime food; claims Charles connections *(Robin Hill, Su and Andy Jones)*

[High St; A4007], *Three Tuns*: Traditional and atmospheric split-level pub, nicely refurbished, with flagstone floors, steps down to low-beamed bar with open fire, cosy alcove; real ales such as Adnams, Ind Coope Burton and Youngs, pubby food from servery up on left, side courtyard and wicker-chair conservatory *(Nigel Gibbs, Mayur Shah)*

Wembley

[397 High Rd], *J J Moons*: Typical Wetherspoons pub in design and decor, very professional service, well kept beers, fair prices, busy but not boisterous atmosphere; parking a problem, even at night *(R Houghton)*

Whitton

[123 Nelson Rd], *Admiral Nelson*: Tastefully refurbished, with well kept Fullers, fine atmosphere, good choice of bar food, friendly service; popular with all ages — perhaps too much so when there's a match at Twickenham *(R Houghton)*

[Chertsey Rd (A316)], *Winning Post*: Nice roomy atmosphere in refurbished open-plan pub/restaurant with good service, spacious dining area in bar, good food in restaurant — two sittings Sun; a Country Carvery, Watneys-related real ales *(E G Parish)*

EAST LONDON
E1

☆ [St Katharines Way], *Dickens Inn*: Lively and attractive position by smart docklands yacht marina, for pastiche of old-world dockside tavern with heavy timber baulks, stripped brickwork, salt-worn floorboards, hard benches, dim lighting, candles in bottles — goes down a treat with tourists; open all day, usual bar food, well kept Courage Best and Directors, John Smiths and a couple of beers brewed for the pub just over the river in Tooley St; upstairs restaurant; signs that they have things a bit too easy, though, and prices high — best enjoyed as a tourist attraction rather than an

ordinary pub *(E G Parish, Gary Scott, Robert Lester, Mrs Richard Stewart, John Fazakerley, Jenny and Brian Seller, LYM)*

☆ [269 Whitechapel Rd], *Grave Maurice*: Popular with staff from London Hospital, quietly comfortable long lounge bar with Victorian plush and polish, well kept Watneys-related real ales, friendly local atmosphere — a real oasis for this area; well cooked and lovingly presented food, inc Sat evening *(Neil Barker, LYM)*

☆ [57 Wapping Wall], *Prospect of Whitby*: Rollicking pub, popular with tourists for its old-style decor and cheerful, hearty evening live music; panelling, flagstones and beamery (but what have they done with the genuine oak beams from above the counter, and the oak staircase balustrade?); well kept Watneys-related real ales, and by any yardstick superb river views (much appreciated by the painter Turner) from flagstoned waterside courtyard *(Neil Barker, LYM)*

☆ [62 Wapping High St], *Town of Ramsgate*: Long, rather narrow bar with squared oak panelling, green plush banquettes and captains' chairs, bric-a-brac, old Limehouse prints, fine etched mirror of Ramsgate harbour, interesting old-London Thames-side setting; well kept Bass and Charrington IPA, usual bar food, has been open all day; it's only a shortage of reader reports that keeps this nice pub out of the main entries *(Marjorie and David Lamb, Gary Scott, LYM — more reports please)*

E2

[211 Old Ford Rd], *Royal Cricketers*: Pleasant canalside pub with almost rural-seeming views from terrace *(Neil Barker)*

E4

[420 Hale End Rd], *County Arms*: Big, busy corner pub, done up with beamery and so forth, but no cheap brass or stained glass — still shows the quality of original 1908 building by Herts & Essex Public House Trust (forerunner of THF); Watneys-related real ales, two pool tables, quiz machines *(R Lester)*

[Kings Head Hill; next to police stn], *Kings Head*: Pleasant and comfortable recently refurbished open-plan pub with Allied beers *(Robert Lester)*

[Larkshall Rd], *Larkshall*: Chingford's only surviving farmhouse, carefully rebuilt with no expense spared by Courage; one end Victorian, the other more interesting end goes back at least to the very early 16th century, with gallery over bar (children allowed up here) and various farm tools; very friendly and pleasant, well kept Best and Directors, good weekday lunches *(Joy and Peter Heatherley, RPH)*

[Hall Lane (A1009)], *Old Hall*: Watneys

pub escaped from Barnabery — now completely reconstituted as proper two-bar pub with plush saloon and pool and darts in tidy public; very friendly atmosphere, real ales *(Robert Lester)*

☆ [Mott St; off Sewardstone Rd (A112) — OS Sheet 177, map reference 384983], *Plough*: Smart, modern roadside pub pleasantly if artificially countryfied, with genuine friendly atmosphere, quick good value food, well kept McMullens Country and AK Mild on handpump; bar billiards and darts in neat public bar; occasional live music Sun *(R P Hastings, Robert Lester, Joy Heatherley)*
[219 Kings Head Hill], *Royal Oak*: Superior McMullens house, very spacious and popular, with spectacular window boxes and baskets, with panelled plush saloon, bar billiards and darts in public bar, good reasonably priced food, McMullens Country and AK Mild on handpump; seats out in front, at side and on back terrace *(Joy Heatherley, Robert Lester)*
[101 Chingford Mt Rd; A112], *Royston Arms*: Large 1930s-style pub with lots of panelling, welcoming atmosphere, Charrington IPA, darts and no less than six pool tables in public bar *(Robert Lester)*

E7
[392 Romford Rd; Forest Gate], *Waggon & Horses*: 1930s tavern with original leaded lights, locally popular for well kept Watneys-related real ales and good value fresh bar food inc exceptional value home-made pies; licensee fluent in German; children allowed, with own menu *(Alan Dean)*

E8
[Martello St], *Martellos*: Boddingtons, Fullers London Pride, Marstons Pedigree, Ruddles County and two guest beers, two stouts, good value food inc three main dishes — one vegetarian — served 12-8; garden backing on to park *(Christy McFadden)*

E11
[31 Wanstead High St], *Cuckfield*: Large open-plan pub with real fire, leather-backed chairs and sofas, terrace; Charrington IPA and Greene King IPA on handpump *(R Lester)* [Nightingale Lane], *Duke of Edinburgh*: Useful for lunch — good choice of ordinary food, well cooked, at good value price; acceptable wine, friendly, cheerful service, beautiful cat *(Mrs J A Blanks)*
[76 Holly Bush Hill; A11], *Eagle*: Large listed three-bar pub with Tottenham Hotspurs mirror, Mr Toby carvery, Bass and Charrington IPA, darts, pool *(R Lester)*

E14
☆ [27 Ropemakers Fields; off Narrow St, opp The Grapes], *House They Left Behind*: Renovated to catch the new Docklands feel (and customers) yet keeping a good local base; fine atmosphere, wine-barish at the edges, good value food cooked in front of you, inc Sun lunchtime roasts and ploughman's, Watneys-related real ales, friendly staff, live music Thurs and weekends *(John and Karen Day)*
[Harbour Exchange Sq; over Millwall Dock], *Spinnaker*: Worth knowing for dockside position, with maybe Thames barge outside, Rhine barge opposite, other barges, lighters and derricks, and the DLR passing; modern, with long bar and food counter, Greene King beers *(Ian Phillips)*

E17
[757 Lea Bridge Rd; A104], *Chestnut Tree*: Large 19th-century local with darts and three pool tables in public bar; live jazz some nights, active folk club *(Robert Lester)*
[807 Forest Rd], *College Arms*: Great choice of guest beers, some good ciders — drinks not cheap but food good value, esp Sun lunch; relaxing friendly atmosphere *(Steve Thomas)*
[199 Shernhall St; Walthamstow], *Lord Raglan*: Pleasant open-plan pub with conservatory; first licensed 1855 — named after Crimean War commander — and rebuilt in 1880s; food evenings, pool, darts, Watneys-related beers on handpump *(Robert Lester)*

Barkingside
[105 Fencepiece Rd (A123)], *Old Maypole*: Allied real ales in smart, spacious two-bar local with various machines in separate children's room off plush saloon; three pool tables and darts in public bar *(Robert Lester)*

Ilford
☆ [553 Ilford High Rd; A118], *Cauliflower*: Large Victorian open-plan pub; good friendly atmosphere, regular live music, Watneys-related real ales *(Robert Lester)*
[182 Cranbrook Rd (A123)], *Cranbrook*: Lively local with Watneys-related real ales, long main bar with small side bar, DJ Sat; can get quite crowded *(R Lester)*
[Eastern Ave; A12/Horns Rd, Newbury Pk], *Farmhouse Table*: Completely refurbished, with plenty of comfortable seats, lots of books, jugs and local old prints, good friendly atmosphere, Bass and Charrington IPA on handpump; restaurant *(R Lester)*
[645 Cranbrook Rd; Gants Hill, A123], *King George V*: Good friendly open-plan pub with plenty of comfortable seating, Courage Best and Directors, darts, quiz machine; all sorts of trophies and shields over bar *(R Lester)*
[57 Roden St; nr A118/A123], *Papermakers Arms*: Friendly and comfortable local which dropped its drinks prices after changing management — Websters Yorkshire on handpump *(R Lester)*

Woodford

[13 Cross Rd; just S of Manor Rd (B173)],
Crown & Crooked Billet: Bass and
Charrington IPA in smart and friendly local,
two bars with beams, panelling and prints of
former pubs around here *(R Lester)*

[735 Chigwell Rd (A113)], *Three Jolly
Wheelers*: Open-plan, with Adnams and
Charrington IPA on handpump, Mr Toby

carvery, good friendly atmosphere, darts,
pool and children's room with two pintables
(Robert Lester)

Woodford Green

[Hale End Rd/Oak Hill], *Royal Oak*: Allied
real ales in spacious pub with two pool
tables, two darts boards and pin table in
public bar *(Robert Lester)*

Scotland

Scotland

Edinburgh stands out as one of the finest places in Britain for pub lovers, with a plethora of interesting places from the most evocative unpretentiously old-fashioned little bars to the grandest of Victorian and Edwardian establishments. Rose Street is a byword for its dense population of worthy pubs – though many of the city's best places are actually well away from it. By comparison, Glasgow still lags well behind on the pub front, though it certainly has some interesting places. With both these cities, we'd point out that the Lucky Dip at the end of the chapter is well worth exploring, alongside the main entries. In general Scottish pubs are very slightly cheaper for drink than English ones – five or six pence a glass, on average. But they score by a more comfortable margin on food. A typical main dish now costs some 40p less than its counterpart south of the border. And a relatively high proportion of pubs up here – particularly in the towns and cities – can beat our targets of £1 or less for snacks and £3 for main dishes. The further one gets from the main centres, the rarer true pubs become. In the remoter parts, inns and hotels serve the pub function much more than they do even in the north of England. So, especially further north, a fair proportion of the entries we list are really dual-purpose places. Sometimes these have a quite separate locals' bar, perhaps quite spartan, as well as a lounge bar. Sometimes the hotel bar does double duty, serving residents as well as the locals: these are often he best places. Scottish pubs we'd pick out for special mention, away from Edinburgh and Glasgow, include the Prince of Wales in Aberdeen (good real ales, plenty of character, very cheap food), the Ardentinny Hotel in its fine waterside position at Ardentinny (new to this edition, with good popular food), the Loch Melfort Hotel, in an even more glorious waterside setting at Arduaine (lots of local seafood), the civilised Riverside Inn at Canonbie (very interesting food, a comfortable place to stay), the Cawdor Tavern a stroll from the castle at Cawdor (very imposing for a village pub), the Tormaukin at Glendevon (currently doing well, in good walking country), the interesting Four Marys in Linlithgow, the obliging Portland Arms in Lybster (a new entry, usefully placed as it fills quite a hole on our map), the ever-reliable Burts Hotel in Melrose, the lively Oban Inn in Oban (flourishing under a new licensee), the cheerful and individual Lairhillock fairly near Peterculter (unusual to find such a warm-hearted place around there), the Killiecrankie Hotel near Pitlochry (good food, a spacious feel – especially in summer), the very congenial Crown on the harbourside at Portpatrick (lots of local seafood, a nice place to stay), the Sheriffmuir Inn for its spendidly remote setting on Sheriffmuir, the Wheatsheaf at Swinton (outstanding food, showing very well indeed in readers' reports), the engagingly unpretentious old Rowan Tree at Uddingston (partly for its amazingly cheap food), the unfortunately named Morefield Motel on the edge of Ullapool (surely far more people would discover its remarkable seafood if it were called something like the Highlands &

*Islands Inn), the Ailean Chraggan at Weem (good food, lovely
surroundings) and the unexpected Old Thistle at Westruther
(especially for its steaks). In the Lucky Dip section at the end of the
chapter, which is split into regions, we'd point particularly to the
Traquair Arms at Innerleithen (Borders); the Carbeth at Blanefield
and Settle in Stirling (Central); the Creebridge House at Creebridge
(Dumfries and Galloway); the Ship at Elie (Fife); the Ferryhill House
Hotel in Aberdeen and the Towie near Turriff (Grampian); the
Applecross Inn, Badachro Hotel, Lock in Fort Augustus,
Glenmoriston Arms at Invermoriston and the Kylesku Hotel
(Highland); the Kilchrenan Inn, and the Lookout in Troon
(Strathclyde); and the Glenview at Culnaknock on Skye.*

ABERDEEN (Grampian)   NJ9305 Map 11
Prince of Wales £

7 St Nicholas La

Boasting the longest bar counter in the city, this individualistic place has a cosy
flagstoned area with pews and other wooden furniture in screened booths, a
log-effect gas fire, and a smart main lounge; sensibly placed darts and fruit
machine. Popular, good value lunchtime food includes soup or sandwiches (80p),
macaroni cheese (£2), tuna and pasta bake (£2.60), and home-made pies or fish
(£2.70). Well kept Bass and Theakstons Old Peculier on handpump, Caledonian
80/- and Youngers No 3 on tall fount air pressure, and two guest beers. The pub is
reached by a Dickensianly narrow cobbled alley twisting right underneath Union
Street. *(Recommended by Richard Sanders, Chris Raisin, Roger Danes, Allan Clarke)*

*Free house   Licensee Peter Birnie   Real ale   Lunchtime meals and snacks (not Sun)
0224 640597   No nearby parking   Open 11–11*

ARDENTINNY (Strathclyde)   NS1887 Map 11
Ardentinny Hotel

A880 N of Dunoon

Popular with yachtsmen and walkers, this inn has a glass wall in one neatly
modern bar that gives excellent views up Loch Long, and to the pier opposite at
Coulport. This room's named after Harry Lauder who used to live at nearby
Glenbranter, and has appropriate memorabilia. There's also a comfortable little
lounge bar with modernist Viking decorations, and the same splendid views; one
of the sitting rooms is no smoking. Sitting outside, you may see yachts mooring at
the bottom of the garden, and the hotel has a courtesy boat for guests, and can
arrange fishing (or deerstalking). Bar food includes home-made soup (£1.45),
venison sausage and onion sauce or smoked herring platter (£3.75), croissant filled
with local prawns (£4.75), crab salad (£6.50), mussel and steak pie (£6.25), lobster
salad (£15), and puddings (from £1.50); Sunday roast lunch served all day. Pool,
dominoes, fruit machine, video game, and piped music. The pub is well placed for
the Younger Botanic Garden at Benmore. *(Recommended by Dorothy and David Young,
I H Rorison, Mrs E M Brandwood)*

*Free house   Licensee John Horn   Meals and snacks   Children in eating area   No
smoking restaurant (evenings)   Ardentinny (036 981) 209   Well behaved children
allowed   Open 12–3, 6–11(till midnight Sat); closed 1 Nov–15 March   Bedrooms;
£37B/£70B*

ARDFERN (Strathclyde)   NM8004   Map 11

Galley of Lorne

B8002; village and inn signposted off A816 Lochgilphead–Oban

Ideally placed across from Loch Craignish (and at the start of *Good Walks Guide* Walk 178), this relaxing inn has a main bar lit with big navigation lamps by the bar counter; there's an unfussy assortment of furniture, including little winged settles and rug-covered window-seats on its lino tiles, and old Highland dress prints and other pictures. A wide choice of malt whiskies and bin-end wines; darts and fruit machine. Very good bar food includes home-made soup (£1.20), baked potato with cheese (£2.35), haggis with neeps or French bread filled with fresh salmon or crab (£3.25), moules marinières (£3.95), scampi (£4.75), Loch Craignish king prawns or Hungarian goulash (£4.95), beef stroganoff (£4), home-made puddings and assorted Scottish cheeses; children's helpings; spacious restaurant. There are good views from the sheltered terrace. *(Recommended by Richard Gibbs, Angus and Rosemary Campbell, Ian Louden, Tim Bishop)*

Free house   Licensee Tim Hanbury   Meals and snacks   Restaurant   Barbreck (085 25) 284   Children in eating area of bar   Open 12–2.30, 5–11   Bedrooms; £22(£27B)/£40(£44B)

ARDUAINE (Strathclyde)   NM7910   Map 11

Loch Melfort Hotel 🛏

On A816 S of Oban and opp Luing

The licensees of this comfortable hotel keep their own lobster pots and nets in the bay, so there's quite an emphasis on seafood. At lunchtime, the bar menu includes home-made soup (£1.30), toasted sandwiches (£1.60), a pint of prawns (£5.75), locally smoked trout (£4.25), quick-fried tiger-tail scampi (£6.50), fresh langoustines (£6.95), half a lobster from Luing (around £10.75) and puddings such as home-made banana and walnut gateau (from £1.55); specials might include home-made crab quiche (£3.95), bowl of mussels in cream and cider sauce or their own cured gravadlax (£4.95), and vegetable curry (£5.50); there's a seafood buffet on Sundays in the restaurant, and with a little notice they will prepare vegetarian meals and high teas for children. The airy and modern bar has low dark brown fabric-and-wood easy chairs around light oak tables, and a freestanding woodburning stove. The walls are papered with nautical charts and there's a pair of powerful marine glasses which you can use to search for birds and seals on the islets and on the coasts of the bigger islands beyond; darts and piped music. From the wooden seats on the front terrace it's a short stroll through grass and wild flowers (where three horses graze) to the rocky foreshore, though from late April to early June the best walks are through the neighbouring Arduaine woodland gardens. Passing yachtsmen are welcome to use their mooring facilities. *(More reports please)*

Free house   Licensee Philip Lewis   Meals and snacks (high season all afternoon)   No smoking restaurant (closed Sun lunchtime)   Kilmelford (085 22) 233   Children welcome   Open 11–10.50; 11–11.30 Sat   Bedrooms; £42.75B/£83.50B

ARDVASAR (Isle of Skye)   NG6203   Map 11

Ardvasar Hotel 🎯 🛏

A851 at S of island; just past Armadale pier where the summer car ferries from Mallaig dock

The far side of the peninsula here, by Tarskavaig, Tokavaig and Ord, has some of the most dramatic summer sunsets in Scotland – over the jagged Cuillin peaks, with the islands of Canna and Rhum off to your left. The views from this comfortably modernised 18th-century inn are spectacular, too – across the Sound of Sleat to the fierce Knoydart mountains. A series of rooms includes the cocktail bar with crimson plush wall seats and stools around dimpled copper coffee tables on the red patterned carpet, and Highland dress prints on the cream hessian-and-wood walls; the public bar, popular with locals, has stripped pews and kitchen chairs, and in a room off the comfortable hotel lounge there are armchairs around the open fire (and a large TV); darts, bar billiards and fruit machine. Friendly and obliging young owners serve good fresh food in the dining room, including local fish and shellfish, and the home-cooked bar food varies day by day. Typically, it might include a good soup (£1), sandwiches (£1.20), smoked shoulder of mutton with redcurrant jelly (£2), vegetarian spiced lentil bake (£4.30), steak and onion pie (£4.50), roast lamb with minted apple (£4.90), fresh dressed squat lobster tails (£5), fresh dressed Sleat crab (£5.60), and puddings like warm rhubarb and ginger tart or heather honey and whisky ice cream (from £1.30); coffee. Handy for the Clan Donald centre. (*Recommended by John Whitehead, P Lloyd, Miss K Bamford, Mr and Mrs G Gittings*)

Free house   Licensees Bill and Gretta Fowler   Real ale   Meals and snacks (12–2, 5–7)   Restaurant   Ardvasar (047 14) 223   Children allowed from 11am–8pm   Open 11–11; 11–2.30, 5–11 winter   Bedrooms; £26B/£52B

BROUGHTY FERRY (Tayside)   NO4630 Map 11

Fishermans Tavern

12 Fort St; turning off shore road

Close to the seafront with its view of the two long, low Tay bridges, this comfortably rambling pub has a diminutive snug with light pink, soft fabric seating on the brown carpet, basket-weave wall panels and beige lamps; in the carpeted back bar, popular with diners, there's a Victorian fireplace and brass wall lights; dominoes, cribbage, and fruit machine. The ample range of real ales on handpump includes Bass, Belhaven 80/-, Flowers, McEwans 70/- and 80/-, Maclays 80/-, Theakstons Best, Timothy Taylors Landlord, and a weekly guest beer, with Youngers No 3 on tall-fount air pressure; there's also a choice of 37 malt whiskies. Bar food includes sandwiches (from 70p), burgers (£1.60), ploughman's (£2.25), curries or scampi (£3.10) and steak pie or lasagne (£3.25), and daily specials such as seafood canelloni (£3.25) or veal à l'orange (£3.45); friendly and professional service. (*Recommended by N J Mackintosh, Robbie Pennington, Celia and David Watt, Alisdair Cuthil*)

Free house   Real ale   Meals and snacks (12–2, 5–7)   Dundee (0382) 75941   Children in snug bar until 6   Open 11-midnight   Bedrooms; £17/£34

CANONBIE (Dumfries and Galloway)   NY3976 Map 9

Riverside ★ ★ ⊘ ⇌

Village signposted from A7

Exacting standards and thoughtful planning combine to make a genuinely interesting bar menu, chalked up by the bar staff each lunchtime: soups like fish and shellfish (£3.25), herring in oatmeal (£4.55), a dozen langoustines (£5.25), cod fillets in beer batter (£6.25), and (from their new chargrill) Barnsley chops, corn-fed chicken or guinea fowl (£6.55); lots of puddings such as spiced brown bread and butter pudding with toffee sauce or baked rhubarb cheesecake with rhubarb and orange sauce. There are lots of careful small touches, like virgin olive oil for the salad dressings, and a concentration on "organic" foods such as undyed smoked fish, wild salmon and naturally-fed chickens; they also have an award-winning range of cheeses; substantial breakfasts. The comfortable and restful communicating rooms of the bar are set out for eating and have open fires, stuffed wildlife, local pictures, good, sensitively chosen chintzy furnishings and a charmingly peaceful atmosphere. Well kept Yates and regularly changing guest beers such as Adnams, Fullers, Hook Norton or Tetleys on handpump; a good range of properly kept and served wines; farm ciders in summer; sympathetic service. Dominoes. In summer – when it can get very busy – there are tables under the trees on the front grass. Bedrooms are notably comfortable and well decorated. Over the quiet road, a public playground runs down to the Border Esk (the inn can arrange fishing permits). *(Recommended by Paul S McPherson, J M Potter, Andy and Jill Kassube, D Morrell, Barry and Anne, Colin and Shirley Brown, Drs M and K Parier, S E Dark, Mr and Mrs D G Wood, C J McFeeters, PLC, John Gillett, Heather Sharland, Stephanie Sowerby, Peter Burton, Syd and Wyn Donald, John Townsend, Dr T H M Mackenzie)*

Free house Licensee Robert Phillips Real ale Meals and snacks (not Sun lunchtime) Children welcome (all ages in bar, from 8 yrs in restaurant) No-smoking restaurant (closed Sun) Canonbie (038 73) 71512 Open 11–2.30, 6.30–11; closed Sun lunchtime and last 2 weeks Feb, first 2 weeks Nov Bedrooms; £20B/£62B

CARBOST (Isle of Skye) NG3732 Map 11
Old Inn

This is the Carbost on the B8009, in the W of the central part of the island

The range of malt whiskies in this old-fashioned and simply furnished stone inn includes the local Talisker – there are guided tours round the distillery, with free samples, most days in summer. The main, bare-board bar has stone walls, part-whitewashed and part-stripped, and red leatherette settles, benches, seats, and a peat fire; a second bar is panelled; darts, pool table (not available in summer), cribbage, dominoes, and piped traditional music. Sustaining and quickly served bar meals include sandwiches, vegetable quiche and ratatouille (£3.85), herring in oatmeal (£3.95), and puddings like apple crumble (£1.60). The pub is by the sea loch and popular with climbers down from the fiercely jagged peaks of the Cuillin Hills. *(Recommended by Tessa Stuart, Alan and Ruth Woodhouse, M S Hancock, Graham Bush, P Lloyd, Miss K Bamford)*

Free house Licensee Deirdre Cooper Meals and snacks (12–2, 5.30–10) (047 842) 205 Children in eating area of bar till 8 Occasional live music Open 11–12; Sat 11–11.30; winter 11–2.30, 5–11 Bedrooms; £13.50/£27

CAWDOR (Highland) NH8450 Map 11
Cawdor Tavern

Just off B9090; Cawdor Castle signposted from A96 Inverness–Nairn

This Highland village pub's proximity to the castle has had a notable effect, particularly in the substantial lounge, with its squared oak panelling and chimneybreast, green plush button-back built-in wall banquettes and bucket chairs, a delft shelf with toby jugs and decorative plates (chiefly game), small tapestries, and attractive sporting pictures. The public bar on the right has an imposing pillared serving counter, elaborate wrought-iron wall lamps, chandeliers laced with bric-a-brac such as a stuffed mongoose wrestling a cobra, banknotes pinned to joists, and a substantial alabaster figurine – not at all what you'd expect from a little Highland village pub. Darts, pool, cribbage, dominoes, fruit machine and video game in the public bar; piped music; no dogs. Sandwiches and home-made bar food such as fresh run Scotch salmon steak with parsley sauce (£5.50), roast haunch of venison in red wine gravy or home-made Scotch beef pie (£5.75), breast of duck in orange sauce (£6), lasagne, and baked trout with celery and walnut stuffing (£6.50). Well kept Flowers Original, Maclays, McEwans 80/- and Theakstons Best on handpump, well over a hundred malt whiskies and some rare blends, a good choice of wines and decent coffee. There are tables on the front terrace, with tubs of flowers, roses, and creepers climbing the supports of a big awning; summer Saturday barbecues roughly once a fortnight. *(Recommended by T Nott, Alan Wilcock, Christine Davidson, Kathy Holt, Dr John Innes)*

Free house Licensee T D Oram Real ale Meals and snacks (12.30–2, 6.30–9) Restaurant (066 77) 316 Children welcome away from public bar until 8.30 Open 11–11.30

CLEISH (Tayside)   NT0998   Map 11

Nivingston House ⊘ 🛏

1 ¹/₂ miles from M90 junction 5; follow B9097 W until village signpost, then almost immediately inn is signposted

The inviting L-shaped bar here is to be redecorated – as is the library; log fire. Belhaven on handpump and a good choice of malt whiskies; freshly squeezed orange juice. Interesting bar snacks might include delicious tomato and orange soup (£1.50), home-made pâté with oatcakes (£3.95), ploughman's or tortellini verdi (£4.25), venison burger (£4.35), smoked trout or croque madame (£4.95), minute steak (£5.50), and Scotch smoked salmon and prawn platter (£5.75); home-made puddings (from £2.50). This civilised country house hotel looks out over a lawn sweeping down to shrubs and trees, with hills in the distance; there are picnic-table sets below the gravel drive. *(Recommended by T Nott, Ian and Sue Brocklebank, Mr and Mrs J H Adam, G R Pearson)*

Free house   Licensee Allan Deeson   Real ale   Meals and snacks (not evenings) Restaurant   Cleish Hills (057 75) 216   Children welcome   Open 11–11.45 Bedrooms; £70B/£90B

CRINAN (Strathclyde)   NR7894   Map 11

Crinan Hotel ⊘ 🛏

A816 NE from Lochgilphead, then left on to B841, which terminates at the village

The emphasis in this harbour-side inn is firmly on local fish: Arbroath smokies (£3.65), grilled fillet of Loch Awe trout (£4.65), Loch Sween mussels (£4.95) and locally smoked wild salmon (£8.75); there's also home-made soup (£1.50) and freshly baked flan (£3.25), and you can get sandwiches from their coffee shop or Lazy Jack's; large wine list and Caledonian 80/-. The picture window in the smart cocktail bar overlooks the busy entrance basin of the Crinan Canal, with its fishing boats and yachts wandering out towards the Hebrides. Seats in the cosy carpeted back part and the tiled front part are comfortable, and the decor includes sea drawings and paintings, model boats in glass cases and a nautical chest of drawers; the latest coastal waters forecast is chalked on a blackboard. The simpler public bar has the same marvellous views and there's a side terrace with seats outside. The smart (jacket and tie) top floor evening restaurant and associated bar look out to the islands and the sea. *(Recommended by Rodney Collins, Gary Melnyk; more reports please)*

Free house   Licensee Nicholas Ryan   Real ale   Lunchtime meals   Children welcome   Evening restaurant (closed Sun and Mon)   Crinan (054 683) 235   Children welcome   Open 11–11   Bedrooms; £65B/£100B

DUMFRIES (Dumfries and Galloway)   NX9776   Map 9

Globe

High St; up a narrow entry at S end of street, between Timpson Shoes and J Kerr Little (butcher), opposite Marks & Spencer

This 17th-century old stone house – not to be confused with a pub of the same name in Market Street – has a big plain public bar at the back with dominoes, a fruit machine, trivia and piped music. But the place to head for is the little museum devoted to Burns in the room that he used most often; on the wall of the old-fashioned dark-panelled Snug Bar there's a facsimile of a letter (now in the J Pierpoint Morgan Library in New York): 'the Globe Tavern here... for these many years has been my Howff' (a Scots word meaning a regular haunt). Upstairs, one bedroom has two window panes with verses scratched by diamond in Burns's handwriting (though not the touching verse he wrote for Anna Park the barmaid here, who had his child). Good value simple bar food includes home-made soup or filled rolls (£1), quiche and salads, a three-course lunch at £5, and apple pie (£1). McEwans 80/- on handpump, very reasonably priced and low alcohol beers.

(Recommended by T Nott, Robert and Fiona Ambroziak; more reports please)

Free house   Licensee Mrs Maureen McKerrow   Real ale   Lunchtime meals and snacks (not Sun)   Restaurant Dumfries (0387) 52335; closed Sun   Children in eating area and restaurant   Nearby daytime parking difficult; car park 5 mins away   Open 11–11; 12.30–11 Sun

EDINBURGH (Lothian)   NT2574   Map 11

The two main areas here for finding good pubs, both main entries and Lucky Dips, are around Rose St (just behind Princes St in the New Town) and along or just off the top part of the Royal Mile in the Old Town. In both areas parking can be difficult at lunchtime, but is not such a problem in the evenings.

Abbotsford £

Rose St; E end, beside South St David St

Something of a long-standing institution for city folk, the bar here has lots of heavy panelling and highly polished wood, particularly around the Victorian island bar counter; there are also old tables, leather-cushioned seats and a handsome high ceiling; a pleasantly formal atmosphere. Broughton, Caledonian 70/-, Greenmantle and McEwans 80/- tapped from the cask, lots of malt whiskies; fruit machine, tucked well away. Good, reasonably priced food includes soup (85p), salads (from £2.70), braised liver and onions, haggis and neeps or kidney casserole (£2.95), curried chicken (£3.30), grilled gammon with pineapple (£3.60), rump steak or mixed grill (£4.05), and puddings such as apple crumble or trifle (from 95p); efficient service from dark-uniformed waitresses. There's a remarkable mixture of customers, especially at lunchtime. *(Recommended by Ian and Sue Brocklebank, Peter Corris, Bob Timmis, Roger Huggins; more reports please)*

Free house   Licensee Colin Grant   Real ale   Lunchtime meals and snacks (not Sun)   Restaurant (closed Sun)   Edinburgh 031 225 1894   Open 11–2.30, 5–11; closed Sun

Athletic Arms £

Angle Park Terr; on corner of Kilmarnock Rd (A71)

Basic, busy and thoroughly unpretentious, this beer-drinker's haven has a gleaming row of tall air-pressure founts dispensing exceptionally well kept McEwans 70/- and 80/-; the team of 15 red-jacketed barmen toil enthusiastically. Opening off the central island servery there are some cubicles partitioned in glossy grey wood with photographs of Hearts and Scotland football teams – a side room is crowded with keen dominoes players; fruit machine; predominantly young customers; filled rolls and pies (from 55p). It's known locally as The Diggers, on account of it originally being frequented by the grave diggers from the nearby graveyard. *(Recommended by Dr G A McLeod, A Neill, Peter Watkins, Pam Stanley; more reports please)*

S & N   Manager Mr O'Toole   Real ale   Snacks   031 337 3822   Open 11–11

Bannermans Bar £

212 Cowgate

Deep in the bowels of some of the tallest buildings in the Old Town, this bare stone-walled, flagstoned cellar of a bar is a warren of little brightly-lit rooms with musty brick barrel-vaulted ceilings. In the front part there are wood panelling and pillars, and rooms leading off have theatrical posters and handbills; furnishings include old settles, pews and settees around barrels, red-painted tables and a long mahogany table. The back area, with tables and waitress service, open when busy, is no-smoking. A remarkably wide range of customers enjoy the well kept Caledonian 70/- and 80/-, McEwans 80/-, Theakstons Best, XB, and Old Peculier and Youngers No 3, all on handpump; malt whiskies and Belgian fruit beers. Filled rolls are served all day, with at lunchtime soup (70p), filled baked potatoes (£1.95), ploughman's (£2.30), vegetarian moussaka (£2.55) and a pork or beef dish. Dominoes, cribbage, chess, draughts and backgammon. *(Recommended by Ralph A Raimi, Ian and Sue Brocklebank, Andy and Jill Kassube; more reports please)*

*Free house Licensee Douglas Smith Real ale Lunchtime meals and snacks 031
556 3254 Children in eating area of bar daytime only Live music Sun-Thurs
evenings Open 11-midnight; closed 25 Dec and 1 Jan*

Bennets Bar £

8 Leven St; leaving centre southwards, follow Biggar, A702 signpost

This compact, 19th-century bar is rich in architectural detail: art nouveau
stained-glass windows, arched and mahogany-pillared mirrors surrounded by
tilework cherubs, Florentine-looking damsels and Roman warriors, and high
elegantly moulded beams supporting the fancy dark maroon ceiling above the long
bar counter; red leather seats curve handsomely around the marble tables and
there are old brewery mirrors. Bar food includes filled rolls (from 80p), soup (90p),
salads and ploughman's (from £2.25), vegetarian lasagne (£2.75), home-made
steak pie (£3.20), a roast of the day (£3.50), and daily specials (from £2.50). Well
kept Caledonian 70/-, McEwans 80/- and Theakstons under air pressure; the
selection of 120 malt whiskies is the largest in Edinburgh. *(Recommended by W T
Aird, Robbie Pennington, Chris Cook)*

*S & N Manager W F Eaton Real ale Meals (lunchtime, not Sun) and snacks 031
229 5243 Open 11–11.45 Mon-Weds, 11–12.30 Thurs-Sat, 7–11 Sun – closed Sun
lunch*

Cafe Royal Circle Bar

West Register St

Built last century as a flagship for the latest in Victorian gas and plumbing fittings,
this attractive bar has been refurbished this year. Over the big island bar counter is
a Victorian gantry (bought at an auction and similar to the original one here), the
seating has been covered in leather, the paintwork restored, the floor and stairway
laid with marble, Victorian-style chandeliers hung, and a new separate food
counter added. They still have the series of highly detailed Doulton tilework
portraits of Watt, Faraday, Stephenson, Caxton, Benjamin Franklin and Robert
Peel (in his day famous as the introducer of calico printing). Caledonian 70/- from
air pressure tall fount, with McEwans 80/-, Theakstons best, Timothy Taylors
Landlord, Youngers No 3 and weekly guest beer on handpump; around 40
whiskies. Simple bar food includes soup, rolls such as brie and tomato (£1.20) or
filled with a hot roast carved to order (£1.80); fruit and trivia machines. The airy
two-roomed bistro upstairs overlooks the street, just at the back of Princes Street
and across from the imposing North British Hotel. *(Recommended by Mel and Phil
Lloyd, Roger Danes)*

*Free house Licensee David Allan Real ale Snacks (12–7) Oyster bar Edinburgh
031 556 1884 Children in oyster bar Open 11–11; 11–12 Thurs; closed 25 Dec and
1 Jan*

Guildford Arms

West Register St

Just along the street from the previous entry, this well preserved Victorian pub has
glorious plasterwork in the main bar – extending up from the walls and carefully
painted in many colours; there's also lots of mahogany, scrolly gilt wallpaper, big
original advertising mirrors and heavy swagged velvet curtains for the arched
windows. The snug little upstairs gallery restaurant gives a dress-circle view of the
main bar (notice the lovely old mirror decorated with two tigers on the way up);
under this gallery a little cavern of arched alcoves leads off the bar. The
atmosphere is lively and welcoming, with the feeling that plenty is going on. Well
kept Bass, Caledonian and 80/-, Courage Directors, Harviestoun 70/-, 80/- and Old
Manor, Malton Double Chance, Orkney Dark Island and Timothy Taylors
Landlord all on handpump; fine choice of malt whiskies; fruit machine. Good
basic pub food includes soup, sandwiches and garlic mushrooms (all £1.50), and
main meals that change daily such as pepper chasseur, sirloin steak au poivre or
steamed cod in lemon butter (all £3.50). *(Recommended by T Nott, S V Bishop, Roger
Huggins, David and Christine Foulkes, Andy and Jill Kassube)*

Free house   Licensee Brian Houston   Real ale   Meals and snacks (lunchtime, not Sundays)   Restaurant (closed Sun)   Edinburgh 031 556 4312   Jazz at Easter and during August festival   Open 11–11 (till midnight Fri and Sat)

I W Frazers Bow Bar ★ £

80 Victoria St

A town bar strong on traditional values, this was actually redesigned only a couple of years ago; decorations consist mainly of a fine collection of appropriate enamel advertising signs and handsome antique trade mirrors, and there's a wealth of careful touches – an umbrella stand by the period gas fire, a (silent) prewar radio, a big pendulum clock, and a working barograph. The rectangular room itself has sturdy leatherette wall seats and heavy narrow tables on its lino floor, cafe-style bar seats and a brass rail around the solid mahogany serving counter, red Anaglypta ceiling and cream Anaglypta walls with a brown panelled dado; look out for the antiqued photograph of the present bar staff in old-fashioned clothes (and moustaches). Simple bar snacks – filled rolls and toasties, hot pies and bridies (from 70p) – and no games or music – just relaxed chat, and the clink of glasses; quick and helpful service. The fine selection of beers includes some making a rare appearance north of the border: Caledonian 60/-, 70/-, 80/- and Merman, Courage Directors, Deuchars IPA, Everards Tiger, Fullers London Pride and ESB, Mitchells Mild, ESB and Bitter, Orkney Dark Island and Raven and Timothy Taylors Best, Golden Best and Landlord, all served on impressive banks of tall founts made by Aitkens, Mackie & Carnegie, and Gaskell & Chambers, dating from the 1920s. The grand carved mahogany gantry has a splendid array of malts (over 140) including lots of Macallan variants and 'cask strength' whiskies, with a good collection of vodkas (nine) and gins (eight), and, particularly, rums (23). It's conveniently located just below the Castle, on the West Bow site. *(Recommended by Graham Bush, Andy and Jill Kassube)*

Free house   Licensee Ian Whyte   Real ale   Lunchtime snacks   031 226 7667   Open 11–11.15; closed Sun

Jolly Judge

James Ct; by 495 Lawnmarket

In one of the earliest of the Old Town tenements and ensconced in one of the many warren-like courtyards just off the Royal Mile, this cosy tavern has captains' chairs around the cast-iron-framed tables on the carpet, a collection of foreign banknotes pinned to a beam near the bar, and a 1787 engraving commemorating Burns's triumphant stay in nearby Lady Stair's Close that January; on the low beam-and-board ceiling are painted fruits and flowers, a characteristic of 16th-century Scottish houses. Caledonian 80/- and Ind Coope Burton on handpump, and a regularly changing range of malt whiskies; space game, dominoes in winter and unobtrusive background music. Bar food includes quickly served filled rolls (from 85p), small local steak or mince pies (£1.05), and lasagne, chilli or curries (all about £3.40). *(Recommended by Graham Bush, David and Christine Foulkes)*

Free house   Real ale   Lunchtime meals (not Sun) and snacks (all day, possibly Sun) 031 225 2669   Children in eating area of bar (12–3 only)   Open 11–3, 5–11 Mon-Thurs, 11–12 Fri and Sat, 6.30–11 Sun

Kays Bar

39 Jamaica St West; off India St

Well worth finding, this cosy and comfortable reproduction of a Victorian tavern has gas-type lamps, casks, vats and old wine and spirits merchant notices, red plush wall banquettes and stools around cast-iron tables, and red pillars supporting a red ceiling. A quiet panelled back room leads off, with a narrow plank-panelled pitched ceiling. Simple bar food includes filled rolls (from 65p), haggis and neeps (£2.50), venison sausage (£2.95), and smoked salmon salad (£3.50); well kept Belhaven 80/-, Caledonian Golden Promise, McEwans 70/- and 80/-, Theakstons Best and Youngers No 3 on handpump, 70 malts and 10 blended whiskies; cribbage, dominoes and Connect 4. *(Recommended by Chris Cook; more reports please)*

S & N   Tenant D W Mackenzie   Real ale   Lunchtime snacks   031 225 1858   Children in library area until 8   Open 11-midnight all year; closed 25 and 26 Dec and 1 and 2 Jan

Peacock

Newhaven; Lindsay Rd

The main lounge in this 200-year-old pub is plushly comfortable, with lots of ply panelling and cosy seats, and the neat back room is cheerfully decorated with trellises and plants that give it the feel of a conservatory (it leads on out to a garden); there's a no-smoking family room. Well kept McEwans 80/- under air pressure on tall fount; malt whiskies. Lunchtime bar food includes home-made soup (95p), salads (from £1.95), fresh haddock (from £2.45), home-made steak pie (£2.55), gammon (£3.95), steak (£5.95) and puddings (from 95p), and there's a larger and more expensive evening menu. Sunday roast lunch, and children's meals (from 50p). The photographs on the walls give some idea of what Newhaven used to be like – before the new development (named after the pub) and other modern changes set in. *(Recommended by D Morrell; more reports please)*

Free house   Licensee Peter Carnie   Real ale   Meals and snacks   031 552 5522   Children welcome in coffee lounge or family/garden room   Open 11-3, 5-11

Sheep Heid

Duddingston; Causeway

The little village of Duddingston is a lovely retreat from the city, and getting to this old-fashioned ex-coaching inn is a pleasant expedition – past Holyroodhouse and around Arthur's Seat and the little nature reserve by Duddingston Loch. The main room has a fine rounded bar counter, seats built against the walls on the Turkey carpet, turn-of-the-century Edinburgh photographs, Highland prints and some reproduction panelling; a side room has some tables divided off by elegant, partly glazed screens; a warm and relaxing atmosphere. Bar food includes soup, soused herring salad, mince pie, ploughman's, and sirloin steak; barbecues in fine weather – you can cook your own if you feel inclined. Tennents 80/- on handpump; dominoes, fruit machine, TV and piped music. The pretty garden has a goldfish pond and fountain, hanging baskets and clematis on the sheltering stone walls of the house, and a skittle alley – it's one of the very few pubs in Scotland to have facilities for the game. *(Recommended by Mark Walker, T M McMillan, Ralph A Raimi, S V Bishop; more reports please)*

Tennents (Bass)   Real ale   Snacks and meals   Restaurant   031 661 1020   Children in restaurant   Open 11-11

Starbank

67 Laverockbank Road, off Newhaven Road

Doing very well under newish management, this popular place keeps around nine well kept real ales on handpump: Belhaven 70/-, 80/- and 90/-, Caledonian Golden Promise, Courage Directors, Greenmantle, Jennings Cumberland, Langstone Bitter, Mitchells ESB and Fortress, Ruddles County and Timothy Taylors Golden Best; good choice of wines, 25 malt whiskies, and helpful, knowledgeable staff. Bar food is good, too, and includes home-made soup (90p), home-made pâté or prawn and smoked chicken vol-au-vent (£2.50), a vegetarian dish or goujons of chicken (£4.25), cold platters (from £4.50), beef stroganoff (£4.75), seafood cassoulet or salmon escalope (£5), whole lemon sole (£5.40), steaks (from £8.50), and puddings (£2.50). The neatly kept and airy bar has a marvellous view over the Firth of Forth from its picture windows; a big mirror reflects the view, and there's a telescope for closer study. There are comfortable plush button-back wall banquettes and elegant stools and dining chairs around the dark tables on the carpet (part by the entrance is quarry-tiled); cribbage, dominoes. A sheltered back terrace (no view) has picnic-table sets and cocktail parasols. *(Recommended by Murrary Dykes; more reports please)*

Free house   Owner Scott Brown, Licensee Mrs Valerie West   Real ale   Meals and snacks (all day)   No smoking restaurant   031 552 4141   Children welcome   Open 11–11 Mon-Weds, till midnight Thurs, Fri and Sat; closed 25 Dec

FINDHORN (Grampian)   NJ0464 Map 11
Crown & Anchor

Coming into Findhorn, keep left at signpost off to beach and car park

Overlooking the jetty where Highlanders would have stayed before taking ship for Edinburgh or even London, this old stone inn has a lively public bar with an unusually big arched fireplace, old photographs of the area on the walls, and games (darts, dominoes, cribbage, fruit machine, trivia and juke box); the comfortable lounge bar is decorated with lots of pictures. There's a decent selection of real ales, including Bass, Boddingtons Bitter, Courage Directors, Fullers ESB, Tetleys Bitter and Theakstons Old Peculier; they also have draught ciders (rare around here), over 100 foreign beers and a good choice of spirits, including over 110 malt whiskies. Bar food ranges from sandwiches, soup and local smoked mackerel (£1.60) or haddock (£2.90), to specials such as home-made chilli con carne, curry, lasagne and vegetarian dishes (£3) and steak (from £5.95), with puddings such as lemon syllabub (£1.70). Residents have the use of boats, and sandy beaches are only a few moments' stroll away. *(Recommended by D Morrell, Ian Louden, Tim Bishop, Ian Baillie; more reports please)*

Free house   Licensees George and Heather Burrell   Real ale   Meals and snacks (11–9.45)   Findhorn (0309) 690243   Children in eating area of bar until 9   Folk Sun evening   Open 11–11; Fri and Sat closing 11.45   Bedrooms; £16B/£28B

GIFFORD (Lothian)   NT5368 Map 11
Tweeddale Arms ⊘ ⇔

High St

Facing an attractive long wooded green and the avenue to Yester House, this old white inn is a civilised place with a wide choice of good lunchtime food. Changing daily, the range includes soup (£1), sandwiches, peach and prawn salad (£2), cold meat salads (£3.70), vegetarian nut cutlets (£3.75), Scottish smoked salmon (£3.80), braised beef olives, casserole of steak and kidney or lasagne (all £4), and puddings like apple pie (£1.90); in the evening you may be able to order dishes in the bar from the restaurant. The comfortably relaxed lounge has big Impressionist prints on the apricot coloured walls (there are matching curtains to divide the seats), modern tapestried settles and stools on its muted red patterned carpet, and brass lamps. The gracious dining room has unusual antique wallpaper. McEwans 80/- under air pressure on tall founts; charming, efficient service. Darts, pool, dominoes, fruit machine, and piped music. The tranquil hotel lounge is a lovely place to sit over a long drink; there are antique tables and paintings, chinoiserie chairs and chintzy easy chairs, an oriental rug on one wall, a splendid corner sofa and magazines on a table. The B6355 southwards from here over the Lammermuirs, and its right fork through Longformacus, are both fine empty moors roads. *(Recommened by Dr T E Hothersall, S D Samuels, S V Bishop, Roger A Bellingham)*

Free house   Licensee Chris Crook   Real ale   Lunchtime meals and snacks (on request in evenings)   Restaurant   Gifford (062 081) 240   Children in restaurant   Open 11–11; 11-midnight Sat   Bedrooms; £47.50B/£60B

GLASGOW (Strathclyde)   NS5865 Map 11
Babbity Bowster ⊘

16–18 Blackfriars St

Something of a Glaswegian institution these days, this Robert Adam town house, down a quiet pedestrian-only street, is strong on the warmth of its welcome and the quality of its food. Usefully available from 8am till 9pm and including morning coffee and afternoon tea, it starts with good breakfasts (served 8am–10.30; till noon Sunday) – either a full Scottish one (£3.15, including Ayrshire bacon), or traditionally smoked Carradale kippers (£2.45); after midday, it includes soup (£1.25), filled baked potatoes (from £2.50), haggis and neeps (from £2.75; vegetarian £3.05), fresh fish and shellfish (check daily blackboard), dishes of the day, and puddings such as seasonal fruit tart or apple strudel (from £1.90). There are pierced-work stools and wall seats around dark grey tables on the stripped boards, an open fire, and fine tall windows; also, well lit photographs and big pen-and-wash drawings of Glasgow and its people and musicians; piped Scottish music (and occasional good-value musical dinners with folk like Dougie McLean). Well kept Maclays 70/-, 80/- and Porter on air pressure tall fount, a remarkably sound collection of wines, freshly squeezed orange juice, Bulmers cider, and even good tea and coffee. A small terrace has tables under cocktail parasols. The pub takes its name from *Bab at the Bowster*, a folk song illustrated by a big ceramic of a kilted dancer and piper. *(Recommended by Ian Phillips, Nigel Hopkins, Geoffrey and Sylvia Donald, Richard Houghton, Diane Duane-Smyth, Nigel Hopkins, Dorothy and David Young)*

Free house   Licensee Fraser Laurie   Real ale   Meals and snacks (12–9)   Restaurant; closed Sun evening   Glasgow 041 552 5055   Children in restaurant   Occasional conerts and Sun evening sessions   Open 11-midnight (and for breakfast); closed 1 Jan   Bedrooms; £36S/£56S

Bon Accord £

153 North St

This simple, traditional and busy pub has padded leatherette seats and little rounded-back chairs on the partly carpeted, partly quarry-tiled floor, and red hessian walls decorated with City of Culture event posters, beer trays and malt whisky boxes; on one side there's quiet booth seating; fruit machine, trivia, Trivial Pursuit and dominoes in a back lobby, with piped music in the lounge bar (which has been redecorated). The outstanding range of real ales on tall founts – well over a dozen – includes Belhaven 60/-, 70/-, 80/-, Caledonian Porter, 60/-, 70/-, 80/-, Golden Promise, and Mermen XXX, Courage Directors, Fullers London Pride and ESB, Marstons Pedigree, McEwans 80/-, Theakstons Best, XB and Old Peculier, Timothy Taylors BB, Golden Best and Landlord and Youngers No 3; over 100 malt whiskies, too. Bar food includes soup (95p), pâté (£1.40), breaded haddock (£2.90), steak pie (£2.95), beef carbonnade (£3.30), and puddings like blackcurrant cheesecake (£1.20). *(Recommended by Alastair Campbell, Peter Watkins, Pam Stanley; more reports please)*

S & N   Manageress Anne Kerr   Real ale   Meals and snacks (12–8)   Restaurant (closed Sun)   Glasgow 041 248 4427   Daytime parking restricted   Open 11–11.45; closed bank hol lunchtimes and 25 Dec

Horseshoe £

17–19 Drury Street

Even when this fine city bar is packed, the atmosphere remains relaxed and friendly. From the horseshoe-shaped promontories of the enormous bar itself, the horseshoe motif spreads through a horseshoe wall clock to horseshoe-shaped fireplaces (most blocked by mirrors now); there's a great deal of glistening mahogany and darkly varnished panelled dado, a mosaic tiled floor, a lustrous pink and maroon ceiling, lots of old photographs of Glasgow and its people, antique magazine colour plates, pictorial tile inserts of decorous ladies, and curly brass and glass wall lamps. The bar counter, which still has pillared snob-screens, has old-fashioned brass water taps (and a house whisky blend); Bass, Belhaven 80/-, Broughton Greenmantle, Caledonian 80/- and Maclays 80/- on handpump; fruit machines and trivia. The upstairs bar is less special, though popular with young people. Amazingly cheap food includes filled rolls (from 40p), pie and beans (60p), fried haddock or lasagne (£1.60), scampi (£2), and a three-course lunch (£1.80). Not far from Central Station. *(Recommended by Ian and Sue Brocklebank, Mel and Phil Lloyd)*

Tennents (Bass) Manager David Smith Real ale Meals and snacks (11–9) 041 221 3051 Children welcome until 8 Keyboard player Sun, Tues and Weds evenings, karaoke Sun morning and Mon and Thurs evenings Open 11-midnight; Sunday 12–12

GLENCOE (Highland)   NN1058 Map 11

Clachaig

Inn signposted off A82; OS Sheet 42, map reference 128567

Dwarfed on all sides by the soaring mountains, this slate-roofed and isolated white house (with only a tucked-away group of chalets for company) is popular with climbers and walkers – it doubles as a mountain rescue post, and the back public bar is equipped for them, with a nice big woodburning stove in one stone fireplace and another in an opposite corner; this room has been refurbished and extended and a new snug added; the atmosphere's lively and cheerful. On the other side, a big modern-feeling lounge bar has tables with green leatherette cushioned wooden wall seats and spindleback chairs around its edges; decorated with good mountaineering photographs, it's usually quieter but can get very lively on folk nights. Simple but robust bar snacks include home-made vegetarian soup (95p), toasties (from 75p), filled baked potatoes (from 95p), with more substantial hot dishes added in winter – curries, gammon, fish, steaks; on air pressure tall founts or on handpump (four at any one time) there might be Arrols 80/-, Caledonian 70/-, Ind Coope Burton, Maclays 80/-, McEwans 80/-, Tetleys, Theakstons Bitter and Youngers No 3; also, a good range of over 110 malt whiskies, tea, coffee and hot chocolate; pool in public bar, piped music. The inn has cheap bunkhouse beds as well as the more orthodox ones in the black clapboarded extension. A little stream, with sycamores and birch trees, is nearby, and the inn arranges courses and activities, such as climbing, walking, skiing, fishing and paragliding. *(Recommended by T and A Kucharski, John Whitehead, S E Dark, Kathy Holt, Tessa Stuart, Heather Sharland)*

Free house   Licensees Peter and Eileen Daynes   Real ale   Snacks (all day) Ballachulish (085 52) 252   Children in lounge   Folk/blues/country & western/cajun music twice a week; winter lecturers eg Chris Bonnington, and regular mountain safety talks   Open 11–11; 11-midnight Fri; 11–11.30 Sat   Bedrooms; £20/£31(£44B)

GLENDEVON (Tayside)   NN9904 Map 11

Tormaukin ⊘ ⇦

A823

On one of the most attractive north-south routes through this part of Scotland, this comfortable and neatly kept inn has a softly lit bar with plush seats against stripped stone and partly panelled walls; gentle piped music. Very good bar food, served in the beamed eating area, includes home-made soup (£1.40), home-made chicken liver pâté (£2.25), mushrooms in garlic butter (£2.40), home-made burger (from £4.10), vegetarian dishes (from £4.20), grilled venison sausages (£4.25), salads (from £4.25), stir-fried chicken with chilli and egg noodles (£4.65), smoked haddock crêpe (£4.95), spicy lamb curry (£5.25), salmon en croûte (£6.75), and puddings like hot syrup sponge or carrot cake with cream cheese topping (from £1.95); they serve soup and coffee throughout the day, and the breakfasts are good. Ind Coope Burton on handpump, a good choice of wines (by the bottle or half-bottle) and malt whiskies. Some of the bedrooms are in a converted stable block. The inn is in good walking country – over the nearby Ochils, say, or along the nearby River Devon; loch and river fishing can be arranged; and there are said to be 90 golf courses within an hour's drive. *(Recommended by Tony and Lynne Stark, Ian and Sue Brocklebank, S E Dark, M Cadenhead, Celia and David Watt)*

Free house   Licensee Marianne Worthy   Real ale   Meals (12–2, 5.30–9.30) Muckhart (025 981) 252   Restaurant (not Sun lunch)   Children in eating area, no young children or babies after 6.30   Open 11–11; middle two weeks Jan   Bedrooms; £44B/£58B

HOWGATE (Lothian)   NT2458   Map 11

Old Howgate Inn

From central Edinburgh, S on A702, then left on to A703 at Hillend; village around 7 miles further on

This civilised hotel has an airy, white panelled bar with red plush window seats and nests of oak stools, a tiled floor and a stone fireplace; a couple of comfortable sitting rooms have easy chairs. As well as a rib-eye steak sandwich and a hot dish of the day such as sweet and sour pork or omelettes (£5.40), there are Danish-style open sandwiches (called finger pieces here): chicken liver pâté with mixed pickle, Danish herring on rye bread, chicken with curry mayonnaise, prawn and lemon mayonnaise, and dill-pickled salmon with mustard dressing (small helping £2, large helping £4). Bass, Belhaven 80/-, McEwans 80/- Timothy Taylors Landlord and a weekly guest on handpump, and frozen aquavit; malt whiskies. There are some slat wood tables on a small back lawn, edged with potentilla and herbaceous borders. (*Recommended by John and Bridget Dean, Mr and Mrs R E Osborne, Mr and Mrs J H Adam, John and Tessa Rainsford, W F Coghill, S V Bishop; more reports please*)

Free house   Real ale   Snacks   No-smoking restaurant   Penicuik (0968) 74244 Children in restaurant   Open 11–2.30, 5–12 Mon-Thurs, 11–12 Fri and Sat

INVERARNAN (Central)   NN3118   Map 11

Inverarnan Inn £

A82 N of Loch Lomond

An early 16th-century house which feels a little like a small baronial hall, this has a notably atmospheric bar – stripped stone or butter-coloured plaster walls, small windows, red candles in Drambuie bottles if not candlesticks, and cupboards of pewter and china; on the walls there are horsecollars and a gun, Highland paintings and bagpipes, green tartan cushions and deerskins on the black winged settles, and a stuffed golden eagle on the bar counter. Lots of sporting trophies (such as a harpooned gaping shark), horns and so forth hang on the high walls of the central hall, where there's a stuffed badger curled on a table, and a full suit of armour. The bar staff wear the kilt, and log fires burn in big fireplaces; piped traditional Scottish music. McEwans 80/- on tall fount, a range of good malts – 60 in the gantry and 60 more in stock, and farm cider; peanuts charged by the handful. Bar food includes sandwiches (toasties 95p), a good stags broth (95p), pâté, herring with oatmeal, and fresh salmon steak (£6.25). Outside, in a field beside the house (also on a small back terrace), there are tables and cocktail parasols, a donkey, pony, and three geese; a stream runs behind. Simple but decent bedrooms. They also call themselves the Drovers. (*Recommended by W T Aird, D Morrell, John Burgan, Hilary Irving, A P Jeffreys, John Whitehead, Alan and Ruth Woodhouse, Cathy Long, Richard Gibbs, GB, CH*)

Free house   Licensee Duncan McGregor   Real ale   Meals and snacks (12–2, 6–8) Inveruglas (03014) 234   Well behaved children allowed until 8   Occasional live music   Open 11–11 Mon-Thurs, 11-midnight Fri and Sat, 12–11 Sunday; closed 25 Dec, 1 Jan   Bedrooms; £16/£32

ISLE OF WHITHORN (Dumfries and Galloway)   NX4736   Map 9

Steam Packet ⇌ £

End of A747 S of Newton Stewart

The picture windows from this comfortably modernised and popular inn have superb views over the harbour; inside, the low-ceilinged, grey carpeted bar is split into two: on the right, plush button-back banquettes, brown carpet, and boat pictures; on the left, green leatherette stools around cast-iron-framed tables on big stone tiles, and a woodburning stove in the bare stone wall. Bar food can be served in the lower beamed dining room, which has a big model steam packet boat on the white walls, excellent colour wildlife photographs, rugs on its wooden floor, and a solid fuel stove, and there's now also a small eating area off the lounge bar; darts, pool and piped music; hospitable service. Bar food includes home-made soup (75p), filled rolls made to order, haggis or jumbo sausage or beefburger (£1.75), fried chicken and bacon (£2.50) or salads (from £2.75; prawn £3.75) and a daily special – fresh fish is the most popular; in the evening there are extras such as chicken curry (£2.50), and sirloin steak (£6.25); fresh lobster is usually available from tanks at the back of the hotel – prices vary according to the market price and it's helpful if you can order in advance; one reader found the sea bass in a light tomato sauce particularly memorable. The fine natural harbour, sheltered by a long quay, is one of the most attractive in South West Scotland; there are interesting buildings, little shops and always something to watch such as people pottering in their yachts or inshore fishing boats, fishermen mending their nets and boys fishing from the end of the pier. Every 1 1/2 to 4 hours there are boat trips from the harbour, and in the rocky grass by the harbour mouth are the remains of St Ninian's Kirk. White tables and chairs in the garden. *(Recommended by Anthony Barnes, D P and M E Cartwright, Peter Burton)*

Free house   Licensee John Scoular   Meals and snacks   Upstairs restaurant (closed Sun evening)   Whithorn (098 85) 334   Children in eating area of bar   Open 11–11; 11–2.30, 5.30–11 winter weekdays   Bedrooms; £21B/£42B

ISLE ORNSAY (Isle of Skye)   NG6912 Map 11

Hotel Eilean Iarmain ★ ⊘ 🛏

Signposted off A851 Broadford–Armadale

The hotel, a sparkling white building and a haunt of the Gaelic-speaking locals (menus and price lists are bi-lingual), has a big and cheerfully busy bar with a swooping stable-stall-like wooden divider that gives a two-room feel: leatherette wall seats, brass lamps and a brass-mounted ceiling fan, good tongue-and-groove panelling on the walls and ceiling, and a huge mirror over the open fire. Well kept McEwans 80/- on electric pump, 34 local brands of blended and vatted malt whisky (including their own blend, Te Bheag, and a splendid vatted malt, Poit Dhubh, bottled for them but available elsewhere), and a good wine list; darts, dominoes, fruit machine and piped music. Bar food includes home-made sandwiches (from 90p), soup (£1), vegetarian dishes (from £3.50), haddock (£3.75), salmon steaks (£8.50), a hot daily special such as curry or lasagne (£3.95) and local seafood such as smoked mussels (£2.95). The pretty dining room has a lovely sea view past the little island of Ornsay itself and the lighthouse on Sionnach (you can walk over the sands at low tide). Some of the simple bedrooms are in a cottage opposite. It's an attractive part of Skye – less austere than the central mountains, and you'll probably see red deer, and maybe otters and seals. *(Recommended by Genie and Brian Smart, Mr and Mrs Tony Walker, P Lloyd, Miss K Bamford, Richard Gibbs, Leith Stuart)*

Free house   Licensee Sir Iain Noble   Real ale   Meals and snacks (12.30–2, 6.30–9) Restaurant; not Sun lunch   Isle of Skye (047 13) 332   Children allowed until 8pm Folk and Scottish music Fri evenings   Open 12–2.30, 5–12 (11.30 Sat); closed 25 Dec and 1 Jan (though hotel is open then)   Bedrooms; I£42.50B(£65B)

KILMARTIN (Strathclyde)   NR8398 Map 11

Kilmartin Hotel

A816 Lochgilphead–Oban

This unassuming white-painted village inn has two snug and softly lit rooms decorated with old Scottish landscape, field sport and genre pictures, and a fine pre-war Buchanan whisky advertisement of polo-players; there are spindleback armchairs, a settee, and a variety of settles including some attractive carved ones; some are built into a stripped stone wall snugged under the lower part of the staircase. Bar food, served generously, includes sandwiches or home-made soup (90p), home-cooked gammon salad or smoked salmon quiche (£4), minute steak or breaded beef cutlet (£5.15) and venison in blackberry sauce (£8); vegetarian dishes; choice of 80 malt whiskies. Sensibly placed cards, darts, dominoes, maybe piped music. Near the start of *Good Walks Guide* Walk 179. *(Recommended by Robbie Pennington, Helen Wilson, Mike Tucker, Richard Gibbs, Steve Dark; more reports please)*

Free house   Meals and snacks (12–2, 6–9)   Restaurant   Kilmartin (054 65) 244 Children in lounge parlour   Maybe accordion and fiddle Fri and Sat evenings   Open 11–11.30 Mon-Fri, 11–12 Sat and Sun   Bedrooms; £22.50(£25B)/£45(£50B)

KILMELFORD (Strathclyde)   NM8412 Map 11

Cuilfail

A816 S of Oban

The distinctly pubby bar of this hotel has stripped stone walls, a stone bar counter with casks worked into it, foreign banknotes on the exposed joists, little winged settles around sewing machine treadle tables on the lino floor and a woodburning stove (open in cold weather). Well kept McEwans and Youngers No 3 on air-pressure tall fount (served in jugs if you wish), and a good range of malt whiskies. An inner eating room has light wood furnishings, and the good choice of imaginative bar food includes soup (£1.35), herring (£2.75), celery and cashew risotto (£4.20), fried haddock (£4.25), chicken in pastry with various fillings (from £4.25), home-made pies (£4.50), scampi (£4.65), and sirloin steak (£8); small helpings for children, and daily specials. Across the road from the Virginia-creeper-covered building is a very pretty tree-sheltered garden with picnic-table sets among pieris and rhododendrons. *(Recommended by H F Boon, John Davidson, Richard Harvey, Richard Gibbs, Kevin Myers, Mrs R M Morris)*

Free house   Licensee David Birrell   Real ale   Meals and snacks   Restaurant Kilmelford (085 22) 274   Children welcome   Open 11–2.30, 5–11   Bedrooms; /£40(£50B)

KIPPFORD (Dumfries and Galloway)   NX8355 Map 9

Anchor

Off A710 S of Dalbeattie

This cheerful waterfront inn – with its colourful window boxes – serves good, home-made bar food, including filled baked potatoes and basket meals, soup (95p), garlic and brandy pâté (£2.05), good open sandwiches (from £2.35, prawn £3.40), basket meals (from £2.85), fresh haddock (£3.85, when available) and 10oz sirloin steak (£7.65), with at least two daily specials such as chicken pie (£3.55), shellfish mornay (£4.25), and beef stroganoff (£5.15); children's dishes (from £1.45) and roast Sunday lunch. The traditional back bar has varnished panelled walls and ceiling, built-in red plush seats (some of them forming quite high booths around sturdy wooden tables), nautical prints and a coal fire. The lounge bar, mainly for eating, has a tremendous variety of old and new prints on the walls of local granite, and dark blue plush banquettes and stools on the patterned carpet; McEwans 80/- and Theakstons Best and Old Peculier on air pressure tall fount; piped music. A games room has a juke box, dominoes, pool table, fruit machine, and video machine. The pub has seats outside and overlooks the big natural harbour to the peaceful hills beyond. *(Recommended by Margaret and Trevor Errington, F J Robinson, R G Goudy, Fiona Mutch, D Morrell)*

S & N   Lease: Simon B Greig   Real ale   Meals and snacks (12–9 summer; 12–2, 6–9 in winter; not 25 Dec or 1 Jan)   (055 662) 205   Children welcome   Occasional impromptu summer music   Open 10.30-midnight; 11–2.30, 6–11 in winter

LINLITHGOW (Lothian)   NS9976 Map 11

Four Marys

65 High St; 2 miles from M9 junction 3 (and little further from junction 4) – town signposted

It comes as no surprise, given this pub's proximity to Linlithgow Palace, Mary Queen of Scots', birthplace, that it has masses of mementoes of her – not just pictures and written records, but a piece of bed curtain said to be hers, part of a 16th-century cloth and swansdown vest of the type she'd be likely to have worn, a facsimile of her death-mask, and of course an explanation of how the pub came by its unique name. The companionable and comfortable L-shaped bar has mainly stripped stone walls, including some remarkable masonry in the inner area; seats are mostly green velvet and mahogany dining chairs around stripped period and antique tables; there are a couple of attractive antique corner cupboards, and an elaborate Victorian dresser serves as a bar gantry, housing several dozen malt whiskies. Well kept Belhaven 70/- and 80/- and two or three interesting guest beers such as Exmoor and Fullers Chiswick, Harviestoun or Marstons Pedigree on handpump, with a twice-yearly beer festival; around 100 malt whiskies; friendly and helpful staff; maybe piped pop music. Enjoyable waitress-served bar food, changing daily, includes good soups such as cullen skink (95p), ploughman's, beef goulash (£4), and chicken basquaise (£4.25); good value Sunday lunch. *(Recommended by Robert Timmis, Ian and Sue Brocklebank; more reports please)*

Free house Licensee Gordon Scott Real ale Meals and snacks (not Sun evening) (0506) 842171 Children in eating area of bar Open 12–2.30, 5–11; 12–11.45 Sat

LOCH ECK (Strathclyde)   NS1391   Map 11
Whistlefield

From A815 along lochside, turn into lane signposted Ardentinny; pub almost immediately to the right

The low-ceilinged lounge bar in this former drovers' inn has winged pine settles and stools upholstered in plush burgundy on the tartan carpet, old guns, fishing rods and prints of sea trout and other fish on the bare stone or rough plaster walls, and a log fire; Tennents 70/- and 80/- on air pressure under tall fount, 40 malt whiskies. Bar food includes sandwiches, soup (£1.05), filled baked potatoes (from £1.50), lasagne (£4.60), venison casserole (£6.25), and specials such as mince and tatties (around £3.95). A games room has a pool table, video game, fruit machine, cribbage, dominoes, and darts; piped music. There are fishing boats for rent and fishing permits can be bought; children's play area outside. Fine views over the loch to the hills beyond. *(Recommended by I H Rorison; more reports please)*

Free house Licensees T Patterson, G E Kibble; Manager R Prime Meals and snacks Strachur (036 986) 250 Children in family room Open 11–2.30, 5.30–11; till midnight Sat Bedrooms; £15(£20B)/£30(£36B)

LYBSTER (Highland)   ND2436   Map 11
Portland Arms 🛏

A9 S of Wick

Our most northerly main entry, this staunch old granite hotel was built as a staging post on the early 19th-century Parliamentary Road. It has a small but cosy and comfortable panelled lounge bar, with a wide choice of very generously served bar food including soup (95p), sandwiches (from £1), snacks such as a lightly soused herring (£2.50), ploughman's (£3), steak pie (£3.50), steaks (from £7.25), excellent puddings (from £1.20) and children's dishes, with local fish such as lemon sole or fresh scampi (£4.10); the same things are served for high tea at slightly higher prices in the dining room. They keep 40 or more malt whiskies (beers are keg). A special point is that service is really friendly and obliging; if there's something they can do for you, they will (squeezing fresh orange, for instance). A separate plain public bar popular with locals has darts, pool and fruit machine, and there's a spacious residents' lounge; there may be unobtrusive piped music. The inn is a good base for this area with its spectacular cliffs and stacks; they can arrange fishing and so forth. *(Recommended by Hazel Church, T Nott, Alan Wilcock, Christine Davidson)*

Free house Licensee Peter Blackwood, Managers Mr and Mrs G B Smith Meals and

snacks   Restaurant   Children welcome   Open 11–11(11.45 Sat)   Bedrooms
£30.75B/£46B

MELROSE (Border)   NT5434 Map 9

Burts Hotel ⊘ ⟻

A6091

Firmly in Border country – Melrose is delightfully quiet and villagey – this
200-year-old inn serves a good range of waitress-served, consistently popular bar
food. At lunchtime this might include cream of leek and bacon soup (£1.20),
chicken liver pâté (£2.55), potted woodpigeon flavoured with Drambuie (£2.65),
ploughman's (£3.10), vegetable cannelloni au gratin (£4.10), grilled Ettrick trout
with mushroom, prawn and butter sauce (£4.35), honey-baked ham (£4.50), roast
rib of beef with Yorkshire pudding (£5.50), and puddings such as sticky toffee
pudding or peach and raspberry crumble (£1.40); evening dishes such as galantine
of duck on a strawberry coulis (£2.75), lentil, tarragon and walnut loaf with spicy
tomato sauce (£5), and hot-pot of local game (£5.75); good breakfasts. The
comfortable, L-shaped lounge bar has cushioned wall seats and Windsor armchairs
on its Turkey carpet, and Scottish prints on the walls; Belhaven 70/- and 80/- on
electric pump; wide range of malt whiskies and wines. There's a well tended
garden, with tables in summer. The town's ruined Abbey is worth a visit.
*(Recommended by Robbie Pennington, John Whitehead, John and Anne McIver, Mr and Mrs J
E Rycroft, Tim Locke, John Townsend, Gordon Smith, Prof H G Allen)*

*Free House   Licensee Graham Henderson   Real ale   Meals and snacks (till 10.30 Fri
and Sat)   Restaurant (not Sun evening)   Melrose (089 682) 2285   Children welcome
until 9   Open 11–2.30, 5–11   Bedrooms; £39B/£64B*

MONIAIVE (Dumfries and Galloway)   NX7790 Map 9

George ⟻

From A76 N of Dumfries, left on to B729 at New Bridge, then left on to A702 after 10
miles

By the time this book comes out, this 17th-century white stone Covenanters' inn
will have new licensees. The Prices who have made it such a friendly, welcoming
and relaxed place are moving on, so we're hoping that the new people will settle in
quickly. The little flagstoned bar has some small seats made from curious conical
straight-sided kegs, high backed pew seats upholstered with tapestry, dark-beamed
ceiling and open fires in winter; the butter-coloured timbered walls have good
antique Tam O'Shanter engravings. The large airy lounge bar and restaurant at the
other end of the building have views over the nearby hills; darts, pool, dominoes,
fruit machine, trivia and a juke box in the adjacent larger bar. Decent bar food has
included home-made soup, filled rolls, sandwiches, home-made chicken liver pâté,
haggis, haddock, and home-made steak and kidney pie or venison in red wine; a
range of malts and selection of wines; piped music in the restaurant. *(Recommended
by S J Ebbutt, Mr and Mrs R Hepburn, Steve Dark, Paul Wreglesworth, Richard Holloway,
Peter Burton, John Gillett; more reports on the new regime, please)*

*Free house   Meals and snacks   Children allowed, but not after 9 in public bar
Restaurant (Fri-Sun evenings; Sun lunch)   Moniaive (084 82) 203   Open 11–2.30,
5–11 Mon-Thurs, 11-midnight Fri and Sat, 12.30–11 Sun   Bedrooms; prices unknown
as we went to press*

MONYMUSK (Grampian)   NJ6815 Map 11

Grant Arms

Inn and village sigposted from B993 SW of Kemnay

In a neat village of dark red woodwork and natural stone, this smart old inn has a
dark-panelled lounge bar divided into two areas by a log fire in the stub wall, and
there are some newly upholstered, burgundy armchairs as well as other seats on the

patterned carpet; the paintings on display by local artists are for sale. The simpler public bar has darts, dominoes, cribbage, fruit machine, video game and piped music; McEwans 80/- and Youngers No 3 on air pressure tall founts, and lots of malt whiskies. Bar food includes soup (£1.25), sandwiches (£1), haddock (£3.70), lemon sole (around £4.30), grilled lamb cutlets (£5.45), and sirloin steak (£6.95); fresh crab, oysters and lobster, with game in season. The inn has exclusive rights to 15 miles of good trout and salmon fishing on the River Don, 11 beats with 29 named pools, and there's a ghillie available. *(Recommended by Peter Burton, Celia and David Watt; more reports please)*

Free house   Licensee Colin Hart   Real ale   Meals and snacks (12–2.15, 6.30–9.15) Restaurant   Monymusk (046 77) 226   Children welcome   Open 11–2.30, 5–11; 11–11.45 Sat; 12–11 Sun   Bedrooms; £31(£38B)/£54(£56B)

MOUNTBENGER (Border)   NT3125   Map 9
Gordon Arms

Junction A708/B709

This little inn is a welcome sight from either of the two lonely moorland roads which cross here: both roads take you through attractive scenery, and the B road in particular is very grand – indeed, it forms part of a splendid empty moorland route between the A74 and Edinburgh. The comfortable public bar has an interesting set of photographs of blackface rams from local hill farms, there's a fire in cold weather and a local 'shepherd song' is pinned on the wall; a hundred and fifty years ago another shepherd poet, James Hogg, the 'Ettrick Shepherd', recommended that this very inn should keep its licence, which Sir Walter Scott, in his capacity as a justice and who also knew the inn, subsequently granted. Well kept Greenmantle 10/- and 80/- on handpump (brewed in Broughton, near Peebles) and Jennings Bitter on air pressure tall fount; a choice of 53 malt whiskies. Bar food includes lunchtime home-made soup (£1.25), sandwiches (from £1.45), lunchtime ploughman's (£1.75), salads (from £3), home-made steak pie (£5.10) and fresh Yarrow trout (5.60), with additional evening dishes such as lamb chops or gammon (£5.10) and steaks (from £5.60); children's dishes (from £1.75). The lounge bar serves high teas – a speciality here. In addition to the hotel bedrooms, there's a bunkhouse which provides cheap accommodation for hill walkers and cyclists. *(Recommended by Robbie Pennington, Helen Wilson, Mr and Mrs J H Adam; more reports please)*

Free house   Licensees Mr and Mrs H M Mitchell   Real ale   Meals and snacks (12–2.30, 7–9 and high teas 4–6)   Restaurant   Yarrow (0750) 82232   Children in eating area of bar   Accordion and fiddle club third Weds every month   Open 11–11 (11–3, 6.30–11 winter); closed Mon Nov-Easter   Bedrooms; £18/£32, also bunkhouse

NEWBURGH (Grampian)   NJ9925   Map 11
Udny Arms 🖛

From A92 N of Aberdeen, right on to A975 at Rashiereive; village 3 miles

The lounge bar in this hospitable and well kept place has carefully chosen furniture that includes prettily cushioned stripped pine seats and wooden chairs around plain wooden tables on the grey carpet, and bird prints, salmon flies, and a pictorial map of the River Dee on the cream walls. A sun lounge has green basket chairs around glass-topped wicker tables. Well kept McEwans 80/- served bright on tall fount air pressure, house wines, and malt whiskies; trivia, piped music and pétanque. Lunchtime food in the downstairs bar includes soups, sandwiches, and cold roast meats; evening food in the upstairs lounge bar is much more restauranty, and in the afternoon they serve tea and shortbread. On the sheltered back lawn there are lots of white tables, and from here a footbridge crosses the little Foveran Burn to the nine-hole golf links, the dunes and the sandy beach along the Ythan estuary. There are three good golf courses and Pitmedden Gardens nearby. *(Recommened by T and A Kucharski, Peter Burton; more up-to-date reports please)*

Free house   Licensees Mr and Mrs Craig   Real ale   Snacks (lunchtime) and meals
Newburgh (Aberdeen) (035 86) 89444   Children in restaurant   Open 11–12.30
Bedrooms; £48B/£60B

OBAN (Strathclyde)   NM8630 Map 11

Oban Inn

Stafford St

The smart upstairs bar, overlooking the harbour, in this late 18th-century inn is
quietly atmospheric, with button-back banquettes around cast-iron-framed tables,
some panelling, a coffered woodwork ceiling, and little backlit arched false
windows with heraldic roundels in 17th-century stained glass. The lively beamed
bar downstairs has small stools, pews and black-winged modern settles on its
uneven slate floor, blow-ups of old Oban postcards on its cream walls, and
unusual brass-shaded wall lamps. Well kept McEwans 80/- and Youngers No 3
from tall founts, a large selection of whiskies; piped music in lounge bar.
Lunchtime bar food includes home-made soup (£1.05), fresh mussels (£1.60),
ploughman's (£3.10), haggis and neeps (£3.55), steak and venison pie or ham and
chicken lasagne (£3.75), and puddings (£1.60). The mix of local customers is very
good. (Recommended by Richard Gibbs, Simon Tormey, Graham and Karen Oddey, Jane
and Calum Maclean, Alan and Ruth Woodhouse, David and Christine Foulkes, Jim and Becky
Bryson, Jon Wainwright, Kevin Myers)

S & N   Manager David Smith   Real ale   Lunchtime meals and snacks (12–2.30; not
Sun)   Oban (0631) 62484   Folk Sun evenings   Open 11–12.45am   Bedrooms – long
term lets only at present

PERTH (Tayside)   NO1123 Map 11

Granary

97 Canal Street; 2 miles from M90 junction 10 – coming in on main road, turn left into
Canal Street in centre; pub is in turning off right, just after multi-storey car park

Once this book is published Mr Nairn will have taken over here; he plans to keep
on the same staff, add more real ales, and concentrate more on the food side (he's a
chef). The bar has brocaded chairs around polished brown tables, stripped stone
walls, and low dark beams – except in one area opened up to roof height, giving
the upstairs candlelit restaurant a galleried effect. Horsebrasses and harness, some
old farm tools and bygones allude to the early 17th-century building's past as a city
granary; there are attractive lamps, old stag prints, open fires (and see if you can
spot all the hot-cross buns, one for each year they've had the pub). Well kept
McEwans 80/- on air pressure tall fount; decent wines; piped classical music at
lunchtime. Efficiently served good value bar food has included soup (80p),
interesting filled baked potatoes such as smoked ham with asparagus (from £1.75),
ploughman's (£2.10), chicken curry or fresh haddock (£3.50), home-made steak
and kidney pie (£3.75), saddle of local lamb, and home-made puddings.
(Recommended by Melvin D Buckner, G and L Owen, Dr Thomas Mackenzie)

Free house   Licensee Kevin Nairn   Real ale   Meals and snacks   Restaurant   Perth
(0738) 36705   Children in restaurant   Open 11.30–2.30, 6–11; closed Sun lunchtime

nr PETERCULTER (Grampian)   NO8493 Map 11

Lairhillock

Netherley; 4 miles S of Peterculter, and a mile N of Netherley itself, turn E off B979 –
you can see fading INN painted on its roof

This much extended 17th-century country pub has a cheerful beamed bar with
panelled wall benches and various other old seats, dark woodwork, harness and
brass lamps on the walls, and a good open fire; it's warmly welcoming, and
relaxing even when crowded. There's a more orthodox if more spacious separate
lounge with a central fire. The food, all carefully home-made by the Polish chef, is

interesting. Bar lunches, no sandwiches, change daily and might include asparagus soup (£1.15), boar or duck terrine (£2.15), ploughman's (£3.65), fresh fish (£6.35) and steak (£8). Evening meals give a much wider choice (changed every month or so), perhaps including mussels (£4.75), vegetarian chow mein (£5.75), chicken and chestnut lasagne (£5.90) and duck in honey and ginger sauce with creole spices (£7.95); Sun lunch is a cold buffet (£5.50). Well kept Boddingtons, Courage Directors, Raven (from Orkney) and Whitbreads Castle Eden on handpump, and several dozen malt whiskies; friendly efficient staff; darts, cribbage, dominoes, maybe piped music. The restaurant in a converted raftered barn behind is cosy, with another log fire. *(Recommended by Chris Raisin, Allan Clarke)*

Free house   Licensee Frank Budd   Real ale   Meals and snacks (till 10, Sat/Sun) Restaurant   Newtownhill (0569) 30001   Open 11–2, 5–11.30

nr PITLOCHRY (Tayside)   NN9458   Map 11

Killiecrankie Hotel   ⊘   ⇌

Killiecrankie signposted from A9 N of Pitlochry

This comfortable country hotel serves a good range of bar food, popular with readers; at lunchtime the well presented range includes home-made soup (£1.35), home-made chicken liver pâté (£2), ploughman's (£4.25), home-cooked smoked Ayrshire ham salad or lightly curried chicken mayonnaise with banana (£5.25), grilled fillets of fresh fish (£5.25), Scottish lamb casserole (£5.50), and fresh Tayside salmon mayonnaise (£6.50); evening dishes include a brochette of marinated pork (£6), fresh pasta (£6.25), and salmon steak with lime and parsley butter (£6.50). Puddings like banoffi pie (£1.90), Sunday roast (£6.50) and half helpings for children; obliging staff, friendly owners; coffee and a choice of teas. The bar has mahogany panelling, upholstered seating and mahogany tables and chairs, as well as stuffed animals and some rather fine wildlife paintings; in the airy conservatory extension there are light beech tables and upholstered chairs, with discreetly placed plants and flowers. The spacious grounds back on to the hills and include a putting course and a croquet lawn – sometimes there are roe deer and red squirrels. The views of the mountain pass are splendid. *(Recommended by B T Smith, W T Aird, S E Dark, Kathy Holt, Mr and Mrs R E Osborne, Alan Wilcock, Christine Davidson, John and Anne McIver, M H Box, D A Wilcock, Miss C M Davidson, Ralph A Raimi, John and Tessa Rainsford, Leith Stuart, T W Hoskins, E J Knight)*

Free house   Licensees Colin and Carole Anderson   Meals and snacks (12–2.30, 6.30–9.30)   Pitlochry (0796) 3220   Children welcome, no infants in evenings   No smoking evening restaurant   Open 12–2.30, 6–11; closed Jan/Feb   Bedrooms; £40.60B/£77.20B

PLOCKTON (Highland)   NG8033   Map 11

Plockton Hotel

Village signposted from A87 near Kyle of Lochalsh

This inn – under new licensees – is part of a long, low terrace of stone-built houses in a lovely Scottish National Trust village, and strung out among palm trees along the seashore and looking across Loch Carron to rugged mountains. The partly panelled and partly bare stone lounge bar is comfortably furnished, with green leatherette seats around neat Regency-style tables on a tartan carpet, an open fire, and a ship model set into the woodwork; window seats look out to the boats on the water. The separate public bar has darts, pool, shove-ha'penny, dominoes, cribbage, and piped music; dogs welcome. Bar food includes home-made soup (95p), filled rolls (from £1) good home-made pâté (£2.95), ploughman's (£2.50), salads (from £4.50), smoked salmon quiche (£3.95), tasty large local prawns (from £3.95), with evening dishes like grilled sirloin steak (£7.95) and fresh wild salmon in season (£6.25); children's dishes (£1.95), good breakfasts. Tennents 80/- on tall fount air pressure and a good collection of whiskies. *(Recommended by T and K Kucharski, Ian Louden, Tim Bishop, Alan Wilcock, Christine Davidson, A E Alcock, Andrew Hazeldine, E J Alcock, Jim and Becky Bryson, P B Dowsett; more reports please)*

*Free house   Licensees Tom and Dorothy Pearson   Real ale   Meals and snacks
(12–2.15, 6–10)   Plockton (059 984) 250   Children in eating area of bar till 9   Open
11–2.30, 5–12 (till 11.30 Sat)   Bedrooms; £17.50/£35(£40S)*

PORTPATRICK (Dumfries and Galloway)   NX0154 Map 9

Crown ★ ⊘ ⇌

SW of Stranraer; down by harbour

The rambling old-fashioned bar in this notably congenial harbour inn serves lots of
local seafood – moules marinières (£3.95), grilled scallops wrapped in bacon with
garlic butter sauce (£4.05), whole grilled jumbo prawns or whole plaice (£5.40),
scallops in white wine sauce (£7.30) and seafood platter (from £16.60); there's
also home-made soup (£1.25), ploughman's (£2.80), salads (from £3.35, fresh crab
(£5.40, lobster from £14.05), steaks (from £9.65), specials such as beef hot-pot
(£3.95), vegetarian pancake (£5.15), and grilled lamb cutlets (£5.90), and
puddings (£1.90); excellent breakfasts. There are lots of little nooks, crannies and
alcoves, and interesting furnishings include a carved settle with barking dogs as its
arms, an antique wicker-backed armchair, shelves of old bottles above the bar
counter, and a stag's head over the coal fire; the partly panelled butter-coloured
walls are decorated with old mirrors with landscapes painted in their side panels;
exceptional service and a really relaxing atmosphere. Piped music; sensibly placed
darts in the separate public bar, and a fruit machine. An airy and very attractively
decorated 1930sish dining room opens through a quiet and attractively planted
conservatory area into a sheltered back garden. Seats outside in front – served by
hatch in the front lobby – make the most of the evening sun. Unusually attractive
bedrooms have individual touches such as uncommon Munch prints. *(Recommended
by Malcolm Ramsay, D Morrell, John C Baker, P Hayes, B Harvey, Robert and Fiona
Ambroziak, D P and M E Cartwright, Lesley Sones, Geralyn Meyler, Peter Burton, Ray and
Gwen Jessop, Ruth Humphrey, George Jonas)*

*Free house   Licensee Bernard Wilson   Meals and snacks (till 10)   Restaurant
Portpatrick (077 681) 261   Children welcome   Open 11–11   Bedrooms; £30B/£56B*

QUEENSFERRY (Lothian)   NT1278 Map 11

Hawes

South Queensferry; A90 W of Edinburgh

The comfortable, airy lounge bar here has a fine view of the Forth stretching out
between the massively practical railway bridge and the elegantly supercilious road
bridge. The small public bar has darts, dominoes, cribbage, fruit machine and
piped music, and there's a Tuesday evening quiz. Until 9pm, the family room is no
smoking. An efficient food counter serves soup, steak pie (£3.45), deep-fried
haddock or cold buffet (£3.55), and baked trout (£4.60). Well kept Arrols and Ind
Coope Burton are served on tall founts. Tables outside overlook the Forth (where
boat trips are available), and a back lawn with hedges and roses has white tables
and a children's play area. In the quieter, older part of the inn, there's still
something of the atmosphere that made it so appealing to R L Stevenson – he used
it as a setting in *Kidnapped*. *(Recommended by Robbie Pennington, S V Bishop, Syd and
Wyn Donald; more reports please)*

*Alloa Brewery Co Ltd   Manageress Moira Cunningham   Real ale   Meals (all day;
lunchtime only Sun)   Restaurant   Edinburgh 031 331 1990   Children in family room
until 9   Open 11–11; till 11.45 summer Sat; 12.30–11 Sun   Bedrooms; £34/£51*

SHERIFFMUIR (Central)   NN8202 Map 11

Sheriffmuir Inn

Signposted off A9 just S of Blackford; and off A9 at Dunblane roundabout, just N of end
of M9; also signposted from Bridge of Allan; OS Sheet 57, map reference 827022

Remotely placed by a single-track road over a sweep of moorland uninhabited except for the sheep, cattle and birds, this white-painted house – one of the oldest inns in Scotland – has a neat, L-shaped bar with pink plush stools and button-back built-in wall banquettes on a smart pink patterned carpet, polished tables, old-world coaching prints on its white walls, and a woodburning stove in a stone fireplace. Well kept Ind Coope Burton and Tetleys on handpump, good choice of whiskies, decent coffee; friendly, neatly uniformed staff, unobtrusive well reproduced piped 1960s music. A wide choice of lunchtime bar food includes soup (£1.15), toasties (£1.25), pâté with oatcakes (£2.40), ploughman's (£2.45), lasagne or deep-fried haddock (£3.95), salads (from £4.25), and scampi (£4.65); evening grills (from £7.75), and puddings (from £1.80). There are tables and a play area outside. The inn was built in the same year as the Battle of Sheriffmuir (1615), on the old drovers/coach road from Stirling to Perth. *(Recommended by Carol and Richard Glover, Martin Aust, P and L Saville, Len Beattie)*

Free house Licensees Peter and Sue Colley Real ale Meals and lunchtime snacks (from 6 evening) Restaurant Dunblane (0786) 823285 Children welcome but no children under 7 after 7pm Sat evening Open 12–11; closed 2.30–5 winter weekdays Bedrooms; £29/£38

SHIELDAIG (Highland) NG8154 Map 11

Tigh an Eilean 🛏

Village signposted just off A896 Lochcarron–Gairloch

The simple bar is at the side of this well kept and friendly hotel and has red brocaded button-back banquettes in bays, with picture windows looking out to sea and three picnic-table sets in a sheltered front courtyard; popular with locals. The residents' side is quite a contrast, with easy chairs, books and a well stocked help-yourself bar in the neat and prettily decorated two-room lounge, and an attractively modern comfortable dining room specialising in good value local shellfish, fish and game. Quickly served, simple bar food includes soup (95p), sandwiches (£1.05), macaroni cheese (£2.50), lasagne (£3), home-made steak and kidney pie (£3.95) and fresh salmon salad (£4.95) with weekly specials such as chicken in white wine or highland rabbit (£3.95). Fruit machine. The grey-shuttered, white hotel is in an outstanding position – overlooking the forested Shieldaig Island to Loch Torridon and then the sea beyond – at certain times of summer, straight down the path of the late-setting sun. They have private fishing and can arrange sea fishing. *(Recommended by S E Dark, A E Alcock, WAH, J A B Darlington, E J Alcock)*

Free house Licensee Mrs E Stewart Meals and snacks (not Sun evening) Evening restaurant summer only Shieldaig (052 05) 251 Children in bar till 8 No dogs Open 11–11 summer; winter 11–2.30, 5–11; meals only summer Sun (no alcohol); closed all day Sun winter, 25 Dec evening and all day 1 Jan Bedrooms; £25.90/£49.70(£55.90B)

SKEABOST (Isle of Skye) NG4148 Map 11

Skeabost House Hotel ★ ⊘ 🛏

A850 NW of Portree, 1 1/2 miles past junction with A856

The high-ceilinged bar in this congenial and smart small hotel has a pine counter, red brocade seats on its thick red carpet and some in a big bay window overlooking a terrace (with picnic-table sets) and the neatly kept lawn; this doubles as a putting course and runs down to the loch, bright with bluebells on its far side. A fine panelled billiards room leads off the stately hall; there's a wholly separate public bar with darts, pool and juke box (and even its own car park). The spacious and airy no-smoking lounge has an attractively laid out buffet table with good home-made soup (90p), generously filled sandwiches, lots of salads (vegetarian £3.10, cold meats from £4.70, fresh salmon £5.40), a hot dish of the day (£3.30), and puddings; good selection of malt whiskies. The grounds around the hotel (at the head of the loch) include a bog-and-water garden under overhanging rocks and rhododendrons, and a nine-hole golf course. The village Post Office here has particularly good value Harris wool sweaters, blankets, tweeds and wools. Loch Snizort has some of the best salmon fishing on the island. *(Recommended by WAH, Mr and Mrs G Gittings, K and G Oddey, J A B Darlington)*

Free house   Licensee Iain McNab   Meals and snacks (not Sun)   No smoking evening restaurant   Skeabost Bridge (047 032) 202   Open 11–2.30, 5–11; public bar closed Sun   Bedrooms; £33(£37B)/£58(£72B)

nr SPEAN BRIDGE (Highland)   NN2281 Map 11

Letterfinlay Lodge Hotel 🛏

7 miles N of Spean Bridge on A82

This secluded and genteel family-run country house has an extensive modern bar, with comfortable brown plush seats clustered around dark tables, and a long glass wall with splendid lochside views over to the steep forests on the far side; there's a games area to one side with darts, pool, dominoes, cribbage and video game. Opening off one side of the main bar is an elegantly panelled small cocktail bar (with a black-bow-tied barman) furnished with button-back leather seats, old prints, and a chart of the Caledonian Canal; malt whiskies, chilled wines (including Scottish wines from Moniack), piped music. Good and popular lunchtime food is served buffet-style, and includes home-made soup (£1.25), sandwiches (£1.75, fresh salmon £2), smoked rainbow trout with horseradish sauce (£2.50), salads such as roast Lochaber venison, Scottish hill lamb and Aberdeen Angus beef (£3.75), pork and pineapple curry (£3.95), roast sirloin of Aberdeen Angus beef or fried fresh fillets of Inverness plaice (£4.25), and puddings (£1.75); friendly, attentive service; coffee. On the side gravel, there are a couple of white tables under cocktail umbrellas. Fishing can be arranged, there are shower facilities for customers on boating holidays, and a small caravan club; dogs welcome. The grounds run down through rhododendrons to the jetty and Loch Lochy. *(Recommended by A D E Lewis, Mr and Mrs B Yearley, John Whitehead, Linda Sewell, Joan and Tony Walker, Mr and Mrs J H Adam)*

Free house   Licensee Ian Forsyth   Lunchtime bar meals and snacks   No smoking restaurant; closed Sun lunch   Invergloy (039 781) 622   Children welcome   Open 11–1am weekdays, till 11.30 Sat; closed mid Nov–March   Bedrooms; £26.50(30.50B)/£53(£61B)

ST MARYS LOCH (Borders)   NT2422 Map 9

Tibbie Shiels Inn 🛏

Just off A708 Moffat–Selkirk

Attractively isolated, this fine old inn has a good range of waitress-served lunchtime bar food, including sandwiches (from £1), home-made soup (£1.20), ploughman's (£2.25), tasty home-made chilli con carne (£3), chicken curry (£3.25), home-baked gammon (£3.50), 4oz rump steak or tasty local trout (£4), lots of vegetarian meals such as cashew nut loaf, mushroom and hazelnut crumble or leek and cheese plait (all £3.50), and puddings like home-made cloutie dumpling or fruit pie (£1.25); in the evening, more elaborate dishes include oak smoked mutton marinated in port or avocado mousse with prawns (£2.10) and gammon in puff pastry with mushrooms (£6.50) or venison in blackberry wine sauce (£7.50); high teas (3.30–6pm). The dining area off the main lounge is no smoking. The cosy stone back bar has well cushioned black wall benches or leatherette armed chairs. Well kept Belhaven 70/- and Greenmantle on handpump; lots of malt whiskies; darts. The Southern Upland Way – a long-distance footpath – passes close by, the Grey Mare's Tail waterfall is just down the glen, and the loch is beautiful (with day members to the sailing club welcome, and fishing free to residents; it's very peaceful – except when low-flying jets explode into your consciousness). The pub is named after a former redoubtable inn-keeper, wife of the local mole-catcher and a favourite character of Age of Enlightenment Edinburgh literary society; her photograph hangs in the bar. *(Recommended by Robbie Pennington, Andy and Jill Kassube, Alan and Lesley Holden, Mr and Mrs B Yearley, Alan Holden, Mrs R M Morris, A McK, Steve Dark)*

Free house   Licensees Jack and Jill Brown   Real ale   Meals and snacks (12–2.30, 3.30–8.30)   Restaurant   Selkirk (0750) 42231   Children welcome until 8pm   Open 11–11; closed Mon and 1 Nov–1 March   Bedrooms; £20/£32

STRACHUR (Strathclyde)   NN0901 Map 11

Creggans 🛏

A815 N of village

The cosy and attractively tweedy lounge in this smart little hotel overlooks the loch to the hills on the far side, and there are more seats in a no smoking conservatory. The public bar, lively with locals, has pool, darts, and fruit machine. McEwans 80/- on tall fount, and a good selection of malt whiskies, including their own vatted malt; coffee and tea. This year they've opened a cappuccino bar and gift shop with home-baked goodies. Popular and quite restaurant bar food includes home-made soup (95p), filled rolls and toasties (from £1.35), ploughman's (£2.95), chicken liver and olive pâté (£3.45), vegetarian burger with potato and onion patties (£3.95), spiced beef and pickle (£4.10), fried fillet of fresh haddock (£4.50), half-a-dozen local oysters or seafood salad (£4.95), Loch Fyne trout in oatmeal (£5.50), fresh langoustines (when available, £8.95), a dish of the day, and puddings (from £1.95). There are white tables outside in front, and you can walk for hours on the owners' land; deerstalking as well as fishing and ponytrekking may be arranged for residents. *(Recommended by W T Aird, Cathy Long, Jon Wainwright, Mrs E M Brandwood; more reports please)*

Free house   Licensee Sir Fitzroy Maclean   Meals and snacks (12.30–2.30, 6–7.30)   Restaurant   Strachur (036 986) 279   Children welcome   Open 11-midnight   Bedrooms; £35(£40B)/£80(£90B)

SWINTON (Border)   NT8448 Map 10

Wheatsheaf 🍽 🛏

A6112 N of Coldstream

The main area in this distinctly foody sandstone hotel has sporting prints and plates on the bottle-green wall covering, an attractive long oak settle and some green-cushioned window seats as well as the wheelback chairs around the tables, and a stuffed pheasant and partridge over the log fire; a small lower-ceilinged part by the counter has pubbier furnishings, and small agricultural prints on the walls – especially sheep. The quite separate side locals' bar has pool and fruit machine, and there's a no-smoking front conservatory with a vaulted pine ceiling and walls of local stone. The outstanding bar food, universally praised by readers, is particularly strong on fish such as devilled whitebait (£2.95), Danish herring with a light curry sauce (£3.20), smoked Tweed salmon (£5.60), baked sea trout with prawn butter (£7.15), sautéed tiger prawns in garlic (£7.80), and fresh scallops sautéed with lemon and parma ham (£9.40). A wide choice of other dishes, generously served, includes soup (£1.65), sandwiches, mushroom, bacon and prawn pancakes (£3.45), Border lamb and vegetable pie (£3.95), tagliatelle carbonara (£4.75), curried chicken madras (£4.85), minute steak platter (£5.25), a dish of the day such as sautéed lamb's liver and onions (£4.20), and puddings like summer pudding (from £1.65). Booking is advisable, particularly from Thursday to Saturday evening. Well kept Greenmantle 70/- and 80/- on air pressure tall fount; decent range of malt whiskies, 36 good wines, and coffee; warmly welcoming friendly service. The garden has a play area for children. *(Recommended by Mrs B Crosland, Viv Middlebrook, Mr and Mrs Y B Dodds, Murray Dykes, B M Jones, Joy Heatherley, Mrs Roxanne Chamberlain, Syd and Wyn Donald, Mr and Mrs M O Jones)*

Free house   Licensee Alan Reid   Real ale   Meals and snacks (12–2, 6–10; till 9.30

Sun; not Mon)   Restaurant (not Mon)   Swinton (089 086) 257   Children welcome
Open 11–2.30, 6–11; 12.30–2.30, 6.30–11 Sat and Sun; closed Mon and one week Oct,
two weeks Feb   Bedrooms; £22.75/£35

TAYVALLICH (Strathclyde)   NR7386 Map 11

Tayvallich Inn ⊘

B8025, off A816 1 mile S of Kilmartin; or take B841 turn-off from A816 two miles N of
Lochgilphead

Bar food in this simple pub veers attractively towards local seafood, especially
shellfish; at lunchtime it includes home-made soup (£1.15), ploughman's (£3),
half-a-dozen Loch Sween oysters (£3.75), burgers (from £3.75), moules marinières
or fusilli with smoked haddock and sweetcorn (£4), cajun chicken (£4.50), Loch
Fyne smoked salmon (£6), whole jumbo prawn salad (£6.50), and Sound of Jura
clams meunière or grilled sirloin steak (£8); home-made puddings (£1.95), and
evening extras like mushrooms on a cream and port sauce (£2.50), seafood hotpot
(£8.50), and panfried turbot with capers (£9.50); decent house wines, coffee. This
year, they have added a dining conservatory (no smoking during mealtimes) which
is proving popular. The small bar has cigarette cards and local nautical charts on
brown hessian walls, exposed ceiling joists, and pale pine upright chairs, benches
and tables on its quarry-tiled floor; sliding glass doors open on to a concrete
terrace furnished with picnic-table sets (which shares the same view); piped music.
The pub looks over the lane to the sheltered yacht anchorage. *(Recommended by
Kevin Myers and others; more up-to-date reports please)*

*Free house   Licensee John Grafton   Meals and snacks (12–2, 6–9)   Restaurant
Tayvallich (054 67) 282   Children welcome   Open 11–11; 11–1am Sat; 11–2.30,
6–11 in winter; closed Mon Nov–March*

THORNHILL (Central)   NS6699 Map 9

Lion & Unicorn

A873

This 17th-century inn has a bar of two communicating rooms, and a lounge with a
log-burning stove. The public bar has darts, dominoes, cards, a fruit machine and
piped music; there's a family room off the lounge bar. Bar food includes soup
(£1.50), ploughman's (£2.30), a large cold meat salad (£3.40), haddock or scampi
(£3.70), chicken kiev (£4) and steak and kidney pie (£4.30), and two daily specials
such as vegetable bake (£3.40) or chicken in orange and rosemary (£4.30);
home-made puddings such as apple pie (£1.70); maybe Greenmantle real ale;
friendly service. The restaurant is in the original part of the building which dates
from 1635 and contains the original massive fireplace (six feet high and five feet
wide). The inn's own bowling green can be used by non-residents. *(Recommended by
Fiona Mutch, Janet and John Towers; more reports please)*

*Free house   Licensees Mr and Mrs Johnstone   Meals and snacks (all day)   Evening
restaurant   Thornhill (078 685) 204   Children in large room adjacent to lounge bar
Ceilidh folk night Sat about once a month   Open 11–midnight Mon–Thurs and Sat, till
1am Fri, 12–12 Sun; winter 11–11 Mon–Thurs and Sat, 11–12 Fri, 11–11 Sun
Bedrooms; £17.50/£33*

TWEEDSMUIR (Border)   NT0924 Map 9

Crook ⊘ ⇐

A701 a mile N of village

A very useful halt on this lonely road through grand, partly forested hills, this old
drovers' inn has a cosy and simply furnished, flagstoned back bar with local
photographs on its walls; one very thick wall, partly knocked through, has a big
hearth, and opens into a large airy lounge with comfortable chairs around low
tables and an open log fire; beyond is a sun lounge. The pub's various art-deco

features are most notable in the lavatories – superb 1930s tiling and cut design mirrors. Well kept Greenmantle on handpump and a good choice of malt whiskies. Bar food includes sandwiches, home-made soup (£1.25), home-made chicken liver pâté (£2.95), baked potatoes with various fillings (from £2.50), ploughman's (£3.50), deep-fried breaded haddock (£3.95), chicken curry, home-made steak pie or pork chop (£4.95), poached salmon steak with cucumber sauce (£6.75), mixed grill (£9.95), daily specials, and puddings like home-made apple tart (£2.50). A separate room has darts, pool, dominoes, cribbage, shove-ha'penny, table skittles, fruit machine and video game. There are tables on the grass outside, with a climbing frame and slide, and across the road the inn has an attractive garden, sheltered by oak trees; maybe pétanque here in summer. Trout fishing permits for about 30 miles fishing on the Tweed and its tributaries are available from the pub at about £5 a day. *(Recommended by R M Macnaughton, JM, PM, Joy Heatherley, John C Baker, John and Joan Wyatt, Dr and Mrs James Stewart)*

Free house   Licensee Stuart Reid   Real ale   Meals and snacks (12–3, 6–9 weekdays; noon–9.30 weekends)   No-smoking restaurant   Tweedsmuir (089 97) 272   Children in restaurant   Open 12–12   Bedrooms; £26B/£44(£52B)

UDDINGSTON (Strathclyde)   NS6960   Map 11

Rowan Tree   £

60 Old Mill Road; in Uddingston High Street, turn into The Cut, which takes you into Old Mill Road with the pub almost opposite. 1 mile from M73 junction 6; leaving M73 from S, turn sharp right immediately at end of motorway, virtually doing a U-turn (permitted here) into A721, then following B7071 into village

The shinily panelled walls in this elegantly old-fashioned town pub have built-in bare benches divided by wooden pillars supporting an arch of panelling, which in turn curves into the embossed ceiling; tall tiers of mirrored shelves rise up behind the high, heavily panelled serving counter, and there are gas-style chandeliers, and Edwardian water fountains on the counter itself, interesting old brewery mirrors, and two coal fires; there's also a lounge. Maclays 70/-, 80/- and Porter on air pressure tall fount, tea and coffee, and good, generously served, simple bar food including pâté (80p), salads (£2), steak pie (£2.20), lasagne (£2.40), fresh fillet of haddock (£2.50), chicken chasseur (£2.80), steaks (£3), and puddings (80p). Dominoes, fruit machine, trivia and piped music. *(Recommended by Ben Wimpenny, Niall and Jane; more reports please)*

Maclays   Manager George Tate   Real ale   Lunchtime meals and snacks (not Sun) Restaurant   (0698) 812678   Children in restaurant   Disc jockey with Golden Oldies Thurs-Sat, folk club Fri   Open 11–11.45

ULLAPOOL (Highland)   NH1294   Map 11

Ceilidh Place

West Argyle St

This white house, in a quiet side street above the small town, has climbing roses and other flowers in front, where tables on a terrace look over the other houses to the distant hills beyond the natural harbour. Inside, the atmosphere is unexpected for so far north in Scotland – a stylish cafe-bar, with bentwood chairs and one or two cushioned wall benches among the rugs on its varnished concrete floor, spotlighting from the dark planked ceiling, attractive modern prints and a big sampler on the textured white walls, piped classical or folk music, magazines to read, Venetian blinds, houseplants, and mainly young upmarket customers, many from overseas. There's a very up-to-date woodburning stove, and they have dominoes. The side food bar – you queue for service – does a few hot dishes such as savoury flans (£2.85), stovies (£3), chilli bean casserole or lentil lasagne (£3.45), and haggis pie or chicken curry (£3.85). Though the beers are keg they have decent wines by the glass (and pineau de charentes), some uncommon European bottled beers, an interesting range of high-proof malt whiskies and a choice of cognacs that's unmatched around here. The hotel, which has an attractive conservatory dining room, includes a bookshop. (*Recommended by Ian Louden, Tim Bishop, T and A Kucharski, John and Daphne Miller; more reports please*)

Free house   Mrs Jean Urquhart   Meals and snacks (10–10 summer, 10–6 winter; not 25 Dec)   No-smoking restaurant (closed Sun lunchtime)   Ullapool (0854) 612103 Children in eating area of bar   Frequent live entertainment – traditional jazz and classical music, poetry and drama   Open 11–11; 12–2.30, 6.30–11 Sun)   Bedrooms; £30(£40B)/£56(£76B)

Ferry Boat

Shire St

The big windows of this simple, genuine two-room bar – with curtain-frills top and bottom – look out to the tall hills beyond the anchorage with its bustle of yachts, ferry boats, fishing boats and tour boats for the Summer Isles. There are quarry tiles by the corner serving counter, patterned red carpet elsewhere, with brocade-cushioned seats around dimpled copper tables; a stained glass door hangs from the ceiling. The quieter inner room has a coal fire, a delft shelf of copper measures and willow-pattern plates. Well kept McEwans 80/- on air-pressure tall fount, a decent choice of whiskies; good value straightforward bar lunches include home-made soup (95p), ploughman's (£2.50), liver and bacon casserole or pasta with fresh basil and pine nuts (£2.95), leek and stilton quiche (£3.45), deep-fried haddock (£3.75), goujons of sole with lime mayonnaise (£4.25), and home-made puddings (£1.50); small helpings (£1.95); unobtrusive piped pop music, fruit machine, and a relaxed mix of locals and visitors. (*Recommended by T and A Kucharski, R and M Wallace, Heather Sharland, Dr T W Hoskins, Jim and Becky Bryson*)

Free house   Licensee Richard Smith   Real ale   Meals and snacks (lunchtime only, summer, but also 6–8.30 winter)   No smoking evening restaurant (they do Sun lunch; closed winter)   Ullapool (0854) 612366   Children welcome   Open 11–11; 11–2.30, 5–11 in winter; closed mid Dec-end Jan   Bedrooms; £20(£29B)/£38(£48B)

Morefield Motel ⊗

North Rd

The most northerly of our west coast main entries, this motel has an L-shaped, squarely modern, partly no smoking lounge with dark brown plush button-back built-in wall banquettes and colourful local scenic photographs. However most of the visitors (often from very far afield) are here to admire the gastronomy – exceptionally fresh fish and seafood. The owners, ex-fishermen and divers, have first-class sources; the bar food, served with a generosity that overwhelms people used to southern ideas of seafood value-for-money, changes seasonally, and in high season might include mussels in wine, tomatoes and herbs (£2.50), fresh local prawn cocktail (£3.95), whole fresh langoustines (£4.95), fillet of fresh haddock (£4.40), whole dressed crab (£5.50), fresh lobster (half £6.95, whole £12.95), poached salmon with local prawn tails in wine (£8.75), a high-heaped platter of fresh seafood which we've never heard of anyone finishing (£13.95), and daily specials such as baby lochside scallops in a cheese sauce (£6.95), split and grilled king prawns with garlic or ginger butter (£7.95) and whole lemon sole filled with prawns, mushrooms and avocado (£8.95). Other dishes include soup (95p), haggis or fresh home-made chicken liver pâté (£1.95), steak pie (£4.50), curries (£4.75), a daily roast (£5.75), and steaks (from £8.75); puddings (from £1.50). In winter (from November to March) the diners tend to yield to local people playing darts or pool, though there's bargain food then, including a very cheap three-course meal. Keg beer (what else, this far north), but a very good range of 90 malt whiskies, decent wines and friendly tartan-skirted waitresses; piped pop music, fruit machine. There are tables on the terrace. The bedrooms are functional. (*Recommended by R Goodger, Ian Baillie; more reports please*)

Free house   Licensee David Smyrl   Meals and snacks (12–2, 5.30–9.30)   Evening restaurant   Ullapool (0854) 612161   Children welcome   Open 11–2.30, 5–11; closed 25 and 26 Dec   Bedrooms; £20B/£40B

WEEM (Tayside)   NN8449 Map 11

Aileen Chraggan ⊘

B846

Bar food in this comfortable and friendly inn is well presented, with a
characteristic emphasis on fresh fish; the selection includes soup (£1.55), pâté
(£2.85), sweetcure herring (£2.75), home-made lasagne (£3.95), six Loch Fyne
oysters (£4.75), fresh cod in beer batter or seafood in creamy tarragon sauce with
tagliatelle (£4.95), salads (from £5.25), moules marinières (£6.25), minute steak
(£6.75), Loch Etive prawn platter (£9.50), and puddings (around £2.65). The
modern lounge has long plump plum-coloured banquettes, and Bruce Bairnsfather
First World War cartoons on the red and gold Regency striped wallpaper; winter
darts, dominoes and piped music; malt whiskies. There are tables on the large
terrace outside. The view is excellent – across the flat ground between here and the
Tay to the mountains beyond that sweep up to Ben Lawers (the highest in this part
of Scotland). Bedrooms are described by readers as spacious and comfortable.
*(Recommended by John Gillett, D I Baddeley, Miss S J Ebbutt, Mr and Mrs R Hepburn, Dr T
H M Mackenzie, Mrs Pauline Spence)*

*Free house   Licensee Alastair Gillespie   Meals and snacks   Restaurant   Aberfeldy
(0887) 20346   Children welcome   Open 11–11   Bedrooms; £23.65B/£47.30B*

WESTRUTHER (Border)   NT6450 Map 10

Old Thistle ⊘

B6456 – off A697 just SE of the A6089 Kelso fork

Firmly an unpretentious village local, this has a tiny, quaint bar on the right with
some furnishings that look as if they date back to the inn's 1721 foundation – the
elaborately carved chimneypiece, an oak corner cupboard, the little
bottom-polished seat by the coal fire. There are some fine local horsebrasses. A
simple back room with whisky-water jugs on its black beams has darts, pool,
dominoes, fruit machine and video game, and doors from here lead out onto their
new terrace; there's a small, plain room with one or two tables on the left. These
three rooms are the real core of the village, full of life in the evenings, with farmers,
fishermen, gamekeepers and shepherds down from the hills – and maybe breaking
into song when Andrew strikes up on the accordion. On the food front, what really
stands out is the quality of the evening steaks – fine local Aberdeen Angus, hung
and cooked to perfection (from 8oz sirloin £6.95; larger sizes, also rump, fillet and
T-bone). Other food is less unusual: soup (90p), sandwiches (from £1.10), decent
home-made lasagne or haddock (£3.95), salads (from £3.95), and evening
gammon (£4.25). A more conventionally comfortable two-room lounge has
flowery brocaded seats, neat tables and a small coal fire, leading into the
restaurant. Friendly young licensees; piped music. *(Recommended by Syd and Wyn
Donald; more reports please)*

*Free house   Licensee David Silk   Meals and snacks (12–2.30, 5–9.30; not Mon)
Restaurant   Westruther (057 84) 275   Children welcome   Open 11–3, 5–11;
11–11.30 Sat; closed Mon lunchtime   Bedrooms; £18B/£35B*

Lucky Dip

Besides the fully inspected pubs, you might like to try these Lucky Dips recommended to
us and described by readers (if you do, please send us reports):

BORDER
Ancrum [off A68 Jedburgh—Edinburgh;
NT6325], *Cross Keys*: Basic friendly pub
with very welcoming landlord, good value
lunchtime rolls, well kept Ind Coope Burton
and guest beers, games room, nice back
garden *(Andy and Jill Kassube, Mr and Mrs M
O Jones)*

Broughton [A701; NT1136], *Greenmantle*:
Recently modernised pub with Greenmantle
from brewery opposite, wide choice of bar
food *(Alastair Campbell)*
Greenlaw [NT7146], *Castle*: Doing
particularly well under new regime, with
huge helpings of good home-made food —
great value, esp Sun lunch; Belhaven 80/-,

Courage Directors and Greenmantle real ale
(Ian Scott Watson)

☆ **Innerleithen** [Traquair Rd; NT3336],
Traquair Arms: Very friendly pub with
interesting choice of good food, especially
Finan savoury and vegetarian dishes;
comfortable lounge bar, friendly service,
well kept Greenmantle and the local
Traquair on handpump — superb in small
quantities; also interesting bottled beers;
good bedrooms, nice breakfasts *(Mr and Mrs
M O Jones, J M Potter, A McK, Andrew
Roberts, Andy and Jill Kassube)*

Kelso [off Market Pl; NT7334], *Waggon*:
Pleasant atmosphere and surroundings;
good choice of good value lunchtime bar
food inc children's dishes, friendly and
efficient service, smaller public bar and
games room opp; McEwans 70/- and 80/-
(M and J Back)

☆ **Lauder** [Market Pl; A68; NT5347], *Eagle*:
Ornate serving counter like Elizabethan
four-poster in otherwise simple lounge bar,
efficient smiling service, limited range of
decent bar food, well kept McEwans 70/-,
games in public bar, summer barbecues in
old stableyard, children welcome, open all
day; bedrooms *(Joy Heatherley, Mr and Mrs J
H Adam, LYM)*

Lauder, *Black Bull*: Dachshund photographs
on plank-panelled bar of 17th-century inn,
bar food; open all day; children welcome;
bedrooms *(W T Aird, LYM)*

Lilliesleaf [NT5325], *Plough*: Good village
pub with well kept beer, small but
interesting range of good value bar meals;
bedrooms recently comfortably refurbished,
with own bathrooms *(K H Frostick)*

Newcastleton [Main St; B6357 N of
Canonbie; NY4887], *Grapes*: Attractive
small hotel serving bar food in public
bar/games room or in dining room in the
hotel part across a corridor (also set menus);
McEwans on handpump, friendly, courteous
licensee and staff; bedrooms *(M and J Back)*

☆ **Selkirk** [NT4728], *Woodburn House*:
Beautifully warm, comfortable and clean,
with well kept ale and good range of bar
food inc really good sandwiches; good
coffee; bedrooms *(Stephanie Sowerby)*

☆ **Selkirk** [28 West Port], *Queens Head*:
Recently refurbished open-plan bar with
copper-topped tables, navy banquettes,
some timber-effect, Scott prints; home-made
food — better than usual, and served till
9.30; friendly service, simpler public bar
with games and so forth; children welcome,
dogs allowed in public bar, open all day
summer *(Mr and Mrs J H Adam, T Nott,
LYM)*

☆ **St Boswells** [A68 just S of Newtown St
Boswells; NT5931], *Buccleuch Arms*:
Relaxed and comfortable sandstone inn with
plushly elegant spacious bar — velvet
curtains, reproduction Georgian panelling,
quietly genteel atmosphere and no smoking
alcove; bar food (not Sun) from soup and
sandwiches to steak (sandwiches all day),
restaurant, tables in garden; nr GWG162;
children welcome; bedrooms *(Leith Stuart,*

*John and Anne McIver, Prof H G Allen, D
Morrell, Graham and Karen Oddey, S V
Bishop, LYM)*

CENTRAL

☆ **Ardeonaig** [S side of Loch Tay; NN6635],
Ardeonaig: Hotel in lovely setting where
burn flows down into loch; nice bar, pubby
atmosphere, good food; bedrooms good
(Cathy Long, T and A Kucharski)

☆ **Blanefield** [West Carbeth; A809
Glasgow—Drymen, just S of B821;
NS5579], *Carbeth*: Low whitewashed
building with unusual pine-panelled bar —
high fringe of tartan curtains, woodburner
one end, log fire the other; fires in smarter
lounge and family room too; good chocie of
generous bar food, sometimes
Whitbreads-related real ales, attentive staff,
lots of tables outside, live music Weds/Fri,
open all day 7 days; bedrooms *(Fiona Mutch,
L A Moignard, Ian Baillie, LYM)*

☆ **Brig o Turk** [A821 Callander—Trossachs;
NN5306], *Byre*: Converted from old byre,
high rafters with modern carved faces on
beam ends, tractor-seat bar stools, friendly
service; McEwans on air pressure tall founts,
good bar food, attractive new restaurant
area with more adventurous evening menu,
spotless lavatories; open all day; children
welcome; bedrooms *(Roger Danes, P and L
Saville)*

Callender [Bridge St; NN6208], *Bridgend
House*: Comfortable leather armchairs in
attractive lounge, well kept McEwans 80/-;
bedrooms *(John Towers)*

☆ **Castlecary** [A80 Glasgow—Stirling;
NS7878], *Castlecary House*: Handily placed
on Glasgow-Stirling route, cheerful main bar
open all day, Belhaven 70/- and 80/-,
Greenmantle and Theakstons Best on
handpump, low-priced bar meals till 10 (Sun
afternoon high teas instead), restaurant
specialising in steaks on hot metal platters,
very friendly staff; bedrooms *(Dr G A
McLeod, A Neill, LYM)*

Dollar [Chapel Pl; NS9796], *Strathallan*:
Good lively bar, with three local real ales,
good value malt of the month, good food,
friendly service, pool, darts, fruit machine
and juke box; comfortable bedrooms *(Nic
James)*

☆ **Drymen** [NS4788], *Salmon Leap*:
Comfortable 18th-century inn with
L-shaped lounge and bar, good log fires and
stove, bric-a-brac, stuffed fish and so forth;
food inc home-made pies, vegetarian dishes,
children's helpings; S&N beers, lots of malt
whiskies; more reports please on service and
bedrooms; children welcome, open all day;
bedrooms *(Frank Cummins, Roger Taylor,
Peter Watkins, Pam Stanley, Cathy Long,
LYM)*

Drymen [The Square], *Winnock*:
Surprisingly English-pub feel if rather
hotelish; well kept McEwans 80/- and
Theakstons, good value food, wide choice of
malt whiskies; bedrooms *(Ian Baillie, Simon
Tormey)*

☆ **Killearn** [Main St (A875); NS5285], *Old*

Mill: Simple bar food in quietly friendly village pub with rustic cushioned built-in settles and wheelback chairs around neat dark tables, open fire, piped music; open all day summer; fine views of Campsie Fells from behind *(LYM)*

☆ **Kippen** [NS6594], *Cross Keys*: Comfortable and friendly lounge with stuffed birds, wildfowl prints, well kept McEwans 80/-, decent waitress-served bar food, log fire; pool and militaria in public bar; well kept McEwans and Greenmantle on handpump, good standard bar food, high teas, family room (with another log fire), nappies and changing shelf in ladies'; small restaurant area; bedrooms *(Roger Danes, LYM)*

☆ **Polmont** [Gilston Crescent; under a mile from M9 junction 7; A803 towards Polmont, then left; NS9378], *Whyteside*: Friendly and well run Victorian hotel with extensive comfortably furnished open-plan bar — most notable for its 300-plus whiskies, dozens of other spirits, over 60 bottled beers and well kept Archibald Arrols 70/- and Ind Coope Burton on handpump; children in eating area (not after 7.30), restaurant; organ music some nights; bedrooms (Anon)

☆ **Stirling** [Easter Cornton Rd, Causewayhead; off A9 N of centre; NS7993], *Birds & the Bees*: Interestingly furnished ex-byre, dimly lit and convivial, with Arrols 70/- and 80/-, Harviestoun 80/-, Maclays 80/- and Youngers IPA on handpump, reasonably priced bar food, loud piped music, live bands most weekends, restaurant; open all day till 1am — very popular with young people, reliably well run; children welcome *(LYM)*

☆ **Stirling** [91 St Mary's Wynd; from Wallace Memorial in centre go up Baker St, keep right at top; NS7993], *Settle*: Small early 18th-century pub, restored to show beams, stonework, great arched fireplace (with open fire) and barrel-vaulted upper room; comfortable back room, bar games, snacks till 7, well kept Belhaven 80/- and Maclays on handpump, piped music (can be loud); open all day; friendly service — staff may wear Highland dress *(Len Beattie, WAH, M Cadenhead, LYM)*

Stirling [Whins of Milton; A872, just off M9 junction 9], *Pirnall*: Recently converted by Whitbreads to smart Brewers Fayre place *(Mr and Mrs J H Adam)*

DUMFRIES AND GALLOWAY

☆ **Auchencairn** [about 2 1/2 miles off A711; NX7951], *Balcary Bay*: Attractive bar and hotel, in nice spot, featuring in smuggling tales; has been praised for good bar food, but no recent reports *(News please)*

= **Auldgirth** [just E of A75, about 8 miles N of Dumfries; NX9186], *Auldgirth*: Old whitewashed stone inn, comfortable lounge in side annexe with brasses, plates and pictures, good plain food, cheerful welcome, good service; bedrooms *(D Morrell)*

Canonbie [NY3976], *Cross Keys*: Good bar food inc fresh fish and notable carvery Sun lunch; children welcome, well kept Youngers Scotch, good service *(Anon)*

☆ **Creebridge** [Minnigaff; NX4165], *Creebridge House*: Country-house hotel in pleasant compact grounds with simple but comfortable public bar, friendly atmosphere, well kept McEwans 80/- and above all good bar lunches inc fine local fish and seafood, mushrooms stuffed with stilton and fried in batter, or silverside thinly sliced, fried and served with a white wine, cream, onion and mushroom sauce — get there early to be sure of full choice; bedrooms *(W C M Jones, Malcolm Ramsay, Fiona Mutch, John C Baker)*

☆ **Dalbeattie** [1 Maxwell St; NX8361], *Pheasant*: Useful for serving bar food till 10 in its comfortable upstairs lounge/restaurant, with good choice; lively downstairs bar, children welcome, open all day till midnight summer; bedrooms *(LYM)*

Drummore [NX1336], *Ship*: Can slow right down out of season, but on form has food inc delicious fresh plaice, and a warm welcome *(Anthony Barnes)*

Dumfries [Lovers Walk, opp stn; NX9776], *Station*: Unpretentious small pub, elegant railway-theme lounge with good range of decent bar food and of drinks inc good cool beer; attentive pleasant staff *(Patrick Godfrey)*

☆ **Gatehouse of Fleet** [NX5956], *Murray Arms*: Carefully rebuilt small 17th-century hotel with strong Burns connections; good buffet, well kept real ales such as Broughton or Youngers, variety of mainly old-fashioned comfortable seating areas, games in separate public bar; open all day for food in summer; children welcome; bedrooms *(D W Huebner, John Watson, LYM)*

☆ **Gatehouse of Fleet** [High St], *Angel*: Small friendly hotel with warm and cosy lounge bar, good service, good popular bar food, sensibly priced restaurant, McEwans ales; bedrooms comfortable and good value *(A D E Lewis)*

Gatehouse of Fleet [Bridge St], *Anwoth*: Doing well under new manager, with pleasant bar, friendly welcome, good straightforward home-made food, riverside garden; a good place for walkers and fishermen; bedrooms pleasant and well equipped, if not large *(D Morrell)*

Glencaple [NX9968], *Nith*: Quick service, good value food — especially fish; pleasant estuary situation; bedrooms *(D Morrell)*

Gretna [Annan Rd; NY3267], *Solway Lodge*: Bright modern lounge bar behind hotel; polite, friendly service, well kept Broughton Special and Tetleys on handpump, small choice of reasonably priced food *(Richard Houghton)*

☆ **Kirkcowan** [NX3260], *Craighlaw Arms*: In quiet village, carefully modernised hotel with imaginative choice of good home-cooked food, welcoming licensees; fishing and shooting; bedrooms clean and comfortable *(Mr and Mrs M J Kelly, M Brooks)*

☆ **Kirkcudbright** [Old High St; NX6851],

Selkirk Arms: A hotel since 18th century, but quiet modern decor in cosy and comfortable partly panelled lounge with good local flavour; decent bar food, restaurant, evening steak bar, tables in spacious garden; fishing; children in restaurant and lounge; good value bedrooms *(Tim Locke, LYM)*

☆ Moffat [High St], *Balmoral*: Fine central village pub, consistently good, with decent simple food quickly served in comfortable peaceful bar *(M H Box, John and Chris Simpson)*

☆ Moffat [1 Churchgate; NT0905], *Black Bull*: Several bar areas inc pubby public bar with railway memorabilia, plush softly lit cocktail bar (not always open out of season), simply furnished tiled-floor dining room and side games bar; bar food from filled rolls and sandwiches up; juke box may be loud; children welcome; open all day all week; bedrooms comfortable, with hearty breakfasts *(KC, Dr T H M Mackenzie, A McK, P Lloyd, Miss K Bamford, LYM)*

Moffat [44 High St; NT0905], *Star*: Narrowest free-standing pub in Britain with plush relaxing lounge, noisier public bar, bright dining room, friendly staff, well kept Tennents 80/- or Theakstons and reasonably priced; interesting food; bedrooms *(Jon Barnes, Genie and Brian Smart)*

New Abbey [NX9666], *Criffel*: Welcoming and lively, popular with locals; nice village with good ruined abbey *(Barry and Anne)*

= Powfoot [NY1566], *Powfoot Golf*: Delightful situation, well stocked bar and good food inc sandwiches and good soups; bedrooms *(Alan Wark)*

☆ Stranraer [George St; NX0660], *George*: Elegant and comfortable lounge bar with good value bar food, huge log fireplace, friendly staff; also wine bar/bistro with world-wide choice of bottled beers; open all day; children welcome; bedrooms most comfortable *(LYM)*

Twynholm [18 Main St; NX6654], *Star*: Friendly and pleasant village pub with McEwans 80/-, good collection of miniature whiskies all around the bar shelves as well as wide range for sale, and good standard bar food inc super steak and kidney pie *(Andrew Triggs, Margaret and Trevor Errington)*

FIFE

☆ Anstruther [High St; NO5704], *Smugglers*: Wide range of good value straightforward bar food (fresh scampi and mixed grill recommended) in friendly old inn with cheerful decor and service; rambling and attractive upstairs lounge bar, good morning coffee; busy downstairs games bar with real ales and whiskies, summer barbecues on pretty terrace, popular if not cheap restaurant; children allowed in eating area; bedrooms small but clean *(John and Ann Prince, Colin Price)*

Anstruther [Bankwell Rd], *Craws Nest*: Good variety of good food inc fresh fish served generously in straightforward lounge; bedrooms *(I S Thomson)*; *Dreel*: Cosy and

friendly old building in attractive position, with garden overlooking Dreel Burn, open fire, pool area, tables outside; has been praised for well kept ale and good bar food inc local seafood, but no recent reports *(News please)*

☆ Carnock [6 Main St; A907 Dunfermline—Alloa; NT0489], *Old Inn*: Good food inc children's helpings and splendid pies and puddings, at neatly spaced tables of tidy low-beamed lounge in cottage-style pub; well kept Maclays (full range); bar with pool table well out of way; children welcome *(Andy and Jill Kassube)*

☆ Ceres [Main St; NO4011], *Meldrums*: Exceptionally good pub food in clean and attractive beamed pub/hotel hidden away between Cupar and Elie; pleasant waitresses; bedrooms *(Hope Chenalls)*

☆ Crail [4 High St; NO6108], *Golf*: Village inn with plenty of atmosphere in bustling little public bar, rather more restrained if not exactly smart lounge; limited choice of simply presented but tasty bar food, well kept McEwans 80/-, good range of malt whiskies, cheerful barman, coal fire; bedrooms clean and comfortable though basic, with good breakfasts *(Ian Baillie)*

☆ Elie [harbour; NO4900], *Ship*: In lovely position by sandy harbour bay, basic and unspoilt, with old-fashioned furnishings, some panelling and beams; very appealing to many even before the much-needed redecoration and tidying-up has been completed, and the waterside garden, with its own bar and barbecues in summer, has been much enjoyed; good value burgers, pizzas and so forth (not Tues), well kept Belhaven 80/-, lively atmosphere; children may be allowed in back room, has been open all day (afternoon closure Sun) *(Kate Sainsbury, Mr and Mrs Hart, T and A Kucharski, W Dennis Dickinson, Peter Fenton, Caroline Muirhead, LYM)*

☆ Falkland [NO2507], *Covenanter*: Attractive, spotless pub with good food and delightful welcoming service; well kept Tennents 70/- on tall fount pressure, usual bar food; children in small bistro bar; nr start GWG165, in beautiful old village with magnificent NT palace; bedrooms good *(Michael Bechley)*

Kilconquhar [NO4802], *Kinneucha*: Good food at attractive prices *(Karen Barclay)*

Lower Largo [NO4102], *Crusoe*: Good choice of decent food, quick and efficient service; bedrooms spacious *(A J Stenson)*

☆ North Queensferry [NT1380], *Queensferry Lodge*: Newly built hotel very handy for motorway, with good views of Forth road and rail bridges and the Firth, from light and airy lounge, tastefully decorated with lots of wood and plants; wide choice of good value bar food 12-2.30, 5-10; also a craft shop; bedrooms *(MH, Roger Huggins, Alan Wark)*

Pitscottie [B939/B940; nr Cupar; NO4113], *Pitscottie*: Wide choice of good well cooked bar lunches served by very pleasant and helpful landlord and staff in two rooms, the main one charmingly upholstered in brocade

— booking advisable at weekends; well stocked bar; clean, with spotless lavatories *(I S Thomson)*

☆ **St Andrews** [Grange Rd — a mile S; NO5116], *Grange*: Good atmosphere in fine old building on outskirts, more restaurant than pub now; spotlessly clean small bar with decent wine, good food here and in restaurant, which has changing set-price meals lunchtime and evening, with interesting cooking *(Mrs N W Biggs, I S Thomson)*

St Andrews [40 The Scores], *Ma Bells*: Seafront pub by golf course, open all day, with popular downstairs bar full of students during term-time, and locals and tourists the rest of the year; has been praised for well kept Greenmantle and Watneys-related real ales, over 75 different bottled beers inc all the Trappists, lots of malt whiskies and reasonably priced bar food served through till 6, but no recent reports *(News please)*; [The Scores], *Russell*: Smart and cosy little bar, Theakstons real ale, bar food; children allowed *(Ian Baillie)*

Strathmiglo [NO2110], *Strathmiglo*: Good food inc fresh veg and home-made pies at attractive prices, obliging friendly service, in simple but comfortable dining lounge *(Mrs J Valentine, LYM)*

Wormit [Naughton Rd; NO4026], *Taybridge Halt*: Good food inc really crisp and juicy steak pie and good children's menu; friendly *(A D E Lewis)*

GRAMPIAN

☆ **Aberdeen** [Bon Accord St], *Ferryhill House Hotel*: Well run small hotel with notable range of six well kept real ales, good choice of malt whiskies, wide choice of bar food and cheap set lunches, comfortable communicating spacious and airy bar areas, lots of well spaced tables out on neat well sheltered lawns; open all day, children allowed in restaurant; bedrooms — only an absence of reader reports keeps this excellent place out of the main entries *(LYM)*

Aberdeen [Kings Gate], *Athol*: Pleasant atmosphere in spacious and popular bar, interesting modestly priced dinners; Aberdonian welcome, good location and parking; bedrooms exceptionally comfortable, good weekend rates *(D Morrell)*; [Dee St], *Gabriels*: Lofty converted chapel turned into showy and pleasantly idiosyncratic bar, nothing tacky; nightclub behind *(LYM)*

☆ **Braemar** [NO1491], *Fife Arms*: Clean and comfortable spacious lounge in big Victorian hotel with appropriate decor; very friendly, efficient service and good value cold buffet with fine range of salads, also good hot dishes; nr start GWG166; children welcome *(G R Pearson, Niall and Jane)*

☆ **Elgin** [Thunderton Pl; NJ2162], *Thunderton House*: 17th-century town-centre pub, sympathetically refurbished, with children's room; has been praised for fast friendly service, real ale and wide range of good value bar food, but no recent reports *(News please)*

Fochabers [NJ3458], *Gordon Arms*: Comfortable traditional small hotel with decent food in bars and restaurant inc some fresh local ingredients, well kept McEwans 80/-, good choice of whiskies; can arrange stalking and fishing for residents; bedrooms *(Bob and Ann Westbrook, LYM)*

Forres [Tolbooth St; NJ0359], *Red Lion*: Small bright and comfortable lounge bar with bar lunches and McEwans real ale; attractive town *(Mr and Mrs J H Adam)*

Laurencekirk [Alma Pl; NO7171], *Alma*: Home-cooked food in bar and restaurant of family-run former coaching inn; well equipped bedrooms — children and pets welcome; also self-catering chalets *(Anon)*

Newmachar [NJ8819], *Beekies Neuk*: Pleasant, neatly kept lounge with wide choice of well cooked food, quick service, good beer *(I S Thomson)*

☆ **Potarch** [B993, just off A93 5 miles W of Banchory; NO6097], *Potarch Hotel*: Attractive granite hotel by R Dee (fishing), with Tennents ales, good food from mushrooms en croûte through mince and tatties or beef and Guinness pie to steaks, friendly service; basic public bar, cosy lounge with open fire, copper-topped tables, local prints and photographs; forest walks, shooting, skiing nearby; seven bedrooms *(Allan Clarke, D A R Glover)*

☆ **Stonehaven** [Shorehead; NO8786], *Marine*: Popular pub in row of houses on front, with seats outside and superb harbour view; lively, friendly atmosphere with young customers, juke box and pool table in room past bar; upstairs lounge; good value food in bars and upstairs restaurant, McEwans 80/- and guest beers such as Timothy Taylors Landlord, coffee and tea; open all day; bedrooms *(Chris Raisin, Mr and Mrs B Hobden, Allan Clarke)*

☆ **nr Turriff** [Auchterless; A947 5 miles S; NJ7250], *Towie*: Stylish upmarket comfort, good friendly atmosphere; emphasis on the beautifully prepared restaurant food, using fresh ingredients, but also has well presented generous bar food inc vegetarian dishes and steaks done on sizzle-plate; quietly efficient service, no smoking or music in dining area; good choice of wines; handy for Fyvie Castle (NT) and Delgatie Castle (traditional archery meet first Sat July); children welcome; bedrooms *(Janet and John Towers, Bernard Phillips)*

HIGHLAND

Achiltibuie [NC0208], *Summer Isles*: Warm, friendly and well furnished, with pretty watercolours and flowers; delicious set menus using fresh ingredients, with a choice of superb puddings and excellent array of uncommon cheeses — a particular interest of the owner; bedrooms comfortable, though the cheapest are not lavish *(Moira and John Cole, T and A Kucharski)*

☆ **Applecross** [NG7144], *Applecross Inn*: Good goal for wonderful scenic drive (don't try the Beallach na Ba pass in bad weather);

friendly welcome, local atmosphere, reasonably priced locally caught lobster, crab, cod, monkfish and oysters, delicious puddings, and above all marvellous scenery — with a breathtaking view of Skye; bar billiards, Tennents 80/-, open all day at least in summer; tables outside *(Joan and Tony Walker, P B Dowsett, Andrew Hazeldine, T and A Kucharski)*

Auldearn [NH9155], *Covenanters*: Welcoming and spacious bar with tidy oak tables and chairs, subdued lighting and piped music; decent straightfoward food, pool and darts at one end; attractive old village; bedrooms clean and modern, of motel standard *(Alan and Margaret Twyford, D Morrell)*

Aultguish [NH3570], *Aultguish*: Isolated highland inn just below Loch Glascarnoch, comfortable, attractive lounge, good range of food, friendly efficient service; bedrooms *(A P Jeffreys, Ian Baillie, LYM)*

Aviemore [NH8912], *Olde Bridge*: Small welcoming inn with good home cooking — curried parsnip soup, lamb casserole and steak pie recommended; well kept Youngers *(S E Dark)*; [Main Road], *Winking Owl*: Useful for upstairs family bar with wide choice of cheerily served bar food, Tetleys and a superb view of Cairngorns; seating outside, climbing frame *(Ian Baillie)*

☆ **Badachro** [B8056 by Gair Loch; NG7773], *Badachro Hotel*: Much more like a pub than most Scottish hotels, friendly and relaxing, the public bar more of a lounge than usual; nice garden, tables on terrace virtually overhanging the bay, part of Loch Gairloch; a must for boat and fishing enthusiasts; friendly helpful staff, idyllic surroundings *(Ian Baillie, A P Jeffreys, T and A Kucharski)*

Ballachulish [Oban Rd, S; NN0858], *Ballachulish*: Old hotel close to Glencoe with upmarket service in lounge bar, West Highland real ale, nice atmosphere, glorious view across Loch Leven to the hills of Ardgour; good if not cheap food lunchtime and evening till 10; also separate basic youth-clubbish bar with well kept Arrols 80/-; bedrooms *(Richard Houghton, Ian Baillie)*

Dornie [NG8827], *Castle*: Clean, white-painted place with friendly staff, well kept McEwans 80/-, really good value meals served in spacious bar; darts, pool, dominoes *(A E Alcock)*; *Clardon Bar*: Nr Eilean Donan Castle, open all day with well kept McEwans 80/-, reasonably priced meals inc locally caught haddock, darts *(A E Alcock)*; [8 Francis St], *Loch Duich*: Overlooking Eileeen Donan Castle (illuminated at night), modest-sized pub part has selecion from the restaurant's dishes; very popular with locals, accommodating staff, well kept McEwans 80/-; bedrooms *(A E Alcock)*

Dulnain Bridge [A938 ½ mile W of village; NH9925], *Muckrach Lodge*: Secluded Victorian former shooting lodge, now a hotel, notable bar lunches, friendly service, good beers; restaurant concentrating on fresh local ingredients; bedrooms with hearty breakfasts *(Leith Stuart)*

Dunnet [A836; ND2171], *Northern Sands*: On lovely bay close to Dunnet Head — on clear day you can see from Duncansby Head to Cape Wrath; pleasant, comfortable bar and lounge with simple standard food; bedrooms *(T Nott)*

☆ **Fort Augustus** [NH3709], *Lock*: A proper pub, so a real rarity up here; at the foot of Loch Ness, run by character ex-Merchant sailor, with lots of atmosphere — can get packed evenings with locals and boating people, especially in season as it's opp first lock on Fort Augustus flight of locks on Caledonian Canal; big fire, half the room reserved for eating the efficiently served reasonably priced bar food, plain but wholesome, with lots of chips; soft Scottish piped music, good choice of whiskies *(Ben Wimpenny, R Sally, Cathy Long, T and A Kucharski, Cdr W S D Hendry)*

Fort William [High St], *Ben Nevis*: Straightforwardly decent low-beamed pub, views behind to Loch Linnhe, limited good value bar food, friendly staff *(Ian Baillie)*; [A82, 2 miles S], *Clan MacDuff Motorlodge*: Not a pub, but worth knowing as a clean, welcoming licensed motel with good evening food and lots of parking; modern building overlooking Loch Linnhe; bedrooms *(John and Daphne Miller)*

☆ **Gairloch** [Just off A832 nr bridge; NG8077], *Old Inn*: Good choice of good value bar food inc fresh fish, attentive friendly service, well kept Youngers No 3, a good few malts, unusually wide range of crisps etc; dimpled copper tables and so forth in two small and rather dark rooms of comfortable lounge, neat and clean public bar with pool table and games, picnic-table sets attractively placed out by stream, splendid beach nearby; open all day; bedrooms *(J A B Darlington, Graham Bush, S E Dark, R Blatch, T and A Kucharski, Peter Watkins, Pam Stanley, BB)*

Garve [A832; NH3961], *Garve*: Small, quiet, comfortable and well stocked bar in welcoming hotel, a useful stop; good plentiful food served quickly; bedrooms comfortable *(Alan Wark, Ian Baillie)*

Glen Shiel [A87 Invergarry—Kyle of Lochalsh, on Loch Cluanie; NH0711], *Cluanie*: In really marvellous countryside miles from anywhere with good value bar food inc very filling soup, fairly new management; bedrooms good value, large, clean and modern in recent extension, with good breakfasts *(Mike Tucker, A E Alcock)*

☆ **Glencoe** [off A82 E of Pass; NN1058], *Kingshouse*: Alone in a stupendous mountain landscape, with basic bar food inc children's dishes, well kept McEwans 80/-; choose your bar carefully — the climbers' one at the back has very basic furnishings, loud pop music, pool and darts, the genteel modernised central cocktail bar has cloth banquettes and other seats around wood-effect tables; open all day; good value bedrooms in inn itself, and in cheaper dormitory-style bunkhouse *(Mr and Mrs J H Adam, BB)*

☆ **Glenelg** [unmarked rd from Shiel Bridge (A87) towards Skye — inn tucked away by bend at road junction and easily missed; NG8119], *Glenelg*: Overlooking Skye across own beach and sea loch; friendly public bar/snack bar with open fire even in summer, plain solid furnishings, pool table, piped music, friendly staff and locals, homely pictures; varied decent bar food, lots of whiskies, nice restaurant, tables on back terrace; drive to inn involves narrow steep roads with spectacular views of Loch Duich — there's a short summer ferry crossing from Skye, too; bedrooms *(E J Alcock, WAH, A P Jeffreys)*

☆ **Invermoriston** [NH4117], *Glenmoriston Arms*: Well kept McEwans 80/-, lots of malt whiskies, decent straightforward bar food and friendly quick staff in cosy lounge and cheery stables bar, good restaurant (book ahead), fishing and stalking by arrangement; not far from Loch Ness; bedrooms good; open all year *(Alan and Lesley Holden, LYM)*

Inverness [Academy St], *Phoenix*: Traditional public bar with central servery, well furnished lounge bar with good atmosphere (though music may be loud); very pleasant and efficient service, well kept Maclays 80/- and a guest beer on handpump; children in family room *(Richard Houghton)*

John O'Groats [ND3773], *John o' Groats*: McEwans ales, plain bar, lounge bar and dining room, all very simple and straightforward — location is the main interest; plans for development in next year or two; bedrooms *(T Nott)*

Kingussie [High St; NH7501], *Royal*: Pleasant bar with good range of food, two real ales and no smoking area; open all day; bedrooms *(Mr and Mrs J H Adam)*

Kinlochbervie [NO2256], *Kinlochbervie*: Good generous low-priced food in restaurant separate from public bar; bedrooms *(Andrew Hazeldine)*

☆ **Kinlochewe** [NH0262], *Kinlochewe*: Public bar and lounge popular with both locals and tourists; good food from toasties and ploughman's up, friendly staff, open fire, piped classical music; stupendous scenery all around, especially Loch Maree and Torridon mountains; bedrooms comfortable and clean *(A P Jeffreys, Joan and Tony Walker)*

☆ **Kylesku** [A894; S side of former ferry crossing; NC2234], *Kylesku Hotel*: Glorious coastal surroundings and short choice of particularly good bar food — esp fresh local seafood inc fish, scallops, delicious mussels, big prawns in garlic butter, also sandwiches and soup; friendly staff, happy mix of locals and visitors, restaurant; five comfortable and peaceful bedrooms; *(D Goodger, Andrew Hazeldine, Neil and Angela Huxter)*

nr **Lairg** [13 miles N on A836; NC5224], *Crask*: Simple but interesting good value food, no piped music, friendly welcome and log fire in basic inn in the middle of nowhere

(S E Dark, KC)

☆ **Lewiston** [NH5029], *Lewiston Arms*: Small public bar with games and lots of locals, decorous well kept lounge, Youngers No 3, good filling bar food, friendly welcome, attractive garden; handy for Loch Ness (nr ruined Urquhart Castle) and Glen Coiltie, with nice drive up to Glen Affric and back; bedrooms *(WAH, Kathy Holt, Cathy Long, LYM)*

Lochcarron [A896; NG9039], *Lochcarron*: Public bar is warm, friendly and nicely furnished, with well kept McEwans 80/- and reasonably priced, well presented decent bar food; very quick service; separate bar with pool table and juke box; views out over Loch Carron; bedrooms *(WAH)*

Mallaig [Side street up hill from harbour; NM6797], *Tigh-a-Chlachain*: A veritable oasis in the west-coast desert of velour upholstery and hotel waiters — very friendly, food filling and not too dear, mixed clientele, nice contrast between serene lounge/restaurant and public bar *(Simon Tormey)*

☆ **Melvich** [A836; NC8765], *Melvich*: Lovely spot with beautiful views of sea and coastline; very civilised lounge, friendly staff, leisurely atmosphere, peat or wood fire even at midsummer, good food in bar and restaurant inc fresh wild salmon; bedrooms *(A D Atienza, D A Wilcock, Miss C M Davidson, Alan Wilcock, Christine Davidson)*

☆ **Nairn** [Viewfield St; NH8856], *Clifton House*: Charming and distinguished small hotel, wonderfully civilised, with delightfully furnished and sumptuously decorated lounge, delectable bar lunches made from the freshest and finest ingredients, fine restaurant, good wines and interesting spirits; was our highest-rated main entry in Scotland, until its evolution into what's clearly no longer a pub even by our elastic definition; comfortable bedrooms *(LYM)*

Nairn [Harbour St], *Taste Bud*: Friendly and amusing staff; good choice of beers and whiskies; bar food, restaurant *(J D Maplethorpe)*

Poolewe [Corriness Guest House; NB8580], *Choppys*: Not a pub, a restaurant with simple modern bar (which has pool table), worth knowing for good value food; very friendly service, guest house behind *(Mrs E M Brandwood, BB)*; *Poolewe*: Plain bar and communicating lounge with big helpings of decent bar food served noon-8.30, well kept McEwans 80/-, good malt whiskies, cheerful service, piped folk music (live too, often), log fire; open all day; bedrooms *(P Lister, BB)*

☆ **Shiel Bridge** [NG9318], *Kintail Lodge*: Fairly simple hotel worth knowing for good well prepared food (inc children's helpings) inc fine game pie and wild salmon; now has Theakstons Best on handpump, good collection of malt whiskies; good value big bedrooms *(M Cadenhead, A E Alcock, Genie and Brian Smart)*

Strontian [NM8161], *Loch Sunart*: Reasonably priced Taste of Scotland bar food, good restaurant dinners; beautiful quiet setting with good walking; bedrooms good value *(D Morrell)*

Struy [B831; NH3939], *Struy*: Clean, pleasant and friendly small pub, recently renovated; McEwans beer, good range of malt whiskies, excellent fresh brown bread sandwiches at low prices; bedrooms *(M J Ridgway)*

Thurso [Traill St; ND1168], *Royal*: Refurbished a year ago in 30s style, but carefully done in good taste; charming efficient service by trained staff; Youngers beer (and Becks), inexpensive but well presented standard food; bedrooms *(T Nott)*

☆ **Tomatin** [NH8029], *Tomatin*: Newly decorated, clean and well run, good atmosphere, friendly staff and keenly priced bar food; seats outside; children welcome *(Neil and Angela Huxter)*

LOTHIAN

Aberlady [off A198 E; NT4679], *Green Craig*: Former private house in enviable position on promontory, now a hotel with bar and restaurant; bedrooms *(W T Aird)*; [A198 towards Edinburgh], *Waggon*: Well run and friendly, view over the salt-flats and Firth to Fife from big windows in the airy high-ceilinged back extension, attractive front family room, decent bar food, well kept McEwans 80/-; restaurant *(LYM)*

Balerno [22 Main St (off A70); NT1666], *Grey Horse*: Traditional Scottish bar, quiet lounge, well kept Belhaven 80/- *(Andy and Jill Kassube)*; [off Marchbank Rd, off A70 SW of Edinburgh], *Kestrel*: Food-oriented bar with wide choice inc delicious vegetable soup and enormous gammon; good service, pleasant surroundings *(Andy and Jill Kassube)*

☆ **Cramond** [Cramond Glebe Rd; signed off A90 leaving Edinburgh W; NT1876], *Cramond Inn*: Old pub tucked into pretty restored fishing village by Firth of Forth, with usual lunchtime bar food, evening restaurant, well kept real ales on tall founts — it's a Sam Smiths pub, but has had others too; open fire in neatly comfortable recently enlarged bar, tables on small side terrace, children allowed lunchtime; open all day Sat *(Ian and Sue Brocklebank, Andy and Jill Kassube, Chris Raisin, LYM)*

☆ **Cramond Bridge** [A90; NT1875], *Cramond Brig*: Good family stop with bar food all day, on main A90 N of Edinburgh; well kept McEwans 80/-, restaurant *(LYM)*

☆ **Dirleton** [village green; NT5184], *Castle*: Pleasant unpretentious but comfortable lounge, generous helpings of well presented food inc well filled sandwiches, well kept McEwans 80/-, friendly service and atmosphere; restaurant; attractive spot, nr GWG175; bedrooms *(S V Bishop, William D Cissna)*

East Linton [NT5977], *Drovers*: Recently renovated 18th-century free house with well kept guest beers, cosy and attractively furnished bar with fresh, interesting food inc local fish and well cooked veg *(Nancy Henderson)*

☆ **Edinburgh** [55 Rose St], *Rose Street Brewery*: Main attraction is the beer they brew on the premises — Auld Reekie 80/- and potent 90/-; downstairs low-beams-boards-and-flagstones saloon with loud but well reproduced pop music from its CD juke box; comfortable partly panelled upstairs lounge (closed at quiet times); bar food, good service, live music some evenings *(P Corris, Mark Walker, Barbara Wensworth, Mel and Phil Lloyd, Bob Timmis, Roger Huggins)*

☆ **Edinburgh** [152 Rose St], *Kenilworth*: Fine Edwardian pub with ornate high ceiling, carved woodwork, etched mirrors and windows; central bar serving Auld Reekie 80/-, Ind Coope Burton, and Tetleys real ales on handpump (at a price), Sun papers out, quick friendly service; good lunchtime food inc tasty haggis, not many seats *(P Corris, Mark Walker, Chris Cook, Simon Tormey)*

Edinburgh [100 Rose St], *Auld Hundred*: Recently brightened up, comfortable furnishings, some stripped stonework, chilled 80/-, staff pleaant, good bar meals upstairs, open all day; CD juke box — evenings this may be loud, with upstairs disco and bouncers on the door *(Peter Corris, M Walker, BB)*; [18-20 Grassmarket], *Beehive*: Good range of well kept real ales in civilised comfortable lounge with cheerful atmosphere, good value food noon-6pm, upstairs restaurant *(Ralph A Raimi, LYM)*; [435 Lawnmarket], *Deacon Brodies*: Snugly refurbished old building, fun for tourists, commemorating the original for Dr Jekyll and Mr Hyde, hanged on the scaffold he designed; leather armchairs upstairs, settles and younger mood down; decent bar food *(Graham Bush, BB)*; [Royal Mile], *Ensign Ewart*: Old-world with Scottish country piped music and good lively atmosphere; Ind Coope beers and Auld Reekie 80/- from Rose Street Brewery pub, limited range of tasty food with friendly service *(Barbara Wensworth, Mark Walker)*; [Grassmarket], *Fiddlers*: Full of locals and not totally aimed at students; one bar has period feel with ornate wooden shelves behind bar and an atmosphere similar to some London pubs; other bar has pool; violins on walls, good lively unthreatening atmosphere, well kept 80/-, plenty of malt whiskies *(Simon Tormey, Graham Bush)*; [17 Market St], *Hebrides*: Feels like you're in the Western Isles here; friendly staff, pleasant atmosphere, piped Scottish music; only food available is pies, sandwiches etc; busy in evening; open all day *(M Walker)*; [74 Grassmarket], *Last Drop*: Dark, cosy, comfortable and friendly with good range of food (reduced prices for students) inc lots of toasted sandwiches; happy to serve coffee or hot chocolate on the little tables out on the street, also real ales; children welcome *(Ian Phillips)*; [Cockburn St], *Malt Shovel*: Cramped bar counter with good choice of well kept real ales inc lots of guests such as Belhaven, Boddingtons and Fullers ESB; good bar food in separate area, friendly if slightly pressurised service *(Roger*

Danes, T and A Kucharski, Mark Walker);
[202 Rose St], *Scotts*: Modernised but still
pleasantly traditional, with low lighting,
old-fashioned efficient service, Allied real
ales (Mark Walker, LYM); [Mortonhall Park,
30 Frogston Rd E], *Stables*: Nicest feature is
the lovely cobbled stone stable quadrangle
outside this cheerful recent conversion —
stripped stonework, harness, big open fire,
Turkey carpet, dark green leatherette stools
and wheelback chairs; open 11-midnight,
also breakfasts from 7.30, pizzas all day,
other bar food noon to 10, Caledonian 80/-
on handpump; very popular with people
using the big caravan site here; children
welcome — and a water bowl for dogs (Ian
Douglas, BB); [Drummond St], *Stewarts*:
Easy-going traditional bar, open all day,
very busy; good value sandwiches, Belhaven
80/- and Youngers IPA (LYM)
Gifford [NT5368], *Goblin Ha'*: Has been
praised for warm welcome, well kept
McEwans 80/-, genuine home cooking,
quick service and good garden, and has
bedrooms, but no recent reports (News
please)
☆ **Gullane** [A198; NT4882], *Golf*: Easy-going
inn with good value bar food, friendly
service, restaurant, garden; open all day, nr
GWG175; very golf-minded; bedrooms (W
D Dickinson, LYM)
Linlithgow [179 High St; NS9976], *Crown
Arms*: Simple but attractive town bar with
friendly atmosphere, well kept Greenmantle
and Tennents 80/- (Ian and Sue Brocklebank)

STRATHCLYDE
Abington [NS9323], *Abington*: Well kept
McEwans 70/-, very friendly, helpful service;
straightforward food (John C Baker)
Auchentiber [A736 Irvine—Glasgow;
NS3647], *Blair*: Good bar lunches served by
young cheery waitresses, good menu; tables
outside (A L Wark)
Ayr [52 Racecourse Rd; NS3321],
Chestnuts: Part of this hotel was once a
synagogue; bar a fine room — once the
snooker room when the place was a
residential villa; Broughtons Special and
Maclays perfectly kept, friendly service;
straightforward bar food; bedrooms (John C
Baker); [2 Victoria Pk], *Old Racecourse*:
Former villa with fine, high-ceilinged rooms;
McEwans 60/- and Youngers No 3 well
kept, service very friendly and helpful; food
enjoyed by older people; bedrooms (John C
Baker)
Balloch [Balloch Rd; NS3881], *Balloch*:
Polite, friendly service, very reasonably kept
Arrols 80/- on handpump and decent
helpings of good bar food (Richard
Houghton)
Biggar [High St; NT0438], *Crown*: Very
smart lounge with extensive use of wood
finish; food lunchtime only; well kept
McEwans 80/- on handpump; piped music,
fruit machine (Alastair Campbell)
Bothwell [27 Hamilton Rd; NS7058],
Cricklewood: Popular revamped local with
smart new lounge bar, food interesting and

varied, three Whitbreads-related real ales
(Ian M Baillie)
Cairndow [NN1810], *Cairndow*: Superb
views over Loch Fyne and reasonable choice
of good value bar food inc cheap local
oysters; Queen Victoria and Keats stayed
here; next to gardens with tallest tree in UK;
bedrooms (W T Aird)
Cardross [NS3477], *Muirfield*: Good choice
of good value food inc interesting starters,
more sophisticated evening dishes (D
Morrell)
Colgrain [A814 Cardross—Helensburgh;
NS3280], *Colgrain*: Really welcoming
young couple in restaurant worth knowing
for good bar lunches and bar suppers, good
choice of food well cooked and presented;
closed Mon (A L Wark)
Failford [B743 Mauchline—Ayr — OS Sheet
77, map reference 460262; NS4626],
Failford: Recently developed and improved;
bar and lounge with back dining room
overlooking River Ayr; wide choice of
freshly made food — bar lunches, high teas
and dinners; quite reasonable prices (T Nott)
Garelochhead [Whistlefield; NS2391],
Green Kettle: Doing well under new young
management, brasserie upstairs with
interesting light meals, sea decor, informal
quick service and bar; gourmet restaurant
downstairs; open fire, cosy friendly
atmosphere; spectacular environment (D W J
Morrell)
☆ **Gartocharn** [A811 Balloch—Stirling —
formerly the Gartocharn Inn; NS4286],
Hungry Monk: Doing well under its new
name, under new ownership, with lavish
new reproduction Victorian decor; friendly
service, good modestly priced food, log fire,
unobtrusive Scottish folk music; no longer
has bedrooms (D W J Morrell)
Girvan [Dalrymple St; NX1897], *Kings
Arms*: Unusual golf bar — serving counter
like giant golf ball, everything else has golf
theme; also spacious lounge, bar food, real
ale, open all day, children welcome;
bedrooms (LYM)
☆ **Glasgow** [83 Hutcheson St], *Rab Has*:
Sensitively converted Georgian town house,
younger brother of Babbity Bowster;
delightfully informal ground floor bar,
basement restaurant, intermittent robust live
music but otherwise relatively quiet; menu
amost entirely seafood — well cooked; good
service; bedrooms elegant and immaculate
(Anthony Sargent, Caroline Gant)
☆ **Glasgow** [154 Hope St], *Pot Still*: Well run
split level bar with slender pillars supporting
high ceiling, comfortable banquettes in bays,
decent bar food, Youngers No 3 on tall
fount, and its great specialisation — a wide
range of malt whiskies (though it has been
found to have promotion of a single brand
instead of those serried ranks of intriguing
bottles for which it is famous) (Ian Baillie,
LYM)
☆ **Glasgow** [1256 Argyle St, corner with
Radnor St], *Montys*: Pleasantly smart and
spacious atmosphere, copious dark wood,
consistently well kept Belhaven,

Greenmantle and other real ales, efficient amiable bar staff, good bar food, pervasive piped music, frequent live entertainment *(Ian Baillie, Alastair Campbell, BB)*

Glasgow [Renfield St/Renfrew St], *Athol*: High-ceilinged, with buttermilk paintwork, mirrored end wall, pillars for upper dining area — some emphasis on food such as soup, sandwiches, good filled baguettes, burgers and chilli; lower area with serving counter and bar stools, good coffee *(Ian Phillips)*; [India St, Charing X], *Baby Grand*: Continental-style cafe-bar, chatty and clattery with terrazzo or tiled floor, long grey marble counter, well kept McEwans 70/- and 80/- on tall founts, espresso machine, good hot chocolate and decent house wines, useful quick food; open all day *(BB)*; [Dumbarton Rd], *Exchequer*: Plush and spacious, with good range of bar food; handy for Art Gallery and new Transport Museum *(Mr and Mrs J H Adam)*; [Sauchiehall St/Renfield St], *Lauders*: Mainly open-plan, rectangular leatherette settees dividing off lounge-like carpeted areas, rest tiled; Harry Lauder prints, fine set of stained-glass sports pictures; central horseshoe bar, friendly efficient service *(Ian Phillips)*; [Custom House Quay], *Morgans Landing*: Modern glasshouse beside the river, inside a cross between the Pompidou centre and QEII; nautical theme, comfortable seating and river views; American bar with restaurant and ice-cream parlour *(Ian Phillips)*

Gourock [Cardwell Bay; NS2477], *Cardwell*: Nice friendly pub overlooking Firth of Clyde, comfortable atmosphere in nicely decorated and well stocked bar; popular and spacious family room, wide choice of good food *(John Drummond)*

Houston [NS4166], *Fox & Hounds*: Reliable local with clean plush lounge, comfortable seats by fire, attentive bar staff, McEwans 70/- and 80/-, good choice of food (can be eaten in restaurant too); livelier bar with video juke box and pool, open all day *(Dorothy and David Young)*

Inveraray [NN0908], *Great Inn*: New — or rather restored original — name for former Argyll Arms, stately old-fashioned hotel overlooking Loch Fyne (especially spacious front conservatory), good choice of bar food and malts, well kept real ale, games in public bar, restaurant; well run, a comfortable place to stay; open all day *(W T Aird, LYM)*; [Main St E], *George*: Corridor through to chummy stripped-stone bar with tiles, flagstones, exposed joists and log fire; Tennents 80/-, good choice of whiskies, bar games, juke box, food served noon to 9pm, also restaurant; friendly service, low prices; nr GWG 180; children welcome; bedrooms *(Mr and Mrs B Yearley, LYM)*

☆ **Kilberry** [B8024; NR7164], *Kilberry*: Unassuming white-washed former post office right off the beaten track, changing choice of good interesting food using fresh ingredients (traditional Sun lunch, no food Sun evening, closed weekdays Oct-Easter;

booking suggested for evening meals); cosy inside, with friendly licensees, interesting bottled beers, and broad views, with Gigha in the distance; scenic drive here from Knapdale *(Kevin Myers, Alistair H Doran)*

☆ **Kilchrenan** [B845 7 miles S of Taynuilt; NN0222], *Taychreggan*: Civilised hotel wih nice garden running down to loch (interesting fishing), airy bar with easy chairs and banquettes around low glass-topped tables, stuffed birds and fish and good local photographs; attractively served interesting lunchtime bar food, polite efficient staff, Sun lunch in no smoking dining room, pretty inner courtyard, children welcome; closed Nov-March, comfortable bedrooms — it does really concentrate more on the hotel side *(Kevin Myers, LYM)*

☆ **Kilchrenan** [B845], *Kilchrenan Inn*: Clean and welcoming inn, bar recently fitted out in local pine, good food inc fresh fish in adjoining eating area, quiet relaxed atmosphere (no TV, darts, music or games); friendly owners, well kept Tennents 80/-, magnificent views of nearby Loch Awe *(Kevin Myers, Dr and Mrs I M Troup, C Gibney)*

Kirkmichael [NS3408], *Kirkmichael Arms*: Attractive whitewashed village inn with most helpful licensee and staff and well kept McEwans 80/-; pleasantly rambling rooms and traditional, freshly prepared bar food *(John C Baker)*

Kirkoswald [A77 — OS Sheet 77, map reference 239075; NS2407], *Kirkton Jeans*: Burns connections might be a reason for coming; plain bar, comfortable lounge with banquettes and stools, standard menu; motel bedrooms *(T Nott)*

Largs [Bath St; NS2058], *Clachan*: Open-plan, with lively atmosphere, piped music, good service, well kept Belhaven 70/- and 80/-, extensive choice of malts and lunchtime food; refurbished but has kept character *(Richard Houghton)*

☆ **Lochaweside** [B840; NN1227], *Portsonachan*: Beautifully placed lochside fishing inn with good service from smartly dressed staff, enormous log fires, loch views from restaurant and library/lounge (lunchtime bar food served here), main bar with fine choice of single malt whiskies, small fishing-minded back public bar, waterside gardens, boat hire — residents get first choice; bedrooms simple but large, light and comfortable, with abundant hot water and exceptionally good breakfasts *(I H Rorison, LYM)*

☆ **Lochgair** [NR9190], *Lochgair*: Popular and attractive bar in quiet, friendly family-run inn with notably good bar food, also restaurant; bedrooms *(Lidunka Vocadlo, W T Aird)*

Lochwinnoch [Lares Rd; NS3558], *Mossend*: Superb environment, good decor, wide range of good food, well kept Flowers Original, helpful staff; popular with families — big play area *(Anon)*

Luss [A82 about 3 miles N; NS3593],

Inverbeg: Very popular for position across rd from Loch Lomond; food served generously in busy informal lounge and restaurant, maybe Caledonian 80/-, games in simple public bar; bedrooms *(Mr and Mrs J H Adam, Ian Baillie, LYM)*

Newbigging [Dunsyre Rd; off A721 E of Carnwath; NT0136], *Nestlers*: Small family-run hotel with nice bar, very friendly staff, good choice of reasonably priced home-cooked food; bedrooms good *(Paul Southward)*

Oban [Airds Pl; NM8526], *Aulays*: Very busy, Tennents beers and very cheap basic food; five mins' walk from ferry terminus *(Ray and Gwen Jessop)*; [Stephenson St], *Lorne*: Well restored, friendly Victorian pub with tile decoration and central bar with ornate brasswork; freshly prepared food inc wild salmon, haggis, local seafood and so forth, and well kept McEwans 80/-, Theakstons and Youngers No 3 *(Kathryn Toledano)*

Old Kilpatrick [Dumbarton Rd; NS4673], *Telstar*: Notable for the very low prices of its bar food, lunchtime and early evening *(Ian Baillie)*

☆ **Port Appin** [NM9045], *Airds*: Friendly and notably well run inn with lovely shoreside position, particularly good food and charming attentive service; has been a main entry in previous editions but is now solely a hotel/restaurant — very much worth visiting; comfortable and well equipped bedrooms *(LYM)*

☆ **Tarbert** [A83 a mile S; NR8467], *Tarbert*: Pleasant little cocktail bar opening into lounge with log fire and attractive easy chairs; woodburner and old fishing photographs in small public bar; comfortable bedrooms; has been well worth knowing for good interesting food using local ingredients, but we've had no reports since its recent change of ownership *(LYM — reports on new regime please)*

☆ **Tarbert** [Harbour], *Tarbert Hotel*: Atmospheric and quaint public bar (sadly not always open) in hotel with lovely outlook over harbour; good value bar lunches and evening meals; bedrooms comfortable, with handsome breakfasts *(Gordon Smith, Jim and Becky Bryson, Penny Fraser)*

☆ **Taynuilt** [NN0030], *Station*: Carefully converted station building with lots of atmosphere and home-brewed beers — the brewhouse (open to visitors) is on the platform; Highland Heavy (OG1036), Severe (OG1058), both good if very hoppy, and HDL (OG1032); guest beers, a good range of malts and spirits and good snacks (from 75p); dogs allowed *(T and A Kucharski)*

☆ **Troon** [Troon Marina; Harbour Rd — from centre go into Temple Hill and keep bearing right; NS3230], *Lookout*: Comfortable plush and wicker-and-bentwood seats in smart first-floor bar of blocky modern building with lively sea and marina views from picture windows, and from barbecue

terrace; huge helpings of good food that for this area is quite adventurous — inc fine open sandwiches; well kept Greenmantle and Theakstons on electric pump, good espresso coffee, children welcome; open all day summer; sailing, windsurfing and waterskiing can be arranged in the marina *(Jim and Becky Bryson, John C Baker, LYM)*

Wemyss Bay [NS1969], *Wemyss Bay*: Good choice of food — not a massive menu or gourmet stuff, but much better than many in an area where moderation is the norm *(Geoffrey and Sylvia Donald)*

TAYSIDE

Almondbank [just off A85 Perth—Crieff; NO0626], *Almondbank*: Well decorated, comfortable free house with an attractive atmosphere, good service and a wide choice of reasonably priced bar and restaurant food; good garden down to River Tay *(M J Ridgway, NH)*

Alyth [Losset Rd; NO2548], *Losset*: Welcoming basic bar and comfortable lounge, good food, fine choice of whiskies, lots of locals; open all day Sun too *(Nic James)*

Bridge of Cally [NO1451], *Bridge of Cally*: Doing well under friendly new family, good food, lovely quiet riverside setting; bedrooms comfortable and well equipped *(Mr and Mrs B Yearley)*

Broughty Ferry [behind lifeboat stn; NO4630], *Ship*: Just behind the lifeboat station, bar downstairs, good choice of decent food upstairs — good friendly service, worth booking to get a nice table by the window *(Mrs N W Biggs)*

Crieff [N, signed off A85, A822; open Mar-Dec Mon-Fri till 5.30, also Apr-Oct Sat till 4; NN8562], *Glenturret Distillery*: Not a pub, but the whisky-tasting bar — which feels like a large self-service restaurant — has very good value malt whiskies, full range of other drinks, and good generously served food; terrace overlooks Scotland's oldest distillery, with good visitors' centre and guided tours *(Kathy Holt)*

Dundee [16 Victoria Rd; about 1 mile N of city centre; NO4030], *Ladywell Tavern*: No-frills small town pub with well kept McEwans 80/- and Youngers No 3, lively friendly atmosphere, sometimes crowded *(BB)*; [South Tay St, Old Hawkhill], *Tally-Ho*: Popular bar, with lots of stuffed animals; well kept Timothy Taylors Landlord and Youngers No 3, good cheap bar food *(T and A Kucharski)*

Kenmore [NN7745], *Kenmore*: Civilised and quietly old-fashioned small hotel with long landscape poem composed here written in Burns's own handwriting on residents' lounge wall, friendly, relaxed back bar with well kept Tennents 80/-, lively separate barn bar; good bar food, restaurant, Tayside gardens, good fishing; nr start GWG185; bedrooms *(Dr T H M Mackenzie, LYM)*

Kinross [2 The Muirs; NO1102], *Green*: Very wide range of bar snacks and McEwans real ales in big comfortable bar, in old coaching inn opp golf course; bedrooms *(Mr and Mrs J H Adam)*; [The Muirs], *Muir*: Recently extended and refurbished in restrained traditional manner, small plain standing bar for serious talking and drinking, second bar named for the small home still on display with captains' chairs and comfortable plain panelled decor, also lounge and supper room with banquettes; well presented individually cooked bar food, Belhaven, Caledonian, Greenmantle, Harviestown and Orkney Dark Island real ales, 20 different foreign bottled beers and some interesting British ones; lavatory for the disabled *(T Nott)*; [The Muirs], *Windlestrae*: Very comfortable open and roomy two-level cocktail bar, good freshly prepared bar food which may be served in second dining room — just as stylishly and splendidly furnished as the main one; well trained polished staff; bedrooms *(T Nott)*

☆ **Kirkton of Glenisla** [NO2160], *Glenisla*: Prettily placed 17th-century coaching inn, beautifully restored with natural unpainted wood throughout; bar with open fire, quite a few prints, happily unmatched furniture, and a raised part with stuffed birds, inc a big capercaillie; cheerful warm atmosphere — very much a local for the community; good bar suppers inc lovely Aberdeen Angus beef, McEwans 80/- and Theakstons Best; bedrooms excellent *(Robbie Pennington)*

THE ISLANDS

Arran
Kildonan [NS0231], *Breadalbane*: Shoreside family pub with spectacular coastal views from bar; two bars, family room and restaurant, and pool, darts, juke box; huge helpings of bar food, notable 3-course set meals *(John Sloboda)*

Benbecula
Creagorry [NF7948], *Creagorry*: Refurbished with very pleasant lounge in hotel, S&N beers; entertaining if rough-and-ready public bar, decent unchanging bar food with a daily special, friendly bar staff; bedrooms *(Alastair Campbell)*

Mull
Craignure [NM7136], *Craignure*: Simple and popular well looked-after pub with good service and atmosphere, good straightforward bar food, pleasant staff; handy for Oban ferry; bedrooms — a nice place to stay *(Jon Wainwright, Tessa Stuart)*
Tobermory [NM5055], *Western Isles*: Pleasantly furnished small bar in big hotel with spectacular views across the Sound; good atmosphere *(Jon Wainwright)*

Orkney
Hoy [ND2596], *Hoy*: Lovely setting on beach with seals playing around corner; good, basic and friendly, with longish opening hours for tea and coffee; plenty of good value food with simply cooked fish and shellfish; also an RSPB information centre *(Linda Sewell)*

Seil
☆ **Clachan Seil** [island linked to mainland by bridge via B844, off A816 S of Oban; NM7718], *Tigh an Truish*: L-shaped bar built of substantial timber, with woodburning stove, prints and oil paintings, piano, tartan curtains, bay windows overlooking bridge and mainland; darts, well kept McEwans 80/- and Tennents 80/-, bar food from burgers to local seafood with home-made mayonnaise, restaurant; tables outside; bedrooms *(Robbie Pennington)*

Skye
☆ **Ardvasar** [A851 towards Broadford; NG6203], *Clan Donald Centre*: Not a pub but licensed to sell alcohol and well worth knowing for its reasonably priced well presented tasty food, all cooked here; converted stable block, with candelabra and clan escutcheons, wonderful atmosphere and service; the nature trail and Clan Donald audio-visual history of the lords of the isles make for a good visit, with majestic gardens and castle ruins *(Genie and Brian Smart, P B Dowsett)*
☆ **Culnaknock** [13 miles N of Portree on Staffin rd; NG5162], *Glenview*: Attractive white-washed house in lovely position below the Old Man of Storr, notable not for decor but for excellent reasonably priced bar and evening restaurant food, home-made (inc the bread and oatcakes), with an inventive approach to traditional tastes and ingredients — anything from simple sandwiches to an elaborate game pie with pheasant, guineafowl, apricots and chestnuts, or superb local lobster; amusing landlord, good view *(Russell and Christina Jones, Mrs E M Higson, A McK)*
Edinbaine [Skye; just off A850; NG3451], *Edinbaine*: Good McEwans 80/- and well cooked, fairly priced food in well kept bar of former hunting lodge, quietly placed by stream *(E J and A E Alcock)*
Sligachan [A850 Broadford—Portree, junction with A863; NG4830], *Sligachan*: Marvellously placed simple inn, remote in central Skye, its public side greatly extended, with fast food and functional decor; plusher more sedate hotel bar with good open fire kept separate for residents; restaurant; bedrooms good value; closed winter *(Genie and Brian Smart, BB)*
Stein [closed Nov—Easter; NG2556], *Stein*: Looking up again in 1991, this little pub set so delightfully above a quiet sea inlet has an extraordinarily friendly atmosphere; clean and tidy, open fire; no real ale at the moment, but bottled Theakstons Old Peculier *(Jerry and Alison Oakes, LYM)*
Uig [NG3963], *Ferry*: Basic bar food in compact lounge with leatherette seats, dimpled copper tables, flock wallpaper, piped music; bedrooms recommendable — comfortable and bright, with lovely views

over pier and loch, good breakfasts *(A McK, Jim and Becky Bryson, BB)*

South Uist

Loch Carnan [signed off A865 S of Creagorry; NF8044], *Orasay*: Marginal qualification as an entry, as you can drink only if you're resident or eating (in bar or restaurant); converted bungalow, small bar in what would have been its lounge; good food, glorious views to Loch Carnan; bedrooms *(Alastair Campbell)*

Lochboisdale [nr ferry dock; NF7919], *Lochboisdale*: Busy bar in hotel overlooking pier, with views to Barra; good generous straightforward food at reasonable prices, good decor, competent friendly staff, Tennents beers *(Alastair Campbell, John Laing)*

Pollachar [at end of road from Daliburgh; NF7414], *Pollachar*: Very basic bar dating back 450 years, with very individual owner; no bar food, but evening meals for residents; friendly atmosphere, view to Barra and Eriskay breathtaking when sun shines — well worth visit for view alone; bedrooms *(Alastair Campbell, Patrick Stapley, Richard Gibbs)*

Wales

Wales

The main entries here have had something of a spring-clean this year;
many of last year's main entries are this year being given a rest in the
Lucky Dip section at the end of the chapter, primarily because we
hear so little about them from readers. So the Dip is perhaps of even
more than usual interest here this year. It's divided into the various
counties. Lucky Dip pubs that we'd single out for special attention
(most of them inspected by us, include in Clwyd the up-and-coming
Britannia at Halkyn and Bridge at Pontblyddyn, and also the Hanmer
Arms at Hanmer, both Llanarmon DC entries, the White Lion at
Llanelian yn Rhos, Hawk & Buckle at Llannefydd and Salusbury
Arms at Tremeirchion; in Dyfed, the New Inn at Amroth, Forest
Arms at Brechfa, Sailors Safety at Dinas, Ship in Fishguard, Ferry at
Pembroke Ferry and, particularly, St Brides at Little Haven and
Salutation at Pont ar Gothi; in Glamorgan, the Black Cock near
Caerphilly, Star at Dinas Powis, Green Dragon at Llancadle,
Llangeinor Arms at Llangeinor, Plough & Harrow at Monknash and
Bush at St Hilary; in Gwynedd, the Olde Bull at Llanbedr y Cennin,
Kings Head in Llandudno and Groes at Tyn y Groes; in Powys, the
Black Lion at Derwenlas and Radnor Arms at Llowes. All these
Gwynedd and Powys recommendations are firmly underlined.
Among the main entries, pubs currently doing particularly well
include the atmospheric Black Lion at Abergorlech (lovely
countryside), the unusual Halfway Inn near Aberystwyth (new
licensees – but you can draw your own beer), the Sportsmans Arms at
Bylchau (so isolated, yet always so well and warmly patronised), the
Courthouse in Caerphilly (lovely views of the castle on the other side
of the moat), the lovely unspoilt Cresselly Arms at Cresswell Quay
(how cheap those lunchtime sandwiches are), the very popular,
civilised and friendly Bear in Crickhowell, the splendid ancient Blue
Anchor at East Aberthaw, the Walnut Tree at Llandewi Skirrid (for
its magnificent food, not cheap but a real revelation), the civilised
Glansevern Arms up in its eyrie near Llangurig, the Maenan Abbey at
Llanrwst (its new landlady is proving very popular with readers), the
Cerrigllwydion Arms at Llanynys (a surprise to find such careful
cooking – and such a nice pub – in so out-of-the-way a place), the
Griffin at Llyswen (a special favourite – outstanding welcome,
excellent food), the heartily popular good value Grapes at
Maentwrog, the We Three Loggerheads near Mold (earning a food
award this year, the Harp on its commanding hill at Old Radnor, the
Ty Coch at Porth Dinllaen (wonderful seaside position), and the
relaxed Royal Hotel in Usk (much less grand than its name implies).
New entries this year, or pubs back in the Guide after an absence and
various changes, include the aptly named Harbourmaster in
Aberaeron (good value food including local fish caught by some of its
customers), the Ty'n-y-Groes at Ganllwyd (lovely Snowdonia
position and walks), the Ty Mawr Arms with its fine garden up above
Lisvane, the Fox & Hounds at Llancarfan (nice country dining pub),

873

the Radnorshire Arms in Presteigne (picturesque timbered and panelled inn, doing well under its present friendly manager), and the Sun at Rhewl (good for families, in a nice spot near Llangollen). Prices of both food and drinks in Welsh pubs are a little lower than the English average. Please note that pubs in Dwyfor (from Porthmadog down through the Lleyn Peninsula) are not allowed to sell alcohol on Sundays and generally close then.

ABERAERON (Dyfed)   SN4462   Map 6

Harbourmaster   £

Quay Parade

The dark-panelled bar of this friendly harbourside pub has good local sea photographs as well as interesting old ones of the town, green button-back banquettes; Bass and Marstons Pedigree on handpump, also Worthington BB tapped from the cask; decent choice of wines. Interesting bar food includes sandwiches (from 90p), delicious home-made soup (£1.20), filled baked potatoes (from £1.55), very good mussels, beef pie with mushrooms or oysters, vegetable lasagne or plaice in lime sauce (all £3.50); children's menu (£1.50). Darts, pool, fruit machine, video game, trivia and juke box. In fine weather you can sit on the harbour wall and look across moored yachts and boats to a neat row of colourfully painted houses opposite. *(Recommended by Drek Patey, J Bramley, Sue Holland, Dave Webster)*

Free house   Licensee Rowland Morris   Real ale   Meals and snacks (12–2, 6(7 winter)–10)   Restaurant (summer only, not Sun lunchtime)   (0545) 570351 Children welcome till 9pm   Open 11–11 (winter 12–3.30, 7–11; maybe longer afternoon opening if trade demands)

ABERGORLECH (Dyfed)   SN5833   Map 6

Black Lion   £

B4310 (a pretty road roughly NE of Carmarthen)

Y Llow Du as it's known in this heart-of-Wales village is a 16th-century black and white pub with traditional furnishings in the atmospheric stripped-stone bar: plain oak tables and chairs, high-backed black settles facing each other across the flagstones by the woodburning stove, horsebrasses on the black beams, and some sporting prints; a pleasant restaurant extension has light-oak woodwork. Bar food includes sandwiches (from 85p), and ploughman's (from £2.20), ham and mushroom tagliatelli (£3.20), home-made steak and kidney pie (£4.95), salads such as beef (from £3.50), vegetarian chilli (£3.75), gammon steak with egg or pineapple (£4.20), prawn and mayonnaise (£4.10), seafood platter (£4.20), and daily specials such as stuffed plaice or chicken, ham and mushroom pie (£3.50); in summer there are afternoon teas with a selection of cakes made by the licensee's mother and Saturday barbecues. Well kept Felinfoel Double Dragon on handpump; cribbage, sensibly placed darts, unobtrusive piped music. The garden, across a quiet road, has picnic-set tables and white metal and plastic seats, and slopes down to the River Cothi where there's a Roman triple-arched bridge; the licensee has fishing rights and the river is good for trout, salmon and sea trout fishing. The car park is over the road, too. Remy is the jack russell and Ben the alsatian (who likes swimming in the river). This valley below the Brechfa Forest is beautiful. *(Recommended by Anne Morris, Tom Haggett, John Nash; more reports please)*

Free house   Licensee Mrs Brenda Entwhistle   Real ale   Meals and snacks (not Mon in winter, except bank hols); afternoon teas in summer   Restaurant   Talley (0558) 685271   Children in eating area   Open 11–11 (winter 12–3, 7–11)   One bedroom with two single beds; £9.50 each

nr ABERYSTWYTH (Dyfed)   SN5882 Map 6

Halfway Inn   ★

Pisgah; A4120 towards Devil's Bridge, 5 3/4 miles E of junction with A487

You're still trusted to tap your own beer from the row of half-a-dozen well kept casks in this fine pub – unless you'd prefer the barman to pull you a pint by handpump: Boddingtons, Felinfoel Double Dragon and Flowers Original are always on, plus approximately 40 different ales per year which may be self service or on handpump. Bar food includes sandwiches, a selection of liver pâtés (£2), vegetarian leek and gruyere pithivier (£3), home-made spaghetti bolognese (£5) and home-made chicken, ham and mushroom pie (£6.50). The bar has bare stone walls, beams, and flagstones, stripped deal tables and settles, and a dining room/restaurant area where tables can be reserved up to 8pm. Darts, pool and piped music (classical at lunchtimes, popular folk and country in the evenings); there may be special events such as sheep shearing contests and Welsh choirs. Outside, picnic-set tables under cocktail parasols have fine views of wooded hills and pastures; there's a play area, free overnight camping for customers, a paddock for pony-trekkers, and even free parking and picnic space for visitors – whether or not they use the pub. It gets particularly busy in summer. *(Recommended by Steve Thomas, N Doncaster, Dr M Owton, Peter Griffiths, M Joyner, Dr John Innes, F A Owens, Jenny and Brian Seller, Alison and Tony Godfrey, Jerry and Alison Oakes, G T Jones, Mr and Mrs Sumner)*

Free house   Licensees Raywood Roger and Sally Wise   Real ale   Meals and snacks all day   Restaurant   (097 084) 631   Children welcome   Open 11–11; 11–3, 6–11 weekdays in winter   Bedrooms; £17.50B/£35B

BEAUMARIS (Anglesey)   SH6076 Map 6

Olde Bulls Head   ★

Castle Street

Interestingly quaint, the rambling bar in this partly 15th-century inn has snug alcoves, low beams, low-seated settles, leather-cushioned window seats and a good open fire. There's a bloodthirsty crew of cutlasses, a rare seventeenth-century brass water clock, copper and china jugs, and even the town's oak ducking stool. Changing daily, the popular lunchtime bar food might include home-made soup (£1.70), sandwiches (from £1.45), good ploughman's (£2.95), main dishes such as ham and chive omelette (£3.95), cold poached salmon salad or braised pork with apples and cider (£4.25), grilled whole local plaice or casserole of beef with Guinness and vegetables (£4.50), and home-made puddings like spiced raisin tart (£1.60). Very well kept Bass on handpump and a good comprehensive list of over 120 wines; dominoes, draughts and chess; cheerful, friendly service. The entrance to the pretty courtyard is closed by the biggest single hinged door in Britain. *(Recommended by Maysie Thompson, P A Crossland, D A Cawley, Mrs Richards, J E Rycroft, Lord Evans of Claughton, John Heritage, RJS, J R Smylie)*

Free house   Licensee D I Robertson   Real ale   Lunchtime meals and snacks (not Sun)   Restaurant   Beaumaris (0248) 810329   Children in bar area lunchtime only   Every Thurs Beaumaris Folk Club meeting   Open 11–11; closed evening 25 Dec   Bedrooms; £38B/£63B

BETWS-Y-COED (Gwynedd)   SH7956 Map 6

Ty Gwyn   ☯   🛏

A5 just S of bridge to village

The furnishings and decorations in this welcoming little 17th-century coaching inn reflect the fact that the owners run an antique shop next door. There's an interesting clutter of unusual antique prints and bric-a-brac in the beamed lounge bar, with an ancient cooking range worked in well at one end and rugs and comfortable chintz easy chairs on its oak parquet floor. Quickly served bar food (the terms of the licence are such that you must eat or stay here) includes generous helpings of home-made soup (£1.60), sandwiches (from £1.60), pâté (£2.95), ploughman's (from £3.25), bulghur wheat and walnut casserole or lasagne (£4.75), fresh plaice, local trout, home-made curry, chilli con carne, or liver stroganoff (all £5), sirloin steak (£7.95) and whole fresh lobster in thermidor sauce (£12.95), also puddings like plum pudding with rum cream or blackberry and apple turnover (£1.95); children's menu (£1.95), highchair and toys available; Sunday lunch (£8.75); friendly, efficient service. McEwans 80/- on handpump. *(Recommended by Stephen R Holman, J Windle, D P and M E Cartwright, Steve Dark, I T and S Hughes, Frank W Gadbois, A Parsons, KC, Mr and Mrs G W Olive, I H Rorison, Mr and Mrs R C F Martin)*

Free house   Licensees Jim and Shelagh Ratcliffe   Real ale   Meals and snacks   Restaurant   Betws y Coed (0690) 710383/710787   Children welcome   Open 12–3, 7–11 (anytime for residents)   Bedrooms; £18/£35(from £52B/S)

BISHOPSTON (W Glam)   SS5789 Map 6
Joiners Arms £

50 Bishopston Rd; village signposted from B4436, on the Gower Peninsula

This warm-hearted, neatly restored local has stripped beams and stonework, fitted carved oak benches on the quarry tiles, a massive solid-fuel stove (perhaps they could light it more often), and a copper-topped stone bar counter. The spiral staircase is quite unusual and there's a white-painted lounge bar decorated with local paintings. A short choice of good value simple home-made bar food includes filled rolls (from 65p), chilli con carne (from £1.70), chicken or beef curry (from £3.10), vegetarian dishes (from £3), gammon steak with pineapple (from £3.70) and chicken kiev (from £3.90); well kept Courage Best, Directors, and John Smiths on handpump; darts, cribbage, dominoes, trivia and backgammon. *(Recommended by Steve and Carolyn Harvey, David and Sandy, Julian Proudman, BHP, M and J Back, S Watkins, Brian Horner, P D Putwain, John and Helen Thompson, David Warrellow)*

Free house   Licensees Philip and Ian Davies   Real ale   Meals and snacks (12–2.30, 6–8)   (044128) 2658   Children welcome   Nearby parking can be difficult   Open 11–11

BODFARI (Clwyd)   SJ0970 Map 6
Dinorben Arms ★

From A541 in village, follow Tremeirchion 3 signpost

Most people come to this carefully extended, popular old pub to eat. At lunchtime, bar food includes filled rolls (£1.40), home-made vegetable soup (£1.45), ploughman's (£3.40), choice of salads (£4.50), and a good value eat-as-much-as-you-like smorgasbord counter; children's menu (£2.80). Evening main courses such as fresh poached salmon (£5.45), shark steak (£5.50), gammon steak (£5.95), and steaks (from £7.85); they also do vegetarian meals. You choose starters and puddings from an attractive list in the Well Bar by a glassed-in well (which is said to have had a spell cast over it 1,300 years ago, so that crying children dunked in it are supposed never to cry again – presumably, that depends on how long you hold them under). Upstairs, there's a carvery on Friday and Saturday evenings and an eat-as-much-as-you-like buffet on Wednesday and Thursday evenings (£8.95); Thwaites ales, over 100 whiskies, many malts, and lots of liqueur coffees; maybe piped music. The three rooms which open off its heart have old-fashioned settles and other seats, beams hung with tankards and flagons, high shelves of china, and three open fires; there's also a light and airy garden room. Outside, the carefully landscaped and prettily planted brick-floored terraces, with lots of tables, have attractive sheltered corners and charming views, and there's a grassy play area which – like the car park – is neatly sculpted into the slope of the hills. *(Recommended by Patrick Godfrey, A M Neal, Mike Tucker, Drs M and K Parier, Neil and Anita Christopher, Jim and Maggie Cowell, David and Jill Roberts; more reports please)*

Free house   Licensee Gilbert Hopwood   Real ale   Meals and snacks (12–3, 6–10.15, Sun lunchtime only smorgasbord)   One no smoking ground floor restaurant (not Sun evening), and 3 other partial no smoking eating rooms   Bodfari (0745 75) 309 Children in eating area   Open 12–3.30, 6–11; closed 25 Dec

BROAD HAVEN (Dyfed)   SM8614   Map 6

Druidstone ⊘ ⇌

From village, take coast road N and bear left, keeping on for about 1 1/2 miles, then follow sign left to Druidstone Haven – after another 1/2 mile or so the hotel is a *very* sharp left turn; OS Sheet 157, map reference 862168 (marked as Druidston Villa)

We must emphasise that this does not have a pub licence; to use it, you have to eat, or stay there (or belong to their club). We keep it in the *Guide* as its unique combination of informality with a glorious coastal setting (and staggering sunsets) pleases a good many readers wanting something out of the ordinary. The unsmart but comfortable public rooms and simple but spacious bedrooms have sweeping clifftop views, and from the informal windswept garden a steep path takes you down to the long and virtually private sandy beach. A flagstoned cellar bar has a strong folk-club feel, with a motley bunch of old sofas and armchairs, and Worthington BB tapped from the cask; there is also a wide range of country wines, a good selection of organic wines and many liqueurs and malt whiskies; darts, chess, backgammon and piped music. But be prepared for random eccentricities, endearing to some, infuriating to others – the old-fashioned plumbing, leisurely service, the way dogs sometimes seem almost more in charge than humans. On the plus side, the food is generous, wholesome and often memorably inventive: bar lunches might include tomato and basil soup (£1.30) with home-baked bread, ploughman's (from £2.20), home-made terrine (£2.80), green lentil lasagne or spinach and cream cheese flan (£4.80), Somerset beef and vegetable pie (£6), curry (£6.80), Celtic baked chicken or Spanish lamb chop with yoghurt and pickled peppers (£7), and whopping puddings (from £1.80) such as Viennese apple pie, rhubarb and rose petal fool or whisky parfait. A seafood quiche turned out to be virtually all lobster, and vegetarian dishes can be imaginative; Sunday roast (about £7.50). Outside, there are all sorts of sporting possibilities, from boules through archery to far more strenuous sports. *(Recommended by Julian Proudman, Mr Junninghan; more reports please)*

Free house – club and supper licence   Licensee Jane Bell   Real ale   Meals and snacks (12.30–2.30, 7.30–10)   Restaurant (not Sun evening)   Broad Haven (0437) 781221 Children welcome   Occasional Ceilidh and jazz evenings   Open 12.30–3, 6-midnight; closed except for party bookings and club evenings Fri-Sun, Nov, 7 Jan to 9 Feb Bedrooms; £24.50/£49

BYLCHAU (Clwyd)   SH9863   Map 6

Sportsmans Arms (Tafarn yr Heliwr)

A543 3 miles S of village

Often snowed-up in winter, this spectacularly isolated 15th-century pub – the highest in Wales – has good moorland and forest views and is popular with the Welsh-speaking people from the surrounding hills. There are old-fashioned high-backed settles and other more modern seats and both a log fire and a massive woodburning stove. Big helpings of bar food include ploughman's (£3.50), home-made deep steak pie or deep chicken, ham and mushroom pie (£4.95), plaice stuffed with mushrooms and in a wine, cream and prawn sauce (£6) and 10oz sirloin steak in a blue cheese sauce (£7.95), with a weekend hot and cold buffet on summer Saturday nights; home-made puddings. It's prepared to order, so there may be a wait if the pub is busy. They do a traditional three-course lunch only on Sundays. Well kept Lees Traditional Bitter and Best Dark Mild on handpump; darts and pool. Nearby Brenig reservoir has sailing, and walks in the forests around it include archaeological trails. *(Recommended by Janet Burd, Andy and Jill Kassube, Mr and Mrs J H Adam, RJS; more reports please)*

Lees   Tenant Ioan Aled Evans   Real ale   Meals and snacks   (0745) 70214   Children in eating area   Organist and Welsh singing Sat evening   Open 11–3, 7–11; closed Mon and Tues lunchtime (and maybe other weekday lunchtimes) winter

CAERPHILLY (Mid Glam)   ST1484 Map 6
Courthouse

Cardiff Road; one-way system heading N, snugged in by National Westminster Bank – best to park before you get to it

From the tables out on the grassy terrace behind this 14th-century pub and from the light and airy modern cafe/bar at the back, there's a marvellous view of the Castle directly over its peaceful lake. The long bar has shutters and curtains on thick wooden rails for the small windows, a formidably large stone fireplace, great stone walls, rugs on ancient flagstones, pews, comfortable cloth-upholstered chairs and window seats; it has a raftered gallery at one end, immediately below its heavy stone slab roof. Bar food includes soup (£1.20), big filled rolls (lunchtime, £1.20), several starters, ploughman's (£1.95 – they make their own caerphilly, here at the pub), shepherd's pie (£3.50), steak and stout pie, lasagne, chicken breast in red wine, scampi or seafood wellington (all £3.95), also vegetarian dishes such as lasagne or nut cutlets (£3.50), and children's menu; barbecue summer weekend evenings. Well kept Courage Best and Directors, John Smiths and Theakstons Best on handpump, good coffee; fruit machine and piped pop music (even outside). *(Recommended by Julian Proudman, M E Hughes; more reports please)*

Courage   Tenant James Jenkins   Real ale   Meals and snacks (12–3, Tues-Thurs 6.30–9)   (0222) 888120   Children in restaurant   Open 11–11

CILCAIN (Clwyd)   SJ1865 Map 7
White Horse

Village signposted from A494 W of Mold; OS Sheet 116, map reference 177652

The cluster of snug rooms in this homely pub, part of a charmingly unspoilt hamlet of stone houses, is made up of a parlour by the bar with mahogany and oak settles, exposed joists in the low ochre ceiling, a snug inglenook fireplace, and a shelf of china and copper, and a room on the right with Lloyd Loom chairs, old local photographs and a goldfish tank. Beyond a further little room with a piano (and a grandfather clock awaiting repair), there's one more conventionally furnished with tables and chairs. A separate quarry-tiled bar at the back allows dogs. Home-made food includes filled rolls (from £1), ploughman's (£2.90), omelettes (from £3), steak and kidney pie, curries or home-baked ham (£4.30), ham and eggs (£5.40) and 8oz rump steak (£7.15), also specials such as home-made chicken and herb pie, vegetarian chilli or pasta with celery and mushrooms in basil sauce, and puddings like home-made raspberry pie with fresh cream (£1.85). Well kept Ansells, Bass, Ind Coope Burton, Marstons Pedigree, and Sam Powells Bitter on handpump; Addlestones cider, decent choice of wines; darts, dominoes, cribbage and fruit machine. There are picnic-table sets at the side, with an attractively naive inn-sign in front of the creeper-covered flower-decked building. *(Recommended by Jenny and Brian Seller, Mr and Mrs J H Adam, P D Putwain, KC, Tony and Lynne Stark, L M Miall, I H Rorison; more reports please)*

Free house   Licensee Peter Jeory   Real ale   Meals and snacks (till 10 Fri/Sat)   (0352) 740142   Open 12–3.30(4 Sat), 7–11

CILGERRAN (Dyfed)   SN1943 Map 6
Pendre

Village signposted from A478

As the pub's Welsh name implies, this is the top end of the village; the other leads down to the River Teifi, with a romantic ruined castle on a crag nearby, where coracle races are held on the Saturday before the August Bank Holiday. The massive-walled medieval pub has armchairs and antique high-backed settles on the broad flagstones and good value bar food: home-made pâté (£1.50), filled rolls (from £1.50), filled baked potatoes (£2), vegetable and cheese crumble (£3.75 lunchtime, £4.75 evening), home-made steak and kidney pie (£3.95 lunchtime, £4.95 evening), beef or chicken curry with bhajee (£4.50), local trout or dressed crab (£4.95) and steak (£6.95, evening only); filled rolls only Sunday lunchtime. Bass and Worthington BB on handpump, friendly service. The public bar has a juke box, darts, pool, and a fruit machine. There are seats outside, with an enclosed play area for small children. Nearby is a good local wildlife park. *(Recommended by Lynne Sheridan, Bob West, Jenny and Brian Seller; more reports please)*

Free house   Licensees P T and M O McGovern   Real ale   Meals and snacks (12–2.30, 6.30–8.30)   Restaurant (not Sun lunchtime)   Cardigan (0239) 614223   Children welcome   Open 11.30–3.30, 6–11

COLWYN BAY (Clwyd)   SH8578   Map 6

Mountain View

Mochdre; take service-road into village off link road to A470, S from roundabout at start of new A55 dual carriageway to Conwy; OS Sheet 116, map reference 825785

A bit like a comfortable clubhouse, this neatly kept, extensive pub spreads through several carpeted areas with plush seats, arched dividing walls, a no smoking area, quite a few houseplants (and bright window-boxes in the large windows), and big pictures of Conwy Castle and, by the entry, the Aberglaslyn Pass. Bar food includes good soup (£1.05), sandwiches (from £2.25), steak and kidney pie (£3.95), curry (£4.35), salmon and broccoli crêpes (£4.95), fresh fish such as local plaice (from £4.85) and steaks (from £7.95), children's menu (about £2.25), also lovely puddings like steamed sponge pudding and fruit crumble (from £1.65). Well kept Burtonwood on handpump; quite a few malt whiskies; darts, pool, dominoes, fruit machine, juke box and unobtrusive piped music (in the lounge). *(Recommended by KC, David and Jill Roberts; more reports please)*

Burtonwood   Manager W M Phillips   Real ale   Meals and snacks (not 25 or 26 Dec)   Restaurant (not Sun evening)   (0492) 544724   Children in eating area   Open 11–11; closed evening 25 Dec

CRESSWELL QUAY (Dyfed)   SN0406   Map 6

Cresselly Arms £

Village signposted from A4075

One reader was delighted to find this lovely old creeper-covered pub just as it had been on a visit 20 years before. Two communicating rooms with red-and-black flooring tiles have a jaunty, friendly atmosphere, built-in wall benches, kitchen chairs and simple tables, a high beam-and-plank ceiling hung with lots of pictorial china, an open fire in one room and a working Aga in another. A third red-carpeted room is more conventionally furnished, with red-cushioned mates' chairs around neat tables. Well kept and attractively priced Hancocks HB is tapped straight from the cask into glass jugs; bar food is limited to sandwiches (from 60p); friendly service, fruit machine and dominoes. Outside, picnic-table sets look out over the beautiful creek and if the tides are right, you can get here by boat. *(Recommended by T Price, Ian Phillips, Julian Proudman, Jed and Virginia Brown, W Bailey)*

Free house   Licensees Maurice and Janet Cole   Real ale   Sandwiches (11–3, not Sun)   (0646) 651210   Open 11–3.30, 5–11

CRICKHOWELL (Powys)   SO2118   Map 6

Bear ★ ⊘ ⊯

Brecon Road; A40

Very civilised and friendly, this popular old coaching inn has a window seat that looks down on the market square and lots of antiques in the heavily beamed lounge, including a fine oak dresser filled with pewter and brass, a longcase clock and interesting prints. Lots of little plush-seated bentwood armchairs, handsome cushioned antique settles and, up by the great roaring log fire, a big sofa and leather easy chairs are spread among the rugs on the oak parquet floor. Snacks range from substantial sandwiches (from £1.40) and home-made soup (£1.75), through pâté such as chicken liver and pink peppercorn pâté (£2.50) and ploughman's (from £2.75), dahl popovers or laverbread and bacon pancake with saffron sauce (£2.95), to avocado pear with prawns and smoked salmon (£4.25); main dishes include omelettes (£3.95), fresh salmon fishcakes (£4.95), parsnip and cashew nut bake or aubergine gallette (£5.25), Elizabethan pork cooked in cider with fruit and spices (£6.50), white fish poached in lobster sauce with orange, ginger and mustard seeds (£6.95) and 14oz rib steak (£8.95); lovely puddings; efficient, helpful service. Bar food is served willingly until much later in the evening than usual for Wales. There are three restaurants, two serving an à la carte menu with main courses that concentrate on Welsh produce (at about £11), and the other, a bistro, serving a cheaper range of French and English dishes such as home-made steak and kidney pie (£5.95) or fresh salmon (£6.50). Well kept Bass, Ruddles County and Best and Websters Yorkshire on handpump; malt whiskies and vintage and late-bottled ports, with some hops tucked in amongst the bottles. The back bedrooms – particularly in the new block – are the most highly recommended. The window boxes are pretty in summer. *(Recommended by Julian Proudman, Jonathan and Polly, Tessa Stuart, A D Atienza, Jed and Virginia Brown, Janet Tomalin, David and Sandy, D A Lloyd, A P Jeffreys, Gwen and Peter Andrews, Anne Morris, G D and J A Amos, R C Morgan, G R Pearson, John and Chris Simpson, Michael and Alison Sandy, Joy Heatherley, Jenny and Brian Seller, Gordon Theaker, E W G and M G Wauton, P B Dowsett, Gwynne Harper, Mrs C S Priest, Mrs D Summers)*

Free house   Licensee Mrs Judy Hindmarsh   Real ale   Meals and snacks (till 10 evening, 9.30 Sun)   Restaurant (not Sun)   Crickhowell (0873) 810408   Children in restaurant   Open 11–3, 6–11   Bedrooms; £49B/£59B

EAST ABERTHAW (South Glamorgan)   ST0367 Map 6

Blue Anchor ★

B4265

The warren of snug, mainly carpeted rooms in this thatched and creeper-covered pub dates back to 1380 and there are massive stone walls (the ones in the restaurant are three feet thick), beams and low doorways. Seats and tables are worked into a series of chatty little alcoves, there are antique oak seats built into the stripped stonework by the inglenook fire (there seem to be open fires everywhere), and the more open front bar has an old lime-ash floor; darts, fruit machine and trivia game. Brains SA, Boddingtons BB, Buckleys Best, Flowers IPA, Marstons Pedigree, Theakstons Old Peculier and Wadworths 6X are kept carefully at a controlled temperature, and served by handpump. Good value bar food includes sandwiches (from £1.50), soup (£1.60), filled jacket potatoes (from £1.75), ploughman's (£2.45), curry, cottage pie or lasagne (£3.25), home-made steak and kidney pie (£3.50), roast lamb (£3.50) and fresh salmon salad (£3.95); children's meals (£1.60). Rustic seats shelter among tubs and troughs of flowers outside, with more stone tables on a newer terrace. From here a path leads to the shingly flats of the estuary. The pub can get packed in the evenings and on summer weekends. *(Recommended by Gordon Theaker, Julian Proudman, Dr John Innes, Gwynne Harper, Steve Thomas, Gwyneth and Salvo Spadaro-Dutturi, John and Chris Simpson, Cathy Long, JMC)*

Free house   Licensee J Coleman   Real ale   Meals and snacks   Restaurant (not Sun evening)   Barry (0446) 750 329   Children in restaurant and eating area of bar   Open 11–11

GANLLWYD (Gwynedd)   SH7224   Map 4

Ty'n-y-groes

A470 S of village

From the little arched windows of the partly-panelled lounge here, there's a splendid view of the Coed y Brenin forests rising above the Mawddach valley (where the hotel has 1 1/2 miles of salmon and sea trout fishing). The walls are decorated with old maps of Wales and so forth; Boddingtons, Flowers IPA and Marstons Pedigree on handpump, and a range of malt whiskies; the choice of bar food includes home-made soup (£1.30), filled baked potatoes (from £1.50), ploughman's (from £2.80), salads (from £2.85), gammon (£4.35), steak (£6.40) and daily specials such as curry or chilli (£3.80) and steak and kidney pudding (£4.30); children's menu (from £1.05); the restaurant is no smoking; friendly service, piped music. The public bar has darts, dominoes and cribbage, there are seats in a narrow sun lounge, and white tables out by the main road. A gold mine at Gwynfynydd – which you can walk to along the river, through the Coed y Brenin forest on the opposite side of the road – dug up about £25 million worth before it closed in 1917 (it's now open again); lots of other hill and forest walks from here. This fine old Snowdonia inn is owned by the National Trust. *(Recommended by W F C Phillips, Anthony Sargent, Caroline Gant, David Evans)*

Free house   Licensees Vicky and Barrie Ruthwell   Real ale   Meals and snacks Restaurant   (034 140) 275   Children in eating area of bar   Open 11–4, 6–11, closed 3–7 in winter   Bedrooms £21B/£38B

GLASBURY (Powys)   SO1739   Map 6

Harp 🏠 £

A438 just N of village turn-off

The red-carpeted lounge in this welcoming, comfortable pub has small red-cushioned Windsor chairs around dark tables, a log fire in its stripped-stone end wall, and sensibly placed darts. The airy games bar, with pine kitchen tables on its wood floor, makes the most of the pub's position above the River Wye, with a good view from its big picture windows: pool, s-ha'penny, dominoes, cribbage and juke box. Bar food includes filled rolls and sandwiches (from 80p), burger (90p), home-made soup (£1), steak and kidney or chicken and mushroom pie (£1, with chips or baked potato £2.25), ploughman's (from £2.50), lasagne, chicken curry, hot-pot or chilli con carne (all £3.50), scampi or salads (£4), and a choice of vegetarian dishes such as vegetable curry or aubergine and mushroom lasagne (from £3.25); children's menu (£1.50), also puddings such as home-made treacle tart (from £1); excellent breakfasts; they warn of delays at busy times, though the service remains friendly. Boddingtons, Flowers Original and Robinsons Best on handpump, Rombouts coffee. At the price, the centrally heated no smoking bedrooms are a real bargain; a cot is available and children under ten are at reduced prices. There are tables out on a crazy-paved terrace, with grass sloping down to the water. *(Recommended by Jed and Virginia Brown, Margaret and Trevor Errington, Anthony Nelson-Smith, Helen and John Thompson, Brian and Anna Marsden, Owen Barder, Eleanor Grey)*

Free house   Licensees David and Lynda White   Real ale   Meals and snacks (till 10 in summer, not Dec 25)   Glasbury (0497) 847 373   Children very welcome   Open 11–3(4 Sat), 6(6.30 winter)–11; closed evening 25 Dec   Bedrooms; £18S/£28S

HAY ON WYE (Powys)   SO2342   Map 6

Old Black Lion 🏠

26 Lion St

Though this neatly kept, friendly place has the character of a 17th-century coaching inn, it actually dates back to the 13th century. The low-beamed and partly black-panelled bar serves well kept Bass and Flowers Original on handpump (the cellar's air-conditioned), as well as an extensive, good value wine list and decent coffee. The wide choice of reasonably priced, home-made food might include soup (£2), pâté with hazelnuts and whisky (£2.60), burgers (£3.10), ploughman's (from £3.20), lasagne (£4.55), a cold table (from £6.10), vegetarian dishes such as nut roast with horseradish sauce (£5.95), steaks (from £8.95), and puddings such as Tia Maria meringue (£2.85); they use fresh local ingredients; breakfasts include special menus 'for salmon fishermen' and 'for all romantics'. On a sheltered back terrace are some tables and the inn has Wye fishing rights and can arrange ponytrekking, as well as golf and the hire of a mountain bike. *(Recommended by Mrs Virginia Brown, B Jeepies, Julian Proudman, A P Jeffreys, Gwen and Peter Andrews, P D Putwain, Bernard Phillips, Mrs Robert Jones, The Revd Wills, Mrs A M Stephenson, Jamie Lyons, Ruth Harrison, Mrs M Mills, D and B Carron)*

Free house   Licensees John and Joan Collins   Real ale   Meals and snacks Restaurant   Hay-on-Wye (0497) 820841   Children in eating area of bar   Open 11–3, 6–11   Bedrooms; £16.95/£33.50(£39.90B)

KENFIG (Mid Glamorgan)   SS8383 Map 6

Prince of Wales

2 1/4 miles from M4 junction 37; A4229 towards Porthcawl, then right when dual carriageway narrows on bend, signposted Maudlam, Kenfig

Close to Kenfig Nature Reserve, this busy pub sells fishing permits during opening hours. The main bar has a splendid, old-fashioned tavern atmosphere with its small storm windows, stripped stone walls, open fire, and heavy settles and red leatherette seats around a double row of close-set cast-iron-framed tables. Well kept Adnams Broadside, Bass, Camerons Strong Arm, Felinfoel Double Dragon, Fullers London Pride and ESP, Marstons Pedigree, Morells Varsity and Wadworths 6X all on tap/gravity and Worthington BB on handpump – the best choice of ales in this area. Simple, good value, home-made bar food is quickly served: pasties, large filled baps (from 70p: the home-roasted meat is well done), faggots (from 90p), cheese and potato pie or cottage pie (£1.30), steak and onion pie (£1.40) or lasagne (£1.70) – prices don't include potatoes or vegetables; basket meals (from £1.50), lunchtime specials change every day (£3.25), fresh eggs from their own hens. Dominoes, cribbage and card games. *(Recommended by Julian Proudman, John Nash; more reports please)*

Free house   Licensee Mr Evans   Real ale   Meals and snacks (all day)   (0656) 740356   Children in separate restaurant   Spontaneous music in side room   Open 11.30–4, 6–11

LISVANE (South Glamorgan)   ST1883 Map 6

Ty Mawr Arms

From central Lisvane follow Mill Road into Graig Road, and continue into the country

The large garden of this country pub (ideal for children) has a patrolling peacock called Peaky, ducks, an aviary of budgies and finches and splendid views over Cardiff and the Bristol Channel. Inside, there are three sizeable, plushly furnished rooms with black beams, rapiers on the walls, and open fireplaces – one with a snug panelled alcove beside it, another elaborately black and gilt. Nearly 100 different ales from all over the country have been served in the last year; scrumpy ciders and imported premium German beers; briskly served food such as sandwiches, California fries (£3), home-made curries and pies (£3.25) and steak cooked with saki (£10.95); only traditional roast Sunday lunchtime; darts, cribbage, dominoes, a couple of fruit machines and piped music. The road past the pub (which is gated) leads on to Rudry Common, and Cefn Onn country park. *(Recommended by Michael and Alison Sandy, Michael Cochrane, R J Collis, Julian Proudman)*

Free house   Licensee Michael Dovey   Real ale   Snacks (not Sunday lunchtime) and meals   Restaurant (not Sun evening)   (0222) 754456   Children welcome until 8 Live bands every Wed and Fri night in the barn   Open 12–3, 6–11 (1am Sat)

LITTLE HAVEN (Dyfed)   SM8512   Map 6
Swan

There are lovely views across the broad and sandy hill-sheltered cove from seats in the bay window here or from the sea wall outside – just the right height for sitting on. The walls of the two communicating rooms inside – partly stripped back to the original stonework – are decorated with old prints, and there are comfortable high-backed settles and Windsor chairs, and a winter open fire. Bar food includes soup (£1.25), sandwiches (£1.25), ploughman's (£2.50), pâté (£2.50), local grilled mussels (£3.25), crab and mayonnaise bake (£3.50), sardine, spinach and egg bake (£3.95), chicken curry (£3.95), ham salad (£4.25), prawns in garlic mousse (£4.95), locally smoked salmon (£5.25) or fresh local crab (£5.25), and a selection of home-made puddings (£1.50); Felinfoel Double Dragon and Worthington BB on handpump from the heavily panelled bar counter. This is one of the prettiest coastal villages in west Wales. *(Recommended by Barbara and Norman Wells, Julian Proudman, Barry and Anne)*

James Williams (who no longer brew)   Tenants Glyn and Beryl Davies   Real ale Lunchtime meals and snacks   Tiny restaurant; closed Sunday evenings in winter Broad Haven (0437) 781256   Children garden only   Open 11–3, 6–11

nr LLANBERIS (Gwynedd)   SH5860   Map 6
Pen-y-Gwryd

Nant Gwynant; at junction of A498 and A4086, ie across mountains from Llanberis – OS Sheet 115, map reference 660558

A great favourite among mountaineers for generations, this inn, isolated high in the mountains of Snowdonia, has a rugged slate-floored climbers' bar, like a log-cabin, which doubles as a mountain rescue post, a smaller room with a collection of boots that have done famous climbs, and a cosy panelled smoke room with more climbing mementoes and equipment. The team that climbed Everest first in 1953, like many other mountaineers, used the inn as a training base, leaving their signatures scrawled on the ceiling. There's also a hatch where you order bar food, and the dining room where residents sit down together for the hearty and promptly served evening meal (check on the time when you book); clean and sensible rather than luxurious bedrooms. At lunchtime, there are good robust helpings of home-made food such as sandwiches, ploughman's using home-baked French bread (£1.80), quiche lorraine (£2), cold meat or pâté salad or a home-made pie of the day (£2.50). They serve Bass and sherry from their own solera in Puerto Santa Maria; darts, pool, bar billiards and shove-ha'penny for residents (who have a charmingly furnished, panelled sitting room too). The Edwardian bath and shower on the first floor is well worth a look. But of course the real reason for coming here is the magnificent surrounding mount countryside – like precipitous Moel-siabod beyond the lake opposite, which you can contemplate from a snug little room with built-in wall benches and sturdy country chairs. *(Recommended by Dr John Innes, Drs G N and M G Yates, Ashley and Annabel Grey, Mr and Mrs R C F Martin; more reports please)*

Free house   Licensee Jane Pullee   Real ale   Meals and snacks (lunchtime) Restaurant (evening)   Llanberis (0286) 870 211/768   Children welcome, except residents' bar   Open 11–10.30 (11 Fri and Sat); no drinks on Suns; closed early Nov to New Year, open weekends only Jan and Feb   Bedrooms; £18.50(£23B)/£37(£46B)

LLANCARFAN (South Glamorgan)   ST0570   Map 6
Fox & Hounds

Village signposted from A4226; also reached from B4265 via Llancadle or A48 from Bonvilston

A comfortably modernised, friendly old pub in a lovely country village with a neatly kept, carpeted bar that rambles through arches in thick Tudor walls: high-backed traditional settles as well as the plush banquettes around its copper-topped cast-iron tables, and a coal fire in winter. Tasty bar food includes sandwiches (from £1, toasted £1.20), ploughman's (£2.75), salads (from £3.50), value-for-money pies (£3.50), vegetarian dishes, chicken curry or lasagne (all £3.50), gammon with pineapple (£4.25), and Sunday roasts (£3.95); summer barbecue on Saturday evenings; children's meals (£1.50) or small helpings of some adult dishes. Well kept Brains, Felinfoel Cambrian and Ruddles and regular guest beers on handpump; espresso, cappuccino and decaffeinated coffee and hot chocolate; video game, fruit machine, unobtrusive piped music. An attractive crazy-paved back terrace, beside a little stream overhung by a thicket of honeysuckle, has tables under flowering trees; the churchyard is close by. *(Recommended by Patrick and Mary McDermott, JV, Julian Proudman, Tom Evans)*

Free house   Licensee Mike Evans   Real ale   Meals and snacks (not Sun evening) Restaurant (not Sun evening)   (0446) 781297   Children in eating area   Open 11–3.30(3 in winter), 6.30–11; all day Sat

LLANDEWI SKIRRID (Gwent)   SO3416   Map 6
Walnut Tree ★ ♦
B4521

Ann and Franco Taruschio have run this stylish eating pub for over 25 years and although they like to think of themselves as a pub and people who drop in for a drink are treated kindly, there are only a couple of token bar stools and most people have come for a meal. There's an extraordinarily wide choice of excellent food – nearly 20 first courses that you might perhaps think of as snacks, such as scallops au gratin (£1.95 each) and crispy crab pancake (£5.95), and even more main dishes like panache of fish and balsam vinaigrette (£14.85), suckling pig (£16.35) and grilled langoustine (£18.95), and though prices are high for a pub, they're a good deal lower than what you'd expect to pay for similar quality in a restaurant. Particular strengths include fresh fish and shellfish, local lamb, game, home-cured meats, interesting fruity and/or herby sauces (orange with coriander has been one successful combination), prettily dressed salads, uncommon cheeses (Welsh and Italian), and the awesome range of imaginative puddings. They don't accept credit cards. The small white-walled bar has some polished settles and country chairs around the tables on its flagstones, and a log-effect gas fire. It opens into an airy and relaxed dining lounge with rush-seat Italianate chairs around gilt cast-iron-framed tables. The attractive choice of wines is particularly strong in Italian ones (they import their own); the house wines by the glass are particularly good value, as is the coffee. Service is efficient and friendly. There are a few white cast-iron tables outside in front. *(Recommended by N P Hopkins, Lynne Sheridan, Bob West, J D Cranston, Gary Melnyk, John Howdler, Frank Cummins, Mr and Mrs M Wall, Pamela and Merlyn Horswell)*

Free house   Licensee Ann Taruschio   Meals and snacks (12–2.30, 7–10)   Restaurant (not Sun)   Abergavenny (0873) 852797   Children welcome   Open 12–3, 7–12; closed Sun and Mon, 2 weeks in Feb and 4 days at Christmas

LLANDRINDOD WELLS (Powys)   SO0561   Map 6
Llanerch
Waterloo Road; from centre, head for station

From the back terrace which has tables and a summer bar and leads on to a garden (where you can play boules), there are lovely views over the Ithon Valley; also, a play area and front orchard. Inside this cheerful 16th-century pub the squarish beamed main bar has old-fashioned settles snugly divided by partly glazed partitions and a big stone fireplace that's richly decorated with copper and glass; there are more orthodox button-back banquettes in communicating lounges. Good value simple bar food such as home-made soup (£1.25), sandwiches (from £1.40), baked potatoes (from 80p), ploughman's (£2.50), omelettes (from £2.25), vegetarian pancakes (£2.75), chicken curry or chilli (£3.50), steak and kidney pie (£3.75), salads (from £3.75), mixed grill (£7.50) and steaks (from £7.50);

children's menu (from £1.50). Well kept Bass, Hancocks HB and Robinsons Best on handpump; fruit machine and trivia machine, piped music; separate pool room, with darts and dominoes; boules in summer. *(Recommended by Steve Thomas, M Joyner, Julian Proudman, A P Jeffreys, Joan and Michel Hooper-Immins, DC)*

Free house   Licensee John Leach   Real ale   Meals and snacks (12–2, 6–9) Restaurant   Llandrindod Wells (0597) 822086   Children welcome   Open 11.30–3, 6–11; winter afternoon closing 2.30   Bedrooms; £18(£22B)/£32(£40B)

nr LLANDUDNO JUNCTION   SH7883   Map 6

Queens Head ⚲

Glanwydden; heading towards Llandudno on A546 from Colwyn Bay, turn left into Llanrhos Road as you enter the Penrhyn Bay speed limit; Glanwydden is signposted as the first left turn off this

Carefully prepared, the generous helpings of good home-made food in this friendly village pub might include soup such as spinach and mushroom (£1.65), open sandwiches and rolls (from £2.35), home-made pâtés such as smoked salmon (£2.95), pizza (from £3.25), mussels sautéed in garlic butter, topped with smoked cheese (£4.45), home-made lasagne (£4.75), lovely quiches (£4.95), salads (from £4.95) or Mediterranean prawns (£7.50), with additional evening dishes like gammon steak, seafood vol au vent, noisettes of lamb with a fresh plum sauce or veal in blue cheese and port sauce (£7.50), baked salmon in filo pastry with wild fennel and white wine sauce (£8.50), 10oz rump steak (£8.95) or sirloin steak. Fish and seafood are always a good bet here, as are the puddings, a huge range, from traditional bread and butter pudding or treacle tart to more exotic orange and grand marnier trifle (£1.95). The spacious and comfortably modern lounge bar has brown plush wall banquettes and Windsor chairs around neat black tables and is partly divided by a white wall of broad arches and wrought-iron screens; there's also a little quarry-tiled public bar. Well kept Burton, Tetleys and a guest like Benskins on handpump, a decent selection of malts, and good coffee maybe served with a bowl of whipped cream; pleasant service – even when things get very busy. There are some tables out by the car park. *(Recommended by Lee Goulding, Maysie Thompson, J R Smylie, Mr and Mrs M Cockram, Mr and Mrs B Hobden, Dennis Jones, David and Jill Roberts, RJS)*

Ansells   Tenant Robert Cureton   Real ale   Meals and snacks   (0492) 546570   Open 11–3.30, 6.30–11

LLANFRYNACH (Powys)   SO0725   Map 6

White Swan

Village signposted from B4558, just off A40 E of Brecon bypass

Handy for the Abergavenny–Brecon canal, this pretty black and white pub has an unusual sheltered back terrace with stone and other tables and is attractively divided by roses and climbing shrubs; it overlooks peaceful paddocks. Inside, the relaxed lounge bar has partly stripped stone walls, plenty of well spaced tables on the flagstones, a big log fire, and rambles back into a series of softly lit alcoves. The emphasis is very much on the wide choice of food: soup (£1.95), light dishes such as ploughman's (from £3.20), lasagne or ratatouille au gratin (£3.90), and more substantial dishes such as chicken curry (£4.85), haddock and prawn pie (£5.60), beef and mushroom pie (£6.90), baked crab or Welsh-style grilled trout with bacon (£7.20) and well hung steaks (from £7.80); puddings such as sherry trifle (from £1.50). They also do children's dishes at lunchtime (£3), and more egg cooking than most pubs. Service is friendly and efficient; Brains and Flowers IPA on handpump. The churchyard is across the very quiet village lane. *(Recommended by Howard and Lynda Dix, David Evans, Mrs D Summers, I D Shaw, Mr and Mrs M Pearman, Julian Proudman, John and Ann Prince, Robert Horler, G R Pearson, Joy Heatherley, John and Chris Simpson, Jenny Cantle, Robert and Kate Hodkinson, Mrs D M Everard, DJW)*

Free house   Licensee David Bell   Real ale   Meals and snacks (until 1.30 Sun lunchtime, not Mon except bank holidays)   (0874) 86276   Children welcome   Open

12–2.30, 7(6.30 *Sat in summer*)–11; *closed Mon lunchtime (except bank holidays) and last three weeks of Jan*

LLANGATTOCK (Powys)   SO2117 Map 6

Vine Tree

A4077; village signposted from Crickhowell

The back part of the bar here is set aside as a dining area with Windsor chairs, scrubbed deal tables, and decorative plates and Highland cattle engravings on the walls. In the front part there are soft seats, some stripped stone masonry, and brass ornaments around its open fireplace. Lunchtime ploughman's comes with stilton, cheddar and brie and their own freshly made bread (from £2.75), and other bar food includes stock-pot soup (£1.25), home-made pâté (£2.35), garlic mushrooms with chilli butter (£2.40), chicken cooked in white wine sauce (£5.45), lamb chop with rosemary and garlic (£6.55), fresh salmon (£7.05) and steaks (from £7.90); lots of puddings; Sunday roast beef, pork, lamb or chicken (£3.95); their fish comes twice a week from Cornwall, and they use local meat and vegetables. Well kept Brains Bitter and Flowers Original on handpump. Tables outside under cocktail parasols give a view of the splendid medieval stone bridge over the River Usk and a short stroll takes you to our Crickhowell main entry, the Bear. *(Recommended by Pamela and Merlyn Horswell; more reports please)*

Free house   Licensee I S Lennox   Real ale   Meals and snacks (12–2.30, 6–10) Restaurant   (0873) 810514   Children welcome   Open 11–3, 6–11

nr LLANGURIG (Powys)   SN9179 Map 6

Glansevern Arms Hotel 🛏

Pant Mawr; A44 Aberystwyth Rd, 4 1/2 miles W of Llangurig; OS Sheets 135 or 136, ref 847824

Quite alone 1,050 feet up among the steep hills and forests of the upper Wye Valley, this welcoming inn has a cosy bar with an open fire, china mugs on its high beams, and cushioned antique settles and captains' chairs; the comfortable residents' lounge has a good supply of books. Besides consistently well kept Bass on handpump, the amiable landlord stocks several good malt whiskies and a well balanced wine list. Bar snacks are confined to home-made soup (£2) and sandwiches with home-baked and roasted meat (£2) or fresh cold salmon during the fishing season (£3); the seven-course dinners (must book) are excellent value; very good breakfasts for residents. *(Recommended by Miss M James, A Clack, Lord Evans, B T Smith, Curt and Lois Stevens, Steve Dark, P B Rea; more reports please)*

Free house   Licensee William Edwards   Real ale   Sandwiches (lunchtime, not Sun) Restaurant (closed Sun evening)   Llangurig (055 15) 240   Children in restaurant Open 11–2.30, 6.30–11   Bedrooms; £35B/£52.50B

LLANGYNIDR (Powys)   S01519 Map 6

Red Lion 🛏

Upper village, off B4558 (the quiet alternative to the A40 Crickhowell–Brecon)

Popular and often imaginative food in this creeper-covered 16th-century building tends to concentrate on daily specials with dishes like sandwiches (£1.25), asparagus (£2.95), ploughman's (£3.75), lamb chops with garlic (£5.95) or pork chop Wellington (£5.95) and a chicken dish named after the village (£4.75). The selection is similar to what's served in the restaurant, but often at much cheaper prices. The old-fashioned bay-windowed bar has fox-brown leather armchairs, red-plush-cushioned settles, antiques, and pictures. Well kept Bass, and a guest beer on handpump; shove-ha'penny, friendly and kindly service. Attractively decorated bedrooms, excellent breakfasts and a beautifully kept, sheltered garden. *(Recommended by Robert Horler, Robert and Kate Hodkinson, David Evans, Mrs V A*

Middlebrook, Mrs M Price, Mr and Mrs Hart, P D Putwain; more reports please – especially on the promising food)

Free house   Licensee Ellie Lloyd   Real ale   Meals and snacks (12–2, 6.30–9.30; not Mon or 24–26 Dec)   Restaurant (closed Mon and Sun evenings)   Bwlch (0874) 730223   Children in eating area only   Open 11–3, 6–11 all year   Bedrooms; £27.50(£30)/£45(£50B)

LLANGYNWYD (Mid Glamorgan)   SS8588   Map 6
Old House

From A4063 S of Maesteg follow signpost Llan 2/4 at Maesteg end of village; pub behind church

One of the oldest in Wales, this partly 12th-century, very popular pub is known locally as Yr Hen Dy. Though it's been much modernised there are comfortably traditional touches in the two thick-walled rooms of its bar – such as the high-backed black built-in settles and lots of china and brass around the huge fireplace, the shelves of bric-a-brac, and the decorative jugs hanging from the beams. Generously served, good bar food includes soup (£1.60), home-made steak and kidney pie or aubergine lasagne (£3.50), beef, ham or pork (£3.60), gammon and eggs (£5.50), fresh fish such as lemon sole (£6.50), and well hung steaks (from £8.50); children's dishes (from £1.25), puddings such as raspberry charlotte (£1.50), also daily specials; well kept Brains SA, and Flowers IPA and Original on handpump; several whiskies. An attractive conservatory extension (with twelve no smoking tables) leads on to the garden where there is a good play area; soft-ice-cream machine for children. *(Recommended by John and Helen Thompson, John and Joan Nash, Joy Heatherley; more reports please)*

Whitbreads   Tenant Mrs W E David   Real ale   Meals and snacks (till 10) Restaurant   Maesteg (0656) 733310   Children in eating area   Open 11–11 (winter 11–4, 6–11)

nr LLANRWST (Gwynedd)   SH8062   Map 6
Maenan Abbey Hotel 🛏

Maenan; A470 towards Colwyn Bay, 2 1/2 miles N

Outside this steep-gabled Victorian house with its battlemented tower, set amongst fine trees, there are plenty of tables on the terraces with more among topiary yews; a good side play area has swings and a castle. Fishing on the River Conwy and nearby lakes and rough or clay-pigeon shooting. The elegant and airy back dining lounge has a spiral-wood-column fireplace with an old-fashioned clock on the mantlepiece above it, a ceiling fan, brocaded chairs and handsome drop-leaf tables on the turkey carpet, and lots of house-plants. A spacious, welcoming bar with Windsor chairs around the tables on its oak parquet floor, tall stone-mullioned windows and Websters Choice and Yorkshire on handpump, has a decent selection of whiskies and liqueurs, and Welsh singing on Saturday night; unobtrusive piped music. Bar food includes starters such as soup (£1.25) and garlic mushrooms (£2.85), also sandwiches (from £1.25, toasted from £1.40), a wide range of ploughman's (from £3.20), main meals such as half roast Caernarfonshire chicken (£4.95), curry (£4.65), gammon steak (£5.25) and steak (£7.75); vegetarian meals, such as lasagne or mushroom and pepper stroganoff (from £3.45); children's dishes, with half portions at half prices on request; good, friendly service. Cribbage, dominoes and piped music. Bodnant Gardens are close by. *(Recommended by KC, Dave Buckley, Mike Tucker, Janet and John Towers, Sylvia and Len Henderson, RJS, Kristine and Peter Guest)*

Free house   Licensee Angela Michelmore   Real ale   Meals and snacks (12–2, 6–9.45)   Partly no-smoking restaurant   Dolgarrog (0492 69) 247/230   Children welcome (young children till 9pm)   Welsh singing Sat evening   Open 11–3, 5.30–11 Bedrooms; £40.50B/£60B

LLANTHONY (Gwent)   SO2928   Map 6

Abbey Hotel

Part of the prior's house, this is surrounded by and really part of the graceful ruins of a Norman priory founded by the Queen's chaplain and William de Lacy (who had been the warlord in charge of Hereford) in 1108. There are lawns among the lofty broken arches and beyond them the soft and tranquil Welsh border hills. The dimly-lit, vaulted crypt bar is basic and simply furnished with half-a-dozen wooden tables, spindleback chairs and wooden benches on the flagstone floor, and serves well kept Flowers Original and Ruddles County on handpump or tapped from the cask, and also Brains Dark, Boddingtons and Wadworths 6X on rotation and according to demand, and farm cider. Bar food is simple too, with good home-made soups (£2.25), toasted sandwiches (from £1.25), decent ploughman's (from £3.25), home-made meaty and vegetarian burgers (£3.50) at lunchtime and, in the evening, meals like lamb with garlic wine and mushrooms (£5.40). On *Good Walks Guide* Walk 201. *(Recommended by Carol and Richard Glover, A P Jeffreys, Julian Proudman, J Bryan, Gwen and Peter Andrews, Jed and Virginia Brown, Brian and Anna Marsden, D and B Carron, Tim Locke, Drs M and K Parier, Dr Zatouroff, D J Penny, Greg Parston)*

Free house   Licensee Ivor Prentice   Real ale   Meals and lunchtime snacks Crucorney (0873) 890487   Well behaved children welcome   Occasional live music Open 11–3, 6–11 (all day Sat and holiday periods); closed weekdays Dec-Feb except 25 Dec and New Year   Bedrooms; £20.50(Sun-Thurs)/£41(£95 for Fri and Sat for two)

LLANWNDA (Gwynedd)   SH4758   Map 6

Goat ⊘ ⇌

Village (a couple of houses or so) signposted as short loop off A499 just S of junction with A487 S of Caernarfon

Run by a friendly, Welsh-speaking landlady, this popular place has a main bar area at the back, divided into two rooms by the almost circular bar counter, with its old-fashioned small-paned rounded screen complete with serving hatch, and an ancient cash register. Visitors go for the bright red plush chairs by the coal fire on the left and the Welsh speakers seem to gravitate to the red leatherette button-back built-in wall banquettes around the four tables on the right. It's the lunchtime cold table in the room on the left which earns the food award – an excellent help-yourself cold table, with well over twenty fresh and attractive dishes laid out on crisp linen (£5 for as much as you like, including starters such as fresh melon in ginger wine and sherry-marinated grapefruit, then over half a dozen fish, several cold meats and freshly baked quiche, and five different cheeses to finish). They also do home-made soup (£1.50), particularly good sandwiches (from £2, open salmon sandwich £3.95), ploughman's (£3.25), and farmhouse grill (£6), and serve breakfasts from 8am–10am; well kept Bass and Boddingtons on handpump, twenty varieties of malt whisky and farmhouse cider; piped music. A genteel front room on the right is reserved for non-smokers. In the evenings the buffet table's stripped down to reveal a pool table, and the darts board comes into use; piped music. Tables on the sunny front terrace, another under a sycamore down in the garden. *(Recommended by Patrick Godfrey, Mr and Mrs R C F Martin, R C Morgan; more reports please)*

Free house   Licensee Mrs L Griffith   Real ale   Meals and snacks (12–2.15, not Sun) Caernarfon (0286) 830256   Children welcome   Open 11–4, 5.30(6 Sat)–11; closed Sun   Bedrooms; £15B/£30B

LLANYNYS (Clwyd)   SJ1063   Map 7

Cerrigllwydion Arms ⊘

Village signposted from A525 by Drovers Arms just out of Ruthin, and by garage in Pentre further towards Denbigh

The careful cooking in this delightfully rambling old place uses good fresh ingredients and might include pheasant in season, and food such as soup, sandwiches (weekday lunchtimes), fresh cod in batter or home-made vegetarian loaf (£4.25), chicken curry (£4.40), poached plaice in lemon sauce (£5.10), chicken breast fillet in white wine sauce (£5.50), and half a fresh duckling (£8.20), with mouth-watering puddings. Well kept Border, Buckleys Best, Marstons Pedigree and guest beers on handpump; quite a few malt whiskies, good coffee. There's a lot of character and a splendidly friendly atmosphere: seats ranging from green plush to older settles, old stonework, dark oak beams and panelling, and interesting brasses, a collection of teapots and other nick-nacks. Darts, fruit machine and piped music; efficient service. Across the quiet lane is a neat garden with teak tables among fruit trees looking across the fields to low wooded hills; the church is interesting. *(Recommended by KC, Tim Locke, Mr and Mrs J H Adam, David and Jill Roberts; more reports please)*

Free house   Licensee Steve Spicer   Real ale   Meals and snacks (Tues-Thurs till 9.30, Fri/Sat till 10; not Mon)   Restaurant   Llanynys (074 578) 247   Children in restaurant   Open 11.30–3, 7–11; closed Mon lunchtime

LLWYNDAFYDD (Dyfed)   SN3755 Map 6

Crown ⊘

Coming S from New Quay on A486, both the first two right turns eventually lead to the village; the side roads N from A487 between junctions with B4321 and A486 also come within signpost distance; OS Sheet 145, map reference 371555

At weekends – even out of season – this attractive country pub fills up very quickly so it's best to get there early if you want a seat. Popular home-made bar food includes decent lunchtime sandwiches and toasted sandwiches, as well as soup (£1.65), tasty garlic mushrooms (£2.45), specials board with local fish dishes (£3.90), steak and kidney or lamb pie (£4.75), good grilled local trout with almonds (£5.75), and steaks (from £7.75); Well kept Bass and Flowers IPA and Original. The friendly, partly stripped-stone bar has red plush button-back banquettes around its copper-topped tables, and a big woodburning stove; piped music. The pretty tree-sheltered garden has picnic-table sets on a terrace above a small pond among shrubs and flowers, with rides and a slide in a play area. The side lane leads down to a cove with caves by National Trust cliffs. *(Recommended by Jerry and Alison Oakes, Derek Patey, Sue Holland)*

Free house   Licensee Keith Soar   Real ale   Meals and snacks (12–2, 6(7 Sun)–9   Restaurant   New Quay (0545) 560396   Children in garden and eating area only   Open 12–3, 6–11; closed Sun evening Oct–March

LLYSWEN (Powys)   SO1337 Map 6

Griffin ★ ⊘ ⇌

A470, village centre

People coming to this warmly welcoming, old-fashioned inn to enjoy the exceptional bar food often end up coming back to stay – it's that sort of place. Very good sandwiches – with a choice of white or brown bread – are filled with sugar-baked ham (£1.70), prawn (£3), and thick, tender slices of salmon (fresh £3.30 or smoked £3.80); also, delicious home-made soup (£2.35), ploughman's with a wide selection of cheeses (£3.90), salads including fresh salmon and local roast chicken (from £4.85), and changing daily dishes like vegetarian chilli (£4.65), curry (£4.95), delicious mushroom and asparagus pancakes (£4.75), grilled fresh trout (£6.85), roast duck and apple sauce (£8.95) and sirloin steak (£9.75); traditional home-made puddings – their most popular being treacle tart (£2.35). Most days after Easter they serve brook trout and salmon, caught by the family or by customers in the River Wye – just over the road; very good jugged hare and other game such as pheasant in season; helpful, friendly service. Boddingtons and Flowers IPA on handpump. The Fishermen's Bar has large Windsor armchairs, leatherette wall benches and padded stools around its low tables, a big stone fireplace with a good log fire, and is decorated with old fishing tackle; at lunchtime there's extra seating in the no-smoking dining room for bar meals. Quoits, a couple of resident cats, and dogs are allowed. *(Recommended by JM, PM, P H Brown, Julian Proudman, Tessa Stuart, Jed and Virginia Brown, G R Pearson, Alan and Marlene Radford, PLC, Mrs R Heaton, Canon K Wills, Mr and Mrs Peter Crane, T R P Rudin, Jamie Lyons, Ruth Harrison, D and B Carron, Mrs M Mills, Steve Dark, Philip King, Mr and Mrs J H Adam, R C Morgan, Joan Harris, Mr Lawson, L G and D L Smith)*

Free house   Licensees Richard and Di Stockton   Real ale   Meals and snacks (not Sun evening except for residents)   Restaurant (not Sun evening)   Llyswen (0874) 754241 Children welcome   Open 11–3, 6–11 (winter 12–2.30, 7–11)   Bedrooms; £28.50B/£50B

MAENTWROG (Gwynedd)   SH6741 Map 6

Grapes ★ ⊘ ⇔ £

A496; village signposted from A470

One of the nice things about this friendly and very busy old coaching inn is that it's popular with a good cross-section of Welsh-speaking locals as well as visitors. All three bars are full of stripped pitch-pine usually salvaged from chapels – pews, settles, pillars and carvings, and good log fires – there's also one in the great hearth of the restaurant where there may be spit-roasts. Hearty helpings of wholesome, home-made bar food include lunchtime sandwiches (from 85p), notably good soup (£1.25), filled baked potatoes (from £1.75), burgers (from £3.10), fried sliced beef with mushrooms in French bread (£3.60), steak and mushroom pie or pork ribs or lasagne (£4.50), Madras curry (£5) and 10oz steaks (from £7.50), with specials running to lobster and local salmon; puddings (from £1.75), vegetarian dishes like tagliatelli or stilton and mushroom bake (from £4.10), children's helpings (£1.50), and large breakfasts. Quick, friendly service even at the busiest times, reliably well kept Bass and Theakstons XB on handpump, a decent selection of malts, and good coffee; unobtrusive piped music. Darts, dominoes and juke box in the public bar, where there's also an interesting collection of brass blowlamps. The good-sized, sheltered verandah (with a shellfish counter at one end) catches the evening sunshine and has lovely views over a pleasant back terrace and walled garden; there's a fountain on the lawn, and magnificent further views. *(Recommended by Brian and Anna Marsden, Anthony Sargent, Caroline Gant, M Joyner, Julian Proudman, Angela and David Graves, R A Corbett, John Towers, DJW, Tom Evans, Patrick Godfrey, RT, S L Hughes, C M Whitehouse, Steve Dark, A Parsons, David Evans, Mr and Mrs R C F Martin, Kate and J O'Malley, Peter Griffiths)*

Free house   Licensee Brian Tarbox   Real ale   Meals and snacks (12–2.15, 6–9.30; not 25 Dec)   Restaurant (not Sun)   Maentwrog (076 685) 208/365   Children in restaurant and patio   Open 11–11   Bedrooms; £23/(£23B)/£46B

MARIANGLAS (Anglesey)   SH5084 Map 6

Parciau Arms

B5110

The high ceiling in the inner bar area here is packed with miners' lamps and horse bits, the dark red hessian walls are hung with local colour photographs, and there's lots of brass (especially car horns), horsebrasses, a mounted jungle fowl and other bric-a-brac. The main seating area has spears, rapiers and so forth on the elaborate chimney-breast over the coal fire, antique coaching prints, comfortable rust-coloured plush built-in wall banquettes and stools around elm tables, and a big settee matching the flowery curtains. An airy family dining room with little bunches of flowers on the tables has attractive Snaffles calendar cartoons. Good value bar food includes sandwiches (from £1.40), home-made soup (£1.60), ploughman's (from £3.50), filled baked potatoes (£3.75), a choice of salads (from £4.25), a big slice of gammon with pineapple or egg (£4.80), home-made steak and kidney pie (£5.60), and 8oz sirloin steak (£8.75), puddings like apple pie or cheesecake (£1.85); good children's dishes (from £1.60), and specials such as fresh baked cod and parsley sauce or lamb chops and creamy mint sauce; also morning coffee and afternoon tea; well kept Bass, Ind Coope Burton, Marstons Pedigree and Tetleys on handpump; decent wines, good choice of malt whiskies, and friendly service. Darts, pool, shove-ha'penny, table skittles, cribbage, dominoes, fruit machine, juke box and piped music; boules area. There are picnic-table sets on a terrace, with pews and other tables under cocktail parasols in a good-sized garden; it also has a good play area including a pensioned-off tractor, a camel-slide, a climber and a children's cabin with video game. *(Recommended by Mr and Mrs B Hobden, C F Walling; more reports please)*

Free house   Licensee Philip Moore   Real ale   Meals and snacks (11.30am–9.30pm, not lunchtime 25 Dec)   (0248) 853766   Well behaved children allowed till 9pm), family cabin in garden   Occasional live entertainment   Open 11–11; closed 25 Dec evening

MOLD (Clwyd)   SJ1962   Map 7

We Three Loggerheads ✿

Loggerheads; A494 3 miles towards Ruthin

Up some steps at the back of this thriving and carefully refurbished old pub is a really spacious area with high rafters, pillars, a false ceiling holding farm machinery and carts, an attractive decor of deep greens and pinks, and comfortable green cloth banquettes set around tables in stripped-wood stalls. Down below, on the right, there are owl prints and other country pictures, stuffed birds and a stuffed fox, and lighting by pretty converted paraffin lamps. On the left a tiled-floor locals' bar has pool, dominoes, shove-ha'penny and table skittles. The arched windows came from a former colliery winding house. Good well cooked bar food includes sandwiches, spicy Greek sausages with yoghurt and mint dip (£3.45), a choice of ploughman's such as home-roast ham (£3.95), home-made chicken and mango curry or home-made steak and kidney pie with Guinness (£4.75), with a huge range of interesting daily specials such as crab and sweetcorn chowder (£1.95), spicy lamb samosas with yoghurt and mint dip (£2.95), garlicky chicken goujons in sour cream and chive dip (£3.25), Elizabethan fishcakes in curry sauce or English meat loaf in a herb crust (£5.25), and Thai spiced chicken in a coconut shell with fresh pineapple salad or Oriental prawns with sweet and sour sauce (£6.95); children's dishes and half portions available. Well kept Bass on handpump and a good selection of wines; friendly, chatty service. Loudish juke box, fruit machine and trivia machine. There are white tables and chairs on a side terrace. *(Recommended by P D Putwain, Mr and Mrs M Cockram, Mr and Mrs J H Adam, Neil and Anita Christopher, I H Rorison, KC, G T Jones, R H Martyn; more reports please)*

Bass   Manager Gary Willard   Real ale   Meals and snacks (12–2.30, 6–10; not Sun evening)   Restaurant (not Sun evening)   (035 285) 337   Children welcome   Open 12–3, 5.30–11 (Fri/Sat 12–11); closed evening 25 Dec

MONTGOMERY (Powys)   SO2296   Map 6

Cottage Inn

Pool Road; B4388 towards Welshpool, just off Newtown road

On the outer edge of this very small quiet town which has many points of historical interest – Offa's Dyke is only couple of miles away and the castle straddles the skyline, hidden from here by the wooded cliffs – this white-painted brick house has a friendly, welcoming atmosphere. Several well kept small rooms have heavy old-fashioned wooden-armed chairs, some dark marine-ply panelling, a mix of carpets, soft lighting, and a careful choice of cottagey old decorations. Good bar food, all freshly made, includes soup, several other starters from egg mayonnaise to smoked salmon, main courses like haddock, chicken, salads, chicken curry (£4.90), gammon, duck in orange sauce (£6.95), and fillet steak (£9.85); prices are lower than this at lunchtime, when they also do sandwiches (from 95p) and ploughman's (the home-made duck pâté and smoked-salmon pâté versions are good). There are plenty of puddings such as home-made apple and blackcurrant tart, and in the evenings they do some more expensive dishes such as salmon and lemon sole. Well kept Tetleys on handpump, decent wines and good coffee; unobtrusive piped music; good hospitable service. There are picnic-table sets on the neat grass behind. *(Recommended by B A Penketh, A A Worthington, B T Smith)*

Free house   Licensees Brendan and Pauline Snelson   Real ale   Meals and snacks (till 10)   Restaurant   Montgomery (0686) 668348   Children in eating area   Open 12–3, 7–11; closed Mon except bank hols

MORFA NEFYN (Gwynedd)   SH2840 Map 6

Bryncynan

Junction A497/B4412

A quiet local in winter but lively and busy in summer, this refurbished pub serves local seafood in summer, including crab and lobster, as well as home-made soup (£1.40), home-made chicken liver pâté (£2.95), clam fries with tartare sauce or whole smoked trout (£3.25), roast chicken or home-made meaty or vegetarian lasagne (all £4.75), vegetarian quiche (£4.95), gammon (£6.25), king prawns or grilled sirloin steak (£8.50); daily specials, children's dishes (£2.75) and puddings such as home-made bread and butter pudding. Service is quick and pleasant even when pushed. Well kept Tetleys and Ind Coope Burton on handpump; dominoes, shove-ha'penny, cards, fruit machine and piped music; pool and a real fire in winter; rustic seats outside. *(Recommended by Janet Bord; more reports please)*

Allied   Tenant Keith Jackson   Real ale   Meals and snacks   Restaurant (not Sun) Pwllheli (0758) 720879   Children in eating area, restaurant and garden, must be out by 9pm   Occasional live music by local entertainers   Open 11–3, 6–11 (winter 11.30–2.30, 7–11); closed Sun

NEVERN (Dyfed)   SN0840 Map 6

Trewern Arms ★ 🛏

B4582 – a useful short-cut alternative to most of the A487 Newport–Cardigan

A lot of readers find their way to this welcoming, extended pub, close to a medieval bridge crossing the River Nyfer. The most atmosphere is to be found in the stripped-stone slate-floored bar – its high rafters strung with nets, ships' lamps, ancient farm and household equipment, shepherds' crooks and cauldrons. There are a couple of high-backed traditional settles by the big log fire, as well as comfortable plush banquette seating. Generous helpings of reasonably priced bar food include sandwiches (from £1), ploughman's (£2.80), cod (£3.95), cold ham or chicken (£3.50), home-made lasagne or steak and kidney pie (£4) and steaks (from £6.95), with children's dishes (£2.50); huge breakfasts. Well kept Flowers Original, Marstons Pedigree and Wadworths 6X on handpump; friendly, efficient service. A back games room has sensibly placed darts, table skittles, pool and dominoes, there's also a fruit machine and a juke box; beyond is a more spacious lounge. The pilgrims' church over the river has a notable Celtic cross and pre-Christian stones set into its windows. The lawn has tables set among shrubs and trees. *(Recommended by Mark Savage, Barbara and Norman Wells, Hilary Roberts, Jed and Virginia Brown, Jenny and Brian Seller, Simon and Ann Ward, FG, JG, Jerry and Alison Oakes, M Badcock)*

Free house   Licensee A Jones   Real ale   Meals and snacks (12–2, 7–10) Restaurant   Newport (0239) 820395   Children welcome until 9.30   Open 11–3, 6–11 (all day in summer)   Bedrooms; £25S/£40S

NOTTAGE (Mid Glam)   SS8178 Map 6

Rose & Crown 🛏

2 miles from M4 junction 37; A4229 towards Porthcawl, then signposted Nottage, Rest Bay

This comfortable and well kept pub – just a stroll from the seaside – has the remnants of really thick stone walls dividing its bar areas. There are well made traditional-style settles and plusher seats on the flagstones or carpet, a log-effect gas fire in the huge fireplace, and in the area on the right, tables arranged more for eating: good value bar food includes sandwiches (from 95p) and a steak sandwich (£1.50), ploughman's (from £2.75), pizza (£2.95), plaice (£4), trout (£4.95) or gammon (£5.25) and steaks (from £7.40), with children's helpings (from £1.50). Well kept Ruddles Best and County and Websters on handpump; Bulmers cider; fruit machine, unobtrusive piped music, efficient service. The bedrooms are attractively decorated and equipped. *(Recommended by Jenny Cantle; more reports please)*

Chef and Brewer (Watneys)   Managers Mr and Mrs Williams   Real ale   Meals and snacks   Restaurant   Porthcawl (0656) 784850   Children in eating area and restaurant   Open 11.30–4, 6–11 (all day Sat)   Bedrooms; £43B/£56B

OGMORE (Mid Glam)   SS8674   Map 6

Pelican £

B4524

A nice old pub used by locals and people from nearby Bridgend. It does good value, very tasty bar food such as jumbo filled rolls (from £1), soup (£1.20), ploughman's (from £1.80), and a choice of home-made hot dishes like steak and onion pie, curries and chillis or salads (all £3.50), fresh fish (from £3.50), and prawns (£3.95); children's dishes (from £2). On the right in the friendly bar are some snug alcoves with pleasantly upholstered seats built into them, swagged pink curtains, harmonising carpet, curly wrought-iron wall lamps with pretty porcelain shades, and a shelf of decorative china; the left-hand part is fairly functional. Well kept Courage Best and Directors, John Smiths Yorkshire, and Wadworths 6X on handpump, and a decent selection of malt and Irish whiskies; darts and shove ha'penny. A side terrace has picnic-table sets, with swings beside it. *(Recommended by Gordon Theaker, John and Helen Thompson, Cathy Long)*

Courage   Tenant Amanda Crossland   Real ale   Meals and snacks (12–2.30, 7–9.30)   Restaurant (Wed-Sat)   Southern Down (0656) 880049   Children in restaurant   Open 11.30–4, 6.30–11; 11.30–11 Sat

OLD RADNOR (Powys)   SO2559   Map 6

Harp ★ 🛏

Village signposted from A44 Kington–New Radnor just W of B4362 junction

We hear this beautifully positioned, hilltop inn is up for sale and can only keep our fingers crossed that it remains as it has been – a very friendly local with lots of character and a lovely place to stay. The old-fashioned brownstone public bar has high-backed settles, an antique reader's chair and other elderly chairs around a log fire; they play table quoits (matches winter Mon, summer Tues), darts (Fri) and cribbage. The cosy slate-floored lounge has a handsome curved antique settle and a fine inglenook log fire, and there are lots of local books and guides for residents. Well kept Boddingtons, Woods Special and Wonderfull, and Wye Valley Hereford and Supreme on handpump or tapped from the cask. Good simple bar food might include sandwiches (from £1.30), ploughman's with stilton cut from the whole cheese (from £2.75), baked potato with prawns (£3.50), faggots (£3.75), chicken curry (£5.50 – very popular) and gammon and egg (£5.90). Evening main dishes in the snug and pretty dining room are mostly about £8. Service is first-class, and breakfasts good. There's plenty of seating outside, under the big sycamore tree, on the green by the fifteenth-century turreted church, and on the side grass (where there are plenty of rabbits as well as a play area). Four resident geese, including Hansel and Gretel, and three ducks. Lots of good walks nearby, including *Good Walks Guide* walk 93. *(Recommended by Lynn Sharpless, Bob Eardley, Kelvin Lawton, JM, PM, A P Jeffreys, L Walker, J G Quick, Drs G N and M G Yates, Ian and Wendy McCaw,*

Jerry and Alison Oakes, Helen and Wal Burns, Philip King, Alison and Tony Godfrey, Gordon and Daphne, C M Whitehouse, Heleen van der Meulen, Anny Kragt, Riet Hoekstra, R J Yates, Alan and Marlene Radford, Peter Griffiths, RJS)

Free house   Licensees Robert and Shirley Pritchard   Real ale   Meals and snacks (not Sun evening)   Restaurant (not Sun evening)   New Radnor (054 421) 655   Well behaved children welcome   Open 12–2.30, 7–11; closed Tues lunchtime   Bedrooms; £25B/£40B

nr PENARTH (S Glamorgan)   ST1871   Map 6

Captains Wife £

Beach Road, Swanbridge, which is signposted off B4267 at Penarth end of Sully

In summer, this seaside pub – opposite Sully Island – is very popular indeed though you can usually find a seat. Several separate areas include snug booths towards the back with Liberty-print-cushioned seats around tables under a glossy red plank ceiling, plush chairs and a high-backed traditional settle around an old tile-surrounded kitchen range in a cosy, low-ceilinged end, exposed stone walls, and Turkey rugs and carpets on its broad bare boards. Brains Bitter, Flowers IPA and Original, and Marstons Pedigree on handpump from the good long bar counter as well as a wide selection of wines from all over the world and various whiskies. Bar snacks include filled rolls (from 80p), ploughman's, baked potatoes, basket meals and salads. If you're hungrier then there are two restaurants attached to the pub, each with their own bar: the Mariners restaurant, and the Smugglers Haunt (reached via a minstrels' gallery); they specialise in charcoal-grilled food, though the Mariners also has lots of fish and seafood. Fruit machine and noticeable piped music. You can sit on the low sea wall in front. *(Recommended by David Shillitoe, Julian Proudman, Patrick and Mary McDermott, Greg Parston, John and Chris Simpson, Mike and Wendy Proctor)*

Free house   Licensee Mr Van Praag   Real ale   Snacks (not Sun)   Two restaurants; Smugglers Haunt open 7 days a week, Mariners closed Sun night, all Mon, and Tues morning   Penarth (0222) 530066/530600   Children welcome   Open 11.30–11 (winter 11.30–3.30, 5.30–11; 11.30–11 Sat)

PENDERYN (Powys)   SN9408   Map 6

Red Lion

From A4059 Aberdare–Brecon, turn off up hill at Lamb Inn, and keep left at T-junction; OS Sheet 160, map reference 945085

Hand-in-hand with an isolated church 950 foot up in the hills, this old stone pub has a splendid range of fourteen well kept real ales, such as Bass, Boddingtons, Brains SA, Cumbrian Premium, Everards Old Original, Exmoor Gold, Felinfoel Double Dragon, Fullers ESP, Marstons Pedigree and Wadworth 6X tapped from the barrel; also fifty malt whiskies. The connecting rooms have stripped stone walls, dark beams hung with flagons, flagstoned floors, traditional furnishings including bare antique settles, and two open fires (one in a singularly big fireplace); a pleasantly cheerful and lively atmosphere. They serve a simple range of sandwiches (70p), pies and pasties; dominoes, cribbage. Outside, sturdy seats and tables look down over the valley below, some built into the wall right on the brink of the pasture that drops away so steeply below. There are good forest walks at Cwm Taf – back down the hill, keep straight across the main road at the Lamb. *(Recommended by A P Jeffreys, Julian Proudman, David Evans; more reports please)*

Free house   Licensees Keith and Beryl James   Real ale   Snacks (may stop after 8pm if very busy)   (0685) 811914   Children in garden, not encouraged inside, side room and must leave by 9pm   Open 1–4 (12–4 Sat), 7–11; closed 25 Dec evening, 26 Dec lunchtime

PENMAENPOOL (Gwynedd)   SH6918 Map 6

George III 🛏

Just off A493, near Dolgellau

Across what used to be a shoreside railway (but is now this 17th-century inn's private drive) are the estuary and waterside meadows with wildfowl and a bird observation tower; the hotel has fishing rights. Inside, the beamed and partly panelled upstairs bar opens into a cosy lounge where armchairs face a big log fire in a stone inglenook and there's an interesting collection of George III portraits. The downstairs bar – usually busy in summer – has long green leatherette seats around plain varnished tables on the flagstones, heavy beams, and stripped stone walls; splendid view from the outside terrace here. Darts, shove-ha'penny, cribbage, dominoes, fruit machine and maybe piped classical music. Home-made lunchtime bar food includes soup (£1.20), pâté (£2.75), steak and kidney pie (£4.45), roast spare rib of pork with barbecue sauce (£4.60), smoked trout (£5.15) and grilled Scotch sirloin steak (£9); Sunday lunch (£8.80); there's simpler food, lunchtime and evening, from Easter till October in the lower bar, such as toasted sandwiches, home-made pizza (£1.90), and a self-service cold buffet. The food in the evening restaurant is imaginative. Some bedrooms are in a very comfortable award-winning conversion of what used to be an adjacent station – the railway closed years ago. There are fine walks in the forested hills around, such as up the long ridge across the nearby toll bridge. The hotel can reserve sea-fishing trips from Barmouth. *(Recommended by Brian and Anna Marsden, Susan and Nigel Siesage, John and Christine Simpson, Mrs K J Betts, Pamela and Merlyn Horswell, Roger and Judy Tame, J Windle, Rt Revd D R Feaver, DJW, W A and S Rinaldi-Butcher, RJS; more reports please)*

Free house   Licensee Gail Hall   Lunchtime meals (Nov-Easter, not Christmas and New Year fortnight), lunchtime and evening snacks Easter-Oct   Restaurant (not Sun evening)   Dolgellau (0341) 422525   Children in restaurant only at lunchtime   Open 11–3, 6–11   Bedrooms; l£43(from £63B), not Christmas and New Year fortnight

PONTYPOOL (Gwent)   ST2998 Map 6

Open Hearth

The Wern, Griffithstown; Griffithstown signposted off A4051 S – opposite British Steel main entrance turn up hill, then first right

Some readers feel this is the best pub in a ten-mile radius and its changing range of real ales is certainly unique to the area: regulars like Bass, Batemans XB, Brains SA, Courage BB, Exmoor, Felinfoel, Fullers London Pride and Morrells Varsity on handpump and also several guest beers from a range of about 50. The smallish lounge bar looks out on a disused stretch of the Monmouthshire & Brecon Canal which runs above the pub and is comfortably modernised in red and grey plush, with a Turkey carpet and big stone fireplace; a back bar has more space and leatherette seating. Reliably good value bar food includes soup (£1.25), garlic mushrooms (£2.25), chicken liver pâté (£2.35), filled baked potatoes (from £2.65), ploughman's (£3.35), salads (from £4), home-cooked ham (£4.20), plaice or popular chicken curries (£4.50, bahjees and so forth extra), vegetarian dishes like courgette and bean bake or vegetable stroganoff (from £4.60), steak, stout and mushroom pie (£5.10), gammon and egg (£5.50) and rump steak (£7); they do their best to suit you if you want something not on the menu, and the downstairs restaurant is something of a local landmark; decent coffee, cheap tea, friendly and efficient service. Cribbage, dominoes, fruit machine and piped music. There are picnic-table sets, boules and swings among shrubs outside. *(Recommended by Pamela and Merlyn Horswell, J M Fletcher, M E Hughes; more reports please)*

Free house   Licensee Glyn Morgan   Real ale   Meals and snacks (till 10)   Restaurant (not Sun evening)   Pontypool (0495) 763752   Children in restaurant   Open 11.30–3(4 Sat), 6–11

PORTH DINLLAEN (Gwynedd) Map 6

Ty Coch £

Beach car park (fee) signposted from Morfa Nefyn; 15-minute walk along beach or over golf links

A small cluster of houses a mile from the nearest public road includes this white-painted house with its dark red facade (hence its name – the red house). The position is idyllic: right on a curve of shallowly shelving beach backed by low grassy hills and the sand-cliffs where the martins nest and overlooking an expanse of water, boats anchored in the foreground, to the shadowy but dramatic hills across the sparkling bay. Inside, the walls and 17th-century beams are hung every inch with pewter old miners' and railway lamps, copper utensils, ale-yard, lanterns, small fishing nets, riding lights, navigation lamps, lots of RNLI photographs and memorabilia, and there are ships in bottles, a working barometer and a Caernarfon grandfather clock. Furnishings are simple, service particularly cheerful, and lunchtime bar food includes filled rolls (from 95p), filled baked potatoes (from £1.60), ploughman's with three cheeses, garlic mussels, and meat or quiche salads from a cold display (all £3.50); decent coffee, a coal fire at each end. There are tables outside. *(Recommended by N P Cox, Andrew Morrissey; more reports please)*

Free house   Licensee Mrs B S Webley   Lunchtime snacks   Pwllheli (0758) 720498 Well behaved children welcome   Open 11ish–10.30; open 12–4 Sun July and Aug only – but no alcohol that day; closed end Oct–mid-March except 25 Dec and 1 Jan (if not Sundays)   Nearby holiday cottages

PRESTEIGNE (Powys)   SO3265 Map 6

Radnorshire Arms ⇐

High Street; B4355 N of centre

Though this picturesque, rambling and timbered THF inn was licensed in 1792, it was actually built some 150 years before by the brother of one of the men who signed Charles I's death warrant, and renovations have turned up secret passages and priest's holes – one priest's diary shows that he was walled up here for two whole years. The lounge bar, like the residents' lounge, has venerable dark oak panelling, and latticed windows, elegantly moulded black oak beams decorated with horsebrasses; its furnishings are discreetly modern. A good range of reasonably priced bar food includes home-made soup (£1.35), sandwiches (from £1.35), ploughman's (£3.10), sausage and mash (£3.60) or home-baked ham salad (£3.85), daily specials such as home-made lasagne (£3.95), pork in calvados sauce or seafood crumble (£4.25), and puddings like treacle pudding or bread and butter pudding (£1.60); children's helpings (about £1.60). Bass and Courage Best on handpump, English wines by the glass, and polite, attentive service; separate no smoking restaurant. Cribbage, dominoes and trivia in winter. There are some well-spaced tables on the sheltered flower-bordered lawn, which used to be a bowling green. *(Recommended by David Williams, A P Jeffreys, Derek and Margaret Wood)*

Free house (THF)   Manager Aidan Tracey   Real ale   Meals and snacks (12–2, 6–9) Restaurant   Presteigne (0544) 267406   Children in eating area and restaurant   Open 11–11   Bedrooms; £49B/£98B – rate inc dinner, staying at least 2 nights

RED WHARF BAY (Anglesey)   SH5281 Map 6

Ship

Village signposted off B5025 N of Pentraeth

Old blue benches against the outside white wall of this solid, slate-roofed, 16th-century house, lots of tables under cocktail parasols on the front terrace, and more rustic tables and picnic-table sets by an ash tree on grass by the side, enjoy the marvellous coastal views here. The two big rooms on either side of the stone-built bar counter have long cushioned varnished pews built around the walls, glossily varnished cast-iron-framed tables, and quite a restrained decor including glossily varnished cast-iron-framed tables, and quite a restrained decor including toby jugs, local photographs, attractive antique foxhunting cartoons and coal fires. Enterprising changing bar food includes sandwiches (from £1.65), ploughman's (£3.60), cold chicken and ham pie or cheese and onion quiche (£3.95), vegetable moussaka (£4.45), lasagne (£4.50), dressed crab (£5.30), gammon in redcurrant and pinapple sauce (£7.10) and turkey steak in creamy mushroom sauce (£7.15), also children's dishes (from £2.25); there may be delays at busy times. The well kept Tetleys Mild and Bitter, and Marstons Pedigree are drawn by handpump with a tight spray to give a northern-style creamy head; a wider choice of wines than usual for the area. Pool, darts and video game in the back room, and a family room; piped music. *(Recommended by Mr and Mrs B Hobden, P A Crossland, D A Cawley, C F Walling; more reports please)*

Free house   Licensee Andrew Kenneally   Real ale   Meals and snacks (not Mon evenings in winter)   No smoking restaurant (some Fri/Sat evenings)   (0248) 852568 Children in family room   Open 11–11 July-Sept (winter 11–3.30, 7–11)

RHEWL (Clwyd)   SJ1744   Map 6
Sun

Off A5 W of Llangollen

This ancient little slate-roofed white village cottage houses a warmly friendly family pub – as they say, they like children who behave well, hate the ones who stand on the pool table (in the detached games room) and trample the roses in the pretty back garden, where there are tables on a terrace. The small black-beamed lounge on the left, with a piano, has a couple of bird pictures, some framed old postcards and so forth, and brasses on the mantlebeam of the fireplace – the old woodburning stove is lit on winter weekends. An old-fashioned hatch serves its back part; a proper counter serves the bar area on the right. Simple good value food includes sandwiches (from £1), ploughman's or burger (£2.95), quiche or salads (from £3.45), plaice, haddock, lasagne, chicken curry or beef in beer pie (all £3.95), trout or braised steak in red wine sauce (£4.75), and steaks (£6.95); well kept Felinfoel on handpump, a good choice of wines and malt whiskies; maybe unobtrusive piped music. The games room has darts, pool, cribbage, dominoes, fruit machine and juke box. The friendly licensees have been in the trade for only a few years, but are certainly making their mark. This is of course a fine walking area, and the garden gives relaxing views of the wooded hills above the Dee. *(Recommended by Mr and Mrs R C F Martin, Brian and Anna Marsden, Mr and Mrs Beugge, Andy and Jill Kassube)*

Free house   Licensee Janet Owens   Real ale   Meals and snacks (till 10, supper licence till midnight)   Llangollen (0978) 861043   Children in dining room   Open 12–3, 6–11

TALYBONT-ON-USK (Powys)   SO1122   Map 6
Star

B4558

It's the wide choice of regularly changing real ales and ciders – unique for the area – that draws people to this unpretentious, old-fashioned pub. The list chalked up by the central servery runs to a dozen, such as Felinfoel, Hook Norton, Marstons Pedigree, Robinsons Best and Wadworths 6X and some that are rare around here, with two or three farm ciders such as Wilkin's on handpump too. Several plainly furnished rooms – unashamedly stronger on character than on creature comforts – radiate from this heart, including a brightly lit games area with darts, pool table and fruit machine; also cribbage, juke box, table skittles and cosy winter fires. Bar food includes filled rolls (80p), soup (£1.50), ploughman's (£2.50), giant sausage (£2.50), home-made lasagne (£4.50), chicken in leek and stilton sauce (£5.50), speciality pies such as chicken, tarragon and orange (£6.50) and steak (£7.50); fish dishes such as fresh trout (from £5.30), vegetarian dishes such as cashew and parsnip roast (from £5.50) and also a separate Indian menu with dishes such as chicken tikka masala. You can sit outside at picnic tables with parasols in the sizeable tree-ringed garden, and the village, with both the Usk and the Monmouth & Brecon Canal running through, is surrounded by the Brecon Beacons national park. *(Recommended by A P Jeffreys, Gwynne Harper, Rob and Gill Weeks, Julian Proudman, Paul Evans; more reports please)*

Free house　Licensee Mrs Joan Coakham　Real ale　Meals and snacks (12–2.15, 6.30–9.45)　(087 487) 635　Children welcome　Live blues Wed, jazz Thurs 8.30 Open 11–3, 6–11 (all day Sat); winter lunchtime opening 12

USK (Gwent)　SO3801　Map 6

Royal

New Market Street (off A472 by Usk bridge)

A splendidly relaxed and atmospheric Georgian country-town inn with a good mix of chatty locals and visitors. The left-hand room of the open-plan bar is the nicest, with a homely mix of tables and chairs, cream-tiled kitchen range flush with the pale ochre back wall, mirrored sideboard, a rug on neat slate flagstones, plates and old pictures on the walls, china cabinets, and tall longcase clock. Generous helpings of good value bar food include chilli con carne or vegetable chilli, salads such as fresh salmon or quiche, half a fresh roast chicken, fisherman's platter or steak and onion pie (all from £4.95), grilled ranbow trout fillets with almonds (from £5.95), grilled lamb chops or beef in red wine (£6.50) and steaks (from £8.50); there are also lots of cheaper lunchtime specials such as burgers, pasties or sausage with egg and chips, home-made steak or ham and chicken pie, apple and brie quiche, boiled ham, haddock or very good lasagne (from £3.75), and fresh salmon salad or 10oz sirloin steak; get there early for Sunday lunch. Particularly well kept Bass, Felinfoel and Hancocks HB on handpump, farm cider, decent wines; open fires, darts, cribbage and dominoes, unobtrusive piped radio. There are some seats out in front, facing a cedar. *(Recommended by Julian Proudman, Graham and Glenis Watkins, Andrew and Helen Hole; more reports please)*

Free house　Licensees Sylvia Casey and Anthony Lyons　Real ale　Meals and snacks (not Sun evening)　(02913) 2931　Children in eating area　Open 11–3, 6–11

Lucky Dip

Besides the fully inspected pubs, you might like to try these Lucky Dips recommended to us and described by readers (if you do, please send us reports): ANGLESEY

Beaumaris [SH6076], *Bishopsgate*: No longer doing bar food, but readers have still been glad to find this hotel for its good cooking and comfortable bedrooms *(I T Parry)*; *[Castle St]*, *Bulkeley Arms*: Quiet pub with good food and good service; bedrooms *(J and D Coates)*; *Liverpool Arms*: Comfortable and friendly, with good fresh bar food *(Dr and Mrs J R C Wallace)* **Menai Bridge** [Glyngarth; A545, half way towards Beaumaris; SH5572], *Gazelle*: Outstanding waterside situation looking across to Snowdonia, steep and aromatic sub-tropical garden behind, lively main bar and smaller rooms off popular with yachtsmen, bar food and restaurants, well kept Robinsons Best and Mild, helpful staff; children allowed away from serving bar; bedrooms *(LYM)*; *[by Menai Straits]*, *Liverpool Arms*: On banks of the Straits with good atmosphere, low beams, and delicious, good value food, all home-made, at reasonable prices; friendly landlord, well kept Greenalls Original *(Mrs G M Roberts, W Dennis Dickinson)* **Trearddur Bay** [London Rd; SH2579],

Beach: Good food, comfortable bedrooms *(T Hutton)* **Valley** [Roscolyn; SH2979], *White Eagle*: Down a narrow country lane half a mile from small sandy bay; recently extended, with particularly good bar food; good choice of real ales *(Eric J Locker)*

CLWYD

Afon Wen [SJ1372], *Pwll Gwyn*: Beamed Tudor pub, attractive and cheerful, with good food and comfortable bedrooms *(Sylvia and Len Henderson)* **Babell** [SJ1674], *Black Lion*: Short but interesting choice of good food, attractive table settings; piped music *(KC)* **Bangor is y Coed** [off A525; SJ3945], *Royal Oak*: By ancient bridge over River Dee, in village now by-passed; very popular, low-beamed pub with wide choice of bar meals, Bass and Stones on handpump; nice terrace *(P Corris)* **Bryneglwys** [A5104 — OS Sheet 116, map reference 149475; SJ1547], *New Inn*: Old beams with various brass instruments of torture hanging from them, well kept

Tetleys; new licensees, food on the up *(G T Jones)*

☆ **Chirk** [SJ2938], *Hand*: Civilised and plush connecting bars in clean and spacious Georgian coaching inn, limited choice of decent straightforward food inc fresh sandwiches and children's dishes from plainer buttery bar, well kept Marstons Pedigree on handpump, welcoming service, games area in public bar; bedrooms *(Chris Raisin, Dr and Mrs J R C Wallace, LYM)*

☆ **Erbistock** [village signposted off A539 W of Overton, then pub signposted; SJ3542], *Boat*: Enjoyed for its tables out in a pretty partly terraced garden sharing a sleepy bend of the River Dee with a country church — enchanting on a quiet day, though at busy times in summer cars parking and leaving are a distraction; the pub's mainly given over to food, especially in the big summer dining annexe, but there is a pleasant small flagstoned bar (used chiefly by people about to eat in the annexe or the beamed dining room, and not always open); children welcome, with half-price helpings *(Laurence Manning, D W Waterhouse, LYM)*

☆ **Halkyn** [Pentre Rd; SJ2172], *Britannia*: Traditional, partly heavily beamed pub in superb location with views across Dee Estuary and Wirrall; horsebrasses, harness, jugs, plates and bric-a-brac in cosy unspoilt lounge, separate public bar; eating area in conservatory, generous bar food from home-made soups and rhes-y-cae bread up, inc children's dishes; Lees ales under light blanket pressure, pleasant service *(Phil Putwain, Neil and Anita Christopher, P Corris, Andy and Jill Kassube)*

☆ **Hanmer** [SJ4639], *Hanmer Arms*: Bustling country inn with fine range of good reasonably priced food from sandwiches to steaks, relaxed atmosphere, well kept bar, big family dining room upstairs — good for Sun lunch; neat and attractive garden, with church nearby making a pleasant backdrop; pretty village; good sensibly priced and well equipped bedrooms in former courtyard stable block *(K H Miller, A F Bond, Alan and Sue Foulkes)*

Knolton [A528 Ellesmere—Overton; SJ3839], *Trotting Mare*: Well renovated pub popular for generous evening meals in bar and restaurant; Greenalls beers *(P Corris)*

☆ **Llanarmon D C** [SJ1633], *Hand*: Very civilised country inn in outstanding scenery, under new ownership; well run, with good value food (evening restaurant meals can be outstanding), quick friendly service, comfortable chairs and sofas, log fire; more locals seem to be coming than before; children welcome; bedrooms comfortable — a nice place to stay *(John and Jane Horn, LYM)*

☆ **Llanarmon D C**, *West Arms*: Very clean, tidy and civilised; lounge bar interestingly furnished with antique settles, sofas, even an elaborately carved confessional stall; sofas in old-fashioned entrance hall, comfortable back bar more of a meeting place for locals, log fires, good bar food, friendly quiet efficiency, peaceful atmosphere, lawn running down to River Ceiriog (fishing for residents); children welcome; bedrooms comfortable *(Janet Burd, M I and G D Winter, D A H Bossom, LYM)*

Llanarmon yn Yal [B5431; SJ1956], *Raven*: Basic country inn with well kept Burtonwood Bitter and Dark Mild, simple bar food, friendly staff and locals, pleasant seats outside — attractive village; bedrooms *(LYM)*

Llanbedr Dyffryn Clwyd [SJ1359], *Griffin*: Very pleasant surroundings, welcoming staff, unobtrusive piped music; nicely served meals; bedrooms *(KC)*

☆ **Llandegla** [SJ1952], *Crown*: Bright, friendly, welcoming and comfortable, with good set of Hogarth prints; good choice of decent straightforward bar food inc vegetarian dishes, well kept Lees real ale, popular restaurant; on Offa's Dyke path *(Neil and Anita Christopher, P J Taylor, Mr and Mrs J H Adam, KC)*

☆ **Llanelian yn Rhos** [S of Colwyn Bay; signed off A5830 (shown as B5383 on some maps) and B5381; SH8676], *White Lion*: Picturesque old place with flagstones, antique high-backed settles and big fire in traditional snug bar, broad steps up to neat and spacious dining area; bar food inc sandwiches, ploughman's, salads and a wide range of hot dishes, half-price children's helpings, well kept John Smiths, good wine list, lots of malt whiskies; dominoes, cribbage, piped music; rustic tables outside, good walking nearby; children in eating area; bedrooms *(Mr and Mrs J H Adam, LYM)*

Llanelidan [B5429 just E of village; signed off A494 S of Ruthin — OS Sheet 116, map reference 110505; SJ1150], *Leyland Arms*: One of the most charming pubs in this part of Wales, and a starred main entry in previous editions, with outstanding food, this was found closed down without warning in autumn 1990 — a great loss *(LYM)*

Llanfair Talhaiarn [off A548; SH9370], *Black Lion*: Bright, welcoming pub with well kept Robinsons and good range of bar food *(Mr and Mrs J H Adam)*

☆ **Llanferres** [A494 Mold—Ruthin; SJ1961], *Druid*: Small soberly plush lounge with attractive view over valley from bay window, some oak settles as well as plainer more modern furnishings in bigger saloon which also looks over to the hills; well run, with well kept Burtonwood Best, limited choice of good food inc vegetarian dishes, with emphasis on fresh produce, served in dining room (may be no food Sat evening if they've done a function); good walking country; bedrooms well furnished, with wide view *(KC, BB)*

Llangedwyn [B4396; SJ1924], *Green*: Country pub in beautiful spot with oak settles, good range of food in bar and evening restaurant, good wine choice; nice big garden, fishing on River Tanat *(Mrs J Gittings, Carrie Wright)*

☆ *nr* **Llangollen** [Horseshoe Pass; A542 N — extreme bottom right corner of OS Sheet 116 at overlap with OS Sheet 117, map reference 200454; SJ2242], *Britannia*: Picturesque inn based on 15th-century core, though much extended and comfortably modernised, with lovely views, generous helpings of good standard food from soup and ploughman's up (inc popular bargain OAPs' meals) in two bars and dining area done out in fairly typical modern style, Boddingtons and possibly Flowers IPA on handpump, pleasant efficient staff; gardens, window boxes and hanging baskets are a fine sight; bedrooms clean, pretty, well equipped and good value (*Mr and Mrs E H Warner, L G and D L Smith, Celia and David Watt, Brian and Anna Marsden, P A Crossland, D A Cawley*)

Llangollen [A542 N], *Jenny Jones*: Plain outside, interesting inside; courtyard-style lounge, back garden, upstairs restaurant, conventional lounge and public bar; Allied beers on handpump; parking difficult (*P Corris*); [Mill St — A539, 200 yds E of bridge (N end)], *Sarah Ponsonby Arms*: Bright Greenalls house with welcoming licensees, well kept beer, good value meals inc unusual curry; big back garden (*Joan and Michel Hooper-Immins, Chris Raisin*)

☆ **Llannefydd** [SH9871], *Hawk & Buckle*: Cleanly run and comfortably modernised hill-village inn, decent bar food inc vegetarian dishes and dining-room meals; good value bedrooms with remarkable views; bedrooms (*Maysie Thompson, LYM*)

Llanrhaeadr [just off A525 Ruthin—Denbigh; SJ0863], *Kings Head*: Recently refurbished by new owners, wide choice of good pub lunches in well furnished, attractive bar; nice village — good Jesse window in church; bedrooms (*John Taylor*)

☆ **Llansannan** [A544 Abergele—Bylchau; SH9466], *Red Lion*: Tiny old-fashioned front parlour with antique furnishings in friendly Welsh-speaking 13th-century hill-village local, other more basic bars; well kept Lees real ale, simple food inc children's dishes — they're welcome; seats in garden; bedrooms (*Andy and Jill Kassube, LYM*)

Nannerch [ST1669], *Cross Foxes*: Welcoming village local, small attractive bar and lounge, Youngers Scotch on handpump, nice fireplace (*Mr and Mrs J H Adam*)

☆ **Pontblyddyn** [A5104/A541, 3 miles SE of Mold; SJ2761], *Bridge*: Very old inn, attractively reconstructed by new licensees, keeping unspoilt feel with good log fires; good range of bar food, candlelit restaurant (good Sun lunches), five real ales inc local Plassey; good place for families, with tables on terrace, gardens by River Alyn (*Mr and Mrs J H Adam, Greenwood and Turner, P Corris*)

☆ **Pontblyddyn** [A5104, just S of A541], *New Inn*: Friendly local, plain and unpretentious, with decent food inc outstanding steak and kidney pie, well kept Watneys-related real ales, darts, juke box and two pool tables upstairs; cooper/licensee will make you a barrel in his cellar workshop (*J P Berryman*)

☆ **Tremeirchion** [off B5429 up lane towards church; SJ0873], *Salusbury Arms*: One of those immaculately civilised N Wales pubs that would be quite at home in the smartest parts of Cheshire, with thick carpet, rich upholstery, interesting bar food using local ingredients inc fish and game in season, well kept John Smiths, dominoes, cribbage, board games; very neat garden, with under-cover barbecue; restaurant (not Sun evening); children allowed if well behaved; closed Mon, except bank hols (*LYM — a shame we don't get more reports on it*)

DYFED

Aberporth [SN2551], *Headland*: Picture windows frame a lovely view of the bay, five real ales such as Bass, Buckleys, Worthington BB and so forth, and bar food; seemed to be a queue of dogs in corridor to gents'; bedrooms (*G T Jones*)

☆ **Amroth** [SN1607], *New Inn*: Lovely traditional atmosphere in three-roomed beamed bar of unspoilt 16th-century seafront pub, cushioned wooden chairs and settles, open fires, no music; upstairs lounge bar, separate games room with pool tables and machines; Felinfoel, Flowers, Pembrokeshire Benfro and Tetleys ales, wide choice of bar food inc local shellfish and children's dishes; picnic-table sets in good garden; holiday flat to let (*B S Bourne, Geoff Wilson*)

Bosherston [SR9694], *St Govans*: Straightforward friendly pub, useful for this interesting stretch of the coast — the hermit's cave-chapel overlooking the sea is worth getting to, as are the nearby lilyponds; bar food inc good fish, Courage Best and Directors and John Smiths Yorkshire on handpump, piped music, bar billiards, tables and friendly grey cat on terrace; nr start GWG190; very simple bedrooms (*Mr and Mrs K J Morris, LYM*)

☆ **Brechfa** [SN5230], *Forest Arms*: Simply renovated and spotless stonebuilt village inn with unusually big inglenook fireplace in its flagstoned bar, cushions on the stone benches built beside it and in its former bread oven, fishing plates on the great mantlebeam; generous home cooking, cheerful quick family service, well kept beer; pub has some fishing, lovely walking and wildlife countryside around, neatly furnished beamed children's room, tables in grassy garden; dogs allowed; bedrooms comfortable and good value (*Mark Savage, BB*)

Burry Port [Stepney Rd; SN4400], *George*: Comfortably plush lounge bar with good range of hot and cold food (no sandwiches), genuinely friendly service, discreet piped music; nr Pembrey Country Park and Welsh Motor Sports Centre; bedrooms splendid value, also self-catering (*John Davidson*)

☆ **Carew** [A4075, just off A477; SN0403], *Carew*: Simple welcome in traditionally furnished country pub with well kept

Worthington, snacks, friendly licensee, pleasant seats outside and play area; attractive position near river, tidal watermill and ruined Norman castle; the Celtic cross by the pub is 9th-century *(LYM)*

Carmarthen [Lammas St; SN4120], *Drovers Arms*: Very good food and beer, newly opened big back restaurant *(Greenwood and Turner)*

Cenarth [SN2641], *Three Horseshoes*: Not outstanding as far as appearance or atmosphere goes, but very close to lovely falls on the Teifi at Cenarth; usual bar food as well as vegetarian dishes, and real ales; children allowed, with own menu *(Lynne Sheridan, Bob West)*

☆ **Cross Inn** [B4337/B4577 — note this is the one at SN5465 in Dyfed; SN5465], *Rhos yr Hafod*: Friendly Welsh-speaking country pub with well kept Sam Powells BB and Marstons Pedigree on handpump, good helpings of food all week from children's dishes through lasagne to steaks, comfortable plush lounge bar, traditional public, open fires, upstairs restaurant *(Lesley Dormer, LYM)*

☆ **Cwm Gwaun** [Pontfaen; Cwm Gwaun and Pontfaen signed off B4313 E of Fishguard; SN0035], *Dyffryn Arms*: Idiosyncratic — even unique — rough-and-ready village tavern known locally as Bessie's, run by same family since 1840 and quite untouched by time — plain deal furniture, well kept Bass and Ind Coope Burton served by jug through a hatch, sandwiches, draughts-boards inlaid into tables; nr start GWG193 *(LYM)*

Dale [SM8006], *Griffin*: Pleasant pub over the road from the sea — in summer people overflow towards the sea wall; friendly atmosphere, good bar food; children welcome *(D J and P M Taylor)*

☆ **Dinas** [Pwllgwaelod; from A487 in Dinas Cross follow Bryn-henllan signpost; SN0139], *Sailors Safety*: One of the best positions in Wales, snugged down into the sand by an isolated cove below Dinas Head; scrubbed-deal tables, pews, keg seats, lively nautical decor, bright side bar with games, four well kept real ales and decent malt whiskies; bar food from sandwiches through fresh fish to steaks (something to eat all day, summer), evening restaurant; hard to beat when it's on form; children welcome *(G T Jones, Mr and Mrs Sumner, W Bailey, H K Dyson, LYM)*

Eglwyswrw [A487 Newport—Cardigan, at junction with B4332; SN1438], *Serjeants*: Antique high-backed settles in snug if basic bar with heavy black beams and capacious inglenook, Worthington BB on handpump, lounge and dining room; friendly licensees, clean and comfortable bedrooms *(LYM)*

Felingwmuchaf [SN5024], *Plough*: Consistently good bar food inc good fish and chicken Kiev; no piped music, friendly staff *(Mrs E Graham)*

☆ **Fishguard** [Lower Town; SM9537], *Ship*: Cottagey fishermen's local with well kept Worthington BB and Dark Mild tapped from the cask in nautically-decorated and dimly lit (if sometimes smoky) bar; homely bar food, welcoming licensees; stroll from old harbour; children welcome, with toys provided *(Julian Proudman, Mr and Mrs Sumner, Kelvin Lawton, LYM)*

☆ **Fishguard** [24 Main St; A487 just E of central roundabout], *Fishguard Arms*: Tiny but welcoming traditional front bar with open fire, Rugby photographs, cheap snacks and well kept Felinfoel Double Dragon, Marstons Pedigree and Worthington BB served by jug at the unusual elbow-high serving counter; traditional games and impromptu music in back room *(LYM)*

Fishguard [The Square, Upper Town], *Royal Oak*: Bigger than it looks, with good food in bar and back restaurant, Felinfoel, Tetleys and Worthington BB on handpump; military prints and pictures, played odd part in Napoleonic Wars; tables outside *(Mr and Mrs Sumner)*

Haverfordwest [Old Quay, Quay St; from A40 E, keep left after crossing river, then first left; SM9515], *Bristol Trader*: A long history but much modernised, in lovely waterside spot; friendly service, popular well priced home-made lunchtime food from sandwiches to scampi and gammon (and using some ingredients grown by the licensees); well kept Ind Coope Burton, decent malt whiskies, CD juke box; children allowed if well behaved; open all day Fri, Sat *(Richard and Ann Jenkins, Barry and Anne, LYM); [Market St]*, *Georges*: Good beer, particularly good value bar food inc many European pot meals and interesting puddings, friendly service; no dogs *(Mr and Mrs D P E Duncombe)*

Jameston [A4139; SS0599], *Swan Lake*: Well kept Bass and good food in old building with tables outside, nr spectacular Manorbier Castle *(Dave Braisted)*

Lampeter [main st; SN5748], *Black Lion Royal*: Old-fashioned coaching inn with ample wholesome food and Worthington BB in comfortable hotel bar and public bar, reasonably big and airy, other side of entry arch; bedrooms well modernised *(G T Jones); [Bridge St]*, *Kings Head*: Friendly, good atmosphere and well run, with good helpings of decent reasonably priced food, several well kept and well priced real ales inc local Pen y Brenin; well used by students; garden; reasonably priced bedrooms *(Hugh Lervy, G T Jones)*

☆ **Little Haven** [in village itself, not St Brides hamlet further W; SM8512], *St Brides*: Neat little cottagey pub with black-beamed bar, a short stroll from the sea; friendly new owners settling in well after kitchen renovation last winter, with quite a wide choice of good filling food inc local fish and seafood, and Worthington BB on handpump; interesting back well may be partly Roman; large comfortable bedrooms in annexe over rd *(Julian Proudman, A P Hudson, H K Dyson, Barbara and Norman Wells, LYM)*

☆ **Llandybie** [6 Llandeilo Rd; SN6115], *Red*

Lion: Unusually shaped spacious and comfortable bar with welcoming landlady, well kept Whitbreads-related real ales and Marstons Pedigree, wide choice of reasonably priced good generous bar food inc local salmon and fresh veg, vegetarian dishes, enormous Sun lunches; efficient service though busy, restaurant, local paintings and photographs for sale; bedrooms *(Greenwood and Turner, Elfed Jones)*

☆ **Llangranog** [SN3054], *Pentre Arms*: Good views from storm-shuttered windows of old pub on seafront of beautiful fishing village, friendly landlord, well kept Buckleys Best on handpump, well chosen jazz or classical piped music, generous bar food (not Sun — roasts then), separate bistro (which may be closed in winter), pool room; simple bedrooms *(Sue Holland, Dave Webster, Lord Evans)*

☆ **Llangranog**, *Ship*: On edge of beach in same picturesque village, basic but well organised pub with friendly atmosphere and service, interesting varied home-cooked food inc tasty vegetarian dishes and fine Sun carvery (as much as you can eat), well kept Flowers IPA and Marstons Pedigree, open fire; photogenic golden retriever, can get busy summer *(Mr and Mrs Nash, Sue Holland and Dave Webster)*

Llanwnnen [B4337 signed Temple Bar from village, on A475 W of Lampeter; SN5346], *Fish & Anchor*: Snug bar with lots of stripped pine, well kept Greenalls on handpump, reasonable food (not Sun) inc interestingly filled baked potatoes, pretty little country dining room, views from garden with good play area; has been closed Sun; children allowed till 9pm if well behaved *(R J Yates, LYM)*; [village centre; A475 Lampeter—Newcastle Emlyn], *Grannell*: Large welcoming pink pub, refurbished but with lots of local character; good choice of generous home-cooked very fresh food in bar and restaurant, real ales; good value bedrooms *(Simon and Ann Ward, M Campbell)*

Marloes [OS Sheet 157, map reference 793083; SM7908], *Lobster Pot*: Has been good family pub, open all day at least in summer, with reasonably priced simple food inc vegetarian dishes and good value children's menu; well kept Felinfoel Double Dragon on handpump, pool and darts; traditional wooden seats, stone floor; don't imagine from the name that it's by the sea — but it is by the start of GWG191 *(Lorrie and Mick Marchington; more reports on new regime please)*

Mathry [off A487 Fishguard—St Davids; SM8732], *Farmers Arms*: Lovely atmosphere in truly old-world workers' pub; collection of 50 or so framed prints from old Guinness calendars; friendly service but bar food has been limited to filled rolls *(Barbara and Norman Wells)*

Milton [A477; SN0303], *Milton Brewery*: Comfortable stone-walled ex-brewery with seats outside, popular food inc good steaks

and puddings, well kept beer *(Greenwood and Turner)*

☆ **Myddfai** [SN7730], *Plough*: Old, beautifully kept building in tranquil village, set in fine hill country; relaxed and warmly welcoming, with big log fire in corner of small cosy bar; imaginative good value food from wide choice of starters such as stuffed mussels to really tender fillet steak, inc lots of puddings such as pancakes — same menu for bar and restaurant; attentive service, games room; bedrooms cheap, clean and simple *(Chris and Robert Marshall, Lorna and Patrick Bisley)*

Newcastle Emlyn [SN3040], *Bluebell*: Small cosy pub with friendly welcome, coal fire and Watneys-related real ales *(Lynne Sheridan, Bob West)*

Newport [East St (A487 E); SN0539], *Golden Lion*: Generous helpings of food which can be very good, inc very fresh fish and superb steak, in seaside-town inn with interesting stripped-stone bar; children allowed in eating area and own bar; bedrooms good value, with huge breakfasts *(Philip King, LYM)*

Pembroke [central; SM9801], *Castle*: Dungeon-style pub with various rooms and corners — interesting themes, though can be very crowded; real ale *(Reg Nelson)*; *Moat House*: More motel/restaurant than pub, but nice setting on castle moat, with good Courage Directors; bedrooms *(Reg Nelson)*; [Main St], *Old Kings Arms*: Taste, character and real ale; bedrooms *(Reg Nelson)*; *Watermans Arms*: Local worth knowing for its fine view of castle and river; real ale *(Reg Nelson)*

Pembroke Dock [Melville St; SM9603], *Navy*: Spacious pub with promising food; pool room *(Alec Lewery, Marie Enright)*

☆ **Pembroke Ferry** [at foot of bridge over estuary; SM9603], *Ferry*: Nice riverside setting, good range of decent bar food inc imaginative but reasonably priced fresh fish dishes, with restaurant and Sun carvery (booking essential for this); busy, but service efficient and friendly, with good atmosphere and well kept Bass and Worthington BB on handpump; good housekeeping, children welcome *(Mr and Mrs D Gilmore, Julian Proudman, Paul and Margaret Baker, Dr A J and M Thomasson)*

Pen y Bryn [A478 S of Cardigan; SN1742], *Penybryn Arms*: Friendly, small pub with good value well cooked bar food *(Dave Braisted)*

Pentlepoir [A478/B4316; SN1106], *Fountains Head*: Appeal wider than the video games and children's amusements suggest, with very reasonably priced bar food, well kept Ansells and very quick, attentive staff *(Dave Braisted)*

☆ **Pont ar Gothi** [6 miles E of Carmarthen on A40 Carmarthen—Llandeilo; SN5021], *Salutation*: Friendly jumble of small rooms in atmospheric old stone inn, little changed by modern inventions like electricity, but notable for very good and generous if not cheap main dishes such as poussin, fresh crab, lobster and sewin, also good snacks and Sun lunch; quick friendly service, Felinfoel Double Dragon on handpump, restricted parking; bedrooms large, breakfasts even larger *(Anne Morris, Joan & Michel Hooper-Immins)*

☆ *nr* **Ponterwyd** [A44 nearly two miles E of village — OS Sheet 135, map reference 774817], *Dyffryn Castell*: Good value bar food in lounge bar and dining room, well kept Marstons Pedigree, John Smiths and Worthington BB in unpretentious but comfortable isolated inn dwarfed by the mountain slopes sweeping up from it; children very evidently welcome; bedrooms clean, comfortable and good value *(G T Jones, LYM)*

Pontfaen [SN0134], *Gelli Fawr*: More hotel than pub, but food in bar and restaurant of very high standard; welcoming staff, idyllic country setting nr coast; bedrooms *(Kelvin Lawton)*

Pontrhydfendigaid [B4343 Tregaron—Devils Bridge; SN7367], *Black Lion*: Simple, well run country pub with helpful locals and remarkable chef; bedrooms *(Drs G N and M G Yates)*

Porthgain [SM8132], *Sloop*: Little mid 18th-century pub full of local character — quarry-worker photographs, shipwreck maps, buoys and nets slung from ceiling; wide choice of food inc local fish, well kept Felinfoel Double Dragon and Hancocks HB on handpump, games room with pool, tables out towards harbour; busy on summer weekends; children welcome *(Lorrie and Mick Marchington)*

Red Roses [A477 Carmarthen—Pembroke, W of St Clears; SN2011], *Sporting Chance*: Not strong on character, but a useful stop — clean, cheerful, good value with good food and parking *(Ian Phillips)*

Rhosmaen [SN6424], *Plough*: Locally popular food pub, plushly comfortable picture-window dining lounge, tiled front bar, restaurant *(LYM)*

Saundersfoot [Wogan Terrace; SN1304], *Royal Oak*: Good atmosphere in comfortable lounge and dining room, wide range of good bar food from sandwiches to local crab, duck and steaks, friendly and efficient staff, well kept Bass and Worthington BB, unobtrusive piped music, separate locals' bar; nice spot just above harbour *(Joy Heatherley, Reg Nelson)*

☆ **Solva** [Main St, Lower Solva; SM8024], *Ship*: Simple, clean and cosy fishermen's pub in quaint street of attractive coastal village, interesting low-beamed bar with lots of old photographs, interesting nautical artefacts and a very miscellaneous hotch-potch of bric-a-brac; big back family dining room with barn-like village hall atmosphere; well kept Bass, Brains, Felinfoel Double Dragon and Worthington BB, simple bar food generously served and reasonably priced inc filled baked potatoes, gammon, scampi and daily specials such as chicken curry; friendly service, maybe radio; close to harbour; little garden has play area over stream *(Joy Heatherley, Reg Nelson, Michael Badcock, Barbara and Norman Wells, M Joyner, H K Dyson)*

Solva [Lower Solva; SM8024], *Cambrian Arms*: Doing well under Italian landlord and wife, with well kept Ansells, Ind Coope Burton and Tetleys, good food — may have to book, as so busy *(H K Dyson)*; [Upper Solva], *Royal George*: Honest local with well kept Bass, Marstons Pedigree and Worthington BB *(H K Dyson)*

St Davids [Goat St; SM7525], *Farmers Arms*: Cheerful pubby atmosphere, decent food, tables in tidy back garden with view of cathedral, Worthington BB on handpump *(Mr and Mrs Sumner, SJC)*; [centre], *Old Cross*: Attractive creeper-clad hotel with trees and shrubs in pleasant front walled garden; civilised and comfortable beamed lounge bar with lots of books and oraments, good sandwiches and snacks though limited hot food, mainly proper oven-cooked baked pots; keg beer, restaurant; bedrooms *(Barbara and Norman Wells)*; [on rd to Porthclais harbour (and lifeboat)], *St Nons*: Cheery hotel, public bar well used by locals for bar lunches (with machines one end, pool the other), lots of life and cheery staff; decent food with generous helpings of vegetables, well kept Bass and Hancocks HB, good wines; restaurant area now has its own bar; jazz Sat; bedrooms airy and reasonably priced *(Mrs M Price)*

St Dogmaels [SN1645], *Ferry*: On Teifi estuary, with Brains Bitter and SA and one named for the pub; good for family meals, if not cheap, with roof garden overlooking water, fine views from good restaurant (closed Mon); good atmosphere *(N Duggan, Jenny and Brian Seller, BB)*

St Florence [SM0801], *Parsonage*: Good spacious garden with well kept borders and trees; interlinking bars, family room and restaurant; straightforward bar food, reasonable beer *(Geoff Wilson)*; *Sun*: Friendly small pub with Buckleys ales on handpump, usual range of pub food; children welcome *(Lynne Sheridan, Bob West)*

St Ishmaels [SM8307], *Brook*: Not smart, but has quietly cheery landlord and good value bar meals in dining area *(Julian Yorke)*

Tenby [SN1300], *Buccaneer*: Fine matchbox collection, real ales *(Reg Nelson)*; [Upper Frog St], *Coach & Horses*: Tasteful with lounge and tap room; real ale *(Reg Nelson)*; [nr rly stn], *Hilton*: Tasteful modern decor, surprisingly quiet, children allowed *(Reg Nelson)*; [High St], *Lamb*: Civil war connections; presentable and comfortable, geared for food, nice atmosphere; real ale *(Reg Nelson)*; *Prince of Wales*: Beamery, subdued lighting; real ale *(Reg Nelson)*; *Tenby House*: Lively multi-roomed pub, real ale *(Reg Nelson)*

Trapp [OS Sheet 159, map reference 653189; SN6518], *Cennen Arms*: Three bars served from one glassed-in servery with hatch to lounge; plain 1950sish decor, simple and comfortable, with friendly staff, low-priced decent standard bar food inc Sun roasts, keg Worthington; handy for Carreg Cennen Castle and craft centre; small garden and terrace with seats; pretty building by bridge in tiny village; children welcome *(Michael and Alison Sandy, Anne Morris)*

☆ **Wolfs Castle** [A40 Haverfordwest—Fishguard; SM9526], *Wolfe*: Yet another management change for this attractively laid out dining pub leaves us still unable to place it firmly on a rating scale; as we went to press its future was unclear; it has previously been very popular for consistently good value food from sandwiches up, in neat red-carpeted lounge, garden room and conservatory-restaurant, with well kept Felinfoel Double Dragon on handpump, games in public bar and tables outside; children welcome, lavatory for the disabled, one twin bedroom; closed Mon lunchtime Sept-Whitsun *(Mr and Mrs Sumner, Barbara and Norman Wells, M Badcock, Howard and Lynda Dix, H K Dyson, Paul and Margaret Baker, Julian Proudman, LYM; news please)*

GLAMORGAN — MID

☆ **Caerphilly** [Watford; Tongwynlais exit from M4 junction 32, then right just after church — OS Sheet 171, map reference 144846; ST1484], *Black Cock*: Neat and comfortable blue-plush bar with particularly well kept Bass, good value bar lunches inc very cheap chippy snacks as well as gammon and eggs, mixed grill, specials such as roast lamb and so forth; sizeable terraced garden among trees with play area and barbecue, restaurant, open fire in pretty tiled fireplace; up in the hills, just below Caerphilly Common *(BB)*

Cefn Cribwr [24 Cefn Rd; handy for M4 junction 37, via Pyle and B4281; SS8582], *Farmers Arms*: Unspoilt pub, very plain but friendly, with collection of coalmining gear, particularly well kept Bass, a couple of traditional settles among more modern seats, views out to sea and across to Devon *(Dr and Mrs A K Clarke, BB)*

Coychurch [SS9379], *White Horse*: Popular local, esp at lunchtime; good value food, well kept Brains Bitter, reasonable prices, good service *(Nigel Pritchard, Peter Williams)*

Cross Inn [nr Llantrisant — note that this is the one in Mid Glam at ST0582], *Barn*: Old barn very successfully converted about 1988, good range of real ales inc guest beers, old farm tools, bags of grain and so forth adding atmosphere, good value evening restaurant; bar lunches *(Anon)*

Laleston [Wind St, behind church; SS8780], *Laleston*: 15th-century stone village pub with big open fire, impressive longcase clock and old harmonium in comfortable bar, newer extension less unusual but comfortable too; interesting choice of reasonably priced real ales with changing guests *(John and Helen Thompson, Julian Proudman)*

☆ **Llangeinor** [SS9187], *Llangeinor Arms*: Remote hill-top pub by church with excellent Bristol Channel view from

conservatory; two bars with fine collection of antique artefacts and porcelain; real fires, choice of real ales, good bar food with adjacent 15th-century restaurant (must book Sun lunch); walks with spectacular views nearby *(John and Helen Thompson, M Joyner)*

Llantrisant [from M4 junction 34; take right turn after traffic lights, to Mwyndy Cross; ST0581], *Barn*: Comfortable red plush and dark wood in former barn, now a long main bar with very popular food from big buttery at one end, steps up to smaller lounge the other; half a dozen well kept ales inc Bass, Felinfoel and Hancocks, back family room, picnic-table sets on terrace and on gravel and grass around big sycamore in back courtyard *(Michael Sandy, R J Collis)*; [Cardiff Rd, Southgate; ST0483], *Pennyfarthing*: Interesting mix of mock Victorian and Edwardian, but tastefully done; something for everyone *(Dr and Mrs A K Clarke)*

☆ **Llanwonno** [off B4275 or B4273; or B4277 in Ferndale — into valley at Commercial Hotel S-bend; OS Sheet 170, map reference 028956; ST0295], *Brynffynon*: Unaffected mountain pub with warmly welcoming high-ceilinged bar, cheap genuine food (the day's specials a usually a good choice), well kept Flowers IPA, obliging service; a marvellous base for walks in the largely forested surrounding hills; children and dogs allowed till 9, occasional live music; open till 4 *(LYM)*

Merthyr Tydfil [SO0709], *Crown*: Outstanding (cheap) food in massive helpings — salads especially good; Flowers and Marstons Pedigree on handpump, friendly staff; made up of bar, lounge and dining room *(John Thorndike)*

Pen y Fai [SS8982], *Pheasant*: Large, comfortable welcoming pub with Courage real ales, popular lunchtime bar food inc traditional puddings *(John and Helen Thompson)*

Pentyrch [ST1081], *Kings Arms*: Attractive old village pub, Brains real ale *(Julian Proudman)*

Pontneddfechan [SN9007], *Angel*: Handy for all the waterfalls around kere, well kept Flowers Original; friendly welcome, good value generous food *(John Nash)*

☆ **Rudry**, [ST1986], *Maenllwyd*: Comfortably furnished traditional lounge in low-beamed Tudor pub with well kept Youngers IPA, polite service, popular bar food, spacious more recent restaurant extension with midnight supper licence; children allowed in some areas *(Gwyneth and Salvo Spadaro-Dutturi, LYM)*

Wick [B4265 4 miles W of Llantwit Major; SS9272], *Lamb & Flag*: Attractive old village pub *(Julian Proudman)*

GLAMORGAN — SOUTH

Cardiff [St Mary St], *Albert*: Big local by Brains Brewery, with well kept Bitter, SA and Dark, friendly staff *(Gwyneth and Salvo Spadaro-Dutturi, Michael Cochrane)*; [St Marys St], *Cottage*: Character carefully restored Brains pub not far from the brewery, particularly well kept SA, Bitter and Dark Mild — a new glass for every pint; popular for good value lunches, handy for shops *(Joan and Michel Hooper-Immins, Julian Proudman)*; [nr Park Hotel], *Dylans*: Big open-plan pub/wine bar with separate food area, popular but not overcrowded; comfortable, with good choice of ciders, lagers and beers, and some happy-hour bargains *(Steve Thomas)*; [Gwyneth St, Cathays], *Gower*: Large bar recently quite tastefully renovated, with full-size snooker table, well kept Brains Bitter and SA Dark, lunchtime bar food *(Elfed Jones)*; [Cathedral Rd], *Halfway*: Recently well modernised Brains pub — one of the best in West Cardiff *(Julian Proudman)*; [Church St], *Old Arcade*: Classic traditional no-nonsense Brains pub, well renovated with plenty of atmosphere, lots of rugby mementoes (less than 300 yds from Arms Park), well kept Brains Dark, Bitter and SA at good prices, big helpings of decent bar food; wide range of customers from students and market traders to lunchtime businessmen; open all day, but back lounge may be closed late afternoon *(Michael Cochrane, Gwyneth and Salvo Spadaro-Dutturi, Julian Proudman)*; [Bute St], *Packet*: Well modernised docklands pub with photographs of sailing ships and old Tiger Bay *(Julian Proudman)*; [David St], *Panorama*: Very pleasant refurbished bar with good food (usual pub range), friendly staff; popular with businessmen, by World Trade Centre due to open 1992 *(Bill Rogers)*; [St Marys St], *Philharmonic*: Bar now knocked through to next door and rather well refurbished in Victorian style — nice Sun lunchtime with cheese, jazz and local singer; downstairs nightclub; can be noisy, but food inc good ploughman's and superb bacon sandwich *(Gwynne Harper, Mrs Virginia Brown)*; [Harbour Rd], *Red House*: Amazing remote city centre location with water's-edge view of dockland developments *(Julian Proudman)*

☆ **Cowbridge** [signed off A48; SS9974], *Bear*: Flourishing atmosphere in neatly kept old coaching inn; beams, flagstones and panelling on left, plush armchairs on right, log-effect gas fires, bar food from sandwiches and baked potatoes to steak and kidney pie (not Sat evening), carvery; half a dozen or more well kept real ales, piped music; children in eating area; bedrooms quiet and comfortable, with good breakfasts *(Patrick and Mary McDermott, LYM)*
Cowbridge [High St], *Duke of Wellington*: Fine old building in country town; atmospheric, well furnished public bar and well kept Brains *(Julian Proudman)*

☆ **Dinas Powis**, [Station Rd; ST1571], *Star*: Well decorated and efficiently run village pub with stripped stone walls, panelling and heavy Elizabethan beams; eating areas, two with welcoming fires, and a no smoking room; friendly licensees, good bar food, well kept Brains ales; good jazz sometimes *(Julian Proudman, LYM)*

Llanbethery [ST0369], *Wild Goose*: Isolated pub trying very hard, worth encouraging *(Julian Proudman)*

☆ **Llancadle** [village signed off B4265 Barry—Llantwit just E of St Athan — OS Sheet 170, map reference 038685; ST0368], *Green Dragon*: Thatched pub with interesting high-raftered stripped-stone main bar, enterprising choice of spirits, several guest beers alongside well kept Courage Best and Directors and John Smiths; lots of bric-a-brac; good bar food (not Mon or Sun evenings), tables outside; promising new management 1991 *(Gordon Theaker, Gwynne Harper, Julian Proudman, LYM)*

☆ **Monknash**, [follow Marcross, Broughton signpost off B4265 St Brides Major—Llantwit Major, turn left at end of Water St — OS Sheet 170, map reference 920706; SS9270], *Plough & Harrow*: Unspoilt and untouched isolated country pub, very basic — flagstones, old-fashioned stripped settles, logs burning in cavernous fireplace with huge side bread oven, good value plain food inc filled granary rolls, Flowers IPA and Original and Marstons Pedigree on handpump; pool, juke box and fruit machine in room on left, picnic-table sets on grass outside the white cottage; nr start GWG195 *(Julian Proudman, Cathy Long, Gwyneth and Salvo Spadaro-Dutturi, BB)*

☆ **Morganstown**, [Ty Nant Rd (not far from M4 junction 32); ST1281], *Ty Nant*: Exceptionally well run and usually busy, with beamed lounge and popular basic bar; consistently well kept real ale, pool table, generous helpings of usual bar food, seats outside *(Anon)*

Penllyn [village signed from A48; SS9776], *Fox*: Up-market pub in smart little village, previously very popular indeed for good food in stylish surroundings; has had real ale too, with good value house wines, and decent malt whiskies; but two changes of ownership in quite quick succession have broken the continuity; should have reopened by now after refurbishment by its latest owner, who is renaming it the Red Fox *(LYM — news please)*

Penmark [ST0568], *Six Bells*: Typical village pub with interesting relics of Hancocks Brewery in public bar *(Julian Proudman)*

Porthcawl [Newton; SS7277], *Jolly Sailor*: Attractive pub by village green in outlying part of village *(Julian Proudman)*

☆ **Sigingstone**, [SS9771], *Victoria*: Beautifully kept pub with antiques, fresh flowers, spotless tables, fast service and good reasonably priced bar food; out of the way, but always busy; some concentration on diners *(Cathy Long, Mr and Mrs E J Chappell, Julian Proudman)*

☆ **St Hilary**, [ST0173], *Bush*: Welcoming and cosy thatched village pub nestling behind church, old settles in traditional flagstoned public bar, comfortable low-beamed lounge with warm atmosphere, well kept Bass, Hancocks and Worthington, generous helpings of good bar food inc some Welsh dishes, cheerful service; separate games bar; restaurant with long menu in Welsh and English — worth booking weekends *(Julian Proudman, LYM)*

GLAMORGAN — WEST

Bishopston [Murton; off B4436 Bishopston—Swansea; SS5889], *Plough & Harrow*: Good choice of food and well kept real ales in well run village pub *(David and Sandy)*

Black Pill [A4067; SS6190], *Woodman*: Smart pub as adjunct to restaurant; well kept Marstons Pedigree *(Dr and Mrs A K Clarke)*

Killay [Gower Rd; SS6092], *Commercial*: Comfortably refurbished, pleasant atmosphere, real ales, piped music, good range of reasonably priced bar food; good with children *(David and Sandy)*

Kittle [SS5789], *Beaufort Arms*: Busy, interesting pub on two levels (nice character on lower level); occasional live music; standard food, quick friendly service *(S Watkins, M Saunders)*

Llangennith [SS4291], *Kings Head*: Old village pub of splendid potential *(Julian Proudman)*

Llangyfelach [B4489 just S of M4 junction 46; SS6498], *Plough & Harrow*: Smoothly comfortable modernised lounge bar with big helpings from food counter, very handy for M4 junctions 46 and 47 *(LYM)*

Llanmadoc [the Gower, nr Whiteford Burrows — NT; SS4393], *Britannia*: Old cottage-type building with low beams, flagstones in bar, beamed dining/lounge area; bar snacks and Sun lunch (best to book), Bass and Marstons Pedigree, pleasant front terrace; Sat evening sing-along; quiet village near NT area, good walks nearby; play area and pets' corner; bedrooms good value *(Gwyneth and Salvo Spadaro-Dutturi)*

☆ **Mumbles** [Newton Rd, Oystermouth; SS6287], *White Rose*: Large, well organised and popular, with cheap bar food, well kept Bass, prompt friendly service, pleasant hubbub of conversation *(Simon Tormey, David and Sandy, S Watkins)*

☆ **Oldwalls**, [SS4891], *Greyhound*: Dark-panelled comfortable lounge bar plenty of tables and well kept Bass, Hancocks HB and interesting guest beers such as Fullers London Pride, reasonably priced bar food; further bar, and restaurant very popular at weekends for generous helpings of good local fish; good coal fire; can get very busy, but service efficient, and atmosphere convivial; big tree-shaded garden with pensioned-off tractor and other play objects *(Michael and Alison Sandy, David Warrellow, Dr and Mrs D A Blackadder)*

☆ **Parkmill** [SS5489], *Gower*: Large, light and airy well organised pub with art deco interior, plenty of tables and wide choice of reasonably priced above-average food inc lasagne, sweet and sour pork, beef carbonade and choice of vegetarian dishes; welcoming service, open Sun evenings in winter too; big car park *(A G Roby, BHP)*

Penclawdd [Berthlwyd; B4295 towards Gowerton; SS5495], *Berthlwyd*: Large, plush, smartly refurbished busy pub, with fine views across Loughor estuary; Courage Best, John Smiths and Felinfoel, helpful staff; open-plan, with banquettes around walls at one end, restaurant area at other; some picnic-table sets on lawn by road *(David and Sandy, M Joyner)*

Pontlliw [Swansea Rd; A48 towards Pontardulais from M4 junction 47; SN6100], *Buck*: Good Watneys Country Carvery dining pub, food good value in bar and carvery restaurant, inc magnificent cold table; well kept Watneys-related real ales *(S Watkins, Tom Evans)*

Reynoldston [SS4789], *King Arthur*: Long Georgian building recently purchased from brewery and attractively restored as free house; big stone log fire, prints, plate rack and warming pans, rugs on bare boards; plusher lounge/restaurant bar and games room behind; clean; blackboard menu varies daily; overlooks village green and common land; very popular with tourists and holiday makers *(J Madel)*

☆ **Swansea** [Kingsway], *Hanbury*: Congenial atmosphere — feels like an old town pub despite post-war development around; very popular for good choice of good value lunchtime food, plenty of dark wood, pictures of old Swansea, showy Edwardian-style lampshades, lots of tables; Watneys beers well kept; full of shoppers; appeals to a different set weekend evenings *(Michael and Alison Sandy, David and Sandy)*

Swansea [Oxford St; SS6593], *Hocks*: Good value food, pleasant staff; no smoking area; handy for a quick lunch when shopping *(S Watkins)*; [56 Wind St], *No Sign Wine Bar*: In oldest street here; line of four narrow rooms; first has mahogany cabinets and other fittings, large portrait in oils, cellars under bar; second is more of an alcove, third is full of church pews, and fourth is flagstoned and rather bare; decent fairly priced bar food, good wines, keg beer; can get crowded lunchtimes, esp with big solicitors *(David and Sandy)*; [Marina], *Tug & Turbot*: Brand new pub overlooking the marina; fits in well in the upmarket nautical atmosphere *(Dr and Mrs A K Clarke)*

West Cross [A4067 Mumbles—Swansea; SS6089], *West Cross*: Nice, comfortable, light and airy modern bar with plush furnishings, pool room, terrace off bar overlooking Swansea Bay, larger one downstairs by seafront path; quickly served, well presented, straightforward food, well kept cheap Flowers *(Michael and Alison Sandy)*

Ynystawe [634 Clydach Rd; A4067 just N of M4 junction 45; SN6800], *Millers Arms*: Pleasant cottagey pub with welcoming landlord, lovely staff, Marstons Pedigree, good lunchtime specials; closed 4-6 weekdays *(Kevan and Alexandra Dutton)*

GWENT

☆ **Abergavenny** [Raglan Rd, Hardwick; B4598

(old A40), 2 miles E; SO3212], *Horse & Jockey*: Pleasant, clean and well furnished with good staff and wide range of popualr good value pub food; well kept Bass *(John and Joan Nash, Pamela and Merlyn Horswell)*

Abergavenny [Station Rd; SO3014], *Great Western*: Basic pub with well kept Bass and Ruddles Best, comfortable lounge bar behind the very local public bar, lots of old railway signs *(Joan and Michel Hooper-Immins); [Flannel St], Hen & Chickens*: Busy, welcoming and unspoilt, good choice of wholesome home-cooked food, well kept real ales inc Bass *(Peter Argent); [The Bryn, Penpergwm; B4598, 3 miles SE], King of Prussia*: Friendly service, good value food, well kept Bass; spotless, with well trained staff; locally very popular *(Col G D Stafford)*

Caldicot [ST4889], *Castle*: Useful, attractive place with spacious open-plan bar, Flowers Original on handpump and reasonably priced food; by drive of historic castle *(John and Joan Wyatt)*

Clydach [Old Black Rock Rd; SO2213], *Rock & Fountain*: This mountainside pub with lovely views down over the valley, a main entry in the last edition for its unusually good food, sadly closed in 1991 *(LYM)*

Croesyceiliog [ST3096], *Green Meadow*: Golf club not a pub, but any visitor is welcome — you don't have to be a player; good bar snacks in old converted barn, farmyard spot without accompanying smells; ideal for quiet drink *(Gwyneth and Salvo Spadaro-Dutturi)*

☆ **Grosmont**, [SO4024], *Angel*: Carefully modernised 17th-century village local with good friendly staff, homely atmosphere, open fires, mining memorabilia on beams, three ales on handpump inc well kept Bass and Buckleys, good varied very reasonably piced food; pool table; next to ancient market hall, nr attractive church; bedrooms *(Brian and Anna Marsden, Chris Aslett, BB)*

☆ **nr Grosmont**, [B4347 N — OS Sheet 161, map reference 408254], *Cupids Hill*: Tiny homely pub, alone on very steep hill in pretty countryside; a quaint survivor — not at all old-world, just basic and homely; bottled beers only (stood on sawn-off former bagatelle table with plyboard top), plain old settles by fire, low white ceiling; table skittles, dominoes, cribbage *(BB)*

Llandogo [SO5204], *Sloop*: Large open-plan dining lounge with distant river view from picture window — a useful stop for good value interesting food, and open all day at least in season; pleasant landlord, Buckleys, Smiles and Wadworths beers on handpump; bedrooms *(Michael and Alison Sandy, Tim and Ann Newell)*

☆ **Llanfihangel Crucorney** [village signed off A465; SO3321], *Skirrid*: Among the oldest pubs in Britain, with parts dating from 1110; ancient studded door lets you into high-ceilinged main bar, all stone and flagstones, dark feel accentuated by furniture inc pews (some padded); two small

rooms, well kept Courage Best and Directors on handpump, big helpings of home-made food, friendly young staff, overall feeling of warmth and age *(Peter Griffiths, Cliff and Karen Spooner, F and J Hamer, LYM)*

☆ **Llangwm**, [B4235 S of Raglan; SO4200], *Bridge*: Relaxed atmosphere in well run pub, varnished pews in bright and airy dining extension with very wide choice of good enterprising food, at a price; well kept Bass in separate pubbier bar with beams, nooks, crannies and traditional furnishings; has been closed Sun evening and Mon lunchtime; children in dining area *(LYM)*

☆ **Llanishen** [SO4803], *Carpenters Arms*: A real pub, with very friendly people, good food, reasonable prices; Bass, Brains and guest beers served from cask, bar meals with huge amounts of veg; real fire, pool table in room off bar, tables in small garden; children welcome and even entertained; lovely bedroom with four-poster, big breakfast, at low price *(Salvo and Gwyneth Spadaro-Dutturi, Andy and Kelli Smith)*

☆ **Llantarnam** [Newport Rd; (A4042 N of M4 junction 26; ST3093], *Greenhouse*: Fine old spacious pub with Courage Best, Directors and John Smiths on handpump and exceptionally wide choice of good if not cheap bar food, served quite quickly; good garden and play area *(C M J Barton, P Corris)*

Llanthony [SO2928], *Half Moon*: Unspoilt single-bar pub divided into two spaces, with log fire and friendly staff; Archers Headbanger, Hook Norton Old Hookey and Hoskins Old Navigation, bar billiards, good value bar food; in remote spot in Llanthony Valley — dramatic scenery — a haven for walkers, riders and motorists; children welcome; bedrooms with mountain views *(Peter Griffiths, Dave Braisted)*

☆ **Llantilio Crosseny**, [SO3915], *Hostry*: 15th-century beamed pub in very quiet pretty village; welcoming staff, well kept Bass and Smiles, good choice of home-cooked bar food inc vegetarian dishes, log fire, lots of character; children allowed in lounge; bedrooms comfortable *(Julian Proudman)*

Llantrisant [off A449; ST3997], *Greyhound*: Very pleasant small country pub with splendid view of Gwent hills beyond road; attractive building; good bar food, friendly service; bedrooms *(Col G D Stafford, Julian Proudman)*

Llanvapley [B4223 Abergavenny—Monmouth; SO3714], *Red Hart*: Good village pub by cricket pitch *(Julian Proudman)*

Llanvihangel Gobion [A40 on Usk turning, about 3 1/2 miles from Abergavenny; SO3509], *Chart House*: Smoothly modernised and relaxing pub with good food in bar and popular restaurant, distant hill views *(Pamela and Merlyn Horswell, BB)*

Magor [a mile from M4 junction 23; B4245; ST4287], *Wheatsheaf*: Pleasant modernised village pub with friendly staff and big helpings of decent straightforward bar food; small restaurant *(David Williams)*

☆ **Mamhilad** [3/4 mile N — OS Sheet 171, map reference 308047; SO3004], *Horseshoe*: Pleasant bar with well kept Brains and Felinfoel, lots of malt whiskies, friendly landlord, well cooked and plentiful straightforward inexpensive food, good service and lovely views, particularly from tables by car park over road *(Gwyneth and Salvo Spadaro-Dutturi, Robert and Kate Hodkinson)*

Michaelston y Fedw [a mile off A48 at Castleton; ST2484], *Cefn Mably Arms*: Tastefully refurbished pub in attractive village setting, with two bars, warm welcome, well kept Allied real ales on handpump, good service and food from bar snacks to Sun lunch; restaurant, garden *(Margaret and Bill Rogers)*

☆ **Monkswood**, [SO3503], *Beaufort Arms*: Notable for outstanding food changing daily, inc delicious unusual soups, fresh seafood, game, good choice of vegetarian dishes and puddings; welcoming atmosphere, well kept Courage Directors and Best tapped from the cask, decent wines — even its own cricket pitch; must book Fri/Sat *(Gwyneth and Salvo Spadaro-Dutturi)*

Monmouth [Agincourt Sq; SO5113], *Bull*: Neatly kept pub with a choice of beers inc Exmoor, decent reasonably priced Spanish omelette *(John and Joan Wyatt)*; [Agincourt Sq], *Kings Head*: Period building with comfortable bedrooms, open inviting atmosphere, flowers everywhere, good food in upmarket dining room with helpful and attentive staff, decent wines; bedrooms *(Anon)*

Nantyderry [between A4042 and B4598 (former A471), N of Pontypool and Usk — OS Sheet 161, map reference 332061; SO3306], *Foxhunter*: In small isolated hamlet; wide range of bar food, well kept Bass and quick service in four interconnected areas around right-angled bar; brass platters and plates and early 19th-century street scenes, toning upholstered wall settles matching the carpet; spotless throughout, quiet piped music; magnificent hanging baskets, garden with fountain, lawn and swing *(Frank Cummins)*

Newport [Baneswell; ST3189], *Engineers*: Authentic town pub with friendly staff and reasonable prices; live jazz or folk weekly, piano player in lounge some nights; Bass and Hancocks HB *(Salvo and Gwyneth Spadaro-Dutturi)*

Peterstone Wentlooge [ST2680], *Six Bells*: Nice old country pub with lots of character and garden *(Anon)*

Pontllanfraith [High St, Pentwynmawr; A472 towards Newbridge; ST1996], *Three Horseshoes*: Friendly staff, nice atmosphere, range of good vegetarian dishes *(J Hines)*

Redwick [ST4184], *Rose*: Quite old, not overmodernised, in very pretty interesting village — lovely setting for long summer evenings, with big play area and a terrace well away from it; Allied beers, comprehensive reasonably priced menu inc Indian dishes, welcoming landlord *(Elfed Jones)*

☆ **Shirenewton**, [signed off B4235 just W of Chepstow; ST4893], *Tredegar Arms*: Usual reasonably priced bar food, well kept Hook Norton Bitter and Marstons Merrie Monk on handpump, good choice of malt whiskies, jolly landlady, tasteful lounge bar with big bay window, comfortable sofa and chairs, plenty of brass and chintz; games in public bar, seats outside; children in eating area; good value bedrooms *(John and Joan Wyatt, C G A Kearney, Jenny and Brian Seller, John and Tessa Rainsford, LYM)*

Shirenewton [on B4235 Chepstow—Usk], *Carpenters Arms*: Lots of little rooms, warm and welcoming, wide choice of reasonably priced food, well kept Bass, Badger Tanglefoot, Marstons Owd Rodger, Ruddles County, Wadworths 6X and two guest beers *(Patrick Godfrey)*

☆ **Talycoed** [B4233 Monmouth—Abergavenny; SO4115], *Halfway House*: Good straightforward food (not Sun evening), excellent atmosphere, real ale and log fires in polished country pub; beautiful setting for a summer's evening, under the wisteria looking over the Trothy Vale to the mewing of buzzards *(PB, HB, Tom Haggett)*

☆ **Tintern** [Devauden Rd; off A446; SO5301], *Cherry Tree*: Unspoilt genuine pub in pretty spot, pleasant licensee, good Hancocks PA and cider tapped from cask; children welcome *(PB, HB)*

Tintern, *Beaufort*: Good bar lunches inc good dish of the day in very attractive and comfortable hotel bar, very quick friendly service; bedrooms *(Joan Harris)*; [A466 Chepstow—Monmouth], *Moon & Sixpence*: Spotlessly clean, beautifully furnished and stylish, with well kept Butcombe, friendly service and real, not frozen chips *(WHBM, John and Pat Smyth)*

Trelleck, [B4293 6 miles S of Monmouth; SO5005], *Lion*: Quiet and unpretentious country pub with pleasant lounge bar; has been praised for unusually good and reasonably priced food, but no recent reports *(News please)*; *Village Green*: Really a restaurant/bistro, but a bar too (with beer as well as its mainstay wine); comfortable, with prints, lots of dried flowers on beams, good staff, good food *(Gwyneth and Salvo Spadaro-Dutturi)*

Usk [centre; SO3801], *Cross Keys*: Good food at reasonable prices, attractively served with pretty matching crockery; good coffee with mint *(Mr and Mrs D Coates)*; [Old Market St], *Kings Head*: Beamed lounge bar with big log fire, assorted tables inc a big dining table, brocaded chairs and wall settles; assorted bric-a-brac above and around fireplace inc old bottles, wind-up gramophone, decanters and fishing rods; quiet piped Radio 2; Badger Tanglefoot, Brains BB, Flowers Original and Tetleys on handpump; decent food inc some home-made dishes; bedrooms *(Frank Cummins)*; [The Square], *Nags Head*: Very obliging landlord, well presented reasonably priced meals inc good Usk salmon, very obliging staff; spotless *(H R Bevan);* [Llangeview; outside town, off A449/A472 junction; first right off B4235 — OS Sheet 171, map reference 396005], *Rat Trap:* Immaculately furnished lounge bar with separate restaurant, bar food and Flowers Original; bedrooms *(Patrick Godfrey)*

GWYNEDD

Remember that pubs on the Lleyn Peninsula from Porthmadog out are not allowed to sell alcohol on Sun

Aberdaron [SH1727], *Ty Newydd:* Windows look out over a furnished terrace to the sea, reasonable choice of beers and good choice of food *(W F C Phillips)*

☆ **Aberdovey,** *Britannia:* Upper floor has superb view over Dovey estuary to mountains of N Cardigan, with balcony open in summer; well kept Bass, good bar food *(Dave Braisted)*

☆ **Aberdovey,** [opp Penhelig rly stn; SN6296], *Penhelig Arms:* Carefully refurbished building in fine position overlooking sea, with cosy bar and good bedrooms; has been popular for good home cooking and well kept Burton, but no recent reports *(News please)*

Bala [High St; SH9336], *Olde Bulls Head:* Oldest inn in town, comfortably refurbished bar, food, Whitbreads ale; bedrooms *(LYM)*

☆ **Beddgelert,** [SH5948], *Prince Llewelyn:* Quietly civilised plush hotel bar with raised dining area, simpler summer bar, good value bar food, straightforward but prepared with real care, well kept Robinsons, cheerful and helpful staff, rustic seats on verandah overlooking village stream and hills; nr GWG206; gets busy at peak holiday times; children allowed at quiet times; bedrooms pleasant, with good breakfasts *(Drs G N and M G Yates, Rt Revd D R Feaver, BB)*

Beddgelert, *Tanronen:* Simply furnished main bar, small but pleasant separate lounge bar, well kept Robinsons real ale, decent straightforward bar food inc good value weekly specials and puddings, friendly; nr GWG206; bedrooms simple but clean — good value *(N P Cox, Gordon Theaker, BB)*

Betws y Coed [SH7956], *Royal Oak:* Not really a pub — more a hotel with coffee shop or grill room, well worth knowing for beautifully fresh fish; bedrooms *(W C M Jones); Waterloo:* Large and comfortable, consistently good bar food; bedrooms *(Anon)*

Capel Curig [SH4682], *Cobdens:* Beautiful spot in Snowdonia, family atmosphere, pleasant staff, good value food *(Mr and Mrs J Manning, KC)*

☆ **Capel Garmon,** [signed from A470 just outside Betws-y-Coed, towards Llanrwst; SH8255], *White Horse:* Comfortable and homely, with friendly atmosphere, magnificent views, good value simple home-made food; delightful countryside; bedrooms reasonably priced and well equipped — marvellous breakfast *(KC)*

Conwy [High St; SH7878], *Castle:* Well furnished bar in THF hotel, usual bar food, decent wines, friendly atmosphere and excellent, willing, speedy service; interesting old building *(Pam Hall, Michael Bechley);* [Quay], *Liverpool Arms:* Outside walls by archway, with some parking on quay — handy for the Smallest House as well as shops and boats; warm inside, with dark wood, stained glass, settles, tables and stools; food inc generously filled baps *(Hazel Morgan)*

☆ **Corris,** [village signed off A487 Machynlleth—Dolgellau; SH7608], *Slaters Arms:* Classic welcoming local with high-backed antique settles and lots of character; open fire in slate inglenook, good value simple bar food, well kept Banks's Bitter and Mild at attractive prices, friendly service; interesting ex-slate-mining village, with railway museum and nearby forest walks *(LYM)*

☆ **Criccieth** [The Square; A497; SH5038], *Prince of Wales:* Open-plan, but with some individual decorative touches, nice pictures, panelling, open fires and some cosy alcoves — neat and well kept; usual bar food, meals rather than snacks in the evening (not Sun), Whitbreads-related real ales, live music Tues; children in eating area till 8; open all day Sat summer, closed Sun *(Kit Read, LYM)*

Deganwy [SH7880], *Deganwy Castle:* Plushly comfortable lounge with fine views, and pleasantly pubby rambling back bar with fat black beams, stripped stone, flagstones and lots of nooks and crannies; good choice of bar food, well kept Watneys-related real ales; bedrooms (big hotel) *(LYM)*

Dinas Mawddwy [SH8615], *Llew Coch:* Lively and traditional friendly village local with hundreds of sparkling horsebrasses, food inc trout or salmon from River Dovey just behind, well kept Bass, family room with pool tables and video games, Sat evening music; lovely steep scenery *(NC, LYM)*

Dolgellau [A487/A470 3 miles E — OS Sheet 124, map reference 766168; SH7318], *Cross Foxes:* Comfortable atmosphere in bars; interesting ornaments, good value bar food inc big chunky sandwiches *(M Joyner)*

Llanbedr [A496; SH5827], *Victoria:* Pleasant riverside pub, big thoroughly refurbished lounge with some traces of the original character inc old-fashioned inglenook, useful choice from food counter in dining area, well kept Robinsons Best; attractive garden with large adventure slide; children welcome; bedrooms *(M Joyner, Brian and Anna Marsden, LYM)*

☆ **Llanbedr y Cennin** [signed from B5106; SH7669], *Olde Bull:* Massive low beams (salvaged from Armada wreck), jaunty furnishings from elaborately carved antiques to brightly striped stools, good log fires, well kept Lees Bitter and Mild, wide choice of straightforward food from sandwiches to steaks; darts, dominoes, cribbage, machines and piped music, tables on terrace, restaurant; children allowed if well behaved;

no dogs *(Mr and Mrs M Cockram, Mike Tucker, Hazel Morgan, LYM)*

☆ **Llanbedrog** [SH3332], *Glyn-y-Weddw*: Friendly and pleasant, with good choice of food served efficiently and courteously; pleasant atmosphere, terrace and garden *(Kit Read, Andrew Morrissey)*

☆ **Llanbedrog** [Bryn-y-Gro (B4413)], *Ship*: Extended refurbished pub with well kept Burtonwood Mild and JBA, lively simple family lounge, good range of popular straightforward food; good outside seating area, reasonable food *(N P Cox, LYM)*

Llanberis [SH5860], *Heights*: Spacious dining area with limited choice of good value food such as hearty home-made vegetable soup, hazelnut roast, local trout *(KC)*

☆ = **Llandudno**, [Old St; SH7883], *Kings Head*: Good atmosphere in friendly and spacious open-plan pub notable for huge range of really good food, not cheap but generously served and with many unusual dishes — they'll also do things not on the menu; can be eaten in dining area (booking needed evening) or elsewhere; open fire, traditional decor — except for the imitation shop windows in one room, filled with unusual things; well kept Ind Coope Burton and Tetleys, good service, pool area, tables on terrace, interesting position by Great Orme Tramway station; open all day *(P A Crossland, D A Cawley, Dr T E Hothersall, Miss G Matthews, Tania Lamberton, Prof S Barnett, Mr and Mrs M J Williams, D Paschke, N Duckworth, J M Watson, RJS)*

Llandudno [Madoc St; SH7883], *Albert*: Recently completely refurbished in mock-olde style, reasonably priced straightforward food, good beer, comfortable *(RJS)*; [1 Market St], *Cottage Loaf*: Timbered pub with nice atmosphere, good lunchtime bar snacks, real ales (free house) and beams that seem to be old ship's masts *(Gordon Theaker)*; [Madoc St], *Cross Keys*: Pleasant and friendly with good range of Whitbreads-related ales, wide range of low-priced bar meals *(B M Eldridge)*

Llandwrog [SH4456], *Harp*: Really well kept Flowers IPA served with geniality, good food; bedrooms first-class *(John Constantine)*

☆ **Porthmadog**, [Lombard St; SH5639], *Ship*: Huge open fireplace in lounge, well kept Ind Coope Burton, Tetleys Mild and Bitter, perhaps their fine own-brew Pencai, and a weekly guest beer such as Batemans XXXB, wide choice of generous and genuine lunchtime food, popular upstairs evening Thai/Malaysian restaurant run by landlord's Malaysian wife; comfortable public bar; small back children's room with video games/fruit machines beyond pool room *(P A Crossland, D A Cawley, John Towers, Brian and Anna Marsden, Gordon Theaker)*

Rhyd Ddu [A4085 N of Beddgelert; SH5753], *Cwellyn Arms*: Lively stone-built pub with fine Snowdon views and good value food; log fires, friendly staff, a welcome for walkers and children, restaurant, garden with barbecue *(J Windle,*

Gordon Theaker)*

Tal y Bont [B5106 6 miles S of Conwy, towards Llanrwst; SH7669], *White Lion*: Two small bars with copper-topped tables, modern furniture, Banks's beers; piped music *(Dr John Innes)*; *Y Bedol*: Well kept and friendly Vale of Conwy village local, dark beams, winter open fire, well kept Tetleys on handpump *(BB)*

Tal y Cafn [A470 Conway—Llanrwst; SH7972], *Tal y Cafn*: Handy for Bodnant Gardens, cheerful and comfortable lounge bar with big inglenook, simple but good value bar food from sandwiches up, Greenalls on handpump; very popular with families, seats in spacious garden *(KC, LYM)*

☆ **Talsarnau** [SH6236], *Caerffynnon Hall*: Interesting bar with raised area overlooking sea, good range of good value meals, esp puddings, from buttery bar, well kept Bass and M & B Mild on handpump; tables in attractive courtyard with water garden, stupendous views from entrance; bedrooms, and self-catering *(John Towers)*

☆ **Tremadog** [SH5640], *Golden Fleece*: Cheerful stone-built inn in attractive village square, with simply furnished rambling beamed lounge bar with unusual arched serving area, nice little snug, games in public bar, tables in sheltered inner courtyard under Perspex roof — even a solarium/sauna; wide choice of food from side food bar, also restaurant meals; Marstons Pedigree tapped from the cask; children in bistro or small room off courtyard; closed Sun *(RT, LYM)*

Tudweiliog [B4417, Lleyn Peninsula; SH2437], *Lion*: Extended and very welcoming village pub with cosy main bar (no music) and noisier bar with pool and TV; excellent value home-made food in big family dining room with children's helpings, well kept ales and wines; back garden with DIY barbecue and lovely views, front one with tables made from old mill wheels, play area; bedrooms clean, well equipped and good value *(Angela and Frank)*

☆ **Tyn-y-Groes**, [B5106 N of village; SH7672], *Groes*: Lovely old low-beamed medieval pub, full of character, good bar food (not Sun evening in winter) inc excellent fresh fish, esp wild salmon, interesting furnishings and decor, two good log fires in winter, lots of fresh flowers in summer, attractive Victorian-style dining room; may be live music summer Sun evenings; tables on pretty terrace and garden with views of Conwy river and Snowdonia *(RJS, LYM)*

POWYS

☆ **Bleddfa** [A488; SO2168], *Hundred House*: Comfortable and attractively furnished stripped stone lounge bar with very fine fireplace stacked with huge logs, antlers on wall, friendly family service, particularly good home cooking, well kept Marstons Pedigree, separate bar and games room; tables outside, lovely countryside *(A P Jeffreys, Gwen and Peter Andrews, Joy Heatherley)*

☆ **Carno** [A470 Newtown—Machynlleth; SN9697], *Aleppo Merchant*: A welcoming and reliable haven, with plushly modernised stripped stone bar, sofas and easy chairs in small lounge, games in public bar, wide choice of bar food from sandwiches to steaks, well kept real ales such as Burtonwood and Marstons Pedigree, restaurant, friendly service; bedrooms comfortable and good value, sharing bathrooms *(Norman and Kathleen Edwardes, A R Nash, Nick Blackstock, Peter Watkins, Pam Stanley, LYM)*

☆ **Crickhowell** [1 1/2 miles NW, by junction A40/A479; SO2118], *Nantyffin Cider Mill*: Popular food pub in handy main-road position, attractive surroundings, enormous log fire in end dining area, good choice of consistent food, ramp provision for disabled people, good parking alongside; keg beers, decent ciders *(Anne Morris, E W B and M G Wauton, David Williams, M E Hughes, A J Madel, Col G D Stafford, BB)*
Crickhowell [New Rd; SO2118], *Bridge End*: Friendly, attractive pub with pretty window-boxes and troughs; well kept Bass and Worthington BB on handpump, attractive food, open all day *(John Nash)*
Cwmdu [A479 NW of Crickhowell; SO1823], *Farmers Arms*: Welcoming cottagey pub with well kept Brains, bar food, pleasant staff, tables in big garden and out in front; bedrooms; handy for Black Mountains *(Gwyneth and Salvo Spadaro-Dutturi)*

☆ **Defynnog**, [SN9228], *Lion*: Carefully restored roadside pub with good value generous straightforward food, warm fires, well kept Flowers real ales, pleasant service, good atmosphere, witty and chatty landlord *(Hilary Roberts, LYM)*

☆ **Derwenlas** [A487 Machynlleth—Aberystwyth — OS Sheet 135, map reference 723992; SN7299], *Black Lion*: Quaint 450-year-old pub in short terrace with huge log fire in low-beamed bar divided by oak posts and cartwheels, friendly quick service, cottagey furnishings with nice individual touches, well kept Marstons Pedigree on handpump, basic choice of decent wines, unobtrusive piped music; good home-cooked bar food inc wide choice of vegetarian dishes in dining area; garden up behind (no dogs), with log cabin in adventure playground and steps up into woods *(Wendy Finch, Gordon and Daphne, DJW)*

☆ **Dolfor** [inn signed up hill from A483 about 4 miles S of Newtown; SO1187], *Dolfor*: Welcoming much modernised inn high in the hills, with easy chairs in beamed lounge opening into neatly modern dining area, generously served food, well kept Davenports and Tetleys on handpump, unobtrusive piped music, good views from terrace; bedrooms comfortable and good value *(Mrs Y M Healey, LYM)*
Elan Valley [B4518, by reservoir; off A44/A470 in Rhayader; SN9365], *Elan Valley*: In nice position by reservoir with

tiled bar, friendly landlord, polite staff and bar snacks; keg beer *(Gwen and Peter Andrews)*

☆ **Gladestry**, [SO2355], *Royal Oak*: Unpretentious welcoming beamed and flagstoned inn on Offa's Dyke, quiet and relaxing, with well kept Bass and Worthington BB, welcoming licensees, good home-cooked bar food inc fine ham ploughman's; refurbished lounge, separate bar, picnic-table sets in lovely secluded garden behind; evenings not open till 6.30; bedrooms sparkling clean, well equipped and good value, with good breakfasts *(A P Jeffreys, Gwyneth and Salvo Spadaro-Dutturi)*
Gwystre [A44 about 7 miles E of Rhayader — OS Sheet 136, map reference 066657; SN0666], *Gwystre Arms*: Warmly welcoming with bar food (inc Sun lunch), keg beer, good collection of foreign banknotes *(Gwen and Peter Andrews)*
Hay on Wye [Bull Ring; SO2342], *Kilvert Court*: Small well furnished hotel bar with friendly staff, well kept Fullers ESB and other real ales on handpump, good range of bar food, ambitious restaurant; outside tables overlooking small town square; bedrooms well done, all with own bathrooms *(Patrick Godfrey, Alan Carr)*

☆ **Knighton** [SO2972], *George & Dragon*: Lots of character in small back lounge with dark old panelling, two fine old carved settles, stone fireplace, stags' heads, old pictures, brassware, swords, mugs and jugs; similar if simpler front public bar, small restaurant; interesting range of good bar food inc home-made beetroot soup, spicy Persian lamb, treacle and nut tart; friendly staff, Tetleys and Whitbreads beers *(Susan and Nigel Siesage)*
Knighton [Broad St], *Knighton*: Recently modernised; pleasant lounge bar with good service and decent choice of bar food; restaurant; bedrooms *(David Williams)*; [OS Sheet 148, map reference 287721], *Swan*: Friendly pub with wider range than usual of reasonably priced bar food, Woods Special; popular with walkers on Offa's Dyke Path *(Neil and Anita Christopher, Dave Braisted)*
Llanbedr [nr Crickhowell; SO2420], *Red Lion*: Village pub in remote valley above Crickhowell; welcoming and popular with pony-trekkers *(Julian Proudman)*
Llandinam [A470 W of Newtown; SO0388], *Poachers Pocket*: Friendly recently refurbished free house with good choice of real ales, good bar snacks and meals, clean beamed lounge bar with new leather settles and deep green carpeting *(Paul and Margaret Baker)*
Llanfair Caereinion [High St; SJ1006], *Goat*: Public bar and comfortable lounge with settees and easy chairs, inglenook fireplace with roaring coal fire; good value straightforward bar food, well kept Felinfoel and Hancocks on handpump, cheerful obliging service, garden; bedrooms good, with own bathroom *(Brian Jones, Andy and Jill Kassube, Cyril Burton)*
Llangenny [SO2417], *Dragons Head*:

Lovely spot in little riverside hamlet tucked below the Black Mountains, low beams, big log fire, pews, housekeepers' chairs and a high-backed settle among other seats, tables outside; has been outstandingly welcoming, with really good food in its small restaurant, but changed hands summer 1991 and no news yet on the new regime *(Graham and Glenis Watkins, R C Morgan, Joan Harris, Julian Proudman, Pearl and Steve Munns, LYM)*

Llangorse [SO1327], *Red Lion*: Friendly large landlord, well kept Welsh beers, good value food and attractive position by stream through village; may be crowded with summer visitors from campsite at nearby Llangorse Lake; bedrooms *(Canon K Wills, LYM)*

☆ **Llangynidr** [B4558, Cwm Crawnon; SO1519], *Coach & Horses*: Sloping canalside lawn, safely fenced — a particular attraction for families; spacious inside, with well kept Watneys-related real ales, open fire, pub games, generous well presented straightforward bar food, also restaurant *(K W J Wood, Dave Irving, A P Jeffreys, LYM)*

Llanidloes [Longbridge St; SN9584], *Unicorn*: Friendly family-run small inn with very helpful and obliging licensees, Bass beer, unobtrusive juke box in main bar, evening meals in small evening restaurant; bedrooms reasonably priced, with good breakfast *(Andrew and Ruth Triggs)*

☆ **Llowes,** [A438 Brecon—Hereford — OS Sheet 161, map reference 192416; SO1941], *Radnor Arms*: Small, modest and very old, with log fire in bar, neat little cottagey dining room, and tables in imaginatively planted garden looking out over fields towards the Wye; particularly wide choice of food from beautifully filled big rye rolls and good soups such as carrot and orange to notably good but restaurant-price main dishes, with tempting puddings; congenial atmosphere, friendly efficient service, well kept Felinfoel Double Dragon, spotless lavatories; closed Sun pm, all day Mon; at weekends it's wise to book *(PLC, David Evans, G R Simpson)*

☆ **Montgomery,** [The Square; SO2296], *Dragon*: Impressive service under new owners, in attractive and welcoming small hotel with pleasant grey-stone tiled hall, comfortable bar on left with stools, settles and tables, prints of local scenes and ducks on walls, an attractive china alcove with china; Felinfoel Double Dragon and Vaux Samson on handpump, good food from bar sandwiches to grillroom and restaurant meals, unobtrusive piped music; very quiet town below ruined Norman castle; bedrooms *(Gwen and Peter Andrews, J and M A Stroh, LYM)*

Newbridge on Wye [SO0158], *New Inn*: Friendly well modernised old village inn nicely set in upper Wye Valley, generous lunchtime hot dishes and wide variety of summer salads, good home cooking in evening restaurant, well kept Flowers IPA,

reasonable prices; spacious carpeted back lounge with button-back banquettes in big bays, good bookmatch collection in public bar with TV, snug Cabin Bar with cushioned wall benches, welcoming licensees; bedrooms *(M Joyner, C E Power, BB)*

Newtown [SO1191], *Eagles*: Upmarket, modernised town pub with good bar food and well kept Sam Powells and Samson on handpump, good wine list *(Andy and Jill Kassube)*

Old Church Stoke [SO2894], *Oak*: Lovely 16th-century pub in delightful countryside, warm welcome, beams and whitewashed stone; good food from sandwiches to steaks; good Sam Powells and Samson on handpump *(Andy and Jill Kassube)*

☆ **Painscastle** [B4594; off A470 Brecon—Builth Wells; SO1646], *Maesllwch Arms*: Village inn up in hills with spacious big-windowed main bar and cosy more traditional public bar; straightforward bar food, cold Flowers Original and a guest beer on handpump, restaurant, children welcome; an attractive area; bedrooms small but comfortable and neat — good value *(John Bowdler, Neil and Anita Christopher, LYM)*

☆ **Pencelli** [B4558 SE of Brecon — OS Sheet 161, map reference 093250; SO0924], *Royal Oak*: Clean and very friendly, with generous helpings of well presented food, Hook Norton Best, Marstons Pedigree and Wadworths 6X, obliging staff; charming terrace backing on to canal and fields, with lovely canal walks with garden in small village; open at 5 on Friday, when made very welcome by landlord and regulars; bar food (not tried) recommended strongly by several other canal boaters *(Dr Robert Hodkinson, Adam and Elizabeth Gorb)*

Pentre Bach [off A40 in Sennybridge; SN9032], *Shoemakers Arms*: Delightful, friendly pub in lovely valley; interesting choice of above-average food (calamares, Welsh lamb steaks); Boddingtons beers *(B C Stevens)*

Talgarth, [from S take first turn into town; 50 yds walk from first car park; SO1534], *Radnor Arms*: Has been marvellously preserved old-fashioned tavern with antique settles, roaring log fire in gleaming kitchen range of flagstoned parlour bar and well kept Flowers Original and Whitbreads; no reports since the long-serving landlord's retirement — can it be still the same? *(LYM)*

Trecastle [SN8729], *Castle*: Imaginative choice of good reasonably priced food under new regime, with extensive renovations; welcoming fire *(Miss E M Thomas, Mrs J Jelliffe)*

Welshpool [Raven Sq — OS Sheet 126, map reference 223081; SJ2207], *Raven*: Comfortable pub with good helpings of straightforward bar food, log fire, friendly staff, Banks's real ale; unobtrusive piped music, fruit machines, pool room, restaurant *(Neil and Anita Christopher, E H and R F Warner)*

Channel Islands

Channel Islands

We've had a thorough re-sort of the Channel Islands entries this year. Barely one in three of last year's main entries have kept their place. This does not mean that the standard of the islands' pubs has fallen abruptly – far from it. It's just that with the other pubs the flow of reports from readers has not been sufficient for us to be convinced that there's still general support for their inclusion. However, this does mean that the Lucky Dip section at the end of the chapter (always relatively strong in the Channel Islands, as we have inspected a high proportion of them and so can vouch for their qualities more directly) is this year even stronger than usual. Three newcomers to the main entries are the Fleur du Jardin at Kings Mills on Guernsey (doing very well after careful refurbishment), the Pony in St Sampsons there (more of a local than many, but well run and accommodating), and the Rozel Bay Inn at Rozel on Jersey (a very genuine little country pub, attractively placed not far from the water). Of the others, the Moulin de Lecq at Greve de Lecq on Jersey has the widest appeal; a well converted watermill, and properly pubby. The Dolphin in Gorey has good fish, in lively harbourside surroundings. On Guernsey, the well run Hougue du Pommier in its attractive and spacious grounds in Castel is probably currently the pick of the island's pubs.

Though drinks prices have been rising even more quickly on the islands than on the mainland, Jersey's pubs are still much cheaper for drinks than those on the mainland, and those on Guernsey and Sark are cheaper than the great majority. Food prices compare well with those in the best value mainland areas.

Note that Guernsey pubs are not allowed to open on Sundays, though hotels, restaurants and cafes are allowed to serve drinks with meals on that day. Jersey pubs, normally open all day, close between 1 and 4.30 on Sundays.

CASTEL (Guernsey)

Hougue du Pommier 🛏

Route de Hougue du Pommier, off Route de Carteret; just inland from Cobo Bay and Grandes Rocques

Once a cider farm (hence the name), this 18th-century house still has fruit trees around its neatly trimmed lawn. There are tables out in their shade, and also by the swimming pool in the sheltered walled garden, and in a tree-shaded courtyard with lots of flowers. Inside is roomy, though even so the appeal of the good value food can fill the oak-beamed bar, with its leatherette armed chairs around wood tables, old game and sporting prints, guns, sporting trophies and so forth. The most prized seats are perhaps those in the snug area by the big stone fireplace with its attendant bellows and copper fire-irons. The food includes home-made soup (£1.10), ploughman's (from £2.25), sandwiches (from £1.70; good open from £2.55), vegetarian dishes like mushrooms stroganoff (from £3.15), salads (from £3.20) and hot dishes such as omelettes (from £3.45), steak and kidney pie (£3.75), gammon and egg (£3.85), and 8oz steak (£5.55), puddings (£1.40), with several children's dishes (£2.15), and a couple of evening carvery roasts (from £5.75); good coffee, decent wines; pool, video game and maybe unobtrusive piped music. Good leisure facilities include a 9-hole pitch-and-putt golf course and an 18-hole putting green (for visitors as well as residents); but even though there's no bowling green one reader's 50-strong bowls touring team enjoyed their stay here so much that they've decided to return. No dogs. *(Recommended by J S Rutter, David Shillitoe, Peter Woods)*

Free house   Licensee Max Trouteaud   Meals and snacks (lunchtime; limited menu Sun)   Partly no smoking restaurant   Guernsey (0481) 56531   Children in eating area and restaurant   Open 11–2.30, 6–11.45 (not Sun unless eating)   Bedrooms; £39B/£78B

GOREY (Jersey) OS714503

Dolphin ⌾

The cheerful bar here has big bow windows looking out over the road to the harbour, sheltered in its sweeping bay by the massive rock on which medieval Mont Orgueil castle perches. The side room in which food is served shares this lively view, though attention's more likely to be focused on the fresh local fish, including grilled sardines (£3.65), stuffed clams (£4.95), moules marinières (£4.95), local plaice (£5.25), a dozen oysters (£5.75) and scallops poached in white wine (around £7.75); they also do sandwiches (from 90p, steak £2.95). The bar's woodwork and high black beams are draped with brown nets and the odd lobster-pot; it has a chatty atmosphere, with efficient largely Portuguese service; piped music. The long bar counter has some high stools, with comfortable backrests, for people eating – in the style of an old-fashioned oyster bar. *(Recommended by John Evans; more reports please)*

Free house   Manager Mr Viaira   Meals and snacks (12.15–1.45, 6.30–10.15)   (0534) 53370   Children in eating area   Live guitarist most Tues and Sat   Open 10–11 Bedrooms; £32B/£64B

GREVE DE LECQ (Jersey) OS583552 Map 1

Moulin de Lecq

Looking taller than it is wide, this serenely placed black-shuttered pink granite building is indeed a former mill – the massive reconstructed waterwheel still turns outside, its formidable gears remorselessly meshing in their stone housing behind the bar. But far from being a touristy gimmick, this is a very proper pub, with plenty of local custom and a warm and pleasant atmosphere. Unusually, it has well kept Bass and a guest such as Ringwood Old Thumper as well as Guernsey Mild and Bitter on handpump. There's a good log fire, toasting you as you come down the four steps into the bar; besides plush-cushioned black wooden seats against the white-painted walls, it has little (some would say too little) low black chairs and tables. In summer there's a lunchtime cold table with ploughman's (£2.90) and salads (from £4.55, crab or prawn £6.85), as well as home-made soup (£1.25), sandwiches (from £2.90), steak and kidney or fish pie (£4.55), with extra dishes in the evening such as chicken (£5.70) and steaks (from £6.85); there's also a good value barbecue outside. In winter they serve traditional Jersey dishes such as bean crock, rabbit casserole and beef in red wine. Service is welcoming and helpful. The terrace has picnic-table sets under cocktail parasols, with swings and a climber in the paddock. The road past here leads down to one of the only north-coast beaches; the valley and nearby coast have pleasant walks. *(Recommended by John and Karen Day, Richard Houghton, Comus Elliott, P Corris, John Evans)*

Ann Street   Licensee Gary Healey   Real ale   Meals and snacks (12–2.30, 6–8) Children in eating area   Occasional Morris dancing and folk music   Open 10(11 winter)–11

KINGS MILLS (Guernsey)

Fleur du Jardin 🕭 🛏

Kings Mills Rd

Originally a 16th-century farmhouse, this attractive steep-tiled inn has just been taken back closer to its origins, in an ambitious project to re-create something of the character of such a building. The formerly rather boxy-seeming lounge bar is now a proper public bar, its white-plastered rough stone walls matching up well with the cushioned pews and other suitable seats; there's a good log fire. The bar on the hotel side has been given an altogether more welcoming feel, with individual country furnishings, in a new lease of life as a lounge bar. But of course it's likely to be summertime when most readers make their acquaintance with the inn – when they'll see the reason for its name, in the quiet and attractive neatly kept garden in which it stands, with picnic-table sets among flowering cherries, flowering shrubs and colourful borders; the stone house itself is bright with hanging baskets, and unusual flower barrels cut lengthwise rather than across. There's a play area. One reader who's been eating here every month or so virtually since it opened reckons that the food, always good, is currently on top form. It includes soup (£1.50), sandwiches (from £1.50, hot char-grilled steak £4.95), filled baked potatoes (from £1.60), ploughman's (£2.45), vegetarian dishes (from £3.25), home-made steak and kidney pie or burger (£3.95), a choice of salads (from £3.95) and half a roast chicken (£4.50); steaks such as the 8oz fillet (£7.95) are particularly recommended. Well kept Guernsey Bitter on handpump, and maybe other guest beers; friendly efficient service; unobtrusive piped music. Part of the restaurant is no smoking. *(Recommended by J T Charman(*

Free house   Licensee Keith Reid   Real ale   Meals and snacks (12–2.15, 6–9)   Partly no smoking restaurant   (0481) 57996   Children lunchtime only (till 3 Sat)   Open 11–2.30, 5–11.45; all day Sat in summer   Bedrooms; £32B/£64B

ROZEL (Jersey)

Rozel Bay

This proper little country local is just moments inland, on the edge of the peaceful and pretty bayside village – where you may see geese stepping cumbersomely along the pebble beach. There are tables under cocktail parasols by the quiet lane past the pub, and more behind, by attractive gardens steeply terraced up the hillside. Inside, the small dark-beamed back bar has old prints and local pictures on its cream walls, and dark plush wall seats and round stools around its low tables. The simple serving bar has a little shelf of toby jugs above it, and its clock claims that Guinness es bouan por te; a pool room leads off. Lunchtime bar food includes sandwiches (prawn £1.50, crab £1.80), salads (from £3.25), scampi (£3.25) and pies in winter (£1.75). Bass on handpump; darts, video game and piped music, cheerful landlord. *(Recommended by John and Karen Day, Julian Yorke, Comus Elliott)*

Randalls   Tenant John Holmes   Real ale   Lunchtime meals and snacks (not Sun)   (0534) 63438   Children welcome   Occasional live entertainment   Open 10–11

ST HELIER (Jersey)

Lamplighter £

Mulcaster Street

The facade, highly ornamental with its elegantly arched windows and proudly carved Britannia surmounting it, might make you expect rather flamboyant plush comfort inside. In fact, the bar is decidedly back to basics, with gas lighting, heavy timber baulks, grainy panelling, scrubbed pine tables, solid old pews and captains' or country-kitchen chairs: the atmosphere is happily pubby and relaxed. Bar food includes generously filled sandwiches (from 90p), sausage and French bread

(£1.90), ploughman's (£2), shepherd's pie (£2.30), cod or plaice (£2.70), salads (from £2.50), scampi (£2.90) and daily specials (£2.50); Bass on handpump, and good cider; darts, cribbage and dominoes. The only pub in this book where you can start drinking well kept real ale at 9am for under £1, and go on drinking it for another fourteen hours. *Recommended by Steve and Carolyn Harvey, Comus Elliott, Alec Lewery)*

Randalls   Tenant David Ellis   Real ale   Lunchtime meals and snacks (not Sat/Sun)
(0534) 23119   Children at one end of bar   Open 9am–11; closed evening 25 Dec

ST MARTIN (Guernsey)
Auberge Divette

Jerbourg; near south-east tip of island

Cheerfully unpretentious, this friendly country pub has button-back banquettes in bays around low tables in its picture-window bar; this leads through folding doors into a small carpeted lounge, with more banquettes and bucket seats. A good straightforward range of bar food includes sandwiches (from £1), ploughman's (£2.50), bacon, egg, sausage and chips (£3), salads (from £3, fresh crab £7)), scampi (£5), steaks (from £7), and children's menu (£1.50); well kept Guernsey Mild on handpump; very friendly staff, maybe piped music. The high-ceilinged back public bar has sensibly placed darts and bar billiards. The pub's glory is the view from the seats under cocktail parasols out in the fairy-lit garden. This is set high above the sea, with the ground falling steeply away below, so you can see right along the coast past St Peter Port to the top of Guernsey, with Herm lying off to the right. *(Recommended by Peter and Bridgett Kitson, John Knighton, Dr and Mrs A K Clarke)*

Guernsey Brewery   Tenant David Lane   Real ale   Meals and snacks (12–1.30, 8.30–10, not Thurs evening or Sun)   (0481) 38485   Children lunchtime only   Open 10.30–11; closed Sun

ST SAMPSONS (Guernsey)
Pony £

Les Capelles

Not one of the island's older buildings, this has quite a spacious and smart lounge, done in warm shades of brown, with plush armchairs, smart neat booth, and dark plank panelling. It has quite a local feel – even more so in the main public bar, with two darts boards, video game, juke box and maybe TV on together, also pool and shove-ha'penny. Bar food includes sandwiches (from 60p), ploughman's (£1.60), sausage (£1.70), ham and egg (£1.90), salads (from £2.20), home-made pasties (from £2.50), home-made pies (from £2.75) and steaks (from £4.60). Well kept Guernsey Mild and Bitter on handpump. There are picnic-table sets under cocktail parasols out in front; the pub's handy for the Oatlands Crafts Centre and Guernsey Candles.*(Recommended by R Houghton, J T Charman)*

Guernsey Brewery   Manager Richard Guillou   Real ale   Meals and snacks (not weekday evenings)   (0481) 44374   Children in lounge bar at lunchtime   Open 10.30–11; not Sun

---

Lucky Dip

Besides the fully inspected pubs, you might like to try these Lucky Dips recommended to us and described by readers (if you do, please send us reports):

ALDERNEY
Newtown, *Rose & Crown*: Clean, smart and welcoming pub with Cries of London prints, Wadworths 6X on handpump, interesting menu inc fish curry *(Graham Gibson)*

St Anne, *Campania*: Traditional pub with games and children's rooms, used by locals and holidaymakers; seat on pavement lets you watch the bustle of the town *(K Flack)*; [Victoria St], *Georgian House*: Relaxing and welcoming friendly bar with good food, restaurant, and comfortable bedrooms *(K Flack)*

GUERNSEY

Castel [Cobo Coast Rd], *Rockmount*: Verandahed small hotel with thickly cushioned leatherette seats in carpeted lounge; generously and happily served seafood bar lunches inc good crab sandwiches, good beer; picture windows overlook attractive beach with windsurfing school in pretty rock channels — and face the sunsets; bedrooms *(J S Rutter, BB)*

Forest [Le Bourg], *Deerhound*: Converted farmhouse with separate rather pleasant restaurant and terrace behind this; pub lounge with well kept beer and chequered-tablecloth bistroish dining area for superb bar food; bedrooms basic *(Dr and Mrs A K Clarke)*

Grande Havre [Rte de Picquerel (part of Houmet du Nord Hotel)], *Houmet*: Big picture windows overlook rock and sand beach; cushioned library chairs and heavy rustic oak tables in high-ceilinged saloon with bar billiards, video game and friendly staff; food from sandwiches to steaks; bedrooms *(BB)*

☆ **Rocquaine Bay**, *Rocquaine Bistro*: Perhaps the best views in Guernsey — splendid outlook over bay filled with fishing or sports boats, little islets, subtle colours; chiefly to be thought of now as a good seafood restaurant, partly no smoking, though the cool winebar-ish quarry-tiled bar is a nice place to enjoy their good wines, and some of the lighter dishes (half a dozen oysters, say) from their magnificent crushed-ice display could be thought of as snacks; one room no smoking, tables on terrace; children welcome, closed winter *(J S Rutter, LYM)*

Rocquaine Bay [Rte de la Lague], *Imperial*: Very good lunchtime snacks inc ploughman's and filled rolls (fresh French bread); hotel with fine sea view, good service; bedrooms *(Julian Yorke)*

St Andrew [nr Little Chapel], *Last Post*: Largeish, with comfortable lounge, genuine public bar, pleasant service, Randalls Mild tapped from the cask; lunchtime food, live entertainment Fri and Sat, open all day *(R Houghton)*

St Martin [La Fosse], *Captains Hotel*: Plenty of atmosphere in the three attractively cosy separate areas of this Tudor-style open-plan bar, in small hotel tucked away in unfrequented area; hot decently presented bar food such as chicken cordon bleu, well kept Guernsey Best from antique handpump, pleasant service, plenty of locals, games area, terrace; open all day, closed Sun; bedrooms *(J S Rutter, Richard Houghton)*; [La Grande Rue], *Queens*: Good service in conventionally pubby lounge of comfortable hotel, well kept Randalls and XXX, nice atmosphere with plenty of locals, bar lunches; open all day; bedrooms *(R Houghton)*

☆ **St Peter Port** [N Esplanade], *Ship & Crown*: Lively yet civilised traditional locals' pub sharing its building with the Royal Guernsey Yacht Club; lots of interesting local sea pictures in main bar, drawings of tall ships in quieter back bar; good reasonably priced bar food, Guernsey Bitter on handpump, a decent range of malt whiskies; only reason it is not a main entry is lack of current readers' reports *(LYM)*

☆ **St Peter Port** [S Esplanade; by bus stn], *Harbour Lights*: Spacious upstairs lounge looking past trees to harbour locally very popular for lunch — neat waitresses bring sandwiches, ploughman's, salads, omelettes, home-made pies and fish (no food evening); downstairs bar with Guernsey Bitter on handpump, darts under pressure; darts in downstairs bar *(P Corris, BB)*

☆ **St Peter Port**, *Salerie*: Blue-painted pub with lovely atmosphere in its friendly open-plan bar, well polished brass, a model ship and other nautical bits and pieces, an oar from a sunken ship, well kept Guernsey Bitter and Mild on handpump, and lunchtime snacks *(Graham Gibson, Ron and Audrey Davidson)*

St Peter Port [Fort Rd/Rte de Sausmarez], *Fermain*: Attractive local with masses of interesting foreign banknotes, in good condition, on the dark brown walls of its parquet-floored saloon; also biggish brightly lit public bar with pool, sensibly placed darts, space game; well kept beer, quick service *(BB)*; [St Jacques], *La Collinette*: Pleasant and relaxing pastiche of small pub bar behind smart hotel, good reasonably priced lunchtime food, good Guernsey Grizzly (mix of Mild and Bitter), darts and shove-ha'penny in separate area; bedrooms *(R Houghton)*; [Rohais Rd], *Pierrots*: Very smart pricey cocktail bar (happy hour 7-8) in cool greens and browns with dark bentwood cane-seat chairs and broad marble-topped tables, well reproduced pop music, small sunken corner dance floor for live music; opens into airy tiled-floor brasserie, and into broad terrace by neat lawn running down to pretty pool and fountain, with tennis courts beyond; part of well run St Pierre Hotel *(BB)*; [The Arcade; off High St, behind Town Church], *Taylors*: Plush upstairs eating bar with a good range of snacky things, downstairs bar more in the style of an airy cafe, with tulip-style brass lamps on the long mahogany counter, pretty Victorian tiles around the fireplace, raj fans; a good choice of wines by the glass *(LYM)*; [S Esplanade], *White Hart*: Plush upmarket town bar by harbour, popular at lunchtime for good fish, meat and other food; quick service, downstairs members-only disco *(R A Corbett)*

St Sampsons, *English & Guernsey*: Spacious modern lounge with green glass-and-brass chandeliers, leatherette cushioned blond captains' chairs, big brass clock, French windows to tables on sheltered lawn (shame about that nearby factory); also small snug bar, big plain harbourside public bar with darts, pool and side games room with pin-table and space game *(BB)*; *Mariners*: Locals' bar not much changed — 1860s

polychrome tiled floor, knotty veneer
panelling, sensibly placed darts, cafe seats
and leatherette wall benches, local punters
watching horse-racing on TV; lounge bar
recently refurbished; on harbour *(BB)*
St Saviour [rue de la Perelle; Perelle Bay],
Atlantique: Pleasant bar with no smoking
area, good value food, well kept Guernsey
beers; bedrooms *(David Shillitoe)*

HERM
Mermaid: Truly idyllic setting, good
Guernsey real ale, basic food; tables out
with the birds *(J S Rutter, Graham Gibson)*;
Ship: Pleasant surroundings on fabulous
island; delicious local oysters and other
seafood, nursery puddings, good wines;
comfortable bedrooms *(J S Rutter)*

JERSEY
☆ **Beaumont** [OS map reference 613498],
Foresters Arms: Pleasant local with tables on
front terrace looking across road to St
Aubins Bay; in fact the island's oldest pub,
with big fire in quarry-tiled low-beamed
main bar, lots of shiny black woodwork in
plush side bar, simple lunchtime bar food
(not Sun); children allowed in lounge; open
all day *(LYM)*
Gorey [just off coast rd about ½ mile N],
Anne Port Bay: Nice comfortable locally
popular front bar, friendly and relaxed, with
good service, well kept Bass and Marstons
Pedigree tapped from the cask; bedrooms *(R
Houghton)*
Greve de Lecq [OS map reference 582554],
Prince of Wales: Huge lounge with battery
of video games and well lit pool tables, also
juke box; picture windows looking over roof
terrace to small pretty sandy bay in pink
granite cove; restaurant; live bands;
bedrooms *(BB)*
Grouville [La Rocque; coast rd St
Helier—Gorey;], *Seymour*: Very
comfortable and locally popular lounge bar
in recent extension, well kept Guernsey LBA
Mild and Bitter, food lunchtime and
evening, pleasant service; genuine public bar
(R Houghton)
☆ **Le Hocq** [St Clements Coast Rd — OS map
reference 685466], *Le Hocq*: The most
southerly pub in the British Isles, just over
road from interesting rocky sand beach;
green plush button-back seats, Turkey
carpet, heavy cast-iron-framed tables, ship
pictures on gold Regency wallpaper — very
popular for quickly served standard bar
food; some tables on front terrace, side
lobby with tortoise rocker; pool, darts and
space game in tiled public; on a clear day
you can see France from the upstairs
restaurant and cocktail bar *(Comus Elliott,
BB)*
☆ **St Aubin** [le Boulevard — OS map reference
607486;], *Old Court House*: Good
atmosphere and friendly service in properly
pubby low-beamed granite-walled basement
bar with dimly lit inner room and tables in
front courtyard — can get very busy with St
Helier's young professionals; also upstairs

cocktail bar elegantly crafted as aft cabin of
a galleon, with good views across the
tranquil harbour to the fort and beyond; a
short choice of genuine bar food inc
vegetarian dishes, and a restaurant that's
been very popular for fish; the bedrooms,
not large but nicely furnished (and with
good views), are attractive though not all
escape noise from the restaurant *(J S Evans,
John and Karen Day, LYM; more reports
please)*
☆ **St Brelade** [Ouaisne Bay — OS map
reference 595476], *Smugglers*: Genuine local
atmosphere in friendly and comfortable
thick-walled black-beamed pub just above
Ouaisne beach and slipway, sensibly placed
darts, cosy black built-in settles, little sun
porch, well kept Bass on handpump, friendly
service, good value quickly served bar food
inc children's dishes (with an activity sheet
to keep them busy); the name refers to
World War Two smuggling; pretty public
gardens further along beach; children in
central lounge *(John and Karen Day, Geoffrey
Pegram, Comus Elliott, BB)*
☆ **St Brelade** [Portelet Bay — OS map
reference 603472], *Old Portelet*: Extensive
series of beamed bars in stonebuilt former
17th-century farmhouse, above fine
distant-view climb down to sheltered cove;
well kept Bass and Marstons Pedigree,
uniformed staff, neatly kept lounge bar, well
equipped children's room, buffet dining
room with good lunchtime food, upstairs
1920s bar, partly covered flower-bower
terrace, spacious garden, pervasive pop
music; open all day; children welcome *(Andy
and Jill Kassube, Comus Elliott, Richard
Houghton, K Flack, BB)*
St Brelade [St Ouen road — OS map
reference 562488], *La Pulente*: Across road
from the island's longest beach; popular
with older local people for lunch, with short
good value choice maybe inc fresh seafood;
more main dishes in evening, inc steaks;
Bass on handpump; green leatherette
armchairs in smallish lounge, sailing ship
prints, leatherette-topped tables; fairy-lit
side terrace *(BB)*
☆ **St Helier** [Charing Cross; King St/Sand St],
La Bourse: Old-fashioned single-room bar
with individual decor inc framed junk
bonds, 19th-century French cartoons; quite
a choice of seafood along with more
ordinary but still good bar food, upstairs
restaurant (where children are allowed);
open all day *(J M Watson, LYM)*
St Helier [Halkett St], *Dog & Sausage*:
Comfortable and neatly refurbished town
pub, handy for shops; some snug small
rooms *(BB)*; [Esplanade; next to Swansons
Hotel], *Esplanade*: Large open-plan bar with
local atmosphere, decent service, well kept
Bass and Ruddles County on handpump,
food lunchtime and evening; open all day,
not Sun *(R Houghton)*; [The Quay; between
English and French Harbour — OS map
reference 649478], *La Folie*: A real
harbourman's pub, quite unpretentious and
untouristy — three little rooms with simple

seats, lots of brightly varnished woodwork, big pictures of fish and ships, chart, nautical brassware; cheerful and clean; on harbour though no views *(BB)*; [Royal Sq], *Peirsons*: Traditionally furnished old town pub with green plush button-back seats, Turkey carpet, cast-iron-framed tables, old prints, some black panelling, Bass on handpump — can get very crowded down here; usual food upstairs (where there's less atmosphere); in quiet chestnut-shaded square near shops *(Andy and Jill Kassube, BB)*

☆ St John [Le Grand Mourier — OS map reference 620565;], *Les Fontaines*: Its great appeal is as an unspoilt country local — not the ordinary biggish main bar with its straightforward food, piped music and machines, but the tucked-away back public bar, with its heavy black beams, irregular granite walls, tiled floor, basic furnishings and cottagey decorations — somewhere you can still hear the local patois, and drink good Bass or cheap French wine; attractive setting near the cliffs of the island's northernmost tip *(LYM)*

☆ St Lawrence [opp parish church], *British Union*: Lively local with welcome for visitors, good friendly service, well kept Guernsey LBA Mild and Bitter on handpump, food lunchtime and evening (not Sun), interior like a mainland town pub — two separate bars, with huge family room where children very welcome; open all day (afternoon closure Sun) *(Richard Houghton)*
St Peter [part of small hotel complex nr airport — OS map reference 592507], *Mermaid*: Pretty creeper-covered pub, separated by pond and swimming pool from modern hotel; black beams, plank ceiling, Spanish-style cream flooring tiles, some seats cut into thick walls, wheelback chairs around black lacquered tables, big fireplace in end stone wall; darts, juke box, space games, and pool room with pin-table and space game; simple bar food; bedrooms *(BB)*; [St Peters Mill — OS map reference 595540], *Windmill*: Neatly rebuilt windmill with partly galleried lounge bar —

cushioned milk churns, pews built into stable-stall-like alcoves, usual bar food reasonably priced, country music; pool, juke box and sensibly placed darts in quarry-tiled public bar; restaurant and diners' cocktail bar in mill tower; tables in neat garden *(P Corris, BB)*

☆ Trinity [Bouley Bay — OS map reference 669546], *Waters Edge*: Comfortable largely modern big hotel with spacious well kept waterside grounds and picture-window sea views; it does have a 17th-century core, and its Black Dog bar has an attractive stripped-stone decor, with a relaxed atmosphere and neatly uniformed staff; lunchtime bar food (not Sun) can range from the ordinary to fresh local crab or lobster; keg Whitbreads, good choice of wines, open all day *(Comus Elliott)*

SARK

Bel Air: First tourist stop (where the tractors climb to from the jetty): big woodburning stove in comfortable Boat Bar with plank ceiling, easy chairs and settees, model ship, boat-shaped counter; old boat pictures in simpler Harbour Bar; darts, piped pop music, tables on terrace outside this pretty cottage *(BB); Mermaid*: A real country local, basketwork chairs and cloth wall seats in lino- floor entrance bar, big and friendly games bar, paperback charity sales, snacks such as sandwiches and ploughman's, keg beers (not too fizzy or chilly), tea and coffee; seats on side terrace; welcoming *(BB)*

☆ *Stocks Hotel*: Cushioned easy chairs and small settees along with the red leatherette banquettes of the snug stone-and-beams bar, with its stormy sailing-ship prints; friendly service, good conservatory food bar with above-average food, partly no smoking restaurant, rustic seats out in sheltered courtyard, bookable tables by swimming pool; loses its place among the main entries only because of a lack of readers' reports this year; comfortable bedrooms *(David Shillitoe, LYM)*

Overseas *Lucky Dip*

We're always interested to hear of good bars and pubs (or — more desirably — their genuine local equivalents) overseas. Readers have recently recommended the following (we start with ones in the British Isles, then go alphabetically through other countries).

IRELAND

Belfast [Grt Victoria St; opp Europa Hotel], *Crown Tap*: Gas mantles, ornate decoration, booths, and a wonderful atmosphere; good lunchtime meals and locally brewed Hilden ale; one of the best pubs we've ever been to *(Dr and Mrs A K Clarke)*; [central], *Garrick*: Comfortable and well kept, with good lunchtime food *(David Simpson)*

Birdhill, *Matt the Thresher*: Well refurbished, with lots of small rooms, good food inc good choice of Irish cheeses, interesting memorabilia *(Alec Lewery, Marie Enright)*

Bray [turn left, coming from Dublin], *Harbour Bar*: Very lively place with lots of little rooms, nice decorations inc a stuffed moosehead and nautical souvenirs; friendly staff, good Guinness, open fires in lounge *(David and Rebecca Killick)*; [1 Castle St; keep straight on when Dublin—Wexford rd bears right], *P McCormack & Sons*: Lots of brass and stained glass, salvaged church furniture, lush plants hanging from skylight, handsome brown and white floor tiles, open fires, two levels — the lower one slightly more intimate; nice combination of modern and traditional seating, wide choice of good weekday lunchtime food from sandwiches through salads to roast chicken, very cheerful helpful staff *(Diane Duane-Smyth, Peter Morwood)*; [seafront], *Tony Doyles*: Long pub with two front rooms, one behind, and back terrace; mixed modern/traditional decor — ceiling fans, old brass cash registers, woodwork salvaged from churches and other old buildings, oak or marble-topped tables, open fires, plenty of seats; popular with young people at weekends, next to the Big Easy jazz/rock club *(Diane Duane-Smyth, Peter Morwood)*

Crawfordsburn [Main St], *Crawfordsburn*: Mainly a hotel (actually Ireland's oldest) but has basic function as a pub; quaint decor with open peat fire; thatched roof, unspoilt interior; small back garden in summer; good bar food, often inc local fish; bedrooms *(Karen Anderson)*

Delgany [off N11 towards Greystones], *Delgany*: Recently redone in pale woods, with spotlighting, hunting prints and paintings, glass etched with horse portraits; very bright and cheerful but booth seating gives feeling of privacy; all well kept, with very attentive staff, open fire, wide-screen TV for sporting events; bedrooms *(Diane*

Duane-Smyth, Peter Morwood); *Wicklow Arms*: Big rambling homely place, plenty of busy staff, good food lunchtime and evening, open fires, tables on back terrace *(Diane Duane-Smyth, Peter Morwood)*

Donnybrook [22 Donnybrook Rd; main Dublin—Wexford rd], *Kielys*: Large and handsome, rather Belle Epoque with its dark blue, gilt and mirrors; huge bar, very friendly efficient staff, lunchtime food, friendly customers *(Diane Duane-Smyth, Peter Morwood)*

Dublin [behind airport], *Boot*: Old building behind the airport — full of character, horse tack and stuffed animals; flagstones, barrel tables and good Guinness; no juke box or machines — all the noise comes from customers and staff *(David and Rebecca Killick)*; [Royal Hibernian Way; off Dawson St], *Buttery Brasserie*: Slightly art deco, with panelling, brass and marble bar, architectural prints; food lunchtime and evening, very busy evening with friendly fashion and media crowd *(Diane Duane-Smyth, Peter Morwood)*; [23/25 Upper Grand Canal St], *Kitty O'Sheas*: Well preserved Victorian pub close to national stadium; splendid place for Guinness if you're prepared to wait; designed now to cater for big numbers of customers with very little seating; friendly, as one would expect, live music *(D P Ryan)*; [Park Gate St], *Ryans*: Original Victorian gem, with huge mirrors, cash booths, very friendly staff *(David and Rebecca Killick)*

Dundrum, *Bay*: Typical Ulster country pub with very lively entertainment most nights, esp Fri; atmosphere friendly if a little smoky *(M McCartney)*

Foynes [High St], *Shannon House*: Good food, friendly staff in pub much like an English one; Sun lunchtime the best time to eat — waitress service then *(Alec Lewery, Marie Enright)*

Galway, *Two Quays*: Interesting high-ceilinged town pub with ochre paintwork, unassuming fixtures and fittings, and a wide ranging clientele *(Phil and Sally Gorton)*

Glencullen [about 4 miles NW of Enniskerry], *Foxs*: Slate floors well scattered with sawdust, panelling, some stripped stone, big open fires — run by Johnny Fo, an auctioneer who filled it with bric-a-brac inc lots of stuffed foxes, chiming clocks, china figures, old mirrors, ancient radios, indescribable farm tools, liberated signposts, overstuffed sofas and other massive furniture; bar food, highly regarded seafood restaurant, hard-worked amiable staff; tables in front with view of Wicklow mountains, live singing most nights *(Diane Duane-Smyth, Peter Morwood)*

Glengormley [585 Antrim Rd (A6)], *Crown & Shamrock*: Typical little Irish bar — good place to meet and talk to the locals *(Dr and Mrs A K Clarke)*

Gormanstown [main Dublin—Belfast rd], *Cock*: Old coaching inn, much added to over the years, with banquette booths around panelled main room, handsome carving, aeronautical and other memorabilia framed or hanging; newly renovated, with own putting green; also known as McAuleys *(Diane Duane-Smyth, Peter Morwood)*

Greystones [Church Rd], *Burnaby*: Sprawly pub done in dark woods, stained glass and brass, with spacious and comfortable lounge, good lunchtime food from sandwiches through lasagne, quiche lorraine, chicken tikka and so forth; tables out behind, occasional summer live music; bedrooms *(Diane Duane-Smyth, Peter Morwood)*

Hillsborough [21 Main St], *Hillside*: Remarkably close to the relaxed atmosphere of a classic country village pub, quite old and genuine; friendly licensee, well kept Hilden from the brewery six miles away, Guinness both chilled and at cellar temperature, good bar food such as vegetarian lasagne or steak, Guinness and honey pie, good restaurant upstairs; unusual wines by the glass; the village itself is attractive, too *(David Simpson, Diane Duane-Smyth, Peter Morwood)*

Kilkenny [N10, 2 miles E], *Pike*: Friendly local with a warm welcome for strangers, particularly good food from sandwiches and children's dishes through starters inc good home-made vegetable soup served with a dollop of crème fraiche to a notable chicken kiev and big sirloin steaks; real fire in lounge, hand-worked hardwoods, comfortable chairs, live Irish music Thurs *(Jody Lynn Nye)*

Killaloe, *Pipers*: Good charcoal grill choice and a lot of garlic-based starters; friendly staff *(Alec Lewery, Marie Enright)*

Kilorglin, *Nicks Piano Bar*: Amazing pub with comfortable bar, bottle-green grand piano played most evenings, the music ranging from pop to classics; well kept beer and fine bar food with good range of seafood dishes *(John Jones)*

Loughgall [Ballyhagan Rd], *Famous Grouse*: Very popular country pub with open fire, traditional furnishings, antiques and old books, and stone fireplace; a variety of home-made bar food inc daily specials like steak and kidney, boiled leg of mutton, seafood crumble, chicken and chips, beef bourguignonne; friendly service even when busy, good beer, decent choice of malts; darts and pool *(David Finan)*

Portlaoise [Abbeyleix], *Morrisseys*: Wonderful old building with wooden walls

stained brown with years of smoke, an old delivery bike on one, and a big cast-iron stove that dominates the maze of snugs; rather like a grocer's shop or Brown Bar in Amsterdam *(Julian Winterborne)*

Schull [Main St], *Bunrattys*: Good food, bar menu till 6 then restaurant menu too, and good choice of drinks in recently extended family-run pub with friendly staff; dogs allowed, gets crowded in summer *(Pat and Clive Sherriff)*

Shannon [N18 towards Limerick; nr Bunratty Castle], *Durty Nellys*: Complex set of bars in heavily beamed and panelled old pub, huge log fires, hidden lights and old-fashioned lamps, sawdust on the stone floor, elks' antlers and other rarities; bar food and good restaurant, live music brings great atmosphere — as well as crowds; pronounced Dorrty Nelly's *(GB, CH, John Innes, Simon Turner)*

Tralee, *Kirbys Brogue*: Nice, old-fashioned stone-floored bar with live bands some evenings; restaurant on top floor *(Alec Lewery, Marie Enright)*

Waterville, *Lobster*: Typical Irish bar with lots of local character outside the main tourist season; good food, pleasant atmosphere, owner a keen fisherman who can give good advice on where to try *(John Innes)*

LUNDY

Lundy, *Marisco*: Only pub on island, doubles as a store — so it's a surprise to find that it brews its own good Puffin ale; modest food *(Simon Reed, Robert Humphreys)*

ISLE OF MAN

Ballasalla [Airport Rd; SC2870], *Whitestone*: Above-average, comfortable with most efficient service — your order may reach the table before you do *(Janet and John Towers)*

Crosby [Peel Rd; SC3390], *Crosby*: Recently refurbished; on the TT course, with Mike Hailwood's TT bike in the lounge *(Dr and Mrs A K Clarke)*

Glenmaye [S of Peel — OS Sheet 95, map reference 236798; SC2480], *Waterfall*: Pleasant and comfortable, interesting choice of well cooked food, Castletown Bitter; on GWG141, in lovely glen *(John Towers)*

Laxey [Tram Stn — OS Sheet 95, map reference 433846; SC4484], *Mines Tavern*: In lovely woodland clearing where Manx electric railway and Snaefell mountain railway connect; old advertisements and tram pictures, home cooking, and Okells ales; can sit outside and watch Victorian trams — one forms the bar counter *(Quentin Williamson, Dr and Mrs A K Clarke)*

Onchan [Avondale Rd; SC4079], *Archibald Knox*: Very comfortable, Okells ales and standard lunches *(Dr and Mrs A K Clarke)*

Port Erin [Station Rd; SC2069], *Haven*: Next to steam rly stn; bright, clean, wood-panelled place with good value food and Okells Castletown ales *(Quentin Williamson)*

Ramsey [Market Pl — OS Sheet 95, map reference 454944; SC4594], *Royal George*: Next to harbour, comfortable modern seating, well kept Okells Castletown ales, fresh cod especially good *(Dr C D E Morris)*

AUSTRALIA

Adelaide [Pultney St; corner with Carrington St], *Earl of Aberdeen*: Own-brew pub — brewery is visible through end wall, and the Scotch Ale is fairly authentic; pleasant brewery memorabilia on wall, wooden bar counter *(Ben Wimpenny)*

Fremantle [64 South Terr; W Australia], *Sail & Anchor*: Closest thing to an English pub here, occasional guitarist in big covered courtyard behind, do-it-yourself barbecues *(Phil Bryant)*

Melbourne [Flemington Rd; Victoria], *Redback Brewery*: Good home-brewed Bitter (not cheap) in art deco pub, very busy in the evenings with young trendy people, upmarket bar servery; view sizeable brewery through side windows; live bands upstairs *(Nick Dowson, Alison Hayward)*

Sydney [George St, The Rocks], *Fortune of War*: Good place for a lunchtime swifty, big bar and impressive beer garden; crowds spill out into the street in the evening *(Ben Wimpenny)*; [Lower Fort St, The Rocks], *Hero of Waterloo*: Good atmosphere, ten beers on tap; can get touristy *(Ben Wimpenny)*; [Argyle Pl, The Rocks], *Lord Nelson*: Solid stone, with beams and bare floorboards — the city's oldest pub; brews up to five of its own beers, good but pricey; nautical theme, upmarket atmosphere, pine furniture; open all day, gets touristy *(Nick Dowson, Alison Hayward, Ben Wimpenny)*; [Glenmore Rd, Paddington], *Rose & Crown*: Founded 1850, with fairly English feel — good for a quiet drink; good Hahn *(Ben Wimpenny)*

BELGIUM

Autelbas [], *Cafe de la Biff*: Well kept Mousel beer from Luxembourg, request for a sandwich au jambon produces massive plate of Ardennes ham; beautifully panelled bar, well kept billiards room *(John C Baker)*

Bruges [Kemelstraat 5], *Brugs Beertje*: Good little tavern serving some 300 of the country's beers, in each beer's distinctive glass; helpful English-speaking staff, good basic bar food *(Peter Adcock)*

BRAZIL

Ipanema [Rua Paul Redfern 63], *Lord Jims*: A surprise to find this successful British pub-pastiche, half-timbered, with red telephone box outside, beams and darts in; lovely spiral stairs to smaller area with good choice of fish and chips, roast beef and Yorkshire, tempting puddings, at quite reasonable prices (pace inflation/exchange rate swings); English landlady, mainly local beers, lots of British customers *(David Warrellow)*

CANADA

Carp [Falldown Lane; Ontario], *Swan*: Northern-style pub with Flowers Mild and mushy peas; three separate rooms, terrace *(Anon)*

Guelph [Yarmouth St; Ontario], *Woolich Arms*: Traditional, uncluttered and relaxing conversion of Victorian house, not pseudo-British, with three well kept real ales from nearby Wellington County Brewery on handpump, good pub food inc fine mixed grill, darts, real fire; no obtrusive music, but TV for Sat night hockey; good mix of professionals, students, locals, with genuinely helpful service; open 7 days *(Craig Walker)*

Kingston [34 Clarence St; Ontario], *Kingston Brewing Co*: Brews its own strong dark Dragons Breath real ale (one of the owners used to work at England's Ringwood Brewery), also a lager and seasonal beers; bar food, properly pubby atmosphere, seats outside — even looks like an English pub; good service, and the beer has more character than many transatlantic own-brews *(John Roué)*; [King St], *Pilot House*: Flowers and Guinness as well as Molsons in English-style pub ornately decorated in 19th-century merchant ship theme; cheap fish and chips all day; very popular, and very small — so can get crowded weekends *(Gordon Mott)*; [Princess St], *Toucan*: Known as Kirkpatricks, with good Guinness and piped (sometimes live) Irish music; ornate bar and frosted windows in Victorian-style front part, more casual saloon behind; pub food, Canadian and US beers *(Byrne Sherwood)*

Nanaimo [Yellow Point Rd, off Cedar Rd Nanaimo—Ladysmith; Vancouver Island], *Crow & Gate*: Out in the country, half-timbered building with tables out by duck and swan pond; good pub food inc steak and kidney pie (the ploughman's could do with a nippier English cheese, perhaps), wonderful atmosphere, friendly and welcoming owners, good beers inc O'Keefs Extra Old Stock, Toby, St Patricks Stout, Okanagon Spring; evokes a real English country pub *(Stephen R Holman)*

Ottawa [a few miles S, towards Kars and Osgoode], *Swan on the Rideau*: Good English-style pub with civilised atmosphere and British beers such as Gales, Sam Smiths and Ruddles County; food inc ploughman's and steak and kidney pie *(John Roué)*

St Johns [265 Duckworth St; Newfoundland], *Ship*: Good location and pleasant local atmosphere, with no piped music or video games; ship prints and models, small corner bar in dining area, ex-Liverpudlian landlord; Quebec heater-type open fireplace, Harp, Guinness and Smithwicks *(John Roué)*

COSTA RICA

San Jose [Avenida 3, Calle 7], *Key Largo*: Largest and best-known gringo bar here — three big circular bars in splendid colonial mansion, also restaurant and casino; open noon-6am, said to have been a Bogart haunt and has that atmosphere *(G T Jones)*

DENMARK

Copenhagen [Stroget; Kongens Nytorv end], *Hivids Vinstue*: Superb atmosphere in very old bar with many interconnecting darkly decorated rooms, unusually wide choice of Carlsberg and Tuborg bottled beers inc the redoubtable Carlsberg Imperial Stout, efficient waiter service; well used by locals, highly distinctive *(Brian Jones)*

FALKLAND ISLANDS

Port Stanley [Snake Hill], *Globe*: Friendly local where servicemen and locals alike meet and socialise, very friendly atmosphere, blazing peat fire *(R A Corbett)*

FIJI

Suva [], *Grand Pacific*: Character hotel, a strong reminder of colonial days — very pleasant to while away an afternoon by the swimming pool; local and Australian lagers *(Phil Bryant)* GERMANY
Darmstadt [Markt Platz; Brauhaus in Ratskeller], *Darmstadter Brauerei*: Brews own unusual beers — served young, with the yeast still in suspension and therefore rather cloudy, but distinctive and palatable; circular central servery, simple furnishings, bare floorboards, simple popular food, upstairs restaurant *(Brian Jones)*
Munich [next to Hauptbahnhof], *Spatenbrau Halle*: Good range of beers from local Spaten brewery, the original lager pioneer; friendly atmosphere — somewhere you could take the family; bar food *(Dave Irving)*
Perl [S of Trier, just off rd to Metz], *Hotel Central*: Large and comfortable, with extremely friendly cheerful service, good beer, wide choice of upper Mosel and other wines, wide range of good food inc wild boar *(John C Baker)*
Rothenburg [Detwang 21], *Gasthof zum Schwarzenbach*: Small place where you share breakfast with farmers having their first beer of the day, great decor and atmosphere; good pork (slaughtering done here); comfortable bedrooms *(Russell Hafter)*
Wincheringen [Trier—Thionville], *Pension Jung*: Village inn, in old village high on hillside above Mosel; good basic food, very cheap local wine, dry and refreshing local Trier Romer beer *(John C Baker)*

GUATEMALA

Guatemala City [Avenida de las Americas], *Dannys Marisco Bar*: Bistro-style place with inside bar area opening into outside terrace — pleasant and informal, with youngish customers *(John Roué)*; [Avenida de la Reforma], *El Establo*: Small, cheerful and friendly library bar full of paperbacks, nice owners; opens into big nightclub area behind *(John Roué)*
Panajachel, *Hotel Atitlan*: Candidate for the best bar view in the world, with glorious outlook over Lake Atitlan and its ring of

three volcanoes around the southern shore — ever-changing panorama of water, sky and mountains; if clouds and mists allow the sunsets are fabulous; the hotel itself with its well tailored lawns and gardens is also outstanding *(John Roué)*

HAWAII

Haliuwa [North Shore, Oahu], *Jamesons by the Sea*: More very informal restaurant than bar, but has imported beers with its good reasonably priced food — and wonderful view of sea across road; quiet at night *(T and A Kucharski);* [North Shore, Oahu], *Steamers*: Small bar area, pleasant atmosphere, good food in informal restaurant *(T and A Kucharski)*
Honolulu [Restaurant Row; Oahu], *Studebakers*: Big, noisy, brash, fun 50s disco-bar, free snacks early evening, staff have been known to dance on the counter *(T and A Kucharski)*
Waikiki [Honolulu/Oahu], *Irish Rose*: Take off your sunglasses for this dim but pleasant and lively bar; sports-oriented, with lots of TVs *(Ben Wimpenny);* *Seagulls: Relatively cheap, but this is not reflected in the decor or the customers — though it is popular with backpackers from nearby hostels (Ben Wimpenny)*

KENYA

Nairobi, *Modern Green*: An experience: it's been open 24 hours a day since it opened a few years ago; pass your money through a gap in the grill around the bar, in exchange for bottled beer — decidedly not a smart place *(Martin Aust)*

MALTA

Bugibba [Triq is Sajjied], *Copper Kettle*: Nice friendly atmosphere in fairly sparse but welcoming atmosphere, evening bar food cooked to order, restaurant daytime too *(Nic James)*
Wied Iz Zurrieq [Blue Grotto], *Congreve Channel*: Good remarkably cheap food, well cooked and presented, upstairs restaurant with terrace; bar decor running to British beer towels and so forth *(Nic James)*

MEXICO

Ensenada [Main St; Baja California], *Hussongs*: Spaghetti-western bar with pavement artist who paints you as you drink, ramshackle juke box with ancient repertoire, thousands of customers' visiting cards *(D P Ryan)*

NETHERLANDS

Amsterdam [422 Prinzengracht], *Café Pieper*: Canalside street-corner brown caf with simple wooden tables and chairs on worn floorboards, small bar serving beer, spirits and coffee, fluted cast-iron column supporting ceiling, stained glass in crazy-angled leaded lights, old posters and photographs on dark walls, carved settle in second small room, friendly service *(Brian*

Jones)

Eindhoven [], *Tappern de Bierelier*: Very lively, with singles-bar feel, antique Andri stove, metal badge and nameplate collection, advertisement highlights in wall panels, loud music, Bavaria beer, back courtyard *(Graham Bush)*

NEW ZEALAND

Auckland [], *Birdcage*: Large but pleasant, even civilised; just outside the centre, and open on Sun — though you're supposed to eat then; decent steinlager *(Ben Wimpenny);* [St Georges Bay Rd/Kenwyn St], *Nags Head*: Roomy former warehouse, cosily converted, with six keg beers, bottled real ale, huge helpings of good lunches and suppers, good staff, occasional live music *(Mr and Mrs T S C Kucharski) [61 Albert St/Wyndham St], Shakespeare: Three-floor pub brewing its own palatable beers and Sir Toby Belch's ginger beer; quite pricey, and* increasingly upmarket as you climb from the cellar level; top lounge bar has a real fire in winter, and live music; friendly staff *(T and A Kucharski, Ben Wimpenny)*

Milford Sound [South Island], *Milford*: Behind the hotel — spectacular location at the head of the Sound, with dazzling view of Mitre Peak soaring 5,000 ft straight out of the water; surprisingly cheap and friendly, free pool tables, cheap pies *(Ben Wimpenny)*
NORWAY

Bergen, *Pirate*: Decked out like a pirate ship; particularly friendly, with Hansa lager and attached steak house; opp Norge Hotel *(Alan Holden) PORTUGAL*

Santa Barbara de Nexe [20 km NW of Faro], *Sues Bar*: English-run traditional building with good British pub atmosphere — not a lager-lout place; local beers *(Nick and Alison Dowson)*

SINGAPORE

Singapore, *Raffles*: Has been magnificent colonial-style hotel, home of the Singapore Sling; no reports since rebuilding *(Phil Bryant) SPAIN*

Fuengirola [Mijas—Alhuarrin mountain rd], *Finca la Motta*: Tiny cobbled bar, hanging vines, little shady courtyards, Sun barbecue, ponies for hire, pups and pet goats — good food, beers, local wine, company and atmosphere, with lots of individualistic regulars *(W Bailey)*

UAE

Dubai [in Marine Hotel], *Thatchers*: Imported British beers — and imported panelling, beams, mugs, barmaids; it works really well, with great atmosphere, mixing rig workers, air hostesses and embassy diplomats; just right after a hard day in the desert; good value Thai and English food — as authentic as possible a pub for this part of the world *(Marion Bollans, W Bailey)*

USA

Berkeley [1920 Shattuck Ave; California], *Triple Rock*: High-ceilinged rather cavernous place with own-brewed light ale and porter, very young owners, rock music *(Joel Dobris)*

Boston [Fanuel Sq; Massachussetts], *Black Rose*: Downtown Irish pub known as the Roisin Dubh; Irish patriot portraits on panelled walls, Guinness as well as domestic and imported beers; live Irish music evenings *(Byrne Sherwood);* [Gt Portland St], *Commonwealth Brewing Co*: Bare wood and gleaming copper for the counter of the pillared island bar, and no less than five plump old brewing kettles (they still use the one in the window to brew); half a dozen ales, most English-style, one a cold proper lager; can see and tour downstairs brewery; food inc regional specialities *(Matt Pringle)*

Cape May [Washington Mall; NJ], *Ugly Mug*: Lager served in frozen mugs in this home of the Froth Blowers' Union, who meet here for annual froth-blowing world championships — their hundreds of mugs hang from the ceiling (and are turned towards the sea when they die); great seafood, especially fresh tuna *(Mrs Elliott Doncrey)*

Captiva Island [Sanibel; Florida], *Mucky Duck*: Good range of beers from around the world, emphasis on food (especially seafood), perfect service — nothing too much trouble; reasonable prices *(Mrs B Y Lockwood)*

Davis [G St, by Ramada Inn; California], *Back Alley Brewery*: Recommended in previous editions, now closed; [132 E St], *Mansion Cellars*: Wide range of bottled beers inc dozens of imports, tables outside, snacks *(Joel Dobris);* [2001 2nd St; Pole Line Rd], *Sudwerk*: Award-winning lager-style own brews based on German recipes — a strong sweet and chewy Christmas Bock as well as their regular Hubschberau Lager, Pilsner, Dunkel and Marzen; popular with respectable suburban crowd, for good German food inc fresh sausages and other bar lunches; windows into brewery at bar, tables outside *(Joel Dobris)*

Dearborn [Greenfield Village; off Oakwood Blvd; Michigan], *Eagle*: Part of Ford's open-air "village" attraction; restored 19th-century country farmhouse/tavern with period-style furnishings in lounge bar, earthy taproom and dining room; Bass in pot mugs, good filling home-cooked beef stew, baked pork, trout and so forth; staff in period costume *(Graham Bush)*

Denver [1634 18th St; junction Wynkoop St; Colorado], *Wynkoop Brewing Co*: Good cross between an English pub and American bar, brewing six decent real ales — four served on handpump, not too cold; in no way a fake pub, genuine attempt to provide English-style beers, and food such as shepherd's pie, bangers and mash, chilli con carne; locally very popular *(Brian Jones)*

Detroit [Franklin; between Schweitzer and Rivard St; Michigan], *River Rock Cafe*: Lively young person's bar, wooden floor and rough panelling, two-tier lower area and stairs to upper gallery and terrace; sports

TV, sporting memorabilia, games machines, Bass among other beers, bar snacks *(Graham Bush)*; [top of Westin Hotel, Level 71 Renaissance Center, *Summit Lounge*: Highest dining bar in the world, rotating completely every 45 mins (the lift up costs $3); chrome and leather seats, glass-topped tables, pricey cocktails and views over America and Canada (or down over diners below) *(Graham Bush)*

Epcot [Florida], *Rose & Crown*: High prices, Bass too cold, and you have to tip the barman — but convivial atmosphere, friendly service, good fish and chips in newspaper, enormous helpings, good seating arrangements *(John Evans)*

Fort Lauderdale [2500 NW 62nd St; Florida], *95th Bomb Group*: Overlooking what is now the executive airport, with earphones to listen to flight control transmissions — replica of English farmhouse with WWII memorabilia, Glen Miller music, nice atmosphere, friendly service, fair to good food *(John Evans)*

Hopland [California], *Hopland Brewery*: From outside, not unlike a neat brick Last of the Summer Wine-country tavern; inside, good Red Tail own brew *(Anon)*

Lititz [14 E Main St; Pennsylvania], *General Sutter*: Good welcome, pleasant relaxing atmosphere, usual drinks, wide range of snacks inc good burgers; gents are in for a shock when they go to the washroom; the pleasant town has America's oldest bakery and a chocolate museum; bedrooms spacious and airy; dates back to 1764 *(John Evans)*

Los Angeles [off Nebraska St; W of S Bundy Dr], *Eureka*: Machinery decor and interesting eclectic really good food in big, bustling restaurant with both the kitchen and its own gleaming brewery on view (it produuces Reinheitsgebot-standard Bavarian-style lager); also a huge special-effects animated caricature of the brewery; owned by Wolfgang Puck, California cooking guru *(Anon)*

Naples [255 13th Ave S; (813) 649 8200; Florida], *Old Naples*: New pub in smart centre, reasonably priced bar food, plans for English beers; takeaways available *(Paul S McPherson)*

New Orleans [Bourbon St, Spanish Qtr], *Ryans Bar*: The live Irish music a contrast to the surrounding old and new jazz; Guinness, warm atmosphere, barman with alternative humour *(D P Ryan)*

New York [40 Thompson St; Spring St], *Manhattan Brewing Co*: Shepherd's pie and chilli con carne in spacious sawdust-floored beer hall with copper-topped tables, live music weekends, and own-brewed City Light, Royal Amber, Rough Draft, Tailspin Brown and bottled Manhattan Gold lager; friendly service, smart restaurant *(Iain Grant)*; [55th and Broadway], *McGees*: Simple inconspicuous Irish pub with Bass as well as Guinness, good staff, some British regulars; handy for theatres, and they let you eat pizzas bought next door here *(T*

Buckland); [235 11th Ave], *New Amsterdam Tap Room*: Now closed; [93 South St Seaport], *North Star*: In the centre of South St Seaport — a group of restored warehouses and quays with a couple of full-rigged ships as background; a good imitation of an English pub with dark green lincrusta ceiling, wall mirrors, oak furniture, handpumps for the Bass and Fullers ESB and London Pride, good choice of English bottled beers, and real English food inc fish and chips, steak and kidney pie, and delicious bangers and mash; obliging and friendly staff *(Duane Klein, Dr C D E Morris)*

Orlando [8282 International Dr; Florida], *Darryls*: One of a small chain with whacky atmosphere (you may be seated in a lift or aloft in the loft); noisy, busy, frantic but friendly service, good food, a good fun place with bizarre decor *(John Evans)*; [Universal Studios], *Finnegans*: Good replica of Irish-American pub, with sporting gear inc curling stones, hurling sticks, horse-racing memorabilia; very friendly welcome, wide range of US beers, Guinness, Bass, Tennents Lager at reasonable prices, from half-pints to yards of ale; good choice of low-priced food such as fish and chips, Irish stew and shepherds' pie in huge helpings; children welcome *(Michael Bechley)*

Sacramento [1001 R St; California], *Fox & Goose*: Landlord from Yorkshire, good food using fresh ingredients and inc English specialities, serving several types of tea and coffee as well as a good choice of English and other beers *(Joel Dobris)*; [2004 Capitol Ave], *Rubicon Brewing Co*: Good food, decent own-brewed beer; open all day, brewery tours by arrangement *(Anon)*

San Francisco [Geary], *Irelands 32*: Really good and really Irish, with particularly good food *(Matthew Barker Kowalsky)*; [155 Columbus Ave], *San Francisco Brewing Co*: Unusual for brewing lagers as well as top-fermented beers; good food such as hot Louisiana sausage and pepper sandwich, turn-of-the-century stained glass and mahogany *(Matthew Barker Kowalsky)*; [Fishermans Quay], *Silhouettes*: Good 50s/60s live music pub, though pool takes over some nights *(T and A Kucharski)*; [Van Ness/Geary], *Tommy's Joynt*: Imported beers from all over the world, vary daily, great atmosphere and conversation (on the macho side), fantastic cafeteria-style food specialising in buffalo-meat stew and Sloppy Joes *(Matthew Barker Kowalsky)*

Sanford [Lake Monroe; extension from Holiday Inn; Florida], *Docke & Shope*: Not in the true sense a bar, but help-yourself coolers of beer, wine and miniature spirits at supermarket prices, and rustic tables and chairs on the deck right by the water *(Mr & Mrs Russell V Bathie, G and R Morris, W and M Morris)*

Tempe [Arizona], *Bandersnatch*: Brews three real ales inc a stout, small choice of good value food; bar and split-level seating area, not a conscious copy of an English pub but a very relaxed pubby feel in appropriate western style; rustic mainly wooden decor, glass panels showing the modern stainless brewery; handy for Arizona State Univ *(Dave Irving)*

Washington [1523 22nd St, NW], *Brickskeller*: Quite remarkable for its astonishing collection of over 550 beers from nearly 50 countries, and particularly pleasing that the more obscure and distant microbrews are not priced appreciably higher than national US brands; good atmosphere, friendly service going well beyond the usual US politeness, good value food from burgers to buffalo steaks served promptly in bare brick, stone-floored and gingham tablecloth dining-room — but it's the tremendous choice of beers which makes this truly special; the microbrewery beers are particularly worth trying, notably Anchor Steam and Special, Olde Heurich Amber (local), Pyramid Wheaten, Samuel Adams, Thousand Oaks *(Brian Jones, Joel Dobris)*

Special interest lists

Open all day (at least in summer)

We list here all the pubs that have told us they plan to stay open all day, even if it's only on a Saturday. We've included the few pubs which close just for half an hour to an hour, and the many more, chiefly in holiday areas, which open all day only in summer. The individual entries for the pubs themselves show the actual details. A few pubs in England and Wales, allowed to stay open only in the last two or three years, are still changing their opening hours – let us know if you find anything different.

BERKSHIRE
Littlewick Green, Cricketers
Yattendon, Royal Oak

BUCKINGHAMSHIRE
Amersham, Kings Arms
Chalfont St Peter, Greyhound
Frieth, Yew Tree
Medmenham, Dog & Badger
Northend, White Hart
Penn, Crown
Stoke Green, Red Lion
West Wycombe, George & Dragon

CAMBRIDGESHIRE AND BEDFORDSHIRE
Cambridge, Anchor; Boathouse; Tap & Spile
Etton, Golden Pheasant
Fowlmere, Chequers
Wansford, Haycock

CHESHIRE
Barbridge, Barbridge
Chester, Boot; Falcon
Church Minshull, Badger
Lower Whitley, Chetwode Arms
Macclesfield, Sutton Hall
Mobberley, Bird in Hand
Ollerton, Dun Cow
Plumley, Golden Pheasant

CORNWALL
Crows Nest, Crows Nest
Lanner, Fox & Hounds
Mousehole, Ship
Mylor Bridge, Pandora
Pendoggett, Cornish Arms
Polkerris, Rashleigh
Polperro, Blue Peter
Porthleven, Ship
St Agnes, Railway
St Mawes, Rising Sun

CUMBRIA
Ambleside, Golden Rule
Askham, Punch Bowl
Braithwaite, Coledale
Coniston, Sun
Dent, Sun
Elterwater, Britannia
Grasmere, Travellers Rest
Hawkshead, Kings Arms
Kirkby Lonsdale, Snooty Fox; Sun
Langdale, Old Dungeon Ghyll
Little Langdale, Three Shires
Loweswater, Kirkstile
Lowick Green, Farmers Arms
Warwick-on-Eden, Queens Arms
Wasdale Head, Wasdale Head

DERBYSHIRE AND STAFFORDSHIRE
Bamford, Derwent
Derby, Brunswick
Grindleford, Maynard Arms
Monsal Head, Monsal Head
Rowarth, Little Mill
Shardlow, Hoskins Wharf
Shraleybrook, Rising Sun
Wardlow, Three Stags Heads

DEVON
Ashburton, London
Broadhembury, Drewe Arms
Burgh Island, Pilchard
Cockwood, Anchor
Combeinteignhead, Coombe Cellars
Dartmouth, Royal Castle
Exeter, Double Locks; White Hart
Exminster, Turf
Moretonhampstead,
White Hart
Newton St Cyres, Beer Engine
Postbridge, Warren House
Sandy Park, Sandy Park
Stoke Gabriel, Church House
Topsham, Globe
Ugborough, Anchor
Welcombe, Old Smithy

DORSET
Abbotsbury, Ilchester Arms
Bridport, George
Cerne Abbas, Royal Oak
Chideock, Anchor
Shaftesbury, Ship
West Bexington, Manor

ESSEX
Great Baddow, Seabrights Barn
Lamarsh, Red Lion
Peldon, Rose
Saffron Walden, Eight Bells
Stock, Hoop

GLOUCESTERSHIRE
Ampney Crucis, Crown of Crucis
Broad Campden, Bakers Arms
Chipping Campden, Lygon Arms
Coates, Tunnel House
Coln St Aldwyns, New Inn
Hyde, Ragged Cot
Lechlade, Trout
Stanton, Mount

HAMPSHIRE
Beaulieu, Montagu Arms
Bentley, Bull
Bursledon, Jolly Sailor
Droxford, White Horse
Fawley, Jolly Sailor
Kings Worthy, Cart & Horses

Langstone, Royal Oak
Linwood, High Corner
Minley, Crown &
Cushion
Romsey, Luzborough
House
Stockbridge, Vine
Turgis Green, Jekyll &
Hyde
Wherwell, Mayfly
Winchester, Wykeham
Arms

HEREFORD AND WORCESTER
Bewdley, Little Pack
Horse
Knightwick, Talbot
Ombersley, Kings Arms
Weobley, Olde Salutation
Worcester, Farriers Arms

HERTFORDSHIRE
Aldbury, Valiant Trooper
Amwell, Elephant &
Castle
Great Offley, Green Man
Puckeridge, White Hart
St Albans, Fighting
Cocks; Garibaldi

HUMBERSIDE
Beverley, White Horse
Hull, Minerva; Olde
White Harte
Pocklington, Feathers
Skidby, Half Moon

ISLE OF WIGHT
Chale, Clarendon (Wight
Mouse)
Shalfleet, New Inn
Ventnor, Spyglass

KENT
Boughton Aluph, Flying
Horse
Chilham, White Horse
Cobham, Leather Bottle
Staple, Black Pig
Stowting, Tiger

LANCASHIRE
Balderstone, Myerscough
Bilsborrow, Owd Nells
Blacko, Moorcock
Brierfield, Waggon &
Horses
Brindle, Cavendish Arms
Broadbottom, Station
Burnley, Coal Clough
House
Darwen, Old Rosins
Edgworth, White Horse
Haslingden, Duke of
Wellington
Liverpool, Philharmonic

Dining Rooms
Lytham, Captains Cabin
Manchester, Lass o'
Gowrie; Marble Arch;
Mark Addy; Royal Oak;
Sinclairs Oyster Bar
Newton, Parkers Arms
Slaidburn, Hark to Bounty
Thornton Hough, Seven
Stars
Tockholes, Rock
Uppermill, Cross Keys
Wheatley Lane, Old
Sparrow Hawk

LEICESTERSHIRE, LINCOLNSHIRE AND NOTTINGHAMSHIRE
Boston, Eagle
Empingham, White Horse
Halton Holegate, Bell
Lincoln, Wig & Mitre
Newark, Old Kings Arms
Nottingham, Fellows
Morton & Clayton; Olde
Inn; Trip to Jerusalem; Sir
John Borlase Warren
Retford, Market
Stamford, George of
Stamford

MIDLANDS (including WARWICKSHIRE AND NORTHANTS)
Brierley Hill, Vine
Himley, Crooked House
Lowsonford, Fleur de Lys
Netherton, Little Dry
Dock; Old Swan
Oundle, Ship
Southam, Old Mint
Stoke Bruerne, Boat
Stratford upon Avon,
Garrick; Slug & Lettuce

NORFOLK
Blakeney, Kings Arms
Norwich, Adam & Eve
Scole, Scole
Snettisham, Rose &
Crown
Thornham, Lifeboat
Tivetshall St Mary, Old
Ram

NORTHUMBERLAND, DURHAM etc
Beamish, Shepherd &
Shepherdess
Corbridge, Wheatsheaf
Durham, Shakespeare
New York, Shiremoor
House Farm
Newcastle Upon Tyne,
Cooperage; Crown
Posada; Tap & Spile

Piercebridge, George
Tynemouth, Tynemouth
Lodge; Wooden Doll

OXFORDSHIRE
Adderbury, Red Lion
Burford, Mermaid
Clifton Hampden, Plough
Cumnor, Bear & Ragged
Staff
Finstock, Plough
Godstow, Trout
Henley-on-Thames, Three
Tuns
Minster Lovell, Old Swan
Newbridge, Rose Revived
Oxford, Bear; Turf Tavern
Tadpole Bridge, Trout
Wytham, White Hart

SHROPSHIRE
Bridgnorth, Hollyhead
Ironbridge, New Inn
Ludlow, Church
Norton, Hundred House

SOMERSET AND AVON
Bath, Coeur de Lion
Bristol, Highbury Vaults
Huish Episcopi, Rose &
Crown
Norton St Philip, George
South Stoke, Pack Horse
Stanton Wick, Carpenters
Arms
Tormarton, Compass
Woolverton, Red Lion

SUFFOLK
Chelmondiston, Butt &
Oyster
Clare, Bell
Hundon, Plough
Orford, Kings Head
Ramsholt, Ramsholt Arms
Wetheringsett, Cat &
Mouse

SURREY
Coldharbour, Plough
Felbridge, Woodcock
Fickleshole, White Bear
Laleham, Three
Horseshoes
Ockley, Punch Bowl
Outwood, Dog & Duck
Pirbright, Royal Oak
Pyrford Lock, Anchor
Shepperton, Kings Head
Thursley, Three
Horseshoes
Walton on the Hill, Fox
& Hounds

SUSSEX
Alfriston, Star
Arundel, Black Rabbit

Blackboys, Blackboys
Chilgrove, Royal Oak
Rye, Mermaid
Scaynes Hill, Sloop
West Ashling, Richmond Arms
Withyham, Dorset Arms

WILTSHIRE
Corton, Dove
Devizes, Bear
Ford, White Hart
Highworth, Saracens Head
Hindon, Lamb
Salisbury, Avon Brewery; Haunch of Venison

YORKSHIRE
Askrigg, Kings Arms
Blakey Ridge, Lion
Buckden, Buck
Cadeby, Cadeby
Cray, White Lion
East Witton, Blue Lion; Cover Bridge
Egton Bridge, Postgate
Harden, Malt Shovel
Helmsley, Feathers
Kilburn, Forresters Arms
Lastingham, Blacksmiths Arms
Ledsham, Chequers
Leeds, Garden Gate; Whitelocks
Linthwaite, Bulls Head
Litton, Queens Arms
Masham, Kings Head; White Bear
Pateley Bridge, Half Moon
Pickhill, Nags Head
Ramsgill, Yorke Arms
Ripponden, Old Bridge
Rosedale Abbey, Milburn Arms; White Horse
Saxton, Greyhound
Settle, Royal Oak
Sheffield, Frog & Parrot
Tadcaster, Angel & White Horse
York, Black Swan; Hole in the Wall; Kings Arms; Olde Starre

LONDON, CENTRAL
Antelope
Argyll Arms
Black Friar
Cittie of York
Coopers Arms
Cross Keys
George
Glassblower
Lamb
Lamb & Flag
Museum Tavern

Nags Head
Old Coffee House
Olde Mitre
Orange Brewery
Princess Louise
Red Lion

LONDON, NORTH
Crockers
Moon Under Water
Spaniards
Waterside
White Lion of Mortimer

LONDON, SOUTH
Alma
Anchor
Angel
Bulls Head
Crown & Greyhound
George
Horniman
Market Porter
Olde Windmill
Phoenix & Firkin
Ship

LONDON, WEST
Bulls Head
Dove
Eel Pie
Ferret & Firkin
Kings Arms

LONDON, EAST
Hollands

SCOTLAND
Aberdeen, Prince of Wales
Ardvasar, Ardvasar
Broughty Ferry, Fishermans Tavern
Carbost, Old Inn
Cawdor, Cawdor Tavern
Cleish, Nivingston House
Crinan, Crinan
Dumfries, Globe
Edinburgh, Athletic Arms; Bannermans Bar; Bennets Bar; Cafe Royal; Guildford Arms; I W Frazers Bow Bar; Kays Bar; Peacock; Sheep Heid; Starbank
Findhorn, Crown & Anchor
Gifford, Tweeddale Arms
Glasgow, Babbity Bowster; Bon Accord; Horseshoe
Glencoe, Clachaig
Glendevon, Tormaukin
Howgate, Old Howgate
Inverarnan, Inverarnan
Isle of Whithorn, Steam Packet

Isle Ornsay, Eilean Iarmain
Kilmartin, Kilmartin
Kippford, Anchor
Linlithgow, Four Marys
Monymusk, Grant Arms
Mountbenger, Gordon Arms
Newburgh, Udny Arms
Oban, Oban Bar
Portpatrick, Crown
Queensferry, Hawes
Sheriffmuir, Sheriffmuir
Shieldaig, Tigh an Eilean
Spean Bridge, Letterfinlay Lodge
St Marys Loch, Tibbie Shiels
Strachur, Creggans
Tayvallich, Tayvallich
Tweedsmuir, Crook
Uddingston, Rowan Tree
Ullapool, Ceilidh Place; Ferry Boat
Weem, Ailean Chraggan
Westruther, Old Thistle

WALES
Aberaeron, Harbourmaster
Abergorlech, Black Lion
Aberystwyth, Halfway
Beaumaris, Olde Bulls Head
Bishopston, Joiners Arms
Caerphilly, Courthouse
East Aberthaw, Blue Anchor
Llanberis, Pen-y-Gwryd
Llancarfan, Fox & Hounds
Llangynwyd, Old House
Llanthony, Abbey
Maentwrog, Grapes
Marianglas, Parciau Arms
Mold, We Three Loggerheads
Nottage, Rose & Crown
Ogmore, Pelican
Penarth, Captains Wife
Porth Dinllaen, Ty Coch
Presteigne, Radnorshire Arms
Red Wharf Bay, Ship
Talybont-on-Usk, Star

CHANNEL ISLANDS
Gorey, Dolphin
Kings Mills, Fleur du Jardin
Rozel, Rozel Bay
St Helier, Lamplighter
St Martin, Auberge Divette
St Sampsons, Pony

No smoking areas

So many more pubs are now making some provision for the majority of their customers – that's to say non-smokers – that we have now found it is worth listing all the pubs which have told us they do set aside at least some part of the pub as a no smoking area. Look at the individual entries for the pubs themselves to see just what they do: provision is much more generous in some pubs than in others.

BERKSHIRE
Cookham, Bel & the Dragon
East Ilsley, Swan
Frilsham, Pot Kiln
Kintbury, Dundas Arms
Knowl Hill, Bird in Hand
West Ilsley, Harrow

BUCKINGHAMSHIRE
Fawley, Walnut Tree
Fingest, Chequers
Ibstone, Fox
Ley Hill, Swan
Skirmett, Old Crown
Stoke Green, Red Lion
Worminghall, Clifden Arms

CAMBRIDGESHIRE AND BEDFORDSHIRE
Barrington, Royal Oak
Bythorn, White Hart
Cambridge, Boathouse; Free Press
Holywell, Olde Ferry Boat
Horningsea, Plough & Fleece
Stilton, Bell
Swavesey, Trinity Foot
Wansford, Haycock

CHESHIRE
Great Budworth, George & Dragon
Mobberley, Bird in Hand
Over Peover, Whipping Stocks
Sutton, Ryles Arms
Weston, White Lion

CORNWALL
Lerryn, Ship
Malpas, Heron
Mawnan Smith, Red Lion
Mylor Bridge, Pandora
Pendoggett, Cornish Arms
Port Gaverne, Port Gaverne
Scorrier, Fox & Hounds

CUMBRIA
Bassenthwaite, Pheasant
Braithwaite, Coledale
Casterton, Pheasant
Coniston, Sun
Dent, Sun
Elterwater, Britannia
Eskdale Green, Bower House
Grasmere, Travellers Rest
Hawkshead, Kings Arms; Queens Head
Langdale, Old Dungeon Ghyll
Little Langdale, Three Shires
Melmerby, Shepherds
Scales, White Horse
Ulverston, Bay Horse

DERBYSHIRE AND STAFFORDSHIRE
Derby, Brunswick
Grindleford, Maynard Arms
Hartington, Jug & Glass
Melbourne, John Thompson
Over Haddon, Lathkil
Wardlow, Three Stags Heads

DEVON
Ashprington, Watermans Arms
Dartington, Cott
Dartmouth, Royal Castle
East Down, Pyne Arms
Exminster, Swans Nest; Turf
Hatherleigh, Tally Ho
Haytor Vale, Rock
Holne, Church House
Knowstone, Masons Arms
Lustleigh, Cleave
Lydford, Castle
Lympstone, Nutwell Lodge
Lynmouth, Rising Sun
Moretonhampstead, White Hart
Tipton St John, Golden Lion
Totnes, Kingsbridge
Winkleigh, Kings Arms

DORSET
Abbotsbury, Ilchester Arms
Bourton, White Lion
Bridport, George
Cerne Abbas, New Inn
Chedington, Winyards Gap
Chideock, Anchor
Corfe Castle, Greyhound
East Chaldon, Sailors Return
Lyme Regis, Pilot Boat
Nettlecombe, Marquis of Lorne
Plush, Brace of Pheasants
Sandford Orcas, Mitre
West Bexington, Manor

ESSEX
Danbury, Anchor
Great Baddow, Seabrights Barn
Great Henny, Swan
Newney Green, Duck
Peldon, Rose

GLOUCESTERSHIRE
Bisley, Bear
Bledington, Kings Head
Blockley, Crown
Coln St Aldwyns, New Inn
Great Rissington, Lamb
Hyde, Ragged Cot
Lechlade, Trout
Moreton in Marsh, Coach & Horses

HAMPSHIRE
Beaulieu, Montagu Arms
Bursledon, Jolly Sailor
Droxford, White Horse
Ibsley, Old Beams
Kings Worthy, Cart & Horses
Linwood, High Corner
Winchester, Wykeham Arms

HEREFORD AND WORCESTER
Bretforton, Fleece
Brimfield, Roebuck
Ombersley, Crown & Sandys Arms
Woolhope, Butchers Arms

HERTFORDSHIRE
Ayot St Lawrence, Brocket Arms
Barley, Fox and Hounds
Rushden, Moon & Stars
St Albans, Garibaldi

HUMBERSIDE
Stamford Bridge, Three Cups

ISLE OF WIGHT
Ventnor, Spyglass

KENT
Boyden Gate, Gate
Smarden, Bell
Southfleet, Black Lion
Whitstable, Pearsons
Crab & Oyster House

LANCASHIRE
Bilsborrow, Owd Nells
Broadbottom, Station
Burnley, Coal Clough House
Goosnargh, Bushells Arms
Haslingden, Duke of Wellington
Manchester, Sinclairs Oyster Bar
Middleton, Olde Boars Head
Thornton Hough, Seven Stars

LEICESTERSHIRE, LINCOLNSHIRE AND NOTTINGHAMSHIRE
Drakeholes, Griff
Hallaton, Bewicke Arms
Scaftworth, King William
Tetford, White Hart
Wellow, Olde Red Lion

MIDLANDS (including WARWICKSHIRE AND NORTHANTS)
Alderminster, Bell
Charlton, Rose & Crown
Oundle, Ship
Priors Marston, Falcon
Twywell, Old Friar

NORFOLK
Blakeney, Kings Arms
Burnham Thorpe, Lord Nelson
Kings Lynn, Tudor Rose
Norwich, Adam & Eve
Ringstead, Gin Trap
Tivetshall St Mary, Old Ram
Warham, Three Horseshoes

NORTHUMBERLAND, DURHAM etc
Eglingham, Tankerville Arms

OXFORDSHIRE
Adderbury, Red Lion
Burford, Lamb

Chinnor, Sir Charles Napier
Clanfield, Clanfield Tavern
Clifton Hampden, Plough
Cumnor, Bear & Ragged Staff
Fyfield, White Hart
Great Tew, Falkland Arms
Newbridge, Rose Revived
Shipton-under-Wychwood, Lamb
Stanton St John, Star
Wytham, White Hart

SHROPSHIRE
Bridgnorth, Hollyhead
Coalport, Woodbridge
Ludlow, Church
Upper Farmcote, Lion of Morfe

SOMERSET AND AVON
Appley, Globe
Aust, Boars Head
Bath, Old Green Tree
Bathford, Crown
Haselbury Plucknett, Haselbury
Kilve, Hood Arms
Montacute, Kings Arms
Oldbury-on-Severn, Anchor
Stoke St Gregory, Rose & Crown
Stoke St Mary, Half Moon

SUFFOLK
Cretingham, Bell
Framlingham, Crown
Hundon, Plough
Orford, Jolly Sailor
Southwold, Crown
Westleton, Crown

SURREY
Blackbrook, Plough
Charleshill, Donkey
Headley, Cock

SUSSEX
Arundel, Black Rabbit
Charlton, Fox Goes Free
Dallington, Swan
Elsted, Three Horseshoes
Heathfield, Star
Houghton, George & Dragon
Kingston near Lewes, Juggs
Oving, Gribble
Ripe, Lamb
Seaford, Golden Galleon
West Firle, Ram
Winchelsea, New Inn

WILTSHIRE
Alvediston, Crown
Barford St Martin, Barford
Devizes, Bear
Everleigh, Crown
Hindon, Lamb
Limpley Stoke, Hop Pole

YORKSHIRE
Arncliffe, Falcon
Askrigg, Kings Arms
Burnsall, Red Lion
Cray, White Lion
Cropton, New Inn
Harden, Malt Shovel
Hetton, Angel
Hubberholme, George
Pickhill, Nags Head
Ramsgill, Yorke Arms
Rosedale Abbey, Milburn Arms
Sawley, Sawley Arms
Sheffield, Fat Cat; Frog & Parrot
Sowerby Bridge, Moorings
Sutton Howgrave, White Dog
Wormald Green, Cragg Lodge

LONDON, CENTRAL
Antelope
Argyll Arms
Lamb

LONDON, NORTH
Crockers

LONDON, SOUTH
Crown & Greyhound
Horniman

LONDON, WEST
Bulls Head
White Horse

SCOTLAND
Arduaine, Loch Melfort
Ardvasar, Ardvasar
Canonbie, Riverside
Edinburgh, Peacock
Howgate, Old Howgate
Kippford, Anchor
Pitlochry, Killiecrankie
Queensferry, Hawes
Skeabost, Skeabost House
Spean Bridge, Letterfinlay Lodge
St Mary's Loch, Tibbie Shiels
Swinton, Wheatsheaf
Tayvallich, Tayvallich
Tweedsmuir, Crook
Ullapool, Ceilidh Place; Ferry Boat

WALES
Bodfari, Dinorben Arms
Colwyn Bay, Mountain View
Ganllwyd, Tyn-y-groes
Llangynwyd, Old House
Llanrwst, Maenan Abbey

Llanwnda, Goat
Llyswen, Griffin
Nottage, Rose & Crown
Red Wharf Bay, Ship

CHANNEL ISLANDS
Castel, Hougue du

Pommier
Kings Mills, Fleur du Jardin

Pubs with good gardens

Special interest lists: gardensThe pubs listed here have bigger or more beautiful gardens, grounds or terraces than are usual for their areas. Note that in a town or city this might be very much more modest than the sort of garden that would deserve a listing in the countryside.

BERKSHIRE
Aldworth, Bell
Chaddleworth, Ibex
Cookham Dean, Jolly Farmer
Hamstead Marshall, White Hart
Hurley, Dew Drop
West Ilsley, Harrow
Winterbourne, Winterbourne Arms

BUCKINGHAMSHIRE
Akeley, Bull & Butcher
Amersham, Queens Head
Bledlow, Lions of Bledlow
Bolter End, Peacock
Chesham, Black Horse
Denham, Swan
Fawley, Walnut Tree
Fingest, Chequers
Hambleden, Stag & Huntsman
Lacey Green, Pink & Lily
Little Horwood, Shoulder of Mutton
Marsh Gibbon, Greyhound
Northend, White Hart
Penn, Crown
Skirmett, Old Crown
West Wycombe, George & Dragon
Whitchurch, White Swan
Worminghall, Clifden Arms

CAMBRIDGESHIRE AND BEDFORDSHIRE
Bolnhurst, Olde Plough
Chatteris, Crafty Fox
Eltisley, Leeds Arms
Fowlmere, Chequers
Horningsea, Plough & Fleece
Southill, White Horse
Swavesey, Trinity Foot
Wansford, Haycock

CHESHIRE
Alvanley, White Lion
Barbridge, Barbridge
Brereton Green, Bears Head
Church Minshull, Badger
Lower Peover, Bells of Peover
Lower Whitley, Chetwode Arms
Macclesfield, Sutton Hall
Over Peover, Whipping Stocks
Smallwood, Bulls Head
Weston, White Lion

CORNWALL
Helford, Shipwrights Arms
Philleigh, Roseland
Trebarwith, Mill House

CUMBRIA
Barbon, Barbon
Bassenthwaite, Pheasant
Eskdale Green, Bower House
Warwick-on-Eden, Queens Arms

DERBYSHIRE AND STAFFORDSHIRE
Alrewas, George & Dragon
Burton on Trent, Albion
Buxton, Bull i'th' Thorn
Grindleford, Maynard Arms
Little Longstone, Packhorse
Melbourne, John Thompson
Onecote, Jervis Arms
Shardlow, Hoskins Wharf
Tatenhill, Horseshoe

DEVON
Broadhembury, Drewe Arms

Cornworthy, Hunters Lodge
Dartington, Cott
Doddiscombsleigh, Nobody
Exminster, Turf
Haytor Vale, Rock
Sidford, Blue Ball
South Zeal, Oxenham Arms
Welcombe, Old Smithy

DORSET
Chedington, Winyards Gap
Child Okeford, Saxon
Farnham, Museum
Lytchett Minster, Bakers Arms
Nettlecombe, Marquis of Lorne
Plush, Brace of Pheasants
Sandford Orcas, Mitre
Shave Cross, Shave Cross
Tarrant Monkton, Langton Arms
West Bexington, Manor

ESSEX
Castle Hedingham, Bell
Chappel, Swan
Great Baddow, Seabrights Barn
Great Henny, Swan
Great Yeldham, White Hart
Hastingwood, Rainbow & Dove
Mill Green, Viper
Newney Green, Duck
Peldon, Rose
Stock, Hoop
Toot Hill, Green Man
Woodham Walter, Cats

GLOUCESTERSHIRE
Alderton, Gardeners Arms
Amberley, Black Horse
Ampney Crucis, Crown

of Crucis
Chipping Campden,
Kings Arms
Fossebridge, Fossebridge
Great Rissington, Lamb
Kingscote, Hunters Hall
Lechlade, Trout
North Nibley, New Inn
Oddington, Horse &
Groom
Redbrook, Boat
Sapperton, Daneway
Southrop, Swan

HAMPSHIRE
Battramsley, Hobler
Bramdean, Fox
Emery Down, New Forest
Fawley, Jolly Sailor
Kings Worthy, Cart &
Horses
Linwood, High Corner
Newtown, Travellers Rest
Ovington, Bush
Petersfield, White Horse
Romsey, Luzborough
House
Steep, Harrow
Stockbridge, Vine
Tichborne, Tichborne
Arms
Turgis Green, Jekyll &
Hyde

HEREFORD AND
WORCESTER
Barnards Green, Blue Bell
Bretforton, Fleece
Fownhope, Green Man
Sellack, Loughpool
Woolhope, Butchers Arms

HERTFORDSHIRE
Amwell, Elephant &
Castle
Ayot St Lawrence,
Brocket Arms
Great Offley, Green Man
Newgate Street Village,
Coach & Horses
Puckeridge, White Hart

HUMBERSIDE
South Dalton, Pipe &
Glass

ISLE OF WIGHT
Chale, Clarendon (Wight
Mouse)
Shorwell, Crown

KENT
Biddenden, Three
Chimneys
Bough Beech, Wheatsheaf
Chiddingstone, Castle
Cobham, Leather Bottle

Dargate, Dove
Groombridge, Crown
Ivy Hatch, Plough
Lamberhurst, Elephants
Head
Newnham, George
Penshurst, Bottle House
Ringlestone, Ringlestone
Smarden, Bell
Southfleet, Black Lion
Stowting, Tiger
Ulcombe, Pepper Box

LANCASHIRE
Burnley, Coal Clough
House
Darwen, Old Rosins
Haslingden, Duke of
Wellington
Newton, Parkers Arms
Uppermill, Cross Keys
Whitewell, at Whitewell

LEICESTERSHIRE,
LINCOLNSHIRE AND
NOTTINGHAMSHIRE
Coningsby, Leagate
Drakeholes, Griff
Exton, Fox & Hounds
Newton, Red Lion
North Muskham,
Muskham Ferry
Old Dalby, Crown
Scaftworth, King William
Stamford, George of
Stamford

MIDLANDS (including
WARWICKSHIRE AND
NORTHANTS)
Ashby St Ledgers, Old
Coach House
Berkswell, Bear
East Haddon, Red Lion
Eastcote, Eastcote Arms
Lowsonford, Fleur de Lys
Stratford upon Avon, Slug
& Lettuce
Thorpe Mandeville, Three
Conies
West Bromwich, Manor
House

NORFOLK
Letheringsett, Kings Head
Reedham, Ferry
Titchwell, Manor

NORTHUMBERLAND,
DURHAM etc
Blanchland, Lord Crewe
Arms
Diptonmill, Dipton Mill
Greta Bridge, Morritt
Arms
Longhorsley, Linden Pub

Piercebridge, George

OXFORDSHIRE
Beckley, Abingdon Arms
Binfield Heath, Bottle &
Glass
Brightwell Baldwin, Lord
Nelson
Burford, Lamb
Chinnor, Sir Charles
Napier
Clifton Hampden, Barley
Mow
Fyfield, White Hart
Goring Heath, King
Charles Head
Hook Norton, Gate
Hangs High
Maidensgrove, Five
Horseshoes
Minster Lovell, Old Swan
Moulsford, Beetle &
Wedge
Newbridge, Rose Revived
Shipton-under-Wychwood,
Shaven Crown
South Leigh, Mason Arms
Stanton Harcourt,
Harcourt Arms
Stanton St John, Star
Stoke Row, Crooked Billet
Tadpole Bridge, Trout
Watlington, Chequers
Woodstock, Feathers

SHROPSHIRE
Bishops Castle, Three
Tuns
Coalport, Woodbridge
Hopton Wafers, Crown
Upper Farmcote, Lion of
Morfe

SOMERSET AND AVON
Ashcott, Ashcott
Bristol, Highbury Vaults
Combe Hay, Wheatsheaf
Dunster, Luttrell Arms
Exebridge, Anchor
Monksilver, Notley Arms
Over Stratton, Royal Oak
Shepperdine, Windbound
South Stoke, Pack Horse
Tormarton, Compass
West Huntspill,
Crossways

SUFFOLK
Chelsworth, Peacock
Hoxne, Swan
Lavenham, Angel
Laxfield, Kings Head
Rede, Plough
Walberswick, Bell
Westleton, Crown
Wetheringsett, Cat &

Mouse

SURREY
Charleshill, Donkey
Chipstead, Well House
Coldharbour, Plough
Fickleshole, White Bear
Hascombe, White Horse
Laleham, Three
Horseshoes
Mickleham, King William
IV
Newdigate, Surrey Oaks
Norwood Hill, Fox
Revived
Outwood, Bell; Dog &
Duck
Pirbright, Royal Oak
Pyrford Lock, Anchor
Warlingham, White Lion

SUSSEX
Ashurst, Fountain
Blackboys, Blackboys
Byworth, Black Horse
Charlton, Fox Goes Free
Coolham, George &
Dragon
Elsted, Three Horseshoes
Fletching, Griffin
Fulking, Shepherd & Dog
Gun Hill, Gun
Heathfield, Star
Houghton, George &
Dragon
Lickfold, Lickfold
Oving, Gribble
Oxleys Green, Jack Fullers
Rowhook, Chequers
Scaynes Hill, Sloop
Seaford, Golden Galleon
Sidlesham, Crab &
Lobster
Stopham, White Hart
West Firle, Ram

Winchelsea, New Inn
Wineham, Royal Oak

WILTSHIRE
Alvediston, Crown
Bradford-on-Avon, Cross
Guns
Brinkworth, Three
Crowns
Castle Eaton, Red Lion
Chicksgrove, Compasses
Everleigh, Crown
Lacock, Rising Sun
Lower Woodford,
Wheatsheaf
Norton, Vine Tree
Seend, Barge

YORKSHIRE
Bolton Percy, Crown
Egton Bridge, Horse Shoe
Harrogate, Squinting Cat
Penistone, Cubley Hall
Threshfield, Old Hall

LONDON, CENTRAL
Cross Keys
Red Lion

LONDON, NORTH
Spaniards
Waterside

LONDON, SOUTH
Crown & Greyhound
Ship
White Swan

LONDON, WEST
Dove

SCOTLAND
Ardfern, Galley of Lorne
Arduaine, Loch Melfort
Cleish, Nivingston House

Edinburgh, Starbank
Gifford, Tweeddale Arms
Kilmelford, Cuilfail
Newburgh, Udny Arms
Pitlochry, Killiecrankie
Skeabost, Skeabost House
Spean Bridge, Letterfinlay
Lodge
Strachur, Creggans
Thornhill, Lion &
Unicorn
Tweedsmuir, Crook

WALES
Aberystwyth, Halfway
Bodfari, Dinorben Arms
Caerphilly, Courthouse
Crickhowell, Bear
Lisvane, Ty Mawr Arms
Llancarfan, Fox &
Hounds
Llandrindod Wells,
Llanerch
Llanfrynach, White Swan
Llanrwst, Maenan Abbey
Llanthony, Abbey
Llwyndafydd, Crown
Marianglas, Parciau Arms
Nevern, Trewern Arms
Old Radnor, Harp
Presteigne, Radnorshire
Arms
Rhewl, Sun

CHANNEL ISLANDS
Castel, Hougue du
Pommier
Kings Mills, Fleur du
Jardin
Rozel, Rozel Bay
St Martin, Auberge
Divette

Waterside pubs
The pubs listed here are right beside the sea, a sizeable river, canal, lake or
loch that contributes significantly to their attraction.

BERKSHIRE
Great Shefford, Swan
Kintbury, Dundas Arms

CAMBRIDGESHIRE
AND BEDFORDSHIRE
Cambridge, Anchor;
Boathouse; Tap & Spile
Holywell, Olde Ferry Boat
Odell, Bell
Sutton Gault, Anchor
Wansford, Haycock

CHESHIRE
Barbridge, Barbridge

CORNWALL
Bodinnick, Old Ferry
Helford, Shipwrights
Arms
Malpas, Heron
Mousehole, Ship
Mylor Bridge, Pandora
Polkerris, Rashleigh
Polperro, Blue Peter
Polruan, Lugger
Port Gaverne, Port

Gaverne
Porthleven, Ship
Portloe, Lugger
St Mawes, Rising Sun

CUMBRIA
Biggar, Queens Arms
Ulverston, Bay Horse

DERBYSHIRE AND
STAFFORDSHIRE
Fradley, Swan
Onecote, Jervis Arms
Shardlow, Hoskins Wharf

DEVON
Ashprington, Watermans Arms
Burgh Island, Pilchard
Combeinteignhead, Coombe Cellars
Dartmouth, Royal Castle
Exeter, Double Locks
Exminster, Turf
Lynmouth, Rising Sun
Plymouth, China House
Torcross, Start Bay
Tuckenhay, Maltsters Arms

DORSET
Chesil, Cove House
Chideock, Anchor
Lyme Regis, Pilot Boat

ESSEX
Chappel, Swan
Great Henny, Swan
Leigh on Sea, Crooked Billet

GLOUCESTERSHIRE
Ashleworth Quay, Boat
Fossebridge, Fossebridge
Lechlade, Trout
Redbrook, Boat

HAMPSHIRE
Bursledon, Jolly Sailor
Fawley, Jolly Sailor
Langstone, Royal Oak
Ovington, Bush
Wherwell, Mayfly

HEREFORD AND WORCESTER
Knightwick, Talbot
Wyre Piddle, Anchor

HUMBERSIDE
Hull, Minerva

ISLE OF WIGHT
Cowes, Folly
Seaview, Seaview
Shanklin, Fishermans Cottage
Ventnor, Spyglass

KENT
Conyer Quay, Ship
Oare, Shipwrights Arms
Whitstable, Pearsons Crab & Oyster House

LANCASHIRE
Bilsborrow, Owd Nells
Garstang, Th' owd Tithebarn
Manchester, Mark Addy

Whitewell, Inn at Whitewell

LEICESTERSHIRE, LINCOLNSHIRE AND NOTTINGHAMSHIRE
North Muskham, Muskham Ferry

MIDLANDS (including WARWICKSHIRE AND NORTHANTS)
Lapworth, Navigation
Lowsonford, Fleur de Lys
Netherton, Little Dry Dock
Oundle, Mill
Stoke Bruerne, Boat

NORFOLK
Reedham, Ferry

NORTHUMBERLAND, DURHAM etc
Haydon Bridge, General Havelock
Piercebridge, George

OXFORDSHIRE
Godstow, Trout
Moulsford, Beetle & Wedge
Newbridge, Rose Revived
Tadpole Bridge, Trout

SHROPSHIRE
Coalport, Woodbridge
Whitchurch, Willey Moor Lock

SOMERSET AND AVON
Exebridge, Anchor
Shepperdine, Windbound

SUFFOLK
Chelmondiston, Butt & Oyster
Orford, Jolly Sailor
Ramsholt, Ramsholt Arms

SURREY
Pyrford Lock, Anchor

SUSSEX
Arundel, Black Rabbit
Stopham, White Hart

WILTSHIRE
Bradford-on-Avon, Cross Guns
Castle Eaton, Red Lion
Salisbury, Avon Brewery
Seend, Barge

YORKSHIRE
Newton on Ouse,

Dawnay Arms
Sowerby Bridge, Moorings
York, Kings Arms

LONDON, NORTH
Waterside

LONDON, SOUTH
Anchor
Angel
Bulls Head
Horniman
Mayflower
Ship

LONDON, WEST
Bulls Head
Dove

LONDON, EAST
Grapes

SCOTLAND
Ardentinny, Ardentinny
Ardfern, Galley of Lorne
Arduaine, Loch Melfort
Carbost, Old Inn
Crinan, Crinan
Edinburgh, Starbank
Findhorn, Crown & Anchor
Isle of Whithorn, Steam Packet
Isleornsay, Eilean Iarmain
Kippford, Anchor
Plockton, Plockton
Portpatrick, Crown
Queensferry, Hawes
Shieldaig, Tigh an Eilean
Skeabost, Skeabost House
Spean Bridge, Letterfinlay Lodge
St Marys Loch, Tibbie Shiels
Strachur, Creggans
Tayvallich, Tayvallich
Ullapool, Ferry Boat

WALES
Aberaeron, Harbourmaster
Abergorlech, Black Lion
Broad Haven, Druidstone
Cresswell Quay, Cresselly Arms
Little Haven, Swan
Nevern, Trewern Arms
Penarth, Captains Wife
Penmaenpool, George III
Pontypool, Open Hearth
Porth Dinllaen, Ty Coch
Red Wharf Bay, Ship

Pubs in attractive surroundings

These pubs are in unusually attractive or interesting places – lovely countryside, charming villages, occasionally notable town surroundings. Waterside pubs are listed again here only if their other surroundings are special, too.

BERKSHIRE
Aldworth, Bell
Frilsham, Pot Kiln
Hurley, Dew Drop
Littlewick Green,
Cricketers

BUCKINGHAMSHIRE
Bledlow, Lions of Bledlow
Brill, Pheasant
Hambleden, Stag &
Huntsman
Ibstone, Fox
Northend, White Hart
Turville, Bull & Butcher

**CAMBRIDGESHIRE
AND BEDFORDSHIRE**
Barrington, Royal Oak
Chatteris, Crafty Fox

CHESHIRE
Barthomley, White Lion
Bottom of the Oven,
Stanley Arms
Great Budworth, George
& Dragon
Langley, Leathers Smithy
Lower Peover, Bells of
Peover
Sutton, Ryles Arms

CORNWALL
Boscastle, Cobweb
Chapel Amble, Maltsters
Arms
Lerryn, Ship
Morwenstow, Bush
Polperro, Blue Peter
Portloe, Lugger
St Breward, Old Inn
St Kew, St Kew
Trebarwith, Mill House

CUMBRIA
Alston, Angel
Bassenthwaite, Pheasant
Biggar, Queens Arms
Boot, Burnmoor
Braithwaite, Coledale
Coniston, Sun
Crosthwaite, Punch Bowl
Dent, Sun
Elterwater, Britannia
Grasmere, Travellers Rest
Hawkshead, Drunken
Duck; Kings Arms
Hesket Newmarket, Old
Crown
Langdale, Old Dungeon

Ghyll
Little Langdale, Three
Shires
Loweswater, Kirkstile
Melmerby, Shepherds
Scales, White Horse
Ulverston, Bay Horse
Wasdale Head, Wasdale
Head

**DERBYSHIRE AND
STAFFORDSHIRE**
Alstonefield, George
Brassington, Olde Gate
Froggatt Edge, Chequers
Hardwick Hall, Hardwick
Holmesfield, Robin Hood
Little Hucklow, Old Bulls
Head
Little Longstone,
Packhorse
Monsal Head, Monsal
Head
Over Haddon, Lathkil
Rowarth, Little Mill

DEVON
Burgh Island, Pilchard
Exminster, Turf
Haytor Vale, Rock
Holne, Church House
Horndon, Elephants Nest
Horsebridge, Royal
Iddesleigh, Duke of York
Knowstone, Masons Arms
Lustleigh, Cleave
Lydford, Castle
Lynmouth, Rising Sun
North Bovey, Ring of Bells
Peter Tavy, Peter Tavy
Postbridge, Warren House
Rattery, Church House
Sandy Park, Sandy Park
Slapton, Tower

DORSET
Abbotsbury, Ilchester
Arms
Askerswell, Spyway
Chedington, Winyards
Gap
East Chaldon, Sailors
Return
Farnham, Museum
Milton Abbas, Hambro
Arms
Plush, Brace of Pheasants
Powerstock, Three
Horseshoes

Sandford Orcas, Mitre
Worth Matravers, Square
& Compass

ESSEX
Belchamp St Paul, Half
Moon
Leigh on Sea, Crooked
Billet
Mill Green, Viper
Purleigh, Bell

GLOUCESTERSHIRE
Amberley, Black Horse
Ashleworth Quay, Boat
Bisley, Bear
Bledington, Kings Head
Brockweir, Brockweir
Chedworth, Seven Tuns
Coates, Tunnel House
Cold Aston, Plough
Coln St Aldwyns, New Inn
Great Rissington, Lamb
Guiting Power, Olde Inne
Nailsworth, Weighbridge
Newland, Ostrich
North Nibley, New Inn
Painswick, Royal Oak
Sapperton, Daneway
St Briavels, George
Stanton, Mount
Stow on the Wold,
Queens Head

HAMPSHIRE
Beaulieu, Montagu Arms
Emery Down, New Forest
Hamble, Olde Whyte
Harte
Linwood, High Corner
Ovington, Bush
Petersfield, White Horse
Soberton, White Lion
Tichborne, Tichborne
Arms
Vernham Dean, Boot

**HEREFORD AND
WORCESTER**
Barnards Green, Blue Bell
Hanley Castle, Three
Kings
Knightwick, Talbot
Ruckhall Common,
Ancient Camp
Sellack, Loughpool
Weobley, Olde Salutation
Woolhope, Butchers Arms

HERTFORDSHIRE
St Albans, Fighting Cocks
Westmill, Sword in Hand

HUMBERSIDE
South Dalton, Pipe &
Glass

ISLE OF WIGHT
Chale, Clarendon (Wight
Mouse)

KENT
Boughton Aluph, Flying
Horse
Chiddingstone, Castle
Chilham, White Horse
Cobham, Leather Bottle
Groombridge, Crown
Lamberhurst, Brown
Trout; Elephants Head
Luddenham, Mounted
Rifleman
Newnham, George
Stowting, Tiger

LANCASHIRE
Blacko, Moorcock
Blackstone Edge, White
House
Downham, Assheton
Arms
Haslingden, Duke of
Wellington
Newton, Parkers Arms
Slaidburn, Hark to Bounty
Tockholes, Royal Arms
Uppermill, Cross Keys
Whitewell, Inn at
Whitewell

LEICESTERSHIRE,
LINCOLNSHIRE AND
NOTTINGHAMSHIRE
Exton, Fox & Hounds
Glooston, Old Barn
Hallaton, Bewicke Arms
Laxton, Dovecote
Lyddington, Marquess of
Exeter

MIDLANDS (including
WARWICKSHIRE AND
NORTHANTS)
Alveston, Ferry
Himley, Crooked House
Warmington, Plough

NORFOLK
Blickling,
Buckinghamshire Arms
Castle Acre, Ostrich
Thornham, Lifeboat

NORTHUMBERLAND,
DURHAM etc
Blanchland, Lord Crewe
Arms
Craster, Jolly Fisherman
Diptonmill, Dipton Mill
Eggleston, Three Tuns
Romaldkirk, Rose &
Crown

OXFORDSHIRE
Brightwell Baldwin, Lord
Nelson
Burford, Mermaid
Chinnor, Sir Charles
Napier
Christmas Common, Fox
& Hounds
Clifton Hampden, Barley
Mow
Cropredy, Red Lion
Goring Heath, King
Charles Head
Great Tew, Falkland Arms
Hailey, King William IV
Maidensgrove, Five
Horseshoes
Minster Lovell, Old Swan
Oxford, Turf Tavern
Pishill, Crown
Shenington, Bell
Shipton-under-Wychwood,
Shaven Crown
Stoke Row, Crooked Billet
Swinbrook, Swan

SHROPSHIRE
Cardington, Royal Oak
Coalport, Woodbridge
Hope, Stables
Ironbridge, New Inn
Llanfair Waterdine, Red
Lion
Wenlock Edge, Wenlock
Edge

SOMERSET AND AVON
Appley, Globe
Ashill, Square & Compass
Combe Hay, Wheatsheaf
Cranmore, Strode Arms
Luxborough, Royal Oak
Stogumber, White Horse
Triscombe, Blue Ball
Wambrook, Cotley
Winsford, Royal Oak

SUFFOLK
Chelsworth, Peacock
Dunwich, Ship
Kersey, Bell
Lavenham, Angel
Ramsholt, Ramsholt Arms
Sutton, Plough
Walberswick, Bell

SURREY
Blackbrook, Plough
Cobham, Cricketers
Headley, Cock
Mickleham, King William
IV
Ockley, Punch Bowl
Outwood, Bell
Reigate Heath,
Skimmington Castle
Shere, White Horse

SUSSEX
Billingshurst, Blue Ship
Burpham, George &
Dragon
Burwash, Bell
Chilgrove, Royal Oak
Dallington, Swan
Ditchling, Bull
Fletching, Griffin
Fulking, Shepherd & Dog
Heathfield, Star
Lickfold, Lickfold
Lurgashall, Noahs Ark
Oxleys Green, Jack Fullers
Seaford, Golden Galleon
Sidlesham, Crab &
Lobster
West Hoathly, Cat
Wineham, Royal Oak

WILTSHIRE
Alvediston, Crown
Bradford-on-Avon, Cross
Guns
Ebbesbourne Wake,
Horseshoe
Lacock, Rising Sun
Wootton Rivers, Royal
Oak

YORKSHIRE
Arncliffe, Falcon
Askrigg, Kings Arms
Blakey Ridge, Lion
Bolton Percy, Crown
Buckden, Buck
Burnsall, Red Lion
Byland Abbey, Abbey
Cray, White Lion
East Witton, Blue Lion
Heath, Kings Arms
Hubberholme, George
Kilburn, Forresters Arms
Kirby Hill, Shoulder of
Mutton
Langthwaite, Red Lion
Lastingham, Blacksmiths
Arms
Levisham, Horse Shoe
Litton, Queens Arms
Masham, Kings Head
Meltham, Will's o' Nat's
Midgley, Mount Skip
Ramsgill, Yorke Arms
Robin Hoods Bay, Laurel
Rosedale Abbey, Milburn
Arms

Rosedale Abbey, White
Horse
Stansfield Moor,
Sportsmans Arms
Sutton Howgrave, White
Dog
Thornton Watlass, Buck
Wath-in-Nidderdale,
Sportsmans Arms
Widdop, Pack Horse

LONDON, CENTRAL
Olde Mitre

LONDON, NORTH
Spaniards

LONDON, SOUTH
Crown & Greyhound
Horniman
Olde Windmill

LONDON, WEST
Kings Arms

SCOTLAND
Arduaine, Loch Melfort
Crinan, Crinan
Edinburgh, Sheep Heid
Glencoe, Clachaig
Loch Eck, Whistlefield
Mountbenger, Gordon
Arms
Pitlochry, Killiecrankie
Sheriffmuir, Sheriffmuir
St Marys Loch, Tibbie
Shiels
Strachur, Creggans
Tweedsmuir, Crook

WALES
Abergorlech, Black Lion
Aberystwyth, Halfway

Broad Haven, Druidstone
Bylchau, Sportsmans
Arms
Caerphilly, Courthouse
Cilcain, White Horse
Ganllwyd, Tyn-y-groes
Kenfig, Prince of Wales
Llanberis, Pen-y-Gwryd
Llangurig, Glansevern
Arms
Llanthony, Abbey
Maentwrog, Grapes
Old Radnor, Harp
Penderyn, Red Lion
Penmaenpool, George III
Porth Dinllaen, Ty Coch
Red Wharf Bay, Ship
Rhewl, Sun

Pubs with good views

These pubs are listed for their particularly good views, either from inside or
from a garden or terrace. Waterside pubs are listed again here only if their
view is exceptional in its own right – not just a straightforward sea view, for
example.

BERKSHIRE
Chieveley, Blue Boar

BUCKINGHAMSHIRE
Brill, Pheasant
Penn, Crown

CHESHIRE
Langley, Hanging Gate;
Leathers Smithy
Overton, Ring o' Bells
Rainow, Highwayman

CORNWALL
Polruan, Lugger

CUMBRIA
Braithwaite, Coledale
Cartmel Fell, Masons
Arms
Hawkshead, Drunken
Duck
Langdale, Old Dungeon
Ghyll
Loweswater, Kirkstile
Ulverston, Bay Horse
Wasdale Head, Wasdale
Head

**DERBYSHIRE AND
STAFFORDSHIRE**
Foolow, Barrel
Monsal Head, Monsal
Head
Over Haddon, Lathkil

DEVON
Burgh Island, Pilchard
Hennock, Palk Arms
Postbridge, Warren House

DORSET
Chedington, Winyards
Gap
West Bexington, Manor
Worth Matravers, Square
& Compass

ESSEX
Purleigh, Bell

GLOUCESTERSHIRE
Amberley, Black Horse
Stanton, Mount
Woodchester, Ram

HAMPSHIRE
Beauworth, Milbury's

**HEREFORD AND
WORCESTER**
Ruckhall Common,
Ancient Camp
Wyre Piddle, Anchor

HERTFORDSHIRE
Great Offley, Green Man

ISLE OF WIGHT
Ventnor, Spyglass

KENT
Penshurst, Spotted Dog
Ulcombe, Pepper Box

LANCASHIRE
Blacko, Moorcock
Blackstone Edge, White
House
Darwen, Old Rosins
Mereclough, Kettledrum
Tockholes, Rock; Royal
Arms
Uppermill, Cross Keys

**NORTHUMBERLAND,
DURHAM etc**
Eggleston, Three Tuns
Seahouses, Olde Ship
Tynemouth, Wooden Doll

SHROPSHIRE
Hope, Stables

SUFFOLK
Hundon, Plough

SUSSEX
Burpham, George &
Dragon
Byworth, Black Horse
Dallington, Swan
Elsted, Three Horseshoes
Fletching, Griffin
Houghton, George &
Dragon

WILTSHIRE
Lacock, Rising Sun

YORKSHIRE
Blakey Ridge, Lion
Kirby Hill, Shoulder of
Mutton
Litton, Queens Arms
Meltham, Will's o' Nat's
Midgley, Mount Skip
Rosedale Abbey, White
Horse

LONDON, SOUTH
Angel

SCOTLAND
Ardentinny, Ardentinny
Ardvasar, Ardvasar
Crinan, Crinan
Edinburgh, Starbank
Glencoe, Clachaig
Isle Ornsay, Eilean
Iarmain
Pitlochry, Killiecrankie
Sheriffmuir, Sheriffmuir
Shieldaig, Tigh an Eilean
St Marys Loch, Tibbie
Shiels
Strachur, Creggans
Ullapool, Ferry Boat
Weem, Ailean Chraggan

WALES
Aberystwyth, Halfway
Bodfari, Dinorben Arms
Broad Haven, Druidstone
Bylchau, Sportsmans Arms
Caerphilly, Courthouse
Ganllwyd, Tyn-y-groes
Llanberis, Pen-y-Gwryd
Old Radnor, Harp
Penmaenpool, George III
Porth Dinllaen, Ty Coch
Rhewl, Sun

CHANNEL ISLANDS
St Martin, Auberge
Divette

Pubs in interesting buildings

Pubs and inns are listed here for the particular interest of their building –
something really out of the ordinary to look at, or occasionally a building that
has an outstandingly interesting historical background.

BERKSHIRE
Cookham, Bel & the
Dragon

BUCKINGHAMSHIRE
Forty Green, Royal
Standard of England

CORNWALL
Morwenstow, Bush

DERBYSHIRE AND
STAFFORDSHIRE
Buxton, Bull i'th' Thorn
Derby, Abbey

DEVON
Dartmouth, Cherub
Harberton, Church House
Rattery, Church House
Sourton, Highwayman
South Zeal, Oxenham
Arms

HAMPSHIRE
Beauworth, Milbury's

HEREFORD AND
WORCESTER
Bretforton, Fleece

HUMBERSIDE
Hull, Olde White Harte

LANCASHIRE
Garstang, Th'Owd

Tithebarn
Liverpool, Philharmonic
Dining Rooms

LEICESTERSHIRE,
LINCOLNSHIRE AND
NOTTINGHAMSHIRE
Nottingham, Olde Trip to
Jerusalem
Stamford, George of
Stamford

MIDLANDS (including
WARWICKSHIRE AND
NORTHANTS)
Birmingham, Bartons
Arms
Himley, Crooked House
West Bromwich, Manor
House

NORFOLK
Scole, Scole

NORTHUMBERLAND,
DURHAM etc
Blanchland, Lord Crewe
Arms

OXFORDSHIRE
Fyfield, White Hart

SHROPSHIRE
Ironbridge, New Inn

SOMERSET AND AVON
Norton St Philip, George

SURREY
Shere, White Horse

SUSSEX
Alfriston, Star
Rye, Mermaid

WILTSHIRE
Salisbury, Haunch of
Venison

LONDON, CENTRAL
Black Friar
Cittie of York

LONDON, NORTH
Crockers

LONDON, SOUTH
George
Phoenix & Firkin

LONDON, EAST
Hollands

SCOTLAND
Dumfries, Globe
Edinburgh, Bennets Bar;
Cafe Royal; Guildford
Arms
Glasgow, Horseshoe

WALES
Llanthony, Abbey

Pubs that brew their own beer

The pubs listed here brew their own brew on the premises; many others not
listed have beers brewed for them specially, sometimes to an individual recipe
(but by a separate brewer). We mention these in the text.

CORNWALL
Helston, Blue Anchor
Tintagel, Min Pin

CUMBRIA
Cartmel Fell, Masons
Arms
Dent, Sun
Hesket Newmarket, Old
Crown

**DERBYSHIRE AND
STAFFORDSHIRE**
Burton-on-Trent, Burton
Bridge
Melbourne, John
Thompson
Shraleybrook, Rising Sun

DEVON
Ashburton, London
Hatherleigh, Tally Ho
Horsebridge, Royal
Newton St Cyres, Beer
Engine

HERTFORDSHIRE
Barley, Fox and Hounds

HUMBERSIDE
Hull, Minerva

LANCASHIRE
Manchester, Lass o'
Gowrie

**LEICESTERSHIRE,
LINCOLNSHIRE AND
NOTTINGHAMSHIRE**
Burrough on the Hill,
Stag & Hounds
Leicester, Tom Hoskins
Nottingham, Fellows
Morton & Clayton

**MIDLANDS (including
WARWICKSHIRE AND
NORTHANTS)**
Brierley Hill, Vine
Langley, Brewery
Netherton, Old Swan

SHROPSHIRE
Bishops Castle, Three
Tuns
Wistanstow, Plough

SOMERSET AND AVON
Trudoxhill, White Hart

SUFFOLK
Earl Soham, Victoria

SUSSEX
Chidham, Old House At
Home

YORKSHIRE
Cropton, New Inn
Linthwaite, Sair
Sheffield, Fat Cat
Sheffield, Frog & Parrot
Todmorden, Staff of Life

LONDON, CENTRAL
Orange Brewery

LONDON, SOUTH
Phoenix & Firkin

LONDON, WEST
Ferret & Firkin

Pubs close to motorway junctions

The number at the start of each line is the number of the junction. Detailed
directions are given in the main entry for each pub. In this section, to help you
find the pubs quickly before you're past the junction, we give in abbreviated
form the name of the chapter where you'll find them in the text.

M1
15: Stoke Bruerne
(Midlands) 3 3/4 miles
18: Ashby St Ledgers
(Midlands) 4 miles
18: Crick (Midlands) 1
mile
20: Walcote (Leics etc)
1 1/2 miles
24: Kegworth (Leics etc)
under a mile
24: Shardlow
(Derbys/Staffs) 3 1/4
miles
29: Hardwick Hall
(Derbys/Staffs) 4 1/2
miles
36: Wentworth (Yorks) 3
miles

M2
1: Cobham (Kent) 2 1/2

miles
6: Luddenham (Kent)
3 1/2 miles
7: Selling (Kent) 3 1/2
miles

M3
5: Mattingley (Hants) 3
miles
5: Rotherwick (Hants) 4
miles

M4
9: Bray (Berks) 1 3/4
miles
9: Littlewick Green
(Berks) 3 3/4 miles
12: Stanford Dingley
(Berks) 4 miles
13: Chieveley (Berks)
3 1/2 miles
13: Hermitage (Berks)

2 1/2 miles
14: Great Shefford (Berks)
1/3 mile
14: Great Shefford (Berks)
2 miles
18: Tormarton
(Somerset/Avon) 1/2
mile
21: Aust (Somerset/Avon)
1/2 mile
37: Nottage (Wales) 2
miles
37: Kenfig (Wales) 2 1/4
miles

M5
2: Langley (Midlands)
1 1/2 miles
9: Bredon
(Hereford/Worcs)
4 1/2 miles
16: Almondsbury

(Somerset/Avon) 1 1/4 miles

19: Clapton in Gordano (Somerset/Avon) 4 miles

23: West Huntspill (Somerset/Avon) 2 3/4 miles

25: Stoke St Mary (Somerset/Avon) 2 3/4 miles

28: Broadhembury (Devon) 5 miles

30: Exeter (Devon) 4 miles

30: Topsham (Devon) 2 miles

30: Woodbury Salterton (Devon) 3 1/2 miles

30: Topsham (Devon) 2 1/4 miles

M6

2: Withybrook (Midlands) 4 miles

6: Birmingham (Midlands) 2 miles

9: West Bromwich (Midlands) 2 miles

15: Whitmore (Derbys/Staffs) 3 miles

16: Barthomley (Cheshire) 1 mile

16: Weston (Cheshire) 3 1/2 miles

16: Shraleybrook (Derbys/Staffs) 3 miles

17: Brereton Green (Cheshire) 2 miles

19: Plumley (Cheshire) 2 1/2 miles

19: Great Budworth (Cheshire) 4 1/2 miles

29: Brindle (Lancs etc) 3 miles

31: Balderstone (Lancs etc) 2 miles

32: Goosnargh (Lancs etc) 4 miles

35: Yealand Conyers (Lancs etc) 3 miles

40: Askham (Cumbria) 4 1/2 miles

40: Stainton (Cumbria) 3 miles

43: Warwick-on-Eden (Cumbria) 2 miles

M9

3: Linlithgow (Scotland) 2 miles

M11

5: Loughton (Essex) 2 1/4 miles

7: Hastingwood (Essex) 1/4 miles

10: Hinxton (Cambs/Beds) 2 miles

M18

5: Hatfield Woodhouse (Yorks) 2 miles

M25

5: Chipstead (Kent) 1 1/4 miles

7: Chipstead (Surrey) 3 1/2 miles

8: Betchworth (Surrey) 4 miles

8: Reigate Heath (Surrey) 3 miles

10: Cobham (Surrey) 3 miles

16: Denham (Bucks) 3 miles

18: Chenies (Bucks) 2 miles

18: Flaunden (Herts) 4 miles

M27

3: Romsey (Hants) 3 miles

8: Bursledon (Hants) 2 miles

8: Hamble (Hants) 3 miles

M40

2: Forty Green (Bucks) 3 1/2 miles

2: Beaconsfield (Bucks) 1 mile

5: Bolter End (Bucks) 4 miles

5: Ibstone (Bucks) 1 mile

6: Watlington (Oxon) 2 1/4 miles

7: Little Milton (Oxon) 2 1/2 miles

8: Worminghall (Bucks) 4 1/2 miles

M55

1: Broughton (Lancs etc) 3 1/2 miles

M56

10: Little Leigh (Cheshire) 4 1/2 miles

10: Lower Whitley (Cheshire) 2 1/4 miles

12: Overton (Cheshire) 2 miles

14: Alvanley (Cheshire) 2 1/2 miles

M62

19: Middleton (Lancs etc) 2 miles

M65

12: Brierfield (Lancs etc) 1/2 mile

M73

6: Uddingston (Scotland) 1 mile

M90

5: Cleish (Scotland) 1 1/2 miles

10: Perth (Scotland) 2 miles

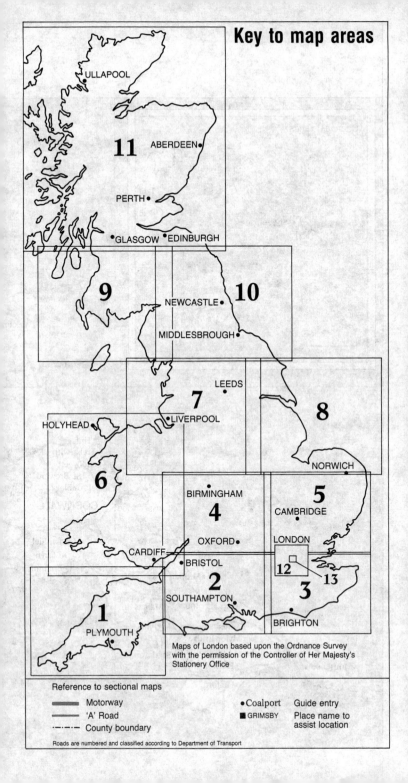

Key to map areas

ULLAPOOL

11 ABERDEEN

PERTH

GLASGOW EDINBURGH

9 NEWCASTLE **10**

MIDDLESBROUGH

LEEDS

7 LIVERPOOL

HOLYHEAD

8

NORWICH

6

BIRMINGHAM **5**

4 CAMBRIDGE

OXFORD LONDON

CARDIFF **12** **13**

BRISTOL

2

SOUTHAMPTON **3**

1 BRIGHTON

PLYMOUTH

Maps of London based upon the Ordnance Survey
with the permission of the Controller of Her Majesty's
Stationery Office

Reference to sectional maps

     Motorway   • Coalport   Guide entry

     'A' Road   ■ GRIMSBY   Place name to
     –·–·– County boundary   assist location

Roads are numbered and classified according to Department of Transport

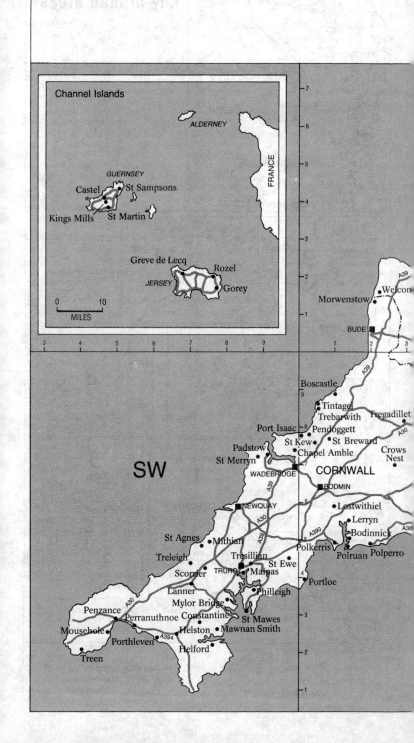

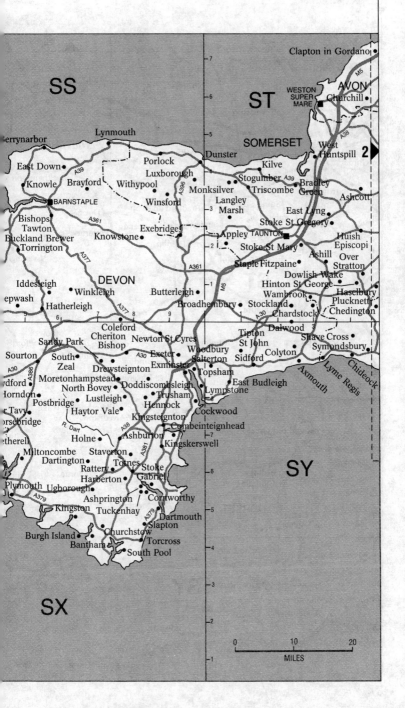

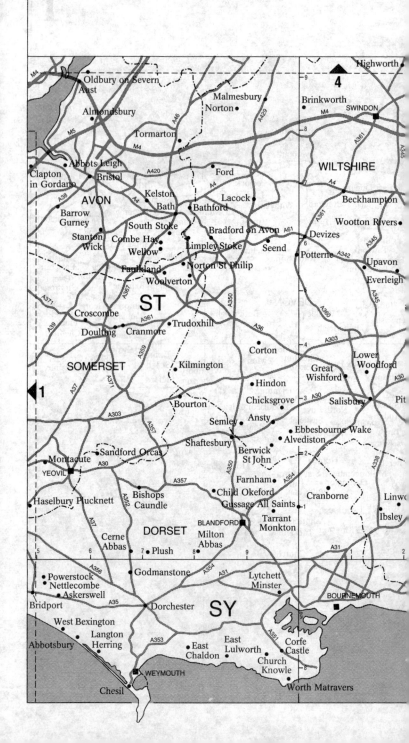

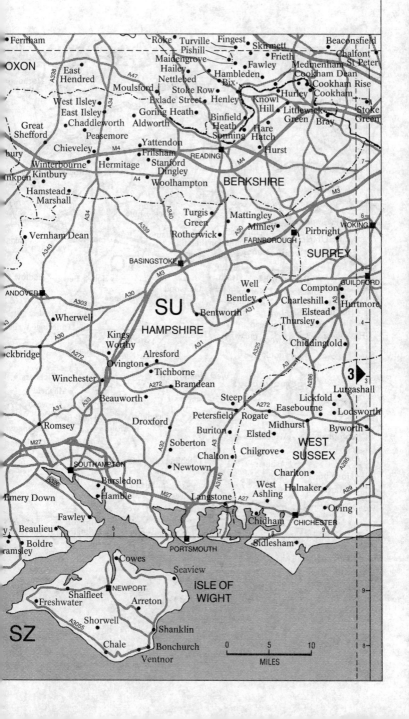

OXON

Fernham •

Roke • Turville • Fingest • Skirmett • Beaconsfield
Pishill • Frieth • Chalfont St Peter
Maidengrove • Fawley • Medmenham • Cookham Dean
Hailey • Hambleden • Bix • Cookham Rise
East Hendred • Nettlebed • Stoke Row • Henley • Hurley • Cookham
Moulsford • Exlade Street • Knowl Hill • Littlewick Green • Bray • Stoke Green
West Ilsley • Goring Heath • Binfield Heath • Hare Hatch
East Ilsley • Chaddleworth • Aldworth • Sonning • Hurst
Great Shefford • Peasemore • Yattendon
Chieveley • Frilsham • READING
Winterbourne • Hermitage • Stanford Dingley • Woolhampton • **BERKSHIRE**
Kintbury • A4
Hamstead Marshall •

Vernham Dean •

Turgis Green • Mattingley • Minley • Pirbright • WOKING
Rotherwick • FARNBOROUGH • **SURREY**

BASINGSTOKE •

ANDOVER •

Wherwell •

SU

HAMPSHIRE

Well • Compton • GUILDFORD
Bentley • Charleshill • Hurtmore
Bentworth • Elstead • A3
Thursley •
Chiddingfold •

Kings Worthy •
Alresford
Ovington • Tichborne
Winchester • Bramdean
Beauworth •

Romsey •

Droxford •

Steep • Lickfold • Lurgashall
Petersfield • Easebourne • Lodsworth
Buriton • Rogate • Midhurst • Byworth
Elsted • **WEST**
Soberton • Chilgrove • **SUSSEX**
Chalton •
Newtown • Charlton
West Ashling • Halnaker
Langstone • Oving
Chidham • CHICHESTER

SOUTHAMPTON •
Bursledon •
Hamble •
Emery Down •
Fawley •
Beaulieu •
Boldre •
ramsley •
PORTSMOUTH
Sidlesham •

Cowes •
Seaview •
NEWPORT • **ISLE OF WIGHT**
Shalfleet • Arreton
Freshwater •
Shorwell •
Shanklin •
SZ Chale • Bonchurch
Ventnor

0   5   10
MILES

3 ▶

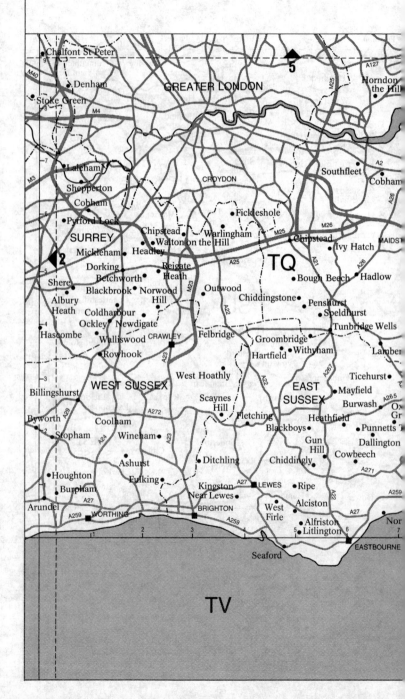

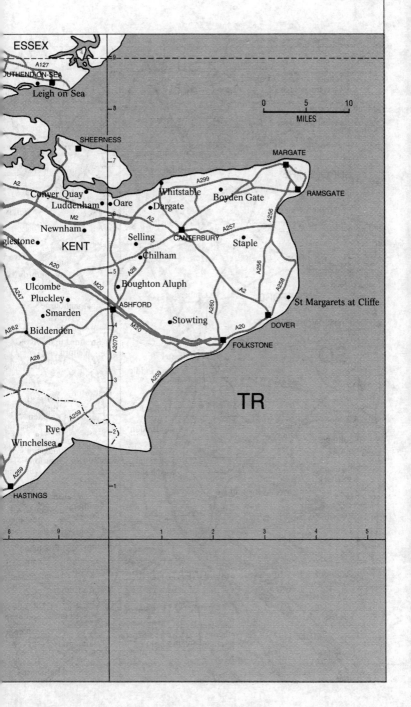

3

ESSEX

A127
UTHEND-ON-SEA
Leigh on Sea

0   5   10
MILES

SHEERNESS

MARGATE

A299
A2
RAMSGATE
Conyer Quay   Oare   Whitstable   Boyden Gate
Luddenham   Dargate
M2   A2
Newnham   CANTERBURY   A257
glestone   KENT   Selling   Staple
A20   Chilham   A256
A28
Ulcombe   Boughton Aluph   A2   A258
A247   Pluckley   M20   ASHFORD   St Margarets at Cliffe
Smarden   Stowting   A260   DOVER
A262   Biddenden   M20   A20
A28   A2070   FOLKSTONE
A259
TR
A259
Rye
Winchelsea
A259
HASTINGS

6   9   1   2   3   4   5

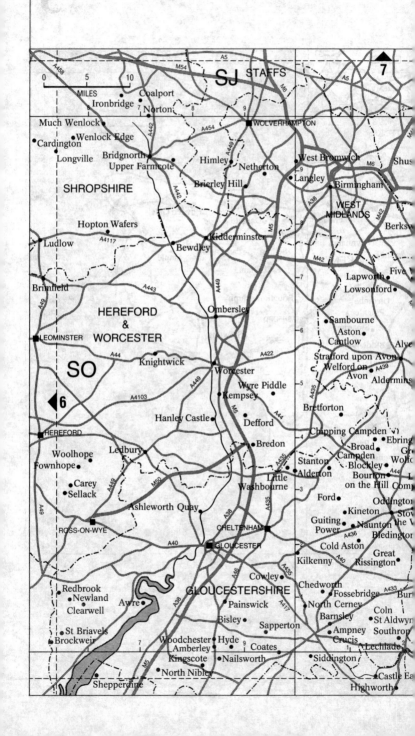

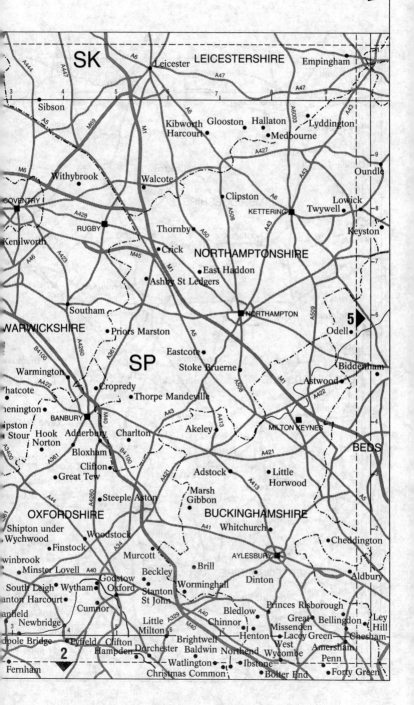

SK

LEICESTERSHIRE

Leicester
Empingham

Sibson

Kibworth Harcourt
Glooston
Hallaton
Lyddington

Withybrook
Walcote
Medbourne

COVENTRY
Clipston
Oundle

Kenilworth
RUGBY
Thornby
KETTERING
Lowick
Twywell

Crick
NORTHAMPTONSHIRE
Keyston

Southam
East Haddon
Ashby St Ledgers

WARWICKSHIRE
Priors Marston
NORTHAMPTON
Odell

Warmington
SP
Eastcote
Stoke Bruerne
Biddenham

hatcote
Cropredy
Astwood

henington
Thorpe Mandeville

ipston
BANBURY
Akeley
MILTON KEYNES
BEDS

Stour
Hook Norton
Adderbury
Charlton

Bloxham

Clifton
Adstock
Little Horwood

Great Tew

Steeple Aston
Marsh Gibbon
BUCKINGHAMSHIRE

OXFORDSHIRE
Whitchurch

Shipton under Wychwood
Woodstock
Cheddington

winbrook
Finstock
Murcott
Brill
AYLESBURY
Aldbury

Minster Lovell
Beckley
Dinton

South Leigh
Wytham
Godstow
Oxford
Worminghall
Princes Risborough
Ley Hill

anton Harcourt
Cumnor
Stanton St John
Bledlow
Great Missenden
Bellingdon

anfield
Little Milton
Chinnor
Lacey Green
Chesham

Newbridge
Henton
West Wycombe
Amersham

pole Bridge
Tyfield
Clifton Hampden
Brightwell Baldwin
Northend
Penn

Fernham
Dorchester
Watlington
Ibstone
Forty Green

Christmas Common
Bolter End

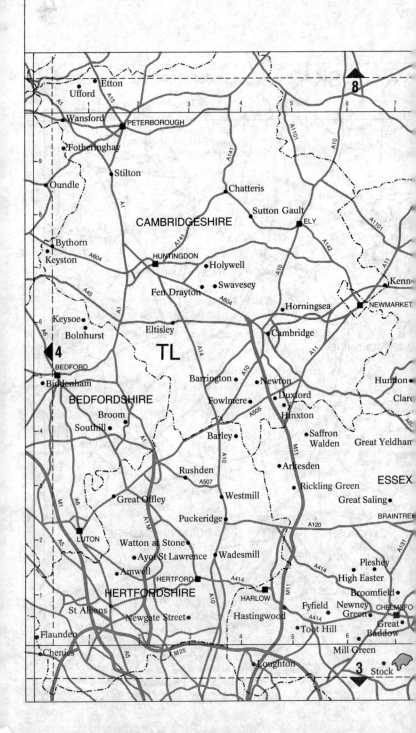

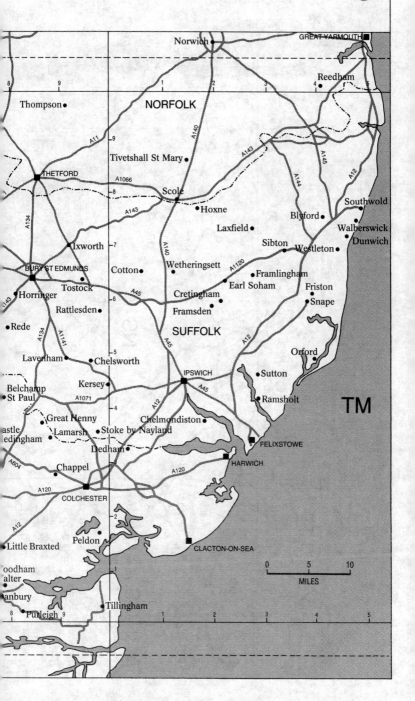

5

GREAT YARMOUTH

Norwich

Reedham

Thompson

NORFOLK

A11

A140

Tivetshall St Mary

A143

THETFORD

A1066

Scole

A145

A12

A134

A143

Hoxne

Blyford

Southwold

Laxfield

Walberswick

Ixworth

A140

Sibton

Westleton

Dunwich

BURY ST EDMUNDS

Cotton

Wetheringsett

A1120

Framlingham

Friston

Horringer

Tostock

Cretingham

Earl Soham

Snape

A45

Rattlesden

Framsden

Rede

A134

A1141

SUFFOLK

Orford

Lavenham

A45

Chelsworth

IPSWICH

A12

Sutton

Kersey

A45

Belchamp
St Paul

A1071

Ramsholt

TM

Great Henny

Chelmondiston

Lamarsh

Stoke by Nayland

astle
edingham

Dedham

FELIXSTOWE

A604

Chappel

A120

HARWICH

A120

COLCHESTER

A12

Little Braxted

Peldon

CLACTON-ON-SEA

oodham
alter

anbury

Tillingham

Purleigh

0   5   10

MILES

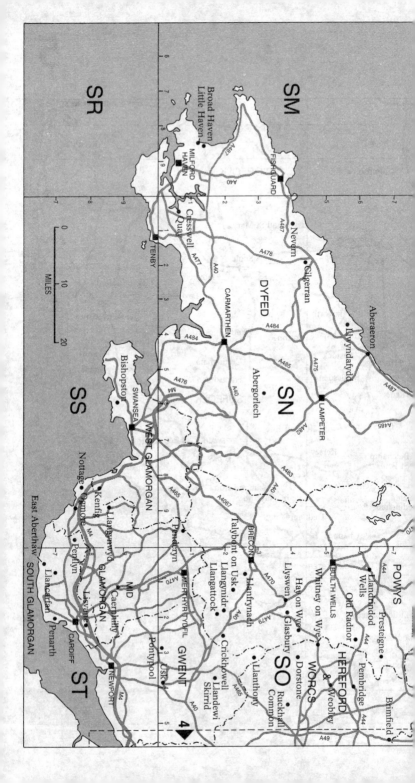

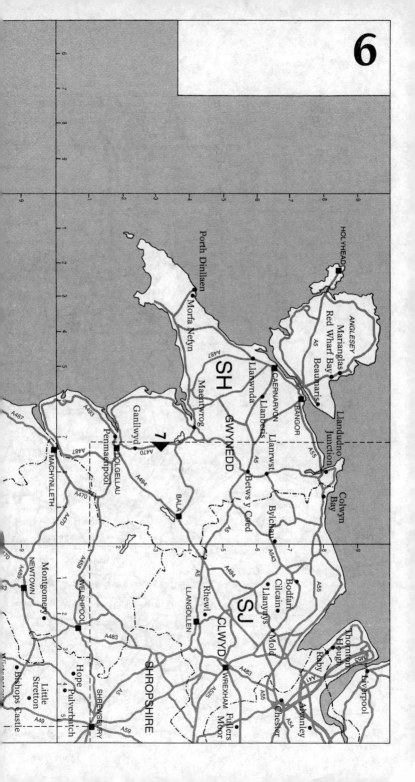

6

7

HOLYHEAD

Porth Dinllaen

Morfa Nefyn

A487

ANGLESEY
Marianglas
Red Wharf Bay
Beaumaris

A5

Llandudno
Junction

Colwyn
Bay

SH

Maentwrog

Llanwnda

CAERNARVON

Llanberis

BANGOR

Ganllwyd

GWYNEDD

Llanrwst

A5

Penmaenpool

A487

A483

7

A470

DOLGELLAU

A494

Llanrwst

Betws y Coed

Bylchau

A5

A543

MACHYNLLETH

A487

BALA

A5

A494

Montgomery

NEWTOWN

A489

A456

A458

WELSHPOOL

A5

LLANGOLLEN

Rhewl

A542

CLWYD

SJ

Bodfari
Clicain
Llanyrys
Mold

A55

A483

Thornton
Hough
Raby

Liverpool

A41

M55

Chester

A55

WREXHAM
Fullers
Moor

A483

A525

Alvanley

A54

A487

A470

A489

A483

A470

Hope
Pulverbatch

A5

SHREWSBURY

A5

A59

SHROPSHIRE

Little
Stretton

Bishops Castle

A49

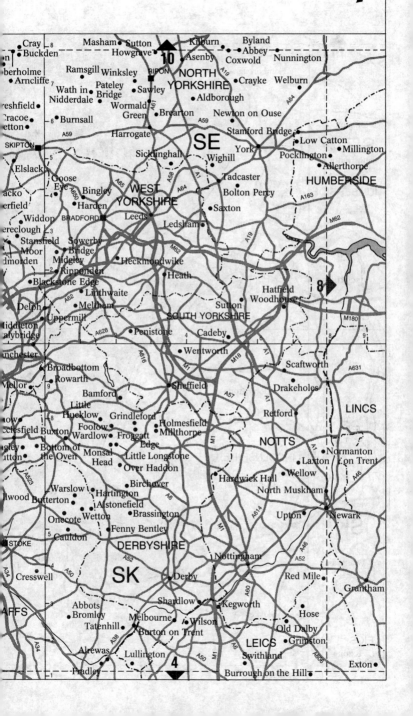

Cray
Buckden
berholme
Arncliffe 7
reshfield
Cracoe
etton

Masham Sutton
Howgrave
Ramsgill Winksley
Wath in Pateley Sawley
Nidderdale Bridge
Wormald Brearton
Green
Burnsall
Harrogate

10
RIPON

Kilburn Byland
Asenby Abbey
Coxwold Nunninton
Crayke Welburn
Aldborough
Newton on Ouse
Stamford Bridge

SKIPTON
5

Elslack
acko
erfield
Widdop 3
ereclough
Stansfield Sowerby
Moor Bridge
dmorden Midgley
2 Ripponden
Blackstone Edge
Linthwaite
Delph Meltham
Uppermill
iddleton
ulybridge
nchester

Goose
Eye
Bingley
Harden
BRADFORD
Leeds

**WEST
YORKSHIRE**

Sicklinghall

Heckmondwike
Heath

SE

York

Wighill
Tadcaster
Bolton Percy
Saxton
Ledsham

SOUTH YORKSHIRE

Sutton

Low Catton
Pocklington Millington
Allerthorpe

HUMBERSIDE

Hatfield
Woodhouse

8

M180

Broadbottom
Rowarth
Mellor 9
Bamford
Little
Hucklow
ccclesfield Buxton
gley Bottom of
tton the Oven
Warslow
lwood Butterton
Onecote Wetton
5 Cauldon
STOKE
Cresswell
3
Abbots
Bromley
Tatenhill
Alrewas
radley

Sheffield

Grindleford
Foolow Holmesfield
Wardlow Froggatt Millthorpe
Edge
Monsal Little Longstone
Head Over Haddon
Birchover
Hartington
Alstonefield
Brassington
Fenny Bentley

DERBYSHIRE

SK

Derby

Shardlow
Melbourne Wilson
Burton on Trent
Lullington

Penistone 4 Cadeby
Wentworth
M18
Scaftworth
Drakeholes
Retford

LINCS

NOTTS

Normanton
Laxton on Trent
Wellow
Hardwick Hall
North Muskham
Upton Newark

Nottingham
Red Mile
Grantham
Kegworth
Hose
Old Dalby
LEICS Grimston
Swithland
Burrough on the Hill
Exton

4

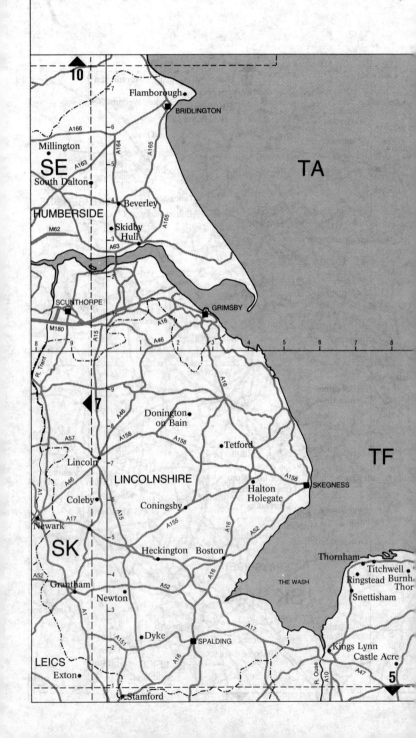

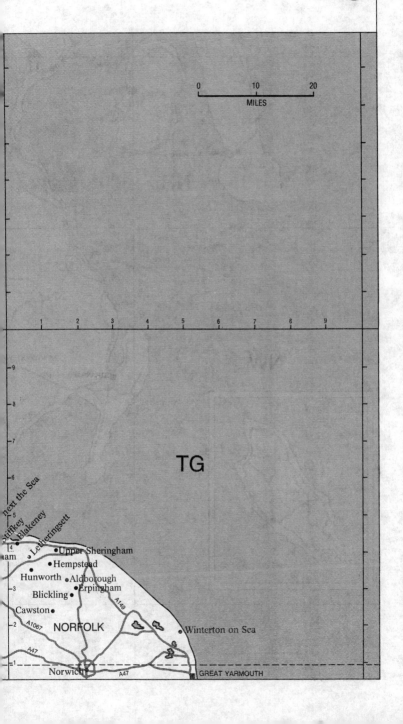

8

0   10   20
MILES

1   2   3   4   5   6   7   8   9

-9

-8

-7

-6

TG

-5

next the Sea

Stiffkey • Blakeney

-4   Letheringsett

am

• Upper Sheringham

• Hempstead

Hunworth • Aldborough

Blickling • Erpingham

-3

Cawston •

A149

-2   A1067

NORFOLK   • Winterton on Sea

A47

-1

Norwich   A47   GREAT YARMOUTH

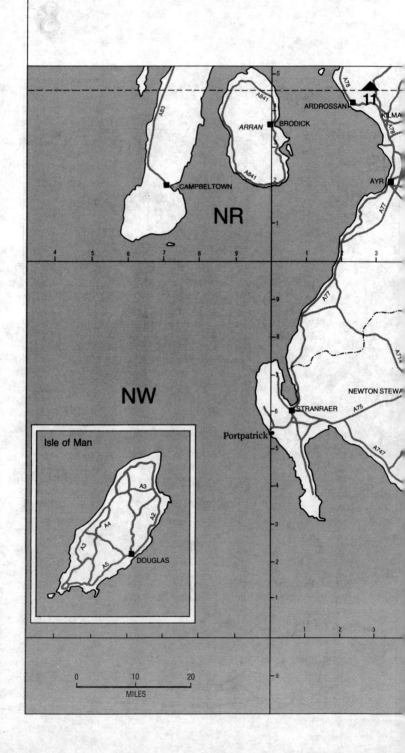

NR

NW

ARDROSSAN
11

KILMA

ARRAN
BRODICK

A841

A841

A83

CAMPBELTOWN

AYR

A77

A78

A78

A77

A77

A714

A75

NEWTON STEWA

STRANRAER

Portpatrick

A747

Isle of Man

A3

A3

A4

A5

A2

DOUGLAS

0   10   20
MILES

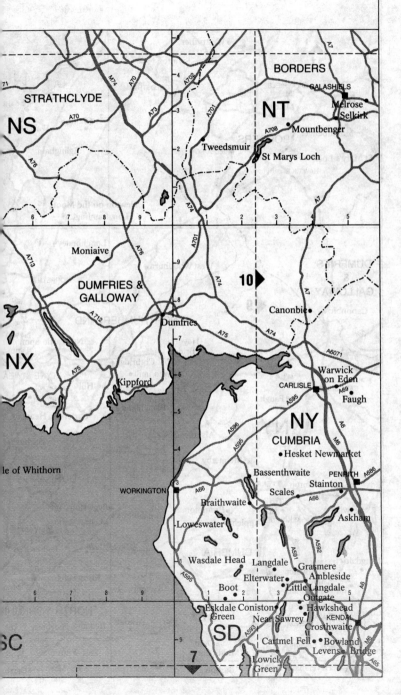

9

STRATHCLYDE

NS

BORDERS

GALASHIELS

NT

Melrose
Selkirk

Mountbenger

Tweedsmuir

St Marys Loch

Moniaive

DUMFRIES &
GALLOWAY

10

Canonbie

Dumfries

NX

Kippford

Warwick
on Eden

CARLISLE

Faugh

le of Whithorn

NY

CUMBRIA

Hesket Newmarket

Bassenthwaite

PENRITH

Stainton

Scales

WORKINGTON

Braithwaite

Askham

Loweswater

Wasdale Head

Langdale

Grasmere

Ambleside

Elterwater

Little Langdale

Boot

Outgate

Eskdale
Green

Coniston

Hawkshead

KENDAL

Near Sawrey

Crosthwaite

SC

SD

Cartmel Fell

Bowland

Levens Bridge

Lowick
Green

7

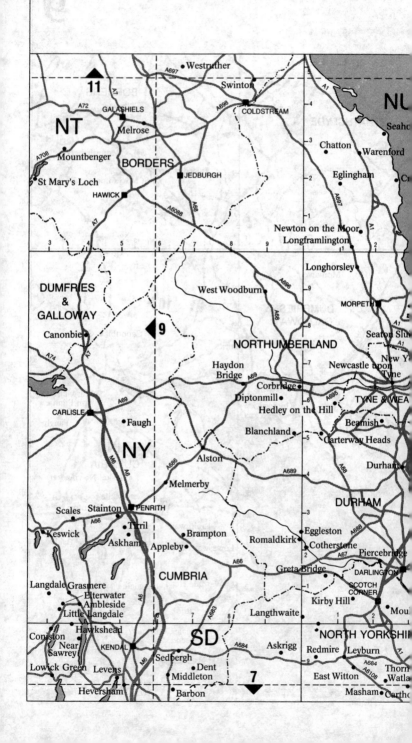

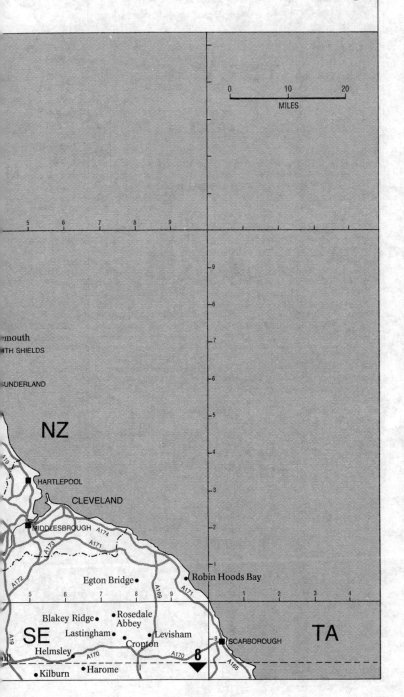

0   10   20
MILES

5   6   7   8   9

9

8

7

6

5

mouth
TH SHIELDS

SUNDERLAND

NZ

4

3

■ HARTLEPOOL

CLEVELAND

■ MIDDLESBROUGH A174

2

A173   A171

1

A172

Egton Bridge●   ● Robin Hoods Bay

5   6   7   8   9   1   2   3   4

Blakey Ridge●   ● Rosedale
Abbey

SE   Lastingham●   ● Levisham   TA

Cropton

Helmsley   A170   ■ SCARBOROUGH

8 ▼

● Kilburn   ● Harome   A170   A165

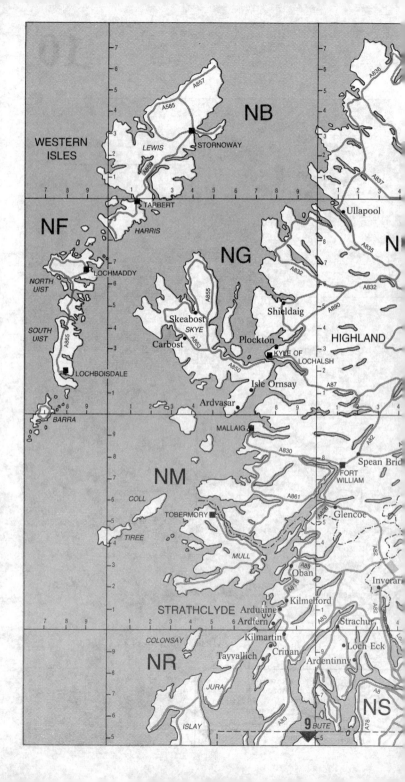

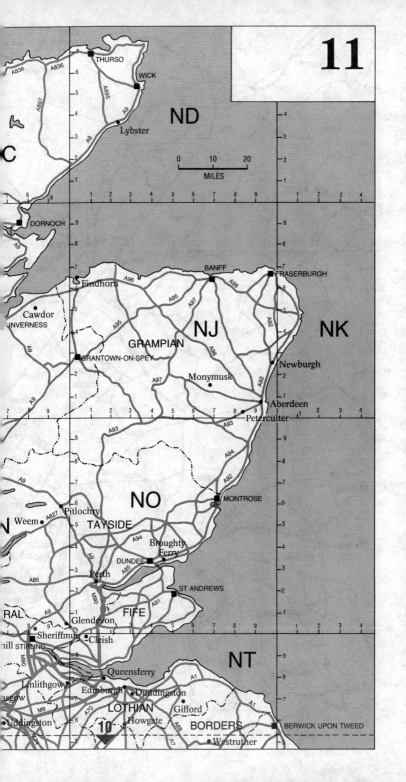

11

ND

THURSO
WICK
Lybster

A836
A836
A897
A895
A9
A9

C

0   10   20
MILES

DORNOCH

A9

Findhorn
BANFF
FRASERBURGH
Cawdor
INVERNESS
NJ
NK
A96
A95
A97
A98
A92
GRAMPIAN
A96
GRANTOWN-ON-SPEY
Newburgh
A97
Monymusk
A92
Aberdeen
Peterculter
A93

A93
A94

A92
NO
MONTROSE
A9
Weem
A827
Pitlochry
TAYSIDE
A94
Broughty
Ferry
A9
DUNDEE
A85
Perth
A85
ST ANDREWS
M90
A91
RAL
FIFE
A9
Glendevon
NT
9
Sheriffmuir
Cleish
hill STIRLING
M80
Queensferry
Linlithgow
A1
asgow
Edinburgh
Duddingston
M8
LOTHIAN
Gifford
A70
10
Howgate
BORDERS
BERWICK UPON TWEED
Uddingston
A68
Westruther

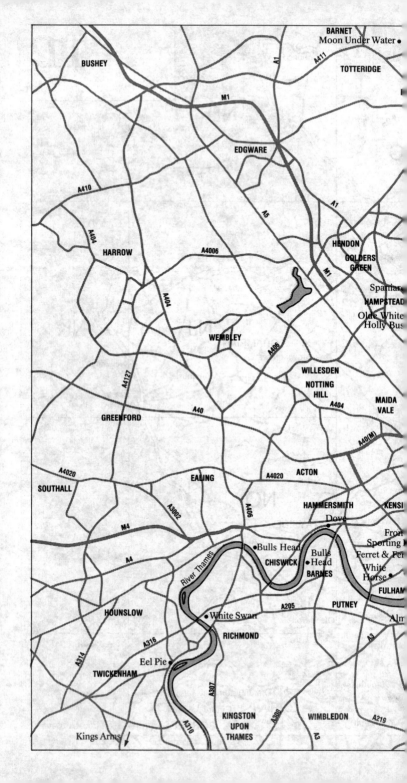

12

A110

A10

A1010

A111

EDMONTON

A406

M11

NCHLEY
406

A406

TOTTENHAM

WALTHAMSTOW

HORNSEY

A112

A12

GHATE

A503

White Lion
of Mortimer

STOKE
NEWINGTON

A11

A1

A10

A118

ISLINGTON

WEST HAM

See map 13

A11

CITY

Hollands

A124

A13

Grapes

Mayflower

Angel

River Thames

Coopers
Arms

A2

GREENWICH

TTERSEA

CAMBERWELL

A202

A2

A2

Phoenix & Firkin

LEWISHAM

CLAPHAM

A20

Olde Windmill

Crown & Greyhound

A3

DULWICH

A205

A21

A24

214

STREATHAM

A215

A23

0   1   2   3

MILES

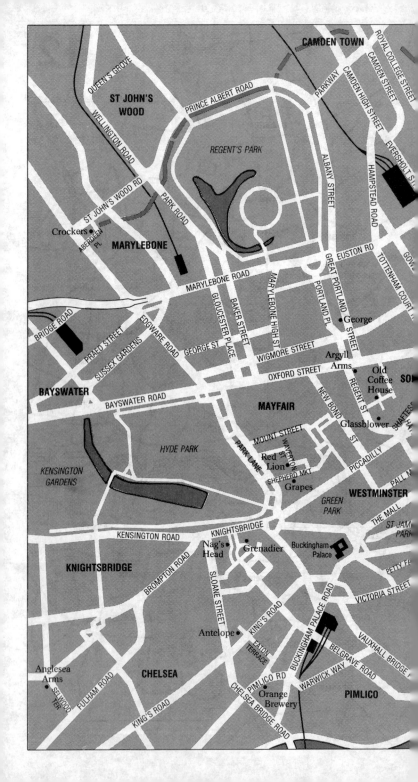

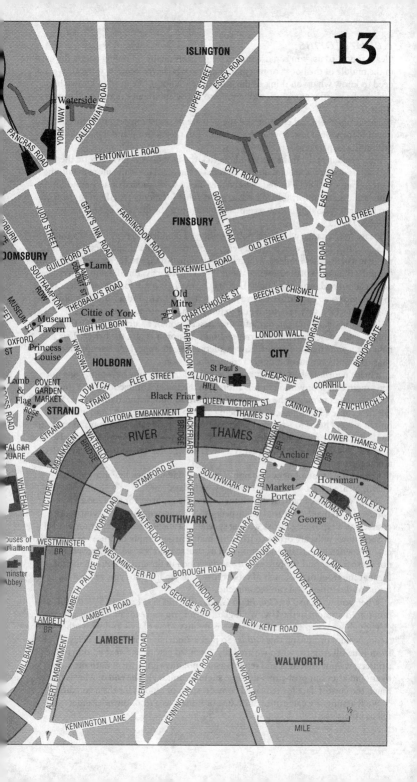

Report forms

Please report to us: you can use the tear-out forms on the following pages, the card in the middle of the book, or just plain paper – whichever's easiest for you. We need to know what you think of the pubs in this edition. We need to know about other pubs worthy of inclusion. We need to know about ones that should not be included.

The atmosphere and character of the pub are the most important features – why it would, or would not, appeal to strangers. But the bar food and the drink are important too – please tell us about them.

If the food is really quite outstanding, tick the FOOD AWARD box on the form, and tell us about the special quality that makes it stand out – the more detail, the better. And if you have stayed there, tell us about the standard of accommodation – whether it was comfortable, pleasant, good value for money. Again, if the pub or inn is worth special attention as a place to stay, tick the PLACE-TO-STAY AWARD box.

Please try to gauge whether a pub should be a main entry, or is best as a Lucky Dip (and tick the relevant box). In general, main entries need qualities that would make it worth other readers' while to travel some distance to them; Lucky Dips are the pubs that are worth knowing about if you are nearby. But if a pub is an entirely new recommendation, the Lucky Dip may be the best place for it to start its career in the *Guide* – to encourage other readers to report on it, and gradually build up a dossier on it; it's very rare for a pub to jump straight into the main entries.

The more detail you can put into your description of a Lucky Dip pub that's only scantily described in the current edition (or not in at all), the better. This'll help not just us but also your fellow-readers gauge its appeal. A description of its character and even furnishings is a tremendous boon.

It helps enormously if you can give the full address for any new pub – one not yet a main entry, or without a full address in the Lucky Dip sections. In a town, we need the street name; in the country, if it's hard to find, we need directions. Without this, there's little chance of our being able to include the pub. And with any pub, it always helps to let us know about prices of food (and bedrooms, if there are any), and about any lunchtimes or evenings when food is not served. We'd also like to have your views on drinks quality – beer, wine, cider and so forth, even coffee and tea.

If you know that a Lucky Dip pub is open all day (or even late into the afternoon), please tell us – preferably saying which days.

When you go to a pub, don't tell them you're a reporter for the *Good Pub Guide*; we do make clear that all inspections are anonymous, and if you declare yourself as a reporter you risk getting special treatment – for better or for worse!

Sometimes pubs are dropped from the main entries simply because very few readers have written to us about them – and of course there's a risk that people may not write if they find the pub exactly as described in the entry. You can use the form at the front of the batch of report forms just to list pubs you've been to, found as described, and can recommend.

When you write to *The Good Pub Guide*, FREEPOST, London SW10 0BR, you don't need a stamp in the UK. We'll gladly send you more forms (free) if you wish.

Though we try to answer letters, there are just a few of us – and with other work to do, besides producing this *Guide*. So please understand if there's a delay. And from June till August, when we are fully extended getting the next edition to the printers, we put all letters and reports aside, not answering them until the rush is over (and after our post-press-day late summer holiday). The end of May is pretty much the cut-off date for reasoned consideration of reports for the next edition.

We'll assume we can print your name or initials as a recommender unless you tell us otherwise.

I have been to the following pubs in The Good Pub Guide in the last few months, found them as described, and confirm that they deserve continued inclusion:

PLEASE GIVE YOUR NAME AND ADDRESS ON THE BACK OF THIS FORM

Your own name and address (block capitals please)

REPORT on   *(pub's name)*

Pub's address:

☐ YES MAIN ENTRY ☐ YES *Lucky Dip* ☐ NO don't include
Please tick one of these boxes to show your verdict, and give reasons and descriptive comments, prices etc:

PLEASE GIVE YOUR NAME AND ADDRESS ON THE BACK OF THIS FORM

☐ Deserves FOOD award ☐ Deserves PLACE-TO-STAY award   92:1

. . . .

REPORT on   *(pub's name)*

Pub's address:

☐ YES MAIN ENTRY ☐ YES *Lucky Dip* ☐ NO don't include
Please tick one of these boxes to show your verdict, and give reasons and descriptive comments, prices etc:

PLEASE GIVE YOUR NAME AND ADDRESS ON THE BACK OF THIS FORM

☐ Deserves FOOD award ☐ Deserves PLACE-TO-STAY award   92:2

REPORT on   *(pub's name)*

Pub's address:

☐ YES MAIN ENTRY   ☐ YES *Lucky Dip*   ☐ NO don't include
Please tick one of these boxes to show your verdict, and give reasons and descriptive comments, prices etc:

PLEASE GIVE YOUR NAME AND
ADDRESS ON THE BACK OF THIS FORM

☐ Deserves FOOD award   ☐ Deserves PLACE-TO-STAY award   **92:3**

REPORT on   *(pub's name)*

Pub's address:

☐ YES MAIN ENTRY   ☐ YES *Lucky Dip*   ☐ NO don't include
Please tick one of these boxes to show your verdict, and give reasons and descriptive comments, prices etc:

PLEASE GIVE YOUR NAME AND
ADDRESS ON THE BACK OF THIS FORM

☐ Deserves FOOD award   ☐ Deserves PLACE-TO-STAY award   **92:4**

Your own name and address *(block capitals please)*

DO NOT USE THIS SIDE OF THE
PAGE FOR WRITING ABOUT PUBS

Your own name and address *(block capitals please)*

DO NOT USE THIS SIDE OF THE
PAGE FOR WRITING ABOUT PUBS

REPORT on _____ *(pub's name)*

Pub's address: _____

_____

☐ YES MAIN ENTRY ☐ YES *Lucky Dip* ☐ NO don't include
Please tick one of these boxes to show your verdict, and give reasons and descriptive comments, prices etc:

PLEASE GIVE YOUR NAME AND
ADDRESS ON THE BACK OF THIS FORM

☐ **Deserves FOOD award** ☐ **Deserves PLACE-TO-STAY award**   92:5

....

REPORT on _____ *(pub's name)*

Pub's address: _____

_____

☐ YES MAIN ENTRY ☐ YES *Lucky Dip* ☐ NO don't include
Please tick one of these boxes to show your verdict, and give reasons and descriptive comments, prices etc:

PLEASE GIVE YOUR NAME AND
ADDRESS ON THE BACK OF THIS FORM

☐ **Deserves FOOD award** ☐ **Deserves PLACE-TO-STAY award**   92:6

REPORT on   *(pub's name)*

Pub's address:

☐ YES MAIN ENTRY ☐ YES *Lucky Dip* ☐ NO don't include
Please tick one of these boxes to show your verdict, and give reasons and descriptive comments, prices etc:

PLEASE GIVE YOUR NAME AND ADDRESS ON THE BACK OF THIS FORM

☐ Deserves FOOD award ☐ Deserves PLACE-TO-STAY award   92:7

REPORT on   *(pub's name)*

Pub's address:

☐ YES MAIN ENTRY ☐ YES *Lucky Dip* ☐ NO don't include
Please tick one of these boxes to show your verdict, and give reasons and descriptive comments, prices etc:

PLEASE GIVE YOUR NAME AND ADDRESS ON THE BACK OF THIS FORM

☐ Deserves FOOD award ☐ Deserves PLACE-TO-STAY award   92:8

Your own name and address *(block capitals please)*

DO NOT USE THIS SIDE OF THE
PAGE FOR WRITING ABOUT PUBS

Your own name and address *(block capitals please)*

DO NOT USE THIS SIDE OF THE
PAGE FOR WRITING ABOUT PUBS

REPORT on _____ *(pub's name)*

Pub's address:

_____

☐ YES MAIN ENTRY ☐ YES *Lucky Dip* ☐ NO don't include
Please tick one of these boxes to show your verdict, and give reasons and descriptive comments, prices etc:

PLEASE GIVE YOUR NAME AND
ADDRESS ON THE BACK OF THIS FORM

☐ Deserves FOOD award ☐ Deserves PLACE-TO-STAY award   92:9

....

REPORT on _____ *(pub's name)*

Pub's address:

_____

☐ YES MAIN ENTRY ☐ YES *Lucky Dip* ☐ NO don't include
Please tick one of these boxes to show your verdict, and give reasons and descriptive comments, prices etc:

PLEASE GIVE YOUR NAME AND
ADDRESS ON THE BACK OF THIS FORM

☐ Deserves FOOD award ☐ Deserves PLACE-TO-STAY award   92:10

Your own name and address *(block capitals please)*

Your own name and address *(block capitals please)*

REPORT on _____ *(pub's name)*

Pub's address: _____

_____

☐ YES MAIN ENTRY ☐ YES *Lucky Dip* ☐ NO don't include
Please tick one of these boxes to show your verdict, and give reasons and descriptive comments, prices etc:

PLEASE GIVE YOUR NAME AND
ADDRESS ON THE BACK OF THIS FORM

☐ Deserves FOOD award ☐ Deserves PLACE-TO-STAY award   92:11

REPORT on _____ *(pub's name)*

Pub's address: _____

_____

☐ YES MAIN ENTRY ☐ YES *Lucky Dip* ☐ NO don't include
Please tick one of these boxes to show your verdict, and give reasons and descriptive comments, prices etc:

PLEASE GIVE YOUR NAME AND
ADDRESS ON THE BACK OF THIS FORM

☐ Deserves FOOD award ☐ Deserves PLACE-TO-STAY award   92:12